UK National Ecosystem Assessment

Understanding nature's value to society

7th November 2011

Dear Colleague

UK National Ecosystem Assessment Technical Report

The UK National Ecosystem Assessment (UK NEA) is the first analysis of the UK's natural environment in terms of the benefits it provides to society and continuing economic prosperity. Part of the Living With Environmental Change (LWEC) initiative, the UK NEA was an inclusive process involving many government, academic, NGO and private sector institutions.

Please find enclosed a copy of the full technical report from the UK NEA. At almost 1500 pages, this technical report is the culmination of the most comprehensive ecosystem assessment undertaken by any nation, and all the more remarkable for being completed in two years.

The Synthesis, launched in June this year, was greeted with widespread acclaim as a significant step forward in our understanding of trends in the delivery of ecosystem services, the drivers of these changes, and the likely consequences for human well-being in the UK. Furthermore, the attempts to ascribe both monetary and non-monetary values to the changes in goods, and exploration of contrasting plausible futures, demonstrate the potential use of ecosystem assessment in decision-making at many levels of governance.

It is heartening that several government departments, including the Treasury, as well as corporate business institutions, increasingly recognise the strong economic arguments for safeguarding and enhancing the natural environment. The work of the UK NEA has had a profound influence on *The Natural Choice: securing the value of nature,* the first White Paper in England on the natural environment in 20 years. Indeed, the first of 34 commitments in the White Paper is *"Building on the National Ecosystem Assessment, the Government will support a further phase of ground-breaking research. It will investigate the mix of future actions most likely to secure the most benefits for nature and for people from our ecosystems. It will also develop practical tools to assist decision-makers in applying the lessons of the NEA."*

http://uknea.unep-wcmc.org/

The UK NEA could not have been achieved without a rigorous evaluation of the evidence base by more than 500 natural, economic and social scientists. The Secretariat, based at UNEP World Conservation Monitoring Centre, coordinated the assessment process.

All the chapters of the technical report along with supporting valuation documents and the Synthesis are available to download from the Resources pages of the UK NEA website.

Kind regards

Jon Hutton
Director
UNEP World Conservation Monitoring Centre
219 Huntingdon Road
Cambridge
CB3 0DL United Kingdom
Tel: +44 (0) 1223 277 314
Fax: +44 (0) 1223 277 136
http://www.unep-wcmc.org/

The UK NEA Secretariat can be contacted at nea@unep-wcmc.org

UK National Ecosystem Assessment

Technical Report

Suggested citation for the UK NEA Technical Report:
UK National Ecosystem Assessment (2011) The UK National Ecosystem Assessment Technical Report. UNEP-WCMC, Cambridge.

For an individual chapter from the UK NEA Technical Report, see this example from Chapter 1:
Brown, C., Walpole, M., Simpson, L. & Tierney, M. (2011) Introduction to the UK National Ecosystem Assessment. *In*: The UK National Ecosystem Assessment Technical Report. UK National Ecosystem Assessment, UNEP-WCMC, Cambridge.

Published by: United Nations Environment Programme World Conservation Monitoring Centre (UNEP-WCMC), 219 Huntingdon Road, Cambridge, CB3 0DL, UK.

Designed by: NatureBureau, 36 Kingfisher Court, Hambridge Road, Newbury, RG14 5SJ, UK.

Printed and bound by: Information Press, Southfiled Road, Eynsham, Oxford OX29 4JB, UK.

Table of Contents

Foreword

The UK National Ecosystem Assessment (UK NEA) provides a comprehensive overview of the state of the natural environment in the UK and a new way of estimating our national wealth. It shows how we have under-valued our natural resources. Valuing them properly will enable better decision making, more certain investment, new avenues to wealth creation and jobs, and greater human well-being in changing times ahead.

Our wealth as a nation and our individual well-being depend critically upon the environment. It provides us with the food, water and air that are essential for life and with the minerals and raw materials for our industry and consumption. Less obviously, it provides the processes that purify air and water, and which sequester or break down wastes. It is also in our environment where we find recreation, health and solace, and in which our culture finds its roots and sense of place. Scientists refer to these services that our environment provides as 'ecosystem services', recognising that it is the interaction between the living and physical environments that deliver these necessities.

Yet we tend to take this largely for granted. While we pay for some ecosystem services like food and fibre, we are often unaware of the importance of others such as natural water or air purification, and would be alarmed at the cost of providing these artificially. This under-estimation of the value of natural processes in economic terms means that we take inadequately informed decisions on how to use these resources. The result is pollution, the loss of species and ecosystems and damage to the processes we need, with real economic costs to either recover them or provide artificial alternatives.

With ever increasing pressures on these natural resources, partly from growing populations but still more from growing levels of individual consumption, it is essential that we learn to take account of the full value of ecosystem services in our decision making. By doing so, we can not only protect what we have and repair damage where needed, but harness these resources more effectively to generate wealth and well-being. The UK NEA represents a first attempt to assess our stocks of natural ecosystem resources, their state and the trends in their development. This ground breaking assessment has been adopted by the partnership that I chair, of Government, Devolved Administrations, Research Councils and other bodies (22 in all) who form the *Living with Environmental Change Partnership* (LWEC). The aim of LWEC is to ensure that decision makers in government, business and society have the knowledge, foresight and tools to mitigate, adapt to and benefit from environmental change.

Funding for the UK NEA has brought together about 500 experts in the natural sciences, economics and the social sciences, under the chairmanship of Professor Robert Watson (Defra's Chief Scientific Advisor and Strategic Director of the Tyndall Centre at the University of East Anglia) and Professor Steve Albon of the James Hutton Institute (formerly the Macaulay Land Use Research Institute). This team has assembled and analysed an enormous body of published information about the UK environment and generated new tools for valuing it, in economic and non-economic terms; this is a world first. It provides for the first time, a coherent body of evidence about the state of our natural environment and the services it provides for each country in the United Kingdom. This can serve as the basis for thinking about how we want to use these services to best effect, for national wealth and national well-being, now and for our nation's children into the future.

John Selborne

Lord Selborne GBE, FRS

Governance Structure for the UK National Ecosystem Assessment

Expert Panel

Co-chairs

Robert T. Watson, Department for Environment, Food and Rural Affairs & the Tyndall Centre, University of East Anglia

Steve Albon, The James Hutton Institute

Members

Melanie C. Austen, Plymouth Marine Laboratory
Ian J. Bateman, University of East Anglia
William Bird, Natural England
Jacquelin Burgess, University of East Anglia
Ian Crute, Agriculture and Horticulture Development Board
Andrew Church, University of Brighton
Bridget A. Emmett, Centre for Ecology & Hydrology
Alastair Fitter, University of York
Chris Gibson, Queen's University, Belfast (retired)
Rosie Hails, Natural Capital Initiative/Centre for Ecology & Hydrology
Roy Haines-Young, University of Nottingham
A. Louise Heathwaite, University of Lancaster
Pushpam Kumar, University of Liverpool
Edward Maltby, University of Liverpool

Georgina M. Mace, Imperial College, London
Stephen J. Malcolm, Centre for Environment Fisheries and Aquaculture Science
Lindsay Maskell, Centre for Ecology & Hydrology
Robert Nicholls, University of Southampton
Ken Norris, University of Reading
Steve Ormerod, University of Cardiff
Juliet Osborne, Rothamsted Research
Jules N. Pretty, University of Essex
Chris Quine, Forest Research
Pete Smith, University of Aberdeen
Kerry Turner, University of East Anglia
Andrew Watkinson, Living With Environmental Change
Michael Winter, University of Exeter

User Group

Association of Electricity Producers (Diane Brooke)
Commission for Architecture and the Built Environment (Edward Hobson, Helen Beck)
Convention of Scottish Local Authorities (Anil Gupta, Gillian Fyfe)
Department of Communities and Local Government (Peter Bide)
Department of Health (Jo Nurse)
EDF Energy (Colin Taylor)
Environment Agency (Jim Wharfe, Steve Killeen)
Forestry Commission (Sallie Bailey)
Her Majesty's Treasury (Will Armitage)
Joint Nature Conservation Committee (Paul Rose, Andrew Stott)

Local Government Association (Kate Hills)
Mineral Products Association (Nicola Owen, Delia Shannon)
National Farmers Union (Diane Mitchell)
National Trust (Stuart Warrington)
Natural England (Ruth Waters)
Scottish Environment Link (Tony King)
Scottish Environment Protection Authority (Martin Marsden)
Scottish Fishermen's Federation (Rory Campbell)
Scottish Natural Heritage (Greg Mudge)
Water UK (Barrie Clarke)
Wildlife and Countryside Link (Paul Morling, Carrie Hume)
Wildlife Trust (Tony Whitbread)

Client Group

Department for Environment, Food and Rural Affairs (David Cooper, Peter Costigan, Robert Bradburne)
Natural Environment Research Council (Dan Osborn)
Economic and Social Research Council (Timothy Wright)
Northern Ireland Environment Agency (Neil McCulloch, Mike Meharg, Mark Wright)

Scottish Government (Joanna Drewitt, Charles Stewart Roper)
Countryside Council for Wales (Keith Davies)
Welsh Assembly Government (Chris Lea, Steve Spode)

Secretariat/UNEP-WCMC

Matt Walpole, Director
Claire Brown, Coordinator
Philip Bubb
Lucy Simpson
Megan Tierney
Simon Blyth

Jonathan Winn
Lindsey C. Elliott
Martin Jenkins
Siobhan Kenney
Chloe Swart

Chapter 1:
Introduction to the UK National Ecosystem Assessment

Coordinating Lead Authors: Claire Brown and Matt Walpole
Lead Authors: Lucy Simpson and Megan Tierney

1.1 The UK National Ecosystem Assessment

The UK National Ecosystem Assessment (UK NEA) is the first analysis of the UK's natural environment in terms of the benefits it provides to society and the nation's continuing prosperity. Carried out between mid-2009 and mid-2011, the UK NEA has been a wide-ranging, multi-stakeholder, cross-disciplinary process, designed to provide a comprehensive picture of past, present and possible future trends in ecosystem services and their values; it is underpinned by the best available evidence and the most up-to-date conceptual thinking and analytical tools. The UK NEA is innovative in scale, scope and methodology, and has involved more than 500 natural scientists, economists, social scientists and other stakeholders from government, academic and private sector institutions, and non-governmental organisations (NGOs).

Supported by the Department for Environment, Food and Rural Affairs (Defra), the Northern Ireland Environment Agency (NIEA), the Scottish Government, the Countryside Council for Wales (CCW), the Welsh Assembly Government (WAG), the Natural Environment Research Council (NERC) and the Economic and Social Research Council (ESRC), the UK NEA was carried out as part of the Living With Environmental Change (LWEC) Initiative. The aim of LWEC is to ensure that decision-makers in government, business and society have the knowledge, foresight and tools to mitigate, adapt to and benefit from environmental change.

1.2 Origins of the UK National Ecosystem Assessment

1.2.1 The Ecosystem Approach
The 'Ecosystem Approach' is a strategy for the integrated management of land, water and living resources that promotes conservation and sustainable use in an equitable way (CBD 1993).

The Ecosystem Approach is much more than accepting ecosystems as the core of environmental management. It recognises that people and society are integral components of ecosystems and their management and conservation. This necessitates a way of working and decision-making that cuts across traditional policy and institutional boundaries. It brings consideration of natural, economic and social sciences into a single methodological framework. The Ecosystem Approach is an underlying element of important agreements to which the UK has significant commitments—notably the Convention on Biological Diversity (CBD), The Ramsar Convention on Wetlands of International Importance and the European Union (EU) Marine Strategy Framework Directive (MSFD).

Defra, the Devolved Administrations and partners are working towards implementing an Ecosystem Approach to conserving, managing and enhancing the natural environment of the UK. This will be achieved by focusing decision-making away from sector-specific or habitat-specific approaches and towards an integrated approach based on whole ecosystems which ensures the value of ecosystem services is fully reflected in decisions (Defra 2007).

The adoption of an ecosystem approach yields a requirement for an evidence base on ecosystem change and ecosystem service provision to inform decision-making. The UK NEA is designed to provide that evidence base. However its origins are most clearly found in the UK's response to an earlier, global assessment process: the Millennium Ecosystem Assessment (MA).

1.2.2 The Millennium Ecosystem Assessment
The MA was called for in 2000, by the then United Nations (UN) Secretary-General Kofi Annan in his report to the UN General Assembly, *We the Peoples: The Role of the United Nations in the 21st Century*. Carried out from 2001 to 2005, the MA assessed the consequences of ecosystem change for human well-being. It comprehensively demonstrated the importance of ecosystems and the services that they provide to human well-being, and found that, at a global scale, many of these services are being degraded or lost (**Box 1.1**). This conclusion is underpinned by state-of-the-art scientific assessment of the condition and trends in the world's ecosystems and the services they provide (such as clean water, food, flood control and recreation). The MA also explored the options to restore, conserve or enhance the sustainable use of ecosystems.

The MA was conducted as a multi-scale assessment, with interlinked assessments undertaken at local (watershed), national, regional and global scales (MA 2005). Some 34 sub-global assessments were undertaken at a variety of scales as part of the MA, responding to the needs of different decision-makers. Since 2005, at least a further 30 sub-global assessments have been initiated at different scales.

1.2.3 Response from the UK Government and House of Commons Environmental Audit Committee to the Findings of the Millennium Ecosystem Assessment
In 2007, the House of Commons Environmental Audit Committee released a report in response to the findings of the MA. Specifically, this report acknowledged the contribution the MA has made globally and reviewed the relevance of the MA findings in the UK context (House of Commons Environmental Audit Committee 2007). A key recommendation was that: "ultimately the Government should conduct a full MA-style assessment for the UK to enable the identification and development of effective policy responses to ecosystem service degradation".

Early 2008, Defra commissioned a Scoping Study to examine the potential benefits of undertaking an ecosystem assessment for England (Haines-Young et al. 2008). The study examined:

1. The policy context in which an ecosystem assessment for England would be set, and the ways in which Defra's involvement or leadership would assist the UK in meeting its wider international commitments and the goals set by national policy.
2. The extent to which the current and planned research portfolio of Defra and its partners had already, or was likely to, put in place all the elements of an ecosystem assessment.
3. Options for an assessment, including benefits and costs.
4. Recommendations on how Defra's requirements for evidence on England's ecosystem services are met.

While the Scoping Study focused primarily on the case for an MA-type assessment for England, it found that there was a strong case for undertaking a UK-scale assessment. The study further recommended that the leadership of a national assessment should rest with the Defra Chief Scientist Group and that a dedicated Scientific Secretariat be established.

In July 2008, the then Secretary of State for Environment, Food and Rural Affairs announced that Defra would commit to supporting an ecosystem assessment for England over two years. Further discussions with the Devolved Administrations led to the expansion of the assessment to include Northern Ireland, Scotland and Wales in order to produce a truly national-scale ecosystem assessment; the decision was taken that the UK NEA would formally begin in March 2009.

1.3 Objectives and Implementation of the UK National Ecosystem Assessment

The objectives of the UK NEA are:
1. Produce an independent and peer-reviewed assessment of the state and value of the UK's natural environment and ecosystem services.
2. Identify and understand what has driven change observed in the natural environment and the services it has provided over the last 60 years, and what may drive change in the future.
3. Foster better interdisciplinary cooperation between natural and social scientists to assist in strengthening policy making in order to ensure effective management of the environment and ecosystem services in the future.
4. Ensure full stakeholder participation and encourage different stakeholders and communities to interact with each other.
5. Use the key messages from the assessment to raise awareness among society of the importance of the natural environment to human well-being and economic prosperity.

Box 1.1 Four main findings of the Millennium Ecosystem Assessment. Source: MA (2005).

1. Over the past 50 years, human have changed ecosystems more rapidly and extensively than in any comparable period of time in human history, largely to meet rapidly growing demands for food, fresh water, timber, fibre and fuel. This has resulted in a substantial and largely irreversible loss in the diversity of life on Earth.
2. The changes that have been made to ecosystems have contributed to substantial net gains in human well-being and economic development, but these gains have been achieved at growing costs in the form of the degradation of many ecosystem services, increased risks of non-linear changes, and the exacerbation of poverty for some groups of people. These problems, unless addressed, will substantially diminish the benefits that future generations obtain for ecosystems.
3. The degradation of ecosystem services could grow significantly worse during the first half of this century and is a barrier to achieving the Millennium Development Goals.
4. The challenge of reversing the degradation of ecosystems while meeting increasing demands for their services can be partially met under some scenarios that the MA has considered, but these involve significant changes in policies, institutions and practices that are not currently under way. Many options exist to conserve or enhance specific ecosystem services in ways that reduce negative trade-offs or that provide positive synergies with other ecosystem services.

Using the ecosystem assessment process developed by the MA (Ash *et al.* 2010) as a starting point, the UK NEA also aims to:
1. Assess the status and trends of the UK's ecosystems and the services they provide at multiple spatial scales.
2. Describe the key drivers of change affecting the UK's ecosystems, including changes in land use, infrastructure development, pollution and climate.
3. Examine plausible futures (scenarios) for the UK's ecosystems and the services they provide.
4. Outline response options to secure continued delivery of the UK's ecosystem services, for the benefit of all of society.
5. Value the contribution of ecosystem services to human well-being through economic and non-economic analyses.

1.3.1 Scope of the UK National Ecosystem Assessment

The UK NEA includes all four of its constituent countries (England, Northern Ireland, Scotland and Wales). It does not incorporate the Isle of Man, the Channel Islands or any of the UK Overseas Territories. At the national scale, the UK NEA assesses terrestrial, freshwater and marine ecosystems, which are categorised into eight Broad Habitats (**Box 1.2**). The picture at country level is captured in four separate individual syntheses, while the local level is addressed through a series of case studies within different chapters.

The UK NEA provides a first attempt at understanding the connection between the environment and people, considering both the ecosystem (Broad Habitat) from which ecosystem services (**Box 1.3**) are derived (**Figure 1.1**) and the people who depend on, and are affected by changes in, the supply of such services. The UK NEA provides an evidence base, highlights gaps in knowledge (research and monitoring), explores plausible futures, and provides a critique of different response options available (including

Box 1.2 The UK's Broad Habitats

Although lacking in extremes—there are no high mountains, no true deserts and no major rivers—the UK is, in fact, remarkably variable biophysically, ecologically and socially, with complex underlying geology, a wide climatic range, (from very wet to semi-arid), and large variations in the distribution of the human population, from extensive areas of near-wilderness (in Scotland) to one of the world's largest metropolitan areas (Greater London). In the UK NEA, this diversity has been captured in eight Broad Habitat types (Figure 1):

 **Mountains, Moorlands and Heaths** cover 18% of the UK's land area. Lowland heaths are highly fragmented, while mountains and upland moors and heaths provide the largest unfragmented semi-natural habitats in the UK. Mountains, Moorlands and Heaths are the source of around 70% of the UK's drinking water, hold an estimated 40% of UK soil carbon, and include some of the country's most iconic landscapes.

 **Semi-natural Grasslands** once covered a large proportion of the UK's land area, largely as the result of low intensity traditional farming. The extent of Semi-natural Grasslands is now extremely reduced, with high diversity grasslands comprising a mere 2% of UK grassland (≥1% of total land area). Semi-natural Grasslands are highly valued culturally—the South Downs, dominated by chalk downland, receives around 40 million visitor days a year.

 **Enclosed Farmland** is the most extensive form of land use in the UK, accounting for around 40% of land area and producing around 70% of the UK's food. Most is managed for cereal, cattle and sheep production. Half of the area of Enclosed Farmland is arable land, mostly in eastern England; almost all the rest is nutrient enriched grassland, mostly in wetter, western parts of the UK. As well as playing a crucial role in provisioning services, Enclosed Farmland is of great cultural significance and is a major determinant of landscape in much of lowland UK.

Dominant UK NEA Broad Habitats (>50%) by area per 1 km cell

- Mountains, Moorlands & Heaths
- Semi-natural Grasslands
- Enclosed Farmland
- Woodlands
- Freshwaters – Open waters, Wetlands and Floodplains
- Urban
- Coastal Margins
- Marine

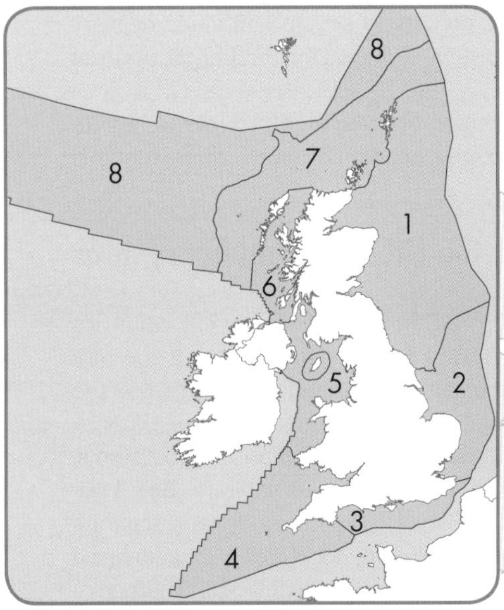

Figure 1 Distribution (%) of the UK NEA Broad Habitat types by area at 1x1 km resolution. Inset: Charting Progress 2, UK Regional Sea boundaries: 1) Northern North Sea; 2) Southern North Sea; 3) Eastern Channel; 4) Western Channel and Celtic Sea; 5) Irish Sea; 6) Minches and Western Scotland; 7) Scottish Continental Shelf; 8) Atlantic North-West Approaches, Rockall Trough and Faeroe/Shetland Channel. Source: Broad Habitat distribution—data from Land Cover Map 2000 (Fuller *et al.* 2002); Regional seas map based on UKMMAS (2010). Coastline: World Vector Shoreline@ National—Geospatial Intelligence Agency. Source: NOASS, NGDC.

Box 1.2 Continued

Woodlands include managed plantations as well as ancient, semi-natural woodlands. Woodlands cover 12% of the UK's land area, making the country one of the least wooded in Europe. At least 80% is less than 100 years old and just 5% is classified as 'ancient woodland'. In the past century, much planting of coniferous trees (often non-native) has taken place. Only in England is Woodland dominated by broadleaved species. Much of the Woodland estate is managed as a source of timber, but Woodlands are increasingly valued for their delivery of other ecosystem services, particularly recreation and carbon storage.

Freshwaters include Openwaters, Wetlands and Floodplains. In the UK, there are more than 389,000 kilometres of rivers, 200,000 hectares of permanent lakes and nearly half a million small ponds. There are also estimated to be at least 390,000 hectares of fen, reedbed, lowland raised bog and grazing marsh, and nearly 1 million hectares of floodplain. Freshwater habitats are a major source of water for a wide range of uses and are important for recreation, including angling, boating and other water sports, and for hazard (notably flood) regulation.

Urban areas in the UK cover just under 7% of the land area. They are home to eight out of ten people, often living at extremely high population densities. Greenspace is very limited in extent, and access to it is unequally distributed; thus it assumes disproportionate cultural significance. Urban areas depend very largely on other habitat types for the provision of most of their ecosystem services.

Coastal Margins, comprising Sand Dunes, Machair, Saltmarsh, Shingle, Sea Cliffs and Coastal Lagoons, cover just 0.6% of the UK's land area. Culturally, Coastal Margins are of immense significance. More than 250 million visits are made to the UK's coast per year, of which, around one third are to natural habitats. These areas are also important in coastal defences, sediment transport and as nursery grounds for fish.

Marine habitats of the UK cover more than three and a half times the land area. They are highly variable, comprising a very wide range of subhabitats. Inshore Marine habitats are of great cultural importance, offering many opportunities for tourism and recreation. Offshore habitats support fisheries and provide a wide range of other ecosystem services such as avoidance of climate stress and waste breakdown and detoxification.

Photo sources: Cairngorm National Park mountain landscape, Scotland by Peter Mulligan available under a Creative Commons Attribution license. Semi-natural Grassland, South Downs, Hampshire by Alistair Young available under a Creative Commons Attribution license. Hay bales © Joingate, 2011 used under license of Shutterstock.com. Veteran oak and beech trees in a mixed lowland woodland, courtesy of FC Picture Library/Isobel Cameron. Glen Cannich, Scotland by Peter Mulligan available under a Creative Commons Attribution license. Housing in Plymouth © Samot, 2011 used under license of Shutterstock.com. Dorset coast © Markus Gann, 2011 used under license of Shutterstock.com. Current swept bed of Zostera marina, courtesy of Keith Hiscock (from www.marlin.ac.uk).

Box 1.3 The UK's Ecosystem Services

Supporting services provide the basic infrastructure of life. They include primary production (the capture of energy from the sun to produce complex organic compounds), soil formation, and the cycling of water and nutrients in terrestrial and aquatic ecosystems. All other ecosystem services—regulating, provisioning and cultural—ultimately depend on them. Their impacts on human well-being are indirect and mostly long-term in nature; the formation of soils, for example, takes place over decades or centuries. Supporting services are strongly interrelated to each other and generally underpinned by a vast array of physical, chemical and biological interactions. Our current understanding of exactly how such ecological interactions influence ecosystem processes and the delivery of supporting services is limited.

Regulating services provided by ecosystems are extremely diverse and include the impacts of pollination and pest and disease regulation on the provision of ecosystem goods such as food, fuel and fibre. Other regulating services, including climate and hazard regulation, may act as final ecosystem services, or contribute significantly to final ecosystem services, such as the amount and quality of available fresh water. As with supporting services, regulating services are strongly linked to each other and to other kinds of services. Water quality regulation, for example, is primarily determined by catchment processes and is thereby linked to other regulating services, such as the control of soil and air quality and climate regulation, as well as to supporting services such as nutrient cycling.

Provisioning services are manifested in the goods people obtain from ecosystems such as food and fibre, fuel in the form of peat, wood or non-woody biomass, and water from rivers, lakes and aquifers. Goods may be provided by heavily managed ecosystems, such as agricultural and aquacultural systems and plantation forests, or by natural or semi-natural ones, for example in the form of capture fisheries and the harvest of other wild foods. Supplies of ecosystem goods are invariably dependent on many supporting and regulating services. Historically, provisioning services have been a major focus of human activity, so are, therefore, closely linked to cultural services.

Cultural services are derived from environmental settings (places where humans interact with each other and with nature) that give rise to cultural goods and benefits. In addition to their natural features, such settings are imbued with the outcomes of interactions between societies, cultures, technologies and ecosystems over millennia. They comprise an enormous range of so-called 'green' and 'blue' spaces such as gardens, parks, rivers and lakes, the seashore and the wider countryside, and including agricultural landscapes and wilderness areas. Such places provide opportunities for outdoor learning and many kinds of recreation; exposure to them can have benefits including aesthetic satisfaction, improvements in health and fitness, and an enhanced sense of spiritual well-being. People's engagement with environmental settings is dynamic: meanings, values and behaviours change over time in response to economic, technological, social, political and cultural drivers, and change can be rapid and far-reaching in its implications.

Photo source: Fly agaric fungus by Dave W. Clarke available under a Creative Commons Attribution-NonCommercial license. Flooded street in Oxfordshire by Dachalan available under a Creative Commons Attribution-NonCommercial license. Stack of wood © Copit, 2011 used under license of Shutterstock.com. Cyclists © Maga, 2011 used under license of Shutterstock.com.

trade-offs between different decisions and outcomes that might need to be made).

The UK NEA focuses on 'ecosystem services' that are derived from ecosystem processes including biotic interactions; as such, it does not provide an assessment of 'environmental services' that may be purely abiotic in origin such as minerals extracted from the ecosystem. Furthermore, when considering plausible futures, the UK NEA does not provide a model, or predictions, of the future. Neither does it provide a recipe book of simple answers for decision-makers. Rather, it lays out the evidence base for informed decision-making, organised in a way to enable easy navigation.

1.3.2 Governance of the UK National Ecosystem Assessment

A key feature of the UK NEA is that it is an inclusive process involving a large number of government, academic and private sector institutions, and NGOs. Each institution or individual can offer valuable information and knowledge from a range of perspectives, and the UK NEA includes various groups and bodies as part of its governance structure.

CoChairs of the Expert Panel, Professor Robert Watson (Chief Scientific Adviser, Defra and Strategic Director, Tyndall Centre, University of East Anglia) and Professor Steve Albon (The James Hutton Institute, formerly the Macaulay Land Use Research Institute), led the assessment. Professor Watson brings his invaluable experience from Chairing the MA and the Intergovernmental Panel on Climate Change (IPCC) to the UK NEA process. Professor Albon brings his extensive knowledge of the natural environment of the UK.

A diverse group of academics—consisting of natural scientists, economists and social scientists—formed the 27-member **Expert Panel**. They provided expertise in all technical focal areas of the UK NEA, advised on the assessment process, and approved all chapters for final 'sign-off' after they had been through the external review process (see below). The Expert Panel also defined the key messages of the UK NEA included in the Synthesis Report (Section 1.4).

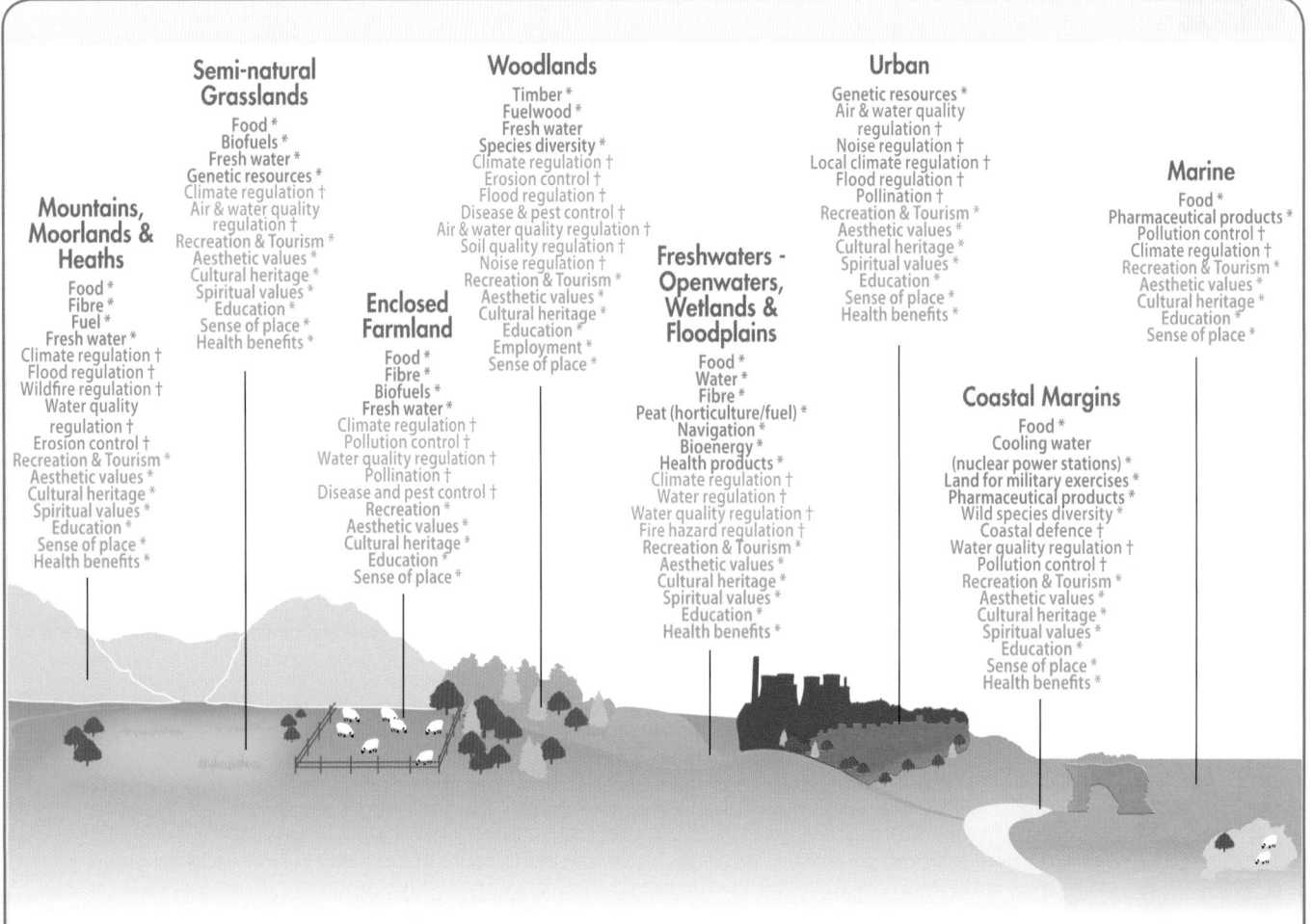

Figure 1.1 The eight Broad Habitats assessed in the UK NEA and examples of the goods and services derived from each. Items marked with an * denote goods, those with † denote services. Items in yellow are considered to be from provisioning services, purple from regulating and green from cultural. The supporting services, including primary production and nutrient cycling, are not listed against individual habitats as they are considered necessary for the production of all other ecosystem services. Source: adapted from the Millennium Ecosystem Assessment (MA 2005).

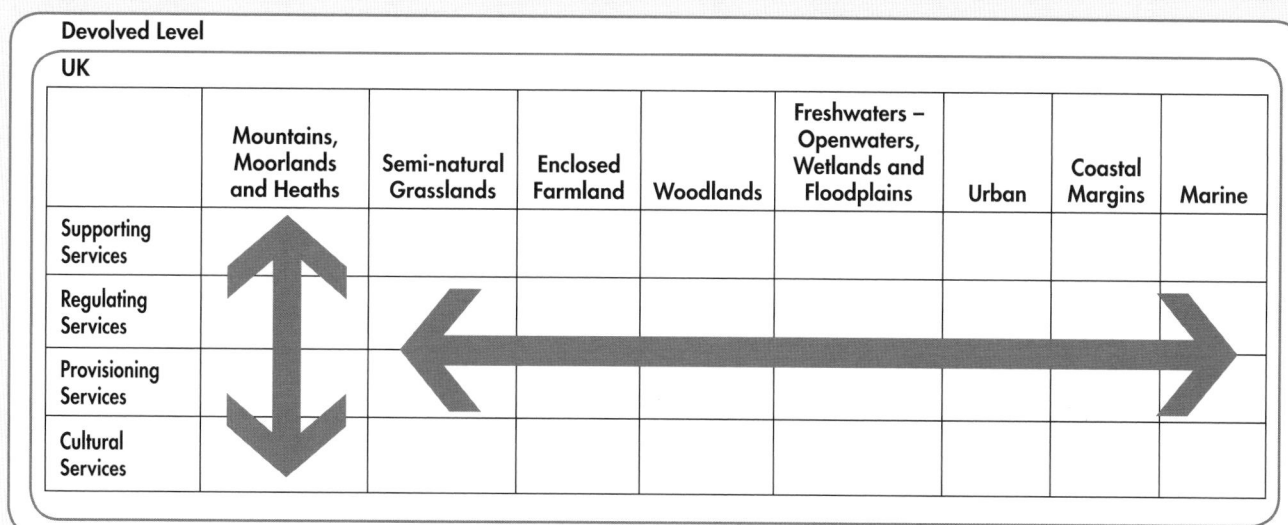

Figure 1.2 Matrix of Broad Habitats and ecosystem services.

The involvement of a wide range of public, private and third sector decision-makers and stakeholders through a **User Group**, as well as a range of wider stakeholder meetings, helped to shape the assessment process and ensure that the outputs are relevant for a variety of different audiences.

The 300-plus authors involved, managed by a group of **Coordinating Lead Authors** (largely natural scientists, but including economists and social scientists), were drawn from more than 50 academic institutions, together with representatives from over 15 government agencies, more than 10 NGOs and 11 private sector institutions.

Each chapter was peer-reviewed by a number of **external reviewers** (on average, seven per chapter, and never less than three for any one chapter) using a standardised review template. After chapters had been revised by the respective Coordinating Lead Author, they were reassessed by the Expert Panel for final approval prior to publication.

Together, the organisations that commissioned the UK NEA—Defra (England), the Devolved Administrations of Northern Ireland, Scotland and Wales (with CCW), NERC and ESRC—formed the **Client Group**, which provided continual oversight and guidance on the whole process.

Coordination was carried out by an independent **Secretariat** based at the United Nations Environment Programme World Conservation Monitoring Centre (UNEP-WCMC). The Secretariat was responsible for coordinating the different assessment activities, and liaising with each of the various author teams, reviewers, data providers, oversight groups and other stakeholders. The Secretariat also provided support to the CoChairs, organised meetings, and managed the timetable, budget, and the review and production processes of the various UK NEA outputs such as the website and communication materials.

1.3.3 Structure of the UK National Ecosystem Assessment

The work was conducted by 26 author teams, working across a matrix (**Figure 1.2**) to answer a set of core questions (**Box 1.4**). Each author team, led by one or two Coordinating Lead Authors, produced a chapter. The three introductory chapters develop the Conceptual Framework for the assessment (Chapter 2), outline the drivers of change operating in the UK (Chapter 3) and examine the links between biodiversity and ecosystem services in the UK (Chapter 4).

Following this, eight author teams assess each of the eight Broad Habitats (Chapters 5–12). These chapters present the state of knowledge of the condition and trends of the Broad Habitat from the end of the Second World War (WWII) to the present day, along with an examination of what is driving that change, the ecosystem services provided and their links to human well-being. They also explore trade-offs and synergies between different ecosystem services, sustainable management options and knowledge gaps. A further four author teams examined the status and trends of four groups of ecosystem services, namely Supporting Services (Chapter 13), Regulating Services (Chapter 14), Provisioning Services (Chapter 15) and Cultural Services (Chapter 16). These chapters further outline the drivers causing change in these services and the consequences of these changes.

The chapters focusing on Broad Habitats and UK-wide ecosystem services are complemented by four chapters which synthesise the evidence and provide the narrative for each of the individual countries within the UK: England (Chapter 17), Northern Ireland (Chapter 18), Scotland (Chapter 19) and Wales (Chapter 20). To assist in putting trends in habitats and ecosystem services within the UK into a global perspective, a short chapter outlines the trends in the dependence of the UK on overseas ecosystem services (Chapter 21). The UK NEA endeavours to understand the contribution that ecosystem services make to the well-being of people in the UK, with three teams assessing the different components of value: Economic values (Chapter 22), Health values (Chapter 23) and Shared Social values (Chapter 24).

The Scenarios assessment team considered possible future trends in ecosystem services under six scenarios, each with two different climate projections (high and low carbon emissions) (Chapter 25). The Economic team then valued changes for a selection of ecosystem services under a range of these plausible futures (Chapter 26). Lastly, the Response Options team considered a range of options for decision-making and the different actors that could play a part in shaping the future for ecosystem services in the UK (Chapter 27).

Chapters 3–27 each begin with a set of key findings. Adopting the approach and terminology used by the IPCC and the MA, those chapters that present the existing evidence base (Chapters 3–21) also include an indication of the level of scientific certainty of each finding: *Virtually certain* (>99% probability of occurrence); *Very likely* (>90% probability); *Likely* (>66% probability); *About as likely as not* (>33–66% probability); *Unlikely* (<33% probability); *Very unlikely* (<10% probability); and *Exceptionally unlikely* (<1% probability). A qualitative scale was also implemented: *well established* (high agreement based on significant evidence); *established but incomplete* (high agreement based on limited evidence); *competing explanations* (low agreement, albeit with significant evidence); and *speculative* (low agreement based on limited evidence). Estimates of certainty were derived from the collective judgement of authors, observational evidence, modelling results and/or theory examined for this assessment.

1.4 Outputs of the UK National Ecosystem Assessment

The UK NEA has been produced in two separate volumes. The **Technical Report** presented here represents the evidence from which the findings and key messages of the UK NEA are derived. It contains each of the chapters prepared by the different author teams (Section 1.4.3). It is not necessarily intended to be read from cover to cover, but is structured as a compendium of the state of knowledge and as a resource for consultation. The Technical Report is fully referenced to enable the reader to explore in depth the supporting literature for any issue of interest.

A **Synthesis Report** (*UK NEA: A Synthesis of the Key Findings* 2011) has also been prepared. This is considerably shorter than the Technical Report and is written for a wider audience of stakeholders and decision-makers. The Synthesis Report presents a series of high-level key messages, together with a summary of the main findings of the UK NEA. It includes consolidated answers to each of the questions in **Box 1.4**, as well as an annex containing the key findings from Chapters 4–16 of the Technical Report. It is comprehensively cross-referenced to the Technical Report in order to enable the reader to source the supporting evidence for the findings it presents. The Synthesis Report was launched by the Secretary of State for the Environment, and by each of the Devolved Administrations, in June 2011.

The Synthesis Report, together with each of the chapters in the Technical Report, has been made available electronically from the UK NEA website, hosted by UNEP-WCMC (http://uknea.unep-wcmc.org). In addition, a series of summary PowerPoint slides, and all major graphics, are also available for download.

1.5 Linkages to Other Initiatives

1.5.1 Links to Other Initiatives Within the UK

The UK NEA is an assessment of the evidence base and, therefore, has drawn on and complements a number of major UK initiatives. These include:

Charting Progress 2: Published by the UK Marine Monitoring and Assessment Strategy community, Charting Progress 2 (CP2; UKMMAS 2010) reports on the state of the UK's seas. It provides the evidence base on progress made since 2005 (Defra, 2005) in five key areas: ocean processes; healthy and biologically diverse seas; clean and safe seas; productive seas; and climate change. One of the attributes of CP2 is the provision of key findings from UK marine research and monitoring for use by policy makers. The evidence base developed for CP2 has been used within the Marine assessment (Chapter 12) of the UK NEA.

Countryside Survey: The Countryside Survey is a regular survey about the state or 'health' of the UK's countryside. The survey has been carried out in 1978, 1984, 1990, 1998 and 2007, which allows change, and the relative rate of change, to be identified. The evidence generated from the Countryside Survey is used to inform polices that influence the management of the countryside. The

Countryside Survey is broken into two components: a field survey using a sample of 1 km² quadrants; and the creation of a Land Cover Map, derived from satellite data.

Foresight Studies: The UK's Foresight Programme, reporting directly to the Government's Chief Scientific Adviser and the Cabinet Office, brings together key people, knowledge and ideas to look beyond normal planning horizons and identify opportunities that could arise from new science and technologies; it then explores the actions that the UK might take to help realise those opportunities. Foresight Studies provide an evidence base, coupled with strategic insights, that helps to inform policy on potential issues. Issues examined by Foresight Studies include: The Future of Food and Farming (2011); Land Use Futures (2010); Sustainable Energy Management and the Built Environment (2008); and Future Flooding (2004).

Making Space for Nature: A Review of England's Wildlife Sites and Ecological Network: Led by Professor Sir John Lawton, and published in 2010, Making Space for Nature (the Lawton Report) is an independent review of England's wildlife sites and the connections between them, specifically looking at where wildlife sites are capable of responding and adapting to climate change and other demands on the land. Key recommendations arising from the Lawton Report include requirements for: better protection and management of designated wildlife sites; the establishment of new Ecological Restoration Zones; and better protection of non-designated wildlife sites.

1.5.2 Links to Other Initiatives in Europe and the World

The UK NEA is framed within an evolving international policy framework. Specifically, the UK NEA will support the UK in meeting a set of global obligations including:

- CBD Decision VIII/9, paragraph 23, which calls for parties to conduct assessments making use of the conceptual framework and methodologies of the MA.
- CBD Decision IX/15, paragraph 1, which invites parties to promote and support integrated national ecosystem assessments, including response scenarios that build on existing frameworks and experiences such as the MA.
- Ramsar Resolution IX.1, Annex A, which updates the 'wise use' concept to include the MA framework and ecosystem services.

The UK NEA also builds on, and contributes to, a number of international science-policy initiatives, some of which are highlighted below:

The MA Follow-up Process: In February 2008, the MA Follow-up Process was established by interested partners of the MA, with the production of A Global Strategy for Turning Knowledge into Action (UNEP/CBD/COP/9/INF/26). The strategy was developed to respond to the recommendations of two independent evaluations of the MA (2005). The evaluations concluded that, despite the advancement in knowledge that the MA contributes, there was little evidence that the MA had made a significant direct impact on policy formulation and decision-making. The key reasons for the lack of impact of the MA have been attributed to:

- gaps in the ecosystem services knowledge base;

- lack of operational tools and methodologies;
- insufficient attention to sub-global assessments;
- limited economic analysis;
- lack of periodic assessments; and
- limited awareness and understanding among decision-makers of the MA findings and the concept of ecosystem services.

In an attempt to give the MA greater traction, a global strategy was created around four objectives:
1. Build the knowledge base.
2. Integrate the MA ecosystem services approach into decision-making at all levels.
3. Disseminate the MA and communicate its findings.
4. Future global assessments.

In particular, under the first objective, ecosystem assessments are encouraged at different scales. Efforts have been made to create a network of such assessments, coordinated by a Secretariat, to ensure consistency with the MA framework and to contribute to international lesson-sharing and a possible further global assessment.

The Economics of Ecosystems and Biodiversity: The Economics of Ecosystems and Biodiversity (TEEB) study is a major international initiative whose findings were published in 2010. The aim of TEEB was to draw attention to the global economic benefits of biodiversity, in turn, highlighting the growing costs of biodiversity loss and ecosystem degradation. Bringing together experts from the fields of science, economics and policy, TEEB produced a series of reports examining: the global economic costs of biodiversity loss, and the costs and benefits of actions to reduce these losses; guidance for policy makers at different scales (including consideration of subsides and incentive, environmental liability, national income accounting and implementing instruments such as Payments for Ecosystem Services); access to tools for measuring business impacts on ecosystems and biodiversity; and raising awareness of the contribution of ecosystem services and biodiversity to human well-being and how individual action can have an impact.

The Intergovernmental Science-Policy Platform on Biodiversity and Ecosystem Services: Since 2008, UNEP has been facilitating discussion on a proposed Intergovernmental Science-Policy Platform on Biodiversity and Ecosystem Services (IPBES). This has been conducted through three Ad Hoc Intergovernmental and Multi-Stakeholder meetings. At the final meeting in Busan, Republic of Korea (7–11 June 2010), the plenary adopted the Busan Outcome (UNEP/IPBES/3/3) which recommends the establishment of IPBES. This recommendation has subsequently been endorsed by the UN General Assembly (resolution number 65/162). It is envisaged that, during 2011, IPBES will be established and that ecosystem assessments at national and regional scales, such as the UK NEA, will make an important contribution.

1.6 Next Steps: Building on the UK National Ecosystem Assessment

The UK NEA provides a major foundation of evidence for Defra's new White Paper on the Natural Environment for England. As such, the assessment process is closely tied to government policy making. The approach taken and methods developed within the UK NEA have significant potential to influence future action on the natural environment and the direction of national development.

To realise this potential will require the findings and messages of the UK NEA to be widely disseminated. Consultation with stakeholders and the User Group identified a number of ways in which the findings might be packaged for specific audiences, and there will be ongoing efforts beyond the launch of the Synthesis Report to ensure the UK NEA reaches audiences across a variety of sectors and scales.

The UK NEA is a first step in assessing the UK ecosystems and their services for human well-being and establishes a comprehensive evidence base to support decision-making by different actors and at different scales. While the UK NEA provides comprehensive answers to a number of the questions posed at the start, many gaps in knowledge were uncovered during the assessment process. Effectively, the UK NEA provides a road map for future research and monitoring needs to better understand the UK's ecosystems, their services and benefits to society. Some of this future research may be undertaken as part of LWEC.

References

Ash, N., Blanco, H., Brown, C., Garcia, K., Henrichs, T., Lucas, N., Raudsepp-Hearne, C., Simpson, R.D., Scholes, R., Tomich, T., Vira, B. & Zurek, M. (2010) Ecosystems and Human Well-being: A Manual for Assessment Practitioners. Island Press, Washington, D.C.

Carey, P.D., Wallis, S., Chamberlain, P.M., Cooper, A., Emmett, B.A., Maskell, L.C., McCann, T., Murphy, J., Norton, L.R., Reynolds, B., Scott, W.A., Simpson, I.C., Smart, S.M. & Ullyett, J.M. (2008) Countryside Survey: UK Results from 2007. NERC/Centre for Ecology & Hydrology, 105pp. (CEH Project Number: C03259).

Defra (Department for Environment, Food and Rural Affairs) (2005) Charting Progress – an Integrated Assessment of the State of UK Seas. Defra Report (Crown copyright). [online] Available at: <http://chartingprogress.defra.gov.uk/feeder/chartingprogress.pdf > [Accessed 21.02.11].

Defra (Department for Environment, Food and Rural Affairs) (2007) Securing a healthy natural environment: An action plan for embedding an ecosystems approach. Defra, London.

Defra (Department for Environment, Food and Rural Affairs) (2010) Fourth National Report to the United Nations Convention on Biological Diversity: United Kingdom. [online] Available at <www.cbd.int/doc/world/gb/gb-nr-04-en.pdf> [Accessed 19.04.11].

Foresight (2004) Future Flooding: Final Project Report. The Government Office for Science, London.

Foresight (2008) Sustainable Energy Management and the Built Environment Project: Final Project Report. The Government Office for Science, London.

Foresight (2010) Land Use Futures Project: Final Project Report. The Government Office for Science, London.

Foresight (2011) The Future of Food and Farming: Final Project Report. The Government Office for Science, London.

Fuller, R.M., Smith, G.M., Sanderson, J.M., Hill, R.A. & Thomson, A.G. (2002) The UK Land Cover Map 2000: construction of a parcel-based vector map from satellite images. *Cartographic Journal*, **39**, 15–25.

Haines-Young, R., Fish, R., Potschin, M., Brown, C., Tindall, C. and Walmsley, S. (2008) Scoping the potential benefits of undertaking an MA-style assessment for England. Full Technical Report to Defra (Project Code NR0118).

House of Commons Environmental Audit (2007) The UN Millennium Ecosystem Assessment. First Report of Session 2006-7; HC77, 58pp.

Lawton, J.H., Brotherton, P.N.M., Brown, V.K., Elphick, C., Fitter, A.H., Forshaw, J., Haddow, R.W., Hilborne, S., Leafe, R.N., Mace, G.M., Southgate, M.P., Sutherland, W.J., Tew, T.E., Varley, J., & Wynne, G.R. (2010) Making Space for Nature: a review of England's wildlife sites and ecological network. Report to Defra.

MA (Millennium Ecosystem Assessment) (2005) Ecosystems and Human Well-being: Synthesis. Island Press, Washington D.C.

TEEB (The Economics of Ecosystems and Biodiversity) (2010) The Economics of Ecosystems and Biodiversity: Ecological and Economic Foundations. EarthScan.

UK NEA (UK National Ecosystem Assessment) (2011) Synthesis of the Key Findings. UNEP-WCMC, Cambridge.

UKMMAS (UK Marine Monitoring and Assessment Strategy) (2010) Charting Progress 2: The State of UK Seas. Published by the Department for Environment Food and Rural Affairs on behalf of UKMMAS. TSO, London. 166pp. ISBN 9780112432937. Available at: <http://chartingprogress.defra.gov.uk/resources> [Accessed 06.06.10].

UNEP/IPBES/3/3 (2010) *Report of the third ad hoc intergovernmental and multi-stakeholder meeting on an intergovernmental science-policy platform on biodiversity and ecosystem services.* UNEP.

Chapter 2:
Conceptual Framework and Methodology

Coordinating Lead Authors: Georgina M. Mace and Ian Bateman
Lead Authors: Steve Albon, Andrew Balmford, Claire Brown, Andrew Church, Roy Haines-Young, Jules N. Pretty, Kerry Turner, Bhaskar Vira and Jonathan Winn

2.1 Introduction

This chapter introduces a conceptual framework and methodology for the UK National Ecosystem Assessment (UK NEA). It is intended that this will provide a readily understood, logical and consistent approach to enhance coherence across chapters and permit the derivation of clear and generally applicable conclusions. A conceptual framework is a representation of the main components of a system or issue of interest, showing their interrelationships or linkages. It serves to develop a common understanding of which issues should be included in an assessment. It provides a basis for different groups to contribute their analyses of specific issues and linkages, and for these analyses to combine in a logical manner in an overall assessment. The framework should also assist in the identification of data or knowledge gaps–in the context of the UK NEA, these gaps may form a focus for extending the assessment in the future.

The framework described here is based on existing methods, especially those used for the Millennium Ecosystem Assessment (MA) (MA 2005). The MA framework—in particular, its broad definition of ecosystem services and their classification into provisioning, regulating, supporting and cultural services—has proven to have traction for both science and policy development. However, the UK NEA also incorporates post-MA advances, especially for the economic valuation of ecosystem services and procedures developed to avoid the double counting of such services. Therefore, we take particular note of conceptual advances proposed for The Economics of Ecosystems and Biodiversity (TEEB) project (Ring *et al.* 2010; Balmford *et al.* 2011), those used for the review of ecosystem services in Europe (Fitter *et al.* 2010), as well as detailed suggestions for enabling economic valuation of ecosystem services (Fisher & Turner 2008) .

The framework has some additional distinctive elements. Firstly, we recognised at the outset that a major objective of the UK NEA was to incorporate, as far as possible, a systematic and comprehensive valuation of ecosystem services. Therefore, we developed a framework which would yield the type of information which economists need for monetary valuation, but also incorporated flexibility to allow non-monetary valuation of services that cannot be meaningfully assessed in monetary terms. Secondly, we have explicitly identified elements for incorporation into the assessment that are relevant for the UK; hence, the classifications of ecosystems (Broad Habitat types), ecosystem services, change processes and outcomes impinging on human well-being are all significant in the UK context. Thirdly, the methodology clearly recognises the remit of the UK NEA to consider policy-relevant changes occurring over a defined timescale. These are implemented through a series of scenarios and response options involving feasible and decision-pertinent changes in the environment, markets and policy. Finally, we have taken a slightly different approach to the treatment of biodiversity and have separated out the underpinning natural processes that depend to a greater or lesser degree on biodiversity, from landscapes, seascapes, habitats and wild species. These latter elements of biodiversity are part of our natural heritage and, through the pleasure they bring to many people, form one kind of cultural ecosystem service.

2.2 Overall Conceptual Framework

The conceptual framework is based around the processes that link human societies and their well-being with the environment (**Figure 2.1**). Taking the core UK NEA questions as a starting point, the conceptual framework emphasises the role of ecosystems in providing services that bring improvements in well-being to people.

Here, we provide an overview of the conceptual framework illustrated in **Figure 2.1**, with each component being described in more detail later in the chapter. Starting at the bottom right of **Figure 2.1**, we see that the basis for ecosystems (Section 2.3) are the fundamental earth processes on land, and in water and air—processes which involve all living things. The most widely accepted definition of an 'ecosystem' is: "A dynamic complex of plant, animal and micro-organism communities and their non-living environment interacting as a functional unit" (MA 2005;). Thus, an ecosystem is a complex where interactions among the biotic (living) and abiotic (non-living) components of that unit determine its properties and set limits to the types of processes that take place there. Ecosystems vary widely in spatial scale and their key processes operate across a range of rates that are overlapping in time and space. In practice, ecosystems are usually defined by the scope of the function, process or problem being studied. For the purposes of the UK NEA, we use the Broad Habitat types from the Countryside Survey as the basis for the classification of ecosystems (Section 2.3).

People are part of ecosystems and, like all other living organisms, affect the processes taking place there, as well as deriving welfare gains from them. Compared to other organisms, people have an enormous influence on ecosystems, both in the UK and elsewhere, as a result of the population numbers and densities, patterns of consumption and use of technology.

The definition of 'ecosystem services' developed by the UK NEA is the outputs of ecosystems from which people derive benefits (MA 2005). In the UK NEA, we distinguish between the 'ecosystem processes and intermediate ecosystem services' (Section 2.4) and the 'final ecosystem services' that directly deliver welfare gains and/or losses to people (Section 2.5). This distinction is important to avoid double counting in the valuation of ecosystem services (Fisher & Turner 2008). Section 2.4 also introduces biodiversity and geodiversity and details the way that these components of the natural environment are related to ecosystems and their services.

There are many outputs from ecosystems, but while ecosystems function and deliver services, people benefit in well-being terms from the outcomes of those services. The

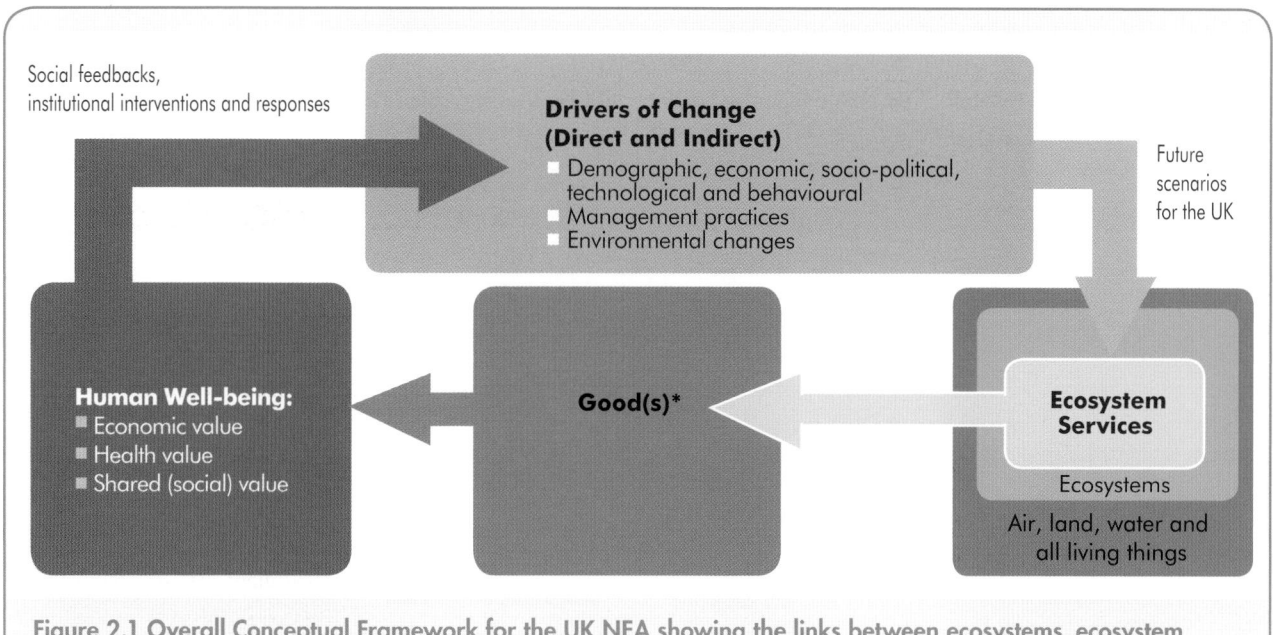

Figure 2.1 Overall Conceptual Framework for the UK NEA showing the links between ecosystems, ecosystem services, good(s), valuation, human well-being, change processes and scenarios. *Note that the term good(s) includes all use and non-use, material and non-material outputs from ecosystems that have value for people.

crucial link between services (as outputs of ecosystems), the outcomes they produce (the 'goods') and the 'values' that these generate for people is explained in Section 2.6. A distinction is also drawn between the overall value of a good and the portion of that value which can be attributed to relevant final ecosystem services. It is clear that the value of a good which can only be produced by applying major inputs of manufactured and/or human capital to some ecosystem service cannot be attributed solely to that service.

While some values can be measured using monetary valuation, certain kinds of benefits to people from ecosystems are not measurable through quantitative economic approaches. Therefore, we define additional well-being measures as health and shared (social) values. The three components of well-being—economic (monetary) value, health value and shared (social) value—are described in Section 2.7. The way that people perceive ecosystems and the extent to which they do or do not obviously provide values affects the choices people make about how to use and manage the environment. These choices may be driven by individuals, communities, societies or governments through a complex series of processes and interactions. However, the ultimate consequences are changes in drivers affecting the environment (Section 2.8).

The UK's ecosystems have changed dramatically over the past 50 years as a result of many direct and indirect drivers, but especially due to land use change to support food production and infrastructure development for the growing population. Over the coming decades, ecosystems will continue to change, transformed by a range of indirect and direct drivers. Increasingly, the many ways that decisions, policies and behaviours influence rates and types of environmental change will be affected by other trends that may be less easy to alter or influence. In particular, there are many ongoing changes in the environment

(especially climate change and land use change), while society itself is continually transforming, with different preferences and markets developing, and trends affecting the demographic structure (age structures, household size, urban-rural distributions, etc.) of different areas of the UK. These changes in the UK NEA are incorporated in analyses of scenarios (Section 2.9) and response options (Section 2.10) for potential futures for the UK's ecosystems and ecosystem services.

2.3 Ecosystems and Broad Habitats

The UK NEA has defined ecosystems based upon recognised 'Broad Habitats' within the UK (Jackson 2000). In the UK and much of Europe, the classification of ecosystems can be considered as significantly overlapping with that of habitats. A definition of a habitat is an ecological or environmental area that is inhabited by a particular animal or plant species. In Europe, Annex I of the EU Habitats Directive lists 231 European natural habitat types including 71 priority types (i.e. habitat types in danger of disappearance and whose natural range mainly falls within the territory of the EU). The Broad Habitats approach is also used in the Countryside Survey—a major source of information on change in the UK's countryside (Carey et al. 2008). For reporting purposes, the UK NEA groups these into categories focusing on the interactions of habitats with their physical and social environments (eight types; Chapters 5–12) (Table 2.1). The field mapping rules from the Countryside Survey explain how these habitats were identified (Maskell et al. 2008).

Table 2.1 Broad Habitat types as defined in the UK NEA.

UK Ecosystem (Broad Habitat)	UK NEA component habitat	UK Biodiversity Action Plan (BAP) priority habitats
Mountains, Moorlands and Heaths	Bracken	• n/a
	Dwarf Shrub Heath	• Lowland heathland • Upland heathland
	Upland Fen, Marsh and Swamp	• Upland flushes, fens and swamps
	Bog	• Blanket bog
	Montane	• Mountain heaths and willow scrub
	Inland Rock	• Inland rock outcrop and scree habitats • Limestone pavements
Semi-natural Grasslands	Neutral Grassland	• Lowland meadows • Upland hay meadows
	Acid Grassland	• Lowland dry acid grassland
	Calcareous Grassland	• Lowland calcareous grassland • Upland calcareous grassland
	Fen, Marsh and Swamp	• Purple moor grass and rush pastures
Enclosed Farmland	Arable and Horticultural	• Arable field margins
	Improved Grassland	• Coastal and floodplain grazing marsh
	Boundary and Linear Features	• Hedgerows
Woodlands	Broadleaved, Mixed and Yew Woodland	• Lowland beech and yew woodland • Lowland mixed deciduous woodland • Upland oakwood • Upland birchwoods • Upland mixed ashwoods • Wet woodland
	Coniferous Woodland	• Native pinewoods
Freshwaters—Openwaters, Wetlands and Floodplains	Standing Open Waters and Canals	• Mesotrophic lakes • Eutrophic standing waters • Oligotrophic and dystrophic lakes • Aquifer fed naturally fluctuating water bodies • Ponds
	Rivers and Streams	• Rivers
	Bog	• Lowland raised bogs
	Fen, Marsh and Swamp	• Lowland fens • Reedbeds
Urban	Built up Areas and Gardens	• Open mosaic habitats on previously developed land (brownfield sites)
Coastal Margins	Sand Dunes	
	Machair	
	Shingle	
	Sea Cliffs	
	Saltmarsh	
	Coastal Lagoons	
Marine	Intertidal Rock	
	Intertidal Sediments	
	Subtidal Rock	
	Shallow Subtidal Sediment	
	Shelf Subtidal Sediment	
	Deep-sea habitats	

2.4 Ecosystem Processes

2.4.1 Physical, Chemical and Biological Processes

Ecosystems are complexes where biotic (living: biological) and abiotic (non-living: chemical and physical) components interact. The interactions between biotic and abiotic components of ecosystems ultimately determine the quantity, quality and reliability of ecosystem services. In **Figure 2.1**, we refer to the fundamental underpinning elements as land, air, water and all living things. Under this heading are the biological, physical and chemical components of the ecosystem and their interactions; these determine the functioning of the ecosystem processes from which ecosystem services result.

As the physical, chemical and biological features and components of ecosystems change, so will the processes that take place there and, consequently, the functions and services that can be delivered. There is much complexity in these interactions, which are not well understood even in relatively simple ecosystems. Importantly, alongside present uncertainties, is the fact that we do not know how these processes and interactions are going to change under complex and global stressors like climate change. It is not the role of the UK NEA to try to disentangle this complexity, which is still an active and growing area of environmental science research, but we do aim to identify particularly significant gaps in knowledge in the chapters dealing with particular habitats or ecosystem services. The implications for the UK NEA and for environmental protection policy are, nonetheless, very important.

The physical and biological underpinning elements of ecosystem processes cannot be ignored since the processes themselves are vulnerable to change (not just the services that we manage ecosystems for) and they have their own characteristic rates and thresholds. In practice, this means that ecosystem responses to environmental change may quite commonly be non-linear, hard to predict and/or irreversible (Carpenter *et al.* 2009). Therefore, as conditions move further away from observed states, say as a result of gradual environmental change, the likelihood of some unexpected shift in the ecosystem and its dynamics will increase. These changes may affect the ecosystem components and have a significant effect on important services (Nicholson *et al.* 2009). For example, increased fertiliser application leading to the eutrophication of rivers and lakes has completely altered ecosystem functions and trophic structures; often, these functions do not recover quickly nor track back on the same trajectory (Scheffer & Carpenter 2003). Another example comes from recent field experiments on the effects of artificially increased levels of atmospheric carbon dioxide on forest production. As expected, primary production increases with carbon dioxide concentrations, but in some of the experiments, a threshold is quickly reached for wood production (Norby *et al.* 2002) and, thereafter, carbon is stored below ground in root systems where it cycles much more quickly back into the atmosphere. The reasons for this are not known (it is likely that some other nutrient, such as nitrogen, becomes limiting (Norby *et al.* 2010)), but the implications for atmospheric carbon capture and storage in forest systems are important. These are just two examples, but illustrate why we emphasise the physical and biological underpinning processes throughout the UK NEA.

Ecosystem processes generally depend on the right combinations of certain biotic and/or abiotic components being present in an ecosystem. However, sometimes what matters for ecosystem functioning is not just the presence of a particular component or its amount, but instead the variety or diversity of types. Biodiversity and geodiversity are terms used to reflect this feature of ecosystems.

2.4.2 Biodiversity

Despite its clear importance to the ecosystem service concept, the term 'biodiversity' is defined in many ways and given various meanings in other ecosystem assessments and other ecosystem services related documents. Previous ecosystem assessments have treated it in a variety of ways including as an underpinning biological process and as an ecosystem service itself. Sometimes biodiversity is equated with ecosystems, sometimes it is equated simply with species richness.

For the UK NEA, we adopt the definition given by the Convention on Biological Diversity (CBD) which is broad and inclusive, and describes biodiversity as the: "variability among living organisms from all sources including, *inter alia*, terrestrial, marine and other aquatic ecosystems and the ecological complexes of which they are part. This includes diversity within species, between species and of ecosystems." This definition includes all the different levels of biological diversity and the interactions between them, and emphasises the importance of variability. Using this definition, there are three different ways in which biodiversity is considered in the UK NEA.

Firstly, biodiversity is important for the fundamental ecosystem processes that underpin final ecosystem services. For example, the dynamics of many soil nutrient cycles are determined by the composition of biological communities in the soil (Hector *et al.* 2000; Bradford *et al.* 2002). Resistance to the effects of pests and environmental change is also increased in more diverse biological communities. Interactions between herbivores and plants, and between carnivores and herbivores, have an impact on the vegetation type affecting both biomass and species composition. Therefore, the biological composition of ecosystems, measured as biodiversity, has a key role to play in ecosystem service delivery (Díaz *et al.* 2006). Broadly speaking, biodiversity, measured as variability, probably contributes more to regulating and cultural services, and to the longer-term resilience of ecosystem processes, than to provisioning services, at least over the short-term (Diaz *et al.* 2007). Some diversity effects may be attributable to composition, i.e. the presence of certain key species or the correlation between species richness and functional trait diversity (Hooper *et al.* 2005). The extent to which species richness is important compared to, for example, biomass or structural and trait diversity, is an area of active research (Suding *et al.* 2008). We include consideration of the insurance role of biodiversity: more diversity buffers systems against change (Hooper *et al.* 2005) and offers more options for the future (Yachi & Loreau 1999).

Secondly, biological diversity at the level of genes and species may directly contribute to some goods and their values. For example, the potential value of medicinal plants and the potential for bio-prospecting increases with the number and evolutionary distinctiveness of species. Genetic diversity of wild crop relatives is important for the improvement of crop strains, and the same will be true for biofuel crops and livestock. Therefore, genetic diversity (or surrogates such as wild species richness or phylogenetic diversity) may itself be a final ecosystem service directly contributing to goods. Hence, we include wild species diversity as a final ecosystem service that contributes to both provisioning and cultural services.

Thirdly, many components of biodiversity are valued by people for other reasons. These include the appreciation of wildlife and of scenic places, and their contribution to spiritual, inspirational, educational, religious and recreational experiences. People value places with a diversity of species, especially the more colourful and spectacular animals and plants. Retaining the full complement of UK wild species is important to many people, and a rich and varied wildlife contributes to cultural cohesion and development. Therefore, biodiversity is sometimes also a good in itself and delivers a distinct value.

2.4.3 Geodiversity

Geodiversity is a term used less commonly than biodiversity, but is defined similarly as the variety of rocks, minerals, fossils, landforms, sediments and soils in a place. Geodiversity supports the provision of basic raw materials and the foundation upon which ecosystems are based. Preserving geodiversity in the landscape is important for several different reasons. Other than for the provision of raw materials, the amount of geological diversity at a site may not be as important as the geodiversity in a landscape. Therefore, geodiversity, like biodiversity, is a good in itself and underpins some important cultural final ecosystem services. People like and wish to preserve rare and distinctive landforms and geological formations. But geodiversity is not only relevant for cultural services. The type and complement of geological forms affects physical, chemical and biological functions, particularly in freshwater systems, coastal areas and uplands. In addition, the heterogeneity of geological formations within landscapes underpins spatial variation in habitats and biodiversity. Spatial heterogeneity of geological formations and habitats in an area will, therefore, be one determinant of the quality and diversity of the ecosystem services that can be delivered there. Finally, the local spatial heterogeneity of landforms, habitats and biodiversity will increase the potential interactions among them, with positive or negative consequences for ecosystem services.

The UK NEA includes a chapter on biodiversity, but not one on geodiversity. Environmental change has a huge effect on biodiversity, but comparatively little effect on the diversity of rocks, minerals, fossils, landforms, sediments and soils. Their quantities and qualities may be changed through direct and indirect extraction, but direct intervention in ecosystems through changed management practices or polices is unlikely to have major impacts on geodiversity or the ability of the ecosystems involved to deliver services. Most processes influencing geodiversity operate on much longer timescales than those influencing biodiversity, although direct changes by people to landforms can affect local geodiversity. Because biodiversity is more likely to be influenced by changed management and environmental change, with consequences for ecosystem service delivery, it warrants more detailed treatment (Chapter 4); geodiversity is considered in most detail in Chapters 16 and 13.

2.5 Ecosystem Services

'Ecosystem services' are the outputs of ecosystems from which people derive benefits. In the UK NEA, ecosystem services are considered under the broad headings of provisioning, supporting, regulating and cultural services. This classification derives from the MA (2005) and is a useful means for distinguishing broad categories of services. 'Final ecosystem services' directly contribute to the good(s) that are valued by people, and people tend to intervene or manage ecosystems to influence the delivery of final ecosystem services. Intermediate ecosystem services and 'ecosystem processes' underpin the final ecosystem services, but are not directly linked to good(s) (**Figure 2.2**) and are less often the focus for management. In fact, ecosystem processes are often inadvertently affected by management for final ecosystem services, sometimes with deleterious consequences.

The goods that are derived from final ecosystem services have a value, only some of which is derived from ecosystems because of capital inputs (from manufacturing and remanufacturing) that add value. Different goods will have different proportions of value attributable to ecosystems versus human capital inputs.

As discussed further in Section 2.6, this separation between ecosystem processes/intermediate services and final ecosystem services is necessary to avoid double counting when valuing the benefits derived from ecosystems (Fisher & Turner 2008). In **Table 2.2** we show the full list of ecosystem services used in the UK NEA, classified according to both ecosystem service type (provisioning, regulating, cultural and supporting) and whether or not they are final ecosystem services or intermediate services/processes.

It should be noted that provisioning and cultural services are always classed as final ecosystem services; regulating services may be either final services or intermediate services/ processes; and supporting services are always intermediate services/processes. The provisioning, regulating, cultural and supporting services classification shown in **Table 2.2** maps on to the MA classification which is already in general use. However, for the UK NEA, we develop the distinction between final ecosystem services and intermediate ecosystem services and/or processes in order to allow the valuation of final ecosystem services.

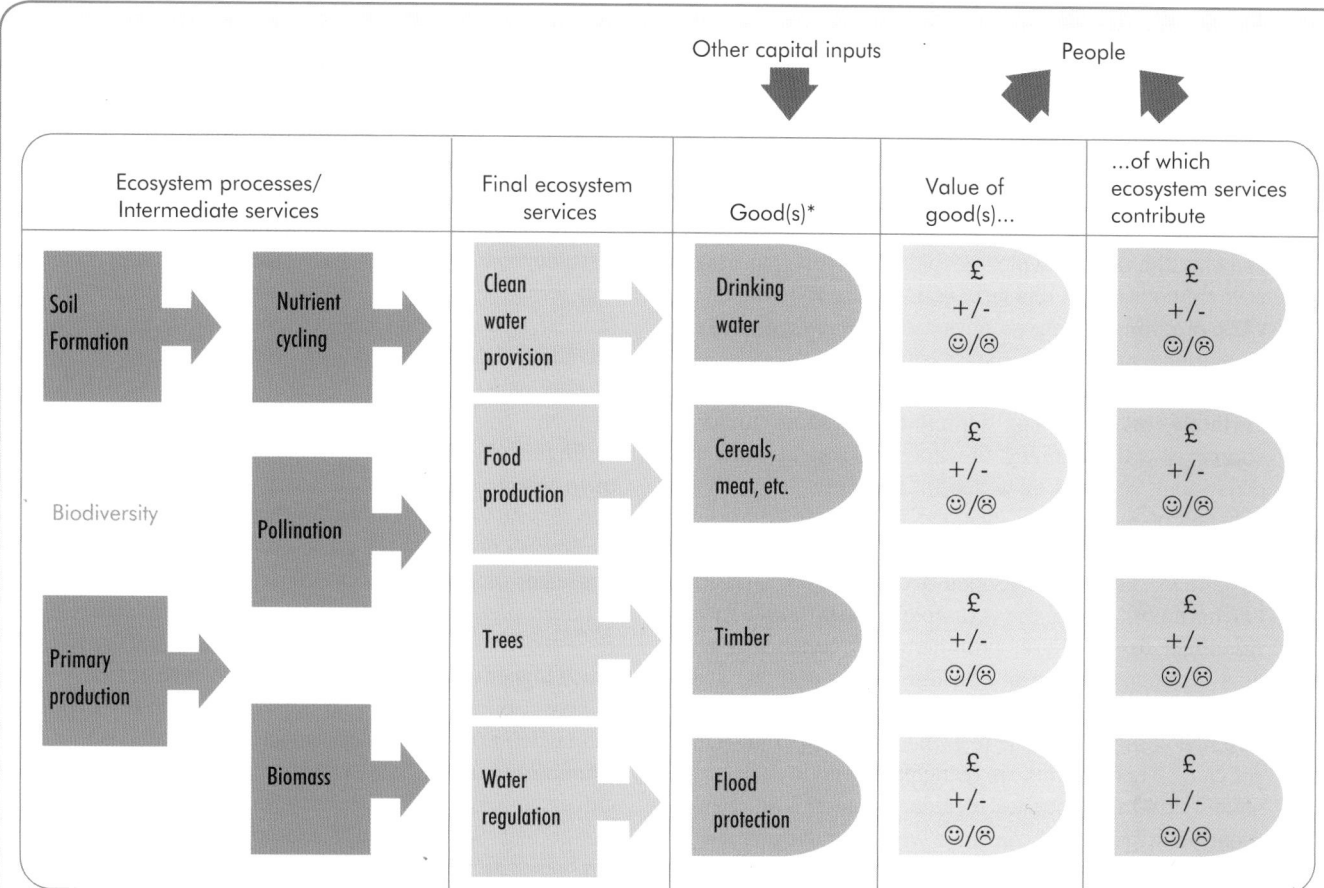

Figure 2.2 Schematic diagram of a small selection of ecosystem processes and services to illustrate how ecosystem processes are linked to final ecosystem services and the goods and values they generate for people. The final ecosystem services are the outcomes from ecosystems that directly lead to good(s) that are valued by people. The full value is not just from the ecosystem, but depends on the addition of inputs from society (other capital inputs) and the value is often context dependent. The final value of the good(s) is, therefore, attributable to both the ecosystem and human inputs. For a fair valuation of ecosystem services, both the separation of final ecosystem services from underpinning processes and the accounting for other capital inputs is necessary. *Note: the term 'good(s)' includes all use and non-use, material and non-material outputs from ecosystems that have value for people. Source: adapted from Fisher et al. (2008).

Table 2.2 Ecosystem services in the UK NEA classified according to both ecosystem service type (provisioning, regulating, cultural and supporting) and whether or not they are final ecosystem services or intermediate services and/or processes. For each final ecosystem service an example of the good(s) it delivers is provided in italics.

Ecosystem processes/intermediate services		Final ecosystem services (example of goods)	
Supporting services	• Primary production • Soil formation • Nutrient cycling • Water cycling	**Provisioning services**	• Crops, livestock, fish (food) • Trees, standing vegetation, peat (fibre, energy, carbon sequestration) • Water supply (domestic and industrial water) • Wild species diversity (bioprospecting, medicinal plants)
	• Decomposition • Weathering • Climate regulation • Pollination • Disease and pest regulation • Ecological interactions • Evolutionary processes • Wild species diversity	**Cultural services**	• Wild species diversity (recreation) • Environmental settings (recreation, tourism, spiritual/religious)
		Regulating services	• Climate regulation (equable climate) • Pollination • Detoxification and purification in soils, air and water (pollution control) • Hazard regulation (erosion control, flood control) • Noise regulation (noise control) • Disease and pest regulation (disease and pest control)

Some services straddle more than one category. Climate regulation, disease and pest regulation, wild species diversity and pollination are both intermediate and final ecosystem services depending on the good(s) being considered. For example, a wider diversity of crop relatives is an intermediate process necessary to sustain the final ecosystem service of crops and livestock that deliver food. Wild species diversity is considered in the biodiversity chapter, but it is a final ecosystem service providing goods related to cultural services, as well as provisioning services as wild species are a source for bioprospecting, natural medicine and genetic variation for the selection of new agricultural crops and livestock breeds.

2.6 Goods

In moving from the consideration of ecosystems and their services, to the well-being that they bring to people, we adopt (and to some extent adapt) the terminology of economics. Specifically, we consider the concept of 'goods' as being the objects which people value. It is important to note that our use of this term goes well beyond the narrow view of goods simply as physical items bought and sold in markets and, hence, possessing market prices which in some (potentially distorted) form reflect their value. Certainly, market-priced commodities are an important source of values, many of which derive, in part, from ecosystem services (e.g. food). However, the UK NEA concept of goods also includes well-being items which either partly or wholly embody ecosystem services, but have no market price (e.g. open-access outdoor recreation). Furthermore, while the examples listed above involve the direct use of the environment, our concept of goods also includes a range of non-use values associated with those ecosystem services which generate well-being in the absence of any direct use (e.g. the knowledge that remote, yet valued, ecosystems are being preserved in their natural state). Note also that we include within this deliberately broad term 'goods' whose value we do not see any realistic prospect of monetising, such as the spiritual dimensions of the environment. This latter example might well cause some to argue against the implied commodification of the environment they perceive in the term 'goods'. However, we make no such implication. Indeed, the term is merely used as shorthand for 'good things' whose presence yields well-being and whose absence lowers that well-being.

Our definition of goods allows us to separate the source of value from the size of that value (**Figure 2.3**). Often we will term the value of welfare improvements as 'benefits' (and by corollary, the value of welfare losses as 'disbenefits', an admittedly ungainly term, but one which allows us to distinguish between this and the 'costs' of delivering benefits). This leads us to some further distinctions. Firstly, distinguishing between the terms 'good' and 'value' allows us to reflect the fact that the value of many goods is context specific and varies over time and space. This is true of a great variety of goods (e.g. the value of a bottle of cold freshwater is greater on a hot day) and those derived from ecosystem services are certainly no exception. So, for example, the recreational services provided by a woodland can yield a much higher value when located on the edge of a large town (where it offers recreational opportunities to the populace) than when a physically identical forest is situated at the top of a remote mountain. Indeed, shifts in the location of a resource can also alter both the value and range of services provided. Continuing our woodland example, alternative locations can generate additional biodiversity habitat, carbon storage

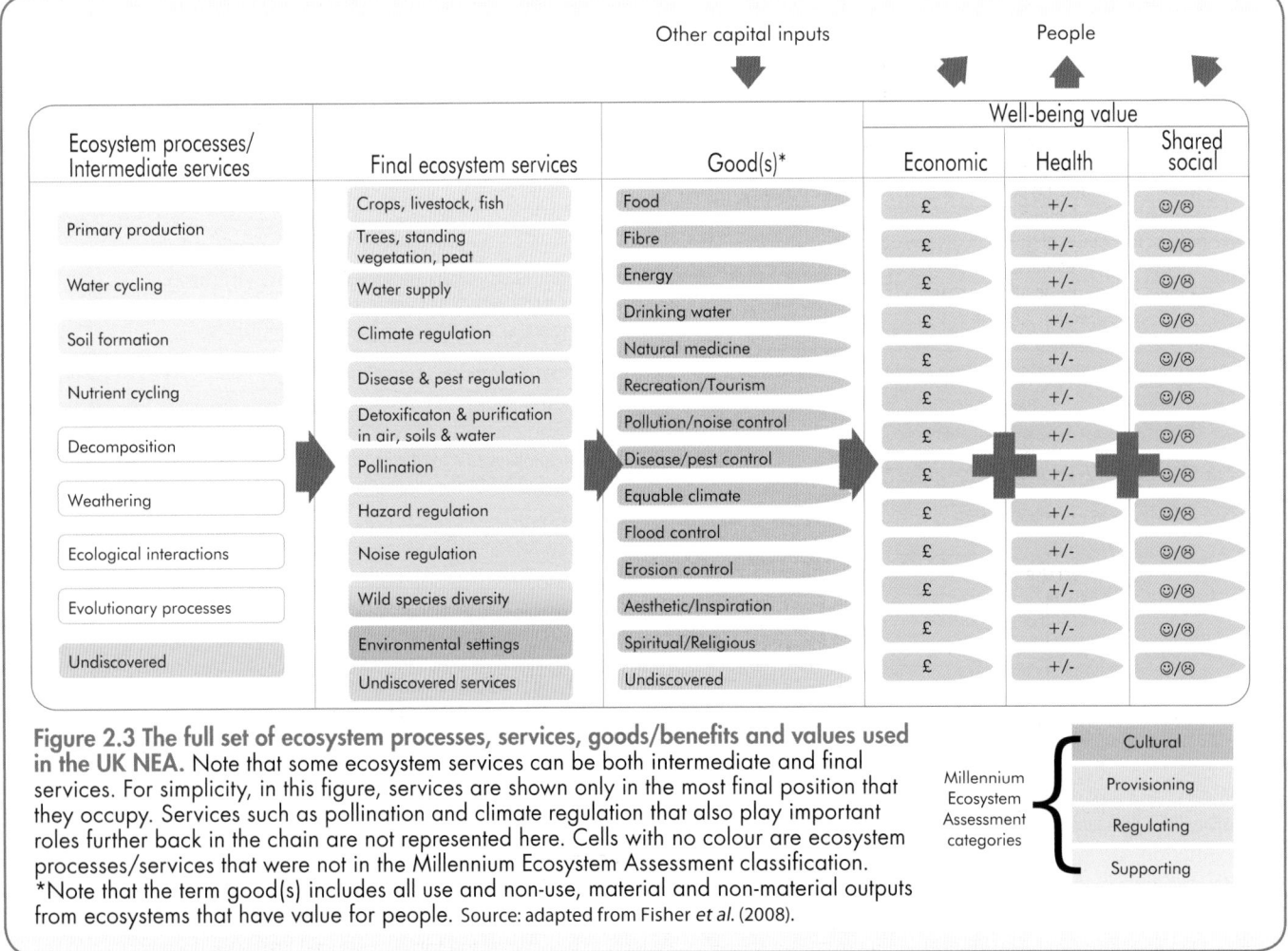

Figure 2.3 The full set of ecosystem processes, services, goods/benefits and values used in the UK NEA. Note that some ecosystem services can be both intermediate and final services. For simplicity, in this figure, services are shown only in the most final position that they occupy. Services such as pollination and climate regulation that also play important roles further back in the chain are not represented here. Cells with no colour are ecosystem processes/services that were not in the Millennium Ecosystem Assessment classification. *Note that the term good(s) includes all use and non-use, material and non-material outputs from ecosystems that have value for people. Source: adapted from Fisher *et al.* (2008).

and visual amenity values. Therefore, much of the analysis contained in the UK NEA is necessarily spatially explicit, while the assessment also stretches both back in time and forward into the future.

A second issue is that, while ecosystem services are vital to the generation of many goods, in many cases we would be in error if we ascribed all of the value of those goods to their corresponding ecosystem services. Many goods can only be generated by applying manufactured capital (e.g. machinery) and human capital (e.g. ingenuity) to ecosystem services (**Figure 2.2**). For example, while nature generates the massive temperate forests of northern latitudes, it is only through the application of human and manufactured capital that we obtain timber. Therefore, it would be incorrect to ascribe all of the value of timber to ecosystem services. Some of that value is due to capital which could be transferred to generate alternative values.

Similarly, we do not consider the value of the subsequent remanufacture of goods. The timber mentioned above might be subjected to further additions of human and manufactured capital to produce furniture. It would clearly be incorrect to add the value of the furniture to that of the timber and ascribe the sum to ecosystem services—such a procedure would massively inflate the value of the latter and undermine the credibility of the assessment. Such an error is analogous to the double counting problem that would arise if we added the value of supporting services to those of final ecosystem services.

There is another type of value which we introduce here, but do not attempt to deal with in this assessment. 'Intrinsic value' refers to the view held by many people that the natural world, and therefore ecosystems, biodiversity and geodiversity, merit conservation regardless of any material benefits or measurable values. This viewpoint is a meta-ethical claim such that the intrinsic value of nature cannot be compared with any other value set. Therefore, it lies outside the UK NEA, but we recognise that this is an important consideration for many people. Intrinsic value should not be confused with the various kinds of extrinsic anthropocentric, but non-market, values such as option, existence and bequest values (**Box 2.1**). They are difficult to estimate, but dominate many people's concerns for the conservation and protection of biodiversity and ecosystems. We do aim to deal with all these kinds of values in the UK NEA.

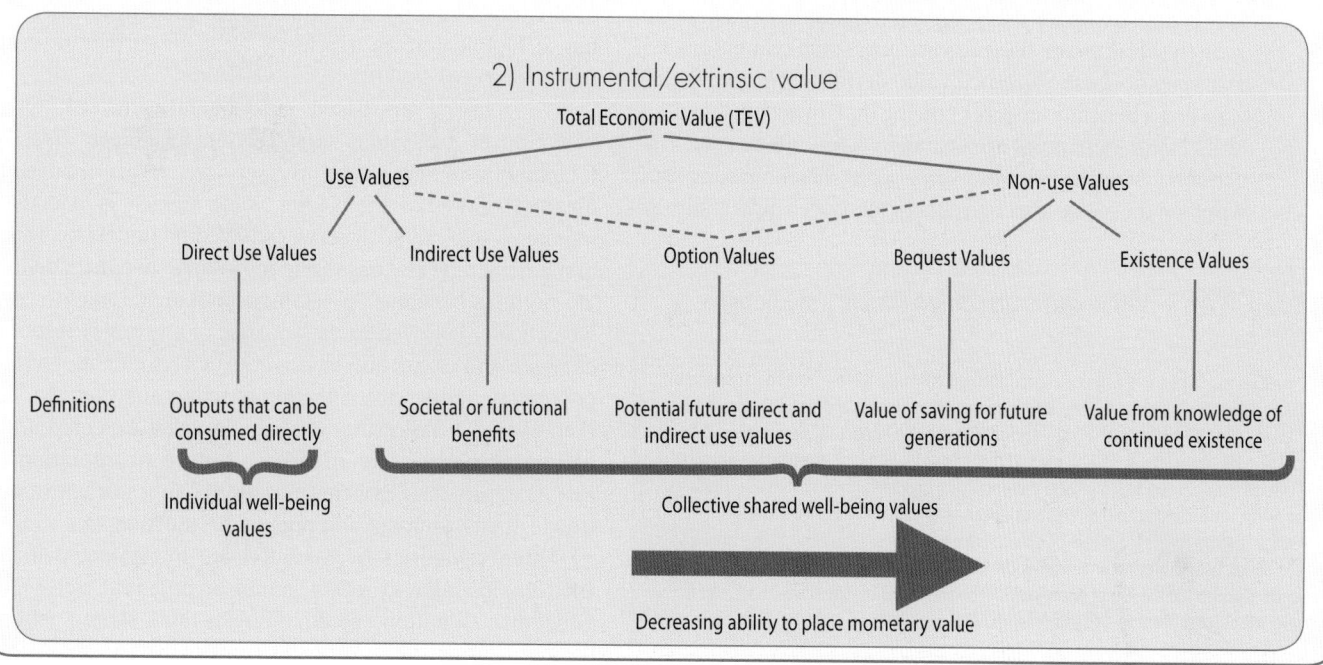

Box 2.1 The different values that people may hold for biodiversity and ecosystems.

There are two different approaches to the valuation of ecosystems and biodiversity - 1) intrinsic/inherent value (see right hand box) and 2) instrumental/extrinsic value (see box below). In the right hand box are some definitions and personal views about 'intrinsic value'. By definition this philosophical position rules out objective valuation. Below is a classification of practical approaches to valuation. In theory, each of the sub-types of value can be estimated and they can be added together for an estimate of the Total Economic Value (TEV) of a system of place. In practice, the methods are best established and available for the use values on the left hand side and become more difficult to define and measure towards the right. It is particularly difficult to estimate non-use values, which are often confused with intrinsic values. Bequest and existence values are often restricted to a subset of species, typically charismatic ones such as large mammals, birds, butterflies and some flowering plants. Note that direct use values are measured by the benefits to individuals, but all other values may be shared (social) values (Section 2.7; **Figure 2.4**).

1) intrinsic/inherent value
Some views and definitions

"The value of something independent of its value to anyone or anything else"

"Nature has a right to exist without any benefit that we may derive from it"

"The non-humanistic value of communities and species is the simplest of all to state: they should be conserved because they exist and because this existence is itself but the present expression of a continuing historical process of immense antiquity and majesty. Long standing existence in Nature is deemed to carry with it the unimpeachable right to continued existence"

D. Ehrenfeld, Conserving Life on Earth 1972

2.7 Human Well-being

A universal definition of 'well-being' is not available as many sources interpret and define it differently. However, well-being is generally considered in a broader context than simply good health. Defra (2007) has collaborated with other government departments and stakeholders to develop a shared understanding of the meaning of well-being within a policy context (**Box 2.2**). This includes good social relationships, financial and personal security, and a healthy and attractive environment.

Therefore, in considering the benefits from ecosystems, a number of different dimensions of value can be discerned and each may be evaluated in different ways, for example: in monetary terms via economic analysis; in biophysical and geochemical terms via natural science; and in more qualitative terms via sociology, geography, arts and humanities. Each of these value dimensions has validity in its own domain and a goal of the UK NEA is to incorporate all these kinds of values and the benefits they can and do provide.

Environmental philosophers have constructed a generic value typology with four categories: 'anthropocentric instrumental value', which maps closely onto the economic concepts of 'use' and most of 'non-use' values, and 'anthropocentric intrinsic value', a culturally dependent concept which is linked to human stewardship of nature and is represented by 'option' and 'existence' 'values' in **Box 2.1**. The other two value categories—'non-anthropocentric instrumental value' and 'non-anthropocentric intrinsic value'—are less directly relevant to the UK NEA initiative.

Anthropocentric instrumental values are usually assessed via economic analysis techniques in terms of an individual person (or sometimes an aggregated household) and their preferences and motivations. In this regard, the literature on the economic valuation of both market and non-market environmental goods has expanded dramatically in recent years, developing a suite of methods which are now extensively applied (Section 2.7.1). However, even in this domain, there are areas of some contention. For example, non-use existence value derives from individuals who feel a benefit from just knowing that an ecosystem and/ or its component parts exists and will continue to exist. The economic valuation literature has yet to reach consensus on whether the value can be reliably measured using survey-based methods (stated preference methods); despite a number of improvements in survey design and testing protocols, debate continues.

In contrast, anthropocentric intrinsic values are more usually viewed in a collectivist way with motivations and preferences which can be assigned to groups and culturally transmitted and assimilated over time as social norms. These cultural values may not be capable of meaningful and full monetary expression; nevertheless, they signal that human well-being and quality of life is a function of both individual wants satisfaction and the fulfilment of a variety of social, health-related and cultural collective needs. These values are shared experiences fostered by, and within, 'groups', often over long periods of time and in connection to specific local places and landscapes. In the UK NEA, these values are assessed within cultural services. **Figure 2.4** introduces a simple typology of valuation as applied in the UK NEA. The typology in **Box 2.1** does not distinguish between the individual versus collective appreciation of value, which is an important component for the social sciences.

We argue that the highlighting of the value of ecosystem service flows provides an important advance over conventional market price-based decision systems. Nevertheless, we recognise the dangers that could result from an over-concentration on the value of ecosystem service flows if this were to lead to the overexploitation of those services threatening system change or collapse. The UK NEA conceptual framework accepts the need to assess and conserve the stocks of natural assets from which services flow, and to maintain the fundamental components and processes which underpin ecosystems. These fundamental processes—labelled 'ecosystem processes/intermediate services' in this framework—are clearly valuable in their own right, and the focus on the flow of assigned ecosystem service values is not meant to deny this. Furthermore, we fully acknowledge the uncertainties that exist regarding the operation of many of these fundamental processes, their contribution to ecosystem services and the existence of thresholds and tipping points regarding their stability. Much of this goes beyond the remit of the present assessment, but is highlighted as a priority area for further research (Nicholson *et al.* 2009).

For reasons discussed subsequently, the UK NEA's valuation of ecosystem services is focused upon feasible incremental changes to those services, rather than some abstract notion of their total value (which is effectively infinite as without such services life could not exist). This is implemented by first assessing the change in values under a 'do-nothing' baseline. For example, looking forward to 2060, we can see that even in the absence of any policy response changes will occur due to drivers such as climate change, population shifts, etc. With this baseline analysed, we can then examine the further changes in value expected under various alternative scenarios for the future incorporating, for instance, proactive policies, societal changes or alternative trends in environment and population (Section 2.8).

Three categories of valuation are implemented in the UK NEA in order to reflect actual or potential well-being. Economic valuation, health benefits and shared (social) values (**Figure 2.4**) are different ways of measuring

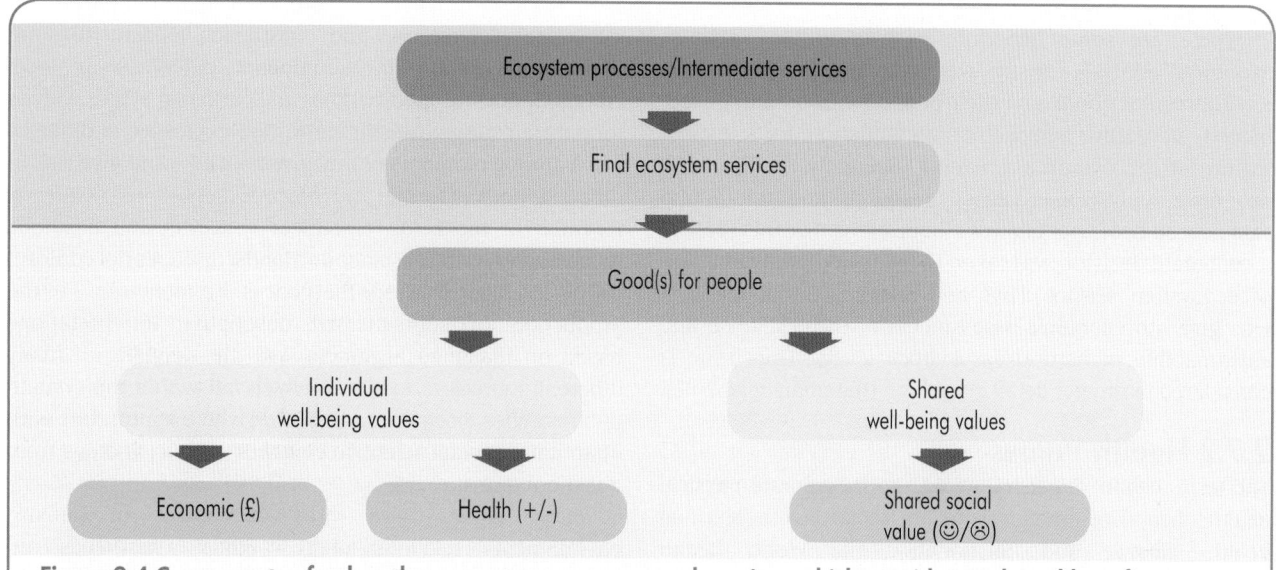

Figure 2.4 Components of value: the ecosystem processes and services which provide goods and benefits to people. These are valued in a variety of ways in terms of both use and non-use values. In the UK NEA, two kinds of individual benefits are recognised (economic and health), as well as shared (social) values that are measured in relative terms.

value and, therefore, overall well-being. Sometimes these categories overlap. For example, health benefits can be expressed in quantitative accounts of the number of persons concerned, qualitative assessments of well-being, or monetary estimates of the benefits or disbenefits concerned.

2.7.1 Economic Value

Economic valuation seeks to determine the monetary value of goods to individuals. Whether these goods are associated with ecosystem services or not, economics attempts to measure value in terms of what people are prepared to give up in order to obtain the goods in question. The most obvious measuring rod (and the one which is most compatible with decision-making) is to examine the amount of money individuals are prepared to pay for a given good: their 'willingness to pay' (WTP).

An immediate problem for valuation is that even goods which are traded in markets may have prices which are distorted by subsidies, non-competitive practices or other imperfections such that they have to be adjusted before we can observe the underlying value of the goods in question. This problem becomes much more complex for the large proportion of environmental goods which are not traded in markets, and so, have no readily observable prices. However, the last thirty years or so has seen the rapid development of numerous methods for estimating monetary values for non-market environmental goods. These are reviewed in the detailed methodology for the economics of the UK NEA (Bateman *et al.* 2011), but, in summary, we can identify several broad categories of economic valuation methods, each being appropriate to different goods and contexts, as follows:

i) Market prices: often not applicable and even then adjustment has to be made for market distortions (e.g. adjusted timber prices).

ii) Production function methods: examining the role of ecosystem services within the production of some goods with an (adjusted) market price (e.g. agricultural crops).

iii) Damage costs avoided and averting behaviour: looks at

the benefits of avoiding costs (e.g. avoidance of storm damage caused by improving coastal wetlands).

iv) Revealed preference methods: estimate the value of environmental goods by examining WTP for goods which permit access to those goods (e.g. looking at travel time and costs as a measure of recreation benefits, or the uplift in house prices in quiet areas).

v) Stated preference methods: directly asks individuals to make choices concerning their WTP for environmental goods (e.g. WTP higher water rates for cleaner rivers).

Most of the above methods can, in principle, be used for valuing either the benefits of improvements or the disbenefits of losses.

For reasons set out previously, the economic analysis conducted for the UK NEA focuses exclusively on the value of changes arising under feasible scenarios (Chapter 26). This is achieved by estimating the value of a single unit change in some environmental goods (the marginal WTP or MWTP) and then multiplying this by the size of the change provided under a given scenario. However, care needs to be taken to allow for the possibility of the per unit MWTP changing with the change in provision. For example, the value of storing a tonne of carbon is very unlikely to change if a given area of the UK is used for carbon storage. This is because the likely damage caused by climate change (which drives the true value of carbon storage) will only be slightly reduced by this storage. A very different situation occurs for other environmental goods. For example, the MWTP for creating a 100-acre recreational wood in an urban fringe area might be very substantial. But once it has been created, the MWTP for extending this by a further 100 acres for recreational use only is likely to be significantly lower due to the fact that the additional recreational benefits are lower than for the initial wood. Because of this and other reasons, it is important that economic valuation incorporates spatial and temporal issues into the analysis, thus capturing the vital impact which these issues can have upon values (Balmford *et al.* 2011).

There are some important caveats to the UK NEA economic analysis. Firstly, we make no claims that all environmental goods and their benefits can be monetised; indeed, alternative perspectives on valuation are a distinct feature of the overall assessment. Secondly, the UK NEA economic analysis was a strictly resource- and time-bound exercise, so could not answer all questions. For this reason, a deliberate decision was taken to focus upon the valuation of ecosystem service flows and relatively little attention was given to economic assessments of the resilience and sustainability of natural asset stock levels. This issue is considered in greater detail elsewhere (Bateman *et al.* 2011).

2.7.2 Health Values

The term 'health' is generally taken to incorporate physical health, mental or emotional health, social health, spiritual health, lifestyle and functionality. The World Health Organization's (WHO) definition of health is still the most widely cited and states that: "health is a state of complete physical, mental and social (individual) well-being, and not merely the absence of disease or infirmity" (WHO 1948).

There is growing evidence to show that ecosystems affect not only the immediate health and well-being of individuals, but also their lifelong welfare (Chapter 23). A funnel of life courses within which all lives are shaped can be envisaged. Some people live longer with a better quality of life; others die earlier and often live years with a lower quality of life. On the healthy pathway, people tend to be active, connected to people and society, engage with natural places, and eat healthy foods. Ecosystem services are, therefore, a critical component of healthy pathways. As a result, individuals tend to have better mental health, be members of groups and volunteer more, keep learning, engage regularly with natural habitats and be more resilient to stress (Foresight 2008; Pretty *et al.* 2009). On the unhealthy pathway, people tend to be inactive and sedentary, disconnected from society and social groups, not engage with natural places, and eat energy-dense and unhealthy foods. They also tend to have lower socioeconomic status, be in more stressful jobs, live where active travel to work or school is difficult, have increased likelihood of being mentally ill (16% of the UK's adult population), and be overweight or obese (Foresight 2007).

2.7.3 Shared (Social) Values

Finding ways to capture collective, cultural values in a scientific assessment of the UK's ecosystem services, goods and benefits is challenging. Over the last thirty years, environmental and ecological economists, working closely with natural scientists, have been developing robust, defensible estimates of the monetary value of ecosystem services and the contributions they make to improving human welfare. However, in making a distinction between anthropocentric instrumental and intrinsic values, environmental philosophers argue that societies maintain a range of beliefs about the 'ethical' basis of people's relationships with nature—what constitutes right and proper conduct towards the non-human world—and also make 'aesthetic judgements' about what is beautiful or, significant in terms of landscapes, species and natural processes.

Ethical concerns and aesthetic judgements are always context-specific: contingent outcomes of local circumstances, of specific times and particular places. Values for nature change over time; they are expressed in different ways among members of any given society; and give rise to different kinds of formal and informal institutions. Academic research in the fields of ethical concerns and aesthetic judgements for nature, place and landscape does not conform to the scientific method; the goal is 'hermeneutic', i.e. the production of sophisticated descriptive interpretations based on reasoned argument and the weighing of many different sources of evidence which fall within the domain of humanities disciplines, supported where appropriate with quantitative social scientific evidence such as findings from questionnaire surveys.

Many argue these three dimensions of human-environment relations—utility, ethics, aesthetics—are basic principles guiding human behaviour and, as such, are incommensurable: ethical and aesthetic principles cannot be meaningfully expressed in monetary terms. At the same time, environmental decision-makers do have to make choices which require trade-offs to be made between them. What is important in such cases is that the decision-making process is seen to be reliable, credible and legitimate. To ensure public trust and confidence when reaching difficult decisions which may well override ethical and/or aesthetic values, it is important that decision-makers are able to demonstrate knowledge and understanding of the philosophical and theoretical bases upon which researchers in the humanities and social sciences present evidence of the cultural values individuals and social groups attribute to their interactions with the natural world. For these reasons, it is increasingly recognised that policy makers require a range of deliberative tools, such as participatory multi-criteria analysis, to integrate the range of quantitative and qualitative information into their choices and to embed the ecosystem approach in decision-making (Fish *et al.* 2011).

Developing a defensible conceptual approach to the definition of final cultural ecosystem services, and the assessment of specific goods and benefits arising from them, has been one of the goals of the UK NEA. What narratives of change in cultural services might fit UK conditions and contexts is an open question. We have sought a framework which reflects our understanding of culture not as determining individuals' values, beliefs and norms, but rather as a process of co-production through the enormous range of social communications and social practices which enfold nature, places and landscapes in everyday life. What is needed is a contribution to the overall conceptual framework that allows humanities and social science disciplines to make their contribution to the UK NEA in such a way as to strengthen the integration of scientific, economic, cultural and socio-political evidence.

We consider cultural services in an economic model, through the benefits they provide in recreation, health and residential property values, but our approach goes beyond these economic values to explore other sorts of value provided by these cultural services (Chapter 16; Chapter 24). The Human-Scale Development Matrix (Max-Neef 1989, 1992) allows analysts to systematically explore how different kinds of 'goods' (material objects, abstract ideas, emotional experiences, social practices, physical settings, living things, etc.) are able to satisfy one or more fundamental human need. It also has potential as a deliberative tool for participatory engagement in ecosystem assessment (Cruz *et al.* 2009). Chapter 16 adapts the Human-Scale Development Index to provide a systematic framework for addressing these issues.

2.8 The Changing UK Environment

The UK's environment has always undergone change. In placing current (and potential future) changes of ecosystems and ecosystem services in context, drivers of positive or negative change can be considered as either direct drivers or indirect drivers. Direct drivers are usually associated with physical changes that can be monitored over time, such as the effects of the overexploitation of fisheries on the status of fish species and the marine environment. Indirect drivers can change the rate of one or more direct drivers at the same time. For example, socioeconomic changes affecting demographic structure and market forces may simultaneously directly affect land use and energy in many different ways. Socioeconomic changes through history have impacted on the extent and state of ecosystems and the services they provide. These changes can be traced though trends in land use, external inputs (such as pollution or fertiliser input to land) and demographics, among others. A further example of socio-political change is the introduction of policies that have impacted on the UK's environment through early reactive protective legislation, such as the Clean Air Act which led to reduced particulate air pollution, and the Water Framework Directive which takes an integrated approach to water use, pollution and quality. Chapter 3 sets out the different drivers of change impacting on the UK's ecosystems and the services they provide (**Table 2.3**).

2.9 Scenarios

Scenarios are an essential part of ecosystem assessments. They provide a bridge between the understanding of the current state and past trends in ecosystem services and the likely policy or management responses that might be appropriate given a range of plausible futures. In the context of the UK NEA, the aim has been to use them to explore how UK ecosystems and their services might change in the future, and to identify what the possible effects might be in terms of human well-being and who might be affected most.

As a sub-global assessment conducted within the MA framework, the latter has been seen as providing a model

Table 2.3 The changing UK environment: drivers of change assessed in the UK NEA.

Direct Drivers of Change	Indirect Drivers of Change
Habitat change (particularly conversion of natural habitat through changes in land use and use of the marine environment)	Demographic changes
Pollution of air, land and water	Economic growth
Overexploitation of terrestrial, marine and freshwater resources	Socio-political changes, especially in policies
Climate change	Cultural and behavioural changes
Introduction of non-native invasive species	Advances in science and technology

and guide for the UK NEA. In the MA, the method of scenario construction was presented as essentially deliberative, involving dialogue between the researchers and user communities to define objectives, to determine the scope of the exercise and to identify the particular issues that the scenarios would be used to explore (Carpenter et al. 2005). The same broad approach has been used for the UK NEA, within which, scenarios have been viewed as devices that can be used to represent alternative ways that land cover and ecosystems may change under different conditions or assumptions about the future (Carpenter *et al.* 2006).

The work started from the premise that scenario-building is not about trying to predict the future, but rather about identifying a range of possible futures that might unfold under contrasting, but 'plausible', (Chapter 25) assumptions. Thus, they allow a comparison of goods and their values that will be available under different plausible futures, and complete the cycle for the assessment used in the UK NEA. They also provide an opportunity to encourage thinking about how future policy may affect ecosystem services. To this end, storylines should not only be plausible and consistent, but should challenge too.

The UK NEA methodology explicitly recognises the need to consider policy-relevant changes occurring over a defined timescale of about 50 years. Given the time-bound nature of the exercise, interactions with stakeholders were prioritised over the development of detailed timelines, and the scenarios were considered in terms of final outcomes only. Nevertheless, the storylines do offer a description of a set of feasible and decision-pertinent changes in the environment, markets, society and policy. The changes anticipated under each scenario are calculated from a consistent baseline and reflect the best estimates of changes in these various drivers in the absence of any policy response. The timeline considered extends to 2060.

From the outset, the development of the UK NEA scenarios was an inherently inclusive and iterative process involving experts and stakeholders, guided by periodic external feedback and internal review. The engagement with people outside the scenarios team was necessary to not only fill in knowledge gaps, but also to ensure that the process remained transparent and flexible. The UK NEA Scenarios team set out to build on what had already been achieved in this area, and so, reviewed and used aspects from a range of existing scenarios in the grey and academic literatures. By asking the UK NEA stakeholders to provide the Scenarios team with focal questions about future ecosystem change, we were able to identify the key issues they wished to consider.

The six storylines developed as a result of the scenario-building process are summarised below. They present a range of socio-political futures that result in considerable diversity in outcomes for ecosystem services and habitats for land and sea. For each scenario, the impacts of high and low climate change effects were considered. This analysis was based on the projections from the outputs of UKCIP.

- *Green and Pleasant Land* is a future where high economic growth has focused on the service, economic and secondary industries, and most primary industry has declined considerably. Consequently, production and housing pressures in rural UK decline, making way for a programme of 'beautifying' the countryside (with many positive benefits for biodiversity).
- *Nature@Work* is a version of today, but with a very strong emphasis on maintaining ecosystem services through all sectors in the UK. It is inherently about trade-offs between ecosystem services, but sustainability forms the backbone in all walks of life.
- *World Market* is a vision of unfettered economic growth and trade. Trade barriers disappear, imports increase and the UK abandons the EU. Environmentalism is given little merit and the countryside becomes more industrialised and developed as a result.
- *National Security* shares many aspects with World Market, but is different in one key area: it is heavily focused on self-sufficiency and economic protectionism.
- *Local Stewardship* presents a slower pace of life and a determined move towards a low-impact, low resource-use society.
- *Go with the Flow* offers a vision of how the UK will evolve if we continue with current socioeconomic and environmental policies.

The qualitative descriptions of plausible changes in ecosystem services and their associated goods and benefits under each storyline represent the basic output from the scenarios exercise. A novel aspect of the work that takes scenario-building further, however, has been the use of Bayesian Belief Networks to create spatially explicit representations of each of the possible futures for land-based ecosystems (Chapter 25).

It has been argued that to be effective scenarios must not be seen as having "lives of their own, divorced from the processes that generated them..." (O'Neill *et al.* 2008). Instead, their real value comes from the way they can be used to help us understand and reflect upon our current understandings and beliefs, and think more broadly about the problems that may confront us. Thus, the scenarios developed as part of the UK NEA must not be viewed as ends in themselves; they should be used as part of the debate about what the UK NEA is telling us about the state we are in and where current trends might lead us. Having constructed the UK NEA scenarios, these materials have also been used as part of the UK NEA workstream dealing with 'responses', which is reported in Chapter 27.

2.10 Response Options

In the light of findings from the assessment of ecosystem services, and informed by the scenarios work that identifies broad policy changes which might influence their future status and trends, the UK NEA also includes an assessment of alternative, policy-relevant response options (Chapter 27). These are considered in a structure that differentiates among relevant sectors, types of interventions and actors.

The different sectors prescribe the general area of policy within which options may be relevant: biodiversity; agriculture; fisheries; forestry; water; recreation and tourism; planning, transport and energy; and integrated, including marine. For each one of these sectors, interventions are considered across seven categories: knowledge; legislation; policy and institutions; social/behavioural responses; markets/incentives; technologies; and voluntary initiatives. For each sector and intervention type, there are also alternative actors: governments; local authorities; the private sector; non-governmental organisations; civil society organisations; and individuals and communities.

The majority of the assessment is undertaken by sector; the response options available to the full range of actors within each sector is assessed according to response type (e.g. legislation and behaviour). The impacts of these responses on habitats, their ecosystem services and, ultimately, human health and well-being is then assessed, often with the use of examples and case studies. A section on Integrated Responses addresses approaches that go beyond sectoral divides, and explores how responses relating to ecosystem services interact with other social and economic objectives.

References

Balmford, A., Fisher, B., Green, R.E., Naidoo, R., Strassburg, B., Turner, R.K. & Rodrigues, A. (2011) Bringing Ecosystem Services into the Real World: An Operational Framework for Assessing the Economic Consequences of Losing Wild Nature. *Environmental and Resource Economics,* **48**, 161–175.

Bateman, I., Mace, G., Fezzi, C., Atkinson, G. & Turner, K. (2011) Economic Analysis for Ecosystem Service Assessments. *Environmental and Resource Economics,* **48**, 177–218.

Bradford, M.A., Jones, T.H., Bardgett, R.D., Black, H.I.J., Boag, B., Bonkowski, M., Cook, R., Eggers, T., Gange, A.C., Grayston, S.J., Kandeler, E., McCaig, A.E., Newington, J.E., Prosser, J.I., Setälä, H., Staddon, P.L., Tordoff, G.M., Tshcherko, D. & Lawton, J.H. (2002) Impacts of soil faunal community composition on model grassland ecosystems. *Science,* **298**, 615–618.

Carey, P. D., Wallis, S., Chamberlain, P. M., Cooper, A., Emmett, B. A., Maskell, L. C., McCann, T., Murphy, J., Norton, L. R., Reynolds, B., Scott, W. A., Simpson, I. C., Smart, S. M. & Ullyett, J. M. (2008) Countryside Survey: UK Results from 2007. NERC/Centre for Ecology and Hydrology, Wallingford, UK.

Carpenter, S.R., Pingali, P.L., Bennett, E.M. & Zurek, M.B. (eds) (2005) Ecosystems and Human Well-Being: Scenarios. Island Press, Washington D.C.

Carpenter, S.R., Bennett, E.M. & Peterson, G.D. (2006) Scenarios for ecosystem services: An overview. *Ecology and Society*, **11**, 29.

Carpenter, S.R., Mooney, H.A., Agard, J., Capistrano, D., DeFries, R.S., Díaz, S., Dietz, T., Duraiappah, A.K., Oteng-Yeboah, A., Pereira, H.M., Perrings, C., Reid, W.V., Sarukhan, J., Scholes, R.J. & Whyte, A. (2009) Science for managing ecosystem services: Beyond the Millennium Ecosystem Assessment. *Proceedings of the National Academy of Sciences of the United States of America*, **106**, 1305–1312.

Cruz, I., Stahel, A. & Max-Neef, M. (2009) Towards a systematic development approach: building on the Human-Scale Development paradigm. *Ecological Economics*, **68**, 2021–2030.

Defra (Department for Environment, Food and Rural Affairs) (2007) Well-being: International policy interventions. Department for Environment, Food and Rural Affairs, London.

Díaz, S., Fargione, J., Chapin, F.S. III & Tilman, D. (2006) Biodiversity loss threatens human well-being. *PLoS Biology*, **4**, 1300–1305.

Díaz, S., Lavorel, S., de Bello, F., Quetier, F., Grigulis, K. & Robson, M. (2007) Incorporating plant functional diversity effects in ecosystem service assessments. *Proceedings of the National Academy of Sciences of the United States of America*, **104**, 20684–20689.

Fish, R., Burgess, J., Chilvers, J., Footitt, A., Haines-Young, R., Russel, D., Turner, K. & Winter, D.M. (2011) Participatory and Deliberative Techniques for Embedding an Ecosystems Approach into Decision Making. Full Technical Report. (NR0124). Department for Environment, Food and Rural Affairs, London.

Fisher, B. & Turner, R.K. (2008) Ecosystem services: classification for valuation. *Biological Conservation*, **141**, 1167–1169.

Fisher, B., Turner, K., Zylstra, M., Brouwer, R., de Groot, R., Farber, S., Ferraro, P., Green, R., Hadley, D., Harlow, J., Jefferiss, P., Kirkby, C., Morling, P., Mowatt, S., Naidoo, R., Paavola, J., Strassburg, B., Yu, D., and Balmford, A. (2008). Ecosystem services and economic theory: Integration for policy-relevant research. *Ecological Applications* **18**, 2050-2067.

Fitter, A., Elmqvist, T., Haines-Young, R., Potschin, M., Rinaldo, A., Setala, H., Stoll-Kleemann, S., Zobel, M. & Murlis, J. (2010) An Assessment of Ecosystem services and biodiversity in Europe. *Issues in Environmental Science and Technology*, **30**, 1–28

Foresight (2007) Tackling Obesities: Future Choices. Government Office of Science, London.

Foresight (2008) Mental health – Future challenge. Government Office of Science, London.

Jackson, D.L. (2000) Guidance on the Interpretation of the Biodiversity Broad Habitat Classification (Terrestrial and Freshwater Types): Definitions and the Relationship with other Habitat Classifications. JNCC Report Series 307. Joint Nature Conservation Committee, Peterborough, UK.

Hector, A., Beale, A.J., Minns, A., Otway, S.J. & Lawton, J.H. (2000) Consequences of the reduction of plant diversity for litter decomposition: effects through litter quality and microenvironment. *Oikos*, **90**, 357–371.

Hooper, D.U., Chapin, F.S. III, Ewel, J.J., Hector, A., Inchausti, P., Lavorel, S., Lawton, J.H., Lodge, D.M., Loreau, M., Naeem, S., Schmid, B., Setälä, H., Symstad, A.J., Vandermeer, J. & Wardle, D.A. (2005) Effects of biodiversity on ecosystem functioning: A consensus of current knowledge. *Ecological Monographs*, **75**, 3–35.

MA (Millennium Ecosystem Assessment) (2005) Ecosystems and Human Well-being: Synthesis. Island Press, Washington D.C.

Maskell, L.C., Norton, L.R., Smart, S. M., Carey, P.D., Murphy, J., Chamberlain, P.M., Wood, C.M., Bunce, R.G.H. & Barr, C. J. (2008) Countryside Survey. Field Mapping Handbook. NERC/Centre for Ecology and Hydrology, Wallingford, UK.

Max-Neef, M. (1989) Human scale development: an option for the future. *Development Dialogue*, **1**, 5–81.

Max-Neef, M. (1992) Development and human needs. Real life Economics (eds P. Ekins & M. Max-Neef), pp. 197–214. Routledge, London.

Nicholson, E., Mace, G.M., Armsworth, P.R., Atkinson, G., Buckle, S., Clements, T., Ewers, R.M., Fa, J.E., Gardner, T.A., Gibbons, J., Grenyer, R., Metcalfe, R., Mourato, S., Muûls, M., Osborn, D., Reuman, D.C., Watson, C. & Miller-Gulland, E.J. (2009) Priority research areas for ecosystem services in a changing world. *Journal of Applied Ecology*, **46**, 1139–1144.

Norby, R.J., Hanson, P.J., O'Neil, E.G., Tschaplinski, T.J., Weltzin, J.E., Hansen, R.A., Cheng, W., Wullschleger, S.D., Gunderson, C.A., Edwards, N.T. & Johnson, D.W. (2002) Net primary productivity of a CO_2 enriched deciduous forest and the impliactions for carbon storage. *Ecological Applications*, **12**, 1261–1266.

Norby, R.J., Warren, J.M., Iversen, C.M., Medlyn, B.E. & McMurtrie, R.E. (2010) CO_2 enhancement of forest productivity constrained by limited nitrogen availability. *Proceedings of the National Academy of Sciences*, **107**, 19368–19373.

O'Neill, B., Pulver, S., VanDeveer, S. & Garb, Y. (2008) Where next with global environmental scenarios? *Environmental Research Letters*, **3**, 1–4.

Pretty, J., Angus, C., Bain, M., Barton, J., Gladwell, V., Hine, R., Pilgrim, S., Sandercock, G. & Sellens, M. (2009) Nature, Childhood, Health and Life Pathways. iCES Occasional Paper 2009–2. University of Essex, Colchester.

Ring, I., Hansjurgens, B., Elmqvist, T., Wittmer, H. & Sukhdev, P. (2010) Challenges in framing the economics of ecosystems and biodiversity: the TEEB initiative. *Current Opinion in Environmental Sustainability*, **2**, 15–26.

Scheffer, M. & Carpenter, S.R. (2003) Catastrophic regime shifts in ecosystems: linking theory to observation. *Trends in Ecology & Evolution*, **18**, 648–656.

Suding, K.N., Lavorel, S., Chapin, F.S. III, Cornelissen, J.H.C., Díaz, S., Garnier, E., Goldberg, D., Hooper, D.U., Jackson, S.T. & Navas, M.L. (2008) Scaling environmental change through the community-level: a trait-based response-and-effect framework for plants. *Global Change Biology*, **14**, 1125–1140.

WHO (World Health Organization) (1948) WHO definition of Health. Preamble to the Constitution of the World Health Organization as adopted by the International Health Conference, New York, 19–22 June, 1946; signed on 22 July 1946 by the representatives of 61 States (Official Records of the World Health Organization, no. 2, p. 100) and entered into force on 7 April 1948.

Yachi, S. & Loreau, M. (1999) Biodiversity and ecosystem productivity in a fluctuating environment: The insurance hypothesis. *Proceedings of the National Academy of Sciences of the United States of America*, **96**, 1463–1468.

Chapter 3:
The Drivers of Change in UK Ecosystems and Ecosystem Services

Coordinating Lead Authors: Jonathan Winn and Megan Tierney
Contributing Authors: A. Louise Heathwaite, Laurence Jones, James Paterson, Lucy Simpson, Amanda Thomson and Carol Turley

Key Findings*

The majority of human influences have driven a decline in both extent and condition of the ecosystems assessed in the UK National Ecosystem Assessment[1]. The exceptions are Enclosed Farmland, Woodlands and Urban ecosystems, where a number of drivers have caused an increase in ecosystem extent. Typically, economic growth and advances in science and technology, coupled with changes in policy, have increased the area of these ecosystems at the expense of others. Of all drivers, habitat and land use change, pollution and nutrient enrichment, and the overexploitation of natural resources have been consistently identified in this assessment as having a major impact on ecosystem extent and condition and service delivery, possibly reflecting the high proportion of managed land within the UK.

[1] well established

Many of the legislative changes that have occurred since 1945 have succeeded in increasing human well-being and limiting ecosystem change. For example, recognition of the negative impacts of poor air quality caused by energy production on human health and well-being, led to the introduction of the Clean Air Act of 1956. This, and others that followed, reduced pollution levels[1]: sulphur deposition in the UK has declined by 70% since the 1970s. There has also been a reduction in the exceedance of critical loads for acidity from 71% to 51% in the same time period. While these indirect drivers were largely driven by the desire to reduce damage to human health, they have also acted to limit potential ecosystem change.

[1] well established

In the absence of regulation, market forces, sometimes in combination with production support mechanisms, have led to unsustainable exploitation of natural resources and the prioritisation of a single ecosystem service above others. For example, entry into the European Union Common Agricultural Policy in 1973, coupled with intensive land use, led to overproduction of foodstuffs, and did not foster substantial increased human well-being[1]. Commercial UK marine fisheries also maximised short-term production beyond sustainable levels[1]. However, overexploitation has been addressed by the development of multi-objective policies and changes in the support for agriculture and forestry that reward environmental sustainability. Enforced changes to fisheries regulation policy is also leading to the recovery of some UK fish stocks. For instance, the number of UK fisheries that are at full reproductive capacity and are sustainably harvested has recently increased from 5–10% in the 1990s to 50% in 2008.

[1] well established

Key direct drivers of change include: habitat modification as a result of alterations in land use and the use of the marine environment; the overexploitation of terrestrial and marine resources; and air and water pollution. Semi-natural vegetation continued to be converted to agricultural land within the UK from the 1940s to the 1990s[1]. Harvest and resource consumption have had important effects on cultural and supporting services and marine ecosystems, for example through overfishing. Inputs of chemicals and nutrients from agriculture and pollution have had important effects on provisioning, regulating and supporting services, and within many ecosystems, causing, among other things, changes in species composition. To date, non-native, invasive species and climate change are thought to have had relatively little impact on ecosystems and ecosystem services; however, the latter is predicted to be a major driver of future change.

[1] well established

The principal drivers shaping ecosystems vary geographically across the UK. Lowland landscapes have become less diverse as farming has become more intensive, large-scale and specialised; whereas the uplands have been subject to high livestock densities and levels of pollution deposition[1].

[1] well established

---

* Each Key Finding has been assigned a level of scientific certainty, based on a 4-box model and complemented, where possible, with a likelihood scale. Superscript numbers and letters indicate the uncertainty term assigned to each finding. Full details of each term and how they were assigned are presented in Appendix 3.1.

There are still significant gaps in our knowledge of what drives ecosystem change and the impacts that changes within ecosystems have on the services they provide. In terms of services, effects on provisioning services are generally well-understood, and are closely followed by our knowledge of effects on regulating services. But much less is known about what affects cultural and supporting services. In many cases, multiple drivers of change are acting on ecosystem service delivery. Often the state of knowledge of the impact of each driver varies, and the combined impact of multiple drivers on an ecosystem service is likely to be difficult to predict.

The direction of change can be successfully guided where strong regulation, legislation and support mechanisms act in conjunction with market forces. Woodland cover has doubled since 1945 in response to Forestry Commission grants and favourable economic and tax conditions[1]. Also, recent agri-environment schemes have been successful in increasing biodiversity in targeted areas: there has been a 145% increase in breeding pairs of cirl bunting (*Emberiza cirlus*) from 1993 to 2009, and a 140% increase of calling male corncrake (*Crex crex*) during the same period[1]. It is often the 'invisible' indirect drivers (e.g. forestry subsidies, demographic change, industrialisation, policy development) whereby society can have the most influence on the direction of environmental change. Therefore, an understanding of the linkage between indirect and direct drivers is critical to any effort to alter or guide the future direction of change.

[1] *well established*

3.1 Introduction

Drivers are the factors, be they natural or human-induced, which cause ecosystem change (Nelson *et al.* 2005). Drivers, as defined by the Millennium Ecosystem Assessment (MA) may be one of two types: direct or indirect. *Direct drivers* have an explicit effect on ecosystem processes (Nelson *et al.* 2005), usually causing physical change that can be identified and monitored (Ash *et al.* 2008). *Indirect drivers* operate more diffusely by altering the level or rate of change of one or more direct drivers (Nelson *et al.* 2005; Ash *et al.* 2008).

It is evident that habitats throughout the UK have changed significantly since the Second World War (WWII; Chapters 5–12). The purpose of this chapter is to provide an overview of the key drivers that have been instrumental in causing such change, and the subsequent effects on the ecosystem services that they provide, while acknowledging that much change may have occurred before this period. Understanding what drives these changes is important in the development of mechanisms, through policy or other means, to influence these drivers and ensure essential ecosystem services can be sustained.

However, it is important to note early on that assessment and management of drivers of change can be complicated for two reasons. Firstly, drivers can affect ecosystem services, and consequently human well-being, at different spatial and temporal scales. Often data may not be available at all scales, or drivers important at one time and place may not be important at a larger (or smaller) scale or over longer (or shorter) time periods (MA 2005b). Secondly, drivers do not act in isolation, but more frequently interact—the pressure from one, exacerbating the impacts of another (CBD 2010). Therefore, an understanding of the linkage between direct and indirect drivers is critical in order to alter or influence future directions of change.

This chapter is structured by first providing an overview of which drivers have had the greatest impact on UK ecosystems and services, and briefly exploring how they inter-relate. We then examine each driver in greater detail, focusing first on the indirect drivers, and second on the direct drivers. For each driver, we will consider trends through time (where possible) and their impact on the extent and condition of the eight Broad Habitats identified by the UK National Ecosystem Assessment (UK NEA) in each of the four constituent countries of the UK (England, Scotland, Wales and Northern Ireland) to provide a picture of how drivers influence the UK as a whole.

As this chapter aims to provide a UK-wide summary of the drivers influencing change, we will, at times, draw on information presented in the habitat and ecosystem services chapters (Chapters 5–16), and may refer the reader to these sections for further details on particular impacts. It should also be noted that this chapter does not include forward projections of how these drivers may change in the future. This is covered in Chapter 25 and Chapter 26, which examines the response of UK ecosystems and their services under six different future sociopolitical and economic ideologies.

3.2 Overview

The combined impacts of various direct and indirect drivers have resulted in significant changes in Broad Habitats throughout the UK since WWII. The key indirect drivers of change which have resulted in significant changes (both positive and negative) in habitats and well-being are:

- Demographic changes
- Economic growth
- Sociopolitical changes, especially in policies
- Cultural and behavioural changes
- Advances in science and technology.

In turn, these have influenced the following direct drivers:

- Habitat change (particularly conversion of natural and semi-habitats through land use change or change in the use of the marine environment)
- Nutrient enrichment and pollution of air, land and water
- Overexploitation of terrestrial, marine and freshwater resources
- Variability and change in climate
- Introduction of invasive alien species.

It is important to understand how these drivers have interacted to bring about change across the UK. These relationships are typically complex; however, we seek to unravel these complexities in this chapter, and provide examples of the interrelatedness of these drivers.

Between the 1940s and 1990s, there was widespread conversion of various semi-natural habitats, such as some grasslands and saltmarshes, to arable land, stimulated by increased demand (due to a growing population and rising wealth) and agricultural production subsidies. Coupled with the intensification of agricultural production and use of agrochemicals, this has resulted in a significant increase in food production. This growth, however, has been at the expense of biodiversity and has caused the degradation of some regulating, supporting and cultural services. Activities other than agriculture, such as the increased demand for water, and air and water pollution from the production and use of energy, have also impacted on UK habitats and ecosystem services.

The drivers described have also interacted in different ways across the UK. For example, lowland landscapes have become less diverse as farming has become more intensive, large-scale and specialised; whereas the uplands have been subject to high livestock densities and levels of pollution deposition. Impacts have changed over time as well, particularly in response to policy changes. For example, while traditional UK and European Union (EU) agricultural production subsidies (such as the Common Agricultural Policy (CAP)) stimulated increased agricultural production, resulting in the conversion of semi-natural ecosystems and the degradation of biodiversity and non-provisioning services, recent reform of such policies means that they now also increasingly support environmentally sustainable practices, particularly through agri-environment schemes. These changes have been linked to, at least in some cases, improving levels of biodiversity and ecosystem sustainability. Falling livestock numbers has also reduced green-house gas emissions.

The direct and indirect drivers vary in their importance in influencing change within and amongst ecosystems and ecosystem services, and in the extent to which their impact is increasing as time goes on. Such patterns could be examined for both types of drivers, but are most easily discerned for direct drivers. In the UK, habitat and land use change, and pollution and nutrient enrichment have had the greatest effect on condition and extent of all habitat types, and are generally thought to have a continuing or increasing impact (**Figure 3.1**). Exploitation of resources has also strongly impacted on all but the Urban and Coastal Margins habitats, as have invasive species, although to a somewhat lesser extent. However, it is thought that the impacts of both these drivers are only going to intensify in the coming decades. To date, climate change has had little impact on ecosystem extent or condition, except in the Mountains, Moorlands and Heaths, Coastal Margins and Marine habitats, where for example shifts in both terrestrial and marine species have been observed (Chapter 4;

Chapter 12), yet in all cases it is thought that climate change will be a major driver of change in the future.

In regards to ecosystem services, habitat and land use change, and over exploitation of resources were consistently identified as the major drivers impacting service delivery (**Figure 3.2**). Pollution and nutrient enrichment are also important drivers, although their impact varies both within and between services. Climate variability and invasive species were rarely identified as major drivers of change in ecosystem services, but again, climate change is predicted to be a major driver in the future.

The state of knowledge on different drivers varies, being particularly poor for cultural and behavioural drivers. As a result of these data gaps, it can be difficult to ascertain or predict how multiple drivers will impact on ecosystems and ecosystem services. On an individual basis, the way in which drivers impact upon provisioning services is relatively well understood, followed by a reasonable understanding of the impacts on regulating services, but there remains poor knowledge of the impacts on cultural and supporting services.

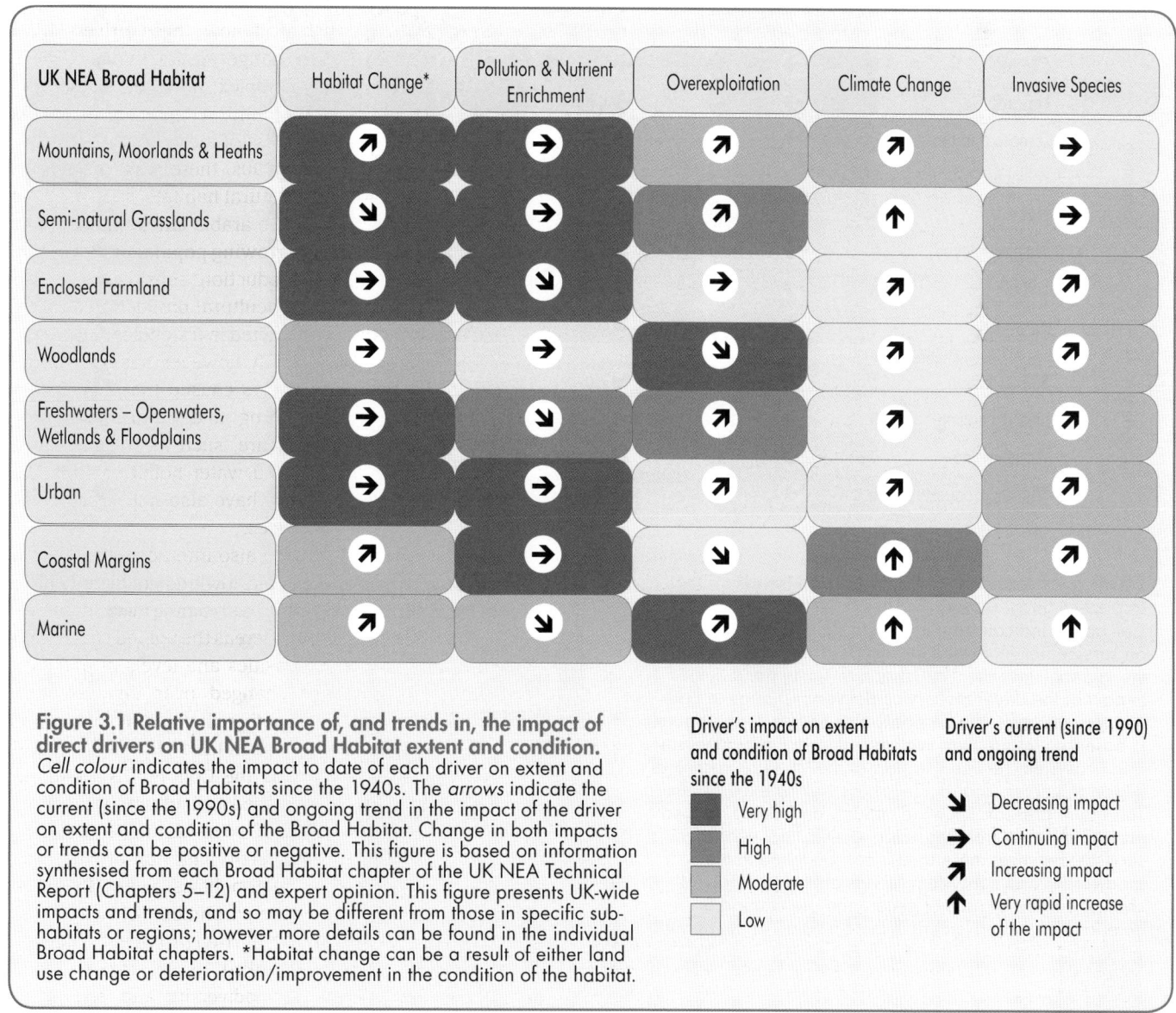

Figure 3.1 Relative importance of, and trends in, the impact of direct drivers on UK NEA Broad Habitat extent and condition. *Cell colour* indicates the impact to date of each driver on extent and condition of Broad Habitats since the 1940s. The *arrows* indicate the current (since the 1990s) and ongoing trend in the impact of the driver on extent and condition of the Broad Habitat. Change in both impacts or trends can be positive or negative. This figure is based on information synthesised from each Broad Habitat chapter of the UK NEA Technical Report (Chapters 5–12) and expert opinion. This figure presents UK-wide impacts and trends, and so may be different from those in specific sub-habitats or regions; however more details can be found in the individual Broad Habitat chapters. *Habitat change can be a result of either land use change or deterioration/improvement in the condition of the habitat.

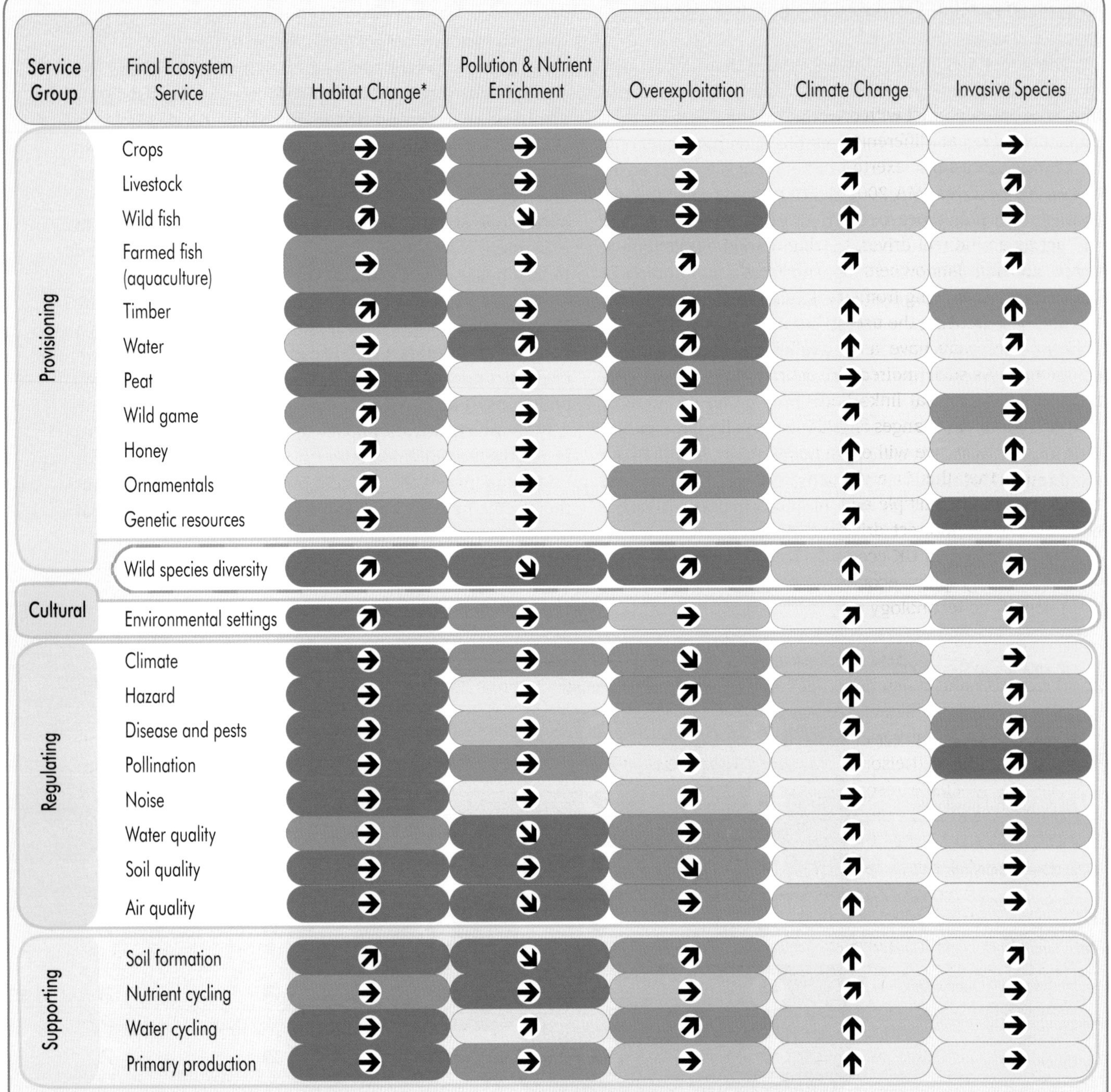

Service Group	Final Ecosystem Service	Habitat Change*	Pollution & Nutrient Enrichment	Overexploitation	Climate Change	Invasive Species
Provisioning	Crops	→	→	→	↗	→
	Livestock	→	→	→	↗	↗
	Wild fish	↗	↘	→	↑	→
	Farmed fish (aquaculture)	→	→	↗	↗	↗
	Timber	↗	→	↗	↑	↑
	Water	→	↗	↗	↑	↗
	Peat	→	→	↘	→	↗
	Wild game	↗	→	↘	↗	→
	Honey	↗	→	↗	↑	↑
	Ornamentals	↗	→	↗	↗	→
	Genetic resources	→	→	↗	↗	→
Cultural	Wild species diversity	↗	↘	↗	↑	↗
	Environmental settings	↗	→	→	↗	↗
Regulating	Climate	→	→	↘	↑	→
	Hazard	→	→	↗	↑	↗
	Disease and pests	→	→	↗	↗	↗
	Pollination	→	→	→	↗	↗
	Noise	→	→	↗	→	→
	Water quality	→	↘	→	↗	→
	Soil quality	→	→	↘	↗	→
	Air quality	→	↘	→	↑	→
Supporting	Soil formation	↗	↘	↗	↑	↗
	Nutrient cycling	→	→	→	↗	→
	Water cycling	→	↗	↗	↑	→
	Primary production	→	→	→	↑	→

Figure 3.2 Relative importance of, and trends in, the impact of direct drivers on UK ecosystem services. *Cell colour* indicates the impact to date of each driver on service delivery since the 1940s. The *arrows* indicate the current (since the 1990s) and ongoing trend in the impact of the driver on service delivery. Change in both impacts or trends can be positive or negative. This figure is based on information synthesised from the biodiversity and ecosystem service chapters of the UK NEA Technical Report (Chapters 4 and 13–16), as well as expert opinion. This figure presents UK-wide impacts and trends, and so may be different from those for specific final ecosystem services; however more details can be found in the biodiversity and ecosystem service chapters. *Habitat change can be a result of either land use change or deterioration/improvement in the condition of the habitat.

Driver's impact on ecosystem service delivery since the 1940s

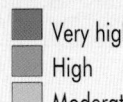

- Very high
- High
- Moderate
- Low

Driver's current (since 1990) and ongoing trend
- ↘ Decreasing impact
- → Continuing impact
- ↗ Increasing impact
- ↑ Very rapid increase of the impact

3.3 Indirect Drivers of Change

Indirect drivers interact with other driving forces in complex ways, including at different spatial and temporal scales, to change pressures exerted on ecosystems and their associated services (MA 2005b). For example, society may exhibit a new preference for certain food types. Such change can act as an indirect driver, altering market demands and hence causing landowners to employ different farming practices like switching from arable- to pastoral-dominated farming or increasing the use of fertilisers to improve yield. This, in turn, may have associated impacts on different ecosystems. As such, indirect drivers rarely act in isolation, and identifying causal links between specific drivers and specific ecosystem changes is seldom possible. However, for the sake of clarity, we will examine each driver separately, recognising that this is a simplification and that driving forces are usually multiple and interactive (MA 2005b). We will discuss five indirect drivers that have been identified as causing change in UK ecosystems and the services they provide: demographic, economic, sociopolitical, cultural, and science and technology.

3.3.1 Demographic Drivers

Population size and consumption patterns (which may vary between age groups, living arrangements and geographic regions) are important variables which influence trends in ecosystem condition (Nelson *et al.* 2005). In turn, these are regulated by available resources, how they are allocated (economic, social and cultural drivers), and the changes in technology that enable the conversion of raw materials into goods and services used by humans (scientific and technological drivers) (Nelson *et al.* 2005). In this section, we will focus on how population growth, demographic change and migration have changed in the UK since WWII, and the consequences these changes have had on ecosystem services.

3.3.1.1 Population growth and distribution

Between 1951 and 2009, the UK population increased by 18% from 50.3 million to 61.8 million people (Jefferies 2005; ONS 2010b; **Table 3.1**). The rate of growth has been variable during this time period, ranging between 0.5–5% per decade (Jefferies 2005). Up until 1998, population growth was primarily due to natural increase (i.e. a greater number of births than deaths); however, since 1998, net migration has been the main contributor (66%) to the increase in population size (Section 3.3.1.3).

Population size and growth varies throughout the UK: with 85% of the UK's population, England has the greatest number of people, followed by Scotland (8%), Wales (5%) and Northern Ireland (3%) (Jefferies 2005; ONS 2010b). Between 1971 and 1981, the fastest growing population was in Wales (2.7% per decade compared to 0.8% for the rest of the UK); in the 1980s, however, the fastest growing population was in Northern Ireland—a trend which continued between 1991 and 2001 (5% increase compared to 3% for the UK). Meanwhile, the population in Scotland has decreased from 5.2 million to 5.1 million during the whole of this period (1971 to 2001).

England is also the most densely populated country (385 people/km^2). Wales and Northern Ireland have similar, but substantially lower, density figures (126 and 142 people/km^2, respectively), while Scotland is the least densely populated country (65 people/km^2) (Shaw & Jefferies 2005).

3.3.1.2 Population demographics

The UK's population is ageing: the current median age is 38.6 years, compared to 34.1 in 1971—an increase of 4.5 years in just three decades (Jefferies 2005; Smith *et al.* 2005; ONS 2010a). Between 1984 and 2009, the proportion of the population aged 65 years and over rose from 15% to 16%—an increase of 1.7 million people. Conversely, the proportion of the population aged 16 years or younger decreased from 21% to 19% during the same period (ONS 2010a). The fastest growing group is the 85 years and over age group, which doubled from 600,000 in 1983 to 1.4 million in 2009 (ONS 2010a). In general, Scotland and Wales tend to have an older demographic, whereas Northern Ireland has a younger one, and England sits in between (Jefferies 2005; Smith *et al.* 2005). However, Northern Ireland's population is aging the fastest of the four component countries, and will continue to do so. Differences in patterns between countries arise due to different patterns of fertility and improvements in mortality at older ages (Smith *et al.* 2005).

The main contributing factors to this change in population structure are low fertility and mortality rates (**Table 3.1**). For example, in 2009, the Total Fertility Rate (TFR) in the UK was 1.94 children per woman, which is below the level needed to

Table 3.1 Population change ('000) and its components in the UK, 1993 to 2008. Source: adapted from Jefferies (2005) and ONS (2010b).

		Components of change (mid-year to mid-year)					
Mid-year to mid-year	Population at start of period	Total change	Births	Deaths	Natural Change*	Net Migration and other changes†	Population at end of period
1993–1994	57,714	148	763	651	112	+36	57,862
1998–1999	58,475	210	711	634	77	133	58,684
2003–2004	59,522	+290	707	603	+104	+186	60,235
2008–2009	61,398	+394	787	570	+217	+177	61,792

* Natural increase refers to the excess of births over deaths in that year. Natural decrease refers to the excess of deaths over births.
† Net migration and other changes refers mainly to international migration. Other small changes include changes in the numbers of armed forces.

replace the population (2.1 children per woman). The TFR has varied through time, peaking at 2.93 in 1964; but since 1973 it has been below 2.1 (Chamberlain & Gill 2005). Life expectancy, on the other hand, has risen: between 1950 and 2008, it increased from 66 to 78 years for men, and 71 to 82 years for women (ONS 2010a).

3.3.1.3 Migration and ethnicity

The arrival of international migrants into the UK has risen substantially since the early 1990s, in particular since the expansion of the EU in 2004 which enabled a greater freedom of movement into the UK for non-UK European citizens. For example, in 2004, 582,000 people migrated to the UK compared to 314,000 in 1994 (Jefferies 2005). The net flow of migrants has been variable over the last 30 years: between 1975 and 1982, the net flow was 300,000 people; between 1983 and 1993, it was 240,000; but between 1994 and 2004 there was a substantial increase in net flow to 1.4 million people (Jefferies 2005; see **Table 3.1**).

Migrants have arrived from a variety of countries; however, the majority have originated from the EU, with numbers showing an increasing trend over time (75,000 in 1994; 123,000 in 2003). Immigrants from the Middle East have also increased (12,000 in 1994; 27,000 in 2003) and there has been a net inflow from Australia since the late 1990s (Jefferies 2005). Ninety per cent of migrants chose to live in England (primarily in London (30%) and the south-east (18%)), followed by Scotland (7%), and Wales and Northern Ireland (2% each). A primary factor driving international migration to the UK is economics: about 20% of migrants who arrived between 1994 and 2003 cited their reason for moving as 'work', although there has also been a 37% increase in the number of people arriving to study (50,000 in 1994; 135,000 in 2003).

Over the past 80 years, the trend in migration within the UK has been for people to move to southern England (Champion 2005; **Figure 3.3**), particularly to coastal villages and retirement districts in the south-west peninsula and along the south coast. There has also been significant migration, in both directions, between urban and rural areas. As an illustration of this point, areas like East Anglia, Lincolnshire and cities on the fringes of the main urban centres of the Midlands and the north of England have seen population growth, while much of western Northern Ireland, northern Scotland, south-west Scotland, Glasgow and several large English cities such as Liverpool and Birmingham, have seen population reductions (Champion 2005). The younger and/or 'skilled' workforce sections of the population tend to migrate to urban areas, while families and the older section of the population are more likely to move to rural areas (Champion 2005).

3.3.1.4 Consequences of demographic change on UK NEA Broad Habitats and ecosystem services

Demographic changes have impacted on all UK habitat types and ecosystem services, and have led to increased urbanisation. The increasing population of the UK, combined with a rise in the number of single-person households (in Great Britain (GB) from 12% to 29% between 1961 and 2004 (Jefferies 2005)), has placed increased pressure on land conversion for housing, and has created higher demands on water and energy resources, hence having the potential to contribute to future climate change. Such pressure is particularly strong in the south-east of England where population growth and migration have been greatest. Here there is potential for the following:

i)   Loss of local provisioning services when high quality farmland is used to house the growing population;

ii) Loss of supporting services, such as soil formation, through the construction of new buildings and the use of non-permeable surfaces; and/or

iii) Loss of regulating services, such as those provided by natural coastal sea defences, when an increase in building exacerbates coastal squeeze (i.e. the reduction and loss of coastal habitat that occurs when natural landward migration of a habitat is prevented by man-made defences and structures).

However, these potential losses can be counteracted, in part, by policy which favours the re-use of previously built land known as 'brownfield'. This has already been demonstrated in England where, although the density of dwellings erected has increased since 1989—from about 25 to 43 dwellings per hectare (ha)—the proportion built on previously developed land had increased from around 55% to 80%, while that on previously agricultural land has reduced from almost 30% to just 14% in 2009 (Planning Statistical Release 2010).

However, the relative impact of these demographic changes on provisioning services at least, has been low compared with other drivers of environmental change. For example, while population increase can be expected to drive provisioning services, such as crops and livestock production, the rates of such service increase in the UK have been far higher than the population increase would have required (Chapter 15). Therefore, it is clear that other drivers, such as economic (e.g. market forces) and sociopolitical (e.g. consumption choices and subsidies) factors, have been more important in impacting on service delivery.

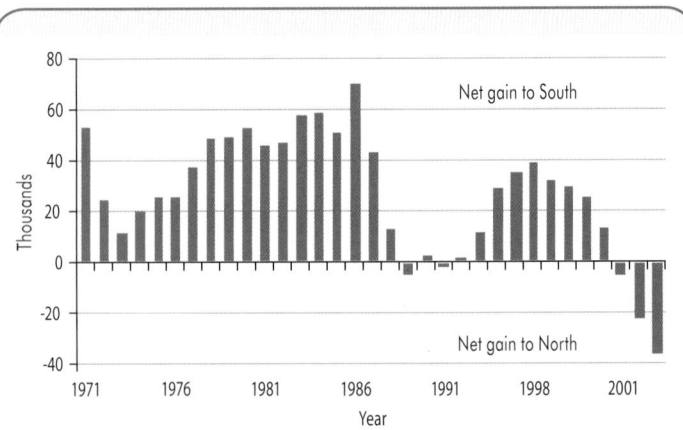

Figure 3.3 Net migration between the North* and South of the UK from 1971 to 2003[†]. *The South comprises the Government Office Regions of London, South East, South West, East and East Midlands; 'the North' is the remainder of the UK. [†]Data refer to calendar years. Source: data from National Health Service Central Register; General Register Office for Scotland; Northern Ireland Statistics and Research Agency; figure reproduced from Champion (2005).

3.3.2 Economic Drivers

Patterns in economic activity often reflect the actions which we take to improve our own well-being (Nelson *et al.* 2005). Economic activity, as described by the MA, "is influenced by the endowment of natural resources, including ecosystem services (natural capital), the number and skills of humans (human capital), the stock of built resources (manufactured capital), [the] nature of human institutions, both formal and informal (social capital)...and by available technologies, [which may] be enhanced by access to international markets" (Nelson *et al.* 2005 p82–83).The latter can change which activities take place at home and the variety of items available for consumption.

The economic drivers affecting UK ecosystems have altered over the last 60 years as the economy has grown (reflected by an increasing trend in Gross Domestic Product) and transformed from an industrial-based to post-industrial service-based economy; currently, developments are towards a low-carbon, high technology-based economy. Market forces at play within the environment have altered as wealth has increased and consumption choices have changed. Typical business and industry sizes have grown, reflecting the development of larger industry bases and the impact that the growth of multinational companies and globalisation have had on the flow of trade and market conditions for many commodities. These drivers are closely related to cultural and demographic drivers, in addition to scientific and technological developments. Economic drivers impact ecosystems by their close association with land and sea use, as well as pollution and exploitation levels as landowners and managers react to market conditions. These economic drivers operate spatially across the whole of the UK but their impact has become more uniform over time as the economic environment, both in the UK, and the world generally, has become more globalised. Hence, in this section, we will discuss economic growth and consumer choice, market forces, and industry size and globalisation.

3.3.2.1 Economic growth and consumer choice

Personal and family wealth in the UK has increased significantly since the 1940s (ONS 2009). The proportion of average family expenditure on essential items, such as food, has decreased, leaving money available to spend on luxury items, travel and leisure. It should also be noted that this improved wealth, combined with population growth and a more general drive towards consumerism (including non-luxury items), has increased the overall level of consumption in society (i.e. the material through-put). Additionally, as spending ability has increased, the origin of consumed items has become ever more global, and the type of products purchased has altered in line with technological developments. Therefore, the potential for proactive consumer choice to drive ecosystem change has been established. For instance, the increase in the demand for organic products (**Figure 3.4**) may act as an incentive for farm conversion and the change of management practices; however, evidence for the full extent of such changes on ecosystem condition and extent are limited.

3.3.2.2 Market forces

Market forces can influence the proportion of land or marine areas managed under different uses (for example, the type and variety of agricultural crops grown, the area of land used for forestry, or the scale of fishing activities), and thereby influence the provision of final goods and benefits. They also affect the way urban land is used, particularly demands for the development of housing and office space.

In recent years, specialist crops, cereals and dairy farming have seen a greater increase in net farm income in the UK than livestock-grazing or mixed farms (Clothier *et al.* 2008; Defra 2010b,c). This has influenced land use management decisions, and, in particular, resulted in greater parcels of land designated for 'set-aside' (when this practise was in place), which may facilitate increased biodiversity. Likewise, economic support and the profitability of producing organic crops and/or high welfare meat from conservation grade farms have influenced management practices. For example, there are now 7,567 organic producers in the UK, a 20% rise on numbers in 2004 (6,038) (Defra 2010d).

Imports and exports to a country reflect dominant market forces and consumer choice. Since the 1960s, the UK markets, as indicated by imports, showed an increase in demand for fruits (+260%), vegetables (+355%) and alcoholic drinks (+526%). Decreases were observed in the import of cereals (-45%), perhaps due to an already sufficient supply within the UK. Although timber exports of sawn wood in 2009 were 15 times greater than those in 1961 (1961: 14,300 cubic metres (m^3), worth USD\$1.5 million, or equivalent to £900,000 in today's terms; 2009: 203,000 m^3, worth £41 million; Forestry Commission 2010b; FAOSTAT 2011a), higher levels have not been attained due to strong competing markets from abroad. The relatively low value for UK timber has reduced the amount of woodland in the UK felled for timber products, and has instead increased the number of woodlands managed for recreation and conservation purposes (Chapter 8).

Market forces in the marine environment have driven high, and often unsustainable harvest levels of economically important species. High returns have also promoted diversification into new areas such as harvesting fish for aquaculture feed and fertiliser.

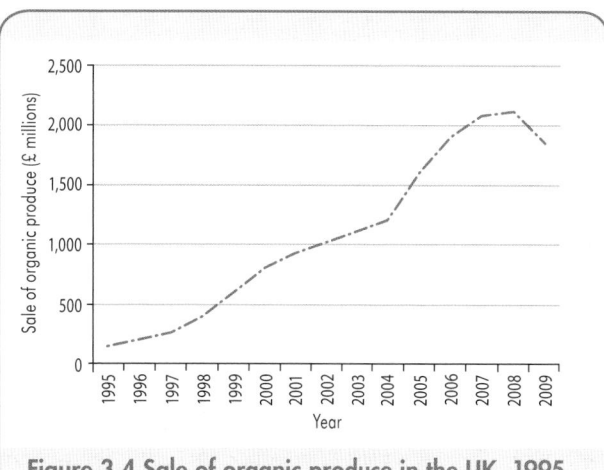

Figure 3.4 Sale of organic produce in the UK, 1995 to 2009. Source: data extracted from Cottingham & Perrett (2010).

3.3.2.3 Industry size and globalisation

Since the 1940s, the business landscape has changed. As global trade increased, the growth of large, chain business and multinational companies expanded to form the globalised economy we see today, where a relatively small number of large companies dominate certain markets and enterprises, including agriculture and food. The scale of business development has paralleled increases in transport infrastructure such that the domestic agriculture, forestry and fisheries trades are linked to European and global markets. These drivers link to consumer choices, market forces, land and sea use, pollution, and exploitation levels of natural resources. Market forces and the move to globalised and larger industries can also be argued to have caused the reduction of cultural services, especially landscapes and seascapes due to the promotion of certain aspects, such as large, uniform field patterns and simplified cropping, which are deemed to detract from the local character.

3.3.3 Sociopolitical Drivers

Sociopolitical drivers operate in connection with economic and cultural drivers. They illustrate the different values that society places on the environment, and how trade-offs between such values are managed. As such, sociopolitical drivers have been identified as some of the most fundamental factors behind the way in which humans influence the environment, although much research still needs to be conducted in order to fully understand how these drivers operate and interact (Nelson *et al.* 2005).

Over the past 60 years, the sociopolitical system within the UK has changed, leading to important consequences for ecosystem condition, extent and delivery of services, primarily in a positive direction. This has been due to the evolution and development of legislation protecting a wider range of public benefits, and the shift in agricultural and forestry support mechanisms from single-focus schemes that promoted large yields and returns, to more multi-objective land use regimes that support diversification, environmental management and amenity; such changes have often been brought about by societal pressure on government. Accordingly, changes have had strong impacts on direct drivers such as land conversion and resource consumption.

Sociopolitical drivers tend to operate across the whole of the UK. However, increasingly, the way legislation is implemented differs between each devolved administration, as well as the relevant agencies and regulatory bodies, and hence impacts may differ between each constituent country (Chapters 17–20). In this section, we will discuss legislation, regulation and support mechanisms, highlighting the consequences these drivers have had on the UK's ecosystems and their services.

3.3.3.1 Legislation, regulation and state versus private relationships

Legislation and regulation. As society has become more aware and concerned about environmental change, legislation and regulation has been developed and implemented to protect human well-being and, consequently, ecosystem health. Following the pioneering Clean Air Act of 1956, a range of legislation has been developed that limits private development rights and increasingly values the common rights of society and the environment (**Table 3.2**). Themes in this developing legislation have included: pollution control and emissions regulation; protection of amenity and natural beauty; provision of access rights; and ecosystem and species protection.

As regulation and legislation has developed there has been a concurrent increase in the scale of responsibility of actions from the individual to society, from local to global, and from reacting to short-term events to assessing the potential impacts of actions over much longer periods (decades or even centuries). There is now regulation of a wide range of human activities with the overarching objective of protecting or enhancing current and future environmental conditions. Some examples are discussed:

■ *Pollution and emissions control*: Pollution control legislation at a national and international level has set standards for air and water pollution levels which, through regulation, monitoring and enforcement by country agencies, have enabled pollution emissions to be tracked and dramatically reduced (Section 3.4.2).

■ *Conservation and protection of nature and ecosystems*: Legislation aimed at nature conservation has led to the designation of areas of land under national (e.g. Sites of Special Scientific Interest (SSSIs)) and international (e.g. Special Areas of Conservation (SACs); Special Protection Areas (SPAs)) designations. These designations exist to protect rare habitats and species, and can provide incentives for ecological restoration or management. Some marine habitats are also covered by such legislation, but there are still large areas that are afforded no protection at all (Chapter 12).

■ *Land use*: Under current land use planning regimes, more attention is now given to the rarity and importance of habitats and land cover types than was seen in the 1940s. Town and country planning laws now regulate land use change discussions, and, through measures such as Environmental Impact Assessments (EIAs), incorporate consideration of the potential impact a change in land use may have on ecosystems. Recent extensions to these regulations now impose restrictions on how different land can be used. For example, the 'uncultivated land' EIA regulations stipulate that land which has not previously been under cultivation or agricultural improvement is now protected from such use, therefore, affecting future land use change decisions.

■ *Access rights*: An evolving range of legislation has addressed access to the countryside, from the National Parks and Access to the Countryside Act of 1949 through to the Countryside and Rights of Way Act 2000 and the Marine and Coastal Access Act 2009. These legislation changes have opened up an ever increasing area of the countryside for public access and enjoyment, although the delivery of these acts has been different in the separate countries of the UK.

■ *Climate variability*: In response to the threats of climate change, the UK government has committed to monitoring greenhouse gases in order to help combat future climate change. Greenhouse gas and carbon

Table 3.2 Important UK, European and global environmental legislation.

Year	UK environmental legislation	Theme
1949	National Parks and Access to the Countryside Act	Access
1956	Clean Air Act	Air pollution control
1974	Control of Pollution Act	Noise management
1981	The Wildlife and Countryside Act 1981 as amended	Ecosystem and species protection
1984	Road Traffic Act	Air pollution control
1990	The Environmental Protection Act	Air pollution, noise, waste management
1991	Water Resources Act	Waste, water management
1991	Water Industry Act	Water management
1993	Clean Air Act	Air pollution control
1993	Noise and statutory nuisance Act	Noise management
1994	Criminal Justice and Public Order Act	Noise management
1994	Waste management licensing regulations (SI1994/1056)	Waste management
1994	The Conservation (Natural Habitats, &c.) Regulations 1994 (the Habitats Regulations)	Ecosystem protection
1995	Environment Act	Air pollution, waste, water, flood management
1996	Noise Act	Noise management
1999	Pollution prevention and control Act	Air pollution control
2000	Pollution prevention and control regulations (England, Wales)	Air pollution control
2000	Countryside and Rights of Way Act 2000	Access
2000	Transport Act	Air pollution control
2000	Finance Act	Air pollution and climate change mitigation
2003	Waste and emissions trading Act	Air pollution control
2003	Water Act	Water management
2004	Environmental information regulations	Freedom of information/justice
2006	Environmental noise regulations (England)	Noise management
2007	Transfrontier shipment of waste regulations SI1711	Waste management
2007	Environmental permitting regulations (England, Wales)	Waste management
2007	Air quality standards regulations	Air pollution control
2008	Climate Change Act	Climate change mitigation
2009	Marine and Coastal Access Act	Access
2009	Environmental damage and liability regulations	Pollution liability
2010	The conservation of habitats and species regulations	Ecosystem and species protection
Year	**European environmental legislation**	**Theme**
1976	Bathing Water Directive 76/160/EEC	Pollution control
1979	Conservation of wild birds (the Birds Directive) 79/409/EEC	Species protection
1986	Single European Act	Environmental assessment
1991	EC Directive 91/689/EEC on hazardous waste	Waste management
1991	Urban Waste Water Directive 91/271/EEC	Waste management
1992	Maastricht Treaty	Sustainable development
1992	Conservation of natural habitats and of wild fauna and flora (the Habitats Directive 92/43/EEC)	Ecosystem species protection
1997	Amsterdam Treaty	Sustainable development
1999	Landfill waste	Waste management
2000	Water Framework Directive 2000/60/EC	Pollution, ecological quality, water management
2001	Integrated pollution prevention and control (IPCC)	Pollution control
2001	Deliberate Release Directive 2001/18/EC	Impact assessment
2003	EU Directive 2003/4/EC Public Access to Environmental Information	Justice/participation
2005	EU emissions trading scheme	Pollution control

Table 3.2 continued. Important UK, European and global environmental legislation.		
Year	**European environmental legislation, continued**	**Theme**
2006	Waste Directive 2006/12/EC	Waste management
2006	Groundwater Directive 2006/118/EC	Water management
2007	Lisbon Treaty	Sustainable development
2007	Floods Directive	Flooding
Year	**International environmental legislation**	**Theme**
1950	International convention for the protection of birds	Species protection
1971	Convention on wetlands of international importance, especially waterfall habitat (Ramsar)	Ecosystem protection
1972	Convention on the Prevention of Marine Pollution by Dumping from Ships and Aircraft	Pollution control
1973	Convention on International Trade in Endangered Species of Wild Fauna and Flora (CITES)	Species protection
1974	Convention for the Prevention of Marine Pollution from Land Based Sources (London Convention)	Pollution control
1979	Convention on Long Range Transboundary Air Pollution	Pollution control
1979	Convention on the Conservation of European Wildlife and Natural Habitats (Bern Convention)	Ecosystem and species protection
1979	Convention on the Conservation of Migratory Species of Wild Animals (CMS or Bonn Convention)	Species protection
1991	Convention on Environmental Impact Assessment in a Transboundary Context (Espo)	Impact assessment
1992	Convention for the Protection of the Marine Environment of the North East Atlantic (OSPAR)	Ecosystem protection
1992	Convention on Biological Diversity	Ecosystem and species protection
1992	UN Framework Convention on Climate Change	Climate change
1997	Kyoto Protocol	Climate change
1998	Aarhus Convention – Convention on Access to Information, Public Participation in Decision-making and Access to Justice in Environmental Matters	Justice
2000	European Landscape Convention	Landscape/amenity protection
2003	Protocol on strategic environmental assessment	Impact assessment

dioxide emissions in the UK have decreased since 1990 (MacCarthy *et al.* 2010; Section 3.4.4.3). Recent legislation (e.g. the Renewable Transport Fuel Obligation; the Renewables Obligation for Electricity Production and the EU Emission Trading Scheme) aims to encourage the use of sustainable and renewable fuel sources which may impact on future land use management decisions. Such legislation was introduced following the Energy Act 2004, and meets requirements under both the EU Renewable Energy Directive 2009/28/EC and UK targets, which aim to ensure 20% and 15%, respectively, of energy is produced from renewable sources by 2020.

State versus private relationships. Recent trends in the development of environmental legislation and regulation have shown a shift from prosecution through criminal courts to more empowered environmental agencies; a move from reactive addressing of individual environmental threats to a consideration of the strategic and long-term implications of plans and policies; and a move to empower society and citizens to monitor environmental change, industry and environmental agency practices by freely accessing environmental information. There has also been a shift from regulation control through enforcement to a market-regulated approach where emission or waste permits can be traded, and market forces and technology can aid in the regulation of emission or pollution levels. The effect of devolution is likely to further impact on future legislation as

the different countries of the UK react to their own particular mix of pressures and societal demands to formulate different policy.

Consequences of legislation and regulation changes on UK ecosystems and ecosystem services. Changing legislation and regulation has protected a number of key ecosystem services in recognition of their importance and value to ensuring human well-being. For example:

■ *Provisioning services*: The range of forestry legislation in place has protected the national resource of trees and timber, preventing undesirable felling and ensuring restocking to maintain both forest cover and a timber resource (Chapter 8; Chapter 15).

■ *Cultural services*: The continual evolution of 'access' legislation has led to a large increase in the area and type of landscape available for public recreation (Chapter 16).

■ *Regulating services*: The wide range of pollution and emissions control legislation has been successful in reducing system inputs, such as nitrogen and phosphorous, to a number of ecosystems (Section 3.4.2) (Chapter 14).

■ *Biodiversity*: There has been a growing list of legislation directed at protecting the diversity of wild species in the UK. While there have been some successes (Section 3.3.3.2), biodiversity continues to be lost which impacts on many ecosystem services (Chapter 4).

Some legislation has resulted in the protection of services that were not the prime focus of the original legislation. For instance, there is a range of European legislation that now protects much of the Mountains, Moorlands and Heaths habitat from being developed for housing or converted to farmland (Chapter 5). As a result, this legislation also affords protection to standing vegetation and peat which are final ecosystem services that are important for carbon storage and climate regulation (Chapter 14). Although it should be noted that there does remain a legacy of sites where permission for peat extraction pre-dates such concerns (Section 3.4.1.4).

Legislative changes are expected to continue to be major drivers of change in the future; the Water Framework Directive, for example, will address the ecological status of ecosystems potentially affected by pollution, and should lead to an improvement in the condition of freshwater and wetlands and the services they provide (such as water, improved biodiversity and flood regulation).

3.3.3.2 Support mechanisms: subsidies and grants

With changing cultural preferences and social and economic conditions, society and governments have encouraged different forms of activity by supplying subsidies and grants in order to affect personal and business behaviour. Ultimately, these influence direct drivers such as land use change, harvest rates and pollution levels.

Agricultural subsidies. There has been a strong post-war tradition of support for productive agriculture and forestry which has influenced land management practices and land conversion. The Agriculture Acts of 1947 and 1967 began a system of price support for agricultural production that was supported by market-aiding organisations such as the Meat and Livestock Commission. These were followed in 1973 and 1991 by EU subsidies under the CAP (Chapter 7; Chapter 15). Over time, these payments greatly supported activities, such as land drainage and land conversion to increase food production from farmland, and also allowed for specialisation, investment and improvement in machinery, livestock breeds, crop growth and drainage systems across the UK. When production levels became too high, financial subsidies were also been offered to farmers to reduce output: for example the 'set-aside' policy that was introduced in 1988, although note this has recently been abolished (**Box 3.1**).

More recently, agricultural support schemes have reduced their focus on production and now include support and rewards for positive management enhancement and 'environmental stewardship' works. Under current initiatives, including agri-environment schemes such as the Defra Environmental Stewardship Schemes (Entry Level, Organic Entry Level, Upland Entry Level and Higher Level Stewardship), support is available for organic farm conversion, energy crop cultivation and farm diversification, and there is also a range of payments that are linked to a system of cross compliance activities that promote traditional and environmentally beneficial management options, such as maintenance of hedges, crop rotations and woodland coppicing.

Forestry subsidies. Financial support for forestry has evolved from the support of traditional timber production to the promotion of multiple uses of forests and forest products, including the consideration of landscape and amenity factors. Initial grant aid encouraged large areas of afforestation, particularly in the uplands and upland fringes of the UK. This caused widespread ecosystem change and damage to peatland and moorland habitats (Chapter 5; Chapter 14).

Although there has long been tension between the promotion of modern productive forestry and its impact on the wider landscape, recent target grants and initiatives, such as Community Forests and the Challenge Schemes for native woodland in National Parks, now provide strong financial support for community- or conservation-based woodland creation programmes which, in turn, influence land cover patterns. Afforestation of sensitive habitats is no longer encouraged by current grants; instead, funding is now often available to allow restoration to other habitat types such as peatland (Patterson & Anderson 2000).

Grants. Since the 1990s, an increasing number of specialist grant schemes have become available to land managers to support conservation activities. Initially, these were focused within designated areas, such as Environmentally Sensitive Areas (ESAs) and targeted upland areas and National Parks, in particular, both of which are difficult to farm and had natural beauty. Ongoing reform to schemes such as the CAP Higher Level Stewardship schemes has led to a shift from site- or protected landscape-based protection to a focus on proactive management within the wider countryside (Natural England 2011). In the UK, the land area supported by such mechanisms has increased by 1,000% between 1992 and the mid-2000s (**Figure 3.5**). Therefore, there is currently less of a distinction between support payments targeted at conservation and those targeted at agriculture as they now mostly fall under the single heading of 'environmental stewardship'.

Government conservation initiatives. The financial support given to biodiversity and conservation initiatives by the UK government has increased by 124% from around £250 million in 2001 to £547 million in 2009 (Defra 2010a). This demonstrates the government's commitment to meeting both national and international obligations—for example, targets set by the Convention on Biological Diversity (www.cbd.int/), which are largely executed through the UK Biodiversity Action Plans (UK BAPs). Elements of this funding are available as grants to support UK BAP work at local levels, such as within local nature reserves, or to support conservation land management. In recent years, significant sums of money have also been provided by the Lottery Fund to support environmental initiatives.

Private support mechanisms. In contrast to state-provided economic support to encourage forestry or agricultural production, there has also been a history of private support for land management and ownership for wildlife and landscape conservation purposes. In this sense, the membership payments to organisations such as The Royal Society for the Protection of Birds (RSPB; www.rspb.org.uk/) and The Wildlife Trusts (www.wildlifetrusts.org) are support mechanisms for conservation management. With the sizeable and growing membership base of the various conservation charities there has been a significant increase in expenditure and action for nature conservation purposes over recent decades. Conservation charities, such as the RSPB, The Wildlife Trusts, the Wildfowl & Wetlands Trust (www.wwt.org.uk/) and the Woodland Trust (www. woodlandtrust.org.uk), are able to buy or lease large areas of land that they manage for conservation purposes but that also bring benefits to human well-being. This can impact on direct drivers, such as land use change and pollution, as seen by the RSPB Fens 'Futurescape' (www.rspb.org. uk/news/276106-rspb-launches-new-landscape-scale-conservation-project) which has acquired farmland areas and is now flooding them to create new wetlands in their place. This project, along with the joint Natural England project, 'Fenland Bird Recovery Project' (www.rspb.org. uk/ourwork/projects/details/218989-fenland-farmland-

---

Box 3.1 How socio-political economic and cultural/behavioural drivers have driven the implementation, abolishment and reform of set-aside policy.

A traditional land management practice used across Europe throughout its agricultural history is the fallowing of land in arable rotation, that is taking parcels of land out of production for various lengths of time. This practice aids in a number of agronomic benefits including: weed control, disease production and improved fertility (IEEP 2008). However, technological improvements during the second half of the 20th Century that gave farmers the capability to have continuous arable crops, including during winter, resulted in a dramatic decrease in the proportion of agricultural land left fallow.

In turn, this contributed to a European-wide surplus of foodstuffs. In response, 'set-aside' was introduced into the Common Agricultural Policy (CAP) (Chapter 7; Chapter 15) as a production control measure, and adopted by EU countries, including the UK, in 1988. At first voluntary, set-aside policy called for land managers (particularly farmers) to take areas of arable land out of production. In 1992, the MacSharry CAP reforms made set-aside obligatory and farmers were required to set-aside 15% of their cropped land for at least five years in return for annual payment from the government, compensating for loss of production revenue (Curry 2008b; IEEP 2008). Since 1992, the percentage of set-aside required has varied from between 5% and 15%, with decisions governed by market fluctuations (Curry 2008b); but, in England, it has typically stood at approximately 500,000 hectares per year, making it England's' third largest category of land use.

Although introduced as a production control measure, set-aside did (in some cases), or could result in three major environmental benefits (Curry 2008b; IEEP 2008):
1. *Increased biodiversity*. Set-aside or fallow land can provid winter food sources (e.g. seed) and spring/summer nesting and brood-rearing habitat for birds. It improves conditions for scarce arable plants (especially in rotational set-aside) or for stands of mixed grass and wild flowers (particularly in non-rotational sea-aside); and it supports higher densities of invertebrates and small mammals (e.g. hares prefer set-aside to other arable fields, and bats can forage on the increased number of invertebrates).
2. *Resources protection*. Fertiliser and pesticide use and soil disturbance is reduced when less land is managed for production, consequently reducing diffuse pollution. Well-placed set-aside land can act as a buffer between cropped land and more sensitive sites, including water courses, and can afford protection to areas typically exposed to the forces of wind and water erosion, such as sloped sites.
3. *Ecological connectivity*. 'Corridors' enabling the movement of species between patches of fragmented habitat can be created by set-aside land, and can also increase the range of habitats available.

Increases in soil carbon sequestration through the conversion of conventional agricultural land to that with high carbon inputs and low-levels of disturbance (e.g. natural regeneration or permanent set-aside) may have also resulted in set-aside contributing to climate change mitigation (IEEP 2008). In July 2007, in response to increased market demands for arable crops, particularly cereals, the European Commission (EC) announced that it would reduce set-aside requirement to 0%; and in November 2008, it agreed to abolish it completely through the CAP Health Check. Although farmers would not necessarily lose future payments received for keeping land as set-aside, it was predicted that between 50% and 70% of set-aside in England in 2007 would be brought back into production by 2009.

The abolition of set-aside has caused concern, particularly among UK environmental agencies and non-governmental organisations (NGOs), that the environmental benefits of set-aside will be lost. This could impact on the UK's ability to meet both national and international commitments, such as: meeting farming and land management targets (e.g. Defra's Departmental Strategic Objectives and Public Service Agreement targets); halting or reducing the loss of biodiversity (e.g. Convention on Biological Diversity targets); improving or maintaining water and soil quality (e.g. as required under the Water Framework Directive, Soil Thematic Strategy and Soil Framework Directive); and mitigating climate change (e.g. meeting commitments to greenhouse gas emissions) (Curry 2008b; IEEP 2008).

The Department for Environment, Food and Rural Affairs (Defra) and farming bodies, such as the National Farmers' Union (NFU), have recognised the environmental benefits that set-aside has delivered. In 2008, Defra commissioned a body of work (undertaken by NFU, Country Land and Business Association, the Royal Society for the Protection of Birds, Environment Agency and Natural England) to assess the impacts of 0% set-aside, to further improve understanding of the environmental benefits set-aside provides, and to formulate mitigation responses for any losses (Curry 2008a).
This review concluded that the implementation of any new policies to counter the loss of environmental benefits brought about the abolition of set-aside could not, realistically, be brought in until the 2009–2010 cropping year. In the interim, farmers were encouraged to retain uncropped land and manage it in such a way that environmental benefits were optimised (Curry 2008a). In July 2009, Defra announced its 'Campaign for the Farmed Environment' initiative—an industry-led, voluntary approach to recapture the environmental benefits of set-aside.

The Campaign, which is supported by a wide variety of organisations across the agricultural sector[1], will bring together the work farmers and land managers already do to benefit wildlife, maintain soil and water resources, and support farmland birds. It will also promote existing stewardship schemes and encourage voluntary management that will benefit the environment, while ensuring efficient and profitable food production. The Campaign has until 2012 to make the voluntary approach work, otherwise regulation will be reinstated (NFU 2011).

---

1 National Farmers' Union (NFU), Country Land and Business Association (CLA), Farming and Wildlife Advisory Group (FWAG), Linking Environment and Farming (LEAF), the Game and Wildlife Conservation Trust (GWCT), the Agricultural Industries Confederation (AIC), the Association of Independent Crop Consultants (AICC) and the Central Association of Agricultural Valuers (CAAV). The Royal Society for the Protection of Birds (RSPB), Natural England and the Environment Agency have also given the Campaign their full backing.

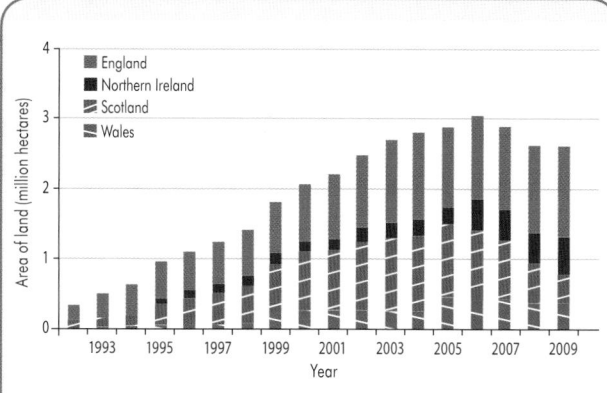

Figure 3.5 Area of land covered by Higher Level Stewardship or targeted agri-environment schemes*† in the UK, 1992 to 2009‡. *The following schemes have been included here as higher level or targeted agri-environment schemes: England – Environmentally Sensitive Areas (ESA), Countryside Stewardship (CS), and new Higher Level Stewardship (HLS); Scotland – ESA, Countryside Premium, and Rural Stewardship; Wales – ESA, Tir Cymen, and Tir Gofal; Northern Ireland – ESA, Countryside Management. †Higher level or targeted agri-environment schemes have stricter criteria for qualification than other agri-environment schemes. ‡Data for 2009 are provisional. Source: data from Welsh Assembly Government, Countryside Council for Wales, Scottish Government, Natural England, Defra; figure reproduced from Defra (2010a). © Crown copyright 2010.

bird-recovery-project#work), is also working with farmers, assisting them to access financial support from government agri-environment schemes to put nature-friendly farm management strategies into practise.

Consequence of change to support mechanisms on UK ecosystems and ecosystem services. Over the past 60 years, subsidies and support mechanisms have greatly enhanced the provisioning services, especially the final service of crops, livestock and fish. Historical support and CAP payments to the agricultural sector have greatly increased crop yields, by both the expansion of agricultural area and by providing stabilised prices that allowed farmers to invest in inputs, mechanisation and improved farming methods (Chapter 7). Support to the forestry sector has encouraged the continued increase in woodland area (Section 3.4.1.2). The recent expansion of these support mechanisms for broader environmental management has benefited the services of climate regulation and landscape amenity, in addition to enhancing the provisioning services (Chapter 14; Chapter 15).

There is evidence of the recent success of agri-environment schemes in bringing areas of Semi-natural Grassland back into 'favourable condition' (Critchley *et al.* 2004; Hewins *et al.* 2005; Chapter 6). Agri-environment schemes have also been successful in increasing the biodiversity ecosystem service within targeted areas. For example, cirl buntings (*Emberiza cirlus*) and corncrake (*Crex crex*) are both identified as being of the highest priority for conservation action in the UK BAP. Targeted conservation action, such as the provision of year-round habitat requirements through agri-environment schemes and the modification of mowing and grazing schemes, are believed to be one driver behind the numbers of both species showing

considerable recovery over the past 17 years: breeding pairs of cirl bunting have risen by 145% from 352 in 1993 to 862 in 2009; while the number of calling male corncrake (an indicator of breeding population size) has increased by 140% from 430 in 1993 to 1,156 in 2009 (Eaton *et al.* 2010).

3.3.4 Cultural and Behavioural Drivers

The value, beliefs and norms shared by a group of people can influence decision-making related to the environment. These values and beliefs are often shaped by cultural influences which mould how an individual perceives the world, what they consider is important and what course of action to take (Nelson *et al.* 2005).

Cultural drivers, which are those aspects of society ranging from knowledge to attitudes and consumption choices, can impact on ecosystems through their links to other drivers such as market forces and legislation. These drivers have changed across the UK over time as the economics and demographics of the country have altered and impacted on a number of habitats and services. Consumption choices by society can, for example, affect market forces, thus impacting on land and sea use, pollution and exploitation levels. Such choices may, therefore, favour the delivery of certain provisioning services over others. When such choices are based upon price alone they would be expected to favour services such as farming and fishing systems that are weighted to maximise production and minimise costs. However, in combination with other cultural drivers, such as societal knowledge and environmental attitudes, there is the potential for consumption choices to cause ecosystem change by favouring alternative farming or fishing practises, such as support for organic farming or sustainable fishing, which can have a positive impact on both ecosystem condition and human well-being. In this section, we will discuss knowledge, and the link between environmental attitudes and the media, as cultural drivers of change.

3.3.4.1 Knowledge

Knowledge is a key driver of ecosystem change as it allows the impact of man's activities on the environment to be seen, understood and acted upon. Knowledge informs legislation, subsidies, science and technology; it was the increased understanding of the detrimental effects that air pollution had on human health, for instance, that led to the development and implementation of the Clean Air Act in 1956—the first piece of legislation directed at reducing pollutants. Likewise, knowledge on the dangers and impacts of acid rain and climate change has stimulated further development and implementation of legislation to reduce levels of sulphur dioxide and greenhouse gas emissions (Section 3.4.2) (Chapter 14).

3.3.4.2 Environmental attitudes and the media

Our attitudes towards the environment can influence ecosystem change through consumer and consumption choice and through public pressure forcing change in legislation. Changes in environmental attitudes can raise public awareness of environmental topics and bring political pressure on particular issues.

The media is one of the biggest influences on environmental attitudes, which, in turn, can influence it. From the first printing presses to today's international internet, the media has had a huge impact on our knowledge and awareness of particular topics. For example, Rachel Carson's book, *Silent Spring* (1962), raised awareness across a wide audience of the threat of agricultural pesticides to wildlife (particularly birds), and eventually resulted in reform, including a ban on the use of the pesticide DDT across the USA in 1972.

More recent issues brought to the attention of the public through the media have included the impact of peat compost on wetlands, and the potential benefits to wildlife and human well-being of organic farming.

The environmental attitudes of UK citizens can be tracked through a variety of means, for example: conducting surveys on public attitudes and behaviours towards the environment and energy issues, such as those undertaken by the Massachusetts Institute of Technology and University of Cambridge in 2005 (Curry *et al.* 2005), and by Defra in 2009 (Thornton 2009); appraising membership figures of environmental campaign groups and political parties; and judging the reaction of the public to specific campaigns. Peoples' concern for the environment and willingness to take action to mitigate their own impact on the environment has shown a continually positive trend over past decades—one indication of this is the 51% increase, between 2001 and 2009, in the time that people spent volunteering in eight UK conservation organisations[1]. In 2009, this equated to approximately 1 million working days (Defra 2010a). However, it should be noted that concern for other issues, such as national security, health care and education, have recently taken precedence for many people (Curry *et al.* 2005).

3.3.5 Scientific and Technological Drivers

Advances in science and technology result in a greater understanding of how the world functions, and in the development of new products, chemicals, electronics, industries and species. These advances can interact with other indirect drivers to influence the rise and fall of economic markets, affect the cultural and religious values of society, or lead to changes in demographics. These drivers have also strongly influenced direct drivers such as land and sea use, pollution levels and climate change. We will discuss innovation and technological change, biotechnology, energy production and transport.

3.3.5.1 Innovation and technological change

Innovative ideas and/or the development of new technologies typically influence other drivers that impact on ecosystem extent or condition. Key technological developments either in, or adopted by, the UK have included the increased mechanisation of farming and fishing practices and the choice of the type of crops sown and livestock reared. Although fishing and farming activities have constantly evolved, changes over the past 60 years, largely resulting from the development of new technology, have had profound effects on ecosystems and the services they provide.

Mechanisation: farming. Improvements to farm machinery and techniques developed since WWII have allowed more frequent and deeper ploughing of agricultural land. Consequently, this has led to changes in farming practices such as a shift to select crops that can be sown in autumn and a reduction in the extent and timing of fallow land (the latter declining to less than a quarter of the area it occupied in 1940).

The introduction of mechanical harvesting began a long-term decline in the traditional management of grasslands for hay, and resulted in a shift to silage production. Although silage is still permanent grassland, the new cutting regime has caused significant, detrimental changes in species composition of these communities. Recently, in recognition of the biodiversity and cultural importance of hay meadow landscapes, many projects have been initiated to restore and retain traditional harvest techniques, particularly in upland areas such as the Yorkshire Dales, Lake and Peak District National Parks, and North Pennines Area of Outstanding Natural Beauty.

Other advancements in mechanical technology have been associated with significant ecosystem change. For instance, the increased use of machinery for peat extraction in the 1970s meant that larger areas and depths of peat could be extracted than had previously been possible by hand. In addition, technological advancements since the 1940s, such as the use of motor pumps, have led to the development of highly effective drainage systems and the consequent introduction of schemes to reclaim land, particularly in the lowlands of England and Northern Ireland. This has led to an increase in productive agricultural land, but a reduction in the area of wetland habitats, seasonally flooded grassland and lowland mires (Chapter 9). The impact of such activities can be considered over time by comparing the modelled historical (last ten millennia) extent of wetlands, against the current extent of wetland habitats (**Figure 3.6**).

Until the 1990s, drainage channels were also installed in the upland moorlands, often with the support of grant aid to help enhance production in poor soils or to boost heather growth in grouse moor areas. Capital grants were also provided in England and Wales for farm improvements which led to an increase in drainage activity. Field drainage was eligible for grant aid of up to 60% of capital expenditure, for example, and by 1972 approximately 100,000 ha per year were being drained (Marshall *et al.* 1978). Because of the devastating impact on ecosystems that such modifications of water flow caused, much of this activity has now ceased and new technology is being used to maintain or increase water levels. As a consequence, the re-wetting of many conservation landscapes in the lowlands has already been achieved, and 'grip blocking' in upland mires has used machinery to maintain water within the landscape, benefiting biodiversity and carbon sequestration.

Mechanisation: fishing. Technological changes during the 1950s led to the development of industrial fisheries.

---

1 Bat Conservation Trust, British Trust for Conservation Volunteers, British Trust for Ornithology, Butterfly Conservation, Plantlife, Royal Society for the Protection of Birds, The Wildlife Trusts, Woodland Trust, and a public body: Natural England.

Enhanced netting equipment and sonar technology enabled fish to be located and captured more efficiently, therefore increasing harvest levels. Increased returns also facilitated a rise in the number of vessels. However, the ability to capture different components of the population, for example juvenile fish in nets with finer mesh sizes, and the destruction of marine habitat through the development of techniques such as bottom trawling, have led to ecosystem-wide changes (Thurstan & Roberts 2010). Advances in fishing technology have also led to overexploitation of fisheries resources, the trends and impacts of which are discussed in Section 3.4.3.1 and in Chapters 12 and 15.

Development and use of chemicals. The development of novel chemicals during the last century has supported the modern agricultural revolution, resulting in an increase in food production and harvest rates. Significant developments have included the discovery of the Haber-Bosch process for ammonia production in the early 1900s resulting in industrial fertilisers, and the development of pesticides, such as the organochlorine DDT, chlordane and endrin, in the 1940s and 1950s. The use of these chemicals removed the constraint of nutrient limitation for crop growth, as well as competitive pests and weeds, resulting in increased yields.

The development of farming chemicals (such as fertilisers, herbicides and pesticides) made it possible for agricultural activity to extend to areas of land that would otherwise have been unsuitable for agricultural use, and has, therefore, influenced land cover patterns. Chemicals have also been used in the forestry sector to aid in the conversion of large areas of broadleaved woodland to conifer plantation in places where mechanical felling and removal of trees would not have been economically viable.

Environmental monitoring. Improvements to information technology and monitoring techniques are enhancing our ability to (rapidly) collect data and build on knowledge that can be used to inform land management decisions and provide input to policy development. For example, increased efforts in monitoring the levels of pollution have provided better information on emission levels (Section 3.4.2). Detailed mapping and modelling of soil fertility status has also led to 'precision farming' where specifically tailored programs of fertiliser application are developed in order to target certain areas of fields, thereby helping to minimise the use of chemicals.

Furthermore, information technology that can be applied to environmental monitoring is increasing our ability to detect ecosystem change, and has facilitated feedback to policy development aimed at the drivers of such change. For instance, remote sensing has aided the Land Cover Map projects undertaken by the Centre of Ecology and Hydrology, and mapping of oceanic environmental variables (e.g. chlorophyll *a* or sea-surface temperature), resulting in improved land-use and land-use change models and ocean processes models, respectively.

3.3.5.2 Biotechnology

Innovation in biotechnology, such as crop selection to produce improved strains and recent advances in genetically

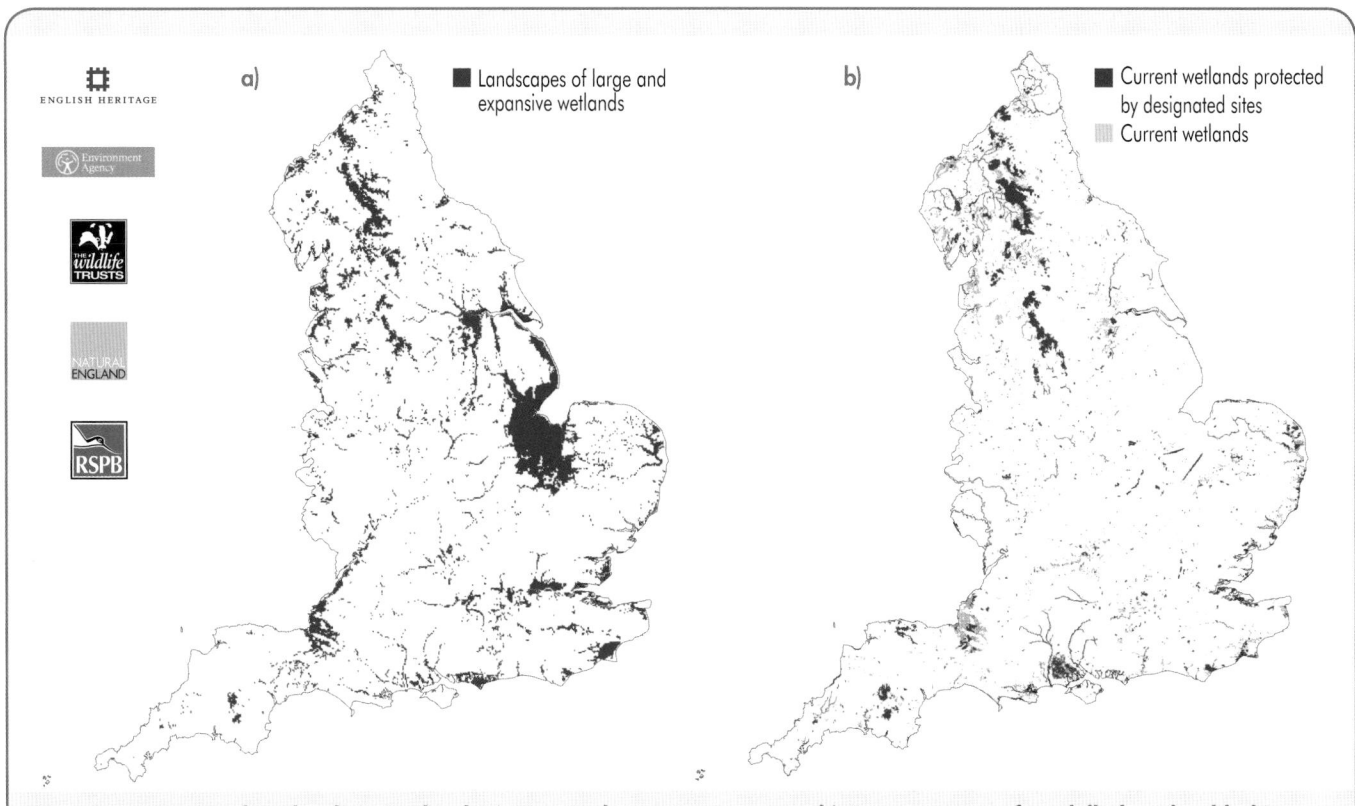

Figure 3.6 Extent of wetlands in England: a) Historical* maximum extent; b) Current extent of modelled wetland habitats.
*Last ten millennia. Source: maps from Hume *et al.* (2008). © Wetland Vision, a partnership between Environment Agency, English Heritage, Natural England, RSPB, and The Wildlife Trusts. Derived from data supplied by Natural England © Natural England 2008. This map is based upon Ordnance Survey material with the permisson of Ordnance Survey on behalf of the Controller of Her Majesty's Stationary Office © Crown copyright. Unauthorised reproduction infringes Crown copyright and may lead to prosecution or civil proceedings. Natural England 100046223 2008.

modified organisms (GMOs), can act as a driver of change by influencing other drivers. For example, while there is a long history of improvement through traditional crop selection techniques, recent changes in GMOs hold scope for increased advances in crop yield. However, it should be noted that considerable concerns exist in some arenas about the potential environmental effects of such technology.

3.3.5.3 Energy production technology

The development of technology used for energy production in the UK is strongly linked to changes in land use and land cover, waste disposal and pollution emissions. During the past 60 years, advances in technology have seen the traditional sources of energy used in the UK, such as coal, peat and wood fuel, supplemented by oil and gas (extracted from undersea reserves), nuclear power and renewable solar, wind and wave power. The uptake of different energy production methods often depends on the mix of market forces, subsides and legislation—this mix can create or amend markets in which these industries develop.

A variety of new technologies are being developed to use biomass for the production of heat, electricity and transport fuels, ranging from direct energy production through to more novel techniques of bio-digestion and fermentation. The production of energy from these sources, and other renewables (wind, wave, solar) have shown a strong increase over recent years (Defra 2010e) and is likely to drive future changes in land use if it proves effective and popular. There is evidence that such changes are already occurring: in England, there has been an increase of land managed for short-rotation coppice (a biomass crop) grown specifically for biofuel (**Figure 3.7**) (Chapter 7; Chapter 15). However, there are concerns that such crops can cause environmental 'sterility'; for example, *Miscanthus* x *giganteus* which is often planted in large fields, can almost completely suppress invertebrates in the crop. Consequently, this may have negative impacts on levels of biodiversity and the delivery of ecosystem services.

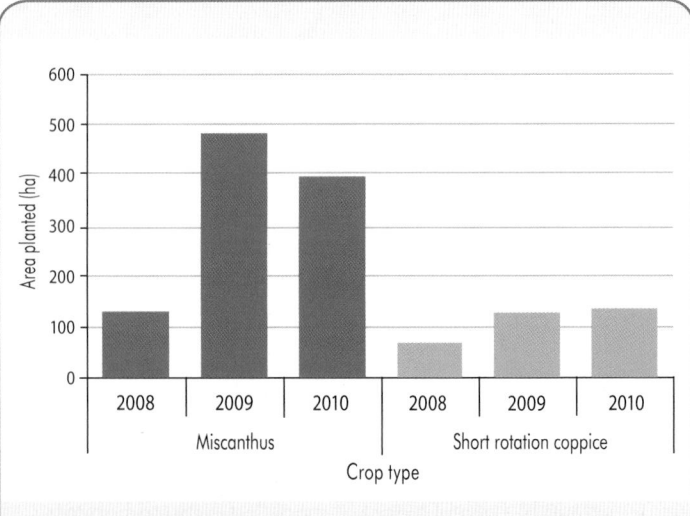

Figure 3.7: Area of energy crops (*Miscanthus* and Short-rotation coppice) planted in England between 2008 and 2010 under the Energy Crops Scheme 2. Source: data provided from Natural England. © Natural England 2010.

3.3.5.4 Transport

Transport technology has altered greatly over the past 60 years, and, as such, has influenced the impact that a number of direct drivers have had on ecosystem change. An illustration of this is the rise in alien and invasive species introductions as a consequence of increased international trade, facilitated through improvements to air and sea transport systems; for instance, the spread of non-native species into UK marine waters has been linked to the increase in movement of ballast water from transport ships. Changing transport technology is also associated with the rise in emission levels and impacts on land use in terms of land being converted to transport infrastructure, such as air and sea ports, rail terminals and road networks.

The use and uptake in these technologies can be linked to legislation and policy, such as the relative promotion of rail versus roads links and the different environmental impacts these have had. A further sociopolitical and cultural driver behind such change has been the promotion of long-distance mobility rather than a focus on facilitating local access and proximity, and reducing the need to travel as the fundamental objective of transport policy. Recently, there has been signs of political interest in 'localism', both as a social value for promoting community well-being and for the benefit of environmental sustainability; although there is yet to be any serious, practical implementation of such action.

3.4 Direct Drivers of Change

As outlined in the introduction to this chapter, direct drivers have an explicit effect on ecosystem processes (Nelson *et al.* 2005), and usually cause physical change that can be identified and monitored (Ash *et al.* 2008). The most important direct drivers identified as causing change in UK ecosystems and to biodiversity are: land use and use of the marine environment, leading to habitat change; pollution and nutrient enrichment (system inputs); overexploitation of terrestrial, marine and freshwater resources (harvest and resource consumption); climate variability and change; and biological drivers, such as invasive alien species.

3.4.1 Habitat Change

Human-induced change in the use and cover of the UK's habitats has been a key driver in altering ecosystem extent, as well as the condition of all habitat types and the ecosystem services that they provide (see **Figure 3.1; 3.2**). The underlying components behind such change include the utilisation and conversion of habitats for agriculture, forestry, fisheries, mineral extraction, and urban and infrastructure development, and the intensity of those uses. Rates of habitat change throughout the UK have varied both in space and time (although they are believed to be slower now than during the period between the end of WWII and the 1970s (Bibby 2009), and are mediated by, or reflect trends in, market forces, demographics and technological developments.

3.4.1.1 Conversion of land for agriculture

The most recent assessments of UK land cover—the Countryside Survey 2007[2] (CS2007; Carey *et al.* 2008a) and the Land Cover Map 2000[3] (LCM2000; Fuller *et al.* 2002)—report that agricultural land[4] dominates habitat, and, by inference, land use in the UK, covering approximately half of the UK land surface (47% LCM2000, 39% CS2007) (**Table 3.3; Figure 3.8**). However, this varies between the four countries with enclosed farmland covering 62% of England, 57% of Northern Ireland, 42% of Wales, but only 23% of Scotland.

Although figures have changed significantly since WWII, the majority of change occurred in the period between the 1940s and 1980s. Historically, the extent of agricultural land was primarily determined by topography and climate, as well as the availability of naturally productive workable soils which influenced what, and where, crops or stock could be managed. However, with the development of chemical fertilisers and mechanised farming practices, steeper and more remote slopes could be utilised and previously infertile soils were rendered productive. These advancements, driven, in part, by the desire for the UK to become more productive and self-sufficient after WWII, plus support from

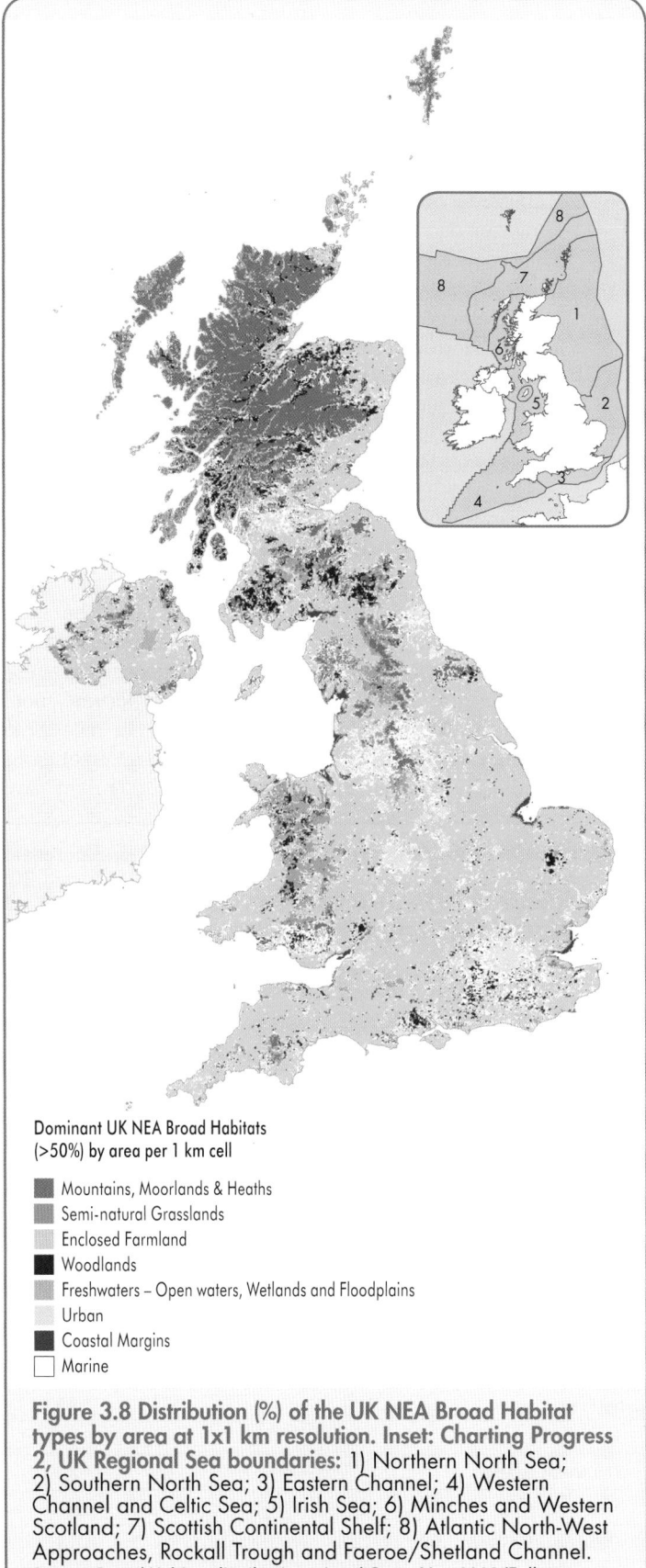

Dominant UK NEA Broad Habitats (>50%) by area per 1 km cell

- Mountains, Moorlands & Heaths
- Semi-natural Grasslands
- Enclosed Farmland
- Woodlands
- Freshwaters – Open waters, Wetlands and Floodplains
- Urban
- Coastal Margins
- Marine

Figure 3.8 Distribution (%) of the UK NEA Broad Habitat types by area at 1x1 km resolution. Inset: Charting Progress 2, UK Regional Sea boundaries: 1) Northern North Sea; 2) Southern North Sea; 3) Eastern Channel; 4) Western Channel and Celtic Sea; 5) Irish Sea; 6) Minches and Western Scotland; 7) Scottish Continental Shelf; 8) Atlantic North-West Approaches, Rockall Trough and Faeroe/Shetland Channel. Source: Broad Habitat distribution – Land Cover Map 2000 (Fuller *et al.* 2002); Regional seas – based on UKMMAS (2010). Coastline: World Vector Shoreline@National – Geospatial Intelligence Agency. Source: NOASS, NGDC.

Table 3.3 Land cover estimates (hectares; ha) of UK NEA Broad Habitat types derived from the Land Cover Map 2000 project (LCM2000; Fuller *et al.* 2002), the Countryside Survey 2007 (CS2007; Carey *et al.* 2008a) and spatial analysis by the UNEP World Conservation Monitoring Programme (UNEP-WCMC) using LCM2000 data*. The Marine area is that encompassed within the 12 nautical mile zone, and was only estimated by UNEP-WCMC.

UK NEA Broad Habitat	LCM2000 ('000s ha)	CS2007 ('000s ha)	UNEP-WCMC ('000s ha)
Mountains, Moorlands & Heaths	4,080	4,603	4,103
Semi-natural Grasslands	3,969	4,065	3,941
Enclosed Farmland	11,670	10,220	11,530
Woodlands	2,914	2,867	2,918
Freshwaters – Openwaters, Wetlands & Floodplains	277	328	272
Urban	1,664	1,398	1,675
Coastal Margins	94	71	336
Marine	-	-	16,477

* The LCM2000 and CS2007 apply different methods to estimate habitat extent (see Section 3.4.1.1). Therefore differences in figures for similar habitat can be expected and likely represent differences in the classification of component habitats and/or the ability to measure extent of a particular habitat type. Likewise, differences observed in estimates between LCM2000 and UNEP-WCMC estimates are due to differences in the way component habitats were aggregated into the UK NEA Broad Habitats (Chapter 1).

2 Estimates of land cover compiled by the Countryside Survey are assessed through ground surveys of 1 km² parcels of land (Carey *et al.* 2008).
3 The Land Cover Map is a digital map of different types of land and vegetation cover compiled from satellite imagery (Fuller *et al.* 2002).
4 Designated as Enclosed Farmland by the UK NEA, and incorporating Arable and Horticultural land plus Improved Grassland habitats.

government subsidies (Section 3.3.3.2) (Chapter 7), not only shifted the balance between arable and pastoral land use, but also resulted in semi-natural habitats being converted to farmland.

It is believed that the rate of change in the conversion of land for agricultural purposes has decreased, yet change is still being observed. Between 1998 and 2007, there was a significant decrease in arable and horticultural land (-9.1%), while some Semi-natural Grassland habitat types increased (Neutral grassland: +6.0%; Acid grassland: +5.5%; **Table 3.4**) (Chapter 6), possibly indicating the de-intensification of farming. However, there has been a concurrent increase in Improved Grassland (which is used for agriculture) by +5% (Carey *et al.* 2008a; **Table 3.4**) (Chapter 7).

Variables such as land use records, field sizes and the presence of field boundaries (e.g. hedgerows and dry stone walls) indicate that the management and use of agricultural land has undergone significant change and simplification since WWII. Records of farm holding sizes kept by the Department for Environment, Food and Rural Affairs (Defra) Observatory Programme indicate that farm size has increased, larger individual fields are maintained (indicated by significant reduction in boundary features), and livestock and cropping patterns have become more simplified and specialised (Foresight 2010). In regards to the latter, while the area of land managed for cereal crops remained relatively stable between 1961 and 2009, there have been significant reductions in the amount of land managed for harvested fruit (-50%), root crops (-49%) and vegetables and melons (-30%); however, the area of harvested pulses increased by 300% during this time (FAOSTAT 2011b; also Chapter 7 and Chapter 15).

3.4.1.2 Conversion of land for forestry

Historically, UK woodlands (incorporating Mixed, Broadleaved and Yew woodland, plus Coniferous woodland) were primarily used for the production of forestry products, such as timber and fuel wood. However, in more recent times, they have also come to be valued for their role in conservation (e.g. of biodiversity) and recreational and cultural pursuits (such as hiking, camping and aesthetics). The decision of land managers to convert land to woodlands (afforestation) or to expand/replace already established stands (reforestation) has been influenced over time by different indirect drivers such as market forces, support mechanisms and cultural attitudes (Chapter 8).

The total amount of woodland cover in the UK has increased by 5.9% since 1947, and currently stands at 11.7% (Forestry Commission 2010a; see **Figure 3.8**). From the 1940s, annual rates of new plantings rose steadily, reaching, in 1976, approximately 27,400 and 900 ha for a coniferous and broadleaved species, respectively; 28,300 ha in total. Since then, however, planting rates have followed a general decline, falling to just 5,400 ha in 2010, with new plantings

Table 3.4 The change in area ('000s hectares (ha) and percentage) of Countryside Survey broad habitats in Great Britain between 1990 and 2007, and in the UK between 1998 and 2007. Arrows denote significant change (p<0.05) in the direction shown. Source: reproduced from Carey *et al.* (2008a). Countryside Survey data owned by NERC – Centre for Ecology & Hydrology.

Countryside Survey Broad Habitats	Great Britain							UK		
	1990–1998		1990–2007		1998–2007		Direction of significant changes 1998–2007	1998–2007		Direction of significant changes 1998–2007
	Change ('000s ha)	% Change	Change ('000s ha)	% Change	Change ('000s ha)	% Change		Change ('000s ha)	% Change	
Broadleaved, Mixed and Yew Woodland	-15	-1.1	63	4.7	78	5.9	↓↑	96	6.9	↑
Coniferous Woodland	147	11.9	80	6.5	-67	-4.8		-69	-4.7	
Linear Features	-70	-12.0	-85	-14.6	-15	-2.9		-13	-2.5	
Arable and Horticulture	43	0.9	-416	-8.3	-459	-9.1	↓	-467	-9.1	↓
Improved Grassland	-368	-8.0	-125	-2.7	243	5.7	↑	261	5.4	↑
Neutral Grassland	338	20.3	507	30.4	169	8.4	↑	136	6.0	↑
Calcareous Grassland	-17	-21.8	-21	-27.2	-4	-7.3		-4	-6.3	
Acid Grassland	-318	-17.5	-232	-12.7	86	5.7	↑	83	5.5	↑
Bracken	43	15.8	-12	-4.4	-55	-17.5	↓	-55	-17.4	↑
Dwarf Shrub Heath	-137	-9.5	-93	-6.5	44	3.4		47	3.6	
Fen, Marsh, Swamp	-1	-0.2	-35	-8.2	-34	-8.0		-40	-8.3	
Bog	172	8.4	182	8.9	10	0.5		7	0.3	
Standing Open Waters	17	8.4	23	11.8	5	2.6	↑	5	1.9	
Rivers and Streams	-3	-3.9	-2	-2.7	0	-0.2		0	0.0	
Montane	na	na	na	na	1	2.4		1	2.4	
Inland Rock	35	46.1	25	32.3	-10	-9.4		-13	-10.9	
Built-up Areas and Gardens	13	1.0	57	4.5	44	3.4		61	4.6	
Other land								6	5.4	↑

of broadleaved species (4,800 ha) greatly outstripping those of coniferous species (500 ha), a pattern which emerged in the mid-1990s (Forestry Commission 2011). Consequently, although there has been a general decline in planting rates across the UK, broadleaved woodland cover has increased significantly from 1.4 million ha in 1998 to 1.5 million ha 2007: a 6% rise in nine years (Carey *et al.* 2008b). The greatest change was recorded in Northern Ireland (+1.3%), followed by England (+0.4%) and Scotland (+0.2%). There was no significant change recorded in Wales during this time period (Carey *et al.* 2008b). These changes in forest management and planting rates reflect changes in forestry management objectives and policy, including afforestation projects and incentives (Chapter 8).

3.4.1.3 Coastal and Marine habitats

The UK has both used, or relied heavily upon, coastal and marine habitats for a variety of purposes, such as food provisioning, infrastructure development (both industrial and domestic) and energy production. Historically, such utilisation has caused widespread habitat change, and, given current rates and projected use, is likely to continue, although at potentially reduced levels due to the implementation of conservation initiatives and policy.

The patterns of change vary spatially, temporally and in the type of habitat found around the UK (Frost 2010). In the Coastal Margins, habitats like Sand Dunes, Saltmarshes and Shingle have been lost to agricultural land-claim and extensive development for housing, tourism and industry (Doody 2001)—it is estimated that these three habitats have suffered a 20% loss in extent since WWII. Sea-level rise is an increasingly important factor in habitat loss of soft coast habitats (French 1997). In the Marine environment, areas in southern UK waters are subject to a greater range of drivers causing habitat change compared to northern regions, and sediment habitats are more extensively degraded than rocky habitats; although these, too, have suffered physical damage due to towed fishing gear (UKMMAS 2010). In the sub-tidal zone, including sediment and reef habitat down to depths of 200 m or more, mobile fishing gear, such as trawls and dredges, have caused substantial damage and loss of habitat, effecting levels of biodiversity and ecosystem function. Although fishing activity has been reduced in some regions, and some fish species are showing signs of recovery, many habitats have suffered so much damage, that this, plus ongoing impacts from other pressures (including climate change and the development of offshore infrastructure such as windfarms), may affect their potential to recover (UKMMAS 2010).

3.4.1.4 Mineral, aggregate and peat extraction

The UK draws on various minerals, fossil fuels (coal) and aggregates to provide, amongst other things, construction materials and fuel for the production of energy. The extraction of mineral and coal deposits has caused widespread ecosystem change including habitat conversion, degradation and fragmentation through both the extraction process and the deposition of waste products. The latter has had major effects on marine and coastal habitats, particularly in the north-east of the UK.

Immediately after WWII, peat extraction for both fuel and horticulture was high and led directly to significant ecosystem changes (e.g. loss of biodiversity) in many areas of accessible mire, especially in England and Northern Ireland (Chapter 5). More recent figures show a reduction in both the amount of land used for peat extraction (14,980 ha in 1994; 10,690 ha in 2009) and in the level of extraction (in GB, 1.6 million m³ sold in 1999; 760,000 m³ in 2009) (Chapter 15). These reductions are primarily due to current legislation that protects mire habitat and largely prevents new applications for the extraction of peat, as well as a drop in demand for peat. However, it should be noted that at existing extraction sites peat removal may continue until the resource has been removed or permissions are rescinded. Removal of permissions may require the government to pay compensation to owners of peat extraction rights.

3.4.1.5 Urbanisation

In the UK, urban habitat (built-up areas and gardens), calculated using the LCM2000 (Fuller *et al.* 2002) directly affects only 6.7% of land area, but approximately 75–80% of the population reside here (Pointer 2005; Chapter 10). Although changes in, and impacts of, UK urbanisation have not been properly quantified since WWII, trends in population growth, domestic migration and the extent of built-up area can be used as indicators. The growth of UK urban populations, in particular, has acted as a direct driver of change of ecosystem condition when habitat (usually highly productive land) has been converted into urban land cover such as residential buildings, infrastructure and amenities (Section 3.3.1) (Chapter 10). Increased urbanisation has also had a major influence on consumption pressure (i.e. demands for food, fuel, water and other natural resources), exerting increased pressure on ecosystems or regions outside urban areas both national and international (Nelson *et al.* 2005; Hannah 2010).

One other way in which the changing pattern of urban cover and infrastructure development can be assessed is by modelling the effects of urban 'intrusion', defined as increasing noise from urban and transport infrastructure. Such studies conducted in England show that the proportion of the country considered disturbed by urban influence or infrastructure noise rose from 26% in the 1960s, to 41% by the 1990s, and to 50% by 2007 (CPRE 2007; **Figure 3.9**).

The direct impact of urban areas could be reduced in the future by evoking various activities including water harvesting, growing local food, promoting local 'green-modes' of accessibility rather than motorised mobility, planting gardens that will increase biodiversity, and developing Sustainable Urban Drainage Systems (SUDS). However, such changes will be dependent on changing cultural views of how people see their relationship with the natural environment.

3.4.1.6 Infrastructure

There have been significant infrastructure development programmes carried out in the UK to ensure water supply for both human consumption and irrigation purposes (e.g. the creation of reservoirs and the canalisation of rivers), to provide public transport systems (road, rail, air and canal networks), deliver protection from flooding (river and coastal flood defences), and supply energy (power stations, hydroelectric schemes and windfarms).

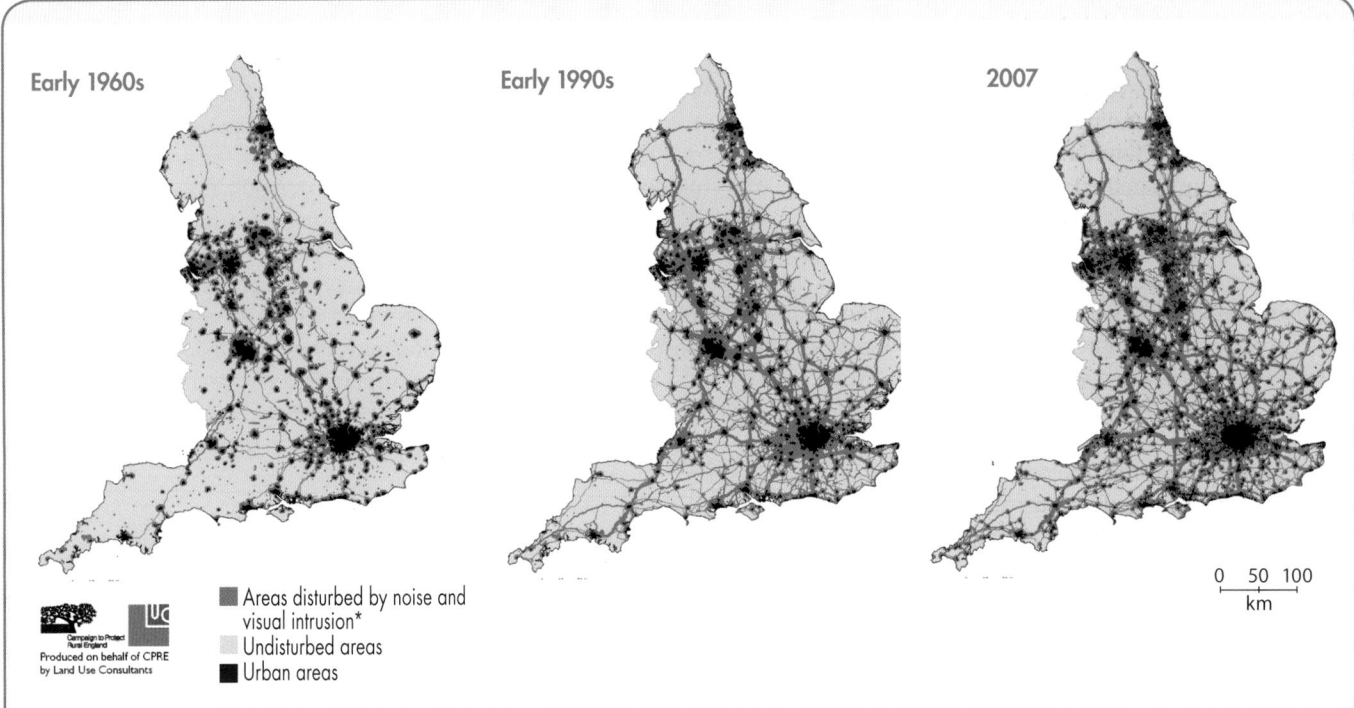

Figure 3.9 Areas of urban intrusion in the 1960s, 1990s and 2007. *Areas disturbed by urban development, major infrastructure projects and other noise and visual intrusion. Source: maps reproduced with permission from the Campaign for the Protection of Rural England (CPRE 2007). Crown copyright 2007. Produced by Land Use Consultants 2007. Licence No. 100019265.

This driver can alter ecosystems when land is directly converted to such infrastructure use, but also, as is the case for water supply, flood defences and renewable energy schemes, where ecosystem processes are affected. For example, river modification can alter levels and flow regimes, which, in turn, can impact on the movement of sediment along the coast (Chapter 11; Chapter 12).

The construction of much of the infrastructure outlined above pre-dates the time frame of this assessment. However, it is constructive to note the long history of public debate over the relative environmental costs and public benefits of large schemes, especially when those receiving the benefits of such schemes are distant from the area of impact. For example, the controversial construction of Haweswater Reservoir in the valley of Mardale in England's Cumbria Lake District. Here, in 1929, Parliament gave permission to Manchester Corporation to build a reservoir to supply water to the conurbations of north-west England. Although not heeded, public outcry was strong, particularly from the farming villages of Measand and Mardale Green which were to be flooded and lost, and the population moved, as result of the construction. Many also considered the valley one of the most picturesque in Westmorland, and voiced opposition against altering its natural aesthetic beauty (Visit Cumbria 2011).

Historically, urbanisation was the major factor behind early water supply infrastructure, while more recently, dominance of motorised transport has driven the expansion of public roads. With the probable future emphasis on renewable energy sources, the development of infrastructure, such as upland, coastal and marine windfarms, is also likely to continue.

3.4.2 Pollution and Nutrient Enrichment

Chemicals and nutrients, particularly nitrogen, phosphorous and sulphur (or their derivatives), entering ecosystems from point source, diffuse pollution and direct agricultural inputs can cause significant habitat change and impact on ecosystem services (see **Figure 3.1; Figure 3.2**). Their impact may be observed both at the point of input as well as at more distant sites due to some chemicals or nutrients moving beyond the area to which they were applied or emitted. For example, nutrient enrichment and runoff can drive shifts in the species composition and structure of both terrestrial and aquatic communities (freshwater, estuarine and marine), while atmospheric pollutants can be transported many thousands of miles.

The relative input of chemicals and nutrients into the environment, and the types used, has varied significantly in the UK since WWII. Consequential pollution and nutrient enrichment have impacted on provisioning, regulating and supporting services (**Figure 3.2**), and affected all eight UK NEA Broad Habitats (**Figure 3.1**). For example, nitrogen pollution from the atmosphere exceeds 'critical pollution loads' for the ground flora and epiphytic lichens of Atlantic Oakwoods, impacting on biodiversity levels and service provision, and increased ozone concentrations which can reduce forest growth (RoTAP 2010). Likewise, high atmospheric nitrogen deposition is linked to a decline in species diversity in Semi-natural Grassland (Stevens *et al.* 2004; Maskell *et al.* 2009; Chapter 6) and in Coastal Margin habitats (Jones *et al.* 2004). It should be noted, however, that often the greatest effect of nitrogen is at low levels (Bobbink *et al.* 2010), and for much of the UK it is likely that the major effects of nitrogen deposition have already taken place.

Due to the potential health risks many pollutants present, levels from both UK sources and transboundary depositions, are now heavily monitored and regulated by a variety of bodies including national and local government authorities, and environment agencies. Long-term research programmes, such as the Environmental Change Network (ECN; www.ecn.ac.uk/), also aim to detect environmental effects over time.

In this section we briefly outline the trends in a variety of nutrients and pollutants that have driven changes in UK habitats. More details can be found in the relevant sections of each of the habitat and service chapters.

3.4.2.1 Air pollution

Impacts on human health. Air quality levels are the result of the interaction of pollution emissions and local weather events (Defra 2010h). Air pollutants are known to impact on human health, contributing to the risk of developing cardiovascular diseases, lung cancer, breathing problems and triggering asthma symptoms (Defra 2010g). Over time, the sources of air pollutants impacting on human health have changed from being dominated by emissions from processes of energy production (sulphur dioxide) to those arising from road transport (i.e. particulates made up of a mixture of carbon, organic chemicals, sulphate, nitrates, ammonium, sodium chloride, mineral dust, water and metals) (Defra 2010g). National monitoring of these emissions began in the 1960s, with a wide range of other pollutants being added to monitoring schemes in the 1970s following the development of automatic recording devices. Road transport emissions,

monitored by the UK Sustainable Development Indicators, show that while roadside and urban background particulate emission levels have fallen by 41% and 48%, respectively, since the 1990s, background urban ozone levels have continued to rise, averaging 55 micro-grams per cubic metre (μg/m³) in 2009 compared with 44 μg/m³ in 1992 (Defra 2010h). The cost of air pollution, and specifically particulates, to the UK in health terms is estimated to be in the order of £15 million annually (Defra 2010g).

Impacts on the environment: Sulphur. Historically, sulphur deposition has been the major cause of acidification in Europe. However, deposition peaked in the 1970s, and there has been a major decline of around 90% since that peak (RoTAP 2010). Nitrogen compounds are now a greater contributor to acidification than sulphur. The effect of acid deposition on habitats can be measured by assessing whether 'critical loads' (i.e. damage thresholds) have been exceeded (RoTAP 2010) (**Figure 3.10**). Exceedance of critical loads for acidity has reduced from 71% to 51%, with some limited recovery in freshwater pH and biological parameters (Monteith *et al.* 2005). Nevertheless, recovery is slow and is not likely to recover to pre-industrial levels (RoTAP 2010).

Impacts on the environment: Nitrogen. Atmospheric nitrogen comes primarily from oxidised nitrogen from combustion sources. Whereas, reduced nitrogen compounds, including ammonia, come primarily from agricultural sources (RoTAP 2010). Since 1990, emissions of nitrogen oxides have declined by 60% (108 million tonnes compared to 288 million tonnes), and ammonia emissions by 22% (288,000 tonnes compared to 368,000 tonnes).

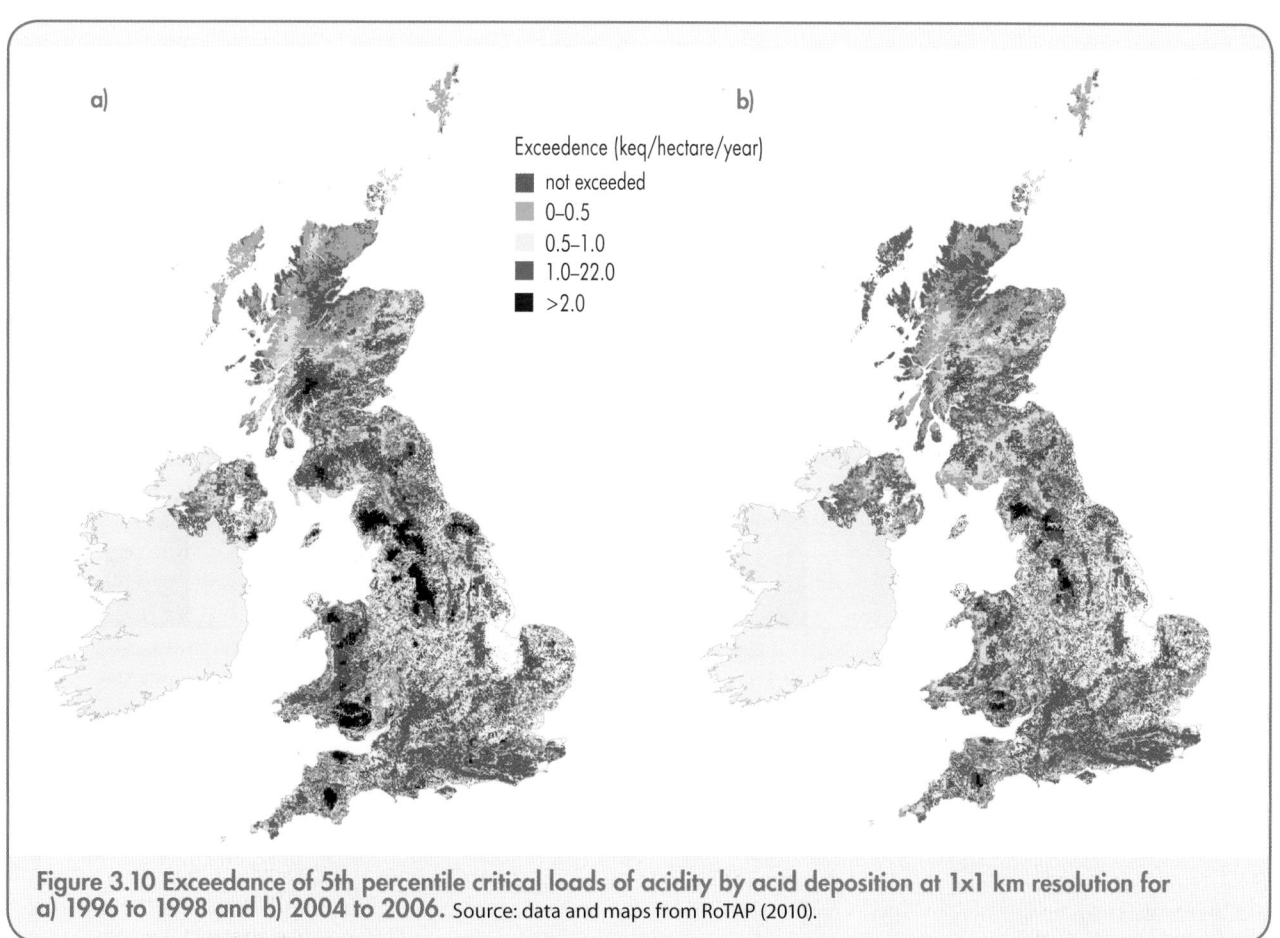

Figure 3.10 Exceedance of 5th percentile critical loads of acidity by acid deposition at 1x1 km resolution for a) 1996 to 1998 and b) 2004 to 2006. Source: data and maps from RoTAP (2010).

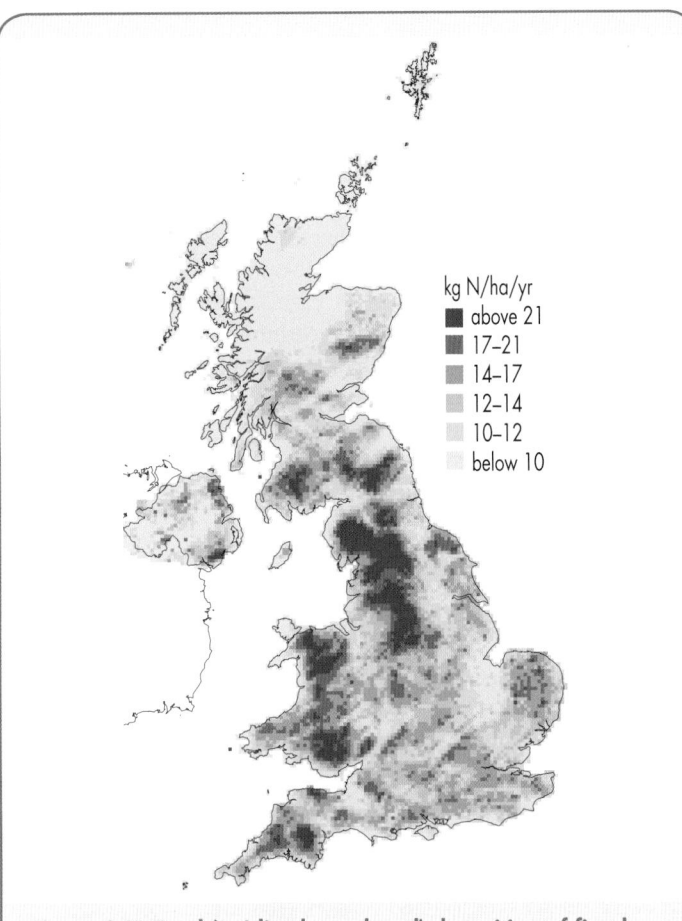

Figure 3.11 Total (oxidised + reduced) deposition of fixed nitrogen over the UK in 2008 (kilograms of nitrogen per hectare per year; kg N/ha/yr). Source: data and map from RoTAP (2010).

Reductions of the former are largely attributable to the introduction of catalytic convertors and stricter regulations on road transport and power stations; reductions in the latter are largely due to a decrease in cattle herds and more efficient fertiliser use (Defra 2010f). However, these declines in emissions have primarily affected transboundary export, and deposition in the UK has changed little (RoTAP 2010). Therefore, nitrogen deposition continues to impact on terrestrial and aquatic ecosystems (Chapter 13). High nitrogen deposition levels tend to be concentrated in the uplands and western areas of the UK (**Figure 3.11**), largely due to greater rainfall in these locations. Exceedance of Critical Loads for nutrient nitrogen varies across the UK and between habitat types (**Figure 3.12**); while there has been some decline in Critical Load exceedance over the past 20 years, this has not been significant.

Impacts of nitrogen deposition include soil and freshwater acidification, eutrophication of ecosystems, losses in plant species diversity (Jones *et al.* 2004; Stevens *et al.* 2004; Maskell *et al.* 2009), increases in emissions of greenhouse gases, and the modification of the transport and deposition patterns of sulphur dioxide (APIS 2010). As ammonia tends to be deposited rapidly, close to its source, it can cause ecosystem change in areas of sensitive habitat close to agricultural systems. On the other hand, nitrogen dioxides are transported longer distances and cause eutrophication far from their source.

3.4.2.2 Point source and diffuse agricultural pollution

Nitrogen, phosphorous and potassium are essential to plant growth (Nelson *et al.* 2005). The development of nitrogen,

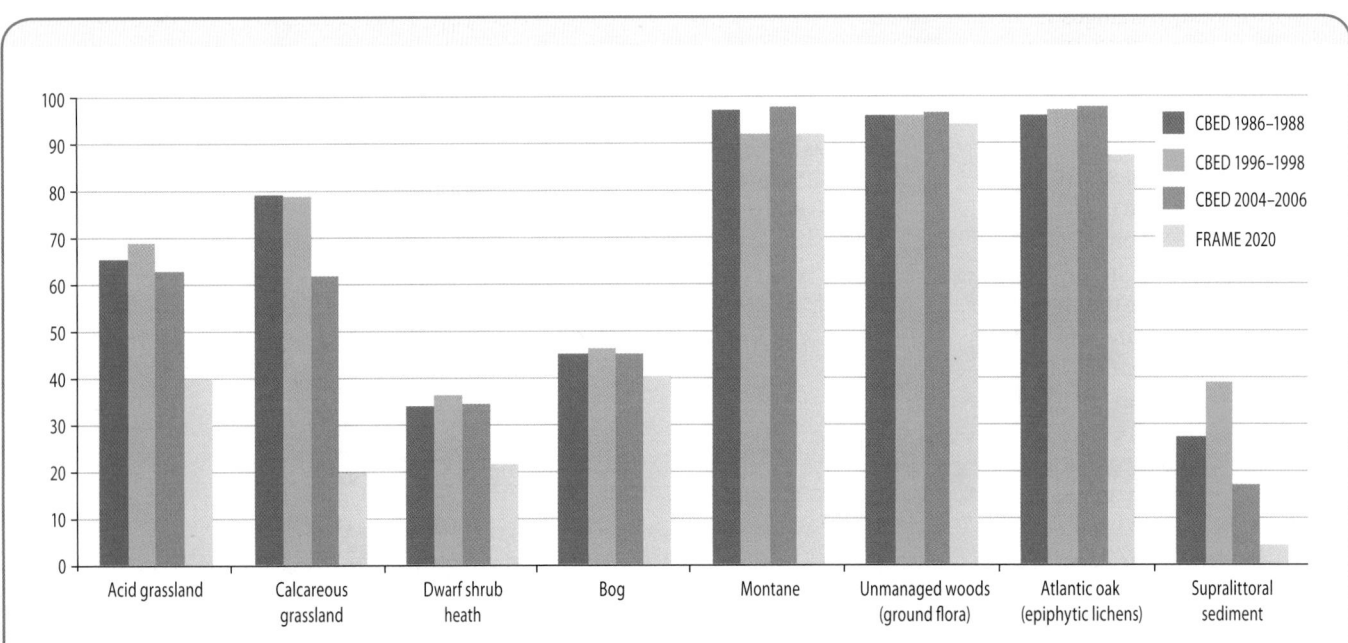

Figure 3.12 Exceedance of critical loads for effects of nitrogen deposition for sensitive semi-natural habitats. This shows the estimated percentage area of each major habitat with exceedance of the relevant critical loads in the mid-1980s, the mid-1990s and the mid-2000s, as well as projected exceedance for 2020. The critical loads used for this estimate were: 7 kilograms nitrogen per hectare per year (kg N/ha/yr) for montane (moss- and lichen-dominated summits); 10 kg N/ha/yr for bogs and for epiphytic lichens (in Atlantic oak woods); 12 kg N/ha/yr for woodland ground flora and dry dwarf shrub heath; 15 kg N/ha/yr for wet dwarf shrub heath, acid grassland and supralittoral sediments (coastal dune grasslands); and 20 kg N/ha/yr for calcareous grassland. Source: data from RoTAP (2010).

phosphorous and potassium based fertilisers and pesticides in the 1940s revolutionised farming and increased crop yields by supplementing natural sources of these nutrients in soils. Following WWII, the application of fertilisers and pesticides in the UK increased rapidly in response to demands for greater food production which were driven by the government's desire to increase security and self-sufficiency, as well as population growth. By 1986, nitrogen application rates had increased to 144 kg/ha, nearly twice that used in 1971, while levels of phosphorous and potassium had increased by almost one-third, to an average of 40 kg/ha and 48 kg/ha, respectively (Thomas 2010; **Figure 3.13**). Since then, fertiliser application rates have declined, particularly in grasslands compared with tilled land. For example, nitrogen application rates on tilled land in GB fell from 139 kg/ha in 1987 to 113 kg/ha in 2009, while application rates on grassland dropped from 132 kg/ha in 1986 to 57 kg/ha in 2009, the second lowest level since 1983 (Thomas 2010).

The primary source of excess nitrogen in ecosystems is derived from runoff from agricultural land, with between 40–60% of the amount of fertiliser applied typically being lost (Nelson *et al.* 2005). On the other hand, the primary source of phosphorous in the waters of GB is household sources (73–78%); this is distantly followed by agriculture (13–20%) and industry (3–4%) (White & Hammond 2009). While levels of nitrogen deposition appear to have changed little over the last 20-years, levels of phosphorous are believed to have declined across all UK habitats between 1998 and 2007 (Emmett *et al.* 2010; Chapter 13).

Pesticides used in the 1960s and early 1970s that were made of novel chemicals, such as DDT, are known to have caused community changes in wildlife such as declines in bird species (Carson 1962; Newton & Wyllie 1992). The types of pesticides used have changed continuously over time, and application rates have also been variable on national and local levels, generally increasing between 1970 and 2000, but decreasing over the last two decades (Ewald & Aebischer 2000; Fera 2011). For example, 20.2 kg of pesticides was used to treat 71 million ha of land in 2009, compared with 34.5 million kg used in 1990 to treat 45 million ha (Fera 2011). However, due to the changing nature of the chemicals applied, their toxicity and longevity, application levels cannot be taken as an indicator of the potential environmental impact of these system inputs. It should also be noted that, in an attempt to reduce the impact of pesticides on wildlife, 85% of the sprayed area in England and Wales is now being treated with tested machines under the National Sprayer Testing Scheme (NSTS) which are operated by members of the National Register of Sprayer Operators (NRoSO). Additionally, more than 2 million ha are now covered by a Voluntary Initiative Crop Protection Management Plan (www.voluntaryinitiative.org.uk).

Pollutants in rivers and streams. Pollution levels within rivers, and the impacts that they may have, can be assessed using measures of chemical and biological quality. In the UK, these metrics are monitored under the UK Sustainable Development Indicators which are reported separately for each country (Defra 2010e). Between 1990 and 2007, water quality was higher in Scotland and Wales

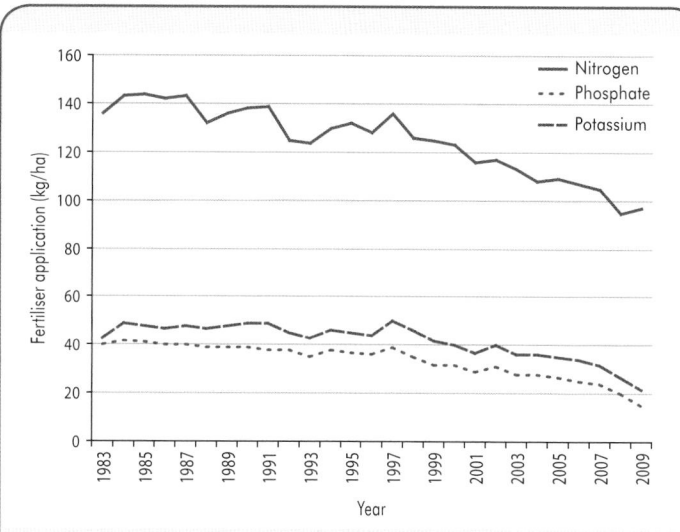

Figure 3.13 Overall nitrogen, phosphate and potassium application rates (kg/ha) on tillage crops and grassland in Great Britain from 1983 to 2009. Source: data extracted from Thomas (2010).

than it was in England and Northern Ireland. In terms of national trends, the biological quality of rivers in Northern Ireland has decreased over the past decade, but chemical quality has increased; rivers in Scotland and Wales have remained stable in terms of both indicators, while both chemical and biological quality of English rivers have been improving (Defra 2010e), demonstrated by a decrease in the percentage of rivers tested showing exceedance levels for phosphorous and nitrate (Defra 2009b). The Countryside Survey Freshwater Stream Report has also shown that headwater streams in GB have continued to improve over the past 17 years (Dunbar *et al.* 2010).

Pollutants in the marine environment. Marine pollution levels can be monitored by testing both the quality of coastal water and bathing water. Such testing has shown that, since 1995, the percentage of sites around the UK that comply with quality standards set by the UK Bathing Water Directive (which are more stringent than standards set by the European Bathing Water Directive) have increased from 41% (189 sites out of 464) to 70% (412 sites out of 587) in 2009 (Defra 2009a). Monitoring has also shown that, between 1995 and 2009, the number of sites complying with standards improved in England (41–71%), Scotland (17–56%) and Wales (38–89%), but declined in Northern Ireland (75–46%; Defra 2009a). Such improvements (i.e. reductions in pollution emissions to marine environments) have largely been attributed to improvements in sewage treatment and new pollution control legislation.

3.4.3 Overexploitation of Resources

Rates of consumption and/or exploitation of biotic resources can have major impacts on biodiversity and ecosystems. In the UK, the overexploitation of commercial fish stocks, the amount and type of timber harvested, the number of livestock, and the levels of abstracted water have all been responsible for directly driving changes in ecosystems and levels of biodiversity (see **Figure 3.1; Figure 3.2**).

3.4.3.1 Fisheries

The UK fishing fleet primarily targets fishing grounds in the north-east Atlantic which are some of the most productive and intensively exploited in the world (Thurstan *et al.* 2010). Excluding declines observed during both World Wars, total landings of demersal fish (i.e. bottom-living fish such as cod, haddock and plaice) in the UK rose rapidly from the late 19th Century to the middle of the 20th Century, corresponding to growth of the fleet, technological advancement and expansion into new grounds. Although fishing power (i.e. a measure of how fishermen increase their catching power over time, for example, through improvements to gear and ability to detect fish) associated with motor trawlers continued to increase up until the late 1970s, commercial landings of demersal fish have undergone a steady, long-term decline since the 1960s (**Figure 3.14**); they are now

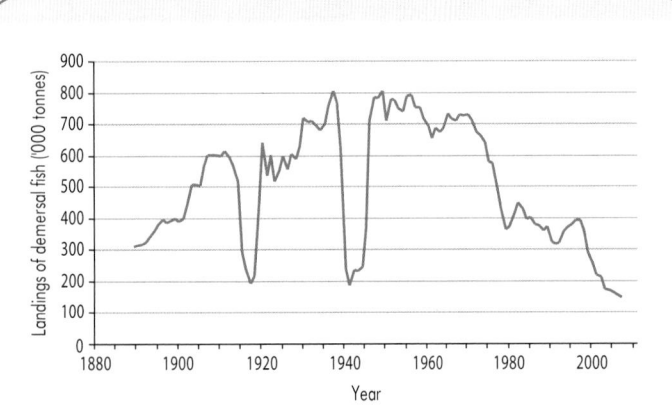

Figure 3.14 Change in total landings of demersal (bottom-living) fish into the UK by British vessels between 1889 and 2007. The two abrupt declines can be attributed to the First and Second World Wars when it was too dangerous to fish and vessels were put to other uses. The general decline since the 1940s can be attributed to overexploitation of fish resources (see text). Source: adapted from Thurstan *et al.* (2010).

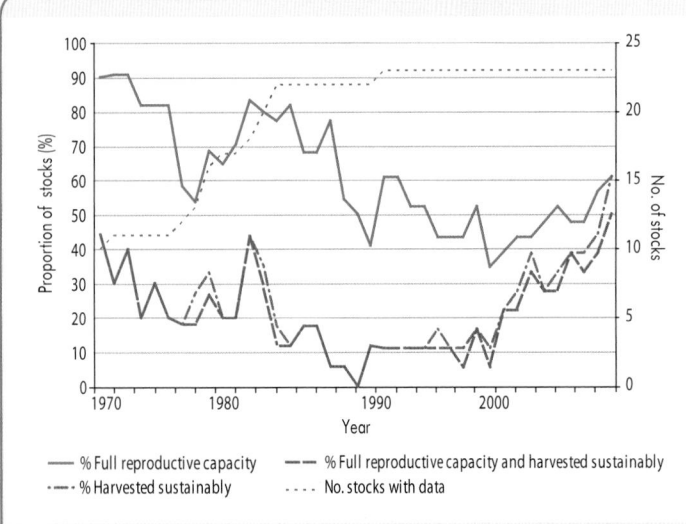

— % Full reproductive capacity — - — % Full reproductive capacity and harvested sustainably
·—·% Harvested sustainably ····· No. stocks with data

Figure 3.15 Percentage of finfish stocks around the UK which are at full reproductive capacity, harvested sustainably, and both at full reproductive capacity and harvested sustainably, 1970 to 2008. Source: Armstrong & Holmes (2010), CEFAS.

5.4 times lower than the historical peak in 1938, dropping from approximately 800,000 tonnes to 150,000 tonnes in 2007 (Thurstan *et al.* 2010). Likewise, landings of pelagic fish have also decreased, but those of shellfish have grown from 34,090 tonnes in 1966 to 144,986 tonnes in 2008 (MMO 2010), largely as a result of the fishing industry switching to shellfish due to both a reduction in, and imposed quotas on, demersal and pelagic stocks.

Since the 1880s, it is thought that the catch rates of individual commercial species in the UK have declined by at least 83% or more, and, in some cases, by more than 99% (e.g. haddock and halibut) (Thurstan *et al.* 2010). Spawning stock biomass of species exploited by UK fleets is also estimated to have fallen by 42.6% since 1982. The decline in fish stocks is primarily thought to be a result of unsustainable catch rates and habitat destruction (e.g. from towed bottom-trawling equipment). This has not only led to reduced levels of productivity in both commercial and non-commercial species, but has also caused the complete collapse or reorganisation of whole marine ecosystems, such as that seen in the Firth of the Clyde in Scotland (Saunders 2010; Thurstan *et al.* 2010; Thurstan & Roberts 2010).

Despite these warnings, which are mirrored in the seas worldwide, the majority of global scientifically assessed stocks continue to be fished at levels above the Maximum Sustainable Yield (MSY), particularly under the current environmental conditions affecting stock productivity (Armstrong & Holmes 2010; Saunders 2010). Yet it should be noted that the diversity and overall abundance of soft-bottom demersal fish in the UK have made significant improvements over the last five to ten years (UKMMAS 2010). For example, it is believed that, of the 18 fish stocks assessed around the UK, the proportion of stocks being fished sustainably and which are at full reproductive capacity has risen from between 5–10% in the 1990s to 50% in 2008; those that are just harvested sustainably from 10% to 61%; and those just at full reproductive capacity from 35% to 61% (Armstrong & Holmes 2010; **Figure 3.15**). This is likely to be a result of enforced reductions in the size of the UK fleet and revised Total Allowable Catches set by the UK government and devolved administrations in line with the EU Common Fisheries Policy (Saunders 2010).

3.4.3.2 Timber harvest

Data collected by the Forestry Commission indicates a trend of continuing decline in the production of hardwoods and a steady increase in the production of softwoods since 1976. These harvest trends reflect the earlier increase in planting of coniferous woodlands with their relatively short harvest times from planting to felling. These figures indicate that management activities remain an active force in UK woodlands and that conifer woodlands can be expected to be more intensively managed than broadleaved woodlands.

3.4.3.3 Livestock stocking rates

Since WWII, the number of livestock in the UK has increased (Chapter 7; Chapter 15). In 2009, there were approximately 10.0 million cattle, 32.0 million sheep and 4.7 million pigs, compared with 8.4, 25.5 and 3.4 million in 1940, respectively. However, these figures mask the range of changes within this period. For example, sheep numbers peaked in 1990 at 44.5

million, which is 44% greater than those in 1950 (19.7 million), but have since declined by 28% to 32.1 million. Until recent times, the increase in stock numbers was associated with increased levels of agricultural improvement. Consequently, grazing pressure increased, leading to ecological change such as the conversion of moorland and mire habitat to grassland communities. Changes in stock numbers have also been driven, at various times, by the incidence of disease (such as Foot and Mouth Disease) and agricultural subsidies.

3.4.3.4 Water abstraction

Water is an essential resource for all life on earth and is heavily utilised by humans for both personal consumption and agricultural production. Water extraction can cause ecosystem change when the levels of rivers or the water table are excessively reduced. The amount of water available for abstraction is largely dependent on rainfall and water use patterns, while the observed increases in the amount abstracted has been linked to economic growth (Defra 2010e). As these factors are not distributed evenly across the UK, some regions, particularly the densely populated and dry south-east of England, suffer greater water stress, resulting in over-abstracted water catchments and rivers (Foresight 2010). In an attempt to avoid detrimental extraction levels, various licensing strategies, such as Catchment Abstraction Management Areas (CAMS) managed by the Environment Agency for England and Wales, have been introduced.

3.4.4 Climate Variability and Change

Change and variability in global climatic variables, such as temperature, precipitation and sea level, can affect biodiversity and ecosystems (Nelson *et al.* 2005). Impacts that have already been observed include changes to species distribution, population sizes, timing of reproduction and migration events, and increased frequency in outbreaks of pests and disease (MA 2005a).

Although climate change has not been identified as a major driver of change in most UK habitats to date, it is expected to play a significant role in future change (see **Figure 3.1)** (Chapter 26), and, in particular, impact on regulating, supporting and provisioning services (see **Figure 3.2)** (Chapters 13–15). For instance, coupled with other drivers and pressures, such as land use intensity, loss of habitat and the introduction of invasive species, increased temperature could result in continued pole-ward movement of species or movement to higher elevations. Higher temperatures and greater prevalence of hot days could increase stress in plants and animals and reduce productivity, but extend the range and activity of pest and disease vectors. And more intense precipitation events could result in increased soil erosion and flood runoff (Nelson *et al.* 2005). In this section, we outline some of the observed trends for key climatic parameters in the UK, including temperature and precipitation, sea levels, greenhouse gas emissions, carbon dioxide and its impact on ocean acidification, as well as patterns in extreme weather events.

3.4.4.1 Trends in temperature and precipitation

Global surface air temperatures have risen by 0.75°C since the late 19th Century, and have been steadily warming by an average of 0.13°C per decade since the 1950s, with the years between 1995 and 2006 being the warmest on record (IPCC 2007). This is mirrored in the UK where the mean annual Central England Temperature (the longest continuous record of surface air temperature in the world) and temperatures in Wales, Scotland and Northern Ireland have risen by approximately 1°C since the beginning of the 20th Century (Jenkins *et al.* 2009; Huthnance 2010; **Figure 3.16**). The greatest regions of warming have occurred in the Midlands, South East England and East Anglia (Perry 2006). Concurrent with rising air temperatures, sea-surface temperatures of UK waters have increased by 0.5–1.0°C during the period between 1870 and 2007 (Huthnance 2010; **Figure 3.17**). Rising sea-surface temperatures are likely to impact on the ability of the ocean to take up carbon dioxide, may affect species distributions, and contribute to sea-level rise (Huthnance 2010).

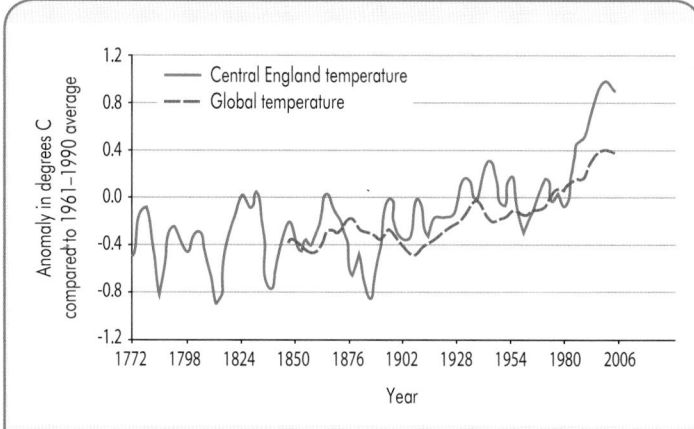

Figure 3.16 Central England surface air temperature (°C) from 1772 to 2008. Source: data from the Hadley Centre; figure reproduced from Defra (2009c). © Crown copyright 2009.

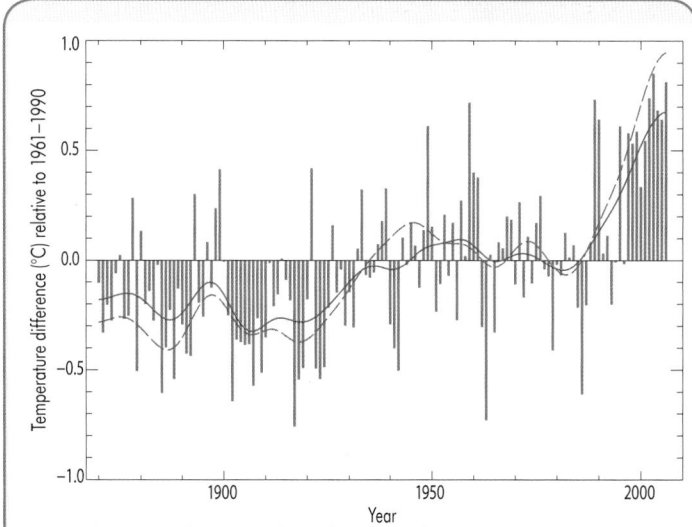

Figure 3.17 Annual mean sea-surface temperature (°C) averaged around the UK coastline, 1870 to 2006 (the orange bars extending from 1961 to 1990 average of 11.3 °C); the smoothed green line emphasises decadal variations. The purple curve (dashed line) shows night marine air temperature over roughly the same area, with the same smoothing. Source: reproduced from Jenkins *et al.* (2009).

Between 1914 and 2004, precipitation patterns (as monitored by the UK Met Office) showed that all districts in the UK experienced a decrease in summer precipitation, although these changes were significant in only three out of ten districts[5]: East Scotland, North West England and Wales, and Northern Ireland (Perry 2006). Despite this, there has been a tendency towards wetter winters in the north and west of Scotland (Huthnance 2010). During the winters of 1961–1962 and 2004–2005, there was a decrease in the number of days with snow across all ten UK districts, of which, four—East and North East England, North West England and Wales, South West England and South Wales, and Central, South and South East England—were strongly significant. The strongest trend is in Central, South and South East England where there are approximately 75% less days with snow compared to 1961 (Perry 2006).

3.4.4.2 Sea-level change

Global sea-level rose by 1.7 mm per year during the 20th Century; while in the UK, and correcting for land movement, the rate of rise was approximately 1 mm per year during the same time period (Jenkins *et al.* 2009; Huthnance 2010). However, this rate of rise was variable, with a much more rapid rise during the 1990s of 3–4 mm

per year. Allowing for land movement, net sea-level rise is greater in England and Wales, but lower in Scotland (**Figure 3.18**). As populations and urbanisation expand into the coastal zones, an increasing number of people will become vulnerable to extreme rises in sea-level, particularly in the south-east of the UK. Change in sea-level will also impact on intertidal habitats and groundwater storage, and may lead to more severe flooding and coastal erosion by waves (Huthnance 2010).

3.4.4.3 Greenhouse gas emissions

There is now strong evidence that the changes to the earth's climate that have occurred during the 20th Century are linked to greenhouse gases emitted as a result of human activities (MacCarthy *et al.* 2010). The 'greenhouse effect' is a natural process that regulates the temperature of the earth; however, the release of excess greenhouse gases by human activities contributes to this process, trapping heat in the atmosphere and resulting in increased temperatures, which can have adverse impacts on ecosystems (MacCarthy *et al.* 2010).

Emissions of the six direct greenhouse gases—carbon dioxide, methane, nitrous oxide, hydrofluorocarbons and perfluorocarbons—have decreased in the UK since 1990 (MacCarthy *et al.* 2010; **Figure 3.19**). Decreases are a result of policy implementation, reduced greenhouse gas-emitting activities (e.g. coal mining) and sources (e.g. livestock numbers and fertiliser application), and changes to processes (e.g. improved methane recovery systems and fluorinated gas abatement equipment) (MacCarthy *et al.* 2010).

3.4.4.4 Carbon dioxide and ocean acidification

Oceans absorb more carbon dioxide than they release, and hence play an important role in mitigating climate change by reducing the amount of carbon dioxide in the atmosphere. However, this also makes oceans more acidic, which not only reduces their capacity to take up carbon dioxide, but alters their carbonate chemistry. Ocean acidification is a direct

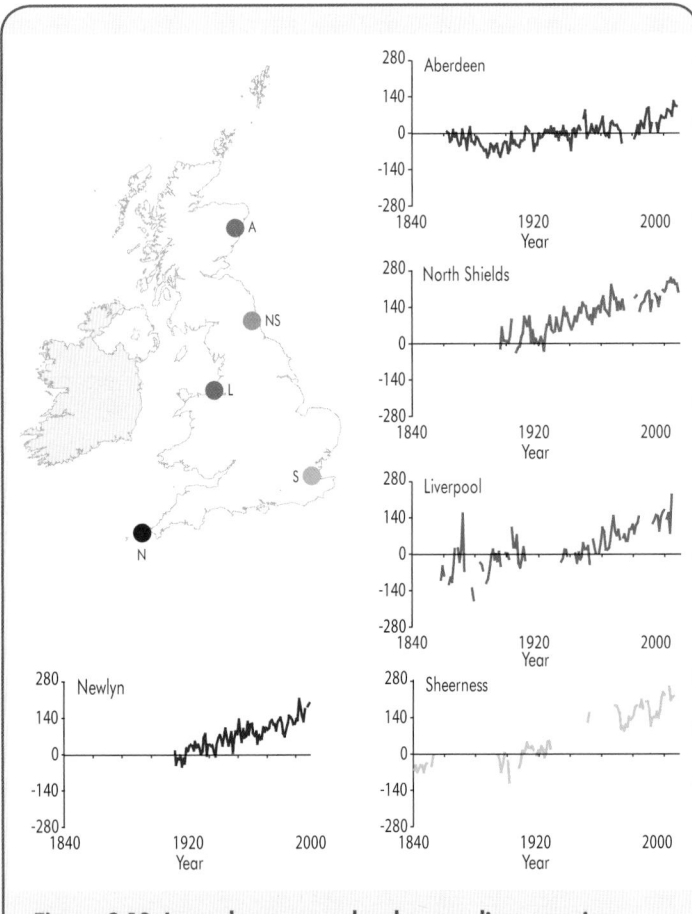

Figure 3.18 Annual mean sea-level anomalies at various sites around the UK compared to the 1920 baseline. Source: data from the Permanent Service for Mean Sea-level (PSMSL; 2011) and Woodworth *et al.* (2009); adapted from Defra (2009c).

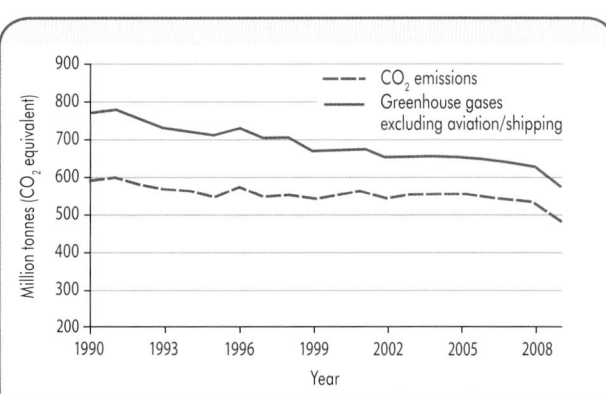

Figure 3.19 Trends in greenhouse gas and carbon dioxide (CO₂) emissions for the UK, 1990 to 2009*. Source: Department for Environment, Food and Rural Affairs, Department of Energy and Climate Change, AEA Energy and Environment; figure reproduced from Defra (2010e). © Crown copyright 2010. *2009 figures are provisional.

5 The ten climate districts used by Perry (2006) to assess the patterns of differentiation and change in UK climate between 1914 and 2004 are:
1. Scotland N; 2. Scotland E; 3. Scotland W; 4. England E and NE; 5. England NW and Wales; 6. Midlands; 7. East Anglia; 8. England SW and Wales S; 9. England SE, Central, S; 10. Northern Ireland.

consequence of anthropogenic carbon dioxide emissions and, if these continue at the same rate, may impact on marine organisms, food webs, ecosystems and ocean biogeochemistry within decades (**Box 3.2**). Currently, there is a lack of knowledge about how ocean acidification impacts on UK waters due to a dearth of baseline measurements and a limited understanding of the processes controlling an ocean's ability to absorb carbon dioxide (Huthnance 2010). Nonetheless, it is projected to be a major contributing factor to future changes in the marine environment.

3.4.4.5 Extreme weather events

Since 1961, there has been a decrease in the length of winter cold spells, and an increase in the length of summer heat waves (Perry 2006), although there appears to be no clear trend in drought frequency in England and Wales (Marsh 2007). Across the UK, heavy precipitation events have made a higher contribution to total winter rainfall levels over the last 45 years (Jenkins *et al.* 2009). In contrast, in summer, all regions except North East England and North Scotland have shown a reduced number of heavy rainfall events in the last 45 years (Jenkins *et al.* 2009). The incidence of extreme stormy weather events has increased over the past 50 years, but these are not above levels recorded in the 1920s (Jenkins *et al.* 2009; Huthnance 2010).

Box 3.2 Carbon dioxide and ocean acidification.

Oceans and seas are becoming more acidic as they absorb increasing amounts of atmospheric carbon dioxide (Zeebe & Wolf-Gladrow 2001; Caldeira & Wickett 2003; Orr *et al.* 2005). Models and measurements suggest about a 30% decrease in surface pH and about a 16% decrease in carbonate ion concentration (used by organisms to make shells, skeletons and liths) since pre-industrial days (Caldeira & Wickett 2003; Feely *et al.* 2004; Sabine *et al.* 2004; Orr *et al.* 2005). By the year 2100, ocean acidity is projected to rise by up to 150% if carbon dioxide emissions continue at their current rate (Caldeira & Wickett 2003; Feely *et al.* 2004; Orr *et al.* 2005). The rate of change in acidity is faster than anything experienced in the last 65 million years (Ridgwell & Schmidt 2010), and it will take tens of thousands of years for these changes in ocean chemistry to be buffered through neutralisation by calcium carbonate sediments (Archer & Brovkin 2008). While evidence of current impacts of these changes to the carbonate system is lacking, there is rising concern for future marine ecosystems and the goods and services they provide as acidification tracks carbon dioxide emissions to the atmosphere (for reviews see Royal Society 2005; Kleypas *et al.* 2006; Fabry *et al.* 2008; Doney *et al.* 2009; Turley & Findlay 2009; Turley & Boot 2010 and references therein).

Ocean acidification may impact some ecosystems directly (e.g. coral ecosystems) or indirectly by reducing the fitness of a keystone species (e.g. echinoderms, pteropods) (Kleypas *et al.* 2006; Fabry *et al.* 2008; Hall-Spencer *et al.* 2008; Turley & Findlay 2009). These future increases in ocean acidity may have major negative impacts on some shell- and skeleton-forming organisms, such as cold water corals (Guinotte *et al.* 2006; Maier *et al.* 2009) and tropical coral reefs (Kleypas *et al.* 2006; Feely *et al.* 2008; Hoegh-Guldberg *et al.* 2008), within this century. While it is a global issue, polar and sub-polar waters (Orr *et al.* 2005; Steinacher *et al.* 2009), deep waters (Orr *et al.* 2005) and some upwelling regions (Feely *et al.* 2008) already naturally rich in carbon dioxide may be the first to experience the impacts of ocean acidification. Projections indicate that European shelf seas will also be vulnerable to changing acidity (Blackford & Gilbert 2007).

3.4.5 Invasive Species

The introduction of invasive and non-native (or 'alien') invasive species, and/or the introduction and naturalisation of domestic forest, crop or livestock species, can drive ecosystem change that affects human well-being through their impacts on economic activities (such as losses in crops or fisheries) or public health (Nelson *et al.* 2005). In the UK, biological drivers are considered to have had important impacts on all UK NEA Broad Habitat types, but especially Semi-natural Grasslands, Enclosed Farmland, Woodlands, Freshwaters and the Urban habitat (see **Figure 3.1**).

3.4.5.1 Invasive non-native species

An invasive species can be taken to mean a species that "spreads in space, either occupying new habitats or increasing its cover in areas previously occupied" (Nelson *et al.* 2005, p209). Typically, invasive species are primarily non-native, but the above definition can also apply to native species that 'invade' after habitat or climate change (Nelson *et al.* 2005).

Invasive species are generally thought to have detrimental impacts on ecosystems and their services, often acting as vectors for disease, changing biodiversity, altering service provision, disrupting cultural landscapes, and reducing the value of land and water for human activities (DAISIE 2011). They can also have significant socioeconomic consequences, especially when they cause damage to livestock, crops and timber plantations. In GB, non-native invasive species are estimated to cost more than £1.7 billion annually in control, mitigation, structural damage to infrastructure or loss of production (Williams *et al.* 2010; **Table 3.5**). The spread of these costs across different sectors are shown in **Table 3.5** for three non-native invasive species in GB (Williams *et al.* 2010):

- Japanese knotweed (*Fallopia japonica*)—originally introduced as an ornamental garden plant in the mid-19th Century, but is now widespread in a range of habitats where it displaces native flora and causes structural damage.
- American signal crayfish (*Pacifastacus leniusculus*)—originally introduced in the late 1970s primarily to farm for food; it soon escaped or was deliberately released and spread rapidly across England and Wales, although its distribution is now limited to Scotland. It out-competes native crayfish, carries a crayfish plague that kills native species, burrows into riverbanks, increasing erosion, and predates on the eggs of wild fish stocks.
- Floating Pennywort (*Hydrocotyle ranunculoides*)—originally introduced from North America in the 1980s through the aquatic plant trade, it now infests at least 150 sites in England and Wales. It forms dense vegetative mats that out-compete most native aquatic plants, can contribute to localised flooding through blocking drainage systems, and may have a negative impact on fish by restricting their access to feeding and resting spots.

Conversely, the effects of introduced non-native species may be benign or even valued. The public may welcome views of rhododendron within upland woodland, for example, or

Table 3.5 Total cost (£ '000s) of three non-native invasive species (Japanese knotweed, signal crayfish and floating Pennywort) to the British economy. Note, Floating Pennywort is not present in Scotland. Source: data extracted from Williams *et al.* (2010).

Sector	England	Scotland	Wales	GB
Japanese knotweed				
Local authorities	270	96	66	432
Research	319	32	19	370
Railways	1,726	174	100	2,000
Roadsides	3,901	757	438	5,096
Riparian	3,444	1,724	469	5,637
House devaluation	963	97	56	1,116
Development	141,358	1,508	7,644	150,510
Householders	383	42	23	448
Total	**152,364**	**4,430**	**8,815**	**165,609**
Signal crayfish				
Management	776	163	363	1,302
River bank restoration	100	50	50	200
Angling	550	325	125	1,000
Research	112	38	37	187
Total	**1,538**	**576**	**575**	**2,689**
Floating Pennywort				
Management	1,815	-	115	1,930
Recreation	23,468	-	69	23,537
Total	**25,283**	**-**	**184**	**25,467**

enjoy sightings of parakeets in the south of England; while grey squirrels (*Sciurus carolinensis*) offer a chance to get close to wildlife for many visitors to urban parks. For these reasons, the control of non-native species by conservation agencies may be controversial.

In GB, 3,473 non-native species have been recorded (Hill *et al.* 2009), with at least 49 being categorised as 'high threat' (**Table 3.6**). Some have been successfully eradicated, while others continue to spread. The number of records of non-native species rose by 23% between 1990 and 2007 (Hill *et al.* 2009). The area in which they occur and are considered invasive has also risen, by 40%, during the same time period (Hill *et al.* 2009), with England being the most affected (2,721 non-native species, of which, 100 are considered to have a negative impact on the environment; Hill *et al.* 2005), followed by Wales and then Scotland (988 non-native terrestrial and freshwater species were identified in 2001, with 76 tagged as potential problem species; Welch *et al.* 2001; SPICe 2010). In England, most non-native flora was introduced in the 18th and 19th Centuries, while most faunal introductions occurred in the second half of the 20th Century and are more prominent in the south of the country (Hill *et al.* 2005). In Scotland, over 100 non-native plants increased their range between the 1950s and 1980s (Welch *et al.* 2001). The rise of global trade and tourism, which facilitates the transfer of species between locations, has been largely responsible for the recent increases in incidence and spread of non-native invasive species (SPICe 2010).

The extent to which current non-native species may become problematic and cause detrimental ecosystem

Table 3.6 Invasive species categorised as 'High Threat' in Great Britain. Common names are provided in parentheses. Source: data extracted from Hill *et al.* (2009).

a) Marine plants
Sargassum muticum (Japweed, Wire Weed)
Undaria pinnatifida (Japanese Kelp, Wakame)
Codium fragile ssp. *tomentosoides* (Green Sea Fingers)

b) Marine animals
Tricellaria inopinata (bryozoan)
Watersipora subtorquata (bryozoan)
Corophium sextonae (amphipod)
Gammarus tigrinus (amphipod)
Elminius modestus (acorn barnacle)
Solidobalanus fallax (barnacle)
Eriocheir sinensis (Chinese Mitten Crab)
Rhithropanopeus harrisii (Dwarf Crab)
Crassostrea gigas (Pacific Oyster)
Crepidula fornicata (Slipper Limpet)
Rapana venosa (Rapa Whelk)
Anguillicola crassus (Swim-bladder Nematode)
Botrylloides violaceus (tunicate)
Corella eumyota (tunicate)
Didemnum vexillum (tunicate)
Styela clava (Leathery Sea Squirt)

c) Freshwater plants
Crassula helmsii (New Zealand Pigmyweed)
Hydrocotyle ranunculoides (Floating Pennywort)
Ludwigia grandiflora (Uruguayan Hampshire-purslane)
Myriophyllum aquaticum (Parrot's-feather)

d) Freshwater animals
Pacifastacus leniusculus (Signal Crayfish)
Procambarus clarkii (Red Swamp Crayfish)
Corbicula fluminea (Asian Clam)
Dreissena polymorpha (Zebra Mussel)
Pseudorasbora parva (Topmouth Gudgeon)
Sander lucioperca (Pikeperch, Zander)
Lithobates catesbeianus (American Bullfrog)
Trachemys scripta (Common Slider Turtle)

e) Terrestrial plants
Carpobrotus edulis (Hottentot Fig)
Disphyma crassifolium (Purple Dewplant)
Fallopia japonica (Japanese Knotweed)
Heracleum mantegazzianum (Giant Hogweed)
Impatiens glandulifera (Himalayan Balsam)
Quercus ilex (Evergreen Oak)
Rhododendron ponticum (Rhododendron)
Rosa rugosa (Japanese Rose)

f) Terrestrial animals
Arthurdendyus triangulata (New Zealand Flatworm)
Harmonia axyridis (Harlequin Ladybird)
Branta canadensis (Canada Goose)
Oxyura jamaicensis (Ruddy Duck)
Cervus nippon (Sika Deer)
Muntiacus reevesi (Reeves' Muntjac)
Mustela vison (American Mink)
Myocastor coypus (Coypu)
Rattus norvegicus (Brown Rat)
Sciurus carolinensis (Grey Squirrel)

change is often unknown due to the lag time between species first invading and subsequently increasing in occurrence within the country. However, to improve records and develop more timely management strategies, a British non-native species secretariat was formed in 2008 (www.nonnativespecies.org). The secretariat manages a risk register and a central depository for data on invasive species. An Invasive Non-Native Species Framework Strategy for GB has also been recently published (Defra 2008).

3.4.5.2 Introduction of domestic species

The majority of the UK's food and timber supply has relied on the introduction of alien domestic species. In many cases, these have now become naturalised (Williamson & Fitter 1996), but introductions have caused significant changes in a variety of UK habitats. For instance, deliberate selection of enhanced forestry species (typically of introduced conifers) led to widespread changes through UK woodlands, resulting in many broadleaved ecosystems becoming shaded, plantation woodlands. In turn, this has led to significant changes in biodiversity levels, particularly ground flora communities.

Breeding and selection of livestock species has also contributed directly to ecosystem change where species have specific grazing requirements and characteristics. The changes in stock type (e.g. sheep versus cattle) and the different breeds selected have contributed to ecosystem changes, especially in the uplands, where this is also interrelated to agricultural improvements and changes in harvest and livestock levels.

References

APIS (Air Pollution Information System) (2010) Ammonia. [online] Available at: <http://www.apis.ac.uk/overview/pollutants/overview_NH3.htm> [Accessed 21.11.10].

Archer, D. & Brovkin, V. (2008) The millennial atmospheric lifetime of anthropogenic CO_2. *Climate Change*, **90**, 283–297.

Armstrong, M. & Holmes, I. (2010) An indicator of sustainability for marine fin-fish stocks around the UK: 1990–2008. Centre for Environment, Fisheries and Aquaculture Science (CEFAS) pp. 13.

Ash, N., Lucas, N., Bubb, P., Iceland, C., Irwin, F., Ranganathan, J. & Raudsepp-Hearne, C. (2008) Framing the link between development and ecosystem services. Ecosystem Services: a guide for decision makers. (eds J. Ranganathan, C. Raudsepp-Hearne, N. Lucas, F. Irwin, M. Zurek, K. Bennett, N. Ash, & P. West). World Resouces Institute, Washington D.C., USA. pp. 13–28.

Bibby, P. (2009) Land use change in Britain. *Land Use Policy*, **26S**, S2–S13.

Blackford, J.C. & Gilbert, F.J. (2007) pH variability and CO_2 induced acidification in the North Sea. *Journal of Marine Systems*, **64**, 229–241.

Bobbink, R., Hicks, K., Galloway, J., Spranger, T., Alkemade, R., Ashmore, M., Bustamante, M., Cinderby, S., Davidson, E., Dentener, F., Emmett, B., Erisman, J., Fenn, M., Gilliam, F., Nordin,

A., Pardo, L. & de Vries, W. (2010) Global assessment of nitrogen deposition effects on terrestrial plant diversity: a synthesis. *Ecological Applications*, **20**, 30–59.

Caldeira, K. & Wickett, M.E. (2003) Anthropogenic carbon and ocean pH. *Nature*, **425**, 365.

Carey, P.D., Wallis, S.M., Chamberlain, P.M., Cooper, A., Emmett, B.A., Maskell, L.C., McCann, T., Murphy, J., Norton, L.R., Reynolds, B., Scott, W.A., Simpson, I.C., Smart, S. & Ullyett, J.M. (2008a) Countryside Survey: UK results from 2007. NERC/Centre for Ecology & Hydrology (CEH Project Number: C03259) pp. 105.

Carey, P.D., Wallis, S.M., Emmett, B.E., Maskell, L.C., Murphy, J., Norton, L.R., Simpson, I.C. & Smart, S. (2008b) Countryside Survey: UK headline messages from 2007. NERC/Centre for Ecology & Hydrology (CEH Project Number: C03259) pp. 30.

Carson, R. (1962) Silent Spring. Houghton Mifflin Company, New York.

CBD (Convention on Biological Diversity) (2010) Global Biodiversity Outlook 3. Secretariat of the Convention on Biological Diversity, Montreal. pp. 94.

Chamberlain, J. & Gill, B. (2005) Fertility and mortality. Focus on People and Migration. (eds R. Chappell). Palgrave and Macmillan, Hampshire. pp. 71–90.

Champion, T. (2005) Population movement within the UK. Focus on People and Migration. (eds R. Chappell). Palgrave and Macmillan, Hampshire, UK. pp. 91–114.

Clothier, L., Langton, S., Boatman, N. & Woodend, A. (2008) Defra Agricultural Change and Environment Observatory Research Report No. 11. Defra pp. 28.

Cottingham, M. & Perrett, T. (2010) Organic market report 2010. Soil Association pp. 39. [online] Available at: <http://www.soilassociation.org/LinkClick.aspx?fileticket=bTXno01MTtM=&tabid=116> [Accessed 08.03.11].

CPRE (Campaign to Protect Rural England) (2007) Developing an Intrusion Map of England. Campaign to Protect Rural England (CPRE) pp. 67. [online] Available at: <http://www.cpre.org.uk/library/results/intrusion> [Accessed 17.12.10].

Critchley, C.N.R., Burke, M.J.W. & Stevens, D.P. (2004) Conservation of lowland semi-natural grasslands in the UK: a review of botanical monitoring results from agri-environment schemes. *Biological Conservation*, **115**, 263–278.

Curry, D. (2008a) Farming and the Environment: Final Report of Sir Don Curry's High Level Set-Aside Group. Defra pp. 40.

Curry, D. (2008b) Farming and the Environment: Interim Report of Sir Don Curry's High Level Set-Aside Group. Defra pp. 55.

Curry, T.E., Reiner, D.M., de Figueiredo, M.A. & Herzog, H.J. (2005) A survey of public attitudes towards energy and environment in Great Britain. Laboratory for Energy and the Environment pp. 35.

DAISIE (Delivering Alien Invasive Species Iventories for Europe) (2011) DAISIE European Invasive Alien Species Gateway. [online] Available at: <http://www.europe-aliens.org> [Accessed 16.01.11].

Defra (Department for Environment, Food and Rural Affairs) (2008) The Invasive Non-Native Species Framework Strategy for Great Britain. The GB Non-Native Species Secretariat pp. 48.

Defra (Department for Environment, Food and Rural Affairs) (2009a) Sustainable development indicators in your pocket: 2009. Defra pp. 163.

Defra (Department for Environment, Food and Rural Affairs) (2009b) River Water Quality Indicator for Sustainable Development – 2008 results. Statistical Release Ref. 203/09. Defra.

Defra (Department for Environment, Food and Rural Affairs) (2009c) The environment in your pocket 2009. Defra. [online] Available at: <http://archive.defra.gov.uk/evidence/statistics/environment/eiyp/index.htm> [Accessed 03.04.11].

Defra (Department for Environment, Food and Rural Affairs) (2010a) UK Biodiversity Indicators in Your Pocket 2010: measuring progress towards halting biodiversity loss. Defra pp. 56. [online] Available at: <http://jncc.defra.gov.uk/page-4229> [Accessed 03.04.11].

Defra (Department for Environment, Food and Rural Affairs) (2010b) Farm Business Survey: farm accounts in England 2009/2010. Defra pp. 166. [online] Available at: <http://archive.defra.gov.uk/evidence/statistics/foodfarm/farmmanage/fbs/published-data/farmaccounts/2010/FAE.pdf> [Accessed 28.01.11].

Defra (Department for Environment, Food and Rural Affairs) (2010c) Agriculture in the United Kingdom 2009. Defra pp. 146. [online] Available at: <http://www.defra.gov.uk/statistics/files/AUK-2009.pdf> [Accessed 19.02.11].

Defra (Department for Environment, Food and Rural Affairs) (2010d) Organic statistics 2009, United Kingdom. Defra pp. 10.

Defra (Department for Environment, Food and Rural Affairs) (2010e) Measuring progress: sustainable development indicators 2010. Defra pp. 140.

Defra (Department for Environment, Food and Rural Affairs) (2010f) UK Emmissions of air pollutants – 2009 results. Defra pp. 8. [online] Available at: <http://ww2.defra.gov.uk/news/2010/12/16/air-pollutants/> [Accessed 14.01.11].

Defra (Department for Environment, Food and Rural Affairs) (2010g) Air pollution: action in a changing climate. Defra, The Scottish Government, Welsh Assembly Government, Department of the Environment pp. 24.

Defra (Department for Environment, Food and Rural Affairs) (2010h) Air quality indicator for sustainable development: 2009 final results. Defra pp. 11.

Doney, S.C., Fabry, V.J., Feely, R.A. & Kleypas, J.A. (2009) Ocean Acidification: The Other CO₂ Problem. *Annual Review Marine Science*, **1**, 169–192.

Doody, J.P. (2001) Coastal Conservation and Management: an ecological perspective. Kluwer, Boston, USA. pp. 306.

Dunbar, M., Murphy, J., Clarke, R., Baker, R., Davies, C. & Scarlett, P. (2010) Countryside Survey: Headwater Streams Report from 2007. Technical Report No. 8/07. NERC/Centre for Ecology & Hydrology. (CEH Project Number: C03259) pp. 67.

Eaton, M.A., Appleton, G.F., Ausden, M.A., Balmer, D.E., Grantham, M.J., Grice, P.V., Hearn, R.D., Holt, C.A., Musgrove, A.J., Noble, D.G., Parsons, M., Risely, K., Stroud, D.A. & Wotton, S. (2010) The state of the UK's birds 2010. RSPB, BTO, WWT, CCW, JNCC, NE, NIEA and SNH, Sandy, Bedfordshire. pp. 44.

Emmett, B.A., Reynolds, B., Chamberlain, P.M., Rowe, E., Spurgeon, D., Brittain, S.A., Frogbrook, Z., Hughes, S., Lawlor, A.J., Poskitt, J., Potter, E., Robinson, D.A., Scott, A., Wood, C. & Woods, C. (2010) Countryside Survey: Soils Report from 2007. NERC/Centre for Ecology & Hydrology. CS Technical Report No. 9/07. (CEH Project Number: C03259) pp. 192.

Ewald, J.A. & Aebischer, N.J. (2000) Trends in pesticide use and efficacy during 26 years of changing agriculture in southern England. *Environmental Monitoring and Assessment*, **64**, 493–529.

Fabry, V.J., Seibel, B.A., Feely, R.A. & Orr, J.C. (2008) Impacts of ocean acidification on marine fauna and ecosystem processes. *ICES Journal of Marine Science*, **65**, 414–432.

FAOSTAT (2011a) FAOSTAT Forestry. [online] Available at: <http://faostat.fao.org/site/626/DesktopDefault.aspx?PageID=626#ancor> [Accessed 18.02.11].

FAOSTAT (2011b) FAOSTAT Crops. [online] Available at: <http://faostat.fao.org/site/567/default.aspx#ancor> [Accessed 18.02.11].

Feely, R.A., Sabine, C.L., Lee, K., Berelson, W., Kleypas, J., Fabry, V.J. & Millero, F.J. (2004) Impact of anthropogenic CO₂ on the CaCO₂ system in the ocean. *Science*, **305**, 362–366.

Feely, R.A., Sabine, C.L., Hernandez-Ayon, J.M., Lanson, D. & Hales, B. (2008) Evidence for upwelling of corrosive "acidified" water onto the continental shelf *Science*, **320**, 1490–1492.

Fera (Food and Environment Research Agency) (2011) Pesticide Usage Statistics. [online] Available at: <http://pusstats.csl.gov.uk/index.cfm> [Accessed 18.02.11].

Foresight (2010) Foresight Land Use Futures Project: Final Project Report. The Government Office for Science, London pp. 325.

Forestry Commission (2010a) Forestry Statistics 2010: a compendium of statistics about woodland, forestry and primary wood processing in the United Kingdom. Forestry Commission pp. 208. [online] Available at: <http://www.forestry.gov.uk/forestry/INFD-88QDFK> [Accessed 16.02.11].

Forestry Commission (2010b) UK wood production and trade 2009. Forestry Commission pp. 12. [online] Available at: <http://www.forestry.gov.uk/pdf/trprod10.pdf/$FILE/trprod10.pdf> [Accessed 17.03.11].

Forestry Commission (2011) Woodland Statistics. [online] Available at: <http://www.forestry.gov.uk/forestry/infd-7aqknx> [Accessed 18.02.11].

French, P.W. (1997) Coastal and Estuarine Management (Routledge Environmental Management Series). Routledge, London.

Frost, M. (2010) Charting Progress 2 Feeder Report: Healthy and Biologically Diverse Seas. Defra, London. pp. 744. [online] Available at: <http://chartingprogress.defra.gov.uk/resources> [Accessed 24.01.11].

Fuller, R.M., Smith, G.M., Sanderson, J.M., Hill, R.A. & Thomson, A.G. (2002) The UK Land Cover Map 2000: construction of a parcel-based vector map from satellite images. *Cartographic Journal*, **39**, 15–25.

Guinotte, J.M., Orr, J., Cairns, S., Freiwald, A., Morgan, L. & George, R. (2006) Will human induced changes in seawater chemistry alter the distribution of deep-sea scleractinian corals? *Frontiers in Ecology and Environment*, **4**, 141–146.

Hall-Spencer, J.M., Rodolfo-Metalpi, R., Martin, S., Ransome, R., Fine, M., Turner, S.M., Rowley, S.J., Tedesco, D. & Buia, M.C. (2008) Volcanic carbon dioxide vents show ecosystem effects of ocean acidification. *Nature*, **454**, 96–99.

Hannah, J. (2010). Personal Communication.

Hewins, E.J., Pinches, C., Arnold, J., Lush, M., Robertson, H. & Escott, S. (2005) The condition of lowland BAP priority grasslands: results from a sample survey of non-statutory stands in England. English Nature Research Reports No. 636, Peterborough. pp. 80.

Hill, M.O., Baker, R., Broad, G., Chandler, P.J., Copp, G.H., Ellis, J., Jones, D., Hoyland, C., Laing, I., Longshaw, M., Moore, N., Parrott, D., Pearman, D., Preston, C., Smith, R.M. & Waters, R. (2005) Audit of non-native species in England. English Nature Research Reports pp. 82.

Hill, M.O., Beckman, B.C., Bishop, J.D., Fletcher, M.R., Marchant, J.H., Maskell, L.C., Noble, D.G., Rehfisch, M.M., Roy, H.E., Roy, S. & Sewell, J. (2009) Developing an indicator of the abundance, extent and impact of invasive non-native species. Final report. Defra pp. 49. [online] Available at: <http://nora.nerc.ac.uk/7796/1/HillN007796CR.pdf> [Accessed 18.01.11].

Hoegh-Guldberg, O., Mumby, P.J., Hooten, A.J., Steneck, R.S., Greenfield, P., Gomez, E., Harvell, C.D., Sale, P.F., Edwards, A.J., Caldeir, A.K., Knowlton, N., Eakin, C.M., Lglesias-Prieto, R., Muthiga, N., Bradbury, R.H., Dubi, A. & Hatziolos, M.E. (2008) Coral reefs under rapid climate change and ocean acidification. *Science*, **318**, 1737–1742.

Hume, C. (2008) Wetland Vision Technical Document: an overview and reporting of project philosophy and technical approach. The Wetland Vision Partnership pp. 80.

Huthnance, J. (2010) Charting Progress 2 Feeder Report: Ocean Processes. Defra, London. pp. 290. [online] Available at: <http://chartingprogress.defra.gov.uk/resources> [Accessed 26.01.11].

IEEP (Institute for European Environmental Policy) (2008) Appendix 5: The environmental benefits of set-aside. In: Farming and the Environment: Interim Report of Sir Don Curry's High Level Set-Aside Group. Defra pp. 18.

IPCC (Intergovenmental Panel on Climate Change) (2007) Climate Change 2007: Synthesis Report. IPCC pp. 52.

Jefferies, J. (2005) The UK population: past, present and future. Focus on People and Migration. (eds R. Chappell). Palgrave Macmillan, Hampshire. pp. 1–18.

Jenkins, G., Perry, M. & Prior, J. (2009) The climate of the United Kingdom and recent trends: UK Climate Impacts project UKCIP08 Report 1. Met Office Hadley Centre pp. 120. [online] Available at: <http://ukclimateprojections.defra.gov.uk/content/view/816/9/> [Accessed 14.11.10].

Jones, M.L.M., Wallace, H.L., Norris, D., Brittain, S.A., Haria, S., Jones, R.E., Rhind, P.M., Reynolds, B., R, & Emmett, B.A. (2004) Changes in vegetation and soil characteristics in coastal sand dunes along a gradient of atmospheric nitrogen deposition. *Plant Biology*, **6**, 598–605.

Kleypas, J.A., Feely, R.A., Fabry, V.J., Langdon, C., C.L., S. & Robbins, L.L. (2006) Impacts of ocean acidification on coral reefs and other marine calcifiers: a guide for future research. Report of a workshop held 18–20 April 2005; NSF, NOAA, US Geological Survey, St Petersburg, FL. pp. 1–88.

MA (Millennium Ecosystem Assessment) (2005a) Ecosystems and Well-being: biodiversity synthesis. World Resources Institute, Washington D.C., USA. pp. 86.

MA (Millennium Ecosystem Assessment) (2005b) Ecosystems and Human Well-being: Synthesis. Island Press, Washington D.C., USA. pp. 155.

MacCarthy, J., Thomas, J., Choudrie, S., Passant, N., Thistlewhaite, G., Murrells, T., Watterson, J., Cardenas, L., Thomson, A., Li, Y., Manning, A., Walker, C., Brophy, N., Sneddon, S., Pierce, M., Brown, K., Matthews, R., Gillam, S., Misselbrook, T. & Gilhespy, S. (2010) UK Greenhouse Gas Inventory 1990 to 2008: Annual Report for sumbission under the Framework Convention on Climate Change. Department of Energy and Climate Change pp. 330.

Maier, C., Hegeman, J., Weinbauer, M.G. & Gattuso, J.-P. (2009) Calcification of the cold-water coral *Lophelia pertusa* under ambient and reduced pH. *Biogeosciences*, **6**, 1875–1901.

Marsh, T. (2007) The 2004–2006 drought in southern Britain. *Weather*, **62**, 191–196.

Marshall, E.J.P., Wade, P. & Clare, P. (1978) Land drainage channels in England and Wales. *The Geographical Journal*, **144**, 254–263.

Maskell, L.C., Smart, S., Bullock, J.M., Thompson, K. & Stevens, C.J. (2009) Nitrogen deposition causes widespread species loss in British habitats. *Global Change Biology*, **16**, 671–679.

MMO (Marine Management Organisation) (2010) United Kingdom Sea Fisheries Statistics Archive. [online] Available at: <http://www.marinemanagement.org.uk/fisheries/statistics/annual_archive.htm> [Accessed 12.11.10].

Monteith, D.T., Hildrew, A.G., Flower, R.J., Raven, P.J., Beaumont, W.R.B., Collen, P., Kreiser, A.M., Shilland, E.M. & Winterbottom, J.H. (2005) Biological responses to the chemical recovery of acidified fresh waters in the UK. *Environmental Pollution*, **137**, 83–101.

Natural England (2011) Funding for land management [online] Available at: <http://www.naturalengland.org.uk/ourwork/farming/funding/default.aspx> [Accessed 03.04.11].

Nelson, G.C., Bennett, E., Berhe, A.A., Cassman, K.G., DeFries, R., Dietz, T., Dobson, A., Dobermann, A., Janetos, A., Levy, M., Marco, D., Naki enovi , N., O'Neill, B., Norgaard, T., Petschel-Held, G., Ojima, D., Pingali, P., Watson, R. & Zurek, M. (2005) Drivers of change in ecosystem condition and services. Ecosystems and Human Well-being: Scenarios. (eds S.R. Carpenter, P.L. Pingali, E. Bennett, & M. Zurek). Island Press, Washington D.C., USA. pp. 173–222.

Newton, I. & Wyllie, I. (1992) Recovery of A Sparrowhawk Population in Relation to Declining Pesticide Contamination. *Journal of Applied Ecology*, **29**, 476–484.

NFU (National Farmers' Union) (2011) Campaign for the Farmed Environment Online. [online] Available at: <http://www.cfeonline.org.uk/> [Accessed 03.04.11].

ONS (Office for National Statistics) (2009) Social Trends – no. 39, 2009 edition. Palgrave Macmillan, New York. pp. 283.

ONS (Office for National Statistics) (2010a) Office for National Statistics: population – latest on ageing. [online] Available at: <http://www.statistics.gov.uk/cci/nugget.asp?ID=949> [Accessed 28.11.10].

ONS (Office for National Statistics) (2010b) Office for National Statistics: population – estimates. [online] Available at: <http://www.statistics.gov.uk/cci/nugget.asp?ID=6> [Accessed 28.11.10].

Orr, J.C., Fabry, V.J., Aumont, O., Bopp, L., Doney, S.C., Feely, R.A., Gnanadesikan, A., Gruber, N., Ishida, A., Joos, F., Key, R.M., Lindsay, K., Maier-Reimer, E., Matear, R., Monfray, P., Mouchet, A., Najjar, R.G., Plattner, G.K., Rodgers, K.B., Sabine, C.L., Sarmiento, J.L., Schlitzer, R., Slater, R.D., Totterdell, I.J., Weirig, M.F., Yamanaka , Y. & Yool, A. (2005) Anthropogenic ocean acidification over the twenty-first century and its impact on calcifying organisms. *Nature*, **437**, 681–686.

Patterson, G.S. & Anderson, A.R. (2000) Forests and peatland habitats. Guideline Note No. 1. Forestry Commission,

Edinburgh. pp. 16. [online] Available at: <http://www.forestry. gov.uk/pdf/fcgn1.pdf/$FILE/fcgn1.pdf> [Accessed 18.01.11].

Perry, M. (2006) A spatial analysis of trends in the UK climate since 1914 using gridded datasets. Met Office National Climate Information Centre. Climate Memorandum No. 21.

Planning Statistical Release (2010) Land use change statistics (England) 2009 – provisional estimates (July 2010). Communities and Local Government pp. 14. [online] Available at: <http://www.communities.gov.uk/publications/corporate/statistics/lucs2009provisionaljuly> [Accessed 17.02.11].

Pointer, G. (2005) The UK's major urban areas. Focus on People and Migration. (eds R. Chappell). Pagrave and Macmillan, Hampshire. pp. 45–60.

PSMSL (Permanent Services for Mean Sea Level) (2011) Global data bank for long-term sea-level change information from tide gauges and bottom pressure recorders. [online] Available at: <http://www.psmsl.org/> [Accessed 21.03.11].

Ridgwell, A. & Schmidt, D.N. (2010) Past constraints on the vulnerability of marine calcifiers to massive CO_2 release. *Nature Geoscience*, **3**, 196–200.

RoTAP (Review of Transboundary Air Pollution) (2010) Review of Transboundary Air Pollution (RoTAP): acidfication, eutrophication, ground level ozone and hevay metals in the UK. Defra pp. 335. [online] Available at: <http://www.rotap.ceh.ac.uk> [Accessed 06.12.10].

Royal Society (2005) Ocean acidification due to increasing atmospheric carbon dioxide. Royal Society Policy Document 12/05.

Sabine, C.L., Feely, R.A., Gruber, N., Key, R.M., Lee, K., Bullister, J.L., Wanninkhof, R., Wong, C.S., Wallace, D.W.R., Tilbrook, B., Millero, F.J., Peng, T.H., Kozyr, A., Ono, T. & Rios, A.F. (2004) The oceanic sink for anthropogenic CO_2. *Science*, **305**, 367–371.

Saunders, J. (2010) Charting Progress 2 Feeder Report: Productive Seas. Defra, London. pp. 432. [online] Available at: <http://chartingprogress.defra.gov.uk/resources> [Accessed 25.02.11].

Shaw, K. & Jefferies, J. (2005) Where people live. Focus on People and Migration. (eds R. Chappell). Palgrave and Macmillan, Hampshire, UK. pp. 19–44.

Smith, C., Tomassini, C., Smallwood, S. & Hawkins, M. (2005) The changing age structure of the UK population. (eds R. Chappell), Hampshire, UK. pp. 61–70.

SPICe (Scottish Parliment Information Centre) (2010) SPICe Brifing: Invasive Non-Native Species. The Scottish Parliment.

Steinacher, M., Joos, F., Frölicher, T.L., Plattner, G.-K. & Doney, S.C. (2009) Imminent ocean acidification in the Arctic projected with the NCAR global coupled carbon cycle-climate model. *Biogeosciences*, **6**, 515–533.

Stevens, C.J., Dise, N.B., Mountford, J.O. & Gowing, D.J. (2004) Impact of nitrogen deposition on the species richness of grasslands. *Science*, **303**, 1876–1879.

Thomas, M. (2010) The British survey of fertiliser practise: fertiliser use on farm crops for crop year 2009. Defra pp. 97.

Thornton, A. (2009) Public attitudes and behaviours towards the environment – tracker survey: a report to the Department for Environment, Food and Rural Affairs. TNS, Defra, London.

Thurstan, R.H., Brockington, S. & Roberts, C.M. (2010) The effects of 118 years of industrial fishing on UK bottom trawl fisheries. *Nature Communications*, **1:15**, 6.

Thurstan, R.H. & Roberts, C.M. (2010) Ecological meltdown in the Firth of Clyde, Scotland: two centuries of change in a coastal marine ecosystem. *PLoS One*, **5**, e11767.

Turley, C.M. & Findlay, H.S. (2009) Ocean Acidification as an Indicator for Climate Change. Climate and Global Change: Observed Impacts on Planet Earth. (eds T.M. Letcher). Elsevier. pp. 367–390.

Turley, C.M. & Boot, K. (2010) UNEP Emerging Issues: Environmental Consequences of Ocean Acidification: A Threat to Food Security. UNEP pp. 9. [online] Available at: <http://www.unep.org/dewa/pdf/Environmental_Consequences_of_Ocean_Acidification.pdf> [Accessed 16.01.11].

UKMMAS (UK Marine Monitoring and Assessment) (2010) Charting Progess 2: The state of UK seas. Defra, London. pp. 194.

Visit Cumbria (2011) Haweswater. [online] Available at: <http://www.visitcumbria.com/pen/haweswater.htm> [Accessed 03.04.11].

Welch, D., Carss, D.N., Gornall, J., Manchester, S.J., Marquiss, M., Preston, C.D., Telfer, M.G., Arnold, H. & Holbrook, J. (2001) An audit of alien species in Scotland. Scottish Natural Heritage Review No. 139 pp. 236.

White, P.J. & Hammond, J.P. (2009) The sources of phosphorus in the waters of Great Britain. *Journal of Environmental Quality*, **38**, 13–26.

Williams, F., Eschen, R., Harris, A., Djeddour, D., Pratt, C., Shaw, R.S., Varia, S., Lamontagne-Gowin, J., Thomas, S.E. & Murphy, S.T. (2010) The economic cost of invasive non-native species on Great Britain. CABI pp. 199.

Williamson, M. & Fitter, A. (1996) The varying success of invaders. *Ecology*, **77**, 1661–1666.

Woodworth, P.L., Teferle, N., Bingley, R., Shennan, I. & Williams, S.D.P. (2009) Trends in UK mean sea level revisited. *Geophysical Journal International*, **176**, 19–30.

Zeebe, R.E. & Wolf-Gladrow, D. (2001) CO_2 in seawater: equilibrium, kinetics, isotopes. Elsevier Oceanographic Series, New York. pp. 360.

Appendix 3.1 Approach Used to Assign Certainty Terms to Chapter Key Findings

This chapter began with a set of Key Findings. Adopting the approach and terminology used by the Intergovernmental Panel on Climate Change (IPCC) and the Millennium Assessment (MA), these Key Findings also include an indication of the level of scientific certainty. The 'uncertainty approach' of the UK NEA consists of a set of qualitative uncertainty terms derived from a 4-box model and complemented, where possible, with a likelihood scale (see below). Estimates of certainty are derived from the collective judgement of authors, observational evidence, modelling results and/or theory examined for this assessment.

Throughout the Key Findings presented at the start of this chapter, superscript numbers and letters indicate the estimated level of certainty for a particular key finding:

1. *Well established:* high agreement based on significant evidence
2. *Established but incomplete evidence:* high agreement based on limited evidence
3. *Competing explanations:* low agreement, albeit with significant evidence
4. *Speculative:* low agreement based on limited evidence

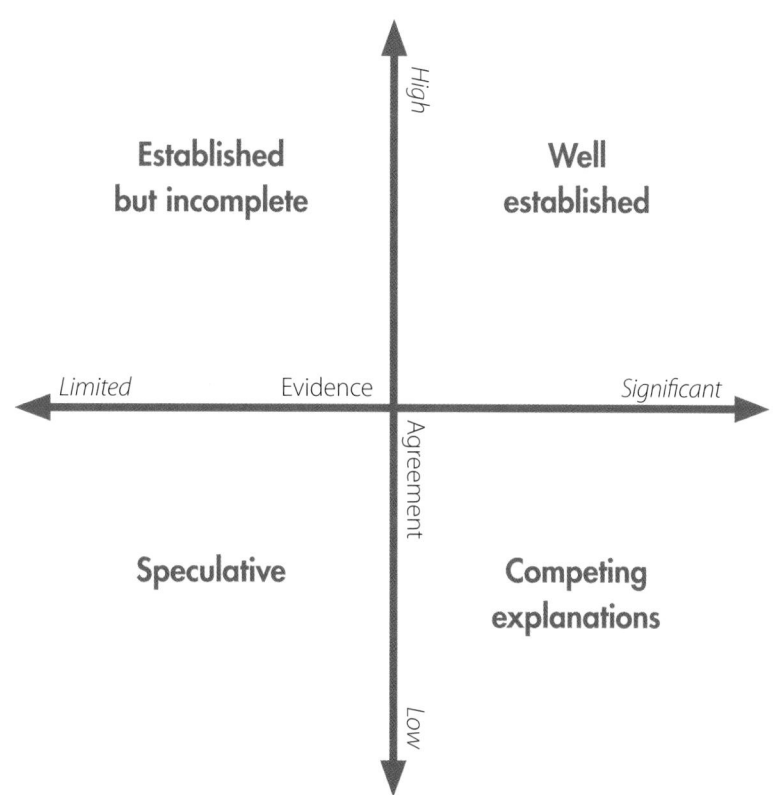

a. *Virtually certain:* >99% probability of occurrence
b. *Very likely:* >90% probability
c. *Likely:* >66% probability
d. *About as likely as not:* >33–66% probability
e. *Unlikely:* <33% probability
f. *Very unlikely:* <10% probability
g. *Exceptionally unlikely:* <1% probability

Certainty terms 1 to 4 constitute the 4-box model, while *a* to *g* constitute the likelihood scale.

Chapter 4:
Biodiversity in the Context of Ecosystem Services

Coordinating Lead Author: Ken Norris
Contributing Authors: Mark Bailey, Sandra Baker, Richard Bradbury, David Chamberlain, Callan Duck, Martin Edwards, Christopher J. Ellis, Matt Frost, Mary Gibby, Jack Gilbert, Richard Gregory, Richard Griffiths, Lauren Harrington, Stephan Helfer, Emma Jackson, Simon Jennings, Aidan Keith, Elizabeth Kungu, Olivia Langmead, David Long, David Macdonald, Heather McHaffie, Lindsay Maskell, Tom Moorhouse, Eunice Pinn, Christopher Reading, Paul Somerfield, Sarah Turner, Charles Tyler, Adam Vanbergen and Allan Watt.

Key Findings*

The term 'biodiversity' describes the diversity of life on Earth. Diversity can occur at a number of levels of biological organisation, from genes, through to individuals, populations, species, communities and entire ecosystems[1].

[1] *well established*

Biodiversity underpins all ecosystem services. Biodiversity plays a wide range of functional roles in ecosystems and, therefore, in the processes that underpin ecosystem services[1]. Examples range from the roles bacteria and fungi play in nutrient cycles which are fundamental processes in all ecosystems, to particular animal groups, such as birds and mammals, which are culturally important to many people. Ecosystem functions are more stable through time in experimental ecosystems with relatively high levels of biodiversity[2]; and there are comparable effects in natural ecosystems[c]. Taken together, this evidence shows that, in general terms, the level and stability of ecosystem services tend to improve with increasing biodiversity.

[1] *well established*
[2] *established but incomplete evidence*
[c] *likely*

Biodiversity plays a wide range of roles in UK ecosystem services. All twelve of the ecosystem services that are important in a UK context are underpinned by a range of biodiversity groups. The number of biodiversity groups playing an important role varies between ecosystem services: water quantity (3/17 of biodiversity groups); socially valued landscapes and waterscapes (6/17 groups); crops, plants, livestock and fish (11/17 groups); and wild species diversity (all 17 groups). The role of different biodiversity groups varies between ecosystem services. Microorganisms, fungi and plants play a role in underpinning all provisioning and regulating services; vertebrate groups contribute to all cultural services, but they only play an important role in 30% (3/10) of the provisioning and regulating services.

Biodiversity is a key component of multifunctional ecosystems. The importance of managing ecosystems to provide multiple services and associated values (so-called 'multifunctional ecosystems') is becoming increasingly recognised both globally and in the UK. The sensitivity of UK ecosystem services to changes in a range of biodiversity groups implies that achieving this multifunctionality will require management measures to support a wide range of biodiversity groups.

Significant biodiversity loss has been documented in the UK over the last 50 years, but monitoring data for a number of biodiversity groups is poor, precluding an assessment of status and trends. The quality of monitoring data in the UK varies between biodiversity groups. For some biodiversity groups, such as marine plankton, land plants, some invertebrate groups, fish, birds and mammals, national-scale data on abundance and range exist for a time-series of 10–20 years. These datasets show clear patterns of biodiversity change. The quality of monitoring data across UK biodiversity groups increases in relation to their cultural importance. As a result, there are only limited data available on several biodiversity groups, such as microorganisms and fungi, which underpin provisioning and regulating services, precluding an assessment of their status and trends.

---

* Each Key Finding has been assigned a level of scientific certainty, based on a 4-box model and complemented, where possible, with a likelihood scale. Superscript numbers indicate the uncertainty term assigned to each finding. Full details of each term and how they were assigned are presented in Appendix 4.2.

Relating changes in UK biodiversity to changes in ecosystem services can be problematic due to a lack of data on associated values and benefits. Interpreting the impact of even well-established trends in UK biodiversity on associated ecosystem services can be problematic where data on values and benefits are lacking. For example, we lack quantitative data on cultural services, so we are currently unable to assess the magnitude of changes in cultural services associated with well-established changes in bird populations. In contrast, specific, well-established biodiversity trends linked to provisioning and regulating services can have clear implications for service provision. For example, declines in the abundance of commercially important marine and freshwater fish species lead directly to a reduction in the output of provisioning services.

Land use change and pollution have been the major drivers of change across biodiversity groups in the UK. Land use change is considered a significant driver of change across all UK biodiversity groups associated with terrestrial and freshwater ecosystems, and for marine groups affected by activities on land. For example, recent evidence suggests that about 67% of 333 farmland species (broadleaved plants, butterflies, bumblebees, birds and mammals) were threatened by agricultural intensification in the year 2000. Pollution impacts reflect a range of human activities including diffuse pollution from agriculture, point source pollution from urban ecosystems, and air pollution (e.g. acid rain).

There is a cultural divide among biodiversity groups and associated ecosystem services in the UK. On one side of this divide are culturally important biodiversity groups; on the other side are biodiversity groups that underpin provisioning and regulating services. For several culturally important biodiversity groups, status and trends are well-established, but data on associated cultural services are frequently lacking. This makes it difficult to quantify the impact of biodiversity change on cultural services. For provisioning and regulating services, quantitative data on changes in the services themselves are often available, but status and trend information for associated biodiversity groups is considered poor. This makes it difficult to understand the role biodiversity plays in changes in associated provisioning and regulating services. Bridging this cultural divide represents a major research and policy challenge.

4.1 Background

Charles Darwin famously described the diversity of life on Earth as "endless forms most beautiful". Over the subsequent 100 years or so, it has become increasingly apparent that human activities have caused, and continue to cause, significant loss of this diversity. This realisation culminated in the Convention on Biological Diversity (CBD) in 1992, which established policies for the conservation of biodiversity, the sustainable use of its components, and the fair and equitable sharing of benefits arising from biodiversity. Subsequently, there has been considerable debate about appropriate indicators that can be used to measure the health of biodiversity (Balmford *et al.* 2003; Green *et al.* 2005) and a number of countries, including the UK, have adopted biodiversity targets and indicators to report on biodiversity status and trends (Gregory *et al.* 2004). These national initiatives complement global targets and indicators, which have recently shown that, despite commitments to halt biodiversity loss by 2010, significant biodiversity loss continues (Butchart *et al.* 2010).

It is widely accepted that biodiversity plays a wide range of key functional roles within terrestrial, freshwater and marine ecosystems (Hooper *et al.* 2005; Raffaelli 2006; Worm *et al.* 2006; Palumbi *et al.* 2009). Nevertheless, it was not until the Millennium Ecosystem Assessment (MA) in 2005 that these functional roles were viewed holistically in the context of ecosystem services and benefits linked to human well-being (MA 2005). The MA recognised the critical roles played by biodiversity in underpinning ecosystem services

(**Figure 4.1**). Subsequent work, such as the European Academies Science Advisory Council's (EASAC) report on Ecosystem Services and Biodiversity in Europe and the report, Reviewing the Economics of Biodiversity Loss: Scoping the Science, produced as part of The Economics of Ecosystems and Biodiversity (TEEB) project, has attempted to be more explicit about how biodiversity underpins the delivery of ecosystem services, and considers the potential consequences of biodiversity loss for future service delivery (Balmford *et al.* 2008; TEEB 2008; EASAC 2009; TEEB 2009). While we often have a broad understanding of which biodiversity groups are important in underpinning specific ecosystem services, such assessments are frequently hampered by a critical lack of quantitative data on biodiversity and ecosystem service relationships at the scales (spatial and temporal) typical of real-world ecosystems (Balmford & Bond 2005; Kremen 2005).

Theoretically, there are a number of potential relationships between biodiversity and ecosystem services (**Figure 4.2a**). Describing these patterns is the key to determining the consequences of biodiversity loss for ecosystem services. While there has been considerable research on the relationships between biodiversity and ecosystem function over the last 20 years (Hooper *et al.* 2005; Raffaelli 2006), much of this work has limitations in terms of understanding real-world ecosystems (Srivastava & Vellend 2005). This is because studies have typically been undertaken on small-scales and within highly simplified experimental ecosystems. Studies using 'model' ecosystems are valuable in exploring the functional roles of biodiversity, but how they relate to biodiversity and ecosystem change in the real world is less clear (Kremen 2005). As a result,

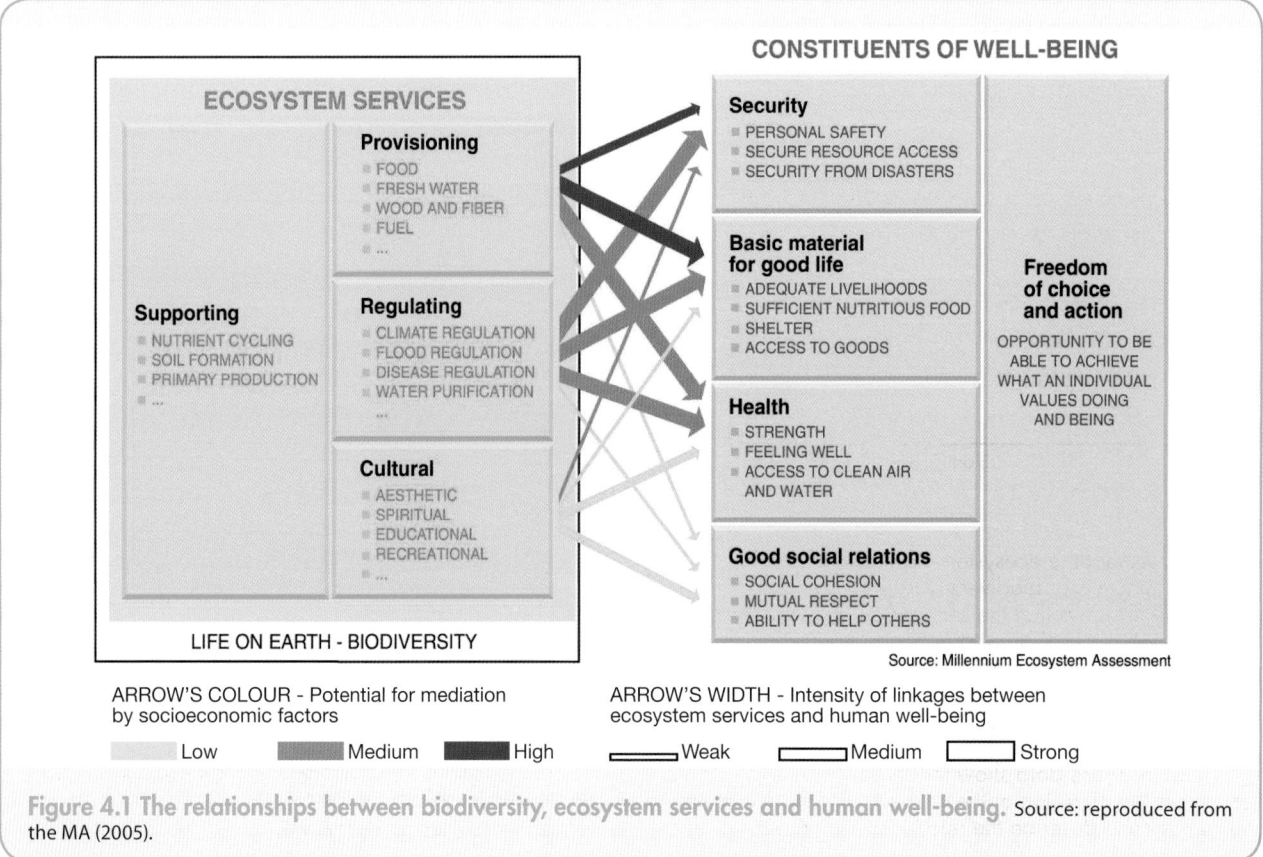

Figure 4.1 The relationships between biodiversity, ecosystem services and human well-being. Source: reproduced from the MA (2005).

there are increasing calls among the scientific community to focus research explicitly on understanding relationships between biodiversity and ecosystem services in the context of real-world ecosystem change (Srivastava & Vellend 2005; Raffaelli 2006); thus insights from natural systems are beginning to accumulate (Benayas *et al.* 2009).

Against this background, it is perhaps not surprising that our understanding of the quantitative links between biodiversity and ecosystem services is, at present, generally rather poor (Kremen 2005), and is limited to a few well-understood case studies such as crop pollination services (Kremen *et al.* 2002) and disease regulation (Keesing *et al.* 2006). There are two important issues relating to this understanding. Firstly, the functional component of biodiversity needs to be identified. It is possible that a service is related to an aspect of diversity *per se* (e.g. species diversity); alternatively, the service may depend on a specific functional group or even an individual species that plays a specific functional role. The functional components of biodiversity may also vary between types of ecosystem service (Diaz *et al.* 2007). Secondly, the data available relating biodiversity to a particular ecosystem service are often relatively sparse (**Figure 4.2a**). Therefore, it is possible to show that a specific ecosystem service is sensitive to changes in a particular biodiversity group, but it is often the case that there is just not enough information available to describe the form of the relationship. As a result, the available evidence is good enough to be able to demonstrate that biodiversity matters to the provision of ecosystem services, but it is often not good enough to allow us to distinguish services that are sensitive to even small levels of biodiversity loss from those that are more resilient to biodiversity loss (**Figure 4.2a**).

There is a general consensus in the literature that biodiversity enhances the stability of ecosystems (Hooper *et al.* 2005). This is believed to occur because increasing biodiversity also increases functional diversity, thereby buffering ecosystem processes against temporal (**Figure 4.2b**) or spatial perturbation (Loreau *et al.* 2003). These concepts are important in the context of ecosystem services because they imply that, as biodiversity is lost from an ecosystem, service provision is not only likely to decrease to some extent (**Figure 4.2a**), but may also get more variable in space or time (**Figure 4.2b**). As a result, biodiversity has a potentially important 'insurance' role to play in maintaining service provision in the face of environmental change.

4.2 Biodiversity in the Context of the UK National Ecosystem Assessment

The general issues discussed in the previous section have important implications for how we consider biodiversity within the UK NEA. The UK has, perhaps, the most comprehensive data on biodiversity status and trends of any country in the world, but these data are not routinely linked

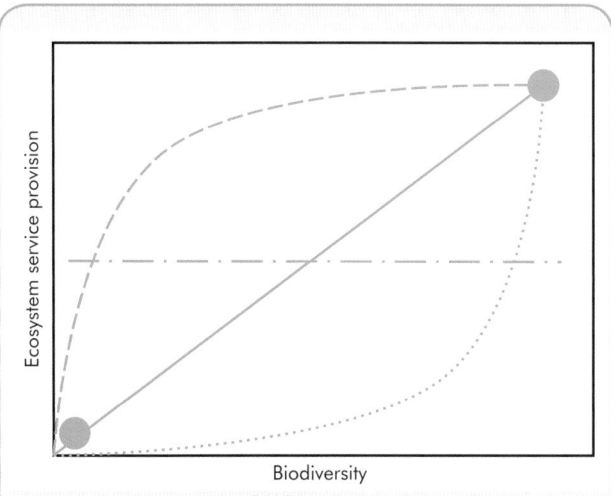

Figure 4.2a Theoretical relationships between biodiversity and an ecosystem service. The dashed line shows that the ecosystem service is resilient to moderate levels of biodiversity loss; whereas the dotted line shows that the service is very sensitive to even small levels of biodiversity loss. The solid line is intermediate between these two. The dashed and dotted line illustrates the case in which an ecosystem service is insensitive to biodiversity change. The green dots illustrate the type of data that are typically available. These data show that biodiversity loss reduces the provision of the ecosystem service, but are too sparse to describe the relationship in any detail.

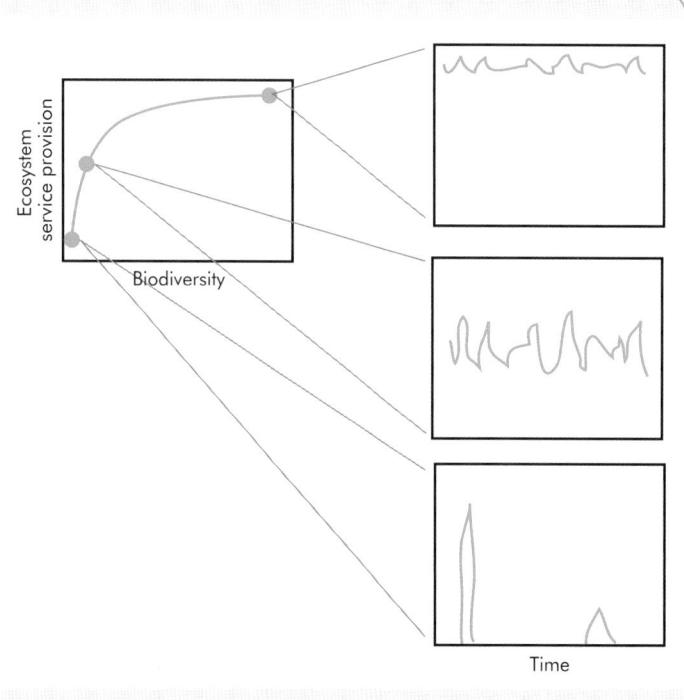

Figure 4.2b The stability of ecosystem services through time in relation to biodiversity. The left hand panel illustrates the theoretical relationship between biodiversity and the provision of an ecosystem service. The right hand panels illustrate how the provision of the service may become more variable through time as biodiversity decreases.

to ecosystem services. For example, it is well known that pollinating insects play a crucial role in providing pollination services to agricultural crops (Klein *et al.* 2007; Zhang *et al.* 2007). While we have evidence of pollinator losses in the UK (Biesmeijer *et al.* 2006), we have a very limited understanding of the consequences of these losses for pollination services, or of how environmental change is likely to impact on pollination systems. Consequently, a £10 million research programme is currently underway to address these knowledge gaps (see www.lwec.org.uk/activities/insect-pollinators-initiative). This is relevant in the context of the UK NEA's consideration of biodiversity because pollination is one of the best understood biodiversity-ecosystem function-ecosystem service relationships. Taken together, this significant lack of evidence means we are currently unable to comprehensively quantify the relationships between UK biodiversity and the ecosystem services it supports (**Figure 4.2a, b**).

For these reasons, we have qualitatively assessed (low, medium or high) the importance of a range of biodiversity groups in underpinning the final ecosystem services being covered by the UK NEA, with the aim of identifying key biodiversity groups associated with each final ecosystem service. This assessment is based on the premise that, while we often understand that a particular ecosystem service (e.g. pollination) is likely to be sensitive to changes in specific biodiversity groups (e.g. pollinating insects), we

are not able to quantify this sensitivity (Section 4.1). We have also reviewed and synthesised the available status and trend information for each of these biodiversity groups, and discussed the linkages between the status and trend data and ecosystem services. Lastly, we synthesised the available information on drivers of biodiversity change to identify important factors that may modify biodiversity in the UK and the ecosystem services it supports.

To undertake this assessment it was necessary to define 'biodiversity'. The CBD defines biodiversity as "the variability among living organisms from all sources, including, 'inter alia', terrestrial, marine, and other aquatic ecosystems, and the ecological complexes of which they are part: this includes diversity within species, between species and of ecosystems". This definition is less than ideal from the perspective of ecosystem services because, as noted in the previous section, diversity *per se* may have only a limited effect on specific ecosystem services. The scientific debate about how best to define biodiversity must also recognise practical constraints imposed by available biodiversity data. In the UK, biodiversity data tends to relate to taxonomic groups distinguished by specific monitoring programmes (e.g. www.nbn.org.uk), which, in turn, provide the data that are used to report on status and trends. While it would be possible, at least in principle, to redefine the biodiversity groups recognised in the UK in terms of their functional roles in ecosystem services, such a task would inevitably be problematic due to the need to combine datasets from a range of monitoring programmes that employ different census methods. This would be a significant undertaking and beyond the scope of this chapter. As a result, this chapter has taken a pragmatic approach by adopting the taxonomic groups recognised by UK monitoring programmes to define UK biodiversity (**Table 4.1**).

These biodiversity groups form the basis of the assessment reported in this chapter. The assessment itself was conducted by a team of 35 scientists with specific expertise in the range of biodiversity groups involved (**Appendix 4.1**). Before reporting the assessment, we briefly outline in the following section how biodiversity fits into the conceptual framework being used by the UK NEA.

Table 4.1 Biodiversity groups distinguished in the UK NEA.

Biodiversity group	Definition
Microorganisms	Bacteria and Archaea, formerly grouped as the prokaryotes, and the single-celled Eukaryotes.
Fungi and Lichens	Mycetozoan (e.g. Myxomycota) and Heterokontophytan (e.g. Oomycota) species; lichenised-fungi include Ascomycetes ('cup'-fungi) and Basidiomycetes.
Phytoplankton	Photoautotrophic microorganisms found in aquatic ecosystems, e.g. diatoms, cyanobacteria, dinoflagellates and coccolithophores.
Macroalgae	Multicellular eukaryotic algae belonging to one of three main groups; red algae (Rhodophyta), green algae (Chlorophyta) and brown algae (Phaeophyceae).
Bryophytes	Liverworts (Marchantiophyta), mosses (Bryophyta) and hornworts (Anthocerotophyta).
Seagrasses	Two species of seagrass; the primarily subtidal *Zostera marina* (eelgrass) and the intertidal *Zostera noltii* (dwarf eelgrass).
Land plants	All vascular plants: Lycopods, Isoetes and Selaginella, ferns and horsetails, conifers (Gymnosperms), and all flowering plants (Angiosperms)—trees, shrubs, herbaceous plants and grasses. The majority are land plants, but some occur in freshwater, brackish or marine habitats.
Invertebrates	All marine, freshwater and terrestrial invertebrates (e.g. annelids, crustaceans, molluscs, arthropods, echinoderms).
Fish	All marine and freshwater fish.
Amphibians	Frogs, toads and newts.
Reptiles	Snakes, lizards and marine turtles.
Birds	Land and seabirds.
Mammals	Land mammals, cetaceans and pinnipeds.

4.3 Biodiversity and the Conceptual Framework

We illustrate how biodiversity fits into the conceptual framework being used by the UK NEA in **Figure 4.3**. Biodiversity can potentially play a role in the primary and intermediate processes that underpin final ecosystem services, and it can also play a role in the final ecosystem services themselves. Our example considers a fruit crop pollinated by insects. Biodiversity is part of the ecosystem processes that provide pollination services to fruit crops, and it is also part of the fruit crop itself (the final ecosystem service) because wild and domesticated plants provide the raw material from which crop varieties are derived. Clearly,

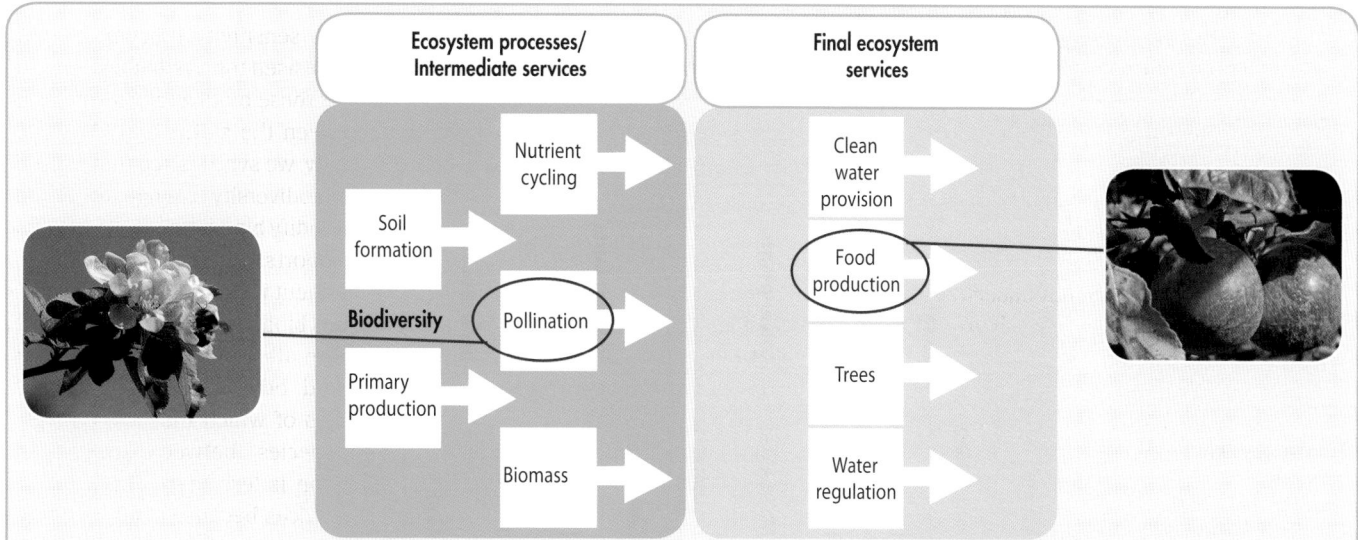

Figure 4.3 The roles of biodiversity within the conceptual framework being used by the UK NEA. The figure illustrates that biodiversity can have a role in the processes underpinning the final services (in this case pollination) or be part of the final service itself (in this case a fruit crop). *Photo sources: Bumblebee, Bombus hortorum, pollinating apples by John Fergusson; Braeburn apples by John Thurm, available under a Creative Commons Attribution-NonCommercial-ShareAlike license.*

the networks of ecological interactions that underpin a final ecosystem service, such as a fruit crop, are more complex than implied by our example. Arguably, all of the primary and intermediate processes play some role (**Figure 4.3**), and biodiversity is likely to play a key role in a number of these. Nevertheless, the important point is that when we talk about biodiversity 'underpinning' the delivery of ecosystem services it is either in the context of biodiversity being part of primary or intermediate processes, or part of the final service itself; often it will be both.

4.4 The Role of Biodiversity in UK Ecosystem Services

In broad terms, we know which biodiversity groups play potentially important roles in UK ecosystem services, but we lack quantitative data that would allow us to link current biodiversity status and trend data with the delivery of ecosystem services. For this reason, we have qualitatively assessed the importance of different biodiversity groups using expert opinion and by adopting a similar approach to that used by the EASAC study (EASAC 2009). The EASAC study assessed the importance of biodiversity using a simple scale of low, medium and high, which we have also adopted. While our approach is similar to EASAC's, it has been specifically tailored to the UK context in terms of the biodiversity groups (**Table 4.1**) and ecosystem services (**Table 4.2**) being assessed. Experts for each biodiversity group were asked to assess the importance of their biodiversity group in underpinning each final ecosystem service being considered in the UK NEA using a simple scale of low, medium or high. This assessment did not consider the precise role played by biodiversity, but simply whether a particular group was considered important irrespective of

the details of its role. In this way, we aimed to identify key biodiversity groups associated with each final ecosystem service. Experts were also asked to identify the level of uncertainty in the available evidence.

This general concept of importance is being used to qualitatively assess the 'sensitivity' of each ecosystem service to changes in each biodiversity group. Where importance is considered 'high', this should be taken to mean that the particular ecosystem service is relatively sensitive to changes in the specific biodiversity group being assessed; where importance is considered 'low', the particular service is relatively insensitive to changes in the specific biodiversity group being assessed. The concept of importance does not reflect the functional mechanism linking the biodiversity group with a specific ecosystem service. As a result, 'high' importance might reflect sensitivity of a specific ecosystem service to levels of diversity present within a particular biodiversity group; but it might also reflect sensitivity to the presence or abundance of specific functional groups, species or genotypes within a particular biodiversity group. In addition, the concept of importance does not explicitly consider the issue of irreplaceability: the idea that the functional role performed by biodiversity cannot be substituted by an artificial process. It simply provides a basis for comparison across a range of biodiversity groups and ecosystem services irrespective of the functional mechanisms involved.

The results of this assessment are summarised in **Table 4.2**. The rows of the table list the final ecosystem services being covered within the UK NEA; the columns identify the different biodiversity groups. The cells in the table are colour-coded to reflect the degree of importance assigned to each service-biodiversity group combination, ranging from high (maroon) to low (green) importance. The size of the circle in each cell is used to illustrate the level of uncertainty in the available evidence.

A number of specific points emerge:

■ All UK ecosystem services are dependent on biodiversity to some extent.

Table 4.2 The importance of different biodiversity groups in underpinning the final ecosystem services based on expert opinion. Importance is colour-coded: high (maroon), medium (beige), low (green), unimportant on the basis of available evidence (blank). The size of the circle in each cell is used to illustrate the level of uncertainty in the available evidence. Further details are given in Appendix 4.1.

Biodiversity groups

Final ecosystem services (based on the UK NEA Conceptual Framework)	Microorganisms — Terrestrial	Microorganisms — Marine	Fungi — Non-lichens	Fungi — Lichens	Lower plants — Phytoplankton	Lower plants — Macroalgae	Lower plants — Bryophytes	Higher plants — Seagrasses	Higher plants — Land plants	Invertebrates — Terrestrial	Invertebrates — Marine	Fish — Freshwater	Fish — Marine	Amphibians	Reptiles	Birds	Mammals
Crops, livestock, fish																	
Trees, standing vegetation & peat																	
Climate regulation																	
Water supply																	
Hazard regulation																	
Waste breakdown & detoxification																	
Wild species diversity																	
Purification																	
Disease & pest regulation																	
Pollination																	
Meaningful places*																	
Socially valued land & waterscapes*																	

* Note: For the purposes of the Cultural Services chapter (Chapter 16), Cultural services have been combined into 'environmental settings'.

- Over 60% (11/17) of the biodiversity groups assessed play an important role in underpinning the crops, plants, livestock and fish upon which we depend for food.
- Microorganisms, fungi and plants play key roles in provisioning and regulating services.
- Higher plants and animals play key roles in cultural services.

The finding that all UK ecosystem services are sensitive to changes in more than one biodiversity group has important implications for the concept of multifunctional ecosystems and the implementation of an 'ecosystems approach' in the UK. The importance of managing ecosystems to provide multiple services and associated values is becoming increasingly recognised both at an international level (Chan *et al.* 2006; Kareiva *et al.* 2007; Naidoo *et al.* 2008; Norris 2008; Bennett *et al.* 2009; Nelson *et al.* 2009) and in a UK context (Anderson *et al.* 2009). In turn, this recognition is stimulating policy responses to explore how a multifunctional ecosystems approach might work in practice (for example, Natural England's ecosystem pilot projects). The evidence summarised in **Table 4.2** suggests that an important objective of these developments should be the management of UK ecosystems to support biodiversity across a wide range of groups to ensure the provision of a range of ecosystem services. The scientific challenges involved with developing the necessary evidence base are significant, but research programmes are emerging that aim to better understand the functional links between biodiversity and ecosystems services in the context of UK ecosystems (e.g. www.nerc. ac.uk/research/themes/tap/tap-phase2.asp). It will be important for the emerging science in this area to interface appropriately with policy development.

4.5 Biodiversity Status and Trends

4.5.1 The Quality of Monitoring Data in Relation to Ecosystem Services

The quality of biodiversity monitoring data in the UK varies between biodiversity groups. In broad terms, the status and trends data tends to be of a higher quality for biodiversity groups closely associated with the cultural services being assessed by the UK NEA (**Figure 4.3**). To investigate this relationship, the trend information available for each biodiversity group was classified as 'good' (UK-wide data on distribution, abundance and population trends over a 20-year or more time period), 'moderate' (UK-wide data on distribution, but limited data on abundance and population trends due to spatial or temporal coverage), 'patchy' (only localised data available on distribution or trends) or 'poor' (negligible data available on distribution or trends) (details are summarised in **Table 4.3**). The pattern in **Figure 4.3** partly reflects technical difficulties associated with monitoring specific groups associated with provisioning and regulating services, such as microorganisms, and suggests that many long-term monitoring schemes were initiated, at least in part, for cultural reasons. As a result, biodiversity groups associated with provisioning and regulating services are often poorly monitored, hence we have a limited understanding of their status and trends.

4.5.2 Status and Trend Information

The Joint Nature Conservation Committee (JNCC) produces a series of UK Biodiversity Indicators, which includes an assessment of the status and trends of components of biodiversity (JNCC 2010b; **Table 4.4**). In general terms, these indicators show improving or stable trends in species, habitats and protected sites of high conservation priority (indicator groups 3–6) over the last decade, but declining trends among biodiversity groups in the wider environment (indicator groups 1–2). Of the 11 specific indicators in these latter two groups, more than 70% (8/11) have shown declining trends in the recent past.

The JNCC indicators represent only part of the status and trend data available for UK biodiversity. The JNCC's online wildlife statistics database (www.jncc.gov.uk/page-3254) contains more than 7,000 trends from over 4,000 species, while the National Biodiversity Network (NBN) (www.nbn. org.uk/) contains more than 57 million species records. For some biodiversity groups, such as marine plankton, land plants, certain invertebrate groups, fish, birds and mammals, national-scale data on abundance and range exist for a

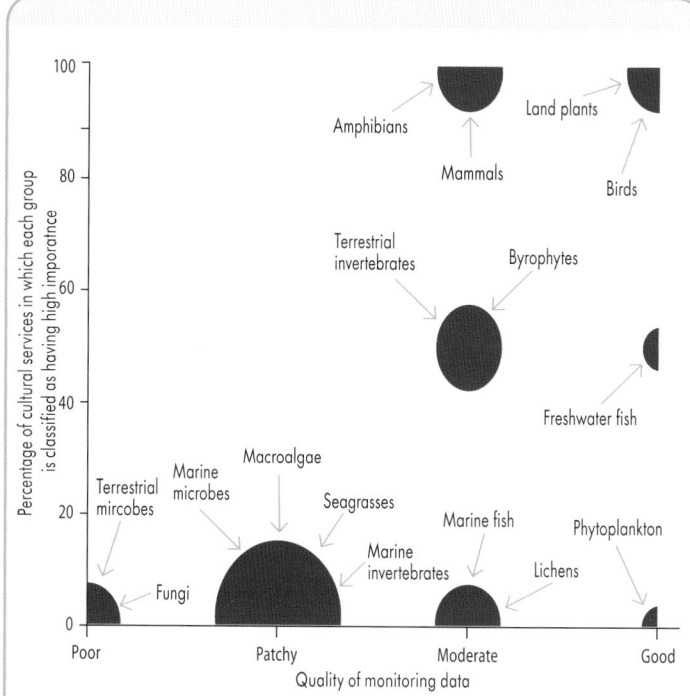

Figure 4.4 The relationship between the quality of monitoring data for each biodiversity group and its role in cultural services. Importance is taken from Table 4.2 in which 'high' importance is coloured maroon. The size of the circle indicates the number of biodiversity groups associated with each point. The relationship can be described by the simple linear model: $y = a+b.x$, in which x takes integer values from 1 (poor) to 4 (good). This model is statistically significant ($R^2_{adj} = 0.30$, $P = 0.016$).

time-series of more than 10–20 years. These datasets show clear patterns of biodiversity change:

- Plankton survey data has documented a northward shift in species diversity in the Atlantic Ocean over the last 20 years (**Figure 4.5a**).
- Atlas data for native land plants show that ranges have, on average, contracted since the 1960s across 1,142 native species.
- Countryside Survey data shows a downward trend in average plant diversity across most habitats between 1978 and 2007 (**Figure 4.5b**), but evidence of increased soil invertebrate abundance in all habitats except arable during the same time period—differences which were largely due to greater mite populations (Emmett et al. 2010). However, the Countryside Survey also indicated a small decrease in soil invertebrate biodiversity with the number of broad invertebrate taxa present in samples generally lower in 2007 than in 1998 (Emmett et al. 2010).
- Results from the Countryside Survey also illustrate improvements to the diversity of freshwater invertebrates in headwater streams across Great Britain (GB) since 1990; however, in lowland ponds, they may have declined.
- The populations of butterfly species that are specialists of semi-natural habitat have more than halved since 1976 (**Figure 4.5c**).
- Marine fish populations and communities have changed significantly since the 1960s, with exploited populations

Table 4.3 Population trends of wild bird species in different habitats. Source: data from the RSPB, BTO and Defra (2010).

Species group (number of species)	Long-term trend	Short-term trend	Key drivers
Breeding birds	**1970–2008**	**1998–2008**	
All species (114)	3%	6%	Multiple and diverse
Seabird species (19)	28%	-5%	Fishery practice and oceanic change
Water and wetland species (26)	1%	9%	Change in agricultural practices
Woodland species (38)	-14%	5%	Change in woodland structure
Farmland species (19)	-47%	-4%	Change in agricultural practices
Urban species (27)	-	11% *	Sympathetic management and food provision
Wintering birds	**1975/1976– 2006/2007**	**1996/1976– 2006/2007**	
All waterbird species (46)	57%	-6%	Site and species protection and management
Wildfowl species (27)	62%	-9%	
Wader species (15)	44%	-5%	

* English trends 1994–2008.

Table 4.4 Status and trends in components of UK biodiversity. The symbols in the cells of the table indicate the direction of trends: declining (↓), increasing (↑) and stable (=). # denotes data is not available. Note: with the long-term change the baseline year varies between categories, see JNCC (2010a) for details. Source: data extracted from JNCC (2010a).

Status and trends in components of biodiversity		Long-term change	Change since 2000
1a. Population trends of selected species (birds)	Breeding farmland birds	↓	↓
	Breeding woodland birds	↓	↑
	Breeding water and wetland birds	=	=
	Breeding seabirds	↑	↓
	Wintering waterbirds	↑	↓
1b. Population trends of selected species (butterflies)	Semi-natural habitat specialists	↓	=
	Generalist butterflies	=	=
1c. Population trends of selected species (bats)		↓	↑
2. Plant diversity	Arable and horticultural land	↑	↑
	Woodland and grassland	↓	↓
	Boundary habitats	↓	↓
3. UK Priority species		#	↑
4. UK Priority habitats		#	=
5. Genetic diversity	Native sheep breeds	#	=
	Native cattle breeds	#	↑
6. Protected areas	Total extent of protected areas	↑	↑
	Condition of Areas/Sites of Special Scientific Interest	#	↑

declining in abundance and some vulnerable species, such as the common skate (*Raja batis*), disappearing entirely from some areas of their range. Since the early 1990s, there is evidence of population recovery in 10–20% of finfish populations (**Figure 4.5d**).

- Among freshwater fish, there is evidence of significant declines in commercially important species, with the number of young European eels (*Anguilla anguilla*) returning to rivers falling to 1% of historical levels since the 1980s.
- Status and trends among wild bird species varies between habitats. Seabird populations have increased by 28% since 1970, but have decreased (-5%) over the last decade; woodland and farmland populations have both declined (-14% and -47% respectively); whereas urban populations have increased (11%) (**Figure 4.5e**).
- Among 37 UK mammal species, 40% appear to be increasing, 12% declining, and 16% stable, with the remaining 32% being considered data deficient (**Figure 4.5f**).

Across biodiversity groups with adequate data, there is clear evidence of significant biodiversity losses (i.e. range contractions and population declines), together with evidence of population increases in certain species and

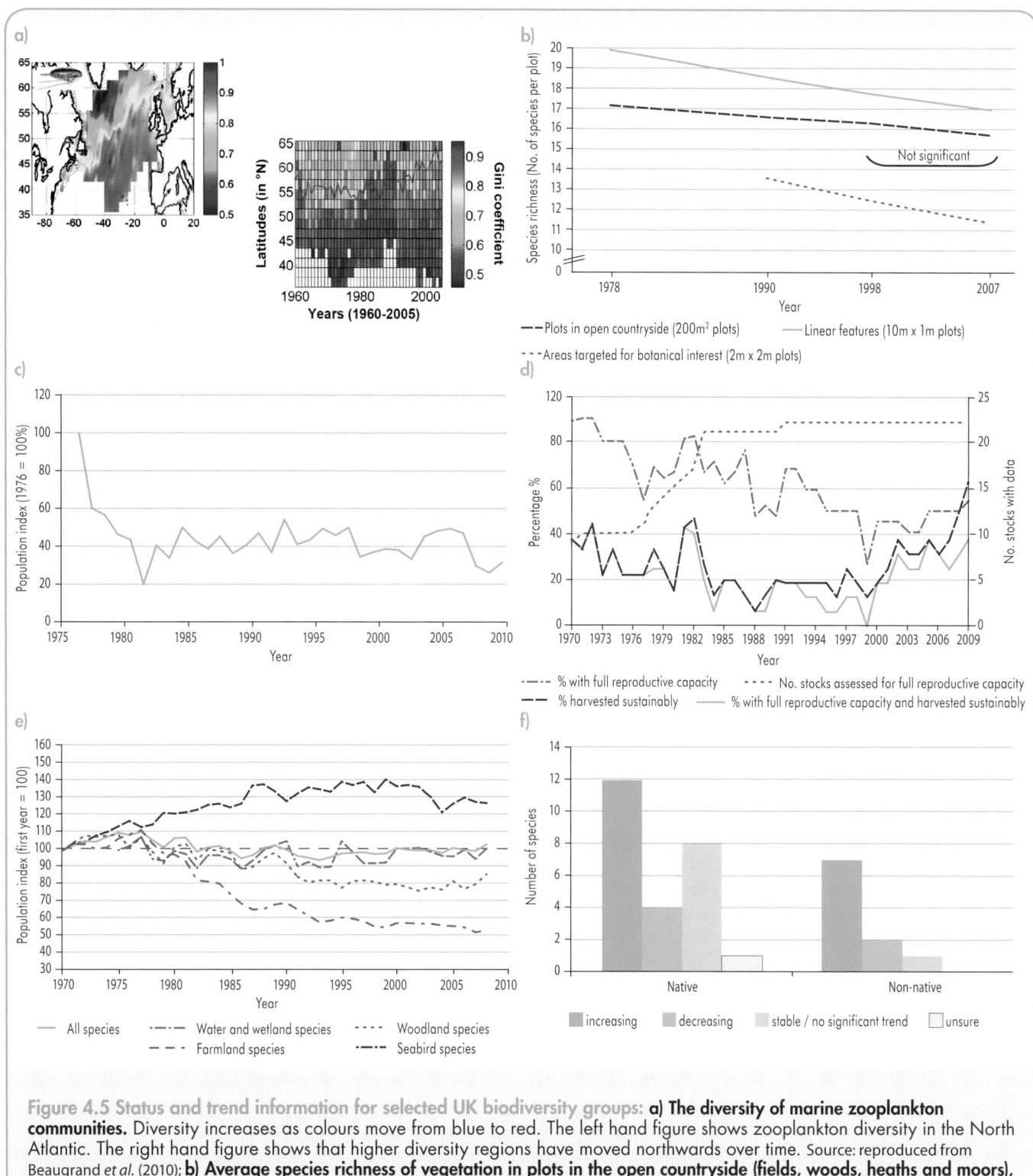

Figure 4.5 Status and trend information for selected UK biodiversity groups: a) The diversity of marine zooplankton communities. Diversity increases as colours move from blue to red. The left hand figure shows zooplankton diversity in the North Atlantic. The right hand figure shows that higher diversity regions have moved northwards over time. Source: reproduced from Beaugrand *et al.* (2010); b) Average species richness of vegetation in plots in the open countryside (fields, woods, heaths and moors), linear features, and areas targeted for their botanical interest in GB between 1978 and 2007. A decline in species richness is apparent in each dataset. Source: reproduced from Carey *et al.* (2008). Countryside Survey data owned by NERC – Centre for Ecology & Hydrology; c) Composite population trend from 1976 to 2009 for 25 species of butterfly which are specialists of semi-natural habitats. This demonstrates that populations have more than halved over the time period. Source: data from Butterfly Conservation, Centre for Ecology and Hydrology and Defra; JNCC (2010c);
d) The sustainability indicator for UK marine fin-fish stocks for 1990 to 2008 showing an improvement in sustainability from the late 1990s. Source: reproduced from Armstrong & Holmes (2010); e) UK 'Quality of Life' indicators: Population trends of wild birds. The graph shows the composite population trends of UK breeding bird species (n=114) with subdivisions showing grouped species' trends for seabirds (n=19), water and wetland birds (n=26), woodland birds (n=38), and farmland birds (n=19). On average, populations of woodland and farmland birds have fallen between 1970 and 2008 by 14% and 47% respectively. Source: data from RSPB, British Trust for Ornithology, JNCC and Defra; f) Population trends in UK wild terrestrial mammal species up to 2007. Sufficient data were available to assess population change for 35 species (n=25 native wild species, n=10 non-native wild species; this represents 53% of all UK terrestrial mammals). The data on the 11 species of native bat included in this summary are for 10 years to 2007; for all other species, trends were assessed over 25 years. Source: data from JNCC (2007).

limited evidence of population recovery in some species of conservation concern. For many other biodiversity groups, particularly some invertebrates, lower plants, fungi and microorganisms, data on status and trends are available for only a few localities and for comparatively short time periods (less than 10 years) in most cases. For these groups, recent status and trends are unclear. Details for each biodiversity group are given in **Appendix 4.1**.

4.5.3 Linking Status and Trend Information to Ecosystem Services

Assessing the impact of trends on ecosystem services, even for cases in which high quality trend information is available, is hampered by a lack of data on associated values and benefits. We illustrate this problem with the role of wild birds in cultural services. About 250 bird species regularly occur in the UK, and we have 40–50 years' worth of data on the distribution and abundance of the majority of these species (**Appendix 4.1**). In broad terms, seabird populations have increased, but have recently begun to decline; water and wetland populations have remained roughly stable, while woodland and farmland populations have declined (the latter to a greater extent); urban species have increased and wintering wader and wildfowl species have shown significant increases, followed by recent declines (**Table 4.3**). Conservation management has improved the status of a number of threatened species over the last 20 years (**Appendix 4.1**). Our assessment of biodiversity and UK ecosystem services suggests that birds play an important role in underpinning cultural services ('meaningful places' and 'socially valued landscapes and waterscapes') in the UK (**Table 4.2**). The impact of the population trends on these ecosystem services is unclear. Population declines in some habitats (e.g. farmland and woodland) might be expected to reduce service delivery (e.g. decreasing the value of socially valued landscapes and waterscapes); whereas increases in urban bird populations and charismatic species of conservation concern might be expected to have the opposite effect (e.g. increasing the value of meaningful places such as gardens or nature reserves). A lack of data on the various values and benefits people derive from wild birds associated with these cultural services, however, makes it impossible to quantify and integrate these potentially opposing effects in order to understand the net impact on each ecosystem service. This illustrates a critically important issue—even for biodiversity groups for which we have comprehensive data on status and trends, a lack of data on associated values and benefits often precludes a quantitative assessment of the impact of biodiversity changes on ecosystem services.

4.6 Drivers of Change

The drivers of change associated with each biodiversity group in the UK are detailed in **Table 4.5**. The drivers we distinguish here broadly follow those used in the MA, with one exception: since most habitat change in the UK occurs because of changes in land use and management, we have used the term 'land use change' to identify habitat changes arising from the way land is used and managed.

The trend information available for each biodiversity group was assessed as 'good' (UK-wide data on distribution, abundance and population trends over a 20-year or more time period), 'moderate' (UK-wide data on distribution, but limited data on abundance and population trends due to spatial or temporal coverage), 'patchy' (only localised data available on distribution or trends) or 'poor' (negligible data available on distribution or trends).

A number of points emerge from this overview:

- Land use change and pollution are considered the major drivers of change across biodiversity groups.
- Exploitation has a significant impact in marine ecosystems, both on target species, but also on non-target species through wider ecosystem changes.
- There is emerging evidence of climate change impacts across most biodiversity groups.
- The impact of invasive species on native biodiversity is considered less important for the majority of biodiversity groups, although there is evidence of impacts across a range of groups.

A comprehensive review of the evidence relating to the drivers of biodiversity change in the UK is beyond the scope of this chapter, but some general points can be made. Land use change is consistently assessed as an important driver of change across a wide range of biodiversity groups based on a large body of consistent, high quality evidence. For example, recent evidence suggests that two-thirds of the populations of 333 farmland species (broad-leaved plants, butterflies, bumblebees, birds and mammals) were threatened by agricultural intensification at the end of the 20th Century (Butler *et al.* 2009). Species with specialist ecological requirements (e.g. food types, nest sites) are more likely to decline in the face of land use change than generalists (Butler *et al.* 2007). There is evidence that land use change has reduced habitat heterogeneity in landscapes (Benton *et al.* 2003), thereby favouring generalist species that are able to reproduce and survive even in simplified landscapes (Smart *et al.* 2006). Biodiversity groups affected by land use change include those associated with estuarine, coastal and marine ecosystems due to the export of sediment and nutrients from land through aquatic ecosystems. Pollution impacts reflect a range of human activities including diffuse pollution from agriculture, and point source pollution from urban ecosystems and air pollution (e.g. acid rain); again, there is a large body of consistent evidence linking these activities with biodiversity changes (Bobbink *et al.* 2010; Maskell *et al.* 2010; Stevens *et al.* 2010). There is also evidence of some recovery from past large-scale pollution issues (Monteith *et al.* 2005). The impact of exploitation on target organisms, particularly in coastal and marine ecosystems, is well-documented (Cook *et al.* 1997). Exploitation also affects non-target organisms through physical and ecological changes to ecosystems (Votier *et al.* 2004).

There is emerging evidence of climate change impacts across a wide range of UK biodiversity groups (**Table 4.5**). The most compelling evidence comes from a northward shift in geographical range margins that have been described in terrestrial (Thomas & Lennon 1999) and marine ecosystems (Beaugrand *et al.* 2009), and from changes in the timing of important ecological events such as flowering in plants and breeding in animals (Thackeray *et al.* 2010). Non-native or invasive species represent a significant and increasing component of UK biodiversity (**Figure 4.5**). For example, recent evidence suggests that 117 non-native freshwater species are established, accounting for 12% of plant, 24% of fish and 54% of amphibian species richness (Keller *et al.* 2009). There is evidence that such species can have significant detrimental impacts on native biodiversity; well-documented examples include the decline of the native white-clawed crayfish (*Austropotamobius pallipes*) (Freeman *et al.* 2010) and water vole (*Arvicola terrestris*) (Rushton *et al.* 2000). There is also growing interest in the impact of non-native species on UK ecosystems (Lecerf *et al.* 2007). Taken together, this evidence suggests that climate change and invasive species are significant current drivers of biodiversity change in the UK, but, to date, these drivers have had a more limited impact than land use change, pollution and exploitation.

In response to these drivers of biodiversity change, there have been a wide range of changes in policy and practice designed to reduce biodiversity losses. There are examples of success in this respect: regulations to control pollution have led to improvements in water quality and the recovery of biodiversity in freshwater ecosystems (Monteith *et al.* 2005); management measures for marine fisheries have resulted in the recovery of some (10–20%) fish populations (**Figure 4.5d**); conservation legislation has promoted recovery among species of conservation concern (Donald *et al.* 2007); and recovery programmes for individual species of conservation concern have been successful (**Appendix 4.1**).

Table 4.5 Drivers of biodiversity change in the UK. This table is a synthesis from the accounts for different biodiversity groups (Appendix 4.1). Importance is colour-coded: high (maroon), medium (beige), low (green), unimportant on the basis of available evidence (blank). The size of the circle in each cell indicates the level of uncertainty. The impact of exploitation includes both the impact of the exploitation itself, but also the indirect consequences of exploitation through physical or ecological changes to the ecosystem.

Biodiversity Group		Trend information	Drivers of biodiversity change				
			Land use change	Climate change	Invasive species	Exploitation (direct and indirect)	Pollutants
Microorganisms	Marine	Patchy	○	○			●
	Terrestrial	Poor	●	○			○
Fungi	Non-lichenised	Poor	●	●	●		●
	Lichens	Moderate	●	○	○		●
Lower plants	Phytoplankton	Good		●	○		○
	Macroalgae	Patchy	○	●	●		●
	Bryophytes	Moderate	●	·	○	○	●
Higher plants	Seagrasses	Patchy	●	●	○	●	●
	Land plants	Good	●	·	○	○	○
Invertebrates	Marine	Patchy	○	○	●	●	●
	Terrestrial	Moderate	●	○			○
Fish	Marine	Moderate		○		●	
	Freshwater	Good	●	○	●	●	●
Amphibians		Moderate	●	●	○		●
Reptiles		Patchy	●	○			
Birds		Good	●	○		●	·
Mammals		Moderate	●	·	○	○	

High importance	Amount of evidence (theory, observations, models) →	Medium importance	Amount of evidence (theory, observations, models) →	Low importance	Amount of evidence (theory, observations, models) →
Level of agreement ↑	(grid of circles)	Level of agreement ↑	(grid of circles)	Level of agreement ↑	(grid of circles)

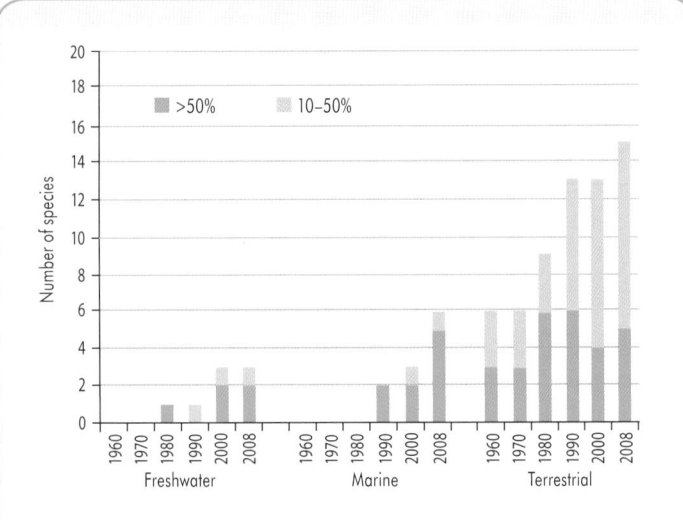

Figure 4.6 Changes in the extent of widely established invasive non-native species in freshwater, marine and terrestrial environments in Great Britain from 1960 to 2008.
Source: data from the Centre for Ecology and Hydrology, British Trust for Ornithology, Marine Biological Association and the National Biodiversity Network Gateway; JNCC (2010d).

Despite these successes, significant biodiversity loss in the UK continues, mirroring recently reported global trends (Butchart *et al.* 2010). Land use change continues to drive the loss of terrestrial biodiversity in the UK despite the significant investment of public funds in schemes, such as agri-environmental management, designed to halt and reverse biodiversity losses. This is occurring because the adverse impacts of land use change on biodiversity have not been adequately removed by policy and practice measures (Butler *et al.* 2007; Butler *et al.* 2009). Addressing these issues requires improved spatial planning mechanisms to ensure that management measures appropriately target the adverse biodiversity impacts of land use change. Other drivers of biodiversity change, such as airborne nitrogen pollution, are difficult to address (Maskell *et al.* 2010). Finally, our understanding of the broad biodiversity impacts of drivers such as climate change and non-native invasive species remains limited, suggesting that further research will be needed on these issues. This need is pressing given that the impacts of climate change and invasive species are likely to increase (**Figure 4.6**). Taken together, this evidence suggests that where the impacts of drivers on biodiversity are relatively well-understood (land use change, pollution and exploitation), the effectiveness of policy and practice responses needs to be improved; whereas for other drivers (climate change and non-native invasive species), our understanding of biodiversity impacts needs to be improved before we can put into place effective responses.

4.7 Conclusions

While there is a clear evidence that biodiversity plays an important functional role in ecosystems and the services they deliver (Balmford & Bond 2005; Hooper *et al.* 2005; MA

2005), the available evidence that enables us to assess the importance of the role of different biodiversity groups in the context of ecosystem services in the UK is less than ideal. As a result, our assessment has been qualitative (low, medium or high) rather than quantitative. Nevertheless, a number of important findings have emerged. It is clear that UK ecosystem services have many important dependencies on biodiversity: all UK ecosystem services are dependent on biodiversity to some extent; more than 60% of the biodiversity groups assessed play an important role in underpinning the crops, plants, livestock and fish upon which we depend for food; and biodiversity is very important in a cultural context (**Table 4.2**). In addition, the finding that all UK ecosystem services are sensitive to changes in more than one biodiversity group is important because it suggests that UK ecosystems will need to support biodiversity across a wide range of groups to ensure the provision of a range of ecosystem services.

The UK has perhaps the most comprehensive data on biodiversity status and trends of any country in the world. These data clearly show that there have been significant range contractions and population declines over the last 40 to 50 years in a number of plant and animal groups; yet conservation efforts for some groups have improved the status of a number of threatened species in recent years (**Appendix 4.1**). Our assessment of drivers of biodiversity change suggests that land use change and pollution have played a major role in terrestrial and some marine ecosystems; whereas exploitation has been important for marine biodiversity groups (**Table 4.5**). There is emerging evidence of climate change impacts, and some evidence of detrimental effects of invasive species. All in all, this evidence shows that human activities in the UK have had significant, detrimental impacts on biodiversity, with important implications for ecosystem services given their dependencies on biodiversity.

Linking biodiversity change with changes in UK ecosystem services is, however, problematic because of the existence of a 'cultural divide' in our knowledge and understanding (**Figure 4.7**). On one side of the divide are biodiversity groups that underpin cultural services. We have shown that the quality of monitoring data on status and trends for a particular biodiversity group is related to its cultural importance (**Figure 4.4**). This means that we have high quality data on status and trends for culturally important biodiversity groups. However, we lack data on changes in cultural services associated with biodiversity change, making it extremely difficult to link the status and trend information to cultural services. We illustrate this problem with a case study on wild bird population trends (Section 4.5.3). On the other side of the cultural divide are provisioning and regulating services. We have high quality data on status and trends for these services (Chapter 14; Chapter 15), but frequently lack high quality monitoring data for key biodiversity groups—microorganisms, fungi and some plants—that underpin these services (**Table 4.2; Table 4.5; Figure 4.4**). This means we have a very limited knowledge of how these important biodiversity groups are changing, what drivers of biodiversity change are involved, and how any changes might affect provisioning and regulating services. Bridging this cultural divide represents

Figure 4.7 The cultural divide in our knowledge of biodiversity and associated ecosystem services. Good quality data are available (✓) on biodiversity associated with cultural services, but limited information (✗) on cultural services. In contrast, good quality data are available (✓) on provisioning and regulating services, but limited information (✗) on associated biodiversity.

Photos: Mackerel by Cory Doctorow*; Water and glass by Stuart Olver†; Wheat © Stocker1970, 2011‡; Cumbrian landscape by HW-Photography¶; Dorset landscape © David Crosbie, 2011‡; Sunset by Gary Tanner†; Microbes by Microbe World†; Phytoplankton by willapalens†; Fly agaric fungus by Dave W. Clarke§; Bluebell wood by Angus Kirk¶; Honeybee (Apis mellifera) © Mirek Srb, 2011‡; Golden plover (Pluvialis apricaria) ©Leksele, 2011‡; Bluebell wood by Angus Kirk¶. Source: * available under a Creative Commons (CC) Attribution license Attribution-ShareAlike license; † available under a CC Attribution-NonCommercial-ShareAlike license; ‡ used under license of Shutterstock.com; ¶ available under a CC Attribution-NonCommercial-NoDerivs license; § available under a CC Attribution-NonCommercial license.

perhaps the most important research and policy challenge relating to biodiversity in the UK.

To address this challenge, we need a shift in emphasis towards a more functional understanding of biodiversity in ecosystem dynamics (Nicholson *et al.* 2009). We need to: 1) *improve our understanding of how different biodiversity groups underpin ecosystem services*; 2) *identify key indicator groups, changes in which have an important impact on ecosystem services*; and 3) *develop a comprehensive, integrated monitoring programme for biodiversity in the UK around these indicator groups*. In making this shift, we need to recognise that the type of functional links between biodiversity and ecosystem services might vary between types of ecosystem service (Diaz *et al.* 2007). This has important implications for the way biodiversity is defined. Biodiversity groups that are currently recognised in a UK context largely reflect monitoring programmes developed around individual species within particular taxonomic groups. Improving our functional understanding of UK biodiversity will require a shift towards a more functionally relevant definition of biodiversity (Feest *et al.* 2009.; Schleuter *et al.* 2010; Vandewalle *et al* 2010.; Diaz *et al.* 2007). Despite the inevitable challenges involved, by adopting a more functional perspective we will be in a much stronger position to understand how biodiversity change in the UK impacts upon our ecosystem services in the face of future environmental and social change.

References

Anderson, B.J., Armsworth, P.R., Eigenbrod, F., Thomas, C.D., Gillings, S., Heinemeyer, A., Roy, D.B. & Gaston, K.J. (2009) Spatial covariance between biodiversity and other ecosystem service priorities. *Journal Of Applied Ecology*, **46**, 888–896.

Armstrong, M. & Holmes, I. (2010). An indicator of sustainability for marine fin-fish stocks around the UK: 1990–2008. CEFAS, Lowestoft.

Balmford, A. & Bond, W. (2005) Trends in the state of nature and their implications for human well-being. *Ecology Letters*, **8**, 1218–1234.

Balmford, A., Green, R.E. & Jenkins, M. (2003) Measuring the changing state of nature. *Trends In Ecology & Evolution*, **18**, 326–330.

Balmford, A., Rodrigues, A., Walpole, M., Ten Brink, P., Kettunen, M., Braat, L. & De Groot, R. (2008) Review of the economics of biodiversity loss: scoping the science. Cambridge, UK: European Commission (contract: ENV/070307/2007/486089/ETU/B2).

Beaugrand, G., Luczak, C. & Edwards, M. (2009) Rapid biogeographical plankton shifts in the North Atlantic Ocean. *Global Change Biology*, **15**, 1790–1803.

Beaugrand, G., Edwards, M. & Legendre, L. (2010) Marine biodiversity, ecosystem functioning and the carbon cycle. *Proceedings of the National Academy of Sciences USA*, **107**, 10120–10124.

Benayas, J.M.R., Newton, A.C., Diaz, A. & Bullock, J.M. (2009) Enhancement of Biodiversity and Ecosystem Services by Ecological Restoration: A Meta-Analysis. *Science*, **325**, 1121–1124.

Bennett, E.M., Peterson, G.D. & Gordon, L.J. (2009) Understanding relationships among multiple ecosystem services. *Ecology Letters*, **12**, 1394–1404.

Benton, T.G., Vickery, J.A., Wilson, J.D., (2003) Farmland biodiversity: is habitat heterogeneity the key? *Trends In Ecology & Evolution*, **18**, 182–188.

Biesmeijer, J.C., Roberts, S.P.M., Reemer, M., Ohlemuller, R., Edwards, M., Peeters, T., Schaffers, A.P., Potts, S.G., Kleukers, R.,

Thomas, C.D., Settele, J. & Kunin, W.E. (2006) Parallel declines in pollinators and insect-pollinated plants in Britain and the Netherlands. *Science*, **313**, 351–354.

Bobbink, R., Hicks, K., Galloway, J., Spranger, T., Alkemade, R., Ashmore, M., Bustamante, M., Cinderby, S., Davidson, E., Dentener, F., Emmett, B., Erisman, J.W., Fenn, M., Gilliam, F., Nordin, A., Pardo, L., De Vries, W. (2010) Global assessment of nitrogen deposition effects on terrestrial plant diversity: a synthesis. *Ecological Applications*, **20**, 30–59.

Butchart, S.H.M., Walpole, M., Collen, B., van Strien, A., Scharlemann, J.P.W., Almond, R.E.A., Baillie, J.E.M., Bomhard, B., Brown, C., Bruno, J., Carpenter, K.E., Carr, G.M., Chanson, J., Chenery, A.M., Csirke, J., Davidson, N.C., Dentener, F., Foster, M., Galli, A., Galloway, J.N., Genovesi, P., Gregory, R.D., Hockings, M., Kapos, V., Lamarque, J.F., Leverington, F., Loh, J., McGeoch, M.A., McRae, L., Minasyan, A., Morcillo, M.H., Oldfield, T.E.E., Pauly, D., Quader, S., Revenga, C., Sauer, J.R., Skolnik, B., Spear, D., Stanwell-Smith, D., Stuart, S.N., Symes, A., Tierney, M., Tyrrell, T.D., Vie, J.C. & Watson, R. (2010) Global Biodiversity: Indicators of Recent Declines. *Science*, **328**, 1164–1168.

Butler, S.J., Brooks, D., Feber, R.E., Storkey, J., Vickery, J.A. & Norris, K. (2009) A cross-taxonomic index for quantifying the health of farmland biodiversity. *Journal of Applied Ecology*, **46**(6), 1154–1162.

Butler, S.J., Vickery, J.A. & Norris, K. (2007) Farmland biodiversity and the footprint of agriculture. *Science*, **315**, 381–384.

Carey, P.D., Wallis, S., Emmett, B.A., Maskell, L.C., Murphy, J., Norton, L.R., Simpson, I.C., Smart, S.M. (2008) Countryside Survey: UK Headline Messages from 2007. NERC/Centre for Ecology & Hydrology, 30pp. (CEH Project Number: C03259).

Chan, K.M.A., Shaw, M.R., Cameron, D.R., Underwood, E.C. & Daily, G.C. (2006) Conservation planning for ecosystem services. *Plos Biology*, **4**, 2138–2152.

Cook, R.M., Sinclair, A. & Stefansson, G. (1997) Potential collapse of North Sea cod stocks. *Nature*, **385**, 521–522.

Diaz, S., Lavorel, S., de Bello, F., Quetier, F., Grigulis, K. & Robson, M. (2007) Incorporating plant functional diversity effects in ecosystem service assessments. *Proceedings Of The National Academy Of Sciences Of The United States Of America*, **104**, 20684–20689.

Donald, P.F., Sanderson, F.J., Burfield, I.J., Bierman, S.M., Gregory, R.D. & Waliczky, Z. (2007) International conservation policy delivers benefits for birds in Europe. *Science*, **317**, 810–813.

EASAC (European Academies Science Advisory Council) (2009) Ecosystem services and biodiversity in Europe. European Academies Science Advisory Council.

Emmett, B.A., Reynolds, B., Chamberlain, P.M., Rowe, E., Spurgeon, D., Brittain, S.A., Frogbrook, Z., Hughes, S., Lawlor, A.J., Poskitt, J., Potter, E., Robinson, D.A., Scott, A., Wood, C., Woods, C. 2010 Countryside Survey: Soils Report from 2007. Technical Report No. 9/07 NERC/Centre for Ecology & Hydrology 192pp. (CEH Project Number: C03259).

Feest, A., Aldred, T.D. & Jedamzik, K. (2009) Biodiversity quality: A paradigm for biodiversity. *Ecological Indicators*, **10**, 1077–1082.

Freeman, M.A., Turnbull, J.F., Yeomans, W.E. & Bean, C.W. (2010) Prospects for management strategies of invasive crayfish populations with an emphasis on biological control. *Aquatic Conservation-Marine and Freshwater Ecosystems*, **20**, 211–223.

Green, R.E., Balmford, A., Crane, P.R., Mace, G.M., Reynolds, J.D. & Turner, R.K. (2005) A framework for improved monitoring of biodiversity: Responses to the World Summit on Sustainable Development. *Conservation Biology*, **19**, 56–65.

Gregory, R.D., Noble, D.G. & Custance, J. (2004) The state of play of farmland birds: population trends and conservation status of lowland farmland birds in the United Kingdom. *Ibis*, **146**, 1–13.

Hooper, D.U., Chapin, F.S., Ewel, J.J., Hector, A., Inchausti, P., Lavorel, S., Lawton, J.H., Lodge, D.M., Loreau, M., Naeem, S., Schmid, B., Setala, H., Symstad, A.J., Vandermeer, J. & Wardle, D.A. (2005) Effects of biodiversity on ecosystem functioning: A consensus of current knowledge. *Ecological Monographs*, **75**, 3–35.

JNCC (Joint Nature Conservation Committee) (2007) Results of the Tracking Mammals Partnership (TMP) Surveillance [online] Available at: <http://www.jncc.gov.uk/page-3744> [Accessed 16.03.11].

JNCC (Joint Nature Conservation Committee) (2010a) UK Biodiversity Indicators in Your Pocket. Overview of assessment of change for all indicators. [online] Available at: <http://www.jncc.gov.uk/page-4231> [Accessed 16.03.11].

JNCC (Joint Nature Conservation Committee) (2010b) UK Biodiversity Indicators. Published by Defra on behalf of the UK Biodiversity Partnership. [online] Available at: <www.jncc.gov.uk/page-1824> [Accessed 16.03.11].

JNCC (Joint Nature Conservation Committee) (2010c) Trends in populations of selected species (butterflies). [online] Available at: <www.jncc.gov.uk/page-4236> [Accessed 16.03.11].

JNCC (Joint Nature Conservation Committee) (2010d) Inpact of invasive species. [online] Available at: <http://www.jncc.gov.uk/page-4246> [Accessed 16.03.11].

Kareiva, P., Watts, S., McDonald, R. & Boucher, T. (2007) Domesticated nature: Shaping landscapes and ecosystems for human welfare. *Science*, **316**, 1866–1869.

Keesing, F., Holt, R.D. & Ostfeld, R.S. (2006) Effects of species diversity on disease risk. *Ecology Letters*, **9**, 485–498.

Keller, R.P., Ermgassen, P. & Aldridge, D.C. (2009) Vectors and Timing of Freshwater Invasions in Great Britain. *Conservation Biology*, **23**, 1526–1534.

Klein, A.M., Vaissiere, B.E., Cane, J.H., Steffan-Dewenter, I., Cunningham, S.A., Kremen, C. & Tscharntke, T. (2007) Importance of pollinators in changing landscapes for world crops. *Proceedings Of The Royal Society B-Biological Sciences*, **274**, 303–313.

Kremen, C. (2005) Managing ecosystem services: what do we need to know about their ecology? *Ecology Letters*, **8**, 468–479.

Kremen, C., Williams, N.M. & Thorp, R.W. (2002) Crop pollination from native bees at risk from agricultural intensification. *Proceedings Of The National Academy Of Sciences Of The United States Of America*, **99**, 16812–16816.

Lecerf, A., Patfield, D., Boiche, A., Riipinen, M.P., Chauvet, E. & Dobson, M. (2007) Stream ecosystems respond to riparian invasion by Japanese knotweed (Fallopia japonica). *Canadian Journal of Fisheries and Aquatic Sciences*, **64**, 1273–1283.

Loreau, M., Mouquet, N. & Gonzalez, A. (2003) Biodiversity as spatial insurance in heterogeneous landscapes. *Proceedings Of The National Academy Of Sciences Of The United States Of America*, **100**, 12765–12770.

Maskell, L.C., Smart, S.M., Bullock, J.M., Thompson, K. & Stevens, C.J. (2010) Nitrogen deposition causes widespread loss of species richness in British habitats. *Global Change Biology*, **16**, 671–679.

MA (Millenium Ecosystem Assessment) (2005) Ecosystems and Human Well-Being: Synthesis. World Resources Institute, pp. 155. Island Press, Washington D.C.

Monteith, D.T., Hildrew, A.G., Flower, R.J., Raven, P.J., Beaumont, W.R.B., Collen, P., Kreiser, A.M., Shilland, E.M. & Winterbottom, J.H. (2005) Biological responses to the chemical recovery of acidified fresh waters in the UK. *Environmental Pollution*, **137**, 83–101.

Naidoo, R., Balmford, A., Costanza, R., Fisher, B., Green, R.E., Lehner, B., Malcolm, T.R. & Ricketts, T.H. (2008) Global mapping of ecosystem services and conservation priorities. *Proceedings Of The National Academy Of Sciences Of The United States Of America*, **105**, 9495–9500.

Nelson, E., Mendoza, G., Regetz, J., Polasky, S., Tallis, H., Cameron, D.R., Chan, K.M.A., Daily, G.C., Goldstein, J., Kareiva, P.M., Lonsdorf, E., Naidoo, R., Ricketts, T.H. & Shaw, M.R. (2009) Modeling multiple ecosystem services, biodiversity conservation, commodity production, and tradeoffs at landscape scales. *Frontiers In Ecology And The Environment*, **7**, 4–11.

Nicholson, E., Mace, G.M., Armsworth, P.R., Atkinson, G., Buckle, S., Clements, T., Ewers, R.M., Fa, J.E., Gardner, T.A., Gibbons, J., Grenyer, R., Metcalfe, R., Mourato, S., Muuls, M., Osborn, D., Reuman, D.C., Watson, C. & Milner-Gulland, E.J. (2009) Priority research areas for ecosystem services in a changing world. *Journal Of Applied Ecology*, **46**, 1139–1144.

Norris, K. (2008) Agriculture and biodiversity – opportunity knocks. *Conservation Letters*, **1**, 2–11.

Palumbi, S.R., Sandifer, P.A., Allan, J.D., Beck, M.W., Fautin, D.G., Fogarty, M.J., Halpern, B.S., Incze, L.S., Leong, J.A., Norse, E., Stachowicz, J.J. & Wall, D.H. (2009) Managing for ocean biodiversity to sustain marine ecosystem services. *Frontiers In Ecology And The Environment*, **7**, 204–211.

Raffaelli, D.G. (2006) Biodiversity and ecosystem functioning: issues of scale and trophic complexity. *Marine Ecology-Progress Series*, **311**, 285–294.

Rushton, S.P., Barreto, G.W., Cormack, R.M., Macdonald, D.W. & Fuller, R. (2000) Modelling the effects of mink and habitat fragmentation on the water vole. *Journal Of Applied Ecology*, **37**, 475–490.

Schleuter, D., Daufresne, M., Massol, F. & Argillier, C. (2010) A user's guide to functional diversity indices. *Ecological Monographs*, **80**, 469–484.

Smart, S.M., Thompson, K., Marrs, R.H., Le Duc, M.G., Maskell, L.C. & Firbank, L.G. (2006) Biotic homogenization and changes in species diversity across human-modified ecosystems. *Proceedings Of The Royal Society B-Biological Sciences*, **273**, 2659–2665.

Srivastava, D.S., Vellend, M. (2005) Biodiversity-ecosystem function research: Is it relevant to conservation? *Annual Review Of Ecology Evolution And Systematics*, **36**, 267–294.

Stevens, C.J., Dupre, C., Dorland, E., Gaudnik, C., Gowing, D.J.G., Bleeker, A., Diekmann, M., Alard, D., Bobbink, R., Fowler, D., Corcket, E., Mountford, J.O., Vandvik, V., Aarrestad, P.A., Muller, S. & Dise, N.B. (2010) Nitrogen deposition threatens species richness of grasslands across Europe. *Environmental Pollution*, **158**, 2940–2945.

TEEB (The Economics of Ecosystems and Biodiversty) (2008) The Economics of Ecosystems and Biodiversity: An interim report. European Commission, Brussels.

TEEB (The Economics of Ecosystems and Biodiversty) (2009) The Economics of Ecosystems and Biodiversity for National and International Policy Makers – Summary: Responding to the Value of Nature. European Commission, Brussels.

Thackeray, S.J., Sparks, T.H., Frederiksen, M., Burthe, S., Bacon, P.J., Bell, J.R., Botham, M.S., Brereton, T.M., Bright, P.W., Carvalho, L., Clutton-Brock, T., Dawson, A., Edwards, M., Elliott, J.M., Harrington, R., Johns, D., Jones, I.D., Jones, J.T., Leech, D.I., Roy, D.B., Scott, W.A., Smith, M., Smithers, R.J., Winfield, I.J. & Wanless, S. (2010) Trophic level asynchrony in rates of phenological change for marine, freshwater and terrestrial environments. *Global Change Biology*, **16**, 3304–3313.

Thomas, C.D. & Lennon, J.J. (1999) Birds extend their ranges northwards. *Nature*, **399**, 213–213.

Vandewalle, M., de Bello, F., Berg, M.P., Bolger, T., Doledec, S., Dubs, F., Feld, C.K., Harrington, R., Harrison, P.A., Lavorel, S., da Silva, P.M., Moretti, M., Niemela, J., Santos, P., Sattler, T., Sousa, J.P., Sykes, M.T., Vanbergen, A.J. & Woodcock, B.A. (2010) Functional traits as indicators of biodiversity response to land use changes across ecosystems and organisms. *Biodiversity And Conservation*, **19**, 2921–2947.

Votier, S.C., Furness, R.W., Bearhop, S., Crane, J.E., Caldow, R.W.G., Catry, P., Ensor, K., Hamer, K.C., Hudson, A.V., Kalmbach, E., Klomp, N.I., Pfeiffer, S., Phillips, R.A., Prieto, I. & Thompson, D.R. (2004) Changes in fisheries discard rates and seabird communities. *Nature*, **427**, 727–730.

Worm, B., Barbier, E.B., Beaumont, N., Duffy, J.E., Folke, C., Halpern, B.S., Jackson, J.B.C., Lotze, H.K., Micheli, F., Palumbi, S.R., Sala, E., Selkoe, K.A., Stachowicz, J.J. & Watson, R. (2006) Impacts of biodiversity loss on ocean ecosystem services. *Science*, **314**, 787–790.

Zhang, W., Ricketts, T.H., Kremen, C., Carney, K. & Swinton, S.M. (2007) Ecosystem services and dis-services to agriculture. *Ecological Economics*, **64**, 253–260.

Appendix 4.1

This section contains accounts for each biodiversity group written by experts from the UK's scientific community. Each account consists of: a broad definition of the group; a brief description of diversity in the UK; an outline of the group's role in ecosystem services; an overview of the available status and trends information; a description of the important drivers of biodiversity change; a view on future prospects; and a short list of key reference material.

A.4.1.1 Microorganisms

Authors: Mark Bailey, Sarah Turner, Paul Somerfield and Jack Gilbert

Taxa included in this group: Microorganisms range in size from 1–500 μm. Molecular systematics has revealed three major domains, the Bacteria and Archaea (Woese *et al.* 1990), formerly grouped as the prokaryotes, and the single-celled Eukaryotes. As a group they are genetically more diverse than all meso- and macro-fauna.

Diversity in the UK: Bacteria are the best described group of microorganisms. They have existed for around 3.5 billion years and represent the most diverse domain of life on Earth. Our understanding of bacterial biodiversity has been revolutionised by the use of molecular tools. More than 70% of bacterial taxa are known only from their DNA sequences and include taxa that are able to live in every known habitat on Earth, including plants and animals, soil, surface and subsurface water, deep in subsurface rocks and under extreme conditions of pH and temperature. The extent of microbial diversity has still to be fully described and, as such, we have little or no understanding of biogeographic or temporal trends either globally or at the UK-scale.

Roles in ecosystem services: Microbes constitute a major portion of the biodiversity and biomass in soils and water and, as a consequence, play an essential role in maintaining soil processes which ultimately regulate the functioning of ecosystems and the biogeochemical cycling of greenhouse gases (e.g. carbon in peat bogs). They are crucial to life, are central to all biogeochemical processes, and exist in spectacular numbers (Torsvik *et al.* 2002; Curtis & Sloan 2005). Yet the precise roles of the majority of microorganisms in ecosystem service delivery remain largely unknown (Raes & Bork 2008; Bell *et al.* 2005; Bardgett *et al.* 2005). It is well-documented that microorganisms recycle organic matter and minerals (carbon, nitrogen, sulphur, phosphorus etc.), purify water, biodegrade pollutants and colonise or infect plants and animals affecting their health status and susceptibility (DeLong 2009; Van der Heijden *et al.* 1998; Fierer & Jackson 2006). Only microbes possess the genes to fix essential nitrogen, and only microbes produce and oxidise biological methane (Battistuzzi *et al.* 2004). Microbial pathogens pose a direct threat to the health of humans and their domesticated animals and crops and hence directly affect food security. Less obviously, pathogens are important drivers of wildlife population dynamics and, as such, influence the net biodiversity of the UK. Microorganisms also provide vital services for food processing/production, for example, breaking down cellulose in the guts of ungulates, being of use in dairy products such as yoghurt and cheese, providing yeasts for the baking and brewing industries, etc.

Status and trends: Over the past three decades, our understanding of microbial biodiversity has been revolutionised by the use of molecular tools to characterise uncultivable communities and sequence entire genomes. For example, studies of the phylogeny of ribosomal gene and internal transcribed sequences (ITS), and other genes, have refined the Tree of Life, providing better insight into evolution and adaptation. Despite these advances, few data are available to determine what threats, if any, are posed to microbial populations.

Drivers of change: At present, we probably know too little to accurately relate microbial community structure to large-scale drivers (Raes & Bork 2008; Fierer & Jackson 2006; Fuhrman *et al.* 2006; Fuhrman 2009). Much is being revealed about the structure of communities (at a high taxonomic level) found in different functional habitats such as polluted streams, agricultural soils, marine waters, etc. (Heemsbergen *et al.* 2004; Pommier *et al.* 2007). Reliable data are emerging, for example, on the impacts of land use change and fertiliser inputs on soil microbial diversity (Bell *et al.* 2005; Fierer & Jackson 2006), or the influence of acidification and temperature on marine microbiota (DeLong 2009; Fuhrman 2009). But we know little of the impacts of these drivers on function and sustainability, or how the structure and functioning of communities is affected by climate or environmental change.

Prospects: This is an area where technological advances are increasing knowledge on a daily basis, and where step changes in understanding ecosystem processes are coming of age. To date, much of the research into microbial ecology has focused on describing diversity and identifying patterns in relation to environmental parameters. More recently, however, the integration of high through-put sequencing approaches with *in situ* process measures is revealing how microbial community structure affects or responds to aspects of human, animal and plant health (including susceptibility to disease), environmental quality, nutrient cycling and status. Because of their short lifecycle, microbes have the potential to act as indicators of immediate and short-term change, and should lead us towards new approaches to manage health and environmental risks.

References

Bardgett, R.D., Bowman, W.D., Kaufmann, R. & Schmidt, S.K. (2005) A temporal approach to linking aboveground and belowground ecology. *Trends in Ecology and Evolution*, **20**, 634–641.

Battistuzzi, F.U., Feijao, A. & Hedges, S.B. (2004) A genomic timescale of prokaryote evolution: insights into the origin of methanogenesis, phototrophy, and the colonization of land. BMC Evolution Biology, **4**, 44–51.

Bell, T., Newman, J.A., Silverman, B.W., Turner, S.L. & Lilley, A.K. (2005) The contribution of species richness and composition to bacterial services. *Nature*, **436**, 1157–1160.

Curtis, T.P. & Sloan, W.T. (2005) Exploring microbial diversity – A vast below. *Science*, **309**, 1331–1333.

DeLong, E.F. (2009) The Microbial ocean from genomes to biomes. *Nature*, **459**, 200–206.

Fierer, N. & Jackson, R. (2006) The diversity and biogeography of soil Bacterial communities. *PNAS*, **103**, 626–631.

Fuhrman, J.A. (2009) Microbial community structure and its functional implications. *Nature*, **459**, 193–199.

Fuhrman, J.A., Hewson, I., Schwalbach, M.S., Steele, J.A., Brown, M.V. & Naeem, S. (2006) Annually reoccuring bacterial communities are predictable from ocean conditions. *PNAS*, **103**, 13104–13109.

Heemsbergen, D.A., Berg, M.P., Loreau, M., van Hal, J.R., Faber, J.H. & Verhoef, H.A. (2004) Biodiversity effects on soil processes explained by interspecific functional dissimilarity. *Science,* **306**, 1019–1020.

Pommier, T., Canbäck, B., Riemann, L., Boström, K.H., Simu, K., Lundberg, P., Tunlid, A. & Hagström, Å. (2007) Global patterns of diversity and community structure in marine bacterioplankton. *Molecular Ecology*, **16**, 867–880.

Raes, J. & Bork, P. (2008) Molecular eco-systems biology: towards an understanding of community function. *Nature Reviews Microbiology*, **6**, 693–699.

Torsvik, V., Øvreås, L. & Thingstad, T.F. (2002) Prokaryotic diversity—magnitude, dynamics, and controlling factors. *Science*, **296**, 1064–1066.

Van der Heijden, M.G.A., Kilronomos, J.N., Ursic, M., Moutoglis, P., Streitwolf-Engel, R., Boller, T., Wiemken, A. & Sanders, I.A. (1998) Mycorrhizal fungal diversity determines plant biodiversity, ecosystem variability and productivity. *Nature*, **396**, 72–75.

Woese, C.R., Kandler, O. & Wheelis, M.L. (1990) Towards a natural system of organisms: proposal for the domains Archaea, Bacteria, and Eucarya. PNAS, **87**, 12– 21.

A.4.1.2 Fungi and Lichens

Non-lichenised fungi

Author: Stephan Helfer

Taxa included in this group: This group includes fungi with the exception of lichenised species, which are dealt with separately below. Although they are parts of other lineages, for this treatment 'fungi' includes Mycetozoan (e.g. Myxomycota) and Heterokontophytan (e.g. Oomycota) species. Fungi are eukaryotic, heterotrophic organisms, and obtain their nutrients by absorption. They reproduce by sexual or asexual spores. Most fungi have a thallus composed of hyphae that elongate by tip growth.

Diversity in the UK: There are approximately 12,000 species of fungi known in Britain (Hawksworth 1991), which represents approximately 1% of global, and possibly 20–30% of European, diversity. They range from single-cell yeasts or purely soil-inhabiting asexual organisms, such as the Glomeromycota, to mutualistic, saprobic or parasitic macromycetes with prominent fruiting bodies, commonly known as 'mushrooms'. Many species are in mycorrhizal associations with higher plants; other species are obligate or necrotrophic plant or animal parasites, or litter decomposers. While some of the fungi, notably sand dune fungi, waxcaps and tooth fungi, have received considerable attention from conservation biologists, the majority of fungi have not been assessed. Conservation for sand dune fungi, waxcaps and tooth fungi is well-established. However, while it has been on the agenda for some time, conservation for fungi in general has only been pursued systematically since the 1990s in GB. Currently, there are 76 priority species of non-lichenised fungi in the JNCC list of UK Biodiversity Action Plan's priority species, 10 of which are micromycetes (Anon 2007).

Roles in ecosystem services: Many crop plants have mycorrhizal associations with fungi (Sawers *et al.* 2008) and benefit greatly from this arrangement with an estimated 100–900% biomass added compared with non-mycorrhizal controls in nutrient-poor soils. This is equally the case for wild plants and some groups of invertebrates

(Bärlocher 1985). Conversely, parasitic fungi cause serious losses in crops (around 10–15% pre-harvest loss) and wild plants (e.g. *Phytophthora* species), and can have devastating effects on wild fauna (e.g. chytrids attacking amphibians). Forest and amenity trees are equally impacted by both sides of the fungal spectrum (e.g. ectomycorrhizal fungi versus Dutch Elm Disease). Common wood-rotting fungi produce high levels of chlorinated aromatics, having a direct impact on pollution and climate regulation (Jong *et al.* 1994). Furthermore, in conjunction with methanogens, fungi in the guts of ruminants are responsible for most of the biogenic production of greenhouse gases (Moss *et al.* 2000). The mycelium of soil fungi is responsible for soil water absorption and retention capacity (Rillig *et al.* 2010). However, overall effects on water quantity are poorly understood. Being capable of degrading lignin, fungi are responsible for the majority of plant litter breakdown and nutrient recycling (Steffen *et al.* 2007). They also assist soil invertebrates in the digestion of plant litter (Douglas 2009). Moreover, fungi are used in the detoxification of oil spills, spoil hills (bings) and even radioactive and other hazardous waste.

Status and trends: While many new species have been added to the UK fungi Red Data List since 1992, and many have increased their rating of vulnerability (69 more extinctions and 21 more Critically Endangered; e.g. *Puccinia scirpi*), some species have had their threat status lessened (7 species no longer Extinct and 24 less Critically Endangered; e.g. *Xeromphalina picta*) (Evans 2007; **Figure A.4.1.2.1**). With this in mind, a general trend for fungi is currently impossible to establish. This is because most, if not all data are deficient, and many fungi 'turn up' or 'disappear' unexpectedly, whereas the mycelium is present all the time.

Drivers of change: The main threats to fungi are pollution, and agricultural and forestry management practices, in particular, nitrogen input and pesticide use, but also the choice of tree species in forest plantations. Land use changes, especially road-building and the development of housing, also threaten species. Conversely, some of these threats have increased the opportunities for fungi.

Prospects: There is little evidence to suggest an overall threat to fungal biodiversity in GB. As with lichens (see A.4.1.2), generally, fungi show a loss of 'northern' species in southern GB and a gain in 'southern' species, coupled with a change in fruiting phenology (Kauserud *et al.* 2010).

References

Anon (2007) JNCC UK Biodiversity Action Plan. UK List of Priority Species and Habitats. [online] Available at: <http://www.ukbap.org.uk/PrioritySpecies.aspx?group=3> [Accessed 07.02.11].

Bärlocher, F. (1985) The role of fungi in the nutrition of stream invertebrates. *Botanical Journal of the Linnean Society*, **91**, 83–94.

Douglas, A.E. (2009) The microbial dimension in insect nutritional ecology. *Functional Ecology*, **23**, 38–47.

Evans, S. (2007) Preliminary Assessment: The red data list of threatened British fungi. [online] Available at: <http://www.fieldmycology.net/Download/RDL_of_Threatened_British_Fungi.pdf> [Accessed 07.02.11].

Hawksworth, D.L. (1991) The fungal dimension of biodiversity: magnitude, significance, and conservation. *Mycological Research* **95**, 641–655.

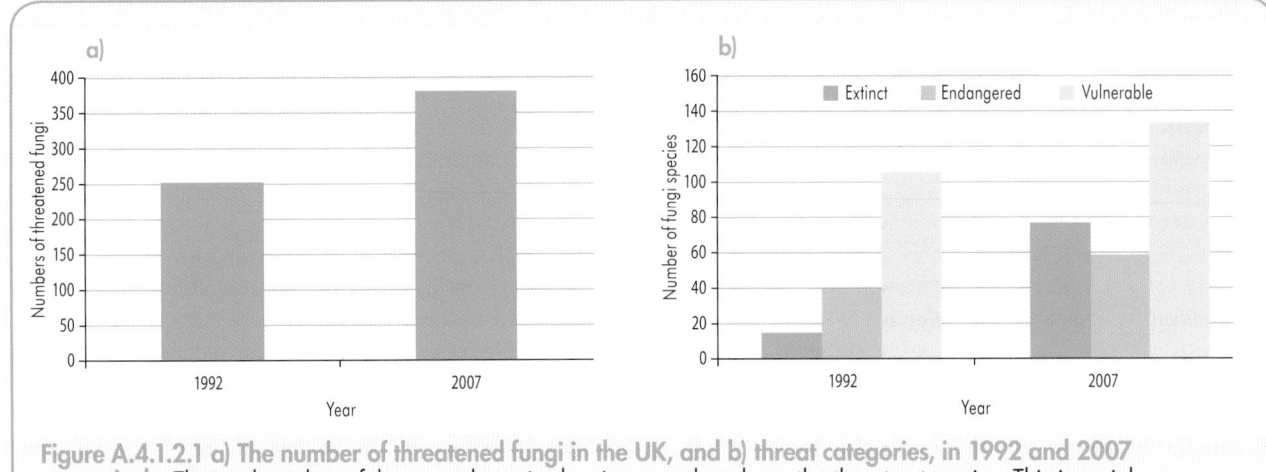

Figure A.4.1.2.1 a) The number of threatened fungi in the UK, and b) threat categories, in 1992 and 2007 respectively. The total number of threatened species has increased, as have the threat categories. This is mainly attributable to greater data availability and does not necessarily indicate an increase in threat. Source: data from Evans (2007).

Jong, E.D.E., Field, J.A.& Spinnler, H.E. (1994) Significant Biogenesis of Chlorinated Aromatics by Fungi in Natural Environments. *Applied and Environmental Microbiology*, **60**, 264–270.

Kauserud, H., Heegaard, E., Semenov, M.A., Boddy, L., Halvorsen, R., Stige, L.C., Sparks, T.H., Gange, A.C., Stenseth, N.C. (2010) Climate change and spring-fruiting fungi. *Proceedings of the Royal Society*, B. **277**, 1169-1177.

Moss, A.R., Jouany, J.P. & Newbold, J. (2000) Methane production by ruminants: its contribution to global warming. *Animal Research*, **49**, 231–253.

Rillig, M.C., Mardatin, N.F., Leifheit, E.F. & Antunes, P.M. (2010) Mycelium of arbuscular mycorrhizal fungi increases soil water repellency and is sufficient to maintain water-stable soil aggregates. *Soil Biology and Biochemistry*, **42**, 1189–1191.

Sawers, R.J.H., Gutjahr, C. & Paszkowski, U. (2008) Cereal mycorrhiza: an ancient symbiosis in modern agriculture. *Trends in Plant Science*, **13**, 93–97.

Steffen, K.T., Cajthaml, T., Šnajdr, J. & Baldrian, P. (2007) Differential degradation of oak (Quercus petraea) leaf litter by litter-decomposing Basidiomycetes. *Research in Microbiology*, **158**, 447–455.

Lichens

Author: Christopher J. Ellis

Taxa included in this group: This group includes the lichenised-fungi. Lichens represent a symbiotic relationship between a heterotrophic fungus and a photosynthetic alga or cyanobacteria, which occurs internally within a fungal-derived macrostructure, the lichen thallus. Approximately 98% of lichenised-fungi are Ascomycetes ('cup'-fungi), with the majority of the remaining 2% being Basidiomycetes. The lichenised-fungi are, therefore, a functional group, and are not monophlyletic; within Ascomycetes, lichens are formed by fungi occurring in several major clades.

Diversity in the UK: There are around 1,900 species of lichenised-fungi (lichens) in the GB, and a further 428 species of lichenicolous fungi (though this number is increasing). This represents about 47% of European lichen diversity. Of the 2,331 taxa representing lichens and lichenicolous fungi, 17% warrant an International Union for Conservation of Nature (IUCN) threat category, with a further 1.3% considered extinct and 11% considered data deficient (Woods & Coppins 2010). GB has 'international responsibility' for 185 species (representing 8% of the flora). This accounts for lichens with viable populations in GB, but which are extremely rare or threatened across Europe or the world, e.g. *Lobaria pulmonaria*.

Roles in ecosystem services: Evidence for the role of lichens in contributing to the diversity of wild species is extremely high (see Diversity in the UK above). *En masse*, lichens also significantly contribute to the aesthetic character of celebrated landscapes in GB, though individual lichens may themselves go unnoticed; for example, the lichen-rich tundra vegetation of the Cairngorm plateau provides an Arctic-feel to the landscape, while epiphyte flora defines the character and sense of place of the 'Celtic Rainforest'. Within these and other ecosystems, lichens may provide an essential ecosystem role, for example, cyanobacterial photobionts fix nitrogen from the atmosphere, contributing to nutrient cycling (Antoine 2004), and there is a functional relationship between lichen-epiphyte biomass and the diversity of food-source invertebrates for birds (Pettersson *et al.* 1995; Gunnarsson *et al.* 2004). This role may extend to hazard regulation: lichens as primary colonisers may play a role in soil stabilisation and vegetation succession, for instance.

Status and trends: For a majority of lichen species there are insufficient data to provide an empirical account of population and metapopulation change. However, a number of general trends are apparent, or have been inferred, indicating a response to both large-scale environmental drivers and local habitat.

Lichen diversity is recovering in regions where biodiversity was decimated during a period of severe industrial pollution from the 19th Century onwards (Coppins *et al.* 2001). This process of recovery is attributed to reduced sulphur dioxide pollution and acid rain, though is curtailed by the concurrent increase in environmental nitrogen inputs, which appear to prevent the full recovery of the lichen flora and may, in fact, have additional and severe negative impacts (van Herk *et al.* 2003; Wolseley *et al.* 2006; Ellis & Coppins 2009). Sensitivity to nitrogen pollution—most commonly examined for epiphytes—extends to include important areas of upland lichen-rich heath (Britton & Fisher 2007), and is thought to be a key factor driving a homogenisation of montane vegetation (Britton *et al.* 2009).

Lichens are sensitive to habitat dynamics, and many species are habitat specialists, growing on particular rock types or as epiphytes on certain tree species, or growing in local climatic settings or on substrata of a particular age. This specialisation makes lichens extremely vulnerable to habitat loss or degradation. Additionally, recent research indicates an 'extinction debt' for lichens (Berglund & Jonsson 2005; Ellis & Coppins 2007): a process by which populations of patch-tracking and long-lived lichens may exist within remnant habitat patches (following the loss of adjacent habitat), but where subsequently declining populations may not be replaced by recolonisation following a process of landscape change. Owing to this delay, extant lichen diversity patterns may not reflect current landscape structure, but may be related to patterns of historic habitat quality. This process indicates a far wider implication of habitat change for lichens (perceived across landscapes), outside the immediate loss and degradation of local habitat.

Lichens are expected to be sensitive to climate change (Ellis *et al.* 2007); there is preliminary observational evidence for declining populations of 'northern' species in southern GB, and newly discovered populations of 'southern' species in northern GB (Ellis & Binder 2007. This preliminary evidence for GB matches with more robust, long-term evidence for continental Europe, which has demonstrated an increase in warm-temperate or subtropical species, and a loss or northward shift in the distribution of boreal species (van Herk *et al.* 2002; Lättman *et al.* 2009).

Drivers of change: Lichens are sensitive to large-scale environmental drivers, such as pollution and climatic setting (including climate change), and, as diminutive organisms nested within a larger-scale habitat matrix, lichens are sensitive to changes in land management impacting local habitat dynamics.

Prospects: The prospects for lichens are uncertain: assuming pollution (a blanket form of 'habitat loss') is reduced, the persistence of lichen diversity is dependent on maintaining a sufficiently high density of high quality mixed habitats within the landscape. This would allow species richness to be maintained through colonisation-extinction dynamics, despite species compositional turnover in response to climate change. Considering the potential importance of habitat quality in buffering an amalgam of human impacts (pollution, climate change), it is of critical importance that 45% of conservation sites, specifically Sites of Scientific Interest (SSSIs), notified for lower plants (including lichens) are in unfavourable condition.

References

Antoine, M.E. (2004) An ecophysiological approach to quantifying nitrogen fixation by *Lobaria oregana*. *The Bryologist*, **107**, 82–87.

Berglund, H. & Jonsson, B.G. (2005) Verifying an extinction debt among lichens and fungi in northern Swedish boreal forests. *Conservation Biology*, **19**, 338–348.

Britton, A.J. & Fisher, J.M. (2007) Interactive effects of nitrogen deposition, fire and grazing on diversity and composition of low-alpine prostrate *Calluna vulgaris* heath. *Journal of Applied Ecology*, **44**, 125–135.

Britton, A.J., Beale, C.M., Towers, W. & Hewison, R.L. (2009) Biodiversity gains and losses: evidence for homogenisation of Scottish alpine vegetation. *Biological Conservation*, **142**, 1728–1739.

Coppins, B.J., Street, S. & Street, L. (2001) *Lichens of Aspen Woods in Strathspey.* Unpublished Report.

Ellis, C.J. & Binder, M. (2007) Inferred shift in the British distribution of Vulpicida pinastri using herbarium and mapping data. *Bulletin of the British Lichen Society*, **101**, 4–10.

Ellis, C.J. & Coppins, B.J. (2007) 19th century woodland structure controls stand-scale epiphyte diversity in present-day Scotland. *Diversity and Distributions*, **13**, 84–91.

Ellis, C.J. & Coppins, B.J. (2009) Quantifying the role of multiple landscape-scale drivers controlling epiphyte composition and richness in a conservation priority habitat (juniper scrub). *Biological Conservation,* **142**, 1291–1301.

Ellis, C.J., Coppins, B.J., Dawson, T.P. & Seaward, M.R.D. (2007) Response of British lichens to climate change scenarios: trends and uncertainties in the projected impact for contrasting biogeographic groups. *Biological Conservation*, **140**, 217–235.

Gunnarsson, B., Hake, M. & Hultengren, S. (2004) A functional relationship between species richness of spiders and lichens in spruce. *Biodiversity and Conservation*, **13**, 685–693.

Lättman, H., Milberg, P., Palmer, M.W. & Mattson, J.-E. (2009) Changes in the distribution of epiphytic lichens in southern Sweden using a new statistical method. *Nordic Journal of Botany*, **27**, 413–418.

Pettersson, R.B., Ball, J.P., Renhorn, K-E., Esseen, P.A. & Sjöberg, K. (1995) Invertebrate communities in boreal forest canopies as influenced by forestry and lichens with implications for passerine birds. *Biological Conservation*, **74**, 57–63.

Van Herk, C.M., Aptroot, A. & Van Dobben, H.F. (2002) Long-term monitoring in the Netherlands suggests that lichens respond to global warming. *The Lichenologist*, **34**, 141–154.

Van Herk, C.M., Mathijssen-Spiekman, E.A.M. & De Zwart, D. (2003) Long distance nitrogen air pollution effects on lichens in Europe. *The Lichenologist*, **35**, 347–359.

Wolseley, P.A., James, P.W., Theobald, M.R. & Sutton, M.A. (2006) Detecting changes in atmospheric lichen communities at sites affected by atmospheric ammonia from agricultural sources. *The Lichenologist*, **38**, 161–176.

Woods, R.G. & Coppins, B.J. (2010) A Conservation Evaluation of British Lichens. British Lichen Society, London.

A.4.1.3 Lower Plants

Phytoplankton

Author: Martin Edwards

Taxa included in this group: Phytoplankton include all photoautotrophic microorganisms found in aquatic ecosystems, e.g. diatoms, cyanobacteria, dinoflagellates and coccolithophores. Collectively, they inhabit more than 70% of the Earth's planetary surface.

Diversity in the UK: The diversity of phytoplankton is not truly quantified in the UK; however, long-term studies suggest an increase in phytoplankton diversity associated with increasing temperature. Phytoplankton diversity around the British Isles is similar to other temperate/boreal marine ecosystems. Diatom diversity is highest in the southern North Sea and other regional seas on the Northern European continental shelf associated with mixed-water habitats. Overall, phytoplankton diversity (including dinoflagellates and coccolithophores) is highest in oceanic waters to the west of the GB where seasonal stability and temperatures are higher.

Roles in ecosystem services: Phytoplankton have roles in: global climate regulation, global oxygen production, global carbon sequestration, nutrient recycling and primary energy transformation; and are the foundation of virtually all marine food chains, leading to global fish production and other marine bioresources.

Status and trends: At the ocean basin-scale, studies on pelagic biodiversity have been related to temperature—an increase in warming over the last few decades has been followed by an increase in diversity. In particular, increases in diversity are seen when previously low diversity systems, such as Arctic and cold-boreal provinces, undergo prolonged warming events. The overall diversity patterns of pelagic organisms, peaking between 20° to 30° north or south of the equator, follow temperature gradients in the world's oceans. Phytoplankton show a relationship between temperature and diversity which is linked to the phytoplankton community having a higher diversity, but an overall smaller size-fraction and a more complex food web structure (i.e. microbial-based versus diatom-based production) in warmer, more stratified environments. Climate warming will, therefore, increase planktonic diversity throughout the cooler regions of the world's oceans as temperature isotherms shift poleward. Long-term phytoplankton data, collected by the Continuous Plankton Recorder since the 1950s, has shown an increase in phytoplankton diversity around the British Isles associated with sea surface warming and climate oscillations.

It has recently been highlighted that Arctic ice is reducing faster than previous modelled estimates. As a consequence, the biological boundaries between the North Atlantic Ocean and Pacific may become increasingly blurred, with an increase of trans-Arctic migrations becoming a reality. The Continuous Plankton Recorder survey has already documented the presence of a Pacific diatom, *Neodenticula seminae*, in the Labrador Sea, which was first observed in the late 1990s and has since spread southwards and eastwards. The diatom species itself has been absent from the North Atlantic for more than 800,000 years and could be the first evidence of a trans-Arctic migration in modern times, as well as the harbinger of a potential inundation of new organisms to the North Atlantic. The consequences of such a change to the function and biodiversity of Arctic systems are, at present, unknown.

Drivers of change: Generally, the changes in phytoplankton biodiversity at the oceanic macroscale appear to be mainly driven by changes in temperature. There is a strong relationship between temperature and pelagic biodiversity with higher temperatures leading to higher biodiversity. Seasonal stability of the water column has also been shown to increase phytoplankton diversity. During the last decade, in open ocean systems around the British Isles, planktonic biodiversity has increased in association with higher sea surface temperatures. There is some evidence that localised nutrient enrichment caused by terrestrial runoff can cause mono-specific phytoplankton blooms in coastal regions (i.e. a decrease in diversity); however, these blooms have tended to be temporally transient events. Ocean acidification may have future consequences for some calcifying phytoplankton such as coccolithophores.

Prospects: In oceanic habitats free from coastal anthropogenic influences (assuming no habitat loss/fragmentation in oceanic systems), it is highly likely that phytoplankton diversity will continue to increase in association with higher temperature projections. Although the traditional anthropocentric viewpoint considers increasing biodiversity as a positive attribute for ecosystems (e.g. increased homeostatic stabilising processes, decreased energy loss from systems, move towards closed nutrient recycling, etc.), increasing phytoplankton diversity may have a number of negative consequences. For example, the increase in phytoplankton diversity is strongly associated with a decrease in the size-structure of the community, leading to the energetic dominance of smaller organisms. In turn, this has consequences for both carbon residence times (increase in carbon residence times in surface waters) and the size-structure of other ectotherms such as fish. Increasing phytoplankton may, therefore, lead to the devaluation of fisheries, with a move towards smaller species and communities. Increasing temperatures and diversity may also lead to floristic shifts from diatoms to flagellates, potentially leading to more occurrences of harmful algal blooms.

References

Beaugrand, G., Edwards, M. & Legendre, L. (2010) Marine biodiversity, ecosystem functioning, and carbon cycle. *Proceedings of the National Academy of Sciences,* **107**, 10120–10124.

Beaugrand, G., Luczak, C. & Edwards, M. (2009) Rapid biogeographical plankton shifts in the North Atlantic Ocean. *Global Change Biology,* **15**(7), 1790–1803. DOI: 10.1111/j.1365-2486.2009.01848.x.

Edwards, M., Reid, P, C. & Planque, B. (2001) Long-term and regional variability of phytoplankton biomass in the north-east Atlantic (1960-1995). *ICES Journal of Marine Science,* **58**, 39–49.

Edwards, M., Johns, D.G., Leterme, S.C., Svendesen, E. & Richardson, A.J. (2006) Regional climate change and harmful algal blooms in the north-east Atlantic. *Limnology and Oceanography,* **51**, 820–829.

Reid, P.C., Johns, D.G., Edwards, M., Starr, M., Poulin, M. & Snoeijs, P. (2007) A biological consequence of reducing Arctic ice cover: the arrival of the Pacific diatom Neodenticula seminae in the North Atlantic for the first time in 800,000 years. *Global Change Biology,* **13**, 1910–1921.

Macroalgae

Authors: Olivia Langmead and Emma Jackson

Taxa included in this group: The taxa in this group include all multicellular eukaryotic algae belonging to one of three main groups: red algae (Rhodophyta), green algae (Chlorophyta) and brown algae (Phaeophyceae).

Diversity in the UK: Macroalgae are a polyphyletic group, which is not only taxonomically diverse, but also displays high functional diversity. There are approximately 800 nationally recorded species of algae in the UK, from about 100 families, 7 phyla and 2 kingdoms (Plantae and Chromista). A recent assessment of global diversity of macroalgae identified UK waters as part of a cluster of endemics in Western Europe (Kerswell 2006).

Roles in ecosystem services: Macroalgal beds are important coastal habitats and support a variety of ecosystem services including providing feeding and nursery habitat for many commercially important fish and shellfish species, and opportunities for direct harvesting for food, biofuels and pharmaceutical products (and historically for fertiliser). Macroalgae also play regulatory roles in the transformation of nutrients to organic matter and their export to other systems, the regulation of oxygen, and the breakdown and removal of pollutants.

Status and trends: No UK-wide assessment of status and trends in marine macroalgae has been undertaken to date, and our perspective of this diverse and functionally important group is incomplete. Data is being collected from Special Areas of Conservation (SACs) in terms of site condition-monitoring for areas designated for rocky reefs, but no overview reports have been produced to summarise the trends or current status. The high functional diversity of this group makes it difficult to generalise about their status and trends. However, there is evidence that changes follow wider European trends where the loss of long-lived, slow-growing, functionally important macroalgae to more opportunistic species has been associated with anthropogenic pressure (Orfandis *et al.* 2003).

Drivers of change: Land use change and pollutants are key drivers of change in status of macroalage. Nutrient enrichment, typically caused by terrestrial runoff of treated sewage and agricultural fertiliser, can lead to changes in macroalgal communities, with outbreaks of opportunistic species, such as *Ulva* species, occurring (Fletcher 1996). These algae compete with other species for space, as well as generating large quantities of biomass which, upon decomposition, may locally reduce oxygen levels among intertidal habitats. In comparison, slow-growing, long-lived algae, such as maerl (calcified red seaweed), are damaged by dredging, anchoring and eutrophication. Between 1982 and 1992, the proportion of dead maerl on the St. Mawes bank, Cornwall, increased significantly from 12% to 23% (Perrins 1995); it also increased at Milford Haven, South Wales, due to industrial coastal development (Jackson *et al.* 2008).

Invasive macroalgal species (e.g. *Sargassum muticum, Undaria pinnatifida, Asparagopsis armata*) are a growing concern, but impacts on native communities have not been consistent (Milneur *et al.* 2008). Assessments of ports show many species are present, potentially acting as reservoirs for further spread in UK waters (Arenas *et al.* 2006). Research on the distribution and abundance of northern (cold water) macroalgal species has shown climate change related range contractions and significant declines in abundance (e.g. cold water brown macroalga, *Alaria esculenta*). This trend is accompanied by range extensions in warm water species (e.g. southern red turf alga, *Chondrocanthus acicularis*, warm water kelp, *Sacchoriza polyschides*) (UKMMAS 2010; Mieszkowkska *et al.* 2006).

Prospects: Our understanding of the status and trends will improve with the implementation of monitoring for the Water Framework Directive. Macroalgae are a biological quality element to be used in defining the ecological status of transitional and coastal water bodies. Opportunistic macroalgae will be assessed in coastal and transitional waters (Scanlan *et al.* 2007), macroalgal community structure will be assessed on rocky shores (Wells *et al.* 2007, and fucoid extent will be assessed in estuaries (Wilkinson *et al.* 2007).

References

Arenas, F., Bishop, J.D.D., Carlton, J.T., Dyrynda, P.J., Farnham, W.F., Gonzalez, D.J., Jacobs, M.W., Lambert, C., Lambert, G., Nielsen, S.E., Pederson, J.A., Porter, J.S., Ward, S. & Wood, C.A. (2006) Alien species and other notable records from a rapid assessment survey of marinas on the south coast of England. *Journal of the Marine Biological Association of the United Kingdom*, **86**, 1329–1337.

Fletcher, R.L. (1996) *The occurrence of "green tides" – a review.* In: Schramm, W., Nienhuis, P.H. (Eds.), Marine Benthic Vegetation: Recent Changes and the Effects of Eutrophication. Springer, Berlin, Heidelberg, New York, pp. 7–43.

Jackson, E.L., Langmead, O., Evans, J., Ellis, R. & Tyler-Walters, H. (2008) Protecting nationally important marine Biodiversity in Wales. Report to the Wales Environment Link from the Marine Life Information Network (MarLIN). Marine Biological Association of the UK, Plymouth.

Kerswell, A.P. (2006) Global biodiversity patterns of benthic marine algae. *Ecology*, **87**, 2479–2488.

Mieszkowska, N., Kendall, M,A., Hawkins, S.J., Leaper, R., Williamson, P., Hardman-Mountford, N.J. & Southward, A.J. (2006) Changes in the range of some common rocky shore species in Britain – a response to climate change? *Hydrobiologia*, **555**, 241–251.

Milneur, F., Johnson, M.P. & Maggs, C.A. (2008) Non-indigenous marine macroalgae in native communities: a case study in the British Isles. *Journal of the Marine Biological Association of the UK*, **88**, 693–698.

Orfandis, S., Panayotidis, P. & Stamatis, N. (2003) An insight to the ecological evaluation index (EEI). *Ecological Indicators*, **3**, 27–33.

Perrins, J., Bunker, F. & Bishop, G. (1995) A comparison of the maerl beds of the Fal Estuary between 1982 and 1992. English Nature, Peterborough.

Scanlan, C.M., Foden, J., Wells, E. & Best, M.A. (2007) The monitoring of opportunistic macroalgal blooms for the Water Framework Directive. *Marine Pollution Bulletin*, **55**, 162–171.

UKMMAS (UK Marine Monitoring and Assessment Strategy) (2010) Charting Progress 2: The State of UK Seas. Published by the Department for Environment Food and Rural Affairs on behalf of UKMMAS. TSO, London. 166pp. ISBN 9780112432937. Available at: <http://chartingprogress.defra.gov.uk/resources> [Accessed 06.06.10].

Wells, E., Wilkinson, M., Wood, P. & Scanlan, C. (2007) The use of macroalgal species richness and composition on intertidal rocky seashores in the assessment of ecological quality under the European Water Framework Directive. *Marine Pollution Bulletin*, **55**, 151–161.

Wilkinson, M., Wood, P., Wells, E. & Scanlan, C. (2007) Using attached macroalgae to assess ecological status of British estuaries for the European Water Framework Directive. *Marine Pollution Bulletin*, **55**, 136–150.

Bryophytes

Authors: David G. Long, David F. Chamberlain and Elizabeth Kungu

Taxa included in this group: The group includes the liverworts (Marchantiophyta), mosses (Bryophyta) and hornworts (Anthocerotophyta), which are quite independent evolutionary lineages, but are placed together for convenience because they are similar in size, share alternation of generations with a dependent sporophyte and occupy very similar ecological and biological roles in nature. The liverworts include the earliest known lineages of land plants.

Diversity in the UK: There are 1,056 species of bryophytes in the GB: 297 liverworts, 755 mosses and 4 hornworts (Hill *et al.* 2008). This constitutes approximately 65% of European species and 6% of the estimated total global species. A recent assessment (JNCC 2007) categorises 22% of British bryophytes (231 species) as Red List species based on IUCN guidelines. Additionally, there are numerous species whose UK populations do not warrant formal conservation status, but are of high international importance, such as liverworts with disjunct global distributions found in rare and vulnerable habitats including Oceanic Liverwort Heath (Rothero 2003) and Atlantic Oakwoods (Hodgetts 1997).

Roles in ecosystem services: Bryophytes contribute significant diversity to almost all GB ecosystems. Where they dominate ecosystems, they are most visible and often highly aesthetically attractive, for example, the rich colours of the 35 British *Sphagnum* species in our northern peatlands, and the sheer luxuriance of mosses and liverworts clothing our oceanic woodlands. In other habitats, they are less conspicuous, but still vitally important, for example, as stabilising colonists of coastal sand dunes, or forming carpets of tiny Arctic species around Cairngorm snowbeds (our own 'tundra'). Peatlands (consisting of both living and decaying *Sphagnum*) are of exceptional importance for carbon sequestration: globally they contain 320 billion tonnes of carbon, about 44% of the amount held in the atmosphere as carbon dioxide (Rydin & Jeglum 2006). Peatlands are also a major source of fuel, energy and horticultural growing mediums (Vanderpoorten & Goffinet 2009). Bryophytes are drought-tolerant (poikilohydric) and have very high water retention properties—up to 1,500% of their dry weight (Proctor 2009)—which is significant in peatlands and mossy forests where high rainfall can be absorbed by the plants preventing rapid runoff and flooding, and maintaining humidity through dry seasons. In many communities, they act as pioneers and stabilise soil crusts. Physically, they provide microhabitats for many invertebrates, which, in turn, provide food for a variety of organisms, particularly in aquatic and mossy forest ecosystems (Lindo & Gonzalez 2010; Parker *et al.* 2000).

Status and trends: Progress in recent years has been considerable in mapping changes to bryophyte distributions in GB (Hill *et al.* 1991–1994), but at the population level, data are in most cases, inadequate to assess trends in any depth. A number of trends can be identified from anecdotal and other evidence, however:

Habitat loss, degeneration and fragmentation. Many bryophytes display highly specialised habitat requirements such as epiphytes showing sensitivity to bark pH, 'copper mosses' restricted to metalliferous rocks, woodland species dependent on shade and high humidity, rheophytes dependent on fast-moving water and montane species dependent on late snow-lie. Such demanding traits render the bryophytes highly vulnerable to habitat loss and degradation, particularly as many of these niches occur on a very small, local scale and may be highly isolated. However, many bryophytes have developed life strategies to deal with ecological instability, and those species with effective dispersal capacity may cope in the face of such changes; others, such as the oceanic-montane liverwort heath species, lack reproductive capacity and have no such defences against habitat change, particularly when it is rapid as a result of ecological calamities such as muirburn (Hobbs 1988).

Pollution. Although primary consideration is often given to air pollution due to its historically destructive impact on bryophyte and lichen epiphytes, both water pollution and agricultural runoff on land can also impact negatively on the bryoflora (Vanderpoorten & Goffinet 2009). The effects of sulphur dioxide pollution have clearly been demonstrated by the historic losses of mosses, such as epiphytic *Orthotrichum* species, in industrial areas, and their recent return to many urban places. However, the effects of nitrogen oxide pollution may be increasing, even in montane areas remote from industrial activity (Woolgrove & Woodin 1996). This may lead to the loss of more demanding and sensitive species.

Climate change. Bryophytes are predicted to show high sensitivity to climate change, with evidence that some northern species are declining in southern GB, and some southern species, such as *Grimmia tergestina*, are moving northwards (Porley & Hodgetts 2005); those already close to their altitudinal limit, such as Arctic bryophytes of snow-beds, may have no way of escape. Not all changes may be temperature-driven, and there is already anecdotal evidence that, in the face of increasing summer rainfall, some oceanic liverworts, such as *Metzgeria temperata*, are moving eastwards. An even more dramatic consequence may be the effect of global warming on peatlands which has been described as a 'ticking time bomb' (Vanderpoorten

& Goffinet 2009) as their decomposition could increase atmospheric carbon dioxide by up to 50% (O'Neill 2000).

Drivers of change: Bryophytes show many similarities to lichens in their sensitivity to environmental drivers such as climatic effects and pollution. Where they occur as components of larger-scale ecosystems, such as in forests and heathlands, they are especially sensitive to human-induced habitat changes at a landscape-scale, such as agricultural intensification, burning, grazing and afforestation.

Prospects: Awareness of the importance of bryophytes in the face of climate and other environmental challenges will surely increase—it is already reflected by their collective description as the 'bryosphere' (Lindo & Gonzalez 2010). The prospects for bryophytes are uncertain. Even with possible reductions in pollution, the relentless pressure on bryophyte-rich habitats shows little sign of diminishing. Historically, our 'protected' areas have been selected to reflect more charismatic interests, and often the richest bryophyte sites are undesignated and under-managed. Even many Sites of Special Scientific Interest notified for cryptogamic plants are in unfavourable condition. A realignment of priorities to more equitably allocate resources on research and conservation to less-charismatic groups, such as cryptogams and invertebrates, is long overdue in GB.

References

Hill, M.O., Preston, C.D. & Smith, A.J.E. (1991–1994) Atlas of the Bryophytes of Britain and Ireland. Colchester: Harley Books.

Hill, M.O., Blackstock, T.H., Long, D.G. & Rothero, G.P. (2008) A checklist and census catalogue of British and Irish Bryophytes. British Bryological Society, Middlewich.

Hobbs, A.M. (1988) Conservation of leafy liverwort-rich *Calluna vulgaris* heath in Scotland. *Ecological change in the uplands* (eds M.B. Usher & D.B.A. Thompson), pp. 339–343. Blackwells, Oxford.

Hodgetts, N.G. (1997) Atlantic bryophytes in Scotland. *Botanical Journal of Scotland,* **49**, 375–386.

JNCC (Joint Nature Conservation Committee) (2007) Threat assessment. Bryophytes. [online] Available at: <http://www.jncc.gov.uk/page-1752> [Accessed 07.02.11].

Lindo, Z. & Gonzalez, A. (2010) The Bryosphere: an integral and influential component of the earth's biosphere. *Ecosystems,* **13**, 612–627.

O'Neill, K.P. (2000) Role of bryophyte-dominated ecosystems in the global carbon budget. Bryophyte Biology ed. 1. (eds A.J. Shaw & B. Goffinet), pp. 344–368. Cambridge University Press, Cambridge.

Parker, J.D., Burkpile, D.E., Collins, D.O., Kubanek, J. & Hay, M.E. (2000) Stream mosses as chemically-defended refugia for freshwater macroinvertebrates. *Oikos,* **116**, 302–312.

Porley, R.D. & Hodgetts, N.G. (2005) Mosses & Liverworts. Collins, London.

Proctor, M.C.F. (2009) Physiological ecology. *Bryophyte Biology,* ed. 2 (eds B. Goffinet &.A.J. Shaw), pp. 595–621. Cambridge University Press, Cambridge.

Rothero, G.P. (2003) Bryophyte conservation in Scotland. *Botanical Journal of Scotland,* **55**, 17–26.

Rydin, H. & Jeglum, J.K. (2006) The biology of peatlands. Oxford University Press, Oxford.

Vanderpoorten, A. & Goffinet, B. (2009) Introduction to Bryophytes. Cambridge University Press, Cambridge.

Woolgrove, C.E. & Woodin, S.J. (1996) Current and historical relationships between the tissue nitrogen content of a snowbed bryophyte and nitrogenous air pollution. *Environmental Pollution,* **91**, 283–288.

A.4.1.4 Higher Plants

Seagrass

Authors: Emma Jackson and Olivia Langmead

Taxa included in this group and diversity in the UK: There are two species of seagrass on the coasts of the UK, the primarily subtidal eelgrass (*Zostera marina*) and the intertidal dwarf eelgrass (*Zostera noltii*). Currently, there is debate as to the status of a possible third species, *Zostera marina var. angustifolia*, which is not widely accepted as a separate species. Dwarf eelgrass is at its most northerly biogeographical limit in the UK.

Roles in ecosystem services: In the UK, seagrass meadows function as important nursery and foraging habitat for fish, shellfish and wildfowl, and they also oxygenate and stabilise sediments and store carbon. They are considered a 'foundation species' i.e. organisms that provide habitat, enhance ecosystem biodiversity and are important indicators of system health.

Status and trends: There is no national monitoring programme for seagrasses in the UK and, therefore, overall trends are difficult to assess. Global trajectories show accelerating losses of seagrasses over the last 100 years (Waycott *et al.* 2009). In the UK, seagrass beds have never fully recovered from large-scale losses attributed to the 1930s outbreak of 'wasting disease' due to the significant changes in sediment dynamics it caused (Wilson 1949). During the 1990s, repeated outbreaks of wasting disease led to further seagrass losses in the Solent (Chesworth *et al.* 2008).

Information from the few UK monitoring studies that do exist demonstrate trends of loss that continued through the 1990s. However, this pattern varies spatially; sublittoral beds in Pembrokeshire have undergone recovery in some areas, such as North Haven, and entirely disappeared in others (Foden & Brazier 2007). Annual diving surveys of seagrass beds in the Isles of Scilly have shown inconsistent trends (in shoot density) between five meadows over the past 13 years suggesting localised effects on the beds rather than large-scale pressures (Cook 2005). The current spatial distribution of seagrass in the Solent appears to be consistent with records from the 1980s (Lefebvre *et al.* 2009).

Intertidal beds (dwarf eelgrass) show similar diverse trends around the UK; seagrass extent does not seem to have greatly changed over the last two decades within the Solent (Lefebvre *et al.* 2009). In Welsh coastal waters the number of intertidal seagrass beds has increased during this century (Boyes *et al.* 2009).

Drivers of change: Changes in seagrass health and distribution are driven primarily by land use change, indirect exploitation and invasive species. Activities which decrease water clarity or quality (for example, eutrophication, aquaculture, coastal development, dredging and spoil disposal) may negatively impact the health or productivity of seagrass (evident in density, biomass or epiphyte cover changes). Increased turbidity may also reduce the depth limit and thus vertical distribution of the seagrasses. While nutrient enrichment may increase production in seagrasses, associated phytoplankton blooms and opportunistic algal growth (including epiphytes and invasive species such as wireweed, *Sargassum muticum*) may cause severe shading. Boat anchoring, propeller scarring, dredging and destructive fishing methods, such as beam trawling, have all been shown to physically damage seagrasses. Damage to UK seagrass beds from such activities are evident in visual surveys (Rhodes *et al.* 2006; Sutton & Tompsett 2000).

Prospects: Improvements in water quality through improved sewerage treatment and national regulations resulting from the Urban Waste Water Treatment Directive and Water Framework Directive have started to negate pressures relating to water clarity and quality. However, continued direct physical pressures on seagrass beds are increasingly resulting in the loss and fragmentation of many beds. Increased storm events predicted as part of a changing climate are likely to have negative effects on the current extent of seagrass beds, making them more vulnerable to more direct human drivers of change. Increased availability of inorganic carbon due to ocean acidification is likely to have positive benefits for the growth and health of seagrasses, but may disrupt the ecosystem services they provide (Hall-Spencer *et al.* 2008).

References

Boyes, S., Brazier, D.P., Burlinson, F., Mazik, K., Mitchell, E. & Proctor, N. (2009) Intertidal monitoring of *Zostera noltii* in the Menai Strait & Conwy Bay SAC in 2004/05. CCW Marine Monitoring report No 31.

Cook, K. (2005) Report on 2004 Isles of Scilly *Zostera marina* survey. Report to Natural England.

Chesworth, J.C., D.G. King, & V. Swales (2008) Inventory of eelgrass beds in Hampshire and the Isle of Wight. Hampshire and Isle of Wight Wildlife Trust, Hampshire.

Foden, J. & Brazier, D.P. (2007) Angiosperms (seagrass) within the EU water framework directive: A UK perspective. *Marine Pollution Bulletin*, **55**, 181–195.

Hall-Spencer, J.M., Rodolfo-Metalpa, R., Martin, S., Ransome, E., Fine, M., Turner, S.M., Rowley, S.J., Tedesco, D. & Buia, M.C. (2008) Volcanic carbon dioxide vents show ecosystem effects of ocean acidification. *Nature,* **454**, 96–99.

Lefebvre, A., Thompsona, C.E.L., Collinsa, K.J. & Amosa, C.L. (2009) Use of a high-resolution profiling sonar and a towed video camera to map a *Zostera marina* bed, Solent, UK. *Estuarine, Coastal and Shelf Science*, **82**, 323–334.

Rhodes, B., Jackson, E.L., Moore, R., Foggo, A. & Frost, M. (2006) The impact of swinging boat moorings on *Zostera marina* beds and associated infaunal macroinvertebrate communities in Salcombe, Report to English Nature, Devon.

Sutton, A. & Tompsett, P.E. (2000) Eelgrass (*Zostera* spp.) Project 1995–1998. Helford River Survey. Helford Voluntary Marine Conservation Area Group.

Waycott, M., Duarte, C.M., Carruthers, T.J.B., Orth, R.J., Dennison, W.C., Olyarnik, S. Calladine, A., Fourquean, J.W. Heck, K.L.J., Hughese, A.R., Kendrick, G.A., Kenworthy, W.J., Short, F.T. & Williams, S.L. (2009) Accelerating loss of seagrasses across the globe threatens coastal ecosystems. *PNAS*, **106**, 12377–12381.

Wilson, D.P. (1949) The decline of *Zostera marina* L. at Salcombe and its effects on the shore. *Journal of the Marine Biological Association of the UK*, **28**, 395–412.

Land plants

Authors: Mary Gibby, Heather McHaffie and Lindsay Maskell

Taxa included in this group: This group includes all vascular plants: Lycopods, Isoetes and Selaginella, ferns and horsetails, conifers (Gymnosperms), and all flowering plants (Angiosperms)—trees, shrubs, herbaceous plants and grasses. The majority are land plants, but some occur in freshwater, brackish or marine habitats.

Diversity in the UK: With approximately 1,500 species, the vascular plant flora of the GB is considered depauperate in comparison with that of mainland Europe, constituting only 13.6% of European species and 0.47% of the estimated total global species. Most of the 1,500 native species are angiosperms; ferns, horsetails and Lycopods account for around 80 taxa, and there are just three conifers (Scots pine, juniper and yew). *The New Atlas of the British and Irish Flora* (Preston *et al.* 2002) includes 1,486 native and 817 introduced species; these latter are classified as 'archaeophytes' (introduced before AD 1500), 'neophytes' (introduced after AD 1500) and 'casuals' (recorded but not forming permanent populations).

Roles in ecosystem services: Vascular plants are significant components of ecosystems, delivering both provisioning and regulating services, with a major role in carbon cycling and oxygen release. Land plants are the basis of productive agriculture and forestry. Forests act as carbon sinks and influence climate change by affecting the amount of carbon dioxide in the atmosphere. Forest cover helps regulate rainfall, slows down runoff and reduces erosion. Wild species diversity is ultimately dependent on vascular plants; they form the base of the food chain and provide shelter and a diversity of habitats. Of the 65 UK Biodiversity Action Plan priority habitats, 33 are dominated by vascular plants, from various woodlands of upland and lowland, heath and scrubland, hay meadows and chalk grassland, to traditional orchards, hedgerows and coastal sand dunes. Vascular plants have a key role in water purification. They are the framework for meaningful places, promote health and well-being, and are valued in green landscapes.

Status and trends: The revised Red Data List (Cheffings *et al.* 2005) includes native species and archaeophytes: 125 species are Endangered or Critically Endangered, 220 are Vulnerable and 98 are Near Threatened. This means that 443 species are of conservation concern—some 25% of the native and archaeophyte flora. The Countryside Survey is a monitoring scheme which provides quantitative data on changes in plant species distribution across GB between 1978 and 2007 (www.countrysidesurvey.org.uk/). It samples a series of plots representing different landscape features within a 1 km square (591 x 1 km² plots were sampled across GB in 2007). Data from the Countryside Survey contributes to the UK Biodiversity Indicators (www.jncc.gov.uk/page-4229). Results from 2007 showed that there had been a decline in mean species richness in most habitats in GB between 1978 and 2007 (Carey *et al.* 2008a; **Figure A.4.1.4.1**).

Within the UK, countries have produced their own analysis of species and habitats giving added conservation status to local species as seen in the Scottish Biodiversity List (2005) and the Vascular Plant Red Data List for Wales (Dines 2008). The Countryside Survey also reports by country and there are summary reports for England, Wales and Scotland. Ireland's National Biodiversity Plan (2010) builds on the Global Strategy for Plant Conservation (2002).

A detailed study of local change was undertaken by members of the Botanical Society of the British Isles (BSBI) compiling datasets gathered in 1987–1988 and again in the same 2 x 2 km areas in 2003–2004 (Braithwaite *et al.* 2006), providing a baseline that can be further extended. Comparisons over a shorter period than between the two Atlases indicate the loss of species from less fertile habitats, calcareous grassland and dwarf shrub heath, probably due to habitat fragmentation. Climate change appears to be favouring the spread of some southern species, but there is less evidence of decline in the uplands as yet.

Drivers of change: There are many reasons for decline. The most outstanding is probably habitat loss, particularly in plants that have suffered from 'improvement' and drainage of wet areas. This is clearly illustrated in the distribution of pillwort (Pilularia globulifera), a small fern that depends on light disturbance to reduce competition and is sensitive to water quality. This species is declining throughout Europe, but the GB populations are comparatively strong which gives them an added importance (**Figure A.4.1.4.2**). The existing records are usually in less populated areas.

Other species have also suffered from more intensive agriculture, and the increased use of herbicide has reduced the abundance of many arable species, which are not nearly as frequent as they used to be, although they are still present in many areas. The archaeophyte, corn spurrey (*Spergula arvensis*), for example, has a change index of -2.30 and if the trend continues might disappear within the next 40 years. Conversely, the native lesser sea spurrey (*Spergularia marina*) has an expanded range inland on salted road margins and has a change index of +1.83.

As well as direct impacts on arable species, as mentioned above, the burning and processing of fossil fuels for energy production, and the manufacture and application of agricultural fertilisers, have resulted in large-scale increases in macro-nutrient inputs to ecosystems. Eutrophication signals have been detected across all habitat types (Smart *et al.* 2003). Eutrophication leads to loss of diversity, particularly when coupled with a decline in management. Significant losses in diversity and increases in competitive species

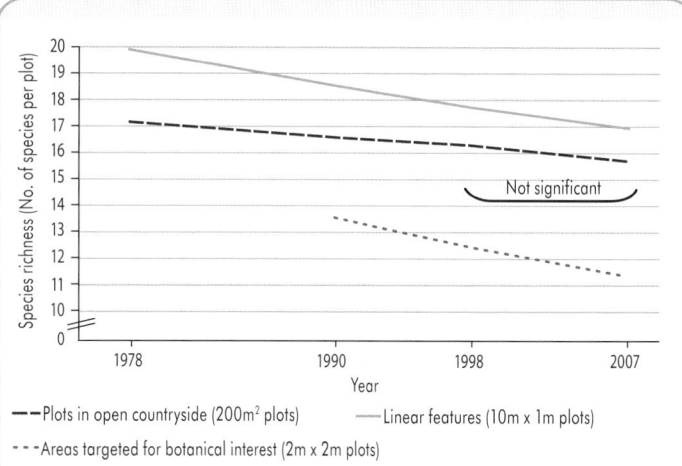

Figure A.4.1.4.1 Average species richness of vegetation in plots in the open countryside (fields, woods, heaths and moors), linear features, and areas targeted for their botanical interest in GB between 1978 and 2007. A decline in species richness is apparent in each dataset. Source: Carey *et al.* (2008). Countryside Survey data owned by NERC – Centre for Ecology & Hydrology.

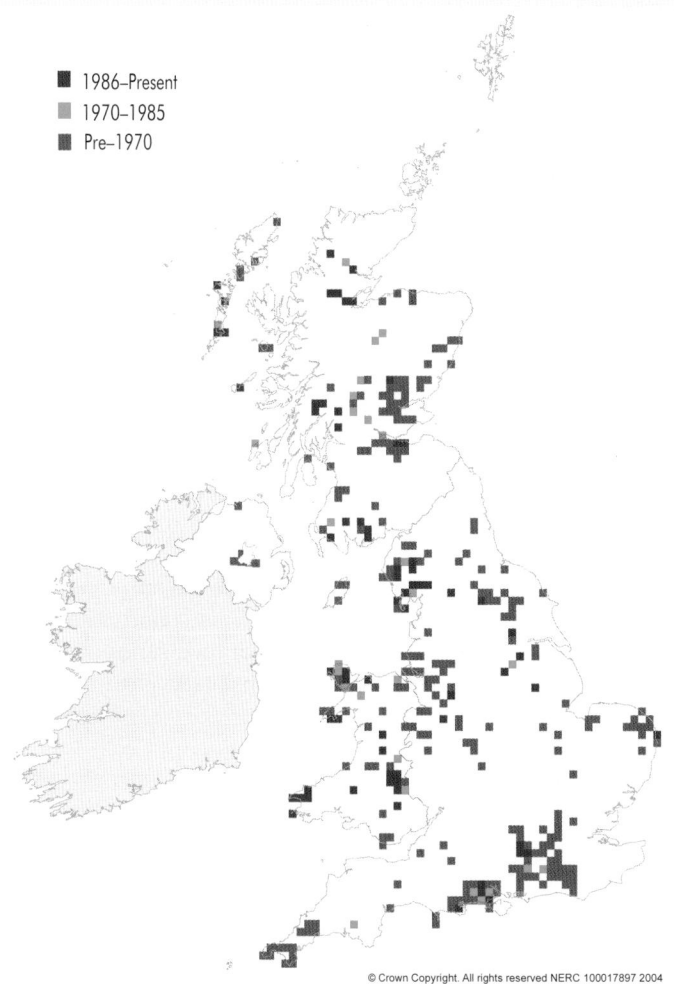

Figure A.4.1.4.2 Map showing distribution of *Pilularia globulifera* (pillwort) in mainland UK at 10x10 km resolution, based on 113 recent records (1986–present), 82 records from 1970 to 1985, and 544 historical records (pre-1970). Change index = -0.03. Most of the losses were pre-1970 and many date back considerably further. Source: data from the National Biodiversity Network Gateway (NBN 2011).

were found across GB between 1978 and 2007, especially along linear features (hedges, streamsides) and in small habitat patches (Carey *et al.* 2008b). Atmospheric nitrogen deposition has been shown to have a significant impact on plant species richness through direct toxicity, acidification and eutrophication (Stevens *et al.* 2004, 2010; Maskell *et al.* 2010; RoTAP 2011).

Global transport networks mix previously isolated biota, exposing more ecosystems to a greater number of potential colonists. There is concern about the impacts of non-native species on native plant diversity. The Atlas showed that some non-natives, such as giant hogweed (*Heracleum mantegazzianum*) (change index +2.0), Himalayan balsam (*Impatiens glandulifera*) (change index +1.85) and common rhododendron (*Rhododendron ponticum*) (change index +1.83), are increasing (Preston *et al.* 2002). Non-natives have been shown to have significant localised effects, but in the wider countryside across GB they are still relatively uncommon (Maskell *et al.* 2006). Invasion is likely to be facilitated by anthropogenic disturbance (intensive farming, atmospheric pollution and land use change), which increases the suitability of a habitat for a smaller number of 'winning' species. It has been shown that as species diversity declines there is an increase in functional similarity as winning trait syndromes dominate (Smart *et al.* 2006). This may have implications for the resilience of communities in providing ecosystem services.

Native vegetation is vulnerable to the increasing spread of non-native invasive fungal pathogens, such as Sudden Oak Death, *Phytophthora ramorum*, possibly linked with climate change. Upland vegetation, including woodland, has been seriously impacted by overgrazing by sheep and deer, resulting in a loss of biodiversity due to habitat fragmentation and the prevention of establishment.

Prospects: The public availability of distributional data (Preston *et al.* 2002) and its comparison with the information from the earlier Atlas (Perring & Walters 1962) has encouraged further data gathering that will be valuable in informing future trends. The BSBI is now recording in decade-long date classes (since 2000), and also aims to get tetrad maps of all species by 2020. Countryside Survey data is also publically available (www.countrysidesurvey. org.uk/) and now provides a 30-year time-series of data for common British plant species and habitats.

References

Braithwaite, M.E., Ellis, R.W. & Preston, C.D. (2006) Change in the British Flora 1987–2004. BSBI, London.

Carey, P.D., Wallis, S, Emmett, B.A., Maskell, L.C., Murphy, J., Norton, L.R., Simpson, I.C. & Smart, S.M. (2008a) Countryside Survey: UK Headline Messages from 2007. NERC/Centre for Ecology & Hydrology, 30pp. (CEH Project Number: C03259).

Carey, P.D., Wallis, S., Chamberlain, P.M., Cooper, A., Emmett, B.A., Maskell, L.C., McCann, T., Murphy, J., Norton, L.R., Reynolds, B., Scott, W.A., Simpson, I.C., Smart, S.M., & Ullyett, J.M. (2008b) Countryside Survey: UK Results from 2007. NERC/Centre for Ecology & Hydrology, 105pp. (CEH Project Number: C03259).

Cheffings, C.M. & Farrell, L. (eds) (2005) The Vascular Plant Red Data List for Great Britain No. 7. JNCC, Peterborough.

Dines, D. (2008) A Vascular Plant Red Data List for Wales. Plantlife Wales, BSBI & CCW.

Forestry Commission (2010) State of Europe's Forest 2011 – UK report. Forestry Commission. [online] Available at: <http://www.interpretscotland.org.uk/forestry/infd-86hchq> [Accessed 07.02.11].

GSPC (Global Strategy for Plant Conservation) (2002) Secretariat of the Convention on Biological Diversity Canada. [online] Available at: <http://www.bgci.org/files/All/Key_Publications/globalstrategyeng223.pdf> with proposed revision 2010 http://www.cbd.int/doc/meetings/sbstta/sbstta-14/official/sbstta-14-09-en.pdf [Accessed 07.02.11].

INBP (Ireland's National Biodiversity Plan) (2010) National Biodiversity Plan – The 91 Actions. [online] Available at: <http://www.botanicgardens.ie/gspc/nbp.htm> [Accessed 07.02.11].

Maskell, L.C., Firbank, L.G., Thompson, K., Bullock, J.M. & Smart, S.M. (2006) Interactions between non-native plant species and the floristic composition of common habitats. *Journal of Ecology,* **94,** 1052–1060.

Maskell, L.C., Smart, S.M., Bullock, J.M., Thompson K. & Stevens, C.J. (2010) Nitrogen Deposition causes widespread loss of species richness in British Habitats. *Global Change Biology,* **16,** 671–679.

NBN (National Biodiversity Network Gateway) (2011) Distribution of *Pilularia globulifera.* [online] Available at: <http://data.nbn.org.uk/gridMap/gridMap.jsp?allDs=1&srchSpKey=NBNSYS0000002089> [Accessed 11.04.11].

Preston, C.D., Pearman, D.A. & Dines, T.D. (eds) (2002) New Atlas of the British and Irish Flora. DEFRA, Oxford University Press, Oxford.

Perring, F.H. & Walters, S.M. (eds) (1962) Atlas of the British Flora. BSBI, Nelson & Sons.

RoTAP (2011) Review of Transboundary Air Pollution: Acidification, Eutrophication, Ground Level Ozone and Heavy Metals in the UK. Contract Report to the Department for Environment, Food and Rural Affairs. Centre for Ecology & Hydrology.

SBL (Scottish Biodiversity List) (2005) [online] Available at: <http://www.scotland.gov.uk/Topics/Environment/Wildlife-Habitats/16118/Biodiversitylist> [Accessed 07.02.11].

Smart, S.M., Robertson, J., Shield, E.J. & van de Poll, M.H. (2003) Locating eutrophication effects across British vegetation between 1990 and 1998. *Global Change Biology,* **9,** 1763–1774.

Smart, S.M., Thompson, K., Marrs, R.H., Le Duc, M., Maskell, L.C. & Firbank, L.G. (2006) Biotic homogenization and changes in species diversity across human-modified ecosystems. *Proceedings of the Royal Society B,* **273,** 2659–2665.

Stevens, C.J., Thompson, K., Grime, J.P., Long, C.J. & Gowing, D.J.G. (2010) Acidification as opposed to eutrophication is the main cause of declines in species richness seen in calcifuge grasslands impacted by nitrogen deposition. *Functional Ecology,* **19,** 355–358.

Stevens, C.J., Dise, N.B., Mountford, J.O. & Gowing D.J. (2004) Impact of nitrogen deposition on the species richness of grasslands. *Science,* **303,** 1876–1879.

A.4.1.5 Invertebrates

Marine and estuarine invertebrates

Author: Paul J. Somerfield

Taxa included in this group: Phyletic diversity is much higher in the sea than it is on land, and marine and estuarine invertebrates belong to most known animal phyla. The most abundant tend to be annelids (worms), molluscs (snails, clams), crustaceans and echinoderms (starfish, sea urchins).

Diversity in the UK: With a long and varied coastline, and a long history of investigation, UK coastal waters and estuaries are among the best studied in the world. Habitat diversity is high and some 9,000 species have been recorded.

Roles in ecosystem services: Many marine and estuarine invertebrates are harvested for food (crabs, lobsters, cockles, clams, oysters, scallops, cuttlefish, shrimp, prawns, urchins) and there is also a large industry harvesting them for bait (worms, crabs). Aquaculture is increasing; invertebrates form structures which provide habitats for commercial fish, and most commercial fish species feed on invertebrates. It should be noted that many marine invertebrates impose economic costs as well, especially those that form fouling communities on ships and structures. Marine sediments form the largest habitat in the UK and are a sink for human waste. The chemistry and functioning of the benthic system is often driven by the activities of invertebrates which turn over the sediment, move material from the surface to depth and vice versa, alter oxygenation, breakdown and recycle organic matter and nutrients, sequester pollutants or make them bioavailable, filter and cleanse seawater, and influence sediment mobility and stability. Habitat formation and modification are both performed by marine and estuarine invertebrates. Apart from their commercial importance, marine and estuarine invertebrates matter to people. Areas rich in invertebrate diversity are popular with scuba divers, and a day on the beach would not be complete without seashells.

Status and trends: For the determination of trends, data from some sort of standardised sampling through time is required. There are very few long- or even medium-term time-series for invertebrates in marine or estuarine environments; most of those available sample plankton. For other marine and estuarine invertebrates there are incomplete time-series available for sediments off the coast of Plymouth and Newcastle. Some studies of invertebrates on hard substrata have demonstrated changes over periods of time, including the fact that some intertidal communities are still recovering from the severe winter of 1962–1963, showing that recovery may be very slow. In general, however, our understanding of biodiversity change in estuarine and marine environments is poor, and much of what we know is based on scattered observations. The same is true of our understanding of status. Arguably, most marine systems were highly impacted before we began studying, and there is a whole branch of marine science attempting to reconstruct historical baselines. What is clear is that few or no marine systems are as they should be.

Drivers of change: The overwhelming factor influencing changes in the distribution and functioning of marine invertebrate biodiversity is human populations. Fishing has direct and indirect effects. It removes large predators which may induce changes in trophic structure throughout food webs. Removing fish which prey on urchins, for example, can lead to overgrazing and the development of urchin barrens instead of kelp forest. Demersal fishing has a direct effect on the benthos. Removal of filter-feeding invertebrates, such as oyster reefs, can alter water quality and benthic-pelagic coupling. Continual seabed disturbance alters the size, structure and composition of invertebrate communities, and hence their ability to cycle nutrients, sequester carbon and pollutants, and stabilise sediment. Removing biogenic (invertebrate) structure also removes habitat for juvenile fish.

Over long time periods, changes in land use and human activities impacts estuarine and marine invertebrates. Conversion of forests to agriculture, mining activity, canalisation of rivers and a range of other activities increase sediment loads in rivers, which either clog estuaries or alter sediment dynamics on coastal seas. Although direct disposal at sea of sewage sludge, untreated sewage, chemical waste and other things has reduced over recent decades, much of our waste still impacts estuaries and seas. Fertilisers applied to the land, petrochemicals and other contaminants, litter and plastics are all washed into rivers, where they join human waste heading for estuaries and the sea. Consequences include eutrophication, hypoxia, blooms of toxic algae, accumulation of persistent organic pollutants and disease. Habitat destruction heavily impacts coastal ecosystems. Marshes and mudflats are 'reclaimed', developments are built and channels are dredged (the dredgings of which are dumped). Many estuaries, particularly those with ports, are heavily modified. Replacement of soft (natural) sea defences, such as marshes, with hard structures, such as seawalls, removes habitat for invertebrates. Add to this sea-level rise (either natural, e.g. eustatic rebound, or anthropogenic, such as the consequences of melting ice) and coastal squeeze results. As a result, the intertidal habitat all but disappears (along with the services intertidal mudflats and marshes provide) and animals which feed on invertebrates, such as seabirds, waders and geese, have to feed elsewhere. Dredging alters hydrodynamics and sediment supply, and hard structures allow species which live on them to spread into areas where they did not live previously. Invasive species are transported on ships' hulls and in ballast water and can have deleterious consequences. Substances applied to prevent fouling by invertebrates can have unforeseen consequences. Tributyltin, for example, severely damaged populations of gastropods and bivalves. The consequences of climate change, such as increased storminess, sea-level rise, warming waters and acidification, may affect trophic interactions, larval production and survival, physiology and health.

Prospects: The overall trend in biodiversity in estuarine and marine invertebrates is unlikely to be an improving one in the foreseeable future. That being said, recent new legislation in the UK and the adoption of international and

European Union initiatives and directives suggest that the marine environment is being taken more seriously than it was. There is evidence that the careful management of the marine environment may lead to recovery of at least some of the biodiversity present in some marine environments. The move towards managing our seas in a more holistic, rather than sectoral, fashion is a start.

References

Angel, M.V. (1993) Biodiversity of the pelagic ocean. *Conservation Biology, 7*, 760–772.

Brierley, A.S. & Kingsford, M.J. (2009) Impacts of climate change on marine organisms and ecosystems. *Current Biology,* **19**, R602–R614.

Briggs, J.C. (1994) Species diversity: land and sea compared. *Systems Biology,* **43**, 130–135.

Diaz, R.J. & Rosenberg, R. (2008) Spreading dead zones and consequences for marine ecosystems. *Science, 321*, 926–929.

Fabry, V.J., Seibel, B.A., Feely, R.A. & Orr, J.C. (2008) Impacts of ocean acidification on marine fauna and ecosystem processes. *Journal of Marine Science, 65*, 414–432.

Grassle, J.F. (1991) Deep-sea benthic biodiversity. *BioScience, 41*, 464–469.

Gray, J.S. (1997) Marine biodiversity: patterns, threats and conservation needs. *Biodiversity Conservation, 6*, 153–175.

Jackson, J.B.C. (2001) What was natural in the coastal oceans? *Proceedings of the National Academy USA, 98*, 5411–5418.

Jackson, J.B.C. (2008) Ecological extinction and evolution in the brave new ocean. *Proceedings of the National Academy USA, 105*(suppl. 1), 11458–11465.

Jackson, J.B.C., Kirby, M.X., Berger, W.H., Bjorndal, K.A., Botsford, L.W., Bourque, B.J., Bradbury, R.H., Cooke, R., Erladson, J., Estes, J.A., Hughes, T.P., Kidwell, S., Lange, C.B., Lenihan, H.S., Pandolfi, J.M., Peterson, C.H., Steneck, R.S., Tegner, M.J. & Warner, R.R. (2001) Historical overfishing and the recent collapse of coastal ecosystems. *Science, 293*, 629–638.

Justic, D., Rabalais, N.N. & Turner, R.E. (1996) Effects of climate change on hypoxia in coastal waters: A doubled CO_2 scenario for the northern Gulf of Mexico. *Limnology and Oceanography, 41*, 992–1003.

Levin, L.A., Boesch, D.F., Covich, A., Dahm, C., Erséus, C., Ewel, K.C., Kneib, R.T., Moldenke, A., Palmer, M.A., Snelgrove, P., Strayer, D. & Weslawski, J.M. (2001) The function of Marine Critical Transition Zones and the importance of sediment biodiversity. *Ecosystems, 4*, 430–451.

Lotze, H.K., Lenihan, H.S., Bourque, B.J., Bradbury, R.H., Cooke, R.G., Kay, M.C., Kidwell, S.M., Kirby, M.X., Peterson, C.H. & Jackson, J.B.C. (2006) Depletion, degradation and recovery potential of estuaries and coastal seas. *Science, 312*, 1806–1809.

Lotze, H.K. & Worm, B. (2009) Historical baselines for large marine animals. *Trends in Ecological Evolution, 24*, 254–262.

May, R.M. (2010) Ecological science and tomorrow's world. *Philosophical Transactions of the Royal Society B, 365*, 41–47.

MA (Millennium Ecosystem Assessment) (2005) Ecosystems and human well-being: Current state and trends, Volume 1. Island Press, Washington D.C.

Myers, R.A. & Worm, B. (2003) Rapid worldwide depletion of predatory fish communities. *Nature, 423*, 280–283.

Pauly, D. (1995) Anecdotes and the shifting baseline syndrome of fisheries. *Trends in Ecological Evolution, 10*, 430.

Pörtner, H.O., Langenbuch, M. & Michaelidis, B. (2005) Synergistic effects of temperature extremes, hypoxia, and increases in CO_2 on marine animals: From earth history to global change. *Journal of Geophysical Research – Oceans, 110*, 1–15.

Ray, G.C. (1991) Coastal-zone biodiversity patterns. *BioScience, 41*, 490–498.

Ray, G.C. & Grassle, J.F. (1991) Marine biological diversity. *BioScience, 41*, 453–461.

Richardson, A.J., Bakun, A., Hays, G.C. & Gibbons, M.J. (2009) The jellyfish joyride: causes, consequences and management responses to a more gelatinous future. *Trends in Ecological Evolution, 24*, 312–322.

Thompson, R.C., Crowe, T.P. & Hawkins, S.J. (2002) Rocky intertidal communities: past environmental changes, present status and predictions for the next 25 years. *Environmental Conservation, 29*, 168–191.

Vaquer-Sunyer, R. & Duarte, C. (2008) Thresholds of hypoxia for marine biodiversity. *Proceedings National Academy Science, 105*, 15452–15457.

Widdicombe, S. & Spicer, J.I. (2008) Predicting the impact of Ocean acidification on benthic biodiversity: What can physiology tell us? *Journal of Experimental Marine Biology and Ecology, 366*, 187–197.

Worm, B., Barbier, E.B., Beaumont, N., Duffy, J.E., Folke, C., Halpern, B.S., Jackson, J.B.C., Lotze, H.K., Micheli, F., Palumbi, S.R., Sala, E., Selkoe, K.A., Stachowicz, J.J. & Watson, R. (2006) Impacts of biodiversity loss on ocean ecosystem services. *Science, 314*, 787–790.

Terrestrial and freshwater invertebrates

Authors: Allan Watt, Adam Vanbergen and Aidan Keith

Taxa included in this group: Terrestrial invertebrates include insects, spiders and other arthropods, snails, nematodes and earthworms.

Diversity in the UK: Terrestrial invertebrates comprise an estimated 95% of species globally. Knowledge of their diversity remains poor, even in the UK. There are, for example, approximately 50 species of woodlice in the UK, 50 centipedes, 60 millipedes, 650 spiders, 200 non-marine molluscs, 13 flatworms, 25 harvestmen, 260 springtails, 50 mayflies, 500 sawflies, 2,500 butterflies and moths, and 4,000 beetles. To put this in context, there are about 20,000 beetle species in Europe and 300,000 globally.

Roles in ecosystem services: Invertebrates play a major role in a range of ecosystem services, particularly as pollinators, natural enemies (predators and parasitoids) of agricultural and forest crops, and as decomposers. They may play a role in meaningful places and socially valued landscapes and waterscapes, but, apart from butterflies, this is probably minor in relation to other species groups.

Status and trends: There are long-term status and trend data for a range of invertebrate groups, including several insects groups (e.g. moths, butterflies, bees, dragonflies), spiders and some molluscs (e.g. land snails), but coverage is biased towards groups that are relatively easy to observe or trap, and groups that are culturally valued, particularly butterflies. As a result, data on these taxa provide limited, rather than comprehensive, information about trends in the invertebrate taxa that are responsible for the delivery of ecosystem services. Data on butterflies (**Figure 4.5**) and insect pollinators (Biesmeijer *et al.* 2006; Carvell *et al.* 2006) show significant recent population declines. The resampling of soil invertebrates as part of the Countryside Survey in 2007 (Emmett *et al.* 2010) established that the abundance of invertebrates in 2007 was greater than in 1998 under all broad habitats except arable (crops and weeds) (**Figure A.4.1.5.1**). The increased invertebrate abundance seen in 2007 was largely due to greater mite populations, suggesting that different soil groups may respond to environmental changes in a specific manner. The 2007 Countryside Survey also reported small, but statistically significant, reductions in the number of soil invertebrate broad taxa (**Figure A.4.1.5.1**) across a range of habitats.

Drivers of change: The key drivers of change in invertebrate abundance and diversity are land use and management, and pollution. There is also increasing evidence of the impact of climate change. Most of the evidence does not, however, relate to invertebrate groups that play a major role in the delivery of ecosystem services. Invertebrate natural enemies of pests have probably declined as a result of changes in crop species (Hicks *et al.* 2001) and agricultural intensification (Wilby & Thomas 2002; Tscharntke *et al.* 2005). Similarly, pollinators have suffered from changes to agro-ecosystems, including hedgerow removal (Hannon & Sisk 2009) and changes to field margins (Carvell *et al.* 2004).

Prospects: Land use change is likely to continue to affect terrestrial invertebrates and climate change will probably have an increasing impact. Unless monitoring of invertebrates is expanded, however, our knowledge and understanding of trends in the abundance and diversity of terrestrial invertebrates will continue to be limited, particularly among the many taxa that play a role in the delivery of ecosystem services. Initiatives such as the Countryside Survey can provide useful information for some taxa; while such a single repeated sampling campaign cannot determine unequivocally whether change in soil invertebrate populations is underway, this kind of large-scale dataset is essential to understand potential drivers of change.

References:

Biesmeijer, J.C., Roberts, S.P.M. & Reemer, M. (2006) Parallel declines in pollinators and insect-pollinated plants in Britain and the Netherlands. *Science*, **313**, 351–354.

Carvell, C., Meek, W.R., Pywell, R.F. & Nowakowski, M. (2004) The response of foraging bumblebees to successional change in newly created arable field margins. *Biological Conservation*, **118**, 327–339.

Carvell, C., Roy, D.B., Smart, S.M., Pywell, R.F., Preston, C.D. & Goulson, D. (2006) Declines in forage availability for bumblebees at a national scale. *Biological Conservation*, **132**, 481–489.

Emmett, B.A., Reynolds, B., Chamberlain, P.M., Rowe, E., Spurgeon, D., Brittain, S.A., Frogbrook, Z., Hughes, S., Lawlor, A.J., Poskitt, J., Potter, E., Robinson, D.A., Scott, A., Wood, C. & Woods, C. (2010) Countryside Survey: Soils Report from 2007. Technical Report No. 9/07 NERC/Centre for Ecology & Hydrology 192pp. (CEH Project Number: C03259).

Hannon, L.E. & Sisk, T.D. (2009) Hedgerows in an agri-natural landscape: Potential habitat value for native bees. *Biological Conservation*, **142**, 2140–2154.

Hicks, B.J., Barbour, D.A., Evans, H.F., Heritage, S., Leather, S.R., Milne R. & Watt A.D. (2001) The history and control of the pine beauty moth, *Panolis flammea* (D&S), (*Lepidoptera: Noctuidae*) in Scotland from 1976 to 2000. *Agricultural and Forest Entomology*, **3**, 161–168.

Tscharntke, T., Klein, A.M., Kruess, A., Steffan-Dewenter, I. & Thies, C. (2005) Landscape perspectives on agricultural intensification and biodiversity – ecosystem service management. *Ecology Letters*, **8**, 857–874.

Wilby, A. & Thomas, M.B. (2002) Natural enemy diversity and pest control: patterns of pest emergence with agricultural intensification. *Ecology Letters*, **5**, 353–360.

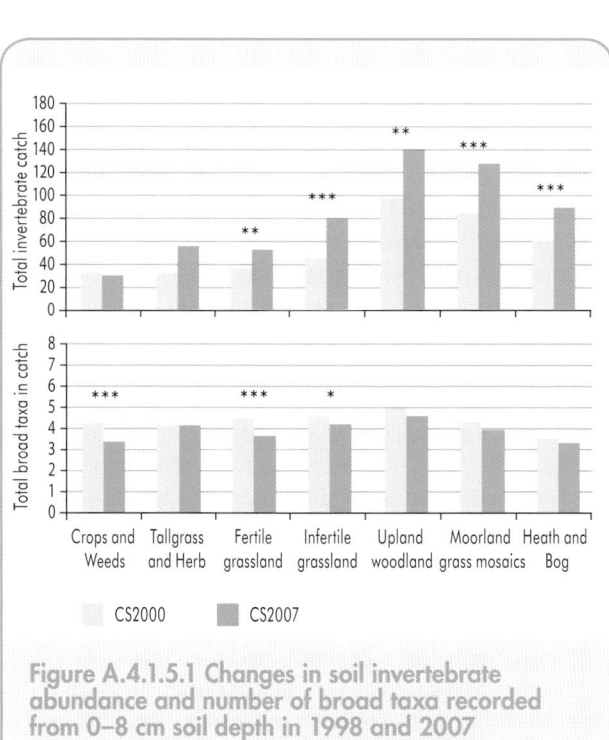

Figure A.4.1.5.1 Changes in soil invertebrate abundance and number of broad taxa recorded from 0–8 cm soil depth in 1998 and 2007 Countryside Surveys (CS2000 and CS2007); separated by Aggregate Vegetation Category. Asterisks indicate significant difference between surveys, * = P <0.05; ** = P <0.01; *** = P <0.001. Source: data from Emmett *et al.* (2010). Countryside Survey data owned by NERC – Centre for Ecology & Hydrology.

A.4.1.6 Fish

Marine fish

Author: Simon Jennings

Taxa included in this group: Marine fishes, including transitional/diadromous species such as the European eel (*Anguilla anguilla*) and sturgeon.

Diversity in the UK: More than 330 fish species inhabit the shelf seas surrounding the British Isles. More than 13,000 species of marine fishes have been recorded globally.

Roles in ecosystem services: Marine fishes support fisheries and contribute to wild species diversity. Their presence can be enjoyed by recreational users of the sea such as divers and sea anglers. The first sale value of fish and shellfish taken by UK vessels from UK waters was £510 million in 2007 with an estimated Gross Value Added (GVA) of £204 million. Fish processing provided an additional GVA of £385 million in 2007. There are 12,729 full- and part-time fishermen in the UK. Participation in recreational sea angling was estimated to be 290,800 people from a boat and 480,950 people from the shore in 2007. The observation of marine fishes contributes to the diving experience and 190,000 recreational divers use the coast each year. The total expenditure by anglers resident in England and Wales in 2003 was estimated at £538 million, which consisted of £178 million for shore-based activities, £82 million for boat charters and £278 million for own-boat activities. Key sources: Frost (2010); Saunders (2010).

Status and trends: Since 1960, there have been major changes in fish populations and communities, primarily driven by the effects of fishing and climate. Trends in fishing mortality broadly reflected trends in fishing effort, with overall fishing mortality rates rising from 1960 to the mid-1990s, before stabilising and starting to fall in response to management measures. The marine environment has generally warmed since the 1960s, with the range of cold water species retracting northwards and warm water species invading from the south. The abundance of species in the cod family generally peaked in the late 1960s, owing to favourable environmental conditions, but subsequently fell, largely as a consequence of very high fishing mortality rates. Some species that were particularly vulnerable to fishing, owing to their low population growth rates, have decreased in abundance throughout the period. For instance, an especially vulnerable, but once abundant, species, the common skate (*Raja batis*), was regionally extinct by the 1970s. A recent taxonomic revision of this species implies that many of the remaining individuals that have been reported from outside the regions of extinction belong to a smaller and less vulnerable species. Thus the true common skate, named as the 'flapper skate' in this revision, may now be confined to very few areas and found only at very low abundance. Other vulnerable species include several deep-water fish species; sharks, rays and skates; and transitional/diadromous species such as the European eel and sturgeon. Many of these animals have recently been 'listed' as requiring statutory protection (OSPAR, CITES, Bern Conventions). As the abundance of many larger species has declined, so smaller species have proliferated, increasing the turnover time of communities. However, community-wide spatial patterns in fish diversity in UK waters, as measured with standard diversity indices that capture richness or evenness, reflect biogeographical factors as well as spatial variation in the effects of fishing. Key sources: Brander (1981); Pope & Macer (1996); Iglésias *et al.* (2009); Frost (2010); Saunders (2010).

Drivers of change: The main large-scale drivers of change in marine fish diversity are overexploitation and climate.

Prospects: In the last few years, there have been reductions in the number of overfished stocks and some signs of increases in the size of individuals in fish communities, but no signs of the recovery of the species most vulnerable to fishing. Thus, of 20 assessed finfish stocks in UK waters, the percentage thought to have full reproductive capacity and to be harvested sustainably has risen from 10% or less in the early 1990s to 20–30% in the 2000s and around 40% in 2007. The proportion of large individuals and species in fish communities has also started to rise in the last five years. The changes are thought to be a response to reductions in overall fishing mortality. Over the last eight years, European Union controls on fisheries have contributed to reductions in total fishing effort in the international demersal fisheries of around 30% or more in the North Sea, west of Scotland and the Irish Sea. During the last ten years, fishing mortality estimates for 67% of assessed fish stocks in UK waters have declined. The monitoring and assessment of fish stocks focuses on commercially exploited stocks and the bottom-dwelling fish community that lives over relatively smooth seabeds which can be sampled with survey trawls. As such, knowledge of changes in these fishes is better documented than changes in many estuarine, coastal, deep-water and highly migratory species, although some estuaries, such as the Thames and Severn, are well monitored using a combination of surveys and samples from power station cooling intake screens. Recent increases in the abundance of some commercial stocks and larger species have to be interpreted against a background of long-term depletion, and current levels of abundance and proportions of large species are still well below the highest levels recorded since 1960. The recent declines in fishing mortality rates appear to have little impact on the abundance of larger and more vulnerable non-target species. Key sources: Frost (2010); Saunders (2010).

References

Brander, K. (1981) Disappearance of common skate, *Raia batis*, from Irish Sea. *Nature*, **290**, 48–49.

Frost, M. (2010) Charting Progress 2 Feeder Report: Healthy and Biologically Diverse Seas. UK Marine Monitoring and Assessment Strategy (UKMMAS), Defra, London. [online] Available at: <http://chartingprogress.defra.gov.uk/healthy-and-biologically-diverse-seas-feeder-report> [Accessed 26.01.11].

Iglésias, S.P., Toulhoat, L. & Sellos, D.Y. (2009) Taxonomic confusion and market mislabelling of threatened skates: important consequences for their conservation status. Aquatic conservation marine and freshwater research. Aquatic Conservation: *Marine and Freshwater Ecosystems,* 10.1002/aqc.1083.

Pope, J.G. & Macer, C.T. (1996) An evaluation of the stock structure of North Sea cod, haddock, and whiting since 1920, together with a consideration of the impacts of fisheries and predation effects on their biomass and recruitment. *ICES Journal of Marine Science*, **53**, 1157–1169.

Saunders, J. (2010) Charting Progress 2 Feeder Report: Productive Seas. Chapters 3.5 and 3.6. UK Marine Monitoring and Assessment Strategy (2010), Defra, London. [online] Available at: <http://chartingprogress.defra.gov.uk/productive-seas-feeder-report-download> [Accessed 26.01.11].

Freshwater fish

Author: Charles R. Tyler

Taxa included in this group: Freshwater fishes in the UK include members of the orders Cypriniforms, Acipenceriforms, Clupeiforms, Perciformes, Siluriformes, Anguilliformes, Atheriniformes, Mugiliformes, Salmoniformes, Esociformes, Gasterosteiformes, Petromyzontiformes and Gadiformes. Not all of these species reside for their full lives in freshwater, but rather move and/or migrate between freshwater and estuarine/marine environments, such as the European eel (*Anguilla anguilla*), Atlantic salmon (*Salmo salar*), river lamprey (*Lampetra fluviatilis*) and thick lipped grey mullet (*Chelon labrosus*).

Diversity in the UK: Sixty-four species of freshwater/brackish water fish have been recorded in the UK (www.wbrc.org.uk/worcRecd/Issue10/fishpopn.htm). Not all of these fish species are native, however, and some have been introduced either purposefully or accidentally. Purposeful introductions include the grass carp (*Ctenopharyngodon idella*) for weed control, rainbow trout (*Oncorhynchus mykiss*) for aquaculture and sport fishing, wels catfish (*Silurus glanis*) for sport fishing, and goldfish (*Carassius auratus auratus*) and orf, (*Leuciscus idus*) for aquaria and ornamental ponds. Accidental releases include the topmouth gudgeon (*Pseudorasbora parva*, sunbleak (*Leucaspius delineatus*) and pumpkin seed sunfish (*Lepomis gibbosus*). Worldwide, there are an estimated total of 26,000 species of fish in freshwater/estuarine and marine environments.

Roles in ecosystem services: Freshwater fishes are of considerable importance to UK ecosystem services and society as a whole. Wild UK freshwater fisheries have a significant economic value. As an example, commercial salmon and eel/elver fisheries in inland waters in England and Wales are thought to be worth up to £4 million annually (www.wbrc.org.uk/worcRecd/Issue10/fishpopn.htm). Recreational fishing, however, is the most important economic consideration for UK freshwater fisheries, and is estimated at £2.7 billion per annum, with an additional estimated £3 billion in the market value of fishing rights. The aquaculture of Atlantic salmon and rainbow trout are further significant economic enterprises in the UK, with annual tonnages in the region of 129,000 and 19,000, respectively (www.marlab.ac.uk/Uploads/ Documents/Survey00.pdf; Trout News 2005). Fish are also of considerable social and cultural importance in the UK. In historical times, commercial inland fisheries supported whole distinctive communities; today, there are approximately 3 million freshwater recreational anglers in England and Wales alone. In addition to their own conservation value, through recreational fisheries, fish ensure the endurance and protection of extensive freshwater habitats and their associated wildlife. Fish species and communities are arguably the best indicators of the well-being of aquatic ecosystems, in terms of both water quality and the physical environment.

Status and trends: In England and Wales there are regional differences in the trends for freshwater fisheries, but 13 species of fish are considered rare or threatened, and some, notably the burbot (*Lota lota*) and the common sturgeon (*Acipenser sturio*), are believed to be extinct in GB waters. Important commercial species in national decline include the Atlantic salmon, brown trout (*Salmo trutta fario*), grayling *(Thymallus thymallus*) and European eel. Considering the trends for Atlantic salmon in England and Wales, commercial catches have declined 40% in the last five years, but interpretation of these data is complicated by the fact that there have been increased regulatory controls and the buy-out of net licences during this time. Adult counts and returning stock estimates in UK rivers over available time-series show clear decline in some rivers (Itchen, Frome, Tamar and Thames); no substantive change in others (Dee, Test and Caldew); and an increasing trend in some (Tees, Fowey, Lune and Kent) (www.environment-agency.gov.uk/research/library/publications/33933.aspx). For eels, the picture is bleak: since the 1980s, the number of elvers (young eels) returning to European rivers has declined catastrophically to just 1% of their historic level; a decline clearly evident in the pattern of catches from the River Severn, the major elver fishery for England and Wales. Almost half of Scotland's 26 native fish species are thought to be declining including the river lamprey, brook lamprey (*Lampetra planeri*), allis shad (*Alosa alosa*), twaite shad (*Allosa falax*), Atlantic salmon, brown trout, Arctic char (*Salvelinus alpinus*), sparling (smelt; *Osmerus eperlanus*), European eel, and nine-spined stickleback (*Pungitius pungitius*). Eleven native species are considered threatened and one species, the vendace (*Coregonus albula*), has become extinct in Scotland. In contrast, pike (*Esox lucius*), minnow (*Phoxinus phoxinus*), roach (*Rutilus rutilus*) and perch (*Perca fluviatilis*) are increasing in Scotland (www.snh.org.uk/publications/on-line/advisorynotes/132/132.htm), favoured by warming due to climate change (Maitland 1991) and eutrophication (Maitland 1984).

Drivers of change: The main pressures affecting freshwater fish species throughout the UK include agricultural practices and habitat loss, pollution, and overfishing. The introduction of alien species, such as the zander (*Sander lucioperca*) which predates heavily on native species, and the topmouth gudgeon (*Pseudorasbora parva*) which can transmit diseases to native species, has impacted on specific freshwater fish populations. River engineering, habitat change and the creation of barriers to migration have also had an impact. The causes of the dramatic and widespread decline in eel populations in England and Wales (see below) are complex, but likely include changing ocean currents, loss of wetlands, disease, pollution and barriers such as dams and weirs (www.environment-agency.gov.uk/research/ library/publications /33933.aspx).

Prospects: Conservation management has brought about local recoveries for some fish species, such as the Atlantic salmon, particularly where water quality has been sufficiently improved (e.g. the Rivers Clyde and Carron). The implementation of restrictions on rod licences (and fish takes) and catch limits for netting have helped to protect the salmon and eel fisheries, but dissecting these factors from other contributing environmental factors is extremely complex. In England, pollution events that result in the decimation of wild local cyprinid fisheries have been (and still are) dealt with through restocking with fish supplied from a national breeding unit run by the UK Environment Agency. But the aim must be to reduce such pollution events through better regulation and control of environmental pollution discharges. Effective management and protection of UK freshwater fishes requires a better understanding of what drives their population dynamics—something that is lacking for almost all UK freshwater fishes.

References

Maitland, P.S. (1984) The effects of eutrophication on wildlife. *Institute of Terrestrial Ecology Symposium,* **13**, 101–108.

Maitland, P.S. (1991) Climate change and fish in northern Europe: some possible scenarios. *Proceedings of the Institute of Fishery Management. Annual Study Course,* **22**, 97–110.

Maitland, P.S. (1999) Priority freshwater fish in Scotland. A report to SNH. Haddington: Fish Conservation Centre.

Trout News (2005) Trout News, Number 40, July 2005, CEFAS, Lowestoft. [online] <www.cefas.defra.gov.uk/publications/troutnews/tnews40.pdf> [accessed 15.04.11].

A.4.1.7 Amphibians

Author: Richard A. Griffiths

Taxa included in this group: Amphibian biodiversity in the UK comprises seven native species. Five of these species have widespread distributions: common frog (*Rana temporaria*), common toad (*Bufo bufo*), smooth newt (*Triturus vulgaris*), palmate newt (*Triturus helveticus*) and great crested newt (*Triturus cristatus*). The other two species are the natterjack toad (*Bufo calamita*), which has more specialist habitat requirements and is largely confined to sand dunes, lowland heath and saltmarsh habitats, and the pool frog (*Rana lessonae*), which is found at a single site as a result of a recent reintroduction.

Diversity in the UK: There are a number of areas within the UK where the five widespread species coexist and all five species may be found breeding within the same water body. Habitats supporting natterjack toad populations may also contain some of the widespread species, but it is uncommon to find six species occurring at the same site. All of the UK species are widespread in other parts of Europe, and are classified as 'Least Concern' on the IUCN Red List.

Roles in ecosystem services: The role of amphibians in ecosystem services is poorly understood, but frogs and newts frequently feature in urban conservation and green space initiatives. The establishment of garden ponds in urban and suburban areas has proved to be an effective way of establishing populations of some species and raising the profile of amphibians locally and nationally. Frogs and toads (and to a lesser extent newts) have featured prominently within literature and are of cultural importance within the UK.

Status and trends: All of our native species have suffered declines over the past 50 years. Since the 1960s, common frogs have made something of a comeback in urban areas through their ability to colonise small garden ponds quickly. Smooth newts—and to a lesser extent palmate newts and common toads—have made similar recoveries in some areas, although it is unlikely that such colonisations have offset declines within the wider countryside.

Drivers of change: For the widespread species, declines have been largely related to changes in agricultural practices that have resulted in the loss of breeding ponds and associated terrestrial habitat. Natterjack toads have suffered similar losses as a result of the development of coastal areas and heathlands for recreation, housing, agriculture and commerce (Beebee & Griffiths 2000). There is evidence that the isolation of populations as a result of development can lead to inbreeding depression. In addition, disease has become a recent issue for UK amphibians, with die-offs of some species regularly observed, particularly in garden ponds.

Prospects: Over the past two decades, interest in the conservation of amphibians has increased considerably within both the voluntary and professional sectors in the UK, and there are now several organisations that are carrying out conservation work, advocacy and public relations. Over the same timeframe, amphibian declines have become a high-profile conservation issue on a global scale, resulting in a range of initiatives to both highlight and tackle the problems. However, within the UK, amphibians frequently come into conflict with development and other activities involving changes in land use; national pressures for housing, food and commercial development are likely to result in the ongoing loss of populations despite mitigation and conservation interventions.

Reference

Beebee, T. & Griffiths, R. (2000) Amphibians and Reptiles. A Natural History of the British Herpetofauna. HarperCollins, London.

A.4.1.8 Reptiles

Terrestrial reptiles

Author: Christopher Reading

Taxa included in this group: In the UK, the native reptiles comprise three snake species from two families (two from the Colubridae and one from the Viperidae) and three lizard species from two families (two from the Lacertidae and one from the Anguidae).

Diversity in the UK: The three snakes are the adder/viper (*Vipera berus*), the grass snake (*Natrix natrix*) and the smooth snake (*Coronella austriaca*). The three lizards are the common lizard (*Zootica vivipara*), the sand lizard (*Lacerta agilis*) and the slow-worm (*Anguis fragilis*). The smooth snake and sand lizard occur in southern England where they are at the northern edge of their geographical range. The grass snake occurs as far as northern England, but is absent from Scotland. The adder, slow-worm and common lizard occur throughout mainland GB. With the exception of the common lizard, there are no reptiles in Ireland.

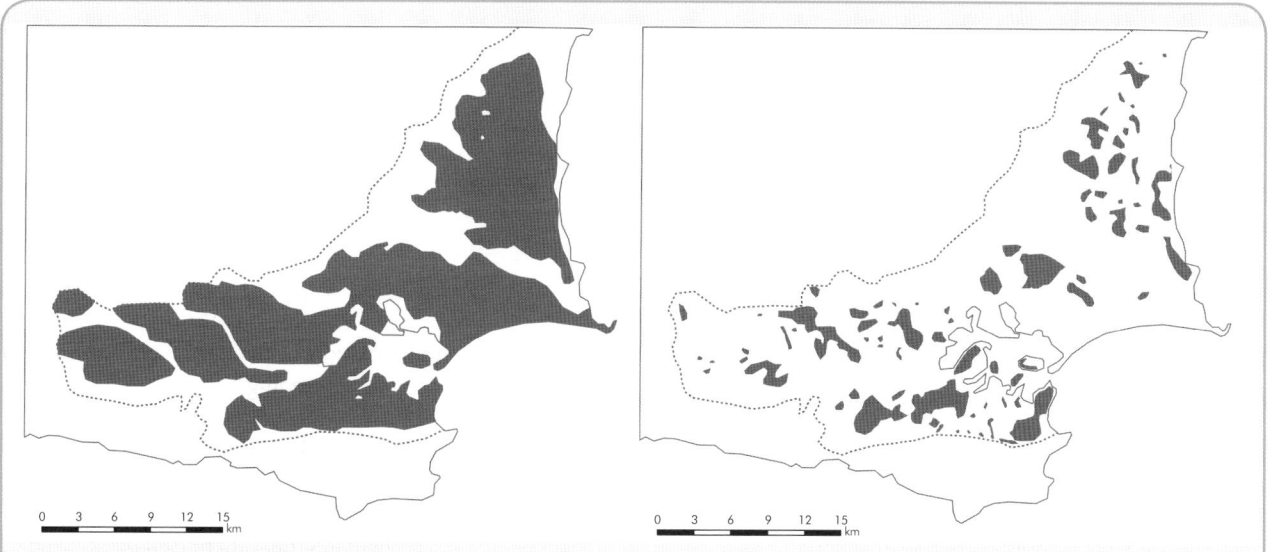

Figure A.4.1.8.1 Changes in the extent of lowland heathland in Dorset between a) 1759 and b) 1978. Source: Webb & Haskins (1980). Copyright (1980), reproduced with permission from Elsevier.

Roles in ecosystem services: With respect to trees and vegetation, the effect of the presence of reptiles relates to the preservation of the habitat where they occur. This is particularly true for the nationally rare sand lizard and smooth snake as the habitats in which they occur gain a significant measure of protection under the Wildlife and Countryside Act, 1981, due to their presence. This also applies to habitats where the other four species occur, though to a lesser degree. In this respect, the presence of rare reptile species can have a financial impact on the potential development of land as Environmental Impact Assessments are required to be completed, which may call for subsequent mitigation measures to be undertaken.

Status and trends: The two rarest species (sand lizard and smooth snake) are almost totally restricted to dry lowland heath in the south of England; being at the northern edge of their geographical range, change in the extent (**Figure A.4.1.8.1**) and area (**Figure A.4.1.8.2**) of this habitat type may be used as an indication of how the status of these two species has changed (declined) over time (Webb & Haskins 1980; Rose *et al.* 2000). With the exception of the smooth snake, there are almost no reliable long-term datasets for any of these species, preventing changes of status over time to be determined. The data that is available cannot be totally relied upon as it has been collected in many different ways, by people with varying degrees of expertise, making comparisons between recorders and between years of dubious value. In general, however, the consensus is that all six species are probably in decline, mainly as a result of habitat loss, though the slow-worm remains relatively widespread and locally abundant.

Drivers of change: The warming effects of climate change in the UK are likely to extend the potential range of all the species northwards. Nevertheless, reptile populations are likely to continue to decline due to habitat loss and disturbance—the adder appears to be particularly susceptible to disturbance.

Prospects: In the future, the main threat to all six species, but to the two rarest reptiles in particular, is likely to be habitat loss as the areas in which they occur are fragmented and lost to development. If the climate warms, as predicted, it is possible that some species may potentially extend their range northwards. However, any benefits from a warming climate are likely to be outweighed by habitat loss and disturbance.

References

Moore, N.W. (1962) The heaths of Dorset and their conservation. *Journal of Ecology* **50**, 369–391.

Rose, R.J., Webb, N.R., Clarke, R.T. & Traynor, C.H. (2000) Changes on the heathlands in Dorset, England between 1987 and 1996. *Biological Conservation* **93**, 117–125.

Webb, N.R. & Haskins, L.E. (1980) An ecological survey of heathlands in the Poole basin, Dorset, England, in 1978. *Biological Conservation* **17**, 281–296.

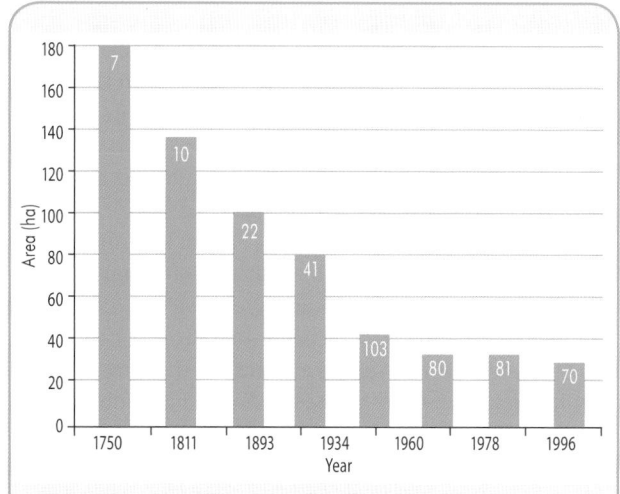

Figure A.4.1.8.2 The change in the area of heathland recorded in surveys between 1750 and 1996. The figures above the bars show the number of heathland fragments greater than 4 hectares that existed (data from the three ITE Dorset Heathland Surveys, 1978, 1987 and 1996, and historical data from Moore, 1962). Source: Rose *et al.* (2000). Copyright (2000), reproduced with permission from Elsevier.

Marine reptiles

Author: Matt Frost

Taxa included in this group and diversity in the UK: The only marine reptiles found in UK seas are turtles. Of the seven species of marine turtle found worldwide, four are known to occur occasionally in seas around the UK: leatherback turtle (*Dermochelys coriacea*); loggerhead turtle (*Caretta caretta*); Kemp's ridley (*Lepidochelys kempii*); and green turtle (*Chelonia mydas*). These species occur in extremely low numbers and only the leatherback turtle is seen frequently enough (an average of 33 records a year since 1998) to be considered a true member of the UK fauna (Marubini 2010). There are also two individual records (1953 and 1983) for hawksbill turtle (*Eretmochelys imbricate*), but this species is not considered a visitor to UK waters (Howson & Picton 1997).

Role in ecosystem services: Marine turtles play a role in marine ecosystems worldwide by "maintaining healthy seagrass beds and coral reefs, providing key habitat for other marine life, helping to balance marine food webs and facilitating nutrient cycling from water to land" (Wilson *et al.* 2010). Wilson *et al.* (2010) also found that, as regards direct human use, the non-consumptive use of turtles (mainly tourism) was of much higher value than consumptive use. In the UK, the value of marine turtles is mainly as flagship species used to promote interest in, and engagement with, the marine environment.

Status and trends: Six of the seven species of marine turtle are classified by IUCN as Endangered or Critically Endangered. The leatherback is listed as Critically Endangered and is also on the OSPAR list of threatened or declining species, along with the loggerhead turtle. On a global scale, there have been very large declines in numbers of marine turtles (Bjorndal & Jackson 2003), but the numbers of turtles in UK waters are too few to make any confident assessment of state or trend for this area (Marubini 2010).

Drivers of change: It is important to note that turtles are wide-ranging species; the leatherback turtle, in particular, migrates throughout the Atlantic, with UK waters representing only a small, peripheral part of its summer foraging habitat (McMahon & Hays 2006; Witt *et al.* 2007). Marine turtle populations are, therefore, affected by drivers operating at larger scales than just the UK level, with pressure from commercial fisheries, habitat loss and climate change being considered the main drivers of change globally (Bjorndal & Jackson 2003). In the UK, entanglement in fishing ropes and nets, and ingestion of plastic debris, constitute the main threats, but occurrences are rare and their impact at the population level has not yet been assessed (Marubini 2010). There is little evidence, as yet, of whether climate change will have any effect on the distribution of turtles in UK waters, although leatherback turtles are expected to expand their range into higher latitudes as ocean temperatures increase (McMahon & Hays 2006).

Prospects: Marubini (2010) recommends that an international effort be made around the entire western approaches to the European shelf (with a focus around the Bay of Biscay) to estimate numbers and trends in marine turtles and inform conservation efforts undertaken in the UK and globally. This is extremely important as species of marine turtle, including the leatherback, remain Critically Endangered and at the risk of ecological and, in some cases physical, extinction (Wilson *et al.* 2010).

References

Bjorndal, K.A. & Jackson, J.B.C. (2003) Roles of sea turtles in marine ecosystems: Reconstructing the past. *The Biology of Sea Turtles Volume II*. (eds P.L. Lutz, J.A. Musick & J. Wyneken), pp. 259–273. CRC Press, Boca Raton, Florida (USA).

Howson, C.M. & Picton, B.E. (eds) (1997) The species directory of the marine fauna and flora of the British Isles and surrounding seas. Ulster Museum and the Marine Conservation Society. Belfast and Ross-on-Wye.

Marubini, F. (2010) Turtles. Charting Progress 2 Feeder Report: Healthy and Biologically Diverse Seas. UK Marine Monitoring and Assessment Strategy (UKMMAS), Defra. [online] Available at: <http://chartingprogress.defra.gov.uk/chapter-3-healthy-and-biologicaly-diverse-seas> [Accessed 24.01.11].

McMahon, C.R. & Hays, G.C. (2006) Thermal niche, large-scale movements and implications of climate change for a critically endangered marine vertebrate. *Global Change Biology,* **12**, 1330-1338.

Wilson, E.G., Miller, K.L., Allison, D. & Magliocca, M. (2010) Why healthy oceans need sea turtles: the importance of sea turtles to marine ecosystems. [online] Available at: <http://na.oceana.org/en/blog/2010/07/new-report-why-healthy-oceans-need-sea-turtles> [Accessed 07.02.11].

Witt, M.J., Broderick, A.C., Johns, D.J., Martin, C., Penrose, R., Hoogmoed, M.S. & Godley, B.J. (2007) Prey landscapes help identify potential foraging habitats for leatherback turtles in the NE Atlantic. *Marine Ecology Programme Series,* **337**, 234–243.

A.4.1.9 Birds

Authors: Richard D. Gregory, Richard B. Bradbury

Taxa included in this group: Here, we consider all birds (Vertebrata: Aves) occurring naturally in the UK.

Diversity in the UK: Around 250 bird species occur naturally in the UK on a regular basis, as resident or summer breeders, or as wintering or passage migrants (Gibbons *et al.* 1996; Gregory *et al.* 2002; Eaton *et al.* 2009). About 85% of these species breed in the UK, of which, 20% are rare breeding species (fewer than 300 pairs). In terms of global significance, the UK is home to large fractions of the global populations of a range of breeding seabirds and wintering wildfowl and waders.

Roles in ecosystem services: It can be argued that birds play a major role in wild species diversity, meaningful places, and socially valued landscapes and waterscapes. Large, enigmatic, flagship bird species hold a special fascination and attraction for people, as do garden birds (Crocker & Mabey 2005). The latter often introduce people to nature for the first time and represent their most common interaction with wildlife. Interest in birds is reflected, for instance, in over half a million people participating in garden birdwatches each January; over a million people being members of the Royal Society for the Protection of Birds (RSPB); and very substantial spending on bird-feeding.

Status and trends: Bird numbers and geographical ranges are tracked by a variety of survey schemes (Gibbons *et al.* 1996; Gregory *et al.* 2002; Eaton *et al.* 2009). Population trends of all but the rarest species are captured in multi-species 'Quality of Life' indicators (**Table A.4.1.9.1; Figure A.4.1.9.1**). The trend for all species with adequate data is relatively stable over four decades, but average trends differ according to the main habitat of the species (**Table A.4.1.9.1**). On average, seabird populations have increased, but they are now in decline. Birds associated with wet breeding habitats show population stability. Woodland and farmland birds have declined markedly, and while the former show greater stability in the last decade, the latter do not. Urban birds have increased over the last decade or so (**Table A.4.1.9.1**). Similar information is not available for the UK uplands, but some wading birds and songbirds at least appear to be in decline (Sim *et al.* 2005). Within habitats, generalist birds have tended to prosper, while specialists have declined. Among a smaller number of rare breeding species (40), occupying various different habitats, around 60% of have increased in number in recent decades. These include charismatic birds such as red kite (*Milvus milvus*), marsh harrier (*Circus aeruginosus*), stone-curlew (*Burhinus oedicnemus*), woodlark (*Lullula arborea*) and Dartford warbler (*Sylvia undata*). Wintering waterbirds have increased substantially in recent decades, but have declined in the most recent decade for which there is data (**Table A.4.1.9.1**).The number of bird species of high conservation concern in the UK has risen steadily over the last two decades (**Table A.4.1.9.2**). The latest assessment identifies 52 species in the highest category of conservation concern, mostly because of population declines.

Drivers of change: Evidence to link the decline of farmland birds with changes in agricultural practices is compelling (Wilson *et al.* 2009). There is also evidence linking change in woodland structure—itself driven by changes in forestry management, forest maturation and increased deer-browsing—with woodland bird populations (Hewson *et al.* 2007). Trends among breeding waterbirds are less well understood and seem to be linked to agricultural intensification and, perhaps, to the predation of ground-nesting birds (Ausden *et al.* 2009). Several of these species are long-distance migrants, with wintering grounds south of the Sahel, so numbers here may be driven by factors on their wintering grounds or migration sites. However, evidence for such effects is limited. Seabird numbers are linked in a complex fashion with fishery practices, marine food chains and oceanic changes (JNCC 2009). Increased discards may, in part, be responsible for the rise of seabird numbers in recent decades. Growing numbers of urban birds may be linked to wildlife-friendly management of green space and gardens, and increased food provision in gardens. Climatic change is frequently cited as a potential driver of trends in birds and there is increasing evidence for impacts in different habitats and speculation about its potential effects. Climatic change might be benefiting southern bird species, but acting to the detriment of those whose southern boundary lies in the UK (Green *et al.* 2008; Gregory *et al.* 2009). Climate change will interact with, and exacerbate, other drivers.

Prospects: The general loss of bird populations, due to the drivers discussed above, will diminish the delivery of wild species diversity, meaningful places, and socially valued landscapes and waterscapes, all of which are enriched by birds. However, increasing numbers of gardens birds, and the recovery and increase in endangered and charismatic bird species, most often through intensive conservation programmes, will increase delivery of the same range of services.

References

Ausden, M., Bolton, M., Butcher, N., Hoccom, D.G., Smart, J., & Williams, G. (2009) Predation of breeding waders on lowland wet grassland – is it a problem? *British Wildlife*, **21**, 29–38.

Table A.4.1.9.1 UK 'Quality of Life' indicators: population trends of wild bird species in different habitats. UK Sustainable Development and England Biodiversity Strategy Indicators. Source: data from the RSPB, BTO and Defra (2010).

Species group (number of species)	Long-term trend	Short-term trend	Key drivers
Breeding birds	**1970–2008**	**1998–2008**	
All species (114)	3%	6%	Multiple and diverse
Seabird species (19)	28%	-5%	Fishery practice and oceanic change
Water and wetland species (26)	1%	9%	Change in agricultural practices
Woodland species (38)	-14%	5%	Change in woodland structure
Farmland species (19)	-47%	-4%	Change in agricultural practices
Urban species (27)	-	11% *	Sympathetic management and food provision
Wintering birds	**1975/1976– 2006/2007**	**1996/1976– 2006/2007**	
All waterbird species (46)	57%	-6%	Site and species protection and management
Wildfowl species (27)	62%	-9%	
Wader species (15)	44%	-5%	
* English trends 1994–2008.			

Table A.4.1.9.2 Number of bird species of high, medium and low conservation concern.

Year	High concern	Medium concern	Low concern	
1990	117		Not assessed	Batten *et al.* (1990)
1996	36	110	Not assessed	Gibbons *et al.* (1996)
2002	40 (16%)	121 (49%)	86 (35%)	Gregory *et al.* (2002)
2009	52 (21%)	126 (51%)	68 (28%)	Eaton *et al.* (2009)

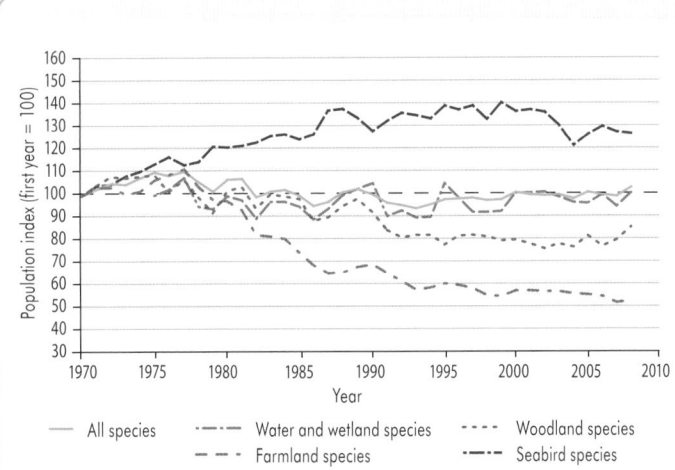

Figure A.4.1.9.1 UK 'Quality of Life' indicators: Population trends of wild birds. The graph shows the composite population trends of UK breeding bird species (n=114) with subdivisions showing grouped species' trends for seabirds (n=19), water and wetland birds (n=26), woodland birds (n=38), and farmland birds (n=19). On average, populations of woodland and farmland birds have fallen between 1970 and 2008 by 14% and 47% respectively. Source: data from RSPB, British Trust for Ornithology, JNCC and Defra.

Crocker, M. & Mabey, R. (2005) Birds Britannica. Chatto & Windus, London.

Eaton, M.A., Brown, A.F., Noble, D.G., Musgrove, A.J., Hearn, R.H., Aebischer, N.J., Gibbons, D.W., Evans, A. & Gregory, R.D. (2009) Birds of Conservation Concern 3: the population status of birds in the United Kingdom, Channel Islands and the Isle of Man. *British Birds.* **102**, 296–341.

Gibbons, D., Avery, M., Baillie, S., Gregory, R.D., Kirby, J., Porter, R., Tucker, G. & Williams, G. (1996) Bird Species of Conservation Concern in the United Kingdom, Channel Islands and Isle of Man: Revising the Red Data list. *Conservation Review,* **10**, 7–10.

Green, R.E., Collingham, Y.C., Willis, S.G., Gregory R.D., Smith K.W. & Huntley, B. (2008) Performance of climate envelope models in retrodicting recent changes in bird population size from observed climatic change. *Biology Letters,* **4**(5), 599–602. DOI:10.1098/rsbl.2008.0052.

Gregory, R.D., Wilkinson, N.I., Noble, D.G., Brown, A.F., Robinson, J.A., Hughes, J. Procter, D.A., Gibbons D.W. & Galbraith, C.A. (2002) The population status of birds in the United Kingdom, Channel Islands and Isle of Man: an analysis of conservation concern 2002–2007. *British Birds,* **95**, 410–448.

Gregory, R.D., Willis, S.G., Jiguet, F., Voríšek, P., Klvanová, A., van Strien, A., Huntley, B Collingham, Y.C., Couvet, D. & Green, R.E. (2009) An indicator of the impact of climatic change on European bird populations. *PLoS ONE,* **4**(3) e4678. doi:10.1371/journal.pone.0004678.

Hewson, C.M., Amar, A., Lindsell, J.A., Thewlis, R.M., Butler, S., Smith, K. & Fuller, R.J. (2007) Recent changes in bird populations in British broadleaved woodland. *Ibis,* **149**(Suppl. 2), 14–28.

JNCC (Joint Nature Conservation Committee) (2009) UK seabirds in 2008. Results from the UK Seabird Monitoring Programme. ISBN–13: 978 1 86107 611 3.

Sim, I.M.W., Gregory, R.D., Hancock, M. & Brown, A.F. (2005) Recent changes in the abundance of British upland breeding birds. *Bird Study,* **52**, 261–275.

Wilson, J.D., Evans, A.D. & Grice, P.V. (2009) Bird Conservation and Agriculture. Cambridge University Press, Cambridge.

A.4.1.10 Mammals

Terrestrial mammals

Authors: David Macdonald, Sandra Baker, Lauren Harrington, Tom Moorhouse

Taxa included in this group: This section includes both native and non-native UK species, as well as domestic livestock, which, although not present in the 'wild', may have significant impacts on the wider environment.

Diversity in the UK: There are 62 species (40 native and 22 non-native) and 4 subspecies of wild terrestrial mammal in the UK (Tracking Mammals Partnership, www.jncc.gov.uk/page-1757). Four species are on the IUCN Red List (IUCN 2009: the Scottish wildcat (*Felis silvestris*), which is listed as Vulnerable; and the otter (*Lutra lutra*), Bechstein's bat (*Myotis bechsteinii*) and barbastelle bat (*Barbastella barbastellus*), all of which are categorised as Near Threatened. The main mammalian livestock species present are beef and dairy cattle, sheep and pigs (Defra 2009).

Roles in ecosystem services: Terrestrial UK mammals have very important impacts upon: crops, livestock and fish through herbivore browsing and grazing (Wallis De Vries 1995; Putman & Moore 1998), potential disease transmission (e.g. badgers and TB; Macdonald *et al.* 2006) and predation (e.g. the potential impact of otters on local fisheries; Kruuk 2006); wild species diversity, primarily through their presence as a conspicuous component of our wild diversity, but secondarily through grazing (essential for the maintenance of certain habitats of high biodiversity value (Defra 2009)) and predation (by invasive mammal species in particular, for example, American mink *Mustela vison*, predate water voles *Arvicola terrestris*, and seabirds; Macdonald & Harrington 2003); meaningful places and socially valued land and waterscapes through their intrinsic existence value (White et al.1997; Dutton *et al.* 2010). Mammals have medium importance impacts upon: trees, standing vegetation and peat, principally through grazing actions (Thalen 1984), but also potentially through the ecosystem engineering effects of beavers (*Castor fiber*) (Rosell *et al.* 2005); and climate regulation, primarily through the production of the greenhouse gas methane by livestock (particularly cattle) (Defra 2009). Finally, terrestrial mammals may impact water purification through the ecosystem engineering action of beavers (e.g. Balodis 2004).

Drivers of change: The drivers of species trends for wild mammals in the UK include habitat- and climate-related factors (such as population increases and increasing urbanisation), human management ('pest' species control, reintroduction, the introduction of invasive species, and protection of species of conservation concern) and natural opportunities (i.e. habitat availability and a lack of predators, for example, for sika deer, *Cervus nippon*). But in many cases trends are unknown (e.g. the hedgehog *Erinaceus europaeus*) or not completely understood (e.g. the American mink). Because there are no common drivers for trends in wild mammals in the UK, and because the trends themselves vary among species, it is difficult to identify 'indicator' species for this group. The table below, therefore, describes recent trends, and their drivers, for a number of 'example' mammals. Drivers of trends in domestic livestock numbers are largely economic (including market prices and agri-environment schemes), but also include new regulations (see, for example, Defra 2009).

Status and trends: Unlike some taxa (e.g. bird species, the majority of which are relatively visible when present), wild mammal species are not always amenable to direct survey. Many species are cryptic and/or nocturnal, and their presence can only be inferred from indirect signs such as scats, footprints, homes (burrows, dens, nests, etc.), spoils (such as molehills or leftovers), or by invasive means such as live trapping. For this reason, nationwide surveys of wild mammal species in the UK are a rare and relatively recent phenomenon; they tend to be species-specific and omit a large number of species. The following information on wild mammal species trends is summarised from the Tracking Mammals Partnership (TMP) report (Battersby 2005), which covers 37 (57%) UK terrestrial mammals. The TMP report highlighted the fact that there are still insufficient data for approximately half of terrestrial mammals. Sufficient data were available to make some assessment of population change for 33 species and one subspecies.

Of the 24 native wild species and one native subspecies, 40% appear to be increasing, 12% declining and 16% remain stable. There were insufficient data to assess population trends for the remaining 32%. Native species currently increasing include several of the bat species, red and roe deer (*Cervus elaphus* and *Capreolus capreolus*) and several carnivore species (polecat *Mustela putorius*, badger *Meles meles*, and otter). Declining native species include the water vole, the dormouse (*Muscardinus avellanarius*) and the hedgehog (**Table A.4.1.10.1**).

Of the nine non-native wild species, 66% appear to be increasing, 11% declining and 22% are stable. Non-native species that are currently increasing include the grey squirrel (*Sciurus carolinensis*), the brown rat (*Rattus norvegicus*), and sika, fallow (*Dama dama*), Chinese water (*Hydropotes inermis*) and muntjac (*Muntiacus reevesi*) deer. The brown hare (*Lepus europaeus*) appears to be stable and the American mink appears to be declining. In most cases, trends appear to be unchanged over the last 25 years, except for the rabbit (*Oryctolagus cuniculus*) and the American mink, both of which appear to have declined in recent years following earlier increases, and for red foxes (*Vulpes vulpes*), red and fallow deer, for which earlier increases appear to have stabilised. For bats, there are insufficient data available to assess longer-term trends.

Over the last 25 years, the UK holdings of key mammalian livestock groups, e.g. cattle, sheep and pigs, have declined (Defra 2009).

Prospects: Prospects for UK mammals may differ greatly between wild and domestic species. Future numbers of domestic mammal species will respond to global and national economics, human population trends and changes in agricultural policy, but may also be affected by climate change, and so, are difficult to predict. Future prospects for wild mammals are most likely to be species-specific rather than general across all taxa. For established non-native species, changes in their populations or geographical range may occur as a result of human intervention (e.g. a national programme for the eradication of American mink or grey squirrels, although none are currently planned). The national population and range of several native species of conservation concern may increase due to reintroduction programmes (e.g. water voles), control programmes or due to strengthening of legislation (in particular the Wildlife and Countryside Act). Additionally, reintroductions may include previously extirpated species, such as beaver and lynx (*Lynx lynx*), so have the potential to increase mammalian biodiversity in the UK.

References

Battersby, J. (2005) UK Mammals: Species status and population trends. JNCC/Tracking Mammals Partnership 2005.

Balodis, M. (2004) Beaver populations of Latvia: history, development and management. Latvijas Zinatnu Akademijas vestis. *Dala B/Proceedings of the Latvian Academy of Sciences, Section B,* **7/8** (564/565) 1–127.

Dutton, A., Edwards-Jones, G., Macdonald, D.W. (2010) Estimating the value of non-use benefits from small changes in the provision of ecosystem services, *Conservation Biology* **24**(6): 1479–1487.

Defra (Department for Environment Food and Rural Affairs) (2009) Agriculture in the UK 2009. [online] Available at: <http://www.defra.gov.uk/statistics/files/defra-stats-auk-2008.pdf> [Accessed 07.02.11].

IUCN (International Union for Conservation of Nature) (2009) IUCN red list of threatened species. Version 2009.2, IUCN, Geneva. [online] < www.iucnredlist.org/> [Accessed 15.04.11].

JNCC (Joint Nature Conservation Committee) (2007) Results of the Tracking Mammals Partnership (TMP) Surveillance [online] Available at: <http://www.jncc.gov.uk/page-3744> [Accessed 16.03.11].

Kruuk, H. (2006) Otters – ecology, behaviour and conservation. Oxford University Press, Oxford.

Table A.4.1.10.1 Examples of trends in mammals (25 years to 2007).

	Common name	Scientific name	Trend	Drivers
Native wild species (by Order) (JNCC 2007)				
Insectivora	Hedgehog	*Erinaceus europaeus*	↓	Unknown
Chiroptera	Common pipistrelle	*Pipistrellus pipistrellus*	↑ (last 10 years)	Increased survival during hibernation (through warmer winters) and increased recording effort?
Lagomorpha	Mountain hare	*Lepus timidus*	No significant evidence	Not applicable
Rodentia	Water vole	*Arvicola terrestris*	↓	Habitat fragmentation and predation by American mink
Carnivora	Otter	*Lutra lutra*	↑	Improvement in water quality since organophosphates banned, end of persecution and reintroductions
Artiodactyla	Roe deer	*Capreolus capreolus*	↑	Increased availability of habitat (through afforestation) and forage (through planting of winter crops)
Non-native wild species (by Order) (JNCC 2007)				
Lagomorpha	Rabbit	*Oryctolagus cuniculus*	↑ (long-term) / ↓ (recent)	Unknown
Rodentia	Brown rat	*Rattus norvegicus*	↑	Increased urbanisation / changes in refuse quantities and collection?
Carnivora	American mink	*Mustela vison*	↓	In part mink removal, potentially other, unknown, factors (otter recovery has been suggested as a driver but the evidence is equivocal)
Artiodactyla	Reeve's muntjac	*Muntiacus reevesi*	↑	Natural dispersal into unoccupied areas and lack of predation in the UK
Domesticated livestock (by Family) (Defra 2009)				
Bovidae	Cattle	*Bos primigenius*	↑ (last 10 years)	Economic and policy drivers
Suidae	Pigs	*Sus domestica*	↓ (last 10 years)	
Bovidae	Sheep	*Ovis aries*	↓ (last 10 years)	

Macdonald, D.W. & Harrington, L.A. (2003) The American mink: the triumph and tragedy of adaptation out of context. *New Zealand Journal of Zoology*, **30**, 421–441.

Macdonald D.W., Riordan P. & Mathews F. (2006) Biological hurdles to the control of TB in cattle: A test of two hypothesis concerning wildlife to explain the failure of control. *Biological Conservation*, **131**, 268–286.

Macdonald, D.W. & Tattersall, F.H. (2001) Britain's Mammals: The Challenge for Conservation. People's Trust for Endangered Species, London.

Putman, R.J. & Moore, N.P. (1998) Impact of deer in lowland Britain on agriculture, forestry and conservation habitats. *Mammal Review*, **28**, 141–163.

Rosell, F., Bozser, O., Collen, P. & Parker, H. (2005) Ecological impact of beavers *Castor fiber* and *Castor canadensis* and their ability to modify ecosystems. *Mammal Review*, **35**(3/4), 248–276.

Thalen, D.C.P. (1984) Large mammals as tools in the conservation of diverse habitats. *Acta Zoologica Fennica*, **172**, 159–163.

Wallis, De Vries, M.F. (1995) Large herbivores and the design of large scale nature reserves in Western Europe. *Conservation Biology*, **9**, 25–33.

White, P.C.L., Gregory K.W., Lindley P.J. & Richards G. (1997) Economic values of threatened mammals in Britain: A case study of the otter *Lutra lutra* and the water vole *Arvicola terrestris*. *Biological Conservation*, **82**(3), 345–354.

Marine mammals

Authors: Callan Duck, Eunice Pinn, Matt Frost

Taxa included in this group and diversity in the UK: The marine mammal groups found in UK waters are the whales, dolphins and porpoises (collectively known as cetaceans) and the seals (pinnipeds). The otter (*Lutra lutra*) is also found in sea lochs and coastal environments but, as a semi-aquatic mammal, is not considered further here. There are 28 species of cetacean recorded in UK waters, which is a high level of diversity considering the UK's comparatively small proportion of the North Atlantic (Pinn 2010). Of these, 11 are known to occur regularly, while the remaining 17 species are considered to be vagrants or rare visitors (Pinn 2010). Although only two species of seal live and breed in the UK, they are of international importance with approximately 36% of the world's population of grey seals (*Halichoerus grypus*) and 4% of the world's population of harbour seals (*Phoca vitulina*; also known as common seals) found in the UK (Duck 2010). The largest populations are in Scotland which has 90% of the UK's population of grey seals and 80% of the harbour seals (Duck 2010). Five species of Arctic seal infrequently visit UK waters (Hall 2008).

Role in ecosystem services: Marine mammals play a key role in the marine ecosystem as top predators and are able to have a major influence on the structure and function of some aquatic communities (Bowen 1997). The main human value for marine mammals in the UK, as in many parts of the world, is in ecotourism and as 'flagship species', defined as: "popular charismatic species that serve as symbols and rallying points to stimulate conservation awareness and action" (Leader-Williams & Dublin 2000). Beaumont *et al.* (2008) point out that marine mammal biodiversity is very important for UK tourism with whales and dolphins being Scotland's number one wildlife attraction and the value of seal-watching to the UK economy in 1996 being at least £36 million.

Status and trends: The conservation status of cetaceans in the eastern North Atlantic has recently been assessed under the requirements of the Habitats Directive. The status of five species is considered favourable. The status of a further six species is unknown, due to a lack of data, while the remaining 17 species are either rare or vagrant so their conservation status in UK waters could not be assessed (Pinn 2010). The grey seal population has steadily increased since routine monitoring started in the 1960s. The increase in pup production is at least partly due to the availability of new breeding sites following the abandonment of human settlements on remote islands, including the automation of lighthouses (Duck 2010). Grey seal pup production is now stabilising, probably due to density-dependent factors affecting the general population. In contrast, harbour seal numbers have declined significantly in a number of areas, with populations in Shetland, Orkney and the on east coast of Scotland declining by more than 50% since 2001; the causes of these declines are not yet known (Duck 2010).

Drivers of change: As wide-ranging migratory species, drivers affecting many cetacean populations operate at a scale larger than just the UK. Marine mammals are apex predators and anthropogenic pressures (mainly commercial hunting and persecution) have had the largest impact on populations in the past (commercial whaling was only banned by the International Whaling Commission in 1986). For UK cetaceans, direct mortality through bycatch in fishing gear remains the most important human impact, with dolphins and porpoises being particularly vulnerable. For seals, since culling ended in the 1970s, the main impacts on UK populations have affected harbour seals. Two outbreaks of Phocine Distemper Virus (PDV) in 1988 and 2002 reduced harbour seal populations, particularly on the east coast of England, by 50% and 22% respectively. Between 2001 and 2009, harbour seal populations in Shetland, Orkney and on the east coast of Scotland declined by up to 60%, the causes of which are unknown.

Prospects: Predicting future trends for UK marine mammals is very difficult for a number of reasons. It is not possible for cetaceans due to uncertainties in the relationship and influence of pressures on population dynamics (Pinn 2010). For seals, although it is thought that the grey seal population is likely to stabilise over the next decade, it is difficult to predict future trends in harbour seals because the causes for recently observed declines have not yet been determined and the future impact of PDV is unknown.

References

Beaumont, N.J., Austen, M.C., Mangi, S.C. & Townsend, M. (2008) Economic valuation for the conservation of marine biodiversity. *Marine Pollution Bulletin*, **56**, 386–396.

Bowen, W.D. (1997) Role of marine mammals in aquatic ecosystems. *Marine Ecology Progress Series*, **158**, 267–274.

Duck, C. (2010) Seals. Charting Progress 2 Feeder Report: Healthy and Biologically Diverse Seas. UK Marine Monitoring and Assessment Strategy (UKMMAS), Defra, London. [online] Available at: <http://chartingprogress.defra.gov.uk/chapter-3-healthy-and-biologicaly-diverse-seas> [Accessed 19.01.11].

Hall A.J. (2008) Vagrant seals. Mammals of the British Isles: Handbook 4th Edition (eds S. Harris, & D.W. Yalden), pp. 547–555. The Mammal Society, Southampton.

Leader-Williams, N. & Dublin, H.T. (2000) Charismatic megafauna as 'flagship species'. Priorities for the conservation of mammalian diversity: has the panda had its day? (eds A. Entwhistle & N. Dunstone), pp. 53–81. Conservation Biology Series, Cambridge University Press, Cambridge.

Pinn, E. (2010) Cetaceans. Charting Progress 2 Feeder Report: Healthy and Biologically Diverse Seas. UK Marine Monitoring and Assessment Strategy (UKMMAS), Defra, London. [online] Available at: <http://chartingprogress.defra.gov.uk/chapter-3-healthy-and-biologicaly-diverse-seas> [Accessed 26.01.11].

Appendix 4.2 Approach Used to Assign Certainty Terms to Chapter Key Findings

This chapter began with a set of Key Findings. Adopting the approach and terminology used by the Intergovernmental Panel on Climate Change (IPCC) and the Millennium Assessment (MA), these Key Findings also include an indication of the level of scientific certainty. The 'uncertainty approach' of the UK NEA consists of a set of qualitative uncertainty terms derived from a 4-box model and complemented, where possible, with a likelihood scale (see below). Estimates of certainty are derived from the collective judgement of authors, observational evidence, modelling results and/or theory examined for this assessment.

Throughout the Key Findings presented at the start of this chapter, superscript numbers and letters indicate the estimated level of certainty for a particular key finding:

1. *Well established:*   high agreement based on significant evidence
2. *Established but incomplete evidence:* high agreement based on limited evidence
3. *Competing explanations:*   low agreement, albeit with significant evidence
4. *Speculative:*   low agreement based on limited evidence

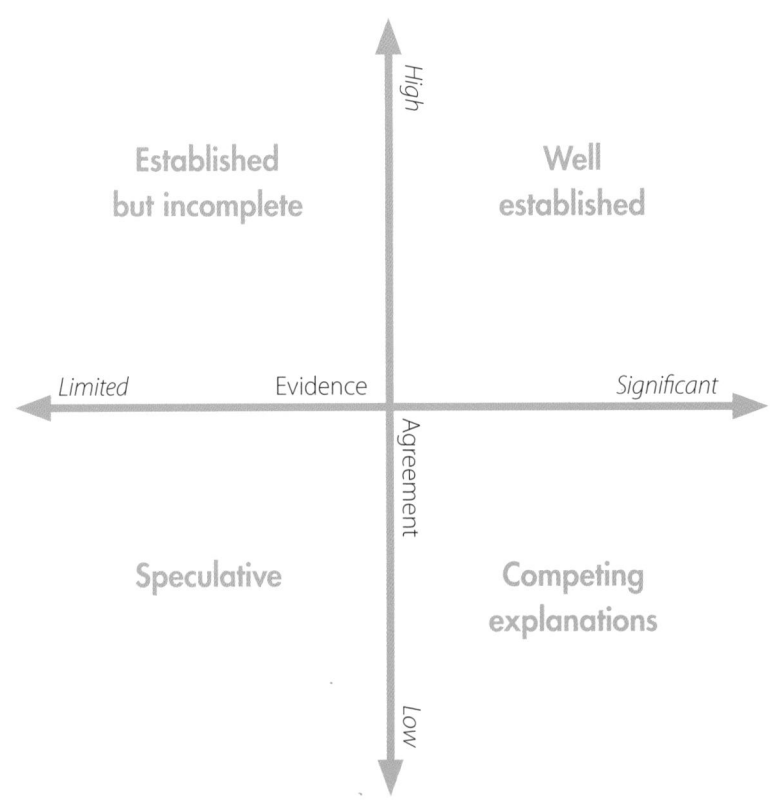

a. *Virtually certain:*   >99% probability of occurrence
b. *Very likely:*   >90% probability
c. *Likely:*   >66% probability
d. *About as likely as not:*   >33–66% probability
e. *Unlikely:*   <33% probability
f. *Very unlikely:*   <10% probability
g. *Exceptionally unlikely:*   <1% probability

Certainty terms 1 to 4 constitute the 4-box model, while *a* to *g* constitute the likelihood scale.

Chapter 5:
Mountains, Moorlands and Heaths

Coordinating Lead Author: René Van der Wal
Lead Authors: Aletta Bonn, Don Monteith, Mark Reed, Kirsty Blackstock, Nick Hanley, Des Thompson, Martin Evans and Isabel Alonso
Contributing Authors: Tim Allott, Heather Armitage, Nesha Beharry, Jayne Glass, Sally Johnson, Julia McMorrow, Louise Ross, Robin Pakeman, Suzanne Perry and Dugald Tinch

Key Findings*

Mountains, Moorlands and Heaths (MMH) cover about 18% of the UK and comprise the great majority of our near-natural and semi-natural habitats and landscapes. Most occur in Scotland (3.4 million hectares (ha)) where they make up 43% of the land surface area, followed by England (693,000 ha), Wales (246,000 ha) and Northern Ireland (228,000 ha), representing 5%, 12% and 12% of the land surface respectively. While Mountains represent some of our least human-influenced ecosystems, the extent and condition of our Moorlands and Heaths have been shaped by, and continue to be dependent on, a range of human activities.

Substantial changes to the extent, condition and use of MMH habitats have taken place since 1945[1]. The greatest losses in extent have been for Bog, and upland and lowland heathland. Much of the once moss-dominated mountain habitats in Wales and England has been converted to grassland. Such losses have been limited during the last two decades. Nonetheless, there is widespread evidence of long-term reductions in habitat condition, notably: greater peat erosion; loss of structural diversity; decreases in species richness; and the expansion of grasses at the expense of moss and dwarf shrub-dominated communities. The economy in MMH areas has shifted from one based largely on farming to one where tourism and recreation are also important. Grouse and deer management continue in the uplands, although associated management practices, such as burning and predator control, have come under increasing scrutiny. More traditional forms of land management have largely ceased in most lowland heaths, except when carried out for conservation purposes.

[1] well established

The key drivers of change in the extent and quality of MMH habitat since 1945 have been afforestation, agricultural development, changes in grazing pressures and airborne pollution, and to a lesser extent climatic changes[2]. Almost invariably, MMH habitats have been affected by multiple pressures; a combination of sheep-grazing and nitrogen deposition, for example, may provide the best explanation for the replacement of dwarf shrub and moss communities by grasses. The changes in land use reflect shifts in markets towards the exploitation of provisioning services (i.e. food, timber and energy) at the expense of other services brought by MMH habitats. Economic reasons also explain the abandonment of many lowland heaths. The impacts of these factors have been moderated by cultural pressures and a number of policy mechanisms, such as nature conservation and pollution control schemes, that do recognise the wider values of MMH.

[2] established but incomplete evidence

About 70% of the UK's drinking water is sourced from MMH, and these habitats buffer water quality against the effects of atmospheric, diffuse and point source pollutants[2]. The high quality water that drains from upland environments sustains healthy aquatic ecosystems and provides drinking water to the majority of UK water customers. The soils and biota of intact MMH ecosystems can retain a significant proportion of airborne pollutants, thereby reducing pollution runoff into freshwater habitats and the drinking water supply.

[2] established but incomplete evidence

About 40% of UK soil carbon is held by MMH, mainly in upland peaty soils. This presents opportunities for short-term reductions in UK carbon dioxide emissions, both through reducing ongoing losses of soil carbon and further sequestration[2]. Any reduction in the volume of peat through its extraction for use as fuel or soil improver, or through the erosion of degrading peat, represents an exacerbation of current carbon dioxide emissions to the atmosphere. Active restoration of Moorland, notably 'degraded' blanket bog, should enhance its capacity for carbon storage and some sequestration.

[2] established but incomplete evidence

---

* Each Key Finding has been assigned a level of scientific certainty, based on a 4-box model. Superscript numbers indicate the uncertainty term assigned to each finding. Full details of each term and how they were assigned are presented in Appendix 5.1.

Mountains, Moorlands and Heaths are nationally treasured landscapes[1] which provide breathing spaces for people[2]. They are particularly cherished for their 'wildness' and as sources of inspiration. Recreation and tourism make significant contributions to their total economic value; their 'non-use' or existence value is also high. The majority of UK National Parks are located within MMH habitat; in England alone, these generate 69.4 million visitor days per year.

[1] *well established*

[2] *established but incomplete evidence*

Steeped in history, MMH are important cultural landscapes[1]. Moorland and Heath habitats are shaped by society's long-term and continuing use of the land, and underpin livelihoods, as well as creating distinctive cultural identities and a sense of place. Mountain landscapes are often part of iconic imagery that is used to convey a national or regional sense of identity. The relatively low levels of physical disturbance (e.g. ploughing, building) makes them valuable sources of palaeo-environmental and archaeological evidence of past landscapes, management and culture.

[1] *well established*

Mountains, Moorlands and Heaths are of great importance for biodiversity: large parts have national and international conservation designations[1]. Whereas lowland heaths are highly fragmented, upland MMH habitats form the largest unfragmented semi-natural landscapes of the UK and are a refuge for many species that used to occur throughout the country. Due to a long history of deforestation, grazing and, more recently, grouse moor management in the uplands, UK MMH contain the majority of the world's heather-dominated landscapes. The blanket bogs and oceanic mountain habitats are also of international importance. They provide a home to some of the UK's rarest species, and communities comprise a unique mixture of temperate, alpine and arctic species.

[1] *well established*

Mountains, Moorlands and Heaths are highly multi-functional, providing different ecosystem services to different people in different places and times[1]. Some of these provide synergistic opportunities such as management for carbon storage, biodiversity and water quality. Others inevitably lead to trade-offs between ecosystem services where the provisioning of different services is mutually exclusive. Given the multi-functional nature of MMH habitats, the continued development of the evidence base must better take into account the (often contradictory and dynamic) objectives of beneficiaries if it is going to inform on sustainable management strategies in the future.

[1] *well established*

5.1 Introduction

"Science says: 'Here is a stone. Its weighs so much. It measures so much. It is so-and-so many years old.' But a man needs to discover that the stone is strong, so that he can stand on it, and cool, so that he can lay his head against it: that it is beautiful and can be fashioned as an ornament, or hard and can be built into his home." (Katharine Steward 1960—A croft in the hills)

5.1.1 Habitat Description and Historic Extent

Mountains, Moorlands and Heaths (MMH) are predominantly open, unenclosed and extensive landscapes (**Figure 5.1**), which many perceive as 'wild land', relatively untouched by people. In reality, the character of these often remote expanses commonly reflects hundreds, if not thousands, of years of human interference. These are, therefore, mostly cultural landscapes, kept in an 'open state' by practices such as grazing, cutting and burning (Webb 1986; Ratcliffe & Thompson 1988; Dodgshon & Olsson 2006). Mountain areas above the climatic tree-line, as well as cliffs, screes and areas of shallow or very wet soil are naturally open as environmental conditions prevent woodland formation (Birks 1988).

For descriptive purposes, MMH can be divided into six broad habitats: Bracken; Dwarf Shrub Heath; Bog; Upland Fen, Marsh and Swamp; Montane; and Inland Rock (See for habitat descriptions **Box 5.1**; extent **Table 5.1**). However, they usually occur in mosaics, and are interspersed with other habitats such as semi-natural grasslands, woodlands and surface water. The latter three habitats fall outside the scope of this chapter but are referred to where they are integral to aspects of ecosystem service provision by MMH.

Whilst the broad habitat classification has useful applications from a nature management perspective,

Figure 5.1 Illustrations of MMH habitat and societal use. a) Craig Goch reservoir overflowing Elan Valley, Wales*; **b)** Heron Pike, Cumbria, England[†]; **c)** Coulin Forest, Scotland[†]; **d)** Cliburn Moss, Cumbria, England[‡]; **e)** Beinn Eighe, Scotland[†]; **f)** Whitendale Fell, Bowland, Lancashire, England[¶]; **g)** Beinn a' Bhuird, Scotland[†]. *Photos courtesy of *© Stephen Aaron Rees 2011 used under license of Shutterstock.com; [†]Andrea Britton/The James Hutton Institute; [‡] Peter Wakely/Natural England; [¶] David J. Glaves.*

MMH habitats are ecological constructs that may not be recognised by others. For instance, recreational visitors might describe their activities in MMH as 'going onto the moors' or 'into the hills', and may not discriminate between MMH broad habitats, or indeed between MMH and other habitats such as woodlands or semi-natural grasslands. It is, therefore, hard to separate MMH components from the wider landscape that people relate to (Swanwick *et al.* 2007). Likewise, many ecosystem services (and the 'biodiversity' underpinning them) are not necessarily specific to MMH habitats, but result from the presence of a range of habitats and the interplay between them; for example, red deer as 'goods' are products of multiple habitats.

Prior to human activity (about 5,000–6,000 years ago) woodland covered much of what is now the tree-less landscape of MMH in the UK (Simmons 2003; Tipping 2003). Over time, the extent of moorland and heath increased through a combination of woodland clearance, managed burning, livestock-grazing and the removal of turf and vegetation, although climatic changes are also believed to have played a part (Crawford 2000). In this increasingly open landscape, herbivores, such as cattle, sheep, goats and deer, kept woodland regeneration in check (Averis *et al.* 2004). Changes in land management for both livestock and, more recently, grouse fostered a further increase in the extent of MMH, with palaeo-ecological evidence pointing to an increase in heather extent from 1500, peaking in about 1800 (Stevenson & Thompson 1993). Until this time, stocking impacts on MMH habitats were generally relatively light due to their limited seasonal and spatial nature (Dodgshon & Olsson 2006). Indeed, it was viewed that "much of the hill pastures was virtually wasteland and could be made much more profitable if systematically grazed by sheep" (Dryerre 1945).

From the 19th Century onwards, cattle-grazing decreased across the whole country. Sheep-grazing started to develop as an industry in the uplands, which caused a step-change in stocking levels, involving larger breeds and the utilisation of ground further uphill. This fostered what was, from a farming perspective, a desired change in vegetation from heather moorland to grass (Dodgshon & Olsson 2006). However, only 40 to 50 years later, with both profitability of sheep farming and opportunities for winter-feeding of livestock increasing, reports of pasture overgrazing started to appear (Dryerre 1945; Dodgshon & Olsson 2006). Meanwhile, many lowland heaths were abandoned and changed into scrub or woodland (Webb 1986).

Loss of MMH area and condition continued into the 20th Century, most notably after the Second World War, due to the increasing use of the UK's uplands for forestry, changes in subsidies for agriculture in marginal areas, changes in the game management of moorland, and increases in the deposition and accumulation of atmospheric pollutants. The main pressures in the lowlands were urban development, agricultural improvements, abandonment of traditional practices, and afforestation (Webb 1986; Dallimer *et al.* 2009). More recently, a variety of conservation-based initiatives have been developed to arrest or reverse long-term decline in MMH area. Reductions in acidic deposition have led to a reduction in soil acidity and reduced the pressure on acid-sensitive plant species. Conservation objectives are also behind the current promotion of natural and assisted regeneration of native woodland which will inevitably be at the expense of open MMH habitats in some areas.

During the last 20 years, MMH is estimated consistently to cover about 18% of the UK (**Table 5.1**; **Figure 5.2**). Most occurs in Scotland (34,310 km²), where it makes up 43% of the land surface area; followed by England (6,930 km²), Wales (2,460 km²), and Northern Ireland (2,280 km²), representing 5%, 12% and 12% of the land surface respectively. The largest share of MMH is found in the uplands, but smaller and often highly fragmented areas also occur in the lowlands.

5.1.2 Environmental Conditions

The basic character of MMH habitats is strongly influenced by three sets of factors. First, local-scale geographic factors, such as slope, aspect and altitude, are fundamental to the vegetation character and associated wildlife in these habitats

Table 5.1 Estimated surface area ('000 ha) for the six MMH broad habitats in the UK by country. Percentage of UK land surface each broad habitat occupied in 2007 is displayed in the final column. Data are available for three points in time for GB: 1990, 1998 and 2007 and two points for Northern Ireland: 1998 and 2007. Source: data from Carey *et al.* (2008). Countryside Survey © Database Right/Copyright NERC – Centre for Ecology & Hydrology. All rights reserved.

All '000 ha	England			Northern Ireland		Scotland			Wales			UK	
	1990	1998	2007	1998	2007	1990	1998	2007	1990	1998	2007	2007	%
Bracken	93	109	91	3	3	107	121	132	71	84	37	**263**	1.05
Dwarf Shrub Heath	309	288	331	14	17	1,007	894	894	120	99	117	**1,360**	5.42
Fen, Marsh and Swamp	78	124	118	53	47	289	239	239	60	40	36	**439**	1.75
Bog	98	138	140	164	161	1,922	2,044	2,044	30	45	48	**2,393**	9.54
Montane	n/a	3.6	3.8	n/a	n/a	n/a	38	38	n/a	0.1	0.1	**42**	0.17
Inland Rock	16	12.1	9.4	n/a	n/a	53	84	84	7	8	8	**106**	0.42
Total MMH	594	675	693	234	228	3,378	3,462	3,431	288	276	246	4,603	
Total surface area	13,180	13,180	13,180	1,774	1,774	8,012	8,012	8,012	2,121	2,121	2,121	25,087	
% MMH in each country		5.3			12.9			42.8			11.6		**18.3**

Box 5.1 Summary characterisation and biodiversity value of the six broad habitats identified to make up Mountains, Moors and Heaths. Lowland raised bog and Lowland Fen, Marsh and Swamp are covered in Freshwaters – Open waters, Wetlands and Floodplains (Chapter 9). Source: modified after www.jncc.gov.uk/page-2433; see also Jackson (2000).

Montane Habitat

These make up the UK's most extensive near-natural habitats. A range of vegetation types occur exclusively in the montane zone, lying above or beyond the natural tree-line. The lowest altitudinal limits occur towards the north and west of Britain, where the compression of life zones is exceptional. Most communities occur on thin soils, which may be acidic or calcareous. Some communities are characteristic of very exposed ridges and summits, whereas others are restricted to sheltered situations where there is late snow-lie. A range of important rock outcrop and scree types, including tall herb ledge vegetation, often occur in close association with this habitat, along with high-altitude springs, flushes and other mire types, and alpine calcareous grasslands.

Characterisation: Exclusively montane habitat types can be recognised by their floristic composition and their physiognomy (prostrate vegetation). It includes dwarf-shrub heaths, grass-heaths, dwarf-herb communities, willow scrub, and snowbed communities. The most abundant vegetation types are heaths dominated by *Calluna vulgaris* and *Vaccinium myrtillus*, typically with abundant bryophytes (e.g. *Racomitrium lanuginosum*) (**Figure 1**; **Figure 2**) and/or lichens (e.g. *Cladonia* species), and siliceous alpine and boreal

grasslands with moss and *Carex bigelowii* sedge heaths. Rarer vegetation types include snow-bed communities with *Salix herbacea* and various bryophytes and lichens, and sub-arctic willow scrub.

Biodiversity value: The invertebrate fauna is diverse, with mountain specialists such as the burnet moth (*Zygaena exulans*), the beetles *Stenus glacialis* and *Phyllodecta polaris*, the flies *Alliopsis atronitens* and *Rhamphomyia hirtula*, and the spider *Micaria alpina*. Several UK Biodiversity Action Plan (BAP) priority species are found here: three vascular plant species, woolly willow (*Salix lanata*), Norwegian mugwort (*Artemisia norvegica*) and juniper (*Juniperus communis*); six bryophyte species including *Herbertus borealis* and *Andraea frigida*; eight lichen species; and two moths, the northern dart (*Xestia alpicola*) and the netted mountain moth (*Macaria carbonaria*). Many other rare and local arctic-alpine plants and invertebrates occur. Notable birds include the montane specialists; dotterel (*Charadrius morinellus*), for which the Scottish Highlands is a significant western outlier of the north European population, and ptarmigan (*Lagopus mutus*), which like the dotterel breeds in some parts at higher densities than recorded anywhere else in the world.

Component priority habitats[1]: Mountain heaths and willow scrub

Figure 1 Montane: *Racomitrium heath* on Creag Meagaidh, Cairngorms, Scotland. *Photo courtesy of René Van der Wal.*

Figure 2 Montane: Woolly fringe-moss (*Racomitrium lanuginosum*). *Photo courtesy of Andrea Britton, The James Hutton Institute.*

Dwarf Shrub Heath

The UK is the worlds' stronghold of *Calluna vulgaris*—dominated heaths, with extensive tracts managed by strip burning (muirburn) or cutting to sustain high densities of red grouse (*Lagopus lagopus scoticus*)—an internationally distinctive habitat (**Figure 3**).

Characterisation: Vegetation that has >25% cover of plant species from the heath family (ericoids) or dwarf gorse (*Ulex europeus*). It generally occurs on well-drained, nutrient-poor, acid soils. Heaths do also occur on more basic soils but these are more limited in extent and contain herbs characteristic of calcareous grassland. Dwarf shrub heath includes both dry and wet heath types and occurs in the lowlands and the uplands. This vegetation is found mainly in the Atlantic biogeographical region in Europe.

Upland heath is typically dominated by a range of dwarf shrubs such as heather (*Calluna vulgaris*), bilberry (*Vaccinium myrtillus*), crowberry (*Empetrum nigrum*), bell heather (*Erica cinerea*) (**Figure 4**); additional characteristic species are western gorse (*Ulex gallii*) in the south and west and northern juniper (*Juniperus communis*) in some northern areas. Wet upland heath is most commonly found in the wetter north and west, and is dominated by mixtures of cross-leaved heath (*Erica tetralix*), deer grass

(*Trichophorum cespitosum*), heather (*C. vulgaris*) and purple moor-grass (*Molinia caerulea*), over an understorey of mosses often including carpets of bog moss *Sphagnum* species. Lowland heathland consists of dwarf shrubs, some gorse, scattered trees and scrub, with areas of grassland and bare ground, and is generally found below 300 m in altitude.

Biodiversity value: Although generally species poor, an important assemblage of birds is associated with upland heath, including red grouse, Eurasian golden plover (*Pluvialis apricaria*), black grouse (*Tetrao tetrix*), merlin (*Falco columbarius*), hen harrier (*Circus cyaneus*), and short-eared owl (*Asio flammeus*). The habitat is also home to high densities of meadow pipit (*Anthus pratensils*) and skylark (*Alauda arvensis*). Charismatic mammals such as red deer (*Cervus elaphus*) and mountain hare (*Lepus timidus*) are widespread in Scotland. Among the few species of reptiles and amphibians are slow worm (*Anguis fragilis*), adder (*Vipera berus*), common frog (*Rana temporaria*) and common toad (*Bufo bufo*). Some forms of heath also have a significant lower plant interest, including assemblages of rare and local mosses and liverworts that are particularly associated with the wetter western heaths. The invertebrate fauna is especially diverse.

Lowland heathlands are more species rich than upland heaths. Among the more high-profile heathland species are the birds nightjar (*Caprimulgus*

1 Full descriptions of UK BAP priority habitats can be found at www.ukbap.org.uk/library/UKBAPPriorityHabitatDescriptionsRevised20100730.pdf

Box 5.1 continued

europaeus), Dartford warbler (*Sylvia undata*) and woodlark (*Lullula arborea*), the reptiles sand lizard (*Lacerta agilis*) and smooth snake (*Coronella austriaca*), many invertebrates including silver studded blue butterfly (*Plebejus argus*), heath tiger beetle (*Cicindela sylvatica*) and solitary wasps,

and plants such as early gentian (*Gentianella anglica*), pale dog violet (*Viola lacteal*) and spring speedwell (*Veronica verna*).

Component priority habitats: Upland heathland, Lowland heathland

Figure 4 Dwarf Shrub Heath: Bell heather (*Erica cinerea*) Kaerloggas Downs heathland restoration site, Cornwall, England. *Photo courtesy of Paul Glendell/Natural England.*

Figure 3 Dwarf Shrub Heath: View of Holt and West Moors Heaths, Dorset, England. *Photo courtesy of Peter Wakely/Natural England.*

Fen, Marsh and Swamp (Upland only)

Characterisation: A variety of vegetation types that are found on minerotrophic (groundwater-fed), permanently, seasonally or periodically waterlogged peat, peaty soils, or mineral soils. Fens are peatlands which receive water and nutrients from groundwater and surface runoff, as well as from rainfall. Flushes are associated with lateral water movement, and springs with localised upwelling of water. Swamps are characterised by tall emergent vegetation. The Upland Fen, Marsh and Swamp broad habitat is typically dominated by sedges and their allies, rushes, grasses (e.g. purple moor-grass *Molinia caerulea*, common reed *Phragmites australis*), and occasionally wetland herbs (e.g. meadowsweet *Filipendula ulmaria*), and/or a carpet of bryophytes (e.g. *Sphagnum* species, *Cratoneuron* species). Vegetation is generally short (<1 m, often <30 cm) but sometimes taller, for example in swamps (**Figure 5**; **Figure 6**).

Biodiversity value: The habitat supports a rich flora of vascular plants with many rare species e.g. scorched alpine-sedge (*Carex atrofusca*), bristle sedge (*C. microglochin*), sheathed sedge (*C. vaginata*), mountain scurvy

grass (*Cochlearia micacea*), alpine rush (*Juncus alpino-articulatus*), two-flowered rush (*J. biglumis*), chestnut rush (*J. castaneus*), three-flowered rush (*J. triglumis*), false sedge (*Kobresia simpliciuscula*), Iceland-purslane (*Koenigia islandica*), yellow marsh saxifrage (*Saxifraga hirculus*) and Scottish asphodel (*Tofieldia pusilla*). Also exceptionally important for bryophytes with notable species including *Sphagnum lindbergii, S. riparium, Hamatocaulis vernicosus, Bryoerythrophyllum caledonicum* and *Campylopus setifolius*. It also forms an important nesting habitats for waders, such as curlew (*Numenius arquata*), snipe (*Gallingo gallingo*) and redshank (*Tringa tetanus*), and supports a varied invertebrate fauna, notably flies and midges (e.g. *Clinocera nivalis, Pseudomyopina moriens*), beetles (e.g. *Gabrius scoticus, Elaphrus lapponicus*), spiders (e.g. *Maro lepidus*) and molluscs (e.g. *Vertigo* species), which in turn provide an important food source for upland breeding birds.

Component priority habitats: Upland flushes, fens and swamps

Figure 6 Fen, Marsh and Swamp: Round-leaved sundew (*Drosera rotundifolia*). *Photo courtesy of Andrea Britton, The James Hutton Institute.*

Figure 5 Fen, Marsh and Swamp: Spring on Ben Avon, Cairngorms, Scotland. *Photo courtesy of Andrea Britton, The James Hutton Institute.*

Box 5.1 continued

Bog (Upland only)

Characterisation: Wetland vegetation that is usually peat-forming and receives nutrients exclusively from precipitation rather than ground water is referred to as ombrotrophic (rain-fed) bog. Two major bog types are identified, namely raised bog and blanket bog. They are for the most part fairly distinctive but at the same time considered extremes of an ecological continuum. Peat depth is highly variable; an average of 0.5–3 m may be typical but depths in excess of 5 m are likewise not unusual.

Blanket bog is the dominant bog, and the north of Scotland has some of the largest single expanses of this priority habitat (e.g. the Peatlands of Caithness and Sutherland Special Area of Conservation (SAC) and Special Protection Area (SPA), the 'Flow Country' (**Figure 7**)). It often forms complex mosaics with other vegetation, such as flush, fen, swamp and upland heathland, reflecting differences in geology and topography. Blanket bog also includes modified bog vegetation that resembles wet or dry dwarf shrub heath but occurs on deep acid peat which would have once supported peat-forming vegetation. Modified bog also includes impoverished vegetation dominated by purple moor-grass (*Molinia caerulea*) or hare's-tail cotton-grass (*Eriophorum vaginatum*). Peat depth, although somewhat arbitrary, is used as the primary criterion to separate types of modified bog vegetation from the 'Dwarf Shrub Heath' and 'Fen, Marsh and Swamp' broad habitat types.

Several of the bog moss *Sphagnum* species (**Figure 8**) occur throughout much of the habitats' geographical range, although their relative abundances vary across the UK. Species that are typically part of blanket bog include heather (*Calluna vulgaris*), cross-leaved heath (*Erica tetralix*), deer grass (*Trichophorum cespitosum*) and cotton grass (*Eriophorum* species) (**Figure 9**). Some other species have requirements that limit their distribution. For example, cloudberry (*Rubus chamaemorus*) is largely confined to high altitude bogs, alpine bearberry (*Arctostaphylos alpines*) to northern bogs, and the black bog rush (*Schoenus nigricans*) to ombrotrophic bogs in the west. *Sphagnum* is a constant element of most blanket bog communities, and is indeed 'habitat forming'. Yet, in the north and west, particularly in the Western Isles, woolly hair moss (*Racomitrium lanuginosum*) can also reach high cover over extensive areas.

Biodiversity value: Blanket bogs support a very wide range of terrestrial and aquatic vertebrates and invertebrates. As with plant species, some of these are widespread and common, others are much more local. Yet, a considerable number of species is of international interest for either their rarity or for the densities on blanket bogs. For birds this includes the breeding populations of red-throated diver (*Gavia stellata*), Eurasian golden plover (*Pluvialis apricaria*), dunlin (*Calidris alpina*) and in the north and west of Scotland, the greenshank (*Tringa nebularia*).

Component priority habitats: Blanket bog

Figure 7 Bog: Blanket bog, Flow Country, Caithness, Scotland. *Photo © Steve Moore/SNH.*

Figure 8 Bog: *Sphagnum* moss. *Photo ©Lorne Gill/SNH.*

Figure 9 Bog: Common cotton grass (*Eriophorum angustifolium*). *Photo © Isabel Alonso/Natural England.*

Inland Rock

This broad habitat includes areas such as inland cliffs, caves, and screes and limestone pavements, as well as various forms of excavations and waste tips such as quarries and quarry waste. The habitat covers a wide range of rock types, varying from acidic to highly calcareous. It occurs throughout the uplands, and is particularly characteristic of high altitudes, but is also found at low altitudes.

Characteristics: Natural rock exposures support a wide range of communities. Screes are typically dominated by ferns (e.g. parsely fern *Cryptogramma crispa*), lichens and bryophytes. On cliff ledges, tall herbs such as rose-root (*Sedum rosea*) and wild angelica (*Angelica sylvestris*) are generally abundant. Chasmophytic (i.e. growing in rock crevices) vegetation is usually dominated by ferns (**Figure 11**) such as green spleenwort (*Asplenium viride*) and small herbs including wild thyme (*Thymus polytrichus*) and *Saxifraga* species. Bryophytes and lichens also occur in crevices but are able to flourish on the open rock surfaces where there is sufficient light but a lack of competition from vascular plants.

Biodiversity value: The inaccessibility of rock habitats to grazing animals, especially of rock ledges, provides a refuge for many vascular plants that

Box 5.1 continued

are sensitive to grazing, including numerous localised and rare species (e.g. **Figure 10**). Notable species of that kind found in upland rock and scree habitats include alpine lady-fern (*Athyrium distentifolium*), oblong woodsia (*Woodsia ilvensis*), rock sedge (*Carex rupestris*), alpine blue-sow-thistle (*Cicerbita alpina*), Norwegian wormwood (*Artemisia norvegica*), Northern hawkweeds (*Hieracium* sect. *Alpestria*), woolly willow (*Salix lanata*), tufted saxifrage (*Saxifraga cespitosa*) and drooping saxifrage (*Saxifraga cernua*).

There are a number of plants consistently found on limestone pavements throughout their geographic range in Britain. The most frequent species include herb Robert (*Geranium robertium*), maidenhair spleenwort (*Asplenium trichomanes*), dog's mercury (*Mercurialis perennis*), harts-tongue fern (*Phyllitis scolopendrium*), wall-rue (*Asplenium ruta-muraria*), male fern (*Dryopteris felix-mas*), common dog violet (*Viola riviniana*) and wall lettuce (*Mycelis muralis*).

The botanically-rich rock habitats support a number of notable invertebrate species. Key groups include beetles (e.g. *Leistus montanus*, *Nebria nivalis*), species of fly (*Tipula* species, *Thricops species*, *Helina vicina*), and spiders (*Pardosa trailli*). Several key species of birds use inland cliffs for nesting, notably peregrine falcon (*Falco peregrinus*), golden eagle (*Aquila chrysaetos*) and raven (*Corvus corax*).

Component priority habitats: Inland rock outcrop and Scree habitats; Limestone pavements

Figure 10 Inland Rock: Serpentine rock with Shetland mouse-ear (*Cerastium nigrescens*), Keen of Hamar, Shetland, Scotland. *Photo courtesy of Andrea Britton, The James Hutton Institute.*

Figure 11 Inland Rock: Black spleenwort (*Asplenium adiantum-nigrum*). *Photo courtesy of Andrea Britton, The James Hutton Institute.*

Bracken

Characteristics: This broad habitat must have a continuous canopy cover (95%) of bracken (*Pteridium aquilinum*) at the height of the growing season. It does not include areas with scattered patches of bracken or areas of bracken that are less than 0.25 ha; these are included in the broad habitat type with which they are associated. Bracken tends to occur on relatively richer soils of heathland, and can mark out areas formerly associated with woodland (**Figure 12**; **Figure 13**).

Biodiversity value: Bracken can harbour a number of rare plant species. Most of these are considered as woodland plants, which survive in bracken after woodland removal. Likewise, its vertical structure provides opportunities for breeding birds, particularly in the lowlands, such as whinchat (*Saxicola rubetra*) and nightjar (*Caprimulgus europaeus*). In general, however, bracken is regarded a habitat of limited biodiversity value, and over substantial parts of upland heaths management is carried out to suppress bracken growth.

Figure 12 Bracken: Autumn view of bracken stands (in red), Crummock Water, Lake District, England. © S J Francis *2011 used under license of Shutterstock.com*

Figure 13 Bracken: *Pteridium aquilinum*. *Photo © Lorne Gill/SNH.*

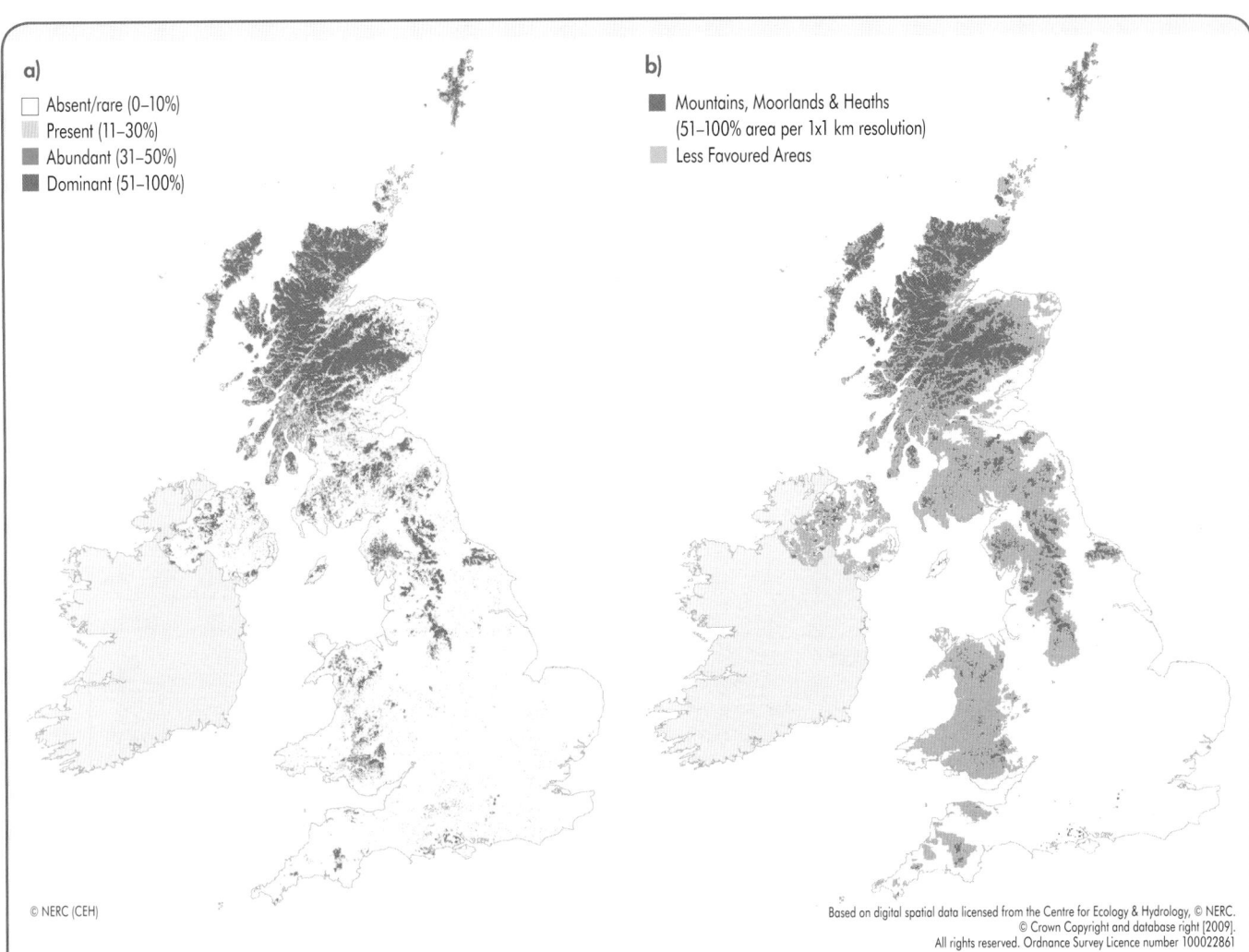

a)
- ☐ Absent/rare (0–10%)
- Present (11–30%)
- Abundant (31–50%)
- Dominant (51–100%)

b)
- Mountains, Moorlands & Heaths (51–100% area per 1x1 km resolution)
- Less Favoured Areas

Figure 5.2 a) Distribution of Mountains, Moorlands and Heaths (MMH) habitat by percent cover per 1x1 km resolution; b) Dominant (>51% area per 1x1 km resolution) MMH habitat in relation to the extent of agriculturally Less Favoured Areas* (LFA). LFA data sources: England and Wales: Natural England. © Natural England (2010), reproduced with the permission of Natural England; Scotland: Scottish Natural Heritage; Northern Ireland: Northern Ireland Environment Agency. This material is based upon Crown Copyright and is reproduced with the permission of Land & Property Services under delegated authority from the Controller of Her Majesty's Stationery Office, Crown copyright and database rights, EMOU206.2. Northern Ireland Environment Agency Copyright 2009. *The percentage overlap between LFA and MMH habitat in Great Britain may be an overestimate due to the coarser resolution of LFA data used. By comparison, Northern Ireland LFA data is at a much finer resolution, (and therefore more fragmented). As a result, the coarser MMH data which overlies some of these gaps reduces the overlap between these data sets in Northern Ireland.

(Köerner & Ohsawa 2005). Local environmental conditions, such as air temperature, wind, cloud cover, rainfall, and snow cover, change rapidly with altitude (**Figure 5.3**) and proximity to the coast, promoting great diversity of life. The more climatically unfavourable conditions experienced in the uplands also serve to restrict human habitation. Second, larger-scale geographic factors that give rise to climatic conditions exert a strong additional influence, notably the strong east-west gradient in oceanicity (Crawford 2000) and north-south gradient in temperature. Both local and larger-scale geographic factors, therefore, determine that Britain tends to be wetter in the west and cooler in the north. Third, the geological substratum is hugely diverse across MMH habitats. It governs landform and drainage; soil pH, rates of nutrient cycling and sensitivity to atmospherically deposited pollutants; opportunities for agricultural use and wider ecosystem services including the exploitation of specific minerals or storage of societal waste products.

Together, and under conditions of anthropogenic influences, these factors have allowed the development of a range of MMH habitats with their communities and species. Notably, moorland and bog developed where cooler and wetter conditions restrict organic matter decomposition rates to encourage the development of peat; heathland resulted where moderate to high rainfall on thin, nutrient-poor soils has led to podsolisation.

5.1.3 Societal Use

The upland environment is such that human occupation has never been extensive, although, in the past, many more people inhabited these landscapes than do so currently. On the other hand, many lowland heaths and some upland habitats, such as the Peak District, are now in relatively close proximity to urban centres. The general low fertility of MMH soils has mostly limited agricultural practices to livestock-grazing. Whilst this and other provisioning services continue

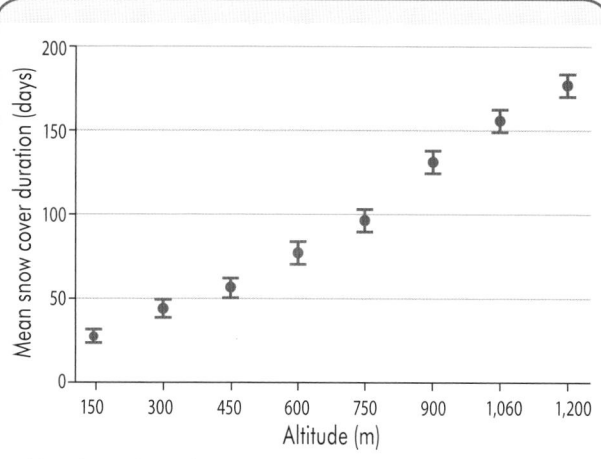

Figure 5.3 The influence of altitude on the duration of snow-lie and, therefore, general opportunities for species, biological processes and human activities. Figures shown are mean and 95% confidence intervals of total snow cover days from October to May on the mountains surrounding Loch Tay, central Scotland, for the period 1954 to 2003. Source: reproduced from Trivedi *et al.* (2007).

to be important in the uplands, agriculture increasingly fulfils additional functions of maintaining cultural landscapes and small-scale rural economies. The once important extraction of minerals, rock, coal and peat from MMH landscapes now takes place at a much reduced scale.

Mountains are known to play a key role in the Earth's water cycle, providing feedbacks to regional climate and modulation of the run-off regime (Köerner & Ohsawa 2005), and there is an increasing awareness that MMH in the uplands provide a wide range of regulating services including water purification, carbon storage and carbon sequestration, as well as potential for some flood regulation (Bonn *et al.* 2009; Bonn *et al.* 2010).

MMH continue to inspire people and form part of our cultural identity (SNH 2008; Natural England 2009b). They offer attractive scenery, exposure to the elements in often remote locations, areas to engage in outdoor pursuits, sites of historic human artefacts and a wide variety of plant and animal species. In so doing, MMH draw people into them, either physically or in their imagination, thus providing a rich set of cultural services to society. Furthermore, MMH include the UK's largest and last unfragmented habitats, which provide a refuge to many species of plants and animals. Collectively, these factors have led to the designation of a major part of MMH as National Parks, Sites of Special Scientific Interest (SSSI)/Areas of Special Scientific Interest (ASSI), Special Areas of Conservation (SAC), Special Protection Areas (SPA) and/or Ramsar sites. While biodiversity has played an important role behind such designations, emphasis on additional MMH aspects, like geodiversity (i.e. the diversity of rocks, minerals and landforms; Gray 2008), is growing. Some of these designations have contributed to a situation where tourism and recreation now form an important source of rural economic revenue (Deloitte 2008), while field sports, such as deer and grouse shooting, remain important market-valued activities. Fundamentally, the continued delivery of provisioning, cultural, regulating and supporting ecosystem services requires well-functioning, extensive and intact

ecosystems; i.e. both losses in scale and deteriorations in quality constrain ecosystem service supply.

5.1.4 Approach

This chapter provides a first assessment of the status and trends in MMH habitats and their use by society from 1945 to 2010, including an evaluation of the prime drivers behind such trends. A number of 'direct' factors, notably land use changes (grazing, development), airborne pollution, climate change and recreational pressures, drive the contemporary changes in MMH habitats and the ecosystem services they provide. In turn, these direct factors depend on a number of underlying factors such as population growth, changes in leisure time and disposable incomes, agricultural prices, the Common Agricultural Policy (CAP), and agri-environmental schemes. Both direct and underlying factors are moderated in terms of their impacts by a number of policy mechanisms (e.g. EC Birds, Habitats, Water Framework and National Emissions Ceilings Directives) and cultural pressures. Here, we aim to cover both drivers and moderating factors directly or indirectly responsible for contemporary changes in MMH.

In five separate sections we provide an overview of: the major changes in habitats and underlying drivers (Section 5.2); associated goods and ecosystem services provided by MMH habitats (Section 5.3); trade-offs and synergies between the delivery of such goods and services (Section 5.4); near-term options for sustainable management (Section 5.5); and major knowledge gaps that need addressing to facilitate the development of such management options (Section 5.6). The longer-term future of MMH habitats is the focus of Chapter 25, Chapter 22 looks at the past and present value of ecosystem services, and Chapter 26 looks at how these values might change under a range of future scenarios.

5.2 Trends and Changes in MMH

5.2.1 Drivers of Change

5.2.1.1 Land use

Forestry. Perhaps one of the greatest losses of MMH habitat area since the Second World War has been to commercial forestry. Supply shortages during the First World War led to the formation of the Forestry Commission in 1919, which was tasked with creating a strategic reserve of timber as a matter of national security (Condliffe 2009). Attention concentrated initially on high quality agricultural land, but focus gradually shifted towards more marginal land including moorland and heath (**Table 5.2**). The 1950s saw the development of powered cableway extraction methods that allowed access to previously unmanageable areas, and access roads across areas of MMH were opened up in many parts of the UK. Since 1990, there has been a steep decline in the afforestation of organic soils due to the disappearance of tax incentives, the recognition that wood production (in what are often wet and nutrient-poor habitats) tends to be poor, concerns about the loss of habitat for plant and animal species of open landscapes, and the development of the UK Woodland Assurance Scheme (UK WAS) (Chapter 8). However, planting on more mineral soils, natural regeneration through reducing grazing pressure, and a localised loss of other management practices, such as cutting and controlled burning, have resulted in the development of (mostly native broad-leaved) woodland at the expense of open MMH (Webb 1986; Marrs *et al.* 1986; Mitchell *et al.* 1997).

Some plantations are being felled for conservation purposes or converted to broad-leaved woodland. A change in market conditions (certification), rising demands from new biomass plants and changes in real prices will drive further changes in MMH forestry. National and regional level targets for new forest planting can also be seen as drivers, although these are currently not being achieved. Planting on deep peat is being discouraged (Forestry Commission 2009) due to negative effects on soil properties, potential long-term reductions in carbon storage and biodiversity goals. Given current grants, land prices and lack of officially sanctioned carbon markets for UK forests, rising imports might be the most likely consequence of increased demand for timber, rather than significant new planting.

Grazing. Arguably the most significant driver of change in MMH habitat quality has been changes in grazing by sheep and deer in the Scottish Highlands, and by sheep, cattle and ponies in England, Wales and Northern Ireland. High grazing pressure throughout much of the uplands has substantially reduced the quality and extent of alpine and sub-alpine dwarf-shrub heath, moss heath, scrub and herb-rich vegetation. Conversely, reduced grazing is considered a prime cause of deterioration of lowland heath. There is also experimental evidence that intermediate grazing pressure can be of benefit to some bird species in the uplands (Evans *et al.* 2006a; Pearce-Higgins & Grant 2006). The effects of grazing and trampling on upland MMH habitat are widely documented (Stevenson & Thompson 1993; Welch & Scott 1995; Lake *et al.* 2001; Hulme *et al.* 2002). Notably, the transition from heather to grass has been observed following an increase in pressure from sheep-grazing

(**Figure 5.4**) with consequences for plant diversity. Sheep preferentially graze grasses but utilise heather and other dwarf shrubs along the edge of grass patches and paths (Palmer *et al.* 2003). Consequently, the condition of heather can be severely impacted by grazers and ultimately leads to grass-dominance across hill slopes, as is the case in much of upland Wales and Northern Ireland. For deer, heather represents a higher quality winter food, so grazing impacts on these shrubs and others, such as bilberry (*Vaccinium myrtillus*) can be greater. Estimates of the number of red deer in the Scottish Highlands indicate a continuing upward trend from the 1920s onwards (**Figure 5.5**), although this may have been more gradual than generally portrayed due to complications of estimating deer in woodland (Clutton-Brock *et al.* 2004).

Livestock numbers in MMH areas reflect changes in agricultural market conditions, technology (e.g. new breeds of sheep; introduction of the turnip in the late 18th Century –Dryerre 1945) and land ownership and management. These determinants had direct impacts on agricultural land use, and indirect effects on biodiversity (Hanley *et al.* 2008). Since the end of the Second World War, the UK government has supported farming in MMH areas through a variety of price support and headage payments schemes, supported by the EC

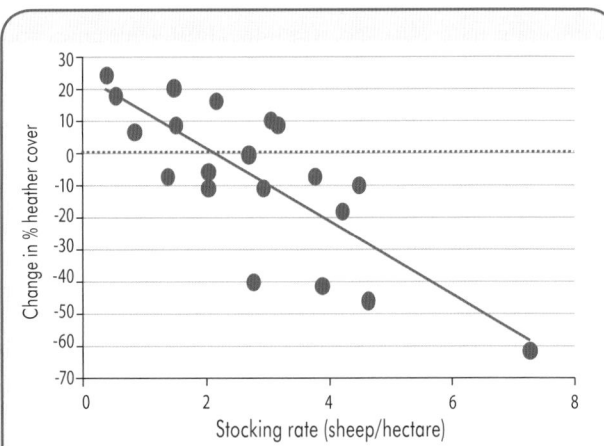

Figure 5.4 Changes in heather cover in relationship to the stocking rate of sheep in north east Scotland. Source: reproduced from Welch *et al.* (1996).

Table 5.2 Losses of lowland heath over time. Earliest estimates of the size of lowland heaths are given, along with the extent of losses at later dates. Source: data from Farrell (1993).

	Earliest figure available (ha)	Date	Losses to forestry (ha)
Breckland (Norfolk/Suffolk)	(By 1900) **28,932**	1918	7,326
		1934–1967	4,432
Dorset	(By 1759) **39,960**	1931–1934	No figure available but by 1934 only 45% left. Losses due to afforestation, agricultural improvement and urban expansion.
Suffolk Sandlings	(By 1783) **16,470**	1930–1968	3,502
Surrey	(By 1762) **22,780**		No figure available but by 1969 only 39% left. Losses due to afforestation and abandonment.
Hampshire	(By 1792) **46,540**		No figure available but by 1980 only 37% left. Losses due to afforestation, abandonment and urban expansion.
The Lizard (Cornwall)	(By 1813) **2,270**; (then by 1908) **3,660**	1963	After a reversion from agriculture, about 10% was lost to forestry, agricultural reclamation and infrastructure.

CAP from 1974 (Condliffe 2009). Key drivers include the 1946 Hill Farm Act, the 1947 Agricultural Act, the 1972 European Economic Community (EEC) livestock headage payments, the 1975 EC Directive with introduction of Less Favoured Area Scheme, the UK Hill Livestock Compensatory Allowance scheme, and subsidies for large-scale drainage schemes. The net effect of these inducements has been a substantial increase in stocking densities, which have damaged and fragmented MMH habitats, particularly in the hills and mountains (Anderson & Yalden 1981; Dallimer *et al.* 2009). In Wales, for example, sheep numbers rose by 71% between 1974 and 1994 (Fuller & Gough 1999); in the Carneddau area of Snowdonia specifically, sheep densities may have risen from 1.2 to between 5–6 sheep per hectare (ha) over the second half of the 20th Century (Britton *et al.* 2005).

In contrast to the problem of land abandonment in mountains encountered in many other countries (MacDonald *et al.* 2000), the lack of herbivore-grazing to maintain a desired vegetation structure and species composition in the uplands of the UK has rarely been an issue of concern. However, a significant reduction in the grazing of lowland heaths over the last century led to the development of scrub and woodland through natural succession (Webb 1986), and consequently to the loss of rare species (Byfield & Pearman 1995). Webb *et al.* (2010) showed that of the 133 UK Biodiversity Action Plan (UK BAP) priority species associated with lowland heath, 53% required bare ground and early successional stages. Since grazing can provide such features when combined with other management options (Lake *et al.* 2001), livestock is now being reintroduced to many lowland heaths, often supported by agri-environment schemes, but mostly by conservation organisations, rather than by farmers. Over the last decade, pressure from sheep-grazing on upland MMH habitats has eased in some regions (RSE 2008), with as yet undetermined impacts on ecosystems. Income support for farmers has gradually moved away from a production-related basis. From 1987 to 1991, the first agri-environment scheme was launched, with Environmentally Sensitive Area (ESA) payments rewarding farmers for caring for the environmental, historical and cultural features on their land, while reducing stocking numbers. The ESA (England and Scotland) and Tir Gofal (Wales) schemes covered a large proportion of MMH habitats. In Scotland, MMH comprises one third of the 19% of total land area under ESA prescription. While these schemes have reduced sheep- and cattle-grazing pressure in some areas, other factors, including decreasing subsidies, unstable market prices, increasing input costs and additional regulatory burdens, have been implicated in a wider, recent reduction in hill sheep, particularly on the west coast of Scotland (SAC 2008).

Ten years is a very short period to gauge environmental trends, and the efficacy of agri-environment schemes in promoting ecological improvement remains contested (Whittingham 2007). The consequence of different grazing pressures on ecosystem services (e.g. carbon sequestration, water purification, tourism) are beginning to be investigated through modelling and land use experiments, but scientific understanding is currently limited.

Grouse Moor Management. Burning is a principal tool in the creation and maintenance of habitat suitable for grouse.

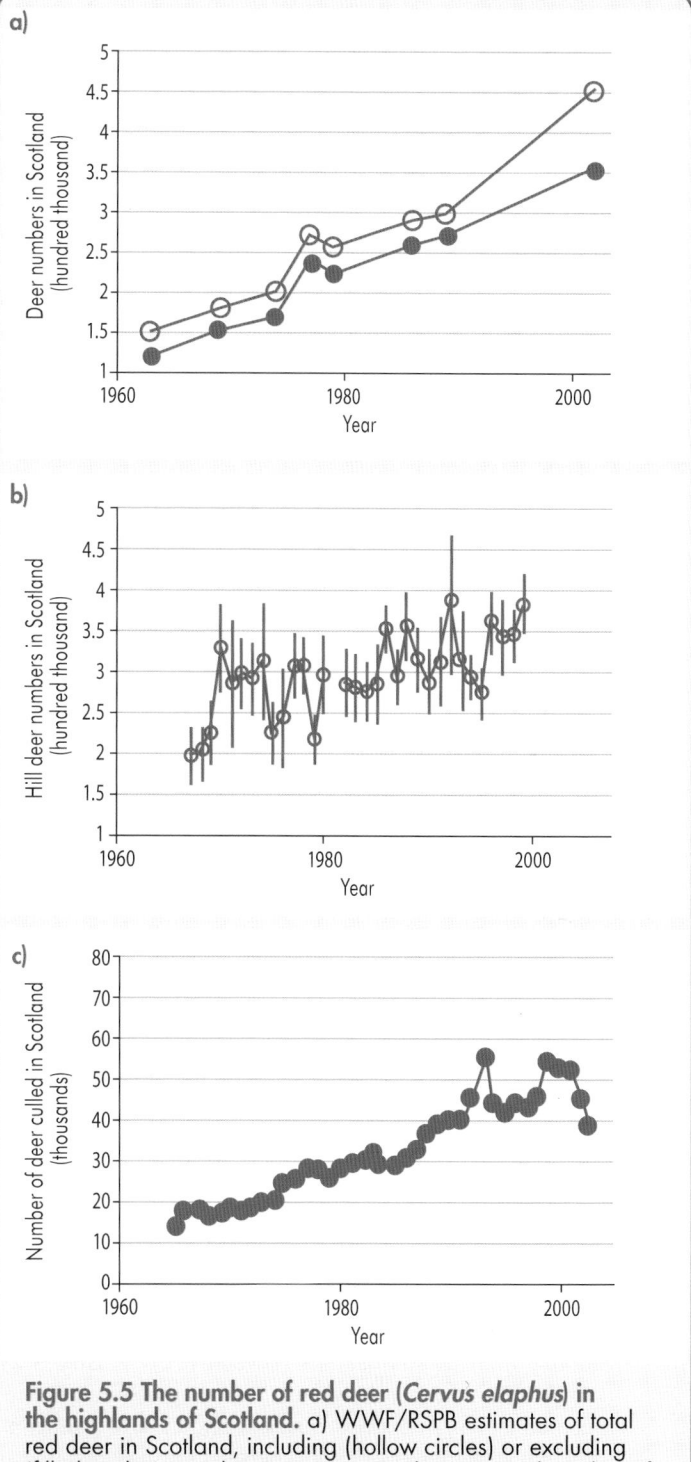

Figure 5.5 The number of red deer (*Cervus elaphus*) in the highlands of Scotland. a) WWF/RSPB estimates of total red deer in Scotland, including (hollow circles) or excluding (filled circles) an arbitrary increase in the estimated number of woodland deer by 70,000 in 2002; b) total hill deer numbers estimated from a multiple regression model and corrected for year of count, showing 95% confidence limits; c) estimates of annual numbers of all deer culled. Source: Clutton-Brock *et al.* (2004). Reprinted by permission from Macmillan Publishers Ltd: Nature, copyright (2004).

Long-term data on red grouse (*Lagopus lagopus*) hunting bags from across 495 estates (Aebischer & Baines 2008; **Figure 5.6**) indicates that high numbers of grouse were shot prior to the Second World War, but that there was a collapse in numbers during the war, partial recovery until the early 1970s, and further, gradual decline during the last 40 years. This long-term reduction may partly be due to a relaxation of

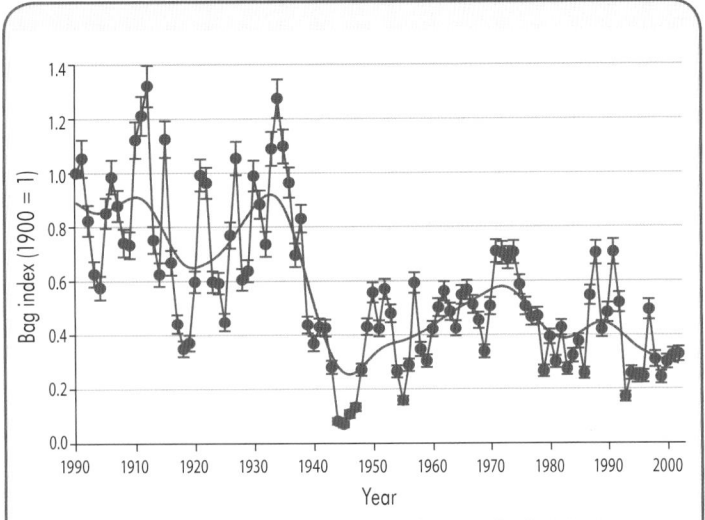

Figure 5.6 Index of red grouse bags since 1900, from the Game & Wildlife Conservation Trust's National Gamebag Census. Source: reproduced from Aebischer & Baines (2008).

Figure 1 A view of the Grampian Hills. *Photo by Hilary Gaunt available under a Creative Commons Attribution-NonCommercial-ShareAlike license.*

Victorian/Edwardian practices of predator eradication and rotational heather-burning to produce a patchwork of small areas with heather growth of different ages (Aebischer & Baines 2008), but increased sheep-grazing and afforestation are also thought to have contributed (Holloway 1996). With the recent decline in income for stocking sheep, some estates are viewing shooting as the most profitable use of the land; as a result, grouse shooting activity in the English uplands increased between 2001 and 2009 (Natural England 2009a).

Grouse management carries cultural importance and contributes to the maintenance of large areas of heather moorland which are of international importance (Thompson *et al.* 1995). However, there are mounting concerns over: i) the visual impact of burning; ii) potential damage to peat structure and subsequent carbon losses through atmospheric exposure in more heavily burnt areas (Yallop & Clutterbuck 2009); and iii) the impacts of associated long-term predator control on some elements of biodiversity. The killing of mammals and birds regarded as 'vermin' to protect agricultural and hunting interests has taken place for at least 450 years, leading to unprecedented species removal, most notably from upland habitats (Lovegrove 2007; **Box 5.2).** Whilst this may benefit ground breeding moorland birds such as lapwing (*Vanellus vanellus*) and curlew (*Numenius arquata*) (Fletcher *et al.* 2010), persecution has resulted in the extermination of several birds of prey, including osprey (*Pandion haliaetus*) and white-tailed eagle (*Haliaeetus albicilla*), well before agricultural pesticides started taking their toll in the 1960s. Several species of raptors, such as red kite (*Milvus milvus*) and white-tailed eagle, are now being reintroduced; yet illegal persecution is still ongoing, for example, of hen harriers (*Circus cyaneus*) (Etheridge *et al.* 1997), golden eagle (*Aquila chrysaetos*) (Whitfield *et al.* 2004) and red kite (Smart *et al.* 2010). This situation indicates the importance of working towards a consensus, whereby the diversity of birds and mammals is enhanced, while also accommodating cultural practices such as grouse management, which are perceived to play a vital role in rural economies (Thirgood & Redpath 2008; White *et al.* 2009).

Urban development. The main loss of MMH to urban development has been in southern England. Webb (1986) indicates that, of the 40,000 ha of lowland heathland present in Dorset in the 1750s, 17,500 ha was lost to agricultural improvements and forestry by 1896, and later losses, mainly to development, left around 6,000 ha by the 1980s (**Table 5.2**). Many towns and cities in southern counties, including London and Bournemouth, have expanded ten-fold in 100 years, often on previous heath (Webb 1986); it is estimated that 12% of the heathland in the Poole-Christchurch-Bournemouth area has been converted to urban sprawl in recent decades (Haskins 2000).

Urban encroachment also impacts on the quality of our remaining heathland through disturbance of wildlife (Liley and Clarke 2003), arson, dumping of rubbish and trampling (Gallet and Roze 2001), and the increased vulnerability of populations of rare species through habitat fragmentation (Haskins 2000).

5.2.1.2 Air pollution

MMH soils and vegetation are sensitive to the atmospheric deposition of sulphur and nitrogen derived primarily from oil and coal burning by the electricity generating sector (both sulphur and nitrogen), motor vehicle exhausts (oxidised nitrogen) and intensive agriculture (reduced nitrogen). Levels of sulphur and nitrogen contamination over most of the past two centuries of industrialisation have generally been highest in the south of the UK and lowest in the far north and west—a consequence of the location of population centres and heavy industry. However, atmospheric pollutant deposition is amplified in the uplands by the presence of hill (orographic) cloud that captures fine pollutant aerosols in cloud droplets (Fowler et al. 1988). Upland areas at mid-latitudes have therefore been some of the most impacted areas of the UK. There are two key effects of particular concern for MMH habitat: acidification and eutrophication; and trends in both are detailed in the current Review of Transboundary Air Pollution (RoTAP 2011).

Acid deposition results from the transformation of sulphur and nitrogen oxides in the atmosphere to sulphuric and nitric acids which are subsequently deposited to the land surface in particles, gases or precipitation. Sulphur has been the primary source of 'acid rain' since the early stages of the industrial revolution, but levels have declined steeply since the 1970s (Chapter 14). Acid deposition acidifies soils by stripping them of their base cations (such as calcium and magnesium) and raising concentrations of hydrogen and inorganic aluminium ions that are damaging to the roots of sensitive plant species and microbial communities involved in nutrient cycling. In the south Pennines, the UK's most heavily impacted area, sulphur deposition has been argued to be the main factor driving long-term decline in sensitive bog vegetation (Lee 1998). Nitrogen deposition can also have an acidifying effect when deposited in a reduced form (as ammonium); acidity is generated if ammonium ions are oxidised to nitrate by bacteria in the soil (nitrification). The prime effect of nitrogen deposition, however, is eutrophication.

Having evolved under conditions of low nitrogen availability, MMH plant species are often vulnerable to even small elevations in nitrogen inputs at low ambient concentrations through the effects of eutrophication (Bobbink et al. 1992). Low nutrient levels encourage the presence of specialist species, which are frequently used as indicators of high biodiversity value, but these may fail to compete with more nutrient-demanding species once nitrogen becomes more abundant. Nitrogen enrichment can also result in phosphorus limitation and other nutrient imbalances (Phoenix et al. 2003), and has been linked to other environmental stresses including pests, diseases and late winter injury (Power et al. 1998; Carroll et al. 1999; Nordin et al. 2009). If these effects open up the dwarf shrub canopy, grasses that are more able to utilise higher levels of nitrogen (and particularly reduced nitrogen), such as purple moor-grass (Molinia caerulea) and wavy hair-grass (Deschampsia flexuosa), may then begin to dominate (Krupa 2003).

Gaseous ammonia appears to be considerably more damaging per unit of nitrogen deposited than either oxidised nitrogen or ammonium (RoTAP 2011), and has been shown to exert clear toxic effects on some bog species including heather (Calluna vulgaris), Sphagnum capillifolium and Cladonia portentosa (Leith et al. 2004; Sheppard et al. 2008). In contrast to nitrogen oxide and ammonium, ammonia tends to be deposited relatively locally, i.e. mostly within a few hundred metres of sources such as animal enclosures, fertilised crops and motor vehicles (Krupa 2003). Therefore, ammonia pollution tends to pose a greater threat to lowland heathland than more remote upland MMH habitats, although critical levels of ammonia set for generally more sensitive lower plants remain exceeded across 69% of the UK's land surface area (RoTAP 2011).

The impact of airborne pollutants within MMH has likely been greatest for moss- and lichen-rich communities, in part due to the large surface area to mass ratios, and also due to physiological adaptations to obtaining nutrients and water directly from the atmosphere rather than via root systems. There are few long-term vegetation monitoring records for upland terrestrial environments in the UK, but it is apparent that some montane communities, such as the prostrate Calluna vulgaris-Cladonia arbuscula heath and Carex bigelowii-Racomitrium lanuginosum moss heath that are common in the Scottish Highlands, are now only found in a degraded condition (reduced cover of mosses, lichens and dwarf shrubs) in more polluted upland areas to the south (Armitage et al. 2011). While eutrophication from nitrogen deposition is frequently implicated in upland ecological change, it is often difficult to separate the effects from those of upland grazing, which have often been more intensive at lower latitudes (Britton et al. 2005; **Box 5.3**). The conversion of lowland heaths into grasslands as a result of high nitrogen deposition is well-documented across Europe (Aerts & Bobbink 1999), but, since the loss of nitrophobe species may have occurred decades ago, it may now be increasingly difficult to demonstrate the impact of particular nitrogen emission sources (e.g. pig or poultry units, power stations) close to sensitive habitats.

The chief controls on national emissions of sulphur and nitrogen to the atmosphere have been a series of protocols under the UN Economic Commission for Europe Convention on Long Range Transboundary Air Pollution and the European Union National Emissions Ceilings Directive that came into force in 1991. Most policy targets are underpinned by Critical Loads modelling. Over the past two decades, acid deposition in the UK has declined by over 50%, largely due to reductions in sulphur deposition. Nitrogen deposition has not fallen as expected, possibly due to changes in atmospheric chemistry associated with the reduction in sulphate. Thus it remains a powerful driver of habitat quality, notably in mountain areas (RoTAP 2011; **Box 5.3**).

5.2.1.3 Climatic changes

Climate and topography have shaped MMH distribution and characteristics and continue to exert a dominant influence. For example, Yeo and Blackstock (2002) concluded that geography, rather than land use, remains the primary predictor of vegetation type for the upland moorlands of Wales. However, whereas topography can be considered static over long timescales, the UK climate has changed significantly (Jenkins et al. 2008), and is predicted to continue to change in response to the accumulation of greenhouse gasses in the atmosphere. Across the UK, a wide range of climatic conditions affect and mould MMH in many different ways, and these habitats are likely to respond differentially

Box 5.3 Synergistic impacts of grazing and nitrogen deposition on mountain habitat.

Racomitrium heath is one of the UK's few remaining near-natural habitats, and is well known for representing the exclusive breeding ground of dotterel (*Charadrius morinellus*), (one of the UK's most charismatic and rare wading birds (**Figure 1**). This moss-dominated mountain summit community (see **Box 5.1**, **Figures 1–2**) is found throughout the upland regions of the UK, and in oceanic mountain areas across Europe including Ireland, the Faroes, Iceland, Norway and Greenland (Ratcliffe & Thompson 1988). Despite such a widespread distribution, the habitat has become the focus of conservation concern due to considerable declines in both its condition and extent in the UK, leading to its fragmentation and virtual disappearance in upland regions south of the Highlands (Thompson *et al.* 1987; Thompson & Brown 1992). During the past 50 to 60 years, replacement of *Racomitrium* heath by grass-dominated communities has been observed in North Wales (Tallis 1957), the Lake District (Pearsall & Pennington 1973) and, more recently, in the Cairngorms (Welch 2005). Two anthropogenic factors, high sheep-grazing pressures and increased atmospheric nitrogen deposition, have been implicated in its degradation and decline. Furthermore, there is evidence (**Figure 2**) that nitrogen deposition and grazing interact and cause an amplification of their deleterious effects on *Racomitrium* heath (Van der Wal *et al.* 2003) as well as in other communities such as heather moorland (Hartley & Mitchell 2005).

Figure 1 Dotterel (*Charadrius morinellus*), the flagship species of *Racomitrium* heath. *Photo courtesy of Jens Fischer.*

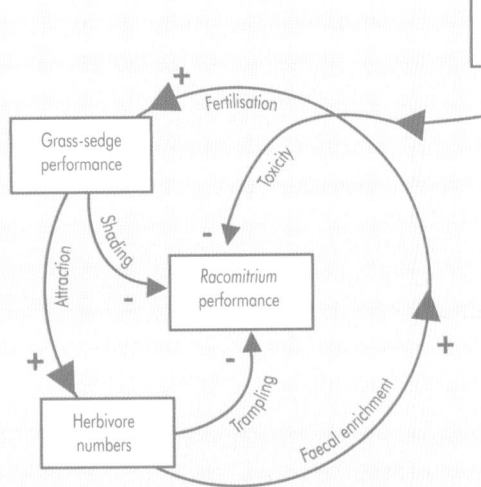

Figure 2 Conceptual model integrating impacts of nitrogen deposition and grazing. This multi-step, positive feedback loop shows how atmospheric nitrogen deposition leads to the replacement of the moss *Racomitrium lanuginosum* by sedges and grasses. Field experimental manipulations showed that nitrogen additions were directly toxic to the moss and indirectly limited light availability through the stimulation of grasses and sedges. These in turn attracted sheep, resulting in greater trampling impact on the moss. Deposition of nutrient-rich faeces enhanced grass/sedge performance and completed this downward spiral of events.

The current condition (tissue chemistry, growth, depth and cover) of woolly fringe-moss (*Racomitrium lanuginosum*), the dominant species of the habitat, was investigated at 29 sites across its geographical range in the UK and at nine European sites (Iceland, Norway and the Faroes). This extensive survey led to an improved understanding of how nitrogen deposition, grazing and climatic conditions contribute to the loss of *R. lanuginosum* cover and degradation of *Racomitrium* heath. Unexpectedly and contrary to experimental studies on this species, nitrogen deposition was found to stimulate, rather than suppress growth. However, results suggest that elevated nitrogen deposition adversely alters the balance between growth and decomposition of moss tissues, leading to increased shoot turnover and reductions in moss mat depth, with higher temperatures shown to exacerbate these effects. A thinner moss mat is more vulnerable to competition from neighbouring vascular plants and also to the physical damage caused by sheep trampling, resulting in loss of moss cover. The worst levels of habitat degradation, seen in Wales and Cumbria, thus represent the cumulative impacts of all three environmental factors.

Field manipulation experiments showed that *Racomitrium* heath has the potential to recover from the effects of nitrogen pollution (Armitage *et al.* 2010; **Figure 3**) and heavy grazing, despite their long history of impacts. Therefore, reduction of nitrogen deposition must be a key policy goal in order to prevent further loss of habitat, and at the local level, a reduction of grazing by sheep can be a positive action.

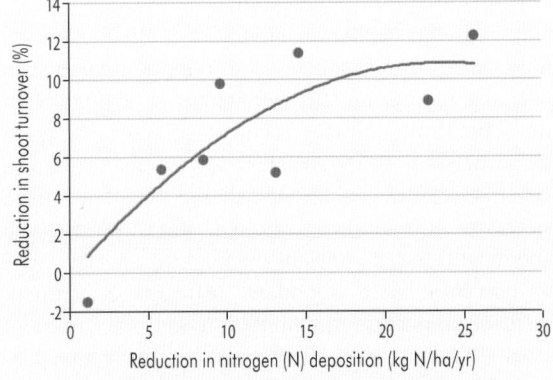

Figure 3 Reduction in nitrogen deposition promotes recovery of *Racomitrium* heath. Greater reductions in nitrogen deposition were associated with lower shoot turnover, indicating recovery of the moss mat. Source: Armitage *et al.* (2011). Copyright (2011) reproduced with permission from Elsevier.

---

to forecast changes in factors such as temperature and rainfall.

In the montane habitat, low temperatures favour hardy, but slow-growing, arctic and alpine plant species, particularly where there is transient snow-lie. Seasonal snow patches support their own unique ecosystems and species, including cold-sensitive mosses and liverworts that depend on snow for winter insulation, and snow buntings that feed upon snow-patch dwelling insects (Hill *et al.* 1999). Bioclimatic envelope models have been used to describe species distribution in 'climate space' and predict how the suitable geographical ranges of species might alter with a changing climate (Berry *et al.* 2002). Such approaches, however, are contested on grounds of associated algorithmic and ecological uncertainties; for a discussion on their reliability for birds, for example, see the disagreement between Beale *et al.* (2008) and Araujo *et al.* (2009). Uphill movement in plant distributions have been observed in various mountain ranges outside the UK and interpreted as a response to a warming climate (Kelly & Goulden 2008; Lenoir *et al.* 2008). Similar distributional changes are predicted for the UK (Trivedi *et al.* 2008), but no strong empirical evidence has yet been provided. While some species may be able to move uphill, there are concerns that arctic-alpine mountaintop species, such as the Snowdon lily (*Gagea serotina*) and the Northern dart moth (*Xestia alpicola*), are at risk of losing their UK refugia (Hossell *et al.* 2000). However, a great range of climatic parameters other than temperature and snow cover (such as wind speed, rainfall and cloudiness, and hence, light availability) are likely to influence species abundance and survival. This makes the study of actual climate change impacts on species in mountain ranges demanding, and predictions uncertain.

At lower altitudes, blanket bog and heath development depend on interactions between a cool, wet, Atlantic climate and the extent of drainage (Lindsay *et al.* 2010; O'Connell 1990). Response to climate change in these environments will depend on how shifts in precipitation, air temperature, humidity and wind speed affect soil moisture balances both seasonally and inter-annually.

Providing that soil moisture does not become limiting, higher temperatures predicted under UK climate change scenarios are expected to result in increased biomass production of heathlands (Peñuelas *et al.* 2004), and may pose management challenges if the open habitat, required by several characteristic species, is to be maintained. Summer drought may curb plant growth and induce changes in plant species composition, such as the suppression of bracken by heather as shown by Gordon *et al.* (1999). Their controlled-environment experiments also revealed the complexities involved in predicting climate-driven vegetation change: a very cold winter spell proved most damaging to heather that had been subject to drought the previous summer, while winter damage occurred in bracken plants that had been subject to raised temperatures in summer.

Spatial relationships are evident between the location of UK peatlands and climate variables responsible for maintaining positive water balance, namely temperature, growing season length and precipitation. This has allowed the development of a range of bioclimatic envelope models for peat occurrence (Clark in 2010b). The majority of models predict that the area with climate suitable for active peat formation in the UK will decline over the next century under a range of UK Climate Impacts Programme 2002 (UKCIP02) scenarios (Clark 2010a), and by as much as 84% according to the most extreme prediction that would see climate favourable for peat formation only in parts of western Scotland (Gallego-Sala *et al.* 2010).

Determination of the influence of recent changes in climatic conditions on MMH habitats is hampered by a limited evidence base, absence of effective 'controls', and strong inter-annual variability in both biological indices and climatic parameters, of which there are many. Moreover, the effects of climatic factors, such as air temperature, rainfall, wind speed or cloud cover, do not present themselves in isolation, but are likely to interact with each other and with effects of anthropogenic drivers such as atmospheric pollutant deposition, stocking levels and burning intensities. Indeed, some potentially significant land use changes might themselves be influenced by changes in climate; for example, wetter winters may influence opportunities for, and hence timing of, burning. But perhaps most importantly, long-term and sufficiently dispersed environmental monitoring programmes, which capture information on both potential environmental drivers and target species at appropriate spatial and temporal scales, are rare. The UK's best established monitoring programmes covering MMH habitats are relatively young and, hence, are only now starting to provide hints of possible 'climate change' impacts (Morecroft *et al.* 2009). With continued data collection and the development of statistical techniques for assessing time-series, their records should increasingly inform us about the vulnerability of MMH habitats to 'global warming'. However, carefully designed experiments, coupled with process-based modelling, and ideally conducted in conjunction with long-term monitoring, will be required to elucidate the precise mechanisms involved.

5.2.1.4 Interactions between drivers of change

Almost invariably, MMH habitats are vulnerable to multiple pressures. For example, sheep-grazing and nitrogen deposition in tandem (**Box 5.4**) may provide the best explanation for the increased dominance of grasses over dwarf shrub (Alonso *et al.* 2001) and moss communities (Van der Wal *et al.* 2003; Britton *et al.* 2005) on mountains and heaths. Heather (*C. vulgaris*) can continue to dominate in experimental conditions under elevated nitrogen deposition providing there is no physical damage from grazing or other factors, such as heather beetle (*Lochmaea suturalis*) outbreaks or severe frosts (Aerts & Bobbink 1999). A loss of plant cover in bogs through grazing can expose peat soils to the actions of frost and desiccation, resulting in material that can be degraded by wind and rain (Bragg & Tallis 2001) as well as biological decomposition. These changes are likely to have much wider implications for biodiversity and to have knock-on impacts on nutrient and water cycling, as well as carbon, nitrogen and pollutant retention. Better understanding of how multiple pressures lead to changes in habitat extent and condition, and how these influence ecosystem service provision, should be a key focus for future research.

5.2.2 MMH Trends

5.2.2.1 Loss of MMH area

Substantial reductions in the total cover of MMH habitats have occurred over the last 60 years, primarily due to afforestation and conversion to rough grassland by drainage, liming, burning and grazing. Loss of lowland heath has been mainly due to the development of towns and roads, afforestation, agricultural improvement and abandonment; the extent today is around 20% of what it was in 1900 (UK Steering Group 1995).

The loss of significant areas of heather moorland to afforestation was acknowledged in the 1980s (Nature Conservancy Council 1984, 1986). Scottish Natural Heritage estimates that the extent of nationally and internationally important heather moorland (falling into both Bog and Dwarf Shrub Heath classifications) in Scotland declined by 15% (from an aerial coverage of 19% in the 1940s to 15% in the 1980s). Simultaneously, the extent of blanket bog was estimated to have declined by 44% (from 0.3% to <0.2% absolute aerial cover).

Countryside Survey data on MMH habitats showed few clear changes over the last decade, with only small areas changing from one broad habitat to another in Great Britain between 1998 and 2007 (Carey *et al.* 2008). Unsurprisingly, given their isolation, there was little indication of significant shifts in the extent of Montane and Inland Rock, while the concept of 'Bracken' as a separate habitat is relatively new, thus limiting the detection of change. More confidence can be placed in estimates for change in Dwarf Shrub Heath and Bog, but even here designations and methods have changed over time. **Table 5.1** demonstrates that the relative contribution of the six broad habitats to overall MMH cover within the Countryside Survey appears to have varied with time, but few changes are deemed statistically significant.

The most striking change observed by the Countryside Survey was a strong increase (15%) in Dwarf Shrub Heath in England between 1998 and 2007 (Carey *et al.* 2008), although this figure has yet to be independently verified. This increase has been attributed to efforts to restore and recreate lowland and upland heathland (to meet UK BAP targets) by programmes such as Tomorrow's Heathland Heritage, Countryside Stewardship and, more recently, the Higher Level Stewardship Scheme. In the uplands, the main instrument to increase heather cover has been a control on grazing pressure, possibly aided by the removal of livestock following the 2001 outbreak of Foot and Mouth Disease. In the lowlands, the main instruments have been the reduction in the extent of scrub and secondary woodland, the creation of new heathland sites (for example, more than 4,000 ha has been recreated or restored in the China Clay country, Cornwall), the chemical and mechanical control of bracken, and the reintroduction of grazing.

Conversely, Countryside Survey data provides an indication of a small reduction in Dwarf Shrub Heath in Scotland during the last 20 years, which is attributed to increases in Acid Grassland and Bracken in the uplands (Carey *et al.* 2008). On the decadal timescale, bracken has clearly expanded in recent decades; Barr *et al.* (1993) estimated a 400,000 ha increase in cover between 1984 and 1990 alone. This is widely perceived as an unwelcome change because the habitat is considered to bring limited benefit (Pakeman & Marrs 1992), but instead to reflect 'poor management of the land' (for example previous overgrazing). Bracken is toxic and carcinogenic to livestock and potentially also humans. For example, there are concerns regarding an increased risk of oesophageal cancer among people in catchments with extensive bracken cover (Alonso-Amelot & Avendano 2002). Bracken stands are also considered a source of ticks, which, through tick-borne diseases, can negatively impact on both livestock and humans. There is no evidence to suggest a

trend towards greater bracken coverage at a millennial scale, however, and palaeo-ecological records indicate that current bracken levels may be no greater than historical maximum levels throughout the Holocene (Pakeman *et al.* 2000).

5.2.2.2 Changes in MMH habitat quality

Although most of the UK land area attributed to MMH broad habitat has not changed in designation in the last 60 years, there is widespread evidence of long-term reductions in ecological status. One of the most notable examples of deterioration is found in the southern Pennines and North York Moors. Here, overgrazing, ecologically damaging levels of burning for livestock and game, and high levels of atmospheric nitrogen deposition in some areas have resulted in a major degradation of upland moorlands and heaths which has been damaging for biodiversity, has increased soil carbon losses and has reduced the aesthetic quality of the landscape.

Slow changes in species composition in less physically disturbed habitats are more subtle and are often difficult to detect with current terrestrial monitoring capabilities. The most widely reported transition has been a progressive increase in grasses, particularly purple moor-grass (*M. caerulea*), wavy hair-grass (*D. flexuosa*) and matt-grass (*Nardus stricta*), at the expense of heather (*C. vulgaris*) in moorland and heathland—trends which are continuing in some areas. The Countryside Survey indicates that between 1998 and 2007 the ratio of grasses to forbs increased in both Dwarf Shrub Heath and Bog in Scotland and also in Dwarf Shrub Heath in England Concomitantly, there has also been a small decline in mean plant species richness in Scottish Bogs and Dwarf Shrub Heaths, and increases in the proportion of competitive species relative to ruderal species in Scottish Bog. Changes in the latter were accompanied by a reduction in the number of species used as food by butterfly caterpillars and farmland birds (Carey *et al.* 2007). It has been argued that the spread of grasses in these habitats has negative impacts on conservation values (Chambers *et al.* 1999; Marrs *et al.* 2004; Milligan *et al.* 2004; **Box 5.4**).

Acidification. The pattern of soil acidification and recovery broadly follows the trend in anthropogenic sulphur deposition. Before the Second World War, soils in many upland areas from central Scotland southward (including parts of the Trossachs, Galloway, the English Lake District, North York Moors, Pennines, Snowdonia, the Cambrian Mountains of central Wales and Dartmoor) had already lost significant acid-buffering capacity. In more geologically sensitive regions, this resulted in a lowering of soil pH and mobilisation of biologically toxic inorganic aluminium, eventually resulting in the acidification of upland streams and lakes in this area and, therefore, the loss of acid-sensitive freshwater biota (NEGTAP 2001). Terrestrial impacts have received less attention, but are also likely to have involved the loss of some sensitive species, particularly as a result of disruption to root function (Stevens *et al.* 2009), to the advantage of acid-tolerant species such as purple moor-grass. Soil acidification continued until at least the period of peak sulphur deposition in the 1970s. Sulphur deposition has since declined, so some recovery in soil base cations and pH is expected. Replenishment of base cations where weathering rates are low (for example in granitic areas and deep organic

Box 5.4 Landscape values for MMH—evidence from a choice experiment study.

Many of our upland landscapes are highly valued by the general public, as well as by recreational users and those that live in such landscapes. But how can we measure the economic value of such benefits, and determine how these benefits might change under a range of future scenarios?

Economists use a variety of stated preference approaches to value non-market benefits from environmental goods such as a landscape: one such approach is 'choice experiments'. Choice experiments proceed from a characterisation of environmental goods into a number of attributes. One of these attributes is a price or cost. Individuals are asked to make choices between different 'bundles' of these attributes, which reveals the rate at which they are prepared to trade-off an increase in heather moorland protection, for, say, a decline in broadleaved woodland. We can then calculate mean 'willingness to pay' measures for changes in each attribute.

Hanley *et al*. (2007) and Colombo and Hanley (2008) report on such a choice experiment applied to upland landscape features in England. **Table 1** shows an example question from their survey, which was carried out with people living in four regions of England with upland areas (the North West, West Midlands, Yorkshire and Humberside, and South West).

The landscape features included in the design were:
- heather moorland and bog;
- rough grasslands;
- broadleaved and mixed woodland;
- field boundaries (stone walls and hedgerows);
- 'cultural heritage'—a term describing traditional farm buildings and animals.

People made choices over future possible changes in these landscape features, or 'attributes', relative to a baseline prediction. 'Payment' for changes in attributes was via an increase in taxes. **Table 2** shows the results for willingness to pay, which demonstrates two things:
- there is large variation in how people in different parts of England value changes in a given landscape attribute, such as increased conservation of cultural heritage;
- there is large variation in the values people within a given region place on changes in different landscape features. For example, people living in the North West are willing to pay considerably more for the conservation of heather moorland and bogs than they are willing to pay for conservation of rough grasslands.

Table 1 An example of a choice card used in the survey. Source: Colombo & Hanley (2008). © 2008 by the Board of Regents of the University of Wisconsin System. Reproduced courtesy of Wisconsin Press.

	Current Policy	Policy Option A	Policy Option B
Change in area of Heather Moorland and Bog	A loss of 2% (-2%)	A gain of 5% (+5%)	A loss of 2% (-2%)
Change in area of Rough Grassland	A loss of 10% (-10%)	A gain of 10% (+10%)	A loss of 10% (-10%)
Change in area of Mixed and Broadleaf Woodlands	A gain of 3% (+3%)	A gain of 20% (+20%)	A gain of 10% (+10%)
Condition of field boundaries	For every 1 km, 100 m is restored	For every 1 km, 200 m is restored	For every 1 km, 50 m is restored
Change in farm building and traditional farm practices	Rapid decline	Much better conservation	No change
Increase in tax payments by your household each year	£0	£40	£17
Which do you like best?	☐	☐	☐

Table 2 Willingness to pay for changes in upland landscape features. All values are in £/household/year. 95% confidence intervals are in parentheses. Source: based on Hanley *et al*. (2007). Copyright © 2007 The Agricultural Economics Society. Reproduced with permission of Blackwell Publishing Ltd.

Attribute	Region			
	North West	Yorks and Humber	West Midlands	South West
Heather moorland and bog; % increase in area	0.23 (0.09 0.41)	0.31 (-0.49 1.05)	0.81 (0.40 1.37)	1.64 (-5.42 11.10)
Rough grassland; % increase in change	0.09 (-0.44 0.20)	0.67 (-0.76. 2.40)	0.76 (-0.15 1.83)	0.23 (-4.94 11.50)
Broadleaved and mixed woodland; % increase in change	0.24 (0.10 0.45)	-0.13 (-1.22 0.47)	0.54 (0.07 1.03)	0.73 (-2.79 6.13)
Field boundaries; length restored	0.02 (0.00 0.03)	0.04 (-0.03 0.13)	0.01 (-0.04 0.06)	-0.01 (-0.32 0.50)
Cultural heritage; no change rather than rapid decline	1.69 (0.18 3.24)	5.96 (0.36 18.64)	3.23 (-1.11 9.71)	16.04 (-0.91 21.35)
Cultural heritage; much better conserved rather than rapid decline	0.49 (-3.14 4.11)	16.73 (0.07 48.57)	23.78 (13.44 41.67)	26.75 (-79.5 134.0)

soils), or the soil surface is poorly connected to underlying mineral horizons, is expected to be an exceptionally slow process and may take many hundreds of years.

There have been widespread increases in soil pH in response to reduced sulphur loads over the last two decades (RoTAP 2011). The Countryside Survey reported upward trends in soil pH (0–15 cm depth) in Bracken, Dwarf Shrub Heath and Bog broad habitats between 1978 and 1998 for Great Britain as a whole. Soil solution chemistry data from Environmental Change Network (ECN) upland moorland sites shows clearer pH increases in deeper mineral soil horizons than in the more organic surface soil of upland moorland sites (Morecroft *et al.* 2009). The damped response at the soil surface indicates that soil organic matter in these habitats may have provided an important ecosystem service by buffering the pH of soil and water runoff against the influence of acid pollutants.

Critical Loads for acidity (and eutrophication—see below) are mapped nationally to identify the sensitivity of terrestrial UK BAP broad habitats. For peaty soils, the critical load for acidity is based on the amount of acid deposition (from sulphur and nitrogen compounds) that would prevent the soil solution pH from falling below pH 4.4 (Calver *et al.* 2004) over long-term 'steady-state' conditions. It is estimated that, over the period 1986 to 2006, the proportion of MMH broad habitat area exceeding the set acidity threshold fell from 92.7% to 46.5% for Dwarf Shrub Heath, 95.9% to 67.1% for Bog, and 99.9% to 96.8% for Montane (RoTAP 2011; **Table 5.3**). This suggests that Montane soils have not yet benefitted significantly from the large reductions in sulphur deposition and thus remain at risk from acidification.

Eutrophication. Control of nitrogen emissions over the last two decades was expected to result in a major decline in nitrogen deposition. However, analysis provided by RoTAP (2011) shows that, despite reductions in oxidised and reduced nitrogen of 50% and 19% respectively, the total deposition of nitrogen in the UK has declined by only 5%, and expectations for short-term recovery are low.

A combination of field experiments and surveys indicate that the effects of nitrogen deposition on MMH habitats have been wide-reaching and detrimental. Field surveys, including the *Calluna* Moorland Survey (Edmondson *et al.* 2007), the Countryside Survey Heath and Bog Survey and the Scottish Moorland Survey (UKREATE 2010) all show significant reductions in total species richness with increased nitrogen deposition, while the Scottish Moorland survey also points to reductions in lichen cover, lichen richness, ericoid richness and graminoid richness (RoTAP 2011).

The extent to which nitrogen deposition has driven observed vegetation change through fertilisation remains unclear. In their testing of nitrogen deposition hypotheses using Countryside Survey data, Maskell *et al.* (2010) found a strongly significant nitrogen deposition effect on species richness of heathland in the 1998 dataset that could not be explained by other potentially important environmental factors. The most vulnerable species were small forbs (e.g. harebell *Campanula rotundifolia*, slender St. John's-wort *Hypericum pulchrum, Viola* species) and bryophytes such as *Hylocomium splendens*. However, no link was apparent between vegetation change and changes in fertility indicators, leaving the authors to propose that the dominant influence of nitrogen deposition had been through acidification rather than eutrophication.

Monitoring programmes, such as the ECN, provide surprisingly little evidence of changes in species richness over the last 15 to 30 years, with the exception of surveys in northern Scotland (**Box 5.5**). Given the widespread evidence from the spatial surveys of nitrogen effects, the most plausible explanation is that most of the damage to vegetation occurred much earlier (nitrogen deposition has been elevated in some areas since the onset of industrialisation), and that the lower deposition areas in northern Scotland are the only ones where nitrogen remains limiting. Given the small reduction in nitrogen deposition in most regions, it is not surprising that the proportion of Dwarf Shrub Heath, Bog and Montane habitats currently deemed to be exceeded by nitrogen with respect to eutrophication has changed little since the mid-1980s (**Table 5.3**). Note that the most widely exceeded habitat is considered to be Montane—the critical load for this habitat of 7 kg nitrogen/ha/yr is currently exceeded almost everywhere, and even by 2020, 90% of this area is expected to be receiving ecologically damaging levels of nitrogen deposition (RoTAP 2011).

Climate change. Instrumental temperature records from around the UK show that air temperatures have been rising for over a century (UKCIP09). Particularly rapid increases have been seen since the 1960s, with several records for extreme high summer and winter temperatures over the last decade. Mean daily air temperatures have risen by similar amounts across all UK regions and seasons between 1961 and 2006, with an annual rise of between 1.05 and 1.67°C. Trends are strongest for winter (December to February) and generally slightly stronger for this season in the south and east of England where MMH habitats are less common.

Nevertheless, there is evidence from the limited number of high altitude weather stations that upland environments

Table 5.3 Exceedance of critical loads for acidification and eutrophication in MMH Broad Habitats. Source: RoTAP (2011).								
Percentage habitat area with critical loads exceeded by deposition data for:								
	Acidity				**Eutrophication**			
Broad Habitat	1986–1988	1996–1998	2004–2006	2020	1986–1988	1996–1998	2004–2006	2020
Dwarf Shrub Heath	92.7	66.9	46.5	22.4	34.0	36.3	34.2	20.7
Bog	95.9	85.1	67.1	41.8	44.7	45.8	44.7	40.1
Montane	99.9	94.7	96.8	76.5	97.5	92.1	98.0	91.5

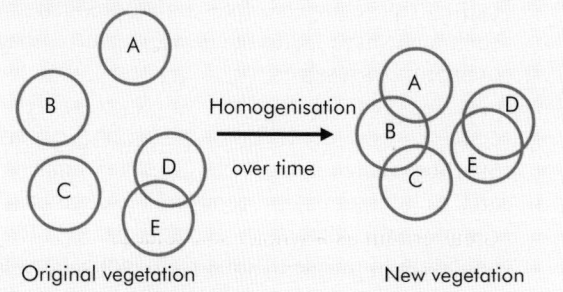
are warming more rapidly than the national average, with particularly clear indications of trends of reductions in frost days and snow-lie. Among ECN sites, warming over the period 1993 to 2007 was more rapid in upland/montane sites (1.2°C) than lowland sites (0.7°C) (Morecroft *et al.* 2009); this is consistent with the observations of Pepin and Lundquist (2008) for upland environments globally. In an altitudinal comparison of air temperature increases, Holden and Rose (2010) concluded that winter warming had dominated at the upland ECN site Moor House in the north Pennines, while summer warming had dominated at the nearby lowland site in Durham. Between 1961 and 2006, the duration of continuous snow cover in Scotland is reported to have shortened (starting later in autumn and ending earlier in spring), the average number of days with frost have declined by 25%, and the growing season (i.e. five consecutive days with a mean air temperature above 5°C) now starts around three weeks earlier and ends two weeks later than was typical during the 1960s (Barnett *et al.* 2006).

Some parts of Scotland and northern England have seen disproportionally large increases in winter precipitation compared to the UK as a whole (70% in northern Scotland and more than 100% in some areas of the West Highlands and Hebrides). There has not been a significant change in summer rainfall in most regions, although parts of north-west Scotland have become up to 45% drier (Barnett *et al.* 2006). Importantly, with respect to potential erosional impacts on degraded MMH soils, Scotland has also experienced a significant trend in the number of days with 'intense' rain (i.e. over 10 mm).

Some key studies are pointing to changes in the distribution patterns of some invertebrate groups, changes in timing of breeding in some birds, and possible changes in diet (Roy *et al.* 2001; Morecroft *et al.* 2009; Pearce-Higgins *et al.* 2010; Thackeray *et al.* 2010) associated with recent changes in climate, and UKCIP projections identify mountain habitats as particularly sensitive to 'climate change', leading to shifts in species distribution. While there is evidence that changes in snow-lie have fostered changes in vegetation, mechanisms are less well understood. However, there are implications for montane birds dependent on insects associated with snow patches, such as snow bunting (*Plectrophenax nivalis*),

dotterel (*Charadrius morinellus*) and golden plover (*Pluvialis apricaria*). Between the 1920s and 1960s, the estimated number of breeding snow bunting fell, but this decrease was followed by a recovery in the 1970s and 1980s. Unfortunately, since the early 1990s, numbers have once again declined: the Scottish breeding population of snow bunting was estimated as just 50 pairs in 2005 (Marquiss *et al.* 2007). Another arctic specialist, the ptarmigan (*Lagopus mutus*), has seen a decline in numbers since the 19th Century; more recently, birds have disappeared from areas where montane heath has been replaced by grassland. Changes in snow-lie are likely to strongly influence the seasonal pattern of runoff and hence are implicated in water quality (notably particulate carbon) and flood management issues. The impacts of reduced snow-lie, including the consequential increase in the number of freeze-thaw cycles, continue, with implications for surface erosion rates and carbon retention. On the other hand, milder winters have been viewed as instrumental for the expansion of other species, such as the Dartford warbler (*Sylvia undata*) in the lowland heathlands of southern Britain (Wotton *et al.* 2009).

5.3 Ecosystem Goods and Services Provided by MMH for Human Well-being

5.3.1 Provisioning Services

5.3.1.1 Food provision: livestock and crops

Mountains, Moorlands and Heaths naturally have low agricultural productivity due to soil properties, waterlogging and topography, and are, therefore, generally classed as poor quality agricultural land (**Figure 5.2b**). MMH habitats are mainly used for grazing sheep and, to a lesser degree, beef cattle at lower altitudes. Land improvements (e.g. drainage, lime and fertiliser additions) have been used to increase productivity; such measures have allowed a small part of MMH to be converted into arable production, but, more commonly, have led to the development of 'rough grazing' or improved grassland.

5.3.1.2 Food provision: venison and gamebirds
Sporting estate management generates supplies of venison and, to a lesser extent, gamebirds (e.g. grouse) for sale in commercial outlets such as game dealers. However, it is important to realise that the main motivations for sporting estates are not commercial sales (Sotherton *et al.* 2009), but rather provision of the hunting experience that such land offers (Section 5.3.2).

5.3.1.3 Fibre provision: sheep wool
Sheep wool is closely associated with sheep meat production, but is currently considered a by-product with little market value; it may, however, become more important as an insulation material in the future. There are small conservation projects that are marketing the products, such as wool, from lowland heathland grazing.

5.3.1.4 Traditional lifestyle products
Past agricultural activities in moorland and heathland required the extensive and creative use of natural material at hand. Bracken and tall rushes were used as convenient bedding material for animal stalls, and heather was used for thatching (Howkins 1997). Living from the land included snaring rabbits, collecting bilberries for jam-making, preparing peat-smoked salmon, cutting willow for basket-making and keeping bees for honey. Today, some MMH plants are still used directly for human benefit; for example, heather cuttings are used as mulch for the restoration of bare peat or for bio-filtration, and bog myrtle is used as midge-repellent ingredient (Sanderson & Prendergast 2002). Also, there are currently 20,000–30,000 beekeepers in the UK, producing approximately 2,000 tonnes of honey each year (British Beekeepers' Association), of which heather honey from upland and lowland heath has twice the value of other types of British honey (Sanderson & Prendergast 2002; Chapter 15). There is an increasing demand for traditional lifestyle products, which can be purchased along with other locally produced goods (including baskets, meat from specialised breeds, game, ale and wine and works of art inspired by natural scenes) in outlets such as farm shops, tearooms and garden centres.

5.3.1.5 Peat extraction
Peat has been used as fuel for many centuries; with a calorific value of around 20 megajoules/kg, it is similar to wood and lignite in its energy capacity. The use of peat for fuel peaked in the 18th and 19th Centuries, but then declined with the advent of electric power. Today, peat extraction for fuel and horticultural use is still a significant, although localised, aspect of MMH (ADAS & Enviros 2008; Tomlinson 2010). Three million cubic metres of peat is extracted for horticultural use every year in the UK (Defra 2010). Although bringing commercial benefits, peat extraction negatively impacts on biodiversity through habitat destruction, and approximately 0.5 million tonnes of carbon dioxide are emitted each year as a result of peat extraction from UK sites (Defra 2010). The UK government is committed to reducing peat use under the UK BAP and has set targets for non-peat soil improvers and growing media to be supplied: 40% by 2005 (met) and 90% by 2010 (not achieved yet) (Defra 2010).

5.3.1.6 Mineral and coal extraction
Considerable amounts of minerals, stone (e.g. crushed rock, granite, limestone) and coal are still being extracted from within the UK through quarries and opencast mining (BGS 2010; Cameron *et al.* 2010), some of which takes place in MMH where it leads to the destruction of the habitat in most cases. Moreover, permission for the opening of new quarries and coal mines continues to be requested and sometimes granted. Coal remains an important fuel for UK power generators and is used by many households, most notably in rural areas.

5.3.1.7 Freshwater provision
Mountains, Moorlands and Heaths are a significant source of water supply: 68% of the UK's drinking water comes from surface water sources (DWI 2008; DWQR 2008), mostly from the uplands. The Peak District National Park, for instance, holds 55 reservoirs and serves as a major water source to surrounding conurbations; abstraction licences total more than 450 billion litres of raw water per year from this area (Bonn *et al.* 2010). Reservoirs also exist in and around lowland heathlands (e.g. Chasewater Heaths SSSI).

There are three key components to this service provision: i) *Upland landscape position*: The uplands are areas of high rainfall because of orographic enhancement (Malby *et al.* 2007). Due to their altitude, water is easily distributed. ii) *Steep slopes, thin soils or peat cover*: Both thin soils and peat soils promote rapid, near-surface runoff of water. Blanket bog runoff is primarily by saturation-excess overland flow or near-surface through-flow, which produces a 'flashy' hydrological regime (i.e. one characterised by flash flood episodes; Evans *et al.* 1999; Holden & Burt 2003a, 2003b). Upland blanket bogs and dwarf shrub heaths are not good regulators of water supply during dry periods as the hydraulic conductivity of the peat mass is very low, thus limiting the maintenance of base flows (Holden & Burt 2003b). In these habitats, stream flow is closely linked to rainfall because water runs off rapidly and soil storage is limited. Therefore, artificial storage, in the form of reservoirs, is important for the continuous supply of drinking water. In catchments with snow lie on higher mountains, run-off may be closely linked to thaw events (Baggaley *et al.* 2009). iii) *Provision of clean (dilute) waters*: An important part of the freshwater provision service is the relatively dilute nature of upland waters due to limited human impacts, relatively low weathering rates, extensive peat cover and widespread overland flow. These clean waters dilute downstream pollutants, reducing water treatment costs, and increasing water quality. However, the increase in dissolved organic carbon (DOC) concentrations in water from upland catchments (see below) provides a treatment challenge for water companies.

The excavation of grips (field drains) in UK upland habitats—largely grant-aided to improve land for hill farming following the 1946 Hill Farming Act (Condliffe 2009)—has dramatically increased drainage density and, in some cases, demonstrably increased the 'flashiness' of upland runoff. However, hydrological processes are complex, and there are also examples of reduced peak flows (Holden *et al.* 2004; 2006); the effects of drainage within a catchment are strongly contingent on the spatial arrangement of the wider drainage network (Holden *et al.* 2004).

5.3.2 Regulating Services

5.3.2.1 Climate regulation

Within the terrestrial biosphere, northern peatlands are the most important carbon store, and have the capacity to act as a further carbon sink. Within the UK, an estimated 44% of all terrestrial carbon (4,562 million tonnes within 0–100 cm depth) is held by unforested semi-natural habitat (Bradley *et al.* 2005); while this also comprises semi-natural grasslands and lowland wetlands, a good proportion of the carbon (2,015 million tonnes) is held within MMH (**Figure 5.7**; Chapter 14). Given the preponderance of MMH in Scotland, much of the UK's total stock of carbon is found here. Other areas with large carbon stocks are the north of England and Northern Ireland. Above-ground and below-ground forest biomass carbon stocks are estimated at 136 million tonnes (Forestry Commission 2009), and are, therefore, small compared to those held in organic soils, i.e. deep peats and organo-mineral soils.

In an active, peat-forming state, MMH soils represent net sinks of carbon dioxide (Gorham 1991) and, in the case of waterlogged soils, sources of methane (Huttunen *et al.* 2003). Changes in climate, notably in rainfall and temperature, are likely to influence the net flux of both gases and hence affect the capacity of ecosystems to store carbon. Therefore, MMH represent both a threat to the global carbon cycle and an opportunity in terms of climate change mitigation policies that encourage adaptive land management to safeguard carbon stores and, to a lesser degree, further carbon sequestration.

Renewable energy schemes within MMH (windfarms, hydroelectric schemes) represent an opportunity to mitigate carbon dioxide emissions. In Scotland alone, 260 developments are currently installed, of which an estimated 30% are in core MMH habitat, mostly at its fringes; many more are approved, proposed or at scoping stage (**Figure 5.8**). While these developments can make a positive contribution to the UK's net emissions, their development is highly contentious and needs careful planning. Their location may negatively influence biodiversity and landscape character (Bergmann *et al.* 2006), and their net effects on carbon flows needs to be evaluated as windfarm construction

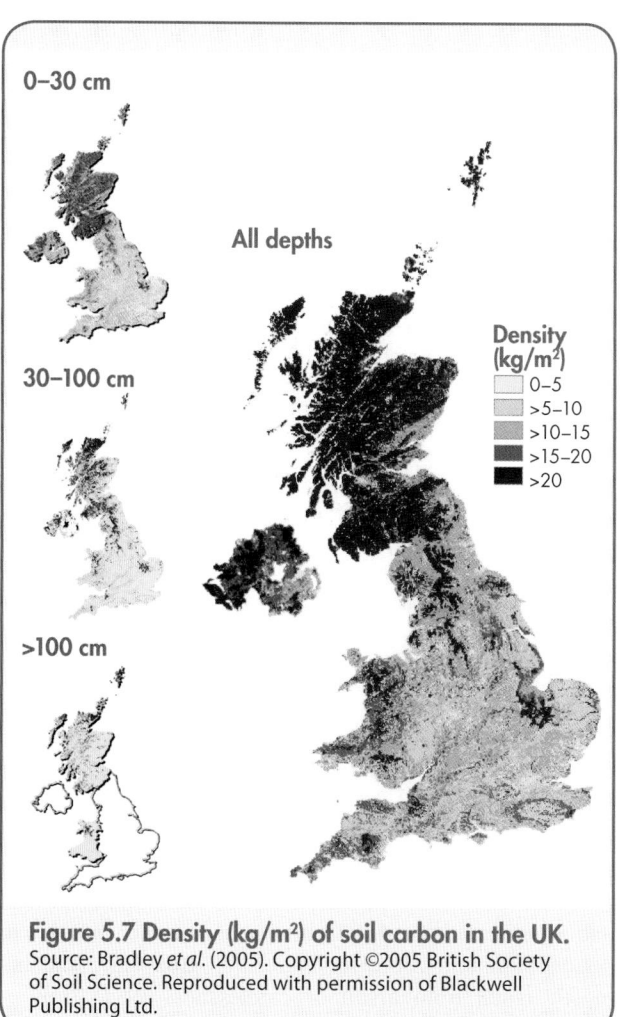

Figure 5.7 Density (kg/m²) of soil carbon in the UK.
Source: Bradley *et al.* (2005). Copyright ©2005 British Society of Soil Science. Reproduced with permission of Blackwell Publishing Ltd.

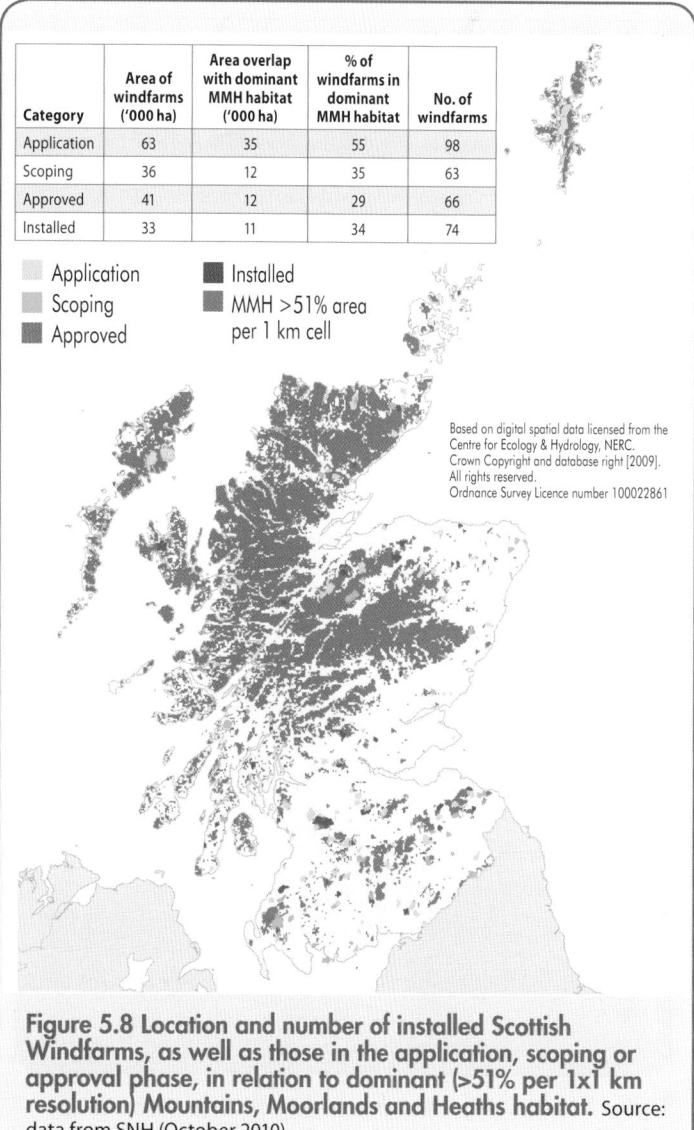

Category	Area of windfarms ('000 ha)	Area overlap with dominant MMH habitat ('000 ha)	% of windfarms in dominant MMH habitat	No. of windfarms
Application	63	35	55	98
Scoping	36	12	35	63
Approved	41	12	29	66
Installed	33	11	34	74

Based on digital spatial data licensed from the Centre for Ecology & Hydrology, NERC. Crown Copyright and database right [2009]. All rights reserved. Ordnance Survey Licence number 100022861

Figure 5.8 Location and number of installed Scottish Windfarms, as well as those in the application, scoping or approval phase, in relation to dominant (>51% per 1x1 km resolution) Mountains, Moorlands and Heaths habitat. Source: data from SNH (October 2010).

and associated drainage of deep organic soils can lead to considerable carbon losses (Nayak *et al.* 2010).

Disturbance of the plant-soil system tends to reduce carbon sequestration (Van der Wal *et al.* 2007; Sjogersten *et al.* 2008), with factors such as soil type, landscape position and exact management interventions all being of influence. Recent studies on peatland at Moor House National Nature Reserve have shown that changes in vegetation composition affect carbon cycling through differential rates of assimilation and transfer of recent photosynthetic carbon to soil, differences in rates of respiration (Ward *et al.* 2007; 2009), and by influencing litter decomposition. However, there is still great uncertainty over the scale of impacts from management practices such as burning and drainage (Wallage *et al.* 2006; Worrall *et al.* 2007; Clay *et al.* 2009; Yallop & Clutterbuck 2009). A particular issue surrounding peatland restoration through reducing drainage (i.e. 'grip blocking') is the potential for increased methane loss to the atmosphere (Baird *et al.* 2009). Nevertheless, Worrall *et al.* (2009) proposed that land management modification might result in significant net gains in carbon storage and foster greater resilience to external changes in climate. The restoration and effective management of peatlands to safeguard their vast carbon store, and potentially enhance their carbon sequestration potential, thus represent important opportunities.

5.3.2.2 Natural hazard regulation: flood risk mitigation

There is currently limited evidence on whether the UK's MMH habitats act to attenuate or exacerbate flooding (O'Connell *et al.* 2005; Holden *et al.* 2007; Orr *et al.* 2008). Steep areas with thin soils are likely to be sources of runoff rather than temporary water storage areas. Peat soils are capable of storing large quantities of water; saturated peat is commonly 90–98% water by mass (Holden 2005). This has led to the mistaken supposition that peatlands act as a sponge to soak up rainfall and prevent flooding, before gradually releasing water to maintain baseflow (Holden *et al.* 2007). In reality, the water table in healthy peatlands is maintained at, or near, the surface so that available water storage is minimal. Consequently, catchments with a high proportion of blanket bog often exhibit a rapid runoff response, with flashy hydrographs so that stream flow rises quickly during rainstorms and returns rapidly to low-flow conditions (Evans *et al.* 1999; Lane *et al.* 2004; Holden *et al.* 2007). Where bog runoff is routed through fen areas, there is some evidence that peak flows may be reduced (Bragg 2002).

The most significant potential gains in flood control from upland systems come from the restoration of degraded systems, for example, through the re-vegetation of bare peat or the afforestation of slopes, which both reduce erosion and enhance vegetation cover. Vegetation cover can reduce flow velocities, with *Sphagnum* mosses inducing the most marked reductions (Holden *et al.* 2008). Extensive moorland gripping across the UK has been shown to increase flow in dry conditions, but the impact on peak flows is variable, although more studies exhibit an increase than a decrease (Holden *et al.* 2004). Grip blocking may decrease flow velocities and discharge from drains (Holden 2005; Holden *et al.* 2008). Most land management interventions designed to modify runoff have been carried out at relatively small scales; it is, therefore, unsurprising that flood risk mitigation at a large catchment scale has not been documented and is an area requiring further research. Nevertheless, the potential to modify runoff regimes, even slightly, should be seen as part of a package of benefits that peatland restoration or adaptive management can deliver.

5.3.2.3 Natural hazard regulation: wildfire risk

Sutherland *et al.* (2008) identified wildfire as one of the top 25 priority risks to UK biodiversity. It already causes substantial environmental and economic losses in MMH habitats (Maltby *et al.* 1990; McMorrow *et al.* 2009; Lindley *et al.* 2009): in 2003, one wildfire on Bleaklow in the Peak District lasted 31 days and fire-fighting costs amounted to around £1million. With predicted climatic changes, wildfire risk is expected to rise as the result of a greater accumulation of potential fuel load following warmer and wetter springs, and a greater ignition risk from increased visitor pressure in hot dry summers (Albertson *et al.* 2009; **Box 5.6**). Wildfires mostly result from arson or carelessness (McMorrow *et al.* 2009; Haskins 2000) and are particularly frequent and

---

Box 5.6 Environmental risk management: managing wildfire risk and recreation in the Peak District National Park, England.

Wildfires pose a serious threat to MMH habitats, their wildlife and their carbon stores (**Figure 1**). Greatest risk is at its south-eastern climatic range, particularly in the late spring and summer months, when the peat is at its driest and most flammable. Increasing summer temperatures with projected climate change and potential increases in visitors may magnify this threat (McMorrow *et al.* 2009). In the Peak District National Park, there have been over 350 reported incidents of wildfires since 1976, which are commonly started by arson, discarded cigarettes, campfires and barbeques. To tackle this issue, the Peak District Fire Operations Group (FOG) was formed bringing together six different fire authorities: three water companies; the National Trust; private estates; and the National Park Ranger Service to help to significantly reduce the impact of wildfires. In addition, the Moors for the Future partnership works in close collaboration with the University of Manchester and other stakeholders to understand the causes and risks of wildfires and raise awareness about them (see www.fires-seminars.org.uk). Risk management measures include: clear protocols and plans for fire fighting; training and use of compatible equipment; predictive mapping of fire risk; and awareness raising programmes with visitors, for example, through the distribution of eco-friendly disposable ashtrays, and the restoration of soils, biodiversity and ecosystem function on wildfire sites.

Figure 1 Fire management on moorland. *Photo supplied by Moors for the Future Partnership.*

---

problematic in highly visited areas, such as the Peak District, or in lowland heaths close to urban centres, such as Dorset heathlands. Costs for fire suppression and prevention through habitat management, such as controlled burns for fire breaks (Davies *et al.* 2008), re-vegetation and re-wetting, can be high, but they need to be assessed against the cost of avoiding damage to ecosystem services (FIRES 2010).

5.3.2.4 Water quality regulation: waste detoxification

Perhaps the upland environments most sensitive to the deposition of long-range transported air pollutants are the acidified streams and lakes draining these habitats. Since the middle of the 19th Century, these habitats have suffered loss of salmonid populations, as well as a much wider, overall decline in aquatic biodiversity (Battarbee *et al.* 1990; Chapter 9).

However, plant-soil systems of MMH habitats intercept and retain a proportion of various atmospheric pollutants, including anthropogenic sulphur, nitrogen and heavy metals, which would otherwise contaminate drainage waters. Furthermore, MMH soils have served to buffer the effects of acid deposition on upland stream and lake ecosystems: deposited acid hydrogen ions are exchanged for base cations (such as calcium and magnesium), levels of which are maintained by the long-term process of geological weathering.

Growing evidence suggests that the reduction in acid deposition has caused an increase in naturally occurring organic acids in the form of DOC, concentrations of which are the result of the incomplete decomposition of organic matter under conditions of anoxia, low temperatures and low pH (Evans *et al.* 2005; Monteith *et al.* 2007). It is possible, therefore, that DOC concentrations may be returning to pre-industrial (and hence pre-water treatment) levels, which, in turn, could have ecological benefits (for instance, through increased energy supply to freshwater ecosystems, and increased protection of freshwater organisms against potentially harmful ultraviolet radiation). However, an increase in DOC concentrations to levels not experienced since the mid 19th Century also represents a treatment challenge (and a major additional cost) for water companies: DOC must be removed at treatment works prior to chlorination to bring levels below those that risk the formation of potentially toxic by-products.

Elevated points in the landscape receive disproportionate amounts of airborne pollutants including sulphur and nitrogen compounds (Caporn & Emmett 2009), heavy metals and Persistent Organic Compounds (POPs) such as pesticide residues. Intact ecosystems, particularly those with well-developed soils and/or those with extensive moss communities, can retain a considerable proportion of these pollutants (Currey *et al.* 2011), thereby minimising pollution runoff into freshwater habitats and drinking water supplies. Organic soils effectively bind a range of heavy metals and POPs by adsorption to organic matter. However, potential physical or biochemical instability of peatlands driven by climatic and land management changes raises the risk of release of some of these contaminants back into the river system (Rothwell *et al.* 2007; Nizzetto *et al.* 2010). Likewise, increased low flows (due to changes in land management or climate), and subsequent reductions in the dilution of pollutants in downstream ecosystems, could greatly increase pollutant pressures on aquatic ecosystems.

5.3.2.5 Soil erosion: particulate organic matter production

Many areas of upland blanket bog and wet heath are degraded and actively eroding (**Figure 5.9**). Estimates of the affected area vary between 10–30% of peatlands (Evans & Warburton 2007). Causes include a range of cumulative anthropogenic impacts over the last millennium such as fire, overgrazing, acid deposition and climatic changes (Evans & Warburton 2007). While erosion is a natural process (and some invertebrate species are associated with open ground), increased soil erosion has a number of negative environmental consequences including the degradation of perceived landscape quality, a reduction in water quality due to release of heavy metals and POPs, and the loss of water storage capacity in reservoirs due to sedimentation of aquatically transported particulate matter. Direct monitoring of suspended sediment outputs from UK upland catchments

Figure 5.9a Eroding blanket bog in the southern Pennines, England. *Photo courtesy of North Pennines AONB Partnership.*

Figure 5.9b Houses encroaching on lowland heath in Dorset, England. *Photo courtesy of Peter Wakely/ Natural England.*

has produced sediment yield estimates of <1 t/km/yr in intact Scottish moorland (Hope *et al.* 1997), compared with around 260 t/km/yr in heavily eroded peatlands of the Peak District (Evans *et al.* 2006b). Studies on sedimentation in UK reservoirs have produced estimates of sediment yields of 25–200 t/km/yr (Yelloff *et al.* 2005). Soil erosion is also a significant factor in carbon loss from eroding moorlands, both directly through the loss of particulate organic carbon, and indirectly through the drainage effects of widespread gullying which enhances peat decomposition (Evans & Lindsay 2010a, b).

5.3.3 Cultural Services

Cultural services of MMH encompass opportunities for recreation, as well as spiritual, religious, aesthetic and educational services. Generally, people value MMH within their landscape context, so cultural benefits also arise from the interactions MMH has with its neighbouring habitats (e.g. grasslands, woodlands and freshwater systems).

Mountains, Moorlands and Heaths are 'socially valued landscapes' as demonstrated by their landscape and biodiversity designations: 28% of the UK's MMH are designated as SSSI/ASSI, and 16% as part of one of the 14 National Parks (**Figure 5.10**). Relatively few people live in, or immediately adjacent to, upland habitats, but areas such as the Peak District, Exmoor, Loch Lomond and the Trossachs are within easy reach for a day trip for many. In stark contrast, lowland heaths are often located close to urban areas and are, therefore, considered to be 'local places' (i.e. places for the daily dog walk).

Engagement with, and appreciation of, landscapes within MMH varies across demographic, socioeconomic and cultural groups (Defra 2008; Natural England 2009b; Hanley

& Colombo 2009; Suckall *et al.* 2009a). Some people enjoy escaping to remote, 'wild' locations to achieve a fulfilling connection to nature (Natural England 2009b), while others may find such places inaccessible, dangerous and forbidding (Askins 2004; Suckall *et al.* 2009b).

5.3.3.1 Religion and spirituality

Mountains, Moorlands and Heaths can provide a setting for spiritual and religious reflection, particularly as travelling through wild and beautiful terrain, with uninterrupted views, can invoke a sense of meaning and, therefore, spirituality (Natural England 2009b; Frey 1998). These habitats may also contain features prompting spiritual reflection, such as ancient burial mounds and historical sacred places and some pilgrimages involve passing through MMH (e.g. St. Cuthbert's Way in Northumbria).

5.3.3.2 Cultural heritage and aesthetics

Peat soils are of considerable archaeological importance as they can preserve records of species, environment, climate and land use for 10,000 years or more (Olivier & Van de Noort 2002; Simmons 2003). Such records provide fascinating insights into our past environment and culture, and are important in informing us about historic climate changes, sea-level rises, land management and fire regimes (Brunning 2001; Blackford *et al.* 2006; Yeloff *et al.* 2007; **Box 5.7**). Ancient landmarks or burial places, land use remains or other historic artefacts are also conserved in much drier soils, such as those of heaths (Hawley *et al.* 2008).

Not only are MMH habitats shaped by grazing, livestock breeds themselves are valued as aspects of regional agrarian heritage (e.g. Welsh black cattle, Highland cattle and New Forest ponies) for their links to the past, as well as their

a)

Protected Area	Area ('000 ha) and proportion (%) of dominant MMH in protected area	England	Northern Ireland	Scotland	Wales	UK
SPA	Area	193	1	709	19	922
	%	55	1	24	23	26
NP	Area	185	0	340	35	560
	%	52	0	11	44	16
SSSI/ASSI	Area	251	204	653	46	970
	%	71	24	22	57	28
SAC	Area	225	15	468	29	737
	%	64	18	16	37	21
AONB	Area	110	54	651	1	816
	%	31	64	22	1	23
NNR	Area	16	1	90	5	111
	%	4	1	3	7	3

Figure 5.10 Protected area designations in relation to dominant (>51% area per 1x1 km resolution) Mountains, Moorlands and Heaths (MMH) Broad Habitat in the UK: a) Area and proportion of protected area in MMH; b) Spatial distribution of protected area and dominant MMH Broad Habitat. SPA=Special Protection Areas; NP=National Parks; SSSI/ASSI=Site/Area of Special Scientific Interest*; SPA=Special Area of Conservation; AONB=Area of Outstanding Natural Beauty; NNR=National Nature Reserves. Protected area data sources: England and Wales: © Natural England (2010), reproduced with the permission of Natural England; Scotland: Scottish Natural Heritage; Northern Ireland: Northern Ireland Environment Agency. This material is based upon Crown Copyright and is reproduced with the permission of Land & Property Services under delegated authority from the Controller of Her Majesty's Stationery Office, Crown copyright and database rights, EMOU206.2. Northern Ireland Environment Agency Copyright 2009. *SSSI is a conservation designation denoting a protected area in Great Britain. ASSI is a conservation designation denoting a protected area in Northern Ireland.

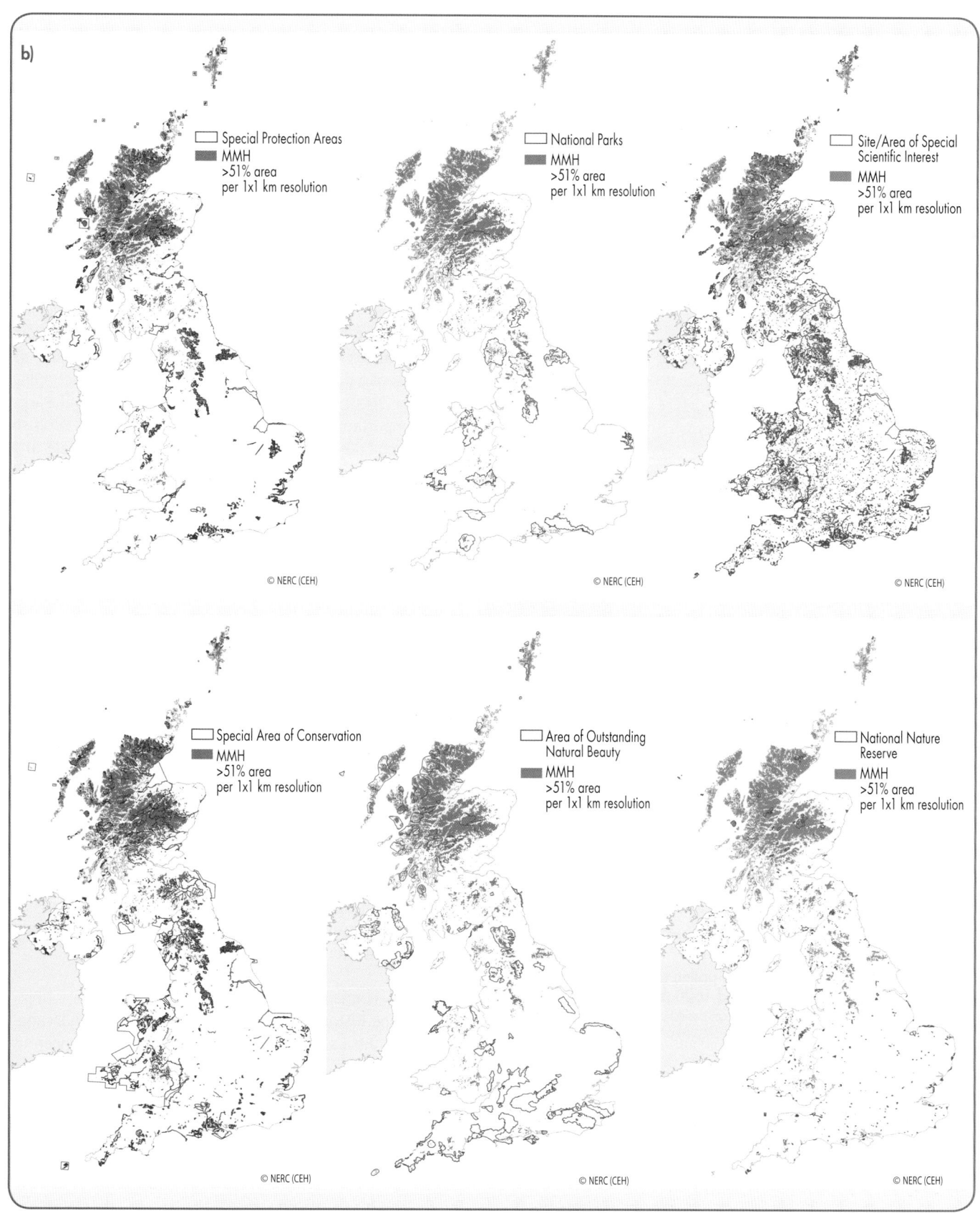

© NERC (CEH)

© NERC (CEH)

© NERC (CEH)

© NERC (CEH)

© NERC (CEH)

© NERC (CEH)

purported benefits for biodiversity and provisioning services (Davies *et al.* 2004). Livestock farming generates important social and economic benefits for local communities, as well as for visitors and the tourism industry, returns from which are not fully captured through markets (LUPG 2009; Hanley *et al.* 2007). Tourists value seeing livestock and associated farm buildings and boundaries (e.g. hedges and dry stone walls) and, for some, these are part and parcel of 'biodiversity' (Fischer & Young 2007).

Although more localised than farming landscapes, and in long-term decline, 'commons' and crofting landscapes also have high social and cultural importance (Oliver 2005; Crofting Inquiry 2009). While the latter are 'local places' for crofters, crofting counties are nationally significant in terms of species, habitats and landscapes (Redpath *et al.* 2010), with a high percentage of land designated under UK and EU environmental legislation.

Aesthetic features valued by people in MMH uplands include remoteness, bleakness, tranquillity, open space and the special plant and animal life (SAC 2005; CPRE 2006; **Table 5.4**). Mountains, Moorlands and Heaths play an important role in providing a sense of freedom and wilderness. In a survey conducted in the Cairngorms National Park, 70% of the respondents and 82% of the residents stated that it was important for Scotland to have such wild places (SNH 2008).

Mountains, Moorlands and Heaths also inspire works of art such as Wordsworth's poems (1800s) or Goldworthy's Sheepfolds sculpture project (Cumbria County Council 2007). In turn, this reinforces the position of MMH as socially valued landscapes.

5.3.3.3 Social cohesion and community development

Mountains, Moorlands and Heaths are often considered emblems for both national identity and social cohesion. For example, MMH in Scotland have been promoted as symbols of a popular national identity (McCrone *et al.* 1995; Lorimer 2000), and the two new Scottish National Parks were important symbolic projects for the devolved Scottish Parliament (Rennie 2006; Thompson 2006; Stockdale and Barker 2009). Likewise, Welsh National Parks illustrate the inter-relationship between cultural identity and sense of place (IWA 2009), with the Countryside Commission for Wales describing Wales as 'a land of mountains' (IWA 2009).

These habitats also support local social networks that foster and sustain relationships. Opportunities for environmental and archaeological volunteering (through Non-Governmental Organisations (NGOs), National Parks, etc.) can engender a sense of ownership and reduce problems of anti-social and damaging behaviour (Natural England 2008). For instance, Mountain Rescue UK retains approximately 3,500 volunteers alone.

Mountains, Moorlands and Heaths are one of the few Broad Habitats that involves the management of 'common pool' resources (e.g. deer management and common grazings); this generates important cultural traditions and bonds of reciprocity which are essential to maintain social capital. Such processes, such as the 'heft' in Cumbria, are cultural heritage in their own right, but also important in sustaining fragile and isolated rural communities when other opportunities for face-to-face interaction have declined (Burton *et al.* 2009).

5.3.3.4 Tourism and recreation

Landscape historians indicate that some MMH landscapes (such as the Lake District) were perceived as dangerous places until the Victorian urban elite, and the artists writing

---

Box 5.7 Biodiversity change and agriculture in the uplands: a long-term historical perspective.

How farmers manage their land is known to have a potentially large impact on species diversity and abundance. But if we look back in time, can we find a long-term relationship between land management in the uplands, and an indicator of biodiversity? Hanley *et al.* (2008) investigated this issue for 11 sites within the Scottish uplands. All sites were chosen to meet two criteria: (i) that they contained suitable undisturbed peat deposits, allowing the extraction of peat cores from which an uninterrupted dating sequence of layers could be obtained; and (ii) that they had farm or estate records which allowed the authors to develop a picture of how land had been managed over the last 400 years (Figure 1). Pollen remains were extracted from dated layers of the peat cores and used to establish plant species diversity. Historical records were examined to build up a picture of land use (e.g. grazing patterns), technological change (e.g. the introduction of new breeds of sheep), land drainage, farm amalgamations or divisions, and changes in land ownership or tenancy. Using original sources, a data set of cattle, sheep and barley prices was also developed. The authors then used panel data methods to estimate a relationship between land use, prices and plant diversity over 400 years. The main results were that increases in grazing pressure (measured using changes in prices) was associated with a statistically significant fall in diversity, while reductions in grazing pressure increased plant diversity. However, land abandonment also reduced diversity. These findings show that the way in which farmers manage land in MMH has had a significant effect on biodiversity over time.

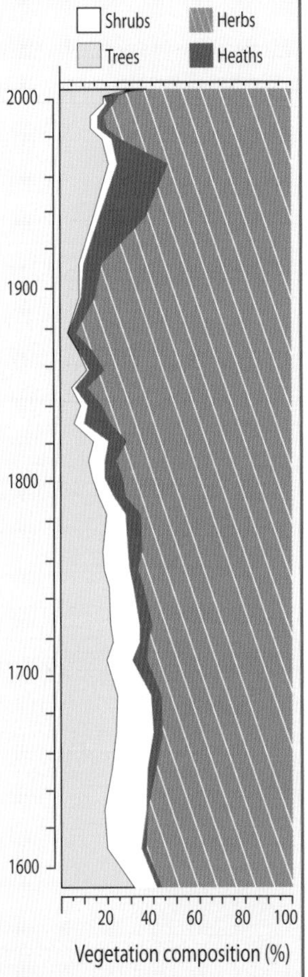

Figure 1 Summary of percentage pollen data for a farm in north-west Scotland, from around 1600 (base of y-axes) to the present day (top of y-axes). Source: based on Hanley *et al.* (2008). Copyright ©2008 British Ecological Society. Reproduced with permission of Blackwell Publishing Ltd.

Table 5.4 An example of the delivery of cultural services by MMH landscapes. Source: reproduced from Natural England (2009b).

Feature	History	Place	Inspiration	Calm	Leisure/ Activities	Spiritual	Learning	Escape
Water, rivers and streams	Low	Medium	High	High	High	High	Medium	High
Bogs and Marshes	Low		Low		Medium	Low	Medium	
Mountains and Hills	Medium	Low	High	Medium	High	High	Low	High
Moorland	Low	High	High	Low	Medium	High	Low	High

and painting for this audience, began to seek out such landscapes as examples of the 'sublime' (Hanley *et al.* 2009). This was the start of appreciating these landscapes for their physical and spiritual recreation opportunities, a trend that now provides alternative livelihoods to the traditional land uses (e.g. sporting estates, extensive grazing). During the 20th Century, outdoor recreation activities, such as hill-walking, increased (Watson 1991; Hanley *et al.* 2002), although broader UK data suggests a recent decline in countryside recreation (Natural England 2006). We have little data on more recent MMH recreation trends, but **Figure 5.11** suggests an increase in contrast to the suggested national downward trends.

While no figures exist for visitor use solely of MMH habitats, overall, 35 million leisure visits were undertaken to English and Welsh National Parks and 19 million to English and Welsh 'open access' land during 2005 (Natural England 2006). In Scotland, 44% of the adult population made at least one visit per week to the outdoors for leisure and recreation purposes (TNS 2009).

Most visitors to MMH are attracted by the scenery (Puttick 2004; Atlantic Consultants 2005; Visit Scotland 2008) and tranquillity (Davies 2006). However, relative proximity to home and ease of access may be strong drivers behind visiting patterns (Bonn *et al.* 2010). For example, more people visit Peak District uplands than remote North Pennines uplands, although the latter may provide greater tranquillity (CPRE 2006). Lowland heathlands tend to be 'local places', visited most often on foot or by short car journeys (Underhill-Day & Liley 2007), with many dog walkers attracted by the open space, the views and the wildlife they encounter (English Nature 2006).

Mountains, Moorlands and Heaths provide tourism and recreational opportunities for climbing, mountaineering, rock scrambling, walking, fell running, skiing, orienteering,

riding and mountain biking. Since the publication of Hugh Munro's list of mountain summits in 1891, 'Munro-bagging'—i.e. attempting to ascend peaks over 3000 feet (914 m)—has become a popular pursuit among British walkers and mountaineers, with Ben Lomond alone attracting more than 50,000 walkers a year (LLTNPA 2005). Several mountaintops are now directly accessible through private company transport (e.g. Snowdon) or newly created walking paths that allow easier access.

Skiing is largely confined to MMH. The Ski Club of Great Britain reports that there were 159,888 Scottish [downhill] skier days in the winter of 2008/9, generating £11million for the economy; 40% of these were associated with the Cairngorms range, NE Scotland, and another quarter with nearby Glenshee range. Skier days vary dramatically from winter to winter but were considerably higher between the mid 1980s to mid 1990s than thereafter (**Figure 5.12a**). The wintry 2009/10 season broke the declining pattern, and indeed, a substantial part of the variation in the number of skier days in Glen Shee between 1994/5 and 2009/10 could be explained by average daytime winter temperature between December and March with colder winters generating more skier days (**Figure 5.12b**). Changes in winter climate have thus economic and social ramifications; the variability in notably snow-lie, and the need for large capital outlays, however, makes it difficult to manage this service adaptively.

Unlike skiing, most leisure activities in MMH are largely informal and non-commercial, such as walking and enjoying the scenery. However, there is a considerable potential for visitor-spending in associated settlements before and after these pursuits. For example, day and overnight visitors to Peak District moorlands spend on average £14.97 and £96.40 respectively per trip for food, accommodation, travel, equipment and souvenirs (Davies 2006). The considerable impact of reduced tourism on local economies was illustrated

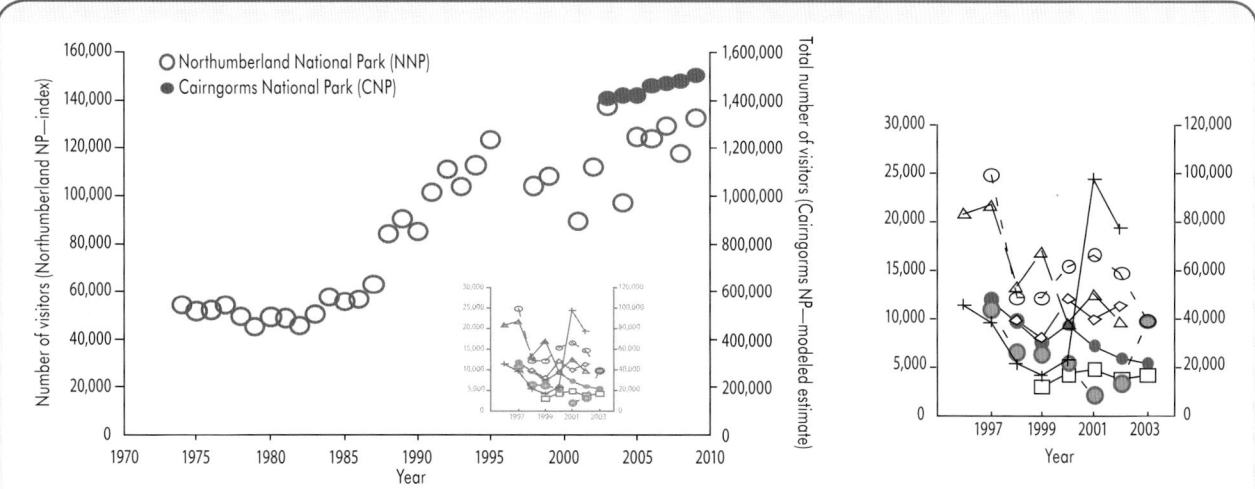

Figure 5.11 Patterns of visitor use of MMH-dominated areas over time. The main graph (left axis; hollow circles) shows an aggregated index of the number of visitors using three MMH areas in the Northumberland National Park (NNP) on the basis of mechanic counter data; and an estimate of the total number of visitors to the Cairngorms National Park (CNP; right axis; filled circles) based on a wide range of tourism indexes. The little graph (inserted in line with the monitored length of time) shows visitor counts in eight areas in the Cairngorms (mechanic counter data), seven of which generally decline (left axis) and one which steeply increases (right axis). Intriguingly, this relatively chaotic pattern coincides with a temporary slump in visitors to the Northumberland National Park. This clearly indicates that long-term trend data from a range of areas is required to determine directional changes in visitor numbers for MMH.
Source: Van der Wal (unpublished data).

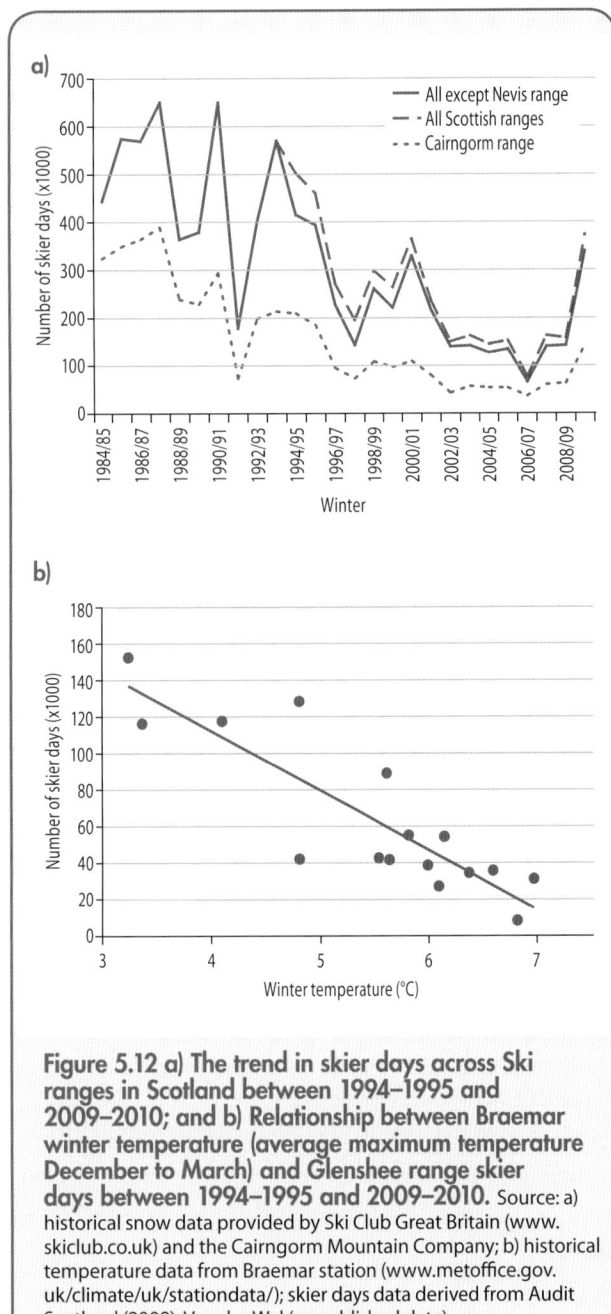

Figure 5.12 a) The trend in skier days across Ski ranges in Scotland between 1994–1995 and 2009–2010; and b) Relationship between Braemar winter temperature (average maximum temperature December to March) and Glenshee range skier days between 1994–1995 and 2009–2010. Source: a) historical snow data provided by Ski Club Great Britain (www.skiclub.co.uk) and the Cairngorm Mountain Company; b) historical temperature data from Braemar station (www.metoffice.gov.uk/climate/uk/stationdata/); skier days data derived from Audit Scotland (2009); Van der Wal (unpublished data).

by the outbreak of Foot and Mouth Disease in 2001 which caused losses to the tourism sector of £3.2 billion across all habitats (Curry 2009).

Charismatic species, such as peregrine falcon, golden eagle, nightjar, mountain hare and red deer, are often associated with MMH habitats. Recent work shows that the public has a considerable willingness to pay for the conservation of raptors found in MMH habitats (Hanley *et al.* 2010). Between 1997 and 2002, the Scottish wildlife tourism market was estimated to be worth £57 million, employed approximately 2,000 people, and demonstrated a 50% increase in employment within wildlife tourism business (A&M 2002).

5.3.3.5 Field sports: wild deer and red grouse

Field sports of relevance to MMH include grouse shooting and stalking wild deer. There have been high private investments in establishing and maintaining moorlands and

heaths for field sports (PACEC 2006). There are approximately 450 grouse shooting moors in the UK, covering 16,763 km² (Richards 2004), i.e. 7% and 36% of the UK and MMH land area respectively (**Figure 5.13**). The majority (296) are in Scotland, with only 10 in Wales, and the rest in England. Furthermore, the average shooting moor in the Scottish Highlands is 40 km²—twice the size of those of the Southern Scottish Highlands and English moors. Although few grouse moors return a profit in their activities (Sotherton *et al.* 2009), Fraser of Allander Institute (2010) estimated that, during 2009, grouse shooting supported 1,072 full-time equivalent employees in Scotland. In England, grouse shooting activity increased from 1,560 potential shooting days per year in 2000 to 1,898 in 2009. During that period, the number of gamekeepers also rose from 196 to 253. Overall, it was estimated that 47,000 people in the UK took part in grouse shooting (PACEC 2006).

5.3.3.6 Education

Within MMH habitats there are substantial opportunities to learn about the natural world and our cultural heritage. For example, MMH are increasingly valued for their geodiversity, as illustrated by the North Pennines Geo-park and North-West Highlands Geo-park (www.northwest-highlands-geopark.org.uk/) projects, communicating a sense of the permanence of nature (Natural England 2009b). Active promotion of learning opportunities, such as those organised by NGOs and National Parks, takes place through guided walks, visitor

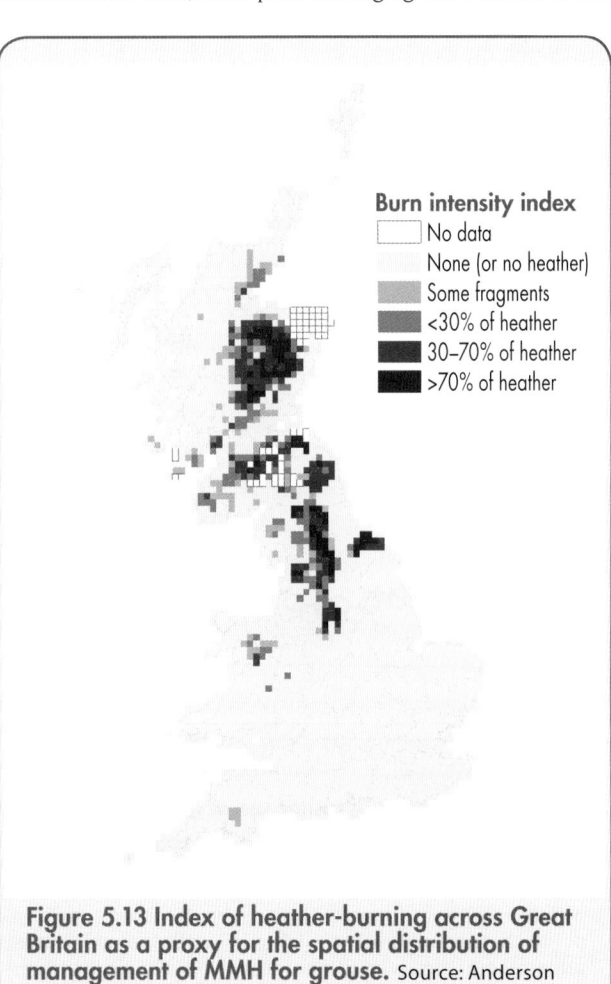

Figure 5.13 Index of heather-burning across Great Britain as a proxy for the spatial distribution of management of MMH for grouse. Source: Anderson *et al.* (2009a). Copyright (2009), reproduced with permission from Elsevier.

centres and school education programmes 'outside the classroom'. Materials, such as onsite interpretation panels, audio-trails, publications and websites, offer opportunities for individual learning.

5.3.3.7 Human health

Mountains, Moorlands and Heaths provide health benefits through the activities undertaken within them, while also providing more 'passive' benefits for mental and emotional health (Pretty *et al.* 2007; Mitchell & Popham 2008). Climbing and walking in MMH, for example, provide both physical and mental health benefits. The openness and remoteness of such landscapes has been linked to feeling calm and relaxed, although other emotions, such as exhilaration, anxiety and fear, can be associated with particular landscape features like high crags (Natural England 2009b). Indeed, MMH can provide spaces for physical and mental recreation that reinforce social bonds of reciprocity. Through memories, inspiring photographs and documentaries, the existence of open, wild spaces may provide important mental 'well-being' for some of the population, even if they do not actually visit them.

However, MMH can be dangerous places, with bogs, slippery rocks, avalanches, rock falls, severe weather and poor visibility among the hazards. Statistics from the Mountain Rescue Committee of Scotland indicate that there were 387 mountain incidents during 2008: 20 of these were fatal and another 60 resulted in serious injury. However, the sense of vulnerability arising from these hazards may well contribute to their attraction, partly through people learning about themselves when undertaking challenging activities in MMH landscapes (Natural England 2009b).

5.3.3.8 Biodiversity

Besides enabling 'life', and thus being a supporting service, 'biodiversity' provides a number of cultural services, which include its conservation. Indeed, Harrison *et al.* (2009) note that often the cultural service aspects of biodiversity conservation have received most attention, with the relationship between biodiversity and provisioning, supporting and regulating services arising at a later date. In other words, biodiversity conservation has often been for moral, ethical or aesthetic reasons, providing spiritual benefits through activating an ethic of care for non-human species and ensuring diversity of life for future generations—these rationales underpin the designations of socially valued habitats (e.g. heathlands). The services arising from biodiversity include the role of species in encouraging an interest in conserving MMH and the role of biodiversity in a landscape setting that provides restorative health benefits.

Although MMH are characterised by their species-poor habitats, they are known for the species indicative to these habitats, i.e. charismatic, flagship species. Visitors include those seeking specific experiences, such as birdwatching for dotterel (*C. morinellus*) or Dartford warbler (*S. undata*), which links biodiversity with recreation and tourism. It is often an interest in a specific charismatic species, habitat or landscape type that stimulates life-long learning about MMH and the environmental processes therein. For example, many naturalists are inspired by species such as golden

eagle (*Aquila chrysaetos*) or red deer (*Cervus elaphus*), which are often used as symbols by NGOs, such as RSPB or the National Trust, to attract new members. Furthermore, biodiversity conservation projects often contribute to community development objectives that combine job creation with environmental education.

The symbolic use of these species highlights the fact that people do not have to visit MMH in order to enjoy and care about them—it is possible that natural history programmes (e.g. Radio Four's World on the Move programme tracking Ospreys returning to nest in the Cairngorms) provide a connection between urban dwellers and the biodiversity found in MMH without visiting. By contrast, it is both biodiversity and geodiversity combined that create a landscape and it is often the individual's experience within this restorative setting that creates the health benefits, rather than species *per se*. Thus, the cultural services arising from biodiversity require us to put the species present in the wider landscape context, understanding both the interconnection between species and also the experiential and cognitive process by which people interpret and derive meaning from these interconnections.

5.4 Trade-offs and Synergies Among MMH Goods and Ecosystem Services

This section will provide a qualitative analysis of the trade-offs and synergies between the provision of the different ecosystem services identified in Section 5.3 (**Table 5.5**; **Box 5.8**). This allows an initial assessment of whether it may be appropriate to prioritise different ecosystem services in different areas for different purposes, and whether multiple delivery of ecosystem services from MMH are likely to provide added value. Certain ecosystem services from MMH are already prioritised in certain locations, but this approach is largely piece-meal (Stockdale & Barker 2009; Reed *et al.* 2009). For example, water quality is prioritised through River Basin Management Plans under the Water Framework Directive, often without reference to likely effects of proposed management activities on other ecosystem services. Similarly, nature conservation is given priority in designated sites such as SSSI's and National Nature Reserves. Although these are multi-functional sites, there is little explicit consideration of the likely consequences of managing land for nature conservation on other ecosystem services such as the provision of food and fibre or carbon storage. It is imperative that trade-offs and synergies between different ecosystem services are more explicitly considered in decisions about the future of MMH habitats.

The management of MMH habitats has changed considerably as managers have adapted to a range of past and present drivers (Section 5.2; Section 5.3). Although

Table 5.5 Main goods and benefits derived from MMH broad habitats. Those that require the actual habitat to be removed (such as coal extraction or woodland regeneration), and thereby transfer into a different MMH broad habitat are not included. Where possible, an indication is given of the relative importance of each habitat for providing the respective service using a four-step scale ranging from negligible (-) to high (+++); o indicate that attribute on to separate MMH broad habitats is difficult.

	MMH goods and benefits	Bracken	Dwarf Shrub Heath	Upland Fen, Marsh & Swamp	Bog	Montane	Inland Rock
Provisioning Services	Food provision—livestock and crops: • Livestock products from sheep and some beef cattle	+	+++	+	++	+	-
	Food provision—deer and game birds: • Wild harvest products including venison and grouse meat	-	+++	+	++	+	-
	Fibre from sheep wool	+	+++	+	++	+	–
	Traditional lifestyle products including honey and whisky	–	+++	+	++	+	–
	Peat extraction for fuel and horticultural use	–	+	+	+++	–	–
	Freshwater provision for domestic and industrial use	o	o	o	o	o	o
	Alternative energy provision: • Opportunity for wind energy schemes • Generation of water flows for hydro-energy in freshwater habitats	+++ o	+++ o	- o	++ o	+ o	- o
Regulating Services	Climate regulation: • Carbon storage; maintenance of plant and soil carbon stores • Carbon sequestration potential	++ ++	++ +++	+++ +	+++ ++	+ +	- -
	Natural hazard regulation: • Potential for flood risk mitigation • Opportunities for wildfire risk mitigation	o +	o +++	o +	o ++	o -	o -
	Pollution mitigation: • Interception and retention of airborne pollutants by plants and soil • Regulation of particulate matter and pH buffering • Dilution by water from uplands of pollutants in downstream locations	+ o o	++ o o	++ o o	+++ o o	++ o o	- o o
	Disease regulation: • Disease transmission through ticks • Disease regulation of waterborne bacteria (e.g. Cryptosporidia)	++ o	++ o	+ o	++ o	+ o	- o
Cultural Services	Religion and spirituality: • Sense of awe; connection to spiritual powers • Opportunities for solitude and reflection	+ +	++ ++	++ ++	++ ++	+++ +++	+++ +++
	Cultural heritage and aesthetics: • Preservation of natural/environmental history and cultural practices • Socially-valued ('natural' and 'cultural') landscapes • Source of inspiration to works of art	+ + o	++ ++ o	+++ +++ o	+++ ++ o	+ +++ o	+ ++ o
	Social cohesion and community development: • Development and maintenance of social networks through management of 'common pool' resources • Landscape as symbols of a popular national identity	+ +	++ +++	++ +	++ ++	+ +++	- ++
	Tourism and recreation: • Outdoor active tourism and recreational opportunities • Tourism and recreation based on watching wildlife • Field sports (e.g. grouse shooting and deer stalking)	+ + +	+++ ++ +++	+ ++ +	++ ++ ++	++ ++ +	+ + -
	Education: • Opportunities to learn about the natural world and cultural heritage • Opportunities to learn about oneself when undertaking challenging recreation in MMH landscapes	+ +	+++ +	+++ ++	+++ ++	+++ +++	+ ++
	Security and personal freedom: • Land used for Military purposes • Existence value (i.e. knowing that MMH and their attributes are there)	o o	o o	o o	o o	o o	o o
	Human health: • Mental and physical benefits from experiencing MMH	o	o	o	o	o	o

the majority of those who benefit from MMH ecosystem services perceive that further extensification of land use and management will occur in these habitats in the future (for example, reductions in managed livestock and/or game populations and associated burning practices, or woodland regeneration), it is likely that some intensive land management practices will continue in certain areas, such as heather-burning for grouse, and others may increase in demand, such as the production of biofuels (Reed *et al.* 2009). The rest of this section, therefore, considers likely trade-offs and complementarities between different MMH ecosystem services under a mix of current (and possible future) extensive and intensive management practices.

Extensive management in MMH habitats may reduce their capacity to sustain provisioning services such as sheep and game production. Intensive sheep-grazing and managed burning have been blamed by some for the poor condition of many upland SSSI's (English Nature 2003), and intensive management may threaten water quality and soil carbon storage (Holden *et al.* 2007). However, the significant reductions in sheep stocking densities currently being reported for some MMH areas (SAC 2008) may potentially lead to a short-term increase in wildfire risk due to fuel-load build up and associated change in vegetation structure. In turn, the enhanced incidence and severity of wildfires could damage soils and release the carbon they contain (Tucker 2003; Reed *et al.* 2009). Fires have indeed been found to spread faster in older heather stands due to a greater amount of fine, available fuel, and increased proportions of dead

material (Davies *et al.* 2010). Yet the dynamics of wildfire in MMH are complex and influenced by a wide range of other factors, such as soil humidity and plant chemical content, that are not necessarily susceptible to changes in sheep-grazing pressure (Johnson *et al.* 2001; Bond & Keeley 2005). Combined with reductions in managed burning, reductions in sheep-grazing are likewise connected to changes in biodiversity (both increases and decreases) through habitat modifications as scrub encroaches into MMH, transforming the drier areas over time into woodland.

A loss of livestock from MMH habitats would most likely be associated with a loss of land managers and farm workers. Depending on how land is managed in the absence of livestock, some land managers may remain, but most probably much fewer than is currently seen (based on a cross-section of opinion from stakeholders consulted over possible scenarios for UK uplands; Reed *et al.* 2009). There is growing concern over the effect this may have on the long-term viability of remote communities already under pressure from demographic change, declining access to public services, limited employment opportunities, limited energy infrastructure, low internet connection speeds and poor mobile phone coverage (Commission for Rural Communities 2010).

Reductions in livestock-grazing may also affect cultural services such as the maintenance of cultural landscapes, social cohesion and tourism. Those who visit MMH for recreation tend to value their uninterrupted views and unique habitats and wildlife, which, according to some

Box 5.8 Diversity of societal uses of the Pentland Hills, 10–12 km south-west of the centre of Edinburgh.
Glencorse Reservoir is below the foreground, with Capelaw Hill (454 m) on the left and Allermuir Hill (493 m) on the right, directly overlooking Edinburgh. The challenge is to recognise the wide range of values multi-functional landscapes such as this bring to society, and develop management strategies that take into account both direct and indirect benefits humans derive from their natural environment. *Photo courtesy of Des Thompson/Scottish Natural Heritage.*

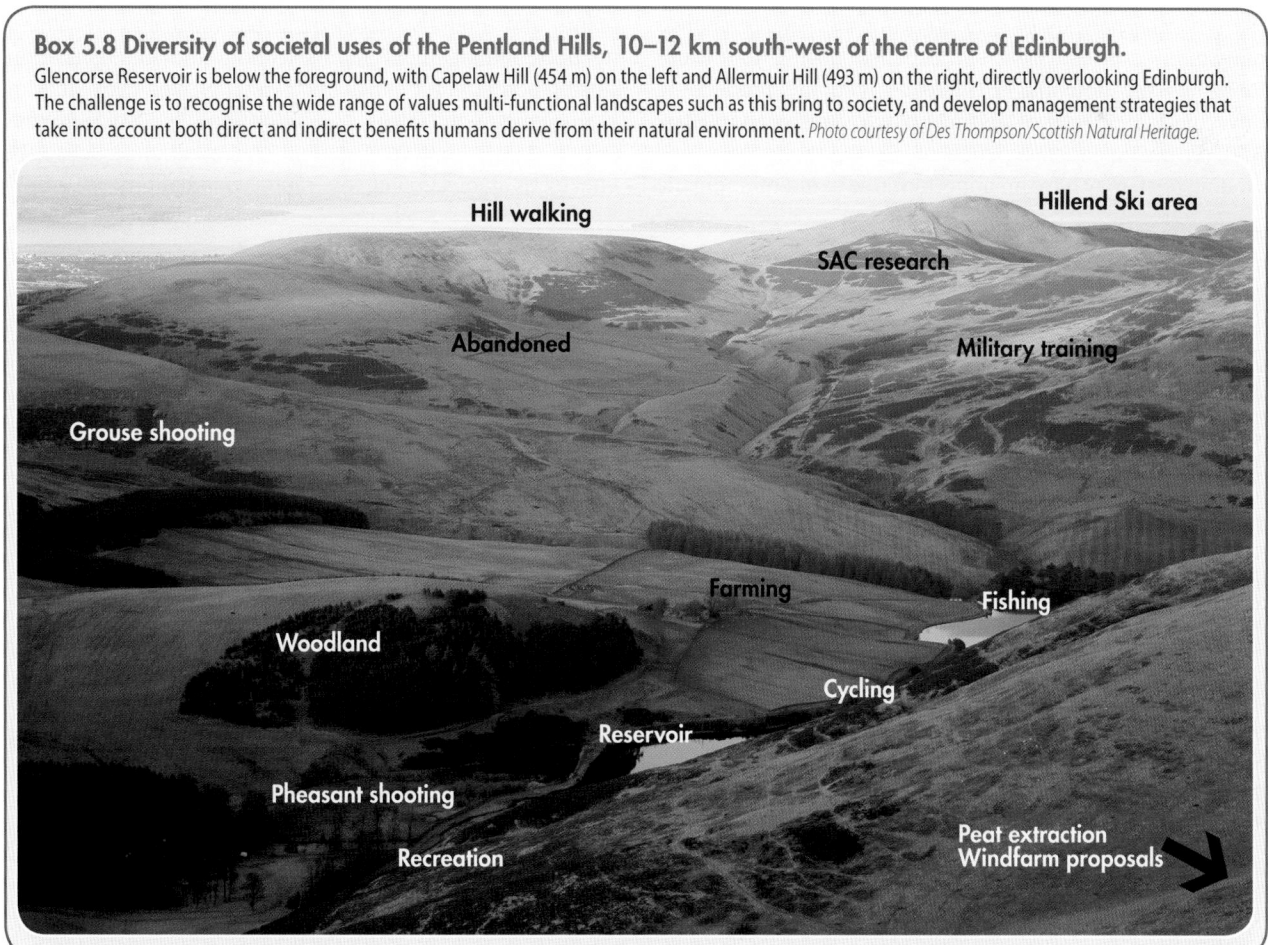

recreationalists, would be compromised by dense scrub and forest (Reed *et al.* 2009). Conversely, it is well-known that respondents to surveys about landscape scenarios tend to express a preference for the status quo over any alternative scenario (Samuelson & Zeckhauser 1988; Hanley *et al.* 2009). However, relationships with, and appreciation of, different landscapes are likely to evolve, and there is a desire to prevent dominance of a single habitat—for example, balancing the prevalence of heather and woodland (Fischer & Marshall 2010). Relaxation of grazing pressure, by both livestock and deer, in certain areas could foster the provision of a more diverse range of landscapes, thus maintaining open MMH and their associated cultural services, whilst allowing scrub and woodland to regenerate. Such a development would increase biodiversity, help fulfil national and international statutory conservation obligations, and create a more diverse landscape to which people can form emotional attachments (Parsons & Daniel 2002). Where MMH habitats do not occur on deep peats, carbon sequestration objectives may become an increasingly strong driver of such landscape change (Forestry Commission 2009).

Indeed, the large number of potential complementarities between carbon management (which, in the short-term may contribute towards climate change mitigation targets) and other ecosystem services (Bonn *et al.* 2010) may represent important opportunities for future sustainable management of MMH habitats. The re-wetting of peat soils by grip blocking might serve to protect the soil carbon store, not only with respect to reducing losses of particulate carbon, but also by making it more resistant to wildfire; however, the potential benefits of grip blocking for 'climate change mitigation' are less clear-cut because raising the water table has the potential to increase methane production. Nevertheless, ecological and hydrological restoration (**Box 5.9**), involving practices such as re-vegetating bare and eroding peat, may have an important role in maintaining the

UK's largest carbon store without increasing net greenhouse gas outputs (Worrall *et al.* 2009; Lindsay 2010). If realised, this could provide synergies between carbon management and the protection of upland biodiversity (and possibly the provision of drinking water) in areas where restoration is viewed as required. Conversely, drainage and extractive uses of MMH habitats (e.g. peat for horticulture or fuel) are mostly in conflict with climate change mitigation and biodiversity protection policies.

Mountains, Moorlands and Heaths also have the potential to contribute towards 'climate change mitigation' in other ways. The altitude of many MMH habitats means they have some of the highest inland average wind speeds in the UK (Orr *et al.* 2008), but the potential for generating wind energy is often limited by the infrastructure costs associated with transmitting energy from sometimes remote locations (Orr *et al.* 2008). There may also be trade-offs between the provision of wind energy and the negative impact of wind turbines and their associated infrastructure on soil carbon storage, upland raptors, waders and wintering geese (Barrios & Rodriguez 2004; Percival 2005; Pearce-Higgins *et al.* 2009b), and people's appreciation of perceived 'wild landscapes' and their desire to maintain the status quo (Woods 2003; SNH 2008). It will be important to minimise such trade-offs and the availability of high quality scientific data to inform decision-making will be crucial; for example, the use of bird sensitivity maps may help identify areas where new windfarm developments are least likely to have adverse effects on important bird populations (Bright *et al.* 2008).

The abundance and diversity of different species of plants and animals that depend on MMH may be altered by both management intensification and extensification, raising potential for conflicts between groups with differing management objectives and priorities. One such conflict within MMH revolves around conservation issues: the effects of gamekeeping on raptor populations in grouse

---

Box 5.9 Ecosystem service recovery through restoration – Bleaklow plateau as case study.

UK upland blanket bog has been in decline for centuries (Lindsay 2010). Land use changes during the last 50 years have further compromised their condition (e.g. Tallis 1997), leading to severe erosion and widespread gullying which have significantly changed bog morphology and drainage patterns (Evans & Lindsay 2010b). This has strong negative impacts on ecosystem services provided by blanket bogs, such as carbon storage and sequestration, water quality regulation and run-off generation, as well as landscape aesthetics and biodiversity (see papers in Bonn *et al.* 2009).

The Bleaklow plateau in the Peak District (53.27.58N, 1.51.09W) has suffered from a legacy of intensive grazing, atmospheric deposition, and a series of large wildfires (McMorrow *et al.* 2009), the last one in 2003. This has led to large-scale degradation with extensive bare peat areas wide-spread gully erosion covering 34% of the plateau (Evans & Lindsay 2010a), increased soil acidity (pH between 2.9 and 3.5), severely elevated heavy metal concentrations (Rothwell *et al.* 2005) and very low water tables (26–451 mm below surface, with a mean of >300 mm in eroded areas; Allott *et al.* 2009). Vegetation of nearby intact areas is characterised by a high plant cover of cotton grasses (*Eriophorum* spp.) and heather (*Calluna vulgaris*) (UK NVC classifications M19 and M20; Rodwell *et al.* 1991).

The Moors for the Future Partnership is engaging in large-scale restoration of the most degraded areas in the Peak District. Since 2003, a total of 6 km² of bare peat area on Bleaklow has been treated with grass nurse crops, heather brash and geojute, while grazing was excluded. Seed germination and root mat development was aided through lime and fertiliser additions, raising pH levels temporarily to around pH 5. These activities act to stabilise the peat soils and enhance soil surface microclimate, thereby allowing subsequent colonisation of blanket bog species such as cotton grasses, crowberry (*Empetrum nigrum*) and bilberry (*Vaccinium myrtillus*).

Within three years, restoration has achieved an average of 45% in vegetation cover, while control areas have remained bare (Anderson *et al.* 2009b). Recovery of blanket bog vegetation is anticipated to take 15–20 years, conditional upon the re-establishment of bog hydrology. High resolution remote sensing is being evaluated as a monitoring tool (Lowe *et al.* 2009). By 2009, the costs of restoration activities over 4.3 km² were £1,235,000, or £2,900/ha (Walker & Buckler, pers. comm.). The current and future restoration impacts on ecosystem services are summarized in **Table 1**. The main benefits are: improvement of regulating services through greatly enhanced carbon storage, significantly reduced erosion losses, enhanced protection against wildfires and associated damage costs, and positive effects on biodiversity and landscape value. Effects of restoration on water quality and flood protection are currently under investigation.

Table 1 Changes to ecosystem services following peatland restoration through the Moors for the Future Partnership on the Bleaklow plateau, Peak District National Park, England. Source: adapted from Eftec (2009).

Ecosystem Services	Pre-restoration (bare peat areas)	Impact of current restoration	Future restoration and its benefits
Provisioning of food & fibre	Low or negative value for livestock production after accounting for farm costs.	No livestock-grazing to allow recovery.	Possibilities for low-intensity grazing possible. However, these are likely to bring only small monetary gains after accounting for farm costs.
Climate regulation	Bare peat is a considerable net carbon source (Worrall et al. 2009, 2011).	Reduced carbon loss after re-vegetation (i.e. smaller carbon source). Carbon storage benefit largely through avoided carbon losses (Worrall et al. 2009, 2011).	Fully recovered blanket bog is expected to be a carbon sink. Future restoration, leading to a reduction of 600 tonnes (t) of carbon dioxide equivalents (conservative estimate) over 6 km², would accrue a net value of ±£370,000 over 50 years (based on current carbon (C) price).
Water quantity regulation	Very flashy catchment with little storage capacity. Severe gullying exacerbates channel run-off.	Water quantity regulation over restored bare peat area alone likely to be negligible at this stage.	Reduction of overland flow velocities, and consequently somewhat reduced peak flows, likely with full establishment of cotton grass/Sphagnum systems (Holden et al. 2008). Flood risk attenuation will, however, be influenced by factors at the catchment level.
Water quality regulation	High rates of dissolved organic carbon (DOC) loss, 20–100 tC/km²/yr (Pawson et al. 2008; Worrall et al. 2011). High sediment losses (Evans et al. 2006).	Currently no measurable benefit of re-vegetation on DOC. Significant reduction in erosion rates of up to an order of magnitude (Worrall et al. 2011).	Potential for reduced DOC and thereby water treatment costs. Reduced sedimentation impacts on reservoirs downstream.
Hazard regulation	High risk areas for wildfires (Lindley et al. 2009), especially under climate change scenarios (Albertson et al. 2009).	Enhanced soil moisture and vegetation cover are likely to have reduced ignition hazard (McMorrow et al. 2009).	Intact water-logged blanket bog is more resistant to fire (i.e. reduced likelihood of outbreak and intensity). Restoration can thus alleviate losses (biodiversity, landscape aesthetics, etc.) caused by fire and prevent the very high expenditure of fire-fighting in remote areas.
Tourism & recreation	Bare peat, particularly when wet, is unsuitable for walking. Yet, the wider area attracts many walkers; ±18,000 visits/yr are made to the southern end of the Pennine Way.	Some improvement for walkers through stabilised peat surfaces.	Restoration is likely to improve suitability for walking, and thereby the quality of visits.
Field sports	Currently no field sports possible.	Likely increase of red grouse use of the area.	Blanket bogs have potential for grouse shooting, as long as associated burning on deep peat does not affect biodiversity, carbon storage and water quality.
Socially valued landscapes	Highly degraded landscape of low visual and cultural-historic value. Negative emotions may be evoked, including guilt regarding the human role in its destruction.	Greater plant cover is likely to have increased landscape appeal.	The blanket bogs and its National Park designation is valued by many people, both locally and nationally. Revealed 'willingness to pay' was £0.12 per household (Eftec 2009); this would translate into an estimated value of ca. £200,000 for the 6 km² Bleaklow restoration site.
Local Biodiversity	Severely degraded habitat with few species.	The enhanced vegetation cover (45% on average) will already provide opportunities for a far greater number of species, both above and below ground.	Active blanket bog species assemblage, including Sphagnum cover and re-colonisation by breeding bird species of conservation importance, such as golden plover (Pluvialis apricaria) and dunlin (Calidris alpina), is expected in the longer term.

moors (Thirgood & Redpath 2008). The associated managed burning and predator control of grouse moors creates heather mosaics which favour gamebirds such as red grouse—the distinctive dark-winged race, *Lagopus lagopus scoticus*, is endemic to Britain and Ireland and lives mostly within the UK. Grouse moor management also favours other ground-nesting birds, such as golden plover (*Pluvialis apricaria*) (Sotherton *et al.* 2009), but species such as such as dunlin (*Calidris alpina*), hen harrier (*Circus cyaneus*) and golden eagle (*Aquila chrysaetos*), are negatively associated with grouse moors (Pearce-Higgins *et al.* 2009a). Redpath and Thirgood (2009) propose various ways in which the trade-off between red grouse and hen harrier populations could be managed to allow hen harriers to co-exist more easily on grouse moors. However, in the absence of alternative forms of management (e.g. grazing), there are concerns that a reduction in grouse moor management intensity may lead to a loss of gamekeepers and subsequent effects on wildlife and landscape (Sotherton *et al.* 2009). Furthermore, the illegal persecution of hen harriers on some grouse moors may produce economic costs for those sectors of the population who care about raptors (Hanley *et al.* 2010). This illustrates how the management of MMH can result in conflicts based on different perspectives and underlying values held by relevant stakeholders (White *et al.* 2009).

As much of MMH are open access country, there seems no shortage of provision of recreation opportunities (Curry 2009). Recreational pressure in MMH can be damaging through a number of factors including: localised disturbance of wildlife, such as nightjar (*Caprimulgus europaeus*) and Dartford warbler (*Sylvia undata*) in lowland heath (Langston *et al.* 2007; Murison *et al.* 2007) and golden plover in upland heath (Finney *et al.* 2005); excessive erosion through trampling and motorised access; and wildfire (Hewins *et al.* 2007; McMorrow *et al.* 2009). As a result, lowland heathland managers might find themselves in conflict with local communities over the appropriate management of some sites. Although common ground can be found with early and appropriate engagement of the neighbours and visitors, some management options, such as grazing large animals (due to both fencing and perceived danger from livestock), burning and cutting trees, regularly result in adverse reactions from the public (**Box 5.10**).

The development and expansion of ski resorts have caused local damage to fragile habitats (Warren 2002). There are several upland footpath and motor vehicle management projects aiming to find a balance between tourism and the conservation of protected sites (Phillip & MacMillan 2006). Indeed, access management through footpath improvement can have joint benefits for visitors and biodiversity (Finney *et al.* 2005).

Although deer can be a tourist attraction and increase recreational use of MMH, concerns about the impact of deer grazing on plant diversity, the knock-on effects on other organisms and the costs to society are mounting (Hunt 2003; Defra 2003), and have led to an explicit call for greater control of their numbers. Despite these concerns, an extensive analysis of data on grazer impact gathered from across Scottish uplands (Albon *et al.* 2007) led to the conclusion that sheep, not deer, were most strongly

associated to grazer impacts on MMH habitats; evidence for strong negative impacts on vegetation from deer grazing appeared limited to certain habitats such as blanket bog (**Box 5.11**). Whilst biodiversity considerations may be seen as legitimate, a diverse range of competing views characterise deer management across the country, as deer present both threat (e.g. to biodiversity, deer traffic accidents) and opportunity (e.g. employment, venison, enjoyment). Carefully balancing different agendas and cultural positions, and a wider exchange of knowledge, are critical to ensuring the best management strategies are employed for this potentially important rural resource.

5.5 Options for Sustainable Management

5.5.1 What is Sustainable Management?

There is considerable disagreement over what constitutes 'sustainable' management and how it should be achieved. Some landowners and managers believe that current land management is sustainable, pointing to its tradition and the current provision of ecosystem services from MMH. Others argue that current management is too intensive, pointing instead to aspects (e.g. biodiversity) that they believe have been compromised by human activities (English Nature 2003; Reed *et al.* 2005; Dougill *et al.* 2006). Hence, on the basis of equally valid but quite different objectives, stakeholders prioritise the provision of ecosystem services in different ways. These priorities are likely to be dynamic—as stakeholder needs and preferences change over time—and to differ from place to place. Management that might be considered sustainable in one location, at one time, may not be considered sustainable in another location, or a different time, rendering universal definitions of 'sustainable' management virtually impossible. Indeed, the Millennium Ecosystem Assessment concluded that "arriving at a comprehensive definition of sustainability in mountains, particularly one that is universally accepted, is itself a mountainous task, and not likely to be a productive effort" (Köerner & Ohsawa 2005). For the remainder of this section, therefore, we will consider how different forms of management may minimise the trade-offs and optimise the complementarities between the provisions of different ecosystem services from MMH that are described in Section 5.3.

5.5.2 Sustainable Management Options

5.5.2.1 Managed burning

Mountains, Moorlands and Heaths are often burned to provide habitats suitable for the production of sheep and red grouse. The effects of burning are complex, and differ between habitats (e.g. heath versus bog) and substrates (e.g. mineral versus organic soils). Burning is primarily carried out to create a mosaic of different aged stands of heather. On heather-dominated moorland, burning stimulates more

Box 5.10 Establishing synergies and trade-offs between ecosystem services: a participatory approach.

The stakeholder meetings allowed identification of key synergies, namely between peatland areas in the Somerset Moors, Thorne and Hatfield as part of a Department for Environment, Food and Rural Affairs project (Defra 2009). The following tables display some of the written comments from the workshop on synergies and trade-offs between ecosystem services for: a) Somerset Moors and Levels (**Table 1**); and b) Thorne and Hatfield (**Table 2**). The different ecosystem services were provided (e.g. provisioning, regulating), however participants were asked to include those services that they deemed were missing.

Table 1 Somerset Moors.

		Benefits to people/synergies	Limitations/Trade-offs
Provisioning Services	Food	Livestock-grazing.	Nutrient content of natural grass is lower than improved grass. Improved livestock-grazing may mean lower biodiversity.
	Freshwater	Freshwater available.	Higher water levels lead to more wet grassland and reeds.
	Peat	Fuel and horticulture resource available.	Peat not renewable in the short term; loss of peat results in loss of many other services.
	Withies and teasels	Wetlands provide withies for basket making and teasels for textile production.	More land for withies and teasels may mean less land for grazing and natural habitats.
Regulating Services	Microclimate	Wetlands modify their own climate.	Synergy with services supported by high water levels.
	Floods	Flood storage available.	Flood water storage assumes low ditch water levels before the flood.
	Carbon	Wetlands have potential to sequester carbon.	High water levels reduce carbon dioxide emissions and increase biodiversity but increase methane emissions.
	Diseases		Wetlands can host insects that carry diseases, especially if water levels are kept high to support biodiversity.
Cultural Services	Archaeology	Anaerobic conditions preserves organic matter.	Synergy with services supported by high water levels.
	Recreation	Wetlands provide a landscape and birdlife favoured by many people, including anglers.	Synergy with services supported by high water levels.
	Education	Wetlands provide a range of opportunities for scientific, social and economic education.	
Supporting Services	Biodiversity	Wetlands support unique plants and animals.	Diversity of wetland species may be lower with a higher water table.

Table 2 Thorne and Hatfield.

		Benefits to people/synergies	Limitations/Trade-offs
Provisioning Services	Food	Low intensity sheep- and deer-grazing.	
	Freshwater	Freshwater available.	Standing water encourages reeds in places.
	Peat	Fuel and horticultural resource available.	Peat is not renewable in the short-term; loss of peat results in loss of many other services.
	Energy provision	Coal seams beneath Thorne (previously mined). Gas reserves below Hatfield. Renewable energy—windfarm permission granted.	
Regulating Services	Microclimate	Peatlands modify their own climate.	Synergy with services supported by high water levels.
	Flood risk prevention		There is little evidence that intact wetlands reduce downstream flood risk.
	Climate regulation	Peatlands have the potential to sequester carbon.	High water table reduces carbon dioxide emissions and increase biodiversity but may increase methane emissions.
	Drinking water provision/ water quality	No provision of drinking water, although there is a borehole at the edge of Hatfield Moor where water comes from an aquifer below the raised mire.	
	Cultural heritage	Sites of archaeological interest including Mesolithic boats and a rare Bronze age pathway at Thorne and a Neolithic wooden trackway at Hatfield.	Synergy with services supported by high water levels and minimum disturbance to peat.
	Recreation	Peatlands provide a landscape and wildlife favoured by many people. 120 km of tracks, many way marked.	Synergy with services supported by high water levels and minimum disturbance to peat.
	Education	Peatlands provide a range of scientific, social, economic and educational subjects.	
Supporting Services	Biodiversity	Peatlands support unique plants, invertebrates, birds and animals.	Biodiversity may be lower with a higher water table.

Box 5.10 continued.

This allowed identification of key synergies between cultural heritage and carbon storage, and between biodiversity, carbon storage and recreation. Key conflicts were also identified: peat extraction versus carbon storage; and emissions of greenhouse gases, cultural heritage and peat extraction (and resultant arable land) versus biodiversity.

There were also a number of relationships between categories that participants indentified as both a synergy and a conflict depending on specific circumstances and points of view, such as between biodiversity and recreation or flood risk and cultural heritage. Services that were consistently seen to provide high trade-offs with other services were arable food production and peat extraction. Spatial and temporal scales of impact were also important, for example, the scale of impact ranging from global in the case of greenhouse gases to local in the case of flood risk.

To take forward our understanding of how people perceive synergies and trade-offs between services, further focus group discussions were held in the Migneint and Peak District. The participants were provided with the former tables and subsequent discussions were used to construct a scoring matrix (**Table 3**): **green** numbers in the top left of a cell represent votes as a synergy and **purple** numbers in the bottom right of a cell as votes for conflicts.

Table 3 Scoring matrix.

Cell values shown as: synergy (green, top-left) / conflict (purple, bottom-right).

	Food	Energy (wind)	Energy (peat)	Carbon storage	Greenhouse gases	Water quality	Flood risk	Recreation	Game	Cultural heritage	Biodiversity
Food	▨										
Energy (wind)	1 /	▨									
Energy (peat)	/ 1		▨								
Carbon storage	1 / 1		3 / 4	▨							
Greenhouse gases		1 / 2	/ 2	3 / 1	▨						
Water quality	1 / 4		/ 1	/ 4	10 / 1	▨					
Flood risk	/ 1			/ 3	3 /	/ 1	▨				
Recreation	/ 1			/ 2	2 / 1			▨			
Game	1 / 3	/ 1	/ 2	/ 2	/ 2	/ 1	/ 1	1 / 2	▨		
Cultural heritage	1 /		/ 1	/ 3				1 /	1 / 1	▨	
Biodiversity	2 / 8			3 /	3 / 2	7 /	2 /	5 / 3			▨

The indentified conflicts were mostly associated with different forms of land use for provisioning services (wind power, peat extraction). As shown in the scoring matrix, water quality and biodiversity were assumed to have excellent synergy. However, when the detail of this was discussed, it was realised that the relationships are quite complex and attempts to aggregate might be difficult. It may, in fact, be that maintaining monocultures of a particular species (e.g. purple moor-grass) could have synergies with water quality, but trade-offs with aspects of biodiversity.

Nevertheless, both approaches proved valuable in terms of foci of discussion, whilst leaving clearly traceable and concise information. There is a long way to go before we have a sufficient understanding of synergies and trade-offs between ecosystem services, but taking into account stakeholders is likely to provide richer insights that may be shared by the wider community.

---

palatable new growth and reduces vegetation height (Yallop et al. 2006). This creates a habitat suitable for red grouse to feed, shelter and nest in (Lovat 1911; Gimingham 1971, 1972), and also favours several other ground-nesting birds (see Section 5.4). However, managed burning may have adverse effects on other bird species, such as meadow pipit (*Anthus pratensis*) (Smith et al. 2001), and on conservation priority plant species, such as common juniper (*Juniperus communis*) which can be killed outright by burning and recovers very slowly from fire damage (Thomas et al. 2007). Gamekeepers also conduct predator control to further favour assemblages of ground-nesting birds, thus altering the competitive balance between species in MMH habitats over vast areas (Fletcher et al. 2010).

There is relatively little scientific evidence to link managed burning to effects on ecosystem services, and where evidence does exist, it is often contradictory. For example, there is currently contradictory evidence about the relationship between managed burning and carbon accumulation and storage where MMH habitats occur on peat soils. Garnett et al. (2000) found that less peat accumulated in North Pennine experimental plots that were burned than in those that were not burned due to the adverse effects of burning on peat-forming species such as *Sphagnum* species; this finding has been supported by peat core evidence from Canada and Finland (Kuhry 1994; Pitkänen et al. 1999). Particulate organic carbon is also lost through soil erosion from burned moorland, but most of this is lost during wildfires, rather than through managed burning (Tallis 1987). Clay et al. (2010), in a plot-scale study on an upland blanket bog, show that burnt sites were smaller sources of carbon than unburnt sites, which were also sources of carbon i.e. there was an avoided loss of carbon under burning management. Clay and Worrall (2011) show that there is a significant proportion of remaining

Between 1997 and 2003, the Macaulay Land Use Research Institute investigated grazing impacts on seven open-hill habitats in seven out of 11 Deer Management Group (DMG) areas across Scotland. They recorded both indicators of current grazing impact (i.e. percentage of shoots and flowers of dominant species eaten) and indicators of longer-term impacts on the physical structure of the vegetation (recorded as heavy, moderate or light). The presence or absence of red deer (*Cervus elaphus*), sheep, cattle, rabbits (*Oryctolagus cuniculus*), mountain hares (*Lepus timidus*) and red grouse (*Lagopus lagopus scoticus*) was recorded on the basis of various visual signs.

The authors found that sheep were associated with the highest impact across habitats in seven out of 11 DMGs, and their presence increased the probability of observing a moderate or greater impact in most habitats, not only those dominated by grasses, but also heath. After sheep, the recorded presence of cattle was most commonly linked with increased impact on open-hill habitats, although their impact was localised. By contrast, rabbits, mountain hares and red deer had relatively little impact. However, red deer were found to exert clear grazer impact in some habitats, such as blanket bog, in which heather was dominant.

The higher impact associated with sheep presence (**Figure 1**) probably reflects their greater aggregation as a result of their limited ranging

behaviour, exacerbated by sheep being herded in places convenient for land managers. Consequently, future reductions in sheep numbers as a result of the reformation of EU farming policies may limit the extent of their impact, but not necessarily the local magnitude. However, reductions in sheep stocks may lead to increases in deer densities (DeGabriel *et al.* In press), with greater impact, particularly in heather-dominated habitats.

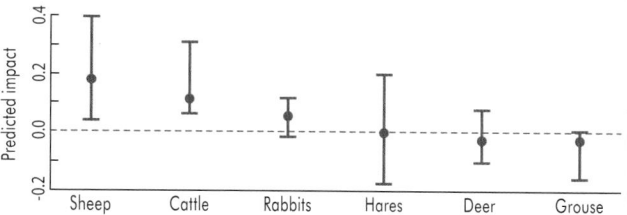

Figure 1 The medium (with 5–95% ranges) grazing and trampling impacts associated with the recorded presence of each herbivore species, averaged across all DMG and all habitats. Predicted impact (y axis) is expressed as estimated change in the probability of observing an impact class of 'moderate' or worse. Source: Albon *et al.* (2007). Copyright ©2007 British Ecological Society. Reproduced with permission of Blackwell Publishing Ltd.

---

biomass following moorland fires which needs accounting for in carbon stocks. This is contrary to previous studies, which assumed that there was no surviving biomass after burning (Garnett *et al.* 2000; Harden *et al.* 2000). Assuming well-managed, cool burns can be achieved, this research suggests that current burning practice is already optimised for carbon through char production. Working on blanket bog in the North Pennines, Clay *et al.* (2009) found that water tables were significantly shallower on burned sites versus those that were not burned, and that there was greater runoff following burning. Although a relationship has been shown between DOC and moorland burning in streams soon after burning (Yallop & Clutterbuck 2009), other research calls this into question (Clay *et al.* 2009; Chapman *et al.* 2010). These studies suggest that the relationship between burning and DOC in soil water and runoff is strongest for the first month after a burn, but is not statistically significant when a range of burn ages are considered (Clay *et al.* 2009; Chapman *et al.* 2010). It should be noted that results to date are specific to certain locations, habitats and substrates, so it is difficult to generalise across MMH habitats.

Heather-cutting is used in some locations, notably in lowland heathland, as an alternative to managed burning. This is the case, for example, in urban heaths, where fire could present a risk and the smoke is a nuisance for people in surrounding private properties or on roads. Cutting heather in autumn allows the seeds to mature, so the material can be used to stimulate heather regeneration in restoration sites; such timing would also avoid harm to breeding birds (Symes & Day 2003). There is evidence that repeated cutting may reduce the cover of purple moor-grass (*Molinia caerulea*) (Milligan *et al.* 2004) but it has also been reported to reduce heather vigour over the long-term, leading to slower re-growth rates (Brown 1990). Cutting operations may be limited by topography, stoniness and access, and are perceived by land managers to be uneconomical compared to burning (Tucker 2003; Reed *et al.* 2005).

5.5.2.2 Grazing

Livestock-grazing and the associated efforts of many generations of farmers have contributed to the cultural and environmental heritage of today's countryside. The provision of several ecosystem services other than food production may be dependent on the existence of viable farming systems within upland and lowland areas in the future.

Grazing impacts on MMH habitats vary between grazer species and breed, for example, cattle are less selective and eat a higher proportion of matt-grass (*Nardus stricta*) or purple moor-grass than sheep or deer. Heather is a valuable winter food for livestock and (particularly) deer after the grasses have died back. However, heather is sensitive to overgrazing; it only thrives when grazing is below a critical limit, which varies with heather growth rates (Grant *et al.* 1978; Pakeman & Nolan 2009; **Figure 5.4**). The effects of grazing on heather are difficult to disentangle from the effects of burning and atmospheric deposition (Yallop *et al.* 2006). Indeed, there is evidence that the behaviour of grazers is influenced by the spatial distribution of burning (Palmer & Hester 2000; Fuhlendorf & Engle 2004). Heavy grazing, combined with frequent burning, may cause heather to be replaced with purple moor-grass (Stevenson *et al.* 1996), particularly under conditions of high atmospheric nitrogen input; this replacement can be difficult to reverse (Ross *et al.* 2003; Marrs *et al.* 2004). Depending on soil type and drainage, heavy grazing and burning may also cause heather to be replaced by other species such as matt-grass or heath rush (*Juncus squarrosus*). Heavy browsing of saplings can prevent the establishment and spread of trees and shrubs. At a smaller spatial scale, heavy grazing pressure is also associated with increased soil erosion, concentrated along sheep tracks and at local depressions in the land (Rawes & Hobbs 1979; Evans 2005). A decrease in grazing pressure will, in many places, enhance vegetation heterogeneity, most notably in its structure, with benefits for several moorland bird species (Evans *et al.* 2006a; Pearce-Higgins & Grant 2006). Destocking is a prerequisite to the re-vegetation of bare and eroding peats, which can, in turn, have benefits for carbon storage. Large-scale removal of sheep from parts of the hills, however, could lead to many unexpected consequences.

Although a reduction in sheep-grazing may bring benefits for certain species in areas that are currently under high grazing pressure (Albon *et al.* 2007), the challenge is to find a sustainable stocking level which is adapted to local conditions (Natural England 2010). Indeed, there are a series of 're-wilding' initiatives across the country (e.g. Wild Ennerdale, Cumbria) aiming to allow natural processes, instead of human management, to shape the landscape and ecology. Although some proponents of 're-wilding' may advocate the cessation of grazing by livestock, a minimum level of grazing, ideally by a mix of species (including cattle in some areas), is likely to be necessary if the objective is to maintain the current range of MMH ecosystem services. Indeed, grazers may play a role in the restoration of some MMH habitats and protect them from encroachment by scrub and trees. Thus, the levels of destocking now being witnessed in parts of MMH (SAC 2008) may have negative implications for some ecosystem services. For example, assuming sheep were not replaced with deer (but see DeGabriel *et al.* under revision), it is likely that a reduction in grazing would mean more areas become dominated by heather at the expense of grass, but scrub and tree encroachment would occur in most areas except the very wet, coastal, high altitude or shallow soil areas. In turn, this may have implications for the value some recreationalists place on more open landscapes.

Given the likely consequences of destocking and other, more unexpected effects, it may be necessary to consider how minimum stocking densities can be preserved in order to maintain MMH, and the ecosystem services they provide, in the future. Ultimately, decisions about what stocking rates are appropriate have to be taken at a local level—depending on management objectives, these could range from very low (to allow woodland regeneration) to high (to maintain species-rich grassland).

5.2.2.3 Deer management

Besides sheep and cattle, the major grazing animals in MMH are deer. In Scotland alone, over 2 million ha (27% of all privately owned land) are managed for game, including deer-stalking activities; a further 17% is in commercial forestry, which is subject to major deer management programmes and, although outside the realms of MMH, of considerable importance for deer populations in open habitats, particularly during periods of adverse weather (Irvine *et al.* 2009).

Despite increased culling, deer numbers have grown considerably over recent years (**Figure 5.5**), which has a range of social, financial and environmental implications. The increasing rate of road traffic accidents involving deer has implications for public safety, and brings significant costs. These may be felt more strongly in less densely populated areas, which are often the areas with highest deer densities. The UK-wide expansion of deer populations has had a negative impact on the profitability of forestry

and agriculture, with damage to the latter being estimated at around £4 million/annum in England (Defra 2003). Also transmission of disease from wild herbivores to livestock, and the subsequent effect on human food safety, is of growing concern. The loss of biodiversity as a consequence of overgrazing by deer is perceived as widespread. For example, deer grazing is known to have a negative impact on invertebrate diversity, the establishment and regeneration of upland birch, *Racomitrium* heath, tall heath, native pinewood regeneration and the diversity of woodland understorey. This has led to the designation of several 'priority sites' where greater control is being achieved by intervention from the statutory authorities. However, evidence for strong negative impacts at the landscape-scale is limited (Albon *et al.* 2007; **Box 5.11**).

Deer also bring benefits in a variety of ways. The presence and role of deer in shaping the landscape has positive effects on tourism and recreation. For instance, the opportunity to see red deer, in itself a cultural icon, is likely to be a significant factor in bringing visitors to the Highlands of Scotland. Deer provide rural employment and income from traditional stalking and hunting activities, as well as for those associated with the downstream venison industry. Yet, exploitation of deer to the benefit of rural economies has been limited, partly because of its associated, centuries-old legislative legacy (Phillip *et al.* 2009).

Deer management across MMH habitats is in different stages of development, and faces the challenge of integrating management across neighbouring landowners (since deer are mobile across property boundaries). Most of Scotland has well-established Deer Management Groups to address this issue, whilst in England and Wales these tend to be more recently established and sometimes absent. The regulation of deer populations is contentious given the different objectives of different (often neighbouring) landowners, some of whom reap the benefits that deer bring, whilst others see mostly the costs (Smart *et al.* 2008). Recent research has shown that collaborative and participatory approaches are required to find locally acceptable solutions to perceived deer problems, as well as to develop creative ways to more effectively capture the associated economic and social gains to the benefit of rural economies. The emergence of Deer Management Groups across the UK is an example of a voluntary approach to managing some of the conflicts around deer numbers and distribution.

5.2.2.4 Grip and gully blocking

During the 1960s and 1970s, government grants were provided to landowners and managers to create drainage ditches or 'grips' in many MMH habitats to improve livestock and game production (Ratcliffe & Oswald 1988). They are particularly prevalent in the English Pennines, with more limited occurrence elsewhere, for example, the Brecon Beacons (Holden *et al.* 2007). However, 'gripping' did little to enhance production (Stewart & Lance 1983), leading instead to hydrological and ecological changes favouring dwarf-shrub heath over blanket bog communities, and increasing fire risk. In many areas, upland peatlands are also dissected by erosional gullies, which are significantly deeper and wider than grips, often occurring in dense, branching networks. Recovery of peat requires a very long time: in the Culoegh Plateau, Fermanagh, mechanised peat extraction led to frequent flooding of 'show' caves and, 15 years after extraction ceased, recovery is still far from complete (Dykes & Kirk 2001).

As a result of gripping, soil is lost through erosion, both of the channels themselves and through increased prevalence of soil pipes in drained peats (Mayfield & Pearson 1972; Holden *et al.* 2006). Gullies may present a hazard to both humans and stock, and sediment can cover salmonid gravel-bed spawning grounds downstream, and infill reservoirs. In actively eroding gully systems, the magnitude of the particulate carbon loss can be sufficient to shift peatlands from carbon-accumulating to carbon-losing status (Evans *et al.* 2006b). As the water table is lowered, carbon is also lost as carbon dioxide through the oxidisation of dried-out peat (Clymo 1983; Evans & Warburton 2010).

It has been proposed that lowering of the water table also enhances dissolved carbon loss, which, in addition to the erosional loss of carbon, means that fluvial carbon losses are significant. Worrall *et al.* (2003) showed that fluvial losses of carbon account for a significant component of the carbon budget in moorlands; the inclusion of fluvial carbon flux estimates into the national carbon budget for peatlands decreased the estimated size of the UK sink from 0.7 to 0.32–0.05 Mt carbon/yr. However, effects of drainage on water quality are mixed, and depend on catchment characteristics and timing of peak flows (Moore 1973; Mitchell & McDonald 1995; Hughes *et al.* 1998; Driscoll *et al.* 2003).

Moorland grips and gullies can be blocked using heather bales or dams made from plastic, wood or peat. Bare and eroding channel walls can be re-vegetated through natural regeneration, re-seeding and mulch (Campeau & Rochefort 1996; Price 1997), or through the use of heather brash (see the Peat Compendium for more restoration options: www.peatlands.org.uk). So far, there has been little research into the effects of grip and gully blocking on water quality. In contrast to Worrall *et al.* (2003), Wallage *et al.* (2006) showed that DOC and associated water colour from a site blocked three years prior to measurement was significantly lower than an adjacent drained site, and also significantly lower than that of undrained moorland.

5.5.3 Future Directions

For MMH to continue providing high levels of ecosystem service flows long into the future, the management of these habitats must be sufficiently flexible to allow adaptation to a range of currently uncertain future conditions. **Table 5.6** provides a range of such adaptive management options as suggested by upland stakeholders and researchers. Some adaptations may be taken at the scale of individual holdings or catchments, while changes to policy may be necessary to facilitate other, wider adaptations. For example, by effectively linking agricultural payments to the provision of ecosystem services in the places that can most efficiently and sustainably deliver those services, it may be possible to give landowners and managers more incentive to provide public goods for which they are currently not paid (Reed *et al.* in press). Finally, if ecosystem services are the benefits humans derive from nature (MA 2005), then we may wish to

consider how the management of MMH habitats can meet the priorities of the people who use and value them. This would require an understanding of regional differences in demand and preferences for different ecosystem services (Christie *et al.* 2010). Clearly communicating the many benefits MMH bring to society may promote greater care and inspiration for people to find their own ways to engage with these special habitats.

5.6 Future Research and Monitoring Gaps

Our work on this chapter has brought into focus a range of limitations in our understanding of changes in extent and perceived quality of MMH habitats since the Second World War, the factors underlying those changes, and what they mean to society. Here, we summarise major knowledge gaps under broad headings.

5.6.1 Changes in Habitat Extent and Quality

We have been surprised by the difficulty of obtaining sound, long-term quantitative (and ideally spatially explicit) data on changes in extent and 'quality' of MMH habitats. Therefore, we recommend a UK-wide programme to bring together our existing, heavily fragmented, datasets. The continuation and development of long-term scientific monitoring programmes, such as the Countryside Survey, the ECN and the UK Acid Waters Monitoring Network (that informs on biogeochemical changes to, and fluxes from, upland soils), provide our best opportunities to quantify future changes in pressures and ecological responses. Yet some coverage, most notably for montane habitats, is poor. Furthermore, we recognise that monitoring data needs to be 'fit for purpose' and able to detect subtle changes in biogeochemical processes resulting from often gradual changes in atmospheric deposition, climate and land use. Hence, we call for a spatial extension of current large-scale scientific monitoring capacity in MMH habitats.

Attributing causes to observed major changes in habitat extent and quality has likewise been difficult. For instance, large-scale changes in plant species composition of MMH habitats may be due to a plethora of factors including changes in land management, atmospheric pollution, climate, or, more likely, a combination of such factors. Strong indications of underlying drivers operating at the national or regional spatial scale can be derived from monitoring networks or other large-scale studies, but currently there is little emphasis on incorporating regular measurements that may best facilitate the identification of factors changing habitat extent and quality. These include: more reliable estimates of grazing pressure, burn size and location; better localised estimates of atmospheric pollutant deposition; and stronger co-location of measurements of soils, vegetation and carbon and nitrogen fluxes. Closer integration of upland terrestrial and freshwater monitoring would greatly benefit

Table 5.6 Options for upland policy and practice to adapt to a scenario where future land use and management in uplands is extensified. Based on a combination of facilitated site visit discussions, an expert workshop as part of the Sustainable Uplands Project, and interviews using the Delphi technique from the Sustainable Estates Project. *Source: a) Reed *et al.* (in press b); b) Reed *et al.* (2009) and c) Glass *et al.* (2009).

Themes	Adaptation strategies	Example	Source*
Restructured financial support: an ecosystem goods and services approach	Provide incentives for management of ecosystem goods and services.	Use financial incentives e.g. to ensure the appropriate combination of moorland burning and grazing.	a, b, c
		Include carbon storage/management payments in Environmental Stewardship grant schemes.	b, c
	Regulate management.	Penalise inappropriate or damaging management outcomes.	a, c
	Develop innovative tax/trading systems.	Individual 'carbon allocations' and collection of 'carbon tax' or 'offsetting schemes'.	a, b
Resilient rural businesses that can withstand future shocks	Plan long-term management visions.	Draw up long-term, integrated spatial plans for future change, e.g. rewetting peat soils, woodland regeneration etc.	a, b, c
	Diversify income streams and add value to products.	Focus on quality rather than quantity e.g. specialised local food products, diversify livestock, create tourism opportunities.	a, b, c
		Inject more cash into non-agricultural economic activity to maintain upland economies (private and public sources).	a, b, c
		Develop biomass and carbon storage opportunities e.g. small-scale wood pellet enterprises, willow plantations etc.	b, c
	Encourage innovation.	Exemplify innovative land managers that make changes rather than allowing change to dictate practices.	a, b, c
Integrated management that delivers environmental and other benefits	Environmental risk management.	Wildfire risk control, ensure designated sites are in favourable condition, maintain viable populations of appropriate species.	a, c
		Ecological restoration projects e.g. gully and grip blocking to reduce erosion, riparian improvements to mitigate flooding.	a, c
		Reduce impacts of upland management resource use e.g. increase energy efficiency/sustainable building design.	c
	Link into local communities.	Release land for development and play a role in housing provision to reduce upland depopulation.	c
		Develop local food markets and encourage self-sufficiency.	c
	Manage increasing upland recreation.	Manage footpaths and access points to reduce impacts, increase ranger provision for education and monitoring.	a, c
	Manage visual impacts of management.	Heather burning, grazing levels, tree planting, bracken control, renewable energy developments, cultural heritage etc.	b, c
Productive knowledge generation and exchange	Join up thinking and dialogue among stakeholders.	Find common ground between interest groups and encourage understanding of the needs and wants of different users.	a, c
		Partner across the region e.g. develop habitat linkages, manage increases in recreational activities etc.	a, b, c
	Share best practice.	Exemplify successful management practices e.g. disseminate moorland restoration techniques/technology.	a, b, c
	Raise public awareness of upland management.	Educate about the multiple uses of moorlands and the role of managers/gamekeepers/farmers/rangers.	a
	Improve scientific evidence, understanding and monitoring.	More research; e.g. on relationship between water quality and local conditions; effects of grouse moor management on ecosystem services.	a
		Integrate local experience and knowledge into management.	a, c
		Well-designed, structured and standardised monitoring e.g. changes in moorland diversity/restoration progress.	a, c

our understanding of both soil biogeochemical processes and the consequences of changes to the terrestrial environment on the quality and biodiversity of upland waters. This also points to the need to spatially link environmental data with socio-economic data on drivers and status over time.

The current paucity of information in this area prevents us from answering what one could view as simple questions, such as: 'how are declining numbers of grazing sheep in MMH influencing biodiversity (e.g. changes in populations of insects, scavenging and predatory birds, vegetation composition, etc.)?' or 'what will happen to deer numbers and the grazing pressure they exert?' Likewise, we still have only a rudimentary grasp of the nature of ecological change in response to seasonal and longer-term variation in temperature, precipitation, wind and cloud cover—all factors that are part and parcel of 'future climate change' and fundamental to MMH and mountain habitats in particular. In addition to ongoing monitoring programmes, there is an urgent need for complementary targeted field experimental approaches to take place at the smaller scale to help determine cause and effect. Such experiments also allow the investigation of interactions between drivers of change, which is one of the largest knowledge gaps we have observed. Regarding climatic changes in particular, we need to develop our horizon-scanning across time periods spanning decades, and to take our thinking beyond basic species range shifts, into understanding how combined pressures from land uses and practices (including the expansion of renewable energy such as wind and hydro-power), atmospheric pollution and climatic changes impact on MMH habitats and their spatial configurations. Better understanding of how multiple pressures lead to changes in habitat extent and condition, and influence ecosystem services, should be a key focus for future research—this should involve both interactive and cumulative effects.

5.6.2 Changes in Ecosystem Services

Most biological monitoring has been driven by ecological and/or nature conservation interests and, during the last two decades, has primarily been conducted from a 'biodiversity' perspective: much information concerns either species or habitats of conservation interest. The more recent 'ecosystem function' approach that formed the precursor of the even younger 'ecosystem services' approach adapted by the UK NEA requires information to be available at multiple levels. It is clear that there has not been sufficient time to allow the development of 'methods' to detect and adequately interpret change in biological, physicochemical, economic and social processes combined, which is required to interpret changes of the 'value' of MMH habitats to society. The development of a more interconnected 'systems approach' in the near future would thus be an important step forward.

5.6.2.1 Provisioning services
Relatively good information is available in terms of provisioning services, although crude recording of, for instance, livestock-grazing (at the parish level) or deer density (at the deer management unit) clearly hinders interpretation of ecological and societal change.

5.6.2.2 Regulating services
A series of large knowledge gaps appear when focusing on regulating services. Regarding land management options that impact on carbon sequestration, we have been struck by the variability of evidence and opinion over the effects of burning practices, grazing intensity, blocking of drainage channels and re-vegetation of actively eroding blanket bog. A range of catchment management responses have been proposed and indeed implemented, at the local scale, including grip blocking and controlling intensity of burns, with the stated aim of controlling losses of dissolved and particulate carbon particularly. However, the scientific justification for such management actions is often thin, while mounting evidence that increases in dissolved organic carbon represent a regional return to more natural water quality, has not been sufficiently acknowledged by those that offer catchment management advice. There is thus a

pressing need to better understand the consequences of moorland and heath management in terms of greenhouse gas emissions across a wide scale of conditions, and identify the mechanisms involved. Importantly, such studies need to be at sufficiently wide scale and take into account both short- and longer-term release of greenhouse gases through various pathways.

From hydrological and geomorphological perspectives, we have an insufficient understanding of the current importance of nitrogen deposition for the processing of carbon within MMH habitats. Improved knowledge in this area is fundamental to developing more accurate predictions of how MMH carbon budgets will respond to future changes in air pollution and climate. Furthermore, there is a need to better understand the fate of fluvial carbon losses from peatland systems, most notably the extent to which particulate and dissolved organic carbon are transformed into climatically active carbon in rivers and other water bodies downstream. A large proportion of the highly organic soils of MMH are impacted by grazing, burning, drainage, air pollution and erosion; thus there is an urgent need to better understand their influences on both carbon stocks and greenhouse gas fluxes.

Likewise, there is a need to develop a much wider evidence-base to understand the influences land management practices have on the provision of water quantity and quality. This includes furthering our understanding of the relationships between vegetation composition, drainage of upland areas and flood risk further downstream. For example, there are currently great uncertainties regarding the effects of blanket bog restoration on stabilising water runoff under conditions of weather extremes. Such knowledge needs to be both mechanistic and spatially explicit as relationships are likely to be highly variable.

While the deposition of sulphur has fallen massively since the 1970s, nitrogen deposition continues to threaten MMH ecosystems. Hence, long-term effects of airborne pollution remain an important area of research, especially for mountain areas which receive disproportionate amounts and are generally susceptible due to their shallow, nutrient-poor soils. Indications are that MMH habitats with deeper moss and soil layers have played an important role in intercepting a wide variety of components, thereby reducing amounts leaching into waterways. However, this buffering principle is still poorly understood and, with respect to nitrogen, it is unclear whether upland soils may ultimately reach a point of saturation and cease to provide this 'service'. Furthermore, the implications of climate change for the continued storage of atmospherically deposited heavy metals that would otherwise be released to drainage waters remains unclear. The potential for land management to mitigate pollutant impacts through interception by the plant and soil system, and factors that regulate pollutant release, requires attention; this includes the currently poorly studied impacts of diffuse pollution. Importantly, such studies need to take into account multiple drivers of change, notably land use and climatic changes.

There are significant gaps in our understanding of disease regulation (e.g. the tick-borne Lyme Disease) and the prevalence of pest insects (e.g. midges and mosquitoes), both of which may be influenced by the numbers of herbivores in MMH, as well as changes in climate (Gilbert 2010), and could have major impacts on recreation and the enjoyment of some areas. The spread of other wildlife diseases, such as Cryptosporidiosis, could also have serious economic impacts on aquatic and terrestrial ecosystems.

5.6.2.3 Cultural services

Given the overwhelming importance of cultural services, and the immense diversity of issues, it is no surprise that our understanding of even the most critically important issues is still in its infancy. Hence, we only touch on a few areas that we view as worthwhile to address in the near future.

The value of nature. We need to develop a richer conceptual and practical understanding of the 'value of nature' which includes people's individual and collective relationships to MMH or its components. Whilst we have impressive lists of habitat, species and site priorities, science and policy groupings articulate these in a language and currency that appears 'alien' to many interest groups. Hence, we need to develop a more effective language and set of instruments to allow greater engagement with the diversity of MMH nature, its intrinsic value, and its importance to certain provisioning services such as water quantity and quality, energy provision, enjoyment, health and general 'well-being'.

Human health and well-being. Whilst the extent of the benefits of the MMH landscape for health and emotional welfare might be clear to those working, for instance, in ecology, attributing engagement with MMH, or any other form of nature, to human health and 'well-being' (which in itself is a highly contested concept) is notoriously difficult, and is in conflict with the 'positivist' outlook related to much of quantitative science. Therefore, we call for a different way of tackling this issue: collaboration between scientists from a range of disciplines with fundamentally different paradigms, and partnership working with members of the public, conservation bodies and other interest groups. This enables the unravelling of the rich relationships between MMH landscapes and human health and well-being in meaningful and mutually accepted ways. Some recent studies report on important 'quality-of-life benefits' which society derives from the MMH landscape, and which go well beyond the notion of relaxation. This area of science is huge and currently poorly understood.

Protected areas. We have been surprised by the national and operational inconsistencies in approaches to evaluating the values and management objectives of protected areas such as SPAs, SACs, National Parks, SSSIs and regionally designated sites. Whilst we recognise the diversity of national and international statutory requirements, it is surely time to harmonise the conservation and land management objectives for protected areas in order to rationalise the development of the evidence base that underpins our understanding of change and the practices and policies needed to bring about improvements. Importantly, such reform would require the realigning of multiple objectives of those impacted by the designations.

In line with the above, there is a need to better understand the ecological, economic and societal implications of (and

diversity in views on) conservation initiatives both within and out with protected areas (e.g. 'rewilding', development of corridors). A careful balancing of different agendas, cultural positions and a wider exchange of knowledge is critical to managing such future developments.

Managing biodiversity conflict. We have reported on a wide range of 'biodiversity conflicts', i.e. issues where the interest of two or more parties towards some aspect of biodiversity compete, and when at least one of those parties is perceived to assert its interest at the expense of another party's interests (White *et al.* 2009). Notably, activities in moorland and heath related to grouse management have been, and continue to be, a strong influence on biodiversity. Likewise, a lack of deer management has been blamed for reduced diversity in plant species abundance. A future conflict is likely to be woodland expansion versus the conservation of open habitats, and, in lowland heaths, controlled grazing against recreation. It is now time to find ways to manage MMH in a manner that encourages the re-establishment of more natural gradients of habitat to the benefit of biodiversity, whilst allowing people to live in, work in, visit and enjoy the countryside.

References

A & M (2002) Review of Wildlife Tourism: Main Report. [online] Available at: <www.greentourism.org.uk/wild-main%20 report.pdf> [Accessed 03.03.11].

ADAS & Enviros (2008) Monitoring of peat and alternative products for growing media and soil improvers in the UK 2007. Defra, London.

Aebischer, N.J. & Baines, D. (2008) Monitoring gamebird abundance and productivity in the UK: The GWCT long-term datasets. *Revista Catalana d'Ornitologia,* **24**:30–43.

Aerts, R. & Bobbink, R. (1999) The impact of atmospheric nitrogen deposition on vegetation processes in terrestrial, non-forest ecosystems. The impact of nitrogen deposition on natural and semi-natural ecosystems. (ed S. Langan) pp. 85–122. Kluwer Academic, Dordrecht.

Albertson, K., Aylen, J., Cavan, G. & McMorrow, J. (2009) Forecasting the outbreak of moorland wildfires in the English Peak District. *Journal of Environmental Management,* **90**: 2642–2651.

Albon, S.D., Brewer, M.J., O'Brien, S., Nolan, A.J. & Cope, D. (2007) Quantifying the grazing impacts associated with different herbivores on rangelands. *Journal of Applied Ecology,* **44**:1176–1187.

Allott, T., Evans, M.G., Lindsay, J.B., Agnew, C.T., Freer, J.E., Jones, A. & Parnell, M. (2009) *Water tables in Peak District blanket peatlands.* Moors for the Future. Edale. [online] Available at: <www.moorsforthefuture.org.uk/sites/default/files/documents/ MFF%20RR17%20Water%20Tables%20in%20Peal%20District%20 blanket%20peatlands.pdf> [Accessed 31.03.11].

Alonso, I., Hartley, S.E. & Thurlow, M. (2001) Competition between heather and grasses on Scottish moorlands: Interacting effects of nutrient enrichment and grazing regime. *Journal of Vegetation Science,* **12**:249–260.

Alonso-Amelot, M.E. & Avendano, M. (2002) Human carcinogenesis and bracken fern: A review of the evidence. *Current Medicinal Chemistry,* **9**:675–686.

Anderson, B.J., Arroyo, B.E., Collingham, Y.C., Etheridge, B., Fernandez-De-Simon, J., Gillings, S., Gregory, R.D., Leckie, F.M., Sim, I.M.W., Thomas, C.D., Travis, J.M.J. & Redpath, S.M. (2009a) Using distribution models to test alternative hypotheses about a species' environmental limits and recovery prospects. *Biological Conservation*, **142**: 488–499.

Anderson, P. & Yalden, D.W. (1981) Increased sheep numbers and the loss of heather moorland in the Peak District, England. *Biological Conservation*, **20**:195–213.

Anderson, P., Buckler, M. & Walker, J. (2009b) Moorland restoration: potential and progress. Drivers of environmental change in uplands (eds A. Bonn, T. Allott, K. Hubacek, & J. Stewart,), pp. 432–447. Routledge, London and New York.

Araujo, M.B., Thuiller, W. & Yoccoz, N.G. (2009) Reopening the climate envelope reveals macroscale associations with climate in European birds. *Proceedings of the National Academy of Sciences of the United States of America*, **106**:E45–E46.

Armitage, H.F., Britton, A.J., Woodin, S.J. & Van der Wal, R. (2011) Assessing the recovery potential of alpine moss-sedge heath: Reciprocal transplants along a nitrogen deposition gradient. *Environmental Pollution*, **159**: 140–147.

Askins, K. (2004) Visible Communities' Use and Perceptions of the North York Moors and Peak District National Parks: A Policy Guidance Document for the National Park Authorities. University of Durham.

Atlantic Consultants (2005) Public perceptions of heathland in Dorset. Report to Urban Heaths Partnership. [online] Available at: < www.dorsetforyou.com/media. jsp?mediaid=81323&filetype=pdf> [Accessed 01.04.11].

Audit Scotland (2009) Key messages Review of Cairngorm funicular railway. Prepared for the Auditor General for Scotland, October 2009.

Averis, A., Averis, B., Birks, J., Horsfield, D., Thompson, D. & Yeo, M. (2004) An Illustrated Guide to British Upland Vegetation. Joint Nature Conservation Committee, Peterborough.

Baggaley, N.J., Langan, S.J., Futter, M.N., Potts, J.M. & Dunn, S.M. (2009) Long-term trends in hydro-climatology of a major Scottish mountain river. *Science of the Total Environment*, **407**:4633–4641.

Baird, A., Holden, J. & Chapman P. (2009) A Literature Review of Evidence on Emissions of Methane in Peatlands. Defra Project SP0574, 54pp.

Barnett, C., Hossell, J., Perry, M., Procter, C. & Hughes, G. (2006) Patterns of climate change across Scotland: Technical Report. SNIFFER Project CC03, Scotland & Northern Ireland Forum for Environmental Research, 102pp.

Barr, C.J., Bunce, R.G.H., Clarke, R.T., Fuller, R.M., Furse, M.T., Gillespie, M.K., Groom, G.B., Hallam, C.J., Hornung, M.,Howard, D.C. & Ness, M. (1993) Countryside Survey 1990: main report. Department of the Environment, London.

Barrios, L. & Rodriguez, A. (2004) Behavioural and environmental correlates of soaring-bird mortality at on-shore wind turbines. *Journal of Applied Ecology*, **41**:72–81.

Battarbee, R.W., Mason, B.J., Renberg, I. & Talling, J.F. (eds) (1990) Palaeolimnology and Lake Acidification. 219pp. Royal Society, London.

Beale, C.M., Lennon, J.J. & Gimona, A. (2008) Opening the climate envelope reveals no macroscale associations with climate in European birds. *Proceedings of the National Academy of Sciences of the United States of America*, **105**:14908–14912.

Bergmann, A., Hanley, N. & Wright, R. (2006) Valuing the attributes of renewable energy investments. *Energy Policy*, **34**:1004–1014.

Berry, P.M., Dawson, T.P., Harrison, P.A. & Pearson, R.G. (2002) Modelling potential impacts of climate change on the bioclimatic envelope of species in Britain and Ireland. *Global Ecology and Biogeography*, **11**:453–462.

BGS (British Geological Survey) (2010) United Kingdom Minerals Yearbook 2009. BGS, Keyworth, Nottingham.

Birks, H.J.B. (1988) Long-term ecological change in the British uplands. *Ecological change in the Uplands*. (ed M.B. Usher & D.B.A. Thompson DBA). 37–56 pp. Blackwell Scientific Publications, Oxford.

Blackford, J.J., Innes, J.B., Hatton, J.J. & Caseldine, C.J. (2006) Mid-holocene environmental change at Black Ridge Brook, Dartmoor, SW England: A new appraisal based on fungal spore analysis. *Review of Palaeobotany and Palynology*, **141**:189–201.

Bobbink, R., Boxman, D., Fremstad, E., Heil, G.W., Houdijk, A. & Roelofs, J. (1992) Critical loads for nitrogen eutrophication of terrestrial and wetland ecosystems based upon changes in vegetation and fauna. Critical Loads for Nitrogen: A Workshop Report (ed P. Grennfelt & E. Thornelof). 111–160pp. The Nordic Council of Ministers in Collaboration with CLRTAP.

Bonn, A., Holden, J., Parnell, M., Worrall, F., Chapman, P.J., Evans, C.D., Termansen, M, Beharry-Borg, N, Acreman, MC, Rowe, E, Emmett, B & Tsuchiya, A (2010) Ecosystem Services of Peat – Phase 1. Defra Project Code SP0572.

Bonn, A., Rebane, M. & Reid, C. (2009) Ecosystem services: a new rationale for conservation of upland environments. Drivers of environmental change in uplands (ed A. Bonn, T. Allott K. Hubacek & J. Stewart). 448–474pp. Routledge, London.

Bond, W.J. & Keeley, J.E. (2005) Fire as a global 'herbivore': the ecology and evolution of flammable ecosystems. *Trends in Ecology & Evolution*, **20**:387–394.

Bradley, R.I., Milne, R., Bell, J., Lilly, A., Jordan, C. & Higgins, A. (2005) A soil carbon and land use database for the United Kingdom. *Soil Use and Management*, **21**:363–369.

Bragg, O.M. & Tallis, J.H. (2001) The sensitivity of peat-covered upland landscapes. *Catena*, **42**:345–360.

Bragg, O.M. (2002) Hydrology of peat-forming wetlands in Scotland. *Science of the Total Environment*, **294**:111–129.

Bright, J., Lanyston, R., Bullman, R., Evans, R., Gardner, S. & Pearce-Higgins, J. (2008) Map of bird sensitivities to wind farms in Scotland: A tool to aid planning and conservation. *Biological Conservation*, **141**: 2342–2356.

Britton, A.J., Pearce, I.S.K. & Jones, B. (2005) Impacts of grazing on montane heath vegetation in Wales and implications for the restoration of montane areas. *Biological Conservation*, **125**: 515–524.

Britton, A.J., Beale, C.M., Towers, W. & Hewison, R.L. (2009) Biodiversity gains and losses: evidence for homogenisation of Scottish alpine vegetation. *Biological Conservation*, **142**: 1728–1739.

Brown, R.W. (1990) The biological interactions between heather management for conservation, shooting, grazing and recreation. Modelling Heather Management. (M. Whitby & S. Grant), University of Newcastle-upon-Tyne, Newcastle-upon-Tyne.

Brunning, R. (2001) Archaeology and peat wastage on the Somerset Moors. Environment and Property Department Somerset County Council.

Burton, R.J.F., Schwarz, G., Brown, K., Convery, I. & Mansfield, L. (2009) The future of public goods provision in upland regions: learning from hefted commons in the Lake District, UK. Drivers of environmental change in uplands (ed A. Bonn, T. Allott K. Hubacek & J. Stewart) 309–322pp. Routledge, London.

Byfield, A. & Pearman, D. (1995) Dorset's disapearing heathland flora: a case for reinstating grazing. *RSPB Conservation Review*, **9**: 84–89

Cameron, G.G., Idoine, N.E., Brown, T.J., Patton, M.A.G., McGinn, C. & Mankelow, J.M. (2010) Directory of Mines and Quarries 2010. 9th Edition. British Geological Survey, Keyworth, Nottingham.

Campeau, S. & Rochefort, L. (1996) Sphagnum regeneration on bare peat surfaces: Field and greenhouse experiments. *Journal of Applied Ecology*, **33**: 599–608.

Caporn, S. & Emmett, B.A. (2009) Threats from air pollution and climate change to upland systems: past, present and future. *Drivers of environmental change in uplands* (ed A. Bonn, T. Allott K. Hubacek & J. Stewart) 34–58pp. Routledge, London.

Carey, P.D., Wallis, S., Chamberlain, P.M., Cooper, A., Emmett, B.A., Maskell, L.C., McCann, T., Murphy, J., Norton, L.R., Reynolds, B., Scott, W.A., Simpson, I.C., Smart, S.M. & Ullyett, J.M. (2008) *Countryside Surevy: UK Results from 2007.* (CEH Project Number: C03259). NERC/Centre for Ecology & Hydrology, 105pp.

Calver, L.J., Cresser, M.S. & Smart, R.P. (2004) Tolerance of Calluna vulgaris and peatland plant communities to sulphuric acid deposition. *Chemistry and Ecology*, **20**: 309–320.

Carroll, J.A., Caporn, S.J.M., Cawley, L., Read, D.J. & Lee, J.A. (1999) The effect of increased deposition of atmospheric nitrogen on Calluna vulgaris in upland Britain. *New Phytologist*, **141**: 423–431.

Chambers, F.M., Mauquoy, D. & Todd, P.A. (1999) Recent rise to dominance of Molinia caerulea in environmentally sensitive areas: new perspectives from palaeoecological data. *Journal of Applied Ecology,* **36**: 719–733.

Chapman, P.J., McDonald, A.T., Tyson, R., Palmer, S.M., Mitchell, G. & Irvine, B. (2010) Changes in water colour between 1986 and 2006 in the headwaters of the River Nidd, Yorkshire, UK. *Biogeochemistry*, **101**: 281–294.

Christie, M., Hyde, T., Cooper, R., Fazey, I., Dennis, P., Warren, J., Colombo, S. & Hanley, N. (2010) Economic Valuation of the Benefits of Ecosystem Services delivered by the UK Biodiversity Action Plan. Defra, London.

Clark, J.M., Gallego-Sala, A.V., Allott, T.E.H., Chapman, S. J., Farewell, T., Freeman, C., House, J.I.. Orr, H.G., Prentice, I.C & Smith. P. (2010a). Assessing the vulnerability of blanket peat to climate change using an ensemble 2 of statistical bioclimatic envelope models. *Climate Research*, doi:10.3354/cr00929.

Clark, J. M., Orr, H.G., Freer, J., House, J.I, Smith, P. & Freeman, C. (2010b) Assessment of projected changes in upland environments using simple climatic indices. *Climate Research*, doi: 10.3354/cr00923.

Clay, G.D., Worrall, F. & Fraser, E.D.G (2009) Effects of managed burning upon dissolved organic carbon (DOC) in soil water and runoff water following a managed burn of a UK blanket bog. *Journal of Hydrology*, **367**: 41–51.

Clay, G.D. & Worrall, F. (2010) Charcoal production in a UK moorland wildfire – how important is it? *Journal of Environmental Management*, **92**: 676–682.

Clay, G.D., Worrall, F. & Rose, R. (2010) Carbon budgets of an upland blanket bog managed by prescribed fire. *Journal of Geophysical Research – Biogeosciences*, **115**: G04037.

Clay, G.D. & Worrall, F. (2011) Charcoal production in a UK moorland wildfire – how important is it? *Journal of Environmental Management*, **92**: 675–681.

Clutton–Brock, T., Coulson, T. & Milner, J. (2004) Red deer stocks in the Highlands of Scotland. *Nature*, **429**: 261–262.

Clymo, R.S. (1983) Peat. Mires: Swamp, Bog, and Moor. Ecosystems of the World (ed A.J.P. Gore) 159–224pp. Elsevier, Amsterdam.

Colombo, S. & Hanley, N. (2008) How can we reduce the errors from benefits transfer? An investigation using the Choice Experiment method *Land Economics,* **84**: 128–147.

Commission for Rural Communities (2010) High ground, high potential: a future for England's upland communities. Commission for Rural Communities, Defra, London.

Condliffe, I. (2009) Policy change in the uplands. Drivers of environmental change in uplands (ed A. Bonn, T. Allott, K. Hubacek & J. Stewart). 59–90pp. Routledge, London.

CPRE (Campaign to Protect Rural England) (2006) Saving Tranquil Places. How to protect and promote a vital asset. [online] Available at: <http://catpaisatge.net/docs/Tria%209%20-%20saving-tranquil-places-report.pdf> [Accessed 02.04.11].

Crawford, R.M.M. (2000) Ecological hazards of oceanic environments. *New Phytologist,* **147**: 257–281.

Crofting Inquiry (2009) Committee of Inquiry on Crofting Final Report. Committee of Inquiry on Crofting, Edinburgh. [online] Available at: <www.croftinginquiry.org/Resource/Doc/0/0000405.pdf> [Accessed 02.04.11].

Cumbria County Council (2007) Sheepfolds [online] Available at: <http://www.sheepfoldscumbria.co.uk/> [Accessed 01.04.11].

Currey, P.M., Johnson, D., Dawson, L.A., Van der Wal, R., Thornton, B., Sheppard, L.J., Leith, I.D. & Artz, R.R.E. (2011) Five years of simulated atmospheric nitrogen deposition have only subtle effects on the fate of newly synthesized carbon in Calluna vulgaris and Eriophorum vaginatum. *Soil Biology & Biochemistry*, **43**: 495–502.

Curry, N.R. (2009) Leisure in the landscape: rural incomes and public benefits. Drivers of environmental change in uplands (ed A. Bonn, T. Allott K. Hubacek & J. Stewart) 277–290pp. Routledge, London.

Dallimer, M., Tinch, D., Acs, S., Hanley, N., Southall, H.R., Gaston, K.J. & Armsworth, P.R. (2009) 100 years of change: examining agricultural trends, habitat change and stakeholder perceptions through the 20th Century. *Journal of Applied Ecology,* **46**: 334–343.

Davies, B.B., Sherlock, K., Brown, K. & Shannon, P. (2004) Challenges in creating local agri-environmental cooperation action amongst farmers and other stakeholders. SEERAD Final Report, Reference MLU/927/03. Scotland.

Davies, G.M., Smith, A.A., MacDonald, A.J., Bakker, J.D. & Legg, C.J. (2010) Fire intensity, fire severity and ecosystem response in heathlands: factors affecting the regeneration of Calluna vulgaris. *Journal of Applied Ecology*, **47**: 356–365.

Davies, G.M., Gray, A., Hamilton, A. & Legg, C.J. (2008) The future of fire management in the British uplands. *International Journal of Biodiversity Science and Management,* **4**: 127–147.

Davies, S. (2006) Recreation and visitor attitudes in the Peak District moorlands. Moors for the Future report. Moors for the Future Partnership, Edale.

De Gabriel, J.L., Albon, S.D., Fielding, D.A., Riach, D.J., Westaway, S. & Irvine, R.J. (in press) The presence of sheep leads to reductions in the impact of deer on heather and increases in plant diversity. *Journal of Applied Ecology*, in press.

Defra (Department for Environment, Food and Rural Affairs) (2003) Current and future deer management options. London, Defra.

Defra (Department for Environment, Food and Rural Affairs) (2008) A Framework for Pro-Environmental Behaviours. London, Defra. [online] Available at: <http://archive.defra.gov.uk/evidence/social/behaviour/documents/behaviours-jan08-report.pdf> [Accessed 02.04.11].

Defra (Department for Environment, Food and Rural Affairs) (2009) Safeguarding our soils. A Strategy for England. Defra, London. [online] Available at: <http://www.defra.gov.uk/publications/2011/04/08/pb13297-soil-strategy/> [Accessed 04.04.11].

Defra (Department for Environment, Food and Rural Affairs) (2010) Monitoring the horticultural use of peat and progress towards the UK Biodiversity Action Plan target. Report SP08020. [online] Available at: <http://randd.defra.gov.uk/Document.aspx?Document=SP08020_9282_FRP.pdf> [Accessed 02.01.11].

Deloitte (2008) The economic case for the visitor economy. Visit Britain. [online] Available at: <www.deloitte.com/assets/Dcom-UnitedKingdom/Local%20Assets/Documents/UK_THL_VisitorEconomy_Sept08.pdf> [Accessed 08.04.11].

Dodgshon, R.A. & Olsson, G.A. (2006) Heather moorland in the Scottish Highlands: the history of a cultural landscape, 1600–1880. *Journal of Historical Geography*, **32**: 21–37.

Dougill, A.J., Fraser, E.D.G., Holden, J., Hubacek, K., Prell, C., Reed, M.S., Stagl, S. & Stringer, L.C. (2006) Learning from doing participatory rural research: lessons from the Peak District National Park. *Journal of Agricultural Economics*, **57**: 259–275.

Driscoll, C.T., Driscoll, K.M., Roy, K.M. & Mitchell, M.J. (2003) Chemical response of lakes in the Adirondack Region of New York to declines in acidic deposition. *Environmental Science & Technology*, **37**: 2036–2042.

Dryerre, H. (1945) Problems of stock feeding. *Proceedings of the Nutrition Society*, **25**: 52–56.

DWI (Drinking Water Inspectorate) (2008) Annual report: Drinking Water. Drinking Water Inspectorate, London. [online] Available at: <www.dwi.gov.uk/about/annual-report/2008/index.htm> [Accessed 02.04.11].

DWQR (Drinking Water Quality Regulator) (2008) Drinking water quality in Scotland 2008. Drinking Water Quality Regulator, Scotland. [online] Available at: <www.dwqr.org.uk/technical/annual-report> [Accessed 02.04.11].

Dykes, A.P. & Kirk, K.J. (2001) Initiation of a multiple peat slide on Cuilcagh Mountain, Northern Ireland. *Earth Surface Processes and Landforms*, **26**: 395–408.

Edmondson, J.L. (2007) Nitrogen Pollution and the Ecology of Heather Moorland. PhD thesis, Manchester Metropolitan University.

Eftec (Economics For the Environment) (2009) Economic valuation of uplands ecosystem services. Report to Natural England NECR029. [online] Available at: <http://naturalengland.etraderstores.com/NaturalEnglandShop/NECR029> [Accessed 02.04.11].

English Nature (2003) England's Best Wildlife and Geological Sites: The Condition of SSSIs in England. English Nature, Peterborough.

English Nature (2006) Dog-walkers on the Dorset Heaths: Analysis of questionnaire data collected by wardens on Dorset's Urban Heaths. Report No 713, Report for English Nature, Peterborough.

Evans, C.D., Monteith, D.T. & Cooper, D.M. (2005) Long-term increases in surface water dissolved organic carbon: Observations, possible causes and environmental impacts. *Environmental Pollution*, **137**: 55–71.

Evans, D.M., Redpath, S.M., Evans, S.A., Elston, D.A., Gardner, C.J., Dennis, P. & Pakeman R.J. (2006a) Low intensity, mixed livestock grazing improves the breeding abundance of a common insectivorous passerine. *Biology Letters*, **2**: 636–638.

Evans, M.G., Burt, T.P., Holden, J. & Adamson, J.K. (1999) Runoff generation and water table fluctuations in blanket peat: evidence from UK data spanning the dry summer of 1995. *Journal of Hydrology*, **221**: 141–160.

Evans, M., Warburton, J. & Yang, J. (2006b) Sediment budgets for erroding blanket peat catchments: global and local implications of upland organic sediment budgets. *Geomorphology*, **79**:45–57.

Evans, M.G. & Lindsay, J.B. (2010a) High resolution quantification of gully erosion in upland peatlands at the landscape scale. *Earth Surface Processes and Landforms*. **35**: 876–886.

Evans, M.G. & Lindsay, J.B. (2010b) The impact of gully erosion on carbon sequestration in blanket peatlands. *Climate Research*. **45**: 31–41.

Evans, M. & Warburton, J. (2007) *The Geomorphology of Upland Peat: Pattern, Process, Form*. Blackwells, Oxford 262pp.

Evans, M. & Warburton, J. (2010) Peatland geomorphology and carbon cycling. *Geography Compass*, **4**: 1530–1531.

Evans, R. (2005) Curtailing grazing-induced erosion in a small catchment and its environments, the Peak District, Central England. *Applied Geography*, **25**: 81–95.

Farrell, L. (1993) Lowland Heathland: The Extent of Habitat Change. English Nature Science Series 12. English Nature.

Finney, S.K., Pearce-Higgins, J.W. & Yalden, D.W. (2005) The effect of recreational disturbance on an upland breeding bird, the golden plover Pluvialis apricaria. *Biological Conservation*, **121**: 53–63.

FIRES (Fire Interdisciplinary Research on Ecosystem Services) (2010) Fire and Climate Change in UK Moorlands and Heaths. Policy brief of FIRES seminar. [online] Available at: <http://www.fires-seminars.org.uk/downloads/FIRES_Policy%20Brief_final.pdf> [Accessed 02.04.11].

Fischer, A. & Marshall, K. (2010) Framing the landscape: Discourses of woodland restoration and moorland management in Scotland. *Journal of Rural Studies*, **26**: 185–193.

Fischer, A. & Young, J.C. (2007) Understanding mental constructs of biodiversity: Implications for biodiversity management and conservation. *Biological Conservation*, **136**: 271–282.

Fletcher, K., Aebischer, N.J., Baines, D., Foster, R. & Hoodless, A.N. (2010) Changes in breeding success and abundance of ground-nesting moorland birds in relation to the experimental deployment of legal predator control. *Journal of Applied Ecology*, **47**: 263–272.

Forestry Commission (2009) Combating climate change – a role for UK forests. An assessment of the potential of the UK's trees and woodlands to mitigate and adapt to climate change. The Stationery Office, Edinburgh.

Fowler, D., Cape, J.N. & Leith, D. (1988) The influence of altitude on rainfall composition at Great Dunn Fell. *Atmospheric Environment*, **22**: 1355–1362.

Fraser of Allander Institute (2010) An Economic Study of Grouse Moors. The Game & Wildlife Conservation Trust Scotland (incorporating the Game Conservancy Scottish Research Trust, Scotland.

Frey, N.L. (1998) Pilgrim Stories: on and off the Road to Santiago. University of California Press, Berkeley.

Fuhlendorf, S.D. & Engle, D.M. (2004) Application of the fire-grazing interaction to restore a shifting mosaic on tallgrass prairie. *Journal of Applied Ecology*, **41**: 604–614.

Fuller, R.J. & Gough, S.J. (1999) Changes in sheep numbers in Britain: implications for bird populations. *Biological Conservation*, **91**: 73–89.

Gallet, S. & Roze, F. (2001) Resistance of Atlantic Heathlands to trampling in Brittany (France): influence of vegetation type, season and weather conditions. *Biological Conservation*, **97**: 189–198.

Gallego-Sala, A., Clark, J.M., House, J.I., Orr, H.G., Prentice, I.C., Smith, P., Farwell, T. & Chapman, S.J. (2010) Bioclimatic envelope model of climate change impacts on blanket peatland distribution in Great Britain. *Climate Research*, doi: 10.3354/cr00911.

Garnett, M.H., Ineson, P. & Stevenson, A.C. (2000) Effects of burning and grazing on carbon sequestration in a Pennine blanket bog, UK. *Holocene*, **10**: 729–736.

Gilbert, L. (2010) Altitudinal patterns of tick and host abundance: a potential role for climate change in regulating tick-borne diseases? *Oecologia*, **162**: 217–225.

Gimingham, C.H. (1971) British heathland ecosystems: the outcome of many years of management by fire. 293–321pp. *Proceedings of the 10th Annual Tall Timbers Fire Ecology Symposium*. Tallahassee, Florida, USA.

Gimingham, C.H. (1972) *Ecology of Heathlands*. Chapman & Hall, London.

Gordon, C., Woodin, S.J., Alexander, I.J. & Mullins, C.E. (1999) Effects of increased temperature, drought and nitrogen supply on two upland perennials of contrasting functional type: *Calluna vulgaris* and *Pteridium aquilinum*. *New Phytologist*, **142**: 243–258.

Gorham, E. (1991) Northern peatlands: role in the carbon cycle and probable response to climatic warming. *Ecological Applications*, **1**: 182–195.

Grant, S.A., Barthram, G.T., Lamb, W.I.C. & Milne, J.A. (1978) Effects of Season and Level of Grazing on the Utilization of Heather by Sheep .1. Responses of the Sward. *Journal of the British Grassland Society*, **33**: 289–300.

Gray, J.M. (2008) Geodiversity: the origin and evolution of a paradigm. *The History of Geoconservation*. (ed Burek, C.V. & Prosser, C.D.) 31–36pp, The Geological Society, London, Special Publications.

Hanley, N., Alvarez-Farizo, B. & Shaw, W.D. (2002) Rationing an open-access resource: mountaineering in Scotland. *Land Use Policy*, **19**: 167–176.

Hanley, N., Colombo, S., Mason, P. & Johns, H. (2007) The reform of support mechanisms for upland farming: Paying for public goods in the severely disadvantaged areas of England. *Journal of Agricultural Economics*, **58**: 433–453.

Hanley, N., Davies, A., Angelopoulos, K., Hamilton, A., Ross, A., Tinch, D. & Watson, F. (2008) Economic determinants of biodiversity change over a 400-year period in the Scottish uplands. *Journal of Applied Ecology*, **45**: 1557–1565.

Hanley, N. & Colombo, S. (2009) The economic value of landscapes in the uplands of England. Drivers of environmental change in uplands (ed A. Bonn, T. Allott K. Hubacek & J. Stewart) 323–338pp. Routledge, London.

Hanley, N., Ready, R., Colombo, S., Watson, F., Stewart, M. & Bergmann, E.A. (2009) The impacts of knowledge of the past on preferences for future landscape change. *Journal of Environmental Management*, **90**: 1404–1412.

Hanley, N., Cjajkowski, M., Hanley-Nickolls, R. & Redpath, S. (2010) Economic Values of Species Management options in Human-Wildlife conflicts: hen harriers in Scotland. *Ecological Economics*, **70**: 107–113.

Harden, J.W., Trumbore, S.E., Stocks, B.J., Hirsch, A., Gower, S.T., O'Neill, K.P. & Kasischke, E.S. (2000) The role of fire in the boreal carbon budget. *Global Change Biology*, **6**: 174–184.

Harrison, P.A. and the Rubicode Consortium (2009) Conservation of Biodiversity and Ecosystem Services in Europe: From Threat to Action. Rubicode Consortium Project Number 036890 for the EC. [online] Available at: <www.eci.ox.ac.uk/research/biodiversity/downloads/rubicode-final.pdf> [Accessed 02.04.11].

Hartley, S. E. & Mitchell, R. J. (2005) Manipulation of nutrients and grazing levels on heather moorland: changes in *Calluna* dominance and consequences for community composition. *Journal of Ecology*, **93**: 990–1004.

Haskins, L. (2000) Heathlands in an urban setting: effects of urban development on heathlands of south-east Dorset. *British Wildlife*, **11**: 229–237.

Hawley, G., Anderson, P., Gash, M., Smith, P., Higham, N., Alonso, I., Ede, J. & Holloway, J. (2008) Impact of heathland restoration and re-creation techniques on soil characteristics and the historic environment. Natural England Research Report 010, Natural England, Sheffield.

Hewins, E., Toogood, T., Alonso, I., Glaves, D.J., Cooke, A. & Alexander, R. (2007) The condition of lowland heathland: results from a sample survey of non-SSSI stands in England. Natural England Research Report No. 2. Sheffield: Natural England.

Hill, M., Downing, T., Berry, P., Coppins, B., Hammond, P., Marquiss, M., Roy, D., Telfer, M. & Welch, D. (1999) Climate changes and Scotland's natural heritage: an environmental audit. Scottish Natural Heritage Research, Survey and Monitoring Report No. 132.

Holden, J. & Burt, T.P. (2003a) Runoff production in blanket peat covered catchments. *Water Resources Research* **39**: 1191 doi:10.1029/2002WR001956.

Holden, J. & Burt, T.P. (2003b) Hydraulic conductivity in upland blanket peat: Measurement and variability. *Hydrological Processes,* **17**: 1227–1237.

Holden, J., Chapman, P.J. & Labadz, J.C. (2004) Artificial drainage of peatlands: hydrological and hydrochemical process and wetland restoration. *Progress in Physical Geography*, **28**: 95–123.

Holden, J. (2005) Peatland hydrology and carbon release: why small-scale process matters. *Philosophical Transactions of the Royal Society A: Mathematical, Physical and Engineering Sciences,* **363**: 2891–2913.

Holden, J., Evans, M.G., Burt, T.P. & Horton, M. (2006) Impact of land drainage on peatland hydrology. *Journal of Environmental Quality,* **35**: 1764–1778.

Holden, J., Shotbolt, L., Bonn, A., Burt, T.P., Chapman, P.J., Dougill, A.J., Fraser, E.D.G., Hubacek, K., Irvine, B., Kirkby, M.J., Reed, M.S., Prell, C., Stagl, S., Stringer, L.C., Turner, A. & Worrall, F. (2007) Environmental change in moorland landscapes. *Earth-Science Reviews,* **82**: 75–100.

Holden, J., Kirkby, M.J., Lane, S.N., Milledge, D.G., Brookes, C.J., Holden, V. & McDonald, A.T. (2008) Overland flow velocity and roughness properties in peatlands. *Water Resources Research,* **44**: 1–11.

Holden, J. & Rose, R. (2010) Temperature and surface lapse rate change: a study of the UK's longest upland instrumental record. *International Journal of Climatology* doi: 10.1002/joc.2136.

Holloway, S. (1996) The Historical Atlas of Breeding Birds in Britain and Ireland: 1875–1900. Poyser, London

Hope, D., Billett, M.F., Milne, R. & Brown, T.A.W. (1997) Exports of organic carbon in British rivers. *Hydrological Processes,* **11**: 325–344.

Hossell, J., Briggs, B. & Hepburn, I. (2000) Climate change and UK nature conservation: a review of the impact of climate change on UK species and habitat conservation policy. DETR, London.

Howkins, C. (1997) Heathland harvest: The Uses of Heathland Plants Through the Ages. Chris Howkins, Old Woking.

Hughes, S., Freeman, C., Reynolds, B. & Hudson, J.A. (1998) The effects of increased drought frequency on sulphate and dissolved organic carbon in peatland dominated catchments. *Proceedings of the Second International Conference on Climate and Water,* **1–3**: 311–319.

Hulme, P.D., Merrell, B.G., Torvell, L., Fisher, J.M., Small, J.L. & Pakeman, R.J. (2002) Rehabilitation of degraded Calluna vulgaris (L.) Hull-dominated wet heath by controlled sheep grazing. *Biological Conservation,* **107**: 351–363.

Hunt, J.F. (2003) Impacts of Wild Deer in Scotland – How fares the public interest? Report for WWF Scotland and RSPB Scotland.

Huttunen, J.T., Nykanen, H., Turunen, J. & Martikainen, P.J. (2003) Methane emissions from natural peatlands in the northern boreal zone in Finland, Fennoscandia. *Atmospheric Environment,* **37**: 147–151.

Irvine, R.J., Fiorini, S., Yearley, S., McLeod, J.E., Turner, A., Armstrong, H., White, P.C.L. & Van der Wal, R. (2009) Can managers inform models? Integrating local knowledge into models of red deer habitat use. *Journal of Applied Ecology,* **46**: 344–352.

IWA (Institute of Welsh Affairs) (2009) Living With Our Landscape. Institute of Welsh Affairs, Cardiff.

Jackson, D.L. (2000) Guidance on the interpretation of the Biodiversity Broad Habitat Classification (terrestrial and freshwater types): Definitions and the relationship with other classifications. JNCC Report 307, 73 pages, ISSN 0963 8091.

Jenkins, G.J., Perry, M.C. & Prior, M.J. (2008) The climate of the United Kingdom and recent trends. Hadley Centre, Met Office, Exeter.

Johnson, E.A., Miyanishi, K. & Bridge, S.R.J. (2001) Wildfire regime in the boreal forest and the idea of suppression and fuel buildup. *Conservation Biology,* **15**: 1554–1557.

Kelly, A.E. & Goulden, M.L. (2008) Rapid shifts in plant distribution with recent climate change. *Proceedings of the National Academy of Sciences of the United States of America,* **105**: 11823–11826.

Köerner, C. & Ohsawa, M. (2005) Mountain systems. Ecosystems and human well-being: Current state and trends: Findings of the condition and trends working group. 683–716pp. Millennium Ecosystem Assessment, Island Press, Washington D.C.

Krupa, S. (2003) Atmosphere and agriculture in the new millennium. *Environmental Pollution,* **126**: 293–300.

Kuhry, P. (1994) The Role of Fire in the Development of Sphagnum-Dominated Peatlands in Western Boreal Canada. *Journal of Ecology,* **82**: 899–910.

Lake, S., Bullock, J.M. & Hartley, S. (2001) Impacts of livestock grazing on lowland heathland in the UK. English Nature, Peterborough.

Lane, S.N., Brookes, C.J., Kirkby, M.J. & Holden, J. (2004) A network-index-based version of TOPMODEL for use with high-resolution digital topographic data. *Hydrological Processes,* **18**: 191–201.

Langston, R.H.W., Liley, D., Murison, G., Woodfield, E. & Clarke, R.T. (2007) What effects do walkers and dogs have on the distribution and productivity of breeding European Nightjar Caprimulgus europaeus? *Ibis,* **149**: 27–36.

Lee, J.A. (1998) Unintentional experiments with terrestrial ecosystems: ecological effects of sulphur and nitrogen pollutants. *Journal of Ecology,* **86**: 1–12.

Leith, I.D., Sheppard, L.J., Fowler, D., Cape, J.N., Jones, M., Crossley, A., Hargreaves, K.J., Tang, Y.S., Theobald, M. & Sutton, M.R. (2004) Quantifying dry NH_3 deposition to an ombrotrophic bog from an automated NH_3 field release system *Water, Air, & Soil Pollution: Focus,* **4**: 207–218.

Lenoir, J., Gegout, J.C., Marquet, P.A., de Ruffray, P. & Brisse, H. (2008) A significant upward shift in plant species optimum elevation during the 20th Century. *Science,* **320**:1768–1771.

Liley, D. & Clarke, R.T. (2003) The impact of urban development and human disturbance on the numbers of nightjar Caprimulgus europaeus on heathlands in Dorset, England. *Biological Conservation,* **114**: 219–230.

Lindley, S., McMorrow, J. & Bonn, A. (2009) Moorland wildfires in the UK Peak District. *Atlas of Biodiversity Risk.* (ed J. Settele, D. Lyubomir, D. Penev, T.A. Georgiev, R. Grabaum, V. Gribelnik, V. Hammen, S. Klotz, M. Kotarac & I Kuehn). 88–89pp. Pensoft Publishers, Sofia-Moscow.

Lindsay, R. (2010) Peatbogs and carbon: a critical synthesis to inform policy development in oceanic peat bog conservation and restoration in the context of climate change. Report for RSPB. [online] Available at: <www.uel.ac.uk/erg/PeatandCarbonReport.htm> [Accessed 02.01.11].

LLTNPA (Loch Lomond and Trossachs National Park Authority) (2005) State of the Park Report 2005: Land Based Recreation.

Lorimer, H. (2000) Guns, game and the grandee: the cultural politics of deer-stalking in the Scottish Highlands. *Ecumene,* **7**: 431–459.

Lovat, L. (1911) Heather burning. The Grouse in Health and Disease (ed A.S. Leslie) 392–412pp. Smith, Elder & Co., London.

Lovegrove, R. (2007) Silent Fields. The long decline of a nation's wildlife. Oxford University Press, Oxford.

Lowe, B., McMorrow, J., Evans, M. & Bonn, A. (2009) High resolution remote sensing for landscape scale restoration of peatland: an overview of work in progress. Poster presented at Remote Sensing and Photogrammetry Society (RSPSoc) annual conference, Leicester, 8–11 September 2009.

LUPG (Land Use Policy Group) (2009) Securing our Common Future through Environmentally Sustainable Land Management. The Land Use Policy Group Vision for the Future of the CAP post 2013. Land Use Policy Group, see www.lupg.gov.uk.

MA (Millennium Ecosystem Assessment) (2005) Ecosystems and Human Well-being. Island Press, Washington D.C.

MacDonald, D., Crabtree, J.R., Wiesinger, G., Dax, T., Stamou, N., Fleury, P., Lazpita, J.G. & Gibon, A. (2000) Agricultural abandonment in mountain areas of Europe: Environmental consequences and policy response. *Journal of Environmental Management*, **59**:47–69.

Malby, A.R., Whyatt, J.D., Timmis, R.J., Wilby, R.L. & Orr, H.G. (2007) Long Term Variations in Orographic Rainfall: Analysis and Implications for Upland Catchments. *Hydrological Sciences – Journal des Sciences Hydrologiques,* **52**: 276–291.

Maltby, E., Legg, C.J. & Proctor, M.C.F. (1990) The Ecology of Severe Moorland Fire on the North York Moors – Effects of the 1976 Fires, and Subsequent Surface and Vegetation Development. *Journal of Ecology,* **78**: 490–518.

Marquiss, M. (2007) Snow bunting. The Birds of Scotland. In (eds R.W. Forrester & I.J. Andrews), Volume 2, pp. 1473–1477. The Scottish Ornithologists' Club, Aberlady.

Marrs, R.H., Hicks, M.J. & Fuller, R.M. (1986) Losses of Lowland Heath through Succession at 4 Sites in Breckland, East-Anglia, England. *Biological Conservation*, **36**: 19–38.

Marrs, R.H., Phillips, J.D.P., Todd, P.A., Ghorbani, J. & Le Duc, M.G. (2004) Control of *Molinia caerulea* on upland moors. *Journal of Applied Ecology*, **41**: 398–411.

Maskell, L.C., Smart, S.M., Bullock, J.M., Thompson, K. & Stevens, C.J. (2010) Nitrogen Deposition causes widespread loss of species richness in British Habitats. *Global Change Biology*, **16**: 671–679.

Mayfield, B. & Pearson, M.C. (1972) Human interference with the north Derbyshire blanket peat. *East Midland Geographer*, **12**: 245–251.

McCrone, D., Morris, A. & Kiely, R. (1995) *Scotland – the Brand: the Making of Scottish Heritage*. Edinburgh University Press, Edinburgh.

McMorrow, J., Lindley, S., Aylen, J., Cavan, G., Albertson, K. & Boys, D. (2009) Moorland wildfire risk, visitors and climate change: patterns, prevention and policy. Drivers of environmental change in uplands (ed A. Bonn, T. Allott K. Hubacek & J. Stewart) 404–431pp. Routledge, London.

Milligan, A.L., Putwain, P.D., Cox, E.S., Ghorbani, J., Le Duc, M.G. & Marrs, R.H. (2004) Developing an integrated land management strategy for the restoration of moorland vegetation on Molinia caerulea-dominated vegetation for conservation purposes in upland Britain. *Biological Conservation*, **119**: 371–385.

Mitchell, G. & Mcdonald, A.T. (1995) Catchment Characterization as a Tool for Upland Water-Quality Management. *Journal of Environmental Management*, **44**: 83–95.

Mitchell, R.J., Marrs, R.H., Le Duc, M.G. & Auld, M.H.D. (1997) A study of succession on lowland heaths in Dorset, southern England: Changes in vegetation and soil chemical properties. *Journal of Applied Ecology*, **34**: 1426–1444.

Mitchell, R. & Popham, F. (2008) Effect of exposure to natural environment on health inequalities: an observational population study. *Lancet,* **372**: 1655–1660.

Monteith, D.T., Stoddard, J.L., Evans, C.D., de Wit, H.A., Forsius, M., Hogasen, T., Wilander, A., Skjelkvale, B.L., Jeffries, D.S., Vuorenmaa, J., Keller, B., Kopacek, J. & Vesely, J. (2007) Dissolved organic carbon trends resulting from changes in atmospheric deposition chemistry. *Nature*, **450**: 537–U539.

Moore, P.D. (1973) Influence of Prehistoric Cultures Upon Initiation and Spread of Blanket Bog in Upland Wales. *Nature*, **241**: 350–353.

Morecroft, M.D., Bealey, C.E., Beaumont, D.A., Benham, S., Brooks, D.R., Burt, T.P., Critchley, C.N.R., Dick, J., Littlewood, N.A., Monteith, D.T., Scott, W.A., Smith, R.I., Walmsey, C. & Watson, H. (2009) The UK Environmental Change Network: Emerging trends in the composition of plant and animal communities and the physical environment. *Biological Conservation*, **142**: 2814–2832.

Murison, G., Bullock, J.M., Underhill-Day, J., Langston, R., Brown, A.F. & Sutherland, W.J. (2007) Habitat type determines the effects of disturbance on the breeding productivity of the Dartford Warbler Sylvia undata. *Ibis*, **149**: 16–26.

Nature Conservancy Council (1984) Nature Conservation in Great Britain. Nature Conservancy Council, Peterborough.

Nature Conservancy Council (1986) Nature Conservation and Afforestation in Britain. Nature Conservancy Council Peterborough.

Natural England (2006) England leisure visits. Report of the 2005 survey. Natural England. Cheltenham.

Natural England (2008) Enjoying the Natural Environment. The State of the Natural Environment 2008, Natural England Commissioned Report NE85, Peterborough.

Natural England (2009a) Vital Uplands. A 2060 vision for England's upland environment. Natural England, Peterbrough.

Natural England (2009b) Experiencing landscapes: capturing the cultural services and experiential qualities of landscape. Natural England, Peterbrough.

Natural England (2010) England's peatlands – carbon storage and greenhouse gases. Natural England Report NE257, Peterborough.

NEGTAP (National Expert Group on Transboundary Air Pollution) (2001) Transboundary Air Pollution: Acidification, Eutrophication and Ground Level Ozone in the UK. [online] Available at: <www.freshwaters.org.uk/resources/documents/ negtap_2001_final_report.pdf> [Accessed 02.04.11].

Nizzetto, L., Macleod, M., Borga, K., Cabrerizo, A., Dachs, J., Di Guardo, A., Ghirardello, D., Hansen, K.M., Jarvis, A., Lindroth, A., Ludwig, B., Monteith, D., Perlinger, J.A., Scheringer, M., Schwendenmann, L., Semple, K.T., Wick, L.Y., Zhang, G. & Jones, K.C. (2010) Past, Present, and Future Controls on Levels of Persistent Organic Pollutants in the Global Environment. *Environmental Science & Technology*, **44**: 6526–6531.

Nayak, D.R., Miller, D., Nolan, A., Smith P. & Smith, J.U. (2010) Calaculating carbon budgets of winds farms on Scottish peatlands. Mires & Peat, 4: Article 09.

Nordin, A., Strengbom, J., Forsum, A. & Ericson, L. (2009) Complex Biotic Interactions Drive Long-Term Vegetation Change in a Nitrogen Enriched Boreal Forest. *Ecosystems*, **12**: 1204–1211.

O'Connell, M. (1990) Origins of Irish lowland blanket bog. Ecology and Conservation of Irish Peatlands (eds G.J. Doyle & P. Dowding), pp. 49–71. Royal Irish Academy, Dublin.

O'Connell, P.E., Beven, K.J., Carney, J.N., Clements, R.O., Ewen, J., Fowler, H., Harris, G.L., Hollis, J., Morris, J., O'Donnell, G., Packman, J.C., Parkin, A., Quinn, P.F., Rose, S.C., Shepherd, M. & Tellier, S. (2005) Review of impacts of rural land use and management on flood generation. Project no. FD2114, Defra, London.

Olden, J.D. & Rooney, T.P. (2006) On defining and quantifying biotic homogenisation. *Global Ecology and Biogeography*, **15**: 113–120.

Oliver, J. (2005) Scottish Gaelic Identities: contexts and contingencies. Scottish Affairs, 51. University of Edinburgh, Institute of Governance, Edinburgh. [online] Available at: <www.scottishaffairs.org/backiss/pdfs/sa51/SA51_Oliver.pdf> [Accessed 02.04.11].

Olivier, A, & Van de Noort, R. (2002) English Heritage strategy for Wetlands. English Nature and University of Exeter.

Orr, H.G., Wilby, R.L., Hedger, M.M. & Brown, I. (2008) Climate change in the uplands: a UK perspective on safeguarding regulatory ecosystem services. *Climate Research*, **37**:77–98.

PACEC (Public and Corporate Economic Consultants) (2006) The economic and environmental impact of sporting shooting. Report on behalf of BASC, CA, and CLA and in association with GCT.

Pakeman, R.J. & Marrs, R.H. (1992) The Conservation Value of Bracken Pteridium-Aquilinum (L) Kuhn-Dominated Communities in the UK, and an Assessment of the Ecological Impact of Bracken Expansion or Its Removal. *Biological Conservation*, **62**: 101–114.

Pakeman, R.J., Le Duc, M.G. & Marrs, R.H. (2000) Bracken distribution in Great Britain: Strategies for its control and the sustainable management of marginal land. *Annals of Botany*, **85**: 37–46.

Pakeman, R.J. & Nolan, A.J. (2009) Setting sustainable grazing levels for heather moorland: a multi-site analysis. *Journal of Applied Ecology*, **46**:363–368.

Palmer, S.C.F. & Hester, A.J. (2000) Predicting spatial variation in heather utilization by sheep and red deer within heather/grass mosaics. *Journal of Applied Ecology*, **37**: 616–631.

Palmer, S.C.F., Hester, A.J., Elston, D.A., Gordon, I.J. & Hartley, S.E. (2003) The perils of having tasty neighbors: Grazing impacts of large herbivores at vegetation boundaries. *Ecology*, **84**: 2877–2890.

Parsons, R. & Daniel, T.C. (2002) Good looking: in defense of scenic landscape aesthetics. *Landscape and Urban Planning, **60**: 43–56.

Pawson, R.R., Lord, D.R., Evans, M.G. & Allott, T.E.H. (2008) Fluvial organic carbon flux from an eroding peatland catchment, southern Pennines, UK. *Hydrological and Earth Systems Science*, **12**: 625–634.

Pearce-Higgins, J.W. & Grant, M.C. (2006) Relationships between bird abundance and the composition and structure of moorland vegetation. *Bird Study*, **53**: 112–125.

Pearce-Higgins, J.W., Grant, M.C., Beale, C.M., Buchanan, G.M. and Sim, I.M.W. (2009a) International importance and drivers of change of upland bird populations. Drivers of

environmental change in uplands (ed A. Bonn, T. Allott, K. Hubacek & J. Stewart) 209–227pp. Routledge, London.

Pearce-Higgins, J.W., Stephen, L., Langston, R.H.W., Bainbridge, I.P. & Bullman, R. (2009b) The distribution of breeding birds around upland wind farms. *Journal of Applied Ecology*, **46**: 1323–1331.

Pearce-Higgins, J.W., Dennis, P., Whittingham, M.J. & Yalden, D.W. (2010) Impacts of climate on prey abundance account for fluctuations in a population of a northern wader at the southern edge of its range. *Global Change Biology* **16**: 12–23.

Peñuelas, J., Gordon, C., Llorens, L., Nielsen, T., Tietema, A., Beier, C., Bruna, P., Emmett, B., Estiarte, M. & Gorissen, A. (2004) Nonintrusive field experiments show different plant responses to warming and drought among sites, seasons, and species in a north-south European gradient. *Ecosystems*, **7**: 598–612.

Pepin, N.C. & Lundquist, J.D. (2008) Temperature trends at high elevations: Patterns across the globe. Geophysical Research Letters, 35: L14701, doi:10.1029/2008GL034026.

Percival, S.M. (2005) Birds and windfarms: what are the real issues? *British Birds*, **98**: 194–204.

Phillip, S. & MacMillan, D.C. (2006) Car park charging in the Cairngorms National Park. *Scottish Geographical Journal*, **122**: 204–222.

Phillip, S., Dandy, N., Gill, R. & MacMillan, D.C. (2009) Is legislation a barrier to the sustainable management of game species? A case study of wild deer in Britain. *Journal of Environmental Planning and Management*, **52**: 993–1012.

Phoenix, G.K., Booth, R.E., Leake, J.R., Read, D.J., Grime, J.P. & Lee, J.A. (2003) Effects of enhanced nitrogen deposition and phosphorus limitation on nitrogen budgets of semi-natural grasslands. *Global Change Biology*, **9**: 1309–1321.

Pitkänen, A., Turunen, J. & Tolonen, K. (1999) The role of fire in the carbon dynamics of a mire, eastern Finland. *Holocene*, **9**: 453–462.

Power, S.A., Ashmore, M.R., Cousins, D.A., & Sheppard, L.J. (1998) Effects of nitrogen addition on the stress sensitivity of Calluna vulgaris. *New Phytologist*, **138**: 663–673.

Pretty, J., Peacock, J., Hine, R., Sellens, M., South, N. & Griffin, M. (2007) Green exercise in the UK countryside: Effects on health and psychological well-being, and implications for policy and planning. *Journal of Environmental Planning and Management*, **50**: 211–231.

Price, J. (1997) Soil moisture, water tension, and water table relationships in a managed cutover bog. *Journal of Hydrology*, **202**: 21–32.

Puttick, R. (2004) Recreational use of Exmoor's Moorlands – a study for the Exmoor National Park Authority. Shell Training and Enterprise Programme – Summer 2004.

Ratcliffe, D.A. & Oswald, P.H. (1988) The Flow Country; the Peatlands of Caithness and Sutherland. Nature Conservancy Council, Peterborough.

Ratcliffe, D.A. & Thompson, D.B.A. (1988) The British uplands: their ecological character and international significance. Ecological change in the uplands. (ed M.B. Usher & D.B.A. Thompson. 3–36pp. Blackwell Scientific Publications, Oxford.

Rawes, M. & Hobbs, R. (1979) Management of Semi-Natural Blanket Bog in the Northern Pennines. *Journal of Ecology*, **67**: 789–807.

Redpath, N., Osgathorpe, L.M., Park, K. & Goulson, D. (2010) Crofting and bumblebee conservation: The impact of land management practices on bumblebee populations in northwest Scotland. *Biological Conservation*, **143**: 492–500.

Redpath, S. & Thirgood, S. (2009) Hen harriers and red grouse: moving towards consensus? *Journal of Applied Ecology*, **46**: 961–963.

Reed, M.S., Hubacek, K. & Prell, C. (2005) Sustainable Upland Management for Multiple Benefits: a multi-stakeholder response to the Heather & Grass Burning Code Consultation. Project report submitted to DEFRA's consultation on the review of the Heather and Grass Etc. (Burning) Regulations 1986 and the Heather and Grass Burning Code 1994.

Reed, M.S., Bonn, A., Broad, K., Burgess, P., Fazey, I.R., Hubacek, K., Nainggolan, D., Roberts, P., Quinn, C.H., Stringer, L.C., Thorpe, S., Walton, D.D., Ravera, F., & Redpath, S. (in press) Participatory scenario development for environmental management: a methodological framework. *Journal of Environmental Management*, in press.

Reed, M.S., Bonn, A., Slee, W., Beharry-Borg, N., Birch, J., Brown, I., Burt, T.P., Chapman, D., Chapman, P.J., Clay, G.D., Cornell, S.J., Fraser, E.D.G., Glass, J.H., Holden, J., Hodgson, J.A., Hubacek, K., Irvine, B., Jin, N., Kirkby, M.J., Kunin, W.E., Moore, O., Moseley, D., Prell, C., Price, M.F., Quinn, C.H., Redpath, S., Reid, C., Stagl, S., Stringer, L.C., Termansen, M., Thorp, S., Towers, W. & Worrall, F. (2009) The future of the uplands. *Land Use Policy*, **26**: S204–S216.

Rennie, A. (2006) The importance of national parks to nation building: Support for the National Parks Act (2000) in the Scottish Parliament. *Scottish Geographical Journal*, 122: 223–232.

Richards, C. (2004) Grouse shooting and its landscape: The management of grouse moors in Britain. *Anthropology Today*, **20**: 10–15.

Rodwell, J.S. (ed.) (1991) British Plant Communities, Vol. 2: mires and heaths. Cambridge University Press, Cambridge.

Ross, S., Adamson, H. & Moon, A. (2003) Evaluating management techniques for controlling *Molinia caerulea* and enhancing *Calluna vulgaris* on upland wet heathland in Northern England, UK. *Agriculture Ecosystems & Environment*, **97**: 39–49.

Ross (2011) Fifty years of vegetation and environmental change in the Scottish Highlands: patterns, processes and lessons for today. PhD thesis University of Aberdeen.

RoTAP (Review of Transboundary Air Pollution) (2011) Review of Transboundary Air Pollution: Acidification, Eutrophication, Ground Level Ozone and Heavy Metals in the UK. Contract Report to the Department for Environment, Food and Rural Affairs. Centre for Ecology & Hydrology.

Rothwell, J.J., Robinson, S.G., Evans, M.G., Yang, J. & Allott, T.E.H. (2005) Heavy metal release by peat erosion in the Peak District, southern Pennines, UK. *Hydrological Processes*, **19**: 2973–2989.

Rothwell, J.J., Evans, M.G. & Allott, T.E.H. (2007) Lead contamination of fluvial sediments in an eroding blanket peat catchment. *Applied Geochemistry*, **22**: 446–459.

Roy, D.B., Rothery, P., Moss, D., Pollard, E. & Thomas, J.A. (2001) Butterfly numbers and weather: predicting historical trends in abundance and the future effects of climate change. *Journal of Animal Ecology*, **70**: 201–217.

RSE (Royal Society of Edinburgh) (2008) Committee of Inquiry into the Future of Scotland's Hills and Islands. (Chair) G. McCrone, Royal Society of Edinburgh, Edinburgh.

SAC (Scottish Agricultural College) (2005) Measuring public preferences for the uplands. Scottish Agricultural College, Centre for the Uplands, Cumbria.

SAC (Scottish Agricultural College) (2008) Farming's retreat from the hills. Rural Policy Centre, Scottish Agricultural College.

Samuelson, W. & Zeckhauser, R. (1988) Status Quo Bias in Decision Making. *Journal of Risk and Uncertainty* **1**: 7–59

Sanderson, H. & Prendergast, H.D.V. (2002) Commercial uses of wild and traditionally managed plants in England and Scotland. Royal Botanical Gardens, Kew, Richmond. Report for Countryside Agency, English Nature and Scottish Natural Heritage.

Sheppard, L.J., Leith, I.D., Crossley, A., Van Dijk, N., Fowler, D., Sutton, M.A. & Woods, C. (2008) Stress responses of *Calluna vulgaris* to reduced and oxidised N applied under 'real world conditions'. Environmental Pollution, 154: 404–413.

Simmons, I.G. (2003) The moorlands of England and Wales. An environmental history 8000 BC–AD 2000. Edinburgh University Press, Edinburgh.

Sjogersten, S., Van der Wal, R. & Woodin, S.J. (2008) Habitat type determines herbivory controls over CO_2 fluxes in a warmer arctic. *Ecology*, **89**: 2103–2116.

Smart, J.C.R., White, P.C.L. & Termansen, M. (2008) Modelling conflicting objectives in the management of a mobile ecological resource: Red deer in the Scottish Highlands. *Ecological Economics*, **64**: 881–892.

Smart, J., Amar, A., Sim, I. M. W., Etheridge, B., Cameron, D., Christie, G., & Wilson, J. D. (2010) Illegal killing slows population recovery of a re-introduced raptor of high conservation concern – The red kite *Milvus milvus*, *Biological Conservation*, **143**:1278–1286.

Smith, A.A., Redpath, S.M., Campbell, S.T. & Thirgood, S.J. (2001) Meadow pipits, red grouse and the habitat characteristics of managed grouse moors. *Journal of Applied Ecology*, **38**: 390–400.

SNH (Scottish Natural Heritage) (2008) Public Perceptions of Wild Places and Landscapes in Scotland. Market Research Partners commissioned by Scottish Natural Heritage.

Sotherton, N., May, R., Ewald, J. & Fletcher, K.D.N. (2009) Managing uplands for game and sporting interest: an industry perspective. Drivers of environmental change in uplands (ed A. Bonn, T. Allott K. Hubacek & J. Stewart) 241–260pp. Routledge, London.

Stevens, C.J., Dise, N.B. & Gowing, D.J. (2009) Regional trends in soil acidification and exchangeable metal concentrations in relation to acid deposition rates. *Environmental Pollution*, **157**: 313–319.

Stevenson, A.C. & Thompson, D.B.A. (1993) Long-term changes in the extent of heather moorland in upland Britain and Ireland: evidence for the importance of grazing. *The Holocene*, **3**: 70–76.

Stevenson, A.C., Rhodes, A.N., Kirkpatric,k A.H. & Macdonald, A.J. (1996) The Determination of Fire Histories and an Assessment of their Effects on Moorland Soils and Vegetation. Survey and Monitoring Report No. 16. Scottish Natural Heritage Research, Edinburgh.

Stewart, A.J.A. & Lance, A.N. (1983) Moor-Draining – a Review of Impacts on Land-Use. *Journal of Environmental Management*, **17**: 81–99.

Stockdale, A. & Barker, A. (2009) Sustainability and the multifunctional landscape: An assessment of approaches to planning and management in the Cairngorms National Park. *Land Use Policy,* **26**:479–492.

Suckall, N., Fraser, E. & Quinn, C. (2009a) How class shapes perceptions of nature: implications for managing visitor perceptions in upland UK. Drivers of environmental change in uplands (ed A. Bonn, T. Allott K. Hubacek & J. Stewart), 393–403pp. Routledge, London.

Suckall, N., Fraser, E.D.G., Cooper, T. & Quinn, C. (2009b) Visitor perceptions of rural landscapes: A case study in the Peak District National Park, England. *Journal of Environmental Management* **90**:1195–1203.

Sutherland, W.J., Bailey, M.J., Bainbridge, I.P., Brereton, T., Dick, J.T.A., Drewitt, J., Dulvy, N.K., Dusic, N.R., Freckleton, R.P., Gaston, K.J., Gilder, P.M., Green, R.E., Heathwaite, A.L., Johnson, S.M., Macdonald, D.W., Mitchell, R., Osborn, D., Owen, R.P., Pretty, J., Prior, S.V., Prosser, H., Pullin, A.S., Rose, P., Stott, A., Tew, T., Thomas, C.D., Thompson, D.B.A., Vickery, J.A., Walker, M., Walmsley, C., Warrington, S., Watkinson, A.R., Williams, R.J., Woodroffe, R., Woodroof, H.J. (2008) Future novel threats and opportunities facing UK biodiversity identified by horizon scanning. *Journal of Applied Ecology,* **45**:821–833.

Swanwick, C., Hanley, N. & Termansen, M. (2007) Scoping Study on Agricultural Landscape Valuation. Defra, London.

Symes, N. & Day, J. (2003) A practical guide to the restoration and management of lowland heathland. Royal Society for the Protection of Birds, Sandy.

Tallis, J.H. (1987) Fire and Flood at Holme Moss – Erosion Processes in an Upland Blanket Mire. *Journal of Ecology,* **75**:1099–1129.

Tallis, J.H. (1997) The Southern Pennine experience: an overview of blanket mire degradation. Blanket Mire Degradation: Causes, Consequences and Challenges (ed J.H. Tallis, R. Meade, & P.D. Hulme), pp. 7–16. Macaulay Land Use Research Institute, Aberdeen.

Thackeray, S.J., Sparks, T.H., Frederiksen, M., Burthes, S., Bacon, P.J., Bell, J.R., Botham, M.S., Brereton, T.M., Bright, P.W., Carvalhos, L., Cluttonbrock, T.H., Dawson, A., Edwards, M., Elliott, J.M., Harrington, R., Johns, D., Jones, I.D., Jones, J.T., Leech, D.I., Roy, D.B., Scott, W.A., Smith, M., Smithers, R.J., Winfield, I.J. & Wanless, S. (2010) Trophic level asynchrony in rates of phenological change for marine, freshwater and terrestrial environments. *Global Change Biology.*

Thirgood, S. & Redpath, S. (2008) Hen harriers and red grouse: science, politics and human-wildlife conflict. *Journal of Applied Ecology,* **45**: 1550–1554.

Thomas, P.A., El-Barghathi, M. & Polwart, A. (2007) Biological flora of the British Isles: *Juniperus communis. Journal of Ecology,* **95**: 1404–1440.

Thompson, D.B.A., Galbraith, H. & Horsfield, D. (1987) Ecology and resources of Britain's mountain plateaux: land use issues and conflicts. Agricultural and Conservation in the Hills and Uplands. (ed M. Bell & R.G. Bunce) 2–31pp. Centre for Ecology and Hydrology, Monks Wood.

Thompson, D.B.A. & Brown, A., (1992) Biodiversity in montane Britain: habitat variation, vegetation diversity and some objectives for conservation. *Biodiversity and Conservation,* **1**: 179–208.

Thompson, D.B.A., MacDonald, A.J., Marsden, J.H. & Galbraith, C.A. (1995) Upland heather moorland in Great Britain: A review of international importance, vegetation change and some objectives for nature conservation. *Biological Conservation,* **71**:163–178.

Thompson, N. (2006) The practice of government in a devolved Scotland: the case of the designation of the Cairngorms National Park. *Environment and Planning C-Government and Policy* **24**: 459–472.

Tipping, R. (2003) Living in the past: woods and people in prehistory to 1000 BC. People and Woods in Scotland – A History (ed T.C. Smout), 15–39pp. Edinburgh University Press, Edinburgh.

TNS (2009) Scottish Recreation Survey: annual summary report 2007. Scottish Natural Heritage Commissioned Report No.321 (ROAME No. F02AA614/6).

Tomlinson, R.W. (2010) Changes in the extent of peat extraction in Northern Ireland 1990–2008 and associated changes in carbon loss. *Applied Geography,* **30**: 294–301.

Trivedi, M.R., Browne, M.K., Berry, P.M., Dawson, T.P. & Morecroft, M.D. (2007) Projecting climate change impacts on mountain snow cover in central Scotland from historical patterns. *Arctic Antarctic and Alpine Research,* **39**: 488–499.

Trivedi, M.R., Berry, P.M., Morecroft, M.D. & Dawson, T.P. (2008) Spatial scale affects bioclimate model projections of climate change impacts on mountain plants. *Global Change Biology* **14**: 1089–1103.

Tucker, G. (2003) Review of the impacts of heather and grassland burning in the uplands on soils, hydrology and biodiversity. Research Reports 550. English Nature.

UKREATE (2010) Terrestrial Umbrella: Effects of Eutrophication and Acidification on Terrestrial Ecosystems. CEH Contract Report C03425. Defra Contract No. AQ0802, pp. 35, Centre for Ecology and Hydrology. [online] Available at: <http://nora.nerc.ac.uk/5880/2/Defra_TU_Report_2008_Final.pdf> [Accessed 18.07.11].

UK Steering Group (1995) Lowland Heathland – A costed Habitat Action Plan. *Biodiversity: The UK Steering Group Report,* Vol. 2: 248–250, HMSO, London.

Underhill-Day, J.C. & Liley, D. (2007) Visitor patterns on southern heaths: a review of visitor access patterns to heathlands in the UK and the relevance to Annex I bird species. *Ibis,* **149**: 112–119.

Van der Wal, R., Pearce, I., Brooker, R., Scott, D., Welch, D. & Woodin, S. (2003) Interplay between nitrogen deposition and grazing causes habitat degradation. *Ecology Letters,* **6**: 141–146.

Van der Wal, R., Sjogersten, S., Woodin, S.J., Cooper, E.J., Jónsdóttir, I.S., Kuijper, D., Fox, T.A.D. & Huiskes, A.D. (2007) Spring feeding by pink-footed geese reduces carbon stocks and sink strength in tundra ecosystems. *Global Change Biology,* **13**:539–545.

Visit Scotland (2008) The Visitor Experience 2008. [online] Available at: <www.visitscotland.org/pdf/visitor_experience-scotland-2008.pdf> [Accessed 02.04.11].

Walker, J, & Buckler, M. (2009) Fire site restoration costs: the Bleaklow 2003 fire, paper presented at Economic impacts of wildfires, wildfire policy and the use of adaptive land management to reduce wildfire risk and impact, FIRES seminar 4, Castleton, Derbyshire. [online] Available at: <www.fires-seminars.org.uk> [Accessed 02.04.11].

Wallage, Z.E., Holden, J. & McDonald, A.T. (2006) Drain blocking: An effective treatment for reducing dissolved organic carbon loss and water discolouration in a drained peatland. *Science of the Total Environment*, **367**: 811–821.

Ward, S.E., Bardgett, R.D., McNamara, N.P., Adamson, J.K. & Ostle, N.J. (2007) Long-term consequences of grazing and burning on northern peatland carbon dynamics. *Ecosystems*, **10**: 1069–1083.

Warren, C.R. (2002) Managing Scotland's Environment. Edinburgh University Press, Edinburgh.

Watson, A. (1991) Increase of People on Cairngorm Plateau Following Easier Access. *Scottish Geographical Magazine*, **107**: 99–105.

Webb, J.R., Drewitt, A.L. & Measures, G.H. (2010) Managing for species: integrating the needs of England's priority species into habitat management. Natural England Research Report, Sheffield.

Webb, N. (1986) Heathlands. A natural history of Britain's lowland heaths. Collins, London.

Welch, D. & Scott, D. (1995) Studies in the grazing of heather moorland in northeast Scotland .VI. 20-Year trends in botanical composition. *Journal of Applied Ecology*, **32**:596–611.

Welch, D., Hartley, S.E. & Buse, A. (1996) Grazing Pressure is the Principle Influence on British Upland Vegetation. *ITE Annual Report 1995–96*, p.27.

White, R.M., Fischer, A., Marshall, K., Travis, J.M.J., Webb, T.J., di Falco, S., Redpath, S.M. & Van der Wal, R. (2009) Developing an integrated conceptual framework to understand biodiversity conflicts. *Land Use Policy*, **26**: 242–253.

Whitfield, D. P., Fielding, A.H., Mcleod, D.R. A., & Haworth, P.F. (2004) The effects of persecution on age of breeding and territory occupation in golden eagles in Scotland, *Biological Conservation*, **118**(2)**:**249–259.

Whittingham, M.J. (2007) Will agri-environment schemes deliver substantial biodiversity gain, and if not why not? *Journal of Applied Ecology*, **44**: 1–5.

Woods, M. (2003) Conflicting environmental visions of the rural: Windfarm development in mid Wales. *Sociologia Ruralis*, **43**: 271.

Worrall, F., Reed, M., Warburton, J. & Burt, T.P. (2003) Carbon budget for a British upland peat catchment. *Science of the Total Environment*, **312**:133–146.

Worrall, F., Armstrong, A. & Adamson, J.K. (2007) The effects of burning and sheep-grazing on water table depth and soil water quality in a upland peat. *Journal of Hydrology*, **339**: 1–14.

Worrall, F., Evans, M.G., Bonn, A., Reed, M.S., Chapman, D. & Holden, J. (2009) Can carbon offsetting pay for upland ecological restoration? *Science of the Total Environment*, **408**:26–36.

Worrall, F., Rowson, J.G., Evans, M.G., Pawson, R., Daniels, S. & Bonn, A. (2011) Carbon fluxes from eroding peatlands – the carbon benefit of revegetation following wildfire. Earth Surface Processes and Landforms, DOI: 10.1002/esp.2174

Wotton, S., Conway, G., Eaton, M., Henderson, I. & Grice, P. (2009) The status of the Dartford Warbler in the UK and the Channel Islands in 2006. *British Birds*, **102**: 230–246.

Yallop, A.R. & Clutterbuck, B. (2009) Land management as a factor controlling dissolved organic carbon release from upland peat soils 1: Spatial variation in DOC productivity. *Science of the Total Environment*, **407**:3803–3813.

Yallop, A.R., Thacker, J.I., Thomas, G., Stephens, M., Clutterbuck, B., Brewer, T. & Sannier, C.A.D. (2006) The extent and intensity of management burning in the English uplands. *Journal of Applied Ecology*, **43**: 1138–1148.

Yeloff, D., Charman, D., van Geel, B. & Mauquoy, D. (2007) Reconstruction of hydrology, vegetation and past climate change in bogs using fungal microfossils. *Review of Palaeobotany and Palynology*, **146**: 102.

Yeo, M.J.M. & Blackstock, T.H. (2002) A vegetation analysis of the pastoral landscapes of upland Wales, UK. *Journal of Vegetation Science*, **13**: 803–816.

Appendix 5.1 Approach Used to Assign Certainty Terms to Chapter Key Findings

This chapter began with a set of Key Findings. Adopting the approach and terminology used by the Intergovernmental Panel on Climate Change (IPCC) and the Millennium Assessment (MA), these Key Findings also include an indication of the level of scientific certainty. The 'uncertainty approach' of the UK NEA consists of a set of qualitative uncertainty terms derived from a 4-box model, and represents a collective judgement by the authors on the basis of observational evidence, modelling results and/or theory examined for this assessment.

A superscript number indicating the estimated level of certainty for each key finding (bold sections only) at the start of this chapter:

1. *Well established:*   high agreement based on significant evidence
2. *Established but incomplete evidence:*   high agreement based on limited evidence
3. *Competing explanations:*   low agreement, albeit with significant evidence
4. *Speculative:*   low agreement based on limited evidence

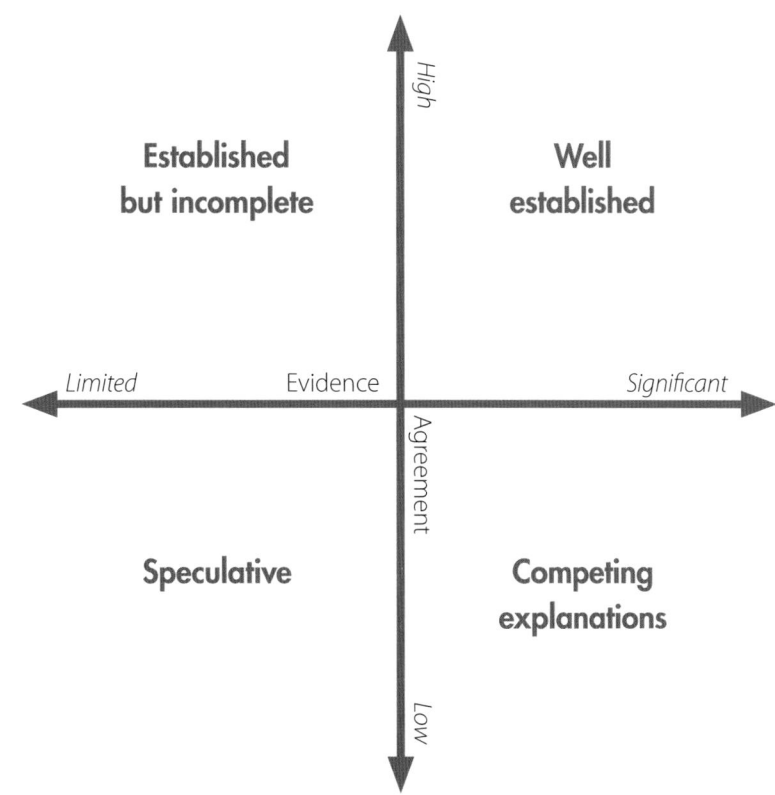

Chapter 6:
Semi-natural Grasslands

Coordinating Lead Author: James M. Bullock
Lead Authors: Richard G. Jefferson, Tim H. Blackstock, Robin J. Pakeman, Bridget A. Emmett, Richard J. Pywell, J. Philip Grime and Jonathan Silvertown
Contributing Authors: Alistair Church, Melina McMullan, Carrie Rimes, Stuart Smith, George Hinton, Keith Porter, Alistair Crowle, Richard Alexander, Steve Peel, Phil Grice, Jane MacKintosh, Vince Holyoak, Ray Keatinge, Ian Middlebrook, Tom Brereton, Mark Crick, Ben Woodcock, Matt Heard, Claire Carvell, Jerry Tallowin, Richard Bardgett and Nigel Cooper

Key Findings*

Semi-natural Grassland has greatly declined in area since 1945, with losses of around 90% in the UK's lowlands. Currently, only 2% of the UK's grassland area comprises high diversity (Biodiversity Action Plans (BAP) priority habitat) Semi-natural Grassland. Two separate studies show a 97% loss of enclosed Semi-natural Grasslands in England and Wales between 1930 and 1984, and an 89% loss of lowland Semi-natural Grassland in Wales between the 1930s and 1990s[1]. Losses continued throughout the 1980s and 1990s[1], with regional English studies indicating declines in specific lowland grassland types ranging from 24% to 62% over various timescales within this period. There are few trend data for Scotland or Northern Ireland, but the scale of loss across the lowlands of these countries is similar to that reported for England and Wales[c]. Changes in upland Acid Grassland since 1945 are poorly documented.

[1] *well established*
[c] *likely*

After 1945, agricultural improvement was the major driver of the loss of Semi-natural Grassland. Technological advances and incentives drove the conversion of high diversity (BAP priority habitat) Semi-natural Grasslands to either 'improved grasslands' or arable land. Today, however, agricultural improvement has decreased in importance as a driver as much Semi-natural Grassland is now protected; for example, in England, 68% is within Sites of Special Scientific Interest (SSSIs) and, in Wales, 52% is within National Parks. There is now evidence for a number of other drivers which continue to cause habitat and species loss in Semi-natural Grassland, particularly nitrogen deposition, inadequate management and habitat fragmentation; although their relative effects are poorly quantified, they are widely recognised as the primary drivers[2]. In the uplands, forestry has been, and continues to be, a major cause of the loss of Acid Grassland. For example, the Scottish Forestry Strategy aims to plant woodland on 270,000 hectares (ha) of 'unimproved grassland'.

[2] *established but incomplete evidence*

The loss in area of Semi-natural Grassland has slowed substantially over the last decade. The Countryside Survey 2007 showed that there was generally no change in area of Acid, Neutral and Calcareous Grasslands in each of the UK countries between 1998 and 2007[1]. However, a few habitats did show some changes in certain countries over that time period; in particular, Acid Grassland increased in extent in the uplands of both Scotland (+9%) and Wales (+7%). The slowed decline is due to the improved protection, restoration and re-creation of grasslands through, for example, agri-environment schemes[c]. Conservation management is important to maintain the quality of Semi-natural Grasslands[1]; for example, only 21% of English non-SSSI Semi-natural Grasslands were found to be in favourable condition, whereas the management of Scottish SSSI lowland grasslands increased the amount of sites in favourable or recovering condition from 45% in the early 2000s to 71% in 2010. The cause of the increase in extent of Acid Grassland is less clear, but may be a continuing impact of overgrazing and degradation of upland heather moorland[d].

[1] *well established*
[c] *likely*
[d] *about as likely as not*

Semi-natural Grasslands are a vital part of the UK's cultural landscape and provide associated services. Most are remnants of traditional farming practices and are the product of thousands of years of human interaction with land and nature. Humans highly value Semi-natural Grassland species and landscapes[1] as shown by the conservation designation afforded to many of these habitats in the UK. Semi-natural Grasslands provide habitat for important and rare species[1]. Of the 1,150 species of conservation concern named in the UK Biodiversity Action Plan (UK BAP), lowland Semi-natural Grasslands are home to 206 UK BAP priority species, while upland Semi-natural Grasslands are home to 41. The UK's National Parks are valued for their greenspace, health, recreation, education and cultural opportunities, and all contain significant areas of Semi-natural Grassland[1]. Calcareous Grassland is the major habitat of the new South Downs National Park. A 2003 study showed that there were about 39 million visitor days per annum to the South Downs and these visitors spent £333 million.

[1] *well established*

Livestock production is low in Semi-natural Grasslands[1], leading to pressures on land use. The annual hay yield for a range of UK lowland Semi-natural Grasslands has been estimated as 2–8 tonnes per hectare (t/ha), which amounts to less than 30% of the dry matter usually obtained in silage over a year from agriculturally improved grassland. The addition of fertilisers increases yearly dry matter yields to about 10–12 t/ha. Upland Acid Grasslands have similarly low yields of about 1.5–5 t/ha, which compares unfavourably to the average of 8 t/ha for reseeded upland grasslands. Digestibility and nutrient content are also lower in forage from Semi-natural Grasslands compared to Improved Grasslands[1]. It has been suggested, however, that livestock grazing on species-rich pasture produce better quality meat than those on species-poor grassland, having, for example higher concentrations of nutritionally beneficial omega-3 fatty acids[4].

[1] well established
[4] speculative

Biodiversity is positively related to many ecosystem services provided by Semi-natural Grasslands. Other than livestock production, many ecosystem services are higher in semi-natural than in agriculturally improved grasslands, and this can be linked partially with the higher plant richness[1]. The Countryside Survey 2007 showed that, within the top 15 cm of soil, Acid Grassland (82.3 t/ha) has the highest carbon stock of any UK NEA broad habitat. Although the stock for Neutral Grassland (62.4 t/ha) is lower, it is above that for Improved Grassland and Arable and Horticultural land. Acid and Neutral Grasslands contain 293 teragrams of the UK's carbon store in the top 15 cm of their soil. Semi-natural Grasslands have high invertebrate abundance and diversity, and may provide pollination and pest control services by the spread of insects to agricultural areas[c]. However, declines in bumblebees since the 1960s are linked to declines in key Semi-natural Grassland plants[1].

[1] well established
[c] likely

Semi-natural Grasslands present opportunities for delivering multiple services while requiring relatively low energy inputs. In contrast to Improved Grassland and Arable and Horticultural land, low input Semi-natural Grasslands generally: store greater densities of carbon and produce less nitrous oxide; produce less methane due to their lower stocking densities; allow greater water infiltration rates and enhanced storage (which should aid flood prevention); and experience less pollution because of the low fertiliser input[2]. Nutrient cycling also seems to be more efficient in unimproved grasslands. Enhancement of plant richness within Semi-natural Grasslands can also increase production in the absence of fertilisers[a]; for instance, one experiment showed a 40% difference in hay yield between species-rich and species-poor plots. Therefore, low input, high service-providing Semi-natural Grasslands form an alternative land use to high input agriculture, albeit with lower overall animal production[a].

[2] established but incomplete evidence
[a] virtually certain

Agri-environment schemes are critical to maintain and enhance the biodiversity and ecosystem services of Semi-natural Grassland. Maintenance of the biodiversity and cultural value of Semi-natural Grassland requires low intensity management related to traditional farming[1]. Restoration of Semi-natural Grassland from, for example, arable and improved grassland, is well-researched and will be critical to prevent further biodiversity loss through habitat fragmentation, and to improve certain services[1]. Maintenance, recreation and restoration are delivered mostly through the country-based agri-environment schemes. For instance, the Tir Gofal scheme in Wales currently has 35,258 ha of Semi-natural Grassland under maintenance options and 1,985 ha being restored. Such protected and restored Semi-natural Grasslands also have the potential to provide recreation and tourism services (particularly if rare livestock breeds are used), and pollinator and pest control services for adjacent intensive farmland[c].

[1] well established
[c] likely

---

* Each Key Finding has been assigned a level of scientific certainty, based on a 4-box model and complemented, where possible, with a likelihood scale. Superscript numbers and letters indicate the uncertainty term assigned to each finding. Full details of each term and how they were assigned are presented in Appendix 6.1.

6.1 Introduction

The vegetation of Semi-natural Grasslands comprises a mixture of grasses and herbaceous plants, along with sedges, rushes, mosses and other low-growing species. In the UK, Semi-natural Grasslands are the remnants of habitats created by low-intensity, traditional farming, or, in some cases, the natural vegetation on poor soils or in exposed locations (Pigott & Walters 1954). Much grassland in the UK has undergone agricultural 'improvement' through the re-sowing of plants, high inputs of inorganic fertilisers and intensive cutting or grazing. These activities have created grasslands dominated by a few agricultural grasses and white clover (*Trifolium repens*). In contrast to the generic and species-poor composition of agriculturally improved grasslands, plant communities in Semi-natural Grasslands often have a rich variety of grasses and herbs, and fall into distinct types which have developed over many decades in response to the local climate, soil, geology and management methods.

From a broad ecological perspective, grasslands can be seen as intermediate stages in the development of vegetation over time. Open areas, such as cultivated soil, burned woodland or silted-up ponds, will usually develop gradually into grasslands of various types. If undisturbed, such grassland will often eventually acquire tree cover. But the intermediate grassland stage may be maintained by grazing, light burning, cutting, flooding or other processes which prevent the establishment and growth of scrub or trees.

The wide extent of grassland in the UK (Improved and Semi-natural Grasslands make up 37% of the land area (Carey *et al.* 2008)) is largely the result of human activity. The extensive coverage of the 'wildwood' following the glacial retreat after the last ice age (the early Holocene, about 10,000 years ago) meant that grassland was a rare habitat (Rackham 1986), although its extent is debated (Hodder *et al.* 2005). Natural disturbances to the woodland allowed grasslands to develop and persist until trees closed over again, while in floodplains or on poor soils, other grasslands may have persisted over longer time periods (Hodder *et al.* 2005). Some of the earliest activities of human settlers in the Holocene involved the clearance of woodland, resulting in the rapid expansion of grasslands which were used for grazing and fodder production (and fertiliser production as manure was applied to crops). Variations in social and economic conditions have caused the area of grassland in the UK to fluctuate over the centuries, especially through changes in the balance of arable and grassland areas. For example, the area of grassland increased at the expense of arable land following the Black Death in the early 14th Century and decreased during the Napoleonic Wars (Thirsk 1997).

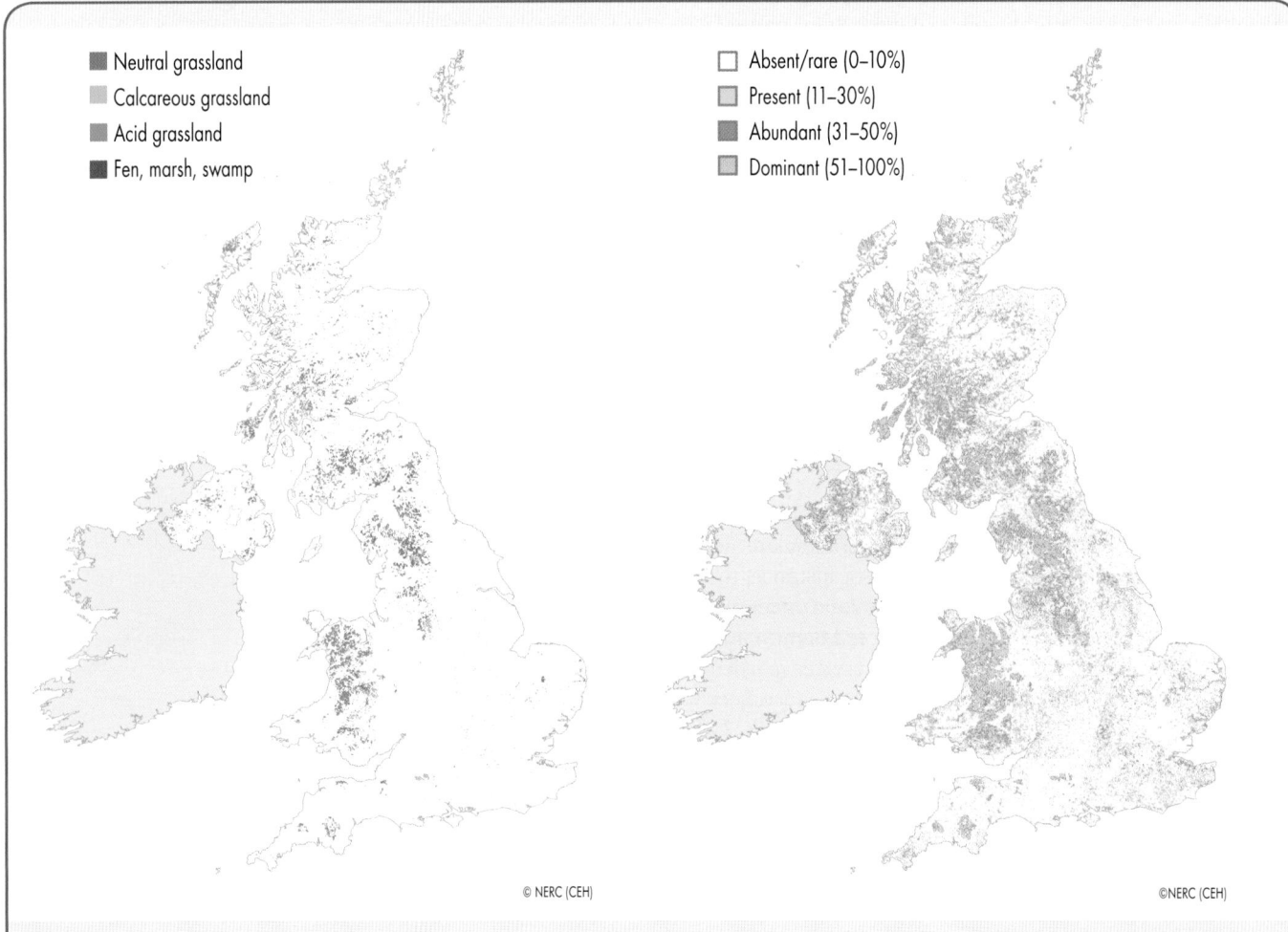

Neutral grassland
Calcareous grassland
Acid grassland
Fen, marsh, swamp

Absent/rare (0–10%)
Present (11–30%)
Abundant (31–50%)
Dominant (51–100%)

© NERC (CEH)

©NERC (CEH)

Figure 6.1 Distribution of UK NEA Semi-natural Grasslands habitat in the UK by a) dominant (>51% area per 1 km cell) type and b) percent cover per 1 km cell.

Semi-natural Grassland is, therefore, a very fluid habitat, which is amenable for conversion to (and from) arable land and to improved grassland through cultivation, re-sowing and fertiliser application. The relaxation of human interventions also causes changes: the cessation of management techniques such as cutting, grazing or burning will lead to colonisation by shrubs and trees which over-top the grasses and herbs and develop into scrub and woodland—a process which, over the last few decades, has occurred on various abandoned Semi-natural Grasslands. These fluctuations, and the fact that grassland farming practices have evolved continually, mean the history of any particular location now classified as a Semi-natural Grassland is complex and reflects human history at both local and national scales.

Semi-natural Grasslands comprise the Acid, Neutral and Calcareous Grassland broad habitats of the Countryside Survey (Carey *et al.* 2008), along with Purple Moor-grass and Rush Pastures which fall within the Fen, Marsh and Swamp broad habitat (**Figure 6.1**, **Figure 6.2**). Within these broad categories, many specific types of Semi-natural Grassland habitat are of conservation concern, particularly the UK Biodiversity Action Plan (BAP) priority habitats, which are lowland meadows, upland hay meadows, lowland dry acid grassland, purple moor-grass and rush pastures, and lowland and upland calcareous grasslands. These are considered important habitats at the European level, with all those listed being afforded protection across the EU, for example, through the Natura 2000 network (Rodwell *et al.* 2007). Upland acid grassland is a major component of UK Semi-natural Grassland, but it is not considered a priority habitat in the UK Biodiversity Action Plan (UK BAP; www.ukbap.org.uk) because it is often the result of overgrazing of moorland.

Because of its fluid nature, its association with human activities and its characteristic as an intermediate stage in the development of vegetation from bare soil to woodland, Semi-natural Grassland also has a close association with many other UK NEA Broad Habitats:

- Semi-natural Grasslands are mostly still within farming systems, but are distinguished from the Improved Grasslands of Enclosed Farmland by their history (lack of recent cultivation, re-sowing or heavy fertilisation) and current low-intensity management: much is managed under agri-environment schemes or is within protected areas.
- Grasslands can closely interact with Freshwater systems; in particular, water meadows were traditionally managed so that they stored seasonal floodwaters, retaining silt that fertilised the grassland for farming. These and other types of wet grassland, such as purple moor-grass and rush pastures, have an important role to play in the flow of water from the land to waterways, for example, by slowing drainage.
- The coastal zone contains many specific types of Semi-natural Grasslands; Machair (Chapter 11), Sand Dunes and the maritime vegetation of Sea Cliffs all comprise Semi-natural Grassland, much of which has high nature conservation value.
- Woodland is the natural endpoint of vegetation development on grasslands, and many woodlands contain grass areas; the New Forest, for instance, is a mosaic of closed wood and grassland, as well as heath. Wood pastures—rare remnants of former parks and Royal Forests—are an intermediate between woodland and grassland, and are a UK BAP priority habitat.
- A variety of grassland types is found in Urban areas, from species-rich Semi-natural Grasslands to highly managed, species-poor amenity grasslands.

In this chapter, we consider all the Semi-natural Grasslands (as distinguished from improved or amenity grassland) associated with other UK NEA Broad Habitats insofar as they represent the general Semi-natural Grassland resource. Roles, goods and services specific to the associated UK NEA Broad Habitat (e.g. coastal defence for sand dunes or water flow in wetlands) are considered in those chapters. Semi-natural Grassland is often an important component of linear features, such as roadside verges and hedgerows. However, the contribution of these linear features to Semi-natural Grassland is poorly quantified and the figures given in this chapter regarding stock and service delivery do not include these small areas.

6.2 Trends and Changes in Semi-natural Grassland

6.2.1 The Current Extent of Semi-natural Grassland

6.2.1.1 Total extent

Priority habitat Semi-natural Grasslands (i.e. excluding upland acid grassland) comprise only 1% of the UK land area and only 2% of the total area of UK grassland (including rough grazing or 3% if rough grazing land is excluded). **Table 6.1** provides estimates of the total area of the UK BAP priority grassland types including estimates of upland acid grassland (UK BAP 2006). Upland acid grassland is not a UK BAP priority habitat as it is often the product of overgrazing of more highly valued upland dwarf shrub heaths and is considered to have low botanical value. However, it does form part of the habitat that supports important upland breeding bird assemblages.

6.2.1.2 Designated sites

Data on designations differ among the countries, having been gathered in different ways and at different times. Therefore, we present each country separately.

Table 6.2 shows the area of Semi-natural Grassland covered by various designations in England. Designations overlap, for example, Special Areas of Conservation (SACs) will also be Sites of Special Scientific Interest (SSSIs), so the percentages sum to more than 100%. However, these figures demonstrate that a large proportion of England's Semi-Natural Grassland resource is protected to some degree.

Figure 6.2 Semi-natural Grasslands comprise Acid, Neutral and Calcareous Grasslands along with Purple Moor-grass and Rush Pastures: a) Acid Grassland with lazy beds from Fermanagh, Northern Ireland. *Photo courtesy of Mark Wright/NIEA*; b) Upland Acid Grassland dominated by mat grass (*Nardus stricta*). Moel Penderyn, Brecon Beacons, Wales. *Photo courtesy of Sam Bosanquet/CCW*; c) Rush Pasture with abundant herbs, including ragged-robin (*Silene flos-cuculi*), marsh thistle (*Cirsium palustre*) and greater bird's-foot trefoil (*Lotus pedunculatus*). Caerau Uchaf, North Wales. *Photo courtesy of Stuart Smith/CCW*; d) Lowland Neutral Grassland, Keltneyburn Scottish Wildlife Trust Reserve, Perthshire, Scotland. *Photo ©Scottish Natural Heritage*; e) Calcareous Grassland, Hambledon Hill National Nature Reserve, Dorset, England. *Photo ©Peter Wakely/ Natural England*; f) Lowland Calcareous Grassland with abundant hoary rockrose (*Helianthemum oelandicum*) and wild thyme (*Thymus polytrichus*). Great Orme's Head, North Wales. *Photo courtesy of Stuart Smith/CCW*; g) Dry Neutral (species-rich variety) Grassland from Northern Ireland. *Photo courtesy of Mark Wright/NIEA*; h) Purple Moor-grass meadow, Chippenham Fen National Nature Reserve, Cambridgeshire, England. *Photo ©Peter Wakely/ Natural England.*

Table 6.3 shows the area of Semi-natural Grassland within SSSIs and National Parks in Wales. Designations overlap, so some SSSIs are in National Parks.

There are no area measurements of grassland features within Scottish SSSIs, so we can present no figures for Scotland. To date, approximately 15% of the Semi-natural Grassland resource in Northern Ireland is within Areas of Special Scientific Interest (ASSI). This is likely to increase in the near future due to further notification of grassland sites (NIEA 2001).

6.2.1.3 Agri-environment schemes

Agri-environment schemes reward farmers and land managers for delivering environmental outcomes on registered agricultural land in the UK. Each of the four countries has its own individual scheme and, therefore, information is presented separately for each country.

England. In England, the Environmental Stewardship Higher Level Scheme (HLS) is the principal mechanism for maintaining existing UK BAP-condition Semi-natural Grassland, restoring grassland in poor condition and creating new Semi-natural Grassland. In England, there are 60,733 hectares (ha) of grassland entered into the maintenance and restoration of grassland options of either the classic schemes (Countryside Stewardship; Environmentally Sensitive Areas) or HLS. In HLS, 2,373 ha have been entered into the creation of species-rich grassland option (Natural England 2009a).

Wales. Table 6.4 summarises data on the area of Semi-natural Grassland types entered into the Tir Gofal options in Wales. These options allow maintaining existing UK BAP-condition Semi-natural Grasslands, restoring grassland in poor condition and expanding the Semi-natural Grassland resource through habitat creation.

Northern Ireland. The Northern Ireland Countryside Management Scheme (NICMS) is the current agri-environment scheme. A total of 12,996 ha are currently under agri-environment management as species-rich grassland

Table 6.2 Area of Semi-natural Grassland* under different designations in England. Source: Natural England (2008).

Designation	Total area (ha)	% of total area of SNG in England
Total resource	109,576 [†]	100
Site of Special Scientific Interest (SSSI)	74,894	68
Special Area of Conservation (SAC)	43,790	40
Special Protection Area (SPA)	33,992	31
Ramsar site	3,134	3
National Nature Reserve (NNR)	6,328	6
Within National Park	10,166	9
Within Area of Outstanding Natural Beauty (AONB)	20,887	19

* Covers upland and lowland meadows, lowland calcareous grassland, upland calcareous grassland, lowland dry acid grassland and purple moor-grass and rush pastures.
† Differs from the estimate in Table 6.1 as the figure is taken from the Natural England habitat inventory data rather than the UK BAP targets review.

Table 6.3 Area of Semi-natural Grassland* under different designations in Wales (upland and lowland). Source: data from UK BAP (2006†); Blackstock *et al.* (1996)‡; Countryside Council for Wales Phase I habitat data¶.

Designation	Total area (ha)	% of total area
Total resource	180,000 [†]	100
SSSI	50,950 [‡]	28
Within National Park	93,000 [¶]	52

* Covers lowland meadows, lowland calcareous grassland, upland calcareous grassland, lowland dry acid grassland and purple moor-grass and rush pastures (UK BAP) and non-BAP upland acid grassland.

Table 6.1 Estimates of the extent of Semi-natural Grassland habitats in the UK. Sources: for priority habitats UK BAP (2006); Upland acid grassland: Countryside Survey – England (CS 2009) and Scotland (Norton *et al.* 2009), Blackstock *et al.* (2010) – Wales, Cooper *et al.* (2009) – Northern Ireland Countryside Survey (2007).

	Area (ha)				
	England	Wales	Scotland	N. Ireland	Total
UK BAP priority grasslands					
Lowland calcareous grassland	38,687	1,146	761	-	**40,594**
Lowland dry acid grassland	20,142	36, 473	4,357	674	**61,646**
Lowland hay meadows	7,282	1,322	980	937	**10,521**
Upland hay meadows	870	-	27	-	**897**
Purple moor-grass & rush pasture	21,544	32,161	6,768	18,476	**79,392**
Upland calcareous grassland	16, 000	700	5,000	936	**22,636**
Totals for priority habitats	104,525	71,802	17,893	21,466	**215,686**
Other Semi-natural Grasslands					
Upland acid grassland	376,000	108,100	983,000	9,695	**1,476,795**
Upland marshy grassland	-	29,200	-	-	
Total Semi-natural Grassland Habitat	**480,525**	**209,102**	**1,000,893**	**31,161**	**1,692,481**

Table 6.4 Grassland under agri-environment schemes in Wales. Tir Gofal prescriptions based on active schedules – lowland grassland. Source: data for 2001 provided by the Wales Assembly Government.

Grassland Habitat Action Plan	Maintenance (ha)	Restoration (ha)	Expansion (ha)
Lowland meadow	1,778	1,461	5,596
Lowland calcareous grassland	181	388	0
Lowland dry acid grassland	13,952		0
Purple moor-grass and rush pasture	19,347	136	0
Total	**35,258**	**1,985**	**5,596**

Table 6.5 Semi-natural Grassland under agri-environment management prescriptions for Environmentally Sensitive Areas and Northern Ireland Countryside Management Scheme. Source: data December 2007 provided by Department of Agriculture and Rural Development.

Management Prescription	Area (ha)
Species rich grassland (dry)	1,456
Species rich grassland (wet)	10,013
Species rich grassland (calcareous)	981
Species rich hay meadow	546
Total	**12,996**

Table 6.6 Semi-natural Grassland agri-environment management options in Rural Priorities and legacy schemes. Source: data for 2010 provided by Scottish Natural Heritage.

Management Option	Area (ha)
Management of species-rich grassland	272,500
Creation and management of species rich-grassland	50,500

(dry/wet/calcareous and hay meadow). It should be noted that habitat definitions under the NICMS are generally broader than UK BAP priority habitat classifications and their application relates to the management of whole field parcels. These factors account for differences between **Table 6.5** and **Table 6.1**.

Scotland. The Scotland Rural Development Programme supports the management, creation and restoration of species-rich grasslands through Rural Development Contracts. Under this competitive funding mechanism, contracts are awarded for proposals which are best able to deliver the agreed regional priorities (**Table 6.6**).

6.2.2 The Current Condition of Semi-natural Grassland

Data from various surveillance and monitoring studies have provided information on the current condition of Semi-natural Grasslands in three of the four countries of the UK (**Table 6.7**). Currently, there are no quantitative data for Wales on the condition of grassland features in SSSIs or non-statutory sites. There are some data for the condition of Annex 1 grassland types on SACs. Of 22 features assessed between 2002 and 2006, all were assessed as 'unfavourable', 18% of which were 'unfavourable recovering'.

For English non-statutory Semi-natural Grassland sites, only 21% of the grassland sample was in 'favourable' condition in 2005. This contrasts with the situation for SSSIs where, in most cases, the percentage of sites which were favourable exceeds that for the non-statutory site sample. Common Standards monitoring data for Scottish SSSIs in 2010 show that recent measures to get features in unfavourable condition into appropriate management have improved the overall proportion of lowland grasslands in favourable or 'recovering' condition from 45% (1999 to 2005) to 71% (2010). The condition of Semi-natural Grassland features on ASSIs in Northern Ireland was assessed between 2002 and 2008. Despite small sample sizes, the data show

Table 6.7 Condition of Semi-natural Grassland types from country surveys demonstrated by the percent of surveyed Semi-natural Grasslands which were in unfavourable recovering or favourable condition*. Note: This does not include sites that were notified as ASSIs between 2002 and 2008; these data are not available at present. Lowland dry acid grassland is not a notified feature on any ASSIs, although it does occur as small areas in a mosaic with upland calcareous grassland (NVC type CG10 *Festuca ovina-Agrostis capillaris-Thymus praecox* grassland [Rodwell 1992]). Sources: data from Natural England SSSI Information System (ENSIS)[‡]; Hewins *et al.* (2005)[¶]; data supplied for 2010 by Scottish Natural Heritage §; Northern Ireland Environment Agency (NIEA 2008)[**].

a) UK BAP Priority Grassland	English SSSIs in 2009[‡]	English non-statutory Semi-natural Grasslands in 2005[¶]	Scottish SSSIs in 2010[§]	Northern Irish ASSIs 2002 to 2008 [**]
Lowland calcareous grassland	92.4	28	71	61
Upland calcareous grassland	92.4	No data	52	
Lowland dry acid grassland	84.5	21	53	No data
Lowland hay meadows	76.2	16	57	25
Upland hay meadows	91.3	7	100	No data
Purple moor-grass & rush pastures	78.1	35	90	39
b) Other				
Upland acid grassland	85.2 [†]	No data	No data	No data

* For definitions see English Nature (2003) and Williams (2006).
† This is the combined figure for unfavourable recovering + favourable and is an assessment for the upland breeding birds associated with upland acid grassland (total area = 27,587 ha).

UK National Ecosystem Assessment: Technical Report

that only 37.5% of all grassland features assessed were in favourable/unfavourable recovering condition.

6.2.3 Historical Trends in the Semi-natural Grassland Habitat

6.2.3.1 Changes in area: historical survey data

The loss and degradation of Semi-natural Grassland, particularly in the lowlands of Great Britain during the second half of the 20th Century, has been well documented (Blackstock *et al.* 1999; Fuller 1987; Green 1990; Ratcliffe 1984). It is clear that there has been a profound and widespread transformation of grasslands across the lowland landscapes of the UK, so that, for the most part, only relatively small, remnant patches survive. Cooper *et al.* (1994) reported that improved and semi-improved grasslands comprised 95.5% of the grassland resource in the UK lowland landscape. In contrast, there are very few data concerning the fate of Semi-natural Grasslands in the unenclosed uplands. Here, the issue is probably less to do with loss, but more to do with degradation resulting from overgrazing or attempts at agricultural improvement, as well as losses to forestry.

Fuller (1987) reported a 97% loss of semi-natural enclosed grasslands in England and Wales between 1930 and 1984. These losses were largely attributable to the conversion of grassland to arable land or the intensification of farming in these areas through ploughing, drainage and reseeding, and improvement with fertilisers and herbicides. This scale of loss is likely to have been similar across the lowland areas of south and east Scotland as the agricultural systems are essentially similar to those in lowland England and Wales. Mackey *et al.* (1998) found that rough grassland declined by 10% between the 1940s and 1980s throughout Scotland, but there was much regional variation. The extent of rough grassland contracted from around 12,300,000 ha (16% of Scotland) to 11,100,000 ha (14% of Scotland). This work was based on the National Countryside Monitoring Scheme (NCMS) and used aerial photography and estimates of change based on visible sward structure, which is not necessarily related to species composition. Grassland was classified as 'rough', 'intermediate' or 'smooth'. The rough grassland category is the one most likely to correspond to Semi-natural Grassland and would probably include purple moor-grass and rush pastures and acid grassland.

During the late 1980s and 1990s, grassland surveys conducted by the statutory, country-based conservation agencies and other, non-governmental organisations, such as The Wildlife Trusts, showed that losses of Semi-natural Grassland continued during this period. For example, a survey of Berkshire's Neutral Grassland in 1995 (previously surveyed in 1984 and 1987), showed that 50% of sites (60% by area) had been damaged or destroyed (Redgrave 1995). In addition, Devon Wildlife Trust (1990) recorded a 62% loss of culm grassland sites (mostly comprising purple moor-grass and rush pasture) between 1984 and 1989/90. These examples of declining extent are also supported by local surveys undertaken by other county Wildlife Trusts during a similar timeframe (Plantlife 2002). More recently, a survey of about 500 non-SSSI Semi-natural Grassland sites in England (Hewins *et al.* 2005) revealed that 24% of these sites more

closely resembled agriculturally improved grassland types than Semi-natural Grassland habitats, indicating further losses of Semi-natural Grassland between 1980 and 2003.

A comparison of lowland grassland cover in Wales between the 1930s and 1980/90s using data from Davies (1936) and the Habitat Survey of Wales (HSW) showed an estimated loss of semi-natural (unimproved) and semi-improved lowland dry grassland to improved grassland of 91% over the 50–60 years between the two surveys (Stevens *et al.* 2010).

Although there are no quantitative trend data for Northern Ireland, similar losses of Semi-natural Grassland have undoubtedly occurred during the second half of the last century. For Eire, Byrne (1996) reported losses of 38% of lowland meadow sites and 43% of acid bent/fescue grassland sites in Leinster over the period from 1979 to 1994. Improved Grasslands now dominate the Northern Ireland landscape, with less than 5% of grasslands classified as being species-rich (Cooper *et al.* 2009; NIEA 2010).

6.2.3.2 Changes in area and condition: recent data from the Countryside Survey 2007

Using a standardised methodology, the Countryside Survey reports changes in broad habitats between 1990, 1998 and 2007. The methodology is less focused on Semi-natural Grassland than the data reported in Section 6.2.3.1, so we will report Countryside Survey trends and consider how they contrast with the data already presented.

England (Countryside Survey 2009):
- There was no significant change in the area of either Calcareous or Acid Grassland broad habitats between 1998 and 2007; but between 1990 and 1998, there was a significant decrease in the area of both habitats.
- There was a significant increase in the area of Neutral Grassland broad habitat between 1990 and 2007.
- There was a significant decrease in plant species richness in botanically rich Neutral and Acid Grasslands between 1998 and 2007.
- The decrease in plant species richness in Neutral Grasslands is also reflected by a significant reduction in the number of foodplants for butterfly larvae and farmland birds.
- There was a significant increase in more competitive, nutrient-demanding plant species in botanically rich Neutral Grassland.

Scotland (Norton *et al.* 2009):
- There was no significant change in the area of Neutral or Calcareous Grassland between 1998 and 2007.
- The area of Acid Grassland increased between 1998 and 2007.
- Plant species richness decreased in both Neutral and Acid Grasslands between 1998 and 2007. Competitive species increased at the expense of species of open ground.
- Some of the plant species lost included those which are important foodplants for particular birds and butterfly larvae.
- Plant species associated with wetter conditions increased in Acid and Neutral Grasslands between 1998 and 2007.

Wales (Smart *et al.* 2009)

- There was no significant change in the area of Neutral, Calcareous or Acid Grassland between 1998 and 2007. However, in the upland zone, Acid Grassland increased in area, while Neutral Grassland decreased.
- Species richness and bird and butterfly foodplants decreased in botanically rich Neutral and Acid Grasslands.

Northern Ireland (Cooper *et al.* 2009)

- There was a decrease (although not statistically significant) in species-rich dry grassland (which includes lowland meadow) from 6,257 ha to 4,345 ha (-31%).
- There was no change in the 1,802 ha of Calcareous Grassland.
- There was a statistically non-significant decrease in fen meadow which contains some of the most species-rich purple moor-grass and rush pasture, from 6,257 ha to 4,345 ha (-31%). However, there was only a small (2%) and non-significant) decline in species-rich wet grassland (13,186 ha) which contains the majority of the purple moor-grass and rush pasture resource.
- There was a statistically non-significant increase in Acid Grassland in lowland classes from 211 ha in 1998 to 549 ha in 2007. However, some of this habitat gain occurred in marginal upland land-classes where there was also a significant decrease in (-22%) Acid Grassland.

The above results generally accord with trends detected by other studies reported in 6.2.3.1. The decrease in plant species richness may be attributable to a combination of both a reduction in, and cessation of, grazing, as well as the continuing effects of atmospheric deposition of nitrogen. The data suggest, however, that the loss of grassland broad habitats has substantially slowed over the last ten years. This finding is in accordance with the UK BAP assessments for priority habitats (**Table 6.8**).Yet there have also been unquantified gains in grassland that conform broadly to the priority UK BAP types through creation, and restoration from arable, semi-improved or improved grassland, as a result of agri-environment incentive measures.

However, there are two surprising findings from the Countryside Survey (2007) results: the increase in the extent of Neutral Grassland (which includes less species-rich, semi-improved grasslands); and the increase in extent of Acid Grassland. The former might be due to the establishment of grasslands through agri-environment incentives or long-term set-aside. The cause of the increase in Acid Grassland is unclear, but could be due to the conversion of dwarf shrub heath to Acid Grassland by overgrazing, along with a reduction in bracken (*Pteridium aquilinum*) cover.

6.2.4 Conservation Status of Semi-natural Grassland

Table 6.8 shows recent assessments of the trend in the extent of UK BAP priority grassland habitats from the 2008 UK BAP reporting exercise, along with assessments of the overall conservation status of grassland Annex 1 habitats as required under Article 17 of the EU Habitats Directive. This reporting is largely based on expert opinion and anecdotal information. The findings illustrate the opinion that, across the UK, Semi-natural Grassland continues to decline in terms of extent, although probably at a slower rate than in the later decades of the 20th Century—a conclusion which

Table 6.8 Overall trends and conservation status for UK Semi-natural Grasslands. Source: UK Biodiversity Action Plan reporting (BARS 2008)*; Favourable Conservation Status reporting (JNCC 2007).

Semi-natural Grassland type	Overall UK trend from 2008 UK BAP reporting*	2007 FCS assessment for grassland Annex 1 habitats†	Annex 1 habitat† assessed and relationship to column 1 grassland type
Lowland calcareous grassland		Unfavourable (Bad) but improving	H6210/H6211 Semi-natural dry grasslands (Festuco-Brometalia). (Direct equivalence)
Lowland dry acid grassland ¶		Unknown	H2330 Inland dunes with open *Corynephorus* and *Agrostis* grasslands (Subset: NVC types SD11 & SD12 only—Rodwell 2000)¶
Lowland hay meadows		Unfavourable (Bad) but improving	H6510 Lowland hay meadows (Subset -NVC type MG4 only—Rodwell 1992)
Upland hay meadows	Declining (slowing)		H6520 Mountain hay meadows (direct equivalence)
Purple moor-grass & rush pastures		Unfavourable (Bad) and deteriorating	H6410 *Molinia* meadows (Subset—NVC types M24 and M26 only—Rodwell 1991)
Upland calcareous grassland		Unfavourable (Bad) but improving	H6210 Semi-natural‡ dry grasslands (Festuco-Brometalia) H6230 Semi-natural dry grasslands H6170 Alpine & sub-alpine calcareous grassland
		Unfavourable (Bad)	H6230 Species-rich *Nardus* grassland
Upland acid grassland	No data—not a priority habitat	-	No Annex 1 habitat

† See www.jncc.gov.uk/PDF/FCS2007_ukapproach.pdf for an explanation of how the Favourable Conservation Status (FCS) assessment was derived. This assessment takes into account trends in range, area and condition of the habitat, as well as threats.
‡ See McLeod *et al.* (2005) for a description of Annex 1 habitats.
¶ Annex 1 habitat 2,330 inland dunes with open *Corynephorus* and *Agrostis* grasslands conforms to NVC types SD11 and SD12.The definition of the lowland dry acid grassland UK BAP priority habitat (UK Biodiversity Group 1999) includes inland types of two dune grassland communities SD10b and SD11b (Rodwell 2000). The main communities that make up the priority habitat (NVC types U1, U2, U3 and U4 (Rodwell 1992)) are not covered by the UK interpretation of Annex 1 types (Rodwell *et al.* 2007).

largely matches the data presented in Section 6.2.3. The condition of these grasslands is generally considered poor but improving, although there are large differences between grassland types and countries. In England, and probably elsewhere, Semi-natural Grasslands in SSSIs are mostly in better condition compared to non-SSSIs.

6.2.4.1 Trends in grassland species

Vascular plants. Many characteristic vascular plants of Semi-natural Grassland have declined markedly over the last 50 years. Preston *et al.* (2002, 2003) examined the *New Atlas of the British and Irish Flora* and compared recent (1987 to 1999) distributions and frequencies of native species and archaeophytes (ancient non-native species) with those recorded in the 1962 Atlas. By assigning each species to its Countryside Survey broad habitat, it was possible to calculate an 'average' change index for species within each broad habitat. They found that Calcareous Grassland and Acid Grassland both had a negative change index: many species associated with these habitats had declined substantially since the 1930s.

Butterflies. Fox *et al.* (2006) concluded that butterflies restricted to semi-natural habitats (including grassland specialists) have fared badly over recent decades. Farmland butterfly populations are considered good long-term biodiversity indicators because they respond to environmental change and agricultural management, occur in a wide range of habitats, and are representative of many other insects. A multi-species index of farmland butterfly abundance has been compiled by Butterfly Conservation and the Centre for Ecology and Hydrology, chiefly from data collated through the UK Butterfly Monitoring Scheme. The indicator includes 48 of the 51 native butterfly species resident in England and occurring on farmland for which sufficient data are available. The indicator includes a breakdown for 23 specialist (low-mobility species restricted to semi-natural habitats) and 25 generalist (mobile species that occur in a broad range of habitats in the wider countryside) species from data collected at 672 lowland farmland sites. Analysis of the underlying trend over the period 1990 to 2009, smoothed to factor out year-to-year fluctuations (structural time-series analysis, with confidence intervals applied by the Kalman filter), indicates a -42% change for all farmland butterflies, a -36% change in specialists and a -47% change in generalists (unpublished analysis supplied by Butterfly Conservation).

Birds. A number of conservation priority bird species are associated with Semi-natural Grassland, primarily during the breeding season. Waders are strongly associated with lowland wet grasslands, twite (*Carduelis flavirostris*) with northern hay meadows and stone curlews (*Burhinus oedicnemus*) with the Brecks and chalk downland (Green & Griffiths 1994). Salisbury Plain holds important populations of several declining passerines, including whinchat (*Saxicola rubetra*), grasshopper warbler (*Locustella naevia*) and skylark (*Alauda arvensis*) (Stanbury *et al.* 2000), along with the only re-established great bustard (*Otis tarda*) population in the UK. There were major declines in the numbers and distribution of breeding and wintering birds associated with grassland habitats in the UK over the second half of the last century (Vickery *et al.* 2001). This has been particularly well

documented for breeding waders associated with lowland damp grassland. The first damp grassland breeding wader survey was conducted in 1982 (Smith 1983) and showed that numbers were already low and that large populations were confined to relatively few sites. Wilson *et al.* (2005) subsequently showed that lapwing (*Vanellus vanellus*), snipe (*Gallinago gallinago*), curlew (*Numenius arquata*) and redshank (*Tringa tetanus*) declined significantly on lowland wet grassland between 1982 and 2002. However, the picture is somewhat complicated because some wintering wildfowl species have increased over the last 30 years (Kershaw & Cranswick 2003). This is thought to be due to a number of factors including increases in nutritious, improved grasslands and winter-sown arable crops, refuge creation and climate change.

In upland grassland landscapes, populations of certain breeding birds (especially waders) declined during the last three decades of the 20th Century (Baines 1988; Fuller *et al.* 2002; Henderson *et al.* 2004; Taylor & Grant 2004). Recent surveys also indicate that since the early 1980s there has been a widespread decline in the breeding population, and a contraction in the breeding range, of yellow wagtails (*Motacilla flava*) in upland hay meadows; this decline accelerated during the 1990s (Nelson *et al.* 2003). Raine *et al.* (2009) showed that the range and numbers of breeding twite have declined considerably since the 1970s in the English uplands. This species nests on open moorlands but requires access to species-rich hay meadows and pastures for feeding during the breeding season (Brown & Grice 2005).

6.2.5 Drivers of Change in the Semi-natural Grassland Habitat

The drivers of change in the Semi-natural Grassland habitat are well-rehearsed. There is qualitative information on the contribution of these drivers to change in Semi-natural Grassland since the war, and their potential role in the near future. However, exact figures—for example, of areas lost to certain land conversion activities—are rarely available. **Table 6.9** combines this qualitative information and our expert judgement to represent the role of each driver of change in Semi-natural Grassland in the past, present and future. It must be noted that degradation of an individual Semi-natural Grassland is often caused by multiple drivers. For example, a re-survey by Bennie *et al.* (2006) during 2001 to 2003 of 92 English Calcareous Grasslands first surveyed in 1952/53 showed declines in plant species richness and replacement of typical Calcareous Grassland plants with more competitive species. Bennie *et al.* (2006) suggested multiple drivers contributed to these losses, including habitat fragmentation, nutrient enrichment and reduced grazing.

Burnside *et al.* (2003) do provide quantitative information on the fate of Semi-natural Grasslands (which they call 'unimproved grassland') between 1971 and 1991, albeit only for the Western South Downs landscape in West Sussex. Analysis of aerial photos suggested a large amount of the 4,729 ha of Semi-natural Grassland present in 1971 was lost by 1991. The greatest losses were to arable land, while plantations and development of woodland and scrub also accounted for a large proportion of losses (**Table 6.10**).

Table 6.9 A summary of drivers of change in Semi-natural Grassland and their impacts at different periods. The role of the driver of change is categorised as major (■), moderate (▣) or minor (□).

Driver of change	Semi-natural Grassland affected	Impact of driver on Semi-natural Grassland	Role since 1940s	Present role	Future role ‡
Agricultural grassland improvement	Priority habitats	Domination by fast-growing plants; loss of plant and animal diversity; soil processes compromised	■	□	□
Conversion to arable	Priority habitats	Cultivation and total loss of habitat	■	□	□
Conversion to forestry	All*	Cultivation, planting and total loss of habitat	■	□/▣	▣ (uplands)
Other conversion: roads, building, quarries, etc.	All	Habitat destruction	▣	□	□
Nitrogen deposition and transfer	All	Increased soil fertility leading to domination by fast-growing plants and loss of plant diversity	■	■/▣	▣
Inadequate management	Priority habitats	Insufficient grazing leading to rank vegetation, scrub and trees	▣	■	■
Overgrazing	Upland acid	Overgrazing (sheep) of moorland causing loss of heather and increase in upland grassland	■	▣	□
Habitat fragmentation	Priority habitats	Remaining Semi-natural Grassland are small and isolated leading to local species losses and invasions	▣	▣	▣
Invasion by non-native plants	All	Exclusion of desirable species; change in soil processes	□	□	□/▣
Agri-environment schemes	Priority habitats	Conservation management of existing Semi-natural Grassland and re-creation of Semi-natural Grassland on agricultural land	□	▣	▣
Agri-environment schemes	Upland acid	Conversion back to heather moorland	□	▣	▣
Protection	Priority habitats	Designation for conservation and so protected and managed against destruction and degradation	■	■	■
Climate change	All	Species losses; colonisation by novel species; increased openness	□	□	■

* 'All' refers to all Semi-natural Grassland habitats; i.e. Priority habitats and Upland acid.
‡ Future roles to 2050 are predicated on the continuation of current environmental and land use policies.

6.2.5.1 Agricultural improvement

A major process in the history of Semi-natural Grassland has been agricultural improvement to increase livestock production. Improvement has involved actions such as: substantial fertiliser addition (especially inorganic fertilisers); tillage followed by re-seeding with productive grass and legume varieties; drainage; lime addition; hay-cutting replaced by silage; and changes in the season and intensity of grazing and the grazing animal. Hodgson *et al.* (2005) show that, for a particular set of English grasslands, the recent economic climate has encouraged the improvement of pasture. Even taking into account the expenditure on fertilisers and other improvements, the economic yield from improved pasture (£600 ha/yr) was vastly greater than that of any unfertilised Semi-natural Grasslands they analysed (£100–300 ha/yr). Along with the loss of other aspects of traditional grassland management (e.g. shepherding and droving of livestock), intensification has caused declines in plant and animal biodiversity, decreased species richness and increased the domination of fast-growing, productive plants. For example, nitrogen additions over 25 kg/ha/yr have the potential to cause loss of botanical diversity, at least in Neutral Grassland (Mountford *et al.* 1993). This amount is small in comparison to the nitrogen rates routinely used on Improved Grasslands, which can be higher than 250 kg/ha/yr, with more moderate applications still in the range of 100–250 kg/ha/yr (Soffe 2003). As illustrated in **Figure 6.3**, improvement—driven by government incentives and grant aid—is considered to have been the main cause of the loss of upland and lowland Semi-natural Grassland priority habitats since the Second World War. Fuller (1987) calculated figures for the change in the area of permanent pasture in England and Wales that received nitrogen fertilisers from

Table 6.10 Average transitions of Semi-natural Grasslands to other land uses and ecosystems in the Western South Downs between 1971 and 1991. Source: based on data from Burnside *et al.* (2003). Reproduced with permission from Cambridge University Press.

Ecosystem or land use	% of Semi-natural Grasslands converted	
	1971–1981	1981–1991
Semi-natural Grassland (% remaining as Semi-natural Grassland)	48	36
Arable	40	39
Wooded and plantation	6	14
Scrub	5	7
Buildings and roads	<1	2
Other	<1	2

UK National Ecosystem Assessment: Technical Report

1938 to 1984. In 1938, no fertiliser was applied to permanent pasture, but by 1944, fertiliser was applied to about 15% of permanent pasture; this figure rose to 28% in 1960, 60% in 1971 and 80% in 1984. Today, agricultural improvement is generally no longer a major cause of loss due to the small area of priority habitat Semi-natural Grassland that remains and the protection much of it is afforded (Section 6.2.1.2).

The classic Park Grass Experiment, which began in 1856, illustrates the impacts of agricultural improvement through fertiliser addition and liming (Silvertown *et al.* 2006). Fertilisers increased the availability of nitrogen, phosphorus and potassium in the soil, which, in turn, led to greatly increased hay yields in some plots (Hill & Carey 1997). Increased fertility, along with greater soil acidity (an effect of the nitrogen fertiliser), led to declines in plant species richness. Compared to plots without the addition of nitrogen, fertilising with 50 kg/ha/yr was calculated to lead to a loss of 6.5 plant species per plot over the period of the experiment. Losses in plant diversity seem to have led directly to changes in the invertebrate fauna such as declines in the species richness of leafhoppers and springtails.

Declines in individual species have been linked to certain aspects of agricultural improvement. Grassland bird declines (Section 6.2.4.1) have been attributed to the intensification of agriculture which has substantially reduced the suitability of grassland as a feeding and breeding habitat (Vickery *et al.* 2001). The switch from hay-making to silage has had a strong impact on some species, with earlier cutting dates resulting in nest destruction before the chicks have fledged (e.g. yellow wagtail; Nelson *et al.* 2003) or the loss of important feeding sites during the breeding season (e.g. twite; Raine *et al.* 2009).

Although we state that agricultural intensification is currently a minor driver of Semi-natural Grassland loss

across the UK, it is continuing in certain regions, for example, where traditional forms of management are still carried out. Crofting is a form of land tenure restricted to the north and west of Scotland. Typically, crofts provided a source of subsistence that had to be supplemented by employment away from the croft, and so, they are often clustered together to form townships. Traditionally, croft land was subject to rotational agriculture and hay production for winter feed. Cattle and sheep were kept on common grazing areas and then allowed to graze the croft land in the winter. The small scale of operations, coupled with low fertility, resulted in a low-intensity land use and often high biodiversity in the Neutral and Calcareous Grasslands associated with the croft land. Croft land is, however, subject to many threats. These have not been quantified and so much of the evidence is anecdotal. However, the following changes in agricultural management are ongoing:

- Abandonment of rotational agriculture and loss of fallow grasslands. Surveys of five areas on North and South Uist and Benbecula showed a 60% reduction in survey points under arable cultivation between 1976 and 2009 (Pakeman unpublished).
- A shift to increased cultivation of grass silage and reduction in the area of hay grown.
- A shift from traditional strip cultivation to management of land in large blocks.
- Fencing of individual holdings.
- Increased use of inorganic fertilisers and deep ploughing.
- Increase in the summer grazing of croft land. This appears to have led to a reduction in bumblebees as pollen and nectar sources are grazed away (Redpath *et al.* 2010).
- Complete abandonment of crofting agriculture due to other employment or absentee crofters.

Contributing to these changes is a diminishing and ageing crofting population opting for lower input agriculture. In contrast, drivers for increased intensity of management are also apparent as some individuals are farming full-time using sublet crofts to build a more efficiently sized management unit.

6.2.5.2 Land use change

The post-Second World War impetus to increase arable production and develop the UK's built infrastructure impacted on Semi-Natural Grassland. For priority habitat Semi-natural Grasslands the major process after improvement was conversion to arable (**Figure 6.3**; **Table 6.10**), which was kick-started by the compulsory 'Cultivation Orders' during the Second World War. Today, the Countryside Survey (2007) indicates that there are no major ongoing losses of Semi-natural Grassland to arable land. There were more moderate post-war losses through conversion to forestry, urbanisation and road building (**Table 6.10**), but these have largely ceased. In the uplands, forestry has been a major cause of losses of Acid Grassland (and associated moorland) (Thompson *et al.* 1995). These losses are likely to continue: the Scottish Forestry Strategy aims to increase Scotland's woodland cover from the current 17% to 25% by the second half of the 21st Century and the current indication is that 270,000 ha

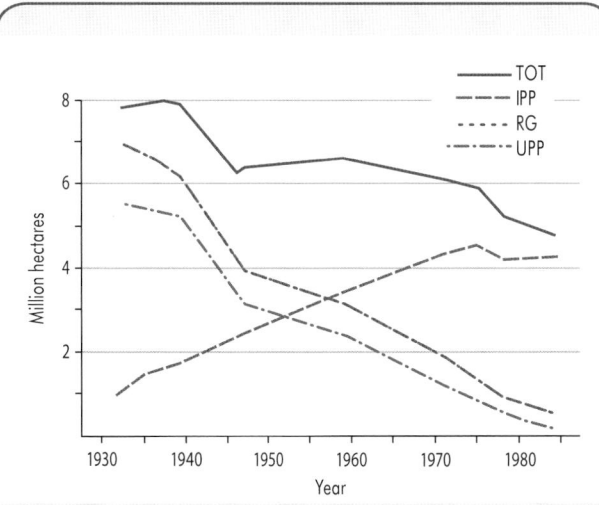

Figure 6.3 The assessment of change in Semi-natural Grassland in England and Wales from 1932 to1984. Using various data sources, the change in Semi-natural Grassland (here, UPP: unimproved permanent pasture; and RG: rough grazing) is explained mostly by the increase in improved pasture (IPP). The loss not explained by improvement—i.e. the decrease in total grassland (TOT)—is mostly due to conversion to arable. Source: Fuller (1987). Copyright (1987), reproduced with permission from Elsevier.

of the 650,000 ha planned will be planted on 'unimproved grassland/bracken' (Forestry Commission 2009).

6.2.5.3 Nutrient deposition and transfer

There is very clear evidence of the effects of atmospheric deposition of nitrogen on Semi-natural Grassland in the UK. Stevens *et al.* (2004) surveyed Great Britain's Acid Grasslands (*Agrostis-Festuca*) across a gradient of nitrogen deposition rates (5–35 kg/ha/yr). Plant species richness showed a negative relationship with nitrogen deposition rate such that the European average nitrogen deposition rate of 17 kg/ha/yr was related with a 23% reduction in species number compared to the lowest deposition rates (5 kg/ha/yr). Maskell *et al.* (2010) carried out a similar study using Countryside Survey 1998 data considering Acid, Neutral and Calcareous Grasslands. Across the whole dataset, plant species richness was negatively related to nitrogen deposition rates for Acid and Neutral Grasslands. The relationship was quite strong in Acid Grasslands and further analysis suggested that the driver was increased soil acidity caused by nitrogen deposition rather than increased fertility. The weaker relationship in Neutral Grasslands was related to the fact that many of these grasslands already have relatively high background soil nutrients. While Calcareous Grassland richness did not relate to nitrogen deposition, species composition did and there was increased representation by species typical of fertile habitats. Using temporal datasets for Acid Grasslands, Duprè *et al.* (2010) found similar nitrogen deposition effects in the UK, Germany and the Netherlands, and showed that these effects have been accumulating since at least the 1930s. It is difficult to predict the future course of changes in Semi-natural Grassland due to nitrogen deposition; it is likely that the major changes have happened already, but ongoing deposition will probably lead to some further change.

Semi-natural Grasslands may also be vulnerable to indirect sources of nutrient enrichment, including runoff from adjacent agricultural holdings, overflow from eutrophicated watercourses, movement of livestock between improved and unimproved pastures, or supplementary feeding (Kirkham 2006); however, these impacts have not been quantified.

6.2.5.4 Inadequate management

The abandonment of low or unproductive land is a major cause of habitat decline across Europe (Strijker 2005). Currently, lowland priority habitat Semi-natural Grasslands are under most threat from inadequate management—generally under-grazing. Only 21% of a sample of non-protected English priority habitat Semi-natural Grasslands was in favourable condition and this was attributed mostly to poor management of the remainder (Hewins *et al.* 2005). Similarly, the low percentages for favourable condition of lowland Semi-natural Grassland SSSIs given in **Table 6.7** are reportedly mostly due to under-grazing (Williams 2006). Under-grazing is a particular issue on Calcareous and Acid Grasslands and purple moor-grass and rush pastures, and results in rank vegetation (such as tor grass, *Brachypodium pinnatum*, on Calcareous Grasslands) and the exclusion of desirable species. Neglect reflects poor financial returns from grazing Semi-natural Grasslands with low productivity, and under-grazing of these habitats is likely to continue into the future because of a lack of funding for conservation grazing. The famous extinction of the large blue butterfly (*Maculinea arion*) in the post-war decades was directly attributable to loss of its niche through under-grazing (Thomas *et al.* 2009); many other warmth-loving invertebrates are also threatened by under-grazing (Thomas *et al.* 1994). The pasqueflower (*Pulsatilla vulgaris*), a perennial herb of Calcareous Grassland in England, declined dramatically during the 18th and 19th Centuries due to the ploughing of its habitat and is now a threatened species. By the 1960s, only 33 populations remained. Since 1968, it has become extinct on 16 sites and has declined on four others; these recent declines have been attributed to a reduction in grazing (Walker *et al.* in prep.).

6.2.5.5 Overgrazing

In contrast, upland acid grassland is under threat (only 23% is in favourable condition) from overgrazing (Williams 2006), particularly through overstocking with sheep. Anderson and Yalden (1981) showed that sheep numbers in an area of the northern Peak District trebled between 1930 and 1976. Of greater concern is the loss of heather moorland

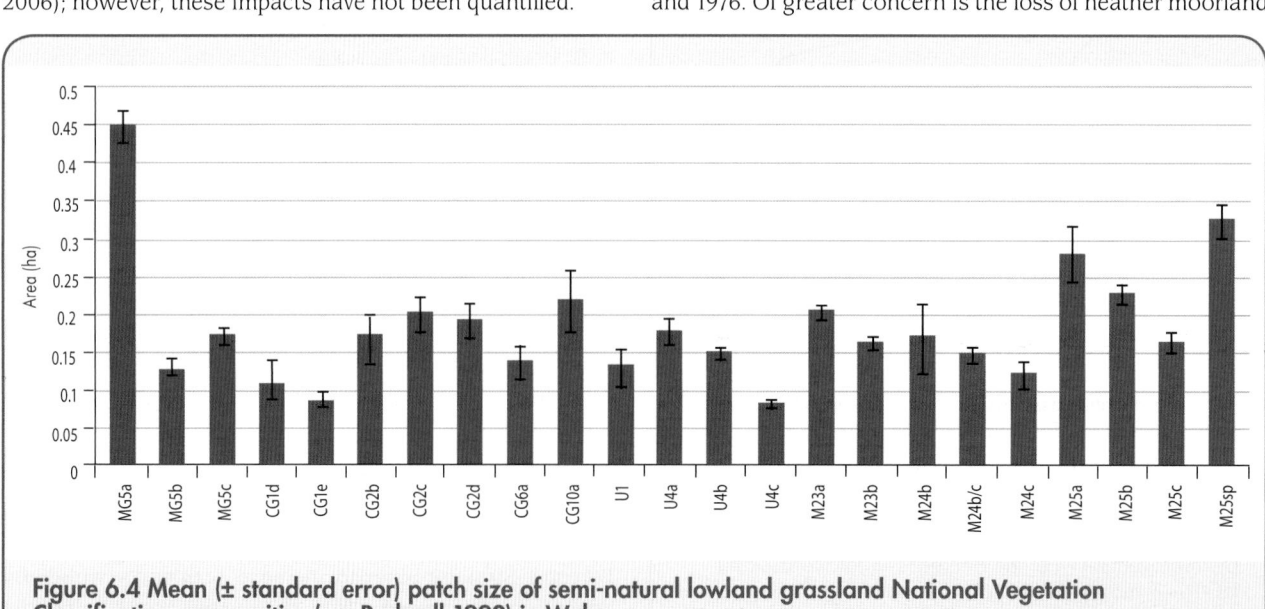

Figure 6.4 Mean (± standard error) patch size of semi-natural lowland grassland National Vegetation Classification communities (see Rodwell 1992) in Wales. Source: data from Stevens *et al.* (2010).

UK National Ecosystem Assessment: Technical Report

through overgrazing, which has caused an increase in the less biodiverse upland acid grassland (Anderson & Yalden 1981); this driver is discussed in more detail in Chapter 5 (Section 5.2.1.1). However, overgrazing has also damaged existing Acid Grassland through the loss of plant species and associated fauna, and the spread of unpalatable plant species such as mat grass (*Nardus stricta*). In addition, the unfavourable status of protected upland calcareous grasslands (again, only 23% are in favourable condition) is mostly due to overgrazing (Williams 2006). In extreme cases, very heavy grazing and trampling can lead to exposure of bare soil and erosion. The Common Agriculture Policy (CAP) reforms are leading to a reduction in livestock numbers in the uplands because payments are no longer linked to production (Chapter 5), thus reducing pressure on upland grasslands, although care will need to be taken that the problems of under-grazing do not now arise as a consequence.

6.2.5.6 Habitat fragmentation

Since the Second World War, Semi-natural Grassland sites have become increasingly fragmented and isolated among intensively managed agricultural land (Burnside *et al.* 2003). As a result, patch sizes of Semi-natural Grasslands, particularly in the lowlands, are now small. Stevens *et al.* (2010) found that mean grassland patch sizes recorded for different grassland NVC communities during the Lowland Grassland Survey of Wales ranged from 0.45 ha for Neutral Grassland MG5a to 0.08 ha for Acid Grassland U4c (**Figure 6.4**).

Table 6.11 provides data on site size of UK BAP priority lowland grassland types from the Natural England inventory. This shows that a high proportion of sites are less than 5 ha in extent. In England, of the sample of 483 non-statutory grassland sites surveyed by Hewins *et al.* (2005), the mean site area was 2.7 ha (range 0.1–10 ha). A study by Cooper *et al.* (1994) found that Semi-natural Grasslands in Northern Ireland were highly fragmented, especially in the lowlands. Mean size of a sample of Semi-natural Grassland field parcels (recorded between 1986 and 1991) ranged from 0.03 ± 0.02 ha (lowland calcareous grassland) to 1.6 ± 0.27 ha (upland species-rich wet grassland). Upland hill pasture, which probably equates to upland acid grassland, however, had a mean size of 2.40 ± 0.54 ha.

Such extreme fragmentation could compromise the long-term conservation of surviving populations of specialist taxa due an 'extinction debt' (Cousins *et al.* 2009). Small and isolated pockets of individuals may become locally extinct during unfavourable conditions and fail to recolonise because there are no populations within dispersal range (Bullock *et al.* 2002). Studies have shown these processes to be important for such iconic Semi-natural Grassland species as the marsh fritillary butterfly (*Euphydryas aurinia*) (Bulman *et al.* 2007) and devil's bit scabious (*Succisa pratensis*) (Soons & Heil 2002). Furthermore, management to reduce the fragmentation of Calcareous Grassland habitat has allowed the recovery of the silver-spotted skipper (*Hesperia comma*) in southern England (Davies *et al.* 2005).

6.2.5.7 Invasion by non-native plants

The spread of undesirable native plants on grassland (e.g. tor grass, mat grass, false oat grass, *Arrhenatherum elatius*, bracken) is a consequence of the drivers described in sections 6.2.5.1–6.2.5.6. Although Calcareous Grasslands can be locally infested by shrubs, such as *Cotoneaster* species, there is little evidence of widespread problems caused by the invasion of non-native plants into Semi-natural Grasslands. Using Countryside Survey 1990 & 1998 data, Maskell *et al.* (2006) found few non-native species in 'infertile grasslands', with 0.09 non-native species per 4 m² plot compared to 0.29 species in 'fertile grasslands'. In general, semi-natural habitats, such as Semi-natural Grassland, bog and moorland, were much less invaded than highly modified habitats, such as crops, Improved Grassland and plantation forestry. Maskell *et al.* (2006) suggest that non-native invasions *per se* will not be a driver of change in Semi-natural Grassland, although they may increase in response to other drivers such as climate change or nitrogen deposition.

6.2.5.8 Habitat protection

Post-Second World War conservation policies have had a huge impact on Semi-natural Grassland, with large areas now protected under a variety of designations (Section 6.2.1.2). While protection may prevent land use change in Semi-natural Grasslands, many are not in favourable condition (Section 6.2.2). However, it seems that the management of protected grasslands is improving, with the high percentages of grasslands recovering from unfavourable condition (Section 6.2.2). Thus, while protection should be maintained and even increased in the future, appropriate management (Section 6.5) is vital to making protection effective.

Table 6.11 Site size classes of BAP priority lowland grassland sites in England. The first figure in each column represents the total number of sites in the inventory. The figure in parentheses represents the sites for which there is greater certainty about the area of priority grassland. The full data will include sites where the area includes other habitats, which inflates the site sizes. For further explanation see Martin *et al.* (2008). Source: data from Natural England (2009b).

UK BAP priority grassland	<5 ha (%)	5–9.99 ha (%)	10–19.99 ha (%)	>20 ha (%)
Lowland calcareous	73 (77)	13 (12)	7 (6)	7 (5)
Lowland meadows	80 (84)	11 (9)	5 (4)	4 (3)
Lowland dry acid grassland	71 (82)	9 (9)	6 (4)	14 (5)
Purple moor-grass and rush pastures	80 (87)	9 (7)	5 (3)	6 (3)
Upland hay meadows	86 (93)	8 (5)	5 (2)	1 (0)

6.2.5.9 Agri-environment schemes

Agri-environment schemes began in the UK in 1987 and large areas of Semi-natural Grassland are now managed under these schemes (Section 6.2.1.3). Current prescriptions which impact Semi-natural Grassland include those targeted at maintaining or restoring the species-rich habitat, but also those focused on maintaining the historic environment, such as water meadows. Much is written about the effectiveness of agri-environment schemes, but the evidence for conservation of Semi-natural Grassland is generally positive. Hewins *et al.* (2005) assessed the condition of about 500 non-SSSI English priority habitat lowland Semi-natural Grasslands and found that those under an agri-environment agreements were twice as likely to be in favourable condition as those outside agreements (27% versus 14%). Considering only grassland under agri-environment schemes, Critchley *et al.* (2004) collated monitoring data for priority habitat lowland Semi-natural Grasslands across the UK. They found that existing high diversity Semi-natural Grasslands were generally maintained well under the schemes, and that there was evidence of some success in restoring diverse grassland on Improved Grassland. It is likely that improved targeting of agreements, and better management strategies and restoration methods will increase the effectiveness of agri-environment schemes in the near future (Anon 2008).

6.2.5.10 Climate change

As with other UK habitats, the direct impacts of climate change on Semi-natural Grassland are currently few, but are likely to become important in the future. For example, projections suggest an altered hydrology (lower rainfall and increased evapotranspiration) in wet grasslands which would negatively affect plant and bird species dependent on a high water table (Thompson *et al.* 2009). The MONARCH study combined analysis of the climate space currently occupied by selected plant and animal species with the climate projections of UKCIP98 for 2020 and 2050 to suggest threats to species of particular UK habitats (Harrison *et al.* 2001; Berry *et al.* 2003). This analysis indicated that the studied species of drought-prone acid grassland (certain acid grasslands found in south-east England), lowland hay meadows and lowland calcareous grassland would be little affected by climate change, while certain species of upland hay meadows, such as globeflower (*Trollius europaeus*) and wood crane's-bill (*Geranium sylvaticum*), may lose climate space. The authors emphasise the uncertainty in both climate projections and in understanding the role of climate in determining species' distributions. Furthermore, the statistical methods used in such 'climate envelope' analyses have been criticised (Beale *et al.* 2008).

It is important, therefore, that recent experimental studies have considered the responses of calcareous Semi-natural Grasslands to climatic manipulations in both the uplands (Buxton, near Sheffield) and the lowlands (Wytham, near Oxford) (Grime *et al.* 2000, 2008). The manipulations comprised elevated winter temperature, summer drought and summer watering. After five years, the lowland site showed increased productivity and large species changes in response to higher temperatures and water availability;

the upland site changed very slowly. Monitoring continues at Buxton and, after 13 years, an analysis has shown that the treatments had little effect on productivity or species. When it was first assessed, the Wytham site had recently reverted from arable cultivation, so the large responses were probably a reflection of the immature state of the vegetation and the presence of fertiliser residues. The Buxton findings suggest that the stable dynamics of unproductive Semi-natural Grassland may mean that the response to climate change will be rather slow, at least in the medium-term (Grime *et al.* 2008).

6.3 Goods and Ecosystem Services from Semi-natural Grassland

The major services provided by Semi-natural Grassland relate to animal production and cultural heritage. These, and other services, are described in **Table 6.12** in categories which are related to the generic UK NEA final services and goods.

6.3.1 Livestock Production

6.3.1.1 Quantity of production

The wide extent of grassland in the UK is the result of the human expansion of this habitat over the centuries to provide grazing and fodder for animal production—meat, dairy products, wool, etc. Modern farming methods were developed to boost production and the consequent improvement activities, such as re-sowing and heavy fertiliser application, have converted much of the Semi-natural Grassland resource to Improved Grassland (Chapter 7, Section 7.1.3). The remaining Semi-natural Grasslands are often still used for animal production, if only to achieve conservation management, but the production is much lower than that on Improved Grassland. Low production is related to the low soil nutrients—particularly phosphorus and nitrogen—compared to Improved Grassland (Janssens *et al.* 1998). For example, Tallowin *et al.* (2005) studied a range of English lowland grasslands, ranging from Semi-natural Grasslands receiving no fertilisers to Improved Grasslands receiving over 400 kg/ha/yr of nitrogen. The most intensive grasslands carried over three times the stocking rate of unfertilised Semi-natural Grasslands. Livestock production on Semi-natural Grasslands must, therefore, be tuned carefully to the specific conditions. For example, the Defra SUSGRAZ project on cattle-grazed, neutral Semi-natural Grassland demonstrated that individual animal growth rates equivalent to those on fertilised grassland (0.8 kg/day) could be achieved, albeit with stocking rates roughly half of those used on the fertilised grassland (Griffith & Tallowin 2007).

Tallowin and Jefferson (1999) carried out an important review of various studies of the agricultural productivity of UK lowland Semi-natural Grassland, which we draw

Table 6.12 The final services and goods provided by Semi-natural Grasslands.

Service Group	Final ecosystem service	Goods and benefits
Provisioning	Livestock: forage for cattle, sheep, etc.	Food (meat, milk), fibre (wool), possibly enhanced quality of meat and milk
	Standing vegetation: biomass crops	Possibly fuel
	Crops: pollination and pest control spillover	Food (crops)
Cultural	Environmental settings: valued species and habitats, agricultural heritage, archaeological heritage, grazing for rare livestock breeds, ecological knowledge, training areas	Physical and psychological health, social cohesion, recreation and tourism, UK research base, UK military training
Regulating	Climate regulation: sequestration and storage of carbon and other greenhouse gases	Avoidance of climate stress
Provisioning	Water quantity: storage of water and recharging of aquifers	Potable water, water for food production, flood protection
	Purification: reduced pollution and storage of pollutants	Clean air, clean water, clean soils
Regulating	Wild species diversity: plant genetic diversity, seed for restoration projects	Genetic resources, bioprospecting, recreation and tourism, ecological knowledge

upon here. The most straightforward measure of grassland production for agriculture is the dry matter yield of cut hay—Tallowin and Jefferson used this measure standardised for a cutting height of about 5 cm above ground level. Hay yield for the first cut in June or July varied greatly across Semi-natural Grasslands, but was between 1.5–6 t/ha. The total annual yield for one or more cuts during the growing season ranged from about 2–8 t/ha. Allowing for losses during haymaking and baling of about 20%, these yields are less than 30% of the dry matter usually obtained from two or more silage cuts on agriculturally improved grassland (ryegrass leys). The addition of inorganic fertilisers to Semi-natural Grassland increases yearly dry matter yields hugely, up to about 10–12 t/ha.

Figure 6.5 Projections of the Macaulay Institute Grazing Management Model for dry matter production of different upland acid grassland types as affected by temperature zone and altitude. The map shows the temperature zones. Source: Armstrong *et al.* (1997). ©1997 British Ecological Society. Reproduced with permission of Blackwell Publishing Ltd.

Crown copyright reproduced with the permission of the controller of HMSO.

Input change	Vegetation type	Other conditions	Impact on annual dry matter production (kg/ha/yr)
Altitude and / or temperature zone varied			Ranges:
	Agrostis-Festuca or Festuca-Agrostis	Temperature zone < 10	1247–4955
	Unburnt Molinia	Temperature zone < 10	1073–2860
	Burnt Molinia	Temperature zone < 10	1073–2860
Altitude increased by 100 m		Adjusted altitude:	Decreases on average by:
	Agrostis-Festuca or Festuca-Agrostis	75–825 m	428
	Unburnt Molinia	75–400 m	166
		400–825 m	144
	Burnt Molinia	75–400 m	231
		400–825 m	202
Temperature Zone increased by 1		Adjusted altitude:	Increases by:
	Agrostis-Festuca or Festuca-Agrostis	75–825 m	348
	Unburnt Molinia	75–400 m	160
		400–825 m	144
	Burnt Molinia	75–400 m	240
		400–825 m	208

The Macaulay Institute Hill Grazing Management Model provides predictions of dry matter yield from various types of upland acid grassland (Armstrong *et al.* 1997a). Yield varies with vegetation type, management, location in the UK (based on temperature zone) and altitude (**Figure 6.5**). The baseline annual yields of 1.5–5 t/ha in the most favourable zones and altitudes are similar to those found by Tallowin and Jefferson (1999) for lowland grasslands. Such annual yields compare poorly with those for reseeded upland grassland, for which the model and empirical studies suggested an average of about 8 t/ha.

The quality of the herbage produced is also important for livestock production. Measured in the laboratory, the digestibility of the organic matter in the hay is a common measure of quality. High content of lignin and structural carbohydrates lowers digestibility and these constituents are generally higher in hay from Semi-natural Grasslands than from Improved Grasslands. Tallowin and Jefferson (1999) report digestibility percentages for lowland Semi-natural Grassland as about 70% for hay cut early in the season (April–May) to about 50% for hay cut later in the season (July–September); this means digestibility is about 20% below that of forage cut for silage from agriculturally improved grassland. Armstrong *et al.* (1997b) report similar values for upland acid grasslands: 48–67% for *Molinia* grassland and 64–72% for *Agrostis-Festuca* grassland, compared to 78% for re-seeded improved grassland. On poor diets, such as those of high fibre content, ruminant livestock become limited by the volume of their guts and the time they can spend feeding. Thus, along with intake and a host of other factors, digestibility has to be taken into account when determining the feed value of Semi-natural Grassland forage and, therefore, the provisioning service of animal production. Tallowin and Jefferson also showed that the mineral (particularly phosphorus and magnesium) and nitrogen content of hay from lowland Semi-natural Grasslands may often be lower than in Improved Grasslands and sub-optimal for the growth and body condition of livestock.

There has been speculation that the secondary metabolites (chemicals which are not essential to a plant's main functions, but are linked with defence against herbivores) of some grassland plants may be efficacious against the gut parasites of livestock (Rook *et al.* 2004). As secondary metabolites vary greatly among species, the greater diversity of plants in Semi-natural Grassland compared to Improved Grassland might enhance parasite control. Athanasiadou and Kyriazakis (2004) examined the evidence for such a process in relation to helminth nematode gut parasites. They concluded that secondary metabolites can have anti-helminthic properties, but that their effectiveness depends on their form and availability. High consumption of secondary metabolites can, however, be harmful to livestock as they have anti-nutritional properties. Indeed, there is considerable evidence that animals learn to avoid plants with high levels of secondary metabolites (Iason & Villalba 2006). Therefore, the balance of harmful and positive effects of plant secondary metabolites is critical and there is a lack of evidence as to how this balance is played out for livestock grazing on Semi-natural Grassland.

6.3.1.2 Quality of production

While the factors described in Section 6.3.1.1 generally lead to a lower quantity of livestock production on Semi-natural Grassland compared to Improved Grassland, the hypothesis that the *quality* of livestock production is higher on Semi-natural Grassland has been receiving attention recently. Quality refers to the nutritional value, taste, appearance and smell of meat and dairy products. A number of studies show that animals fed forage rather than concentrates produce meat which is more attractive to (better taste, appearance and smell), and healthier for (greater concentrations of omega-3 fatty acids), consumers (Wood *et al.* 2007). However, the evidence for such benefits from animals fed on biodiverse grasslands (i.e. Semi-natural Grassland) compared to agriculturally improved grasslands is less clear. Many studies are not well controlled, for example, so the conditions under which livestock develop vastly differ between 'biodiversity' treatments (Wood *et al.* 2007).

Some recent studies have been better designed. Whittington et al. (2006) compared lamb raised on semiimproved grasslands (control), saltmarsh, grass moor and heath. The meat from the control lambs was scored by a panel as having worse taste and odour compared to the semi-natural habitats. The moor and heath lambs had meat with higher amounts of polyunsaturated fatty acids than the other two groups, which may be linked to the improved flavour. A study by the University of Bristol (2008) analysed beef produced from cattle grazing on improved compared to neutral lowland Semi-natural Grassland. In one experiment, cattle produced fatter carcassess on the improved grassland, but the fatty acid composition and quality did not differ between the pasture types. In a second experiment, the cattle on improved pasture had a much higher fat concentration than those on Semi-natural Grassland. In this case, the low fat content of the latter allowed the nutritionally beneficial omega-3 fatty acids to reach higher concentrations. It should be noted that neither of these studies has been published in the peer-reviewed literature.

In a peer-reviewed publication, Fraser et al. (2009) reported a study in the Welsh uplands which compared cattle raised on improved pasture with cattle raised on Moliniadominated rough pasture (i.e. upland acid pasture). In comparison to the rough pasture, the improved pasture carried more than twice the stocking rate, the rate of liveweight gain was about four times higher, and the final carcasses were about 15% heavier. The meat from the rough pasture animals contained less fat, reflecting the lower weight gain. However, the fatty acid composition differed only slightly between pasture types, with a marginally higher proportion of polyunsaturated fats in the animals from rough pasture. A taste panel found no effect of pasture type on meat quality. Therefore, Semi-natural Grasslands may produce better quality meat than Improved Grasslands, but the evidence remains inconsistent.

There is good evidence from France that the taste, aroma and texture of cheeses is affected by the botanical diversity of pasture or forage fed to livestock. This work is summarized in an excellent review by Coulon et al. (2004). Cheeses made by the same process, but using milk from animals grazed on different Semi-natural Grasslands, can differ strongly Broad

19 in taste, aroma and texture. When such comparisons have been made contrasting animals fed hay from Semi-natural Grassland with those fed from agriculturally improved grasslands, the Semi-natural Grassland-derived cheese were less bitter with less rancid odours. It is thought that grassland botanical composition directly affects the sensory characteristics of the resulting cheese through the transfer of plant species-specific chemicals, such as terpenes and carotenes, into the milk, but also indirectly affects it by influencing both the quality and quantity of milk proteins, fats and enzymes, and the diversity of microbes in the milk. These findings, especially the fact that the characteristics of the Semi-natural Grasslands on which animals graze influence the sensory characteristics of the resulting cheeses, provide support for the French terroir movement, which places value on the effects of regional variations in environment and culture on food, wine and other produce.

6.3.2 Cultural Services: Heritage, Recreation, Tourism, Education and Ecological Knowledge

Semi-natural Grasslands are part of the cultural landscape (environmental settings) of the UK.. Most are remnants of traditional farming practices and are the product of thousands of years of human interaction with the landscape and wildlife. Semi-natural Grasslands are both ubiquitous and important throughout the UK, adding to the complexity and diversity of our landscapes. As well as the prominent, large fields of Semi-natural Grassland, there are numerous smaller patches, often found along streamsides and roadsides, which provide a refuge for many species that have been reduced elsewhere through intensification. The value placed by humans on Semi-natural Grassland species and landscapes can be seen in the conservation designations that are afforded to so much of the grasslands resource in the UK (Section 6.2.1.2).

6.3.2.1 Conservation and heritage

A measure of the cultural value of Semi-natural Grasslands is their provision of habitat for species of conservation interest, such as UK BAP priority species of which there are 1,150 in total. Lowland grassland priority habitats (dry acid and calcareous grasslands, lowland meadows, purple moor-grass and rush pastures) are home to 206 UK BAP species, while upland grassland priority habitats (calcareous grasslands and upland hay meadows) are home to 41. For lowland and upland grasslands respectively, the UK BAP species comprise: 9 and 2 fungi, 24 and 0 lichens and bryophytes, 51 and 13 vascular plants, 86 and 13 invertebrates, 6 and 0 amphibians and reptiles, 23 and 11 birds and 7 and 2 mammals (Webb *et al.* 2009). Many of these species are restricted in their ranges (**Figure 6.6**), emphasising the importance of the grassland habitat. Important species of Semi-natural Grassland include the: date waxcap fungus (*Hygrocybe spadicea*); lady's slipper (*Cypripedium calceolus*), monkey (*Orchis simia*), green-winged (*O. morio*) and greater butterfly (*Platanthera chlorantha*) orchids; pasqueflower; adonis blue (*Lysandra bellargus*), large blue (*Maculinea arion*), marsh fritillary and silver-spotted skipper butterflies; brown-banded carder (*Bombus humilis*),

great yellow (*B. distinguendus*) and large garden (*B. ruderatus*) bumblebees; stone curlew; skylark; chough (*Pyrrhocorax pyrrhocorax*); corn crake (*Crex crex*); and twite. The BAPs for these, and many other, species require the conservation of relevant Semi-natural Grasslands.

As well as their importance in wider conservation planning, Semi-natural Grasslands are also the subject of more focused and local conservation activities. The Grasslands Trust promotes the maintenance and restoration of Semi-natural Grasslands, as well as their use as a local nature resource. The Parish Grasslands Project in the Wye Valley is a 'grass-roots' initiative started by a local group of friends. This project has promoted local interest in Semi-natural Grassland, provided valuable information on the location and status of local grasslands, and given advice to landowners on management and funding sources for the conservation of Semi-natural Grasslands. This initiative, and others like it (Peterken & Tyler 2006), allow a more proactive role for local people in appreciating and caring for natural resources.

6.3.2.2 Recreation and tourism

A Natural England report (Anon 2009) used social research to assess the cultural services derived by people from landscapes. The report is not of great use to this chapter as Improved Grasslands and Semi-natural Grasslands were not well differentiated. However, many of the reported positive attitudes towards particular areas of England (described in terms of 'Joint Character Areas') were related to grasslands or pastoral farming, and thus related to Semi-natural Grasslands. Comments include: "fields of different shapes and sizes" (the Devon Redlands); "chalk downland" (the North Downs); "valley between two sides" (the Eden Valley); "gently rolling hills" (the Yorkshire Wolds); "gently undulating plateau" (the Durham Magnesian Limestone Plateau); and "areas of wildlife importance within grasslands..." (the North Thames Basin).

More direct evidence of public use of Semi-natural Grassland comes from the UK National Parks, which are valued for recreation, greenspace, education, and other services, and which all contain significant areas of Semi-

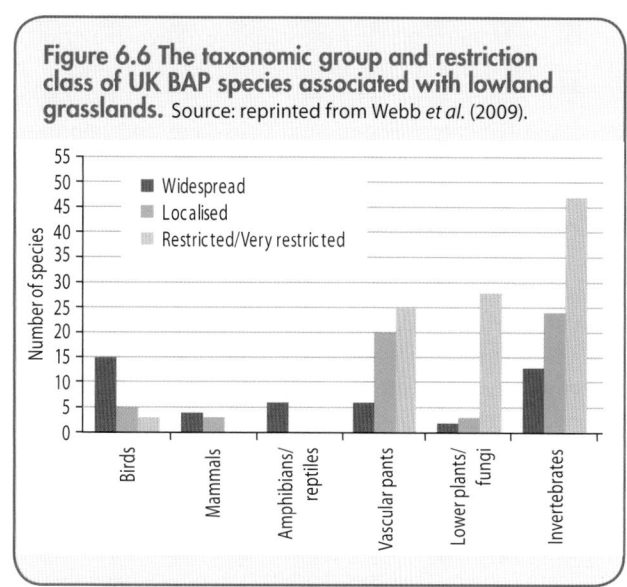

Figure 6.6 The taxonomic group and restriction class of UK BAP species associated with lowland grasslands. Source: reprinted from Webb *et al.* (2009).

natural Grassland. For example, upland and lowland hay meadows contribute greatly to the wildlife, historical and landscape value of the Yorkshire Dales National Park, while species-rich neutral and calcareous grasslands and purple moor-grass and rush pastures are important in the Pembrokeshire Coast National Park. The Marble Arch Caves Global Geopark, which is the first international Geopark and covers the Fermanagh/Cavan border, includes important areas of calcareous grassland and purple moor-grass and rush pasture. There is also significant use by visitors of other Semi-natural Grassland conservation sites. A survey of all 222 English National Nature Reserves (Natural England unpublished) showed that the 41 sites that contained large areas of Semi-natural Grassland each had an average of about 21,000 visitors over a 12-month period during 2006/07.

Calcareous downland is the major habitat of the new South Downs National Park. An unpublished visitor survey of the South Downs took place in 2003 as part of the assessment of the proposal for National Park status (Tourism South East 2003). Of 7,342 people interviewed, more than 90% visited the area to indulge in relaxation or recreation within the South Downs landscape. Allowing for multiple responses, the landscape and scenery was the most cited (73%) aspect of the South Downs that was enjoyed by respondents, and 27% specifically mentioned wildlife as an attraction. Over a 12-month period, the study estimated there were about 35 million visitor days from outside the South Downs and over 4 million visitor days from residents. More than £177 million was spent in the South Downs by these visitors and about 5,200 jobs were supported in this area by visitor spend. If the total trip was considered (i.e. including activities on the way to and from the South Downs), then visitor spend was about £333 million and the jobs that it supported reached over 8,000. To such direct economic gains must be added others such as the physical and psychological benefits of visiting and exercising in the green spaces provided by these and other Semi-natural Grasslands (Barton & Pretty 2010).

6.3.2.3 Archaeological heritage

Scheduled Monuments represent our most valued archaeological sites and monuments, but a large number have been destroyed since the Second World War. English Heritage's Monuments at Risk Initiative (English Heritage 2011) showed that, of the 19,709 Scheduled Monuments in England, only 23% are in optimal condition, and 35% are in grassland habitats (Semi-natural Grassland and Improved Grassland). A survey undertaken in 2004/5 of 1,500 sites on the Northern Ireland Sites and Monuments Record (about 10% of the total number of sites catalogued) found that the 10% which were in Semi-natural Grasslands ('unimproved grassland') had survived well and were in generally good condition, while those in Improved Grassland and Arable had the poorest condition and survival rates (Gormley et al. 2009). In general, the lower the intensity of land use, the higher the chances of survival for archaeological features and the information they contain. Semi-natural Grassland is probably the most benign environment for the preservation of archaeology. Arable cultivation causes features to be degraded or effaced by the physical impact of tillage, chemical fertilisers (which affect metal artefacts), or drainage (which

will cause desiccation of previously waterlogged remains). Direct physical impacts will be less in intensive grassland, but the latter two factors may still apply. Scrub growth on poorly managed grassland can also damage archaeological features. Obviously, once archaeology has been degraded or destroyed, it cannot be replaced. Many distinctive regional features have all but disappeared as a result of post-war intensification and improvement, including: Iron Age 'banjo enclosures'—a form of prehistoric stock corral—which were synonymous with the Wessex chalklands; and the ridge and furrow earthworks produced by medieval agriculture, which were once ubiquitous in the English East Midlands, but are now rare (Anderton & Went 2002).

The UK agri-environment schemes afford protection to monuments. Natural England (2009a) reports that 59% (by area) of English Scheduled Monuments on agricultural land are under agri-environment schemes, and provides evidence that a large proportion of sites under these schemes are showing improved condition. More than 90% of the archaeological sites in Northern Ireland which are specially protected, including by agri-environment schemes, have survived well (Gormley et al. 2009).

6.3.2.4 Ecological knowledge

Semi-natural Grasslands have also probably contributed more than any other ecosystem to the development of the UK's ecological knowledge. During the 20th Century, the UK's ecological pioneers (such as Alexander S. Watt, Sir Arthur G. Tansley) defined the science of ecology and its underpinning theory, often using grassland systems as a focus (Tansley & Adamson 1925; Watt 1947). Semi-natural Grassland in the UK have since been the testing ground for key ecological concepts, of which, the following is a small selection: ecological stability (Silvertown et al. 2006); the productivity-diversity relationship (Hector et al. 1999); the regeneration niche (Grubb 1977); plant strategy theory (Grime 1974); population biology (Sarukhan & Harper 1973); and interaction webs (Muller et al. 1999). This focus on Semi-natural Grasslands is related to their highly dynamic and fluid nature (Section 6.1), which makes them ideal for experimental work, and their extremely high local diversity of plants and animals. Thus, research on Semi-natural Grasslands has been critical to the UK's ecological research reputation, and is an area in which the UK punches above its weight internationally, as evidenced by international comparison of UK research papers in environmental and biological sciences (www.bis.gov.uk/assets/biscore/corporate/migratedd/publications/i/icpruk09v1_4.pdf).

6.3.2.5 Religious and spiritual benefits

Many churchyards and cemeteries comprise Semi-natural Grassland (although many others have been re-sown, or are recent or Improved Grassland) and provide a specific example of the role of these habitats in the religious and spiritual life of people. Many churchyard Semi-natural Grasslands have conservation value as remnants of old meadow and pasture. As such, churchyards can provide important areas for recreation and access to nature, especially in Urban areas (Swanwick et al. 2003; Chapter 10). However, as part of the church estate, churchyards also have an important religious and spiritual role. In an unpublished sermon, Reverend Nigel Cooper of Anglia Ruskin University has developed this theme further. Cooper suggests a churchyard managed to benefit its wildlife, in contrast to those neglected or managed with fertilisers and frequent mowing, is a potent symbol of the Christian gospel: "neither hiding the reality of death, nor defeated by it". In other words, caring for the churchyard's wildlife and experiencing the natural processes of replacement and decay affords a continual reminder of the Christian belief in the resurrection. These spiritual aspects are also reflected in the widespread use of the churchyard as a motif in English literature. Some of these works link aesthetic and spiritual values with the mundane natural world; one of the most famous examples is Thomas Gray's 'Elegy Written in a Country Churchyard'—a meditation on human mortality in which the living wildlife of the churchyard forms an important metaphor.

There is much interest in managing churchyards for biodiversity (Cooper 1995, 1997). Indeed, the Church of England has more than 12,000 churchyards in which biodiversity projects are taking place (Hansard 2010), including the national Living Churchyards and Cemeteries Scheme which is delivered by various county Wildlife Trusts, among others, and the dedicated charity, Caring for God's Acre.

6.3.3 Greenhouse Gases

6.3.3.1 Carbon
The Countryside Survey (2007) reports estimated average carbon stocks for the top 15 cm of soil of Acid and Neutral Grassland broad habitats (**Table 6.13**). Insufficient samples were available to allow a figure to be estimated for Calcareous Grasslands.

While grassland is often perceived as storing little carbon, it should be noted that Acid Grassland is on organo-mineral soils and has the highest carbon stock of any UK broad habitat. The stock for Neutral Grassland is only above that of Improved Grassland (61 t/ha) and Arable and Horticultural land (43 t/ha). The grassland figures can also be compared against other land uses to which Semi-natural Grasslands might be converted: deciduous (66.3 t/ha) or coniferous (73.0 t/ha) woodland, dwarf shrub heath (81.6 t/ha), or bracken (77.1 t/ha). Using the Countryside Survey (Carey et al. 2007) estimates, and accounting for their land cover, Acid and Neutral Grasslands contain 144 Tg and 149 Tg, respectively, of the UK carbon store in the top 15 cm soil layer (Chamberlain et al. 2010). These figures account for 21% of the soil carbon across the Countryside Survey broad habitats. Furthermore, Janssens et al. (2005) produced figures

suggesting that UK grasslands (Semi-natural Grasslands and Improved Grasslands were not differentiated) sequester large amounts of carbon at a rate of 242 ± 1,990 kg/ha/yr, which is higher than that of more slowly growing forests (106 ± 40 kg/ha/yr) and contrasts with a net loss from arable land (-137 ± 103 kg/ha/yr).

It should be emphasised that the Countryside Survey (2007) figures are for the top 15 cm of soil only. The National Soil Resources Institute holds soil data taken to a depth of 1 m, which Bradley et al. (2005) used to estimate carbon content. Unfortunately, these estimates are less precise as to habitat and the general classes used include 'pasture' and 'seminatural' which include Semi-natural Grassland. Respectively, these habitats are estimated to have 16 kg/m^2 and 32 kg/m^2 of carbon in the 1 m depth of soil, and to hold UK-scale stocks of 1,345 Tg and 2,015 Tg. It is difficult to reconcile these data specifically for Semi-natural Grassland.

6.3.3.2 Other greenhouse gases
Most of the greenhouse gas emissions from grasslands will be linked to methane from animals and, therefore, are positively correlated with stocking rates (Soussana et al. 2004), which are lower on Semi-natural Grasslands than on Improved Grasslands (Section 6.3.1.1). Soil methane production is important only in waterlogged systems, and so, is only an issue for a minority of Semi-natural Grasslands such as purple moor-grass and rush pastures, and upland *Molinia* grassland. Few data exist for these wetter grasslands, as most methane work has been done on peatlands, so more research is needed. However, examination of patches of wet grassland within such peatlands has indicated high methane fluxes (McNamara et al. 2008) which suggests other wet grasslands may also produce appreciable quantities of methane. Nitrous oxide emissions are of greater concern and are higher on clay-rich soils and positively correlated with nitrogen fertilisation rates. In unimproved Semi-natural Grasslands, an assessment quantified production rates of nitrous oxide at 1–10% of total current day nitrogen deposition and equivalent to 1–2 kg nitrogen/ha/yr (Curtis et al. 2006).

6.3.3.3 Trends and drivers for greenhouse gases
The Countryside Survey provides information on carbon stocks in the top 15 cm of soils from 1978 to 2007; these data suggest no consistent change in carbon stocks in either Neutral or Acid Grassland broad habitats (Chamberlain et al. 2010). Over a similar period (1978 to 2003), Bellamy et al. (2005) report losses in grassland carbon from a large number of samples across England and Wales, also taken from a 15 cm soil depth. It is not possible to extract figures for Semi-natural Grassland carbon loss from the latter study. The cause of the differences between the studies is not clear, although there is some debate about the statistical analysis in the Bellamy study (Potts et al. 2009).

Increased soil nutrients in Semi-natural Grassland due to agricultural improvement or nitrogen deposition might be expected to affect soil carbon, but effects on soil chemical processes are complex. There are very few projects which study soil carbon in grasslands under simulated nitrogen deposition. Long-term nitrogen addition over a period of 12 years had no effect on soil carbon stocks in a mid-Wales Acid

Table 6.13 UK Semi-natural Grassland carbon stocks estimated in the Countryside Survey 2007.
Source: data from Carey et al. (2007). Countryside Survey data owned by NERC – Centre for Ecology & Hydrology.

Grassland broad habitat	Soil carbon concentration (0–15 cm depth)	Soil carbon stock (0–15 cm depth)
Neutral	61.9 g/kg	62.4 t/ha
Acid	208.2 g/kg	82.3 t/ha

Grassland at Pwllpeiran (UKREATE 2009). Fertilising *per se* can increase carbon sequestration in grasslands through greater plant production (Conant *et al.* 2001; Jones *et al.* 2006), but the lower carbon storage reported in the Countryside Survey (2007) for Improved Grasslands compared to Semi-natural Grasslands (Section 6.3.1.3) indicates that other activities, such as re-sowing, more than counteract this effect. In the Park Grass experiment, the increasing acidity in some nitrogen-fertilised plots led to increases in soil carbon, but, in general, there were few effects of fertilising on carbon sequestration (Hopkins *et al.* 2009).

Considering other greenhouse gases, adding nitrogen stimulates nitrous oxide emissions (Conant *et al.* 2005). In addition, soils associated with semi-natural dry grassland have a relatively high fungus to bacterial biomass ratio compared to those of improved grasslands (Bardgett & McAlister 1999), which may be linked to other ecosystem properties; for example, fungus-rich soils appear to retain nitrogen more effectively (Gordon *et al.* 2008). However, studies are needed to assess the totality of grassland management impacts on greenhouse gases. A study on the Northern Great Plains in the USA calculated the 'Global Warming Potential' of grassland management practices by calculating carbon dioxide emissions associated with fertiliser production and use, methane production from grazing cattle, soil organic carbon changes, and fluxes of methane and nitrous oxide (Leibig *et al.* 2010). It found that native grassland with moderate stocking rates acted as a net sink of greenhouse gases, while heavily grazed, agriculturally improved grassland was a net source of greenhouse gases.

Liming has been widely used to increase productivity in acidic grasslands, with the greatest use (supported in some countries by agricultural subsidies) occurring during the middle of the 20th Century. Because decomposition rates in many upland soils are constrained by acidity, increases in pH due to liming consistently lead to accelerated carbon turnover, carbon dioxide production and carbon export (Andersson & Nilsson 2001; Rangel-Castro *et al.* 2004). Increased pH may also increase nitrous oxide losses (Yamulki *et al.* 1997). Although liming has become less prevalent since the mid-20th Century, historical liming is likely to have residual effects on soil acidity.

6.3.4 Pollination and Pest Control

Because they support more species and a greater abundance of animals than Improved Grassland or Arable and Horticultural land (Cole *et al.* 2002), and are often positioned within farmed areas, Semi-natural Grasslands have the potential to provide services for farming, in particular, pollination and pest control. It is suggested that both services should be delivered by the spread from Semi-natural Grassland to farmed land of species which pollinate crops or which attack pests—so-called 'spillover'.

Globally, there is some evidence of spillover of pollinators (Ricketts *et al.* 2008), and in mainland Europe the abundance and species-richness of bees, butterflies or hoverflies in arable fields has been shown to be related to the distance of the fields from Semi-natural Grasslands (Ockinger & Smith 2007; Jauker *et al.* 2009). Ricketts *et al.* (2008) report a UK study which showed that the proximity of field bean (*Vicia faba*)

crops to 'natural habitat' influenced pollination within the crops by native bees. The distance that the crops needed to be from natural habitat in order for the measures of pollination to decline by 50% was about 1.4 km for pollinator species-richness and 900 m for visitation rate by pollinators to flowers.

Comparing data from before and after 1980, Biesmeijer *et al.* (2006) reported widespread declines in the species-richness of British bee faunas, but did not find the same pattern for hoverflies. Individual bumblebee species have also declined; Williams (1982) reported that, by the 1980s, only six of Britain's 19 native (true) bumblebee species remained throughout their pre-1960s ranges. Goulson *et al.* (2005) attributed bumblebee declines directly to the loss of Semi-natural Grassland over the 20th Century. Carvell *et al.* (2006) provided evidence for this link by detailing the diminution of the range and local-scale frequency of the principal forage plants of British bumblebees. The plants which showed notable declines were all from Semi-natural Grassland: knapweed (*Centaurea nigra*), meadow vetchling (*Lathyrus pratensis*), oxeye daisy (*Leucanthemum vulgare*), bird's-foot-trefoil (*Lotus corniculatus*), yellow rattle (*Rhinanthus minor*) and red clover (*Trifolium pratense*).

Spillover of natural enemies of pests has been little studied. While there is good evidence for positive effects on predators of habitat enhancement within crop fields, such as wildflower strips (Landis *et al.* 2000; Haenke *et al.* 2009), there is little evidence for the effect of nearby semi-natural habitats.

There is some evidence for declines in pest control services that have been caused by Semi-natural Grassland losses. The Carabid Recording Scheme (but note that not all carabids are predatory), summarised by the JNCC (1997), suggests that 134 of 251 species for which there are sufficient data declined in British range size between the 1960s and 1980s (only 20 species increased). Kotze and O'Hara (2003) show that the greatest declines, in terms of decreasing range sizes, of carabid beetles in northern Europe are of those species associated with open or grassland habitats.

6.3.5 Genetic Resources: Plant Wild Relatives and Rare Breeds

The plants sown to improve grasslands for agricultural production are derived from some of the species of traditional pastures and meadows. From an early date, native grassland species were subjected to selective breeding, which led to a trade in improved cultivars. For example, perennial ryegrass (*Lolium perenne*) and white clover (*Trifolium perenne*) cultivars were available commercially from the 18th Century onwards, and were sown widely. There has been no bio-prospecting in UK Semi-natural Grasslands for new pasture plant species for a very long time. Current plant breeding tends to explore the genomic potential of these long-cultivated varieties, such as a project at Aberystwyth University to develop a physical map of the perennial ryegrass genome. 'Xenogenomics' examines the genomics of non-agricultural grassland species which are well adapted to certain environmental stressors, such as drought or salinity, thus exploring their potential contribution to further breeding of pasture plant varieties (John *et al.* 2005); but this idea is not being explored in the UK.

In the UK, many traditional garden plants have been sourced from Semi-natural Grassland, for example: bugle (*Ajuga reptans*), clustered bellflower (*Campanula glomerata*), greater knapweed (*Centaurea scabiosa*), viper's-bugloss (*Echium vulgare*) and ragged-robin (*Silene flos-cuculi*). Domestic Semi-natural Grassland no longer benefits the horticulture trade as the UK's novel garden plants are now sourced from other countries (Dehnen-Schmutz *et al.* 2007). However, a significant amount of seed is sourced from Semi-natural Grasslands for use in creating species-rich grasslands under agri-environment schemes and other conservation initiatives. Natural England's GENESIS database indicates that, of the 2,486 current (April 2010) Higher Level Stewardship agreements (under the English agri-environment scheme) which involve the maintenance, restoration or creation of species-rich grassland, 421 receive a supplement for using native seed sourced from Semi-natural Grassland. There is also a significant trade in seed for such projects, sourced by seed merchants from Semi-natural Grasslands, although figures are not available.

Rare or traditional livestock breeds are often associated with Semi-natural Grassland. It is often suggested that these breeds, which date from times of less intensive farming, are more useful than modern breeds for managing this habitat (The Rare Breeds Survival Trust, www.rbst.org.uk) as they are better adapted to rough grazing and more able to utilise the poorer quality forage. There is little evidence to support this contention, prompting a call for more research (Anon 2006). The few studies that have been published have found little difference in performance between traditional and modern cattle breeds grazing on Semi-natural Grassland (Isselstein *et al.* 2007; Fraser *et al.* 2009). Recently, the Defra-funded BEFORBIO project found that commercial Simmental x Hereford Friesian and traditional North Devon cattle had similar grazing behaviours and effects on Semi-natural Grassland botanical composition. Indeed, rare breeds perform well on improved pasture and many Semi-natural Grasslands are grazed with modern breeds. It is probably more accurate to suggest that the use of rare breeds for grazing of Semi-natural Grassland can provide dual benefits for conservation of the breed and the habitat, but not that one is essential to the other. Rare breeds themselves are valued as providing aesthetic, cultural and historical benefits, as well as genetic resources for future breeding programmes (Anon 2006).

6.3.6 Water Quantity and Quality

Information about the impact of Semi-natural Grassland on water quantity and quality is generally in relation to alternative land uses. Water storage is less than under more woody vegetation, such as trees (Weatherhead & Howden 2009) or even bracken (Williams *et al.* 1987). Conversely, conversion to intensive grazing and the resulting compaction of the soil causes decreased infiltration and increased runoff, which both increases the risk of flooding and reduces the recharging of aquifers (Weatherhead & Howden 2009). Measures of streamwater quality in upland and lowland Britain across gradients from low-intensity grassland to arable and intensive livestock pastures show higher concentrations of polluting nutrients derived from agriculture, such as nitrogen

and phosphorous, in the more intensive landscapes (Jarvie *et al.* 2008, 2010). Water pollution is a result of a number of processes including soil erosion, fertiliser inputs and contamination from manure and slurry. These studies suggest the lower intensity management of Semi-natural Grassland is critical in maintaining water quality and quantity. Phoenix *et al.* (2008) also showed that Semi-natural Grassland soils are able to store significant amounts of deposited nitrogen, which would reduce the pollution of groundwater. Within the Peak District, Calcareous Grasslands accumulated up to 89% of deposited nitrogen, while Acid Grasslands stored up to 38%. These results suggest the need for more research into the role of Semi-natural Grassland vegetation and soils in ameliorating water quality.

6.3.7 Soil Structure and Pollution

Soil compaction in grasslands is caused by high stocking rates, winter grazing and the use of heavy machinery. A recent review for Defra (Anon 2007) showed that compaction can decrease water infiltration and increase runoff, increase emissions of nitrous oxide and ammonia, decrease uptake of methane, reduce the abundance of soil fauna, decrease plant growth and yield, and limit food availability for some birds. Agricultural intensification is generally to blame for increased soil compaction—including increased wheel loads of farm machinery and higher stocking rates—and so will be less of a problem on Semi-natural Grassland than on Improved Grassland. However, where soil compaction does occur on Semi-natural Grassland, it can cause long-term changes in plant growth and composition (Hirst *et al.* 2003).

As in most UK ecosystems, heavy metal concentrations in Semi-natural Grassland soils are elevated above their pre-industrial levels. However, atmospheric heavy metal pollution has declined in recent years and the Countryside Survey (2007) assessed whether this was reflected in declines in soil concentrations between 1998 and 2007. It found that concentrations of heavy metals in Semi-natural Grassland (Neutral and Acid Grassland broad habitats) remained elevated and unchanged in Acid Grassland. In Neutral Grassland, there were significant declines in concentrations of chromium, zinc and nickel, while cadmium, copper and lead were unchanged.

6.3.8 Biomass Cropping

While plant biomass for fuels is generally considered in terms of planted crops, it has been suggested that hay from Semi-natural Grasslands might provide an alternative source of fuel which does not monopolise cropland. No studies relevant to Semi-natural Grassland have taken place in the UK and so figures for costs or potential production are not available; but Tilman *et al.* (2006) showed that a high diversity prairie grassland in the USA could produce reasonable biomass for fuel with low fertiliser inputs.

6.3.9 Military Use

Large areas of Semi-natural Grassland are owned, leased and used for training by the Ministry of Defence (MOD). A submission to the UK NEA by the Defence Estates reports that the Salisbury Plain Defence Training Estate is the largest (38,000 ha) and most important training area in the UK. Because of the nature of the terrain (resilient chalk soils), it is the only site in the UK where extensive armoured manoeuvre training can be undertaken. The majority of the Salisbury Plain Estate is Semi-natural Grassland (56%) and is used for the principal training activities including live firing and other training facilities for armoured vehicles, artillery, engineers, infantry and aircraft, and cross-country driver training. During the 2009/10 financial year, 740,560 personnel training days were spent on the estate; in 2008/9, this figure was 803,361, and in 2007/8, it was 858,347. It should also be pointed out that the Defence Estates carries out extensive conservation activities on this internationally important area of chalk grassland.

6.4 Trade-offs and Synergies Among Goods Ecosystem and Services

The fundamental trade-off in Semi-natural Grassland is the tension between production and many of the other services. Increased production from Semi-natural Grassland has been at the expense of biodiversity, cultural heritage, increased greenhouse gas production, water pollution, and many other negative effects. These impacts arise through decreased biodiversity and compromised soil and hydrological processes following agricultural improvement. However, the straightforward nature of the trade-offs suggests the potential for maintenance and restoration of Semi-natural Grasslands to provide a *range* of services which are not well provided by Improved Grasslands.

In **Table 6.14** we list possible trade-offs and synergies in services from Semi-natural Grassland. Many of these are simply our judgement as there are few data to test the suggested relationships. In the following sections, we describe in more detail the relationships for which there are critical data. Biodiversity—generally plant species richness—is often the process through which relationships are formed, so **Table 6.14** also links biodiversity to these services. To avoid confusion we consider only *direct relationships* between services.

It should be noted that biomass cropping from Semi-natural Grassland may be a future use which could impact positively on many services and biodiversity if it is not accompanied by intensive management to increase production (Tilman *et al.* 2006). However, the outcomes would depend on the precise management used and its compatibility with the traditional management needed to maintain biodiverse grasslands (Ceotto 2008). Clearly, biomass cropping is incompatible with grazing. There are many unknowns concerning biomass cropping of Semi-natural Grassland, so we will not consider it further here.

Table 6.14 Suggested direct relationships between major ecosystem services of Semi-natural Grassland. + positive, — negative, 0 no relationship. Biodiversity (plant species richness) is included to illustrate its important role in many services. In each case, the relationship is one of cause and effect (hence the focus on a direct relationship); the cause is the column title and the affected service is in the row. Unfilled cells indicate that no direct relationship is expected.

Cause / Effect	Rare breeds	Plant wild relatives	Pollination	Pest control	Livestock production quantity	Livestock production quality	Greenhouse gas storage	Water quality	Water flow	Soil structure	Biodiversity
Cultural services	+	+	+		—	+					+
Rare breeds					—						0
Plant wild relatives					—						+
Pollination					—						+
Pest control					—						0
Livestock production quantity	0					—				+	+
Livestock production quality	0				—						+
Greenhouse gas storage, etc.					—/0					+	+
Water quality					—					+	+
Water flow					—					+	
Soil structure					—						
Biodiversity	0		+		—					+	

6.4.1 The Effects of Livestock Production on Other Services

Grazing is important to maintain many Semi-natural Grasslands. Inadequate grazing can cause the loss of the Semi-natural Grassland habitat (Section 6.2.5.4). Here, we take the need for grazing as read and consider the impacts of actions to increase livestock production on grazed grasslands. Excess stocking impacts are considered in Section 6.2.5.5. As described earlier, agricultural improvement to increase production negatively impacts plant biodiversity (Section 6.2.5.1) and associated services, pollination, pest control (Section 6.3.4), and wild relative diversity. Rare breeds have become so as they are not perceived as suited to modern production livestock systems (Section 6.3.5). Linked to this is the possible higher fat content and so lower quality of intensively produced meat (Section 6.3.1). Section 6.3.2 suggested that landscapes of Improved Grassland have lower cultural value than those with Semi-natural Grassland, in terms of cultural heritage, recreation, archaeology, etc. As described in Section 6.3.3, despite the increased productivity, actions to increase livestock production overall have a negative or no effect on greenhouse gas storage. Chapter 7 describes the major role of intensive agriculture in diminishing air quality (e.g. ozone, ammonia; Chapter 7, Section 7.3.2.2) and water quality (leaching of nitrogen, phosphorus, etc; Chapter 7, Section 7.3.2.2). Finally, there is evidence that practices to intensify agriculture lead to soil compaction, increased runoff and flooding risk, poorer recharging of aquifers, and water pollution (Section 6.3.6; Section 6.3.7).

It should be said that all these trade-offs concern the agricultural improvement of Semi-natural Grassland. Increased production on grasslands maintained as Semi-natural Grassland is difficult to do without such improvement as the Semi-natural Grasslands are the outcome of traditional management optimised for production in a less technological world. Changing stocking densities, grazing season, livestock breed, cutting date, the degree of manuring and other management practices has complex effects on biodiversity depending on the grassland type (Crofts & Jefferson 1999). The impacts on services are neither well-studied nor straightforward.

6.4.2 The Effects of Biodiversity on Ecosystem Services

Higher plant species richness in grasslands, whether in Semi-natural Grassland compared to Improved Grassland, or among Semi-natural Grasslands, is linked to increased pollinator species richness (Carvell 2002; Potts et al. 2003). There may also be a reverse influence, such that declines in pollinators may cause plant losses (Biesmeijer et al. 2005). In contrast, invertebrate predators are more affected by the vegetation structure of grasslands than by plant diversity (Morris 2000). As discussed in Section 6.3.5, there is little evidence for a link between the use of rare livestock breeds and plant biodiversity. More complex plant community composition (functional diversity) and, to some extent, species richness, reduces leaching of inorganic nitrogen from grasslands (Scherer-Lorenzen et al. 2003; Phoenix et al. 2008).

There are many studies which show an effect of increased plant species richness on grassland productivity (Hector et al. 1999). This has caused some confusion because increased soil fertility leads to increased production and decreased plant diversity in grasslands (Thompson et al. 2005). However, if soil fertility is not altered, an increase in plant diversity can cause higher production (such as hay yield), and this effect can persist for many years (Bullock et al. 2007). This may arise because more species lead to a greater efficiency in using energy and other resources and/or because a species-rich community is more likely to contain species which are highly productive. The mechanisms are debated, but the outcome that increased species richness increases production is clear (Hooper et al. 2005). Recently, it has been shown that, in certain circumstances, experimental grasslands with low agricultural inputs and high plant diversity are as productive as high input, low diversity grasslands (Weigelt et al. 2009). In such circumstances, if higher plant diversity increases production, without a change in inputs, this leads to increased carbon sequestration rates (Tilman et al. 2006; Klumpp & Soussana 2009).

Positive effects of plant diversity for soil carbon sequestration have also been reported in USA and European grassland experiments (Fornara & Tilman 2008; Steinbeiss et al. 2008). The mechanisms involved are likely to be highly complex, involving a range of biotic interactions between plants, their symbionts (i.e. mycorrhizal fungi and nitrogen-fixing bacteria), and decomposer organisms whose activities determine the rate of decomposition and, hence, the loss of carbon from soil through respiration and leaching of dissolved organic carbon (Bardgett et al. 2008).

As described in Section 6.3.1, there is also some evidence of increased meat quality from animals grazing on Semi-natural Grassland compared to improved pasture. The evidence is not great and the mechanism seems to relate to slower growth rates in poorer quality pasture than a direct effect of plant richness. We retain this relationship in **Table 6.14**, but it is a poorly tested hypothesis. Section 6.3.1 also presents evidence for the role of Semi-natural Grasslands in determining cheese quality and local character in France; it would be interesting to explore this possibility in the UK.

Evidence is emerging that higher Semi-natural Grassland plant species richness not only increases individual ecosystem services, but is required to maximise a variety of services within a Semi-natural Grassland, such as soil carbon, herbage production, forage quality, and insect richness and abundance (Zavaleta et al. 2010). Thus, ecosystem services might be optimised by a high plant diversity within and among the Semi-natural Grasslands found in a landscape.

6.4.3 Impacts of Other Services and Biodiversity on Cultural Services

As described in Section 6.3.2, we ascribe the cultural heritage value of Semi-natural Grasslands directly to the richness of their flora and fauna, including pollinating bees and butterflies. Rare breeds are considered to provide aesthetic, cultural and historical benefits (Section 6.3.5).

In providing a greenspace for visitors, the wildflower species richness of Semi-natural Grassland may be directly related to the aesthetic appreciation and enjoyment of visitors. A study in Germany showed that non-expert visitors were able to recognise Semi-natural Grasslands with higher plant richness and that their stated aesthetic appreciation of the grasslands increased with plant diversity (Lindemann-Matthies *et al.* 2010). This important study counters suggestions that there is a lack of connection between people's aesthetic appreciation of landscapes and the ecological value of ecosystems. As described in Section 6.3.2.5, it is suggested that the maintenance of biodiversity in churchyards may enhance the resulting spiritual and religious experience of visitors.

6.5 Near-term Options for Sustainable Management

In this Section, we consider options for management to optimise individual ecosystem services. This is done partly to illustrate any conflicts among alternative objectives. However, we end with a consideration of how Semi-natural Grasslands might be managed for multiple services, that is, how they may be 'multifunctional'.

6.5.1 Maintenance of Semi-natural Grassland Biodiversity

Biodiversity of Semi-natural Grassland has effects on cultural values and a range of physical services such as pollination (Section 6.4.2). Maintenance of the Semi-natural Grassland habitat requires extensive (i.e. non-intensive) management such as no or light fertiliser additions (usually manure rather than inorganic fertilisers), traditional grazing or cutting regimes and appropriate seasonal water levels. These traditional farming methods were fine-tuned to the grassland type, the geographic region and the required products (e.g. wool, beef or dairy; hay for winter feed or an extended grazing season; etc.). Alternative extensive management regimes and their impacts on grassland biodiversity are well-researched and described (Crofts & Jefferson 1999, Jefferson 2005). The optimal management varies among different groups of species (Bullock *et al.* 2001). For example, bumblebees are more

abundant in cattle-grazed than in sheep-grazed Calcareous Grassland on the Salisbury Plain, probably because the former activity encourages bumblebee forage plants (Carvell 2002). Indeed, an important aspect of traditional management was the variation in practices from one field or farm to the next and from one year to the next. This would lead to dynamic habitat characteristics which would maintain a high diversity of species. For example, Smith and Jones (1991) showed how historical variation in cutting dates among hay meadows in the Pennines had large effects on the plant species composition. Therefore, a critical aspect of the conservation of Semi-natural Grassland is to allow variation in management practices over space and time, and within a region.

6.5.2 Restoration of Semi-natural Grassland Habitat

Several issues require the Semi-natural Grassland habitat to be expanded in order to conserve its intrinsic biodiversity. Fragmentation of Semi-natural Grasslands into small, isolated sites is a major issue for the persistence of the grassland and the possible local extinction of plants and animals (Section 6.2.5.6). For example, persistence of the marsh fritillary butterfly on purple moor-grass and rush pastures is largely dependent on the connectivity and area size, as well as the quality of the grassland patches (Bulman *et al.* 2007). Climate change is likely to exacerbate these problems as species will need to migrate to track suitable habitat. Therefore, conservation planning requires the restoration of Semi-natural Grassland habitats and the creation of linked networks of Semi-natural Grasslands (e.g. the European Ecological Network and The Wildlife Trusts' 'Living Landscapes'. The UK BAP has ambitious restoration targets for Semi-natural Grassland (**Table 6.15**).

Restoration techniques are well-developed for all types of Semi-natural Grassland, for example, upland (Smith *et al.* 2008) and lowland (Pywell *et al.* 2002) hay meadows, calcareous grasslands (Pywell *et al.* 2002) and purple moor-grass and rush pastures (Tallowin & Smith 2001). Restoration is implemented through various conservation organisations, as well as the national agri-environment schemes. Agri-environment schemes provide detailed prescriptions for habitat restoration and, in some cases, are aiming to target such actions in the regions where environmental outcomes are likely to be greatest (www.naturalengland.org.uk/ourwork/farming/funding/es/hls/targeting/approach.aspx).

Semi-natural Grassland creation is most fruitfully carried out on ex-arable land or improved grassland (Walker *et al.* 2004). Problems to be overcome in such schemes include reducing soil fertility, introducing target species and establishing appropriate management. Residual soil fertility can be addressed through soil stripping (Walker *et al.* 2004), but appropriate grazing or cutting management can also ameliorate the effects (Pywell *et al.* 2002, 2007). However, restoration techniques require further research. Fagan *et al.* (2008) surveyed 40 English Calcareous Grassland restorations and found that even after 60 years restored grasslands were not identical to target ancient grasslands. Indeed, a meta-analysis by Pywell *et al.* (2003) showed that during restorations, generalist and competitive plant species tend to out-perform the Semi-natural Grassland specialists.

Table 6.15 UK BAP targets for restoration of Semi-natural Grassland priority habitats from the Biodiversity Action Reporting System. Source: date from www.ukbap-reporting.org.uk/outcomes/targets.asp . Estimated achieved restorations are given under 2005.

Habitat	UK restoration target (ha)			
	2005	2010	2015	2020
Lowland acid grassland	31	313	597	879
Upland calcareous grassland	0	250	362	0
Lowland calcareous grassland	10	399	789	1,176
Purple moor-grass and rush pasture	260	642	926	1,408
Lowland meadows	1,259	1,736	2,210	2,687
Upland hay meadows	0	25	51	75

6.5.3 Increasing Livestock or Arable Production

Agricultural improvement methods used to optimise livestock production or to convert grassland to arable systems are described in Sections 6.3.1 and 6.4.1. Semi-natural Grasslands can be moderately 'improved' to increase livestock production, but even small increases in fertiliser and other intensive practices leads rapidly to biodiversity loss (Mountford *et al.* 1993; Hodgson *et al.* 2005; Isselstein *et al.* 2005). Issues of food security may increase the pressure to convert Semi-natural Grasslands to increase productivity. Opportunities for improvement on much of the remaining priority habitat Semi-natural Grasslands are probably limited by their topography which includes steep slopes, poor drainage and other such obstacles. However, the potential for improvement remains. A report on the land capability for agriculture in Scotland suggested that climate change may increase the potential for conversion of upland rough grazing to improved agricultural land (Brown *et al.* 2008).

6.5.4 Increasing Biomass Fuel Production

Similarly, requirements for increased biomass fuel might, hypothetically, lead to pressure to destroy Semi-natural Grasslands in order to plant biomass crops such as *Miscanthus* and short rotation willow. However, good quality agricultural land would be the prime focus of such planting (Haughton *et al.* 2009). The potential for harvesting biomass from Semi-natural Grassland (Section 6.3.8) is currently not being considered in the UK.

6.5.5 Enhancing Greenhouse Gas Sequestration and Storage

Increased carbon storage may be achieved simply by the conversion of Semi-natural Grassland to habitats with higher above- and/or below-ground storage potential. Conversion of grassland to forest is often suggested (Dawson & Smith 2007); for example, a desire to increase Scotland's carbon sink is a key driver of the Scottish Forestry Strategy aim to increase Scotland's woodland cover to 25% (Section 6.2.5.2). A less radical approach might involve limited tree planting. For example, the Pontbren Project in mid-Wales involves introducing tree shelterbelts into upland grassland (Marshall *et al.* 2009); here, carbon storage has been enhanced, as along with rainfall infiltration rates. However, tree planting on small, fragmented lowland Semi-natural Grasslands is likely to be less straightforward or desirable.

Several other ideas for the enhancement of carbon storage in temperate grasslands have been mooted, such as the introduction of legumes, irrigation and nitrogen addition to enhance production (Conant *et al.* 2001; Soussana *et al.* 2004). But these ideas are more relevant to Improved Grasslands. Indeed, conversion of Improved Grassland or Arable and Horticultural land to Semi-natural Grassland may be an effective approach to increasing carbon storage (Soussana *et al.* 2004; Ostle *et al.* 2009). A recent study provides support for this idea; restoration activities on an Improved Grassland, which involved sowing a variety of plant species and the cessation of fertiliser applications, increased the rates of soil nitrogen and carbon accumulation (de Deyn *et al.* 2011). In the best treatment, carbon and nitrogen accumulated at 317 kg/ha/yr and 35 kg/ha/yr respectively, compared to net losses of 8 kg carbon/ha/yr and 1 kg nitrogen/ha/yr in the treatment with continued fertiliser addition and no seed-sowing.

A decrease in grazing intensity is also suggested to increase carbon storage, through both decreased carbon removal and lower methane production (Dawson & Smith 2007; Leibig *et al.* 2010). However, given the wide range of mechanisms by which herbivores can influence soil carbon dynamics, it is unsurprising that the effects of grazing on carbon stores and fluxes are highly variable, and depend on the physical properties of soil (e.g. texture and depth), the depth of soil sampling, and the responsiveness of the plant community to grazing (Bardgett & Wardle 2010). While carbon removal associated with animals is relatively minor in low-productivity Semi-natural Grasslands (Allard *et al.* 2007), modelling by Soussana *et al.* (2004) of an upland French grassland suggests that the carbon dioxide sink would be greatest, and methane production associated with the grazing cattle smallest, at low stocking densities. At an Acid Grassland on organic soils in Wales, experimental grazing intensification caused a loss of organic horizon carbon (Emmett unpublished); whereas at a nearby grassland on mineral soils, 12 years of experimental grazing removal did not change soil carbon stocks (Rowe unpublished).

6.5.6 Multiple Services from Semi-natural Grasslands

The agricultural origin of Semi-natural Grasslands presents opportunities for their management to provide multiple services and goods while requiring relatively low energy inputs. In contrast to Improved Grassland and Arable and Horticultural land, Semi-natural Grassland in general: a) stores greater densities of carbon and produces less nitrous oxide (Section 6.3.3); b) has lower stocking densities, resulting in lower methane production; c) allows greater water infiltration rates and enhanced storage, preventing flooding and resulting in less atmospheric (e.g. ammonia and ozone) and water (e.g. nitrogen, phosphorus) pollution (Section 6.3.6; Section 6.3.7). Nutrient cycling also seems to be more efficient in unimproved grasslands (Lovell *et al.* 1995). The current emphasis on production and the relatively low cost of agricultural inputs outweighs these benefits, but increasing energy costs may change the balance and encourage farming to address such issues as energy flows and nutrient cycling as a priority (Pretty 2008).

Conserved and restored Semi-natural Grasslands also have the potential to provide cultural services related to recreation and tourism (Section 6.3.2), especially if rare livestock breeds are used (Section 6.3.5), and pollinator and pest control services for surrounding intensive farmland (although the current evidence for these services from Semi-natural Grassland is extremely limited; Section 6.3.4). As suggested by Lawton *et al.* (2010), this combination of broad services would be best delivered by linked habitat networks (including large-scale restoration) which are better able to maintain Semi-natural Grassland species and which may enhance synergies in cultural benefits and the delivery of physical services (Wardle *et al.* 1997).

References

Anderson, P. & Yalden, D.W. (1981) Increased sheep numbers and the loss of heather moorland in the Peak District, England. *Biological Conservation, 20*, 195–213.

Andersson, S. & Nilsson, S.I. (2001) Influence of pH and temperature on microbial activity, substrate availability of soil-solution bacteria and leaching of dissolved organic carbon in a mor humus. *Soil Biology & Biochemistry, 33*, 1181–1191.

Anderton, M. & Went, D. (2002) Turning the plough: loss of a landscape legacy. *Conservation Bulletin, 42*, March 2002. [online] Available at: <http://www.english-heritage.org.uk/publications/turning-the-plough-loss-of-a-landscape-legacy/turningplough.pdf> [Accessed 10.02.11].

Anon (2006) UK National Action Plan on Farm Animal Genetic Resources. Defra, London. [online] Available at: <http://www.defra.gov.uk/fangr/> [Accessed 09.02.11].

Anon (2007) Scoping study to assess soil compaction affecting upland and lowland grassland in England and Wales. [online] Available at: <http://randd.defra.gov.uk/Default.aspx?Menu=Menu&Module=More&Location=None&ProjectID=14699&FromSearch=Y&Publisher=1&SearchText=bd2304&SortString=ProjectCode&SortOrder=Asc&Paging=10> [Accessed 09.02.11].

Anon (2008) Environmental stewardship review of progress. Defra, London.

Anon (2009) Experiencing landscapes: capturing the cultural services and experiential qualities of landscape. Natural England Report NECR0124. Natural England, Sheffield.

Armstrong, H.M., Gordon, I.J., Grant, S.A., Hutchings, N.J., Milne, J.A. & Sibbald, A.R. (1997a) A model of the grazing of hill vegetation by sheep in the UK. I. The prediction of vegetation biomass. *Journal of Applied Ecology, 34*, 166–185.

Armstrong, H.M., Gordon, I.J., Hutchings, N.J., Illius, A.W., Milne, J.A. & Sibbald, A.R. (1997b) A model of the grazing of hill vegetation by sheep in the UK. II. The prediction of offtake by sheep. *Journal of Applied Ecology, 34*, 186–207.

Athanasiadou, S. & Kyriazakis, I. (2004) Plant secondary metabolites: antiparasitic effects and their role in ruminant production systems. *Proceedings of the Nutrition Society, 63*, 631–639.

Baines, D. (1988) The effects of improvement of upland, marginal grasslands on the distribution and density of breeding wading birds (Charadriiformes). *Biological Conservation, 45*, 221–236.

Bardgett, R.D. & McAlister, E. (1999) The measurement of soil fungal : bacterial biomass ratios as an indicator of ecosystem self-regulation in temperate meadow grasslands. *Biology and Fertility of Soils, 29*, 282–290.

Bardgett, R.D., Freeman, C. & Ostle, N.J. (2008) Microbial contributions to climate change through carbon-cycle feedbacks. *The ISME Journal, 2*, 805–814.

Bardgett, R.D. & Wardle, D.A. (2010) Aboveground-Belowground Linkages: Biotic Interactions, Ecosystem Processes and Global Change. Oxford University Press, Oxford.

BARS (Biodiversity Action Reporting System) (2008) [online] Available at: <http://www.ukbap-reporting.org.uk/status/uk.asp> [Accessed 02.02.11].

Barton, J. & Pretty, J. (2010) What is the best dose of nature and green exercise for improving mental health? A multi-study analysis. *Environmental Science and Technology, 44*, 3947-3955.

Beale, C.M., Lennon, J.J. & Gimona, A. (2008) Opening the climate envelope reveals no macroscale associations with climate in European birds. *Proceedings of the National Academy of Sciences of the United States of America, 105*, 14908–14912.

Bellamy, P.H., Loveland, P.J., Bradley, R.I., Lark, R.M. & Kirk, G.J.D. (2005) Carbon losses from all soils across England and Wales 1978–2003. *Nature, 437*, 245–248.

Bennie, J., Hill, M.O., Baxter, R. & Huntley, B. (2006) Influence of slope and aspect on long-term vegetation change in British chalk grasslands. *Journal of Ecology, 94*, 355–368.

Berry, P.M., Dawson, T.P., Harrison, P.A., Pearson, R. & Butt, N. (2003) The sensitivity and vulnerability of terrestrial habitats and species in Britain and Ireland to climate change. *Journal for Nature Conservation, 11*, 15–23.

Biesmeijer, J.C., Roberts, S.P.M., Reemer, M., Ohlemuller, R., Edwards, M., Peeters, T., Schaffers, A.P., Potts, S.G., Kleukers, R., Thomas, C.D., Settele, J. & Kunin, W.E. (2006) Parallel declines in pollinators and insect-pollinated plants in Britain and the Netherlands. *Science, 313*, 351–354.

Blackstock, T.H., Stevens, D.P. & Howe, E.A. (1996) Biological components of Sites of Special Scientific Interest in Wales. *Biodiversity and Conservation, 5*, 897–920.

Blackstock, T.H., Rimes, C.A., Stevens, D.P., Jefferson, R.G., Robertson, H.J., Mackintosh, J. & Hopkins, J.J. (1999) The extent of semi-natural grassland communities in lowland England and Wales: a review of conservation surveys 1978–96. *Grass and Forage Science, 54*, 1–18.

Blackstock, T.H., Howe, E.A., Stevens, J.P., Burrows, C.R. & Jones, P.S. (2010) Habitats of Wales. A comprehensive field survey 1979–1997. University of Wales Press, Cardiff.

Bradley, R.I., Milne, R., Bell, J., Lilly, A., Jordan, C. & Higgins, A. (2005) A soil carbon and land use database for the United Kingdom. *Soil Use and Management, 21*, 363–369.

Brown, A.F. & Grice, P.V. (2005) Birds in England. T. & A.D. Poyser, London.

Brown, I., Towers, W., Rivington, M., Black, H., Booth, P. & Barrie, D. (2008) The Implications of Climate Change on Land Capability for Agriculture. Macaulay Institute. [online] Available at: <www.programme3.net/LCAREPORTweb.pdf> [Accessed 09.02.11].

Bullock, J.M., Franklin, J., Stevenson, M.J., Silvertown, J., Coulson, S.J., Gregory, S.J. & Tofts, R. (2001) A plant trait analysis of responses to grazing in a long-term experiment. *Journal of Applied Ecology, 38*, 253–267.

Bullock, J.M., Kenward, R.E. & Hails, R. (2002) Dispersal ecology. Blackwell Science, Oxford.

Bullock, J.M., Pywell, R.F. & Walker, K.J. (2007) Long-term enhancement of agricultural production by restoration of biodiversity. *Journal of Applied Ecology, 44*, 6–12.

Bulman, C.R., Wilson, R.J., Holt, A.R., Bravo, L.G., Early, R.I., Warren, M.S. & Thomas, C.D. (2007) Minimum viable metapopulation size, extinction debt, and the conservation of a declining species. *Ecological Applications, 17*, 1460–1473.

Burnside, N.G., Smith, R.F. & Waite, S. (2003) Recent historical land use change on the South Downs, United Kingdom. *Environmental Conservation*, 30, 52–60.

Byrne, C. (1996) Semi-natural grassland communities in Eastern Ireland: classification, conservation and management. PhD thesis, University of Dublin.

Carey, P.D., Wallis, S., Chamberlain, P.M., Cooper, A., Emmett, B.A., Maskell, L.C., McCann, T., Murphy, J., Norton, L.R., Reynolds, B., Scott, W.A., Simpson, I.C., Smart, S.M. & Ullyett, J.M. (2008) Countryside Survey: UK Results from 2007. NERC/Centre for Ecology & Hydrology, 105pp. (CEH Project Number: C03259).

Carvell, C. (2002) Habitat use and conservation of bumblebees (*Bombus* spp.) under different grassland management regimes. *Biological Conservation,* **103**, 33–49.

Carvell, C., Roy, D.B., Smart, S.M., Pywell, R.F., Preston, C.D. & Goulson, D. (2006) Declines in forage availability for bumblebees at a national scale. *Biological Conservation,* **132**, 481–489.

Ceotto, E. (2008) Grasslands for bioenergy production. A review. *Agronomy for Sustainable Development,* **28**, 47–55.

Chamberlain, P.M., Emmett, B.A., Scott, W.A., Black, H.I.J., Hornung, M. & Frogbrook, Z.L. (2010) No change in topsoil carbon levels of Great Britain, 1978–2007. *Biogeosciences Discuss,* **7**, 2267–2311.

Cole, L.J., McCracken, D.I., Dennis, P., Downie, I.S., Griffin, A.L., Foster, G.N., Murphy, K.J. & Waterhouse, T. (2002) Relationships between agricultural management and ecological groups of ground beetles (Coleoptera : Carabidae) on Scottish farmland. *Agriculture Ecosystems & Environment,* **93**, 323–336.

Conant, R.T., Paustian, K. & Elliott, E.T. (2001) Grassland management and conversion into grassland: Effects on soil carbon. *Ecological Applications,* **11**, 343–355.

Conant, R.T., Paustian, K., Del Grosso, S.J. & Parton, W.J. (2005) Nitrogen pools and fluxes in grassland soils sequestering carbon. *Nutrient Cycling in Agroecosystems,* **71**, 239–248.

Cooper, A., McCann, T. & Power, J. (1994) Grassland diversity in relation to field parcel size and management. Fragmentation in Agricultural Landscapes (ed J.W. Dover), pp. 62–70. Proceedings of the third International Association for Landscape Ecology (UK) Conference. IALE, Reading.

Cooper, A., McCann, T. & Rogers, D. (2009) Northern Ireland Countryside Survey 2007: Broad Habitat Change 1998–2007. *Northern Ireland Environment Agency Research and Development Series,* No. 09/06.

Cooper, N.S. (1995) Wildlife in churchyards: plants, animals and their management. Church House Publishing, London.

Cooper, N.S. (1997) A sanctuary for wildlife. *Biologist,* **44**, 417–419.

Coulon, L.B., Delacroix-Buchet, A., Martin, B. & Pirisi, A. (2004) Relationships between ruminant management and sensory characteristics of cheeses: a review. *Lait,* **84**, 221–241.

Countryside Survey (2009) Countryside Survey: England Results from 2007 (published September 2009). NERC/Centre for Ecology & Hydrology, Department for Environment, Food and Rural Affairs, Natural England, pp. 119 (CEH Project Number: C03259).

Cousins, S.A.O. (2009) Extinction debt in fragmented grasslands: paid or not? *Journal of Vegetation Science,* **20**, 3–7.

Critchley, C.N.R., Burke, M.J.W. & Stevens, D.P. (2004) Conservation of lowland semi-natural grasslands in the UK: a review of botanical monitoring results from agri-environment schemes. *Biological Conservation,* **115**, 263–278.

Crofts, A. & Jefferson, R.G. (1999) The lowland grassland management handbook, 2nd edition. English Nature, Peterborough.

Curtis, C.J., Emmett, B.A., Reynolds, B. & Shilland, J. (2006) How important is N_2O production in removing atmospherically deposited nitrogen from UK moorland catchments? *Soil Biology & Biochemistry,* **38**, 2081–2091.

Davies, W. (1936) The grasslands of Wales – a survey. A Survey of the Agricultural and Waste Lands of Wales (ed R.G. Stapledon), pp. 13–107. Faber and Faber, London.

Davies, Z.G., Wilson, R.J., Brereton, T.M. & Thomas, C.D. (2005) The re-expansion and improving status of the silver-spotted skipper butterfly (*Hesperia comma*) in Britain: a metapopulation success story. *Biological Conservation,* **124**, 189–198.

Dawson, J.J.C. & Smith, P. (2007) Carbon losses from soil and its consequences for land-use management. *Science of the Total Environment,* **382**, 165–190.

De Deyn, G.B., Shiel, R.S., Ostle, N.J., McNamara, N.P., Oakley, S., Young, I., Freeman, C., Fenner, N., Quirk, H. & Bardgett, R.D. (2011) Additional carbon sequestration benefits of grassland diversity restoration. *Journal of Applied Ecology,* **48**, 600–608.

Dehnen-Schmutz, K., Touza, J., Perrings, C. & Williamson, M. (2007) The horticultural trade and ornamental plant invasions in Britain. *Conservation Biology,* **21**, 224–231.

Devon Wildlife Trust (1990) Survey of Culm grasslands in Torridge District. Devon Wildlife Trust, Exeter.

Dupré, C., Stevens, C.J., Ranke, T., Bleeker, A., Peppler-Lisbach, C., Gowing, D.J.G., Dise, N.B., Dorland, E., Bobbink, R. & Diekmann, M. (2010) Changes in species richness and composition in European acidic grasslands over the past 70 years: the contribution of cumulative atmospheric nitrogen deposition. *Global Change Biology,* **16**, 344–357.

English Heritage (2011) Scheduled monuments at Risk. [online] Available at: < http://www.english-heritage.org.uk/caring/heritage-at-risk/scheduled-monuments-at-risk/> [Accessed 28.03.11].

English Nature (2003) England's best wildlife and geological sites: The condition of Sites of Special Scientific Interest in England in 2003. English Nature, Peterborough.

Fagan, K.C., Pywell, R.F., Bullock, J.M. & Marrs, R.H. (2008) Do restored calcareous grasslands on former arable fields resemble ancient targets? The effect of time, methods and environment on outcomes. *Journal of Applied Ecology,* **45**, 1293–1303.

Forestry Commission (2009) The Scottish Government's Rationale for Woodland Expansion. Scottish Government. [online] Available at: <www.forestry.gov.uk/pdf/ForestExpansion.pdf/$FILE/ForestExpansion.pdf> [Accessed 09.02.11].

Fornara, D. & Tilman, D. (2008) Plant functional composition influences rates of soil carbon and nitrogen accumulation. *Journal of Ecology,* **9**, 314–322.

Fox, R., Asher, J., Brereton, T., Roy, D. & Warren, M. (2006) The state of Butterflies in Britain and Ireland. Pisces Publications, Newbury.

Fraser, M.D., Davies, D.A., Vale, J.E., Nute, G.R., Hallett, K.G., Richardson, R.I. & Wright, I.A. (2009) Performance and meat quality of native and continental cross steers grazing improved upland pasture or semi-natural rough grazing. *Livestock Science,* **123**, 70–82.

Fuller, R.J., Ward, E., Hird, D. & Brown, A.F. (2002) Declines of ground-nesting birds in two areas of upland farmland in the south Pennines of England. *Bird Study,* **49**, 146–152.

Fuller, R.M. (1987) The changing extent and conservation interest of lowland grasslands in England and Wales – a review of grassland surveys 1930–84. *Biological Conservation,* **40**, 281–300.

Gordon H., Haygarth, P.M. & Bardgett, R.D. (2008) Drying and rewetting effects on soil microbial community composition and nutrient leaching. *Soil Biology and Biochemistry,* **40**, 302–311.

Gormley, S., Donnelly, C., Hartwell, B. & Bell, J. (2009) CAMSAR: a condition and management survey of the archaeological resource in Northern Ireland. Northern Ireland Environment Agency. [online] Available at: <http://www.doeni.gov.uk/niea/camsarreport.pdf > [Accessed 10.02.11].

Goulson, D., Hanley, M.E., Darvill, B., Ellis, J.S. & Knight, M.E. (2005) Causes of rarity in bumblebees. *Biological Conservation,* **122**, 1–8.

Green, B.H. (1990) Agricultural intensification and the loss of habitat, species and amenity in British grasslands: a review of historical change and assessment of future prospects. *Grass and Forage Science,* **45**, 365–372.

Green, R.E. & Griffiths, G.H. (1994) Use of preferred nesting habitat by Stone-curlews *Burhinus oedicnemus* in relation to vegetation structure. *Journal of Zoology,* **233**, 457–471.

Griffith, B.A. & Tallowin, J.R.B (2007) Agronomic value of Biodiverse Grasslands. High Value Grassland: providing biodiversity, a clean environment and premium products. (ed J.J. Hopkins), pp. 225–228. British Grassland Society Occasional Symposium No. 38. British Grassland Society, Cirencester.

Grime, J.P. (1974) Vegetation classification by reference to strategies. *Nature,* **250**, 26–31.

Grime, J.P., Brown, V.K., Thompson, K., Masters, G.J., Hillier, S.H., Clarke, I.P., Askew, A.P., Corker, D. & Kielty, J.P. (2000) The response of two contrasting limestone grasslands to simulated climate change. *Science,* **289**, 762–765.

Grime, J.P., Fridley, J.D., Askew, A.P., Thompson, K., Hodgson, J.G. & Bennett, C.R. (2008) Long-term resistance to simulated climate change in an infertile grassland. *Proceedings of the National Academy of Sciences of the United States of America,* **105**, 10028–10032.

Grubb, P.J. (1977) The maintenance of species richness in plant communities: the importance of the regeneration niche. *Biological Reviews,* **52**, 107–145.

Haenke, S., Scheid, B., Schaefer, M., Tscharntke, T. & Thies, C. (2009) Increasing syrphid fly diversity and density in sown flower strips within simple vs. complex landscapes. *Journal of Applied Ecology,* **46**, 1106–1114.

Hansard (2010) Questions for Short Debate: Biodiversity. 28 July 2010. [online] Available at: <www.publications.parliament.uk/pa/ld201011/ldhansrd/text/100728-0002.htm#10072821000829> [Accessed 09.02.11].

Harrison P.A., Berry P.M. & Dawson T.P. (eds) (2001) Climate change and nature conservation in the Britain and Ireland: modelling natural resource responses to climate change (the MONARCH project). UKCIP Technical Report, Oxford. [online] Available at: <http://www.ukcip.org.uk/index.php?option=com_content&task=view&id=331&Itemid=9> [Accessed 09.02.11].

Haughton, A.J., Bond, A.J., Lovett, A.A., Dockerty, T., Sunnenberg, G., Clark, S.J., Bohan, D.A., Sage, R.B., Mallott, M.D., Mallot, V.E., Cunningham, M.D., Andrew, B., Shield, I.F., Finch, J.W., Turner, M.M. & Karp, A. (2009) A novel, integrated approach to assessing social, economic and environmental implications of changing rural land-use: a case study of perennial biomass crops. *Journal of Applied Ecology,* **46**, 315–322.

Hector, A., Schmid, B., Beierkuhnlein, C., Caldeira, M.C., Diemer, M., Dimitrakopoulos, P.G., Finn, J.A., Freitas, H., Giller, P.S., Good, J., Harris, R., Högberg, P., Huss-Danell, K., Joshi, J., Jumpponen, A., Körner, C., Leadley, P.W., Loreau, M., Minns, A., Mulder, C.P.H., O'Donovan, G., Otway, S.J., Pereira, J.S., Prinz, A., Read, D.J., Scherer-Lorenzen, M., Schulze, E.-D., Siamantziouras, A.-S.D., Spehn, E.M., Terry, A.C., Troumbis, A.Y., Woodward, F.I., Yachi, S. & Lawton, J.H.(1999) Plant diversity and productivity experiments in European grasslands. *Science,* **286**, 1123–1127.

Henderson, I.G., Fuller, R.J., Conway, G.J. & Gough, S.J. (2004) Evidence for declines in populations of grassland-associated birds in marginal upland areas of Britain. *Bird Study,* **51**, 12–19.

Hewins, E.J., Pinches, C., Arnold, J., Lush, M., Robertson, H. & Escott, S. (2005) The condition of lowland BAP priority grasslands: results from a sample survey of non-statutory stands in England. English Nature Research Reports, No 636. English Nature, Peterborough.

Hill, M.O. & Carey, P.D. (1997) Prediction of yield in the Rothamsted Park Grass Experiment by Ellenberg indicator values. *Journal of Vegetation Science,* **8**, 579–586.

Hirst, R.A., Pywell, R.F., Marrs, R.H. & Putwain, P.D. (2003) The resistance of a chalk grassland to disturbance. *Journal of Applied Ecology,* **40**, 368–379.

Hodder, K.H., Bullock, J.M., Buckland, P.C. & Kirby, K.J. (2005) Large herbivores in the wildwood and in modern naturalistic grazing systems. English Nature Research Report 648.

Hodgson, J.G., Montserrat-Marti, G., Tallowin, J., Thompson, K., Diaz, S., Cabido, M., Grime, J.P., Wilson, P.J., Band, S.R., Bogard, A., Cabido, R., Caceres, D., Castro-Diez, P., Ferrer, C., Maestro-Martinez, M., Perez-Rontome, M.C., Charles, M., Cornelissen, J.H.C., Dabbert, S., Perez-Harguindeguy, N., Krimly, T., Sijtsma, F.J., Strijker, D., Vendramini, F., Guerrero-Campo, J., Hynd, A., Jones, G., Romo-Diez, A., Espuny, L.D., Villar-Salvador, P. & Zak, M.R. (2005) How much will it cost to save grassland diversity? *Biological Conservation,* **122**, 263–273.

Hooper, D.U., Chapin III, F.S., Ewel, J.J., Hector, A., Inchausti, P., Lavorel, J.H., Lodge, D.M., Loreau, M., Naeem, S., Schmid, B., Setälä, H., Symstad, A.J., Vandermeer, J. & Wardle, D.A. (2005) Effects of biodiversity on ecosystem functioning: A consensus of current knowledge. *Ecological Monographs,* **75**, 3–35.

Hopkins, D.W., Waite, I.S., McNicol, J.W., Poulton, P.R., Macdonald, A.J. & O'Donnell, A.G. (2009) Soil organic carbon contents in long-term experimental grassland plots in the UK (Palace Leas and Park Grass) have not changed consistently in recent decades. *Global Change Biology,* **15**, 1739–1754.

Iason, G.R. & Villalba, J.J. (2006) Behavioral strategies of mammal herbivores against plant secondary metabolites: The avoidance-tolerance continuum. *Journal of Chemical Ecology,* **32**, 1115–1132.

Isselstein, J., Griffith, B.A., Pradel, P. & Venerus, S. (2007) Effects of livestock breed and grazing intensity on biodiversity and production in grazing systems. 1. Nutritive value of herbage and livestock performance. *Grass and Forage Science,* **62**, 145–158.

Isselstein, J., Jeangros, B. & Pavlu, V. (2005) Agronomic aspects of biodiversity targeted management of temperate grasslands in Europe – A review. *Agronomy Research,* **3**, 139–151.

Janssens, F., Peeters, A., Tallowin, J.R.B., Smith, R.E.N., Bakker, J.P., Bekker, R.M., Verweij, G.L., Fillat, F., Chocarro, C. & Oomes, M.J.M. (1998) Relationship between soil chemical factors and grassland diversity. *Plant and Soil,* **202**, 69–78.

Janssens, I.A., Freibauer, A., Schlamadinger, B., Ceulemans, R., Ciais, P., Dolman, A.J., Heimann, M., Nabuurs, G.J., Smith, P., Valentini, R. & Schulze, E.D. (2005) The carbon budget of terrestrial ecosystems at country-scale – a European case study. *Biogeosciences,* **2**, 15–26.

Jarvie, H.P., Haygarth, P.M., Neal, C., Butler, P., Smith, B., Naden, P.S., Joynes, A., Neal, M., Wickham, H., Armstrong, L., Harman, S. & Palmer-Felgate, E.J. (2008) Stream water chemistry and quality along an upland-lowland rural land-use continuum, south west England. *Journal of Hydrology,* **350**, 215–231.

Jarvie, H.P., Withers, P.J.A., Bowes, M.J., Palmer-Felgate, E.J., Harper, D.M., Wasiak, K., Wasiak, P., Hodgkinson, R.A., Bates, A., Stoate, C., Neal, M., Wickham, H.D., Harman, S.A. & Armstrong, L.K. (2010) Streamwater phosphorus and nitrogen across a gradient in rural-agricultural land use intensity. *Agriculture Ecosystems & Environment,* **135**, 238–252.

Jauker, F., Diekotter, T., Schwarzbach, F. & Wolters, V. (2009) Pollinator dispersal in an agricultural matrix: opposing responses of wild bees and hoverflies to landscape structure and distance from main habitat. *Landscape Ecology,* **24**, 547–555.

Jefferson, R.G. (2005) The conservation management of upland hay meadows in Britain: a review. *Grass and Forage Science,* **60**, 322–331.

JNCC (Joint Nature Conservation Committee) (1997) The Carabid Recording Scheme. [online] Available at: <www.jncc.gov.uk/default.aspx?page=3257&DatasetID=4&type=analysis> [Accessed 09.02.11].

JNCC (Joint Nature Conservation Committee) (2007) Conservation Status Assessment [online] Available at: <http://www.jncc.gov.uk/page-4096> [Accessed 09.02.11].

John, U.P. & Spangenberg, G.C. (2005) Xenogenomics: genomic bioprospecting in indigenous and exotic plants through EST discovery, cDNA microarray-based expression profiling and functional genomics. *Comparative and Functional Genomics,* **6**, 230–235.

Jones, S.K., Rees, R.M., Kosmas, D., Ball, B.C. & Skiba, U.M. (2006) Carbon sequestration in a temperate grassland; management and climatic controls. *Soil Use and Management,* **22**, 132–142.

Kershaw, M. & Cranswick, P.A. (2003) Numbers of wintering waterbirds in Great Britain, 1994/1995–1998/1999: I. Wildfowl and selected waterbirds. *Biological Conservation,* **111**, 91–104.

Kirkham, F.W. (2006) The potential effects of nutrient enrichment in semi-natural lowland grasslands through mixed habitat grazing or supplementary feeding. Scottish Natural Heritage Commissioned Report No 192.

Klumpp, K. & Soussana, J.F. (2009) Using functional traits to predict grassland ecosystem change: a mathematical test of the response-and-effect trait approach. *Global Change Biology,* **15**, 2921–2934.

Kotze, D.J. & O'Hara, R.B. (2003) Species decline – but why? Explanations of carabid beetle (Coleoptera, Carabidae) declines in Europe. *Oecologia,* **135**, 138–148.

Landis D.A., Wratten S.D. & Gurr G.M. (2000) Habitat management to conserve natural enemies of arthropod pests in agriculture. *Annual Review of Entomology,* **45**, 175–201.

Lawton, J.H., Brotherton, P.N.M., Brown, V.K., Elphick, C., Fitter, A.H., Forshaw, J., Haddow, R.W., Hilborne, S., Leafe, R.N., Mace, G.M., Southgate, M.P., Sutherland, W.J., Tew, T.E., Varley, J. & Wynne, G.R. (2010) Making space for nature: a review of England's wildlife sites and ecological network. Defra.

Leibig, M.A., Gross, J.R., Kronberg, S.L. & Phillips, R.L. (2010) Grazing management contributions to net Global Warming Potential: a long-term evaluation in the Northern Great Plains. *Journal of Environmental Quality,* **39**, 799–809.

Lindemann-Matthies, P., Junge, X. & Matthies, D. (2010) The influence of plant diversity on people's perception and aesthetic appreciation of grassland vegetation. *Biological Conservation,* **143**, 195–202.

Lovell, R.D., Jarvis, S.C. & Bardgett, R.D. (1995) Soil microbial biomass and activity in long-term grassland – effects of management changes. *Soil Biology & Biochemistry,* **27**, 969–975.

Mackey, E.C., Shewry, M.C. & Tudor, G.J. (1998) Land Cover Change: Scotland from the 1940s to the 1980s. The Stationery Office, Edinburgh.

Marshall, M.R., Francis, O.J., Frogbrook, Z.L., Jackson, B.M., McIntyre, N., Reynolds, B., Solloway, I., Wheater, H.S. & Chell, J. (2009) The impact of upland land management on flooding: results from an improved pasture hillslope. *Hydrological Processes,* **23**, 464–475.

Martin, D., Alexander, R., Pinches, C.E. & Hurst, A. (2008) Updating and Disseminating England's Grassland Biodiversity Action Plan Priority Habitat Inventories. Final Contract report to NBN Trust and Defra. Natural England, Peterborough.

Maskell, L.C., Firbank, L.G., Thompson, K., Bullock, J.M. & Smart, S.M. (2006) Interactions between non-native plant species and the floristic composition of common habitats. *Journal of Ecology,* **94**, 1052–1060.

Maskell, L.C., Smart, S.M., Bullock, J.M., Thompson, K. & Stevens, C.J. (2010) Nitrogen deposition causes widespread loss of species richness in British habitats. *Global Change Biology.* **16**, 671–679.

McLeod, C.R., Yeo, M., Brown, A.E., Burn, A.J., Hopkins, J.J. & Way, S.F. (eds) (2005) The Habitats Directive: selection of Special Areas of Conservation in the UK. 2nd edition. Joint Nature Conservation Committee, Peterborough. [online] Available at: <www.jncc.gov.uk/SACselection> [Accessed 09.02.11].

McNamara, N.P., Plant, T., Oakley, S., Ward, S., Wood, C. & Ostle, N. (2008) Gully hotspot contribution to landscape methane (CH_4) and carbon dioxide (CO_2) fluxes in a northern peatland. *Science of the Total Environment,* **404**, 354–360.

Morris, M.G. (2000) The effects of structure and its dynamics on the ecology and conservation of arthropods in British grasslands. *Biological Conservation,* **95**, 129–142.

Mountford, J.O., Lakhani, K.H. & Kirkham, F.W. (1993) Experimental assessment of the effects of nitrogen addition under hay-cutting and aftermath grazing on the vegetation of meadows on a Somerset peat moor. *Journal of Applied Ecology,* **30**, 321–332.

Muller, C.B., Adriaanse, I.C.T., Belshaw, R. & Godfray, H.C.J. (1999) The structure of an aphid-parasitoid community. *Journal of Animal Ecology,* **68**, 346–370.

Natural England (2008) State of the Natural Environment 2008. Natural England, Sheffield.

Natural England (2009a) Agri-environment schemes in England 2009. A review of results and effectiveness. Natural

England, Sheffield. [online] Available at: <http://www. naturalengland.org.uk/Images/AE-schemes09_tcm6-14969.pdf> [Accessed 09.02.11].

Natural England (2009b) UK BAP priority habitat inventories version 2.01. Natural England.

Nelson, S.H., Court, I., Vickery, J.A., Watts, P.N. & Bradbury, R.B. (2003) The status and ecology of the yellow wagtail in Britain. *British Wildlife,* **14**, 270–274.

NIEA (Northern Ireland Environment Agency) (2003) A Forward Programme for the Declaration of Area of Special Scientific Interest in Northern Ireland. [online] Available at: <http://www.doeni.gov.uk/niea/a_forward_programme_for_the_declaration_of_assis_in_ni.pdf> [Accessed 09.02.11].

NIEA (Northern Ireland Environment Agency) (2008) The condition of Northern Ireland's Areas of Special Scientific Interest: the Results of the First Condition Assessment Monitoring Cycle 2002–2008. Research and Development Series, No. 08/10.

NIEA (Northern Ireland Environment Agency) (2010) Farmlands and Grasslands. [online] <http://www.ni-environment.gov.uk/biodiversity/habitats-2/farmlands_and_grasslands.htm> [Accessed 09.02.11].

Norton, L.R., Murphy, J., Reynolds, B., Marks, S. & Mackey, E.C. (2009) Countryside Survey: Scotland Results from 2007. NERC/Centre for Ecology & Hydrology, The Scottish Government, Scottish Natural Heritage, 83pp. (CEH Project Number: C03259).

Ockinger, E. & Smith, H.G. (2007) Semi-natural grasslands as population sources for pollinating insects in agricultural landscapes. *Journal of Applied Ecology,* **44**, 50–59.

Ostle, N.J., Levy, P.E., Evans, C.D. & Smith, P. (2009) UK land use and soil carbon sequestration. *Land Use Policy,* **26**, S274–S283.

Peterken, G. & Tyler, S.J. (2006) Flowers in the fields: community conservation in the Lower Wye Valley. *British Wildlife,* **17**, 313–320.

Phoenix, G.K., Johnson, D., Grime, J.P. & Booth, R.E. (2008) Sustaining ecosystem services in ancient limestone grassland: importance of major component plants and community composition. *Journal of Ecology,* **96**, 894–902.

Pigott, C.D. & Walters, S.M. (1954) On the interpretation of the discontinuous distributions shown by certain British species of open habitats. *Journal of Ecology,* **42**, 95–116.

Plantlife (2002) England's Green Unpleasant Land? – Why urgent action is needed to save England's wild flower grasslands. Plantlife, London.

Potts, J.M., Chapman, S.J., Towers, W. & Campbell, C.D. (2009) Comments on 'Baseline values and change in the soil, and implications for monitoring' by RM Lark, PH Bellamy & GJD Kirk. *European Journal of Soil Science,* **60**, 481–483.

Potts, S.G., Vulliamy, B., Dafni, A., Ne'eman, G. & Willmer, P. (2003) Linking bees and flowers: How do floral communities structure pollinator communities? *Ecology,* **84**, 2628–2642.

Preston, C.D., Telfer, M.G., Arnold, H.R., Carey, P.D., Cooper, J.M., Dines, T.D., Pearman, D.A., Roy, D.B. & Smart S.M. (2002) The changing flora of the UK. Department for Environment, Food and Rural Affairs, London.

Preston, C.D., Telfer, M.G., Roy, D.B., Carey, P.D., Hill, M.O., Meek, W.R., Rothery, P., Smart, S.M., Smith, G.M., Walker, K.J. & Pearman, D.A. (2003) The changing distribution of the flora of the United Kingdom: technical report. Centre for Ecology and Hydrology, Huntingdon.

Pretty, J. (2008) Agricultural sustainability: concepts, principles and evidence. *Philosophical Transactions of the Royal Society B-Biological Sciences,* **363**, 447–465.

Pywell, R.F., Bullock, J.M., Hopkins, A., Walker, K.J., Sparks, T.H., Burke, M.J.W. & Peel, S. (2002) Restoration of species-rich grassland on arable land: assessing the limiting processes using a multi-site experiment. *Journal of Applied Ecology,* **39**, 294–309.

Pywell, R.F., Bullock, J.M., Roy, D.B., Warman, E.A., Walker, K.J. & Rothery, P. (2003) Plant traits as predictors of performance in ecological restoration. *Journal of Applied Ecology,* **40**, 65–77.

Pywell, R.F., Bullock, J.M., Tallowin, J.B.R., Walker, K.J., Warman, E.A. & Masters, G.J. (2007) Enhancing diversity of species-poor grasslands: an experimental assessment of multiple constraints. *Journal of Applied Ecology,* **44**, 81–94.

Rackham, O. (1986) The history of the British countryside. Dent & Sons, London.

Raine, A.F., Brown, A.F. Amano, T. & Sutherland, W.J. (2009) Assessing population changes from disparate data sources: the decline of the Twite *Carduelis flavirostris* in England. *Bird Conservation International,* **19**, 1–16.

Rangel-Castro, J.I., Prosser, J.I., Scrimgeour, C.M., Smith, P., Ostle, N., Ineson, P., Meharg, A. & Killham, K. (2004) Carbon flow in an upland grassland: effect of liming on the flux of recently photosynthesized carbon to rhizosphere soil. *Global Change Biology,* **10**, 2100–2108.

Ratcliffe, D.A. (1984) Post-medieval and recent changes in British vegetation: the culmination of human influence. *New Phytologist,* **98**, 73–100.

Redgrave, L. (1995) Berkshire unimproved neutral grassland survey. English Nature unpublished report.

Redpath, N., Osgathorpe, L.M., Park, K. & Goulson, D. (2010) Crofting and bumblebee conservation: The impact of land management practices on bumblebee populations in northwest Scotland. *Biological Conservation,* **143**, 492–500.

Ricketts T.H., Regetz, J., Steffan-Dewenter, I., Cunningham, S.A., Kremen, C., Bogdanski, A., Gemmill-Herren, B., Greenleaf, S.S., Klein, A.M., Mayfield, M.M., Morandin, L.A., Ochieng, A., Potts, S.G. & Viana, B.F. (2008). Landscape effects on crop pollination services: are there general patterns? *Ecology Letters,* **11**, 499–515.

Rodwell, J.S. (ed) (1991) British Plant Communities. Volume 2, Mires and Heaths. Cambridge University Press, Cambridge.

Rodwell, J.S. (ed) (1992) British Plant Communities. Volume 3, Grasslands and Montane Communities. Cambridge University Press, Cambridge.

Rodwell, J.S. (ed) (2000) British Plant Communities. Volume 5, Maritime Communities and Vegetation of Open Habitats. Cambridge University Press, Cambridge.

Rodwell, J.S., Morgan, V., Jefferson, R.G. & Moss, D. (2007) The European Context of British Lowland Grasslands. Joint Nature Conservation Committee Report 394, Peterborough.

Rook, A.J., Dumont, B., Isselstein, J., Osoro, K., WallisDeVries, M.F., Parente, G. & Mills, J. (2004) Matching type of livestock to desired biodiversity outcomes in pastures – a review. *Biological Conservation,* **119**, 137–150.

Sarukhan, J. & Harper, J.L. (1973) Studies on plant demography: *Ranunculus repens* L., *R. bulbosus* L. and *R. acris* L. I. Population flux and survivorship. *Journal of Ecology,* **61**, 675–716.

Scherer-Lorenzen, M., Palmborg, C., Prinz, A. & Schulze, E.D. (2003) The role of plant diversity and composition for nitrate leaching in grasslands. *Ecology,* **84**, 1539–1552.

Silvertown, J., Poulton, P., Johnston, E., Edwards, G., Heard, M. & Biss, P.M. (2006) The Park Grass Experiment 1856–2006: Its contribution to ecology. *Journal of Ecology,* **94**, 801–814.

Smart, S.M., Allen, D., Murphy, J.; Carey, P.D.; Emmett, B.A., Reynolds, B., Simpson, I.C., Evans, R.A., Skates, J., Scott, W.A., Maskell, L.C., Norton, L.R., Rossall, M.J. & Wood, C. (2009) Countryside Survey: Wales Results from 2007. NERC/Centre for Ecology & Hydrology, Welsh Assembly Government, Countryside Council for Wales, 94pp. (CEH Project Number: C03259).

Smith , K.W. (1983) The status and distribution of waders breeding on wet lowland grassland in England and Wales. *Bird Study,* **30**, 177–192.

Smith, R.S. & Jones, L. (1991) The phenology of mesotrophic grassland in the Pennine dales, Northern England: historic hay cutting dates, vegetation variation and plant species phenologies. *Journal of Applied Ecology,* **28**, 42–59.

Smith, R.S., Shiel, R.S., Bardgett, R.D., Millward, D., Corkhill, P., Evans, P., Quirk, H., Hobbs, P.J. & Kometa, S.T. (2008) Long-term change in vegetation and soil microbial communities during the phased restoration of traditional meadow grassland. *Journal of Applied Ecology,* **45**, 670–679.

Soffe, R.J. (ed) (2003) Primrose McConnell's The Agricultural Notebook. 20th edition. Blackwell Science, Oxford.

Soons, M.B. & Heil, G.W. (2002) Reduced colonization capacity in fragmented populations of wind-dispersed grassland forbs. *Journal of Ecology,* **90**, 1033–1043.

Soussana, J.F., Loiseau, P., Vuichard, N., Ceschia, E., Balesdent, J., Chevallier, T. & Arrouays, D. (2004) Carbon cycling and sequestration opportunities in temperate grasslands. *Soil Use and Management,* **20**, 219–230.

Stanbury, A., Branston, T., Sheldrake, P. & Wilson, S. (2000) Breeding Bird Survey of Salisbury Plain Training Area. Unpublished Royal Society for the Protection of Birds report.

Steinbeiss, S., Bessler, H., Engels, C., Temperton, V.M., Buchmann, N., Roscher, C., Kreutziger, Y., Baade, J., Habekost, M. & Gleixner, G. (2008) Plant diversity positively affects short-term soil carbon storage in experimental grasslands. *Global Change Biology,* **14**, 2937–2949.

Stevens, C.J., Dise, N.B., Mountford, J.O. & Gowing, D.J. (2004) Impact of nitrogen deposition on the species richness of grasslands. *Science,* **303**, 1876–1879.

Stevens, D.P., Smith, S.L.N., Blackstock, T.H., Bosanquet, S.D.S. & Stevens, J.P. (2010) Grasslands of Wales: A survey of lowland species-rich grasslands, 1987–2004. University of Wales Press, Cardiff.

Strijker, D. (2005) Marginal lands in Europe – causes of decline. *Basic and Applied Ecology,* **6**, 99–106.

Swanwick, C., Dunnett, N. & Woolley, H. (2003) Nature, role and value of green space in towns and cities: an overview. *Built Environment,* **29**, 94–106.

Tallowin, J.R.B. & Jefferson, R.G. (1999) Hay production from lowland semi-natural grasslands: a review of implications for ruminant livestock systems. *Grass and Forage Science,* **54**, 99–115.

Tallowin, J.R.B. & Smith, R.E.N. (2001) Restoration of a *Cirsio-Molinietum* fen meadow on an agriculturally improved pasture. *Restoration Ecology,* **9**, 167–178.

Tallowin, J.R.B., Smith, R.E.N., Goodyear, J. & Vickery, J.A. (2005) Spatial and structural uniformity of lowland agricultural grassland in England: a context for low biodiversity. *Grass and Forage Science,* **60**, 225–236.

Tansley, A.G. & Adamson, R.S. (1925) Studies of the vegetation of the English chalk.III. The chalk grasslands of the Hampshire-Sussex border. *Journal of Ecology,* **13**, 177–223.

Taylor, I.R. & Grant, M.C. (2004) Long-term trends in the abundance of breeding Lapwing *Vanellus vanellus* in relation to land-use change on upland farmland in southern Scotland. *Bird Study,* **51**, 133–142.

Thirsk, J. (1997) Alternative agriculture: A history from the black death to the present day. Oxford University Press, Oxford.

Thomas, J.A., Morris, M.G. & Hambler, C. (1994) Patterns, mechanisms and rates of extinction among invertebrates in the United Kingdom. *Philosophical Transactions of the Royal Society of London Series B-Biological Sciences,* **344**, 47–54.

Thomas, J.A., Simcox, D.J. & Clarke, R.T. (2009) Successful conservation of a threatened *Maculinea* butterfly. *Science,* **325**, 80–83.

Thompson, D.B.A., MacDonald, A.J., Marsden, J.H. & Galbraith, C.A. (1995) Upland heather moorland in Great Britain: A review of international importance, vegetation change and some objectives for nature conservation. *Biological Conservation,* **71**, 163–178.

Thompson, J.R., Gavin, H., Refsgaard, A., Sorenson, H.R. & Gowing, D.J. (2009) Modelling the hydrological impacts of climate change on UK lowland wet grassland. *Wetlands Ecology and Management,* **17**, 503–523.

Thompson, K., Askew, A.P., Grime, J.P., Dunnett, N.P. & Willis, A.J. (2005) Biodiversity, ecosystem function and plant traits in mature and immature plant communities. *Functional Ecology,* **19**, 355–358.

Tilman, D., Hill, J. & Lehman, C. (2006) Carbon-negative biofuels from low-input high-diversity grassland biomass. *Science,* **314**, 1598–1600.

Tourism South East (2003) Visitor Survey of the Proposed South Downs National Park. Tourism South East. [online] Available at: <www.southdowns.gov.uk/rte.asp?id=92> [Accessed 09.02.11].

UK BAP (UK Biodiversity Action Plan) (2006) UK BAP Targets Review (2006) [online] Available at: <http://www.ukbap. org.uk/BAPGroupPage.aspx?id=98> [Accessed 02.02.11].

UKBD (UK Biodiversity Group) (1999) Tranche 2 Action Plans. Volume VI: Terrestrial and freshwater species and habitats. UKBG/English Nature, Peterborough.

UKREATE (2009) Terrestrial Umbrella: Effects of Eutrophication and Acidification on Terrestrial Ecosystems. CEH Contract Report C03425. Defra Contract No. AQ0802.

University of Bristol (2008) Healthiness and quality of beef produced from traditional and modern breeds reared in species-rich, unimproved grasslands. Defra. [online] Available at: <http://randd.defra.gov.uk/Default.aspx?Menu=Menu&Mo dule=More&Location=None&Completed=0&ProjectID=13134> [Accessed 09.02.11].

Vickery, J.A., Tallowin, J.R., Feber, R.E., Asteraki, E.J., Atkinson, P.W., Fuller, R.J. & Brown, V.K. (2001) The management of lowland neutral grasslands in Britain: effects of agricultural practices on birds and their food resources. *Journal of Applied Ecology,* **38**, 647–664.

Walker, K.J., Pinches, C.E. & Wells, T.C.E. (in prep) Reduced grazing and the decline of the threatened grassland herb *Pulsatilla vulgaris* Mill. (Ranunculaceae) in England, UK.

Walker, K.J., Stevens, P.A., Stevens, D.P., Mountford, J.O., Manchester, S.J. & Pywell, R.F. (2004) The restoration and re-creation of species-rich lowland grassland on land formerly managed for intensive agriculture in the UK. *Biological Conservation,* **119**, 1–18.

Wardle, D.A., Zackrisson, O., Hornberg, G. & Gallet, C. (1997) The influence of island area on ecosystem properties. *Science,* **277**, 1296–1299.

Watt, A.S. (1947) Pattern and process in the plant community. *Journal of Ecology,* **35**, 1–22.

Weatherhead, E.K. & Howden, N.J.K. (2009) The relationship between land use and surface water resources in the UK. *Land Use Policy,* **26**, S243–S250.

Webb, J.R., Drewitt, A.L. & Measures, G.H. (2009) Managing for species: integrating the needs of England's priority species into habitat management. Research Report NERR024. Natural England, Sheffield.

Weigelt, A., Weisser, W.W., Buchmann, N. & Scherer-Lorenzen, M. (2009) Biodiversity for multifunctional grasslands: equal productivity in high-diversity low-input and low-diversity high-input systems. *Biogeosciences,* **6**, 1695–1706.

Whittington, F.M., Dunn, R., Nute, G.R., Richardson, R.I. & Wood, J.D. (2006) Effect of pasture type on lamb product quality. 9th Annual Langford Food Industry Conference. Proceedings of the British Society of Animal Science, pp. 27–31. Bristol, UK.

Williams, A.G., Kent, M. & Ternan, J.L. (1987) Quantity and quality of bracken throughfall, stemflow and litterflow in a Dartmoor catchment. *Journal of Applied Ecology,* **24**, 217–229.

Williams, J.M. (ed) (2006) Common Standards Monitoring for Designated Sites: First six year report. Joint Nature Conservation Committee, Peterborough.

Williams, P.H. (1982) The distribution and decline of British bumblebees (*Bombus* Latr). *Journal of Apicultural Research,* **21**, 236–245.

Wilson, A.M., Vickery, J.A., Brown, A., Langston, R.H.W., Smallshire, D., Wotton, S. & Vanhinsbergh, D. (2005) Changes in the numbers of breeding waders on lowland wet grasslands in England and Wales between 1982 and 2002. *Bird Study,* **52**, 55–69.

Wood, J.D., Richardson, R.I., Scollan, N.D., Hopkins, A., Dunn, R., Buller, H. & Whittington, F.M. (2007) Quality of meat from biodiverse grassland. High Value Grassland (eds J.J. Hopkins, A. J. Duncan, D. I. McCracken, S. Peel & J.R.B. Tallowin), pp. 107–116. British Grassland Society, Cirencester.

Yamulki, S., Harrison, R.M., Goulding, K.W.T. & Webster, C.P. (1997) N_2O, NO and NO_2 fluxes from a grassland: Effect of soil pH. *Soil Biology & Biochemistry,* **29**, 1199–1208.

Zavaleta, E.S., Pasari, J.R., Hulvey, K.B. & Tilman, G.D. (2010) Sustaining multiple ecosystem functions in grassland communities requires higher biodiversity. *Proceedings of the National Academy of Sciences of the United States of America,* **107**, 1443–1446.

Appendix 6.1 Approach Used to Assign Certainty Terms to Chapter Key Findings

This chapter began with a set of Key Findings. Adopting the approach and terminology used by the Intergovernmental Panel on Climate Change (IPCC) and the Millennium Assessment (MA), these Key Findings also include an indication of the level of scientific certainty. The 'uncertainty approach' of the UK NEA consists of a set of qualitative uncertainty terms derived from a 4-box model and complemented, where possible, with a likelihood scale (see below). Estimates of certainty are derived from the collective judgement of authors, observational evidence, modelling results and/or theory examined for this assessment.

Throughout the Key Findings presented at the start of this chapter, superscript numbers and letters indicate the estimated level of certainty for a particular key finding:

1. *Well established:*   high agreement based on significant evidence
2. *Established but incomplete evidence:*   high agreement based on limited evidence
3. *Competing explanations:*   low agreement, albeit with significant evidence
4. *Speculative:*   low agreement based on limited evidence

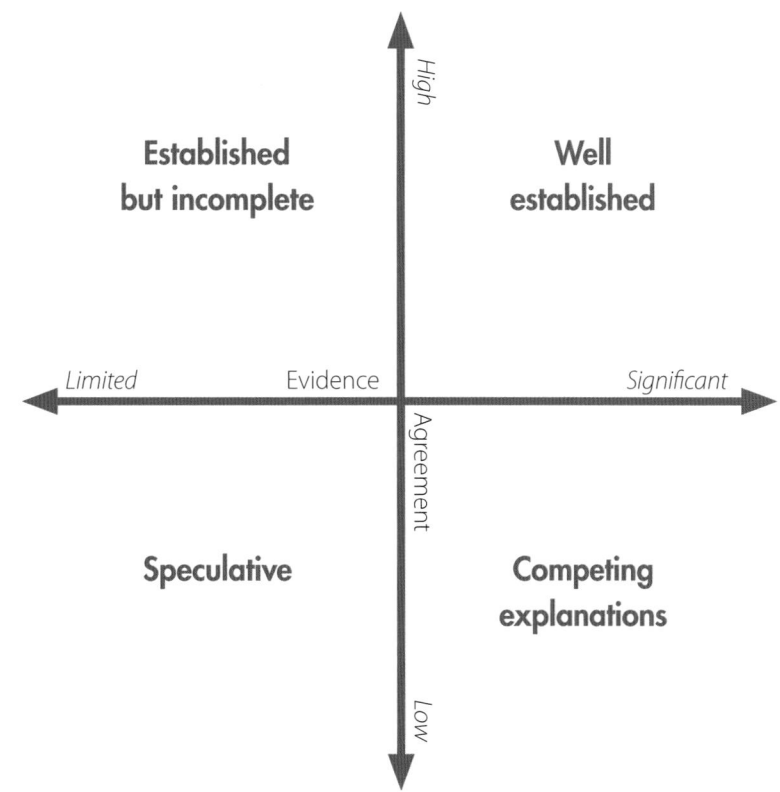

a. *Virtually certain:*   >99% probability of occurrence
b. *Very likely:*   >90% probability
c. *Likely:*   >66% probability
d. *About as likely as not:*   >33–66% probability
e. *Unlikely:*   <33% probability
f. *Very unlikely:*   <10% probability
g. *Exceptionally unlikely:*   <1% probability

Certainty terms 1 to 4 constitute the 4-box model, while *a* to *g* constitute the likelihood scale.

Chapter 7:
Enclosed Farmland

Coordinating Lead Authors: Les Firbank and Richard Bradbury
Lead Authors: Davy McCracken and Chris Stoate
Contributing Authors: Keith Goulding, Ralph Harmer, Tim Hess, Alan Jenkins, Emma Pilgrim, Simon Potts, Pete Smith, Ragab Ragab, Jonathan Storkey and Prysor Williams

Key Findings*

Enclosed Farmland is a vital habitat in the UK in terms of food production and the provision of landscape, recreation and other cultural benefits[1]. However, it also imposes important negative effects on the UK, including greenhouse gas emissions, diffuse water pollution and losses to biodiversity[1]. The challenge for the future will be to enhance the multiple ecosystem services that Enclosed Farmland provides despite a rapidly changing environment.

[1] *well established*

Enclosed Farmland is managed largely for food production. Changes in this habitat are driven mainly by changes in technologies, markets and policies. Climate change[a] and greater cultivation of bioenergy crops[c] are likely to become important drivers in the future[c]. Arable and Horticultural land occupies an estimated 19% of the UK land area (concentrated in eastern England) and Improved Grassland a further 21% (concentrated in the wetter, western parts of the UK)[1]. The 20th Century saw a trend for specialisation and landscape homogenisation, which was driven by mechanisation, markets and policies, among other factors[1]. The area of enclosed grassland increased by 5.4% between 1998 and 2007, due to agri-environment and former set-aside schemes, which restored some landscape diversity[1]. The length of hedgerows in Great Britain fell from an estimated 624,000 km in 1984 to 506,000 km by 1990[1]. This loss was caused more by poor management than by outright removal, and was largely stemmed by policy changes[a]. The area of farm woodlands in the UK increased from 280,000 ha to 700,000 ha between 1981 and 2008[1]. Pond numbers and quality have declined, especially in arable areas[a]. Climate change and increasing pressure on water supplies are expected to influence land management in the future through both mitigation and adaptation measures[a], including planting an estimated 350,000 ha of perennial bioenergy crops[c].

[1] *well established*
[a] *virtually certain*
[c] *likely*

Provisioning is the major ecosystem service provided by Enclosed Farmland, underpinning the UK agri-food sector, which contributes more than 6% of UK GDP[1]. Until the 1990s, levels of agricultural production increased greatly, causing an increase in external environmental costs and at the expense of other ecosystem services[1]. The increases in total agricultural productivity slowed during the 1990s, and hence the deterioration in other ecosystem services was reduced[b]. Production has increased since 1945, driven by new technologies and supported by deliberate policy interventions; for example, wheat yields increased from 2.5 tonnes per hectare per year (t/ha/yr) in 1940 and have stabilised at around 8 t/ha/yr since 2000[1]. The value of many UK agricultural products fell in the late 1990s, but recently rose again. Self-sufficiency in production of indigenous foods increased from 30% to 40% in the 1930s, and is now 73%[1].

[1] *well established*
[b] *very likely*

The contributions of the habitats of Enclosed Farmland to regulating services have often been negative, but are improving[2]. Levels of carbon in Arable and Horticultural soils fell between 1998 and 2007, while stocks under Improved Grassland remained steady at 61 t/ha[2]. The burden placed by agricultural inputs on regulating services, through local and exported pollution, is declining as nutrients are used more efficiently and livestock numbers fall[b]. For example, absolute values of non-carbon dioxide greenhouse gas emissions from UK agriculture have fallen by 19% since 1990, although they still accounted for 45% of the UK total in 2006[2]. Similarly, over 91% of UK ammonia emissions come from agricultural sources, and were estimated at 0.29 megatonnes (Mt) in 2007, compared to the 1990 estimate of 0.36 Mt[2]. Reductions in fertiliser use are contributing to falls in nitrate levels in rivers[a]. Pollination and biological pest control are provided by many invertebrates of Enclosed Farmland. However, numbers of honey bee colonies in England have declined by 54% since 1985[1]. Little is known of national trends in populations of biological control agents, nor of the relationships between the various organisms providing regulating services and crop yield.

[1] *well established*
[2] *established but incomplete evidence*
[a] *virtually certain*
[b] *very likely*

---

* Each Key Finding has been assigned a level of scientific certainty, based on a 4-box model and complemented, where possible, with a likelihood scale. Superscript numbers and letters indicate the uncertainty term assigned to each finding. Full details of each term and how they were assigned are presented in Appendix 7.1.

Millions of people enjoy the cultural benefits of Enclosed Farmland landscapes and their associated species[1]. Many Areas of Outstanding Natural Beauty and National Parks contain areas of Enclosed Farmland, and some landscapes are characterised by their patterns of crops, grass, woodlands, linear features and farm buildings[1]. The UK's farmland provides health benefits in terms of both the opportunities to exercise within it and the food produced[2]. Many species of plants, birds, invertebrates and mammals are directly associated with farmland cultural services[1], although quantitative data are lacking on their values and benefits. During the 20th Century, agriculture was associated with major declines in the diversity and numbers of plants, terrestrial invertebrates and vertebrates; for example, by 2000, the numbers of specialist farmland birds had fallen to 40% of their 1970 levels, and they have fallen a further 4% since then[1]. Only 26 out of 710 Areas/Sites of Special Scientific Interest on Enclosed Farmland are in favourable condition[1]. The UK's agricultural sector employs 470,000 people today, which is fewer than 2% of the workforce and half the number employed in 1973[1].

[1] *well established*
[2] *established but incomplete evidence*

Many interactions between provisioning and other ecosystem services are negative, partly because of releases of nutrients from agriculture as greenhouse gas emissions and diffuse pollution, and partly because of competition between crops and other habitats and taxa[2]. Better management of nutrients at crop, farm and catchment scales will improve regulating services without affecting food production[a]. However, productive agriculture involves removing weeds and pests, and simplifying landscapes, with inevitably negative consequences for biodiversity[1]. Extensive agriculture cannot meet all the UK's food production needs[3], so delivering both food and other ecosystem services requires the management of parcels of land for different purposes, from field to catchment scales[c]. Even then, it is not known whether the demand for ecosystem services can be met. Targeted regulations and guidance are being used to enhance levels of ecosystem services with some success; for example the control of diffuse water pollution[1]. Proposals to increase the area of bioenergy cropping will affect food production unless grown on poor quality farmland[a].

[1] *well established*
[2] *established but incomplete evidence*
[3] *competing explanations*
[a] *virtually certain*
[c] *likely*

Agriculture in the UK needs to: produce more food and energy; be more efficient in terms of resource utilisation; better provide ecosystem services other than production; and be resilient to climate and other changes[1]. Low-input agriculture provides higher levels of many services per unit area, but cannot meet expected requirements for food production, unless demand for food and energy is also met in other ways[1]. There is scope for increasing the productivity of food production both per unit area and per unit of resource, while the diversification of crop types and using trees or housing to create cooler conditions for livestock will help to manage the risks of climate change[b]. The volatile and complex nature of regulations and markets makes delivery of other ecosystem services difficult[1]. Values for such services are changing rapidly, and it is not clear whether agri-environment schemes are cost-effective mechanisms for delivering all ecosystem services from Enclosed Farmland[c].

[1] *well established*
[b] *very likely*
[c] *likely*

New research is needed to discover ways to enhance other ecosystem services while continuing to increase food production[1]. Some of this research should focus on traditional agricultural areas, such as breeding[1]; whereas some may be required in newer areas, such as the manipulation of biogeochemical processes through an improved understanding of soil function[c]. We need more information on how ecosystem services interact if we are to generate optimum farmed landscapes[1]. In particular, we lack information on the contribution of regulating services to food production[1]. In many cases, we only have access to proxy data, for example, declining pollinator numbers rather than the impacts of those declines on food production[1]. This is because the critical experiments are difficult and expensive to conduct at appropriate scales. It may not be possible to meet future demands for all ecosystem services[c]. Public engagement is needed to establish priorities, values and mechanisms for the delivery of ecosystem services from Enclosed Farmland, not least because the full cost of these services may prove far greater than allowed for in current policies and markets[c].

[1] *well established*
[c] *likely*

7.1 Introduction

Enclosed Farmland encompasses the cropped and grass fields that cover much of the UK's lowlands, along with the networks of hedges and ditches and the small woodlands interspersed among them. Enclosed Farmland is largely managed to produce food, using practices that result in some undesirable losses of nutrients and sediments into water, and greenhouse gases and ammonia into the atmosphere, as well as some that have caused large losses in the abundance and diversity of many species. By contrast, Enclosed Farmland is often also managed to provide positive outcomes or benefits, especially for providing landscape character, habitats for wildlife and opportunities for leisure. The management of UK Enclosed Farmland impacts on ecosystem services globally through the import and export of food, and through the use and alteration of energy and water, and emissions of greenhouse gases (Chapter 21). In this chapter we look at the ecosystem services provided by Enclosed Farmland and how they have changed in response to different drivers. This analysis helps us to consider how Enclosed Farmland might be managed sustainably in the UK in order to meet the expected global demands for more food and bioenergy, biodiversity conservation, and the enhancement of other ecosystem services.

7.1.1 Description of the Enclosed Farmland Broad Habitat

In the UK NEA, Enclosed Farmland comprises the two component habitats 'Arable and Horticultural' and 'Improved Grassland' (Jackson 2000), defined by vegetation, rather than land use (**Box 7.1**). Arable and Horticultural is identified on the basis of crops, grass leys, ploughed land and weedy vegetation characteristic of early succession set-aside. Improved Grassland occurs when palatable grasses (mainly perennial rye-grass (*Lolium perenne*), timothy (*Phleum pratense*), cock's-foot (*Dactylis glomerata*), crested dog's-tail (*Cynosurus cristatus*), and Yorkshire fog (*Holcus lanatus*)) exceed 75% cover and there is a restricted range of broadleaved species (Howard *et al.* 2003; Maskell *et al.* 2008). Hedgerows, ditches, ponds, farm woodlands and buildings interspersed among arable and grassland are also included in this chapter. The more species-rich habitats of Acid, Neutral and Calcareous Grasslands are dealt with separately within the Semi-natural Grassland chapter of the UK NEA (Chapter 6).

In 2007, Enclosed Farmland covered 39.3% of the UK's land area, with Arable and Horticultural and Improved Grassland habitats accounting for 18.8% and 20.5% of UK land cover, respectively (Carey *et al.* 2008; **Figure 7.1**). The extent of Enclosed Farmland, and the ratio of extent of Arable and Horticultural and Improved Grassland, differs between the four countries of the UK. This reflects the drier conditions in the south and east of the UK (which are more conducive to arable) and the wetter conditions in the west. Thus, divided by country:

- 52.1% of land area in England is Enclosed Farmland, consisting of 30.4% Arable and Horticultural and 21.7% Improved Grassland (Carey *et al.* 2008);

- 17.8% of land area in Scotland is Enclosed Farmland, consisting of 6.6% Arable and Horticultural and 11.2% Improved Grassland (more than 72% of the combined extent of both habitats is concentrated on the most nutrient-rich soils in the eastern lowlands of the country) (Norton *et al.* 2009a);
- 44% of land area in Northern Ireland is Enclosed Farmland, consisting of 3.5% Arable and Horticultural and 40.5% Improved Grassland (Cooper *et al.* 2009); and,
- 37.4% of land area in Wales is Enclosed Farmland, consisting of 3.4% Arable and Horticultural and 34% Improved Grassland (Carey *et al.* 2008).

7.1.1.1 Fields: Arable and Horticultural

Most arable land is cultivated to grow annually harvested crops. Cereals are the dominant crops sown, occupying 66.7% of the total area under crops in 2009 (Defra 2009a; Chapter 15). Wheat and barley alone now account for almost 95% of the total cereal area. Wheat grows well on heavier soils, but less well in areas of high rainfall. It is grown mainly for animal feed and milling. Barley can tolerate greater rainfall, but prefers lighter soils. Oats can tolerate more acidic soils, and so, traditionally, have been grown in Scotland, Wales and north-western England. Rape provides culinary and industrial oils, feedstock for biodiesel, livestock feed, and provides a break in cereal rotations for improved control of weeds and crop diseases. A wide variety of other crops are grown, usually for food or animal fodder, seldom occupying more than 10% of the agricultural area in a given county or region. These crops include sugar beet, forage brassicas, field beans, peas and forage maize. Potatoes grow best in deep, well-drained and stone-free soils, so are mostly grown on the silt and peat soils of eastern England, Shropshire, Cheshire, Fife and Angus. In Northern Ireland, only 17% of farms have arable or horticultural crops. Barley (26,700 hectares; ha) is the main crop grown, followed by wheat (10,100 ha) (DARD 2010). Only 43,000 ha of Welsh arable land is occupied by cereals, potatoes and horticulture, along with some oilseeds (3,000 ha) and livestock feeds, such as maize (19,000 ha); while 95,000 ha is sown to improved grasslands which are less than five years old.

A small, but growing, amount of land is used to grow crops for other uses, particularly in England. These include flax and hemp for fibre, as well as high market value crops grown for

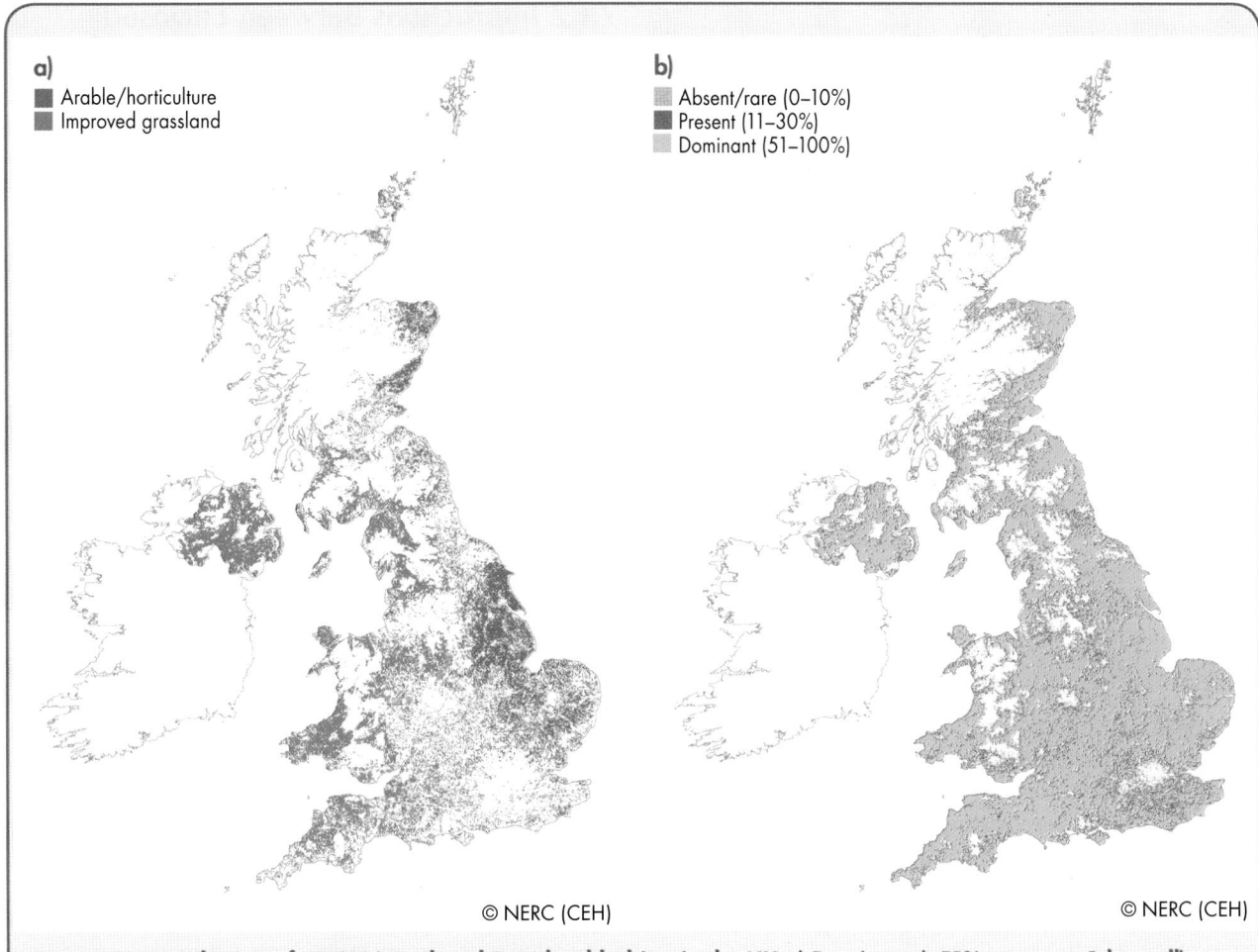

a)
■ Arable/horticulture
■ Improved grassland

b)
■ Absent/rare (0–10%)
■ Present (11–30%)
■ Dominant (51–100%)

© NERC (CEH)

© NERC (CEH)

Figure 7.1 Distribution of UK NEA Enclosed Farmland habitat in the UK a) Dominant (>51% area per 1 km cell) Enclosed Farmland type and b) percentage cover per 1 km cell.

pharmaceutical and medicinal extracts, essential oils, dyes, flavours, fragrances, cosmetics and nutritional supplements. Examples of speciality crops include borage and viper's-bugloss, which are grown for their oil; and dill, foxglove and chamomile which are grown for high-value medicinal or herbal extracts. Arable land has also included early successional set-aside (voluntary from 1987 and compulsory since 1992): over 180,000 ha was set-aside in 2007/08, the last year before the policy was discontinued.

At present, production horticulture accounts for 3% of the UK's agricultural area (The Smith Institute 2009). Orchards are concentrated in Kent, Herefordshire and Worcestershire; soft fruit production is very widespread, but the production of raspberries in Fife is worthy of note; vegetable-growing is largely found between Humberside and Essex; and flowers are mainly produced in Lincolnshire, Cornwall and the Isles of Scilly.

7.1.1.2 Fields: Improved Grassland
Most Improved Grassland is managed to provide food for livestock, mainly sheep and beef and dairy cattle. It is typically in the form of 'improved' pasture or long-term leys, managed using herbicides, fertilisers, ploughing, reseeding, liming and drainage to favour competitive, nitrogen-responsive grasses which provide silage to feed livestock over the winter and grazing for the rest of the year (Fuller 1987). There is a continuum from high-input, monoculture swards to low-

input, botanically diverse Semi-natural Grassland (treated as a separate UK NEA Broad Habitat). Improved Grassland is concentrated in Wales, western and northern Scotland, Northern Ireland, northern England and south-west England. These places are less suitable for arable crops because of their topography, high rainfall and more acidic soils.

7.1.1.3 Fields: biomass crops
Biomass crops are perennial crops that remain in the ground for successive harvests, potentially for more than 25 years. The two most common biomass crops in the UK are short rotation coppice (SRC), mainly willow (*Salix* species), and *Miscanthus* x *giganteus*, a dense, tall, perennial rhizomatous grass. These crops currently occupy only about 15,500 ha (Booth *et al.* 2009).

7.1.1.4 Farm woodland
Farm woodlands are typically small patches of woodland embedded within an agricultural landscape. There is no agreed definition of 'farm woodland', but it is generally accepted that 0.25 ha is a reasonable minimum area (FCS 2007). The most recent survey found more than 250,000 woodlands with areas from 0.1–2 ha in Great Britain (GB) (Forestry Commission 2003), many of which would have been in Enclosed Farmland. Such woodlands can be high forest, coppice or scrub, with variable amounts of open space (Evans 1984). Small woodlands are predominantly

broadleaved (most frequently oak (*Quercus* species) and ash (*Fraxinus excelsior*), especially in England and Wales. Spruce species (*Picea* species) are the most common conifers.

7.1.1.5 Field boundaries and ponds

Hedgerows, stone walls, dykes, fences and earth banks are all common field boundary features across the UK, originally created to enhance agricultural production, notably by stock proofing. Hedgerows usually consist of a linear strip of low, woody vegetation, sometimes punctuated by standard trees and often associated with other boundary features such as banks, ditches and uncultivated field margins. The planting of many of the UK's hedgerows was triggered by the Enclosure Acts of the 18th Century and before, creating a landscape with a social and historical dimension that is unusual on Earth (Rackham 1986). Hedgerows are concentrated in southern England and Wales, and are relatively scarce in Scotland. Northern Ireland has the UK's highest density of field boundaries, with 118,000 km of hedges in 1998 (Cooper & McCann 2000).

7.1.1.6 Buildings and gardens

Farm buildings, yards, houses, gardens and green lanes are not included in the definition of Enclosed Farmland, but play a major part in landscape character and hence the cultural services from farmland. They also provide habitat for barn swallows (*Hirundo rustica*), bats and other species. We are not aware of national data on the numbers, distribution and types of these features.

7.1.1.7 Enclosed Farmland landscapes

Enclosed Farmland has evolved in response to interactions between cultural, economic, technological and environmental factors, giving rise to distinctive yet dynamic landscapes of fields, buildings, linear and point features, woodlands and other habitats. These landscapes have been classified by country into Landscape Character Areas (they are termed National Character Areas in England). Historically, they have been considerably influenced by the development of agricultural systems, especially the 'planned countryside' associated with the Enclosure Acts of the 18th Century and the contrasting 'ancient countryside' which reflects a longer history of gradual evolution (Rackham 1986). Today, large, tilled fields dominate the farmed landscape in southern England, with scattered woodland patches and farm buildings. Further north and west in England, fields are smaller and less regular in shape, with more hedgerow trees and pasture. Pasture dominates even more in Wales and Northern Ireland, but tilled fields once again prevail in parts of the east and south-east of Scotland.

Crofting is a unique land use system, important socially and culturally, and often accompanied by a rich and varied fauna and flora (SNH 2009). It is associated with distinctive, small-scale cropping patterns, and is dominated by mixed farming; fields are lined with stone dykes and sparse stands of gorse instead of stock-proof hedges (Wilson *et al.* 2009). Crofting covers nearly 10% of Scottish farmland, mostly in the north-west; there are currently around 10,000–12,000 crofters on nearly 18,000 crofts (Slee *et al.* 2009).

7.1.2 Interactions Between Enclosed Farmland and Other UK NEA Broad Habitats

The major direct interactions Enclosed Farmland has with other UK habitats are in terms of exchanges of land into and out of agriculture through land use change and through agricultural management that cuts across Broad Habitat boundaries (especially in the uplands). Imports and exports of water, energy, nutrients and pollutants are dealt with in Section 7.3.

The greatest net transfer of land into and out of Enclosed Farmland in recent decades has been the large-scale conversion from Semi-natural Grassland (Chapter 6) to more intensive agriculture during the mid-20th Century. Fuller (1987) reported that, between 1930 and 1984, 97% of grasslands in England and Wales had been improved. In recent decades, this conversion has slowed, with large fields close to more intensive grassland the most likely to change (Petit & Firbank 2006). Flows between habitats other than Neutral Grassland were negligible between 1998 and 2007 (Carey *et al.* 2008). While there remains pressure to convert Enclosed Farmland into built land, the actual proportion of new dwellings built on agricultural land has fallen from around 28% during the 1990s to less than 15% since 2005 (FLUFP 2010).

Upland farming in the north and west of Britain is dominated by the extensive rearing of cattle and sheep. The Enclosed Farmland areas on such farms may be relatively small, but their management dictates the intensity of grazing across the farm as a whole, and hence on the semi-natural vegetation used as grazing land (permanent grassland, moorland and bog, rush pasture and marsh, Machair and Sand Dunes). The intensification of grassland and cropping management practices in enclosed areas has allowed an overall increase in the livestock carrying capacity of these areas, resulting in overgrazing of many upland habitats (Samsom 1999). Changes in support payments as a result of the reform of the Common Agricultural Policy (CAP) are now driving stocking densities back down and raising the prospect of under-grazing in some parts of the uplands (Scottish Agricultural College 2008).

7.2 Trends and Changes in Enclosed Farmland

This section looks at the change in extent and status of Enclosed Farmland habitats and the main causes of these changes.

7.2.1 Changes in Extent and Status

7.2.1.1 Fields

According to official agricultural statistics for England, the total area for arable and permanent grass (excluding rough grazing, but including Semi-natural Grassland) fell during the 20th Century, with some substitution of grass by cereals (**Figure 7.2**). The GB area of Arable and Horticultural

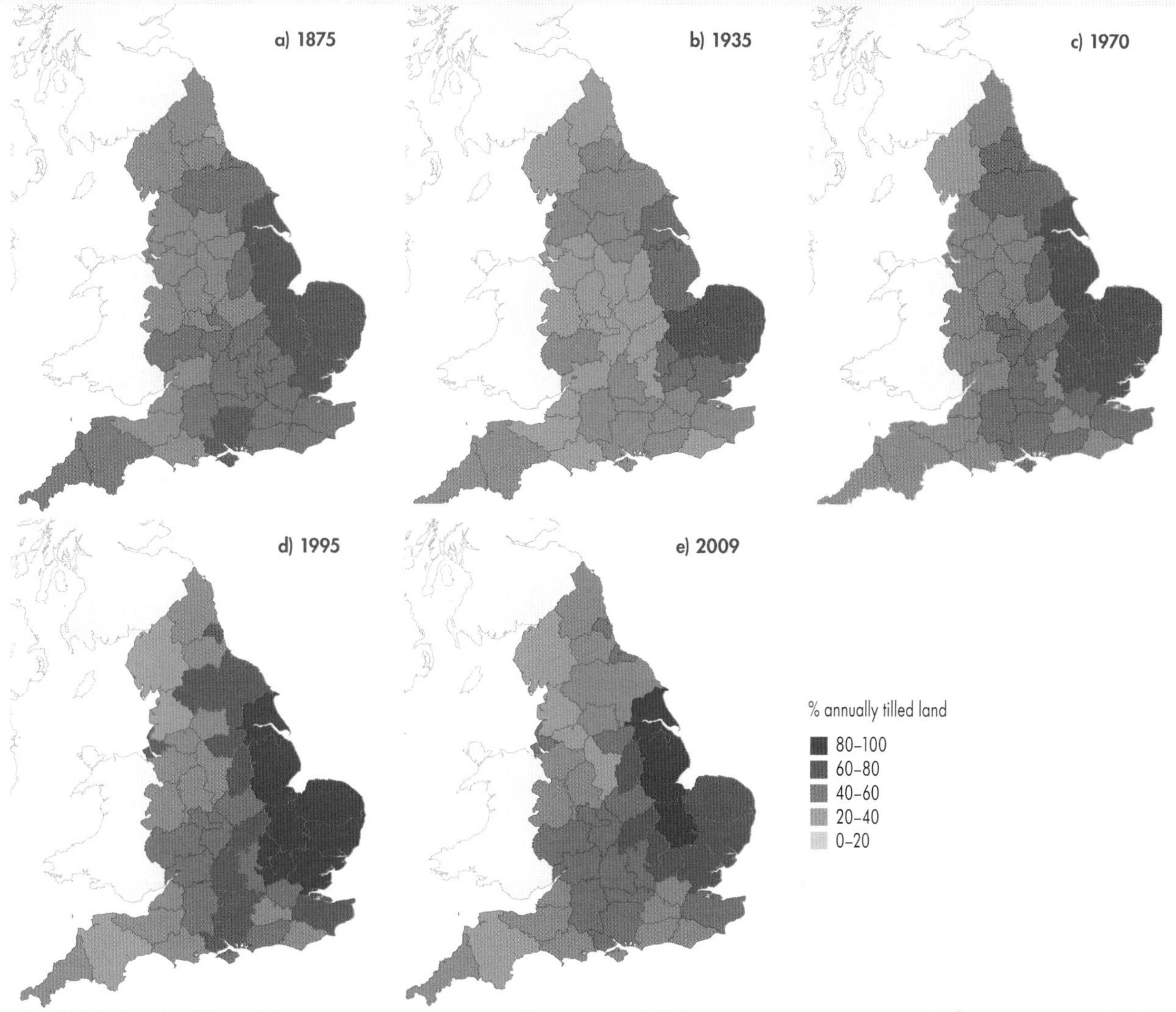

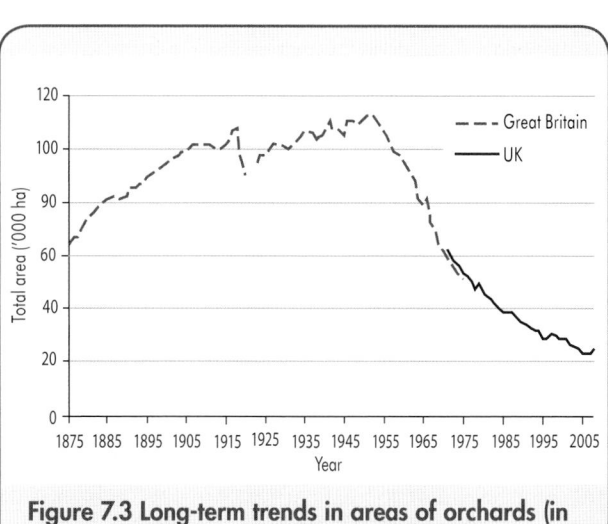

Figure 7.2 The amount of annually tilled land in England, as a percentage of total farmed area by county in a) 1875, b) 1935, c) 1970, d) 1995 and e) 2009, based on agricultural census returns. Source: adapted and updated from Robinson & Sutherland (2002).

a) 1875   b) 1935   c) 1970   d) 1995   e) 2009

% annually tilled land

- 80–100
- 60–80
- 40–60
- 20–40
- 0–20

land fell from 5.3 million ha in 1984 to 4.1 million ha in 2007, while the area of Improved Grassland also fell from 5.9 million ha to 4.5 million ha over the same time period (note: these latter changes were concentrated in England). The major transfers were to Neutral Grassland, reflecting less intensive management; the extent to which this was due to agri-environment schemes, as opposed to neglect, is not known (Carey *et al.* 2008). Note that Countryside Survey data conflicts with evidence from agricultural statistics in ways that could be accounted for by the conversion of some agricultural land to woodland (Bibby 2009).

Maize and oilseed rape have increased dramatically in area in recent decades, while areas of turnips, swedes and fodder rape have declined. Changes in dominance of different cereals are illustrated by the situation in Scotland where, from the mid-1940s to mid-1950s, about 80% of the area planted was to oats, 15% to barley and the rest to wheat. By around 1980, oats had declined to less than 10% of the area planted, while barley area increased to about 80–85%. Since then, wheat has increased to about 25% of area planted, at the expense of barley (Miller *et al.* 2009). The area of orchards rose steadily until the 1950s, but has since

been in decline (**Figure 7.3**). Further details of inter-country variation in changes in extent of different crops are given in Chapter 15.

Figure 7.3 Long-term trends in areas of orchards (in thousands of ha) in GB followed by UK. Source: reproduced from Keep (2009). © Crown copyright.

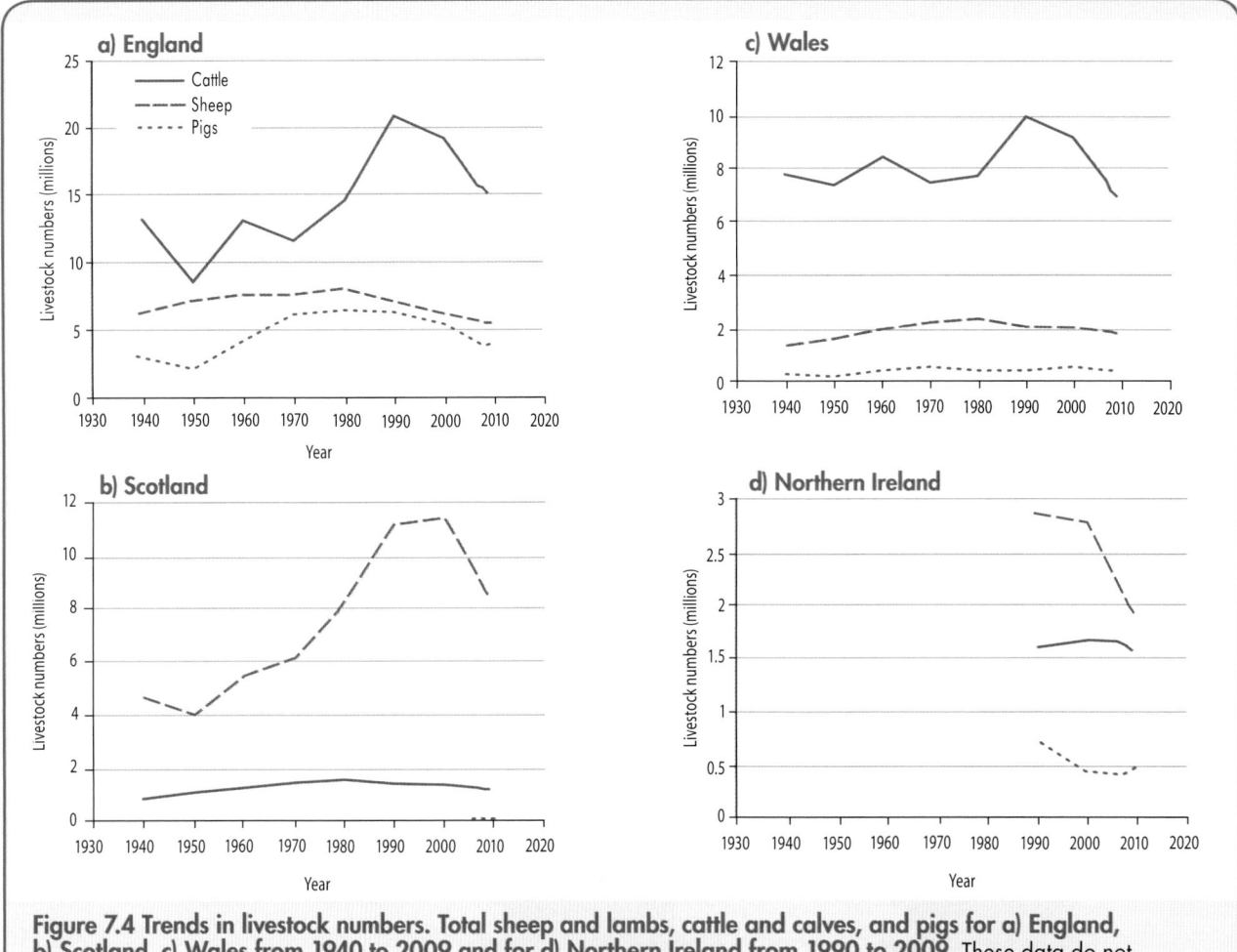

Figure 7.4 Trends in livestock numbers. Total sheep and lambs, cattle and calves, and pigs for a) England, b) Scotland, c) Wales from 1940 to 2009 and for d) Northern Ireland from 1990 to 2009. These data do not distinguish between livestock in enclosed and unenclosed farming habitats. Source: June census data from Defra, Department of Agriculture and Rural Development, Scottish Government and Welsh Assembly Government; data available from http://www.defra.gov.uk/statistics/foodfarm/landuselivestock/junesurvey/.

Historically, most young grasslands were grass-clover mixes, in rotation with arable crops, to restore fertility and provide hay. During the course of the 20th Century, these have been replaced by regularly reseeded long-term leys, designed to maximise production of grazing or silage (Chapter 15). The resulting forage is fed to stock over the winter, along with concentrates and sometimes forage crops. Livestock numbers rose from the mid-20th Century to the 1990s, sustained by increasing inputs of inorganic fertilisers and feed; since then, they have fallen (**Figure 7.4**; Chapter 15). Stocking densities have increased because of the tendency to concentrate the remaining livestock on the more productive, enclosed areas of grazing on farms.

Turnover between arable crop types and grassland has been extensive and complex, has occurred at scales from national to rotations on individual farms, and has been happening for decades (Haines-Young *et al.* 2003; Swetnam 2007; **Table 7.1**). For instance, there was a 14.5% decrease in area of Arable and Horticultural broad habitat in Northern Ireland between 1998 and 2007 (Cooper *et al.* 2009), including a 32% decrease in the area of land in potatoes (DARD 2010). In Scotland, there was a 14% decrease in the extent of Arable and Horticultural broad habitat between 1998 and 2007 (in contrast to the relative stability seen between 1990 and 1998), but there was a significant increase (9%) in the extent of Improved Grassland (Norton *et al.* 2009a).

The area of agricultural land under bioenergy crops is increasing in the UK, but from a very low baseline (Lovett *et al.* 2009; Chapter 15). By 2007, the area of *Miscanthus* was 12,600 ha and SRC 2,600 ha in England. In Scotland, the area planted with bioenergy crops, or approved for planting up until the end of 2006, was 300 ha, with applications for planting in 2007 and 2008 amounting to around 600 ha. In Northern Ireland, 800 ha of SRC have been planted or approved for planting, while in Wales there is only known to be 40 ha of SRC and 72 ha of *Miscanthus* (Sherrington & Moran 2010).

7.2.1.2 Hedgerows

The original agricultural functions of linear features have often been lost, not least due to declines in stock numbers in now arable-dominated areas. Yet hedgerows remain important for the habitats they provide, the connections they make between habitats, for their role in reducing diffuse pollution, and for their contribution to the cultural landscape (Barr & Petit 2001; Ballantine *et al.* 2009). The first national data on hedgerows were collected in 1984 (Barr & Gillespie 2000), before which it is believed that many hedgerows were removed as fields were enlarged to facilitate the use of tractors and other machinery. Between 1951 and 2007, the number of hedgerow trees fell dramatically across Britain from over 56 million to less than 2 million (Carey *et al.* 2008); around half of these were elm trees killed by Dutch Elm Disease (Forest Research 2010). The estimated length of 624,000 km of 'managed' hedge in GB recorded in 1984 decreased to 506,000 km by 1990 (Petit *et al.* 2003). Subsequent protection (e.g. under the Hedgerow Regulations in England and Wales) has severely restricted the removal of hedgerows and much reduced the rate of subsequent losses (**Figure 7.5**), which were often the result of poor management rather than outright removal (Smart *et al.* 2009). Under half (48%) of managed hedges in GB were classified as being in good structural condition in 2007 (Carey *et al.* 2008).

We are unaware of published data on national trends in ditches and their status.

7.2.1.3 Farm woodland

Farm woodlands have been planted with a variety of intentions, including providing productive alternative land uses to agriculture, shelter for stock, and improving biodiversity, landscape and recreation (John Clegg *et al.* 2002). According to the Forestry Commission, between 1981 and 2008, the area of land recorded as farm woodland increased from about 280,000 ha to 700,000 ha (Forestry Commission 2009), with 45% being in England, a similar amount in Scotland, 8% in Wales and the remainder in Northern Ireland (**Figure 7.6**).

Throughout the 20th Century, game-shooting has been one of the main reasons for the planting of farm woodlands (Duckworth *et al.* 2003). Pheasant (*Phasianus colchicus*) shooting is a major recreational activity that is normally dependent on a matrix of farmland and woodland habitats, and an estimated 830,000 ha of UK woodland is being managed primarily for this sport (PACEC 2006). Management of woodlands for game species contributes directly to the conservation of birds and other wildlife (Draycott *et al.* 2008).

Farm woodlands are rarely planted primarily for timber and fuel; they are often isolated from other woodlands and have poor access, which makes management and extraction of harvested material difficult. However, some are now being better managed, and the recent widespread adoption of wood fuel boilers on farms and larger premises has encouraged the production of woodchip from a wide range of woodland types.

Table 7.1 Changes in areas of Improved Grassland and Arable and Horticultural habitats across England, Scotland and Wales since 1990 showing statistical significance of changes between adjacent times (*p < 0.05; **p< 0.01). Data collected using field sampling rather than agricultural census returns. All values are thousands of hectares (ha). Source: reproduced from Keep (2009). ©Crown copyright. Countryside Survey data owned by NERC – Centre for Ecology & Hydrology.

		Arable & Horticulture			Improved Grassland		
		'000 ha					
		1990	1998	2007	1990	1998	2007
England	Easterly lowlands	3,191	3,127	2,907 **	928	926	1,056 *
	Westerly lowlands	1,147	1,223 *	1,061 **	1,809	1,537 **	1,576
	Uplands	41	39	34	284	250	225
Scotland	Lowlands	511	519	462	539	526	580
	Intermediate uplands and islands	75	95 *	71	214	245	267
	True uplands	7	4	2	62	60	60
Wales	Lowlands	46	55	63	501	457 *	467
	Uplands	6	6	10 **	228	249 **	263

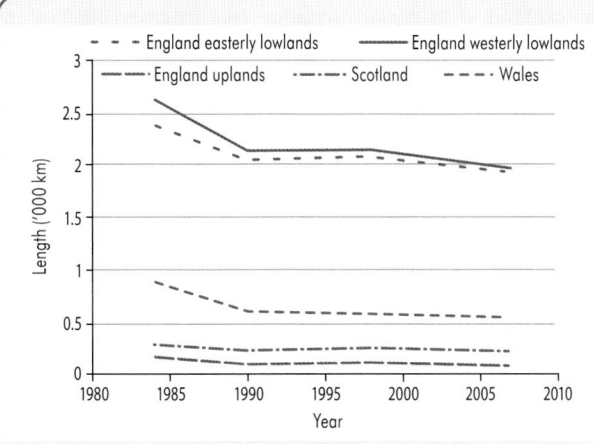

Figure 7.5 Trends in the overall length (thousands of km) of managed hedgerows. Source: data from Countryside Survey (Carey *et al.* 2008). Countryside Survey data owned by NERC – Centre for Ecology & Hydrology.

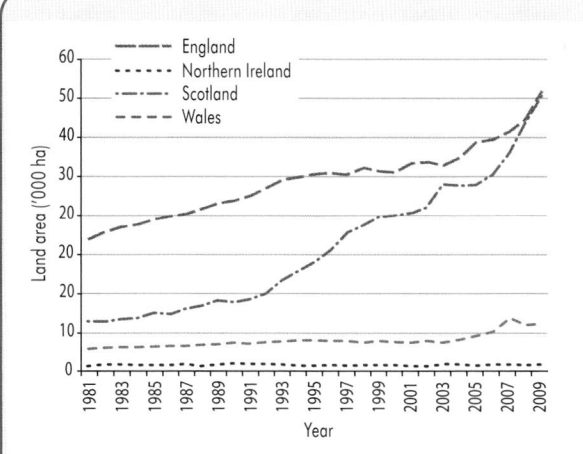

Figure 7.6 Trends in the overall land area (thousands of hectares) covered by farm woodlands from 1981 to 2009. Source: data from Forestry Commission (2009).

7.2.1.4 Ponds

In the late 19th Century, the number of ponds in England and Wales is estimated to have been about 800,000 (Rackham 1986). Many ponds were lost, however, largely due to the drainage of the land and the infilling of ponds that had become redundant as livestock watering sites or hindered large-scale agricultural operations. Numbers fell to an estimated 200,000 in the 1980s, but are now recovering; an estimated 478,000 ponds existed across GB in 2007 (Williams *et al.* 2010). Over the same period, the invertebrate species richness of lowland ponds declined by 20%, and the proportion of ponds in 'poor' or 'very poor' condition increased by 17% (Williams *et al.* 2010). Causes of this ecological degradation include elevated nitrate concentrations, runoff from roads, increased tree shading and the transport of sediment through stream inflows.

7.2.2 Drivers of Change in Enclosed Farmland Habitats

Management of Enclosed Farmland results from the decisions of individual land managers in the light of markets, policies, the characteristics of the land, environmental conditions, available knowledge and technology, and the attitudes and objectives of the land managers themselves (McIntyre *et al.* 2009; Chapter 15). This means that the extent and vegetation of this habitat, and the ecosystem services provided, may change very rapidly. A summary of the drivers of change in the extent and status of Enclosed Farmland habitats, and their relative importance, is shown in **Table 7.2**.

7.2.2.1 Climate change (temperature/precipitation) and sea-level rise

During the 20th Century, the UK's climate was stable enough not to drive major changes in the extent and management of Enclosed Farmland. That situation is changing rapidly as agriculture must increasingly adapt to climate change and meet political expectations to reduce greenhouse gas emissions, sequester carbon and produce bioenergy. Here, we address adaptation options directly related to the management of Enclosed Farmland, and not the rest of the food chain. Options for mitigating greenhouse gas emissions and the potential indirect impacts of climate change on Enclosed Farmland resulting from reduced agricultural productivity in other parts of the world are addressed in Section 7.3.2.1.

Adaptation to climate change. There is the potential for an increase in the productivity of UK agriculture due to climate change (Parry *et al.* 2008). The UK's climate is expected to become warmer (Jenkins *et al.* 2009), and expected increases in atmospheric carbon dioxide are likely to have a fertilising effect on plant growth (Long *et al.* 2004), but with a potential cost of reduced plant protein content (DaMatta *et al.* 2010; Cotrufo *et al.* 1998).

However, patterns of rainfall are expected to change, with wetter winters in the grassland-dominated north and west, and drier summers in the south-east, as well as more extreme weather events overall (Jenkins *et al.* 2009). Arable farming may be compromised by droughts in summer and waterlogging in winter, preventing timely agricultural operations. While agriculture currently accounts for only 2% of water abstracted in the UK, this is mostly used in the summer in the south and east of England (Defra 2010a), a time and place of peak demand. Climate change could increase this need, placing additional strain on water supplies that are already stretched.

Warmer winters facilitate the use of outdoor livestock systems, but extremes of weather threaten the resilience of livestock management, for example, if the land is too wet or hot for cattle to be put out to graze without compromising their welfare (Pilgrim *et al.* 2010). Such risks can be controlled using fully housed systems to protect livestock from heat stress in the summer; there is also scope for using more trees in grazing areas to provide cooler conditions outdoors. All year-round housing can have mixed environmental outcomes: compared with systems more reliant on grazing, housing livestock should result in reduced losses of nitrous oxide and nitrates (Pilgrim *et al.* 2010); by contrast, there is the potential for ammonia emissions to be increased (Chadwick *et al.* 2008).

Responses by farmers are likely to include more use of on-farm reservoirs and alternative crops and varieties more suited to the new climates. Italian ryegrass, for instance, could be used for summer grazing as it is drought-tolerant (Bartholomew & Williams 2009). The benefits of using this crop may include reduced nitrogen excretion, nitrous oxide emissions and enteric methane emissions by livestock, as well as reduced nitrates leaching from soils.

Sea-level rise. Sea-level rise has not been a driver of Enclosed Farmland management in the past, and while there is potential for inundation of low-lying agricultural land at some point in the future, it is not anticipated in the coming decades. Nor is a major increase in storm surges anticipated (Jenkins *et al.* 2009). However, some coastal areas may be lost to coastal realignment as part of a national response to cope with flooding in the future (FPFCD, undated).

7.2.2.2 Habitat change

Most changes in cover and management of Enclosed Farmland have been the indirect result of other social, economic and policy drivers, which are described separately. In recent years, however, there is renewed interest by national governments in developing policies for rural land use. In Scotland, A Forward Strategy for Scottish Agriculture was developed in 2001 (Scottish Executive 2001) and A Forward Strategy for Scottish Agriculture: Next Steps was produced in 2006 (Scottish Executive 2006). The Scottish Government is currently in the process of developing their land use strategy: Getting the Best From Our Land (Scottish Government 2010). In 2009, the Welsh Assembly Government produced their strategy: Farming, Food and Countryside: Building a Secure Future. A New Strategy for Farming (WAG 2009). Land use policy is evolving rapidly in England too. As recently as 2006, a major report on land use planning did not mention agriculture in its primary recommendations, which mainly addressed streamlining the English planning system to promote economic growth in other sectors (Barker 2006). However, the spike in food prices in 2008 raised the issue of food security, which has since been addressed in several key strategies (HM Government 2010; Defra 2010c).

The Foresight Land Use Futures final report (2010) highlighted the importance of both agricultural production and other ecosystem services from agricultural land, and promotes a more integrative, holistic view of land planning. This report recognises some of the major challenges currently facing land use policy in the UK, namely: increasing competition for land in the south-east of England, where much arable farming is concentrated; climate change, and the need to reduce greenhouse gas emissions and set appropriate mechanisms to value carbon; and the delivery of public goods and services from private land.

7.2.2.3 Species introduction and/or removal

Crop species have been introduced into the UK over the centuries—a process likely to be given new impetus as crops change their geographic range of suitability because of climate change. Indeed, some UK farms are already introducing melons, kiwi fruit, olives and even tea (The Times, 9 August 2010). However, climate change will also influence the spectrum of crop and livestock diseases, weeds and pests (Iglesias et al. 2007; Pilgrim et al. 2010). For example, the cattle disease Bluetongue was considered a minor threat in the UK until its appearance in northern Europe in 2006; previously, its midge vectors (Culicoides species) had been restricted further south, but warmer summers enabled it to spread north (Szmaragd et al. 2010).

There are several other mechanisms of species introductions (Davies 2007). The muntjac deer (Muntiacus reevesi) was deliberately introduced into the UK in the early 20th Century, and now degrades the flora of farm woodlands and impacts on the fertility of native roe deer (Capreolus capreolus) (Dolman & Waber 2008). The New Zealand flatworm (Arthurdendyus triangulates), which predates on native earthworms (Lumbricidae), has been introduced via garden centres (Cannon 1999) and is now spreading with unknown effects on soil function. Attempts to eradicate species have been largely restricted to economic diseases of livestock, although certain other species are notifiable and should be removed if seen (for example, the Colorado beetle (Leptinotarsa decemlineata), which is an invasive pest of potatoes, and ragwort (Senecio jacobea), which is poisonous to livestock). The outbreak of Bluetongue Virus in 2006 was controlled by vaccination (Szmaragd et al. 2010), and had little impact on other species or on ecosystem services.

By contrast, the eradication of the virus that caused the massive outbreak of Foot and Mouth Disease (FMD) in the UK's sheep flock in 2001 involved closing access to large areas of land valued for leisure (Phillipson et al. 2002). The costs to agriculture and the food chain of controlling the outbreak were estimated at around £3.1 billion (or 20% of total farming income in 2001). There were also losses to tourist businesses of a similar amount, although much of these were displaced to other businesses within the UK. The net cost of controlling the outbreak was around 0.2% of Gross Domestic Product (GDP) (Thompson et al. 2002). Current plans for controlling an FMD outbreak involve closing only those footpaths within 3 km of infected premises.

The UK Government has recently consulted over whether to allow the culling of badgers (Meles meles) as part of a package to control Bovine Tuberculosis (bTB) (Defra 2010c). In 2009, control of this disease involved slaughtering over 25,000 cattle, which cost £63 million in England alone and caused trauma to many farming households. Badger control is being considered as populations often harbour bTB, and it is proposed that their presence makes the elimination of the disease more difficult, if not impossible. Such control would impact on the cultural value of Enclosed Farmland, as the badger is a legally protected, iconic species, with societies dedicated to its conservation. The proposal is highly contentious and has been characterised as being political, rather than evidence-based (Monbiot 2010; Kendall 2010).

For a more detailed discussion of disease and pest regulation, see Chapter 14.

Table 7.2 Major drivers of change in Enclosed Farmland habitats. ⊚ denotes high agreement with much evidence and ⊙ denotes high agreement with limited evidence.

Driver	Relevant to farmland now and in future	Major driver on farmland	Evidence base
Climate change (temperature/precipitation)	✓ and increasing	Mitigation and adaptation	⊚
Climate change (sea level)	✗ but increasing	Some land loss in UK, loss of global agricultural land	⊚
Habitat change	✓	Especially interchange between grass and arable, and between crops	⊚
Species introduction and/or removal	✓	Potential for new crops, control of new pathogens, pest control	⊚
Pollution (nutrients etc.)	✓	Fertiliser and pesticides have resulted in pollution, likely to reduce as inputs lessen	⊚
Overexploitation (harvest / resource use)	✓	Responds to other drivers	⊚
Demography—population growth	Expected to be a future driver	Increasing population growth and consumption increase demand for agricultural production	⊙
Demography—demographic change	✓	Impacts on patterns of labour and management	⊙
Demography—ethnicity	✗		⊙
Demography—migration	✓	Impacts on patterns of labour and management	⊙

7.2.2.4 Pollution (nutrients, agrochemicals)

The advent of inorganic fertilisers in the early 1900s reduced the need for livestock manures and nitrogen-fixing legumes in farming systems and enabled the switch from hay to faster-growing silage, along with the cultivation of taller and denser cereal swards. It is estimated that 40–50% of the world's food is now produced using nitrogen fertiliser (Smil 2002; IFA 2009).

Over the past 25 years, there has been an ongoing decline in inorganic fertiliser applications. In 2008, the total amount of phosphate fertiliser used in GB was only 43% of that used in 1984 (Defra 2010a). While the application rate for synthetic nitrogen on arable land has remained fairly constant at around 140–150 kg/ha, the synthetic nitrogen application rate on grassland fell from 129 to 55 kg/ha (57%) between 1990 and 2008 (CCC 2010). This has coincided with reduced livestock numbers as a result of CAP reform, and, as such, may be attributable to reduced stocking densities more than improved efficiency in fertiliser use. Other factors that are likely to influence fertiliser use include rising prices (they climbed from £100/tonne (t) to more than £400/t between 1998 and 2009, and are likely to increase further given the high energy costs of producing nitrate fertiliser and the potential reduction in supplies of phosphates), and the regulations controlling diffuse water pollution (e.g. Nitrate Vulnerable Zones, the Nitrates Action Programme and the England Catchment Sensitive Farming Initiative).

Since the 1970s, the use of pesticides has been driven by the policy context. When price support was fixed to tonnage payments, prophylactic, often excessive, spraying regimes dominated. Since the 1992 switch to area-based payments, farmers have tended to adopt more targeted applications based on pest infestation thresholds, so the application rates of pesticide active ingredients per unit area have fallen (CSL data, http://pussstats.csl.gov.uk). The new EU Thematic Strategy for Pesticides is likely to reduce pesticide use on farmland even further. Pesticide use is now influenced by the industry-led Voluntary Initiative (VI), such that 85% of the sprayed area in England and Wales is now being treated with tested machines under the National Sprayer Testing Scheme and more than 2 million ha are now covered by a VI Crop Protection Management Plan (www.voluntaryinitiative.org.uk).

The spectrum of pesticides and herbicides has changed in response to technologies and policies. For example, the non-selective herbicide atrazine was used for pre-emergence weed control until its recent withdrawal because of concerns over groundwater contamination. Another non-selective herbicide, glyphosate, was widely used to control weeds and self-seeded crop plants (volunteers) on fallow land under the set-aside scheme. More recently, Genetically Modified (GM) crops have been developed to be tolerant to such herbicides, facilitating weed management (Champion et al. 2003), although they are not grown commercially in the UK (see Section 7.2.2.8).

Pesticides are used to enhance crop yield by controlling unwanted plants that compete with the crop, animals that feed on the crop, disease vectors and fungal infections. While modern pesticides tend to be more environmentally benign in terms of unwanted effects than the ones they replaced (Lutman & Marsh 2009), these deliberate removals have important indirect impacts on other species, discussed in Section 7.3.5.

7.2.2.5 Overexploitation (harvest and/or resource use)

The intensity of production (yields, stocking rates, etc.) is the result of more external drivers, namely markets, technologies and policies, dealt with seperately.

7.2.2.6 Demography (population growth, demographic change, ethnicity and migration)

There is little evidence of demography driving changes in UK Enclosed Farmland in recent decades, and, at a global level, agricultural production has kept pace with consumer demand. However, concerns are rising that a combination of increasing global population (to an estimated 9 billion by 2050), increasing demands for meat and dairy products, and the challenges of climate change may result in food shortages (Godfray et al. 2010). This driver will impact on Enclosed Farmland indirectly by influencing markets and policies to increase food production at the potential expense of other services.

7.2.2.7 Technological adaptation and knowledge

The impacts of technology as a driver of ecosystem service delivery from Enclosed Farmland cannot be exaggerated. The replacement of draught animals by tractors removed the need to grow cereals to feed them (Chapter 15), while the introduction of inorganic fertilisers removed the need for manures for arable crops (Shrubb 2003). The result was the polarisation of Enclosed Farmland between the arable east and pastoral west that can be seen today (**Figure 7.2**; Robinson & Sutherland 2002; Haines-Young et al. 2003). Loss of livestock, plus economies of scale for use of machinery, led to large increases in field size and the loss of field boundary habitats and ponds in the arable areas of the east.

From the 1970s, the process of agricultural intensification and increased productivity was associated with the widespread use of several technologies including agrochemicals and new varieties and breeds (Chamberlain 2000). For example, genetic improvement explains more than 50% of the milk productivity improvements seen on UK farms over the past two decades (The Smith Institute 2009). However, there was widespread concern that agricultural production was being promoted at the expense of other ecosystem services and human well-being (McIntyre et al. 2009). Policy responses included agri-environment schemes and regulations such as the Water Framework Directive (WFD); consumer responses included resistance to GM crops and increasing markets for food produced locally and less intensively; and technological responses included ways to manage agrochemical and nutrient inputs through precision, integrated and organic farming systems.

Precision farming systems use technology to help the grower to manage inputs more exactly, for example, using soil mapping and GPS to locate precisely where fertilisers should be applied. Therefore, they facilitate the optimal use of farm inputs, reducing costs, maximising yields and reducing environmental impacts. However, take-up is low; in England in 2009, the percentage of holdings using precision technology was divided thus: GPS, 11%; soil mapping, 14%; yield mapping, 7%; rate application, 13%; telemetry, 1%; guidance, 11%; and auto steering, 6%. The nutrient content of soil was regularly tested on only 68% of holdings (Defra 2010a).

Integrated Farm Management is a whole farm system intended to provide efficient and profitable production that is environmentally responsible. It integrates beneficial natural processes into modern farming techniques, ensuring that high standards of stewardship and environmental care are practised. In the UK, integrated farming is promoted by Linking Environment and Farming (LEAF; www.leafuk.org/leaf/home.eb). For instance, parasitoids and predatory insects, such as carabid and staphylinid beetles, that eat crop pests like aphids can be encouraged through the provision of rough grass banks in field centres or along field edges (Collins et al. 2003), reducing the need for summer aphicides. The abundance of flying predators of aphids has been shown to have a greater impact on aphid numbers than the abundance of epigeal predators, independently of grass margins immediately adjacent to the crop (Holland et al. 2008). In addition, pollinator numbers can be enhanced using nectar-rich plant mixtures in field margins (Carvell et al. 2007).

Organic farming promotes the internalisation of inputs for crop and livestock production (especially in the case of nutrients), precludes the use of many external inputs, such as mineral fertilisers and most pesticides, and incorporates biological processes such as pest control by rotation (Lampkin 1990; Norton et al. 2009b). Production levels are typically lower than non-organic systems, but prices are normally higher than other farm products. National standards for organic production and labeling, such as those of the UK Soil Association, are underpinned by European Council Regulation 834/2007. In 2008, the total area of land that was organically managed (either fully organic or in-conversion) was 743,000 ha, half of which (375,000 ha) was in England. In all, there were 320,000 cattle, 1.2 million sheep, 71,000 pigs, 4 million poultry and 5,000 other livestock being reared organically in the UK (Defra 2010a). Organic farms are concentrated in south-west England, where climate, soils and topography are unfavourable for intensive arable farming and facilitate the rotations involving both crops and livestock that enable the efficient use of organic nutrients. Here, the proportion of registered organic farmers reaches 29% of crop producers and 27% of livestock farms.

It is now argued that the medium-term threats to food security require new technological investment. The goal is to increase production but without compromising the delivery of other ecosystem services (Royal Society 2009). There is new interest in technologies aimed at promoting the co-management of multiple ecosystem services. For instance, genetic improvement, diet manipulation and containment are increasingly being adopted to reduce greenhouse gas emissions from livestock (Abberton et al. 2007; Garwes 2009). Technologies that could be applied to adapt to summer droughts in arable areas include more water-efficient crops, irrigation systems with high efficiency (such as low pressure sprinklers), drip irrigation, the use of sub-surface partial root drying (PRD) systems, the use of greenhouses and plastic tunnels, and the use of non-conventional water resources (brackish groundwater, treated waste water, rainfall-harvested water, etc.). Genetic Modification technology will remain an important option for the development of new crop varieties with, for example, improved drought tolerance, among other qualities.

7.2.2.8 Market forces

Farmers typically aim for profit maximisation in the light of farm climate and soil type, as well as prices, grants, exchange rates, etc. (Bateman et al. 1999). Normally, this results in yields less than maximum because a point is reached where additional input costs are not recouped by returns on marginal increases in outputs. Changes in global market conditions and policy can bring a rapid response by farmers; for example, in 2007, the area of uncropped land (set-aside and fallow land) fell by over one fifth following rising cereal prices and the removal of the requirement for farmers to set aside land under the CAP (Section 7.2.2.9).

Over the last half-century, agri-food systems have become more integrated, with supermarkets increasing in size and increasing their market share and control over the whole supply chain, from farm to shop. Meanwhile, fragmented markets supply more of the higher-value products including organic and local food (McIntyre et al. 2009). Sales of organic produce accounted for only 5.3% of total fruit and vegetable sales in 2006, most of which was imported (The Smith Institute 2009). Supermarkets are increasingly promoting local produce and reduced environmental impact throughout the food chain in order to meet the markets for more environmentally and socially benign consumption.

Markets in the UK operate using various standards and assurance schemes. For example, for the milling of bread flour, the protein levels of wheat must normally exceed 13% of dry matter. Otherwise, it is sold more cheaply for animal feed. The setting of this level influences both farm management decisions and the proportion of crop production that can be sold directly for human food. Between 2000 and 2008, an average of 49% of the UK annual wheat crop was used for animal feed and 42% for flour (Defra 2010a).

Consumer concerns about intensive agriculture came to a head in the debate about the introduction of GM crops that started in the late 1990s. While the first GM product in the UK market place sold well, consumer resistance built up, making the approval of the first commercial planting of GM crops (a herbicide-tolerant variety of maize) very contentious. The UK Farm Scale Evaluations (FSEs) were established to improve the evidence base for the environmental risks of herbicide-tolerant maize, sugar beet, spring and winter oilseed rape (Firbank et al. 1999). They found that environmental impacts resulted from the herbicides used on the crops, not from the way in which the crops themselves had been developed (Firbank et al. 2003a). This project was intended to provide part of the evidence for the much wider assessment of environmental and health risks required to approve any releases of GM organisms. However, this was only one of the concerns expressed in public debates held at the time of the FSEs; concerns also included risks to human health, food safety, the power of multinational agrochemical companies, and the contamination of non-GM and organic produce. At present, there is no commercial planting of GM crops in the UK, and very little across Europe.

7.2.2.9 Government subsidies and regulation

The Common Agricultural Policy (CAP) and agri-environment schemes. Following the food shortages of WWII, the 1947 Agriculture Act mandated an intensification of food production to ensure self-sufficiency, which was facilitated by price support (Tracy 1989). Price support for increased productivity continued following the UK's accession to the EEC in 1973 and the implementation of the CAP (Young *et al.* 2005). These policies were highly successful, to the extent that, in the early 1980s, the CAP changed in emphasis, introducing measures to control surplus production. These actions included the imposition of milk quotas in 1984 and the introduction of set-aside from 1987. Set-aside involved taking arable land out of food production. While this measure was economic in intent, it also provided food and habitats for many farmland species as large areas of land were allowed to regenerate naturally (Firbank *et al.* 2003b). Environmental benefits were sought more actively through the UK's first agri-environment scheme in 1987 (see next paragraph). Subsequent CAP reviews in 1992, 1998 and 2003 increased support for environmental management and for activities other than food production (Bignal & McCracken 2000; Bignal *et al.* 2001; Dwyer *et al.* 2007). The 1992 CAP reforms 'fossilised' existing patterns of arable land use to a significant extent (Winter 2000). Most financial support provided to farmers is no longer dependent on them growing specific areas of crops or retaining a certain number of animals. Instead, a Single Payment Scheme is available to farmers, provided they meet cross compliance standards (ADAS 2009). That is, they undertake to comply with a range of conditions to ensure basic standards of environmental management, animal welfare and food safety, and keep their land in Good Agricultural and Environmental Condition (GAEC).

The main policy vehicles for delivering ecosystem services other than food production from Enclosed Farmland are agri-environmental schemes developed within the CAP, in which farmers are paid to manage the land for particular environmental benefits. Starting with the Environmentally Sensitive Areas Scheme in 1987, these have evolved differently in each country in the UK. More than 8 million ha of farmland in the UK are currently managed under agri-environment scheme agreements, although the actual area covered by specific agri-environment scheme management plans within farms is much smaller (Defra 2010a).

In England, the most recent scheme is Environmental Stewardship. This currently takes the form of Entry Level Stewardship (including an organic version), which is non-competitive and based on a threshold of points awarded for management measures, and the Higher Level Stewardship, which is targeted and competitive and provides funding towards more specific environmental management actions (such as habitat and species maintenance and enhancement, pollution mitigation, flood prevention, etc.). In 2009, there were 1,000 ha still in the Organic Farming Scheme (the predecessor of Organic Entry Level Stewardship), 372,000 ha still in the Countryside Stewardship Scheme (a predecessor of Environmental Stewardship), 462,000 ha still in the Environmentally Sensitive Areas Scheme, 5.6 million ha under Entry Level Stewardship and 453,000 ha under Higher Level Stewardship (Defra 2010a).

In Wales, Tir Gofal is a comprehensive scheme and is applicable on a whole farm basis throughout the country, while Tir Cynnal is a less demanding 'entry level' scheme.

In 2009, there were 377,000 ha in Tir Cymen/Tir Gofal and 281,000 ha in Tir Cynnal, along with 126,000 ha still in the older Organic Farming/Maintenance Schemes and 26,000 ha still in the Environmentally Sensitive Areas Scheme (Defra 2010a). From 2012, these schemes will be replaced by a single scheme, Glastir.

In Scotland, in 2009, 115,000 ha were in the Organic Aid Scheme, 174,000 ha were still in the Environmentally Sensitive Areas Scheme, 239,000 ha were in the Countryside Premium Scheme/Rural Stewardship Scheme, and 492,000 ha were in Land Management Contracts/Land Managers Options (Defra 2010a).

In Northern Ireland, in 2009, 468,000 ha, or 39% of farmland, was registered in an agri-environment scheme, including 7,000 ha in the Organic Farming Scheme, 352,000 ha in the Countryside Management Scheme, and 109,000 ha in the new Environmentally Sensitive Areas Scheme.

These payments have largely resulted in the preservation of existing habitats and features. For example, in England, 41% of hedgerows are now managed through the schemes and more than 6,000 archaeological features on farmland are protected under the schemes, including more than half of all scheduled monuments and registered battlefields (Natural England 2009a). There have also been benefits to educational access and landscape quality (Carey *et al.* 2003). New areas of habitat have been created, notably 116,000 km of grass buffer strips. Recent agri-environmental and set-aside policies are thought to be responsible for the 5.4% increase in enclosed grassland between 1998 and 2007 (Carey *et al.* 2008), restoring some landscape diversity to arable landscapes, although some of this area has since been returned to arable cropping (Section 7.2.2.8). They have produced increases in species abundance, yet so far only when focused on designated sites and targeted actions for particular range-restricted populations or experimental pilots (Aebischer *et al.* 2000; Kleijn & Sutherland 2003; Wilson *et al.* 2009). For instance, Countryside Stewardship projects helped cirl buntings (*Emberiza cirlus*) in England to increase by 133% between 1993 and 2009, and corncrakes (*Crex crex*) in Scotland to increase by 181% between 1994 and 2008 (McCracken & Midgley 2010). Widespread deployment of agri-environment scheme agreements has so far failed to reverse national declines of widespread species (Section 7.3.5). This may be because these schemes have had insufficient time to take effect, although there is also evidence that the most commonly adopted agri-environment measures are not necessarily those that benefit wildlife the most (Butler *et al.* 2007; McCracken & Midgley 2010).

Support for farm woodlands. The establishment of farm woodlands on land formerly in agricultural use has been supported by grants that compensate farmers for loss of agricultural income. The Woodland Grant Scheme (WGS), the Farm Woodland Scheme (FWS) and their successors led to the establishment of about 120,000 ha of new woodland between 1988 and 2005 (Usher *et al.* 1992; John Clegg *et al.* 2002; Forestry Commission 2009). Many of these woodlands have been created to support game shooting and wildlife conservation, rather than timber production (Duckworth *et* al. 2003). The impacts of woodland creation depend on a variety of factors including the taxa observed, and the size and location of the woodland (Usher et al. 1992; Usher & Keiller 1998).

Support for bioenergy. The UK aims to obtain 15% of all its energy from renewables by 2020, a target which will require significant increases in the contribution of renewables to each of the three energy sectors: electricity, heat and transport. While opportunities to use materials such as municipal solid waste and forestry waste are considerable (Gove et al. 2010), agricultural bioenergy in the form of biomass or biofuel crop products, or biogas from anaerobic digestion of agricultural or food waste, can contribute to each of the energy sectors.

The planting of perennial biomass crops on more marginal land is being encouraged to help relieve potential conflicts over land use (Lovett et al. 2009). Government incentives have been introduced to encourage establishment of bioenergy crops (e.g. Natural England's 2010 Energy Crops Scheme). The UK Biomass Strategy (DTI, DFT & Defra 2007) concluded that 350,000 ha of perennial energy crops were needed by 2020; this could be achieved without greatly affecting food production if they are grown on less productive land (Lovett et al. 2009). This forecast needs to be set against current biomass crop production, comprising willow from SRC and Miscanthus of 15,500 ha, indicating that a sharp increase in area of production is needed to meet demand. At present, a considerable amount of material, including timber and oil palm co-products, is imported to plug this gap (Gove et al. 2010). This analysis also excludes the estimated 740,000 ha required to grow crops for transport fuels (Booth et al. 2009).

Targets and regulations. Standards of environmental management of Enclosed Farmland are being set through European-wide legislation. In particular, the WFD sets objectives to improve the chemical and ecological status of watercourses, groundwater and coastal waters by 2015, and is likely to have a major impact on the way agricultural land is managed, as currently exemplified by the England Catchment Sensitive Farming Delivery Initiative (McCracken & Midgley 2010). The Scottish Environment Protection Agency and the Scottish Government have recently announced a new target for the restoration of Scotland's water bodies: they aim to bring 97% into 'good status' by 2027. This is very ambitious, especially as the hydrological cycle is likely to be altered by climate change, and changes in the amount, timing and distribution of precipitation and runoff will lead to changes in water availability.

Targets are also being established for improvements in climate regulation from Enclosed Farmland. These focus on reductions in emissions of the greenhouse gases methane and nitrous oxide, as they have high global warming potentials (carbon dioxide equivalent (CO_2e) values of 72 and 289 over a 20-year time horizon, respectively), and agriculture is a major source, accounting for 38% of all UK methane emissions and 69% of all UK nitrous oxide emissions in 2008 (Defra 2010a; Section 7.3.2.1). For example, the UK Low Carbon Transition Plan encourages English farmers to make and maintain a reduction in greenhouse gas emissions to a level (3 megatonnes (Mt) of carbon dioxide emissions) at least 11% lower than currently predicted for 2020. To help

meet this ambition, a farming industry Greenhouse Gas Action Plan was developed and published in February 2010 by the Climate Change Task Force. The Welsh Assembly Government set up an independent Land Use Climate Change Group in January 2009, which developed recommendations for reducing emissions by 2040 (CCC 2010). At the time of writing, the Welsh Assembly Government is reviewing report recommendations in order to develop an action plan to take forward various mitigation proposals. Scotland published its Climate Change Delivery Plan in June 2009, which proposes a reduction target for the agricultural land use sectors of 1.3 Mt CO_2 emissions by 2020. Northern Ireland's Department of Agriculture and Rural Development (DARD) established an internal Steering Group during 2009 to develop a range of primary production mitigation measures based on a review of available scientific evidence.

7.3 Ecosystem Goods and Services Provided by Enclosed Farmland for Human Well-being

An overview of the provision of the UK NEA classification of goods and services by Enclosed Farmland is shown in **Table 7.3**.

7.3.1 Provisioning Services

7.3.1.1 Food

The vast majority of parcels of Enclosed Farmland are managed primarily for a single ecosystem service, the provisioning of food, either directly for human consumption or feed for livestock. This service is met by the removal of large amounts of net primary production and the manipulation of nutrient cycles.

During the 19th Century, arable crops were usually grown within a rotation, most commonly the Norfolk four-course rotation of turnips, spring barley, clover or a grain, legumes and wheat (Johnston & Poulton 2009). Pest and disease infestation greatly limited yields and there was little understanding of basic crop nutritional requirements, with the exception that livestock manure boosted yields which was generally only applied to the most valuable root crops in the rotation. Agricultural productivity per unit area grew four-fold after WWII (Defra 2010a; Chapter 15), driven by the introduction of high-yielding varieties of crops, an ability to control pests and diseases effectively, and an all-round effective agronomy (including the introduction of selective herbicides and fungicides, and more effective use of nitrogen), supported by deliberate policy interventions. The relationship of wheat yields to these technological changes can be seen in the record of the long-term Broadbalk Experiment at Rothamsted Research (**Figure 7.7**); more than 90% of yield improvement in winter wheat over the

Table 7.3 Overview of final ecosystem services provided by Enclosed Farmland. Note: the impact values range from ++ to --, depending on the magnitude and direction of influence. ⊙ denotes high agreement with much evidence; ⊙ indicates high agreement with limited evidence. Ecosystem services are categorised as provisioning (P), regulating (R) or cultural (C).

Final ecosystem service	Importance of enclosed farmland for service	Impact of enclosed farmland on service	Evidence base	Comments
Crops, plants, livestock, fish, etc. (wild and domesticated)	High	++	⊙	Strong positive score: farmland is largely managed for crop and livestock production.
Trees, standing vegetation & peat	Low	+	⊙	Positive score, due to small but increasing areas of biomass crops.
Climate regulation	High	--	⊙	Strong negative score, due to emissions of Greenhouse gases and depletion of carbon in soils.
Water quantity	High	+ / -	⊙	Important for catching water for ground and surface waters, though flood risk mitigation potential often compromised by management.
Hazard regulation –vegetation & other habitats	High	--	⊙	Negative impact on sediment loss to watercourses, increasing flood risk downstream.
Waste breakdown & detoxification	High	-- / +	⊙	Negative score due to diffuse (mainly) pollution leaving farmland; positive score for ability to compost green waste / AD, and sewage disposal.
Wild species diversity including microbes	High	--	⊙	Negative impacts; status of microbes unknown.
Purification	Low	--	⊙	Negative impacts on water quality as a result of diffuse pollution.
Environmental settings – meaningful places incl. green & blue space	Low	Zero	⊙	Individual sites have less significance than spaces in cities or mountain tops.
Environmental settings – socially valued landscapes and waterscapes	High	++	⊙	Farming management is largely responsible for the landscapes that many people cherish.

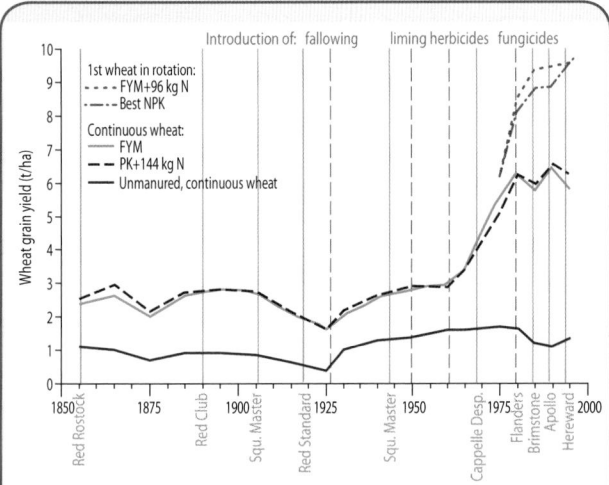

Figure 7.7 Yields of wheat grain (t/ha) through time on the Broadbalk Wheat Experiment at Rothamsted Research, plotted against variety, fertiliser treatment and agronomy (liming, herbicides, etc.). Source: reproduced from Goulding *et al.* (2009), with permission from the Philosophical Transactions of The Royal Society B.

new varieties with higher yields in experimental plots. This may be due to farmers managing the crop to maximise profit rather than yield, and also to more variable weather patterns (The Smith Institute 2009).

In grassland systems, both yield and digestibility of grass have increased greatly since 1945 (Hopkins 1999), while high milk-yielding Holstein Friesians have been crossed with breeds such as Herefords and Simmental to produce beef from dairy herds. Steady improvements in the efficiency of beef and sheep production have taken place over the past decade, resulting from improved genetics, fertility and feeding, better health measures, the use of artificial insemination, and industry-wide development and knowledge transfer initiatives. Genetic and management improvements in dairy cattle have seen the average cow increase milk production from 5,000 litres/year in 1989 to 7,600 l/yr in 2007 (The Milk Roadmap 2008), while the number of animals required to produce each tonne of meat fell by 5% from 3.23 in 1998 to 3.07 between 1998 and 2008 (EBLEX 2009). For more details on yield increases see Chapter 15.

Current levels of production mean that the UK is 60% self-sufficient in all foods, and 73% self-sufficient in indigenous foods (UK Agriculture 2010; Chapter 15; Chapter 21; **Figure 7.8**). In 2009, the area of cereals planted in the UK was 3.1 million ha, producing just over 22 million tonnes of grain (Defra 2010a). Cereal production in the UK is now

past 25 years has been due to new varieties that are able to respond to the application of fertilisers, although the use of pesticides has also been important. Over the past decade, there is little evidence of national yield increases in wheat, barley or oilseed rape, in spite of the regular introduction of

worth over £2.5 billion and is more than sufficient for the country's processing needs. Exports total 2–4 million tonnes, depending on the season, while the UK imports about 1 million tonnes of bread-quality wheat (The Smith Institute 2009). Between 1988 and 1993, approximately 55% of the fruit and vegetables consumed in the UK were domestically produced; subsequently, production went into decline and the proportion fell to 33% in 2006.

For most of the period since the 1980s, the UK's imports and exports of milk and other dairy products have broadly balanced. However, from 2004, the UK became a net importer. The main dairy herd was 1.9 million animals and the beef herd was 1.6 million animals, while there were 32 million sheep and lambs. The female pig breeding herd was 445,000 animals, and the poultry breeding flock was 9.6 million birds, but neither fulfilled all of the UK's needs (**Figure 7.8**). Today, UK farms produce 1.1 million tonnes of meat (EBLEX 2009) and over 13 billion litres of raw milk each year, around 6 billion litres of which is processed into liquid milk, mainly for drinking (The Milk RoadMap 2008; **Table 7.4**). In addition, the UK imports a further 1.1 billion l of milk (The Smith Institute 2009).

The contribution of food production to the UK GDP has fallen from almost 3% in 1973 to 1.5% in 1996 and around 0.6% in 2009, although the agri-food sector as a whole contributes 6.7% (Defra 2010a). In 2008, agriculture's share of Gross Value Added was greatest in Northern Ireland (1.20%) and least in England (0.56%) (note: these figures include production from the uplands as well as from Enclosed Farmland). Recent trends in the production, value and self-sufficiency of wheat, and a selection of other agricultural commodities produced principally on Enclosed Farmland, are shown in **Figure 7.8**, while trends in trade of various commodities are shown in **Figure 7.9.** These data shows the sharp rise in food prices in 2008. The real costs of major foods to UK consumers have also declined: in 1973, 19.7% of final household expenditure was on household food; by 2008 it had fallen to 8.8% (Defra 2010a).

7.3.1.2 Wild food

Enclosed Farmland provides a number of species that are valued as food such as field mushroom, blackberry and watercress (Mabey 1972). In addition, gamebirds and mammals are shot as part of crop protection activities (e.g. deer, rabbits (*Oryctolagus cuniculus*), pigeons) and recreational shooting (e.g. grey partridge, red-legged partridge (*Alectoris rufa*), pheasant). Although game species are technically wild animals, many are non-native and the subject of often intensive management. Many game species are hunted for pleasure, but, despite this, the majority of game animals that are killed in the UK will enter the human food chain in some form, either by being eaten by their hunter or after being sold to consumers, retailers or game dealers (see Chapter 15 for more detailed accounts of particular game species).

7.3.1.3 Bioenergy

The production of bioenergy is currently low but is expected to increase over the coming decade. Kilpatrick *et al.* (2008) suggested that the biomass resource required to achieve

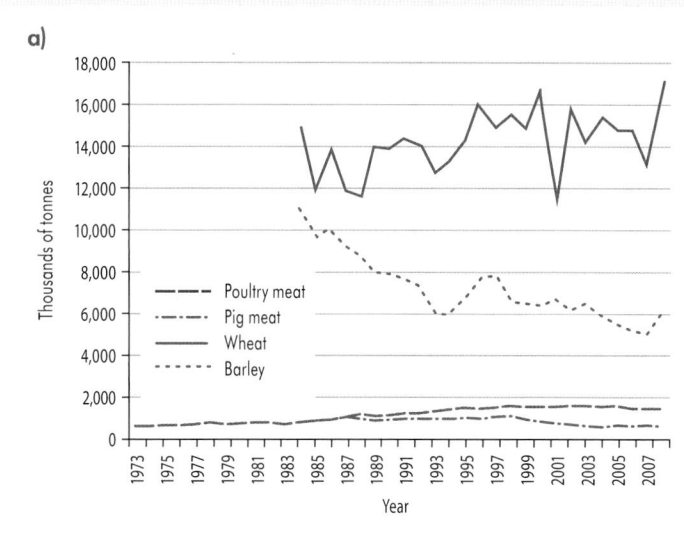

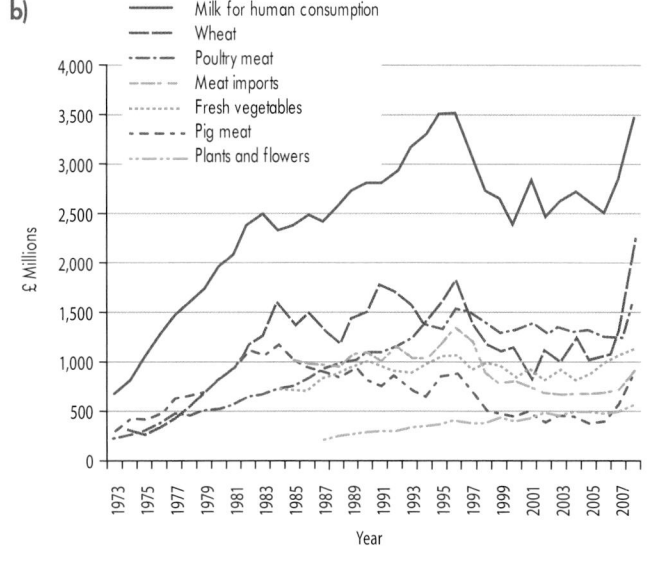

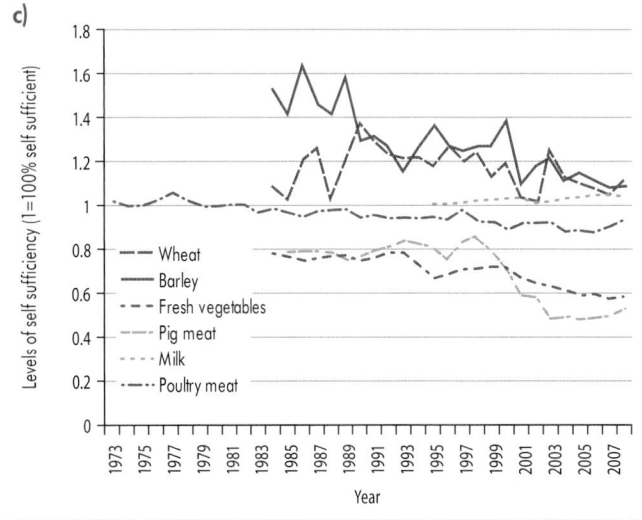

Figure 7.8 a) Amount (thousand tonnes) of production, b) value of production (£ million at market prices) and c) levels of self-sufficiency of exemplar agricultural products for the UK over time. Data focuses on those goods for which production is based in Enclosed Farmland, excluding protected crops. Source: data from Defra (2010a).

Table 7.4 Production of major agricultural commodities in the UK in 2008. At the time of writing, 2008 was the most recent year for which confirmed data were available. Data for cattle and sheep meat include production from non-enclosed farmland. Source: data from Defra (2010a).

Commodity	Production	Value at market prices	% of new supply for use in UK
Wheat	17 million tonnes	£2,245 million	110
Barley	6.1 million tonnes	£817 million	108
Oats	780,000 tonnes	£90 million	110
Oilseed rape	2.0 million tonnes	£618 million	102
Linseed	30,000 tonnes	£10 million	111
Sugar beet	7.6 million tonnes	£208 million	60 *
Potatoes	6.1 million tonnes	£767 million	82
Fresh vegetables	120,000 hectares	£1,104 million	58
Plants and flowers	20,000 hectares	£799 million	-£897 million [†]
Total fruit [‡]			11
Orchard fruit	18,000 hectares	£145 million	
Soft fruit	10,000 hectares	£359 million	
Beef and veal [¶]	860,000 tonnes	£2,068 million	82
Pigmeat [¶]	710,000 tonnes	£867 million	52
Mutton and lamb [¶]	330,000 tonnes	£798 million	88
Poultrymeat [¶]	1.5 million tonnes	£1,578 million	92
Milk [§]	13,000 million litres	£3,447 million	104
Hen's eggs	750 million dozen	£520 million	79

* refined sugar.
[†] % supply not available, here we give trade gap of value of exports— value of imports x gross indigenous production.
[‡] % supply only available for total fruit.
[¶] dressed carcass weight, gross indigenous production.
[§] for human consumption.

Table 7.5 Likely impacts of biomass crops on ecosystem services and biodiversity. ↑ positive impact; ↓ negative impact; ↔ no change; * limited data. Source: Rowe *et al.* (2009). Copyright (2009), reproduced with permission from Elsevier.

Environmental impact	Short rotation coppice (SRC)	*Miscanthus*	Biofuel crops (wheat, oilseed rape, sugarbeet)
Soil organic carbon	↑	↑	↔
Nitrogen leaching	↑↑↑	↑↑↑	↔
Visual impacts	↓	↓	↔
Energy and carbon balance	↑↑↑	↑↑↑	↑
Hydrology (at catchment scale)	↓	↓	↔
Biodiversity	↑↑	↑ *	↔
Avian	↑↑	*	↔
Flora	↑↑	*	↔
Invertebrates	↑↑ *	*	↔
Mammal and amphibians	*	*	↔

policy targets (Section 7.2.2.9) can be generated from straw from cereals and oilseed rape, along with energy and root crops on arable land. Much greater changes in land cover may occur on grassland, with the conversion of temporary grassland to energy crops and the conversion of permanent grassland and rough grazing to short rotation forestry (SRF).

The impacts on other ecosystem services depend greatly on how and where the bioenergy crops are introduced and managed (Firbank 2008; Lovett *et al.* 2009; Karp *et al.* 2009, Rowe *et al.* 2009; **Table 7.5**). The major benefit would be in terms of contribution to climate regulation. In theory, perennial crops, such as SRC, SRF and *Miscanthus*, can be close to carbon neutral because the quantities of carbon dioxide released to the atmosphere on combusting the crop are equal to those absorbed by photosynthesis during crop growth. The production of energy from straw entails only minimal additional carbon inputs over and above the food crop within the field. There are additional net carbon dioxide emissions associated with the management, harvesting and transport of bioenergy crops, and, in some instances, there may be loss of soil and vegetation carbon from the habitats bioenergy crops replace, although using arable soils for *Miscanthus* increases soil carbon stocks. Therefore, the total greenhouse gas mitigation potential of energy crops depends largely upon how they are grown, the energy costs of transport and the land use which they replace (St Clair *et al.* 2008; Hillier *et al.* 2009; Gove *et al.* 2010). Booth *et al.* (2009) suggest that replacing 12% of the total cropped area on an example arable farm with SRC would reduce total greenhouse gas emissions by 10.3%, mainly as a result of lower fertiliser use reducing nitrous oxide emissions. This reduction would be 7.7% if SRC willow replaced 12% of Improved Grassland area on an example mixed livestock farm (producing beef and lamb on a grass-based system), largely achieved by a reduction in livestock numbers.

Perennial bioenergy crops have high water requirements that would need to be accounted for in planning water regulation, but they have low nutrient requirements, with

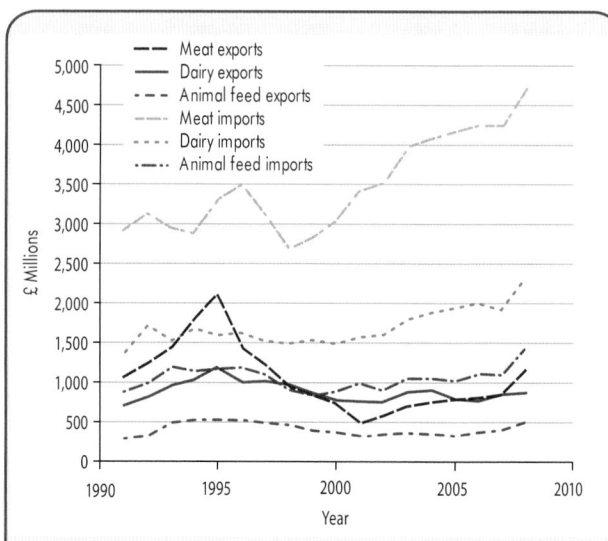

Figure 7.9 UK trade in meat, dairy and animal feed with the rest of the world (£ million at 2008 prices). Source: data from Defra (2010a).

little risk of diffuse pollution. Biodiversity should benefit, too: SRC and SRF would provide new habitats for taxa of small woodlands and perennial crops should not result in major impacts on species if planted on species-poor grasslands and avoiding locations important for species of open habitats. As *Miscanthus* is not native to the UK, it may support less biodiversity than SRC, and its biodiversity value may decline as it matures due to increased crop density. Plantings of energy crops could also be planned not to compromise the landscape quality of culturally valued areas.

7.3.2 Regulating Services

Enclosed Farmland regulates biogeochemical cycles of water, nutrients and carbon. Soil organisms cycle nutrients and carbon, though our understanding of the mechanisms by which soil biodiversity influences ecosystem processes and the delivery of supporting services, and how it responds to land management, is limited (Bardgett & Wardle 2010). The status of soil microbial and fungal functional diversity and their trends remains under-researched at the national level; although there is evidence that they can contribute to soil moisture retention and the attenuation of runoff, for example (Allton *et al.* 2007). The large area of Enclosed Farmland gives it a potentially important role in regulating services. However, current agricultural management often generates emissions of greenhouse gases and releases nutrients to air and water, resulting in Enclosed Farmland causing net disbenefits.

7.3.2.1 Climate regulation

Here, we focus on carbon sequestration, storage and greenhouse gas emissions within the fields and housing for livestock; emissions from the rest of the food chain are excluded from this analysis.

Permanent grassland soils are already close to carbon saturation (Bradley *et al.* 2005), making them important carbon stores rather than potential sinks. The large-scale loss of permanent grassland during the 20th century must have resulted in large releases of carbon (Smith *et al.* 2000a,b): they currently hold around 43 t/ha in the top 15 cm, which is a decline from 1998. Meanwhile, stocks under Improved Grassland have remained steady at 61 t/ha

(Carey *et al.* 2008). Conversion of temporary grassland or arable to permanent grassland or woodland will tend to lead to an increase in carbon sequestration, and the cessation of cultivation (especially of peat soils) will reduce carbon dioxide losses (Smith *et al.* 2008). Some techniques may help to enhance soil carbon in arable soils, for example, the input of organic materials such as green waste compost or digestate material derived from anaerobic digestion (Banks *et al.* 2009). In general, however, inputs of organic materials maintain soil carbon or slightly uplift the equilibrium level, resulting in a state which then needs to be maintained by continued inputs. Evidence of the success of no-tillage and minimum tillage regimes for maintaining and enhancing soil carbon is equivocal (Baker *et al.* 2007; Bhogal *et al.* 2008; Smith *et al.* 1998, 2008).

Despite this sequestration and store potential, UK agriculture generates net greenhouse gas emissions (**Figure 7.10**). Indeed, emissions from agriculture account for around 7.0% of the UK total, although there is variation between UK countries (LUCCG 2010).

While nitrous oxide emissions (53% of total agriculture emissions in 2008) arise naturally in agricultural soils through biological processes, they are especially associated with the oxidation of the nitrogen in inorganic and organic fertilisers on both arable and grassland. Emissions are greatly influenced by a variety of agricultural practices and activities, including the quantity of fertiliser applied, the deposition of manure onto soils by grazing animals, the nitrogen in crop residues returned to soils, the timing of fertiliser application, and other land management practices (such as drainage) which affect the proportion of nitrogen taken up by the crop, retained in the soil or released as nitrous oxide or other pollutants (CCC 2010).

Methane emissions (38% of agriculture emissions in 2008) within the agriculture sector mainly arise from enteric fermentation that occurs in the digestive systems of ruminants (e.g. cattle and sheep) and from manures. They are driven by the number of livestock animals, the characteristics of those animals (i.e. their breed, size, yield, digestive systems, etc.), what livestock are fed (for example, a diet with a higher maize content can maintain animal performance while decreasing the production of methane), and how manures are managed (CCC 2010).

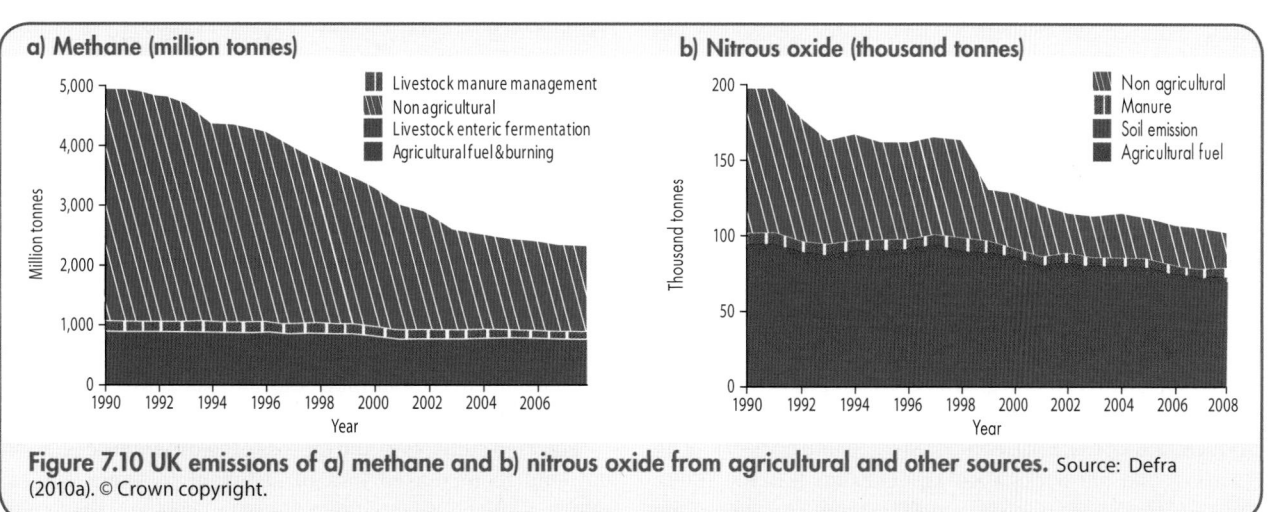

Figure 7.10 UK emissions of a) methane and b) nitrous oxide from agricultural and other sources. Source: Defra (2010a). © Crown copyright.

Carbon dioxide from agriculture accounts for less than 1.0% of the UK total, and is generated from the use of machinery in agriculture and, to some extent, from soil disturbance.

Since 1990, agricultural greenhouse gas emissions have fallen from 61 Mt CO_2e to 48 Mt CO_2e, decreasing from all direct sources: soils (-23%), enteric fermentation (-16%), wastes/manure management (-21%), and stationary/mobile combustion (-19%). Agricultural emissions have also declined across the range of greenhouse gases: nitrous oxide (-23%), methane (-18%) and carbon dioxide (-19%). Reductions in nitrous oxide emissions have been concentrated on grassland and are correlated with decreased fertiliser use (Defra 2010a), while reductions in methane emissions have resulted largely from decreases in the sizes of animal herds (note: there is an assumed correlation between animal numbers and emissions from manure management as the latter is calculated from the former) (CCC 2010). While reductions in ruminant numbers have had the greatest impact on agricultural emissions in the UK to date, these reductions contribute to improved climate regulation only if ruminant numbers do not increase elsewhere as a result of shifts in trade (Gill *et al.* 2010). Also, rising nitrous oxide emissions from fertiliser use is more than offsetting the reduction in methane emissions from lower livestock numbers, so much so that, without additional interventions, Scottish emissions from agriculture are projected to rise slightly in the future to about 7.3 Mt CO_2 emissions/yr in 2020 (Slee *et al.* 2009).

There is potential to reduce greenhouse gas emissions from arable systems through improved soil, fertiliser and agrochemical management (Smith *et al.* 2008; Macleod *et al.* 2010). Nitrous oxide emissions arising from crops and soils can be decreased by good nutrient planning, including improving efficiency in using fertiliser by, for example, taking full account of nitrogen in manure applications, timing applications to match crop requirements, using composts and straw-based manures in preference to slurry where practical, and separating slurry and mineral nitrogen application. Reductions in fertiliser use will also have emissions benefits beyond the farm gate, as fertiliser manufacture and transport is associated with high industrial carbon oxide emissions (CCC 2010). Other mitigation options include soil management measures (such as improved drainage), the use of nitrification inhibitors (which can reduce nitrous oxide emissions arising from fertiliser application, but do not necessarily lead to a reduction in fertiliser application levels), and the use of more nitrogen-efficient plants (including the introduction of different species) (CCC 2010).

There is scope to reduce greenhouse gas emissions from the livestock sector per kilogram of product (EBLEX 2009). Animal diet can have a profound impact on emissions. For instance, the poorer quality nutrition and longer production times of hill sheep mean that much higher greenhouse gas emissions per kilogram of lamb are produced because lower quality forages tend to generate higher methane emissions and slow growth results in greater emissions than more rapid growth and earlier slaughter. Thus, lowland sheep flocks produce 12.6 kg CO_2e/kg, compared to upland flocks (13.8 kg CO_2e/kg) and hill flocks (18.4 kg CO_2e/kg) (EBLEX 2009). Gaseous emissions from livestock systems can, therefore,

be reduced by breeding to influence productivity and fertility (respecting animal welfare concerns), modifications to diet to reduce enteric fermentation (such as using maize-silage instead of low quality forage that stimulates methane production), and, subject to satisfactory resolution of animal welfare concerns, a shift to utilising dietary additives such as propionate precursors (CCC 2010). Methane emissions from stored manures and slurries can be reduced through the installation of on-farm or centralised anaerobic digestion plants to generate energy, and by covering and aerating slurry and manure while stored (CCC 2010). However, many of these practices are not yet widely adopted.

7.3.2.2 Water quantity, hazard regulation, waste breakdown and detoxification, and purification

The management of Enclosed Farmland has large impacts on the management of water, pollutants and waste products, not least because of the large areas of land involved. Farmland can be both a source and a sink for waste and toxins. As these functions are interlinked through hydrological and biogeochemical processes, they are considered together here.

Water quantity and flood risk. River water and groundwater are important resources for agriculture. Although water used for agriculture represents about 2.0% of that abstracted in the UK, much is used in the south and east of England during summer, already areas of particular pressure for water resources (Defra 2010a). Also, 62% of water needed to produce goods consumed in the UK is so-called 'virtual water', i.e. embedded in the water needed to produce those goods (agricultural and non-agricultural) overseas (HM Government 2010; Chapter 21). Recently, WWF estimated the water needs for agricultural production in the UK at 34,000 million m^3/yr, with a net UK water footprint of 28,000 million m^3 /yr, contrasting with an external footprint of 46,000 million m^3/yr of food imported into the UK (Chapagain & Orr 2008).

Agricultural use of water can have both positive and negative contributions to flooding, soil erosion and the recharge of aquifers. Plant cover, root architecture, drainage and field and watercourse boundary management all contribute to speeding up or slowing the movement of water across farmland, albeit at a local level, and these effects are easily masked at the catchment scale. Under waterlogged conditions agriculture is very severely restricted, so much agricultural land is drained in order to shift water off the land surface as quickly as possible; this increases the flood risk downstream, however. In addition, biomass crops are fast-growing and consume large amounts of soil water which can, in turn, have a negative impact on groundwater recharge. By contrast, grasses, trees and other waterside vegetation can slow down runoff and help reduce diffuse pollution (Pilgrim *et al.* 2010; Bilotta *et al.* 2007). Some Enclosed Farmland in floodplain areas is managed through grazing to hold water and contribute to flood management, but the size of such areas declined considerably during the 20th Century, in conjunction with increased river canalisation.

Powered cultivation and the loss of field margin vegetation can lead to increased loss of sediment to watercourses, reducing habitat quality for biodiversity (including economically important salmonids), blocking channels and increasing flood risk. Analysis of sediment cores in recent years has revealed that sedimentation of UK reservoirs has intensified in response to an increase in arable area and the adoption of field drains, thus contributing to reduced water storage capacity (Foster 2006).

Air quality. The major impacts of the management of Enclosed Farmland on air quality are the emissions of methane (covered in Section 7.3.2.1) and ammonia. Ammonia is a nitrogen compound released by the breakdown of urea and uric acid from urine, poultry faeces and inorganic fertilisers. It can be dispersed through the air and in rainfall, to be deposited on soils and vegetation, acidifying and adding nitrogen to systems, and causing an odour nuisance and negative impacts on biodiversity in both terrestrial and aquatic environments. Because it is soluble and reactive, it tends to be deposited quite quickly, and the effects are particularly damaging to vegetation close to major sources (Maier *et al.* 2008). In 2007, 91% of UK ammonia emissions were from agriculture (Defra 2010b). Emissions arise predominately from livestock housing and from the spreading of animal manure—each accounting for around a quarter of the total from agriculture—and the majority are associated with cattle. Inorganic nitrogen fertilisers account for around 12% of the total from agriculture. Urea fertiliser, in particular, is associated with much greater ammonia emissions than other fertiliser types, and the relative proportion of urea to total fertiliser applied (largely influenced by relative costs) is responsible for much of the year-to-year variability in soil emissions (Defra 2010b). The total emissions of ammonia for 2007 are estimated at 0.29 Mt, compared to the 1990 estimate of 0.36 Mt, representing a 21% reduction, primarily due to declining livestock numbers, especially cattle and pigs (Jackson *et al.* 2009), and reduced fertiliser use (Defra 2010b).

Diffuse pollution to watercourses. From a European perspective, diffuse pollution from agricultural land remains the biggest threat to recreational waters through reductions in water quality caused by contaminated runoff water. Contaminants include nitrogen, phosphorus, sediments and pesticides, as well as parasites that impact on human health (McIntyre *et al.* 2009; Section 7.3.1.2). As reported in Chapter 9, there has been a major improvement in lowland river quality over the past two decades, with chemical and biological classification of several rivers being improved between 1990 and 2008. Yet this is thought to reflect improvements in waste water treatment more than changes in agricultural practice. There has been some overall improvement in chemical river quality in Northern Ireland since 2003; however, biological river quality has deteriorated (DARD 2010).

In Enclosed Farmland, nitrogen compounds are removed through the harvesting of crops, and so need to be replaced. However, they are not used by plants with perfect efficiency, it is not always practical to apply them at the correct levels at the correct time, and economic agricultural production entails adding more nitrogen than the plants actually require, albeit at levels that are declining nationally (Section 7.2.2.4). Excess nitrogen compounds from fertilisers, manures or any other sources may be released as nitrate leaching to ground and surface waters, may contribute to soil acidification, or

may be released as atmospheric emissions of ammonia, nitrous oxide and methane. Agriculture accounts for about 60% of nitrates in rivers (Hunt *et al.* 2004) and, consequently, influences coastal water quality and fisheries (EEA 2001). The increasing levels of soil fertility in and around Enclosed Farmland are associated with the rising trend of lowland vegetation becoming more homogenous and typical of higher nutrient status (Smart *et al.* 2006b; Firbank *et al.* 2008). Although nitrate concentration increased in almost 4,000 km of lowland rivers in England and Wales between 1995 and 2008, nitrate levels in English rivers have fallen overall since 2000 (despite an increase in 2004), reflecting a decrease in fertiliser use (Defra 2010a; **Figure 7.11a**). The proportion of river length with nitrate levels greater than 30 mg nitrate per litre is low in Northern Ireland, Wales and Scotland compared to England (DARD 2010).

Agriculture is also a major source of phosphorus, the primary nutrient responsible for eutrophication in freshwater (Jarvie *et al.* 2010), affecting the ecological balance of the aquatic environment and leading to changes in animal community structure (Maier *et al.* 2008; Jarvie *et al.* 2010; Chapter 9). Phosphorus from fertilisers tends to bind with soil particles, so sediment loss is associated with elevated phosphorus concentrations in waters and accounts for around 29% of phosphates in rivers (White & Hammond 2006; DARD 2010). Jarvie *et al.* (2010) reported diffuse sources of phosphorus contributing more than 90% of total load across three differing agricultural catchments. Dudley and May (2007) suggest as much as 20% of the phosphorus load in a rural catchment may be derived from septic tanks, and losses from sewage treatment works may well be responsible for continued elevated phosphorus levels in many waters (Jarvie *et al.* 2008a,b; Withers *et al.* 2009). Sediment and phosphorus loads are generally higher under arable systems than grassland ones, although pathways are highly site-specific and grassland loads can be high where grazing pressure is intense or there are additional inputs of phosphorus from manure (Watson & Foy 2001). Sediment fluxes depend on land use history and weather variability; over the past 40 to 100 years, they have tended to increase in the most intensively managed catchments but have recently fallen (**Figure 7.11b**).

Environmental risks caused by agricultural pesticides reaching watercourses from Enclosed Farmland are now very low (Chapter 9). In England and Wales, 10.1% of river length is at risk, or probably at risk, from agricultural pesticides and sheep dip, but these areas are concentrated in the uplands, rather than in Enclosed Farmland (Environment Agency 2011).

Diffuse pollution can be managed using many different approaches according to location, farming system and resources available. For example, precision farming techniques can be used to target inputs and reduce waste. Minimum tillage can reduce the transport of sediment and associated phosphorus to water via surface runoff, relative to conventional ploughing (SOWAP 2007; Deasy *et al.* 2008). Strategically sited grass buffer strips can also reduce overland sediment and nutrient runoff to watercourses (Borin *et al.* 2004), though the sediment can still sometimes be flushed out in large storm events. Field edge detention ponds can be used to trap phosphorus lost from field drains (Stoate *et al.* 2006), while ditches also reduce the impacts of agricultural pollutants on watercourses (Herzon & Helenius 2008). While it is possible, in principle, to consider which measures are most cost-effective, we lack the data that takes into account how different measures can interact at the catchment scale (Haygarth *et al.* 2009).

Anaerobic digestion and composting. Enclosed Farmland can provide waste breakdown services if the farmer imports waste biological material for anaerobic digestion or composting. Anaerobic digestion is widely used in Germany and Austria, and uptake is increasing in the UK. Agricultural manures, domestic organic waste materials and crops such as maize are digested in a vat to produce methane for use as an energy source; digestates that can be returned to the land to enhance soil organic matter, carbon and, potentially, industrial feedstocks, depending on the substrate and conditions in the digester (Banks *et al.* 2009).

7.3.2.3 Pollination

Many of the UK's field crops (e.g. oilseed rape, field beans, linseed), top fruits (e.g. apples, pears, plums), soft fruits (e.g. strawberries, raspberries, blackcurrants) and vegetables (e.g. tomatoes and peas) are dependent, at least in part, on insect pollination (Free 1993). Pollinator-dependent crops covered 20% of the UK's cropped area in 2007 (England: 23%; Northern Ireland: 5%; Scotland: 8%; Wales: unknown), and this area has increased by 41% since 1989 (Defra 2009a; Basic Horticultural Statistics 1999, 2008). Pollinators also support uncropped biodiversity by mediating seed and fruit set of many plants which feed invertebrates, birds and mammals (Jacobs *et al.* 2009).

Pollination is provided by managed honey bees (*Apis mellifera*) and a wide range of wild insect species including bumblebees, solitary bees, hoverflies, butterflies and moths. Between 1985 and 2005, honey bee colonies severely declined in number: in England, they dropped by 54%; in Northern Ireland declines are unknown; in Scotland they declined by 15%; and in Wales by 23% (Potts *et al.* 2010a). Wild bees and hoverflies are also in serious decline, with more than half of UK landscapes studied showing a significant loss of bee diversity (Biesmeijer *et al.* 2006). These declines in our pollinators have multiple causes, but a key driver is the loss of flower-rich, semi-natural landscape elements in farmland (Tscharntke *et al.* 2005; Winfree *et al.* 2009; Le Féon *et al.* 2010) such as flower-rich field margins, species-rich meadows and arable plants in crops. The loss of grass and clover leys, and the legumes they contain, has also been important (Carvell *et al.* 2006), and pesticides have been shown to have lethal and sub-lethal effects on bees (Morandin *et al.* 2005), resulting in local losses in bee diversity (Brittain *et al.* 2010).

The impacts of declines in pollinators on food production are not known. Yet the presence of semi-natural features in the landscape provides an ongoing supply of nectar and pollen which can maintain and increase crop pollination services (Kremen *et al.* 2007; Ockinger & Smith 2007; Ricketts *et al.* 2008). Several studies suggest that proximity to 'natural habitat' can influence crop pollination by native bees (Ricketts *et al.* 2008).

Pollination can be enhanced by providing high quality bee habitat such as flower-rich field margins in arable (Carvell *et al.* 2007) and grassland systems (Potts *et al.* 2009); such habitat management is supported by agri-environment schemes.

7.3.2.4 Biological pest control

Biological pest control is provided by a wide range of invertebrate predators and parasitoids, such as carabids, spiders and ladybirds (Collins *et al.* 2002; Schmidt *et al.* 2003), but it is extremely difficult to demonstrate causal relationships between such enhancement and increased food production. This is because it is not possible to establish the ideal experimental comparisons at the scale of whole fields and landscapes. In addition, natural enemies tend to be best at keeping pest populations at low levels, rather than at controlling major pest outbreaks. There is good evidence of habitat enhancement within crop fields, such as the upkeep of grass field margins, having positive effects on the abundance of natural enemies of many pest species (Landis *et al.* 2000; Collins *et al.* 2003). Yet little is known about trends in national populations of these invertebrates.

7.3.3 Supporting Services

The major supporting services provided by Enclosed Farmland include soil formation, nutrient cycling and primary production (Chapter 13). These all contribute to provisioning services described in Section 7.3.1, and also to

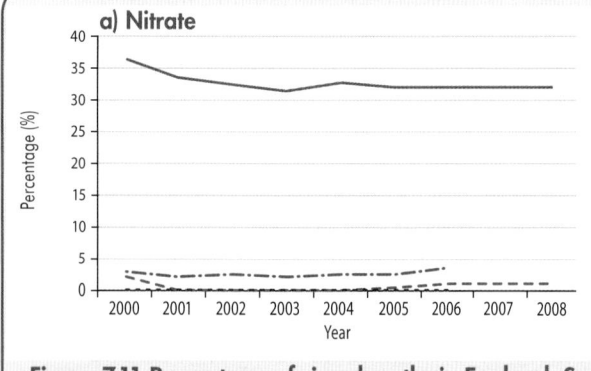
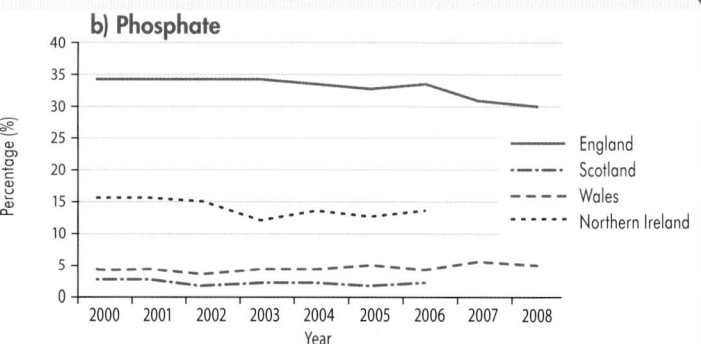

Figure 7.11 Percentage of river lengths in England, Scotland, Wales and Northern Ireland with high levels of a) nitrate (NO₃*; levels greater than 30 mg NO₃/l) and b) phosphate (P; levels greater than 0.1mg P/l) from 2000 to 2008. * Note: no values for Northern Ireland exceeded zero. Source: Defra (2010a) © Crown copyright.

some of the regulating services described in Section 7.3.2, and so are not considered separately here.

7.3.4 Cultural Services

The Enclosed Farmland of the UK is characterised by a diversity of scenery and habitat which is influenced, and valued, by many people and institutions. Enclosed Farmland provides cultural services (environmental settings; Chapter 16) to those people who live and work within it, to those who make journeys to it, and to those who enjoy less direct interactions with it, such as through reading, art, television, or by purchasing goods and services that have some form of positive association with conserving lowland farming landscapes. It can play an important role in providing contacts with nature and the living world for those who can not, or do not wish to, travel to more remote locations (Harrison *et al.* 1987; Crouch & Lubbren 2003). Here, we treat different kinds of services separately, but in practice the benefits they bring to people are often highly interactive.

7.3.4.1 Employment

Mechanisation and the economies of scale have impacted on the number of people working in agriculture, which declined from about 4 million in 1850 to around 1 million in the 1950s and 1960s (5% of the workforce); now, there are only 470,000 agricultural workers, fewer than 2% of the total UK workforce (Defra 2010a). Horticulture employs over 95,000 people (The Smith Institute 2009). The workforce for the agri-food sector as a whole is much higher at 3.6 million people, or 13.7% of the UK workforce (Defra 2010a).

7.3.4.2 Sense of place and aesthetics

The degree to which agricultural landscapes provide meaningful places for individuals varies greatly according to the nature of the landscape itself, its accessibility and the variation in values, attitudes and behaviours of individuals. In the UK, the defining sense of place appears to be built around typically rural landscapes (Weiner 2004), although preferences vary across the country. In Scotland, for example, the landscape and habitats of the Highlands provide the popular national identity. In Wales, an urban, industrial and largely English-speaking identity prevails in the south, but a rural, agricultural and Welsh-speaking one dominates in the north.

Enclosed Farmland landscapes are more important for the English sense of place. The English value the notion of 'deep England' (Matless 1998), with lowland agricultural landscapes symbolising continuity, social stability and a productive nature (Lowenthal 1991).

A recent report (Natural England 2009b) concluded that: "grassland was regarded as a flatland, which (on the whole) was not regarded as a highly interesting type of landscape. However, if people thought of it as a wild untouched meadow with wild flowers, then it was considered to be very beautiful and inspirational for painters." Indeed, while the term 'grassland' was associated with low delivery of cultural services relating to history, sense of place, leisure and spirituality, 'field systems' were generally highly valued and were felt by the same people to have worth for a sense of history, place and calm. Within 'field systems', small, irregular field systems, such as those of traditional pastoral (grassland) landscapes, were valued more highly than large arable fields; such systems also tend to be rich in biodiversity (Benton *et al.* 2003; Section 7.3.5). For many, hedgerows are quintessential and locally distinctive features which reflect cultural history, conserve outlines of past land use and define many rural landscapes. An improved knowledge of land use history enhances a sense of place and ownership of current environmental problems and opportunities (Stoate 2010).

In 2002–2003, the English Leisure Day Visits survey found that 25% of British adults had visited National Parks over the last 12 months and 7% had visited an Area of Outstanding Natural Beauty (AONB). Across the UK, there there are 49 AONBs and 14 National Parks. Although many of these are associated with open upland or coastal landscapes, a large proportion contain areas of Enclosed Farmland, while much of the character of the remainder comes from their Enclosed Farmland and mixture of crops, grass, hedgerows and woodlands (for example, the Cotswolds AONB and South Downs National Park). In England, the Enclosed Farmland at the edges of larger cities is protected from urban development by its designation of 'Green Belt land' which, in 2009, was estimated to be about 13% of the land area (Commission for Rural Communities 2008).

Traditional farm buildings provide a wide range of cultural benefits across all but the most remote landscapes of England (Gaskell & Owen 2005; Countryside Agency 2006). They provide an essential contribution to local character and to the sense-of-place enjoyed by rural communities and visitors alike, especially in certain areas such as the Cotswolds and Yorkshire Dales. They are critical to our understanding of settlement patterns and the development of the countryside. They tell us much about how our ancestors farmed and lived, and represent a historical investment in materials and energy that can be sustained through conservation and careful reuse. They are repositories of local crafts, skills and techniques, and were built using traditional materials (often closely related to the local geology) that are sometimes not available or too expensive for new building projects. They can also alleviate pressure to build on green-field land and reduce the demand for new buildings. They provide economic assets for farm and rural businesses. Some provide habitats for wildlife, particularly more generalist and common species.

Some farmland taxa have strong cultural importance and particular resonance with the public, given their widespread distribution and proximity to settlements (Mabey 1997; Donald 2004; Crocker & Mabey 2005). Examples include skylarks (*Alauda arvensis*) and other songbirds, butterflies and hedgerow flowers. One expression of this appeal is the mass participation in volunteer surveys such as the Breeding Bird Survey, Butterfly Monitoring scheme and Moths Count scheme (Defra 2009b).

7.3.4.3 Leisure

There are around 188,700 km of public rights of way in England, much of which crosses Enclosed Farmland; 78% are public footpaths giving a right of way on foot; 17% are bridleways giving access to pedestrians, horse riders and cyclists; and 5% are restricted byways along which vehicles may travel (Commission for Rural Communities 2008). According to Natural England's 2005 English Leisure Visits Survey, approximately one third of visits were to the countryside, with coast and woodlands the most favoured destinations. The duration of the visits was split equally between more than and less than three hours, with nearly 60% using a car and 25% walking, suggesting that there is likely to be a fairly even division between visits to meaningful local places and visits to socially valued landscapes. More than 184,000 people attended events on 420 farms for Linking Environment and Farming (LEAF)'s Open Farm Sunday in 2010. In 2006, it was estimated that there were around 1 million horses in the UK, and 4.4 million people (or 7% of the GB population) had ridden horses in the previous 12 months. Of these, 1.1 million are estimated to be 'regular riders' (Commission for Rural Communities 2008). It is not clear how much Enclosed Farmland is being managed primarily for horses and other leisure uses.

Game shooting is widely associated with lowland farmland, which is modified to meet the requirements of (mainly) released non-native pheasants and red-legged partridges (Dickson et al. 2009). Around 370,000 people regularly shoot game in England and this activity supported around 54,000 full-time equivalent jobs and influenced the management of over 8.5 million ha of countryside (PACEC 2006). Twenty-two percent of shoots are operated as businesses (PACEC 2006), but, in a wider sense, shooting is an economic activity involving the purchase of poults for releasing, the trade in shot game, and other employment associated directly or indirectly with the shoot.

7.3.4.4 Human health

Enclosed Farmland provides a vital health benefit to the UK's population by providing safe, nutritious food; UK foodstuffs are monitored to ensure pesticide residues are kept well below safety levels. Enclosed Farmland also provides health benefits associated with exercise and recreation in the countryside (Barton & Pretty 2010). Moreover, living in the countryside reduces inequalities in death rates between rich and poor (Mitchell & Popham 2008). Health risks from Enclosed Farmland are greatest from mechanical injury to the workforce, but primary airborne particulates arising from intensive livestock housing and field operations can cause human respiratory problems (Foley et al. 2005). Opponents of GM crops have raised the issue of health risks to people, but there are no examples of human health being affected by exposure to these crops.

Health risks arise to users of bathing water from parasites found in livestock faeces, such as Escherichia coli 0157:H7 (FAO 2006) and Cryptosporidium (Patz et al. 2004), being transported by surface water into ditches, streams and rivers. In practice, it is hard to distinguish between microbial pollution arising from agricultural diffuse and domestic point sources, in particular, septic tanks (Neal et al. 2010). As well as affecting water quality in the immediate vicinity of the septic tank and downstream, such pollution may have implications for marine water quality and the associated bathing areas and shellfish industry (Harris 1995; Geary & Davies 2003). In addition to generic faecal coloniforms, the microorganisms

discharged from septic tank effluents may include pathogenic types, such as Salmonella species, various E. coli and Enterococcus species (Harris et al. 1995; Geary & Davies 2003), and enteric viruses (Scandura & Sobsey 1997). To date, no human infections within the UK have been directly linked to pathogens from septic tanks, although such links have been proven elsewhere. The majority of septic tank systems in agricultural catchments are thought to be old and the costs of retrospective fitting of treatments systems (Harrison et al. 2000; Tanner et al. 2002) could prove prohibitive.

Other risks to human health include releases of antibiotics and sediments from eroded pastures (Fewtrell et al. 2005; FAO 2006); however, the emergence of antibiotic resistance in the UK is unlikely as antibiotics are not allowed as growth promotors. For more detail on disease regulation see Chapter 14, Tables 14.9–14.11.

7.3.5 Wild Species Diversity

Enclosed Farmland is associated with a suite of species favoured by habitats that are early successional, open, disturbed and/or in ecotones and mosaics with woodland. It is home to both specialist and generalist plants and animals, which contribute in various ways to provisioning, regulating, cultural and supporting services (see Section 7.3), although quantitative data are usually lacking on the values and benefits they provide. Arable specialists are typically associated with relatively stable, early successional conditions; for example, many of the UK's rarest plants are associated with long-term cereal agriculture. Species-rich grasslands in farmed landscapes are addressed in Chapter 6.

In agricultural landscapes, biodiversity is greatest where there is heterogeniety of habitats over multiple scales of space and time (Benton et al. 2003). This is because such landscapes provide a range of ecological niches, turnover of habitats for those species that require it, the possibility of dispersal between habitats, and conditions for those species that require more than one habitat. Most species that are regarded as emblematic of high quality countryside, such as songbirds, butterflies and hedgerow flowers, are adapted to such complex mosaics. Farming systems that promote such diversity, notably organic, tend to support such species in greater abundance per unit area (Fuller et al. 2005).

The Enclosed Farmland UK NEA Broad Habitat contains two Biodiversity Action Plan (BAP) habitats, namely arable field margins and hedgerows. In turn, these include BAP priority species (65 and 83 in the two habitats, respectively) such as pheasant's-eye (Adonis annua), grey partridge and brown hare (Lepus europaeus). Hedgerows provide primary habitat for 13 globally threatened or rapidly declining species and, where they are ancient or remnants of ancient woodland, may act as refuges for characteristic woodland plants and ancient trees. Although they are often small in area, long-established farm woodlands may have high conservation value, especially if they are ancient woodland (Goldberg et al. 2007). Farm ponds contribute considerably to the biodiversity of agricultural ecosystems, supporting more species, more unique species and more scarce species than other types of waterbody (Williams et al. 2004). Ditches (most of which are seasonal) are the least species-rich aquatic habitat associated with farmland, but support uncommon species, including temporary water invertebrates not recorded in other waterbody types (Williams *et al.* 2004)

Declines in species diversity and abundance. Changes in agricultural practices must have always resulted in population ebbs and flows according to which species were best suited to the prevailing land management regimes (Stoate 1995, 1996; Shrubb 2003). But changes in Enclosed Farmland during the 20th Century changed the balance between provisioning of food and biodiversity. The result has been major declines in the diversity and numbers of plants, terrestrial invertebrates and vertebrates (Potts 1986; Rich & Woodruff 1996; Ewald & Aebisher 1999; Chamberlain *et al.* 2000; Robinson & Sutherland 2002; Holloway 2002; Shrubb 2003; Wilson *et al.* 2009). It is hard to quantify long-term declines, given that they started well before biological recording systems had been established, but indications of trends can be seen from wild game counts (Tapper 1999), biodiversity on traditionally managed areas, such as hay meadows and some plots in the Rothamsted classic experiments, and from archaeological records.

The majority of agricultural grassland is now species-poor and structurally uniform (Wilson *et al.* 2005) because of greater fertiliser inputs (Firbank *et al.* 2008), increased stocking levels and a switch from hay-making to silage production (Chamberlain *et al.* 2000; Petit & Elbersen 2006). While most species-rich grassland had been lost by the 1980s (Fuller 1987), the process of species loss continued until 1998, with no significant change detected between 1998 and 2007 (Carey *et al.* 2008). These trends do, however, vary nationally; for example, plant species richness in Scottish Improved Grasslands declined by 7% between 1998 and 2007 (Norton *et al.* 2009a).

Similarly, the use of fertilisers, selective herbicides and the switch from spring-sown to autumn-sown cereals has impacted on the arable flora. Many broadleaved arable plants declined markedly between 1960 and 2000 (Preston *et al.* 2002), and probably before; arable plants now comprise the most nationally threatened element of the UK's flora. By contrast, there have been increases in some competitive grass plants that are less sensitive to herbicide control in cereals and are better suited to autumn-sown crops (e.g. blackgrass, *Alopecurus myosuroides*). Plant species diversity and abundance now tend to be higher at field margins (Marshall *et al.* 2003) and in those relatively few fields where management has not been so intensive (Watkinson *et al.* 2000).

The flora of field boundaries has also changed, with increases in plants that are competitive and have high nutrient requirements, and decreases in plants that are important food resources for pollinators and farmland birds. This has been largely driven by the increasing nutrient status of Enclosed Farmland (Smart *et al.* 2000). Other possible causes include changes in management and drift of pesticides, although this is not considered a major problem with modern methods of spraying (Roy *et al.* 2003). Plant species diversity in grassland has become largely confined to field edges (Smart *et al.* 2002, 2006c; Walker *et al.* 2009) as these areas have been impacted less by these changes.

Changes in the plant composition of Enclosed Farmland have inevitably impacted species higher up the ecological food chain (**Box 7.2**). Within arable fields, numbers of invertebrates at higher trophic levels are related to numbers of foodplants (Hawes *et al.* 2003). There is evidence of

Box 7.2 The Sussex Study: a long-term study of a farmland ecosystem.

In the late 1960s, a national decline in numbers of grey partridges (*Perdix perdix*) was causing concern, so a programme of research and monitoring was set up in Sussex to elucidate what was happening, and has continued uninterrupted ever since (Potts *et al.* 2010b). Grey partridges and other wildlife, especially insects, have been monitored by the Game & Wildlife Conservation Trust on 12 farms across the South Downs between Arundel and Worthing. Forming the first ever study of the wildlife associated with cereal farming, results revealed that the decline of the grey partridge in the 1960s was a consequence of a fall in chick survival rate caused by a shortage of insects in the chicks' diet during the first two weeks after hatching. As a result, from 1970 onwards, information regarding grey partridge abundance and productivity, crop types, invertebrate densities and overall weed abundance has been collected from 32 km² in June and September every year using the same methods. Pesticide data is also available for most farms. Thus this 40-year study is the longest of its type anywhere in the world and spans some substantial changes in agriculture including the introduction and widespread use of insecticides and fungicides, the switch from spring to autumn sowing of cereals and the decline of mixed farming (arable and livestock).

Early findings from the study were instrumental in highlighting the indirect effects of pesticide use, in particular, the effects of herbicides. The removal of weeds through herbicide use led to a reduction in the abundance of insects, especially those that feed on weeds. This disrupted the food chain on which grey partridge productivity depended. Consequently, the Sussex Study is considered to have accumulated the best and most continuous evidence for the indirect effects of pesticides on farmland birds. Over the duration of the project, the overall abundance of invertebrates has declined by 43%. The decline was steepest between 1970 and 1985, but there has since been some recovery. Of these invertebrates, the fungus-feeding species have declined by 77% and the predators and parasites by 47%.

The Sussex Downs are recognised as one of the hot spots for rare arable plants and 171 species have been identified in the project area. Although the total number of weed species has remained stable over the last 40 years, 19 species have been lost or become very rare, while 18 species have been added. Analysis of herbicide data has revealed that the timing of their use is important, with spring herbicide applications being most damaging to the arable flora, and, in turn, having the greatest effect on the abundance of insects and the subsequent productivity of grey partridge.

Long-term study site of farmland in Sussex. Initial work on invertebrates and arable flora on this study site led to conservation headlands (in foreground). Photo courtesy of Peter Thompson / Game & Wildlife Conservation Trust.

declines in pollinators (Section 7.3.2.3.) and aerial insects occurring over several decades, though not in all locations (Benton *et al.* 2002; Shortall *et al.* 2009).

Reductions in safe nest sites, invertebrates during the breeding season and in seed resources in the autumn and winter have resulted in major reductions in numbers of farmland birds (Chamberlain *et al.* 2000; Krebs *et al.* 1999; Boatman *et al.* 2004). Between the start of the time-series of annual bird surveys in the 1970s and the early 1990s, the UK population of farmland birds almost halved, remaining relatively stable ever since (**Figure 7.12**). There is some variation in pattern between the four UK countries; for instance, numbers have been essentially stable in Scotland. With regards to species trends, populations of farmland generalists, including corvids and pigeons, have remained around or above the 1970 level. However, those specialist species that rely on plants and invertebrates of Enclosed Farmland, such as grey partridge and corn bunting (*Emberiza calandra*) have continued to decline and numbers are now about a third of what they were in 1970 (**Figure 7.12**).

In grasslands, birds have been directly affected by the reduction in botanic species richness and subsequent declines in weed seeds and key invertebrate prey (Woodcock *et al.* 2009). They have also been indirectly affected by other changes in field management (Vickery *et al.* 2001) including: increased defoliation pressure from both silage-cropping and grazing removing seeds and sward-dwelling invertebrate prey (Buckingham *et al.* 2006); earlier and more frequent mowing of forage grass impacting breeding productivity of ground-nesting birds (Wilson *et al.* 2007); poor access in crops made dense and tall by high nutrient inputs (Wilson *et al.* 2005); and changes in soil drainage and soil structure impacting on soil invertebrate prey availability (Peach *et al.* 2004; Smart *et al.* 2006a).

Landscape simplification is an important mechanism of biodiversity loss from Enclosed Farmland (Robinson & Sutherland 2002; Firbank *et al.* 2008). More complex

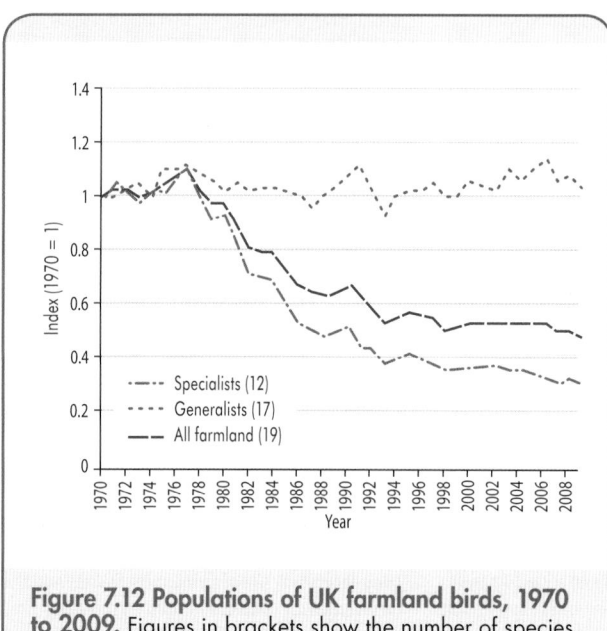

Figure 7.12 Populations of UK farmland birds, 1970 to 2009. Figures in brackets show the number of species. Source: data from RSPB; BTO; Defra (2011).

agricultural landscapes support a greater diversity of species (Benton *et al.* 2003; Fuller *et al.* 2005; Firbank *et al.* 2008), partly because of the amounts of habitat, partly due to the fact that several species of conservation concern require spatial and temporal variation in land cover (Bignal & McCracken 2000) (e.g. breeding lapwings, *Vanellus vanellus*, require cover and more open ground for feeding, while bats tend to hunt along hedgerows), and partly because other species need to disperse between features such as ponds or woodlands (e.g. amphibia, nuthatches *Sitta europaea*). For example, the extent of arable land in the crofting area of the Western Isles has declined to about 230 ha, with concomitant declines in birds and plants associated with crops (SNH 2009).

Another way of looking at trends in biodiversity of Enclosed Farmland is to look at the condition of sites designated for conservation, i.e. Sites of Special Scientific Interest (SSSIs) in GB and Areas of Special Scientific Interest in Northern Ireland (ASSIs). Across the UK as a whole, in 2006, Arable Horticultural sites and Improved Grasslands were in the worst condition of any habitats, even compared with other agricultural habitats, with only 26 out of 710 in favourable condition, and 536 unfavourable or destroyed (Defra 2009c).

Restoration of biodiversity. The past 20 years has seen the development of several techniques for increasing biodiversity and leisure services in Enclosed Farmland. They include bare patches in fields for nesting skylarks (Morris 2007), game cover for granivorous birds (Stoate *et al.* 2004; Parish & Sotherton 2008), flower mixes that provide pollen and nectar for foraging bumblebees (Carvell *et al.* 2007), beetle banks to support generalist predators (Collins *et al.* 2003), and conservation headlands (Sotherton 1991) to support grey partridge and associated taxa. Such management for biodiversity has been embraced within BAPs, and is often funded through agri-environment and similar schemes. There is a great deal of voluntary action: 92% of farmers in England have hedges on their farm, 82% of farmers cut their hedges at specific times (October–March) to avoid harming nesting birds and 53% of cereal farmers have used beetle banks or field margin management to encourage natural predators (Defra 2008).

Recent trends in species diversity and abundance. During the 1990s, there were changes to the management of Enclosed Farmland that were expected to benefit biodiversity. These included set-aside, agri-environment schemes, cross compliance, the application of technology to improve the efficiency of fertiliser and pesticide applications, the restoration of habitat features such as field boundaries and hedgerows under BAPs, and an increasing awareness of the cultural value of biodiversity by the agricultural and food chain industries.

It is difficult to detect impacts on wild species associated with Enclosed Farmland, given that high quality, national data is collected on an annual basis for only a few groups (e.g. birds, butterflies), it is not always easy to separate out species which are wholly Enclosed Farmland-specific, and that there are likely to be time lags before species show a response. Nevertheless, it seems that some population declines have been halted, if not reversed. At the UK level, overall plant species richness in arable habitats increased between 1990 and 2007, after showing a decline between 1978 and 1990 (Carey et al. 2008), while the numbers of farmland bird and butterfly foodplant species in arable fields increased by 22% and 24%, respectively, between 1998 and 2007 (these trends were most evident in England, with the situation in Scotland and Wales remaining stable from 1990) (Carey et al. 2008). However, while the proportion of ground covered by common plant species used as food by butterflies or birds has increased in arable land at the UK level, it was still less than 1% of the cropped land between 1998 and 2007 (Carey et al. 2008).

7.4 Trade-offs and Synergies Among Enclosed Farmland Goods and Services

Agricultural production is essentially an extractive service: plant cover and soils are frequently disturbed; community structure is highly manipulated to favour some species at the expense of others; plant and animal production is removed

from the system; and lost nutrients are reintroduced using organic and inorganic fertilisers that are not taken up with perfect efficiency. These properties all tend to create conflicts with those ecosystem services that are best delivered by ecosystems subject to much less intervention (Henle et al. 2008); such conflicts become increasingly hard to avoid at higher intensities and volumes of production.

Pilgrim et al. (2010) looked at the interactions among the delivery of ecosystem services from European temperate grasslands, namely agricultural production, climate regulation, air quality regulation, water quality regulation, hydrological regulation, soil erosion regulation, nutrient cycling, biodiversity conservation and landscape quality. Of the 72 direct pair-wise interactions studied, 37 were positive and 21 were inconclusive (**Figure 7.13**). All six negative relationships arose from the effects of agricultural production as a driving force on the delivery of other ecosystem services, with consistent evidence of negative impacts on air quality, water quality, erosion regulation, nutrient cycling, biodiversity conservation and landscape quality. Of all the potential driving ecosystem services, only erosion regulation and efficient nutrient cycling were consistently reported to enhance agricultural production. By contrast, interactions among the non-agricultural production ecosystem services tend to be positive or the evidence is currently inconclusive.

The situation in arable systems may well be different. In

		Responding Factor								
		Agricultural production	Climate regulation	Air quality	Water quality	Hydrological regulation	Erosion regulation	Nutrient cycling	Biodiversity conservation	Landscape quality
Driving Factor	Agricultural production	■	↕ ***	↓ ***	↓ ***	↕ **	↓ **	↓ ***	↓ ***	↓ ***
	Climate regulation	↕ **	■	↑***	↑***	↑ **	↑ **	↕ **	↕ **	↕ **
	Air quality	↕ **	↕ **	■	↑ ***	↑ *	0	↑ **	↑ ***	↑ ***
	Water quality	↔	↕ **	↕ **	■	↕ **	0	0	↑ **	↑ **
	Hydrological regulation	↕ **	↕ **	↔	↑ **	■	0	↑ ***	↑ **	↑ **
	Erosion regulation	↑ **	↕ **	↑ **	↑ ***	↑ *	■	↕ **	↑ **	↔
	Nutrient cycling	↑ ***	↑ **	↑ *	↑ ***	↑ **	↑ *	■	↑ **	↑ **
	Biodiversity conservation	↕ **	↕ **	↔	↑ **	↑ **	↑ **	↑ *	■	↑ ***
	Landscape quality	↕ *	↕ *	↕ *	↑ *	↑ *	↑ **	↕ **	↑ ***	■

Figure 7.13 The relationship between the ecosystem service A (ES A) as a driving factor and ecosystem service B (ES B) as a responding factor in grasslands in North West Europe. The form of the relationship is given by the arrows: 0 = no direct relationship, ↓ = decline in ES B, ↑ = an increase in ES B, ↕ = evidence of the relationship between ES A and ES B is divided or inconclusive, ↔ = no current evidence in the literature of an interaction between ES A and ES B. The strength of the relationship between ES A and ES B is reflected in the number of stars ***= highly confident about evidence **= mixed confidence about evidence *= poor confidence in evidence. Cell colour reflects scenario type: ▨ : win-win; ■ : lose-lose; ☐ : variable outcome; ☐ no known interaction. Pilgrim et al. (2010). Copyright (2010), reproduced with permission from Elsevier.

particular, the regulating services of biological pest control and pollination are enhanced through the provision of habitat features that benefit other taxa, implying a win-win between provisioning of food and at least some other ecosystem services. Yet critically, we are not aware of any solid evidence showing an increase in food production in the UK following the introduction of such features. The extent to which these services can be substituted by the use of domestic honey bees and the use of cultural and chemical pest control measures is not known, but likely to be high given that national levels of food production have increased as biodiversity has declined.

7.5 Options for Sustainable Management

It is envisaged that the global demands for agricultural production of food, energy and materials will increase greatly in the coming decades as a result of increased UK and global population and changing diets; during this time, the potential costs of key inputs of water, nutrients and energy are likely to rise. Other ecosystem services from Enclosed Farmland are becoming more valued and controlled through regulation, subsidy and markets. It is also envisaged that climate change will introduce increased uncertainty and risk to ecosystem service delivery. Therefore, UK agriculture needs to become more productive in terms of food and energy (so it does not make additional demands upon agricultural habitats elsewhere), more efficient in terms of resource utilisation, more productive in terms of other ecosystem services, and more resilient to climate and other changes; such alterations must be sustainable over time.

7.5.1 Increasing Food and Energy Production

To increase the provisioning of food and bioenergy, productivity per unit area must be intensified and/or the area of production must be expanded. The area of land used for bioenergy production is likely to increase given current policy drivers. Ideally, competition with land used for food production can be reduced by using land of low agricultural value for growing bioenergy crops, or by generating bioenergy as a co-product of food production, whether by using straw as biomass or slurries for anaerobic digestion. Nevertheless, there is scope for the replacement of some areas of arable farming with biofuels. This, plus existing pressures on land use, makes it likely that the area of Enclosed Farmland available for UK food production will decrease rather than increase. Therefore, there is a need to improve provisioning of food per unit area in the UK.

There is an important role for technological developments—such as cultivating new varieties, improving the protection of crops and livestock from pests, weeds and disease, and enhancing the resilience of food production against climate change impacts—and knowledge transfer, coupled with appropriate economics to ensure the adoption of such developments (Royal Society 2009).

7.5.2 Increasing the Resource Use Efficiency of Food Production

Many of the drawbacks of agricultural production arise from the loss of nutrients from the farming system (including diffuse pollution with nitrate and phosphorus), and emission of ammonia, methane and nitrous oxide to the atmosphere. Therefore, increasing the efficiency that plants and animals use these materials will result in improved ecosystem regulation. For instance, recent reductions in fertiliser inputs and emissions to air and water are partly due to increasing resource use efficiency, as well as reduced livestock numbers.

Techniques to increase resource use efficiency are already available, but are likely to become more widespread as productivity is increasingly reported per unit of water, carbon or other resource, and as the resources themselves become more expensive. Waste can be reduced by more precise application of irrigation water and nutrients in space and time. Greenhouse gas emissions from livestock can be reduced by improving growth rates, changing diets and changing storage methods for slurries and manures. Mixed livestock and arable farming may once again make economic sense should transport costs of nutrients increase, albeit at larger scales than before. Pigs may prove more valuable than ruminants because of their ability to feed on a greater variety of protein sources and their lower levels of greenhouse gas emissions. There is also scope for more efficient use of the food that is already produced, for example, by reducing food waste throughout the food chain and reducing the proportion of arable production that is used for livestock feed.

7.5.3 The Delivery of Regulating and Cultural Services

The delivery of ecosystem services is strongly influenced by both regulation and financial support and is likely to be increasingly influenced by markets.

Regulations include the WFD, Pesticides Directive, Habitats Directive, Nitrates Directive and Landscape Directive. They tend to control different aspects of the agro-ecosystem singly, imposing spatial boundaries within which land management can operate to deliver ecosystem services. The cost-benefit of current and proposed regulations in terms of ecosystem services is rarely known. It is possible to replace some regulations with taxes, but their effectiveness depends on the detail. For example, a nitrogen tax should result in reduced diffuse pollution, but could encourage farmers to use cheaper, urea-based fertilisers resulting in increased greenhouse gas emissions.

Support measures currently include rural development and agri-environment schemes. In Scotland, CAP-based policy instruments presently have the greatest impact on land management decisions (Miller *et al.* 2009). While cross compliance and agri-environment measures have had some successes to date (Section 7.2.2.9), the cost of meeting publicly defined objectives from agri-environment schemes in the UK (including in the uplands) is estimated at just under £2 billion per year (Cao *et al.* 2009; **Table 7.6**): more than three times the funding currently available from existing CAP Rural Development Programme allocations.

Table 7.6 A breakdown of the annual cost of agri-environment scheme options to deliver environmental policy objectives across the UK (£ million). Note that a number of assumptions were made in the analyses (e.g. incentives, such as provided through agri-environment schemes, are assumed to be the primary delivery mechanism used to achieve environmental gains; and existing income-foregone calculations are used to calculate land management costs). Taken together, the overall impact of these assumptions means that the costs in the report may significantly underestimate the total funding necessary within the UK. Source: Cao *et al.* (2009).

	England	Scotland	Wales	Northern Ireland	UK	% Total
Biodiversity	624	250	72	57	1,003	**51%**
Landscape	107	86	19	9	220	**11%**
Climate change mitigation	173	37	29	31	270	**14%**
Flood risk management	43	28	14	7	92	**5%**
Farmland historic environment	9	3	2	2	15	**1%**
Soil quality	95	18	0.3	0.6	114	**6%**
Water quantity	70	*	*	*	69	**3%**
Resource protection	99	19	23	13	154	**8%**
Public access	38	4	7	0.2	48	**2%**
Total (£ million)	**1,258**	**444**	**165**	**119**	**1,986**	
% Total	**63%**	**22%**	**8%**	**6%**		

*Indicator currently only applies to England but may extend to other regions by 2020 due to climate change; additionally, actions may be given priority in terms of resource efficiency.

It is not always clear that scheme resources are being targeted in the most effective way. Payments are often on the basis of actions by the farmer; thus the new Welsh Glastir scheme will make payments according to a national points system for different management actions, each intended to have some form of environmental benefit. Such payments assume that the prescriptions are correct, yet the evidence for prescriptions is variable in quality, the added value of combinations of actions is not well understood, and there may be local variations in efficacy that could be dealt with by a more flexible approach than rigid prescriptions allow. However, while it may seem to make sense to pay farmers by results (Schwarz *et al.* 2009), and to prioritise according to the local environmental context, the increased costs and complexity of scheme management may not be worthwhile.

There are two kinds of market support for ecosystem services other than food and energy production. One is direct payment, for example, for holiday accommodation in the countryside, for which there is a mature market, or for carbon sequestration, the market for which is in its infancy. Another type of support is to seek increased market share by adding value to food items. For example, Conservation Grade, the LEAF marque and organic production all have mechanisms for incorporating environmental objectives into production and marketing of food. Conservation Grade incorporates wildlife habitat into farming systems, while both LEAF and organic production assure an integrated approach to resource use and land management, the former promoting integrated and precision crop management, and the latter greatly restricting the use of inorganic fertilisers and agrochemicals. The promotion of products with added environmental value by supermarket chains is ensuring market penetration of such approaches.

7.5.4 The Joint Delivery of Food, Energy and Other Ecosystem Services

Increasing agricultural production is currently associated with reductions in other ecosystem services (Section 7.4.). But new research is showing that not all of these reductions are inevitable: there is more scope for joint production of multiple ecosystem services than has been previously realised (**Box 7.3**). For example, varieties of forage grass are being developed with roots that can improve the water-holding capacity of soils, in turn, improving water regulation on farmland. In addition, grass varieties with high sugar content are reducing methane emissions from cattle. Greenhouse gas emissions from livestock are reduced when the animals are healthy, well-nourished and grow rapidly. In arable systems, minimum tillage and no-tillage are often proposed as a key mechanism for reducing the negative impacts of cultivation on water quality, increasing carbon sequestration, improving soil function, and delivering biodiversity benefits (Holland 2004; Field *et al.* 2007a,b). However, there is evidence to suggest that carbon may be redistributed within the soil, rather than sequestered, and that nitrous oxide emissions may be increased because of low soil aeration and increased waterlogging (Bhogal *et al.* 2008).

It has been suggested that a switch to perennial crops may be beneficial for carbon sequestration and reducing diffuse pollution, as regular soil disturbance is avoided (although this may be detrimental to some arable plants). It is possible that advances in plant breeding and post-harvest processing will facilitate this in the future (Glover *et al.* 2010).

But win-win solutions may not always be possible. It is not clear to what extent UK soils can act as carbon sinks without major conversion of arable to grassland or forest, while there are clear conflicts between increased agricultural production and habitat and species diversity on the same units of land.

General rules about when to expect beneficial trade-offs among ecosystem services in agricultural landscapes are lacking (Bennett *et al.* 2009). Getting the balance right is a political issue as the values attached to different ecosystem services vary between people; it is also a scientific issue as the chosen balance requires technical knowledge to be implemented successfully. It raises the question, is it better to have reduced production and enhanced environmental quality on the same areas of land, or to have distinct units of land allocated to different functions?

This question is referred to as 'land sharing versus land sparing'. Land sharing involves the adoption of more extensive farming systems which provide multiple services from the same area, but probably with lower efficiency per unit area for given services than a more intensive approach might achieve (Balmford *et al.* 2005). Organic farming, for instance, usually has positive effects on species richness and abundance (depending on taxa and landscapes) in the order of 10% increases compared with non-organic systems. These positive effects arise largely from the greater diversity of land covers (Bengtsson *et al.* 2005, Fuller *et al.* 2005; Macfadyen *et al.* 2009). However, these advantages are per unit area, and do not take into account the reduced yield. It has been estimated that a national shift to organic-only farming could reduce UK wheat yield to about a third of current production (Jones & Crane 2009). This is because

Box 7.3 Case study 2: reconciling the provision of multiple ecosystem services on farmland.

In recent decades, much effort has been directed to reconciling the two objectives of continued production of provisioning services and biodiversity conservation. Here, we examine three examples, involving both empirical and modelling approaches, to explore how the provision of multiple ecosystem services might be achieved on UK farmland.

The first example is the RSPB's **Hope Farm**, a conventional arable farm in Cambridgeshire that shows how production and conservation can be reconciled by excluding a small proportion of the potential cropped area from food production. Hope Farm was bought by the RSPB in 1999 with many donations from RSPB members and other members of the public. The 181-hectare farm is on heavy clay, with 5 ha under permanent pasture and 7 ha of semi-natural habitats such as farm woodlands. The majority of the remainder is farmed by a contractor to grow a rotation of autumn-sown wheat, oilseed rape and spring beans. Efforts to increase farmland bird numbers have focused on Environmental Stewardship options, such as grass margins and seed-rich habitats, and good practice farming such as cutting hedgerows and ditch vegetation just once every three years. There have also been trials of management techniques for particular species, such as the provision of skylark plots. Since the baseline year in 2000, when all 169 ha of the potential cropped area was cropped, an average of 18 ha has been devoted to set-aside and non-crop features, with the latter mainly in low-yielding, field edge locations (Morris *et al.* 2010).

At Hope Farm, breeding bird numbers increased substantially between 2000 and 2009 (**Figure 1**), while farmland bird populations in the wider countryside remained steady across eastern England. This is due to increases in numbers of both common and rare (e.g. BAP) species. Changes include increased numbers of skylark (10 pairs in 2000, increasing to 44 in 2009) and yellowhammer (*Emberiza citrinella*; 16 pairs increasing to 39), and colonisation by lapwing and grey partridge (Morris *et al.* 2010). Doubling the farmland bird index has not compromised crop yields (**Figure 1**); Hope Farm has consistently exceeded the national wheat yield average, for example, the

harvest in 2009 was 9.35 tonnes/hectare, compared to the national level of 7.6 tonnes/hectare (Morris *et al.* 2010).

The Game & Wildlife Conservation Trust's **Allerton Project** shows how food production can be reconciled with the provision of a wider range of cultural services. The Allerton Project is based at a 333 ha mixed arable/pastoral farm at Loddington, Leicestershire. Management practices researched and implemented for biodiversity include grass margins, beetle banks and wild bird seed crops as part of a game management system designed to increase numbers of wild gamebirds for shooting. Summer aphicides are no longer used on cereals at Loddington as sufficient control is achieved by predatory invertebrates associated with grass margins and beetle banks. The farm produces 410 to 538 lambs each year, and sheep wool and flax are sold for fibre. Wood chip is harvested from farm woods during thinning operations and provides an important source of fuel for the Project's headquarters and other local premises, reducing carbon emissions associated with the procurement, transport and use of fossil fuels.

Breeding bird numbers increased substantially at Loddington until 2001, but subsequently declined due to the cessation of some components of the game management system. As at Hope Farm, increases in bird numbers were achieved while crop yields remained consistent (**Figure 2**).

At Loddington, the provision of two other services has been quantified: recreational and educational opportunities. The farm has been managed as a recreational pheasant shoot and has a suite of associated management measures including the provision of grain in winter, the control of nest predators and the creation and management of a range of habitats (Boatman & Brockless 1998; Stoate 2002). This provided recreational opportunities for shooters, beaters and dog handlers (**Figure 2**), without compromising crop yields. In addition, the Allerton Project provides education, demonstration and knowledge exchange opportunities for policy makers, regulators, farmers, agronomists and students (Stoate 2004; **Figure 2**), as well as community engagement outside the farm boundary at the stream catchment scale (Stoate 2010).

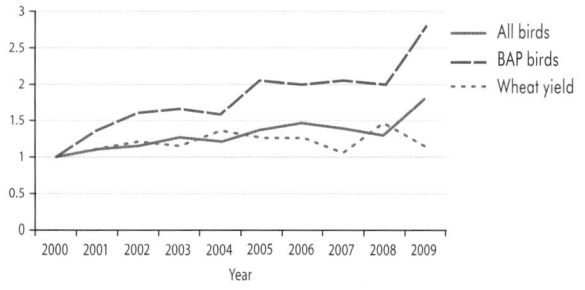

Figure 1 Trends in wheat yields and birds at Hope Farm.
To enable comparison of trends, all variables are converted to an index with the value in the first year set to 1. Source: RSPB pers. comm.

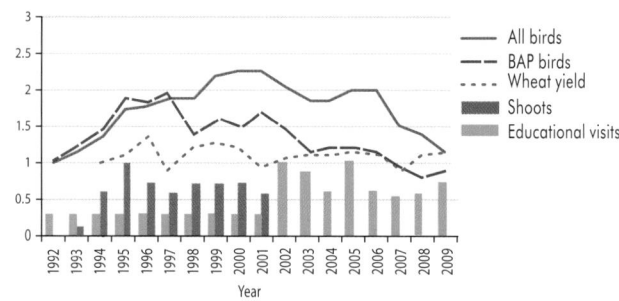

Figure 2 Trends in various services at the Allerton Project.
Note that visitor numbers were not captured prior to 2001, and so are estimated prior to that year. As with Hope Farm, variables are converted to indices for ease of comparison of trends. Source: data from Game & Wildlife Conservation Trust (2010).

yields of wheat grown organically are about two-thirds of those grown conventionally with fertilisers and chemical pest and disease control, and wheat can only be grown for half of an organic rotation at most, the rest of the rotation needing legumes to restore soil fertility or root crops to control pests and diseases (Goulding *et al.* 2009). National data are not available for livestock organic yields. Extensive agriculture alone will not meet the challenge of increased joint production of food and other ecosystem services.

Land sparing, on the other hand, involves concentrating agricultural production into certain areas of land, so that other areas are available to provide other services, which need not be in the UK. The optimum solution depends on the relative productivity of both shared and distinct land units for the services of interest, and how the services are valued (Hodgson *et al.* 2010). Land sparing is only an effective strategy if the spared land actually delivers ecosystem services. Land sparing can take place at all scales, including individual patches within fields, and will depend on the landscape context (Bradbury *et al.* 2010; Hodgson *et al.* 2010). The segregation of ecosystem services need not be complete; for example, the pioneering Conservation Headlands approach developed by the Game Conservancy and Wildlife Trust (Sotherton 1991) involves reducing pesticide sprays at the less productive field edge. Conservation Headlands still produce food, but with a yield penalty that is considered to

How, though, might one attempt the reconciliation of food production with a wider range of other benefits? One approach is that taken by Posthumus *et al.* (2010) who estimated the provision of a range of ecosystem services by **The Beckingham Marshes** under the current, and various alternative, future land use scenarios (**Figure 3**).

The Beckingham Marshes consist of 900 ha of floodplain by the River Trent in Nottinghamshire. Flood defences were built in the 1960s to provide 2 million m³ of controlled flood storage in order to reduce the probability of inundation of Gainsborough. Land drainage improvements and a new pumping station improved conditions for arable farming throughout the 1970s, so much so that, by 1983, 82% of the area was arable. In 2005, 90 ha of arable land was reverted to extensive grassland under a collaboration between the Environment Agency and the RSPB (RSPB 2009). Posthumus *et al.* (2010) used a modelling approach to compare four alternative future scenarios with the current situation:
1. Maximum agricultural production: with land under intensive arable agriculture.
2. Biodiversity: with land used to enhance local and national BAP targets.
3. Agri-environment: as (2) but with the constraint that land remains predominantly agricultural.
4. Floodwater storage: with land used to provide maximum flood water storage.

The more intensive farming system had the greatest scores for global warming potential and nitrate leaching, and the lowest scores for habitat conservation: marginally lower than the conservation value of the current land use and much lower than the biodiversity scenario. Habitat conservation value under the agri-environment scenario was marginally higher than under the biodiversity scenario, primarily due to the high nature conservation value of alluvial hay meadows. Flood risks varied between scenarios as the frequency of flooding varied: the higher the flood frequency, the higher the average annual costs of flood damage. Flood damage costs were low (in comparison to the monetary values of other indicators) under all scenarios due to the low density of infrastructure and residential homes in the floodplain.

Although some benefits can be delivered simultaneously, this was not always the case. The floodwater storage and production scenarios delivered similar levels of ecosystem services, scoring highly on production and floodwater storage, at the expense of environmental indicators. Not surprisingly, the agri-environment and biodiversity scenarios generally had a positive environmental impact. However, the biodiversity scenario resulted in increased flood risk for settlement and transport, and reduced floodwater storage as the existing flood banks would be breached. Under the agri-environment scenario, as flooding is controlled with sluices and pumps, there was little increase in flood risk and the floodplain can be used for floodwater storage.

This floodplain example illustrates how a careful combination of scenarios and indicators, set in an ecosystem services framework, can help to assess options for management of multiple services.

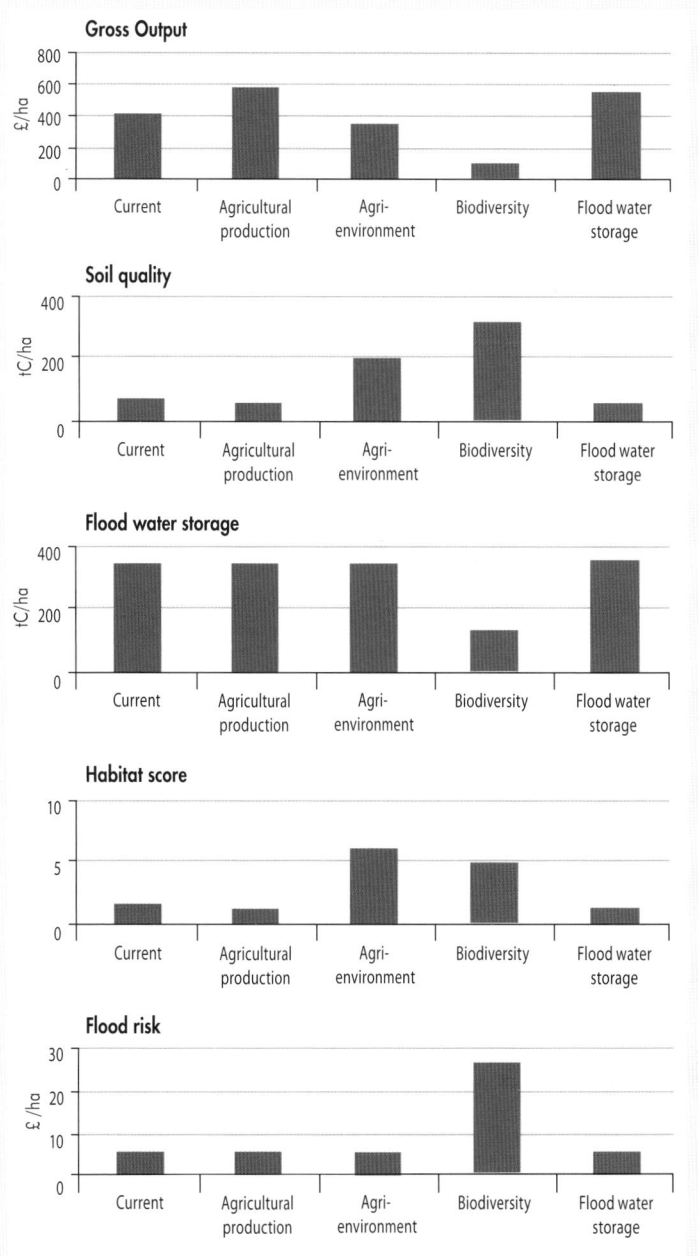

Figure 3 Relative levels of selected ecosystem services under five alternative scenarios. Source: data from Posthumus *et al.* (2010). Copyright (2010), reproduced with permission from Elsevier.

be outweighed by enhanced biodiversity and opportunities for game shooting. Similarly, many semi-natural habitats, such as upland heaths and species-rich grasslands, require extensive grazing for their persistence, and the grazing animals provide meat that can be sold at a premium.

This approach can be taken a step further by allocating land to different combinations of ecosystem services according to topography and soil type, both at the farm and at larger, catchment or landscape scales. For example, grass field margins can reduce the transport of soil and nutrients to water, and provide habitat for pollinating insects, predators of crop pests and nesting birds (Stoate et al. 2009). Constructed wetlands can reduce the transport of sediment and nutrients from field drains and ditches to watercourses, while also providing benefits to terrestrial and aquatic biodiversity within the farmland ecosystem (Stoate et al. 2006). Species-rich legume grassland supports higher insect abundance and richness, including pollinating species, and provides greater carbon sequestration potential than monocultural grassland (De Deyn et al. 2008). Such changes would result in landscapes that are more diverse but less familiar, with impacts on cultural services varying from place to place (Firbank 2005).

7.6 Future Research and Monitoring Gaps

The sustainable management of Enclosed Farmland involves the long-term co-delivery of agricultural production and other ecosystem services by land managers in response to the potential of the land (climate, soils, topography) and economic, policy and societal drivers. The major driver is likely to be the projected rise in human population causing increases in global demands on ecosystem services from farmland over the coming decades (Tilman et al. 2002; MA 2005). There is an expectation that food production will have to increase by as much as 50%, alongside increases in fuels and biomaterials. Agricultural production in the UK is likely to be affected less by climate change than in many other parts of the world, implying that an even greater increase in food output will be required here. This also implies that the market and policy situation may well change more rapidly than the research base. There are major knowledge gaps at all levels regarding the supply of ecosystem services from Enclosed Farmland.

7.6.1 Enhancing the Provision of Multiple Ecosystem Services

Research is needed into the development of more productive, resilient, multifunctional agro-ecosystems. The challenge is that these properties are not necessarily synergistic.

Increased food production must be supported by research that stresses increasing productivity within traditional agricultural areas, such as breeding, crop protection and animal disease management, using new technologies

including genetic modification, genomics, metabolomics, etc. (Royal Society 2009).

There is a great need to optimise the efficiency of nutrient use across the food chain in order to reduce releases of nitrogen compounds and phosphates to air and water, to cope with potential increasing costs of artificial fertiliser and shortages of phosphorus, and to minimise the competition for protein from arable crops between human and livestock consumption. Some of this work will involve further developments in precision agriculture and storage of manures; some will address nutrient management at the farming system and catchment scales. Research is needed into how to balance the efficient use of food processing wastes with food safety. There may be scope to manipulate biogeochemical processes directly by manipulating soil biota once their role is better understood; the broader question of the importance of biodiversity in underpinning stability of ecosystem service provision, including agricultural production, remains under-researched (Loreau 2010).

Farming systems in the UK have proved extremely resilient to date, not least due to the mild climate, good soils and a highly adaptive farming industry. But, as ever, the industry faces multiple pressures. Social pressures include changes to the farming community itself, competing pressures on the land, access to new technologies, and the changing attitudes of food consumers and users of Enclosed Farmland for leisure, exercise and culture. Economic pressures include fluctuating financial returns to the farming community, the rapidly evolving policy requirements, and a potential decline in the availability of phosphorus for fertiliser. Climate change poses major challenges to food production. It may be possible to design farming systems that are resilient to climate change, for example, protecting livestock from heat stress in controlled buildings or using greater woodland cover in grasslands to provide cooler microclimates. A substantial increase in the price of fossil fuels could generate an important tipping point, forcing farming systems to optimise or replace tractors, road transport and inorganic fertilisers. It is not clear what low-carbon agriculture would look like.

The co-production of multiple ecosystem services in multifunctional agricultural landscapes remains under-researched. Clearly, a better understanding of management of ecosystem services, and how they interact, is critical (Bennett et al. 2009). We lack sound evidence of the relationships between provisioning and regulating services; instead, we tend to rely on proxy data, such as numbers of pollinators. This is because the critical experiments are often difficult and expensive to make at appropriate scales. Existing quantitative data are not amenable to complex optimisation modelling at farm, landscape and catchment scales. New experiments are needed at scales from controlled environment to catchment, combining different forms of land management; this should be supplemented by systems modelling because the actual outcomes of different land management combinations on multiple services are likely to be sensitive to soils, location and weather patterns. Long-term monitoring over multiple scales of space and time is needed to validate and refine the models (Bennett et al. 2009; Carpenter et al. 2009).

7.6.2 The Governance of Delivery of Ecosystem Services

The governance of ecosystem service delivery is currently highly complex and not well adapted to the cost-effective delivery of ecosystem services from Enclosed Farmland. At the moment, delivery is sensitive to volatile commodity markets, government support and regulation. In principle, ecosystem benefits and disbenefits could be considered in terms of value to society, and so could be costed and funded through agri-environment schemes or other mechanisms. Unfortunately, the values of such benefits are changing rapidly (e.g. the recent rise in importance of greenhouse gas mitigation) and are perceived very differently by different members of society. For instance, how does the public trade off food supply, local produce, prices of food and biodiversity in the UK countryside and abroad? Differences in responses to such questions help drive the diversity of agricultural production methods, from smallholdings right through to large-scale suppliers of commodity crops.

It is difficult to value long-term needs as opposed to short-term gains (Bennett *et al.* 2009); currently, most land managers are only rewarded for short-term success (MA 2005). Also, agricultural land use is fundamentally controlled by the market and the priorities of individual landowners and land managers, and so, even if the research base were strong enough to suggest optimum ways of producing multiple ecosystem services at landscape, catchment and larger scales, there is no clear governance mechanism for delivering such wider-scale benefits without compromising the benefits of farm-scale innovation and diversity.

7.6.3 Cultural Barriers to Implementation of Solutions and Knowledge Transfer

A third barrier is knowledge exchange. There needs to be greater dissemination of best practice; as noted above, take-up of precision arable farming remains low despite its benefits in terms of more efficient use of inputs. Knowledge exchange is needed to address conflicts between production and environmental knowledge cultures (Tsouvalis *et al.* 2000; Ingram 2008), and to enable the introduction of new skills in ecosystem management to profitable rural enterprises. There is also a need for much broader public engagement in order to better establish priorities, values and mechanisms for the delivery of ecosystem services from Enclosed Farmland, not least as the full cost for these services may prove far greater than allowed for in current policies and markets.

7.7 Conclusion

To conclude, Enclosed Farmland has been, and remains, a vital habitat in the UK in terms of food production and the provision of landscape and other cultural benefits. Yet it also imposes disadvantages to the UK in terms of greenhouse gas emissions, diffuse water pollution and losses to biodiversity. Greater demand is expected of multiple ecosystem services including food, bioenergy, greenhouse gas mitigation and

cultural services, some of which can be delivered using current knowledge, while others could be met by novel approaches including spatial optimisation of land management. But there are major challenges and knowledge gaps regarding how such integrated land use could be determined and delivered given that the drivers of decision-making (e.g. marked changes in weather, changes in the price of carbon, the desire for biodiversity conservation, the need for pest control, nutrient cycling and the control of diffuse pollution, etc.) are becoming more complex, and cross scales and ownership boundaries; that relationships between regulating services and food production are not clear; and that the values of different ecosystem services are not well defined.

References

Abberton, M.T., MacDuff, J.H., Marshall, A.H. & Humphreys, M.W. (2007) The Genetic Improvement of Forage Grasses and Legumes to Reduce Greenhouse Gas Emissions. Food and Agriculture Organisation, Rome.

ADAS (2009) Evaluation of cross compliance. Defra Agricultural Change & Environment Observatory. [online] Available at: <http://www.defra.gov.uk/evidence/statistics/foodfarm/enviro/observatory/research/documents/Xceval_mar09.pdf> [Accessed 07.03.11].

Aebischer, N.J., Evans, A.D., Grice, P.V. & Vickery, J.A. (eds) (2000) Ecology and Conservation of Lowland Farmland Birds. British Ornithologists' Union, Tring.

Allton, K.E., Harris, J.A., Rickson, R.J. & Ritz, K. (2007) The effect of microbial communities on soil hydrological processes: A microcosm study utilising simulated rainfall. *Geoderma*, **142**, 11–17.

Baker, J.M., Ochsner, T.E., Venterea, R.T. & Griffis, T.J. (2007) Tillage and soil carbon sequestration – What do we really know? *Agriculture, Ecosystems & Environment*, **118**, 1–5.

Ballantine, D., Walling, D.E. & Leek, G.J.L. (2009) Mobilisation and transport of sediment-associated phosphorus by surface runoff. *Water, Air and Soil Pollution*, **196**, 311–320.

Balmford, A., Green, R.E. & Scharlemann, J.P.W. (2005) Sparing land for nature: exploring the potential impact of changes in agricultural yield on the area needed for crop production. *Global Change Biology*, **11**, 1594–1605.

Banks, C., Swinbank, A. & Poppy, G. (2009) Anaerobic digestion and its implications for land use. What is Land for? (eds M. Winter & M. Lobley), pp. 101–134. Earthscan, London.

Bardgett, R.D. & Wardle, D.A. (2010) Aboveground-Belowground Linkages: Biotic Interactions, Ecosystem Processes, and Global change. Oxford Series in Ecology and Evolution, Oxford University Press.

Barker, K. (2006) Barker review of land use planning: final report and recommendations. HMSO, London.

Barr, C.J. & Gillespie, M.K. (2000) Estimating hedgerow length and pattern characteristics in Great Britain using Countryside Survey data. *Journal of Environmental Management*, **60**, 23–32.

Barr, C. & Petit, S. (2001) (eds) Hedgerows of the World: their ecological functions in different landscapes. International Association of Landscape Ecologists, Guelph, Canada.

Bartholomew, P.W. & Williams, R.D. (2009) Establishment of Italian ryegrass (*Lolium multiflorum* Lam.) by self-seeding as affected by cutting date and degree of herbage removal in spring in pastures of the southern Great Plains of the United States. *Grass and Forage Science*, **64**, 177–186.

Barton, J. & Pretty, J. (2010). What is the best dose of nature and green exercise for improving mental health? A multi-study analysis. *Environmental Science and Technology*, **44**, 3947–3955.

Bateman, I.J., Ennew, C., Lovett, A. & Rayner, A.J. (1999) Modelling and mapping agricultural output values using farm specific details and environmental databases. *Journal of Agricultural Economics*, **50**, 488–511.

Bengtsson, J., Ahnstrom, J. & Weibull, A.C. (2005) The effects of organic agriculture on biodiversity and abundance: a meta-analysis. *Journal of Applied Ecology*, **42**, 261–269.

Bennett, E.M., Peterson, G.D. & Gordon, L.J. (2009) Understanding relationships among multiple ecosystem services. *Ecology Letters*, **12**, 1394–1404.

Benton, T.G., Bryant, D.M., Cole. L. & Crick, H.Q.P. (2002) Linking agricultural practice to insect and bird populations: a historical study over three decades. *Journal of Applied Ecology*, **39**, 673–687.

Benton, T.G., Vickery, J.A. & Wilson, J.D. (2003) Farmland biodiversity: is habitat heterogeneity the key? *Trends in Ecology & Evolution*, **18**, 182–188.

Bhogal, A., Chambers, B.J., Whitmore, A.P. & Powlson, D.S. (2008) The effects of reduced tillage practices and organic material additions on the carbon content of arable soils. Summary report for Defra Project SP0561. ADAS, Gleadthorpe & Rothamsted Research, Harpenden.

BHS (Basic Horticultural Statistics) (1999) Basic Horticultural Statistics for the United Kingdom, 1999. [online] Available at: <http://www.intute.ac.uk/cgi-bin/fullrecord.pl?handle=20080723-1019205> [Accessed 07.03.11].

BHS (Basic Horticultural Statistics) (2008) Basic Horticultural Statistics for the United Kingdom, 2008. [online] Available at: <http://www.defra.gov.uk/evidence/statistics/foodfarm/landuselivestock/bhs/index.htm> [Accessed 07.03.11].

Bibby, P. (2009) Land use change in Britain. *Land Use Policy*, **26S**, S2–S13.

Biesmeijer, J.C., Roberts, S.P.M., Reemer, M., Ohlemuller, R., Edwards, M., Peeters, T., Schaffers, A.P., Potts, S.G., Kleukers, R., Thomas, C.D., Settele, J. & Kunin, W.E. (2006) Parallel declines in pollinators and insect-pollinated plants in Britain and the Netherlands. *Science*, **313**, 351–354.

Bignal, E. & McCracken, D.I. (2000) The nature conservation value of European traditional farming systems. *Environmental Reviews*, **8**, 149–171.

Bignal, E., Jones, G. & McCracken, D. (2001) Comment: Future directions in agriculture policy and nature conservation. *British Wildlife*, **13**, 16–20.

Bilotta, G.S., Brazier, R.E. & Haygarth, P.M. (2007) The impacts of grazing animals on the quality of soils, vegetation, and surface waters in intensively managed grasslands. *Advances in Agronomy*, **94**, 237–280.

Boatman, N.D. & Brockless, M. (1998) The Allerton Project: farmland management for partridges (*Perdix perdix, Alectori rufa*) and pheasants (*Phasianus colchicus*). *Gibier Faune Sauvage*, **15**, 563–574.

Boatman, N.D., Brickle, N.W., Hart, J.D., Milsom, T.P., Morris, A.J., Murray, A.W.A., Murray, K.A. & Robertson, P.A. (2004) Evidence for the indirect effects of pesticides on farmland birds. *Ibis*, **146**, 131–143.

Booth, E., Walker, R., Bell, J., McCracken, D.I., Curry, J., Knight, B., Smith, J., Gottschalk, P. & Biddle, A. (2009) An assessment of the potential impact on UK agriculture and environment of meeting renewable feedstock demands: final report for National Non-Food Crops Centre (NNFCC). Scottish Agricultural College, Aberdeen University & PGRO.

Borin, M., Bigon, E., Zanin, G. & Flava, L. (2004) Performance of a narrow buffer strip in abating agricultural pollutants in the shallow subsurface water flux. *Environmental Pollution*, **131**, 313–321.

Bradbury, R.B., Stoate, C. & Tallowin, J.R.B. (2010) Lowland farmland bird conservation in the context of wider ecosystem service delivery. *Journal of Applied Ecology*, **47**, 986–993.

Bradley, R.I., Milne, R., Bell, J., Lilly, A., Jordan, C. & Higgins, A. (2005). A soil carbon and land use database for the United Kingdom. *Soil Use and Management*, **21**, 363–369.

Brittain, C.A., Vighi, M., Bommarco, R., Settele, J. & Potts, S.G. (2010) Impacts of a pesticide on pollinator species richness at different spatial scales. *Basic and Applied Ecology*, **11**, 106–115.

Buckingham, D.L., Peach, W.J. & Fox, D.S. (2006) Effects of agricultural management on the use of lowland grassland in the UK by foraging birds. *Agriculture, Ecosystems and Environment*, **112**, 21–40.

Butler, S.J., Vickery, J.A. & Norris, K. (2007) Farmland biodiversity and the footprint of agriculture. *Science*, **315**, 381–384.

Cannon, R.J.C., Baker, R.H.A., Taylor, M.C. & Moore, J.P. (1999). A review of the status of the New Zealand flatworm in the UK. *Annals of Applied Biology*, **135**, 597–614.

Cao, Y., Elliott, J., McCracken, D.I., Rowe, K., Whitehead, J. & Wilson L. (2009) Estimating the scale of future environmental land management requirements for the UK. A report for the UK Land Use Policy Group (LUPG). ADAS UK Ltd and Scottish Agricultural College. [online] Available at: <http://lupg.org.uk/pdf/LUPG_estimating_scale_correctionFeb2010.pdf> [Accessed 27.01.11].

Carey, P.D., Short, C., Morris, C., Hunt, J., Priscott, A., Davis, M., Finch, C., Curry, N., Little, W., Winter, M., Parkin, A. & Firbank L.G. (2003) The multi-disciplinary evaluation of a national agri-environment scheme. *Journal of Environmental Management*, **69**, 71–91.

Carey, P.D., Wallis, S., Chamberlain, P.M., Cooper, A., Emmett, B.A., Maskell, L.C., McCann, T., Murphy, J., Norton, L.R., Reynolds, B., Scott, W.A., Simpson, I.C., Smart, S.M. & Ullyett, J.M. (2008) Countryside Survey: UK Results from 2007. NERC/Centre for Ecology & Hydrology. (CEH Project Number: C03259).

Carpenter, S.R., Mooney, H.A., Agard, J., Capistrano, D., DeFries, R.S., Diaz, S., Dietz, T., Duraiappah, A.K., Oteng-Yeboah, A., Pereira, H.M., Perrings, C., Reid, W.V., Sarukhan, J., Scholes, R.J. & Whyte, A. (2009) Science for managing ecosystem services: Beyond the Millennium Ecosystem Assessment. *Proceedings of the National Academy of Sciences of the United States of America*, **106**, 1305–1312.

Carvell, C., Roy, D.B., Smart, S.M., Pywell, R.F., Preston, C.D. & Goulson, D. (2006) Declines in forage availability for bumblebees at a national scale. *Biological Conservation*, **132**, 481–489.

Carvell, C., Meek, W.R., Pywell, R.F., Goulson, D. & Nowakowski, M. (2007) Comparing the efficacy of agri-environment schemes to enhance bumble bee abundance and diversity on arable field margins. *Journal of Applied Ecology*, **44**, 29–40.

CCC (Committee on Climate Change) (2010) Meeting Carbon Budgets – ensuring a low-carbon recovery. 2nd Progress Report to Parliament. Chapter 5: Opportunities for reducing emissions from agriculture. Committee on Climate Change, London.

Chadwick, D.R., Chambers, B.J., Crabtree, R., Anthony, S. & Harris D. (2008) Benefits and 'Pollution Swapping': Cross-Cutting Issues for Diffuse Pollution Mitigation. Land Management in a Changing Environment (eds K. Crighton and R. Audsley), pp. 41–47. SAC and SEPA (Agriculture and the Environment VII).

Chamberlain, D.E., Fuller, R.J., Bunce, R.G.H., Duckworth, J.C. & Shrubb, M. (2000) Changes in the abundance of farmland birds in relation to the timing of agricultural intensification in England and Wales. *Journal of Applied Ecology*, **37**, 771–788.

Champion, G.T., May, M.J., Bennett, S., Brooks, D.R., Clark, S.J., Daniels, R.E., Firbank, L.G., Haughton, A.J., Hawes, C., Heard, M.S., Perry, J.N., Randle, Z., Rossall, M.J., Rothery, P., Skellern, M.P., Scott, R.J., Squire, G.R. & Thomas, M.R. (2003) Crop management and agronomic context of the Farm Scale Evaluations of genetically modified herbicide-tolerant crops. *Philosophical Transactions of the Royal Society B-Biological Sciences*, **358**, 1801–1818.

Chapagain, A. & Orr, S. (2008) UK Water Footprint: the impact of the UK's food and fibre consumption on global water resources Volume two: appendices. WWF-UK, Godalming.

Collins, K.L., Boatman, N.D., Wilcox, A., Holland, J.M. & Chaney, K. (2002) Influence of beetle banks on cereal aphid predation in winter wheat. *Agriculture, Ecosystems and Environment*, **93**, 337–350.

Collins, K.L., Boatman, N.D., Wilcox, A. & Holland, J.M. (2003) A five-year comparison of overwintering polyphagous predator densities within a beetle bank and two conventional hedgebanks. *Annals of Applied Biology*, **143**, 63–71.

Cooper, A. & McCann, T. (2000) Northern Ireland Countryside Survey 2000. Environment and Heritage Service, Belfast.

Cooper, A., McCann, T. & Rogers, D. (2009) Northern Ireland Countryside Survey 2007: Broad Habitat Change 1998–2007. Northern Ireland Environment Agency Research and Development Series No.09/06. [online] Available at: <http://ni-environment.gov.uk/nics2007_broad_habitat_change_1998-2007.pdf> [Accessed 27.01.11].

Cotrufo, M.F., Ineson, P. & Scott, A. (1998) Elevated CO_2 reduces the nitrogen concentration of plant tissues. *Global Change Biology*, **4**, 43–54.

Countryside Agency (2006) Living Buildings in a Living Landscape: finding a future for traditional farm buildings. The Countryside Agency.

CRC (Commission for Rural Communities) (2008) State of the Countryside 2008. Commission for Rural Communities, Cheltenham Glos.

Crocker, M. & Mabey, R. (2005) Birds Britannica. Chatto & Windus, London.

Crouch, D. & Lubbren, N. (2003) Visual culture and tourism. Berg, London.

DaMatta, F.M., Grandis, A., Arenque, B.C. & Buckeridge, M.S. (Buckeridge, Marcos S.) (2010) Impacts of climate changes on crop physiology and food quality. *Food Research International*, **43**, 1814–1823.

DARD (Department of Agriculture and Rural Development) (2010) Statistical review of Northern Ireland agriculture: 2009. Department of Agriculture & Rural Development. [online] Available at: <http://dardni.gov.uk/statistical_review_of_northern_ireland_agriculture_-_2009.pdf> [Accessed 27.01.11].

Davies, D., Evans & Oxley, S. (2007) Impact of Climate Change in Scotland on Crop Pests, Weeds and Disease. Technical Note 605. Scottish Agricultural College.

Deasy, C., Quinton, J.N., Silgram, M., Jackson, R.J. & Bailey, A.P. (2008) Controlling sediment in arable landscapes: experiences from the United Kingdom. Final Cost 634 International Conference, On- and Off-site Environmental impacts of Runoff and Erosion, 30 June–4 July, Aveiro, Portugal.

De Deyn, G.B., Conelissen, J.H.C. & Bardgett, R.D. (2008) Plant functional traits and soil carbon sequestration in contrasting biomes. *Ecology Letters*, **11**, 516–531.

Defra (Department of Environment, Food and Rural Affairs) (2008) Farm Practices Survey – England 2008. Defra. [online] Availbale at http://www.defra.gov.uk/evidence/statistics/foodfarm/enviro/farmpractice/index.htm [Accessed 07.03.11].

Defra (Department of Environment, Food and Rural Affairs) (2009a) June Survey of Agriculture and Horticulture 2009. [online] Available at: <http://www.defra.gov.uk/evidence/statistics/foodfarm/landuselivestock/junesurvey/index.htm> [Accessed 27.01.11].

Defra (Department of Environment, Food and Rural Affairs) (2009b) Biodiversity indicators in your pocket 2009. Defra, London.

Defra (Department of Environment, Food and Rural Affairs) (2009c) Agriculture in the United Kindom 2008. Defra, DARDNI, SEERAD, WAG Department for Rural Affairs and Heritage.

Defra (Department of Environment, Food and Rural Affairs) (2010a) Agriculture in the United Kindom 2009. Defra, DARDNI, SEERAD, WAG Department for Rural Affairs and Heritage. [online] Available at: <http://www.defra.gov.uk/evidence/statistics/foodfarm/general/auk/latest/index.htm> [Accessed 27.01.11].

Defra (Department of Environment, Food and Rural Affairs) (2010b) e-digest of environmental statistics. [online] Available at: <http://www.defra.gov.uk/evidence/statistics/environment/airqual/aqemammonia.htm> [Accessed 27.01.11].

Defra (Department of Environment, Food and Rural Affairs) (2010c) Bovine Tuberculosis: The Government's approach to tackling the disease and consultation on a badger control policy.

Defra (Department of Environment, Food and Rural Affairs) (2010d) Wild bird populations: Farmland birds in England 2009. [online] Available at: <http://www.defra.gov.uk/evidence/statistics/environment/wildlife/download/pdf/100729farmland-birds-release.pdf> [Accessed 07.03.11].

Dickson, B., Hutton, J. & Adams, W.M. (2009) Recreational Hunting, Conservation and Rural Livelihoods: Science and Practice. Blackwell, Oxford.

Dolman, P.M. & Waber, K. (2008) Ecosystem and competition impacts of introduced deer. *Wildlife Research*, **35**, 202–214.

Donald, P.F. (2004) The Skylark. T. & A.D. Poyser, London.

Draycott, R.A.H., Hoodless, A.N. & Sage, R.B. (2008) Effects of pheasants management on vegetation and birds in lowland woods. *Journal of Applied Ecology*, **45**, 334–341.

DTI (Department of Trade and Industry), DFT (Department For Transport) & Defra (Department for Agriculture, Food and Rural Affairs) (2007). UK Biomass Strategy. DTI, DFT, Defra, London.

Duckworth, J.C., Firbank, L.G., Stuart, R.C. & Yamamoto, S. (2003) Landscape changes in British lowland woodlands over the last century in relation to game management. *Landscape Research*, **28**, 171–182.

Dudley, B. & May, L. (2007) Estimating the phosphorus load to waterbodies from septic tanks. A Report to the Scottish Environment Protection Agency and Scottish Natural Heritage. Centre for Ecology and Hydrology, Lancaster, UK.

Dwyer, J., Ward, N., Lowe. P. & Baldock, D. (2007) European rural development under the common agricultural policy's 'second pillar': Institutional conservatism and innovation. *Regional Studies*, **41**, 873–887.

EBLEX (English Beef and Lamb Executive) (2009) Change in the air: the English Beef and Sheep Production Roadmap – Phase 1. [online] Available at: <http://www.eblex.org.uk/documents/content/publications/p_cp_changeintheairtheenglishbeefandsheepproductionroadmap.pdf> [Accessed 21.06.11].

Environment Agency (2011) Diffuse source pressure on rivers, Environmental Agency. [online] Available at: <http://www.environment-agency.gov.uk/research/planning/33312.aspx> [Accessed 27.01.11].

EEA (European Environment Agency) (2001) Eutrophication in Europe's Coastal Waters. Technical Report. European Environment Agency, Copenhagen, Denmark.

Ewald, J.A. & Aebischer, N.J. (1999) Pesticide use, avian food resources and bird densities in Sussex. JNCC Report No. 296. JNCC, Peterborough, UK.

Evans, J. (1984) Silviculture of broadleaved woodland. Forestry Commission Bulletin 62. HMSO, London.

FAO (Food and Agriculture Organisation) (2006) Livestock's Long Shadow: environmental issues and options. Food and Agriculture Organization of the United Nations, Rome.

Fewtrell, L., Kaufmann, R.B., Kay, D., Enanoria, W., Haller, L. & Colford, J.M. (2005) Water, sanitation, and hygiene interventions to reduce diarrhoea in less developed countries: a systematic review and meta-analysis. *Lancet Infectious Diseases*, **5**, 42–52.

Field, R.H., Benke, S., Badonyi, K. & Bradbury, R.B. (2007a) Influence of conservation tillage on bird use of winter arable fields in Hungary. *Agriculture, Ecosystems & Environment*, **120**, 399–404.

Field, R.H., Kirby, W.B. & Bradbury, R.B. (2007b) Conservation Tillage encourages early breeding by Skylarks *Alauda arvensis*. *Bird Study*, **54**, 137–141.

Firbank, L.G. (2005) Striking a new balance between agricultural production and biodiversity. *Annals of Applied Biology*, **146**, 163–175.

Firbank L.G. (2008) Assessing the ecological impacts of bioenergy projects. *Bio-Energy Research*, **1**, 12–19.

Firbank, L.G., Dewar, A.M., Hill, M.O., May, M.J., Perry, J.N., Rothery, P., Squire, G.R. & Woiwod, I.P. (1999) Farm-scale evaluation of GM crops explained. *Nature*, **399**, 727–728.

Firbank, L.G., Perry, J.N., Squire, G.R., Bohan, D.A., Brooks, D.R., Champion, G.T., Clark, S.J., Daniels, R.E., Dewar, A.M., Haughton, A.J., Hawes, C., Heard, M.S., Hill, M.O., May, M.J., Osborne, J.L., Rothery, P., Roy, D.B., Scott, R.J. & Woiwod, I.P. (2003a) The implications of spring-sown genetically modified herbicide-tolerant crops for farmland biodiversity: A commentary on the Farm Scale Evaluations of Spring Sown Crops. Centre for Ecology and Hydrology, Merlewood.

Firbank, L.G., Smart, S.M., Crabb, J., Critchley, C.N.R., Fowbert, J.W., Fuller, R.J., Gladders, P., Green, D.B. & Henderson, I. (2003b) Agronomic and ecological costs and benefits of set-aside in England. *Agriculture, Ecosystems and Environment*, **95**, 73–85.

Firbank, L., Petit, S., Smart, S., Blain, A & Fuller, R. (2008) Assessing the impacts of agricultural intensification on biodiversity. *Philosophical Transactions of the Royal Society B-Biological Sciences*, **363**, 777–787.

Foley, J.A., DeFries, R., Asner, G.P., Barford, C., Bonan, G., Carpenter, S.R., Chapin, F.S., Coe, M.T., Daily, G.C., Gibbs, H.K., Helkowski, J.H., Holloway, T., Howard, E.A., Kucharik, C.J., Monfreda, C., Patz, J.A., Prentice, I.C., Ramankutty, N. & Snyder, P.K. (2005) Global consequences of land use. *Science*, **309**, 570–574.

FLUFP (Foresight Land Use Futures Project) (2010) Final Project Report. The Government Office for Science, London.

FPFCD (Foresight Project Flood and Coastal Defence) (undated) Foresight future flooding. Volume 2; managing future risks. Foresight Directorate, London.

Forest Research (2010) Dutch Elm Disease in Britain. [online] Available at: <http://www.forestry.gov.uk/fr/HCOU-4U4JCL> [Accessed 02.02.11].

Forestry Commission (2003) National inventory of woodland and trees: Great Britain, Forestry Commission, Edinburgh.

Forestry Commission (2009) Forestry statistics. Forestry Commission, Edinburgh. [online] Available at: <http://www.forestry.gov.uk/website/forstats2009.nsf/LUContents/E5088599199CE3FF8025736100394E3B> [Accessed 02.02.11].

FCS (Forestry Commission Scotland) (2007) Woodland creation explanatory note: 2007/08 planting season. Forestry Commission, Edinburgh. [online] Available at: <http://www.forestry.gov.uk/pdf/WCS0708ExplanatoryNote.pdf/$FILE/WCS0708ExplanatoryNote.pdf> [Accessed 02.02.11].

Foster, I.D.L. (2006) Lakes in the Sediment Delivery System. Soil Erosion and Sediment Redistribution in River Catchments (eds P.N. Owens & A.J. Collins), pp. 128–142. CAB International, Wallingford.

Free, J.B. (1993) Insect Pollination of Crops (2nd Edition). Academic Press Ltd, London.

Fuller, R.J., Norton, L.R., Feber, R.E., Johnson, P.J., Hamberlain, D.E., Joys, A.C., Mathews, F., Stuart, R.C, Townsend, M.C, Manley, W.J, Wolfe, M.S., Macdonald, D.W. & Firbank, L.G. (2005) Benefits of organic farming vary among taxa. *Biology Letters*, **1**, 431–434.

Fuller, R.M. (1987) The changing extent and conservation interest of lowland grasslands in England and Wales: a review of grassland surveys 1930–1984. *Biological Conservation*, **40**, 281–300.

Garwes, D. (2009) Increasing efficiency in livestock production: benefits for producers, consumers and the environment. *The Journal of the Royal Agricultural Society of England*, **170**, 34–39.

Gaskell, P. & Owen, S. (2005) Historic farm buildings: constructing the evidence base, University of Gloucestershire, English Heritage, and the Countryside Agency, (English Heritage Product Code: 51168), ISBN: 1 86174 172 3.

Geary, P.M. & Davies, C.M. (2003) Bacterial source tracking and shellfish contamination in a coastal catchment. *Water Science and Technology*, **47**, 95–100.

Gill, M., Smith, P. & Wilkinson, J.M. (2010) Mitigating climate change: the role of domestic livestock. *Animal*, **4**, 323–333.

Glover, J.D., Culman, S.W., DuPont, S.T., Broussard, W., Young, L., Mangan, M.E., Mai, J.G., Crews, T. E., DeHaan, L.R., Buckley, D.H., Ferris, H., Turner, R.E., Reynolds, H.L. & Wyse, D.L. (2010) Harvested perennial grasslands provide ecological benchmarks for agricultural sustainability. *Agriculture Ecosystems & Environment*, **137**, 3–12.

Godfray, H.C.J., Beddington, J.R., Crute, I.R., Haddad, L., Lawrence, D., Muir, J.F., Pretty, J., Robinson, S., Thomas, S.M. & Toulmin, C. (2010) Food Security: The Challenge of Feeding 9 Billion People. *Science*, **327**, 812–818.

Goldberg, E., Kirby, K., Hall, J. & Latham, J. (2007) The ancient woodland concept as a practical conservation tool in Great Britain. *Journal for Nature Conservation*, **15**, 109–119.

Goulding, K.W.T., Jarvis, S.C. & Whitmore, A.P. (2008) Optimising nutrient management for farm systems. Philosophical Transactions of the Royal Society series B, 363, 667–680.

Goulding, K.W.T., Trewavas, A. & Giller, K.E. (2009) Can organic farming feed the world? A contribution to the debate on the ability of organic farming systems to provide sustainable supplies of food. Proceedings No 663, International Fertiliser Society, York.

Gove, B., Flower, K.A. & Bradbury, R.B. (2010). A review of environmental consequences of biomass production for UK energy consumption. RSPB Research Report 38. RSPB, Sandy.

Haines-Young, R., Barr, C.J., Firbank, L.G., Furse, M., Howard, D.C., McGowan, G., Petit, S., Smart, S.M. & Watkins, J.W. (2003) Changing landscapes, habitats and vegetation diversity across Great Britain. *Journal of Environmental Management*, **67**, 267–281.

Harris, P.J. (1995) Water quality impacts from on site waste disposal systems to coastal areas through groundwater discharge. *Environmental Geology*, **26**, 262–268.

Harrison, C.M., Burgess, J. & Limb, M. (1987) Nature in the city: popular values for a living world. *Journal of Environmental Management*, **25**, 347–362.

Harrison, R.B., Turner, N.S., Hoyle, J.A., KrejsL, J., Tone, D.D., Henry, C.L., Isaksen, P.J. & Xue, D. (2000) Treatment of septic effluent for fecal coliform and nitrogen in coarse-textured soils: Use of oil-only and sand filter systems. *Water, Air and Soil Pollution*, **124**, 205–215.

Hawes, C., Haughton, A.J., Osborne, J.L., Roy, D.B., Clark, S.J., Perry, J.N., Rothery, P., Bohan, D.A., Brooks, D.R., Champion, G.T., Dewar, A.M., Heard, M.S., Woiwod, I.P., Daniels, R.E., Young, M.W., Parish, A.M., Scott, R.J., Firbank, L.G. & Squire, G.R. (2003) Responses of plants and invertebrate trophic groups to contrasting herbicide regimes in the Farm Scale Evaluations of genetically modified herbicide-tolerant crops. *Philosophical Transactions of the Royal Society B- Biological Sciences*, **358**, 1899–1913.

Haygarth, P.M., Ap Simon, H., Betson, M., Harris, D., Hodgkinson, R & Withers, P.J.A. (2009) Mitigating diffuse phosphorus transfer from agriculture according to cost and efficiency. *Journal of Environmental Quality* **38**, 2012–2022.

Henle, K., Alard, A., Clitherow, J., Cobb, P., Firbank, L., Kull, T., McCracken, D.I., Moritz, R., Mühle, H., Niemelä, J., Nowicki, P., Rebane, M., Wascher, D., Watt, A. & Young, J. (2008) Identifying and managing the conflicts between agriculture and biodiversity conservation in Europe– a review. *Agriculture, Ecosystems & Environment*, **124**, 60–71.

Herzon, I. & Helenius, J. (2008) Agricultural drainage ditches, their biological importance and functioning: literature review. *Biological Conservation*, **141**, 1171–1183.

Hillier, J., Whittaker, C., Dailey, G., Aylott, M., Casella, E., Richter, G.M., Riche, A., Murphy, R., Taylor, G. & Smith, P. (2009) Greenhouse gas emissions from four bioenergy crops in England and Wales: Integrating spatial estimates of yield and soil carbon balance in life cycle analyses. *Global Change Biology Bioenergy*, **1**, 267–281.

HM Government (2010) Food 2030. Defra, London.

Hodgson, J.A., Kunin, W.E., Thomas, C.D., Benton, T.G. & Gabriel, D. (2010) Comparing organic farming and land sparing: optimising 1 yield and 2 butterfly populations at a landscape scale. *Ecology Letters*, **13**, 1358–1367.

Holland, J.M. (2004) The environmental consequences of adopting conservation tillage in Europe: reviewing the evidence. *Agriculture, Ecosystems & Environment*, **103**, 1–25.

Holland, J.M., Oaten, H., Southway, S. & Moreby, S. (2008) The effectiveness of field margin enhancement for cereal aphid control by different natural enemy guilds. *Biological Control*, **47**, 71–76.

Holloway, S. (2002) The Historical Atlas of Breeding Birds in Britain and Ireland, *1875–1900*. Poyser.

Hopkins, A. (1999) *Grass: Its Production and Utilisetion*. Blackwell Scientific Publications, Oxford.

Howard, D.C., Watkins, J.W., Clarke, R.T., Barnett, C.L. & Stark, G.J. (2003) Estimating the extent and change in Broad Habitats in Great Britain. *Journal of Environmental Management*, **67**, 219–227.

Hunt, D.T.E., Dee, A.S. & Oakes, D.B. (2004) Updating the estimates of the source apportionment of N to UK waters. Phase 2. Report to Defra by WRc and ADAS.

IFA (International Fertiliser Industry Association) (2009) Feeding the earth. Energy efficiency and CO_2 emissions in ammonia production. International Fertiliser Industry Association, Paris.

Iglesias, A., Avis, K., Benzie, M., Fisher, P., Harley, P., Hodgson, N., Horrocks, L., Moneo, M. & Webb, J. (2007) Adaptation to climate change in the agriculture sector. Agri-2006-G4-05. Report to European Commission Directorate General for Agriculture and Rural Development. EAE Energy and Environment and Universidad de Politecnica de Madrid, Spain.

Ingram, J. (2008) Agronomist-farmer knowledge encounters: an analysis of knowledge exchange in the context of best management practices in England. *Agriculture and Human Values*, **25**, 405–418.

Jackson, D.L. (2000) JNCC Report No. 307. Guidance on the interpretation of the Biodiversity Broad Habitat Classification (terrestrial and freshwater types): definitions and the relationships with other habitat classifications. Joint Nature Conservation Committee, Peterborough.

Jackson, J., Li, Y., Murrells, T.P., Okamura, S., Passant, N., Sneddon, S., Thomas, J., Thistlethwaite, G. & Misselbrook, T.

(2009) Inventories for England, Scotland, Wales and Northern Ireland: 1990 – 2007. AEA group, Didcot.

Jacobs, J.H., Clark, S.J., Denholm, I., Goulson, D., Stoate, C. & Osborne, J. (2009) Pollination biology of fruit-bearing plants and the role of flower-visiting insects in fruit set. *Annals of Botany*, **104**, 1397–1404.

Jarvie, H.P., Haygarth, P.M., Neal, C., Butler, P., Smith, B., Naden, P.S, Joynes, A., Neal, M., Wickham, H., Armstrong, L., Harman, S. & Palmer-Felgate, E.J. (2008a) Stream water chemistry and quality along an upland-lowland rural land-use continuum, south west England. *Journal of Hydrology*, **350**, 215–231.

Jarvie, H.P., Withers, P.J.A., Hodgkinson, R., Bates, A., Neal, M., Wickham, H.D., Harman, S.A. & Armstrong. L. (2008b) Influence of rural land use on streamwater nutrients and their ecological significance. *Journal of Hydrology*, **350**, 166–186.

Jarvie, H.P., Withers, P.J.A., Bowes, M.J., Palmer-Felgate, E.J., Harper, D., Wasiak, K., Wasiak, P., Hodgkinson, R.A., Bates, A., Stoate, C., Neal, M., Wickham, H.D., Harman, S.A. & Armstrong, L.K. (2010) Streamwater phosphorus and nitrogen across a gradient in rural-agricultural land use intensity. *Agriculture, Ecosystems and Environment*, **135**, 238–252.

Jenkins, G.J., Murphy, J.M., Sexton, D.M.H., Lowe, J.A., Jones, P. & Kilsby, C.G. (2009) UK Climate Projections: Briefing report. Met Office Hadley Centre, Exeter.

John Clegg & co, Firn Crichton Roberts Ltd., CJC Consulting and Ecoscope (2002) Evaluation of woodland creation in England under the woodland grant scheme and the farm woodland premium scheme. Report to Defra and Forestry Commission.

Johnston, A.E. & Poulton, P.R. (2009) Nitrogen in agriculture: an overview and definitions of nitrogen use efficiency. Proceedings No 651, International Fertiliser Society, York.

Jones, P. & Crane, R. (2009) England and Wales under organic agriculture. How much food could be produced? CAS Report 18. Centre for Agricultural Strategy, Reading.

Karp, A., Haughton, A.J., Bohan, D.A., Lovett, A.A., Bond, A.J., Dockerty, T., Sunnenberg, G., Finch, J.W., Sage, R.B., Appleton, K.J., Riche, A.B., Mallott, M.D., Mallott, V.E., Cunningham, M.D., Clark, S.J. & Turner, M.M. (2009) Perennial energy crops: implications and potential. What is Land for? (eds M. Winter & M. Lobley), pp. 47–72. Earthscan.

Keep, M. (2009). Agriculture: historical statistics. Standard Note: SN/SG/3339. House of Common Library, London.

Kendall, l.P. (2010) Badger cull needed to fight bovine TB. The Guardian. [online] Available at: <http://www.guardian. co.uk/uk/2010/nov/19/badger-cull-to-fight-tb> [Accessed 03.02.11].

Kilpatrick, J., Tubby, I., Matthews, R., Mackie, E., Hogan, G., Heywood, C., Smith, C., Wilson, L., Proctor, C. & Spink, J. (2008) Addressing the land use issues for non-food crops, in response to increasing fuel and energy generation opportunities. ADAS report to National Non-Food Crops Centre (NNFCC). [online] Availlable at: <http://www.nnfcc.co.uk/metadot/index.pl?id=82 53;isa=DBRow;op=show;dbview_id=2539> [Accessed 02.02.11].

Kleijn, D. & Sutherland, W.J. (2003) How effective are European agri-environment schemes in conserving and promoting biodiversity? *Journal of Applied Ecology*, **40**, 947–969.

Krebs, J.R., Wilson, J.D., Bradbury, R.B. & Siriwardena, G.M. (1999) The second Silent Spring? *Nature*, **400**, 611–612.

Kremen, C., Williams, N.M., Aizen, M.A., Gemmill-Herren, B., LeBuhn, G., Minckley, R., Packer, L., Potts, S.G., Roulston, T., Steffan-Dewenter, I., Vazquez, D.P., Winfree, R., Adams, L., Crone, E.E., Greenleaf, S.S., Keitt, T.H., Klein, A.M., Regetz, J. & Ricketts, T.H. (2007) Pollination and other ecosystem services produced by mobile organisms: a conceptual framework for the effects of land-use change. *Ecology Letters,* **10**, 299–314.

Lampkin, N. (1990) Organic Farming. Farming Press, Ipswich.

Landis, D.A., Wratten, S.D. & Gurr, G.M. (2000) Habitat management to conserve natural enemies of arthropod pests in agriculture. *Annual Review of Entomology*, **45**, 175–201.

Le Féon, V., Schermann-Legionnet, A., Delettre, Y., Aviron, S., Billeter, R., Bugter, R., Hendrickx, F. & Burel, F. (2010) Intensification of agriculture, landscape composition and wild bee communities: A large scale study in four European countries. *Agriculture Ecosystems & Environment,* **137**, 143–150.

Long, S.P., Ainsworth, E.A., Rogers, A. & Ort, D.R. (2004) Rising atmospheric carbon dioxide: Plants face the future. *Annual Review of Plant Biology*, **55**, 591–628.

Loreau, M. (2010) Linking biodiversity and ecosystems: towards a unifying ecological theory. *Philosophical Transactions of the Royal Society Series B – Biological Sciences*, **365**, 49–60.

Lovett, A.A., Sünnenberg, G.M., Richter, G.M., Dailey, A.G., Riche, A.B. & Karp, A. (2009) Land use implications of increased biomass production identified by GIS-Based suitability and yield mapping for *Miscanthus* in England. *Bioenergy Research*, **2**, 17–28.

Lowenthal, D. (1991) British national identity and the English landscape. *Rural History*, **2**, 205–230.

LUCCG (Land Use Climate Change Group) (2010) *Land Use Climate Change Report to Welsh Assembly Government.* Land Use Climate Change Group. [online] Available at: http://wales. gov.uk/docs/drah/publications/100310landuseclimatechangegr oupreporten.pdf [Accessed 02.02.11].

Lutman, P. & Marsh, J. (2009) Environmental, economic and social aspects of NAE Agriculture and AKST. Agriculture at a crossroads: International Assessment of Agricultural Science and Technology for Development, Volume IV; North America and Europe (eds B.D. McIntyre, H.R. Herren, J. Wakhungu, & R. Watson), pp. 79–115. Washington, Island Press.

MA (Millennium Ecosystem Assessment) (2005) Ecosystems and human well being: Synthesis. Island Press, Washington DC.

Mabey, R. (1972) Food for Free. Collins, London.

Mabey, R. (1997) Flora Britannica. Sinclair-Stevenson, London.

Macfadyen, S., Gibson, R., Polaszek, A., Morris, R.J., Craze, P.G., Planque, R., Symondson, W.O.C. & Memmott, J (2009) Do differences in food web structure between organic and conventional farms affect the ecosystem service of pest control? *Ecology Letters*, **12**, 229–238.

Macleod, M., Moran, D., Eory, V., Rees, R., Barnes, A., Topp, C., Ball, B., Hoad, S., Wall, E., McVittie, A., Pajot, G. Matthews, R., Smith, P. & Moxey, A. (2010) Developing greenhouse gas marginal abatement cost curves for agricultural emissions from crops and soils in the UK. *Agricultural Systems*, **103**, 198–209.

Maier, G., Nimmo-Smith, R.J., Glegg, G.A., Tappin, A.D. & Worsford, P.J. (2008) Estuarine eitrophication in the UK: current incidence and future trends. *Aquatic Conservation: Marine and Freshwater Ecosystems*, **19**, 43–56.

Marshall, E.J.P., Brown, V.K., Boatman, N.D., Lutman, P.J.W., Squire, G.R. & Ward, L.K. (2003) The role of weeds in supporting biological diversity within crop fields. *Weed Research*, **43**, 77–89.

Maskell, L.C., Norton, L.R., Smart, S.M., Carey, P.D., Murphy, J., Chamberlain, P.M., Wood, C.M., Bunce, R.G.H. & Barr, C.J. (2008) CS Technical Report No.1/07 Field Mapping Handbook. Centre for Ecology and Hydrology, Wallingford.

Matless, D. (1998) Landscape and Englishness. Reaktion, London.

McCracken, D.I. & Midgley, A. (2010) How well is farmland biodiversity being maintained? Rural Scotland in Focus (eds S. Skerratt, C. Hall, C. Lamprinopoulou, D. McCracken, A. Midgley, M. Price, A. Renwick, C. Revoredo, S. Thomson, F. Williams. & A. Wreford), pp. 70–79. Rural Policy Centre, Scottish Agricultural College, Edinburgh.

McIntyre, B.D., Herren, H.R., Wakhungu, J. & Watson, R. (eds) (2009) Agriculture at a crossroads: International Assessment of Agricultural Science and Technology for Development, Volume IV; North America and Europe. Island Press, Washington.

Miller, D., Schwarz, G., Sutherland, L-A., Morrice, J., Aspinall, R., Barnes, A., Blackstock, K., Buchan, K., Donnelly, D., Hawes, C., McCrum, G., McKenzie, B., Matthews, K., Miller, D., Renwick, A., Smith, M., Squire, G. & Toma, L. (2009) Changing land use in rural Scotland: drivers and decision makers. Rural Land Use study Project 1. Report for the Scottish Government by The Macaulay Land Use Research Institute, Forest Research, Humboldt University of Berlin, Scottish Agricultural College and Scottish Crop Research Institute. [online] Available at: <www.scotland.gov.uk/Resource/Doc/294685/0091117.pdf> [Accessed 02.02.11].

Mitchell, R. & Popham, F. (2008) Effect of exposure to natural environment on health inequalities: an observational population study. *Lancet*, **372**, 1655–1660.

Monbiot, G. (2010) Control landowners, not badgers – that's the real answer to bovine TB. The Guardian. [online] Available at: <http://www.guardian.co.uk/commentisfree/2010/nov/15/control-landowners-badgers-bovine-tb> [Accessed 03.02.11].

Morandin, L.A., Winston, M.L., Franklin, M.T. & Abbott, V.A. (2005) Lethal and sub-lethal effects of spinosad on bumble bees (Bombus impatiens Cresson). *Pest Management Science*, **61**, 619–626.

Morris A J. (2007) An Overview of the Sustainable Arable Farming for an Improved Environment (SAFFIE) project. *Aspects of Applied Biology*, **81**, 23–30.

Morris, A.J., Bailey, C.M., Winspear R, Gruar, D.J. & Dillon, I.A. (2010) Drivers of population increase on an arable farm delivering a comprehensive suite of measures for farmland birds. *Aspects of Applied Biology*, **100**, 201–209.

Natural England (2009a) Agri-environment schemes in England 2009: A review of results and effectiveness. Natural England. [online] Available at: <http://www.naturalengland.org.uk/Images/AE-schemes09_tcm6-14969.pdf> [Accessed 02.02.11].

Natural England (2009b) Experiencing landscapes: capturing the cultural services and experiential qualities of landscape. Natural England Report NECR0124. Natural England, Sheffield.

Natural England (2010) Energy Crops Scheme. [online] Available at: <http://www.naturalengland.org.uk/planning/grants-funding/energy-crops/default.htm> [Accessed 02.02.11].

Neal, C., Jarvie, H.P., Withers, P.J.A., Whitton, B.A. & Neal, M. (2010) The strategic significance of wastewater sources to pollutant phosphorus levels in English rivers and to environmental management for rural, agricultural and urban catchments. *Science of the Total Environment*, **408**, 1485–1500.

Norton, L.R., Murphy, J., Reynolds, B., Marks, S. & Mackey, E.C. (2009a) Countryside Survey: Scotland Results from 2007. NERC/Centre for Ecology & Hydrology, The Scottish Government, Scottish Natural Heritage, 83pp. (CEH Project Number: C03259). [online] Available at: <http://www.countrysidesurvey.org.uk/scots_reports2007.html> [Accessed 02.02.11].

Norton, L., Johnson, P., Joys, A., Stuart, R., Chamberlain, D., Feber, R., Firbank, L., Manley, W., Wolfe, M., Hart, B., Mathews, F., Macdonald, D. & Fuller, R.J. (2009b) Consequences of organic and non-organic farming practices for field, farm and landscape complexity. *Agriculture, Ecosystems and Environment*, **129**, 221–227.

Ockinger, E. & Smith, H.G. (2007) Semi-natural grasslands as population sources for pollinating insects in agricultural landscapes. *Journal of Applied Ecology*, **44**, 50–59.

PACEC (Public and Corporate Economic Consultants) (2006) The Economic and Environmental Impacts of Sporting Shooting. Research for the British Association of Shooting and Conservation, County Land and Business Association and Countryside Alliance, in association with the Game Conservancy Trust. Public and Corporate Economic Consultants, Cambridge.

Parish, D.M.B. & Sotherton, N.W. (2008) Landscape-dependent use of a seed-rich habitat by farmland passerines: relative importance of game cover crops in a grassland versus an arable region of Scotland. *Bird Study*, **55**, 118–123.

Parry, M.L., Canziani, O.F., Palutikof, J.P., van der Linden, P.J. & Hanson, C.E. (eds) (2008) Contribution of Working Group II to the Fourth Assessment Report of the Intergovernmental Panel on Climate Change, 2007. Cambridge University Press, Cambridge.

Patz, J.A., Daszak, P., Tabor, G.M., Aguirre, A.A., Pearl, M., Epstein, J., Wolfe, N.D., Kilpatrick, A.M., Foufopoulos, J., Molyneux, D. & Bradley, D.J. (2004) Unhealthy landscapes: Policy recommendations on land use change and infectious disease emergence. *Environmental Health Perspectives*, **112**, 1092–1098.

Peach, W.J., Denny, M., Cotton, P.A., Hill, I.F., Gruar, D., Barritt, D., Impey, A. & Mallord, J. (2004) Habitat selection by song thrushes in stable and declining populations. *Journal of Applied Ecology*, **41**, 275–293.

Petit, S., Stuart, R.C., Gillespie, M.K. & Barr, C.J. (2003) Field boundaries in Great Britain: stock and change between 1984, 1990 and 1998. *Journal of Environmental Management*, **67**, 229–238.

Petit, S. & Elbersen, B. (2006) Assessing the risk of impact of farming intensification on calcareous grasslands in Europe: a quantitative implementation of the MIRABEL framework. *Ambio*, **35**(6), 297–303.

Petit, S. & Firbank, L. (2006) Predicting the risk of losing parcels of semi-natural habitat to intensive agriculture. *Agriculture, Ecosystems and Environment*, **115**, 277–280.

Phillipson, J., Lowe, P. & Carroll, T. (2002) Confronting the Rural Shutdown: Foot and Mouth Disease and the North East Rural Economy. Centre for Rural Economy Research Report, University of Newcastle.

Pilgrim, E.S., Macleod, C.J.A., Blackwell, M.S.A., Bol, R., Hogan, D.V., Chadwick, D.R., Cardenas, L., Misselbrook, T.H., Haygarth, P.M., Brazier, R.E., Hobbs, P., Hodgson, C., Jarvis, S., Dungait, J., Murray, P.J. & Firbank, L.G. (2010). Interactions among agricultural production and other ecosystem services delivered from European temperate grassland systems *Advances in Agronomy* **109,** 117–154.

Posthumus, H., Rouquette, J.R., Morris, J., Gowing, D.J. & Hess, T.M. (2010) A framework for the assessment of ecosystem goods and services; a case study on lowland floodplains in England. *Ecological Economics*, **69**, 1510–1523.

Potts, G.R. (1986) The Partridge: Pesticides, Predation and Conservation. Collins, London.

Potts, G.R., Ewald, J.A. & Aebischer, N.J. (2010b) Long-term changes in the flora of the cereal ecosystem on the Sussex Downs, England, focusing on the years 1968–2005. *Journal of Applied Ecology*, **47**, 215–226.

Potts, S.G., Roberts, S.P.M., Dean, R., Marris, G., Brown, M., Jones, R. & Settele, J. (2010a) Declines of managed honeybees and beekeepers in Europe. *Journal of Apicultural Research*, **49**, 15–22.

Potts, S.G., Woodcock, B.A., Roberts, S.P.M., Tscheulin, T., Ramsay, A.J., Pilgrim, E., Brown, V.K. & Tallowin, J.R. (2009) Enhancing pollinator biodiversity in intensive grasslands. *Journal of Applied Ecology*, **46**, 369–379.

Preston, C.D., Pearman, D.A. & Dines, T.D. (2002) New Atlas of the British and Irish Flora: An Atlas of the Vascular Plants of Britain, Ireland, The Isle of Man and the Channel Island. Oxford University Press, Oxford.

Rackham, O. (1986) The History of the Countryside. J.M. Dent, London.

Rich, T.C.G. & Woodruff, E.R. (1996) Changes in the vascular plant floras of England and Scotland between 1930–1960 and 1987–1988: The BSBI monitoring scheme. *Biological Conservation*, **75**, 217–229.

Ricketts, T.H., Regetz, J., Steffen-Dewenter, I., Cunningham, S.A., Kremen, C., Bogdanski, A., Gemmill-Herren, B., Greenleaf, S.S., Klein, A.M., Mayfield, M.M., Morandin, L.A., Ochieng, A., Potts, S.G. & Viana B.F. (2008) Landscape effects on crop pollination services: are there general patterns? *Ecology Letters*, **11**, 499–515.

Robinson, R.A. & Sutherland, W.J. (2002) Post-war changes in arable farming and biodiversity in Great Britain. *Journal of Applied Ecology*, **39**, 157–176.

Rowe, R.L., Street, N.R. & Taylor, G. (2009) Identifying potential environmental impacts of large-scale deployment of dedicated bioenergy crops in the UK. *Renewable & Sustainable Energy Reviews*, **13**, 271–290.

Roy, D.B., Bohan, D.A., Haughton, A.J., Hill, M.O., Osborne, J.L., Clark, S.J., Perry, J.N., Rothery, P., Scott, R.J., Brooks, D.R., Champion, G.T., Hawes, C., Heard, M.S. & Firbank, L.G. (2003) Invertebrates and vegetation of field margins adjacent to crops subject to contrasting herbicide regimes in the Farm Scale Evaluations of genetically modified herbicide-tolerant crops. *Philosophical Transactions of the Royal Society B- Biological Sciences.* **358**, 1879–1898.

Royal Society (2009) Reaping the Benefits: science and the sustainable intensification of global agriculture. The Royal Society, London.

RSPB (Royal Society for the Protection of Birds) (2009) Clock wound back 5000 years at Beckingham Marshes.

[online] Available at: <http://www.rspb.org.uk/news/details.asp?id=tcm:9-219651> [Accessed 02.02.11].

RSPB (Royal Society for the Proteciton of Birds), BTO (British Trust for Ornithology), JNCC (Joint Nature Conservation Committee) & Defra (Department for Agriculture, Food and Rural Affairs) (2011). UK Wild Farmland Bird Indicator 1970-2009.

SAC (Scottish Agricultural College) (2008) Farming's retreat from the hills. Scottish Agricultural College, Edinburgh. [online] Available at: <http://www.sac.ac.uk/mainrep/pdfs/retreatreport.pdf> [Accessed 02.02.11].

Samsom, A.L. (1999) Upland vegetation management: The impacts of overstocking. *Water Science & Technology*, **39**, 85–92.

Scandura, J.E. & Sobsey, M.D. (1997) Viral and bacterial contamination of groundwater from on-site sewage treatment systems. *Water Science & Technology,* **35,** 141–146.

Schmidt, M.H., Lauer, A., Purtauf, T., Thies, C., Schaefer, M. & Tscharntke, T. (2003) Relative importance of predators and parasitoids for cereal aphid control. *Proceedings of the Royal Society of London* B-Biological Sciences, **270**, 1905–1909.

Schwarz, G., Moxey, A., McCracken, D., Huband, S. & Cummins, R. (2009) An analysis of the potential effectiveness of a Payment-by-Results approach to the delivery of environmental public goods and services supplied by Agri-Environment Schemes (23192). Report to the UK Land Use Policy Group (LUPG). Macaulay Institute, Pareto Consulting and Scottish Agricultural College. [online] Available at: <http://www.lupg.org.uk/pdf/LUPG_Payment_by_Results_Feb09.pdf> [Accessed 02.02.11].

Scottish Executive (2001) A Forward Strategy for Scottish Agriculture. Scottish Government, Edinburgh. [online] Available at: <http://www.scotland.gov.uk/Resource/Doc/158242/0042839.pdf> [Accessed 02.02.11].

Scottish Executive (2006) A Forward Strategy for Scottish Agriculture: Next Steps. Scottish Government, Edinburgh. [online] Available at: <http://www.scotland.gov.uk/Resource/Doc/94965/0022832.pdf> [Accessed 02.02.11].

Scottish Government (2010) Getting the best from our land. A draft land use strategy for Scotland: Consultation for discussion and feedback. Scottish Government, Edinburgh.

Sherrington, C. & Moran D. (2010) Modelling farmer uptake of perennial energy crops in the UK. *Energy Policy*, **38**, 3567–3578.

Shortall, C.R., Moore, A., Smith, E., Hall, M.J., Woiwod, I.P. & Harrington, R. (2009) Long-term changes in the abundance of flying insects. *Insect Conservation and Diversity*, **2**, 251–260.

Shrubb, M. (2003) Birds, Scythes and Combines: A History of Birds and Agricultural Change. Cambridge University Press, Cambridge.

Slee, W., Bergman, H., Brown, I., Huband, S., McCracken, D., Renwick, A., Sutherland L-A., Thomson S. & Reed, M. (2009) Rural Land Use Study Project 2: Realising the potential contributions of Scotland's rural land to delivering sustainable economic growth. Report to Scottish Government's Rural and Environment Research and Analysis Directorate. [online] Available at: <http://www.scotland.gov.uk/Publications/2009/12/04154104/16> [Accessed 02.02.11].

Smart, J., Sutherland, W.J. & Watkinson, A.R. (2006a) Grassland-breeding waders: identifying key habitat requirements for management. *Journal of Applied Ecology*, **43**, 454–463.

Smart, S.M., Firbank, L.G, Bunce, R.G.H. & Watkins, J.W. (2000) Quantifying changes in abundance of food plants for butterfly larvae and farmland birds. *Journal of Applied Ecology,* **37**, 398–411.

Smart, S.M., Bunce, R.G.H., Firbank, L.G. & Coward, P. (2002) Do field boundaries act as refugia for grassland plant species diversity in intensively managed agricultural landscapes in Britain? *Agriculture Ecosystems & Environment,* **91**, 73–87.

Smart, S.M., Thompson, K., Marrs, R.H., Le Duc, M.G., Maskell, L.C. & Firbank, L.G. (2006b) Biotic homogenisetion and changes in species diversity across human-modified ecosystems. *Proceedings of the Royal Society,* **273**, 2659–2665.

Smart, S.M., Marrs, R.H., Le Duc, M.G., Thompson, K., Bunce, R.G.H., Firbank, L.G. & Rossall, M.J. (2006c) Spatial relationships between intensive land cover and residual plant species diversity in temperate farmed landscapes. *Journal of Applied Ecology,* **43**, 1128–1137.

Smart, S.M., Allen, D., Murphy, J., Carey, P.D., Emmett, B.A., Reynolds, B., Simpson, I.C., Evans, R.A. Skates, J., Scott, W.A., Maskell, L.C., Norton, L.R., Rossall, M.J. & Wood, C. (2009) Countryside Survey: Wales Results from 2007. NERC, Swindon.

Smil, V. (2002) Nitrogen and Food Production: Proteins for Human Diets. *Ambio,* **31**, 126–131.

Smith, P., Powlson, D.S., Glendining, M.J. & Smith, J.U. (1998) Preliminary estimates of the potential for carbon mitigation in European soils through no-till farming. *Global Change Biology,* **4**, 679–685.

Smith, P., Milne, R., Powlson, D.S., Smith, J.U., Falloon, P.D. & Coleman, K. (2000a) Revised estimates of the carbon mitigation potential of UK agricultural land. *Soil Use and Management,* **16**, 293–295.

Smith, P., Powlson, D.S., Smith, J.U., Falloon, P.D. & Coleman, K. (2000b) Meeting Europe's climate change commitments: quantitative estimates of the potential for carbon mitigation by agriculture. *Global Change Biology,* **6**, 525–539.

Smith, P., Martino, D., Cai, Z., Gwary, D., Janzen, H.H., Kumar, P., McCarl, B., Ogle, S., O'Mara, F., Rice, C., Scholes, R.J., Sirotenko, O., Howden, M., McAllister, T., Pan, G., Romanenkov, V., Schneider, U., Towprayoon, S., Wattenbach, M. & Smith, J.U. (2008) Greenhouse gas mitigation in agriculture. *Philosophical Transactions of the Royal Society B,* **363**, 789–813.

SNH (Scottish Natural Heritage) (2009) Farming and the natural environment. Paper prepared for the inquiry into future agricultural support for Scotland. Scottish Natural Heritage. [online] Available at: <http://scottish-schools.gov.uk/Topics/farmingrural/Agriculture/inquiry/background> [Accessed 02.02.11].

Sotherton, N.W. (1991) Conservation Headlands: A practical combination of intensive cereal farming and conservation. The Ecology of Temperate Cereal Fields (eds L.G. Firbank, N. Carter, J.F. Darbyshire & G.R. Potts), pp 373–397. Blackwell Scientific Publications, Oxford.

SOWAP (Soil and Water Protection) (2007) Soil and surface water protection using conservation tillage in Northern and Central Europe. EU/LIFE03/ENV/UK000617.

St Clair, S., Hiller, J. & Smith, P. (2008) Estimating the pre-harvest greenhouse gas costs of energy crop production. *Biomass & Bioenergy,* **32**, 442–452.

Stoate, C. (1995) The changing face of lowland farming and wildlife. Part 1: 1845–1945. *British Wildlife,* **6**, 341–350.

Stoate, C. (1996) The changing face of lowland farming and wildlife. Part 2: 1945–1995. *British Wildlife,* **7**, 162–172.

Stoate, C. (2002) Multifunctional use of a natural resource on farmland: wild pheasant (*Phasianus colchicus*) management and the conservation of farmland passerines. *Biodiversity and Conservation,* **11**, 561–573.

Stoate, C. (2004) Preparing for a new agri-environment scheme in England: influences on farmer participation. Proceedings of the 6th European International Farming Systems Association conference (ed A. Cristóvão), pp. 459–466. Vila Real, Portugal.

Stoate, C. (2010) Exploring a Productive Landscape – from a long history to a sustainable future in the Eye Brook catchment. GWCT, Fordingbridge. 144pp.

Stoate, C., Henderson, I.G. & Parish, D.M.B. (2004) Development of an agri-environment scheme option: seed-bearing crops for farmland birds. *Ibis,* **146** (suppl. 2), 203–209.

Stoate, C., Whitfield, M., Williams, P. & Driver, K. (2006) Wetland creation and mitigation of water pollution from field drains: Use of buffer strip pools within an arable landscape. Water and Landscape: The Landscape Ecology of Freshwater Ecosystems, pp. 331–334. IALE, Oxford.

Stoate, C., Amos, M. & King, P. (2009) Land use history as a foundation for catchment management planning in the Eye Brook, England. European Landscapes in Transformation: Challenges for Landscape Ecology and Management (eds J. Brueste, M. Kozova & M. Finka), pp. 336–339. European IALE Conference 2009, Salzburg.

Swetnam, R.D. (2007) Rural land use in England and Wales between 1930 and 1998: Mapping trajectories of change with a high resolution spatio-temporal dataset. *Landscape and Urban Planning,* **81**, 91–103.

Szmaragd, C., Wilson, A.J., Carpenter, S., Wood, J.L.N., Mellor, P.S. & Gubbins, S. (2010) The Spread of Bluetongue Virus Serotype 8 in Great Britain and Its Control by Vaccination. PLoS One, **5**, e9353.

Tanner, B.D., Kuwahara, S., Gerba, C.P. & Reynolds, K.A. (2002) Electrochemical ozone generation as a means of water and wastewater disinfection. *Abstracts of the General Meeting of the American Society for Microbiology,* **102**, 415–416.

Tapper, S.C. (1999) A Question of Balance: game animals and their role in the British Countryside. The Game Conservancy Trust, Fordingbridge.

The Milk Roadmap (2008) Dairy Supply Chain Forum's Sustainable Consumption & Production Taskforce. Defra. [online] Available at: <http://www.defra.gov.uk/foodfarm/food/industry/sectors/milk/supplychainforum/taskforce.htm> [Accessed 03.02.11]

The Smith Institute (2009) Feeding Britain (eds J. Bridge & N. Johnson). The Smith Institute.

Thompson, D., Muriel, P., Russell, D., Osborne, P., Bromley, A., Rowland, M., Creigh-Tyte, S. & Brown, C. (2002) Economic costs of the foot and mouth disease outbreak in the United Kingdom in 2001. *Revue Scientifique et Technique de l'Office Internationa des Epizooties,* **23**, 756–687.

Tilman, D., Cassman, K.G., Matson, P.A., Naylor, R. & Polasky, S. (2002) Agricultural sustainability and intensive production practices. *Nature,* **418**, 671–677.

Tracy, M. (1989) Government and Regulation in Western Europe, 1880–1988. New York University Press, New York.

Tscharntke, T., Klein, A. M., Kruess, A., Steffan-Dewenter, I. & Thies, C. (2005) Landscape perspectives on agricultural intensification and biodiversity – ecosystem service management. *Ecology Letters*, **8**, 857–874.

Tsouvalis, J., Seymour, S. & Watkins, C. (2000) Exploring knowledge-cultures: precision farming, yield mapping, and the expert-farmer interface. *Environment & Planning* A, **32**, 909–924.

Usher, M.B., Brown, A.C. & Bedford, S.E. (1992) Plant species richness in farm woodlands. *Forestry*, **65**, 1–13.

Usher, M.B. & Keiller, S.W.J. (1998) The macrolepidoptera of farm woodlands: determinants of diversity and community structure. *Biodiversity & Conservation*, **7**, 725–748.

Vickery, J.A., Tallowin, J.R., Feber, R.E., Asteraki, E.J., Atkinson, P.W., Fuller, R.J. & Brown, V.K. (2001) The management of lowland neutral grasslands in Britain: effects of agricultural practices on birds and their food resources. *Journal of Applied Ecology* **38**, 647–664.

WAG (Welsh Assembly Government) (2009) Farming. Food and countryside; building a secure future. A new strategy for farming. Welsh Assembly Government, Cardiff. [online] Available at: <http://wales.gov.uk/docs/drah/publications/090507ffcmaindocen.pdf> [Accessed 02.02.11].

Walker, K.J., Preston, C.D. & Boon, C.R. (2009) Fifty years of change in an area of intensive agriculture: plant trait responses to habitat modification and conservation, Bedfordshire, England. *Biodiversity & Conservation*, **18**, 3597–3613.

Watkinson, A.R., Freckleton, R.P., Robinson, R.A. & Sutherland, W.J. (2000) Predictions of biodiversity response to genetically modified herbicide-tolerant crops. *Science*, **289**, 1554–1557.

Watson, C.F. & Foy, R.H. (2001) Environmental impacts of nitrogen and phosphorus cycling in grassland systems. *Outlook on Agriculture*, **30**, 117–127.

Weiner, M.J. (2004) English Culture and the decline of the industrial spirit 1850–1980 (2nd Edition). Cambridge University Press, Cambridge.

White, P.J. & Hammond, J.P. (2006) Updating the estimates of the sources of phosphorus in UK waters. Defra Final Report for Project WT0701CSF. [onoline] Available at: <http://randd.defra.gov.uk/Document.aspx?Document=WT0701CSF_4159_FRP.pdf.> [Accessed 02.02.11].

Williams, P., Whitfield, M. & Biggs, J. (2004) Comparative biodiversity of rivers, streams, ditches and ponds in an agricultural landscape in Southern England. *Biological Conservation*, **115**, 329–341.

Williams, P., Biggs, J., Crowe, A., Murphy, J., Nicolet, P., Weatherby, A., Dunbar, M. (2010) Countryside Survey: Ponds Report from 2007. Technical Report No. 7/07 Pond Conservation and NERC/Centre for Ecology & Hydrology, 77pp. (CEH Project Number: C03259).

Wilson, J.D., Whittingham, M.J. & Bradbury, R.B. (2005) The management of crop structure: a general approach to reversing the impacts of agricultural intensification on birds? *Ibis*, **147**, 453–463.

Wilson, J., Anderson, G., Perkins, A., Wilkinson, N. & Maggs, H. (2007) Adapting agri-environment management to multiple drivers of decline of corn buntings *Emberiza calandra* across their UK range. *Aspects of Applied Biology*, **81**, 191–198.

Wilson, J.D., Evans, A.D. & Grice, P.V. (2009) Bird Conservation and Agriculture. Cambridge University Press, Cambridge.

Winfree, R., Aguilar, R., Vazquez, D.P., LeBuhn, G. & Aizen, M.A. (2009) A meta-analysis of bees' responses to anthropogenic disturbance. *Ecology,* **90**, 2068–2076.

Winter, M. (2000) Strong policy or weak policy? The environmental impact of the 1992 reforms to the CAP arable regime in Great Britain. *Journal of Rural Studies*, **16**, 47–59.

Withers, P.J.A., Jarvie, H.P., Hodgkinson, R.A., Palmer-Felgate, E.J., Bates, A., Neal, M., Howells, R., Withers, C.M. & Whickham, H. (2009) Characterisetion of phosphorus sources in rural watersheds. *Journal of Environmental Quality*, **38**, 1998–2011.

Woodcock, B.A., Potts, S.G., Tscheulin, T., Pilgrim, E., Ramsey, A.J., Harrison-Cripps, J., Brown, V.K. & Tallowin, J.R. (2009) Responses of invertebrate trophic level, feeding guild and body size to the management of improved grassland field margins. *Journal of Applied Ecology*, **46**, 920–929.

Young, J., Watt, A., Nowicki, P., Alard, D., Clitherow, J., Henle, K., Johnson, R., Laczko, E., McCracken, D., Matouch, S. & Niemela, J. (2005) Towards sustainable land use: identifying and managing the conflicts between human activities and biodiversity conservation in Europe. *Biodiversity & Conservation*, **14**, 1641–1661.

Appendix 7.1 Approach Used to Assign Certainty Terms to Chapter Key Findings

This chapter began with a set of Key Findings. Adopting the approach and terminology used by the Intergovernmental Panel on Climate Change (IPCC) and the Millennium Assessment (MA), these Key Findings also include an indication of the level of scientific certainty. The 'uncertainty approach' of the UK NEA consists of a set of qualitative uncertainty terms derived from a 4-box model and complemented, where possible, with a likelihood scale (see below). Estimates of certainty are derived from the collective judgement of authors, observational evidence, modelling results and/or theory examined for this assessment.

Throughout the Key Findings presented at the start of this chapter, superscript numbers and letters indicate the estimated level of certainty for a particular key finding:

1. *Well established:*   high agreement based on significant evidence
2. *Established but incomplete evidence:* high agreement based on limited evidence
3. *Competing explanations:*   low agreement, albeit with significant evidence
4. *Speculative:*   low agreement based on limited evidence

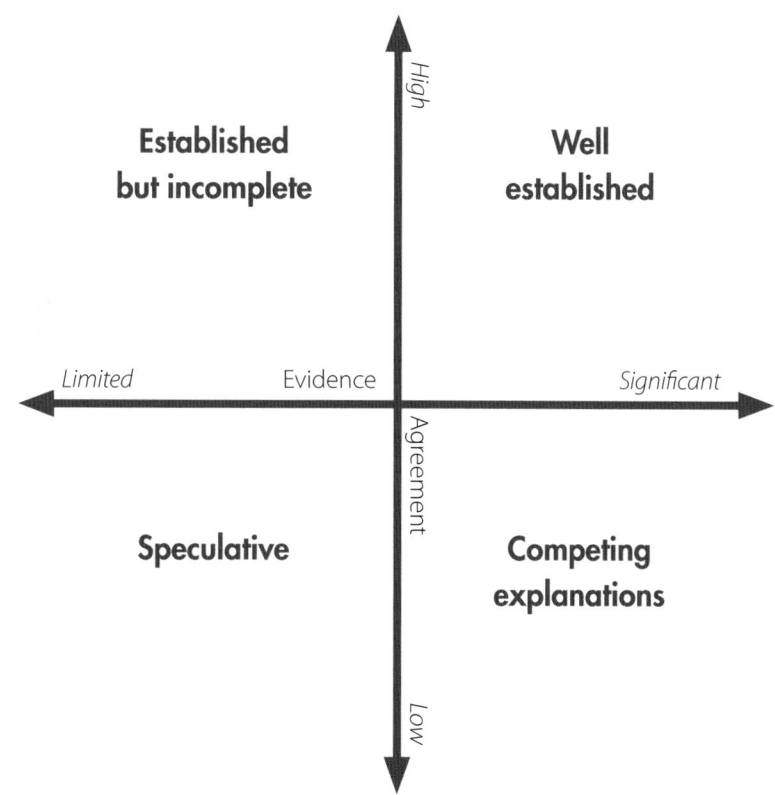

a. *Virtually certain:*   >99% probability of occurrence
b. *Very likely:*   >90% probability
c. *Likely:*   >66% probability
d. *About as likely as not:*   >33–66% probability
e. *Unlikely:*   <33% probability
f. *Very unlikely:*   <10% probability
g. *Exceptionally unlikely:*   <1% probability

Certainty terms 1 to 4 constitute the 4-box model, while a to g constitute the likelihood scale.

Chapter 8:
Woodlands

Coordinating Lead Author: Chris Quine
Lead Authors: Christine Cahalan, Alison Hester, Jonathan Humphrey, Keith Kirby, Andy Moffat and Gregory Valatin

Key Findings*

Since 1945, the area of woodland has doubled to cover 12% of the UK, but still remains well below the EU average of 37%1. Much of this increase is due to afforestation for timber production, leading to the dominance of coniferous species. These comprise 81% of current woodland in Scotland, 55% in Wales and 35% in England. Recently, more broadleaved species have been planted, resulting in an increase of 6.9% in the area of broadleaved mixed and yew woodland in the UK between 1998 and 2007.

[1] *well established*

There is no primary woodland in the UK; all remaining woodland has been influenced by human activities[1]. Nevertheless, the woodland that remains contains significant biodiversity: a quarter of all UK Biodiversity Action Plan priority species are associated with trees and woods. Trends in the condition of habitats and species vary, but that of woodland SSSIs and seven priority native woodland habitats is improving. Short-term trends can be misleading, however[2]. Recent plantations gain native species, albeit with different assemblages from those of semi-natural woods[c].

[1] *well established*
[2] *established but incomplete evidence*
[c] *likely*

Many factors, at all scales, effect change in woodland ecosystems. Key drivers include climate change, pollution, government policy on land use, society, global trade and domestic markets, and the endogenous dynamics of ageing woodland. Although recent climate change has had little effect on woodland structure and composition, mobile species, such as insects and birds, have shown range changes, and increasing temperatures have led to faster tree growth and altered phenology in some areas[2]. Despite recent reductions in emissions, nitrogen deposition and ozone levels are still above 'critical loads' for habitats such as UK Atlantic Oakwoods. Wild herbivores, particularly deer, have increased in number over the past 30 years to the detriment of woodland habitats[1].

[1] *well established*
[2] *established but incomplete evidence*

Timber production is an important provisioning service from woodlands. Domestic production has increased from an estimated 4% in the 1940s to 20% of UK consumption of timber, pulp and panel products today[1]. In 2009, 8.5 million green tonnes of softwood was produced in the UK—approximately 60% of annual growth increment—and production is predicted to rise to 11–12 million tonnes in the 2020s. A total of 0.4 million tonnes of hardwood were produced from broadleaves—about 20% of annual growth increment. Non-timber products from woodlands can also be important; for example, game shooting is estimated to contribute £640 million per annum to the UK economy[2].

[1] *well established*
[2] *established but incomplete evidence*

Woodlands are highly valued by people for social and cultural services*; there are approximately 250–300 million day visits to woodlands per year. Woodland includes nearly 5,000 Scheduled Ancient Monuments, plus many areas managed for geological study. The social and environmental benefits of woodlands in Great Britain (GB) were valued in 2002 at more than £1.2 billion per annum (at 2010 prices), with the landscape value of woodland estimated at £185 million (2010), and recreational visits valued at £484 million (2010). However, only 55% of the population has access to woods larger than 20 ha within 4 km of their home.

[2] *established but incomplete evidence*

---

* Each Key Finding has been assigned a level of scientific certainty, based on a 4-box model and complemented, where possible, with a likelihood scale. Superscript numbers and letters indicate the uncertainty term assigned to each finding. Full details of each term and how they were assigned are presented in Appendix 8.1.

Carbon sequestration is one of the most important regulating services provided by woodlands*. The total carbon (C) stock in UK forests (including soils) is around 800 megatonnes (Mt) of carbon (2,900 Mt of carbon dioxide (CO_2) equivalent), and is estimated to be a further 80 Mt C in timber and wood products. The strength of the UK forest carbon sink increased from 1990 to 2004, but may now start to decline due to a fall off in planting rates in the last 20 years and harvesting of mature trees. At peak growth, coniferous forest can sequester around 24 tonnes of CO_2 per hectare per year, with a net long-term average of around 14 t CO_2/ha/yr. Rates of around 15 t CO_2/ha/yr have been measured in oak forest at peak growth, with a net long-term average likely to be around 7 t CO_2/ha/yr.

[2] established but incomplete evidence

The social value of net carbon sequestration by UK woodlands is currently at least double the market value of wood production per hectare; and the total value of net carbon sequestration by UK woodlands planted after 1921 increased more than six-fold over the period between 1945 and 2004, falling thereafter[2]. Carbon sequestration currently has the highest annual social value of the woodland ecosystem services considered; however, as it remains largely a non-market value, there is little incentive for landowners to increase its provision or to maintain existing carbon storage at present.

[2] established but incomplete evidence

Forest policy and woodland management have changed over time as different goods and services have been required[1]. There are both trade-offs and synergies between goods and services produced by woodlands. The diversification of forest structure for biodiversity benefits may improve cultural services (including aesthetics), while increases in forest cover may benefit carbon regulation and flood regulation. However, maximising provisioning services through the use of highly productive species and intensive site treatments may have negative effects upon the value of woodland for biodiversity and for cultural services.

[1] well established

A spectrum of techniques within a framework of sustainable forest management can deliver different goods and services[2]. Certification schemes encourage appropriate action. Around half of the UK's woodlands are certified under independent sustainability assessment schemes. There are multiple spatial (and temporal) scales at which choices can be made, limited evidence for some of the consequences, and a variety of planning frameworks to assist with choices. Achieving coordinated action across multiple ownerships at broad scales is challenging, but has become the target of recent forest policy and research; coordination across land uses to secure integrated landscapes now needs to be pursued.

[2] established but incomplete evidence

8.1 Introduction

"[Trees] ...Nothing can compete with these larger-than-life organisms for signalling the changes in the natural world." (Roger Deakin 2007)

8.1.1 Woodlands of the UK

The forests and woodlands of the UK provide an important range of ecosystem services and associated goods and benefits, such as timber, soil protection, amenity and biodiversity (Sections 8.2 & 8.3).

The climate of the UK has a strong maritime influence that, over time, has led to the development of a number of distinctive cool temperate and boreal native forest types, which are a subset of those found in continental Europe (Barbatti *et al.* 2007) and observable despite the substantial loss of natural woodland cover. There is considerable variation in composition in response to climatic gradients, lithology and soil type. Distinctive 'Atlantic' woodland, dominated by oak (*Quercus petraea*) and birch (*Betula* species), occurs in wetter and cooler north and west areas, with Scottish native Scots pine (*Pinus sylvestris*) woodland on nutrient-poor acid soils. In the south and east of the UK, the dominant native woodland habitat is mixed lowland broadleaved woodland consisting of oak (*Q. petraea* and *Q. robur*) and ash (*Fraxinus excelsior*), and with localised areas of beech (*Fagus sylvatica*) and hornbeam (*Carpinus betulus*). Wet woodlands of alder (*Alnus glutinosa*), willows (*Salix* species) and birch (*B. pubescens*) occur in sites with regularly wet soils (Rodwell 1991; Malcolm *et al.* 2005; Barbatti *et al.* 2007). The same climatic constraints have influenced the development of woodland management, for example, by enabling a wide range of potential temperate species to be considered, but also by presenting some particular issues, such as wind, rather than fire, being a dominant abiotic disturbance (Quine & Gardiner 2006).

The post-glacial history of native woodland in the UK is largely one of loss, degradation and fragmentation (Rackham 1986). Tree species, such as oak, recolonised from refugia in southern Europe (e.g. Iberia) (Petit *et al.* 2002) and possibly from the west, but others like Norway spruce (*Picea abies*) failed to establish, despite being present in previous interglacial periods (Rackham 2003). From a post-glacial high of perhaps 70–80%, there was a progressive decline in woodland cover, partly due to climate and partly human-driven; by medieval times there was little extant native woodland, especially in Scotland and Northern Ireland (Section 8.2). A number of notable woodland species, such as bear, wolf, wild ox, beaver, lynx and capercaillie, became extinct (Corbett & Yalden 2001; Smout 2002), although some have since been reintroduced. Soil changes towards increased podzolisation also occurred in many upland areas after the loss of woodland cover (Dimbleby 1962; Chapter 5). By the beginning of the 20th Century, woodland comprised less than 5% of the country (Rackham 1986; Peterken 1996). Major forest types associated with tree-lines and floodplains were largely lost,

as was the lime-dominated forest over much of southern Britain. Nevertheless, many other species contributing to our woodland biodiversity were conserved through the retention of ancient broadleaved woodland, some of which was managed on a coppicing system (Rackham 1986; Peterken 1991), the preservation of larger tracts of wood pasture and parkland with ancient trees (Rackham 2003) and the survival of areas of old-growth native pinewood in Scotland (Mason *et al.* 2004).

Concern over the further loss and degradation of ancient and native woodland in the decades following the Second World War (WWII) led to the development of policies, firstly, for the protection of key sites (e.g. National Nature Reserves and Sites of Special Scientific Interest), and later, for the protection, management and expansion of priority woodland habitats (Kirby 2003; Latham *et al.* 2005; UK BAP 2006; Section 8.2).

Notable woodland planting by private estate owners began in the late 17th and 18th Centuries, but substantial re-afforestation efforts began in the 20th Century (Linnard 2000; Smout 2002). Successive governments attempted to address the shortage of timber by encouraging the creation of large plantations of non-native conifer species, but this effort was compounded by wartime fellings. There was considerable criticism of such conifer-planting on open moors and bogs (Avery 1989) and on existing ancient woodland sites (NCC 1984; Humphrey & Nixon 1999) due to the loss of valued habitats and the rapid pace of change in upland areas; afforestation, together with development and agriculture, contributed to major reductions in the extent and fragmentation of lowland heath (Webb 1986). Opposition to 'commercial forestry' from the conservation sector and other changes, such as those relating to government taxation policy, have led to a dramatic decrease in new planting of conifers over the last 20 years (Section 8.2), although they continue to be used extensively in the restocking of existing forests. In contrast, over this period, there has been an increase in the area of native woodland and the use of broadleaved tree species for planting or natural regeneration (Section 8.2).

Methods of woodland management have evolved, reflecting woodland type, markets and labour availability and affordability. Economic production of a narrow range of timber and wood products has led to the neglect of multiple products and services in favour of the simplification of practices. In the latter part of the 20th Century, there was an almost complete cessation of traditional coppice management systems in native woodlands (Buckley 1992). Commercial plantations were, and in many cases still are, managed on an even-aged basis, with large-scale felling of stands at economic maturity to maximise timber production (Section 8.5).

In recent decades, there has been a shift in forestry policy and practice with the adoption of the principle of Sustainable Forest Management (SFM) for multiple benefits (Mason 2007) (Section 8.5). Woodlands are managed as a resource for people, providing timber, wood products, recreation, amenities and well-being, as well as being managed for the benefit of local wildlife.

8.1.2 What is Woodland?

In this chapter, we use the term 'woodland' interchangeably with 'forest'. **Table 8.1** summarises the definitions used in the various major survey and reporting schemes covering woodland in the UK. The National Inventory of Woodlands and Trees (NIWT) provides the most comprehensive information on woodland in GB (Forestry Commission 2003a), but only recently have NIWT data been combined with inventory data from Northern Ireland to give an annual UK picture (Forestry Commission 2009a). NIWT also provides the British information for the Food and Agriculture Organization's (FAO) Global Forest Resource Assessments (FAO 2005).

The UK NEA broad habitat 'woodlands' is based on the broad habitat definitions in the UK Biodiversity Action Plan (BAP) (**Box 8.1**). These definitions are also used by the UK-wide Countryside Survey (Carey *et al.* 2008) with slight variation. Two woodland habitats are recognised in the UK BAP: coniferous woodland and broadleaved mixed and yew woodland. Within these two categories, further priority

Table 8.1 Definitions of woodland used in recent surveys.

UK BAP Broad Habitats*	Countryside Survey 2007	National Inventory of Woodlands and Trees†	Food and Agriculture Organization 2005	Native Woodland Survey of Scotland	Ancient Woodland Inventories (AWI)
Definition of woodland					
Vegetation dominated by trees >5 m in height when mature; >20% canopy cover.	Trees and shrubs >1 m in height (from vegetation key 2007) with >25% canopy cover; felled or recently planted woodland not included. Minimum area of woodland 400 m², minimum width 5 m.	A minimum area of 0.5 ha; and a minimum width of 20 m; tree crown cover ≥20% or the potential to achieve it; a minimum height of 2 m, or the potential to achieve it.	Trees >5 m in height in areas >0.5 ha; canopy cover >10%; minimum width 20 m or able to make these thresholds *in situ*. Does not include agro-forestry or parks and gardens.	Wooded polygons larger than 0.5 ha with a canopy cover of ≥20% of which ≥40% is native species.	Areas ≥2 ha marked as woodland on 1920s base maps and supporting woodland since at least 1600 in England and Wales, 1750 in Scotland, 1830 in Northern Ireland¶ (date under review in Wales). Woods less than 2 ha were considered in the Northern Ireland inventory and in more recent revisions to the inventory in south-east England and Wales.
Definition of woodland types					
Coniferous woodland >80% of canopy comprising conifer species; includes areas temporarily cleared of woodland. **Broadleaved, mixed and yew woodland** >20% canopy to be dominated by broadleaved species or yew; woody scrub <5 m tall included in some circumstances.	Divided by UK BAP woodland broad habitats; coniferous woodland and broadleaved woodland.	Indicative forest types interpreted from aerial photographs: broadleaved, conifer, mixed conifer, mixed broadleaved, young trees, scrub, felled.	**Other wooded land** Land not classified as forest, spanning >0.5 ha; with trees >5 m tall and a canopy cover of 5–10%, or trees able to reach these thresholds *in situ*; or with a combined cover of shrubs, bushes and trees above 10%. It does not include land that is predominantly under agricultural or urban land use. **Other land with tree cover** Agricultural land, meadows and pastures, built-up areas, barren land, with groups of trees >0.5 ha; canopy cover >10% of trees capable of >5 m height at maturity.	Polygons are ascribed to HAP and NVC‡ types.	Ancient semi-natural woodland—no recent evidence of planting. Ancient replanted woodland Long-established woodland category in Scotland and Northern Ireland used for sites wooded since the middle of the 19th Century.

* From Jackson (2000).
† Based on Patenaude *et al.* (2005).
‡ HAP = Habitat Action Plan; NVC = National Vegetation Classification (Rodwell 1991).
¶ The Northern Ireland AWI was undertaken separately to the GB AWI and included areas 0.5 ha and more; where the origin of woodland in Scotland and Northern Ireland is unknown, but presence can be verified in 1750 or 1830 respectively the woodland is termed "long-established".

Box 8.1 Woodland habitats and species within the UK Biodiversity Action Plan (UK BAP).

The UK BAP recognises two **broad** woodland habitats and eight *priority* habitat types. In addition, about a quarter of the UK BAP priority species are associated with woodland or tree habitats to varying degrees. For example, in England 256 species are associated with tree and woodland habitats (Webb *et al.* 2009).

Bluebells under mixed broadleaved woodland. Photo courtesy of FC Picture Library / George Gate.	*Conservation area. Non-native tree species have been removed to allow the Caledonian pines and sensitive ground vegetation to expand. Photo courtesy of FC Picture Library / Isobel Cameron.*
Broadleaved, mixed and yew woodland	**Coniferous woodland**
Lowland mixed deciduous woodland	*Native pine woods* (Scotland only)
Lowland beech and yew woodland	
Wet woodland	
Wood-pasture and parkland *	
Upland mixed ash woodland	
Upland oak woodland	
Upland birch woodland (Scotland only)	

* Note that wood-pasture and parkland is considered in Chapter 6.

habitats are recognised (Section 8.2). Habitat Action Plans (HAPs), which suggest measures for the conservation and restoration of priority habitats, cover the range of native woodland types in the UK; these may either be planted, semi-natural, ancient or recent stands.

There is not a clear division between provision of goods and services by priority habitats and those from other types of woodland. As a generalisation, however, priority habitats contribute more to biodiversity and some cultural services, and less to the provision of wood fibre and carbon sequestration. Despite this, there are many overlaps between them, so we have not separated out the contribution that specific priority habitats make to ecosystem service provision, but have tried to distinguish the difference between the two broad habitat types where appropriate.

8.1.3 Interactions with Other UK NEA Broad Habitats

Woodlands and, perhaps most notably, native woodlands share many of the species and vegetation assemblages of non-wooded broad habitats; for example, native pinewood vegetation is very similar to heathland vegetation (Rodwell 1991). Riparian zones form a key ecotone between woodland and the aquatic environment, so recently developed guidelines recommend the amount and type of woodland that should be grown alongside watercourses in order to ensure the continuation of this habitat (Forestry Commission 2003b). There is a dynamic interplay between woodlands and other habitats, with successional pathways operating at

multiple temporal and spatial scales, and directions (Hester *et al.* 1991a, 1991b, 1991c). In addition, organisms may move between different habitats to secure their full range of food and shelter requirements.

During the 20th Century, there was considerable afforestation of upland heath and bog habitats (Thompson *et al.* 1995), and in the lowlands, many heathland ecosystems were converted to conifer plantations (Mason 2007). Restoration has recently been undertaken to repair some of the damage incurred by these changes, including extensive removal of woodlands in the Flow Country and other peatlands (Patterson & Anderson 2000; Lindsay 2010). In England, a new framework policy has been developed to guide woodland clearance to meet UK BAP targets for priority open habitats (Forestry Commission 2010a). However, there remains pressure upon woodlands from other uses such as urban development and energy development (e.g. windfarms). The Countryside Survey (Carey *et al.* 2008) provides some data on stocks and flows (which are summarised below), while net gains and losses of woodland can be derived from successive national forest inventories.

More recently, there has been a focus on landscape-scale planning as a framework for deciding on the balance and configuration of woodland and other habitats over large areas (Humphrey *et al.* 2009). Tools such as BEETLE (Watts *et al.* 2010) and the Native Woodland Model (Towers *et al.* 2002), have been developed to provide an ecological basis for planning frameworks within the context of regulations such as the EU Water Framework Directive (WFD) and Strategic Environmental Impact Assessments.

Table 8.2 Extent of ancient and semi-natural woodland in the UK ('000 ha). Source: Forestry Commission (2009a) based on data from Pryor and Peterken (2001) with Northern Ireland data from Woodland Trust (2007).

Woodland type	England	Scotland	Wales	Northern Ireland	UK
ASNW *	206	89	31	0	326
PAWS *	135	59	30	1	225
OSNW *	210	44	52	15	320
Total ancient †	**341**	**148**	**61**	**1**	**551**
Total semi-natural †	**416**	**133**	**82**	**15**	**646**

* ASNW (Ancient Semi-Natural Woodland) is both ancient and semi-natural; PAWS (Plantation on an Ancient Woodland Site) is ancient but not semi-natural; OSNW (Other Semi-Natural Woodland) is semi-natural but not ancient.
† Ancient woodland is woodland that has been in continuous existence since 1600 (1750 in Scotland, 1830 in Northern Ireland); semi-natural woodland is woodland with natural characteristics (predominantly native species of trees, ground plants and animals).

8.2 Trends and Changes in Woodlands

"The great accomplishments of foresters in deforested Great Britain are admirable... The first step was to establish the material base of the forest, i.e. to create biomass. It is possible to progress only after such a base has been created...." (Prof. D. Mlinsek 1979)

8.2.1 Current Extent, Location and Composition

Woodland area in the UK currently amounts to 2.84 million hectares, representing 12% of the total land area. Approximately 9% of England is wooded, 17% of Scotland, 14% of Wales and 6% of Northern Ireland according to the Forestry Commission (2009a); the Countryside Survey (Carey *et al.* 2008) suggests that 9% of England, 15% of Scotland, 13% of Wales and 10% of Northern Ireland are wooded. Despite the small discrepancies between estimates, it is widely accepted that there is substantially less woodland cover in the UK in comparison to the global average of 30% and the EU average of 37% (FAO 2005).

There are major concentrations of planted coniferous woodlands in Wales, south and west Scotland, Northumberland, and in Thetford Forest, Norfolk. The Scottish Highlands have significant cover of native woodland of various HAP types, as does the New Forest, Forest of Dean/Wye Valley and the south-east of England; elsewhere native woodland is largely fragmented and dispersed (**Figure 8.1a,b**).

All UK woodland has been modified by management to some extent. There are no areas of primary woodland left in the UK (FAO 2005): the majority of woodland area (66.8%) is classed as Productive Plantation, with Modified Natural and Semi-natural representing 32.3% of woodland area, 0.7% is classed as Protective Plantation. Each of these categories delivers a different set of ecosystem services (Section 8.3).

The Modified Natural category (22.7% of woodland area) can be sub-divided further into Ancient Semi-natural Woodland (ASNW), Plantations (of mostly non-native tree species) on Ancient Woodland Sites (PAWS) and Other Semi-natural Woodland (OSNW), i.e. non-ancient semi-natural woodland (FAO 2005) (**Table 8.2**). Within the UK, ancient semi-natural woodland has long been recognised as being of the highest value for nature conservation and biodiversity (Peterken 1977), but more recent semi-natural woodland and plantations can also be of value in delivering other services, such as providing recreational and educational opportunities.

8.2.2 Stand Age and Structural Stages

Any one point in a forest or woodland might naturally go through a series of structural stages over time (**Figure 8.2a,b**). The extent and distribution of the different stages across the landscape is then largely determined by natural disturbance regimes, or their emulation and replacement by patterns of woodland management (Hopkins & Kirby 2007; Mason 2007), in particular, the patterns of felling. In general, management truncates the age-class distribution. Conifers in commercial stands are felled at economic maturity (e.g. for Sitka spruce 40–50 years old) and only 1% of commercial forests are managed as natural reserves to develop old-growth features (Forestry Commission 2004; UKWAS 2008). Such management decisions result in different structures (Quine *et al.* 2007) and different combinations of goods and services (Sections 8.3, 8.4 & 8.5).

The most recent data for forest structure and age suggest that 7% of the current forest area is less than 15 years old; 31% 15–50 years; 43% 51–100 years and 20% over 100 years (Mason 2007). These age classes equate broadly with the ecological definitions of stand stages developed in North America (Oliver & Larson 1996; Frelich 2002). Stands less than 15 years old are typically in the 'stand initiation' phase, where the canopy is not yet closed and understorey vegetation has not been shaded out. These stands can have considerable value for biodiversity (Warren & Key 1991). Stands of 15–50 years represent the 'stem exclusion' stage, where there is a closed canopy and little understorey. Stands of 51–100 years old characterise the 'understorey reinitiation' or 'demographic transition' phase, where shrubs and ground vegetation recolonise. Stands older than 100 years are entering the last phase, termed 'old-growth' or 'multi-aged', which is characterised by a high frequency of large-diameter trees, a mix of tree ages and significant accumulations of fallen and standing deadwood of importance for biodiversity (Warren & Key 1991).

The precise age demarcation of the stand stages, especially with respect to old-growth, varies between tree species, soil types and localities (Mason *et al.* 2004; Humphrey 2005). Stands older than 100 years are generally dominated by broadleaves; although native Scots pine woodland contains current stands of 250 years or more (Humphrey *et al.* 2003).

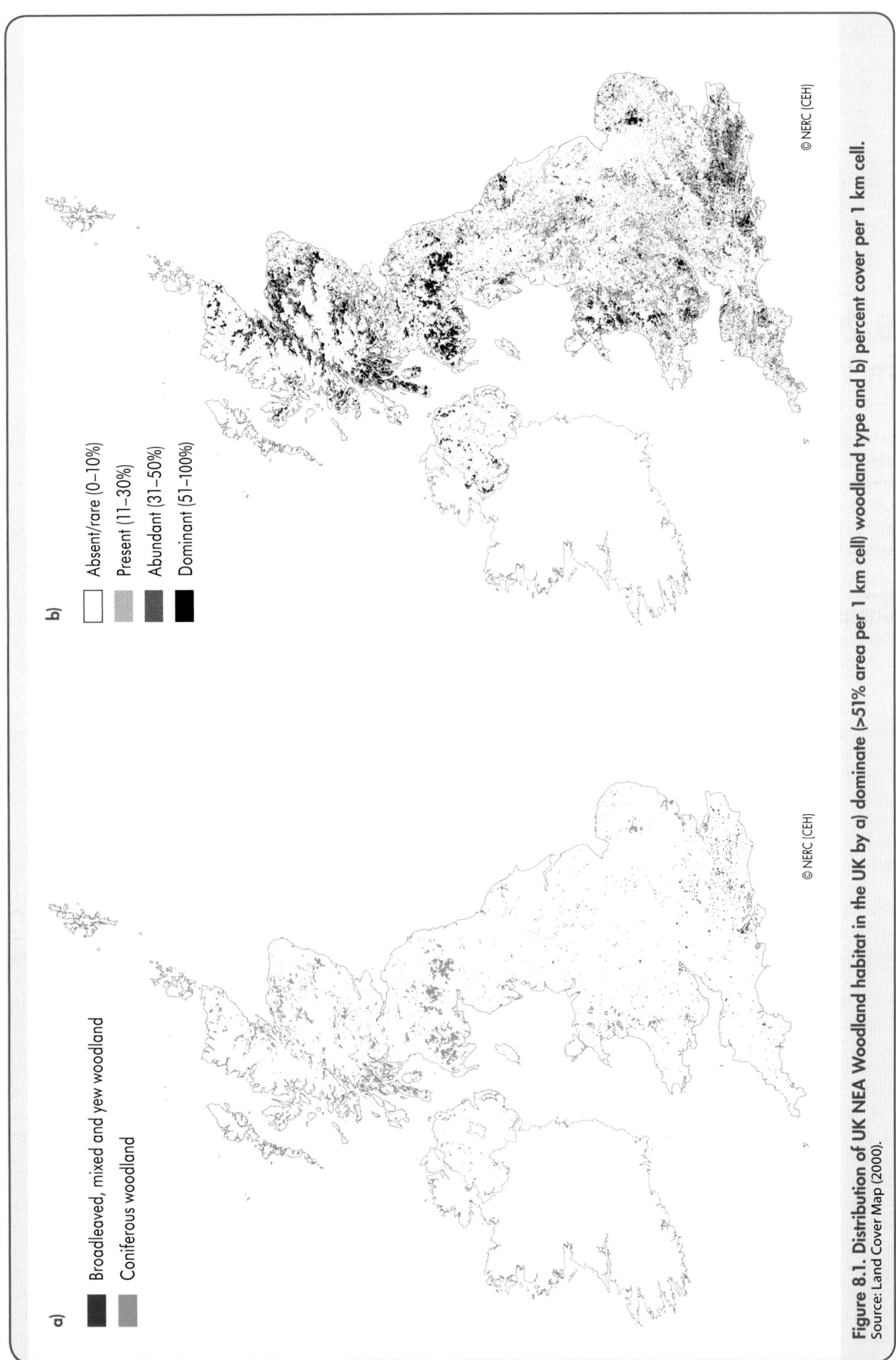

a)

■ Broadleaved, mixed and yew woodland

■ Coniferous woodland

© NERC (CEH)

b)

☐ Absent/rare (0–10%)

▨ Present (11–30%)

▨ Abundant (31–50%)

■ Dominant (51–100%)

© NERC (CEH)

Figure 8.1. Distribution of UK NEA Woodland habitat in the UK by a) dominate (>51% area per 1 km cell) woodland type and b) percent cover per 1 km cell.
Source: Land Cover Map (2000).

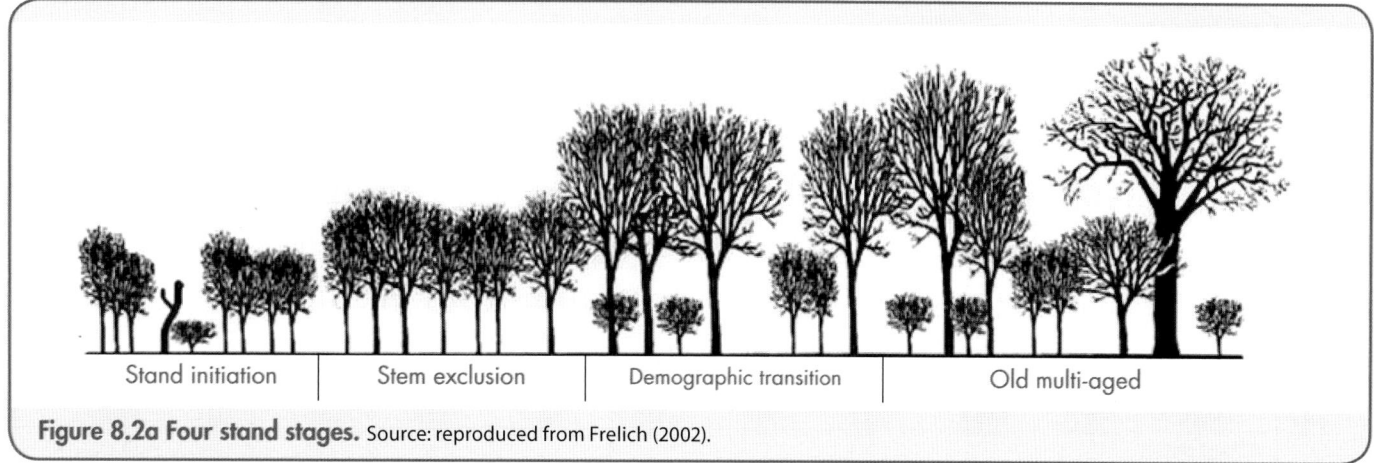

| Stand initiation | Stem exclusion | Demographic transition | Old multi-aged |

Figure 8.2a Four stand stages. Source: reproduced from Frelich (2002).

8.2.3 Composition and Management Types

In the past, the natural composition of UK woodland would have been predominantly broadleaved, with local concentrations of yew and juniper, and more significant areas of pine in the highlands of Scotland and possibly as part of tree-line woods on wooded bogs and acid sands further south (Peterken 1996). According to the FAO (2005), the UK has 66 native tree and shrub species. Among these are a number of whitebeams which are unique to the UK and Ireland and are considered by the International Union for Conservation of Nature to be threatened: three are classified as Critically Endangered (*Sorbus leptophylla, S. leyana, S. wilmottiana*), one is Endangered (*S. bristoliensis*), and six are Vulnerable (*S. anglica, S. arranensis, S. eminens, S. pseudifennica, S. subcuneata, S. vexans*) (see www.iucnredlist.org for definitions of the categories).

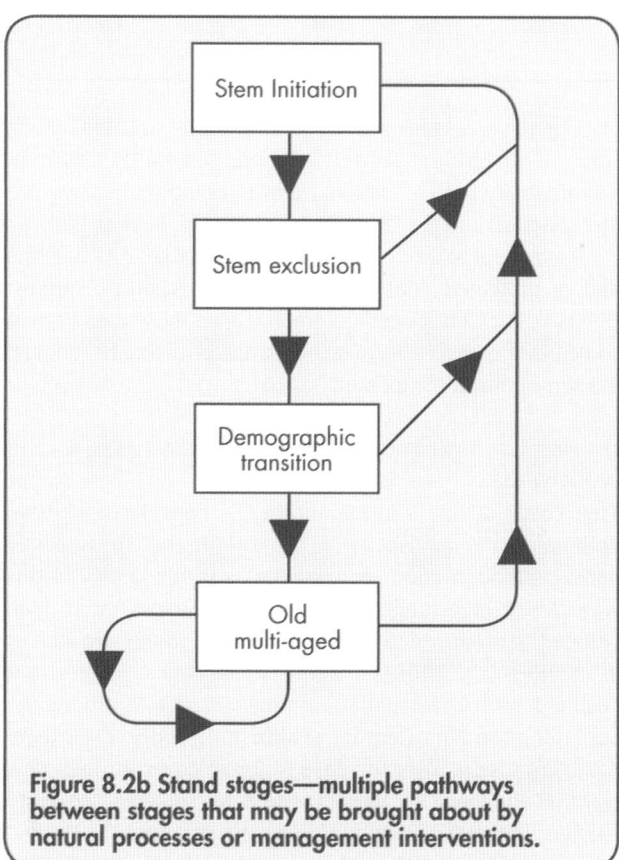

Figure 8.2b Stand stages—multiple pathways between stages that may be brought about by natural processes or management interventions.

Climate, soils, land availability and productive potential have all influenced the location of plantations and the selection of species within them. In the 20th Century, Sitka spruce (*Picea sitchensis*) was the dominant choice of commercial species in northern and western areas, with extensive forests planted on upland heaths and grasslands. Scots pine (now only native in Scotland) and Corsican pine (*Pinus nigra* subspecies *Laricio*) were more popular in the south and east, but Douglas fir (*Pseudotsuga menziesii*) and various species of larch and other conifers were also planted extensively across the UK. Sitka spruce is the commonest tree species in Britain (29% by area) followed by Scots pine (9.5%) and oak (9.4%) (**Table 8.3**); in Northern Ireland, Sitka spruce accounts for the largest volume of growing stock (6.5 million m³ in 2010), followed by Scots pine (0.7 million m³), Norway spruce (0.5 million m³) and oak (0.4 million m³) (FAO 2010). The vast majority of woodland in the UK is managed as high forest, with clear-felling and restocking on a 40- to 50-year rotation for conifers. Thinning of woodland has been limited by threat of windthrow and by lack of markets for small dimension produce. The small amount of coppicing (0.9% by area) that takes place in the UK is undertaken almost exclusively in England.

Veteran trees (Read 2000), often managed in the past by pollarding, tend to be commoner in non-woodland situations or in open parks and wood-pastures, but may still be found in forested landscapes; for example, in Savernake, Wiltshire, over 5,000 veteran trees have been mapped (P. Crow pers comm.). Such trees, often several hundred years old, are not only living evidence of past land management, but provide habitats for rare and specialist organisms. The UK is widely believed to have a higher density of veteran trees than most other northern European countries and, hence, has a particular responsibility for protecting them for their high conservation value.

All trees in the UK form mycorrhizal associations; these are mutualistic associations between the trees and some soil fungi, where the relationship is based upon transfer of soil-derived nutrients from the fungus to the host in exchange for photosynthate. These relationships between trees and mycorrhizal fungi are essential to the functioning of the whole system (Smith & Read 2007; Chapter 13), and yet, are rarely used in measures of woodland biodiversity status or condition.

Table 8.3 Area of woodland in GB by main tree species ('000 ha). Source: Forestry Commission (2003a).

Species	England	Scotland	Wales	GB*
Conifers				
Scots pine	82	140	5	227
Corsican pine	41	2	3	47
Lodgepole pine	7	122	6	135
Sitka spruce	80	528	84	692
Norway spruce	32	35	11	79
European larch	14	9	1	23
Japanese/hybrid larch	33	56	22	111
Douglas fir	24	10	11	45
Other conifer	19	5	6	30
Mixed conifer	9	8	0	18
Total conifers	**340**	**916**	**149**	**1,406**
Broadleaves				
Oak	159	21	43	223
Beech	64	10	9	83
Sycamore	49	11	7	67
Ash	105	5	19	129
Birch	70	78	13	160
Poplar	11	0	1	12
Sweet chestnut	12	0	1	12
Elm	4	1	0	5
Other broadleaves	84	18	18	120
Mixed broadleaves	91	62	8	160
Total broadleaves	648	206	118	971
Total—all species	**988**	**1,123**	**266**	**2,377**
Felled	15	23	9	47
Coppice †	22	1	0	24
Open space ‡	72	134	11	217
Total woodland	**1,097**	**1,281**	**287**	**2,665**

* Note no equivalent data are available for Northern Ireland.
† Coppice includes coppice with standards.
‡ Areas of integral open space, each <1 ha.

8.2.4 Trends and Indicators of Change in Woodland

The following sections explore changes in the condition of woodland in the UK, and how such changes are currently assessed by a number of indicators.

The European Environment Agency (EEA) defines an environmental indicator as "a measure, generally quantitative, that can be used to illustrate and communicate complex phenomena simply, including trends and progress over time" (EEA 2005). The EEA distinguish indicators of driving forces, pressures, states, impacts and responses. In relation to forests and woodlands, indicators have been adopted which relate mostly to states and impacts. Conceptually, these indicators represent easily measured features, such as an organism, forest structure or productivity, which can be used as an index of attributes (e.g. diversity) that are too difficult or expensive to measure for other aspects of woodland ecosystem supply and services (Williams & Gaston 1998; EEA 2009). Following the Ministerial Conference on the Protection of Forests in Europe (MCPFE 1993), countries have developed indicator sets which assess progress in sustainable forestry and relate to ecosystem supply (biodiversity, condition and extent) and ecosystem services

(supporting, regulating and cultural). The UK indicators, some of which form subsets of more general indicators of sustainability both at national and international scales, are incorporated into the UK Forestry Standard (Section 8.5).

We do refer to the condition and status of UK BAP habitats and of protected Sites/Areas of Special Scientific Interest (SSSIs/ASSIs), but place less emphasis on these data than in some other chapters because our scope is all forests, not just the semi-natural component.

8.2.4.1 Change in extent and connectivity of woodlands

Tree cover of one sort or another is considered to have dominated the landscape in the UK in the pre-Neolithic period, although there are disputes as to how much of this was closed high forest and how much was a more open wooded system (Vera 2000; Rackham 2003; Hodder *et al.* 2005, 2009). Throughout the Middle ages, forest cover declined, until it reached an all-time low of 4.7% around the beginning the 20th Century (**Table 8.4**). Since 1945, there has been a significant increase in forest cover through new planting and forest creation (**Table 8.5**). This has also led to changes in the distribution of forest cover across the UK and within regions. The largest increases have been of coniferous woodland in Wales and Scotland, although changes have been positive throughout the country (**Figure 8.3**).

Periodic forestry and land-cover surveys (Forestry Commission 2003a; Carey *et al.* 2008) provide regular information on gains and losses of trees and woodland.

Since the mid 1980s, the rate of increase has slowed (the increase from 2001 to 2006 being only 40% of that in the period 1971 to 1976). There has been a shift towards expansion of broadleaved/native woodland (Forestry Commission 2003a), rather than coniferous woodland, and usually in smaller blocks (**Table 8.5**). For example, the development of the 'National Forest' in the English Midlands has been largely through relatively small, scattered, new woods (Anon 2009). Countryside Survey data show that the area of broadleaved woodland increased by 6.9% (from 5.6–6.0% of land-cover) in the UK between 1998 and 2007 (**Table 8.6a**) and that there was no detectable change in the area of coniferous woodland in the UK, although it decreased by 7.2% in Scotland (from 12.9–11.9% of land-cover) between 1998 and 2007 (**Table 8.6b**). Reporting of the UK BAP priority woodland habitats also suggest that change is modest and largely positive in character, and showed that most were stable or increasing extent (**Table 8.7**).

There has been a revival of interest in afforestation as part of the future climate change adaptation/mitigation programmes, which may shift the balance back towards conifers and highly productive broadleaved species (Read *et al.* 2009). This renewed interest is consistent with the increased emphasis on conifer-planting in England over the last eight years (**Table 8.5**), but rates of planting are influenced by many factors.

Ancient and semi-natural/native woodland—a particular concern from a biodiversity perspective (Peterken 1977)—has declined due to losses to agriculture and, to a lesser extent, development. In addition, before 1985, large areas of ancient semi-natural woodland were converted to plantations predominantly of non-native species, generally conifers

(Spencer & Kirby 1992; Roberts *et al.* 1992). Since then, policy changes have reduced the rates of clearance and encouraged restoration of replanted stands to native species (Forestry Commission 1985; Defra & Forestry Commission 2005; Goldberg *et al.* 2007). Individual sites do still come under threat from development (Woodland Trust 2010) and from insidious loss through overgrazing, especially in the Scottish Highlands (Mackenzie 1999).

There is some turnover of other woodland cover. The Countryside Survey (Carey *et al.* 2008) showed that felled conifers have been replaced by neutral grassland, acid grassland or bog broad habitats in some places. Woodland removal in Scotland (e.g. for wind turbines) is discouraged by recent policy guidance, and there is an expectation that the rate of such clearance will not exceed the rate of afforestation (Scottish Government 2009) with mechanisms of compensatory planting being introduced. Deforestation in England is permitted in some circumstances, notably where clearance of recent woodland, particularly plantations or scrub, is proposed to restore priority open habitats (Forestry Commission 2010a). More generally, clearance of any woodland is controlled largely through the operation of Felling Licences (though not applicable in Northern Ireland) and Environmental Impact Assessment (Forestry) regulations. Further discussion on drivers of change in woodlands is found in Section 8.2.5. Information on changes in the numbers and extent of small clumps and individual trees is available in Chapters 6, 7 and 10. Non-woodland trees declined in the post-war period (Peterken & Allison 1989) as a consequence of agricultural intensification. Dutch Elm Disease also had a major effect during this time (Burdekin 1983).

There is increasing interest in the extent to which woodlands are functionally connected, and whether new woodland has contributed to, or could make a further contribution to, reducing the isolation of fragments of biodiversity (Bailey 2007). Schemes such as JIGSAW have sought to target new woodland planting to make a

Table 8.4 Woodland area in the UK: changes over 10 centuries. Source: Forestry Commission (2009a).

Year	England		Scotland		Wales		Northern Ireland †		UK	
	Area ('000 ha)	%*	Area ('000 ha)	%*	Area ('000 ha)	%*	Area ('000 ha)	%*	Area ('000 ha)	%*
1086		15 ‡								
c.1350		10 ‡			4 ‡					
17thC		8 ‡			4 ‡			5 ‡		
1905	681	5.2	351	4.5	88	4.2	15	1.1	1,140	4.7
1924	660	5.1	435	5.6	103	5.0	13	1.0	1,211	5.0
1947	755	5.8	513	6.6	128	6.2	23	1.7	1,419	5.9
1965	886	6.8	656	8.4	201	9.7	42	3.1	1,784	7.4
1980	948	7.3	920	11.8	241	11.6	67	4.9	2,175	9.0
1995–1999	1,097	8.4	1,281	16.4	287	13.8	81	6.0	2,746	11.3
2009 ¶‡	1,128	8.7	1,341	17.2	284	13.7	88	6.5	2,841	11.7

* % of the total surface area including inland water. The total surface areas, including inland water are taken from the Annual Abstract of Statistics 2008 (published by the Office for National Statistics).
† For Northern Ireland, the 17th Century figure is an estimate for all of Ireland; the 1905 figure is an estimate for Ulster 1908; the 1947 figure assumes no change from the 1939 to 1940 Census.
‡ An approximation.
¶ The non-Forestry Commission woodland figures for 2008 for England, Scotland and Wales are based on the 1995 to 1999 National Inventory of Woodland and Trees (NIWT) and adjusted for new planting and sales of Forestry Commission woodland, but at present no adjustment is made for woodland converted to another land-use. The NIWT did not include Northern Ireland.

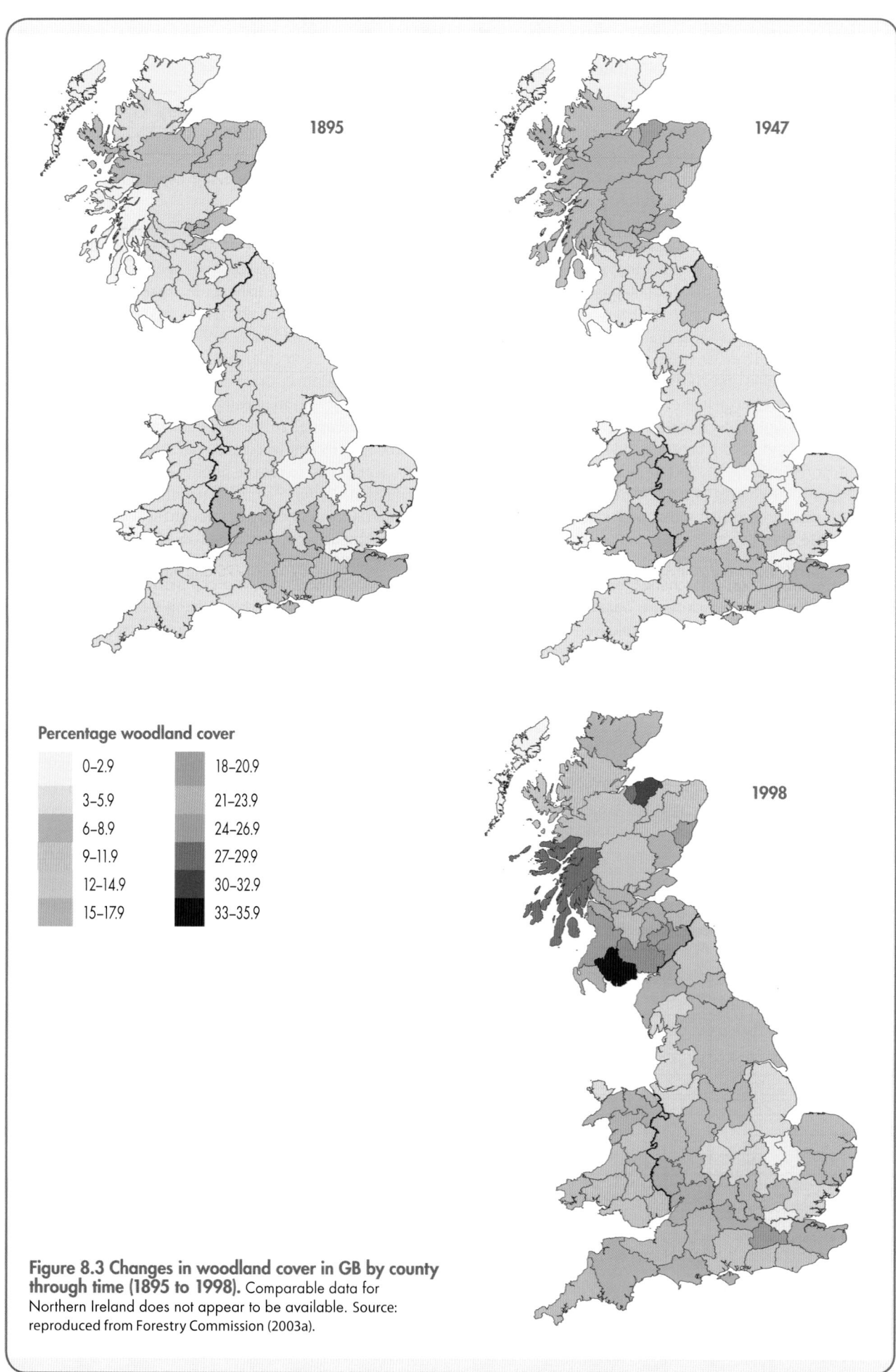

Figure 8.3 Changes in woodland cover in GB by county through time (1895 to 1998). Comparable data for Northern Ireland does not appear to be available. Source: reproduced from Forestry Commission (2003a).

Percentage woodland cover

0–2.9	18–20.9
3–5.9	21–23.9
6–8.9	24–26.9
9–11.9	27–29.9
12–14.9	30–32.9
15–17.9	33–35.9

1895

1947

1998

Table 8.5 New woodland creation ('000 ha); five year totals. Source: Forestry Commission (2009a).

		\multicolumn{8}{c}{Five year period ending 31 March}
		1976	1981	1986	1991	1996	2001	2006	2009*
England	Conifer	18.3	7.0	5.3	3.9	3.2	3.2	13.0	5.7
	Broadleaves	2.4	1.5	2.3	9.2	21.5	21.2	27.8	11.6
	Total	**20.7**	**8.5**	**7.5**	**13.1**	**24.7**	**24.4**	**40.8**	**17.3**
Scotland	Conifer	148.6	90.9	100.1	94.6	38.3	27.1	11.5	3.9
	Broadleaves	0.6	0.8	0.9	9.2	21.0	28.5	19.7	10.3
	Total	**149.3**	**91.7**	**100.9**	**103.8**	**59.3**	**55.6**	**31.2**	**14.2**
Wales	Conifer	12.9	6.8	5.6	3	0.5	0.7	0.0	0.0
	Broadleaves	0.1	0.2	0.3	1.1	2.0	2.1	1.9	0.7
	Total	**12.9**	**6.9**	**5.9**	**4.1**	**2.5**	**2.7**	**1.9**	**0.7**
Northern Ireland	Conifer	5.0	4.3	3.4	4.4	3.9	2.1	0.5	0.1
	Broadleaves	0.1	0.3	0.4	1.0	1.4	1.5	2.2	1.3
	Total	**5.1**	**4.6**	**3.8**	**5.4**	**5.3**	**3.6**	**2.7**	**1.4**
UK	Conifer	184.7	108.9	114.3	105.8	45.9	33.0	25.0	9.7
	Broadleaves	3.2	2.7	3.8	20.4	45.9	53.3	51.6	23.9
	Total	**188.0**	**111.7**	**118.2**	**126.3**	**91.8**	**86.4**	**76.6**	**33.6**

* Three year total to and including 2009.

Table 8.6 Estimates of the woodland habitat area ('000 ha) and percentage of land area in the UK from 1998 to 2007 and in GB from 1984 to 2007. Arrows denote significant change (p<0.05) in the direction shown. Note that because of changes in definitions that have been applied retrospectively, the estimates from 1990 and more especially 1984 are not in all cases directly comparable with later surveys. # denotes data not available. Source: reproduced from Carey et al. (2008). Countryside Survey data owned by NERC – Centre for Ecology & Hydrology.

a) Broadleaved, mixed and yew woodland	1984		1990		1998		2007		Direction of significant changes 1998–2007
	Area ('000 ha)	%	Area ('000 ha)	%	Area ('000 ha)	%	Area ('000 ha)	%	
GB	1,317	5.6	1,343	5.8	1,328	5.7	1,406	6.0	↑
England	#	#	887	6.7	927	7.0	981	7.4	↑
Scotland	#	#	284	3.5	229	2.9	251	3.1	↑
Wales	#	#	173	8.2	172	8.1	174	8.2	
Northern Ireland	#	#	#	#	64	4.5	82	5.8	↑
UK	#	#	#	#	1,392	5.6	1,488	6.0	

b) Coniferous woodland	1984		1990		1998		2007		Direction of significant changes 1998–2007
	Area ('000 ha)	%	Area ('000 ha)	%	Area ('000 ha)	%	Area ('000 ha)	%	
GB	1,243	5.3	1,239	5.3	1,386	5.9	1,319	5.7	
England	#	#	241	1.8	260	2.0	257	1.9	
Scotland	#	#	913	11.4	1,030	12.9	956	11.9	↓
Wales	#	#	85	4.0	96	4.5	106	5.0	
Northern Ireland	#	#	#	#	62	4.4	61	4.3	
UK	#	#	#	#	1,448	5.9	1,380	5.6	

Table 8.7 Summary of trends for Priority woodland habitats as reported in the 2008 reporting round. Source: Biodiversity Action Reporting System (2008).

Priority woodland type	Extent is
Lowland mixed deciduous	Increasing
Lowland beech and yew	Fluctuating, probably increasing
Wet woodland	Report not available
Upland mixed ash	Increasing
Upland oak	Increasing
Upland birch	Report not available
Native pinewood	Increasing

contribution to linking fragments of woodland, and appear to be successful compared to standard planting grants (Quine & Watts 2009). Recently, a landscape connectivity indicator has been developed (Watts & Handley 2010) and applied to Countryside Survey 2007 data for the purposes of biodiversity reporting. Preliminary results indicate regional changes, but overall, still low values in connectivity.

8.2.4.2 Trends in woodland condition

While there is increasing appreciation of the value of woodland for biodiversity, there are concerns as to its condition overall (**Box 8.2**) as reflected in:

- Threats and issues noted in returns under the 2008 reporting round of the Biodiversity Action Plan (UK BAP 2008);
- Threats recorded in the 2005 report on the state of UK protected sites (Williams 2006);
- The UK's submission on the degree to which Annex 1 Habitats are achieving Favourable Conservation Status (JNCC 2007);
- Results from monitoring of various woodland species groups (**Table 8.8**).

The trends identified are likely to continue to be significant in the short- to medium-term. In the longer-term, changes in woodland assemblages as a consequence of climate change will become more important and there is likely to be re-sorting, not just of the plant communities (Keith *et al.* 2009), but of faunal groups as well.

The key threats to semi-natural woodland identified from these activities are overgrazing, habitat fragmentation and isolation, invasion by non-native species, unsympathetic forestry practices, lack of appropriate management, air pollution and new pests and diseases. In addition, more localised pressures include losses to built development (including quarries), inappropriate game management, recreational pressures and drainage or water quality issues. In the long-term, species and assemblages will also be affected by climate change.

Most surveys of woodland condition focus on the semi-natural component of our woodland because, despite its limited extent, it remains one of our richest habitats, with a rich association of rare and priority species. For example, about a quarter of the SSSIs in England, and about one third in Scotland, include woodland; there are 10 Annex 1 types listed under the European Habitats and Species Directive (www. jncc.gov.uk/ProtectedSites/SACselection/SAC_habitats. asp) and eight types included in the UK BAP Priority Habitats List (www.ukbap.org.uk). Woodland Condition Assessment for biodiversity has been developed largely as part of the SSSI Common Standards Monitoring process (Kirby *et al.* 2002; Williams 2006). Woods are assessed in terms of their extent (Section 8.2.4.1) and four attributes: Structure and Natural Processes, Tree and Shrub Composition; Regeneration Potential and Quality Indicators (changes in species). Summary reports for SSSIs in Scotland have been published and will be published soon for England (Kirby *et al.* 2010a; Mackey & Mudge 2010; Natural England in prep, SNH 2010). These show that around 65% of woodland features on Scottish SSSIs are either in Favourable Condition or are

Recovering (appropriate management is in place to bring the site into Favourable Condition in future); while in England, the corresponding figure is more than 90%. The positive trend in SSSI condition over the last decade reflects the considerable effort that has been put in to securing positive management, which has not always been the case in non-SSSI woodland, particularly semi-natural woodland. Hence, the indications are that the condition of non-SSSI woodland is generally worse, but surveys currently underway (Scottish Native Woodland Survey; Defra survey of non-SSSI woodland condition) will allow this to be more accurately assessed.

Where non-native coniferous plantations are included in condition surveys, they are often viewed in a negative light because the priority is to restore them to open habitats, such as heathland, or to native tree species. However, there is also increasing interest in the contribution that coniferous plantations created over the last century can make to future woodland biodiversity, not as substitutes for the open ground habitats they replaced or for native woodland, but as new cultural landscapes in their own right (Humphrey *et al.* 2003; Quine & Humphrey 2010). This aspect is not routinely addressed by current monitoring, but could become more important in the future.

8.2.4.3 Changing composition, structure and species

Changes that have been taking place in varying degrees to woodland processes and structure across the UK are discussed here (**Box 8.2**). Overall, while the tendency is towards an increase in structural diversity, there are specific issues in particular areas and woodland types requiring action.

Shifts in the abundance of different tree and shrub species have occurred through the selective clearance of forests, the favouring of particular species, either directly or indirectly, through the management system, and the spread of introduced species both through planting and self-seeding. The abandonment of past forms of management, and responses to climate change (Section 8.2.3), have been associated with changes to the composition of semi-natural woodland, generally towards more mixtures. For example, over the past 40 years, there has been an increase of ash in beech woodland, birch in oak woods, oak in northern birch woods, and the spread of holly in the understorey (Kirby *et al.* 2005; Kirby *et al.* 2009; Amar *et al.* 2010). Grey squirrels (*Sciurus carolinensis*) are likely to reduce the competitive potential of beech in woods where previously it has been dominant.

The effects on woodland biodiversity (i.e. ignoring the declines in open habitat biodiversity through plantations on open ground) from this changing composition can be summarised as follows:

1. Increased abundance of conifer specialists, such as siskin (*Carduelis spinus*), responding to expanding forest area (Baillie *et al.* 2009); and increased woodland generalists (both plants and animals) capable of tolerating deep shade or found in the open habitats in forests (such as rides). The latter tend to already be widespread species, which have seen little change in their range. There are also indications that distinctive assemblages and species are building up in plantations, particularly as many are

now entering their second rotation (Humphrey *et al.* 2003; Quine & Humphrey 2010), and in future, their composition may become more varied (Mason *et al.* 2009). Green and great-spotted woodpeckers (*Picus viridis* and *Dendrocopos major* respectively) have increased rapidly (Baillie *et al.* 2009) and may be benefiting from the maturation of new forests, an increase in standing deadwood due to Dutch Elm Disease and self-shading in unthinned woodlands, and from the increasing provision of winter food in gardens.

2. Loss of habitat area for broadleaved woodland specialists or those of lightly shaded conditions because of the conversion of broadleaved woodland to conifers after 1945 (**Table 8.8**).

3. Since 1986 and the introduction of HAPs, in particular, there has been increasing restoration of plantations to native species on ancient woodland sites (Thompson *et al.* 2003; Goldberg 2003). There are few accounts of the accompanying changes in woodland communities in restored sites (Kirby & May 1989; Harmer & Kiewitt 2007), but a major study carried out for the Woodland Trust is to be published soon (Tim Hodges pers. comm.).

The impact of climate change on regeneration may mean that the classification of 'native', either at the species or provenance level, will need to be reconsidered; species currently restricted to southern Britain may be accepted further north, along with species from the near continent (such as sycamore, *Acer pseudoplatanus*) that are currently often treated as undesirable elements of semi-natural woods from a biodiversity perspective (Wesche *et al.* 2006; Kirby 2009; Kirby *et al.* 2009).

Traditional broadleaved woodland management in England tended to rely on vegetative regrowth from coppice stools and pollard. As these systems have declined, there has been increased interest in natural regeneration of broadleaves from seed (Evans 1988; Harmer *et al.* 2010). Similar concerns have arisen in discussions of the native pinewoods (although their past management was different),

with the added factor of the possible role of fire in site preparation (Mason *et al.* 2004; Summers & Wilkinson 2008; Hancock *et al.* 2009). Afforestation in the 20th Century was necessarily based around planting. While the restocking of most of these plantations is likely to continue to be by planting, there is increasing interest in natural regeneration as an alternative (Mason *et al.* 2009).

The major uncertainty with achieving regeneration lies with the levels of wild herbivores, mainly deer, but also grey squirrels and, locally, rabbits (Gill 1992a, 1992b; Section 8.2.5.4). Deer densities have long been seen as a problem for achieving natural regeneration in Scotland (Staines & Welch 1989), but for at least the last 30 years (and probably substantially longer), deer populations and distributions have spread in England and Wales (Ward 2005) and now constitute a major limitation on maintaining or restoring coppice, as well as natural regeneration from seed (Fuller & Gill 2001).

Good practice in deer management across landscapes is promoted via the Deer Commission for Scotland (now part of Scottish Natural Heritage) and the Deer Initiative in England and Wales, but achieving effective collaborative management across multiple ownerships remains challenging (Phillip *et al.* 2009).

Systematic monitoring of woodland species as quality indicators in recent years is best documented for the six taxonomic groups summarised in **Table 8.8**. In general, woodland birds appear to be declining, together with some mammals such as the red squirrel (*Sciurus vulgaris*). In particular, specialist woodland bird species have shown a decline since 1970, but a modest recovery has been noted in recent years (Defra 2009a; **Figure 8.4**), along with regional variation with, for example, largely positive trends in the index for Scottish woodland birds (Eglington & Noble 2010). For the other groups, there are gains and losses, but there is a lack of information for many taxa. Despite the importance of the relationship between trees and mycorrhizal fungi, there is no routine assessment of their status or condition, although methods are currently being explored (Mueller *et al.* 2004; Feest *et al.* 2010).

Box 8.2 Summary of changes to woodlands.

- The broadleaved resource has aged following the abandonment of coppicing (notably in southern Britain) and limited thinning in the last 60 years (Kirby *et al.* 2005; Amar *et al.* 2006; Hewson *et al.* 2007; Mason 2007). This has contributed to a tendency towards increased shadiness, reductions in understorey and open space, and increases in deadwood (Kirby *et al.* 1998).
- Maturing coniferous forests are showing increased structural diversity in, and have also been impacted by the deliberate restructuring of plantations through smaller felling coupes, and the identification of areas to be kept as open or broadleaved along stream corridors (see Kielder case study in Section 8.5).
- There is an increasing interest in alternatives to clear-fell silviculture; for example, a target was set to transform 50% of state forests in Wales from clear felling to continuous cover by 2012 (Mason 2007).
- Windthrow (Quine & Gardiner 2006), localised forest dieback due to disease, and the intrusion of non-crop species (Humphrey *et al.* 1998) have all had a marked effect.
- Changing levels of grazing within woodland are influencing structure. Typically, high-levels of stock- or deer-browsing are leading to a reduced understorey (Fuller & Gill 2001) and, in due course, to limited recruitment of new canopy trees. However, in local areas, the converse also occurs, with reduced grazing and browsing by stock leading to a dense understorey that may shade out ground flora and lichens low-down on tree trunks, and compete with veteran trees (Read 2000).
- There is an increasing 'generation gap', whereby sites with many veteran trees frequently lack mature and younger generations to replace them; in hedges with mature trees, there are seldom younger ones coming along. The apparently increasing threats (Broadmeadow *et al.* 2009) to mature trees from disease (Dutch Elm Disease, Alder dieback, Ash dieback, various syndromes affecting oak, new strains of *Phytophthora* affecting a broad range of trees, etc.) makes a lack of replacement trees even more acute.
- New types of woodland (agro-forestry, short-rotation forestry and energy crops grown as short rotation coppice) may add a new type of structural pattern to rural landscapes.

8.2.4.4 Tree and woodland health

Pests, pathogens, climate and other events which cause tree death play an important role in the dynamics of woodland ecosystems; dead and decaying wood provides important micro-habitats, dying trees allow more light and warmth to reach the forest floor, and nutrient cycles depend upon turnover of biomass (Kirby *et al.* 2010b). However, rapid, widespread tree death can threaten provision of ecosystem services such as production (effects on tree growth), visual amenity (loss of cherished views) and nature conservation (loss of rare species and valued habitats).

There have been issues around woodland health throughout the 20th Century, but in the past decade, new threats have raised the level of concern. During the 1950s, air pollution was a focus for concern regarding tree health, particularly in proximity to large industrial areas in the Midlands and northern England. In the 1980s, attention shifted to the threat of acid rain to trees (as well as water quality) in upland areas (Section 8.2.5). However, annual surveys of crown condition of five forest species, undertaken from 1984 to 2005 (Binns *et al.* 1985; Hendry *et al.* 2005), showed fluctuating canopy condition in response to climate conditions and impact of insects, such as the green spruce aphid (*Elatobium abietinum*), but no major overall deterioration in health.

During the latter half of the 20th Century, the threat to woodland health and the productivity of commercial woodland, in particular, from a range of endemic insects and fungi, resulted in the development of management techniques,

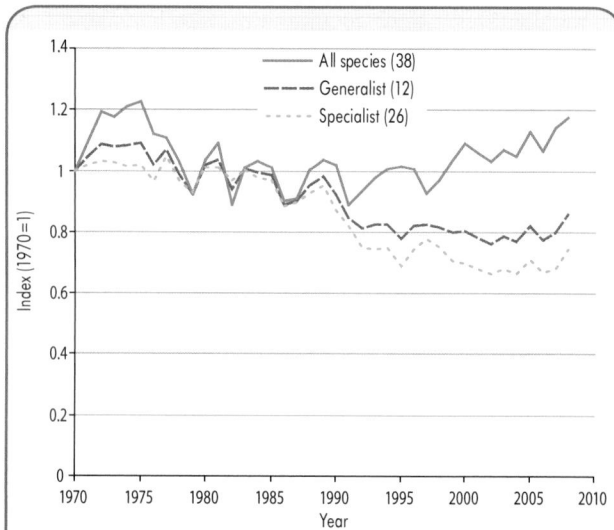

Figure 8.4 UK woodland bird index trends, 1970 to 2008. Figures in brackets show the number of species. Source: data from RSPB/BTO/Defra.

Table 8.8 Examples of changes in status of woodland species.	
Vascular plants	Woodland vascular plants have generally shown relatively little change in overall distribution compared with those from other habitats (Preston *et al.* 2002; Braithwaite *et al.* 2006). Within broadleaved woodland, various studies indicate reductions in species-richness and shifts towards more competitive species at different scales (Kirby *et al.* 2005; Keith *et al.* 2009; Carey *et al.* 2008). The following factors appear to be working across a number of landscapes to cause these changes: increasing shade, increasing eutrophication, increasing browsing and grazing.
Lower plants	Relatively little is known about recent trends in lower plants and fungi—apparent changes in distribution and abundance may reflect differences in survey effort rather than real change. However, reductions in air pollution, in particular sulphur, appear to be associated with the recovery and spread of some lichen species (RoTAP 2011).
Woodland birds	There have been increases in birds, such as goshawk (*Accipiter gentilis*) and crossbill (*Loxia curvirostra*), which are associated with large conifer forests in particular. Within broadleaved woodland, eight out of a total of 35 species showed large national declines (>25%) whereas 11 showed large national increases (>25%). All long-distance migrants have declined, whereas the two medium-distance migrants, blackcap (*Sylvia atricapilla*) and chiffchaff (*Phylloscopus collybita*), have increased. Common generalist species, such as blue tit (*Cyanistes caeruleus*) and great spotted woodpecker, have fared better than more specialised and less common species, such as willow tit (*Poecile montanus*) and lesser spotted woodpecker (*Dendrocops minor*). The reasons for the different changes are complex, but in part, related to changing woodland structures (Amar *et al.* 2007; Quine *et al.* 2007; Hewson & Noble 2009).
Lepidoptera	Amongst Lepidoptera there are two clear trends. One is a response to changing woodland structures: of six butterfly species associated with clearings in woodlands, three have shown marked declines, of which, the high brown fritillary (*Argynnis adippe*) showed a 77% decline from 1970 to 1982 (Asher *et al.* 2001). By contrast Hambler and Speight (1995) have argued that leaf-mining Lepidoptera have benefitted from the increase in high forest canopies; lichen-feeding species have also shown increases (Fox *et al.* 2006). However, in practice, many of our moth species are declining, with a decrease of almost a third in the species-richness index for Rothamsted light traps from 1968 to 2002. This decline includes tree-feeding species such as the dusky thorn (*Ennomos fuscantaria*). In parallel, Lepidoptera as well as some other invertebrates may be starting to respond to climate change: there has been considerable northward range expansion by the speckled wood butterfly (*Pararge aegeria*; Hill *et al.* 1999); more localised distribution responses may be shown through species changing their habitat preferences. Thus, butterflies which currently use 'hotspots' in glades may become more common under canopy shade, just as they are in southern Europe (Thomas 1991).
Other invertebrates	The increasing proportion of closed-canopy forests may benefit some canopy species (Hambler & Speight 1995). Deadwood species should benefit from the increases in deadwood reported (Winter 1993; Kirby *et al.* 2005; Amar *et al.* 2006). However, specialist saproxylic species tend to be poor colonists so may be in decline where the veteran trees on which they depend are under threat (Warren & Key 1991).
Mammals	Some mammals have increased over the last 60 years, notably deer in southern Britain (Ward 2005), and grey squirrels and badgers (*Meles meles*); while others have declined, such as red squirrels and dormice (*Muscardinus avellanarius*). For some, such as pine martens (*Martes martes*), yellow-necked mice (*Apodenius flavicollis*) and some bats, there is insufficient evidence to be certain as to the long-term trend (Battersby 2005). While the potential habitat cover for woodland mammals is likely to increase further as forest expansion continues, individual species may be limited by factors such as disease (red squirrel), poor dispersal (dormouse), lack of suitable roost sites (some bats).

such as the treatment of stumps to prevent colonisation by the fungus *Heterobasidion annosum* (Rishbeth 1952; Redfern *et al.* 2001; Redfern *et al.* 2010), and the chemical treatment of planting stock against the weevil *Hylobius* species (Moore *et al.* 2004; Wainhouse *et al.* 2007). Localised outbreaks of particular insect pests were controlled by aerial application of chemicals or the introduction of biocontrol agents; examples include pine beauty moth (*Panolis flammea*) outbreaks on lodgepole pine (*Pinus contorta*) stands in north Scotland (Hicks *et al.* 2001) and the control of the introduced bark beetle (*Dendroctonus micans*) (Gilbert *et al.* 2003) through the introduction of a biological predator (*Rhizophagous grandis*). Some health declines were noted to reflect combined climatic and pest/pathogen stress, or combined insect and pathogen attack (Redfern *et al.* 1987). A number of pests and pathogens present in Europe (including *Ips typographus*) were seen as potential threats to woodland health, and measures such as import controls and port inspections were established to prevent their arrival. The pandemic of Dutch Elm Disease, involving the fungus *Ophiostoma novo-ulmi*, was perhaps unusual because it largely affected non-woodland trees (Chapter 7).

Recently the focus of concern has switched to damaging, or potentially damaging, invasions of newly introduced or newly occurring pests and pathogens. Examples of newly introduced insect pests from Europe include the pine-tree lappet moth (*Dendrolimus pini*), a defoliator of Scots pine, and the oak processionary moth (*Thaumetopoea processionea*) which defoliates oak and can be a threat to human health. Introductions from further afield include the Asian longhorn beetle (*Anoplophora glabripennis*) and emerald ash borer (*Agrilus planipennis*), both of which pose threats to native broadleaved trees in urban and rural settings. A number of serious pathogens have also appeared in the last 20 years, including *Phytophthora ramorum* which has been responsible for widespread oak death in the USA and a bacteria (*Pseudomonas syringae pv. aesculi*), implicated in a disease of horse chestnut (Green *et al.* 2010). A bacteria, together with other factors not yet fully understood, may be responsible for Acute Oak Decline (Denman & Webber 2009; Denman *et al.* 2010). There is evidence of organisms, such as *Phytophthora*, switching host species in an unpredictable way, so that each invasive pathogen represents an uncontrolled, open-ended experiment in evolution (Brasier 2008; Brasier & Webber 2010). Recent widespread death of Japanese larch (*Larix kaempferi*) from *Phytophthora ramorum* (Brasier & Webber 2010) illustrates the dynamic nature of the threat and the scale of possible impact to woodland health, productivity and visual amenity. There is evidence of Red Band Needle Blight (*Dothistroma septosporum*) affecting native Scots pine trees, after initially (from the 1990s) being a problem on Corsican pine and then lodgepole pine. In late 2010, *Phytophtora lateralis* was found in the UK for the first time, killing Lawson's cypress trees in a country park near Glasgow. Understanding of the routes of entry and potential impact is developing rapidly through application of molecular techniques. It is clear that a number of the introductions have pathways which can be traced back to Asia, and there is growing concern about the risks posed by the global trade in large plants and plant material, and the challenges of regulating unknown organisms (Brasier & Webber 2010).

There is also evidence that woodland health does decline, both locally and regionally, through the additional contribution of climatic stress (Tubby & Webber 2010): for example, through drought lowering tree resistance (Green & Ray 2009; Gregory & Redfern 1998) or wetter springs aiding fungal sporulation (Brown & Webber 2008). Such impacts may well increase in future, with climate change predictions suggesting significant drought stress, especially in the south and east (Broadmeadow *et al.* 2009; Ray *et al.* 2010). In addition, the further arrival and establishment of exotic pests and pathogens may well threaten valued woodland habitats, as well as production from managed woodlands. This would lead to woodland health becoming more than a local issue within productive plantations (or an intrinsic part of the stand dynamics of semi-natural woodlands), but one with landscape-scale effects on a range of ecosystem services.

8.2.5 Drivers of Change in Woodlands

A broad definition of 'drivers of change' is: "any natural or human-induced factor that directly or indirectly causes a change in an ecosystem" (MA 2003). The UK NEA has adopted this definition and a modified classification of direct and indirect drivers (Chapter 3). Many drivers act synergistically, and across a range of scales, so that the individual effects can be hard to distinguish. The main drivers affecting forests and woodlands in the UK are climate change, pollution and land-use practice (directly via competition with other land uses, or indirectly through socio-political, demographic and economic drivers). In addition, the particular age structure of woodlands (and the legacy of long-past events, policies and management decisions) is an endogenous driver that is bringing about spontaneous change in provision of goods and services.

Some drivers of change have particular relevance to semi-natural woodland compared with other woodland. **Table 8.9** summarises the direction and magnitude of the main drivers of change in forest and woodland biodiversity. We attempt to summarise the influence of the drivers on extent and on characteristics that govern goods/service provision. This also gives a clear indication of which effects are more complex and where the main knowledge gaps exist.

8.2.5.1 Climate change

Climate has an important influence in shaping the composition and character of woodlands within the UK, with regional forest types reflecting major spatial patterns in climate; palaeoecological studies indicate how such patterns changed as the climate improved after the last glaciations. The main climatic factors affecting tree-growth in forests and woodlands (Pyatt *et al.* 2001) are:

1. Temperature—growing season temperature affects tree-growth; winter/spring temperature affects the degree of frost damage; and range of temperature (continentality) is also influential;

2. Moisture deficit—different tree species differ in their seasonal moisture requirements and drought tolerance; snowfall can physically damage trees or protect them from winter desiccation, especially when small;

3. Wind—can cause physical damage and affect tree-growth form; combinations of wind and temperature also drive tree-line and forest-line limits.

These give rise, in combination with the effects of geology and soil type, to strong spatial patterns in tree suitability and productive potential, as shown for pedunculate oak (*Quercus robur*) and Sitka spruce (**Figure 8.5**).

Change, rather than simply variability, in these factors will be an influential driver of extent and condition. Climate may operate at different stages of the life of trees, and so, particular events may differ in their effects on tree establishment versus mature trees; this is an important distinction to make as it affects the pattern and speed of response to climatic change (Kirby *et al.* 2009).

There is only limited evidence of major climate-related change in the composition of UK forest and woodlands in recent years (Kirby *et al.* 2005). This is partly because most tree species are long-lived, adapted to cope with considerable climate variability and relatively resilient to the small changes in climate that have happened in recent years (Broadmeadow *et al.* 2009). Thus, the total extent

and diversity appear to have been little altered by climate drivers. However, recent climate-related changes have been documented in more mobile species, such as insects and birds from woodland and other habitats (Section 8.2), and these variations are predicted to increase, leading to more rapid changes in the complement of species using woodland areas. Increasing summer temperatures have led to faster tree-growth in some areas (Cannell 2002; Broadmeadow *et al.* 2009), but drought has had the opposite effect; increased windiness and storm frequency (Broadmeadow *et al.* 2009), and increased winter wetness, could also affect tree survival, rooting and slope stability (Ray 2008).

Advances in leafing date in response to increasing spring temperatures have been recorded for some tree and ground-layer plant species (Broadmeadow *et al.* 2009), but this has probably also increased the prevalence of late spring frost damage. Changes in phenology may be linked with knock-on effects on associated flora and fauna, and to declines if such species are unable to adapt to changes. In some cases, such adaptation has happened; for example, in Wytham Woods, blue tits and great tits are breeding about two weeks earlier than they did in the 1980s (Perrins & Gosler 2010). However,

Table 8.9 Summary of main driver effects (magnitude and direction) identified as important for forests and woodland. Main effects to date are indicated together with predictions about their future importance. Arrow indicates positive and/or negative effect; multiple arrows indicate strong magnitude and brackets indicate lesser magnitude; = denotes no major effect; ? denotes little is known.

UK NEA Driver		Effect on: total area		Effect on: tree growth and yield		Effect on: service provision and woodland condition (including biodiversity)	
		Past (since 1945)	Future (to 2060)	Past (since 1945)	Future (to 2060)	Past (since 1945)	Future (to 2060)
DIRECT							
Land use / cover	Grazing (livestock)	=	↓ ↑	↓	↓ =	↓ (↑)	↓ ↑
	Grazing (wild herbivores)	↓	↓ ↑	↓	↓ =	↓ (↑)	↓ ↑
	Afforestation policies	↑ ↑	↑	↑=	↑ =	↓ (↑)	↑ (↓)
	Biodiversity policies	(↑)	↑	=	=	(↑)	↑
	Agricultural policies	↓ (↓)	↓ ↑	n/a	n/a	↓	↓ ↑
Introduced & invasive species	Species introduction / removal	=	↓ =	=	↓	↓	↓ ↓
Pollution	Nitrogen deposition	=	=	↓ ↑	?	↓	↓?
	Sulphur deposition	=	=	(↓)	=	?	?
	Ozone	=	=	↓	↓	?	?
Overexploitation	Harvest / resource consumption	↓ ↓	↓ ↑	=	=	↓ ↓	↓ ↑
Climate change	Temperature	=	↓ ↑	↑	↑	↓ ↑	↓ ↑
	Drought	=	↓ ↓	↓	↓ ↓	↓ ?	↓ ?
	Windiness	=	=	Form: ↓	Form: ↓	↑ ?	↑ ?
Other	Age structure of woodlands	=	=	↑	↑	↑	↓ ↑
INDIRECT							
Demographic	Population growth	↓	↓	=	=	↓	↓ ↑
	Demographic change	↓ ↑	↓ ↑	=	=	↑	↑
	Ethnicity	?	?	?	?	?	?
	Migration	?	?	?	?	?	?
Economic	Market forces	↑	↑	↑	↑	↓ ↑	↓ ↑
Socio-political	Government subsidies	↓ ↑	↑	↓ ↑	↑	↓ ↑	↓ ↑
	Legislation	↓ ↑	↑	↓ ↑	↑	↓ ↑	↓ ↑
Technology adaptation		↓	=	↑	↑	↓ ↑	↓

there might come a point when insects may emerge when their food sources are unavailable, vernal plant species may emerge when forest canopies have already closed, and chicks may hatch when the peak invertebrate abundance has passed. These indirect effects of climate change may have substantial effects upon woodland biodiversity as a consequence of reduced habitat specialisation when the temporal synchrony between hosts and herbivores breaks down. If generalist species become more common, there may be increased homogeneity between habitats; there are already indications of this from data on long-term plant species compositional change in UK woodlands and alpine habitats (Keith *et al.* 2009; Britton *et al.* 2009).

It is possible that both semi-natural and planted forests will be able to grow to higher altitudes than they have previously. This is highly dependent on: (i) the balance between increasing temperature and increasing windiness/storminess; and (ii) the degree of invasiveness of the vegetation occupying the areas above the current tree-limit (Hester & Brooker 2007; Broadmeadow *et al.* 2009).

Impacts of climate change are predicted to increase in future, under all scenarios of change. Some changes are already being made in forest and woodland management plans, such as recommendations on the 'most suitable' species for planting in different areas (Ray, 2008; Broadmeadow *et al.* 2009; Quine & Ray 2010). Forest management requires long-term planning appropriate to the long-lived nature of the main species. Much activity is, therefore, currently focused on the best way for the forest industry to 'prepare' for future change (Broadmeadow & Ray 2005; Freer-Smith *et al.* 2007; Ray *et al.* 2008, 2010). The impact of increased frequency and severity of summer droughts upon forest fires has yet to be firmly established, but past drought years (e.g. 1994–1995) have seen increases in wildfires.

The scope for woodlands to contribute to the mitigation of, and adaptation to, climate change is discussed in Section 8.3.3.

8.2.5.2 Pollution
Aerial deposition of pollutants, originating from fossil fuel combustion and food production, has affected air quality and rainfall chemistry across the UK (NEGTAP 2001; RoTAP 2011). There is some evidence of air pollution impacts on growth and composition of UK forests and woodlands, although reports from surveys of commercial forests

Figure 8.5 Spatial variability in productivity of pedunculate oak and Sitka spruce. The 'suitability' (defined as productivity relative to maximum productivity achievable by that species under current climatic conditions) for a) pedunculate oak, and b) Sitka spruce under Baseline (1961–1990) scenarios. The results are based upon Ecological Site Classification. Dark green = very suitable (>70% of current maximum productivity); light green = suitable (50–70% of maximum productivity); orange = marginal (40–50% of maximum productivity); blue = poor (30–40% of maximum productivity); red = unsuitable (<30% of current maximum productivity). Source: reproduced from Read *et al.* (2009).

indicate 'no widespread forest damage' overall (e.g. Defra-funded UKREATE programme: www.bangor.ceh.ac.uk/terrestrial-umbrella/). Recent policy-driven reductions in nitrogen oxides and sulphur have been recorded, and these have had knock-on effects on soils, waters and foliar sulphur concentrations. However, nitrogen deposition, and ozone levels in particular, are still above 'critical loads' for some habitats—for example, it has been estimated the critical loads for ground flora and epiphytic lichens is exceeded in almost 100% of UK Atlantic oak woodlands (RoTAP 2011). In a few woodlands, however, there is some evidence of recovery in woodland lichens (Section 8.2 & 8.3). Past concerns about acidification of afforested catchments led to the development of the Forests and Water Guidelines (Forestry Commission 2003b).

Nitrogen deposition increases the growth rates of some forest trees, but is known to have strong detrimental effects on many lower plants. Nitrogen deposition is also cited as a major factor in the overall decline in fungal diversity (especially mycorrhizal diversity) in Europe. Many species show a very rapid response to nitrogen deposition—some decline and others increase—but there is no uniform response and the reasons for the different responses are not yet fully understood (Nygren et al. 2008). Nitrogen deposition has been implicated in recent increases in cover of nitrogen-demanding ground-layer species and reductions in overall species diversity in, for example, UK broadleaved woodlands (Haines-Young et al. 2003; Kirby et al. 2005; RoTAP 2011; **Table 8.8**). So far, increases in carbon dioxide concentrations are predicted to have had relatively little effect on forests as compared to nitrogen deposition (van Oijen et al. 2008; RoTAP 2011); future increases in carbon dioxide levels are predicted to interact with nitrogen deposition to favour faster-growing species (Jarvis et al. 2009). Conversely, cumulative ozone concentrations are apparently reducing both forest growth and carbon sequestration across Europe (RoTAP 2011). Furthermore, faster growth following nitrogen addition is likely to increase shoot vulnerability to winter damage or other stressors, as found for some woody shrubs (Power et al. 1998; Power et al. 2004). Therefore, predicting the nature and importance of both current and future changes in pollutant deposition is complex, difficult and highly dependent on changes in other drivers, particularly climate (RoTAP 2011). Aerial pollutant experimentation is difficult in forest habitats, so most current pollutant data from forests are derived from spatial and temporal correlations between forest survey and deposition data (which makes direct allocation of causality impossible), with limited data from semi-natural woodlands (Kennedy & Pitman 2004; Vanguelova et al. 2007). Most manipulative experiments on pollutant effects in the UK have been carried out in open-ground habitats and so, are not directly applicable to forested habitats (RoTAP 2011).

There is currently limited evidence of the impact of point source pollution from smelters and livestock facilities. However, interest in the latter is increasing because changes in the regulatory regime now require this impact to be assessed.

The scope for woodlands to contribute to the capture and immobilisation of pollutants is discussed in Section 8.3.3.3.

8.2.5.3 Land Use

Land use change has undoubtedly caused substantial changes in forests and woodlands in the UK, but it involves many different 'drivers', both direct and indirect, including human behaviour and values, policy and economic drivers, and climate. The major expansion of woodland area since 1945 was driven by a perceived need to increase strategic timber reserves (Section 8.1) and domestic timber supply, and was achieved with government support in the form of grants and favourable tax regimes, and direct investment in public forests. Policy priorities have evolved over time to include rural employment, support for a domestic wood-using industry and, most recently, a broad mix of 'public good' targeting environmental quality and social value (Rollinson 2003). Longer-term drivers, influential in the decline of UK semi-natural woodland both in terms of area and composition, include felling and free-range livestock grazing (Birks 1988; Mitchell & Kirby 1990; Hester et al. 1998).

Economic forces partially underlie several of the relevant land use drivers. In particular, the domestic markets for wood products are affected by factors such as global forestry demands, forest cover in other countries, import/export costs and exchange rates, and food/fibre 'security' issues (Thomson 2004). UK- and European-level policies directly and indirectly affect many of these factors—some of the most important indirect effects act by driving other 'competing' land uses, such as livestock management (and associated subsidies) and EU targets for using biomass as a source of renewable energy. Road-building and expansion of settlements have also contributed to woodland loss and fragmentation across the UK, although there are measures in place to reduce the rate of such loss; for example, Environmental Impact Assessments for new construction projects and recent deforestation policies requiring compensatory planting (Section 8.2). Technological adaptation has included the adoption of chainsaws, the mechanisation of harvesting and extraction operations, and the development of highly mechanised sawmills. These have influenced the costs of production and the demands from the domestic market; this, in turn, influences the objectives for the management and profitability of woodland enterprises, and the market for woodlands. Harvesting from the public forest estate is required to maintain the viability of the domestic industry, while harvesting from private woods is more responsive to market trends. The extent of coppicing has reduced as labour costs have increased and traditional niche markets declined. However, a trend towards 'getting back to nature' is increasing interest in small-scale workings and the use of natural regeneration, rather than planting, in woodland re-establishment. There are also changes in the ownership of woodlands with a decline in public ownership (FAO 2010) and an increase in private ownership. There have been increases in the amount owned by environmental charities, such as the Woodland Trust, the National Trust and The Wildlife Trusts, and by individual owners for whom production is not a primary concern.

Woodland fragmentation and loss are regarded as having long-term detrimental effects upon biodiversity and other woodland values. This has led to direct action to improve the condition and extent of semi-natural woodland across the UK, particularly for 'biodiversity aims', with national and international obligations to protect and expand a number of woodland habitats and species through HAPs and BAPs (Section 8.2.4). Direct policy drivers causing increases in semi-natural woodland area and condition mainly involve grant-aid—until recently, 'nested' within a range of land use policies such as Environmentally Sensitive Areas (ESAs) and farm woodland schemes. In Scotland, the grant-aid for native woodland expansion and increases in connectivity has recently been brought under the Scotland Rural Development Programme (SRDP). Changes in area of commercial forestry (both public and private) are still mostly driven by economics, although 'multifunctionality' benefits are increasingly being recognised, and the balance of importance is changing towards biodiversity and landscape issues in these forests. Carbon sequestration may become a major driver of UK forest policy in the future (Section 8.3.3), but there is much debate about the costs/benefits of temperate forests versus open-ground habitats for carbon sequestration terms, particularly on highly organic soils (Broadmeadow & Matthews 2003; RoTAP 2011; Lindsay 2010).

Other increasingly important social and demographic drivers of land use change affecting the composition and extent of both woodland and forest include recreation (responding to increased leisure time and mobility, and a greater range of activities, e.g. mountain biking) (Section 8.3.4) and construction activities. There have been substantial developments of facilities in coniferous woodlands to accommodate walks and cycle tracks, and to enhance visual appearance; much of this has been grant-aided for private owners. Use of volunteers to undertake traditional management, such as coppicing, has also increased in popularity, but the benefits to semi-natural woodland structure and composition in some areas may still be hampered by high densities of deer (Fuller & Gill 2001). These activities have significantly changed the diversity and form of forested areas but have not led to major changes in total area across the UK as a whole.

8.2.5.4 Biotic pressures from herbivores, pests, pathogens and invasive species

Despite the recent large-scale reductions in livestock in some areas of the UK, grazing-related impacts have led to significant net losses in overall area and diversity of semi-natural woodland (Section 8.2.4.2) to date, and significant costs in terms of tree/seedling damage in commercial forests. The main exceptions are in the lowlands where areas traditionally managed by livestock, such as common land, are no longer grazed, and scrub encroachment is occurring. There has been a gradual increase in wild herbivores across the UK in recent decades, particularly deer of several species (Staines et al. 1995; Ward 2005; Gill 2006). Smaller herbivores like hares, rabbits, small mammals, can also reduce regeneration, but their impacts are usually more local. However, past experience shows that they can become national pests, for example, rabbits prior to 1955.

Grazing and browsing by both wild and domestic herbivores (primarily sheep and deer) is arguably the primary driver of biodiversity change in UK woodlands and forest. These herbivores remove tree regeneration

(ultimately leading to loss of total area and fragmentation) and affect both species and structural diversity (Gill 1992a, 1992b, 2006; Broadmeadow et al. 2009). Most semi-natural woodlands are not fenced, so have no protection against deer and other wild herbivores, and even commercial plantations, which are normally fenced, have resident populations of these species.

The biggest driver of changes in free-ranging livestock numbers is agricultural policy, but disease can also cause rapid and dramatic variations, as recently illustrated by the response to the Foot and Mouth outbreak of 2001. At a national level, policy drivers include stocking level requirements within ESAs. At a European level (with local modification), the Common Agricultural Policy (CAP) has been a major driver of livestock numbers for some time. The recent CAP reform has led to massive reductions in free-ranging sheep in the uplands of the UK (SAC 2008), which could start to reverse the long-term decline in semi-natural woodland cover and diversity. However, the benefits may be restricted if wild herbivore numbers increase in response to the reduction of stock. Changes in wild herbivore numbers, particularly in deer, are partly human-driven, such as winter-feeding, and partly climate-driven in terms of greater over-winter survival in warmer winters. Policies and legislation related to wild herbivore control (for example, the Wild Deer Act) have had relatively few effects to date (Phillip et al. 2009). There are moves, however, to provide greater powers to government agencies (particularly the Deer Commission in Scotland and, to a lesser degree, the Deer Initiative in England and Wales) to cull deer.

Increasing outbreaks of certain insect pests, particularly in commercial plantations, are compounded by winter-warming, but also driven by the increasing volume of global trade in plant products (Broadmeadow et al., 2009); this is also the case for a number of pathogens. For example, some Phytophthora species are thought to have been introduced in nursery stock and now represent a major threat to many woody species in the UK (Chavarriaga et al. 2007).

The spread of invasive species, such as rhododendron, insect pests and pathogens, has greatly reduced forest and woodland diversity in many parts of western Britain in particular. Grey squirrels, for example, are limiting the growing of quality broadleaved timber (Mayle et al. 2009), the survival of the red squirrel, and may affect canopy composition by impacting upon thin-barked tree species such as beech. Feral boar are increasing in number and range, with possible effects on woodland ecology and with local impacts on recreation (e.g. in the Forest of Dean).

8.2.5.5 Ageing of woodland stock

An endogenous driver of change is the ageing of woodlands within the UK. Age determines many characteristics of woodlands, including size and structural diversity (see Section 8.2.2). Very large areas of woodland were cleared in the First and Second World Wars; combined with the regeneration of felled woodland and the new planting triggered by concerns over timber supply, this has produced a particular, unbalanced, age class distribution (Mason 2007). The ageing of these cohorts changes the delivery of, and potential for, goods and services arising from the woodlands. Such changes also impact upon habitat quality (Quine *et al.* 2007) and are thought to be influential in the changes to the woodland bird indicator (Hewson *et al.* 2007; **Table 8.8, Figure 8.4**).

8.3 Ecosystem Goods and Services Provided by Woodlands for Human Well-being

"such forests...are of considerable service to neighbourhoods that verge upon them by furnishing them with peat and turf for their firing; with fuel for the burning of their lime; and with ashes for their grasses; and by maintaining their geese and their stock of young cattle at little or no expense" (Gilbert White 1789)

The concept of ecosystem services is based on an understanding that sustainable human life depends not just on the raw products that different types of ecosystem produce (such as food and timber), but on a much wider range of goods and services. Many of these are unseen, many go unnoticed, and many are unrewarded.

An early modern reflection on the concept of ecosystem services came from Krutilla (1967) who considered them as: "present and future amenities associated with unspoiled natural environments, for which the market fails to make adequate provision". Other definitions have since been used, including that from the Millennium Ecosystem Assessment (MA): "those processes of ecosystems that support (directly and indirectly) human wellbeing" (MA 2003; Patterson & Coelho 2009). Several typologies of ecosystem services have been put forward such as those of de Groot *et al.* (2002) and Campos *et al.* (2005); but Costanza (2008) argues that a pluralism of typologies is needed. In the UK NEA, the definition of ecosystem services identifies 'benefits' rather than 'processes' following Defra (2007), and the typology of services (provisioning, regulating, cultural and supporting) is fully described in Chapter 2.

8.3.1 Multifunctional Forestry and Ecosystem Services

There is evidence that the multiple use of forests was a goal of Anglo-Norman landowners in the 12th Century (Wilson 2004); for instance, the combination of hunting deer and managing trees by pollarding is just one example of the combination of uses parkland offered our ancestors. The evolution of modern-day multi-functional forestry to encompass a range of ecosystem services can be traced through successive editions of the manual "Forestry Practice", published by the Forestry Commission from 1933 onwards. In the first edition, there was no reference to any goods and services other than timber production (Forestry Commission 1933), and this position was

sustained up to, and including, the eighth edition (Edlin 1964). In the ninth edition (Blatchford 1978), a chapter was provided on recreation as an objective for woodland management, reflecting a government instruction in 1973 for the Forestry Commission to "give still further emphasis to recreational provision". A chapter on wildlife management acknowledged the amenity, scientific, economic and educational services that woodland fauna provide. Conservation of ecosystems, landscape design and consideration of water and soil were introduced in the tenth edition (Hibberd 1991). Gradually, forestry policy started to shift from multiple-use (e.g. a forest used for production and recreation) to multifunctionality, i.e. management to bring the forest to a state that several services can be delivered and possibilities are kept open to fulfil new services in the future, without endangering or impoverishing the ecosystem.

Modern multifunctional forestry policy in GB stems from the principles of Sustainable Forest Management (SFM) first enunciated at the United Nations Conference on Environment and Development—the Rio Earth Summit—in 1992 (Rollinson 2003; Forestry Commission 2004; Section 8.5). The concept of ecosystem services, including the development of methodologies for monetising some of the most important services, provides the potential for optimising decision-making with regards to habitat management.

A classification of the principal types of services considered important in UK woodlands/forestry is presented in **Table 8.10** using the UK NEA typology, and developed in the following sections.

8.3.2 Provisioning Services

For millennia, wood has been a key raw material for society, providing fuel, construction materials, chemicals (from tan bark), utensils and many other necessities. Traditional forest products, such as timber, are included as goods derived from provisioning services (i.e. trees) (Chapter 15). Arguably, these could also appear in regulating services as options for reducing carbon dioxide emissions into the atmosphere through the substitution of wood for building materials such as steel or concrete (with higher embedded carbon), and the substitution of woody biomass to generate heat and/or power instead of fossil fuels (Chapter 14). Perhaps to a lesser extent in the UK than in some other cultures (Shvidenco *et al.* 2003), forests and trees have also been the source of non-wood products such as food (fruit, fungi), meat (domestic stock grazing, wild game), animal bedding (litter and bracken), foliage, medicines and cosmetics.

8.3.2.1 Trees for timber, fibre, fuel

Timber remains a major component of various industries, especially construction and pulp- and paper-making. Currently, about 80% of the UK's wood and wood-product needs are met by imports (Forestry Commission 2009a); this compares with approximately 96% in the 1940s (Taylor 1946). Most of this demand is for coniferous wood, but there are imports of hardwoods as well. There are complex pathways of products from forest to processing to end use (Scottish Forest Industries Cluster 2004).

From 1999 to 2007, the total consumption of wood-products tended to increase, but dropped in 2008 (Forestry

Table 8.10 Types of ecosystem service provided by woodlands.

Ecosystem service provided by woodlands	Examples of goods and benefits in the UK	Key references
Provisioning services		
Crops, livestock and **fisheries**	Little tradition of agro-forestry other than grazing particularly as part of wood-pasture systems; non-timber forest products (NTFPs) for commercial and domestic use, e.g. meat (including from culled deer), berries, honey, fungi, medicinal derivatives and drugs.	Martin *et al.* (2006); Emery *et al.* (2006); Kirby *et al.* (1995)
Trees for timber	Provision of raw timber materials for use in commercial and domestic enterprises; provision of wood chips for boards and pulp for paper. Use of timber as an alternative for other building materials such as steel and concrete in order to reduce use of fossil fuels and enhance building standards.	Forestry Commission (2003a) Suttie *et al.* (2009)
Trees for bio/woodfuel	Timber products (e.g. harvesting residues, stumps and roots, recycled wood) as fuel for heat and power plants, as domestic firewood, for biochar and as raw material for processed hydrocarbon fuels.	Chapter 14 Ireland *et al.* (2004)
Woodlands and **water supply**	Wooded catchments especially in the uplands provide important water supplies for major urban areas (e.g. Thirlmere and Manchester).	Ritvo (2009)
Regulating services		
Climate	Avoidance of climate stress. Tree cover can help dampen the climatic effects experienced in the open, thus protecting soils, animals and humans from extremes of temperature, strong winds and UV light.	Mason *et al.* (2009)
	Carbon sequestration. Woodlands and their soils are important reserves of terrestrial carbon, and timber products can also be considered.	Morison *et al.* (2009); Lorenz & Lal (2010)
Hazard	Soil protection. Tree cover can offer protection from soil erosion and slope failure. Forest management will reduce exposure to chemicals and pesticides and likelihood of soil compaction compared to agriculture.	Moffat (1991); Nisbet *et al.* (2008)
	Flood and water protection. Woodlands moderate rainfall events and river and stream hydrographs, delaying and reducing flood events.	Nisbet *et al.* (in press)
Disease and pests	Woodland dwelling organisms can help in regulating the incidence and spread of insect pests of crops and pathogens of importance to humans, livestock, crops and ecosystems.	Chapter 14
Detoxifixation and Purification	Water quality. Because of minimal use of pesticides and fertilisers, woodlands managed under sustainable principles also offer benefits of water quality.	Nisbet *et al.* (in press)
	Soil quality. Woodland cover can stabilise contaminated brownfield land and hinder the pathways between source and receptors.	Moffat & Hutchings (2007)
	Air quality. Capture of atmospheric pollutants in tree canopies can lead to consequent reduced exposure for humans, crops, buildings etc.	NEGTAP (2001)
	Noise reduction. Belts of trees between residences and transport routes can absorb sound.	Huddart (1990)
Pollination	Woodlands likely provide habitat for diverse wild pollinator communities of importance to trees, crops and other plants.	Devoto *et al.* (2011)
Cultural services		Edwards *et al.* (2009)
Wild species diversity	Biodiversity. UK forests, including plantations, provide habitat for a wide range of fauna and flora but a limited genetic resource (e.g. compared to tropical forests).	Humphrey *et al.* (2003)
Environmental settings	Trees and woodlands are valuable for personal enlightenment and as places or catalysts for social activity and cohesion.	O'Brien (2006); Lawrence *et al.* (2009)
	Forests are increasingly acknowledged for their educational value.	O'Brien & Murray (2007)
	Trees have been perpetual motifs in fine art, and influenced many other art forms.	Phythian (1907); Hohl (1998)
	Many forests are open to the public for the enjoyment of outdoor pursuits and recreational activities. Their access facilitates exercise and benefits human health and longevity.	Woodland Trust (2004); O'Brien & Morris (2009)
	Trees and woodlands increase the diversity of landscape character; their existence provides a link with the past when man's existence was more closely linked to woodlands and their products; woodlands reduce the rate of, or eliminate the need for, cultivation, a significant cause of archaeological destruction.	Rackham (1976); Smout (2002); Crow (2004)
Supporting services		
Soil formation, nutrient cycling, water cycling, oxygen production	Forests facilitate soil formation and other biogeochemical processes essential to life.	Fisher & Binkley (2000)
Biodiversity	Little in way of unique species (endemism) at least amongst the well-know groups, but locally adapted provenances and distinctive assemblages associated with some species being at the edge of their range in Britain; a distinctive maritime climate; and historical differences. These include 'Atlantic' elements such as the abundance of bluebells, rich bryophyte communities in western oak woods, ash-hazel dominated woods (beyond range of beech), abundance of veteran trees with associated lichen and saproxylic associated species.	Rodwell (1991); Peterken (1996); Kirby *et al.* (2005)

Commission 2009a). Use of timber in construction—both home-produced and imported—could increase in future because of its potential to substitute for products such as concrete and brick, the use and production of which involves higher emissions (Suttie *et al.* 2009).

A total of 8.4 million green tonnes of softwood was produced in the UK in 2008 (Forestry Commission 2009a). This level of production has grown slightly over the last ten years and is substantially greater than that of 50 years ago. Over the same period, hardwood production has declined and currently stands at 0.4 million green tonnes (69% of which was used as fuel; Section 8.3.6).

About 60% of the gross annual increment of conifers is harvested (Forestry Commission 2002). The age structure and changing composition of softwood plantations have led to the forecast that production will to rise to 11–12 million tonnes in the 2020s, but will decline thereafter. Any subsequent increase will depend on future rates of afforestation and forms of restocking.

Only about 20% of the gross annual increment of broadleaves is currently harvested, so that production could increase substantially from the existing woods (Forestry Commission 2002). There is considerable interest in encouraging further use of this resource, but there are thought to be operational, market and attitudinal barriers to harvesting a greater proportion of the increment; the fragmented ownership and typical location of small woodlands within an agricultural landscape are particular barriers. The only market that seems likely to be able to expand sufficiently to take advantage of this potential resource is wood-fuel. The markets for traditional coppice products remain steady, or are increasing slightly, and seem unlikely to increase much (Sanderson & Prendergast 2002).

The gross value added in forestry and primary wood-processing (Forestry Commission 2009a) had been fairly stable from 2003 to 2006 at about £1.7 billion, but increased to £2.05 billion in 2007 (note that this includes processing of imported timber). About half of this is in the pulp and paper sector, with the other half split between the panel, sawmilling, and forestry/logging/related-services sectors.

Across much of country, wood was the major source of fuel until the widespread availability of cheap coal (and later oil, gas and electricity) during the 19th Century (Rackham 2003). It was not just used for domestic purposes, but also for industrial functions, such as iron smelting which contributed to the maintenance and expansion of broadleaved woodland in some regions at particular times. Industrial uses of wood-fuel had effectively disappeared by 1950, and its use as a domestic fuel continued to decline, in part because of Clean Air Acts and the greater convenience of coal, oil and gas.

The oil crisis in 1974, and interest in 'self-sufficiency', sparked a limited revival of wood-fuel through the use of wood-burning stoves. Throughout the 1990s, much work was done on wood-chip as a potential fuel based on short-rotation coppice (Tubby & Armstrong 2002), but little came of this in Britain; interest has been more sustained in Northern Ireland (McCracken 2007).

More recently, the general firewood market has been very buoyant, as has the demand for wood-burning stoves, due to factors such as increases in gas and electricity prices, and interest in reducing carbon footprints. The Stove Industry Alliance estimates 186,000 stoves were sold in 2008 alone, largely as secondary heating sources (Angela Duignan pers. comm.). Modern stoves can be more than 90% efficient, whereas logs burnt on an open fire are only about 30% efficient. A well-stocked, mixed broadleaved coppice woodland might produce about 3 tonnes of air-dried wood/ha/yr; 7–9 tonnes per year are needed to heat an average three-bedroom house. The popularity of barbecues has helped to increase interest in the charcoal market—much of the charcoal (about 75%) is still imported (Sanderson & Prendergast 2002), but there are initiatives such as BioRegional that seek to coordinate and increase local supply to the major charcoal markets (www.bioregional.com/what-we-do/our-work/bioregional-charcoal/).

Government subsidies allied to more consistent fuel type, quantity and quality (e.g. www.southwestwoodshed.co.uk/static/wp-content/uploads/woodfuel-standards.pdf) have encouraged active interest in wood-chip for small to medium-sized combined heat and power units. Wood-use is also being considered as a fuel for major power stations through co-firing (e.g. www.power-technology.com/projects/drax) and the dedicated wood-burning E.ON plant at Lockerbie. In England, a wood-fuel strategy envisages increasing the harvest of wood-fuel from existing woods to 2 million tonnes per annum (Forestry Commission 2007a).

There is likely to be an increase in fuel demand and provision from UK woodland. There are some suggestions that demand might outstrip domestic supply, leading to an increase in imports.

8.3.2.2 Wild food, medicines and ornamental products

Non-timber Forest Products (NTFPs), such as fruit, fungi, moss and foliage, are harvested every year from forests on both a commercial and non-commercial basis (FAO 2010). Across the country as a whole, the amounts are relatively small (Sanderson & Prendergast 2002), but these products can be important in supporting local industries and preserving traditions and skills. In Scotland, 18–24% of people regularly access forests for wild fruit, fungi and other NTFPs, such as lichens for dyes and foliage for floristry. In 2005, the total commercial value of these NTFPs was estimated at greater than £9.2 million (Chapter 15). The harvest and trade of Scottish wild moss alone is worth approximately £0.5 million a year and supports 125 jobs (Staddon 2006). Information on species and products, as well as guidance on gathering, trading and managing woodlands for NTFPs, is provided by the Forest Harvest Project (www.forestharvest.org.uk/). However, there is a need to improve knowledge of the reproductive systems, ecology and population structure of NTFP species (especially fungi) to be sure about sustainable harvesting levels.

Woods and forests are critical to the success of many game shoots (Gray 1986; Robertson 1992) and organised pheasant and partridge shooting has increased substantially over the last 20 years (Chapter 15). Shooting can make significant contributions to the income of individual estates and their local communities (PACEC 2006). According to data presented in PACEC (2006), of the 1.9 million ha of shooting land in the UK, approximately 40% is woodland. This equates to an approximate value of £640 million to the UK economy and the support of around 28,000 jobs. The long-term sustainability of intensively run shoots may be questioned, however, because they depend on breeding and releasing large numbers of birds each year. Release pens are present in around 5% of woods (Sage *et al.* 2005) and there can be conflicts with biodiversity conservation, although other management activities associated with shooting may benefit biodiversity (Draycott *et al.* 2008). Small-scale shoots or those involving wild birds are likely to be more compatible with other woodland uses (Chesterton 2009).

The increase in deer populations in recent years requires management to reduce their impact on woodland composition, structure and regeneration, as well as on the prevalence of road-traffic accidents, crop damage and other, non-woodland impacts. There is some potential income from the venison market, although this will rarely be enough to cover the costs (Chapter 22). In England, most deer stalking for sport takes place within woodland; in Scotland, hill stalking is more typical, but woodlands are vital to provide food and shelter for deer, especially in winter. Unless carefully managed, wintering deer cause woodland to deteriorate, as they eat young seedlings, preventing them from developing into a new generation of trees. The need for deer management is likely to increase further, so there could be benefits from developing these markets further (www. macaulay.ac.uk/RELU/ ; also www.scottish-venison.info/).

Woodlands also provide valuable shelter for livestock production, as shown in studies at Kirkton Glen SAC farm (Pollock 2005).

8.3.2.3 Genetic resources

There is little in way of unique species (endemism) in UK woodlands, at least amongst the well-known groups of organisms. There are locally adapted provenances and distinctive assemblages, however, which have developed through a combination of: some species that are common on the continent being absent or at the edge of their range in Britain; the distinctive maritime climate; and historical differences. These result in a good representation of ash-hazel dominated woods (beyond the range of beech), 'Atlantic' elements, such as the abundance of bluebells and rich bryophyte communities in western oak woods, and the abundance of veteran trees with associated lichen and saproxylic species. There are likely to be genetic differences associated with such distinctiveness, but these are largely unknown.

The area of woodland for *in situ* genetic conservation is nearly 18,000 ha, for *ex situ* genetic conservation is 250 ha, and for seed production is nearly 2,250 ha.

8.3.2.4 Biodiversity

As well as being a key supporting service, biodiversity, can also be considered as a provisioning service because resources are invested in forest management (e.g. through the BAP process, agri-environment schemes and support for SSSI management) to generate particular types of diversity and species assemblages. These assemblages can have value as goods and services in their own right. Both

the cost of providing biodiversity and benefits to people of this provision can be monetised. The costs of delivering biodiversity for the first set of BAPs produced in 1994 were estimated (Shepherd *et al.* 2002), but since then, both the targets and the range of habitats covered have changed. A study commissioned by Defra to estimate the economic value of biodiversity benefits delivered by the BAPs is currently being finalised.

In a recent survey, people recognised the provision of 'places for wildlife to live' and, hence, biodiversity, as one of the main benefits of forests (70–80% of respondents) (Forestry Commission 2009b). Biodiversity has also been included as part of the estimation of non-timber values associated with woodland. In one study, for example, the marginal benefits of woodland were estimated to be 35p per household/year for enhanced biodiversity in 12,000 ha (1%) of commercial Sitka spruce forest; 84p per household/year for a 12,000 ha increase in Lowland New Broadleaved Native forest; and £1.13 per household/year for a similar increase in Ancient Semi-natural Woodland (Willis *et al.* 2003). Several studies provide estimates of values for protecting habitats, increasing populations, or reintroducing particular species of woodland animals. These include estimates of median annual values for increasing red squirrel populations under the BAPs by 25–50% of £2.67 per person in North Yorkshire (White *et al.* 2001), mean annual values for protecting red squirrel habitat in Kielder Forest by the Northumberland Wildlife Trust of £2.94 per member (Garrod & Willis 1994), and of around £28 per household/year in the Aberdeen area for increasing capercallie populations in Scotland over a 10-year period (Philip & Macmillan 2005). For reintroductions, estimated values include £22–£24 per household/year in the Aberdeen area over a 10-year period for a pilot project to reintroduce beavers in Argyll, Scotland (Philip & Macmillan 2005), and reported lump sum values of £8–£10 for the reintroduction of pine marten populations in England (Bright & Helliwell 1999; White *et al.* 2001). Values associated with the conservation and extension of woodland habitats are also partly reflected in charitable giving to bodies such as the Woodland Trust (which received total legacy and membership income of £12 million in 2009).

8.3.3 Regulating Services

Across the globe, forests are one of the main habitats providing regulating services for the environment. Their current and future role in UK conditions has often been under-estimated because of the limited extent of tree cover, and because of the negative impacts that have arisen in some conditions such as reduced water quantity or poorer water quality (acidification) in upland catchments, and carbon losses through the drainage of peatlands for planting. There are still risks from inappropriate woodland creation or management, but these can be dealt with by following good practice set out in UK Forest Standard and associated guidelines (Section 8.5). The role of trees and forests in helping to regulate our environment is likely to increase in future under climate change scenarios (Handley & Gill 2009). While only limited work has been done on monetising this role (CJC Consulting 2005), it is likely to be significant.

8.3.3.1 Avoidance of climate stress

Timber products can have an important role in substitution as alternatives for other building materials, such as steel and concrete, which have higher embedded energy (ECCM 2006).

One of the most important regulating services that woodlands provide is their capacity to sequester carbon. The total carbon stock in UK forests (including their soils) is around 800 megatonnes of carbon (Mt C) (approximately 2,900 Mt of carbon dioxide (CO_2) equivalent) and the stock in timber and wood products outside forests is estimated to be a further 80 Mt C. Broadleaved woodland in southern England is currently the most important vegetation carbon store (Milne & Brown 1997), though this is dwarfed by the carbon stored in soils, particularly in heathlands and blanket bogs. It has been estimated that the average carbon content across non-organic forest soils in GB is 288 t CO_2 equivalent/ha, while on peaty soils and deep peats, carbon stocks of 160–700 t CO_2 equivalent/ha are found depending on peat-layer depth. The choice of forest management systems influences the rate of sequestration and the amount of carbon stored on site, and forests can capture up to 800 t CO_2 equivalent/ha in tree components (Mason et al. 2009; Morison et al. 2009). Measurements suggest that annual removal from the atmosphere of around 24 t CO_2/ha/yr can be achieved in a coniferous forest at peak growth, with a net long-term average for productive coniferous crops of around 14 t CO_2/ha/yr (Jarvis et al. 2009). Rates of around 15 t CO_2/ha/yr have been measured in oak forests at peak growth, with a net long-term average likely to be around 7 t CO_2/ha/yr. Further studies are required to fully determine long-term rates of carbon storage, taking into account the type of use of timber products which influences the amount of carbon stored away from woodlands.

The strength of the UK forest carbon sink increased from 1990 to 2004, but may now start to decline as a result of the uneven age class distribution, the rotational harvesting of mature trees and the fall off in planting rates over the last 20 years. There is renewed policy interest in forest expansion in England, Scotland and Wales (Read et al. 2009; Moffat et al. 2010). Woodland planted since 1990, coupled with an enhanced woodland creation programme of 23,000 ha/yr over the next 40 years, could be delivering emissions abatement equivalent to 10% of the total greenhouse gas emissions at that time. Woodland creation is judged to be a highly cost-effective and achievable form of emission abatement at less than £100/t CO_2 equivalent, and while conifer plantations and energy crops were, not surprisingly, judged the most cost-effective options for carbon sequestration, mixed and broadleaved woodland that deliver a wider range of other benefits were still only about £41/t CO_2 equivalent (Matthews & Broadmeadow 2009; Section 8.3.6). Tree-planting on high carbon soils can lead to emissions of carbon dioxide, though these are progressively counterbalanced by uptake in the growing trees. Other types of land-cover can also support carbon sequestration, such as peatland (Lindsay 2010), but forests are less limited in where they can be grown, have a greater potential to generate income as a land use (through timber, etc.), and have potentially high value for other services.

Forests can also reduce some of the effects of climate change, notably in dampening temperatures in the soil and beneath the canopy, and in providing shade and shelter for animals and human visitors. Woodland cover can provide shade, reducing overheating and the need for air conditioning, and shelter from strong winds, reducing heat loss and soil erosion (Gardiner et al. 2006). Increasing temperatures will increase the shade and shelter value of trees in towns (Handley & Gill 2009), and also for livestock in the country. Shading of streams can aid thermal regulation and fish survival.

8.3.3.2 Avoidance of hazard

Tree cover can offer protection from soil erosion and slope failure. Recent soil strategies, such as those from Defra (2009b) have focused attention on soil loss and degradation, although mainly in the context of agricultural land use (POST 2006). There has been little attempt to estimate the contribution of British forests to soil protection, yet ancient woodland has a value in protecting relatively undisturbed soils (Ball & Stevens 1981).

Erosion in the forest itself can occur following large-scale and badly implemented forest operations, particularly large clear-fells. Good practice guidelines have, therefore, been developed (Forestry Commission 2003b; Forestry Commission in press a). In erosion prone sites, there is likely to be greater use of low-impact silvicultural systems, and continuous cover forestry may become more favoured. Increasingly dry summers and heavier winter rainfall (particularly extreme events) will increase the importance of this service, highlighting the need for more research in this area.

Forests moderate rainfall, delaying and reducing flood events. Forest and tree cover can help to regulate flows in streams and rivers, and also affects the quality of that water (Calder et al. 2008; Nisbet et al. in press). The effects can be either positive or negative, depending on the context, and are localised. In general, benefits from increased cover are likely in the upland and upland fringes, and may not require very large changes to the land cover of whole catchments. There is likely to be some benefit from increasing tree cover in floodplains (Thomas & Nisbet 2007). Any increase in cover will need to be carefully planned, identifying where a slowing of water movement may be desirable, and ascertaining the possible implications of trees caught in floods blocking bridges downstream (Nisbet et al. in press).

8.3.3.3 Detoxification and purification of water, air and soil

Forest cover of catchments may reduce yield, but has been used as a way of minimising the need for water treatment by excluding livestock from watercourses and their immediate catchments, therefore reducing the risk of potential water contamination. Forestry operations have the potential to cause problems for water quality, but these can be addressed through application of the Forestry and Water Guidelines (Forestry Commission 2003b). The presence of trees can also contribute to water quality by maintaining cool temperatures for fish, intercepting pollution from point sources and capturing diffuse pollution (Nisbet et *al.* in press). Trees and woodland can contribute to water management, for example, more sustainable surface drainage in urban areas (Handley & Gill 2009; Chapter 10).

Trees are effective scavengers of pollutants from the atmosphere both through internal absorption of pollutants, and external adsorption on to leaf and bark surfaces; hence, problems arise when the acidity scavenged finds its way into watercourses. While some atmospheric pollutants, such as sulphur dioxide, have reduced in concentration, some remain of concern, and climate change will exacerbate others—there is the potential for increased ozone, for instance (Section 8.2.5.2). Targeted tree and woodland development around intensive livestock units (Pitcairn *et al.* 1998) and alongside roads (Bignal *et al.* 2004) can limit the spread of pollutants on to more sensitive habitats such as heathland.

Net pollution absorption by trees was considered to reduce the number of deaths brought forward by air pollution by 5–7 per year, and to reduce hospital admissions by about 4–6 per year. With a discounted value of life and cost of hospital admission, this suggests a benefit of £0.9 million per year for Britain (Powe & Willis 2004). This is small compared to some other non-market benefits, but in urban areas, the relative benefit of small woods (high edge-ratio) will be comparatively high in this respect.

Forest cover may have a remedial role on post-industrial and contaminated soils as an alternative, potentially productive, land use (Lynch & Moffat 2005). This may be considered a viable low-cost alternative to more expensive engineering solutions (Duggan 2005; Pulford & Watson 2003).

Belts of trees and shrubs can be effective at reducing noise pollution—a 33 m-wide tree buffer may reduce noise levels by 6-8 dB (Leonard & Parr 1970). While a relatively minor effect in most situations, this could provide an additional argument for trees and shrubs, rather than other forms of greenspace, in some urban situations, on roadsides and adjacent to industry such as quarries.

8.3.4 Cultural Services

The cultural services offered by woodlands and forests must not be underestimated (Edwards *et al.* 2009; Chapter 16). Their importance for recreation and informal leisure activities is hugely significant, with between 250–300 million visitors to British forests each year. Most visitors undertake various forms of physical activity, such as horse riding, cycling, walking or jogging, and thus, enhance their general health. A range of pilot initiatives have begun where members of the public with certain ailments will be referred to local woods or forests in order to take physical exercise; an NHS Forest Project has also begun (**Box 8.3**). Research has shown both the physical and mental health benefits that woodlands can facilitate, even to those who simply live amongst them. Increasingly, community activities are being held in or around woodlands, in order to promote healthy outdoor pursuits, but also to develop community cohesion. In the public forest estate, Forest Rangers are employed to provide an informal educational role. In addition, there are nearly 150 Forest Schools in GB set up to promote outdoor play and learning (Knight 2009). Such opportunities can improve self-confidence and self-esteem, especially for those who find indoor classrooms less conducive to learning (O'Brien & Murray 2007; Lovell 2009).

Depending on their character and location, forests and woodlands can have significant aesthetic appeal, and can enhance landscape character. These services are appreciated by those who live amongst, or visit, such places. In urban areas, even small woodland blocks can improve the visual appearance and, therefore, the 'feel' of a neighbourhood, and property values often correlate with the degree of trees present (O'Brien *et al.* 2007). The tree and woodland motifs are used extensively in the arts, and form the inspiration for fine art, poetry and music. Woodlands also provide a 'sense of place', a community focus and a spiritual resource. Such services are probably taken for granted by most, but are immeasurably life-enhancing.

Trees and woods are highly valued by people for their historic and cultural values, and as places for quiet (and not so quiet) recreation. It is increasingly acknowledged that UK woodlands contain a diverse array of historic environment assets which are often well-preserved when compared to those in cultivated landscapes, and which provide links to past woodland management or an earlier, pre-wooded landscape. They offer not only a valuable educational resource, but help to create a sense of place and contribute to cultural identity. Historic buildings and monuments in England received an estimated 51 million visitors during 2009, 71% of which expressed an interest in their local history (English Heritage 2010). But while this can offer some indication of heritage value at monitored sites, the contribution of heritage in woodland remains unknown and unvalued.

8.3.4.1 Recreation and tourism, health and well-being

Woodlands provide a setting for a wide range of activities from dog walking to mountain biking, for the short and longer-stay visitor.

Box 8.3 The NHS forest

The NHS has realised that sustainability is part of the core business of the health service, rather than a green add-on. It is one of the biggest resource-users and carbon-generators in the UK, and there are many efforts underway both nationally and locally to reduce its carbon footprint. The creation of an NHS forest is one response. There are 1.3 million employees in the NHS, and the NHS Forest aims to have 1.3 million mature trees in 20 years' time. It is hoped that at the centenary of the birth of the NHS, the forest will play a significant part in offsetting the carbon footprint of the health service by as much as 10%.

The NHS Forest will consist of trees on every NHS campus, and in the local surrounding area, giving opportunities for involvement from the wider community and contributing to a 'Natural Health Service' through the benefits of the greenspace. The NHS Forest will also be available for commemoration and celebration by patients, relatives and professionals. The Campaign for Greener Healthcare is working with the Forestry Commission, the Woodland Trust, Natural England, the Sustainable Development Unit and others to develop partnerships to identify suitable land for planting and existing woodlands close to NHS sites which could be 'adopted' as part of the NHS forest.

Woodland is listed as one of the most popular destinations for countryside visits (around 250 million day visits per year (Forestry Commission 2009a). Three-quarters of respondents in the Public Opinion of Forestry Survey (Forestry Commission 2009b) had visited forests or woodland in the last three years for walks, picnics or other recreational activities. This was an increase over the results in 2005, but similar to the results in 2007. An annual aggregate value for recreation in GB forests has been estimated as £393 million (Willis *et al.* 2003). National Nature Reserves containing woodland provide an example of popular, individual, woodland locations, with Burnham Beeches (220 ha) attracting an estimated 750,000 visitors and Hatfield Forest (392 ha) attracting 250,000 visitors in 1997–98 (English Nature 2002).

Access to woodland has been promoted, particularly by the Woodland Trust (Woodland Trust 2004). In Scotland, there is a general right of responsible access to all land and water, including woodland. In England, over half the area of woodland has public access, some of which is secured under the Countryside and Rights of Way Act, mainly through the dedication of the Forestry Commission's public estate, and voluntary and public bodies. Much of the population, however, still does not have the opportunity to experience woodland in their local area; only 55% of the population have access to woods greater than 20 ha within 4 km, and 10% have access to woods greater than 2 ha within 500 m of their home (Woodland Trust 2004).

More specifically walking in the outdoors is increasingly promoted as part of encouraging healthy life-styles (www.whi.org.uk). The benefits of being in woodland are not just a physical effect: trees and woods are seen as affecting our spiritual and emotional sides as well, as illustrated in the modern writings of Roger Deakin (2007). In the Judeao-Christian faith tradition, trees and woodlands are often seen as reflections of the strength, majesty and creative skill of a transcendent God. In other religious traditions, such as animism, trees and woodlands themselves are imbued with a spiritual presence and power.

Woods may also be the venue for more organised commercial events such as orienteering and paintball games, venues for pop concerts and by the adventure company GoApe which provides a mixture of canopy walkways and zip-wires. Across all its UK sites, GoApe have over 30,000 users per annum (www.countrysiderecreation.org.uk/events/Activity%20Tourism/Go%20Ape!.pdf). In Scotland, the Enchanted Forest (www.enchantedforest.org.uk/) sound and light show at Pitlochry is a popular event every autumn. Forestry Commission Scotland's 7stanes mountain biking network throughout south Scotland has a range of tracks, including one suitable for disabled riders. Developments of facilities at Bedgebury Forest have resulted in a four-fold increase in visitors in recent years. There are also substantial facilities in North Wales (Coed y Brenin) and the Lake District (Grizedale and Whinlatter).

The value of forests for recreation is likely to increase as part of the transition to low-carbon living, through greater interest in holidays and recreational activities in Britain and better local access to greenspace. There is also remote appreciation of woodland through membership of bodies, such as the Woodland Trust, or books such as *Meetings with Remarkable Trees* (Pakenham 1996) and the related television programmes.

Woodlands can have substantial biodiversity, valued for its existence by many different people from casual walkers to wildlife enthusiasts; the opportunities that woodlands provide for viewing wildlife is a major motivation for woodland visits.

8.3.4.2 Heritage goods—citizenship and other cultural services including historical and landscape values

Trees and woodlands are valued for personal enlightenment: they provide special moments, places of sanctuary and even burial areas. They also provide a link with the past, contributing to cultural memory and development. Woodlands can be places of learning, providing evidence of the workings of the natural world. They can be a focus for community development around both their formation and management—there are a substantial number of volunteer groups utilising woodlands.

Ancient woodland and veteran trees are historic features in their own right and provide a link to past society and culture (Rackham 2003). Many 'Royal Forests' have hundreds of years of history, tradition, myth and legend associated with them, helping to create important historic landscapes. Ancient woodland is also increasingly appreciated for its archaeological content. This includes the archaeology of the woods—banks, sawpits, old coppice stools and other features that relate to the history of the land as woodland—and also the archaeology in the woods: the traces of earlier land uses that have survived because the woodland soil surface has often been less disturbed than surrounding land (Rotherham *et al.* 2008). There is increasing interest in these services: amongst the public with regards to local history, as evidenced by TV programmes such as 'Who do you think you are' and 'Time Team'; amongst policy makers with regards to the added protection given to ancient woods and veteran trees in England through Planning and Policy Statement 9 (ODPM 2005); and amongst organisations and initiatives such as the Ancient Tree Hunt (www.ancient-tree-hunt.org.uk/). There are now many community-based heritage projects where local interest groups and volunteers are helping to record veteran trees and archaeological features within some of Britain's forests. Woodlands can also contribute to the protection of soil profiles, cultural artefacts and archaeological remains beneath them—providing a link with the past. British forests include nearly 5,000 Scheduled Ancient Monuments and a much larger, but unknown, number of sites of archaeological interest. Forests can help protect such evidence from disturbance, unless events such as catastrophic windthrow occur. Forest operations have also contributed to access for education and research into geological sites of interest (**Box 8.4**).

Trees and woodlands increase the diversity of landscape character. They provide a sense of place in key locations and form the major components of many landscapes, from the pinewoods of Glen Affric and the hanging oak woods of North Wales, to the beech woods of the Chilterns. The

Box 8.4 Geodiversity and woodlands

Britain is arguably the most geologically diverse landmass of its size in the world with a sequence of rocks representing every major Period of geological history, permitting a variety of sediments, fossils, igneous and metamorphic rocks and structures to be seen. Many of the pioneers of the science of geology were British, and the names of several geological Periods, Series and Stages (e.g. Cambrian, Devonian, Wenlock, Tremadoc, Bathonian) refer to areas or places in the UK.

Woodland character responds to the geological diversity and its influence on soil type and wetness (Pyatt *et al.* 2000; Section 8.2.5). In addition, woodlands cover some key sites of geological interest, which may be of value for research and education. For example, in England, approximately 50 of the 1,200 nationally important geological SSSIs are found on Forestry Commission land, along with an unknown number of Regionally Important Geological and Geomorphological Sites (RIGS). These include sites where active geomorphological processes are taking place, as well as sites that provide evidence of Britain's geological history and may take a variety of forms from quarries and road cuttings, to stream sections and natural rock exposures, amongst others. In some cases, the activities required for the development and management of commercial or sustainable forest have exposed the now-designated features. Features of geological or geomorphological interest may require various forms of management in order to maintain access to the features, or to maintain the geomorphological processes related to the features (Prosser *et al.* 2006).

Two examples provide an indication of the variety of interests that occur on these sites:

Geological history—Mortimer Forest SSSI, near Ludlow, on the Herefordshire/Shropshire border

This SSSI consists of a series of exposures formed by disused quarries, extensive forest road-cuttings and stream sections. Together, these quarries, cuttings and stream sections provide extensive exposures through a succession of rocks belonging to the Wenlock and Ludlow Series of the Silurian, and contain the internationally recognised reference section for the boundary between the Wenlock and Ludlow Series and the boundary between the Gorstian and Ludfordian Stages of the Ludlow Series. The term Ludlow Series was first proposed by the pioneering geologist Sir Roderic Impey Murchison in 1833 based on the rocks exposed around Ludlow, Mortimer Forest and adjacent areas. Since that time, there has been an almost continuous history of research on the rocks, fossils and ancient environments represented in Mortimer Forest, with the investigation of the ages of thin bands of volcanic ashes within the succession being one of the most recent. The importance of the rocks themselves, and their fossiliferous nature, has meant that Mortimer Forest is frequently used for teaching by schools and universities, and is also visited by geology societies and interested individuals. Much of the research of the past 50 years has relied on the presence of the cuttings and disused quarries in the forest. During the late 1970s, the then Nature Conservancy Council (NCC), together with the Forestry Commission, cleared a series of 13 roadside exposures along the Wigmore Road, providing representative sections in all the rocks comprising the Ludlow Series to form the basis of a geological trail. This was accompanied by a trail guide initially published by the NCC and later by the Forestry Commission. Today, the exposures within Mortimer Forest and the geological trail are managed by the Forestry Commission with advice from Natural England, so that they remain visible and accessible.

Active geomorphology—Slade Brook SSSI in Gloucestershire

This (illustrated below) contains a long series (about 700 m) of spectacular, actively forming tufa dams. Although the management of this site relies, in part, on the hydrogeological conditions of the surrounding area, the degree of shade surrounding the stream, the humidity and temperature, the availability of dead vegetation, such as twigs, and the presence of certain algae and mosses are all factors controlling the precipitation and formation of the tufa.

Tufa dam. *Photo courtesy of Natural England.*

---

contribution may be solely aesthetic, or linked to how that landscape has developed historically and culturally, such as the Binsey poplars that were celebrated in the poem of Gerald Manley Hopkins. Individual trees, like the Birnam and Major Oaks, are strongly associated with the character of particular sites. Trees contribute to amenity values and their presence can even increase property values. The UK adoption of the European Landscape Convention is likely to mean that the significance of landscape issues can be expected to increase.

There is some association between perceptions of landscape value and woodland characteristics: for example, woodland type (broadleaves tend to be more favoured than conifers), tree age (large, old trees tend to be favoured over young ones), openness (valued more than dense, closed areas) and diversity (mixtures and variation valued over uniformity) (Willis *et al.* 2003). Willis and others have explored expressing these preferences in value terms, via willingness-to-pay or hedonic pricing methods. For instance, they have estimated a marginal value of £269 per annum/household for those households on the urban fringe with a woodland landscape view, and £1,500–£2,000 (present value per hectare) for the contribution of new planting to the landscape in Central Scotland (CJC Consulting 2005). Overall, Willis *et al.* (2003) give annual values attributable to landscape values of £150 million for GB forests (**Table 8.11**).

Large-scale afforestation, almost from its inception, has been criticised as damaging valued open landscapes (Symonds 1936; Tompkins 1989; Smout 2000). Pioneering work was done by Sylvia Crowe in the 1960s to improve the fit of new forests into the landscape and this has been followed with research and guidance (Bell 2003; Forestry Commission in press b). Despite this, objections are often raised to the clearance of trees and woods in order to restore heathland and other open habitats. People do not like sudden change: communities may object to the planting of new woodland but, when it is mature, object to its felling. In turn, this may be reflected in the use of Tree Preservation Orders which, while more usually applied to individual trees, have been applied to areas of woodland as well. Environmental Impact Assessments (Forestry Commission

2007b) are now required for any large-scale schemes, both woodland creation and clearance; and Landscape Character Assessments can contribute to identifying how and where changes in tree and woodland cover may best be achieved.

The heritage associated with this widespread landscape change has achieved some recognition. There are a number of initiatives to capture the oral history of the large-scale afforestation, and its impacts on the landscape, from forest workers and surrounding communities (Smout & Tittensor 2008), and to summarise the evolution of organisations and objectives (Tsouvalis 2000; Foot 2010).

8.3.5 Supporting Services

Underpinning the three groups of ecosystem services discussed above are the supporting services of soil formation, nutrient cycling, water regulation and oxygen production. These are common to almost all terrestrial ecosystems which support vegetation (Chapter 13). Woodland biodiversity, including genetic diversity, can be regarded as another supporting service. In particular, below-ground fauna and flora (including mycorrhizal relationships) promote essential biogeochemical processes that, in turn, lead to the renewal of soil, plant nutrients and fertility. Above-ground fauna both help and hinder woodland dynamics and natural woodland regeneration. But biodiversity is an important management objective for many woods and forests in Britain in its own right—in other words, in order to promote a rich fauna and flora because these land uses are seen as having the capacity to do so. In this respect, one can view biodiversity as a provisioning service, but for some it may even take on the role of a cultural one.

8.3.6 Valuation of Services Over Time

As has been illustrated in respect of individual services (see Section 8.3 above) there have been some previous attempts to assess the value of the services provided by woodlands and forests. One of the most comprehensive (Willis *et al.* 2003), is summarised in **Table 8.11**.

The UK NEA valuation exercise has focused on assessing changes both in past benefits associated with ecosystem service provision, and in potential future benefits (Chapter 22). Woodlands provide a wide range of ecosystem services, of which seven provisioning services, 12 regulating services, four supporting services and 10 cultural services were initially considered as potential candidates for valuation (Chapter 22). The extent to which the service could be attributed exclusively to woodlands, and the availability of time-series data, led to the following being selected for description here:

i) Wood production (timber and fuel): an example of a provisioning service;

ii) Carbon sequestration: an example of a regulating service.

8.3.6.1 Provisioning services: wood production values

Wood production. Overall, total wood production in the UK has risen substantially since the mid-1970s as forests planted earlier in the 20th Century have matured. For

Table 8.11 Annual and capitalised social and environmental benefits of forests in GB (at 2010 prices).

Environmental benefit	Annual value (£ millions)	Capitalised value (£ millions)
Recreation	484	13,825
Landscape	185	5,290
Biodiversity	476	13,592
Carbon sequestration*	115	2,676
Air pollution absorption*	0.5	14
Total	**1,261**	**36,019**

* An approximation, since carbon sequestration, and probability of death and illness due to air pollution, varies over time. More carbon is sequestrated in early rotations than in later rotations, resulting in an annuity stream that is inconsistent over multiple rotations. Similarly for air pollution, that results in an individual's life being shortened by a few days or weeks at the end of the individual's life at some point in the future. More recent work puts a much higher value on the carbon sequestration benefits (Read *et al.* 2009).

softwood, production by the Forestry Commission is the major element, while for hardwood most production comes from the private sector (Chapter 22). The quantity of wood produced from Forestry Commission land tends to be more stable between years compared with wood harvested from private woodlands; the former reflects commitments to support domestic wood-using industries, while the latter is influenced to a greater extent by prevailing price levels.

Softwood production has increased substantially since 1945, (Chapter 15) but detailed annual data are only available since 1976. Much of the increase in softwood production since the mid-1990s has been in Scotland (**Figure 8.6**).

By contrast, hardwood production has declined since the mid-1970s, and is largely concentrated in England (**Figure 8.7**). High volumes of production during the period 1988 to 1990 were probably partly due to clearance after the storms of 16 October 1987 in south-east England (resulting in windthrow of 3.9 million m³ or 13–24% of the growing stock), and of 25th January 1990 in south and west Britain

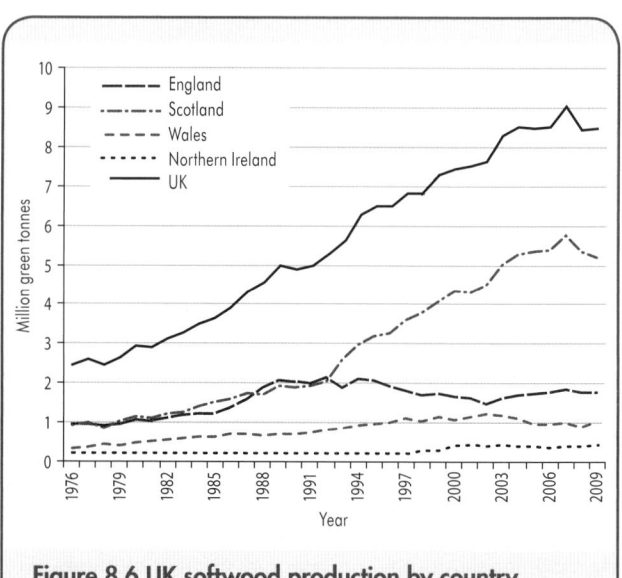

Figure 8.6 UK softwood production by country (million green tonnes). Source: Forestry Commission (2009e).

(resulting in windthrow of 1.3 million m³ or 1–3% of the growing stock) (Quine 1991).

Price. Forest management decisions concerning rotation length can affect the prices of wood. Prices tend to be higher for larger (i.e. generally older) trees and lower for small trees as they cannot be used for producing sawlogs (which tend to be relatively high-value). Relationships between tree size and price are traditionally modelled as price-size curves (Mitlin 1987; Whiteman 1990; Whiteman *et al.* 1991; Sinclair & Whiteman 1992; Pryor & Jackson 2002; Bateman *et al.* 2003). However, the largest trees are not invariably the most valuable (Chapter 22), and a range of other factors including species mix, quantity sold, timber quality, site conditions, and strength of local demand, also influence prices.

Over the period 1971/72 to 2009/10 mean softwood standing sales prices for the Forestry Commission estate fell in real terms by about two thirds from around £30/m³ overbark (£35 per green tonne) to £10/m³ overbark (£12 per green tonne) at 2010/11 prices (**Figure 8.8**). This appears to follow a longer-term downward trend: the British softwood standing sales price index reported by the Forestry Commission in 1977 indicated a fall of around one quarter in real terms over the period 1958 to 1972 (Mitlin 1987; Insley *et al.* 1987).

Time series data on hardwood standing sales prices are not available. The mean price for all hardwood sales in 2007/08 by the Forestry Commission in England (which accounted for over 90% of hardwood sales by the Forestry Commission that year, although less than 10% of total UK hardwood production) was around £15/m³ (equivalent to about £18 per green tonne at 2010/11 prices). Comparison of recent Forestry Commission hardwood price data with prices for all British woodlands reported in Whiteman *et al.* (1991) suggests that, in real terms, hardwood prices probably fell by at least a third from around £90 per green tonne in 1989, to somewhere in the range £18–£61 per green tonne

in 2007/08 at 2010/11 prices (Chapter 22). A drop in average hardwood prices in real terms appears consistent with the apparent decline in demand for UK-grown hardwood by some upstream sectors. The past decade has been characterised by a collapse in purchases of British hardwood by UK sawmills, and by pulp- and paper-mills, which fell from 227,000 and 191,000 green tonnes respectively in 1999, to 67,000 green tonnes and zero green tonnes in 2008—the numbers of UK sawmills processing hardwoods roughly halving (Forestry Commission 2009a). Overcapacity and investment in Eastern European mills are also considered important factors in this decline (Lawson & Hemery 2007).

With domestically grown wood accounting for less than a fifth of the total wood used in the UK (Forestry Commission 2009a), this country is generally assumed to be a price-taker with respect to global prices (McGregor & McNicoll 1992; Thomson & Psaltopoulos 2005; Lawson & Hemery 2007), and the supply of imported timber perfectly elastic at the world price (Bateman & Mellor 1990). To the extent that UK standing sales prices simply reflect those on the world market, the marginal value of wood produced by UK woodlands can be considered independent of the quantity produced.

Value. Wood production can be valued at standing sales prices, at roadside prices, or using an average of these. Standing sales prices appear to provide the better basis for estimating the contribution of woodland habitats to ecosystem services.

Valued at standing sales prices, the gross value of UK softwood production has shown little trend from 1976 to the present. Falling real prices for softwood were largely offset by increasing volumes as coniferous plantations matured, with removals of roundwood apparently more than trebling from 2.4 million green tonnes of softwood in 1976 to 8.5 million green tonnes in 2009 (Forestry Commission 2010b). However, despite little overall trend, gross values varied considerably in real terms over this period, with peaks in the

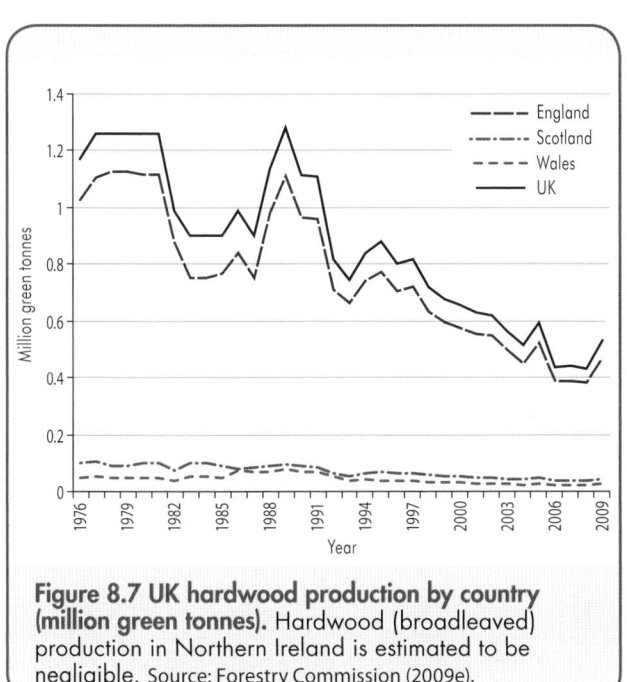

Figure 8.7 UK hardwood production by country (million green tonnes). Hardwood (broadleaved) production in Northern Ireland is estimated to be negligible. Source: Forestry Commission (2009e).

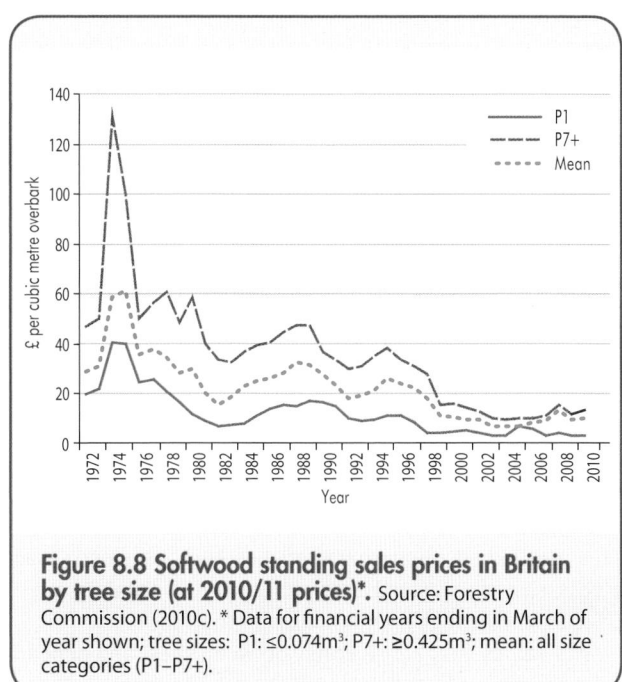

Figure 8.8 Softwood standing sales prices in Britain by tree size (at 2010/11 prices)*. Source: Forestry Commission (2010c). * Data for financial years ending in March of year shown; tree sizes: P1: ≤0.074m³; P7+: ≥0.425m³; mean: all size categories (P1–P7+).

late 1980s and mid 1990s, including a maximum of over £190 million in 1995 at 2010 prices, and troughs in the early 1980s and early 2000s, including a minimum of under £60 million in 1981 at 2010 prices. The total area of predominantly coniferous woodland in the UK has remained at around 1.5 million ha over the past two decades, while there has been an expansion in predominantly broadleaved woodland in the UK from 0.9 million ha in 1990 to 1.1 million ha in 2010 (Forestry Commission 2010b). Indicative per hectare values for softwood production, derived by dividing total production by the total area of coniferous woodlands, suggest gross production values fell from £95/ha/yr in 1990 to around £66/ha/yr in 2009 at 2010 prices.

Information to construct trends in hardwood values is sparse. However, the reduction in the total volume of UK hardwood sold (which more than halved from over 1.2 million in 1989 to 0.4 million green tonnes in 2007–08), combined with an apparent fall in hardwood prices, suggests total gross values of UK hardwood sold fell sharply over this period. Gross values for hardwood production were around £120/ha in 1989. Valued using the above lower- and upper-bound mean price estimates (of £18 and £61 per green tonne at 2010/11 prices), gross values in 2007/08 would have been £7–£25/ha at 2010/11 prices. The decline is consistent, with reports that it is often less expensive at present to buy imported hardwood than to process UK-grown wood; this could change in the future.

How forestry costs are apportioned between wood production and other ecosystem services (such as carbon sequestration), combined with the range of costs covered, and the assumed shadow price of labour, may all affect estimates of marginal values of wood production net of capital and labour costs and of subsidies. More fundamentally, whether expenditures and revenues are simply compared for individual years, or annual equivalents computed over a single or series of rotations, also affects estimated values, with annualised estimates sensitive to the discount rate adopted in comparing costs and revenues over time.

Regular surveys of forestry costs, incomes and expenditures were undertaken from the 1960s until the early 1990s for private woodlands and typically showed expenditure exceeding income (Todd et al. 1988; Dolan & Russell 1988; Chapter 22). Reflecting a market perspective, no account is taken of shadow values for labour, non-market values of wood production (e.g. carbon substitution benefits associated with using wood instead of fossil fuels or more fossil fuel-intensive materials) or non-market ecosystem services (to the extent that these costs are partly associated with provision of these wider benefits). Therefore, they can be considered to significantly under-estimate marginal social values of wood production. However, in the absence of mechanisms that value such wider, non-market ecosystem services, profitability has tended to be low, with woodland grants and tax incentives being major influences on woodland planting rates. Forestry costs per hectare of woodland vary between sites, depending upon characteristics such as slope, road access, size of woodland and species planted. Establishment costs tend to be higher for broadleaves than conifers.

Net values vary considerably between sites, and depend upon species and rotation length choices; for example, Pryor and Jackson (2002) report mean net annual income estimates (that take no account of changing values over time and discounting) for 11 species/yield class (YC)/rotation length combinations considered typical of plantations on ancient woodland sites. These range from -£2/ha for birch YC6 to £262/ha for ash YC10 (both over a 70-year rotation) for broadleaves, and from £77/ha for larch YC12 to £247/ha for Douglas fir YC18 (both over a 45-year rotation) for conifers.

8.3.6.2 Regulating services: carbon sequestration

Estimates of the net amount of carbon (in the form of carbon dioxide) sequestered by woodland, and of changes in carbon stored in Harvested Wood Products (HWP), are available from the Centre for Ecology and Hydrology (CEH) (Dyson et al. 2009). Based upon a carbon accounting model (C-Flow) for woodlands planted after 1921 that includes transfers of carbon from living biomass (roots, trunk, branches, foliage) to litter and soils, estimates are produced on behalf of the government as part of the UK's commitments under the Kyoto Protocol (Chapter 22). The CEH estimates show net carbon sequestration in UK woodlands rising from 2.4 Mt of carbon dioxide in 1945 to a peak of 16.3 Mt of carbon dioxide in 2004, and then falling back to 12.9 Mt of carbon dioxide in 2009. Net sequestration rates for the period 2001 to 2009 have been estimated at around 5.2 t CO_2/ha across all UK woodlands (and 0.3 t CO_2/ha for HWP). An increase in net carbon sequestration by UK woodlands since 1945 is consistent with increased afforestation rates from the 1950s to 1980s, although exclusion of forests planted before 1921 probably results in lower estimates for the early part of the period than would otherwise have been the case. Carbon accounting methodology is still evolving and it is probable that current estimates from existing models underestimate carbon sequestration rates (Robertson et al. 2003; Dyson et al. 2009; Matthews & Broadmeadow 2009).

Permanence can be a key influence on valuation of carbon benefits, with the present value of the carbon at the point at which it is re-released to the atmosphere generally needing to be subtracted in valuing current gross sequestration. Where future carbon values are expected to rise, the present value of future emissions can even exceed the value of the original sequestration in some cases (Valatin 2010). However, permanence issues can be ignored if the total carbon stock in UK woodlands and HWP combined is expected to remain at least at the current level in perpetuity once account has been made for carbon substitution benefits (associated with using wood instead of fossil fuels or more fossil fuel-intensive materials).

A wide range of values have been used to value carbon. UK government guidance on valuing carbon (DECC 2010) is currently based upon a target-consistent approach which, at 2010 prices, includes using a central value of around £53/t CO_2 (equivalent to £193/t C) for 2009 for the 'non-traded' sector (i.e. that not covered by the EU emissions trading scheme). As forestry carbon sequestration is not covered by the ETS at present, values for the 'non-traded' (rather than the 'traded') sector are relevant, and in the absence of a consistent time-series of values back to 1945, the 2010 value is applied to value sequestration in previous years.

Valued at the DECC central estimate of £53/t CO$_2$ in 2009, the CEH estimates suggest that the gross value of net carbon sequestration by UK woodlands increased five-fold, from £124 million in 1945, to £680 million in 2009 at 2010 prices, with Scotland currently accounting for around two thirds of the total (**Figure 8.9**).

Values per hectare at the DECC central social value of carbon of £53/t CO$_2$ rise from £270/ha in 2001 to a peak of £304/ha in 2004, before falling back to a minimum of £239/ha in 2009 (Chapter 22); a mean of £276/ha is seen over this period. For woodland planted since 1921, per hectare values are significantly higher. Dividing by CEH estimates for these woodland areas suggests values of net carbon sequestration at 2010 prices of around £590/ha in 1945, falling to about £400/ha in 2009, valued at the DECC central social value of carbon of £53/t CO$_2$; a zero value is assumed for net carbon sequestration by woodlands planted prior to 1921.

The mean value of net carbon sequestration by woodlands and in HWP combined over the period 2001 to 2009 was £286/ha at 2010 prices valued at the central estimate of the social value of carbon (with £143/ha and £429/ha as the low and high social value estimates). The combined value remained fairly stable, rising from £279/ha in 2001 to £293/ha in 2004, before falling to £281/ha in 2009.

In addition to net sequestration (i.e. change in carbon stored), existing carbon storage in woodlands can also be valued relative to its release to the atmosphere; forest carbon stock estimates have been recently published (Forestry Commission 2010b). Valuing the total stored (803 Mt C) in 1990 at the central DECC estimate of £193/t C (£53/t CO$_2$) would imply a total value of £155 billion and an average gross value of around £59,000/ha at 2010 prices, increasing slightly over the past decade consistent with a positive per hectare net carbon sequestration rate*. However, over four fifths of this total is soil carbon which may vary relatively little with land use change in the short-run. Valuing carbon storage in above- and below-ground biomass, dead wood and litter alone (which may be more sensitive to land use change) at the central DECC estimate of £193/t C would imply a total value of £28 billion, and a per hectare value of around £11,000/ha at 2010 prices (equivalent to an annuity value of £380/ha/yr at a 3.5% discount rate). In contrast to the net sequestration values, carbon storage values could be expected to be highest in woodlands planted prior to 1921, other factors being equal.

8.3.6.3 Valuation: summary and concluding remarks

Paucity of data and different reporting periods precludes identification and comparison of trends in values for each ecosystem service provided by UK woodlands. Nonetheless, the review of changes in values of two ecosystem services has highlighted some clear differences in magnitude and trend (**Table 8.12**). The sharp decline in hardwood prices is consistent both with reports of low import price and with a shift in woodland management objectives away from timber production towards provision of multiple ecosystem services. In the case of the per hectare hardwood values, a decline is also consistent with an expansion in the total area covered by broadleaves and the associated transition to a lower average age of stands.

The estimates of gross values take no account of capital and labour costs, but surveys of private woodland owners

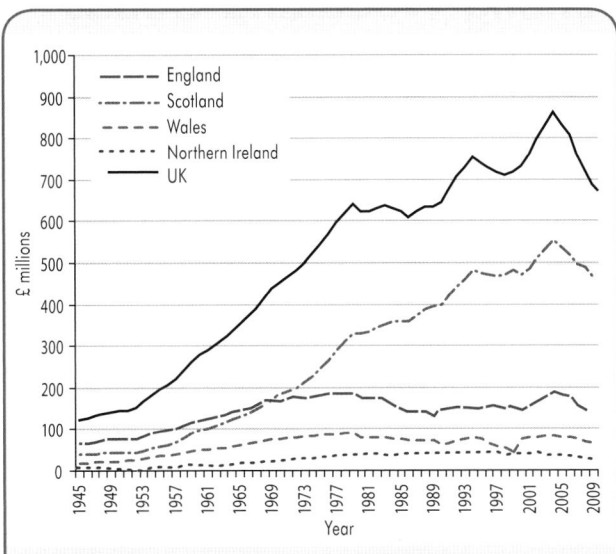

Figure 8.9 Value of annual carbon sequestration by UK woodlands (at 2010 prices). Based upon CEH estimates and the DECC (2010) central estimate of £53/tCO$_2$.

* Based instead upon the carbon stock estimate of 790 Mt C cited in the Read Report (Read *et al.* 2009) and elsewhere in this chapter, the estimates are £125 billion and £58,000/ha respectively.

Table 8.12 Changes in values of ecosystem services from UK woodlands (at 2010 prices).

Ecosystem service	Annual value (£ millions)				Annual value per ha (£/ha)		
	1945	1976	1990	2009	1990	2001	2009
Softwood production *		112	145	105	95	55	68
Hardwood production †			110	8–26	120		7–25
Net carbon sequestration by woodlands ‡	124	563	642	680	246	270	239
Net carbon sequestration in harvested wood products ‡	0	13	77	119	29	8	42

* Estimates based upon prices for standing sales from Forestry Commission land.
† Dates differ: the first year is 1989 and second 2007/08. Estimates based upon average prices for both standing sales and direct production (data comparability unclear).
‡ Based upon the central estimate of the social value of carbon for 2009 recommended for non-ETS sectors (DECC 2010) at 2010 prices; per ha estimate for 1990 derived by dividing by UK forest area from Forestry Commission (2010a).

suggest these averaged around £200/ha–£300/ha during 1961 to 1986 at 2010/11 prices (recent information on total Forestry Commission expenditure in England of £275/ha in 2007/08 suggests these costs are currently of a similar magnitude). To the extent that these costs are common to the provision of each ecosystem service provided by woodlands (including those considered in other chapters), gross estimates provide a useful rough indication of relative social value.

Although sensitive to the social values of carbon used and to assumptions of permanence, at present, the highest values are for carbon sequestration by woodlands. Remaining largely a non-market value, however, there is little incentive currently for landowners to increase provision of this ecosystem service or to maintain existing carbon storage.

The extent both of ecosystem service provision, and to which trade-offs or synergies exist in their provision, is sensitive to land management approaches and objectives (Chapter 5). For example, stalking and venison production are complementary activities to wood production and habitat conservation in many cases, but where the primary focus of land management may largely be substitutes.

Significant data gaps include the lack of consistent time-series data on hardwood standing sales prices, on woodfuel, on venison and stalking revenues, and on forestry costs. Given this lack of data, knowledge gaps remain concerning

spatial differences in marginal values between regions, different woodlands types and forestry management approaches. More fundamentally, the marginal value of individual ecosystem services net of capital and labour costs remains indeterminate in the absence of an accepted approach to apportioning forestry establishment and management costs between different ecosystem services. Under these circumstances, any analysis of issues of trade-offs and synergies, and of optimal land use, will have to rely on comparisons of differences in the total net value (including non-monetised contribution to human well-being) of ecosystem services provided. However, in view of existing data and knowledge gaps, including the need still to develop a suitable methodology to quantify some ecosystem services (e.g. spiritual values), robust estimates of total net values to facilitate comparisons of alternative land uses seem elusive at present.

8.4 Trade-offs and Synergies Among Woodland Goods and Ecosystem Services

"Newly planted forests may, at times, offend the aesthetic conscience, and feelings are stirred by some aspects of their early growth and by fears regarding their future development." (W.L. Taylor 1946)

"All these examples, from Burns onwards, demonstrate the post-Romantic, post-Enlightenment conflict between use and delight which is the constant theme in the environmental history of the last two centuries. After all, the various landowners....were only trying to realise a timber crop, or to plant efficiently to suit the tree species to the soil. In the eyes of their critics, however, they were destroying the natural and the beautiful which, by being in the public eye, belongs to us all." (Christopher Smout 2000)

8.4.1 Introduction

Previous sections have highlighted the trends in policy and management of woodland since 1945. Some of these changes have reflected the shift in emphasis of woodland expansion and management from a dominant production focus, to one targeting a wider set of values (as espoused in the terminology of 'multipurpose forestry' and 'sustainable forest management'). Implicit in these shifting objectives is the requirement to make choices about the combination of goods to be sought, and which methods are to be deployed to achieve them. These decisions and techniques are further elaborated in Section 8.5. In this section, examples are provided of particular trade-offs and synergies (**Table 8.13**); note that interactions between UK NEA Broad Habitats are covered in Section 8.1.3.

Figure 8.10 Carbon sequestration is one of the most important ecosystem services of woodlands; at peak growth, coniferous forest can sequester around 24 tonnes of carbon dioxide per hectare per year, with a net long-term average of around 14 t CO_2/ha/yr. Fresh needles signal spring growth in Sitka spruce. *Photo courtesy of: FC Picture Library / Isobel Cameron.*

8.4.2 Synergies in the Provision of Services

The following examples illustrate where focusing on the delivery of one group of services can provide the simultaneous supply of other services.

8.4.2.1 Achieving provisioning and regulating services

New forests have been identified as a means of increasing carbon storage and achieving some climate change mitigation through the expansion phase (i.e. before the forests reach a steady state). Faster growing species or the use of better quality sites will not only fix carbon quicker, but also produce timber of an utilisable size quicker (**Figure 8.10**). Felling may take place sooner and, provided that the carbon is then stored (e.g. through embedding in construction), another rotation can be established to further sequester carbon. Such synergies have attracted policy support, with new woodland expansion targets for Scotland, Wales and England.

8.4.2.2 Achieving provisioning and cultural services

The character of many of the UK's woodlands reflects the interaction between past policies, past management and site quality. Many lowland woodlands still show the legacy of wartime felling and subsequent regeneration, or planting, leading to a cohort of woodlands that have now reached a particular stand stage (Section 8.2.2; **Figure 8.2a,b**). This stage is known in ecological literature as 'stem exclusion' and is characterised by dense canopies, the shading of the understorey and the restriction of physical access. Natural stand dynamics, driven by storms, insect infestation or disease, will eventually lead to the opening up of such woods, but the length of time this will take is at odds with the demands of today's society. Stand management, in the form of thinning, can harvest some of the production (provisioning). In doing so, it will increase the light levels within the stand, leading to improved conditions for ground and shrub layers (and those organisms, such as woodland birds, that depend upon them), and improved access for recreational activities (including the gathering of non-timber forest products). Reinstatement of a coppice regime could foster crafts and traditional skills, maintain a supply of niche products and woodfuel, and bring biodiversity benefits.

8.4.2.3 Achieving regulating and cultural services

Natural flood management is being increasingly promoted as a way of reducing the costs of flooding to society, coping with intense rainfall events as a result of climate change, and reducing the cost of hard-engineering solutions. Restoration of riparian/floodplain woodland may delay and reduce flood peaks. Such restoration would also lead to the reinstatement of habitats that have been lost over large parts of Europe, favouring a range of aquatic and terrestrial organisms, providing wildlife corridors and making a significant contribution to landscape quality and diversity.

8.4.3 Trade-offs in the Provision of Services

The following examples illustrate where focusing on the delivery of one group of services can negatively impact on the supply of other services.

8.4.3.1 Trade-off between provisioning and regulating services

Trees must be felled in order to make fibre available for use in timber products, construction, paper-making, or fuel. However, this felling removes the carbon store in the above-ground parts of the tree, and may lead to increased rates of soil carbon loss as a result of changes in the microclimate and soil. The magnitude of this trade-off depends upon the end use of the tree products (including the extent to which these products become an off-site store), and the rate of restoration of forest conditions after felling. The former depends upon markets, the latter on management options, including the scale of the felling intervention, and the manner by which a successor tree crop is established. Similarly, water quantity may be increased, but quality decreased, by felling, and regulation is diminished until vegetation cover re-establishes.

Table 8.13 Six examples of trade-offs and synergies in provision of ecosystem services and human well-being provided by woodlands.

	Provisioning services	Regulating services	Cultural services
Provisioning services		**Synergy 1:** Increased growth and production can increase carbon storage.	**Synergy 2:** Thinning of neglected woodland can open access for visitors and improve habitat for wildlife (enhancing opportunities to observe); opportunities may be provided for employment, volunteering and craft development.
Regulating services	**Trade-off 1:** Increased harvest reduces carbon sink/store unless products are long-life.		**Synergy 3:** Restoration of riparian woodland to aid flood regulation may enhance landscape and opportunities for recreation (including fishing).
Cultural services	**Trade-off 2:** Increased production may reduce quality of woodland environment for recreation (e.g. increased traffic and machinery), and reduce visual quality (e.g. clearfells).	**Trade-off 3:** Most efficient carbon capture may be with novel crops/species that are not familiar or liked.	

8.4.3.2 Trade-off between provisioning and cultural services

Removal of trees, as part of the supply of a provisioning service, is increasingly mechanised in developed countries such as the UK both for cost reasons and because of the unattractiveness of the manual forms of harvesting to the labour pool. Large machines bring a form of industrialisation to what is regarded as a natural habitat by many, and may require a large-scale of working. There are potential conflicts between harvesting operations and recreational use as access may be restricted to prevent accident, and the resulting change of character may influence the perceived attractiveness of the area. Heavy machinery may also disturb wildlife and reduce opportunities to view charismatic species, at least in the short-term (in the medium-term, the habitat manipulation may be beneficial). Clear-felling silvicultural systems are an efficient way of growing fibre, particularly when using pioneer, light-demanding species, and are well-suited to mechanisation. But clear-felling creates rapid and large-scale change in the landscape that attracts unfavourable comment and dramatically affects visual appearance.

8.4.3.3 Trade-off between regulating and cultural services

Trials of eucalyptus and other fast-growing species are under way as a source of biomass for biofuel. Their very rapid growth rates (which result in swift carbon capture), are expected to be many times greater than those of native broadleaved tree species on the same site type (Matthews & Broadmeadow 2009). The rate of carbon sequestration and renewable fuel production will have to be considered in the light of obvious trade-offs. These include:

- concerns over eucalyptus and its high water-usage;
- potential invasiveness into other ecosystems (something associated with use of the genus in other countries such as Spain and Portugal);
- poor quality habitat due to leaf-fall and slow leaf decomposition leading to suppression of the ground flora;
- uncertainties over impact on landscape aesthetics, with conflicting public opinion (distinguishing eucalypts from other species may be difficult for many, especially at a distance, but large-scale harvesting is unlikely to be appreciated: Section 8.4.3.2);
- extensive recreational use is unlikely to be compatible with the optimal stand structure for fuel production; and
- the increased fire hazard of using eucalypts, particularly in light of predictions of increased summer drought.

8.4.4 Choices in Trade-offs and Synergies

Section 8.5 provides a review of the policy and management instruments that govern the specification of woodland management, and how a balance is struck between competing or synergistic demands. Choices are governed by planning tools such as cost-benefit analysis, standards, consultation and Environmental Impact Assessment.

8.5 Options for Sustainable Management

"A culture is no better than its woods." (W.H. Auden 1955)

8.5.1 Introduction

The concept of sustainability in woodland management has a long history. Osmaston (1968) describes the development of forest management for sustained yields of timber in Continental Europe over 700 years ago. A 14th Century French ordinance required management such that "forests can perpetually sustain a good state" (Huffel cited in Osmaston 1968), and by the mid-19th Century, the principle of sustained yield was understood and applied in France, Germany and Austria. During the latter part of the 20th Century, the concept of sustainable forest management evolved to encompass the wider ecological and social functions of forests (FAO 1993).

Today, UK forestry is making substantial progress in the elaboration of approaches to sustainability and active land use, and in developing the concepts of management to provide for multiple goods and services. A number of recent developments exemplify the options available to enhance ecosystem services. An increasing area of both state and privately owned woodland has gained certification status under the United Kingdom Woodland Assurance Standard (UKWAS 2008); this is recognised as the standard for sustainable forest management in the UK by the Forest Stewardship Council (FSC). As a consequence, there has been increased interest in lower-impact silvicultural systems used in continuous cover forestry (*sensu* Mason). Many of the ancient woodlands planted with non-native conifers are being restored to native woodland communities (Thompson *et al.* 2003). There is developing interest in adaptation to climate change (Ray 2008) and to the opportunities for woodlands to play a role in climate change mitigation through sequestration and substitution (Broadmeadow & Matthews 2003; Read *et al.* 2009). The broader context and specific options are now examined in more depth. Note that much of the literature on this subject uses the term "sustainable forest management" (rather than sustainable woodland management); this and the word 'forest' are retained where they are used in the source literature.

8.5.2 Sustainable Forest Management in Europe

The Ministerial Conference on the Protection of Forests in Europe (MCPFE) was founded in 1990 to develop common strategies for its 46 member countries and the EU on the protection and management of forests. In 1993, the Second Ministerial Conference produced general guidelines for the sustainable management of forests in Europe, defining sustainable forest management as:

"the stewardship and use of forests and forest lands in a way, and at a rate, that maintains their biodiversity, productivity, regeneration capacity, vitality and their potential to fulfil, now and in the future, relevant ecological, economic and social functions at local, national and

Table 8.14 MCPFE criteria and quantitative indicators for sustainable forest management at the national level.

Criteria	No.	Indicator
Maintenance and appropriate enhancement of forest resources and their contribution to global carbon cycles	1.1	Forest area
	1.2	Growing stock
	1.3	Age structure and / or diameter distribution
	1.4	Carbon stock
Maintenance of forest ecosystem health and vitality	2.1	Deposition of air pollutants
	2.2	Soil conditions
	2.3	Defoliation
	2.4	Forest damage
Maintenance and encouragement of productive functions of forests (wood and non-wood)	3.1	Increment and fellings
	3.2	Roundwood
	3.3	Non-wood goods
	3.4	Services
	3.5	Forests under management plans
Maintenance, conservation and appropriate enhancement of biological diversity in forest ecosystems	4.1	Tree species composition
	4.2	Regeneration
	4.3	Naturalness
	4.4	Introduced tree species
	4.5	Deadwood
	4.6	Genetic resources
	4.7	Landscape pattern
	4.8	Threatened forest species
	4.9	Protected forests
Maintenance, conservation and appropriate enhancement of protective functions in forest management (notably soil and water)	5.1	Protective forests—soil, water and other ecosystem functions
	5.2	Protective forests—infrastructure and managed natural resources
Maintenance of other socio-economic functions and conditions	6.1	Forest holdings
	6.2	Contribution of forest sector to GDP
	6.3	Net revenue
	6.4	Expenditure for services
	6.5	Forest sector workforce
	6.6	Occupational health and safety
	6.7	Wood consumption
	6.8	Trade in wood
	6.9	Energy from wood resources
	6.10	Accessibility for recreation
	6.11	Cultural and spiritual values

global levels, and that does not cause damage to other ecosystems" (MPCFE 1993)

Pan-European criteria and indicators for sustainable forest management were agreed at the Third Ministerial Conference (MPCFE 1998) and revised in 2002 (MCPFE 2002). The current set of quantitative indicators is summarised in **Table 8.14** (there are also 17 qualitative indicators which are not shown). Progress towards sustainable forest management at the national level in the 46 MPCFE member countries, assessed using these criteria and indicators, is described in The State of Europe's Forests 2007 (MPCFE 2007). Forests in the UK, like most of those elsewhere in Europe, appear to be in "a comparatively good state" and delivering a range of ecosystem services.

The criteria and indicators used for monitoring and reporting at a national level are of little practical help to owners and managers trying to practise sustainable management at the level of an individual forest or a forested landscape (Forestry Commission 2004; Bell & Apostol 2008). Pan-European operational-level guidelines for sustainable forest management (MCPFE 1998) go some way to addressing this problem, but need to be modified for local economic, environmental, social and cultural conditions.

8.5.3 Sustainable Forest Management in the UK: the UK Forestry Standard

In GB, the publication of Forestry Commission guidelines on environmental and cultural aspects of forest management started in the early 1990s, before the appearance of the MPCFE guidelines for the sustainable management of forests in Europe. The Forestry Commission guidelines do not use criteria and indicators, but take a practical approach to management of a particular component of the forest ecosystem, or of particular forest features that have cultural or social value. The current guidelines cover nature conservation, recreation, landscape design, historic environment, soil conservation and water, and revised guidelines have recently been prepared (Forestry Commission in press a,b&c).

Starting in 1995, the existing guidelines and developing ideas on criteria, indicators and standards were brought together into a single document, the UK Forestry Standard. Consultations took place in 1996 and 1997, and the first edition was published in 1998; a second edition was produced in 2004 to reflect devolution in the UK (Forestry Commission 2004), and the third edition is due to be published in 2011 following consultation (Forestry Commission 2009c; R. Howe pers. comm.). In the international arena, the UK Forestry Standard shows how international protocols on sustainable forest management are implemented here. It applies to all forests and woodlands in the UK and provides a performance standard for sustainable management at the level of the forest management unit, normally the area subject to a forest management plan or proposal (Forestry Commission 2009c).

The third edition of the UK Forestry Standard identifies eight elements of sustainable forest management: general forestry and legal conformity; forest planning and general forestry practice; forests and landscape; forests and biodiversity; forests and water; forests and climate change; forests and soils; and forests and people. For each element, legal requirements and good forestry practice requirements are identified, and sustainable forest management is demonstrated by full compliance with both sets of requirements. There are about 90 requirements in total, of which about a third are legal requirements. Many of the legal requirements relate to legislation that implements EU Directives and is not specific to forestry (e.g. the EU Habitats Directive and the EU WFD). A few, such as the requirement to obtain a licence for felling trees, relate to GB legislation under the Forestry Act (and its amendments). A Woodland Carbon Code is also being developed (www.forestry.gov.uk/website/forestry.nsf/byunique/infd-863ffl) to set standards for voluntary carbon sequestration projects that incorporate core principles of good carbon management as part of modern sustainable forest management.

8.5.4 Forest Certification: the UK Woodland Assurance Standard (UKWAS)

Increasingly, buyers of wood and wood products wish to be assured that these products have been sourced from sustainably managed forests. Forest certification schemes provide independent verification of sustainable forest management, allowing forest-managers to claim that they are meeting specified standards of management and, therefore, to market their wood more effectively. Two certification schemes operate in the UK (Bills 2001)—the Forest Stewardship Council (FSC) and the Programme for Endorsement of Forest Certification (PEFC)—and 45% of the UK's forests are certified (Forestry Commission 2009d). In addition, all wood currently produced from Forestry Commission land in Britain, and from Forestry Service land in Northern Ireland, as well as around 70% of wood from non-Forestry Commission/Forestry Service land, is certified as meeting sustainable forest management criteria.

The UKWAS is a voluntary certification standard that can be used by independent certification organisations, such as FSC and PEFC, for the certification of UK woodlands. The certification standard has eight sections that deal with different aspects of woodland management: compliance with the law and conformance with the requirements of the certification standard; management planning; woodland design (creation, felling and replanting); operations; protection and maintenance; conservation and enhancement of biodiversity; the community; and forestry workforce. The standard sets out a number of requirements (criteria) in each of the eight aspects of woodland management, and suggests means of verifying (indicators) that the requirements have been met.

Although its eight sections do not map exactly on to the nine elements identified in the UK Forestry Standard, UKWAS is "designed to ensure that it reflects the requirements of the Government's UK Forestry Standard" (UKWAS 2008). UKWAS emphasises the operational aspects of sustainable woodland management, which is helpful for woodland owners and managers. Thus, rather than identifying landscape, water, climate change and soils as distinct elements of sustainable woodland management (as is done in the UK Forestry Standard), UKWAS includes them in guidance on management planning, woodland design and operations. UKWAS claims that its process attracts international interest from countries setting up their own national processes, and that this is a measure of its success. But it is not clear if the process has resulted in improved woodland management, nor whether certified woodlands are any better managed than the 55% of UK woodlands that are not currently certified.

8.5.5 Implementing Sustainable Forest Management

Innes *et al.* (2009) discuss the scale at which planning for sustainable forest management should take place. Strategic plans should be used for the long-term management of all the forest resources in a large area; this is planning at the catchment- or landscape-scale. Tactical plans, equivalent to forest management plans in the UK, cover a shorter period and focus on the implementation of strategic plans. Operational plans describe what is to be done on small areas in the short-term (one to five years), and are equivalent to the work programmes that form part of many forest management plans in the UK. It is important that the different levels of plan are consistent with each other, and problems can arise if they are drawn up by different individuals or organisations. In the UK, tactical plans (forest management plans) and operational plans (work programmes) are usually prepared by the same person (the forest manager or planner), while strategic plans are normally the responsibility of organisations such as local authorities or national park authorities.

Efforts have been made to translate higher-level policies into operational guidelines. But however willing woodland owners and managers may be to deliver the ecosystem services demanded by society, their ability to do so depends on the size and location of their woodlands, and the cost of the management required to provide particular goods and services.

8.5.5.1 Management objectives for woodlands

Owners have different objectives for their woodlands, and different ways of achieving them. The UK Woodland Assurance Standard recognises the diversity of woodland management in the UK, considers this to be valuable in its own right, and acknowledges that owners and managers will decide how best to meet the requirements of the certification standard. Many management objectives are directly related to ecosystem services (e.g. timber production is a provisioning service, recreation is a cultural service and biodiversity is a supporting service), but few, if any, woodland owners and managers think in terms of ecosystem services when setting objectives.

Many authors, such as Bell and Apostol (2008), have suggested that the mix of goods and services that a forest provides should be a matter of negotiation between the forest owner and the local community, and should also take account of wider interests in forests. But who pays the management costs of delivering such negotiated goods and services? Owners can receive revenue from the sale of goods (provisioning services) and sometimes from recreation (cultural services), and these may offset or exceed management costs. At the present time, payments are not made to owners who are providing supporting or regulating ecosystem services from their forests (Valatin 2010).

8.5.5.2 Size of woodland management units

Small (less than 10 ha), individual woodlands can make an important contribution to the delivery of ecosystem services at the larger, landscape-scale. Yet, the owners of small woodlands will often only have a very limited number of objectives.

Larger woodlands (several hundred hectares) can deliver more services, and the owners of larger woodlands will normally have several objectives. The current edition of the UK Forestry Standard warns that "[while] compromise is accepted as necessary in these circumstances, loss of potential benefits through neglect or mismanagement must be avoided" (Forestry Commission 2004). More than half (55%) of the UK's forests are multipurpose and managed for more than one objective, but how do owners ensure that there is no "loss of potential benefits" from their forests? If the forest is in single ownership, it may be possible to divide it into a number of zones, concentrating different activities (e.g. recreation, intensive timber production) in different zones. This is a straightforward way of ensuring that multiple objectives are achieved, but it may not optimise the delivery of ecosystem services, and may not be a practical option for every woodland.

At the landscape-scale, woodlands may cover several thousand hectares and could, in theory, deliver the full range of ecosystem services. However, the problem of optimising the delivery of ecosystem services is the same as for a large woodland block, and is compounded by the fact that the woodlands are likely to be in different ownerships, with owners who may have different objectives.

8.5.5.3 Management plans

The importance of management plans is recognised in both the UK Forestry Standard and the UKWAS. Only half of UK woodlands currently have a management plan; increasing the coverage of management plans is central to sustainable forest management and the delivery of ecosystem services.

In Wales, the Better Woodlands for Wales scheme paid grants for activities against an approved 20-year management plan that identified the main features of the woodland; the features were chosen from a list, some of which were clearly ecosystem services. In the plan, the desired characteristics were listed, current and target levels of each desired characteristic were stated, and the monitoring of progress towards target levels was explained. This approach allowed managers to identify management conflicts and complementarities, and consider ways of resolving them or arriving at compromises. The scheme closed at the end of 2010, after only five years of operation. This illustrates the wider problem of forestry policies changing more rapidly than management plans can be implemented, resulting in a lack of continuity and a potential waste of public funds.

8.5.5.4 Silviculture

Achieving most (though not all) of the objectives of forest management requires the use of silviculture. Indeed, silviculture can be defined as the manipulation of forest stands to accomplish a specified set of objectives (Lorimer 1982). Operational forest plans (work programmes) are largely concerned with silviculture and the application of silvicultural treatments such as thinning, pruning, site preparation, planting/direct-seeding, establishment and protection. Silvicultural treatments can be organised into planned, long-term programmes for tending, protecting, harvesting and regenerating forest stands; these are 'silvicultural systems' (Matthews 1991; Smith et al. 1997). In some respects these systems are stylised ideals, but the concept provides a useful framework for thinking about long-term management at the level of the individual stand.

The silvicultural system used for a stand determines its age structure and (through the methods of harvesting and regeneration) species composition, which both influence the ecosystem services that can be provided from the stand. In the last decade, there has been considerable interest in moving away from clear-cutting, the most common silvicultural system in the UK, to alternatives such as shelter-wood and selection systems. This is expected to have a positive impact on the delivery of ecosystem services such as soil protection, flood and water protection, carbon sequestration and the character of the wider landscape, although internal landscapes may be negatively affected. There are particular challenges in developing systems that permit the transformation of forests from plantations to more diverse structures (Mason 2006).

8.5.6 Future Developments to Enhance the Provision of Ecosystem Services

The MCPFE concept of sustainable forest management is useful at a national level, but cannot be achieved at the woodland level in the UK. Here, as elsewhere in the world, the majority of individual woodlands fulfil only a proportion of the requirements of sustainable forest management (Innes et al. 2009). Bell and Apostol (2008) question whether criteria, indicators, standards and guidelines really help responsible forest owners and managers to do what they are trying to do: sustain the forest's capacity to deliver goods and services, and meet the needs of future generations. What else can be done to help these people enhance the ecosystem services provided by the UK's forests and woodlands?

Multi-criteria decision analysis is a technique used by decision-makers for evaluating alternative courses of action in situations where there are conflicts. Because it incorporates the preferences of the decision-maker, it is a subjective method, but it has potential for optimising the delivery of ecosystem services from woodlands at national or regional level.

At woodland level, owners and managers need *decision support tools* to help them choose between alternative, and perhaps conflicting, management options. Several decision support tools are already available such as the wind risk model ForestGALES (Gardiner *et al.* 2004), the Ecological Site Classification (Pyatt *et al.* 2001) and a knowledge management system for habitats and species HARPPS (Ray & Broome 2007). So far, these are mainly implemented at site or stand level, rather than woodland level, not least because of the lack of appropriate digital soil data.

Payments for ecosystem services may encourage and enable owners to manage their woodlands to deliver services that currently have little or no financial value. Public payment schemes and both regulatory and voluntary markets for ecosystem services exist in a number of countries and natural resource sectors (Perrot-Maître 2006; Richards & Jenkins 2007; Jack *et al.* 2008; Turpie *et al.* 2008), and these should be explored for the forestry sector in the UK.

Adaptive management, in which the effects of different management options are tested either experimentally or by modelling, can be particularly valuable at times of change or uncertainty. Experimental testing of options is problematic in forest management, given the timescale on which forestry operates, but there is scope for learning from implementation. However, in addition, a modelling approach has considerable potential for examining the effects of management on the flows of ecosystem services from forests, and for ensuring that these flows are maintained under future climates (Innes *et al.* 2009).

8.5.7 Kielder Forest: a Case Study of Changing Objectives and Adaptive Management

The parallel evolution of growing forests, changing policies, developing markets, and shifting societal demands, has been an underlying theme of this chapter. The integration of these to shape the development of a forest and its services is exemplified by this case study of Kielder Forest.

Covering some 50,000 ha, Kielder Forest in Northumberland in northern England is one of the largest man-made forests in Europe (McIntosh 1995). Over the past 80 years, Kielder has been at the forefront of delivering forest ecosystem services in response to changing economic demands, public aspirations and government policies relating to the environment. A summary of the changes in importance over time of the various ecosystem services is shown in **Table 8.15**.

Afforestation began in 1926 and continued into the 1980s with a focus on raw timber as the primary provisioning services (**Table 8.15**). At first, a mix of non-native conifer species were planted, including Sitka spruce, Norway spruce, and Scots and lodgepole pine, but over time the superior growth rate of Sitka spruce was recognised and used to a such a degree that it currently comprises 72% of the forest (McIntosh 1995).

In the early part of the 20th Century, state forestry policy was largely focused on creating a strategic timber reserve and providing rural employment (Edlin 1952; McIntosh 1995). In Kielder, this led to the establishment of a village to house forestry workers (with pre-chainsaw predictions of the community developing from tens to hundreds of workers) and a large-scale planting programme. Timber production remains one of the key ecosystem services provided by

Table 8.15 Changes over time in the delivery of different ecosystem services over time at Kielder Forest.
- no delivery; -/+ some delivery but not significant; + delivery; ++ significant delivery; +++ very significant delivery.

Ecosystem service category	Main services	Time periods			
		1920–1960	1960–1980	1980–1995	1995–2010
Provisioning services	Food	-	-	-/+	-/+
	Freshwater	-	-/+	+++	++
	Wood, fibre, employment	+++	+++	++	++
	Fuel	-/+	-/+	-/+	+
Regulating services	Climate regulation	-	-	-	++
	Flood regulation	-	-	+	+
	Disease regulation	-	-	-	-
	Water purification	-	-	+	+
Cultural services	Aesthetic	-	++	+++	+++
	Spiritual	-	-/+	++	++
	Educational	+	+	++	++
	Recreational	-	++	+++	+++
Supporting services	Biodiversity	-	-/+	++	+++
	Soil formation and nutrient cycling	+	+	+	+

Figure 8.11 Kielder Forest showing its patchwork of forest stands of different ages, rides, open habitats, and felled areas.
Source: Forestry Commission Kielder Forest District derived from IKONOS 2004 imagery.

Kielder Forest, yielding approximately 1,400 tonnes of timber a day on a sustainable basis and providing the UK with 5% of its softwood requirements (GPFLR 2001).

By the 1960s, public dislike of large, even-aged blocks of conifer woodland initiated action to visually 'soften' forest edges, ensure that areas of new planting were designed to be in-keeping with the landscape, and create a more aesthetically pleasing experience for the visitor (**Table 8.15**). From 1974 to 1980, over 400 ha of forest were cleared to make

way for the establishment of the Kielder Water reservoir. Together with an improved road network, the creation of this resource had a significant impact on recreational use of the forest; today, over half a million visitors make use of the forest for sight-seeing, cycling, horse riding and other outdoor pursuits (GPFLR 2001). The forest also continues to have a role, albeit a minor one, in regulating, water quality and quantity in the Kielder Water catchment area (Dunn & Mackay 1995).

In the early 1980s, it became clear that biophysical constraints of the Kielder Forest area placed a significant restriction on tree growth. In particular, shallow, wet soils and high exposure combine to increase the risk of windthrow, so that stands rarely survive beyond 50 years of age (McIntosh 1995; Mason & Quine 1995). A programme of restructuring to create a more diverse and mixed-aged forest was initiated, not only to address the problem of windthrow, but to ensure a more sustainable timber supply over the longer-term and to enhance recreation, visual impact and biodiversity (Hibberd 1985). Today, the forest landscape is made up of a patchwork of different types and age of forest stand, open space and rides (**Figure 8.11**). By the 1990s, the value of the forest for wildlife conservation and biodiversity was being increasingly recognised (Petty et al. 1995). A wide range of habitats are provided for species groups such as raptors (Petty et al. 1995), songbirds (Patterson et al. 1995; Fuller & Browne 2003), plants, fungi and invertebrates (Butterfield et al. 1995; Humphrey et al. 2003). Today, amongst general objectives for increasing habitat and species diversity, there is a special focus on the restoration and management of mire habitats (Smith et al. 1995) and the protection and enhancement of red squirrel populations (Lurz et al. 1995). In the Strategy for England's Woods, Trees and Forests (Forestry Commission 2007c) there is specific mention of the forests of the north-east as having key strategic importance in sustaining England's red squirrel population. The strategy also reflects a sharpening of government forestry policy with respect to ecosystem services. In the 1990s, the Forestry Commission was charged with managing the public forest estate for 'public benefits' (Forestry Commission 1993), and now those benefits are more specifically articulated and costed (Forestry Commission 2007c).

Three recent developments in government policy have also initiated a shift in emphasis for forest management: The Climate Change Act; the Renewable Energy Strategy and the implementation of the EU WFD. Not only do forests need to protect and enhance environmental resources of water, soil, air, biodiversity and landscapes, they also have a role in mitigating the impact of climate change, and promoting new and improved markets for sustainable wood products such as wood fuel (**Table 8.11**). Translation of policy objectives into practice is achieved through forest design planning. The forest area is divided into management units ranging from 1,000–10,000 ha and felling and restocking plans drawn-up in relation to strategic objectives (Graham Gill pers. comm.). The planning process allows a range of environmental, social, and economic priorities to be considered at the appropriate spatial scale, and a number of computer-based decision support tools are available to help determine management priorities. These include site evaluation tools, such as Ecological Site Classification (Pyatt et al. 2001), and ForestGALES (Gardiner et al. 2004), as well as tools for modelling ecological connectivity and biodiversity enhancement, such as BEETLE (Watts et al. 2007). Research is also beginning to make available tools for assessing the sustainability of whole forest-wood-chains ([FWC] i.e. from forest to wood product), which allows modelling and evaluation of the impacts of different management options on the provision of ecosystem services throughout the chain (Lindner et al. 2009). In the future, Kielder Forest is likely to provide an important test area for how effectively the forest industry can continue to deliver a mix of ecosystem services in response to evolving environmental and policy drivers.

8.6 Future Research and Monitoring Gaps

Identification of gaps in data, knowledge and understanding is a benefit of the integration of knowledge stimulated by the UK NEA. The following are amongst the key areas that require further investigation as shown by the material drawn together for this chapter.

8.6.1 Climate Change and Other Threats

- Development and monitoring of approaches to adaptation to climate change in forest management;
- Understanding the interaction of climate change and some forms of service delivery; meeting the challenges of perpetuation of cherished species and habitats;
- Effective management and control of new/emerging pests and diseases, and established (expanding) populations of deer and grey squirrels.

8.6.2 Valuation

- Methods of monetising or finding ways of comparing the value of different services;
- Comparison of marginal versus absolute benefits of changing extent or management of woods;
- Improved understanding of differences in marginal values between regions, between different woodlands types and forestry management approaches;
- An accepted approach to apportioning forestry establishment and management costs between the provision of different ecosystem services.

8.6.3 Condition

- Comprehensive data on the extent and condition (including components of supporting services) of the broad habitat, in particular, native woodland/semi-natural woodland;
- The status and trends of novel woodland habitats and improved biodiversity monitoring of plantation forests.

8.6.4 Integrated Land Use and Landscape-scale Action

- Planning methods and incentivisation of owners to achieve landscape-scale action across large spatial scales (e.g. catchments);
- Promotion and monitoring of changing, landscape-scale impact of new woodland and tree cover.

References

Amar, A., Hewson, C.M., Thewlis, R.M., Smith, K.W., Fuller, R.J., Lindsell, J.A., Conway, G., Butler, S. & MacDonald, M.A. (2006) What's happening to our woodland birds? Long-term changes in the populations of woodland birds. RSPB and BTO, Sandy and Thetford.

Amar, A., Smith, K.W., Butler, S., Lindsell, J.A., Hewson, C.M., Fuller, R.J. & Charman, E.C. (2010) Recent patterns of change in vegetation structure and tree composition of British broadleaved woodland: evidence from large-scale surveys. *Forestry,* **83**, 345–356.

Anon (2009) National Forest Company annual report and accounts 2008–09. The Stationery Office, London.

Asher, J., Warren, M., Fox, R., Harding, P., Jeffcoate, G. & Jeffcoate, S. (2001) The Millennium Atlas of Butterflies in Britain and Ireland. Oxford University Press, Oxford.

Avery, M.I. (1989) Effects of upland afforestation on some birds of the adjacent moorland. *Journal of Applied Ecology,* **26**, 957–966.

Bailey, S-A., (2007) Increasing connectivity in fragmented landscapes: an investigation of evidence for biodiversity gain in woodlands. *Forest Ecology and Management,* **338**, 7–23.

Baillie, S.R., Marchant, J.H., Leech, D.I., Joys, A.C., Noble, D.G., Barimore, C., Grantham, M.J., Risely, K. & Robinson, R.A. (2009) Breeding Birds in the Wider Countryside: their conservation status 2008. BTO Research Report No. 516. BTO, Thetford. [online] Available at: <http://www.bto.org/birdtrends> [Accessed 17.01.11].

Ball, D.F. & Stevens, P.A. (1981) The role of ancient woodlands in conserving undisturbed soils in Britain. *Biological Conservation,* **19**, 163–176.

Barbatti, A., Corona, P. & Marchetti, M. (2007) European forest types: categories and types for sustainable forest management reporting and policy. EEA Technical Report No 9/2006. European Environment Agency, Copenhagen.

Bateman, I., & Mellor, C. (1990) The UK Timber market: an econometric model. *Oxford Agrarian Studies,* **18**, 53–61.

Bateman, I.J., Lovett, A.A. & Brainard, J.S. (2003) Applied Environmental Economics: a GIS Approach to Cost-Benefit Analysis. Cambridge University Press, Cambridge.

Battersby, J. (2005) UK Mammals: Species Status and Population Trends, JNCC/Tracking Mammals Partnership 2005, ISBN 1 86107 568 5. [online] Available at:< http://www.jncc.gov.uk/page-3311#download> [Accessed 17.01.11].

Bell, S., (ed) (2003) The potential of applied landscape design to forest design planning. Forestry Commission, Edinburgh.

Bell, S. & Apostol, D. (2008) Designing sustainable forest landscapes. Taylor and Francis, London.

Bignal, K., Ashmore, M. & Power, S. (2004) Ecological effects of diffuse air pollution from road transport. English Nature Research Report 580. English Nature, Peterborough.

Bills, D. (2001) The UK Government and certification. *International Forestry Review,* **3**, 323–326.

Binns, W.O., Redfern, D.B., Rennolls, K. & Betts, A.J.A. (1985). Forest health and air pollution: 1984 survey. Research and Development Paper 142. Forestry Commission, Edinburgh.

Biodiversity Action Reporting System (2008) [Online] Available at: <http://www.ukbap-reporting.org.uk/> [Accessed 20.02.11].

Birks, H.J.B. (1988) Long term ecological change in the British uplands. Ecological Change in the Uplands (eds M.B. Usher & D.B.A. Thompson), pp 37–56. Blackwell Scientific Publications, Oxford.

Blatchford, O.N. (ed) (1978) Forestry Practice. Forestry Commission Bulletin 14. HMSO, London.

Braithwaite, M.E., Ellis, R.W. & Preston, C.D. (2006) Change in the British flora 1987–2004. BSBI, London.

Brasier, C.M. & Webber, J.F. (2010). Sudden larch death. *Nature,* **466**, 824–825.

Brasier, C.M. (2008) The biosecurity threat to the UK and global environment from international trade in plants. *Plant Pathology,* **57**, 792–808.

Bright, P.W. & Halliwell, E.C. (1999) Species recovery programme for the pine marten in England, 1996–1998. English Nature Research Report N. 306. English Nature, Peterborough.

Britton, A.J., Beale, C.M., Towers, W. & Hewison, R.L. (2009) Biodiversity gains and losses: evidence for homogenisation of Scottish alpine vegetation. *Biological Conservation,* **142**, 1728–1739.

Broadmeadow, M.S.J., Webber, J.F., Ray, D. & Berry, P.M. (2009) An assessment of the likely future impacts of climate change on UK forests. Combating climate change—a role for UK forests (eds D.J. Read, P.H. Freer-Smith, J.I.L. Morison, N. Hanley, C.C. West & P.R. Snowdon) pp. 67–98. The Stationery Office, Edinburgh.

Broadmeadow, M. & Matthews, R. (2003) Forests, carbon and climate change. Forestry Commission Information Note 48. Forestry Commission, Edinburgh.

Broadmeadow, M. & Ray, D. (2005) Climate change and British woodland. Forestry Commission Information Note 69. Forestry Commission, Edinburgh.

Brown, A. & Webber, J. (2008) Red band needle blight of conifers in Britain. Research Note 002, Forestry Commission, Edinburgh.

Buckley, G.P. (1992) Ecology and management of coppice woodland. Chapman and Hall, London.

Burdekin, D.A. (1983). Research on Dutch elm disease in Europe. Forestry Commission Bulletin 60, HMSO, London.

Butterfield, J., Luff, M., Baines, M. & Eyre, M.D. (1995) Carabid beetle communities as indicators of conservation potential in upland forests. *Forest Ecology and Management,* **79**, 63–78.

Calder, I.R., Harrison, J., Nisbet, T.R. & Smithers, R.J. (2008) Woodland actions for biodiversity and their role in water management. Woodland Trust, Grantham.

Campos, J.J., Alpízar, F., Louman, B. & Parrotta, J. (2005) An integrated approach to forest ecosystem services. Forests in the Global Balance: Changing Paradigms (eds G. Mery, R. Alfaro, M. Kanninen & M. Lobovikov), pp. 97–116. IUFRO World Series, vol. 17, Helsinki.

Cannell, M. (2002) Impacts of climate change on forest growth. Climate change: impacts on UK forests. (ed M. Broadmeadow), Bulletin 125. Forestry Commission, Edinburgh.

Carey, P.D., Wallis, S., Chamberlain, P.M., Cooper, A., Emmett, B.A., Maskell, L.C., McCann, T., Murphy, J., Norton, L.R., Reynolds, B., Scott, W.A., Simpson, I.C., Smart, S.M., Ullyett, J.M.

(2008) Countryside Survey: UK Results from 2007. NERC/Centre for Ecology & Hydrology, 105pp. (CEH Project Number: C03259).

Chavarriaga, D., Bodles, W.J.A., Leifert, C., Belbahri, L. & Woodward, S. (2007) Phytophthora cinnamomi and other fine root pathogens in north temperate pine forests. *Microbiology Letters,* **276**, 67–74.

Chesterton, C. (2009) Management for lowland gamebirds. Environmental impacts of land management, (Natural England) pp. 100–109. Natural England Research Report 30, Peterborough. [online] Available at: <http://naturalengland.etraderstores.com/NaturalEnglandShop/product.aspx?ProductID=4e8af97d-83cc-4720-87e5-d9ce614f5def> [Accessed 17.01.11].

CJC Consulting (2005) Review of evidence for the formulation of forestry policy in England. Unpublished report for Defra, London.

Corbett, G.B. & Yalden, D.W. (2001) Mammals. The changing wildlife of Great Britain and Ireland (ed. D.L. Hawksworth), pp. 399–409. Taylor and Francis, London & New York.

Costanza, R. (2008) Ecosystem services: multiple classification systems are needed. *Biological Conservation,* **141**, 350–352.

Crow, P. (2004) Managing the historic environment in woodland: the vital role of research. In Forest Research Annual Report and Accounts 2002–2003. Forest Research, Farnham, pp 46–55.

de Groot, R.S., Wilson, M.A. & Boumans, R.M.J. (2002) A typology for the classification, description and valuation of ecosystem functions, goods and services. *Ecological Economics,* **41**, 393–408.

Deakin, R. (2007) *Wildwood: a journey through trees.* Hamish Hamilton, London.

DECC (Department of Energy and Climate Change) (2010) Valuation of energy use and greenhouse gas emissions for appraisal and evaluation, Department of Energy and Climate Change, London. [online] Available at: <http://www.decc.gov.uk/en/content/cms/statistics/analysts_group/analysts_group.aspx> [Accessed 17.01.11].

Defra (Department for Environment, Food and Rural Affairs) & Forestry Commission (2005) Keepers of time: a statement of policy for England's ancient and native woods, Bristol and Cambridge. [online] Available at: <www.forestry.gov.uk/pdf/anw-policy.pdf/$FILE/anw-policy.pdf> [Accessed 17.01.11].

Defra (Department for Environment, Food and Rural Affairs) (2007) Securing a healthy natural environment: An action plan for embedding an ecosystems approach. Defra, London.

Defra (Department for Environment, Food and Rural Affairs) (2009a) Wild bird populations 2008. Defra, London.

Defra (Department for Environment, Food and Rural Affairs) (2009b) Safeguarding our soils—a strategy for England. Defra, London.

Denman, S. & Webber, J.F. (2009) Oak declines. New definitions and new episodes in Britain. *Quarterly Journal of Forestry,* **103**, 285–290.

Denman, S., Kirk, S. & Webber, J. (2010) Managing acute oak decline. Practice Note 15. Forestry Commission, Edinburgh.

Devoto, M., Bailey, S. & Memmott, J. (2011) The 'night shift': nocturnal pollen-transport networks in a boreal pine forest. *Ecological Entomology,* **36**, 25–35.

Dimbleby, G.W. (1962) The development of British heathlands and their soils. Oxford Forestry Memoirs, 23, pp. 121. Oxford.

Dolan, A.G. & Russell, B.P. (1988) Economic report of private forestry: England and Wales income and expenditure, Twentieth report. Oxford Forestry Institute, Oxford.

Draycott, R.A.H., Hoodless, A.N. & Sage, R.B. (2008) Effects of pheasant management on vegetation and birds in lowland woods. *Journal of Applied Ecology,* **45**, 334–341.

Duggan, J. (2005) The potential for landfill leachate treatment using willows in the UK—A critical review. *Resources, Conservation and Recycling,* **45**, 97–113.

Dunn, S.M. & Mackay, R. (1995) Spatial variation in evapotranspiration and the influence of land use on catchment hydrology. *Journal of Hydrology,* **171**, 49–73.

Dyson, K.E., Thomson, A.M., Mobbs, D.C., Milne, R., Skiba, U., Clark, A., Levy, P.E., Jones, S.K., Billett, M.F., Dinsmore, K.J., van Oijen, M., Ostle, N., Foeried, B., Smith, P., Matthews, R.W., Mackie, E., Bellamy, P., Rivas-Casado, M., Jordan, C., Higgins, A., Tomlinson, R.W., Grace, J., Parrish, P., Williams, M., Clement, R., Moncrieff, J. & Manning, A. (2009) Inventory and projections of UK emissions by sources and removals by sinks due to land use, land use change and forestry. Annual report, CEH, Edinburgh. [online] Available at: <www.edinburgh.ceh.ac.uk/ukcarbon/docs/2009/Defra_Report_2009.pdf> [Accessed 17.01.11].

ECCM (2006) Forestry Commission Scotland greenhouse gas emissions comparison—carbon benefits of timber in construction. Edinburgh Centre for Carbon Management Report ECCM-EM-196-2006.

EEA (European Environment Agency) (2005) EEA Core Set of Indicators. Technical Report 1/2005. [online] Available at: <http://www.eea.europa.eu/publications/technical_report_2005_1> [Accessed 17.01.11].

EEA (European Environment Agency) (2009) Progress towards the European 2010 biodiversity target. Pp. 52. ISBN 978-92-9167-993-5. EEA, Copenhagen. [online] Available at: <http://biodiversity-chm.eea.europa.eu/information/indicator/F1090245995> [Accessed: 17.01.11].

Edlin, H.L. (1952) Britain's new forest villages. *Unasylva,* **6** (4). [online] Available at: <http://www.fao.org/docrep/x5365e/x5365e02.htm> [Accessed 17.01.11].

Edlin, H.L. (ed) (1964) Forestry Practice. 8th edition. Forestry Commission Bulletin 14, HMSO, London.

Edwards, D., Elliott, A., Hislop, M., Martin, S., Morris, J., O'Brien, L., Peace, A., Sarajevs, V., Serrand, M. & Valatin, G. (2009) A valuation of the economic and social contribution of forestry for people in Scotland. Forestry Commission Research Report. Pp. 190, Forestry Commission Scotland, Edinburgh.

Eglington, S. & Noble, D. (2010) Final Report for 2009 on the Scottish Woodland Breeding Bird Surveys. BTO, Thetford.

Emery, M., Martin, S. & Dyke, A. (2006) Wild harvests from Scottish woodlands: social, cultural and economic values of contemporary non-timber forest products. Forestry Commission, Edinburgh.

English Heritage (2010) Heritage Counts 2010. [online] Available at: <http://hc.english-heritage.org.uk/content/pub/HC-Eng-2010> [Accessed 17.01.11].

English Nature (2002) Revealing the value of nature. English Nature, Peterborough.

Evans, J. (1988) Natural regeneration of broadleaves. Forestry Commission Bulletin 78. HMSO, London.

FAO (Food and Agriculture Organization) (1993) The Challenge of Sustainable Forest Management. FAO, Rome.

FAO (Food and Agriculture Organization) (2005) Global Forest Resources Assessment 2005. FAO, Rome.

FAO (Food and Agriculture Organization) (2010) Global Forest Resources Assessment 2010. FAO, Rome.

Feest, A., Timothy D. Aldred, T.D & Jedamzik, K. (2010) Biodiversity quality: A paradigm for biodiversity. *Ecological Indicators*, **10**, 1077–1082.

Fisher, R.F. & Binkley, D. (2000) Ecology and management of forest soils. John Wiley and Sons, New York.

Foot, D. (2010) Woods and people: putting forests on the map. The History Press, Stroud.

Forestry Commission (1933) Forestry Practice. 1st edition. Forestry Commission Bulletin 14, HMSO, London.

Forestry Commission (1985) The Policy for Broadleaved Woodland. Forestry Commission, Edinburgh.

Forestry Commission (1993) Forest Enterprise Corporate Agenda 1993–94. Forestry Commission, Edinburgh.

Forestry Commission (2002) UK Indicators of Sustainable Forestry. Forestry Commission, Edinburgh.

Forestry Commission (2003a) National Inventory of Woodlands and Trees. Great Britain. Forestry Commission, Edinburgh.

Forestry Commission (2003b) The Forests and Water guidelines. (Fourth edition). Forestry Commission, Edinburgh.

Forestry Commission (2004) The UK Forestry Standard: the government's approach to sustainable forestry. Second edition. Forestry Commission, Edinburgh.

Forestry Commission (2007a) A wood-fuel strategy for England. Forestry Commission, Edinburgh.

Forestry Commission (2007b) Environmental impact assessments of forestry projects. Forestry Commission, Edinburgh. [online] Available at: <http://www.forestry.gov.uk/pdf/wgseia.pdf/$FILE/wgseia.pdf> [Accessed 17.01.11].

Forestry Commission (2007c) Strategy for England's Woods Trees and Forests. Forestry Commission England, Cambridge.

Forestry Commission (2009a) Forestry Statistics 2009. [online] Available at: <http://www.forestry.gov.uk/pdf/ForestryStatistics2009.pdf/$FILE/ForestryStatistics2009.pdf> [Accessed 17.01.11].

Forestry Commission (2009b) Public opinion of forestry, 2009, UK. Forestry Commission, Edinburgh.

Forestry Commission (2009c) The UK Forestry Standard: Consultation Draft July 2009. Forestry Commission, Edinburgh

Forestry Commission (2009d) Forestry Facts & Figures 2009. Forestry Commission, Edinburgh.

Forestry Commission (2009e) Time series data for wood production (roundwood removals) for 1976 to 2009. [online] Available at: <http://www.forestry.gov.uk/forestry/infd-7aql5b> [Accessed 01.02.11].

Forestry Commission (2010a) Open habitats Policy: when to convert woods and forests to open habitat in England: Government policy. Forestry Commission England, Bristol. [online] Available at: <http://www.forestry.gov.uk/forestry/INFD-7FCH5D> [Accessed 17.01.11].

Forestry Commission (2010b) State of Europe's Forests 2011—UK report. Forestry Commission, Edinburgh. [online] Available at: <http://www.interpretscotland.org.uk/forestry/infd-86hchq>. [Accessed 01.02.11].

Forestry Commission (2010c) Timber Price Indices: Date to September 2010. Forestry Commission, Edinburgh. [online] <http://www.forestry.gov.uk/forestry/infd-8asdz9> [Accessed 20.02.11].

Forestry Commission (in press a) Forests and soils guidelines. Forestry Commission, Edinburgh.

Forestry Commission (in press b) Forests and landscape guidelines. Forestry Commission, Edinburgh.

Forestry Commission (in press c) UKFS Historic Environment Guidelines. Forestry Commission, Edinburgh.

Fox, R., Conrad, K.F., Parsons, M.S., Warren, M.S. & Woiwod, I.P. (2006) The state of Britain's larger moths. Butterfly Conservation/Rothamsted Research, Wareham, Dorset.

Freer-Smith, P.H., Broadmeadow, M.S.J. & Lynch, J.M. (2007) Forests and climate change: the knowledge base for action. Forestry and climate change (eds P.H. Freer-Smith, M.S.J. Broadmeadow & J.M. Lynch). CABI, Wallingford.

Frelich, L.E. (2002) Forest dynamics and disturbance regimes: studies from temperate evergreen-deciduous forests, Cambridge University Press, Cambridge.

Fuller, R. & Browne, S. (2003) Effects of plantation structure and management on birds. Biodiversity in Britain's planted forests. Results from the Forestry Commission's biodiversity assessment project. (eds J.W. Humphrey, R. Ferris & C.P. Quine), pp. 93–99. Forestry Commission, Edinburgh.

Fuller, R.J. & Gill, R.M.A. (2001) Ecological impacts of deer in British woodland. *Forestry*, **74**, 193–299.

Gardiner, B., Suarez, J., Achim, A., Hale, S. & Nichol, B. (2004) ForestGALES. A PC-based wind risk model for British forests. Version 2.0. Forestry Commission, Edinburgh.

Gardiner, B.A., Palmer, H. & Hislop, A.M. (2006) The principles of using wood for shelter. Information Note 81, Forestry Commission, Edinburgh.

Garrod, G.D. & Willis, K.G. (1997) The non-use benefits of enhancing forest biodiversity: A contingent ranking study. *Ecological Economics,* **21**, pp.45–61.

Gilbert, M., Fielding, N., Evans, H.F. & Gregoire, J.C. (2003) Spatial pattern of invading *Dendroctonus micans* (Coleoptera: Scolytidae) populations in the United Kingdom. *Canadian Journal of Forest Research*, **33**, 712–725.

Gill, R. (2006) The influence of large herbivores on tree recruitment and forest dynamics. Large Herbivore Ecology and Ecosystem Dynamics (eds K. Danell, R. Bergström, P. Duncan & J. Pastor), pp. 170–202. Cambridge University Press, Cambridge.

Gill, R.M.A. (1992a) A review of damage by mammals in north temperate forests. 1.Deer. *Forestry*, **65**, 145–169.

Gill, R.M.A. (1992b) A review of damage by mammals in north temperate forests. 3. Impact on trees and forests. *Forestry*, **65**, 363–388.

Goldberg, E. (2003) Plantations on ancient woodland sites. *Quarterly Journal of Forestry*, **97**, 133–138.

Goldberg, E.A., Kirby, K.J., Hall, J.E. & Latham, J. (2007) The ancient woodland concept as a practical conservation tool in Great Britain. *Journal of Nature Conservation*, **15**, 109–119.

GPFLR (Global Partnership for Forest Landscape Restoration) (2001) Kielder Forest, United Kingdom. Global Partnership for Forest Landscape Restoration. [online] Available at: <http://www.ideastransformlandscapes.org/about-us/sites/great-britain/> [Accessed 17.01.11].

Gray, N. (1986) Woodland management for pheasants and wildlife. David & Charles, Newton Abbott.

Green, S. & Ray, D. (2009) Potential impacts of drought and disease on forestry in Scotland. Forestry Commission Research Note 004. Forestry Commission, Edinburgh.

Green, S., Studholme, D.J., Laue, B.E., Dorati, F., Lovell, H., Arnold, D., Cottrell, J.E., Bridgett, S., Blaxter, M., Huitema, E., Thwaites, R., Sharp, P.M., Jackson, R.W. & Kamoun, S. (2010) Comparative genome analysis provides insights into the evolution and adaptation of *Pseudomonas syringae* pv. *aesculi* on European horse chestnut. *Public Library of Science ONE* **5**(4), e10224. i:10.1371/journal.pone.0010224

Gregory, S.C. & Redfern, D.B. (1998) *Diseases and disorders of forest trees*. Forestry Commission Field Book 16. The Stationery Office, London.

Haines-Young, R., Firbank, L., Furse, M., McGowan, G. & Petit, S. (2003) Changing landscapes, habitats and vegetation diversity across Great Britain using Countryside Survey. *Journal of Environmental Management*, **67**, 267–281.

Hambler, C. & Speight, M.R. (1995) Biodiversity conservation in Britain: science replacing tradition. *British Wildlife*, **6**, 137–147.

Hancock, M.H., Summers R.W., Amphlett, A. & Willi, J. (2009) Testing prescribed fire as a tool to promote *Pinus sylvestris* regeneration. *European Journal of Forest Research*, **128**, 319–333.

Handley, J.F. & Gill, S.E. (2009) Woodlands helping society to adapt. Combating climate change—a role for UK forests (eds D.J. Read, P.H. Freer-Smith, J.I.L. Morison, N. Hanley, C.C. West & P.R. Snowdon), pp. 180–195. The Stationery Office, Edinburgh.

Harmer, R. & A. Kiewitt. (2007) Restoration of PAWS, testing some of the advice. *Quarterly Journal of Forestry*, **101**, 213–218.

Harmer, R., Kerr, G. & Thompson, R. (2010) Broadleaved woodland management. Forestry Commission, Edinburgh.

Hendry, S.J., Poole, E.J., Craig, I. & Proudfoot, J.C. (2005) Forest condition 2004. Forestry Commission Information Note 75. Forestry Commission, Edinburgh.

Hester, A.J., Gimingham, C.H. & Miles, J. (1991a) Succession from heather moorland to birch woodland. III. Seed availability, germination and early growth. *Journal of Ecology*, **79**, 329–344.

Hester, A.J., Miles, J. & Gimingham, C.H. (1991b) Succession from heather moorland to birch woodland. I. Experimental alteration of specific environmental conditions in the field. *Journal of Ecology*, **79**, 303–315.

Hester, A.J., Miles, J. & Gimingham, C.H. (1991c) Succession from heather moorland to birch woodland. II. Growth and competition between *Vaccinium myrtillus, Deschampsia flexuosa* and *Agrostis capillaris. Journal of Ecology*, **79**, 317–328.

Hester, A.J., Kirby, K.J., Mitchell, F.J.G., Gill, R., Latham, J. & Armstrong, H. (1998) Ungulates and forest management in the British Isles. Grazing as a management tool in European forest ecosystems (eds J.W. Humphrey, R.M. Gill & J. Claridge), pp. 25–36. Forestry Commission Technical Paper 25. Forestry Commission, Edinburgh.

Hester, A.J. & Brooker, R.J. (2007) Threatened habitats: marginal vegetation in upland areas. Biodiversity Under Threat (eds R.E. Hester & R.M. Harrison), pp. 107–134. IEST Vol. 25. RSC Publishing, Cambridge.

Hewson, C.M. & Noble, D.G. (2009) Population trends of breeding birds in British woodlands over a 32-year period:

relationships with food, habitat use and migratory behaviour. *Ibis*, **151**, 464–486.

Hewson, C.M., Amar, A. Lindsell, J.A. Thewlis, R.M., Butler, S., Smith, K. & Fuller, R.J. (2007) Recent changes in bird populations in British broadleaved woodland. *Ibis*, **149**, 14–28.

Hibberd, B.G. (1985) Restructuring of plantations in Kielder Forest District. *Forestry*, **58**, 119–129.

Hibberd, B.G. (ed) (1991) Forestry Practice. 10th edition. Forestry Commission Handbook 6, HMSO, London.

Hicks, B.J., Barbour, D.A., Evans, H.F., Heritage, S.G., Leather, S.R., Milne, R. & Watt, A.D. (2001) The history and control of the pine beauty moth, *Panolis flammea* (D. & S.) (Lepidoptera: Noctuidae), in Scotland from 1976 to 2000. *Agricultural and Forest Entomology*, **3**, 161–168.

Hill, M.O., Mountford, J.O., Roy, D.B. & Bunce, R.G.H. (1999) Ellenbergs' indicator values for British plants. ECOFACT Volume 2, Technical Annex. ITE Monkswood, Huntingdon. London: Department of the Environment, Transport and the Regions.

Hodder, K.H., Bullock, J.M., Buckland, P.C. & Kirby, K.J. (2005) Large herbivores in the wildwood and modern naturalistic grazing systems. Peterborough: English Nature (Research Report 648).

Hodder, K.H., Buckland, P.C., Kirby, K.J. & Bullock, J.M. (2009) Can the pre-Neolithic provide suitable models for re-wilding the landscape in Britain? *British Wildlife*, **20** (supplement), 4–15.

Hohl, R. (1998) Pictures about trees. The Magic of Trees (eds M. Brüderlin, B. Gardi, R. Hohl & C. Kaufmann), pp. 9–20. Fondation Beyeler, Riehen/Basle.

Hopkins, J. & Kirby, K.J. (2007) Ecological change in British broadleaved woodland since 1947. *Ibis*, **149**, 29–40.

Huddart, L. (1990). The use of vegetation for traffic noise screening. Department for Transport, TRL Research Report RR238, Transport Research Laboratory, Crowthorne.

Humphrey, J.W. (2005) Benefits to biodiversity from developing old-growth conditions in British upland spruce plantations: a review and recommendations. *Forestry*, **78**, 33–53.

Humphrey, J.W., Ray, D., Brown, T., Stone, D., Watts, K. & Anderson, A.R. (2009) Using focal species modelling to evaluate the impact of land use change on forest and other habitat networks in western oceanic landscapes. *Forestry*, **82**, 119–134.

Humphrey, J.W., Ferris, R. & Quine, C.P. (eds) (2003) Biodiversity in Britain's planted forests. Results from the Forestry Commission's biodiversity assessment project, pp. 118. Forestry Commission, Edinburgh.

Humphrey, J.W., Holl, K. & Broome, A.C. (1998) Birch in spruce plantations: management for biodiversity. Technical Paper 26, Forestry Commission, Edinburgh.

Humphrey, J.W. & Nixon, C.J. (1999) The restoration of upland oakwoods following the removal of conifers: general principles. *Scottish Forestry*, **53**, 68–76.

Innes, J., Joyce, L.A., Kellomäki, S., Louman, B., Ogden, A., Parrotta, J., Thompson, Ayres, M., Ong, C., Santosa, H., Sohngen, B. & Wreford, A. (2009) Management for adaptation. Adaptation of Forests and People to Climate Change (eds R. Seppälä, A, Buck & P. Katila), pp. 135–185. IUFRO World Series Volume 22, IUFRO, Helsinki.

Insley, H., Harper, W. & Whiteman, A. (1987) Investment appraisal handbook, Forestry Commission, Edinburgh.

Ireland, D., Hall, A. & Jones, D.H. (2004) Woodfuel Information Pack. Forest Research, Farnham.

Jack, B.K., Kousky, C. & Sims, K.R.E. (2008) Designing payments for ecosystem services: lessons from previous experience with incentive-based mechanisms. *Proceedings of the National Academy of Sciences,* **105,** 9465–947.

Jackson, D. (2000) Guidance on the interpretation of the Biodiversity Broad Habitat Classification (terrestrial and freshwater types): Definitions and the relationship with other classifications JNCC Report 307. Peterborough.

Jarvis, P.G., Clement, R.J., Grace, J. & Smith, K.A. (2009) The role of forests in the capture and exchange of energy and greenhouse gases. Combating climate change—a role for UK forests (eds D.J. Read, P.H. Freer-Smith, J.I.L. Morison, N. Hanley, C.C. West & P.R. Snowdon), pp. 21–47. The Stationery Office, Edinburgh.

JNCC (2007) Second Report by the UK under Article 17 on the implementation of the Habitats Directive from January 2001 to December 2006. Peterborough: Joint Nature Conservation Committee. [online] Available at: <http://www.jncc.gov.uk/article17> [Accessed 17.01.11].

Keith, S.A., Newton, A.C., Morecroft, M.D., Bealey, C.E. & Bullock, J.M. (2009) Taxonomic homogenization of woodland plant communities over 70 years. *Proceedings of the Royal Society Series B-Biological Sciences,* **276,** 3539–3544.

Kennedy, F. & Pitman, R. (2004) Factors affecting the nitrogen status of soils and ground flora in Beech woodlands. *Forest Ecology and Management,* **198,** 1–14.

Kirby, K.J. (2003) Woodland conservation in privately-owned cultural landscapes: the English experience. *Environmental Science and Policy,* **6,** 253–259.

Kirby, K.J. (2009) Guidance on dealing with the changing distribution of tree species. Technical Information Note TIN053, Natural England, Sheffield.

Kirby, K.J. & May, J. (1989) The effects of enclosure, conifer planting and the subsequent removal of conifers in Dalavich oakwood (Argyll). *Scottish Forestry,* **43,** 280–288.

Kirby, K.J., Thomas, R.C., Key, R.S., McLean, I.F.G., & Hodgetts, N. (1995) Pasture woodland and its conservation in Britain. *Biological Journal of the Linnean Society,* **56** (b), 135–153.

Kirby, K.J., Reid, C.M., Thomas, R.C. & Goldsmith, F.B. (1998) Preliminary estimates of fallen dead wood and standing dead trees in managed and unmanaged forests in Britain. *Journal of Applied Ecology,* **35,** 148–155.

Kirby, K.J., Latham, J., Holl, K., Bryce, J., Corbett, P. & Watson, R. (2002) Objective setting and condition monitoring within woodland sites of special scientific interest. English Nature (Research Report 472), Peterborough.

Kirby K.J., Smart, S.M., Black, H.I.J., Bunce, R.G.H., Corney, P.M. & Smithers, R.J. (2005) Long term ecological change in British woodland (1971–2001). English Nature (Research Report 653), Peterborough.

Kirby, K.J., Quine, C.P. & Brown, N.D. (2009) The adaptation of UK forests and woodlands to climate change. Combating climate change—a role for UK forests (eds D.J. Read P.H. Freer-Smith J.I.L. Morison N. Hanley C.C. West & P.R. Snowdon) pp. 164–179. The Stationery Office, Edinburgh.

Kirby, K.J., Jefferson, R., Larwood, J., Russell, D., Le Bas, B. & Wright, R. (2010a) What has the SSSI improvement programme achieved for nature conservation in England? *British Wildlife,* **22,** 16–25.

Kirby, K.J., Perry, S.C. & Brodie-James, T. (2010b) Possible implications of new tree diseases for nature conservation. *Quarterly Journal of Forestry.* **104,** 77–84.

Knight, S. (2009) Forest Schools & Outdoor Learning in the Early Years, pp. 144. Sage Publications, London.

Krutilla, J.V. (1967) Conservation reconsidered. *The American Economic Review,* **57,** 777–786.

Latham, J., Miller, H., Mountford, E.P., Kirby, K.J., & Ioras, F. (2005) Country Report—United Kingdom. COST Action E27—Protected Forest Areas in Europe—Analysis and Harmonisation (PROFOR)—Reports of Signatory States (eds J. Latham G. Frank O. Fahy, K. Kirby, H. Miller & R. Stiven), pp. 399–413. BFW, Vienna.

Lawson, G. & Hemery, G.E. (2007) World timber trade and implementing sustainable forest management in the United Kingdom. Report to the Woodland Policy Group.

Lawrence, A., Anglezarke, B., Frost, B., Nolan, P. & Owen, R. (2009) What does community forestry mean in a devolved Great Britain. *International Forestry Review,* **11,** 281–297.

Leonard, R.E. & Parr, S.B. (1970) Trees as a sound barrier. *Journal of Forestry,* **68,** 282–283.

Lindner, M., Suominen, T., Palosuo, T., Garcia-Gonzalo, J., Verweij, P., Zudin, S. & Risto Päivinen, R. (2009) ToSIA—A tool for sustainability impact assessment of forest-wood-chains. *Ecological Modelling,* **221**(18), 2197–2205. [online] Available at: <doi:10.1016/j.ecolmodel.2009.08.006> [Accessed 17.01.11].

Lindsay, R. (2010) Peatbogs and carbon: a critical synthesis. University of East London, London. [online] Available at: <www.uel.ac.uk/erg/PeatandCarbonReport.htm> [Accessed 17.01.11].

Linnard, W. (2000) Welsh Woods and Forests: A History. Gomer Press, Llandysul, Wales.

Lovell, R. (2009) Physical activity at Forest School. Forestry Commission Scotland, Edinburgh.

Lorimer, C. (1982) Silviculture. Introduction to Forest Science (ed R.A. Young) John Wiley & Sons, Chichester.

Lorenz, K. & Lal, R. (2010) Carbon sequestration in forest ecosystems. Springer, Dordrecht.

Lurz, P.W.W., Garson, P.J. & Rushton, S.P. (1995) The ecology of squirrels in spruce dominated plantations: implications for forest management. *Forest Ecology and Management,* **79,** 79–90.

Lynch, J.M. & Moffat, A.J. (2005) Bioremediation—prospects for the future application of innovative applied biological research. *Annals of Applied Biology,* **146,** 217–221.

MA (Millennium Ecosystem Assessment) Ecosystems and Human Well-being: A Framework for Assessment, Island Press, Washington, D.C., 245 pp.

MacKenzie, N.A. (1999) The Native Woodland Resource of Scotland: a Review 1993–1998. Forestry Commission Technical Paper 30. Forestry Commission, Edinburgh.

Mackey, E.C. & Mudge, G. (2010). *Scotland's Wildlife: An assessment of biodiversity in 2010.* Scottish Natural Heritage, Inverness.

Malcolm, D.C., Cochrane, P., Cottrell, J. & Chamberlain, D.E. (2005) Atlantic Oakwoods. *Botanical Journal of Scotland,* **57** (1–2) Special Issue.

Martin, S., Emery, M. & Dyke, A. (2006) Wild Harvests from Scottish Woodlands: an exploration of the health and well-being benefits of non-timber forest product collection and use. *Scottish Forestry,* **60,** 21–26.

Mason, W.L. (2006) Transformation of conifer plantations to mixed forests: initial guidance from an experiment in Wykeham forest, North Yorkshire. *Quarterly Journal of Forestry*, **100**, 1–12.

Mason, W.L. (2007) Changes in the management of British forests between 1945 and 2000 and possible future trends. *Ibis*, **149**, 41–52.

Mason, W.L., Hampson, A. & Edwards, C. (2004) Managing the pinewoods of Scotland. Forestry Commission, Edinburgh.

Mason, W.L., Nicoll, B.C. & Perks, M. (2009) Mitigation potential of sustainably managed forests. Combating climate change—a role for UK forests (eds D.J. Read, P.H. Freer-Smith, J.I.L. Morison, N. Hanley, C.C. West & P.R. Snowdon) pp. 100–118. The Stationery Office, Edinburgh.

Mason, W.L. & Quine, C.P. (1995) Silvicultural possibilities for increasing structural diversity in British spruce forests: the case of Kielder Forest. *Forest Ecology and Management,* **79**, 13–28.

Matthews, J.D. (1991) Silvicultural Systems. Second edition. Clarendon Press, Oxford.

Matthews, R.W. & Broadmeadow, M.S.J. (2009) The potential of UK forestry to contribute to Government's emissions reduction commitments. Combating climate change—a role for UK forests (eds D.J. Read, P.H. Freer-Smith, J.I.L. Morison, N. Hanley, C.C. West & P.R. Snowdon) pp. 139–161. The Stationery Office, Edinburgh.

Mayle, B.A., Proudfoot, J. & Poole, J. (2009) Influence of tree size and dominance on incidence of bark stripping by grey squirrels to oak and impact on tree growth. *Forestry*, **82**(4), 431–444. DOI: 10.1093/forestry/cpp015.

McCracken, A. (2007) Guidelines for establishing short rotation coppice in Northern Ireland. Forest Service/Department of Agriculture and Rural Development, Belfast.

McGregor, P. & McNicoll, I.H. (1992) The impact of forestry on output in the UK and its member countries. *Regional Studies*, **26**, 69–79.

McIntosh, R. (1995) The history and multi-purpose management of Kielder Forest. *Forest Ecology and Management*, **79**, 1–12.

MCPFE (Ministerial Conference on the Protection of Forests in Europe) (1993) General Guidelines for the Sustainable Management of Forests in Europe. Second Ministerial Conference on the Protection of Forests in Europe.

MCPFE (Ministerial Conference on the Protection of Forests in Europe) (1998) Pan-European Criteria and Indicators for Sustainable Forest Management. Third Ministerial Conference on the Protection of Forests in Europe.

MCPFE (Ministerial Conference on the Protection of Forests in Europe) (2002) Improved Pan-European Indicators for Sustainable Forest Management. MCPFE Expert Level Meeting, 7–8 October 2002, Vienna, Austria.

MCPFE (Ministerial Conference on the Protection of Forests in Europe) (2007) State of Europe's Forests 2007: The MCPFE Report on Sustainable Forest Management in Europe. Ministerial Conference on the Protection of Forests in Europe.

Milne, R. & Brown, T.A. (1997) Carbon in the vegetation and soils of Great Britain. *Journal of Environmental Management*, **49**, 413–433.

Mitchell, F.J.G. & Kirby, K.J. (1990) The impact of large herbivores on the conservation of semi-natural woods in the British uplands. *Forestry*, **63**, 333–354.

Mitlin, D.C. (1987) Price-size curves for conifers. Forestry Commission Bulletin 68, HMSO, London.

Moffat, A.J. (1991) Forestry and soil protection in the UK. *Soil Use and Management,* **7**, 145–151.

Moffat, A.J. & Hutchings, T.R. (2007). Greening brownfield land. In: Sustainable Brownfield Regeneration. Liveable places from problem spaces (eds T. Dixon, M. Raco, P. Catney and D. N. Lerner). Blackwells, Oxford.

Moffat, A.J., Quine, C.P. & McKay, H. (2010) The state of the natural environment: Land use and the future of forestry. In: Land Use Futures: making the most of land in the 21st century. Final Project Report, Government Office for Science, London.

Moore, R., Brixey, J.M. & Milner, A.D. (2004). Effect of time of year on the development of immature stages of the large pine weevil (*Hylobius abietis* L.) in stumps of Sitka spruce (*Picea sitchensis* Carr.) and influence of felling date on their growth, density and distribution. *Journal of Applied Entomology,* **128**, 167–176.

Morison, J., Matthews, R., Perks, M., Randle, T., Vanguelova, E., White, M. & Yamulki, S. (2009) The Carbon and GHG Balance of UK Forests—a Review. Report to Forestry Commission, Forest Research, Farnham.

Mlinsek, D. (1979) On ecology of even-aged monocultures. The ecology of even-aged forest plantations (eds E.D. Ford D.C. Malcolm & J. Atterson), pp. 3–6. Institute of Terrestrial Ecology, Cambridge.

Mueller, G.M., Bills, G.F. & Foster, M.S. (eds) (2004) Biodiversity of Fungi: Inventory and Monitoring Methods. Elsevier Academic Press, San Diego.

NCC (Nature Conservancy Council) (1984) Nature Conservation in Great Britain. Nature Conservancy Council, Peterborough.

NEGTAP (National Expert Group on Transboundary Air Pollution) (2001) Transboundary Air Pollution: Acidification, Eutrophication and Ground-level Ozone in the UK. NEGTAP, Edinburgh.

Nisbet, T.R., Silgram, M., Shah, N., Morrow, K. & Broadmeadow, S. (in press) Woodland for water: woodland measures for meeting Water Framework Directive objectives. Environment Agency, Bristol.

Nisbet, T.R., Orr, H. & Broadmeadow, S.B. (2008) Using woodland for soil protection and sediment control. Land management in a changing environment: Proceedings of the SAC and SEPA biennial conference (eds K. Crighton & R. Audsley). SAC, Auchincruive.

Nygren, C.M.R., Eberhardt, U., Karlsson, M., Parrent, J.L., Lindahl, B.D. & Taylor, A.F.S. (2008) Growth on nitrate and occurrence of nitrate reductase-encoding genes in a phylogenetically diverse range of ectomycorrhizal fungi. *New Phytologist,* **180**, 875–889.

O'Brien, L. (2006) Strengthening the heart and mind: using woodlands to improve mental and physical well-being. *Unasylva*, **224**, 56–61.

O'Brien, L. & Murray, R. (2007) Forest School and its impacts on young children: case studies in Britain. *Urban Forestry and Urban Greening*, **6**, 249–265.

O'Brien, L. & Morris, J. (2009) Active England. The Woodland Projects. Forest Research, Farnham. [online] Available at: <http://www.forestresearch.gov.uk/pdf/active_england_final_report.pdf/$FILE/active_england_final_report.pdf> [Accessed 17.01.11].

O'Brien, L., Foot, K. & Doick, K.J. (2007) Evaluating the benefits of community greenspace creation on brownfield land. *Quarterly Journal of Forestry*, **101**, 145–151.

ODPM (the Office of the Deputy Prime Minister) (2005) Planning Policy Statement 9: Biodiversity and geological conservation. ODPM, London.

Oliver, C.D., & Larson, B.C. (1996) Forest Stand Dynamics. 2nd edition. John Wiley and Sons, New York.

Osmaston, F.C. (1968) The Management of Forests. George Allen and Unwin Ltd.

PACEC (Public and Corporate Economic Consultants) (2006) The economic and environmental impact of sporting shooting. PACEC, London (report produced on behalf of BASC, CA, CLA in association with GCT).

Pakenham, T. (1996) Meetings with remarkable trees. Pp. 192. Wiedenfeld and Nicholson, London.

Patenaude, G., Milne, R. & Dawson, T.P. (2005) Synthesis of remote sensing approaches for forest carbon estimation: reporting to the Kyoto Protocol. *Environmental Science and Policy*, **8**, 161–178.

Patterson, G.S. & Anderson, A.R. (2000) Forests and peatland habitats. Guideline Note No.1. Forestry Commission, Edinburgh.

Patterson, I.J., Ollason, J.G. & Doyle, P. (1995) Bird populations in upland spruce plantations in northern Britain. *Forest Ecology and Management*, **79**, 107–132.

Patterson, T.M. & Coelho, D.L. (2009) Ecosystem services: foundations, opportunities, and challenges for the forest products sector. *Forest Ecology and Management*, **257**, 1637–1646.

Pearce, D. (1991) Assessing the returns to the economy and to society from investments in forestry. In Forestry expansion: a study of technical, economic and ecological factors. Occasional Paper, Forestry Commission, Edinburgh.

Perrins, C.M. & Gosler, A.G. (2010) Birds. Wytham woods, Oxford's Ecological Laboratory (eds P.S. Savill, C.M. Perrins, K.J. Kirby & N. Fisher), pp. 145–172. OUP, Oxford.

Perrot-Maître, D. (2006) The Vitell payments for ecosystem services: a "perfect" PES case? International Institute for Environment and Development, London.

Peterken, G.F. (1977) Habitat conservation priorities in British and European woodland. *Biological Conservation*, **11**, 223–236.

Peterken, G.F. (1991) Ecological issues in the management of woodland nature reserves. The scientific management of woodland nature reserves (eds I.F. Spellerburg, F.B. Goldsmith & M.G. Morris), pp. 245–272. Blackwell, Oxford.

Peterken, G.F. (1996) Natural Woodland: Ecology and Conservation in Northern Temperate Regions. Cambridge University Press, Cambridge.

Peterken, G.F. & Allison, H. (1989) Woods, Trees and Hedges: a Review of Changes in the British Countryside. Focus on Nature Conservation 22. Nature Conservancy Council, Peterborough.

Petit, R.J., Brewer, S., Bordacs, S., Burg, K., Cheddadi, R., Coart, E., Cottrell, J., Csaikl, U., Deans, D., Fineschi, S., Finkeldey, R., Goicoechea, P., Jensen, J., Konig, A., Lowe, A., Madsen, S.F., Matyas, G., Munro, R.C., Oledska, I., Slade, F.P.D., Tabbener, H., Van Dam, B., Ziegenhagen, B., de Beaulieu, J. & Kremer, A. (2002) Postglacial colonisation routes of European white oaks inferred from the variation of chloroplast DNA and from the analysis of fossil pollen. *Forest Ecology and Management*, **156**, 49–74.

Petty, S.J., Garson, P.J. & McIntosh, R. (eds) (1995a) Kielder—the ecology of a man-made spruce forests. *Forest Ecology and Management*, **79** (Special Issue).

Petty, S.J., Patterson, I.J., Anderson, D.I.K., Little, B. & Davison, M. (1995b) Numbers, breeding performance, and diet of the sparrowhawk *Accipiter nisus* and merlin *Falco columbarius* in relation to cone crops and seed-eating finches. *Forest Ecology and Management*, **79**, 133–146.

Philip, L.G. & MacMillan, D.C. (2005) Exploring values, context, and perceptions in contingent valuation studies: the CV market stall technique and willingness to pay for wildlife conservation. *Journal of Environmental Planning and Management*, **48**, 257–274.

Phillip, S., Dandy, N., Gill, R. & MacMillan, D.C. (2009) Is legislation a barrier to the sustainable management of game species? A case study of wild deer in Britain. *Journal of Environmental Planning and Management*, **52**, 993–1012.

Phythian, J.E. (1907) Trees in nature, myth and art. Methuen & Co., London.

Pitcairn, C.E.R., Leith, I.D., Sheppard, L.J., Sutton, M.A., Fowler, D., Munro, R.C., Tang, S. & Wilson, D. (1998) The relationship between nitrogen deposition, species composition and foliar nitrogen concentrations in woodland flora in the vicinity of livestock farms. *Environmental Pollution*, **102**, 41–48.

Pollock, M. (2005) Future directions for integrated land use in the hills—The Hill Sheep & Native Woodland Project. SAC Sustainable Livestock Systems Research Notes 2005. SAC Edinburgh.

POST (2006) UK soil degradation. Postnote 265. Parliamentary Office of Science and Technology, London.

Powe, N.A. & Willis, K.G. (2004) Mortality and morbidity benefits of air pollution (SO_2 and PM10) absorption attributable to woodland in Britain. *Journal of Environmental Management*, **70**, 119–128.

Power, S.A., Ashmore, M.R. & Cousins, D.A. (1998) Impacts and fate of experimentally enhanced N deposition on a British lowland heath. *Environmental Pollution*, **102**, 27–34.

Power, S.A., Ashmore, MR., Terry, A.C., Caporn, S.J.M., Pilkington, M.G., Wilson, D.B., Barker, C.G., Carroll, J.A., Cresswell, N., Green, E.R. & Heil, G.W. (2004) Linking field experiments to long-term simulation of impacts of nitrogen deposition on heathlands and moorlands. *Water, Air and Soil Pollution: Focus*, **4**, 259–267.

Preston, C.D., Pearman, D.A. & Dines, T.D. (2002) New Atlas of the British and Irish flora. Oxford University Press, Oxford.

Prosser, C.D., Murphy, M. & Larwood, J.L. (2006) Geological Conservation: a guide to good practice. English Nature, Peterborough. [online] Available at: <http://naturalengland.etraderstores.com/NaturalEnglandShop/ST118> [Accessed 17.01.11].

Pryor, S. & Peterken, G.F. (2001) Protected Forest Areas in the UK. WWF, Godalming.

Pryor, S.N. & Jackson, T.J.F. (2002) The cost of restoring planted ancient woodland sites. The Woodland Trust. [online] Available at: http://www.woodlandtrust.org.uk/SiteCollectionDocuments/pdf/Cost_restoring_PAWS_report3.pdf [Accessed 17.01.11].

Pulford, I.D. & Watson, C. (2003) Phytoremediation of heavy metal-contaminated land by trees—a review. *Environment International*, **29**, 529–540.

Pyatt, D.G., Ray, D. & Fletcher, J. (2001) An Ecological Site Classification for Forestry in Great Britain. Forestry Commission Bulletin 124. Forestry Commission, Edinburgh.

Quine, C.P. (1991) Recent storm damage to trees and woodlands in southern Britain. Research for Practical Arboriculture (ed S.J. Hodge), pp. 83–94. Forestry Commission Bulletin 93. HMSO, London.

Quine, C.P. & Gardiner, B.A. (2006) Understanding how the interaction of wind and trees results in windthrow, stem breakage and gap formation. Plant disturbance ecology: the process and the response (eds E.A. Johnson & K. Miyanishi), pp. 103–155. Academic Press (Elsevier), New York.

Quine, C.P. & Watts, K. (2009) Successful de-fragmentation of woodland by planting in an agricultural landscape? An assessment based on landscape indicators. *Journal of Environmental Management*, **90**, 251–259.

Quine, C.P. & Humphrey, J.W. (2010) Plantations of exotic tree species in Britain: irrelevant for biodiversity or novel habitat for native species? *Biodiversity and Conservation,* **19**, 1503–1512.

Quine, C.P., & Ray, D. (2010) Sustainable forestry—which species for which site for which world? Species Management; Challenges and Solutions for the 21st Century (eds J. Baxter & C.A. Galbraith), pp. 417–434. TSO and SNH, Edinburgh.

Quine, C.P., Fuller, R.J., Smith, K.W. & Grice, P.V. (2007) Stand management: a threat or opportunity for birds in British woodland? *Ibis*, **149**, 161–174.

Rackham, O. (1976) Trees & woodland in the British landscape. J.M. Dent, London.

Rackham, O. (1986) The history of the countryside. Dent, London.

Rackham, O. (2003) Ancient woodland (revised edition). Castlepoint Press, Dalbeattie.

Ray, D. (2008) Impacts of climate change on forests in Scotland—a preliminary synopsis of spatial modelling research. Forestry Commission Research Note 001. Forestry Commission, Edinburgh.

Ray, D. & Broome, A.C. (2007) An information retrieval system to support management of habitats and rare priority protected species (HARPPS) in Britain. Sustainable Forestry: from monitoring and modelling to knowledge management and policy science (eds K.M. Reynolds, A. J. Thomson, M. Kohl, M.A. Shannon, D. Ray & K. Rennolls), pp. 480–496. CAB International, Wallingford.

Ray, D., Wainhouse, D., Webber, J. & Gardiner B.A. (2008) Impacts of climate change on forests and forestry in Scotland. Forest Research Report, January 2008. FR, Edinburgh.

Ray, D., Morison, J. & Broadmeadow, M. (2010) Climate change: impacts and adaptation in England's woodlands. Forestry Commission Research Note 201. Forestry Commission, Edinburgh.

Read, H.J. (2000) Veteran tree management handbook. English Nature, Peterborough.

Read, D.J., Freer-Smith, P.H., Morison, J.I.L., Hanley, N., West, C.C. & Snowdon, P.R. (eds) (2009) Combating climate change—a role for UK forests. The Stationery Office, Edinburgh.

Redfern, D.B., Stoakley, J.T., Steele, H. & Minter, D.W. (1987) Dieback and death of larch caused by *Ceratocystis laricicola* sp. nov. following attack by *Ips cembrae*. *Plant Pathology*, **36**, 467–480.

Redfern, D.B., Pratt, J.E., Gregory, S.C. & Macaskill, G.A. (2001) Natural infection of Sitka spruce thinning stumps in Britain by spores of *Heterobasidion annosum* and long-term survival of the fungus. *Forestry,* **74**, 53–71.

Redfern, D.B., Pratt, J.E., Hendry, S.J. & Low, J.D. (2010) Development of a policy and strategy for controlling infection by *Heterobasidion annosum* in British forests: a review of supporting research. *Forestry* **83**, 207–218.

Richards, M. & Jenkins, M. (2007) Potential and Challenges of Payments for Ecosystem Services from Tropical Forests. Forestry Briefing 16. Overseas Development Institute.

Rishbeth, J. (1952) Control of *Fomes annosus* Fr. *Forestry* **25,** 41–50.

Ritvo, H. (2009) The dawn of green: Manchester, Thirlmere, and modern environmentalism. University of Chicago Press, Chicago: Pp 248

Roberts, A.J., Russell, C., Walker, G.J. & Kirby, K.J. (1992) Regional variation in the origin, extent and composition of Scottish woodland. *Botanical Journal of Scotland*, **46**, 167–189.

Robertson, P.A. (1992) Woodland management for pheasants. Forestry Commission Bulletin 106, Edinburgh.

Robertson, K., Ford-Robertson, J., Matthews, R.W. & Milne, R. (2003) Evaluation of the C-FLOW and CARBINE carbon accounting models. In UK Emissions by Sources and Removals due to Land Use, Land Use Change and Forestry Activities. [online] Available at: <http://ecosystemghg.ceh. ac.uk/docs/2006andOlder/DEFRA_Report_2003.pdf> [Accessed 01.02.11].

Rodwell, J.S. (ed) (1991) British Plant Communities. Volume 1: Woodlands and Scrub. Cambridge University Press, Cambridge.

Rollinson, T.J.D. (2003) Changing Needs—Changing Forests: The UK Experience. in UNFF Intersessional Experts Meeting on the Role of Planted Forests in Sustainable Forest Management, pp. 13. 24–30 March 2003, Wellington, New Zealand.

RoTAP (Review of Transboundary Air Pollution) (2011) Review of Transboundary Air Pollution: Acidification, Eutrophication, Ground Level Ozone and Heavy Metals in the UK. Contract Report to the Department for Environment, Food and Rural Affairs. Centre for Ecology & Hydrology.

Rotherham, I.D., Jones, M., Smith, L. & Handley, C. (2008) The Woodland Heritage Manual. Wildtrack Publishing, Sheffield.

SACRPC (Scottish Agricultural College, Rural Policy Centre) (2008) 'Farming's Retreat from the Hills'. Scottish Agricultural College, Edinburgh.

Sage, R.B., Ludorf, C. & Robertson, P.A. (2005) The ground flora of ancient semi-natural woodlands in pheasant release pens in England. *Biological Conservation*, **122**, 243–252.

Sanderson, H. & Prendergast, H. (2002) Commercial uses of wild and traditionally managed plants in England and Scotland. Unpublished Research Report (RBG, CA, English Nature, SNH).

SFIC (Scottish Forest Industries Cluster) (2004) Scotland's Forest Industries. Scottish Enterprise, Edinburgh.

Scottish Government (SG) (2009) The Scottish Government's Policy on Control of Woodland Removal. Scottish Government, Forestry Commission Scotland, Edinburgh.

Shepherd, P.A., Gillespie, J., Garrod, G. & Willis, K. (2002) An initial investigation of the actual costs of implementing UK biodiversity action plans. Baker Shepherd Gillespie, Bakewell/ Defra, London. [online] Available at: <http://www.defra.gov.uk/ evidence/economics/foodfarm/reports/index.htm> [Accessed 21.01.11].

Shvidenko, A., Barber, C.V. & Persson, R. (2003) Forest and Woodland Systems. Chapter 21. Millennium Ecosystem Assessment, Island Press, 585–621.

Sinclair, J. & Whiteman, A. (1992) Price-size curve for conifers. Forestry Commission Research Information Note 226, Forestry Commission, Edinburgh.

Smith, D.M., Larson, B.C., Kelty, M.J. & Ashton, P.M.S. (1997) The Practice of Silviculture: Applied Forest Ecology. Ninth edition. John Wiley & Sons.

Smith, R.S., Lunn, A.G. & Newsom, M.D. (1995) The Border Mires in Kielder Forest: A review of their ecology and conservation management. *Forest Ecology and Management*, **79**, 47–62.

Smith, S.E. & Read, D.J. (2007) Mycorrhizal Symbiosis, Third Edition. Academic Press, London.

Smout, T.C. (2000) Nature contested. Pp.210. Edinburgh University Press, Edinburgh.

Smout, T.C. (ed) (2002) People and woods in Scotland: a history. Edinburgh University Press, Edinburgh.

SNH (Scottish Natural Heritage) (2010) Condition of designated sites. [Online] Available at: <http://www.snh.gov.uk/docs/B686620.pdf> [Accessed 01.02.11].

Smout, T.C. & Tittensor, R. (2008) A stab in the dark: an oral history of an Ayrshire forest. *Scottish Forestry, 62*, 1–8

Spencer, J.W. & Kirby, K.J. (1992) An inventory of ancient woodland for England and Wales. *Biological Conservation*, **62**, 77–93.

Staddon, C. (2006) The harvest and trade of moss in Scotland. Forest Harvest, Scotland. [online] Available at: http://rbg-web2.rbge.org.uk/ethnobotany/ntfp/reports.htm [Accessed 21.01.11].

Staines, B.W. & Welch, D. (1989) Impact of red and roe deer on Scottish woodlands. Mammals as Pests (ed R.J. Putman), pp. 128–130. Chapman & Hall, London.

Staines, B.W., Balharry, R. & Welch, D. (1995). Heaths and Moorlands: Cultural Landscapes. (eds D.B.A. Thompson, A.J. Hester & M.B. Usher). HMSO, Edinburgh.

Summers, R.W. & Wilkinson, N.I. (2008) Age structure and history of stand types of *Pinus sylvestris* in Abernethy Forest, Scotland. *Scandinavian Journal of Forest Research*, **23**, 28–37.

Suttie, E., Taylor, G., Livesay, K. & Tickell, F. (2009) Potential of forest products and substitution for fossil fuels to contribute to mitigation. Combating climate change—a role for UK forests (eds D.J. Read, P.H. Freer-Smith, J.I.L. Morison, N. Hanley, C.C. West & P.R. Snowdon) pp. 119–138. The Stationery Office, Edinburgh.

Symonds, H.H. (1936) Afforestation in the Lake District. Dent, London.

Tabbush, P.M. (2004) Public money for public good? Public participation in forest planning. *Forestry*, **77**, 145–156.

Taylor, W.L. (1946) Forests and forestry in Great Britain, Crosby Lockwood, London.

Thomas, H. & Nisbet, T.R. (2007) An assessment of the impact of floodplain woodland on flood flows. *Water and Environment Journal*, **17**, 65–85.

Thomas, J.A. (1991) Rare species conservation: case studies of European butterflies. *The Scientific Management of Temperate Communities for Conservation* (eds I.F. Spellerberg F.B. Goldsmith & M.G. Morris), pp. 149–198. Blackwell, Oxford.

Thompson, D.B.A., MacDonald, A.J., Marsden, J.H. & Galbraith, C.A. (1995) Upland heather moorland in Great Britain: A review of international importance, vegetation change and some objectives for nature conservation. *Biological Conservation*, 71, 163–178.

Thompson, R., Humphrey, J.W., Harmer, R. & Ferris, R. (2003) Restoration of native woodland on ancient woodland sites. Forest Practice Guide, Forestry Commission, Edinburgh.

Thomson, M. (2004) International markets in wood products. Information Note 60, Forestry Commission, Edinburgh.

Thomson, K.J. & Psaltopoulos, D. (2005) Economy-wide effects of forestry development scenarios in rural Scotland. *Forest Policy & Economics*, **7**, 515–525.

Todd, J.D., Kupiec, J.A. & Baptie, M.A. (1988) Economic surveys of private forestry income and expenditure Scotland. University of Aberdeen, Aberdeen.

Tompkins, S. (1989) Forestry in crisis: battle for the hills. Christopher Helm, London.

Towers, W., Hester, A.J. & Malcolm, A. (2002) The use of the Native Woodland Model in the calculation of local targets for Habitat Action Plans. *Scottish Forestry*, **56**, 196–199.

Treasury (1972) Forestry in Great Britain. An interdepartmental cost/benefit study. HMSO, London.

Tsouvalis, J. (2000) A critical geography of Britain's State forests. Oxford University Press, Oxford.

Tubby, I. & Armstrong, A. (2002) Establishment and management of short rotation coppice. Forestry Commission Practice Note, Edinburgh.

Tubby, K. & Webber, J.F. (2010) Pests and diseases threatening urban trees under a changing climate. *Forestry*, **83**, 451–459.

Turpie, J.K., Marais, C. & Blignaut, J.N. (2008) The working for water programme: evolution of a payments for ecosystem services mechanism that addresses both poverty and ecosystem service delivery in South Africa. *Ecological Economics*, **65**, 788–798.

UKBAP (United Kingdom Biodiversity Action Plan) (2006) The UK Biodiversity Action Plan: Highlights from the 2005 reporting round. Defra, London.

UKBAP (United Kingdom Biodiversity Action Plan) (2008) The UK Biodiversity Action Plan: results from the 2008 reporting round. [online] Available at: <http://www.ukbap-reporting.org.uk> [Accessed 17.01.11].

UKWAS (United Kingdom Woodland Assurance Standard) (2008) The UK Woodland Assurance Standard. Second edition (amended). UKWAS, Edinburgh. [online] Available at: <http://www.ukwas.org.uk/assets/documents/UKWAS%20Second%20Edition%20%28Amended%20November%202008%29%20Web.pdf>[Accessed 01.02.11].

Valatin, G. (2010) Forestry carbon: valuation, discounting and risk management. Discussion Paper. Forest Research, Edinburgh. [online] Available at: <http://www.forestry.gov.uk/pdf/Carbon_valuation_and_risk_management_%28Feb2010%29.pdf/$FILE/Carbon_valuation_and_risk_management_%28Feb2010%29.pdf> [Accessed 01.02.11].

Valatin, G. & Starling, J. (2010) Economic assessment of ecosystem services provided by UK Woodlands. The Economics Team of the UK National Ecosystem Assessment, Forest Research.

Van Oijen, M., Agren, G.I., Chertov, O., Kellomaki, S., Komarov, A., Mobbs, D. & Murray, M. (2008) Evaluation of past and future changes in European forest growth by means of four process-based models. Causes and Consequences of Forest Growth Trends in Europe (ed Kahle, H.P.), pp. 183–199. European Forest Institute Research Report 21, Brill.

Vanguelova, E.I., Barsoum, N., Benham, S., Broadmeadow, M., Moffat, A., Nisbet, T. & Pitman, R. (2007) Ten years of intensive environmental monitoring of British forests. Forestry Commission Information Note 88, Edinburgh.

Vera, F.M.W. (2000) Grazing Ecology and Forest History. CABI Publishing, Oxford.

Wainhouse, D., Brough,S. & Greenacre, B. (2007) Managing the pine weevil on lowland pine. Practice Note 14. Forestry Commission, Edinburgh.

Ward, A.I. (2005) Expanding ranges of wild and feral deer in Great Britain. *Mammal Review*, **35**, 165–173.

Warren, M.S. & Key, R.S. (1991) Woodlands: past, present and potential for insects. The conservation of insects and their habitats (ed N.M Collins & J.A. Thomas), pp. 155–211. Academic Press, London.

Watts, K. & Handley, P. (2010) Developing a functional connectivity indicator to detect change in fragmented landscapes. *Ecological Indicators,* **10**, 552–557.

Watts, K., Ray, D., Quine, C.P., Humphrey, J.W. & Griffiths, M. (2007) Evaluating biodiversity in fragmented landscapes: applications of landscape ecology tools. Forestry Commission Information Note 85, Edinburgh.

Watts, K., Eycott, A.E., Handley, P., Ray, D., Humphrey, J.W. & Quine, C.P. (2010) Targeting and evaluating biodiversity conservation action within fragmented landscapes: An approach based on generic focal species and least-cost networks. *Landscape Ecology,* **25**(9), 1305–1318.

Webb, J.R., Drewitt, A.L. & Measures, G.N. (2009) Managing for species: integrating the needs of priority species into habitat management. Natural England Research Report NERR 024, Sheffield.

Webb, N. (1986) Heathlands. A natural history of Britain's lowland heaths. Pp. 223. Collins, London.

Wesche, S., Kirby, K.J. & Ghazoul, J. (2006) Plant assemblages in British beech woodlands within and beyond native range: Implications of future climate change for their conservation. *Forest Ecology and Management,* **236**, 385–392.

White, G. (1789) The natural history of Selborne, in the county of Southampton: with Engravings, and an Appendix. B. White and Son, London.

White, P.C.L., Bennet, A.C. & Hayes, E.J.V. (2001) The use of willingness-to-pay approaches in mammal conservation. *Mammal Review,* **31**, 151–167.

Whiteman, A. (1990) Price-size curves for conifers. Research Information Note 192, Forestry Commission, Edinburgh.

Whiteman, A., Insley, H. & Watt, G. (1991) Price-size curves for broadleaves. Occasional Paper 32, FC, Edinburgh.

Williams, J. (2006) *Common Standards Monitoring for Designated Sites: First Six Year Report*. Joint Nature Conservation Committee, Peterborough.

Williams, P.H. & Gaston, K. (1998) Biodiversity indicators: graphical techniques, smoothing and searching for what makes relationships work. *Ecography,* **21**, 551–560.

Willis, K.G., Garrod, G., Scarpa, R., Powe, N., Lovett, A., Bateman, I.J., Hanley, N. & Macmillan, D.C. (2003) The social and environmental benefits of forests in Great Britain. Forestry Commission, Edinburgh.

Wilson, D. (2004) Multi-Use Management of the Medieval Anglo-Norman Forest. *Journal of the Oxford University History Society*, **2,** 1–16.

Winter, T. (1993) Dead wood—Is it a threat to commercial forestry? Dead wood matters: the ecology and conservation of saproxylic invertebrates in Britain (eds K.J. Kirby & C.M. Drake). English Nature Science No. 7., Peterborough.

Woodland Trust (2004) Space for People. Targeting action for woodland access. Woodland Trust, Grantham. [online] Available at: <http://www.woodlandtrust.org.uk/SiteCollectionDocuments/pdf/spaceforpeople.pdf> [Accessed 17.01.11].

Woodland Trust (2007) Back on the Map. Woodland Trust, Grantham.

Woodland Trust (2010) Woodwatch. [online] Available at: <http://frontpage.woodland-trust.org.uk/woodsunderthreat/tell-us/register-a-threat.htm> [Accessed 17.01.11].

Appendix 8.1 Approach Used to Assign Certainty Terms to Chapter Key Findings

This chapter began with a set of Key Findings. Adopting the approach and terminology used by the Intergovernmental Panel on Climate Change (IPCC) and the Millennium Assessment (MA), these Key Findings also include an indication of the level of scientific certainty. The 'uncertainty approach' of the UK NEA consists of a set of qualitative uncertainty terms derived from a 4-box model and complemented, where possible, with a likelihood scale (see below). Estimates of certainty are derived from the collective judgement of authors, observational evidence, modelling results and/or theory examined for this assessment.

Throughout the Key Findings presented at the start of this chapter, superscript numbers and letters indicate the estimated level of certainty for a particular key finding:

1. *Well established:*   high agreement based on significant evidence
2. *Established but incomplete evidence:*   high agreement based on limited evidence
3. *Competing explanations:*   low agreement, albeit with significant evidence
4. *Speculative:*   low agreement based on limited evidence

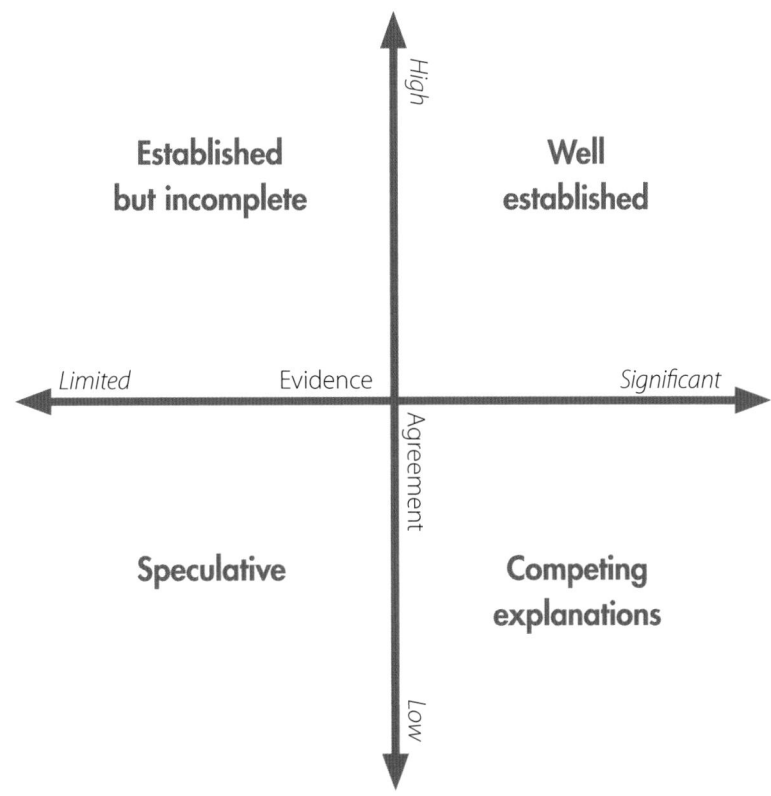

a. *Virtually certain:*   >99% probability of occurrence
b. *Very likely:*   >90% probability
c. *Likely:*   >66% probability
d. *About as likely as not:*   >33–66% probability
e. *Unlikely:*   <33% probability
f. *Very unlikely:*   <10% probability
g. *Exceptionally unlikely:*   <1% probability

Certainty terms 1 to 4 constitute the 4-box model, while *a* to *g* constitute the likelihood scale.

Chapter 9:
Freshwaters – Openwaters, Wetlands and Floodplains

Coordinating Lead Authors: Edward Maltby and Steve Ormerod
Lead Authors: Mike Acreman, Martin Blackwell, Isabelle Durance, Mark Everard, Joe Morris and Chris Spray
Contributing Authors: Jeremy Biggs, Phil Boon, Bill Brierley, Lee Brown, Alastair Burn, Stewart Clarke, Ian Diack, Catherine Duigan, Michael Dunbar, David Gilvear, Angela Gurnell, Alan Jenkins, Andy Large, Steve Maberly, Brian Moss, Jonathan Newman, Anne Robertson, Martin Ross, John Rowan, Matthew Shepherd, Ann Skinner, Julian Thompson, Ian Vaughan and Rob Ward

Key Findings*

Rivers, lakes, ponds, groundwaters and wetlands provide major services, but their benefits are inadequately identified and valued[1]. This has resulted in habitat losses that are among the fastest in the UK. When managed appropriately, Freshwaters should transport water, matter, energy or organisms within and between terrestrial systems, riparian zones, estuaries and near-coastal waters. They provide: consumptive and non-consumptive uses of water; organisms for food, recreation and conservation; and energy. They can regulate flooding, erosion, sedimentation, local climates and water quality, while facilitating the dilution and disposal of pollutants. They support dispersal through, and resilience in, adjacent ecosystems (for example, though water or nutrient supply), and act as a medium for key biogeochemical cycles. They have large cultural value for recreation, tourism, education, heritage and as inspiration for arts and religion. Costs for people include their role in waterborne diseases and their propensity to flood low-lying infrastructure.

[1] well established

Rivers, lakes and wetlands are present throughout UK landscapes. Historically, they were highly connected to each other and to their catchments, but are now fragmented and disconnected[1]. There are more than 389,000 km of rivers in the UK, almost 6,000 permanent large lakes covering around 200,000 ha and nearly half a million ponds (covering less than 2 ha); but the true extent of the UK's wetlands is less well defined. Distribution is also uneven, with Scotland holding more than 90% of the volume and 70% of the total surface area of Freshwater in the UK—it has over 30,000 openwater bodies, as well as some 40% of active raised bog. The llynnau of North and mid-Wales and the tarns of Cumbria form distinctive clusters of natural lake systems on the west coast. In central and southern England, where natural lakes are rare, artificial reservoirs provide important standing water habitats. Natural, small water bodies are also widespread, such as the pingo ponds of the Norfolk and Suffolk Breckland and the smaller Cheshire and Shropshire meres and pools. There are at least 392,000 ha of fen, reedbed, lowland raised bog and grazing marsh, but the true extent is uncertain. Floodplains are the most widespread (963,700 ha) and productive Freshwater systems and are shaped by the natural dynamics of river flows. However, they have been extensively impacted by engineering, including flood embankments and channel modifications, so that over two-fifths (42% by area) of all floodplains in England and Wales (defined by the 100-year flood envelope) have been separated from their rivers.

[1] well established

No completely pristine Freshwater ecosystems remain in the UK; almost all have been affected by human activity, including drainage, changes in land cover and atmospheric deposition, and most are now managed to a lesser or greater extent[1]. Habitat fragmentation and degradation have reduced their service value[2]. **However, while the least damaged are expected to provide the most natural service profile[2]**, some managed Freshwaters and artificial habitats can be locally important, such as chalk rivers, reservoirs, fenlands, water meadows and ponds[2]. More information is still required about ecosystem services provided by Freshwaters under various levels of management or condition.

[1] well established
[2] established but incomplete evidence

There is considerable uncertainty about how ecosystem services are related to ecosystem structure, functioning, habitat type, size, spatial extent and fragmentation[1]. The functions Freshwater ecosystems provide depend on their type, size, condition and position within a catchment[2]. Water connects diverse habitat types along gradients through catchments (with interaction in both directions) via exchanges between the atmosphere, uplands and lowlands, terrestrial and aquatic systems, fresh and saline waters, and between surface and groundwater. We lack precise knowledge of the importance of connectivity, and, in particular, the role of the many small wetlands or water bodies whose number remains poorly estimated and location often unrecorded[1].

[1] well established
[2] established but incomplete evidence

---

* Each Key Finding has been assigned a level of scientific certainty, based on a 4-box model and complemented, where possible, with a likelihood scale. Superscript numbers indicate the uncertainty term assigned to each finding. Full details of each term and how they were assigned are presented in Appendix 9.5.

Despite the multiple benefits of naturally functioning wetlands and floodplains, many have been degraded, lost or converted (for example, by drainage) to other uses designed to deliver specific services incompatible with their original condition (such as crop production)[1]. Where wetlands are intact, the major reason has been for nature conservation, often due to the important habitat they provide for birds. Wetlands comprise the largest proportion of Sites of Special Scientific Interest (SSSIs), but protection or management for the wide range of other benefits they provide to human well-being is only now beginning to influence policy and decision-making. The past focus on the conservation of species and communities now needs to be complemented with the maintenance of ecosystem functions if services are to be delivered in the future.

[1] well established

To date, our approach in the classification and mapping of different Freshwaters as 'priority habitats' does not necessarily indicate their actual or potential contribution to ecosystem services[2]. We have little idea about the actual areas of different Freshwater habitat required to provide a specified quantity and/or combination of services[2]. Evidence-based tools are becoming increasingly available to enable the assessment of the functioning of wetlands, together with their capacity to deliver ecosystem services[1]. New partnership concepts, such as the Association of Rivers Trusts, and the emergence of innovative implementation strategies, including covenants on land use and rewards for providing ecosystem services that serve the public good, offer considerable scope to recover previously impaired benefits, particularly at the local scale[1].

[1] well established
[2] established but incomplete evidence

Rivers are among the UK's most extensively monitored habitats; systematic, long-term data are available from over 25,000 km of the channel network in England, Wales and Scotland. Rivers in urban or intensively farmed areas have significantly lower sanitary quality and elevated nutrients (e.g. nitrate greater than 5 milligrams per litre) than elsewhere. The chemical quality of rivers has been progressively improving since the 1980s, but trends are locally variable[1]. Since 1990, the biological and chemical classification of what were formerly the most polluted rivers in England and Wales has now improved[1], although the quality of some of the best Welsh rivers has recently declined for reasons that are unclear[2]. More widely, nitrate concentrations have increased and phosphorus is still a problem in some locations[1]. Some upland or western regions are still affected by diffuse agricultural pollutants, while biological recovery from acidification lags behind chemical recovery[1]. More than 50% of English and Welsh rivers have been modified physically[1]. The numbers of ponds are now increasing following losses prior to 1980, but, in many, water quality is poor and declining, possibly due to increasing nutrient concentrations[2]. A similar pattern emerges for lakes, where evidence indicates that pressures from water level regulation and catchment developments are compounding water quality issues resulting from excessive nutrient loads[2]. There has been very limited monitoring of lakes and wetlands (with local exceptions including the Lake District and East Anglian fens). Even where monitoring has taken place, it has generally not been oriented towards the assessment of ecosystem services. In Scotland, a change in the monitoring network in 2006 makes a similar overall trend assessment difficult, but up until that time, rivers and canals showed a gradual, continuous improvement[2]. Again, very little monitoring has been directed towards the assessment of ecosystem services.

[1] well established
[2] established but incomplete evidence

Freshwater ecosystems appear particularly vulnerable to 'regime' shifts that, once incurred, can lead to large service losses which are difficult to restore[2]. Past adverse effects include acidification, impoundment, flow modification, eutrophication, siltation, habitat degradation, fragmentation, loss and drainage, toxic pollution, over-abstraction and invasion by non-native species[1]. New pollutants (e.g. endocrine disrupting substances, personal care products, nanoparticles, the effects of synthetic biology) are emerging issues for Freshwaters[2]. Urbanisation and climate change are likely to lead to increased water demand and lower resource availability, as well as increased pressure from saline intrusion on freshwater coastal habitats[2]. Climate change has also driven biologically significant water temperature increases of 1.5–3°C in many rivers over the past two decades, although the full effects on river biodiversity are, as yet, unclear[2]. In some catchments, juvenile populations of trout (*Salmo trutta*) and salmon (*S. salar*) have declined by about 50–60%, and there are major declines among other species, such as eels[2]. Invasive species of vegetation, fish, crustaceans and other organisms, including those causing diseases of wildlife, are of growing concern[2].

[1] well established
[2] established but incomplete evidence

Throughout human history, the integrity of Freshwater ecosystems has been traded-off against specific management objectives, with little or no understanding of the true costs[2]. Along with wetland drainage, flood defence and the purposeful and accidental use of Freshwaters for waste disposal have led to degraded ecological quality, loss of asset value and adverse health impacts[2]. The largest potential synergies in the delivery of different Freshwater ecosystem services are likely to arise where surrounding habitats are managed positively to enhance service delivery; indeed, some agri-environment measures now emphasise the importance of protecting the land-water interface[2].

[2] established but incomplete evidence

Understanding the linkages between physical, biogeochemical and ecological processes (from genes to ecosystems) that regulate the services of Freshwater systems remains a scientific challenge. Examples include: the role of Freshwaters in element cycles (e.g. carbon, silicon); the importance of microbial processes; the up- and down-scaling effects of modifications to catchments and flow regimes; the identity of critical ecosystem resources that underpin key services; and factors affecting resistance, resilience and critical thresholds to support service delivery. We also lack models predicting how Freshwater ecosystems may be altered by future environmental change and variability.

Only small proportions of wetlands and less than 1% of the UK's entire river length are part of formal protection networks[1]. Sustainable freshwater management will depend on better use of existing legislation, improved casework planning and better decision-support tools capturing ecosystem service delivery[2]. Key needs will include 'slowing-down' water, avoiding adverse runoff quality, and protecting sensitive ecosystem assets[2]. For wetlands, floodplains and catchments ecosystems, there is a need for improved inventory and assessment, including the ecosystem services and benefits they currently, or could potentially, provide[2]. Enhanced stakeholder and community involvement is an important factor in improved Freshwater valuation. Freshwater science is already highly inter-disciplinary, but further development to encompass socioeconomics will bring extra sustainability gains[2].

[2] established but incomplete evidence

We need to restore and recreate Freshwater ecosystems in order to maximise and reap the benefits of the ecosystem services they provide[2]. Restoration may provide cost-effective solutions to the enhancement of key services such as flood risk reduction and water quality improvement[2]. There is a growing inventory of practical actions and experience throughout the UK which are improving both the technical knowledge base and our understanding of the operational, policy and governmental actions required to reverse the degradation of our Freshwater ecosystems[2].

[2] established but incomplete evidence

9.1 Introduction

The hydrological cycle, along with the rivers, lakes, ponds, wetlands and groundwaters that form its terrestrial phases, provides some of the most critical of all resources for human well-being (Acreman 2001a). These freshwater-based ecosystems are some of the UK's most prominent landscape features and occur wherever rainfall, snowmelt or groundwater collects into flowing channels, standing waters, or associated bogs, fens, grazing marshes and floodplains. In nature, they form a continuum between these habitat types and their wider catchments (Gregory et al. 1991; Ward 1998). Not only are these habitats important geographical or management units, but they also control key processes and characteristics that have important ecological influences downstream through the supply of energy, solutes and water (often 'pulsing' during flood conditions) (Junk et al. 1989; Tockner et al. 2000). Catchment characteristics also influence downstream changes in temperature, hydrology, habitat character and species composition, affecting relative energy sources between litter-fall and in-stream production, and influencing the way nutrients 'spiral' through different organisms (Vannote et al. 1980; Newbold et al. 1981).

More than 389,000 km of river channels flow across England, Wales and Scotland, while almost 6,000 permanent large lakes cover a total area of almost 200,000 hectare (ha) (Ordnance Survey data). Scotland alone contains some 70% of all surface waters in the UK by area, and more than 90% by volume (Lyle & Smith 1994). There are about 0.5 million ponds (Carey et al. 2008), at least 392,000 ha of fens, reedbed, lowland raised bog and grazing marsh, and floodplains comprise 963,700 ha. It is estimated that there are almost 570 lakes (covering more than 1 ha) in Wales and a much larger number of smaller ponds and wetland pools. Many of these lakes are glacial in origin and are located in the mountains of North and mid-Wales. Over 20 major river systems drain the total surface area of Wales (2,077,000 ha). The UK has major groundwater resources, primarily in rock formations of chalk, Permo-Triassic sandstones, Jurassic limestone and Lower Greensand, which provide significant flow to rivers and wetlands, as well as water for public supply, irrigated agriculture and industry.

Flowing waters vary from headwaters and rivers to estuaries, while standing waters vary in size (i.e. ponds to lakes); the characteristics of both are determined by catchment features such as climate, latitude, altitude, soils, geology and land use. From the uplands to the coast, Wetlands constitute further freshwater diversity as intermediate states between fully terrestrial and permanently inundated habitats. The UK also has numerous artificial Freshwaters, such as reservoirs, gravel pits, canals and sewage lagoons, which often provide key ecosystem services in their own right (**Figure 9.1**).

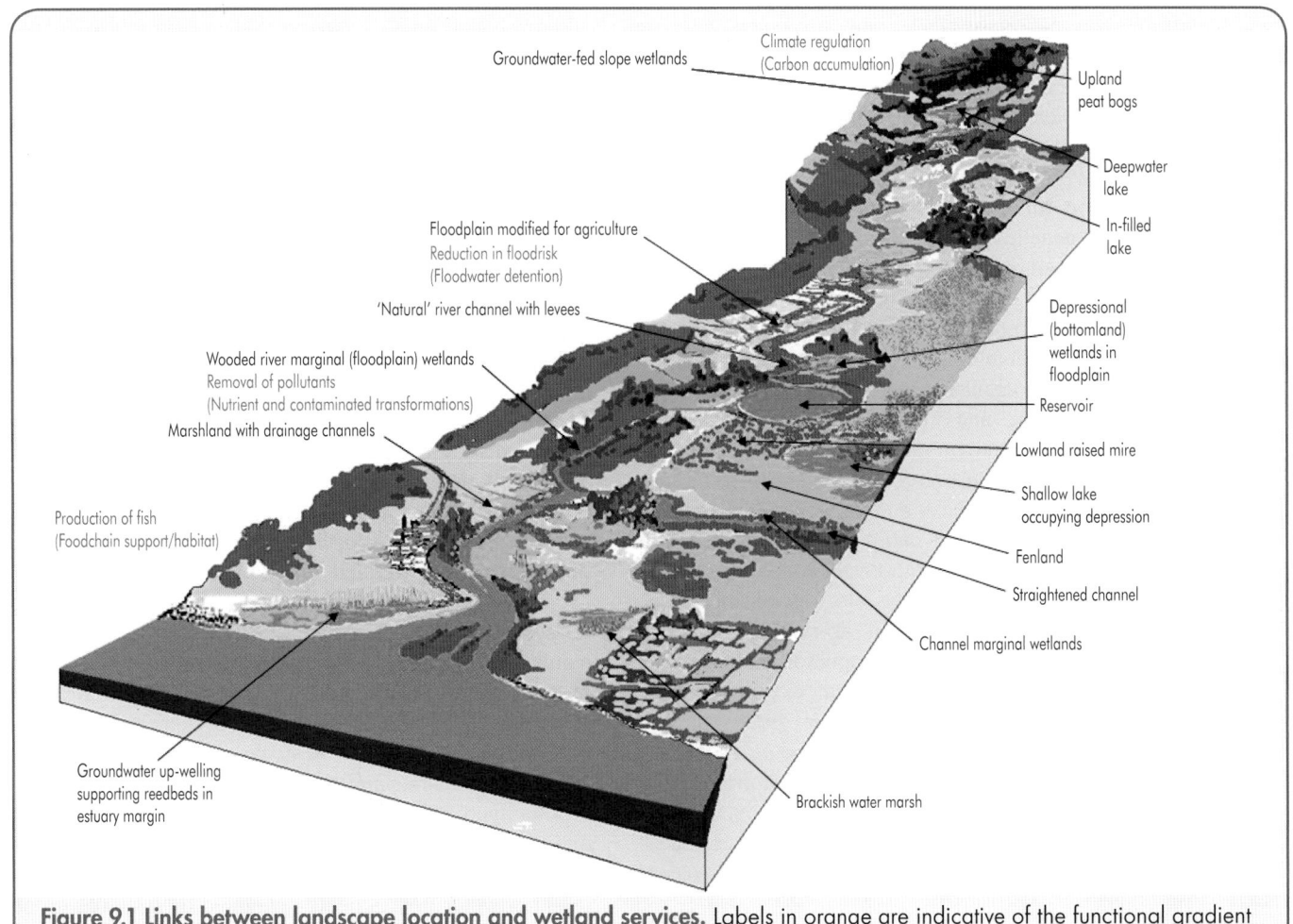

Figure 9.1 Links between landscape location and wetland services. Labels in orange are indicative of the functional gradient in importance of wetland ecosystem services, with text in parentheses providing an indication of the underpinning processes/intermediate services. Source: modified from art work of Aidoud in Maltby (2009a).

Functionally, Freshwaters move water, matter, sediments, solutes, organisms and energy across landscapes, gradients and habitats, linking the atmosphere, terrestrial systems, groundwaters, estuaries and ultimately the marine environment. In particular, Freshwaters control runoff processes from the land to rivers, floodplain inundation, floods and droughts, groundwater recharge (Bullock & Acreman 2003) and water quality (Fisher & Acreman 2004). These processes and movements are vital for the associated ecosystems to which they supply water, nutrients, energy (for example as carbon flux), solutes, sediments and migratory organisms. Freshwater systems also remove and dilute pollutants, store floodwaters and capture carbon. Throughout Freshwater catchments, there is considerable variation in the different ecosystem services provided (**Figure 9.1**), but critical among them are clean waters, flood protection, climate change mitigation, food, recreation, wild species, cultural inspiration and support for other associated systems (**Table 9.1**). However, there are also negative effects when Freshwaters transport undesirable materials such as pollutants from point or diffuse sources in their catchments, excessive loads of sediment, or invasive alien organisms. The flooding of human population centres or infrastructure located in areas which historically would have been inundated represents another negative effect of freshwater movement.

Freshwaters are among the UK's most productive and naturally diverse ecosystems, and are essential in the lifecycles of both freshwater specialists and species that move between Freshwaters and adjacent ecosystems. They have a disproportionately large biological diversity and relative abundance of organisms. This reflects their dynamic and physically varied nature, as well as the natural fragmentation among watersheds that is important for maintaining genetic diversity. Most freshwater species are highly specialised, and important groups include plants (e.g. algae, bryophytes and angiosperms), invertebrates (e.g. protozoa, rotifers, molluscs, micro- and macro-crustaceans, insects), and vertebrates (e.g. fish, amphibians, birds and mammals). Microorganisms, such as bacteria and fungi, are also abundant, and in aggregate drive production, decomposition and nutrient regulation.

In UK Wetlands alone, over 3,500 species of invertebrates, 150 aquatic plants, 22 ducks and 39 wader species occur, while all of the UK's seven native amphibians depend on Wetlands for breeding (Merritt 1994). Ponds, ditches and other small water bodies have also increasingly been recognised over the last 20 years as rich and important habitats in the UK. This follows recognition that, at least in lowland landscapes, ponds contribute disproportionately to the regional biodiversity of aquatic groups such as invertebrates and macrophytes (Williams *et al.* 2004; Oertli *et al.* 2009). While, on average, rivers support more species per location (known as 'alpha richness'), ponds contribute more species across lowland regions ('gamma richness'), and, in particular, hold unique and scarcer species (Davies *et al.* 2008).

The cool, damp microclimate of the often wooded Welsh river corridors supports an exceptional diversity of bryophytes (Hatton-Ellis *et al.* 2009). Aquatic species are most dominant in the fast-flowing upland headwaters, while additional taxa are associated with a distinct splash and spray zone. Deep gorges and waterfalls provide streamside habitat with especially high humidity, often with a distinctive, local composition of taxa that are of conservation importance.

For Wetlands specifically, this chapter deals with the four UK Biodiversity Action Plan (BAP) priority habitats of grazing marsh, fen, reedbeds and lowland raised bog (**Table 9.2**). Freshwaters also include additional components of the hydrological cycle, notably groundwater, which has its own distinctive ecosystem. Floodplains may contain one or more of the priority habitats, together with other habitats in various combinations resulting from changes in elevation, geomorphology, drainage and other management. Upland Wetlands, especially blanket bog, are dealt with in Chapter 5; rush pasture and Culm grassland is covered in Chapter 6; and wet woodland is covered in Chapter 8. The distinction between different Wetland habitats results from the variation and interaction among natural environmental factors including the magnitude and timing of saturation (waterlogging) and inundation; local topography and connectivity to other water bodies; vegetation cover; substrate and sediment; nutrient status; and management.

The importance of Freshwaters and their organisms means that they are emphasised in major conservation legislation such as the EU Habitats Directive (92/43/EEC) and Birds Directive (74/409/EEC). Rivers and lakes are often recognised as Sites of Special Scientific Interest (SSSIs), reflecting the diversity and naturalness of water bodies in the UK. Freshwaters also figure in specific aquatic policy or legislation, such as the EU Water Framework Directive (2000/60/EC; WFD) which requires the attainment of at least 'Good Ecological Status' (defined as minimal departure from reference (natural) conditions) throughout the UK's water systems. As we discuss later, many highly managed ecosystems in the UK provide important ecosystem services, thus restoration to reference conditions may mean the loss of these services. Wetlands are not explicitly recognised as separate elements in the WFD, but are included as part of the water bodies to which they are connected (lakes or rivers), or as groundwater-dependent terrestrial ecosystems when fed by groundwater (European Commission 2003). The international Ramsar Convention on Wetlands is the only example of an international convention for a specific ecosystem type and achieved a significant turning point in our perception of wetland value (Maltby 1986; Davis 1993) by focusing specifically on delivery of a wide range of ecosystem services. However, Ramsar sites have no legal status. Six priority types of Openwater are also recognised in the UK BAP (**Table 9.2**). In Scotland, 'freshwater and wetlands' forms one of the five ecosystem groups of the new Scottish Biodiversity Strategy, and has some nine UK BAP priority habitats and 75 priority species associated with it. This approach is supported by the Water Environment and Water Services (Scotland) Act 2003 and the Nature Conservation (Scotland) Act 2004. In Wales, work towards the Freshwater BAP is being generated by a similar group consisting of the major environmental bodies including the Environment Agency, Countryside Council for Wales and Forestry Commission.

Table 9.1 Ecosystem services provided by the Freshwater Broad Habitat. Component and sub-component habitats potentially delivering ecosystem services are river (R), lake (L), pond (P), grazing marsh (GM), reedbed (RB), fen (F), and lowland raised bog (LRB).

Final services of Freshwater habitat	Habitats potentially delivering services							Conditions or characteristics of habitats required
	R	L	P	GM	RB	F	LRB	
Provisioning								
Fish	•	•	•	•				Commercially significant fisheries (crayfish, salmon, trout) based on rivers, lakes and ponds in suitable conditions.
Dairy and beef				•		•		Wetland grasses provide grazing, silage and hay. Nutrition level depends upon management.
Reeds, osiers and watercress	•	•	•	•	•	•		Reeds grow in saturated soils and slow flowing or still water up to 0.3 m deep. Osiers produce withies for basket making; requiring saturated soil conditions. Cress-beds need swiftly flowing high pH clean water.
Water	•	•	•		•	•		Open water habitats provide a water source for public supply, irrigated crops, power station cooling, industrial processing and fish farming, but high evaporation rates may suppress total water availability.
Peat		•	•	•	•	•	•	Peat provides the basis of some composts for horticulture. Peat needs to be >0.5 m deep to be commercially exploitable due to recent planning guidance.
Navigation	•	•						Navigable waterways need sufficient water depth and low velocity.
Health products	•	•	•			•		Mineral spas, medicinal plants (e.g. bogbean), medical leeches.
Regulating								
Carbon regulation		•	•	•	•	•	•	Carbon accumulates where production of plant litter exceeds decomposition and generally under waterlogged, predominantly anaerobic conditions. Deposition of organic sediments within lakes, ponds and reservoirs is an important component of the carbon budget.
Flood regulation	•	•	•	•	•	•		Flood reduction relies on available water storage. Permanently saturated habitats with no storage may generate or augment floods.
Flow regulation	•	•	•	•	•	•	•	River flow, groundwater recharge influenced by landscape location, water storage characteristics and connection with other water bodies.
Water quality regulation	•	•	•	•	•	•		Freshwater systems can dilute, store and detoxify waste products and pollutants, however there are threshold levels and some systems may accumulate substances to toxic levels.
Local climate regulation	•	•	•	•	•	•	•	Temperature and humidity may be different within the habitat and without; degree depends on size. Important moist microclimates can develop.
Fire regulation	•	•	•	•	•			Open water bodies can act as natural fire breaks.
Human health regulation	•	•	•	•	•	•	•	Natural freshwater systems can increase well-being and quality of life if visually attractive and supportive of physical recreation. Mismanaged freshwaters can be sources of water borne diseases and disease vectors (e.g. mosquitoes), but also sources of biocontrol agents.
Cultural								
Science and education	•	•	•	•	•	•	•	Lake, floodplain and mire sediment sequences contain palaeo-environmental archives and human (pre)history, artefacts that may be lost if disturbed or desiccated. Freshwater ecosystems are important outdoor laboratories.
Religion	•					•		Freshwaters are sites of historical baptism and religious festivals.
Tourism and recreation	•	•	•	•	•	•	•	Extensive recreational fisheries (game species and coarse fisheries depend on good habitat). Tourism depends on landscape appeal and iconic species, such as rare birds, flowers or amphibians. Good water quality and visual appearance required for natural swimming and boating.
Sense of place	•	•	•	•	•	•	•	Water is important in defining specific landscape character and features strongly in art and local culture. Literary and cultural identities embodied in distinctive landscapes such as Snowdonia, the Lake District, the Somerset Levels, Gwent Levels or the Norfolk Broads.
History	•	•	•	•	•	•	•	Freshwaters and especially wetlands have played a key role in human history and settlement since prehistoric times. Water is a recurrent feature at the heart of many historically important places, battlefields, territorial boundaries and many local folklore connections.
Supporting services								
Biodiversity	•	•	•	•	•	•	•	All freshwater habitats with open water: species depend on conditions such as, temperature, oxygen level, depth and velocity of water and area with suitable conditions. Some habitats may provide temporary habitat for fish (e.g. for spawning), such as floodplains.

Table 9.2 Priority habitats emphasised in the UK Biodiversity Action Plan (UK BAP). Source: UK Biodiversity Action Plan http://jncc.defra.gov.uk/.

Habitat type	Outline attributes	Extent and conservation status
Rivers	Varied, but encompassing all natural and near-natural running waters in the UK, ranging from torrential headwaters through to meandering lowland rivers. Key types are headwaters, *Ranunculus*-rich rivers, chalk rivers, active shingle rivers, designated Sites of Special Scientific Interest (SSSI)/Areas of Special Scientific Interest (ASSI), those containing UK BAP species (such as salmon and lamprey), or those of high hydromorphological or ecological status.	Recently added to the UK BAP and still being evaluated.
Ponds	Permanent and seasonal waters up to 2 hectares in size with particular conservation importance, i.e. meeting designation criteria under the Habitats Directive, holding UK Red Data Book or BAP species, exhibiting exceptional assemblages of organisms, or having exceptional ecological quality or other special attributes.	About 478,000 in the UK, of which, 20% probably meet these conservation criteria.
Oligotrophic and dystrophic lakes	Mainly greater than 2 hectares, with low nutrient concentrations and productivity. Usually occurring on hard, base-poor, upland rocks, these are among the least disturbed assemblages in the UK. Oligotrophic lakes have very clear water, while dystrophic waters are generally peat-stained.	Recently added to the UK BAP and will comprise examples of known conservation importance, as well as those that are damaged but suitable for remediation.
Mesotrophic lakes	Characterised by a narrow range of nutrients, typically 0.3–0.65 mg nitrogen/litre and 0.01–0.03 mg phosphorus/litre and high macrophyte diversity, often with rare fishes.	Infrequent in the UK and confined to north-west upland margins. Many significant mesotrophic lakes are SSSIs, and some are notified under the Ramsar Convention and/or managed as National Nature Reserves.
Eutrophic standing waters	Highly productive and nutrient rich (>0.035 mg phosphorus/litre and 0.5 mg nitrogen/litre) waters, occurring naturally or as a result of enrichment. Characterised by dense algal populations in mid-summer.	Approximately 178.5 hectares in the UK (including Northern Ireland); about 240 designated as SSSI or ASSI, and around 20 Ramsar sites and 6 Special Areas of Conservation.
Aquifer-fed naturally fluctuating water bodies	Natural water bodies with intrinsic regimes of extreme fluctuation in water level, with natural periods of complete or almost complete drying out. They have no inflow or outflow.	Very rare. Three intact turloughs in County Fermanagh (Northern Ireland) and one in South Wales. At least six fluctuating meres in the Norfolk Breckland. All are designated SSSIs, ASSIs or SACs.
Grazing marsh	Periodically inundated grassland, largely occurring within the flat landscapes of floodplains or coastal plains. Ditches divide the fields and are used to control water levels within the marshland; they can support an extremely diverse aquatic flora and fauna. Grazing marsh is an important habitat for ground-nesting wading birds such as lapwing (*Vanellus vanellus*) and curlew (*Numenius arquata*).	This is by far the most common type of lowland wetland, and is widespread throughout the UK. As a consequence, it comprises a large number of SSSIs, but a relatively small proportion of the overall resource is notified.
Fens	This habitat encompasses a very wide range of wetland types on peat and mineral soil, but all have a water table close to, or above, ground level for much of the year. Fens receive water from groundwater, surface water and rain. They include single-species stands in standing water, species-rich tall fen in floodplains, *Sphagnum*-dominated vegetation in basins and valley mires, and very species-rich vegetation around calcareous springs.	These are the second most widespread lowland wetland habitat throughout the UK, and the majority of them are subject to notification, e.g. SSSI. About 70% of fen, marsh and swamp SSSIs are considered to be in unfavourable condition.
Reedbed	Wetlands dominated by stands of common reed (*Phragmites australis*), wherein the water table is at or above ground level for most of the year.	These are the rarest lowland wetland habitat considered here. Most of the larger blocks of the resource are notified.
Lowland raised bogs	Exclusively rain-fed, peatland ecosystems which develop primarily, but not exclusively, in lowland areas such as the head of estuaries, along river floodplains and in topographic depressions. The vegetation is dominated by peat-forming *Sphagnum* mosses and other species such as bog rosemary (*Andromeda polifolia*), cranberry (*Vaccinium oxycoccus*) and cotton-grasses (*Eriophorum vaginatum* and *E. angustifolium*).	Most of the remaining bogs are found in the wetter northern and western parts of the UK, although bogs were once found in all regions. Only 7% of bog SSSIs are in favourable condition as most of the resource is recovering from peat extraction and drainage.

The long-standing recognition of the importance of water supply, pollutant disposal and other Freshwater goods and services, means that Openwaters are amongst the most intensively monitored of all the UK's environments (Section 9.3.6). Available indicators of change are extensive and include:

i) biological features, for example phytobenthos, phytoplankton, macrophytes, invertebrates, fish, microbiological indicators, phyto- and zooplankton and invasive species);

ii) physical features, for example, flow volume and variability, morphological features, modification and fragmentation;

iii) physico-chemical indicators of naturally occurring solutes, sanitary discharges, priority substances, eutrophication, acidification, thermal discharges and inert sediments;

iv) and energetic measures, such as production, decomposition and heat or light budgets.

Many specific tools have been developed for monitoring, classifying and predicting the biological status of Freshwaters; for example, the WFD emphasises fish, macrophytes, phytobenthos and invertebrates for rivers. For standing waters and wetlands, systematic monitoring has historically been restricted to a few locations without any overall inventory or assessment (Raven & Diamond 2010). However, comprehensive biodiversity surveys of lakes and wetlands have been undertaken in Scotland,

Wales, England and Northern Ireland and used for habitat classification.

Despite increasing knowledge of the significance of Freshwater ecosystems in underpinning a sustainable economy, the services they provide remain generally undervalued. Moreover, few data available on UK Freshwaters specifically offer an ecosystem services context. In this chapter, we outline some of the principal ecosystem services provided by Freshwaters, and exemplify them through case studies. We also appraise trends in the condition of the UK's Freshwaters and provide some insight into possible short-term policy options for their improved management.

9.2 Ecosystem Services from Freshwaters

Freshwaters contribute significantly to the delivery of the entire range of ecosystem services (**Table 9.1**). The concept of goods and services of Freshwaters is well-established for Wetlands (e.g. Maltby 1986; Barbier *et al.,* 1991; Dugan 1993) and was subsequently developed for broader ecosystem services (Turner *et al.* 2008; Fisher *et al.* 2009; Maltby 2009a). The approach taken in the UK National Ecosystem Assessment (UK NEA) defines the link between ecosystem processes into intermediate services first, and then defines final services that form the basis of subsequent assessments (**Figure 9.2**).

Final ecosystem services have important economic benefits, but these are underpinned by physical, chemical and biological processes and functions, many of which remain only partially understood (**Figure 9.3**). Examples include the aggregate role of Freshwater organisms on the diversity, temporal and spatial dynamics of ecosystem functions, and interactions between habitat heterogeneity and Freshwater ecosystem processes. The historical focus on the conservation of species/communities needs to be complemented with the maintenance of ecosystem functions if services are to be delivered in the future.

Not all freshwater habitats perform all processes, functions and services to the same degree (Maltby 1986; Dugan 1993; Maltby *et al.* 1994; Bullock & Acreman 2003), with the production of many services varying according to position in the catchment (**Figure 9.1**). There is increasing recognition of the need to understand better the interactions of various different freshwater and land types within a catchment to assess how their processes and functions combine to deliver ecosystem services. Additionally, individual Wetlands may comprise one or several distinct functional units more or less connected by water flows, which in turn depend on overall catchment dynamics. Functional analysis of such areas through characterisation of these areas as 'hydrogeomorphic units' is well advanced for Wetlands, linking ecosystem structure to the delivery

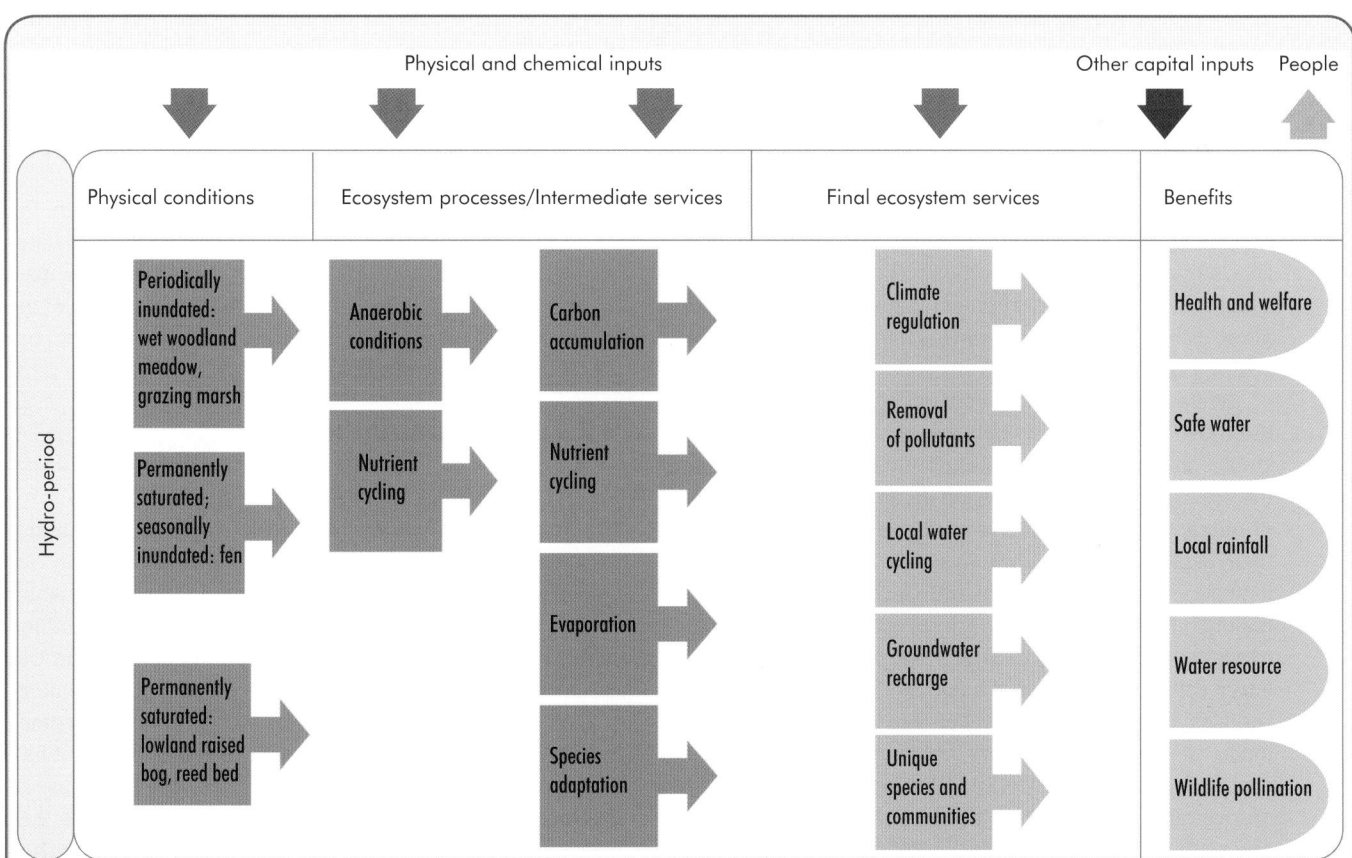

Figure 9.2 Schematic diagram of the relationship between the physical conditions, ecosystem services and benefits of Wetlands. Schematic follows the philosophy of the UK NEA Conceptual Framework (Chapter 2), and is adapted from Fisher *et al.* (2008).

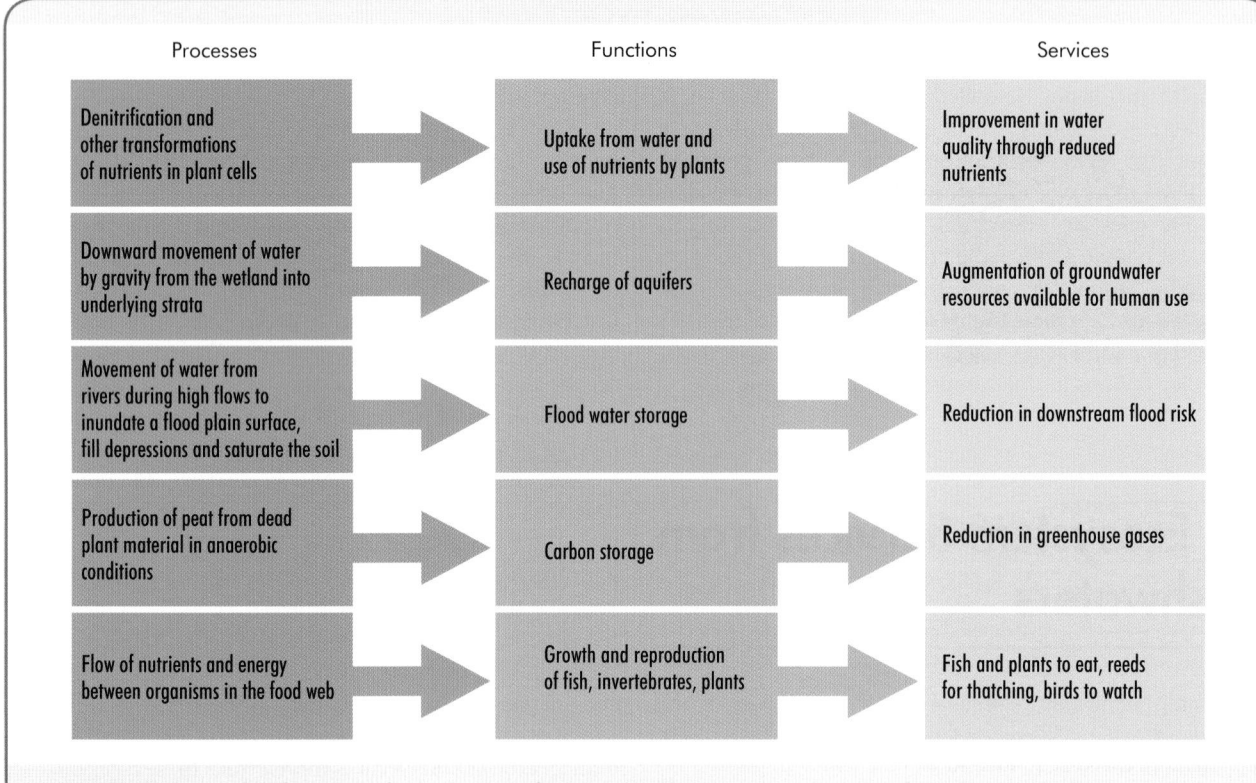

Processes	Functions	Services
Denitrification and other transformations of nutrients in plant cells	Uptake from water and use of nutrients by plants	Improvement in water quality through reduced nutrients
Downward movement of water by gravity from the wetland into underlying strata	Recharge of aquifers	Augmentation of groundwater resources available for human use
Movement of water from rivers during high flows to inundate a flood plain surface, fill depressions and saturate the soil	Flood water storage	Reduction in downstream flood risk
Production of peat from dead plant material in anaerobic conditions	Carbon storage	Reduction in greenhouse gases
Flow of nutrients and energy between organisms in the food web	Growth and reproduction of fish, invertebrates, plants	Fish and plants to eat, reeds for thatching, birds to watch

Figure 9.3 Relationship between the processes, functions and ecosystem services of Freshwater habitats. Source: adapted from Maltby *et al.* (1994), Acreman & Mountford (2009) and Maltby (2009a).

of services (Maltby 2009a,b; **Figure 9.4**). For rivers the approach of the Riverine Ecosystem Synthesis (Thorp *et al.* 2008) similarly describes the structure and functioning of riverine landscapes via functional process zones.

In addition to spatial heterogeneity, services from Freshwaters depend on catchment and temporal hydrological dynamics. For rivers, broad relationships exist between the flow regime, channel form and habitat provision (Acreman 2001b). For example, flow regimes have essential elements that maintain ecosystem functions and services; large floods maintain channel geometry; low flows allow fish fry to mature; small floods stimulate migration; and high flows allow fish access to spawning grounds (Acreman *et al.* 2009a; **Figure 9.5**).

While many of the final ecosystem services provided by the UK's Freshwaters are well-documented (**Table 9.1**), few studies are available that: i) explicitly quantify the value of the services provided; ii) develop quantitative understanding of interactions among the provision of goods and services, their exploitation and ecological functions; or iii) give an indication of the specific area and/or condition necessary to maintain particular services. These represent major research needs, some examples of which are provided below. Even fewer estimates have been made of Freshwater ecosystem services in aggregate. However, in 2002, estimates were made of the total monetary value of Scotland's natural capital and ecosystem services (Williams *et al.* 2003): within an overall annual figure of around £17 billion, lochs, rivers and estuaries generated more than £3 billion. Many of these ecosystem service benefits are used by industry, becoming incorporated in their final goods and services, while other benefits are spread throughout the wider population or

enjoyed by recreational users. An economic analysis of water use in Scotland was undertaken by the Scottish Environment Protection Agency (SEPA) in 2005 and showed links to whisky distilling, hydropower, water supply, recreational angling and agriculture (SEPA 2006). The report also included a number of case studies covering these and other uses including aquaculture, the exploitation of coal, paper and pulp production, canal water supply and leather tanning.

Considerable efforts are being made currently in the UK to identify clearly and value the benefits of Freshwater management. These efforts are being increasingly focused on the identification of strategies that can enhance the realisation of ecosystem services; some examples are presented in **Appendix 9.2**.

9.2.1 Provisioning Services

9.2.1.1 Direct use of water

The provision of water resources supports agricultural irrigation, public domestic supply and abstraction for industry, but there is substantial variation in rainfall, water supply and abstraction across the UK. Of the 16.8 billion cubic metres (m^3) of water abstracted annually in the UK, around 40% comes from tidal sources (as cooling water), around 50% comes from surface waters and 10% comes from groundwaters. These abstractions represent about half of the volumes that are actually licensed. The major use of abstracted water is for piped domestic supply (**Figure 9.6**) which is generally provided by water companies, but over 70% of this volume is subsequently returned as treated effluent. Farmers use less than 1% of the total amount of abstracted water for spray irrigation, but this varies regionally and

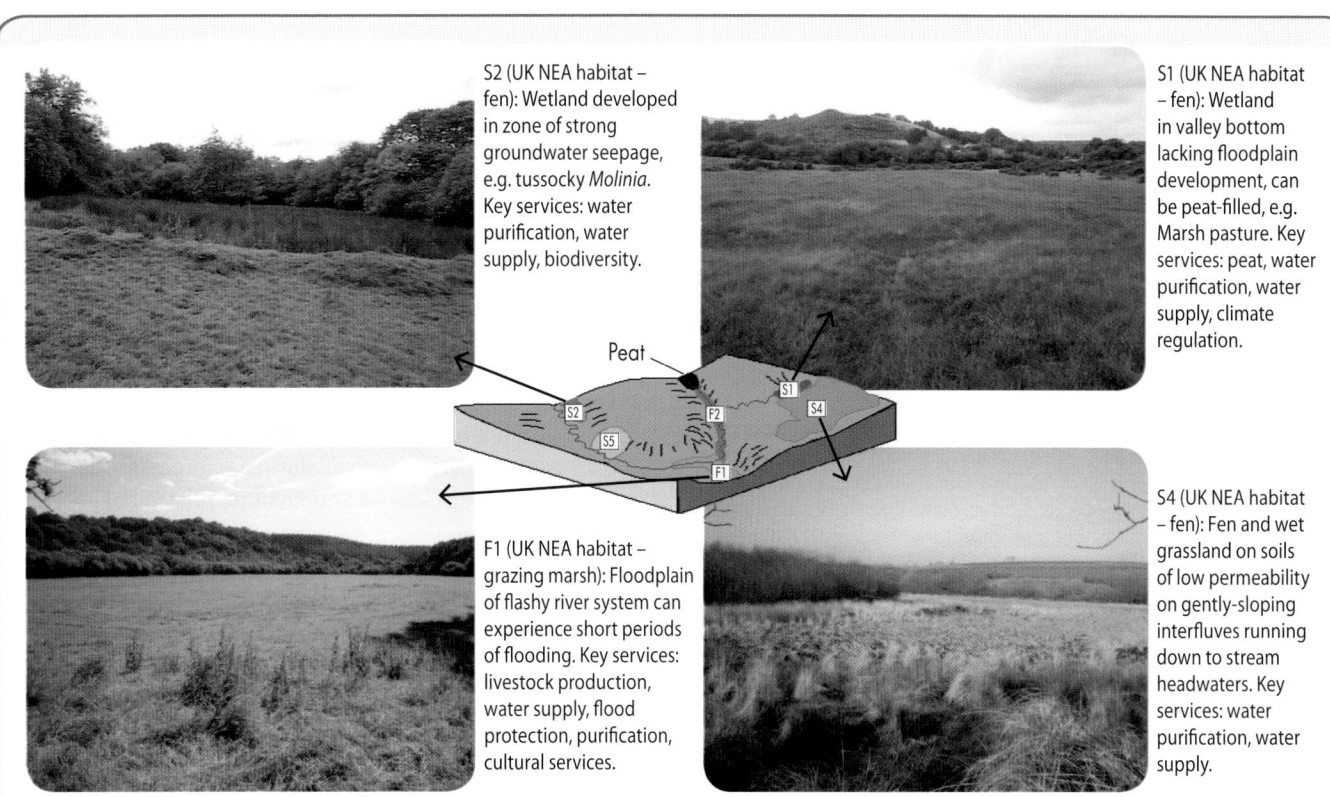

S2 (UK NEA habitat – fen): Wetland developed in zone of strong groundwater seepage, e.g. tussocky *Molinia*. Key services: water purification, water supply, biodiversity.

S1 (UK NEA habitat – fen): Wetland in valley bottom lacking floodplain development, can be peat-filled, e.g. Marsh pasture. Key services: peat, water purification, water supply, climate regulation.

F1 (UK NEA habitat – grazing marsh): Floodplain of flashy river system can experience short periods of flooding. Key services: livestock production, water supply, flood protection, purification, cultural services.

S4 (UK NEA habitat – fen): Fen and wet grassland on soils of low permeability on gently-sloping interfluves running down to stream headwaters. Key services: water purification, water supply.

Figure 9.4 Examples of functional units in Wetlands at the landscape-scale from the Tamar catchment. Source: adapted from Blackwell *et al.* (2009).

seasonally; for example, in East Anglia, abstraction for irrigation during the summer months can average 20% of the total for all uses of freshwater. The ultimate fate of this water—it is lost through evaporation—means that there are potentially larger environmental consequences associated with the use of abstracted water for irrigation than other uses (Environment Agency 2008a).

Groundwater is an important source of water for the public in the UK, and has a vital role in maintaining supplies during dry summers and prolonged droughts (Acreman *et al.* 2000). The principal aquifers of the UK (**Figure 9.7**) are in the English lowlands and include: chalk, Permo-Triassic sandstones, Jurassic limestone and Lower Greensand. Aquifers also occur in the Devonian and Carboniferous strata of South Wales, northern England, central Scotland and parts of Northern Ireland, but these are much more compact rocks, so are considered to be less important for water supply. The older rocks (Silurian, Ordovician, Cambrian and Precambrian) are regarded as an 'impermeable basement', though even these can provide water in significant quantities relative to the scale of individual wells and springs (Groundwater Forum 2002). Groundwater provides 6% of public water supply in Scotland, 8% in Northern Ireland, and 33% across England and Wales (a figure that rises to over 70% when considering the south-east of England alone). Groundwater is also important for rural water supplies in remote parts of the UK. The most productive aquifers in Scotland are in Fife, Strathmore and Moray, as well as south-west Scotland, although surface deposits of alluvium, sands and gravels are also important. Groundwater also plays an important role in sustaining flows in Scottish rivers through the summer months, accounting for up to 30% of total annual flow in 60%

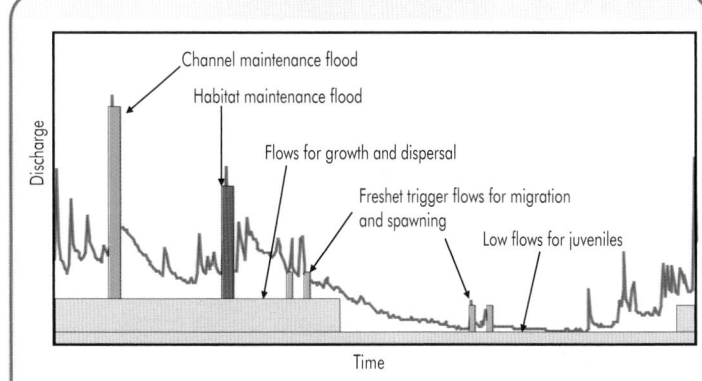

Figure 9.5 Elements of the flow regime required for UK rivers to meet Good Ecological Status in the Water Framework Directive. Source: Acreman *et al.* (2009a).

of our rivers; despite this, overabstraction of groundwater is not a widespread problem in Scotland (Spray 2011). Extensive hard bedrock in Wales has limited underwater storage, so the country's rivers are highly responsive to rainwater runoff or drought (Duigan 2009).

Across England and Wales, water abstraction equates to an average of 10% of total water availability (excluding abstraction to support power production, the water from which is often returned to Openwaters as effluent, although some returns to rivers outside the source catchment). However, this 'Water Exploitation Index' (EEA 2003) varies regionally. It exceeds 22% in south-east and eastern England, for example, so these areas are regarded as 'under stress from water abstraction' to the same extent as countries that are usually considered drier than UK (e.g. Cyprus, Malta,

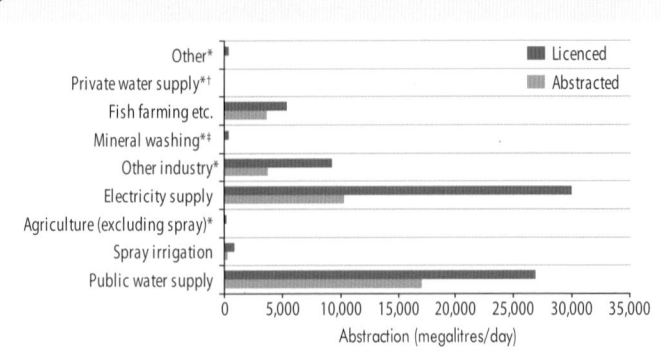

Figure 9.6 Uses of water abstracted from non-tidal sources in England and Wales, 2006–2007. *Return requirements were changed from 01/04/2008 whereby licences that abstract under 100 m³/day no longer had to send returns back this has mainly affected agricultural, private water supply/other and small industrial licences. ‡In 1999, mineral washing was not reported as a separate category. Licences for mineral washing are contained in 'Other industry'. †Private abstractions for domestic use by individual households. Source: Environment Agency (2008a). © Environment Agency and database right.

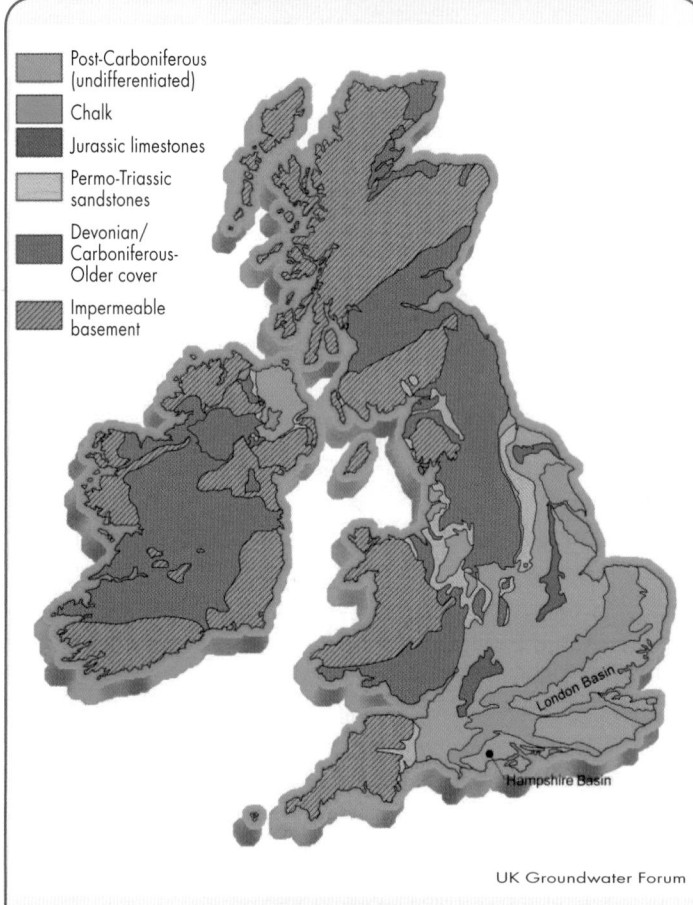

Figure 9.7 Principal aquifers of the British Isles. Source: map obtained from the UK Groundwater Forum (Downing 1998).

significant link to the iconic Scottish whisky industry which is of economic importance, supporting over 40,000 jobs. The whisky industry as a whole consumes some 2–3 million m³ of water per annum, along with 30–40 million litres for cooling which is abstracted and then returned. The Welsh water resource supplies a population of almost 3 million people, with about two thirds concentrated in the south-east around Cardiff. In addition, there are significant cross border demands to supply metropolitan areas of England.

The value of reservoirs often exceeds their role as solely supply features. For example, when evaluated in the early 1990s, Rutland Water had a total annual value of up to £215 million, of which, at least 64% was attributable to ecosystem services (principally recreation) in addition to its primary purpose as a source of potable supply (Gaterell *et al.* 1995). Wetlands may also be locally important in the provision of water supply either directly or through the recharge of aquifers, but there are no national data to indicate the full extent of this service.

The availability of water does not remain fixed over time. Natural interannual meteorological variation has substantial effects on both supply and demand, particularly during droughts (e.g. 1984, 1990–1991, 1995–1996, 2003). Climate change is likely to change flow conditions and availability in the future (e.g. Romanowicz *et al.* 2006; Johnson *et al.* 2009), while also altering demands; although current evidence for trends in low and high flows are equivocal (Hannaford & Marsh 2007, 2008). Water is required for the dilution of pollutants and the consequences of altered flow for organisms and natural ecosystem function are still only partly understood. Many river regimes are now substantially altered from their natural state (Petts 2009). This not only results in ecological effects, but also in consequences for other ecosystem services, particularly where other stressors are involved such as increasing river temperature (Clews *et al.* 2010; Dunbar *et al.* 2010a,b). Subsequently, potential conflicts in use may arise, as exemplified by case studies (Spillett *et al.* 2003).

9.2.1.2 Water for power generation

Water has been used for thousands of years to drive water wheels and watermills. More recently, water has been harnessed to drive turbines for electricity generation. Different configurations exist, but principally consist of schemes where power is generated at a dam or weir, and schemes where water is diverted at a dam or weir and transported via a penstock or leat to generators located some distance away. The UK currently generates more than 1,500 megawatts (MW) of electricity from hydropower sources, which represents a little over 2% of total national energy generation. Most of the large hydropower stations are in Scotland, but the largest of all, Dinorwig (a pumped storage scheme with a capacity of 1.7 gigawatts GW), is in North Wales. Reservoirs held back as part of Scotland's 23 main hydropower schemes cover over 800,000 ha, and affect the ecological status of 117 water bodies. Along with drinking water supply (117 water bodies) and agriculture, abstraction and flow regulation from these activities affect 21% of Scotland's rivers and 25% of its lochs.

The recent large increase in small-scale (<2 MW), run-of-river hydropower schemes is causing severe local impacts

Spain and Italy). Some catchments outside the south-east of England are also considered to be overexploited for both surface and groundwaters, while others are considered to have water available.

In Scotland, water supply has a direct influence on the food and drink sector, especially with regards to its

on flow regimes where they involve off-line turbines; they are generating controversy because of possible effects on longitudinal connectivity of rivers. Although hydropower is non-consumptive, it can affect connectivity, and may have additional effects on flows depending on the configuration and operation of the particular scheme—it can deplete flows in bypassed sections of river and cause artificially rapid flow fluctuations. By regulating the Afon Prysor in Wales, Llyn Trawsfynydd was built in 1931 as the storage reservoir for the Maentwrog hydroelectric power station (Whitehouse 2002). It was also used as the source of cooling water for the Trawsfynydd nuclear power station, which has now been decommissioned. Nonetheless, the reservoir water continues to be used for fishing and hydropower generation.

9.2.1.3 Crops, plants, livestock and fish

The majority of the UK's permanent, Openwater bodies support fish, whether coarse species, such as carp, bream, roach and pike, which prefer slow-flowing or still lowland waters, or game fish, such as trout, grayling and salmon, which prefer fast-flowing waters. Historically, protein from coarse fish was an important element of human diet, and so, medieval fish ponds were widespread in the UK. Today, coarse fish are far less widely eaten. The capture of migratory salmon has also declined, although a few commercial fishermen have continued to net wild salmon in tidal sections of rivers. The Salmon and Freshwater Fisheries Act (1975) regulates and bans fishing licences, fishing seasons and size limits, and banned obstructing the salmon's migratory paths. As a result, most UK salmon fishing is now undertaken for sport and only 30–40% of the 90,000 salmon caught annually in Scottish rivers are eaten, with the remainder being released. Floodplains and Wetlands also provide fish habitats, especially nurseries for coarse species, such as pike, eel and carp. Consequently, the fishing industry is reliant upon these habitats for fish recruitment, although these fish may not be harvested commercially within the habitats themselves (provisioning and regulatory services). Again, much of the harvesting or catch-and-release of these fish is related more to the leisure and recreation industries (cultural services) than to provisioning services.

By far the most important Freshwater systems for food and fibre production are Floodplains, which are naturally fertilised by rivers during floods and are, therefore, amenable to seasonal grazing and arable production (**Box 9.1**). Many are used for intensive agriculture (for example, the Humberhead Levels are used for arable root crops and turf production), while the cutting of natural vegetation on Floodplains provides hay crops and on fens provides sedges used in thatching. The harvesting of reedbeds for thatching is also a significant industry of Floodplains, although not as important today as it was historically. In the 1980s, problems of premature decay in another thatching material, long wheat straw, were traced to high nitrogen contents following intensification of their cultivation with nitrogen fertilisers. The same problem was also claimed for reed roofs, but despite high nitrogen levels causing problems for floating mats of reed (Boar *et al.* 1989), which were disappearing rapidly from Floodplains in East Anglia, there was little evidence of problems in the soil-rooted reed of the managed beds (Boar *et al.* 1999). Perception of the problem may have led to greater imports of cheaper reed from the Danube Delta and Poland, and reduced sales of UK reed. Currently, there seems to be no steady trend in supply and demand of UK-grown reed, but this position is determined largely on anecdotal evidence.

Managed Floodplains and grazing marshes are used for the intensive (and sometimes extensive) farming of dairy, beef and sheep products. Agricultural grassland is the most extensive land cover within Welsh Floodplains and, as a

---

Box 9.1 Agriculture on floodplains.

In England, 1.02 million hectares of agricultural land are within the indicative floodplain, that is, they have an annual risk of flooding of 1% or greater from rivers, or 0.5% or greater from coastal waters (**Table 1**). Although the indicative floodplain accounts for only 9% of the total agricultural area of England, it includes some of the most fertile and productive areas, having been 'reclaimed' and 'improved' for agricultural purposes over hundreds of years. Fifty-seven percent of Grade 1 agricultural land falls within the indicative floodplain, and the capital value of agricultural land at risk of flooding has been estimated at £15 billion using 2008 values. The management of hydrological regimes, in the form of flood alleviation and land drainage, has been key to maintaining the agricultural productivity of this land. The cost in terms of loss of other goods and services has yet to be properly assessed.

Table 1 Classification of agricultural land in indicative floodplains in England, 2002. Source: Natural England (2011).

Agricultural Land Classification	Typical land use	Total ('000s ha)	Indicative floodplain ('000s ha)	Proportion of total area in indicative floodplain (%)
Grade 1	Intensive arable	355	204	57%
Grade 2	Intensive arable	1,849	239	13%
Grade 3	Extensive arable	6,292	379	6%
Grade 4	Dairy and grazing livestock	1,840	186	10%
Grade 5	Grazing livestock	1,101	11	1%
Total potential agricultural land		11,437	1,019	9%
Non-agricultural land		657	31	5%
Urban areas		952	72	8%
Total		**13,046**	**1,122**	**9%**

---

consequence, Floodplain semi-natural habitat is scare, with 60% of the area within just ten river systems (Jones *et al.* 2009, Chapter 6, Chapter 20). Neutral and marshy grassland is the most common component of semi-natural habitat, together with secondary woodland, swamp, fen, bog and standing water.

Wetlands provide habitat for wild game such as woodcock, snipe, ducks and deer, although these are generally now harvested for sporting reasons than for food. This is in sharp contrast to the historic importance of undrained areas, such as The Fens, which supplied London and other urban markets with large quantities of game, eels and other food items (Darby 1983; Maltby 1986).

9.2.1.4 Trees, standing vegetation and peat

Many semi-natural woodlands on Floodplains produce timber that is sustainably managed, while, historically, many grazing marshes produced coppiced and pollarded willow as an important local source of wood for fuel.

Willow has been used for centuries as a construction material, particularly for baskets (Cole 1990), and is prized for its quality in the crafting of cricket bats. Giraldeus Cambrensis provides a 12th Century description of a coracle as a round boat made of willow and covered with raw hides which was used for fishing. Willow is harvested by pollarding: trees are cut back to the main trunk and new shoots, called 'withies', grow out of the trunk and are cut periodically for use. During the 1930s, over 3,600 ha of willow was grown commercially on the Somerset Levels and Moors, but since the 1950s, this industry has declined as packaging has become dominated by plastic and cardboard. By 2000, only around 140 ha of willow was grown commercially in the UK, and only the Somerset Levels and Moors remain today in commercial willow basket production (Acreman *et al.* 2011).

The native black poplar (*Populus nigra* subspecies *betulifolia*) is an attractive, rare and highly valued tree, persisting largely on river floodplains (Jones *et al.* 2009). Many individual trees are now old and in decline. Traditionally, its sturdy timber was used for making carts and stable partitions, in particular, but it had multiple uses in pre-industrial society.

Lowland raised bogs provide peat for the horticultural industry and were historically dug for fuel (**Box 9.2**). However, the pace of peat formation versus its extraction, and the subsequent impacts on biodiversity and hydrology, raise serious questions about its sustainability.

Together with Walton Moss in Cumbria, Cors Caron, which dominates the inland floodplain of the Afon Teifi in Wales, and Cors Fochno, at the mouth of the Dyfi also in Wales, represent the best surviving examples of raised bog landscape in the UK. Yet depressions created by historic peat digging are still visible in these areas. The Fenn's, Whixall, Bettisfield, Wem and Cadney Mosses complex on the Welsh border is the only other surviving relatively large-scale, raised bog, with the remainder of the Welsh resource comprising sites between 1 and 50 ha (Jones 2009). Thorne and Hatfield Moors in England were once among the largest raised bogs, but declined following many years of peat-cutting; they are now being restored. Other natural products from peatlands

include water for whisky production, *Sphagnum* moss for hanging baskets and wild flowers for floristry.

A recent assessment carried out on UK peatlands has examined the full range of services they provide. A summary is given in **Appendix 9.3**.

Fibre, timber and thatch have well-established market values. Other goods may have significant local importance, but most are hard to quantify. In some cases, such as peat extraction or drainage for more intensive agriculture, exploitation may not be consistent with sustainable Wetland or Floodplain management. Other Wetland goods include:

- fibre and fuel including thatch and timber, animal fur, bulb fibre, flax, peat, osiers and withies;
- genetic resources including the grazing of rare breeds and the heritage of the natural diversity of plants which may be used for human benefit (for example, genes for crop resilience);
- biochemicals, natural medicines and pharmaceuticals including known valuable agents such as salicylic acid from willow bark, fungal extracts and local herbal remedies, as well as yet unknown resources;
- and ornamental resources including insectivorous plants, bulrushes and other plants of decorative interest, pebbles, gravel, cobbles and sand.

9.2.1.5 Reedbeds

Reedbed management in the UK supports around 90 direct full-time equivalent jobs and further contract work to a value of up to £4 million per year (GHK 2004). Commercial reed-harvesting provides further direct employment that helps

---

Box 9.2 Peat.

In the UK, peat is still extracted from lowland raised bogs to supply the amateur and commercial horticultural market. In Northern Ireland, Scotland and parts of Wales there is also still peat-cutting for local domestic fuel and export. Extraction continues at around 10 sites in England, covering some 1,300 ha. Consents have been granted on 2,237 ha of peatland and the total area of peatland covered by a current active consent is 520 ha (Lindsay & Immirzi 1996; Brooks 2003; Headley & Dargie 2004; Thomas & Walker 2004; Capita Symonds 2005). Around 77% of raised bogs in Northern Ireland have been cut for fuel, the majority for domestic purposes, but with some relatively limited commercial extraction also. In Scotland, there were 72 extraction sites in 2003: 20 were active, 16 had expired, 3 were pending and 33 were awaiting confirmation (Brooks 2003).

Demand for peat use in horticulture increased in the 1990s, rising by 46% between 1993 and 1999 (ADAS & Enviros 2008). Since 1999, the absolute amount of peat used in the UK has stabilised, and even declined in 2007. Total peat use for horticulture in the UK was 3.01 million m^3 in 2007, of which, around 1.31 million m^3 was derived from UK sources, with 221,000 m^3 from Scotland; extraction of peat for other uses in the UK was around 10,000 m^3.

Extraction of peat for horticultural uses requires the vegetation to be stripped, thus removing the floral and faunal biodiversity. In addition, site preparation for peat extraction requires drainage by cutting deep arterial drains to take away the water collected in the superficial drains around the cutting areas. It therefore interferes with the existing biodiversity, water quality, carbon storage and nutrient dynamics in an intact bog, as well as with the rates of, or potential for, restoration of degraded bogs.

---

to support the thatching industry. Major reedbeds such as those at the Royal Society for the Protection of Birds (RSPB) Ham Wall, Titchwell Marsh, Minsmere and Leighton Moss nature reserves in England, together with the Tay Reedbeds in Scotland, are also important for wildlife tourism. In Wales, swamp habitat is widespread, but occurs most frequently and extensively along the coast (Jones 2009). The total extent of all forms of Welsh swamp is around 1,800 ha, of which, about 460 ha are dominated by reed sufficiently extensive to be regarded as reedbed. There is strong demand for quality, UK-produced thatching reed. Along with other fen products, such as biofuel and pet litter, thatching reed can be produced viably while sensitively managing the reedbeds for wildlife. Reedbeds can also provide water management functions (Fisher & Acreman 2004), as well as making significant contributions to improving water quality (Moss et al. 1984; 1988).

Some conservation bodies have re-established semi-natural reedbeds, particularly for birds such as bittern (*Botaurus stellaris*), and manage them with minimum cutting (RSPB 1994). Northumberland Wildlife Trust has a target of increasing the reedbed resource by 20 ha/annum within their own reserves. However, many pre-war reedbeds have reverted to scrub and carr, and are unlikely to be recovered. The market for thatch is believed to be buoyant—thatched roofs are considered valuable features and need replacing every few decades.

9.2.2 Regulating Services

9.2.2.1 Flood regulation

Openwaters are both agents of flood risk and also dissipate floodwaters. Both outcomes have been a key feature of their management. The frequency and magnitude of floods from Openwaters are influenced by human uses of land in their wider catchments including urbanisation, increased drainage and other conversions that alter hydraulic retention, such as embankments that separate rivers from their floodplains. Although these alterations can provide part of the solution to flood risk management, maintenance of such engineered solutions is expensive. Floodwater retention occurs where water is retained in catchment soils or Wetlands, and where flood storage capacity is enhanced by green roofs, permeable surfaces, channels, lakes, Wetlands and Floodplains functioning in natural ways. These notions were expressed partly in the Department for Environment, Food and Rural Affairs (Defra) (2005) report, 'Making Space for Water', and also in the concept and development of Sustainable Urban Drainage Systems (SUDS).

Most flooding occurs from the overspill of rivers or the sea, or from the failure of local drainage. However, groundwater flooding can also occur in areas underlain by aquifers, such as chalk, or in river valleys with thick deposits of alluvium or river gravel. This latter type of flooding typically happens in response to a combination of already high groundwater levels and lengthy rainfall events, and lasts far longer than fluvial flooding (Macdonald et al. 2008). There are currently around 380,000 properties at risk of groundwater flooding and the cumulative cost of these events has been estimated at £4–14 million/year.

In Scotland, a new Flood Risk Management (Scotland) Act 2009 has been approved. This Act deliberately focuses attention on the extent to which a reduction in flood risk can be achieved through both structural and non-structural options (Spray et al. 2010). It also highlights the importance of assessing whether interventions in the upper catchment could assist in reducing flood risk to communities lower down the valley. It directs relevant authorities (working in partnership) to consider flood risk management in a holistic manner and instructs SEPA to map natural features and artificial structures in terms of their contribution to flood risk management.

In Wales, riverbank reinforcement and embankment for flood control are widespread, especially in urban environments, with almost the entire length of rivers such as the Taff being impacted in this way (Dobson et al. 2009). From Environment Agency River Habitat Survey data, there is evidence of slightly more reinforcements at sites in the 2007/2008 baseline survey compared with 1995/1996, particularly in the South Wales Valley area towards Cardiff.

The extensive modifications to river channels and floodplains undertaken in the recent past for flood control and land drainage purposes have had serious consequences for habitats and their inhabitants (Dunbar et al. 2010a,b). At the same time, when carried out sensitively and in conjunction with natural processes, flood defence works offer a major potential route for river rehabilitation and restoration, including the restoration of important ecosystem functions. However, to judge whether the overall costs and benefits of flood defence are positive or negative for ecosystem services or functions requires further, careful evaluation of the evidence in order to guide action.

The storage of floodwater on Floodplains can reduce flood magnitude downstream (Bullock & Acreman 2003). A modelling study of the River Cherwell in Oxfordshire (Acreman et al. 2003) showed that separation of floodplains from the river by embankments increases the peak flows downstream by up to 150%. The majority of flood storage in Wetlands is above ground; for example, at a flood level of 5 m Above Ordnance Datum (AOD), the floodplains of the Parrett (Currymoor, Northmoor and Haymoor) in Somerset have a combined volume of 6.8 million m³ through the inundation of 1,710 hectares of land. Saturated soils, with a water table near the surface, occur in many Wetlands and have no, or limited, flood storage capacity (Acreman et al. 2007). However, it is important to note that drained agricultural soils may also reach saturation during the heavy rain that precedes a flood. Areas of saturated soils in headwater areas are defined as 'runoff contributing areas' by hydro-geomorphologists (e.g. Hewlett & Hibbert 1966); this relationship forms the basis of rainfall-runoff models used by hydrologists, such as 'TOPMODEL' (Beven & Kirkby 1979; Beven et al. 1984). Taken as a whole, the available evidence suggests that the widespread belief that Wetlands act as sponges, storing large quantities of water during times of high rainfall, is misplaced. However, storage is just one factor that determines how floods are generated and transmitted through a catchment. For example, the presence of Wetland vegetation, and particularly wet woodland, can significantly increase the hydraulic roughness of a Floodplain when compared to alternative land uses (Baker *et al.* 2009). This has the effect of holding up water levels locally during extreme events, slowing the movement of the flood peak downstream, and reducing the height of the peak. This may synchronise or desynchronise flood peaks, thus implications at the catchment-scale are difficult to generalise. Surface roughness can also be a factor in runoff generation in upland catchments; overland flow is slower through vegetation than bare soils (Holden *et al.* 2008). Land drainage can have an additional, significant impact on runoff-generation, but whether it increases or decreases floods depends on the soil type (Robinson 1990).

Objectives for re-wetting Floodplains for biodiversity and for flood risk management are combined in the Great Fen Project in Cambridgeshire. It aims to store winter floodwater for the protection of the Middle Level System and the houses, farms and businesses that depend on it, while also providing water to restore and maintain fenland habitat on previously arable land. Other objectives include improving water quality, increasing recreation and tourism opportunities, and improving quality of life for local people.

The Insh Marshes, an internationally important Wetland in the Spey Valley, provides flood defence benefits to Aviemore and other downstream settlements (Alveres *et al.* 2007). The marshes cover some 1,100 ha of Floodplain and have a role in water storage that has been valued at more than £83,000/annum, were it to be replaced by 7 km of flood defence banks around Aviemore. Alongside their flood defence services, the marshes provide many other functions that add economic, recreational and cultural value to the local community and visitors. Tourists contribute around £132,000 to the local economy each year, while fishing revenue provides a further £35,000. Additional ecosystem services, such as farming, water quality, education, training and conservation management, are also provided by the marshes; their total value, along with that of biodiversity, has not yet been quantified.

Secondary impacts on flood behaviour may result from the experimental reintroduction of the European beaver (*Castor fiber*) into the Scottish landscape. Beaver dams that create ponds on headwater streams may have a role in flood attenuation, while also providing biodiversity benefits. The Scottish Beaver Trial, jointly run by the Scottish Wildlife Trust and Royal Zoological Society of Scotland, is monitoring the effects of their reintroduction on high and low river flows, as well as their effects on the wider habitat and species diversity.

9.2.2.2 Carbon sinks and sources

In global terms, Freshwaters are small in comparison with the marine environment, so have smaller absolute roles in carbon uptake through, for example, algae or macrophytes. However, peat soils can store more carbon than forests and woodland.

Lowland peatlands are often deeper than upland peatlands; their enhanced accumulation is a result of their topography and the higher growth rate of plants in milder, lowland climates, particularly in nutrient-rich systems. As a result, lowland peatlands often store more carbon per unit area than their upland counterparts. Peat deposits exceeding

12 m deep can occur in valleys like Fen Bog in North Yorkshire, and deposits up to 12 m deep occur in the former fenland of the Somerset Levels (Cope & Colborne 1981). Many raised bogs also have peat deposits which exceed 10 m deep in places (Burton & Hodgson 1987). Natural England (2010) estimated that the remaining lowland fen in English peatlands stored 1,004–2,576 tonnes of carbon/ha, and raised bog peats stored 1,575–1,629 tonnes of carbon/ha. However, when peatlands are drained for agriculture, peat-cutting or forestry, their stored carbon is no longer protected from decomposition by waterlogging. Thus the peats begin to degrade, becoming shallower through slumping, compression and erosion, and gradually rot away, releasing carbon dioxide as they decompose. These areas, known as 'wasted' peatlands, may still store considerable quantities of carbon (around 850 tonnes/ha) in their remnant peat. However, Natural England (2010) recognises that these calculations are mostly based on data that is 25 to 30 years old, and that loss of peat carbon is likely to have progressed at a greater rate more recently (Holman 2009). The National Peat Depth and Carbon Storage Project, funded by Natural England, is underway to collate more peat depth and carbon storage data, and promote new and coordinated surveys to improve estimates of peatland carbon storage. In addition to the significant store of carbon in the peat deposits, lowland wetland vegetation can be an important store of carbon. Lindsay (2010) estimates that a 15 cm deep *Sphagnum* mat can represent a carbon store of 45 tonnes carbon/ha—a figure comparable to some woodlands.

Peatlands retaining a high water table continue to store new carbon through the build-up of plant material that has captured atmospheric carbon through photosynthesis. While some plant material decomposes in the upper, more aerobic peat layers, a proportion becomes more or less permanently waterlogged and anaerobic, decomposing far more slowly. This very slow anaerobic decomposition is outstripped by the deposition of newer plant material and peat builds up. However, this anaerobic decomposition releases methane, a greenhouse gas much more powerful than carbon dioxide (Immirzi & Maltby 1992). This means that waterlogged peatlands are not only carbon sinks, but may also be overall sources of greenhouse gases. This effect is strongest in the short-term, because the potency of methane as a greenhouse gas declines over time as it is degrades in the atmosphere (Baird *et al.* 2009). However, the carbon dioxide emissions from drained and cultivated peatlands are so large that they are likely to have five to six times the global warming effect of waterlogged peatlands, even allowing for the greater potency of methane. Natural England (2010) used figures generated from a range of European sites (Couwenberg *et al.* 2008) to estimate that drained intensive agricultural peatlands emit the greenhouse gas equivalent of 22–26 tonnes of carbon dioxide/ha/yr.

A major and extensive phenomenon over recent years has been a marked and progressive increase in the export of dissolved organic carbon (DOC) from peatlands discharging through upland rivers, lakes and reservoirs (Worrall *et al.* 2002, 2003). Although the exact cause is debated (Freeman *et al.* 2001, 2004; Monteith *et al.* 2007), observed trends correlate with increasing average summer temperatures coupled with peat-drying and local land use modification. There are serious concerns about this alteration in carbon dynamics and soil storage, which also have implications for water treatment costs, particularly due to water discolouration.

A series of projects, including the United Utilities' Sustainable Catchment Management Programme (SCaMP) and the Exmoor Mires Project, are now assessing how catchment-scale restoration can help attenuate DOC export, while also meeting the target of returning SSSIs to favourable condition. There is also a focus on sediment load and downstream flooding with the intention to "ensure a sustainable future for the company's agricultural tenants and support United Utilities' Biodiversity Strategy". The measures taken include large-scale drain-blocking, revegetation of extensive bare peat and the introduction of more sustainable grazing regimes. Partnerships are extensive in these projects, including government bodies, universities, water companies and non-governmental organisations (NGOs) such as the RSPB. It is still not clear whether drain-blocking consistently reduces DOC loads and water discolouration once peat has undergone significant physical and chemical change. However, meta-analysis by Armstrong et al. (2010), using data from 32 study sites, revealed 28% lower DOC and colour in blocked drains than in unblocked drains. Other conclusions about biodiversity and atmospheric gas exports (e.g. of methane) are still emerging.

In Scotland, SEPA has used long-term monitoring data to investigate recent trends in carbon dynamics, and has shown that 39 out of 58 rivers have significantly increasing Total Organic Carbon (TOC), with rates equal to a doubling of the concentration over 20 years. All of the sites showing an increase were south of the Cromarty Firth, while 11 of the 18 that did not were north of Inverness. Fewer long-term data were available for lochs, but decreasing trends in DOC were found at 23 sites about which more than five years' worth of data had been collected. For both lochs and rivers, increasing TOC concentrations caused darkening of water colour, reducing light and energy levels entering these ecosystems.

Sea-level rise is a specific concern for coastal Welsh peatlands, such as Cors Fochno, which suffers from marginal drainage and is at risk of saltwater flooding if coastal defences fail (Jones 2009).

Wetland restoration, particularly of peat, is often cited as a means of combating climate change and the wider societal benefits of this have been examined by Maltby (2010). Carbon dioxide and methane are the most important components of the peatland carbon budget, although methane is 25 times more potent as a greenhouse gas. The Somerset Levels and Moors is one of the UK's largest Wetlands containing around 10.9 million tonnes of carbon (Brown 2009a); estimates of carbon dioxide and methane available for this Wetland (**Box 9.3**) show it to be broadly carbon neutral, but the balance depends on site management, particularly water level and the grazing/hay-cutting regime.

9.2.2.3 Climate regulation
In addition to the above effects on carbon dynamics, Freshwater ecosystems can moderate extreme temperature.

Box 9.3 Greenhouse gas fluxes on the Somerset Levels and Moors.

In 2002, the net flux of carbon dioxide was measured at Tadham Moor, a lowland wet grassland on the Somerset Levels and Moors (Lloyd 2006). Carbon assimilated into the wetland during 2002 exceeded the carbon produced by 169 grams carbon/m², making the site an apparent sink for carbon. These measurements, however, include the assimilation of carbon dioxide into the meadow vegetation, but not the loss of carbon dioxide that would have occurred if the vegetation had been left to senesce and decompose in the field. Instead, the hay was harvested and taken away, and some of the new meadow growth was consumed by cattle which also removed the vegetation in the form of their increased body weight. From harvest yields and established relationships between cattle weight gain per kilogram of herbage eaten, it was estimated that 228 grams carbon/m² had been removed from the field. Subtracting this from the overall balance turned the site from a carbon sink to a carbon source losing 59 grams carbon/m² during the year. By using a model of the site, it was estimated that raising water levels would have reduced carbon losses by 243 grams carbon/m² over the year, making the site at least carbon neutral (Acreman et al. 2011).

Measurements of soil methane fluxes were made during three campaigns between 2003 and 2004 (Acreman et al. 2011). Strong relationships were apparent between water table depth (which varied between -0.81 and +0.18 m) and average methane flux (which ranged from -85 to +19 micrograms/m²/hr). The wetland generates methane during high water table levels and consumes methane when water levels are low. The critical water table level at which this switch takes place is around 10 cm below the soil surface.

Box 9.4 Microclimate regulation.

Enhanced evaporation over a wetland, compared to dry land, would be expected to increase relative humidity and cool the lower atmosphere with feedback consequences for evaporation in surrounding habitats. There is also the possibility that cloud cover will change over a wetland, linked to the modified evaporation and surface energy fluxes, and to modified rainfall. The magnitude of these influences will depend on the size of the wetland, the contrast with the surrounding region and the overlying weather patterns. The Somerset Levels and Moors is one of the UK's largest wetlands and shows some microclimate alterations. Meteorological data from Yeovilton airstation (25 km to the south-west and outside the Wetland) shows the air over Tadham Moor has higher daytime humidity and slightly lower temperature leading to a substantially lower vapour pressure deficit in the day (Acreman et al. 2011). The vapour pressure deficit is one of the primary drivers to evaporation and we would infer that the potential evaporation over the Wetland would be 10–20% lower (Acreman et al. 2011).

The supply of water to the atmosphere is also an essential contribution to fundamental climate control at all scales, but can be especially marked at the local level (**Box 9.4**).

9.2.2.4 Waste disposal and dilution
Openwaters are used extensively for the disposal and dilution of wastes and pollutants. As with water supply, the financial (not to mention energy, chemical and land take) costs of providing the same service through other methods would be very high. Equally, the costs incurred in treating this material before disposal are a measure of how much value is placed on good quality Freshwater ecosystems: annual water treatment costs across the UK are estimated at around £1.2 billion.

There are an estimated 100,000 consented wastewater discharges across England and Wales. Many are small, domestic sewage discharges (<5 m³/day), but around 8,000 are 'significant' sewage or trade effluent discharges. A further 20,000 discharge consents are for intermittent discharges, such as storm overflows, that serve joint purposes of voiding floodwaters and bypassing sewage treatment works that would otherwise be overloaded. Discharges have been a very significant source of ecological impact on river ecosystem quality, illustrating how, in the past, Openwaters were used for pollutant disposal and regulation without full recognition of the environmental costs (Section 9.4). General compliance with consents is high, and has improved through time, but problems remain in some locations. Water quality issues are also increasingly likely to reflect the inadvertent disposal of diffuse pollutants through non-consented routes.

Parallel data for Scotland reveals around 1,250 consented discharges, divided between trade discharge (approximately 370), public sewage (660) and private sewage (165). Compliance with consent requirements across Scotland is in the range of 80–90%. Northern Ireland has about 280 consented sewage outfalls and 655 trade outfalls, with compliance at around 66%.

Waste purification in constructed Wetlands provides a further example of waste regulation services. However, in contrast to the situations described previously, which deal with waste from point sources (usually pipes), these services address the much more challenging issue of diffuse pollution whether from agricultural or urban sources.

The ability of Freshwater ecosystems to trap, breakdown, process and transform pollutants, especially those derived from diffuse agricultural pollution, means they perform the services of waste breakdown, detoxification and purification to a significant degree (Maltby 2009a) and with an associated high societal value that is often overlooked. Key processes occurring in Wetlands that enable delivery of this service include bacterially driven denitrification, nitrification and mineralisation, plant uptake and the trapping or filtering of particulates (Kadlec & Knight 1996). Wetland systems, particularly reedbeds, have combinations of highly oxic and anoxic sites within their soils due to stratification in the sediment or soil profile and/or the release of oxygen from plant roots; these conditions are conducive to the breakdown and transformation of many pollutants including organic and inorganic compounds derived from agriculture and denitrification (a major mechanism for 'cleaning' groundwaters of their nitrogen content). It should be noted, however, that overloading a Wetland's natural capacity to cope with chemical transformations may cause ecological changes resulting in the loss of biodiversity. Consequently, constructed Wetlands are often created to deal with pollutants rather than trying to use natural ecosystems.

Detoxification of polluted waters, such as those containing high concentrations of heavy metals, can occur through the uptake of toxic materials by Wetland plants, such as reeds or bulrushes, or through the deposition of particulate matter. However, there is growing concern that these accumulated nutrients or pollutants may escape from Wetlands into rivers as pulses (Prior & Johnes 2002), resulting in significant pollution events. In addition, many persistent pollutants are stored rather than metabolised, leading to Wetland toxicity in extreme cases. Removal or harvesting of the plant material cannot ensure complete removal of these

pollutants, although excavation and disposal of trapped sediment is more effective.

Welsh Freshwater ecosystems are still suffering from an industrial legacy, but there is evidence of improvement following remediation interventions. The Afon Goch, which drains the currently inactive copper mine on Parys Mountain, Anglesey, has been described as one of the most acid- and metal-contaminated streams in the UK (Boult et al. 1994). Abandoned coal mines are releasing acidic, sulphate-rich water, often with negative effects on biota (Ormerod & Jüttner 2009). The most recent Welsh review identified 90 mine discharges, with around 60 km of Welsh rivers judged to be affected. Within and around those river stretches that were affected, deposits of 22 ha of ochreous pollutants were conspicuously visible, and clearly linked to biological impacts at around 70% of the sites sampled. Despite the fact that Welsh rivers are still polluted, more than 50 metal mine locations have remediation strategies in place (Environment Agency 2002) and there have been some success stories. For instance, the Afon Pelenna Wetlands were constructed between 1995 and 1999 to remediate an acid-mine discharge; regardless of occasional episodes of pollution, the abundances of invertebrates, trout and river birds have recovered (Wiseman et al. 2004). Treatment of these discharges have probably aided the wider ecological recovery within the Welsh Valley Rivers, with salmon returning to the Ebbw, the Rhymney, the Taff and the Rhondda (data from the Environment Agency; Holmes & Gough 2009).

The capacity of naturally occurring Wetlands to improve water quality depends on them occupying locations that intercept polluted waters such as agricultural runoff (Blackwell et al. 2009). The use of constructed Wetlands for water treatment has seen enormous growth over the past 50 years and, in some cases, they are now seen as a more sustainable and cost-effective solution to the problem of treating various types of polluted water than their engineering counterparts. Appropriate planning and management of the Wetland is necessary to ensure lasting, effective treatment; without this, the Wetland is, at best, ineffective and, at worst, may add to the pollutant load. Constructed treatment Wetlands can also provide a range of secondary benefits such as habitat provision and production of reeds for thatching. However, management for these additional benefits should not compromise the primary objective of water treatment (Stratford et al. 2010). There are now more than 1,000 examples of such systems in the UK (Cooper 2007) including: the constructed Wetland at Slimbridge which treats wastewater from the Wildfowl & Wetlands Trust's bird collection; the Wheal Jane Wetland in Cornwall which treats mine wastewater; and the Heathrow Wetland which treats runoff from the airport's runways (Nuttall et al. 1997).

South West Water estimates that water treatment costs rise by between 17% and 20% for managing raw river water with heavy sediment loads. In extreme floods, river intakes may be closed for short periods while the turbidity in the raw water declines; during this time, the treated water system relies on stored water. Modelling has shown that a £10 million investment could save £650 million in costs of treating nutrient- and topsoil-laden water over a 30-year period. South West Water has, therefore, put forward a proposal to OFWAT (the Water Services Regulation Authority) under Price Review 2009 (PR09) to make payments to farmers to alter the management of their land (i.e. private land, not owned by South West Water) for the benefit of particular ecosystem services (Martin Ross pers. comm.).

Economic choice experiments to estimate the value of improving water quality (as required by the WFD) have been carried out in two Scottish catchments impacted by agricultural non-point source pollution and water abstraction (Hanley *et al.* 2006). Encouragingly, 90% of the respondents interviewed in each catchment expressed a 'willingness to pay' for better river water quality. These benefit estimates are potentially 'transferable' to other sites with similar characteristics. The Scottish Environment Protection Agency has consequently set up a river restoration fund, in part, to help achieve this goal (Gilvear *et al.* 2010).

9.2.2.5 Firebreaks
Freshwater can provide important fire breaks, as in gaps in combustible material that act as a barrier to slow or stop the progress of a bushfire or wildfire.

9.2.2.6 Health and diseases
Freshwaters can be very important for sustaining human health through recreation and quality of life. However, historically, they were often described as unhealthy. For example, in 1794, George Kay (a well known writer of the day on agricultural issues) described Anglesey: "The climate is moist and unhealthy, producing frequent agish complaints. This is imparted to the fogs from the Irish Sea by which it is surrounded. I am however rather inclined to think that it arises from the great number of fens and morasses which, if drained, would not only be a great acquisition to the proprietors but would lend much to the healthiness of the island" (Kay 1794).

Today, Freshwaters remain potential sources of infection (Acreman *et al* 2011); our current knowledge is very limited, so risks are difficult to calculate, but the issue warrants some reporting. For example, Freshwaters support large numbers of migratory waterbirds, such as ducks, geese and swans, that can be reservoirs for Low Pathogenic Avian Influenza viruses and have also played a role in the transmission of Highly Pathogenic Avian Influenza (HPAI), specifically H5N1 (Gilbert *et al.* 2008) which represents a threat to wildlife, poultry and humans (Snow *et al.* 2007). In 2008, an outbreak of HPAI H5N1 was recorded in a mute swan (*Cygnus olor*) population at Abbotsbury, Dorset (Defra 2008); however, direct contact with such birds would be needed for humans to become infected.

In Wetland systems, the abundance of mosquitoes has been shown to be reduced by the presence of the diverse communities of invertebrate predators (including water beetles such as *Dytiscus, Laccornis, Hydaticus* and *Hydrophilus* species) that are generally present in mature water bodies (Carlson *et al.* 2009). Key human-biting mosquitoes have been found in UK Wetlands including *Anopheles claviger*, a species capable of transmitting *Plasmodium vivax* (the probable causal agent of historical malaria in the UK), and

Coquillettidia richiardii, a species that bites humans and birds and is implicated as a bridge vector involved in the transmission of West Nile Virus in the USA (Medlock *et al.* 2005). Wetlands in the south of England are currently warm enough to support the transmission of *P. vivax* for two to three months per year (Lindsay & Thomas 2001)—a period that is likely to extend with future global warming. However, there is currently no evidence for the existence of insect vector-borne diseases associated with Wetlands in the UK, even though the data suggests that several Wetland-associated UK mosquito and midge species have the potential to vector a range of exotic diseases. While the expansion of Wetland habitats may have the potential to increase the risk of disease transmission, particularly via some mosquito species, it is possible to mitigate against such effects with well-considered Wetland design and management (Zimmer *et al.* 2010). Where Wetlands are reasonably remote from large population centres, mosquitoes produce only limited biting nuisance to people in the foreseeable future. However, stagnant areas of water in urban areas (e.g. water butts and tyre dumps) also provide good mosquito habitat and may pose a risk to humans.

9.2.3 Supporting Services

9.2.3.1 Resistance and resilience in surrounding ecosystems
In addition to the support of organisms and internal ecosystem processes, Freshwaters also support other surrounding ecosystems. This includes the export of energy or carbon in the form of emerging insects or exploited fishes which are used as prey by terrestrial organisms; for some birds, bats and spiders, this subsidy can contribute 25–100% of total energy used (Briers *et al.* 2005; Baxter *et al.* 2005). The export of water and sediments into terrestrial zones and Floodplains inundated during flood cycles may also be significant.

The hyporheic zone (the zone beneath and lateral to a stream bed, where mixing of shallow groundwater and surface water takes place) provides a refuge habitat for surface-dwelling taxa during disturbance events such as droughts; thus, it has the capacity to add resilience to the whole river ecosystem (Brunke & Gonser 1997; Robertson & Wood 2010).

9.2.3.2 Wild species diversity including microbes
Wetlands, in particular, are ecologically diverse, and more than a quarter of the Wetland area in England is designated as a SSSI. In some cases, the individual habitat may not appear overly diverse (e.g. reedbeds), but they support specialised species. But often, much of the diversity of Wetlands is hidden in the soil, where varied and sometimes unique microbial communities are found. In these frequently anoxic environments, microbes have developed novel adaptations including the ability to respire anaerobically and to use reduced organic compounds in the soil as energy sources (nitrate, manganese, iron and sulphur). Diverse and unique communities of microorganisms include: nitrifiers such as *Nitrosomonas* species and *Nitrobacter* species which are capable of oxidising ammonium to nitrate; denitrifiers such as *Pseudomonas* species and *Thiobacillus* species,

capable of reducing nitrate to nitrogen gases; methanogens such as *Methanobacterium* species and *Methanococcus* species, capable of removing excess hydrogen from anaerobic environments in the form of methane; and sulphate-reducing bacteria such as *Desulphobacterales* and *Desulphovibrionales* which are capable of reducing sulphates to sulphites. These communities are essential for nutrient cycling and the performance of the water purification and detoxification services operated by Wetlands. Many of these same organisms can occur locally in river environments, and form part of a range of organisms that have been 'domesticated' for use in treating a wide variety of domestic and trade wastes.

9.2.3.3 Biogeochemical cycling

In addition to conveying the all-important water cycle, Freshwaters have close links with other cycles, for example, through providing nitrogen, phosphorous, carbon and other trace elements into marine environments and other adjacent systems. These effects are expanded in Chapter 12.

9.2.3.4 Contribution to biological and genetic diversity

Freshwater habitats cover less than 1% of the Earth's surface, yet support about 10% of all known species, and around one third of all vertebrate species. Regardless of this, they are also hotspots for human activities that have led to widespread habitat alteration, pollution, flow regulation, abstraction, fish exploitation and alien species introductions. As a consequence, impairments to biodiversity and extinction rates are faster in Freshwaters than in any other ecosystem types (Denny 1994; MA 2005; Strayer & Dudgeon 2010).

The importance of the biodiversity of the UK's Freshwaters is recognised in a range of ways, including:

- in the UK BAP (see **Table 9.2**);
- through the inclusion of UK Freshwater organisms in the Habitats Directive (92/43/EEC) such as fish like brook lamprey (*Lampetra planeri*), river lamprey (*Lampetra fluviatilis*), sea lamprey (*Petromyzon marinus*), Atlantic salmon (*Salmo salar*), bullhead (*Cottus gobio*), twaite shad (*Alosa fallax*) and allis shad (*Alosa alosa*); invertebrates like the snail, *Anisus vorticulus* and the bivalve, *Margarifiter margarifiter*; and *Callitriche–Batrachion* plant communities characteristic of chalk rivers;
- and through additional national and international conservation legislation (e.g. Wildlife and Countryside Act, Ramsar Convention) and the UK statutory designation system.

With regards to statutory designations, using England as an example, there are 28,693 ha of Openwater within SSSIs, of which, 20,458 ha are standing waters (including 10,391 ha designated for their bird interest), 354 ha are canals and 7,881 ha are rivers and streams. Forty-four rivers have at least a part of their length notified as an SSSI, covering just over 2,500 km of river length. Among the most important internationally are England's chalk rivers, which cover a greater length here than any other country in Europe (around 3,900 km). About 2,500 km of river in England and Wales have water-crowfoot (*Ranunculus* species),

recognised as important both in the EU Habitats Directive and UK Biodiversity Action Plan.

Special Areas of Conservation (SACs) cover 9,308 ha of Openwater habitat (**Table 9.3**) including: 33 lakes or groups of lakes totalling 4,628 ha; 17 rivers, which are mainly large, whole-river sites, covering a length of 1,744 km; the Rochdale and Cannock Extension canals; and hundreds of temporary ponds throughout the New Forest and pond complexes on 32 sites around the UK designated specifically for great crested newts (*Triturus cristatus*). Large areas of Openwaters (6,615 ha or more) are also designated as Special Protection Areas (SPAS), mainly for wintering waterbirds (**Table 9.3**) (Natural England 2009).

Fresh water is considered a key biodiversity, landscape and recreational resource in the UK. The Freshwaters and Wetlands of Wales, for example, represent a nationally and internationally important conservation resource. More than 75% of Welsh designated conservation sites (SSSIs/SACs/SPAs) contain freshwater-dependent biological features (data from Countryside Council for Wales). There are designated sites on six major river systems and over 140 lakes (data from Countryside Council for Wales). Approximately 320 Wetland SSSIs depend upon groundwaters (data from Countryside Council for Wales). More than 50% of the land area of Wales is within the catchments of these rivers, lakes and wetlands. Some river stretches have also been recognised as the best examples of fluvial geomorphological features as part of the Geological Conservation Review (Duigan *et al.* 2009). These sites (approximately 20) serve as illustrations of the evolution of the Welsh landscape and cover landforms, processes, channel features, channel change and examples of human impact.

There are 284 SSSIs notified for their 'fen, swamp and mire' habitats in Scotland, 147 notified standing waters and canals, and just 10 notified rivers and streams. In terms of the UK BAP priorities for Freshwaters and Wetlands, Scotland holds 9 priority habitats and 75 priority species including 1 alga, 7 bryophytes, 4 fungi and lichens, 24 invertebrates, 13 vascular plants and 26 vertebrates.

In England, ponds support more UK BAP priority species than lakes, and a similar number to streams, rivers and river floodplains combined (**Figure 9.8**).

This richness of ponds reflects both the intrinsic productivity of this water body type when not degraded and the heterogeneity among pond types, with permanence,

Table 9.3 Areas (hectares) of Openwater in England under different statutory designations in 2008.
Source: Natural England (2009).

Designation	Total area (ha)
Sites of Special Scientific Interest	28,693
Special Areas of Conservation	9,308
Special Protected Areas	6,615
Ramsar sites	6,013
National Nature Reserves	1,972
Within National Parks	9,339
Within Areas of Natural Beauty	4,058

depth, flow, altitude, age, surrounding vegetation, underlying geology and chemistry all contributing to marked differences in their ecology and species composition.

Alongside ponds, drainage ditches are also abundant with an estimated 600,000 km in Great Britain (**Table 9.4**). Lowland grazing marsh ditches are among the most species-rich Freshwater habitats (Brown *et al.* 2006). Although ditches in other landscape areas often support fewer species (i.e. alpha richness) (Biggs *et al.* 2007), there is not enough data on the biota of this extensive Freshwater habitat to make a full assessment.

9.2.3.5 Hyporheic zones and groundwaters

Water-bearing rocks (aquifers) and stream sediments (the hyporheic zone), where surface water mixes with groundwater, provide habitats for uniquely adapted organisms. These habitats include open and interconnected pore spaces, caves, mines, wells and boreholes which may contain diverse assemblages such as obligate groundwater species (stygobites), species with an affinity for subterranean environments (stygophiles), and those which occur accidentally (stygoxenes) (Gibert *et al.* 1994). In the UK, the composition, distribution and biology of subterranean assemblages is poorly understood (see Proudlove *et al.* 2003; Gilvear *et al.* 2006; Knight 2008; Robertson *et al.* 2009). In mainland UK, 10 stygobitic crustacean species are currently recognised: 6 amphipods, 1 isopod, 1 syncarid, 1 copepod and 1 ostracod. Only one species (*Niphargus glennei*; listed on the UK BAP) is endemic and, so far, has been found in Devon and Cornwall (Knight 2008). Stygophilic assemblages have been collected from groundwaters throughout the UK, but stygobites are largely restricted to areas that were not glaciated (Robertson *et al.* 2009; **Figure 9.9**). Existing records are strongly biased towards chalk geology, although other aquifers, including other fractured carbonate aquifers, have been under-sampled. Systematic studies of invertebrate ecology of groundwater habitats are now taking place in parts of England, but there are no similar surveys of the hyporheic zone in the UK as a whole.

The hyporheic zone is important in biogeochemical filtration which is largely mediated by microbial biofilms (Butterini *et al.* 2000) that fuel rapid biogeochemical cycling of nutrients while retarding their downstream transport (Fischer *et al.* 2005). Intense cycling of nitrogen, phosphorous and carbon occurs in the hyporheic zone; these zones are also locations of denitrification, nitrogen mineralisation and ammonification (Hill *et al.* 1998; Duff & Triska 1990). Porous hyporheic media increase water residence time, thus increasing the opportunities for

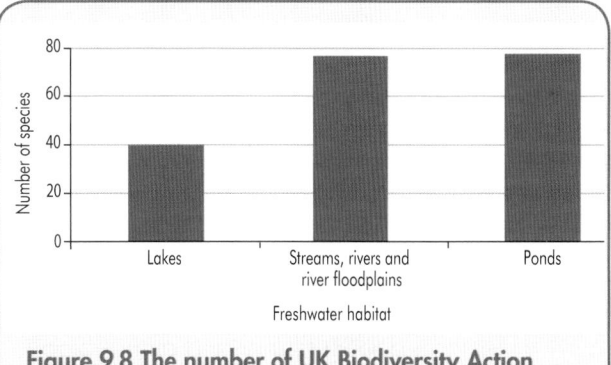

Figure 9.8 The number of UK Biodiversity Action Plan (UK BAP) priority species recorded in lakes, streams, rivers and river floodplains, and ponds in England. Source: data from Webb *et al.* (2010).

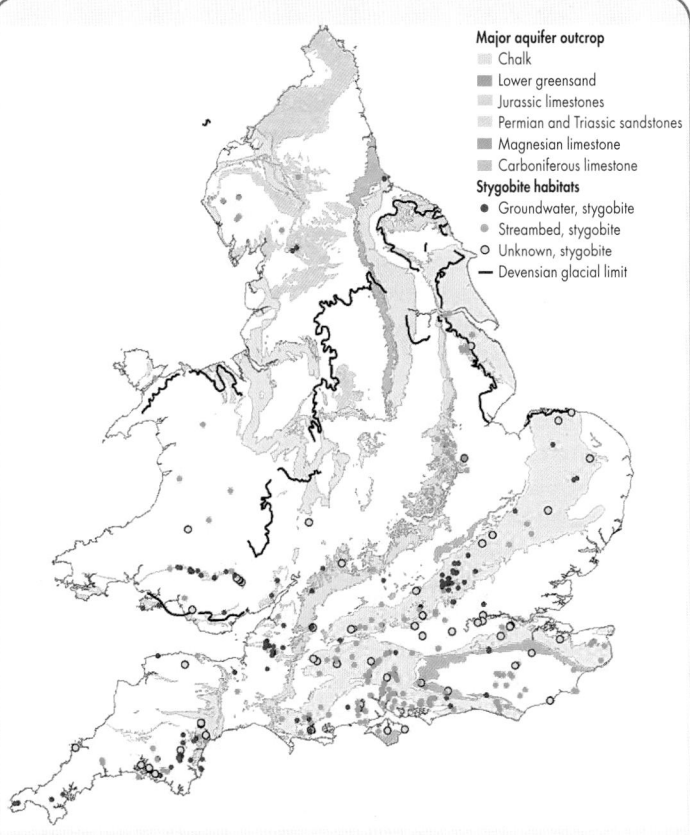

Figure 9.9 Hyporheic and groundwater stygobite records in England and Wales overlain on a map indicating the outcrop of principal aquifers. Source: Robertson *et al.* (2009).

microbial-mediated reactions relative to surface water. The movement of larger invertebrates (e.g. amphipods, isopods, oligochaetes) through sediments may reduce clogging and increase hydraulic conductivity within substrates, thus enabling the penetration of oxygen, nutrients and other bacterial substrates (e.g. Mermillod-Blondin *et al.* 2000). The hyporheic zone can moderate stream discharge by absorbing or releasing water (Environment Agency 2009b), while providing habitat for salmonid eggs (Malcolm *et al.* 2008). Refuge habitat is also available for surface organisms during disturbance events, such as droughts (Wood *et al.* 2001) and spates, and organisms that live in the hyporheic zone may add resilience to whole river ecosystems (Brunke & Gonser 1997; Robertson & Wood 2010).

Table 9.4 Linear lengths (km) of rivers, streams and ditches in the ten main Defra agricultural landscape classes in Great Britain. Source: Brown *et al.* (2006).

Water body type	Total linear length (km)
Rivers	91,499
Streams	175,975
Ditches	604,405

There is no firm understanding of how groundwater invertebrates influence ecosystem services in aquifers (Boulton *et al.* 2008), although they may assist remediation following organic pollution. However, hyporheic and groundwater assemblages are vulnerable to disturbance, pollution (Danielopol *et al.* 2003), groundwater abstraction and fine sediments (Malcolm *et al.* 2010).

9.2.4 Cultural Services

9.2.4.1 Heritage goods: history and archaeology
Recently excavated from the peat-infilled, former, post-glacial lake, the Starr Carr House in Pickering, North Yorkshire, has been dated at 8,500 BP and is the oldest known dwelling in the UK. Mesolithic (from 8,500 to 4,000 BP in the UK) communities favoured lake margins for the establishment of villages as they could exploit the Freshwater habitats for food, shelter and security. Following this, Neolithic (from 4,000 to 2,500 BP in the UK) people continued to exploit Wetlands for their natural resources and started to construct wooden trackways. More than 40 different trackways have been discovered in the UK; the best preserved is the Sweet Track, dating from 3,806 BP and crossing nearly 2 km of Wetland that lay between dry land and a mid-marsh island in the Somerset Levels and Moors (Coles 1990). Its single plank walkway was held about 40 cm above the soft ground by pairs and groups of obliquely crossed pegs retained by a ground-level rail.

The most complete representation of the material culture of the Iron Age (from 750 to 300 BP in the UK) is the Glastonbury Lake Village (Adkins & Adkins 1992), England, formerly inhabited by around 200 people living in 14 roundhouses. The Isle of Avalon (the high land around Glastonbury, including the hill of Glastonbury Tor, which is surrounded by Wetlands) is said to be the burial place of King Arthur and Guinevere, although there is no archaeological evidence to support this enduring legend.

The waterlogged peat and clay deposits of the Somerset Levels and Moors also contain a wealth of palaeo-environmental data in the form of plant and animal remains such as pollen, seeds, snails, beetles, diatoms and foraminifera. These provide a unique record of the changing climate, sea-level and landscape during the Holocene (which began about 10,000 years ago), including during the Medieval Warm Period (approximately 950 to 1250 AD) and the Little Ice Age (1350 to 1850 AD) (Lamb 1972). The peat deposits are up to 8.5 m thick and are believed to contain the longest Holocene peat record of any lowland location in the UK.

The aesthetic value of Freshwaters has been an inspiration for painters, poets, bards and writers. Charles Dickens was, for example, inspired by the landscape of the North Kent Marshes which he recreated in *Great Expectations*. The development of tourism and the concept of picturesque landscapes are particularly associated with tours of the River Wye in the 1700s: 'Wild Wales' became a place where people could escape the urban landscapes and pollution created by the Industrial Revolution, and pastimes in botanising and fishing evolved. Today, several river valleys feature in the Register of Landscapes of Historic Interest in Wales (Cadw: Welsh Historic Monuments 1998, 2001).

There has always been a close relationship between water resources and the development of Welsh society and the regional economy; for example, the 13th Century native laws of Wales, 'Cyfraith Hywel', set the price for valuable otter (*Lutra lutra*) and beaver skins. Rivers have acted as boundaries, lines of defence and transport and communications routes. Lakes and Wetlands have been shown to hold valuable archaeological deposits and environmental records (Rees 1997). For example, an ancient Celtic fortification (crannog) was built in Llangorse Lake and has been subject to archaeological excavation; the accumulated lake sediment represents an environmental record extending back to the Devensian Late Glacial period (13,000 to 10,000 BP).

9.2.4.2 The multiple values of Freshwaters
Cultural services provided by Freshwaters are many and include unique opportunities for recreation, boating, fishing, tourism, education, history, religion, inspiration and art, while also providing a sense of place, physical boundaries and barriers, and the notion of mythical creatures, which are a source of inspiration in their own right. Many Freshwaters are valued for their mere existence, even if people do not necessarily visit them.

Among all the recreational uses of Openwaters, the asset value of the UK's Freshwater fish populations is particularly significant and reflects several key features. From an economic perspective, coarse fisheries alone contribute £850 million to the economy out of a total spend by rod fishermen exceeding £3 billion in England and Wales (Environment Agency 2006). In December 2006, there were 18,250 full-time employees in the angling industry and 5,500 part-time employees. At this time, there were 2,700 angling outlets, with an average annual turnover of £191,000. For migratory salmonids, the capital value of fishing rights alone is estimated at £140 million (Aprahamian *et al.* 2010), and several case studies show how associated angler spending within game fisheries is particularly important to rural economies and job creation (Peirson *et al.* 2001; Butler *et al.* 2009). From a recreational perspective, in excess of 2.6 million Freshwater anglers make this the most widespread participant sport in the UK across all social strata. However, there is also more fundamental ecological importance, with many species key to energy and nutrient transfer through Freshwater food webs (a supporting service).

Salmon fishing is particularly important to the economy of rural Scotland. A study in 2007 estimated it brought in £18 million to the local Borders economy and directly supported 487 jobs. Annually, 35,876 rod days of fishing are let, with 75% of salmon anglers travelling from outside Scotland; these visiting anglers spend an average of £189 per day in the Borders compared to an average of just £56 spent by other, non-fishing visitors. At a national level, Freshwater angling in Scotland is estimated to support around 2,800 jobs and generates nearly £50 million in wages and self-employment, as well as a spend of £100 million during the 1 million angler days involved.

Angling is not the only water sport generating large amounts of income. A study on the River Spey, Scotland, in 2004 estimated the number of water sports days to be over

38,000, contributing about £1.7 million to the local economy and supporting 48 jobs.

Wildlife tourism also plays a vital part in Scotland's rural economy. Since its return to Scotland over 50 years ago, the iconic osprey (*Pandion haliaetus*) has attracted hundreds of thousands of people to Wetland sites such as the Scottish Wildlife Trust nature reserve at Loch of the Lowes. In 2006, it was estimated that 125,000 visitors went to the five osprey viewing sites (nests) across Scotland, spending some £2.2 million, with birdwatching boosting the overall Scottish economy by £5 million (SNH 2008)

A Welsh Assembly sponsored study in 2000 estimated that the contribution of inland recreational fisheries to Wales was around £50 million per year (Anon 2002); but this is thought to be an underestimation by other interested parties. Approximately 60,000 rod licences are sold in Wales each year, while around 700,000 fishing trips to Wales are undertaken, generating a spend of about £75 million. Knowledge of fish and fishing is respected in Welsh communities, where tales of anglers (and poachers) are part of the oral tradition (Evans *et al.* 2009). The art of tying fishing flies has a number of world famous patterns derived in Wales—Coch Y Bonddu, the Diawl Bach, the Welshman's Button—with a correspondingly rich mythology on their use (Gee & Fowles 2009).

In England, the creation of the London Wetland Centre increased the value of adjacent, overlooking property significantly. The Centre supports rare species, such as bittern, employs many local people, supports volunteers, generates income for the Wildfowl & Wetlands Trust, and contributes to local cohesion. It provides a unique education and research facility in the centre of London.

9.2.4.3 Health goods: meaningful places including green and blue space

Wetlands are often associated with nature and provide both green (e.g. forests, meadows) and blue (Openwater, e.g. The Broads) space. Habitats such as rivers and their floodplains and grazing marsh comprise key facets of locally characteristic and valued landscapes, with associated tourism, aesthetic and recreational interest.

In English and Scottish literature, Wetlands have often been symbolic of mystery and the unknown, remoteness, and sometimes the supernatural. Freshwater has also always been an important component of Welsh Celtic heritage. Water was considered a magical substance associated with spirits and legends, and requiring ceremonial offerings. And holy wells are a Christian expression of a religious connection with water.

9.2.4.4 Socially valued landscapes and waterscapes

Wildlife groups, angling clubs, grazing communities and other associations have formed around the services provided by Wetland habitats of multiple types, such as the Somerset Levels and Moors, and East Anglian Fens. The Lake District is England's largest national park and covers 229,200 ha. In 2007, 8.3 million visitors came to enjoy the spectacular landscape and rich cultural heritage in a peaceful setting; Romantic poets found inspiration in the beauty of 'untamed' countryside, with Wordsworth describing the Lake District as "a sort of national property, in which every man has a right and an interest who has an eye to perceive and a heart to enjoy". Loch Lomond and its landscape were celebrated by Sir Walter Scott in his famous poem, *Lady of the Lake*, two hundred years ago, and later by Gerard Manley Hopkins in his poem, *Inversnaid*, in 1881. Ponds, lakes, waterfalls and other watercourses are an intrinsic part of landscape history and dominant components of estates and parklands, especially from the 18th Century onwards (Rees 1997).

9.3 Freshwater Condition and Trends

9.3.1 Status of Freshwaters

Despite their functional importance, ecological value and various forms of protection, Freshwaters have been extensively modified physically, chemically and biologically. Human impacts on river flow and sediment regimes, channel size, form and mobility, and the widespread management of riparian and aquatic vegetation, have all affected the entire assemblage of aquatic, wetland and terrestrial habitats (Gurnell & Petts 2010). It is almost certain that there are now no completely pristine Freshwater ecosystems in the UK—almost all have been impacted by human activity and are managed to a lesser or greater extent. Management has increased over the past few centuries, and has progressed from the local enhancement of natural processes, such as natural irrigation of water meadows, to major interventions to prevent natural processes, such as the building of dams. While the least damaged are expected to provide the most natural profile of services, more managed systems and artificial habitats can be very important locally; for instance, chalk rivers, reservoirs, fenlands and ponds and some water management structures have been protected for their cultural heritage.

A key element of change has been the disruption of the natural continuum, such that Freshwater has become highly fragmented over time, resulting in habitat degradation and loss. This is particularly significant with regard to connections among or within Wetlands, Floodplains and rivers, where the movement of water would normally reduce flood magnitude, encourage infiltration to aquifers, and allow the exchange of organisms and nutrients with adjacent habitats. Loss of connectivity has occurred through dams, weirs, land drainage, embankments, channel deepening, straightening and widening (Newson 2002), and infrastructure development adjacent to rivers. For example, the River Habitat Survey (Environment Agency 2003) records the presence of Floodplains, bank-top land use, artificial embankments and features of special interest on the Floodplain including natural open water, water meadow, fen, bog, carr and marsh. Of the 24,000 river sites (along 12,000 km of river) surveyed, 1,705 had a Floodplain on either bank for at least a third of the 500 m survey length. Some

13% of the 1,705 Floodplain sites had embankment close to the watercourse and 6% had embankments set back (**Table 9.1**); in both cases, this prevented water from inundating the 'natural' Floodplain, resulting in fragmentation of the hydrological continuum vital for the maintenance of ecosystem services. Many of these changes occurred before environmental safeguards, such as environmental impact assessments and cost-benefit analyses, and most have gone unrecorded.

9.3.2 Changes in River Dynamics

In addition to responses to longer-term climate and land cover changes (e.g. Macklin & Lewin 2008), the dynamics of the UK's rivers have been heavily impacted by centuries of agricultural development and land drainage, as well as management for water supply, flood defence, navigation and other human activities (Newson 2002). Many dynamic rivers, particularly in England, were affected by significant floodplain alluviation with fine sediment during the medieval period following the intensification of agriculture through the use of the open field system (e.g. Brown 2009b). This increased the strength of riverbanks and reduced river lateral dynamics. Since the medieval period, numerous direct and indirect human pressures have modified river flows and their hydrological connectivity, the sediment load available to river systems, and the degree to which river channels, banks and Floodplains are able to respond to changes in flow and sediment supply (e.g. Gregory 2006; Gregory et al. 2008).

Human impacts have affected the entire assemblage of habitats that characterise river corridors (Gurnell & Petts 2011), yet the monitoring of these physical changes remains a relatively neglected area (Sear & Newson 2003). The impact of particular types of human activity on river and Floodplain form and dynamics has been evaluated, including: dam construction (Petts & Gurnell 2005); the realignment, simplification and reinforcement of river channels (Brookes et al. 1983); sediment dredging (Sear et al. 1995); the cutting and pruning of riparian vegetation; and the removal of wood from river systems (Gregory et al. 2003, Gurnell & Petts 2002). Investigations of historical documentary and aerial photography sources, alongside sedimentary and morphological evidence, have illustrated major changes on individual rivers; but these investigations have largely focused on relatively dynamic case studies (e.g. Hooke & Yorke 2010), so the integrated impact of human activities on rivers and their Floodplains remains difficult to quantify. However, as national datasets are assembled, particularly to meet the hydromorphological requirements of the WFD, it is becoming possible to gain some broader insights. For example, over-plotting data (drawn from the Environment Agency's River Habitat Survey) on established relationships between river gradient, discharge and riverbed sediment size for a sample of river reaches in England and Wales suggests that multi-thread rivers should be far more widespread than at present (**Figure 9.10**). The loss of multi-thread rivers is often indicated in Floodplain sedimentological sequences, as well as cultural artefacts such as complex historical bridge structures. Such multi-thread systems supported the side channels, Floodplain ponds and Wetlands whose importance and status as a diminishing resource is described in other sections of this report. Today, we are left in many catchments with a fossilised and more or less fixed arterial drainage system that responds only to large flood events, such as those in Cumbria in 2009.

As noted in a global context by Tockner and Stanford (2002), "there is an urgent need to preserve existing, intact flood plain rivers as strategic global resources and to begin to restore hydrologic dynamics, sediment transport and riparian vegetation to those rivers that retain some level of ecological integrity".

While there is some understanding of the dynamics of Freshwaters, quantitative evidence of the effects on ecosystem services is limited and uncertain, and monitoring remains a relatively neglected area (Sear & Newson 2003). We understand some of the basic processes within relatively unaffected environments, but we need to know more about how different Freshwater systems in various levels of management/condition impact on, or deliver, ecosystem services. This is required to meet hydromorphological objectives under the WFD.

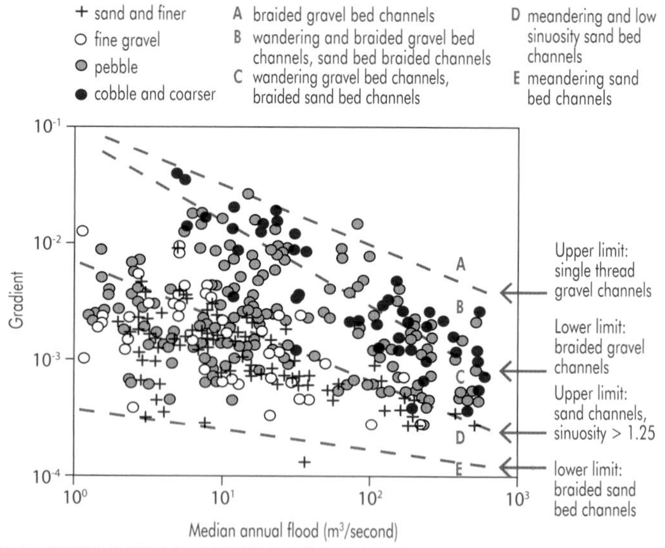

9.3.3 Condition of Designated Sites

By area, 18.4% of SSSI rivers in England are in favourable condition and 29.9% are recovering; for standing waters, the figures are 50.5% and 30.5% respectively (statistics provided by Natural England, October 2010). Those standing waters notified for their bird interest are in the best condition, that is 86% favourable or recovering (Natural England 2009). But overall, these values are among the worst for all habitats protected in England's SSSIs, mainly as a consequence of eutrophication from both point and diffuse sources. In general, there is less monitoring in Wetlands and information is based on site condition monitoring for SSSIs to determine trends.

Figure 9.10 Mean riverbed sediment size estimated from River Habitat Surveys of 467 sites in England and Wales. Over-plotted on sand- and gravel-bed river channel style thresholds defined by Church (2002) in relation to the median annual flood (as an index of bankfull discharge) and valley slope. Source: Gurnell et al. (2010). Copyright (2010), reproduced with permission from Elsevier.

Based on some 559 condition assessments on protected areas in Scotland, by 2009, 61% were judged to be in favourable condition, with 8% recovering and the remaining 31% unfavourable. The main reasons for poor condition were the presence of invasive species and lack of management (Mackey & Mudge 2010).

Of the UK BAP priority habitats associated with Freshwaters and Wetlands in Scotland, 40% were assessed as declining, 20% show no trend, 20% are fluctuating probably stable, and 20% are fluctuating probably increasing (Spray 2011). The comparative picture for the 75 UK BAP priority species showed 42% declining, 11% no clear trend, 31% fluctuating probably stable and 16% fluctuating probably increasing. Some native species, such as otters and Greylag geese (*Anser anser*), have shown major increases, but so have many invasive non-native species including signal crayfish (*Pacifastacus leniusulus*) and Australian swamp stonecrop (*Crassula helmsii*).

Freshwater ecosystems in Wales are undergoing serious environmental degradation from a variety of human induced pressures, including pollution, sedimentation, fisheries management, invasive and non-native species introductions, and water regulation. The majority of Freshwater sites or features within designated sites in Wales are in unfavourable or declining condition.

9.3.4 Openwaters and Groundwater Monitoring and Assessment in the UK

Rivers are the UK's most extensively monitored Freshwater habitats. Water quantity is measured through a network of around 1,500 gauging stations located along rivers, and 160 index wells or boreholes that provide details on groundwater (Marsh & Hannaford 2008) in summary reports (www.ceh.ac.uk/data/nrfa/nhmp/monthly_hs.html). The Environment Agency has many more groundwater monitoring sites for chemistry and water level. For the WFD Article 8 report on monitoring, the Environment Agency reported to the European Commission (EC) that, for England, there were 1,217 monitoring points for groundwater level (used for WFD assessment) and 3,373 for groundwater quality (used for groundwater body status and trend assessment). For biological trends, systematic, long-term data are available from over 20,000 sites on 25,000 km of rivers in England, Wales and Scotland. For physical structure (i.e. hydromorphology), in excess of 24,000 locations have been sampled along rivers throughout the UK using River Habitat Survey methods developed by the Environment Agency (Raven *et al.* 1998). These extensive surveys are complemented by the sampling of 300–400 headwaters in 1990, 1998 and 2007 for macrophytes, macroinvertebrates, habitat structure and chemistry, and a similar number of ponds sampled for macrophytes in 2007 as part of the Countryside Survey (Dunbar *et al.* 2010c; Williams *et al.* 2010). Several major river systems have also been the subject of detailed long-term research. This effort to assess status and trends reflects the legislative importance placed on Freshwaters; the importance of water quality to its uses; the array of pressures affecting water; and the indicator value of river organisms in revealing change.

For lakes, trend data are less systematic, but good insights are available from well-known case studies, for example, Lake Windermere (George & Harris 1985) and the English Lake District in general (Maberly *et al.* 2002; Thackeray *et al.* 2008), Loch Leven, Scotland (Spears & Jones 2010), Lough Neagh, Northern Ireland (Griffiths 2007), the UK Acid Waters Monitoring Network (Monteith & Evans 2005; Kernan *et al.* 2010), the Norfolk Broads (Sayer *et al.* 2010), the Anglesey Lakes (Bennion *et al.* 1996), Llangorse Lake (Duigan *et al.* 1999) and Llyn Tegid in Wales (Gritten *et al.* 2003), and a range of smaller water bodies (Jeffries 2008). New data are also emerging as a consequence of the surveillance monitoring programmes required for implementation of the WFD.

9.3.5 Limitations of the Available Trend Data

While trend data for lakes and rivers are numerous, there are some limitations. The most important is that the ecological methods used are based largely on static, structural measures of taxonomic composition, rather than on functional measures linked to ecosystem processes or services. In addition, sampling locations for most purposes are not representative, with headwaters, upland and smaller water bodies often under-represented. Pressures specifically affecting these locations, such as habitat degradation, acidification, metals or sheep dips, are, therefore, overlooked to an extent, but are best identified in specialised studies (e.g. UK Acid Waters Monitoring Network, Countryside Survey). There are also some mismatches in the availability or timing of trend data from different parts of the UK, with England and Wales covered most fully and consistently. By comparison with sanitary aspects of water quality, some sources of ecosystem change in Freshwaters are appraised less effectively in systematic monitoring, such as physical modification, inert sediments and climate change. Quality varies among datasets; for example, some of the most extensive biological monitoring data cover only a limited taxonomy. Finally, Freshwater monitoring throughout the UK has recently been changed radically to support the WFD and this has important bearings on interpretation.

The situation in Scotland is particularly challenging with two recent, major changes in the nature and extent of the water monitoring network. Relative to the rest of the UK, Scotland has an abundance of surface waters. However, up until the requirements of the WFD were enacted through the Water Services Water Environment Act (2003), little attention had been paid to groundwater resources, to the impacts of abstraction (which was largely unregulated) or to hydromorphological alterations of surface waters. Furthermore, while invertebrate monitoring had been undertaken on a systematic basis, there was no systematic fish monitoring, except for salmon catches. With the implementation of the WFD, and following extensive consultation with other bodies, SEPA introduced a new Scottish aquatic monitoring strategy that addressed these shortcomings by developing a groundwater monitoring network, for example, as well as introducing new controls on abstraction and flow regulation (The Controlled Activities Regulations).

Across the whole of the UK, WFD developments include augmenting the array of indicators used for ecological quality assessment (fish, macrophytes, and invertebrates, plus phytobenthos in rivers and phytoplankton in lakes) as well as assessment of hydromorphology and chemistry. These and other changes have increased the sensitivity of assessment for some effects, notably eutrophication through the stronger inclusion of diatoms and macrophytes. Nevertheless, differences remain between the constituent countries of the UK, for example Scotland's measurement of hydromorphological change uses a different tool (MIMAS) to that elsewhere and to date Scotland still has limited fish monitoring. Recently, the extent of the Scottish recently-introduced freshwater monitoring network and frequency parameters have been severely cut back as a response to financial pressures, with many sites previously monitored annually being dropped or reduced to less frequent sampling.

9.3.6 Trends for Openwater

Trends in water quality in the UK's Freshwater habitats have been determined from extensive, systematic surveys of rivers, case studies in lakes and Wetlands, and recent systematic surveys of ponds. These data provide a valuable indication of: i) how the uses of the UK's Freshwaters for flood defence or waste disposal have affected their quality; ii) how Freshwater trends reflect catchment use for fibre production, agriculture or urban land; iii) how Freshwater quality can limit the uses of water for final goods and services, for example, abstraction, fisheries, recreation and aesthetics; and iv) the potential costs of degrading Freshwaters, either assessed through the costs of restoring quality or through the loss of services that occur where Freshwater ecological functions are degraded. These issues also illustrate a long-standing trade-off in which terrestrial goods and services have often been exploited without recognition of the full cost of ecological consequences downstream.

In general, several aspects of long-term monitoring data illustrate a major improvement in the quality of many UK rivers as a result of actions over the last two decades. In England and Wales, the biological and chemical classification of 7,000 km and 12,000 km of rivers, respectively, improved significantly from 1990 to 2008. Although still short of full recovery, effects have been most marked across formerly polluted catchments with extensive urbanised land, particularly those in central England, northern and southern England and South Wales (**Figure 9.11**). Measured in terms of sanitary quality (such as biochemical oxygen demand, dissolved oxygen, ammonia and associated biological indicators), these improvements reflect investments in wastewater treatment and other point source discharges.

Against this generally improving trend, recovery patterns are much more variable at a local level. For example, biological quality declined by one or more classes in 2,500 km of the best hill-rivers in Wales and the Welsh borders for reasons that are unclear (**Figure 9.11**). This trend was corroborated in the Countryside Survey at the locations originally sampled (**Figure 9.12**). Whereas, across 168 headwaters in Scotland and 132 in England there was a general gain in taxa and significantly improved index values over the period 1990 to 2007. By contrast, 46 headwaters in Wales have not sustained the same improvement, with a tendency for richness to fall against expectations between 1998 and 2007 (**Figure 9.12**). The most likely explanations are continuing problems with diffuse pollutants. Declines have also been observed in macroinvertebrate status in the Scottish Highlands which had the highest proportion of sites at good or high status in 1998; by 2007, this proportion has dropped to a level comparable to that of the rest of Scotland and upland England but it is not currently possible to pinpoint causes of this decline.

Nitrate concentrations increased in almost 4,000 km of English and Welsh rivers between 1995 and 2008, mostly in the lowlands (**Figure 9.13**). Other eutrophication indicators, such as phosphorus concentrations, also remain

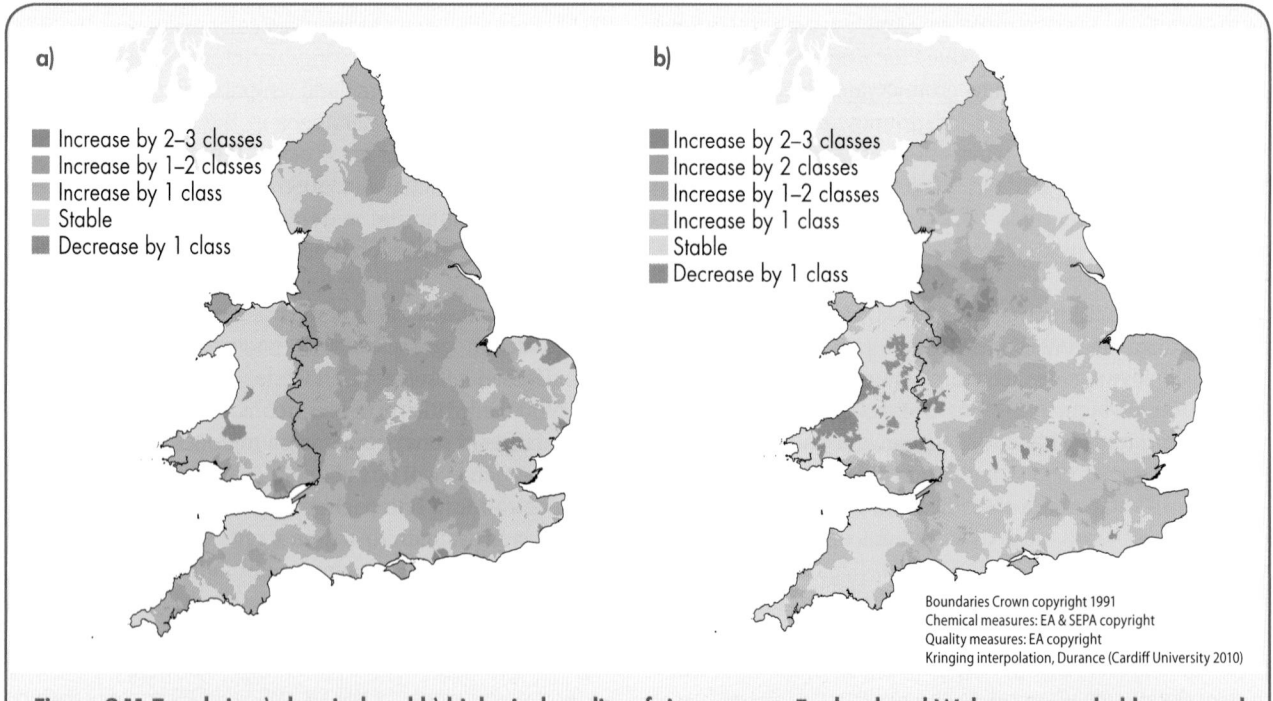

a)
- Increase by 2–3 classes
- Increase by 1–2 classes
- Increase by 1 class
- Stable
- Decrease by 1 class

b)
- Increase by 2–3 classes
- Increase by 2 classes
- Increase by 1–2 classes
- Increase by 1 class
- Stable
- Decrease by 1 class

Boundaries Crown copyright 1991
Chemical measures: EA & SEPA copyright
Quality measures: EA copyright
Kringing interpolation, Durance (Cardiff University 2010)

Figure 9.11 Trends in a) chemical and b) biological quality of rivers across England and Wales as revealed by general quality surveys from 1990 to 2008. Source: data from the Environment Agency and complied by I. Durance (Cardiff University).

elevated in many locations despite some stabilisation or reversal of long-term increase (*e.g.* Mainstone *et al.* 2008; Neal *et al.* 2010; **Figure 9.14**). Sources probably reflect continued discharge from wastewater treatment, with more modest contributions from agriculture (*e.g.* Jarvie *et al.* 2010), although the importance of contributions from minor, unconsented point sources, such as septic tanks, is increasingly recognised (May *et al.* 2010). Implications for ecosystem services arise from the costs of remediating damaged systems, from the costs of sewage treatment, and from increased risks of cyanobacteria in receiving waters. Lost recreational opportunity, as well as increased human and livestock health risks, can be substantial.

In upland locations, data on acidification caused by acid rain show that chemical recovery continues to track reductions in acidifying emissions (Davies *et al.* 2005). However, associated biological recovery is more modest, probably because of continuing acid episodes (Kowalik *et al.* 2007; Ormerod & Durance 2009). Ore-bearing regions in some acid-sensitive locations still produce local problems through metal-rich drainage, while more extensive background metal loadings also occur from atmospheric deposition (Lawlor & Tipping 2003). Out of 7,815 water bodies across England and Wales, 465 appear to be impacted by pollution from non-coal mines, with around half of these likely to affect in-stream pollution (Mayes *et al.* 2009).

There is widespread regulation of priority substances under the WFD (WFD Annex VIII). Monitoring shows limited exceedence of Environmental Quality Standards (EQS) for pesticides in most surface waters. However, breaches of EQS values, or standards set by the EU for drinking water supply, do still occur and, in some cases (e.g. metaldehyde used as slug pellets), this requires targeted action to minimise entry to water. General population recovery across the whole of the UK among sensitive organisms, such as otters (listed on the Habitats Directive 92/43/EEC), illustrates how previous pesticide effects, notably from organochlorine compounds, such as dieldrin, have diminished. On the other hand, EQS over the last decade were exceeded on scores of occasions in sheep-rearing areas by two active ingredients in sheep dips: the synthetic pyrethroid, cypermethrin, and the organophosphate, diazinon (Sinclair *et al.* 2007). However, licensing changes have now reduced, if not fully eliminated, these risks.

Agricultural developments and increased livestock density across Wales have probably more than doubled catchment phosphorus loadings to rivers and trebled nitrogen loadings (Johnes *et al.* 2007). Based on an analysis of Welsh Local Environment Agency Plans (Ormerod & Jüttner 2009), agricultural runoff is identified as a particular problem in mid-Wales, with sheep dip an issue throughout the region, and especially in west Wales. Tens of major or significant pollution incidents involving sheep dip have occurred annually across England and Wales, with the increased numbers recently reflecting targeted investigations. Wales contributes strongly to the Environment Agency sheep dip statistics. In 2000/01, sheep dip residues were found at 86–92% of Welsh survey sites, with cypermethrin responsible for most EQS failures; the cypermethrin marketing licence has now been suspended (Ormerod and Jüttner 2009).

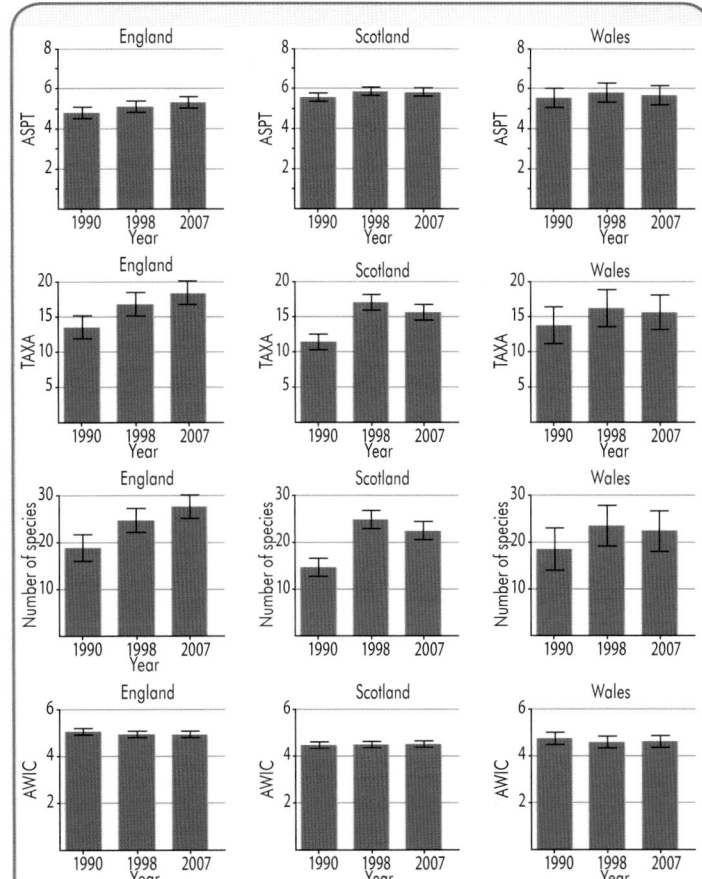

Figure 9.12 Trends in quality measures from a stratified random sample of headwaters in Great Britain as shown by the Countryside Survey in 1990, 1998 and 2007. Means (± 95% CI) of four macroinvertebrate indices: Average Score Per Taxon (ASPT); number of BMWP (Biological Monitoring Working Party) scoring taxa (TAXA); number of species; and Acid Waters Indicator Community (AWIC). Source: Dunbar *et al.* (2010c). Countryside Survey data owned by NERC – Centre for Ecology & Hydrology.

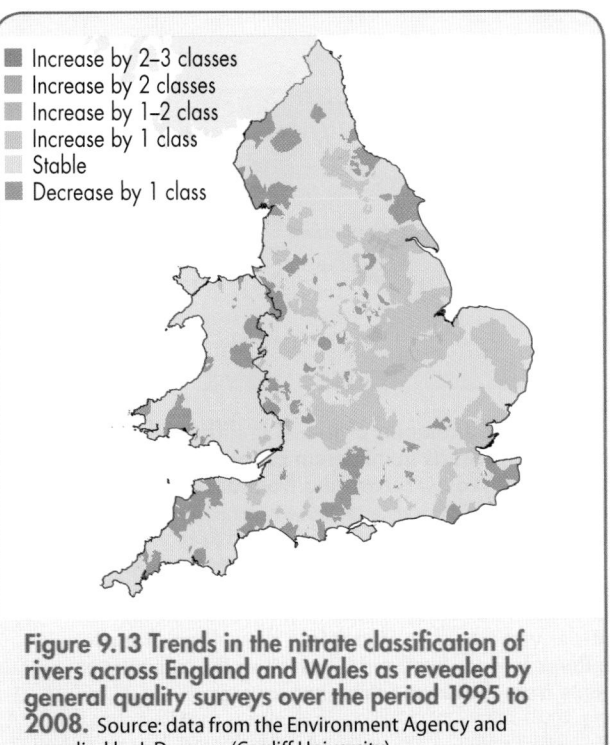

Figure 9.13 Trends in the nitrate classification of rivers across England and Wales as revealed by general quality surveys over the period 1995 to 2008. Source: data from the Environment Agency and compiled by I. Durance (Cardiff University).

Inert and nutrient-bearing sediments are thought to be increasingly problematic, and possibly widespread, but there is insufficient monitoring, and trends through time vary among locations. Patterns reflect changes in key sources such as agriculture or forestry, and climate variability (Owens & Walling 2002; Orr & Carling 2006; **Figure 9.14**). The most intensively used catchments have often had amplified sediment fluxes over the last 40 to 100 years (Walling *et al.* 2003; Small *et al.* 2005; Hatfield & Maher

2009). Increasing evidence shows how river organisms and ecosystem processes can be sensitive to such effects at surprisingly low levels, particularly in upland regions (e.g. Larsen & Ormerod 2010). Several species of importance to nature conservation are affected, notably the freshwater pearl mussel (*Margaritifera margaritifera*) (Hastie *et al.* 2003; Geist & Auerswald 2007) and white-clawed crayfish (*Austropotamobius pallipes*); salmon spawning success has also been impacted upon. There are also problems for public water supply or regulating reservoirs as a result of treatment costs and reduced capacity (e.g. Holliday *et al.* 2008). In addition to their physical effects, sediments are also a vector for pollutants such as phosphorus (Neal *et al.* 2010). Sediment loads to some rivers, particularly chalk streams, are now exacerbating anoxia in bed sediments to the extent that methane exports to the atmosphere have increased (Sanders *et al.* 2007). Absolute emissions are small, but this illustrates how unexpected changes in ecosystem function can arise from poor catchment management. The understanding of the role of nanoparticles (produced by the cosmetics industry, for example) in Freshwaters is increasing, and solutions to treat them are evolving (Jarvie & King 2010).

Dissolved organic carbon has relevance to both water supply and climate, and extensive data now reveal widespread increasing trends (Evans *et al.* 2005; Worrall & Burt 2007; Dawson *et al.* 2009). Exact causes are debated (see section 9.2.2.1), but there is growing evidence that underlying increases may be driven by the greater mobilisation of Soil Organic Matter as a result of recovery from acidification (Monteith *et al.* 2007); short-term peaks and interannual variations, on the other hand, are linked to climatic factors, such as temperature, droughts and high flows (e.g. Clark *et al.* 2005; Erlandsson *et al.* 2008), or land management, such as moorland drainage ditches ('grips'). There are potential costs for freshwater organisms, potable supply and carbon balances.

9.3.7 Changes in River Flow Since 1950

Annual mean precipitation over England and Wales has not changed significantly since records began in 1766. Seasonal rainfall is highly variable, but appears to have decreased in summer and increased in winter; although there has been little change in the latter over the last 50 years. All UK regions have seen an increase over the past 45 years in the contribution of heavy precipitation events to winter rainfall; in summer, all regions, except north-east England and north Scotland, show decreases in rainfall. Between 1961 and 2006, all regions have also experienced an increase in average annual and seasonal temperatures, which suggests increases in evaporation.

Examination of flow timeseries data for 15 rivers across England and Wales revealed positive trends in both winter and summer flows in some rivers since 1940 (Wilby 2006); however, the majority of summer flow trends were not significant. Autumn and winter flows increased in 95 'benchmark' natural catchments during the period between 1969 and 2008 (Hannaford & Harvey 2010). The strongest winter increases were generally found in the north and west of the UK, whereas autumn trends were most prevalent in

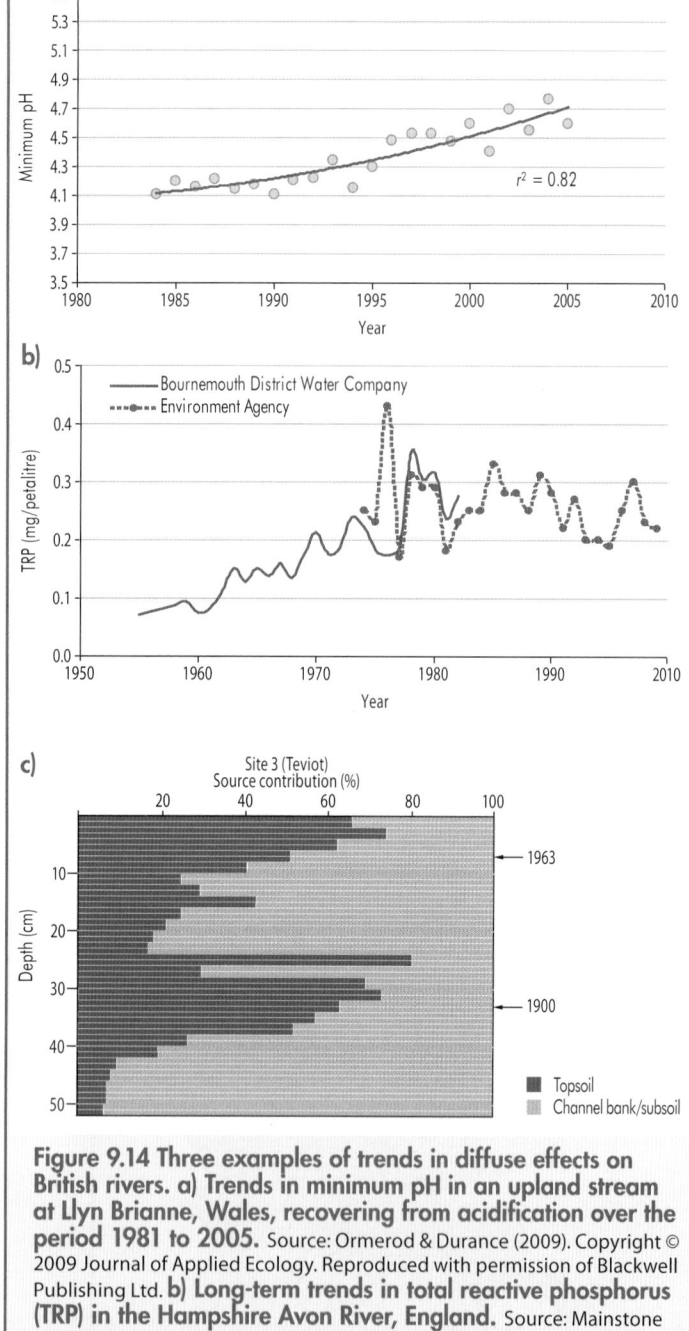

Figure 9.14 Three examples of trends in diffuse effects on British rivers. a) Trends in minimum pH in an upland stream at Llyn Brianne, Wales, recovering from acidification over the period 1981 to 2005. Source: Ormerod & Durance (2009). Copyright © 2009 Journal of Applied Ecology. Reproduced with permission of Blackwell Publishing Ltd. **b) Long-term trends in total reactive phosphorus (TRP) in the Hampshire Avon River, England.** Source: Mainstone *et al.* (2008). Copyright (2008), reproduced with permission from Elsevier. **c) Core-derived trends in Floodplain deposition at a site on the River Tweed, Scotland, illustrating the delivery of sediments from different catchment sources.** Source: Owens & Walling (2002). Copyright © 2002 Earth Processes and Landforms. Reproduced with permission of Blackwell Publishing Ltd.

south-west and central England. Trends in summer and spring flows were weaker and regional patterns were very mixed, although spring flows have decreased in some areas during the last 40 years. The winter and autumn trends observed were resilient to changes in the study period, whereas the decline in spring flows seen in recent records is not apparent over longer periods.

Based on 34 benchmark catchments across the UK, there is little evidence for trends in low flows over the period 1963 to 2002 (Hannaford & Marsh 2006). Certain positive trends seen during 1973 to 2002 were influenced by a sequence of notably dry years at the start of the period, but were not evident over a 40-year time period. Furthermore, these authors found little compelling evidence for low flow trends in longer hydrometric records; there is some evidence for an increase in naturalised 30-day minimum flows on the Thames since 1880, but this is likely to be influenced by a lack of homogeneity in the long Thames record. Lane (2008) has identified flood-rich and flood-poor periods.

Significant trends in high flows and floods were found across upland, maritime northern, and western areas of the UK in a study of 87 benchmark catchments (Hannaford & Marsh 2007). In western Scotland, there are some dramatic examples of a flood-rich period post-1990: eight out of the ten largest floods gauged since 1973 on the River Forth at Stirling have occurred post-1990, with six of these since 2000. However, there was little conclusive evidence for trends in the occurrence of high flows in English lowland rivers. From the late 1980s onwards, flood peaks on the River Avon at Amesbury are more pronounced than before

1988/1989, with similar changes to varying degrees on other chalk rivers (Solomon & Lightfoot 2007). Groundwater records from Chilgrove House, Chichester, show a similar pattern, with more extreme levels (especially low autumn and high winter levels) since 1989 compared with the more stable period between 1962 and 1988. It is not clear, however, whether this is part of cyclic or persistent behaviour, a long-term trend, or a step change.

9.3.8 Current General Quality in Rivers

Despite improvements, the current quality of rivers across the UK is still uneven. Rivers in the urban regions of England, Wales and Scotland still have the poorest quality (**Figure 9.15**), and reflect a range of factors including: elevated organic loadings (often from storm overflows); elevated metal loadings from industrial or combustion sources (**Figure 9.16**); and enhanced indicator values for waterborne pathogens. Relatively new urban pollutants, such as endocrine-disrupting substances, are giving rise to increasing concern with regards to their effects on fish. The risk of these effects occurring is greatest in locations where the contribution of treated sewage to river flow is largest (Williams *et al.* 2009).

Chemical indicators reveal continued problems in the extensively cultivated lands to the south and east of the Severn-Humber line. Here, and in south-west Wales and eastern Scotland, elevated nutrient concentrations (e.g. nitrate >5 milligrams per litre) contrast markedly with the UK's upland areas in Exmoor, Dartmoor, Wales, the Pennines and large parts of Scotland (**Figure 9.17**). The intensive

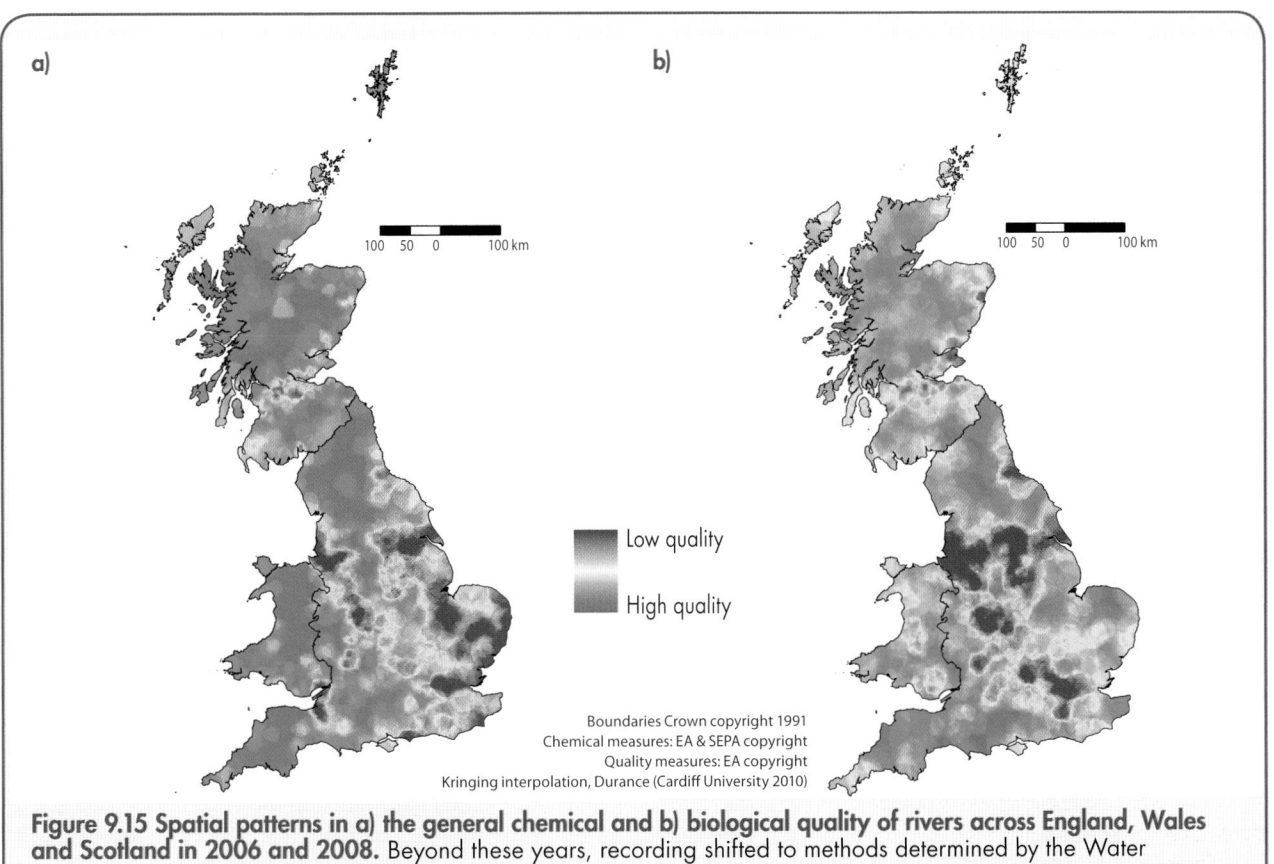

Boundaries Crown copyright 1991
Chemical measures: EA & SEPA copyright
Quality measures: EA copyright
Kringing interpolation, Durance (Cardiff University 2010)

Low quality

High quality

Figure 9.15 Spatial patterns in a) the general chemical and b) biological quality of rivers across England, Wales and Scotland in 2006 and 2008. Beyond these years, recording shifted to methods determined by the Water Framework Directive (WFD). Source: data from the Environment Agency and SEPA, and compiled by I. Durance (Cardiff University).

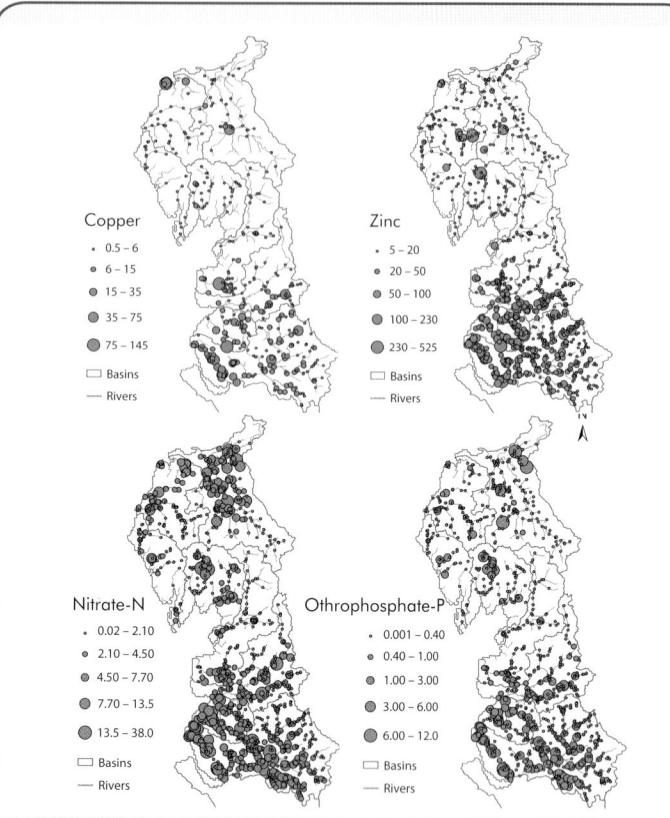

Figure 9.16 Spatial variations in water quality in North West England as shown by 800 individual locations sampled by the Environment Agency between 1995 and 2001. Water quality impairments at these scales reflect catchment land uses for agriculture and urban land. Source: Rothwell *et al.* (2010). Copyright (2010), reproduced with permission from Elsevier.

agricultural areas of Scotland, such as the Ythan Valley and eastern seaboard, also show continuing problems with nutrient enrichment and impacts from nitrates and other diffuse pollutants. The Scottish Environment Protection Agency is tackling the issue through the identification of priority catchments for remediation (e.g. Lunan Water, Angus).

Impaired quality in both urban and agriculturally intensified locations is reflected in the recent water body classification for the WFD (**Figure 9.18**). Newly added WFD tools for assessing the physical modification of rivers provided by River Habitat Surveys, (which are based on stratified random sampling) reveal that more than 50% of English and Welsh rivers have been modified physically (**Figure 9.19**). Rivers in urban or central English regions are most affected by bank reinforcement, where artificial materials are used to strengthen bank or bed structures, and re-sectioning, where the banks or bed are mechanically reprofiled for flood defence purposes (Boitsidies *et al.* 2006). Similar data from Scotland show that hydromorphological alterations are one of the most widespread causes of the failure of the country's water bodies to reach good ecological status, with 17% suffering from modifications to channels and banks, and 16% having barriers to fish migration. Trend data from the Countryside Survey 2007 (Carey *et al.* 2008) suggest a tendency towards increasing modification in Scotland, although this may reflect improved recording (Dunbar *et al.* 2010c). The effects of modification on total ecosystem services have not been

quantified, but the effects on biota are likely to be negative, decreasing habitat heterogeneity, for example, and rendering biota more sensitive to low flows (Dunbar *et al.* 2010a,b).

9.3.9 Microbiology and Microbial Quality

In terms of their microbiology, the UK's inland waters have improved during the past 30 to 50 years, reflecting investment in wastewater treatment and disposal. However, significant problems remain where poorly performing sewage treatment works and sewer overflows, along with livestock, are sources of pathogens. Some pathogens, such as *Cryptosporidium* species, can still lead to reservoir closures, while other organisms can affect potable supply, bathing waters or shellfisheries downstream (e.g. Pickup *et al.* 2006; Kay *et al.* 2008). Fluxes of faecal indicator organisms, such as coliform bacteria, increase at high flow compared with base flow, and are greater in summer than in winter. Catchments also vary widely in export, with urban areas and lowland improved pastures most likely to be key sources (Kay *et al.* 2008). In the northern English Ribble system, for example, more than 90% of the total coliform load to the estuary arises from sewage-related sources during high flow events (Stapleton *et al.* 2008; **Figure 9.20**).

Myobacterium avium subspecies *paratuberculosis* has been discovered in the Afon Taff, Cardiff, and has been implicated in chronic inflammation of the intestine in humans. The increased occurrence of such illness in the area appears to be related to how close the affected residents live to the rivers where they may be exposed to aerosols bearing this pathogen (Pickup *et al.* 2005).

9.3.10 Groundwater Status and Trends

Groundwater contributes significantly to our water resource needs and is essential to maintain a healthy natural environment. Although groundwater occurs everywhere, it is not always accessible due to the properties of the subsurface. Where it is accessible, and not contaminated by pollutants, it can provide clean, fresh water for a range of human uses, as well as meeting the needs of the environment (surface waters and wetlands). To aid the protection and management of groundwater, aquifers have been divided into 'groundwater bodies' for the purposes of the WFD. There are 714 groundwater bodies in the UK: 304 in England and Wales, 343 in Scotland and 67 in Northern Ireland. The status of each groundwater body was assessed for the first time as part of the implementation of the WFD (**Table 9.5**). This comprised an assessment of the quantitative (flow rate) status and the chemical (water quality) status. It should be noted that groundwater status is based only on chemical quality, and not on biological quality as is applied to other water bodies. However, there is a biological test for groundwater-dependent terrestrial ecosystems under the WFD; and if the terrestrial ecosystem is not considered to be in good status, then neither is the aquifer.

For each assessment, a number of tests (four quantitative and five chemical) were applied to check whether the groundwater body was meeting the criteria for good status as set in the WFD. In addition, a review of environmentally significant trends in pollutant concentrations in groundwater was undertaken as there is a specific objective in the WFD

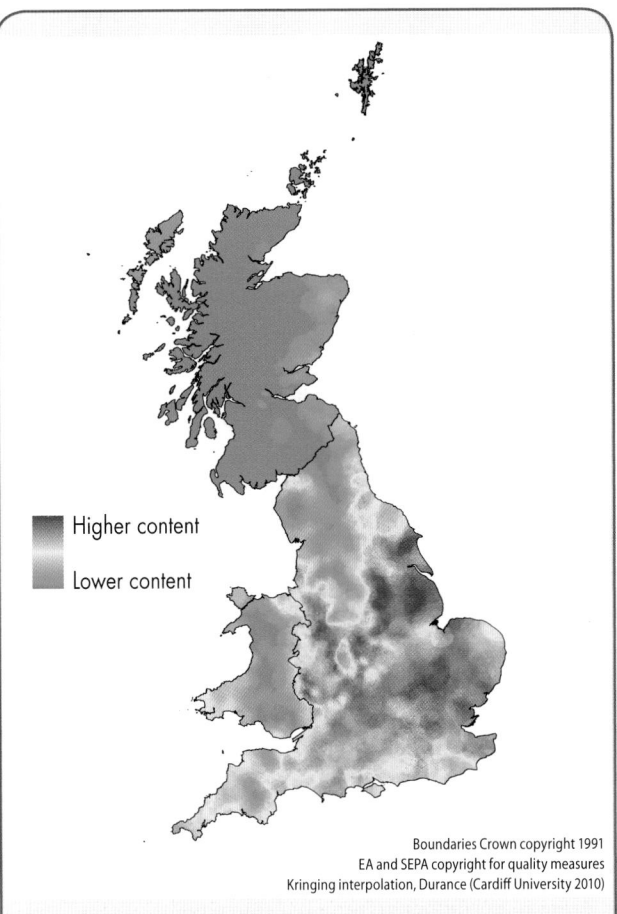

Higher content

Lower content

Boundaries Crown copyright 1991
EA and SEPA copyright for quality measures
Kringing interpolation, Durance (Cardiff University 2010)

Figure 9.17 Spatial patterns in nitrate concentrations of rivers across England, Wales and Scotland in 2006 and 2008. Source: data from Environment Agency and SEPA and compiled by I. Durance (Cardiff University).

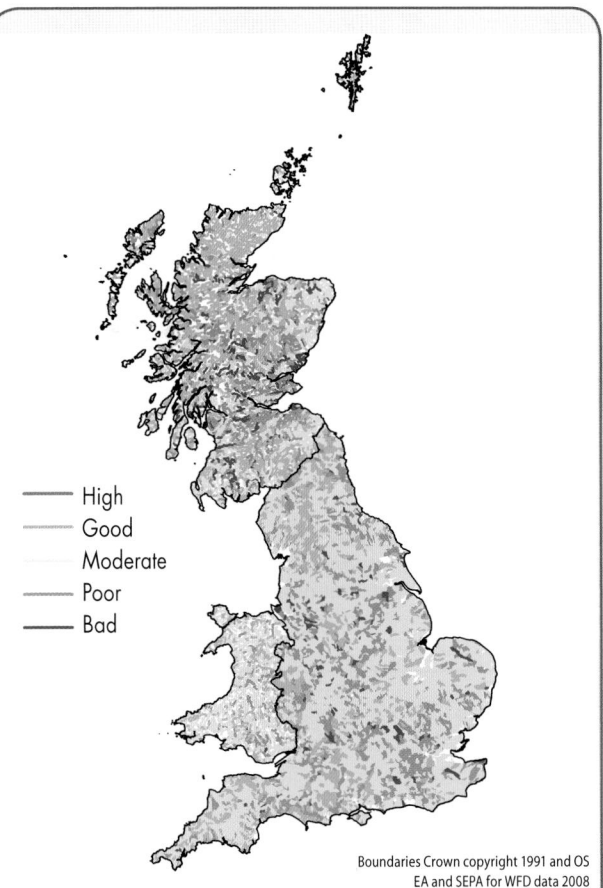

—— High
—— Good
—— Moderate
—— Poor
—— Bad

Boundaries Crown copyright 1991 and OS
EA and SEPA for WFD data 2008

Figure 9.18 Ecological status classes for rivers and river basins in England, Wales and Scotland as determined by the Environment Agency and Scottish Environment Protection Agency (SEPA) in 2008 for the purposes of the Water Framework Directive (WFD). The classes reflect the most sensitive indicator element in each location relative to the prevailing risks. Source: data from Environment Agency and SEPA and compiled by I. Durance (Cardiff University).

Table 9.5 Status of groundwater bodies across the UK. Source: data derived from River Basement Management Plans produced by the Environment Agency, Northern Ireland Environment Agency and Natural Scotland.

Country	Overall Status		Chemical Status		Quantitative Status		Ground-water bodies with upward trend
	Good	Poor	Good	Poor	Good	Poor	
England & Wales	180	124	194	110	130	174	81
Northern Ireland	65	2	63	4	63	4	Not assessed
Scotland	271	72	318	25	259	84	Not assessed

to reverse such trends. For this purpose, an environmentally significant trend was defined as one where concentrations are showing a statistically significant upward trend in pollutant concentrations and this trend has led/will lead to a failure of one or more environmental objectives.

The most significant cause of groundwater bodies not meeting the good quantitative status was the impact of groundwater abstraction on the flow of surface waters and groundwater-dependent terrestrial ecosystems. The largest

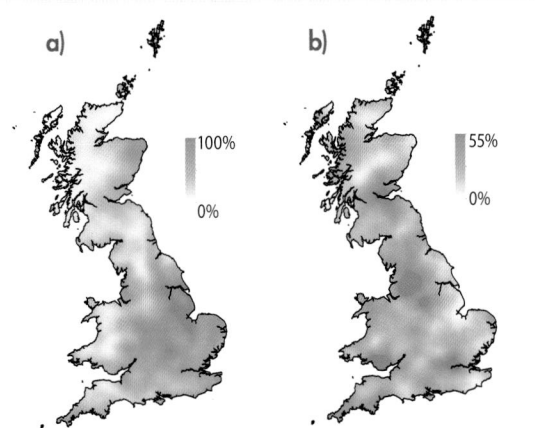

a)   100%   0%

b)   55%   0%

Figure 9.19 The extent (percentage of channel length) of two major physical modifications to rivers: a) re-sectioning of the channel and b) reinforcement of the bed and/or banks. Source: data derived from the Environment Agency baseline River Habitat Survey of England and Wales (2006 to 2008) and the Scottish Environment Protection Agency/Environment Agency baseline survey of Scotland (1995 to 1996). Both sets of data derive from randomly selected locations, stratified by 10 km grid squares. Data compiled by I. Vaughan (Cardiff University).

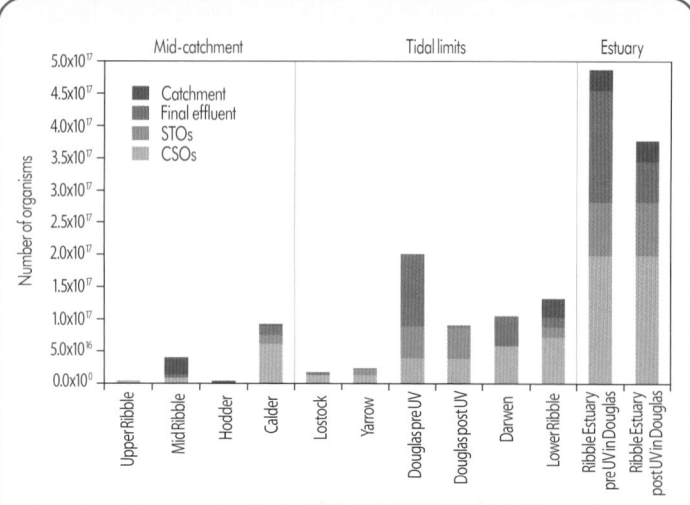

Figure 9.20 Estimated high flow faecal coliform loads discharged to the Ribble Estuary and selected sub-catchments from diffuse catchment sources and sewage effluents. Source: Stapleton *et al.* (2008). Copyright (2008), reproduced with permission from Elsevier.

contributors to a poor chemical status were failure to achieve drinking water protected area objectives and groundwater pollution contributing significantly to surface water bodies (rivers and lakes).

For the 81 groundwater bodies (27%) in England and Wales with environmentally significant upward trends, the main pollutant was agriculturally derived nitrate; this was followed by pesticides and industrial solvents. Due to the paucity of data, however, it is likely that the number of groundwater bodies with upwards trends in pollutant concentrations has been underestimated. Insufficient monitoring data were available in Scotland and Northern Ireland to undertake a trend assessment.

9.3.11 Fish Populations

Freshwater fish populations in Openwaters reflect natural habitat character as well as the effects of pollution, eutrophication, acidification, afforestation, channel engineering and exploitation, which have driven some stocks to local extinction (Maitland *et al.* 2007). Fragmentation, introgression from hatchery releases, climate change and the effects of exploitation at sea on Freshwaters are also issues (Ormerod 2003; Clews *et al.* 2010). Non-native species, such as Asian topmouth gudgeon (*Pseudorasbora parva*), are also a potentially growing threat to nature conservation value and some native fish (Britton *et al.* 2007). Stock movements threaten the stability or viability of local species; for example, the relatively recent extinction of vendace (*Coregonus albula*) in Bassenthwaite Lake, Cumbria, was largely due to the introduction of coarse fish species.

Native populations of fish that require clean water, such as Atlantic salmon, have reappeared or re-established and increased (though not necessarily bred) in formerly polluted rivers, such as the Thames, Clyde and Taff, commensurate with general improvements in water quality (e.g. Doughty *et al.* 2003; Evans *et al.* 2009). However, there are areas of concern. For example, the demographic structure of Atlantic salmon populations in many rivers suggests a shift from multiple sea-winter fish to one sea-winter fish

(known as grilse) because exploitation effects have been disproportionately large on those fish with longer lifecycles (e.g. Welton *et al.* 1999; Youngson *et al.* 2003). Additionally, rod catches have followed similar declining trends during recent years over geographically extensive areas from Scotland to Wales and the south-west of England (**Figure 9.21**), but the extent to which rod catches reflect population trends is still debated (e.g. Thorley *et al.* 2005; Hendry *et al.* 2007). Changes in marine temperature and survival and exploitation at sea are implicated, although diffuse effects in river catchments also appear to be involved because non-migrant salmonids have declined too (**Figure 9.21**). Climate is an emerging factor, with hot, dry summers apparently reducing juvenile populations of both brown trout and salmon (Clews *et al.* 2010).

Trends in populations of European eels (*Anguilla anguilla*) are now a cause for major concern. This is the most valuable commercial inland fishery in England and Wales, but declared catches of glass eel have fallen from 10–70 tonnes/yr in the 1970s and 1980s, to less than 1–2 tonnes/yr today. Declared catches for yellow and silver eels have fallen from 280 tonnes/yr in the mid-1990s to 28 tonnes/yr. Overall, glass eel recruitment in the western UK is now thought to be around 30% of what it was before 1980, while yellow and silver eel stocks are at 20% of their late 1980s levels (Aprahamian & Walker 2008). Adverse feeding conditions in the Sargasso Sea appear to have had large effects on recruitment (Friedland *et al.* 2007).

9.3.12 Lakes and Standing Waters

There are around 8,818 permanent large (>2 ha) lakes in the UK covering over 196,700 ha. The vast majority by number, volume and surface area are in Scotland, with English lakes being focused in Cumbria and Welsh lakes in Snowdonia and mid-Wales. In central and southern England, where natural lakes are rare, artificial reservoirs provide important standing water habitats. Many UK lakes are oligotrophic, although others, such as the Machair lochs of the Western Isles, are calcareous in nature. However, they do exhibit a very wide range of ecological diversity and have been classified in the UK into 11 distinct lake groups mainly based on their aquatic plant assemblages (Duigan *et al.* 2006; 2007). Together, these different lakes hold a range of important plant species, such as slender naiad (*Najus flexilis*) and Shetland pondweed (*Potamogeton rutilus*), as well as many algae; associated wetland flora includes locally distributed species such as Irish ladies' tresses (*Spiranthes romanzoffiana*) and marsh saxifrage (*Saxifraga hirculus*).

The nature conservation agencies in England, Scotland and Wales have surveyed over 3,400 lakes, but, with local exceptions like the Lake District, there has been very limited systematic monitoring of lakes in the UK. Even where monitoring has taken place, it has generally not been oriented towards the assessment of ecosystem services.

Trends in the UK's Openwaters are more difficult to appraise systematically, although many trends are consistent with river data. For example, at upland, acid-sensitive lake sites in the Acid Waters Monitoring Network, sulphate, hydrogen ion and aluminium concentrations have declined progressively over the last 20 years (Davies *et al.*

Table 9.6 The ecological status of lakes in the UK under the terms of the Water Framework Directive (WFD). Source: data derived from the Environment Agency, Northern Ireland Environment Agency and Natural Scotland.

Country	Number of lakes (>50 ha)	Proportion (%) achieving good ecological status or better
England & Wales*	762	36
Northern Ireland	22	33
Scotland	309	66

* In England and Wales, there are 433 lakes of more than 50 hectares in size, most of which are reservoirs or excavated pits. The figure given here of 762 includes smaller water bodies where they are deemed to be of significance for conservation.

2005). Modest biological recovery among macrophytes and invertebrates is also now underway (Monteith *et al.* 2005). In contrast, but in keeping with trends in streams, DOC concentrations have increased which has consequences for water supply.

Table 9.6 provides a summary of the overall ecological status of the UK's lakes as reported by the environmental agencies of England, Wales, Northern Ireland and Scotland. Currently, 66% of Scotland's 309 lochs reach good ecological status, while 36% of England and Wales' and 33% of Northern Ireland's lakes achieve the same status. This reflects the much higher proportion of reservoirs and excavated pits in the countries, and more widespread hydromorphological and water quality pressures. At Loch Leven, Kinross, nutrient loads have been controlled progressively by active catchment management. As a result, the ecological quality of the lake has improved. In particular, macrophytes have returned to deeper areas of the lake in response to increased water clarity, and this has resulted from the lowering of phosphorus inputs (**Figure 9.22**). Although macrophyte communities have not yet reached the lake's former condition, which included characteristic soft water species (Salgado *et al.* 2010), their overall abundance and species composition have improved considerably. This is an important sign of sustainable recovery, because macrophytes play a critical role in nutrient cycling, sediment stability and community composition across multiple trophic levels. The lake provides an important lesson on the requirements for restoring openwaters and the benefits that can be gained (D'Arcy *et al.* 2006).

9.3.13 Status and Trends in Ponds

Ponds are defined as bodies of standing water 0.0025–2 ha in size and containing water for more than four months of the year. They have been counted in the Countryside Survey since 1984, and most recently in 2007. For the first time, however, the 2007 Countryside Survey also appraised pond physico-chemical condition and biological quality throughout GB, with trends also assessed in a lowland subset (Williams *et al.* 2010).

In 2007, there were around 478,000 ponds in GB at densities of roughly 1.8/km² (in England) to 250/km² (in

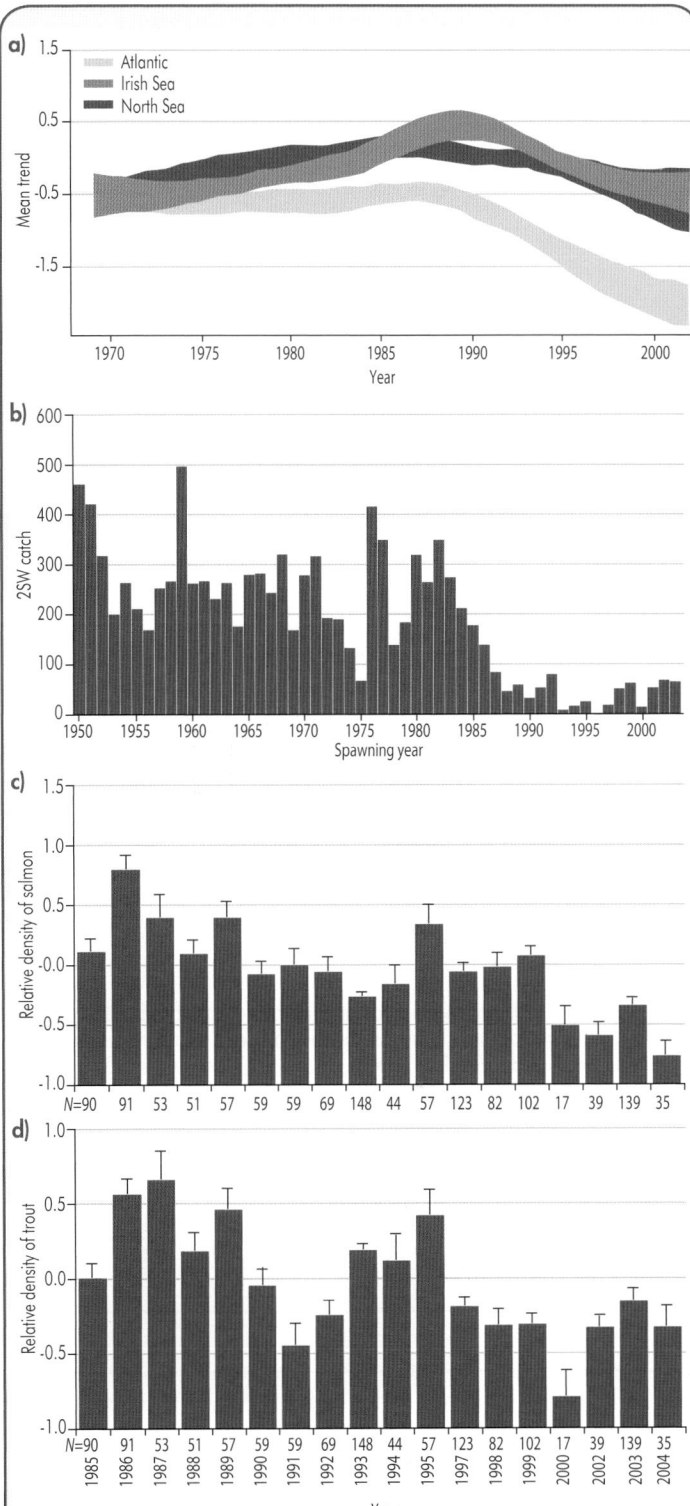

Figure 9.21 Examples of recent trend data for salmonids in the UK: a) Scottish rod catches (with 95% confidence envelopes) of Atlantic salmon (pale green line, Atlantic; medium green line, Irish Sea; darkest green line, North Sea). Source: Vøllestad *et al.* (2009). **b)** rod catches in May and June of Atlantic salmon in the River Avon Hampshire four years after the spawning year shown. Source: Solomon & Lightfoot (2007). Contains Environment Agency information © Environment Agency and database right. **c) & d)** standardised densities (± SE) of juvenile (> 0+) salmon and trout averaged across tributaries of the Welsh River Wye, from 1985 to 2004 (N indicates the number of rivers contributing to mean annual density in each year). Source: Clews *et al.* (2010). Copyright © 2010 Global Change Biology. Reproduced with permission of Blackwell Publishing Ltd.

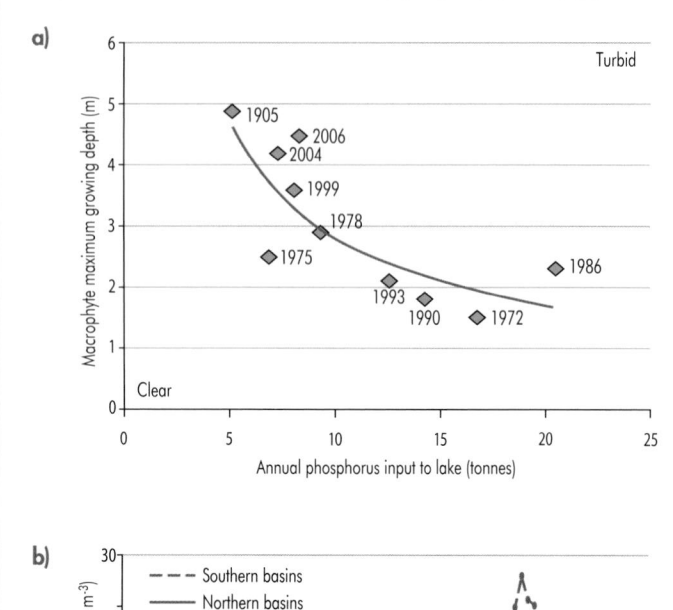

a)

b)

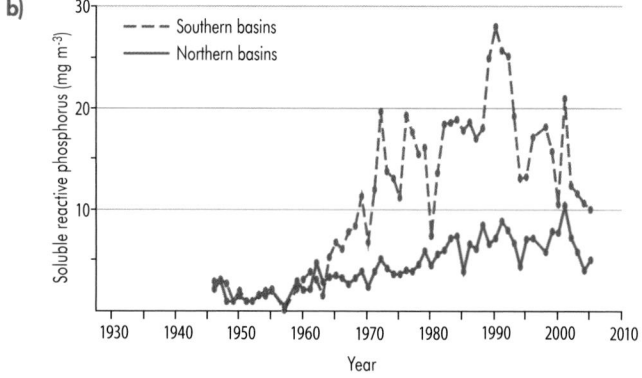

Figure 9.22 a) Maximum growing depth of macrophytes in relation to historical changes in phosphorus input to Loch Leven, Scotland, 1905 to 2006. Source: May & Carvalho (2010). Reproduced with kind permission from Springer Science+Business Media. © Springer Science+Business Media B.V. 2010. **b) Mean concentrations of soluble reactive phosphorus during the first 4 weeks of the year for the north (closed symbols, continuous line) and south (open symbols, broken line) basins of Windermere from 1945 to 2005.** Source: Winfield *et al.* 2008. Reproduced with kind permission from Springer Science+Business Media. © Springer Science+Business Media B.V. 2008.

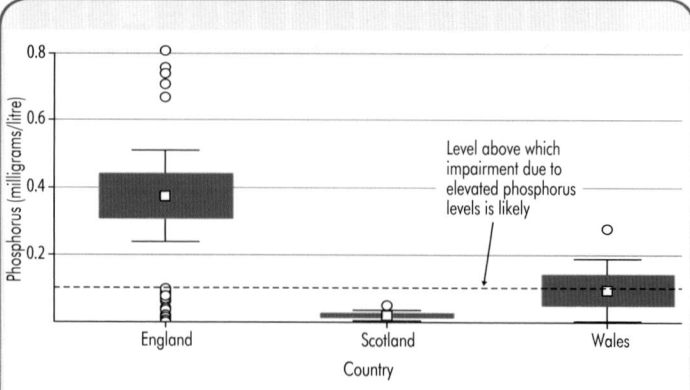

Figure 9.23 Soluble reactive phosphorus in ponds across Great Britain in 2007. All values are means with standard errors (green) and 95% CIs (lines). Source: reproduced from Williams *et al.* (2010). Countryside Survey data owned by NERC – Centre for Ecology & Hydrology.

Scotland). Between 1998 and 2007, more ponds were created (almost 71,000) than were lost (18,000), so pond numbers in GB are probably now increasing by about 1.4% per year after sustaining losses up to and during the 1980s (**Table 9.7**).

The 2007 Countryside Survey Ponds Report (Williams *et al.* 2010) showed that Scottish ponds appeared to be in a better state than those in England and Wales (**Figure 9.23**). In these latter countries, ponds were often degraded (80% poor or very poor) and, on average, supported only a third of the expected total number of wetland plants and one fifth of the expected uncommon plants. Where trend data were available for lowland England and Wales, quality fell between 1996 and 2007 as plant species richness decreased by 20% and the proportion of poor or very poor quality ponds increased by 17%. Pollution by nutrients was probably a major cause of poor status and deterioration (**Figure 9.23**), this is of particular significance given the current increase of nitrate concentrations across England and Wales. Ponds on arable land or under shade from trees were also of lower quality, while climate variability was largely responsible for the increased tendency of ponds to dry out during more arid years. In contrast, ponds near or connected to other Wetlands fared better, while newly created ponds also appeared to be of better quality.

The protection of ponds in the UK appears to depend on the management of surrounding landscapes rather than specific statutes. The Habitats Directive (92/43/EEC) lists eight 'habitats of high conservation importance' that either partly or wholly include ponds, while a range of species listed on Annex II of this Directive are also pond species. However, except for incorporating ponds and ditches within larger designated areas, SACs created by the Directive mostly involve water bodies larger than the UK's typical pond area (generally <0.4 ha). The WFD overwhelmingly emphasises standing waters of more than 50 ha in size. By contrast, the UK BAP has now given specific emphasis to high quality ponds, with national targets and action plans for those that have conservation importance or particular ecological characteristics (Williams *et al.* 2010).

The current poor condition of the pond stock, and the scarcity of unpolluted freshwater throughout the landscape, is being partially addressed through the multi-partner Million Ponds Project, led by the NGO Pond Conservation. Phase 1 of the project (2008 to 2012) is creating 5,000 new clean water ponds in England and Wales, with 1,000 specifically targeted towards the 80 or so pond-associated UK BAP species. In the long-term, the aim is to double pond numbers over the next 50 years and reinstate clean water widely in the landscape. Specifically, the project is using the creation of new, clean water ponds as a tool for Freshwater biodiversity protection.

9.3.14 Status and Trends of Ditches

The Defra aquatic habitats study assessed the extent of ditch and stream habitats, and patterns in biological diversity. The Countryside Survey (2007) also assessed ditch quality to a limited extent (Carey *et al.* 2008). However, no systematic national data on ditch quality trends are available despite the fact that ditches are part of the condition assessment for specific Wetland SSSIs such as the Somerset Levels and Moors.

9.3.15 Invasive, Non-Native Species

Non-native species that become invasive and problematic are a growing issue in both running and standing Freshwaters (Strayer 2010). Examples include many groups of organisms in the riparian zones or shorelines of Freshwaters, as well as some beneath the water line. Adverse effects from the spread of such species have emerged rapidly in UK lakes and rivers over the last 20 to 30 years, some of which are outlined below for particular fishes and molluscs.

In England and Wales, at least 24 Freshwater fish species occur in lakes and rivers as a result of introduction, of which, 15 have established self-sustaining populations in at least one location. Among these, five long-standing introductions now occur in over 100 water bodies and have a high risk of further expansion; these are: common carp (*Cyprinus carpio*), European catfish (*Silurus glanis*), goldfish (*Carassius auratus*), ide (*Leuciscus idus*), European pikeperch (*Sander lucioperca*) and rainbow trout (*Oncorhynchus mykiss*). These and other more recent introductions could pose significant risks to ecological function, particularly if climate change progresses as expected. Among them, common carp is an interesting example as it is favoured by some anglers, but can have significant impacts on habitats, macrophyte communities, nutrient dynamics and turbidity where it is introduced (Britton *et al.* 2010a). Such instances illustrate tensions between the exploitation of some ecosystem services (such as for food, fisheries, sport or ornamentation) and other fundamental ecological processes in Freshwaters. Other effects of introduced fish include vectoring pathogens, competition with native species, impairing recruitment in native species, altering food web structure, and enhancing natural enemies that prey on scarce species (Britton *et al.* 2007, 2010b; Inger *et al.* 2010).

Few non-native species have such marked effects as the zebra mussel (*Dreissena polymorpha*). Initially recorded in the UK in the 19th Century, the incidence of this species in the UK has increased dramatically in lowland lakes and rivers across extensive areas since the 1980s. It has even recently been recorded in the Scottish canal system on the hull of a boat. On hard surfaces, zebra mussels can reach densities as high as 100,000/m³. The consequences of such invasions include: effects on oxygen dynamics, both through direct uptake and effects on primary producers; effects on turbidity, sediment and nutrient dynamics; and competition for resources with native species. In the newly formed Cardiff Bay, closed by impoundment in 2001, zebra mussel larvae have become one of the most abundant zooplanktonic organisms, settling in densities of 3,000–5,000/m² on all hard surfaces, including the Bay's aeration system (M. Alix unpublished thesis). At this site, zebra mussels also harbour large populations of the recently arrived invasive crustacean, *Dikkerogammarus villosus*. There are also problems at water treatment installations, where they occlude flow, but, so far, there is no safe method of control other than physical removal (**Figure 9.24**).

The recent occurrence of the invasive, non-native gammarid shrimp (*Dikerogammarus villosus*) at Grafham water in Cambridgeshire, Cardiff Bay and one other Welsh site, illustrates the need for vigilance over the movement of such species, which often pose major risks for Wetland

biodiversity, into and around the UK. The prevention of further spread of this species is reliant on voluntary cooperation between landowners and recreational water users (Natural England & Environment Agency 2010). There are expectations that similar problems will increase in future as environmental change progressively favours non-native species, but the consequences for ecosystem services have yet to be fully evaluated.

Other examples of the damaging effects of invasive, non-native species are already well-known, such of the impact of introduced crayfish species on the UK's native white-clawed crayfish (Freeman *et al.* 2010). The likely ecosystem service impacts of the introduced signal crayfish (*Pacifastacus leniusculus*) have been explored by Everard *et al.* (2010). There are also concerns about the risks of new arrivals, such as the potentially highly damaging ectoparasite of salmon, *Gyrodactylus salaris* (Johnsen & Jensen 1991; Peeler & Thrush 2009).

The spread of non-native plant species in, and alongside, watercourses has been due to supply by the horticultural industry and the increase in water gardening since the 1960s. Non-native aquatic species and their date of introduction into the UK include: New Zealand swamp stonecrop, *Crassula helmsii* (1911); parrot feather, *Myriophyllum aquaticum* (1964); water pennywort, *Hydrocotyle ranunculoides* (1989); and water primrose, *Ludwigia grandiflora* (1991). The particularly invasive Canadian pondweed (*Elodea canadensis*) was introduced into the UK towards the end of 19th Century. One of the earliest colonisations took place at Bosherston, Pembrokeshire, and is recorded in correspondence by Lord Cawdor who remarked that, prior to 1895, it was a favoured food for the large mute swan population (Duigan & Haycock 1995). Today, it is widespread in lowland lakes in Wales and can be found across the UK in streams, ditches and ponds, often choking the waters with its rapid growth.

Other species of concern are Himalayan balsam (*Impatiens glandulifera*), Japanese knotweed (*Fallopia japonica*) and giant hogweed (*Heracleum mantegazzianum*). Catchment-wide control programmes for giant hogweed in

Table 9.7 Change in the estimated number of ponds ('000s) and pond density (per km²) across Great Britain between 1998 and 2007. Arrows denote significant change (p<0.05) in the direction shown. Source: reproduced from Williams *et al.* (2010). Countryside Survey data owned by NERC – Centre for Ecology & Hydrology. Williams *et al.* (2010).

	Density (per km²)		Number of ponds ('000s)		% change	Direction of significant changes 1998–2007
	1998 (95% CIs)	2007 (95% CIs)	1998 (95% CIs)	2007 (95% CIs)		
GB	1.86 (1.41, 2.54)	2.1 (1.64, 2.78)	425 (321, 580)	478 (374, 634)	12.5	↑
England	1.55 (1.30, 1.81)	1.83 (1.53, 2.14)	197 (165, 230)	234 (195, 272)	18.3	↑
Scotland	2.35 (1.25, 4.14)	2.48 (1.37, 4.30)	187 (100, 330)	198 (110, 344)	5.5	↑
Wales	1.91 (0.85, 3.31)	2.24 (1.23, 3.70)	40 (18, 70)	47 (26, 78)	16.9	↑

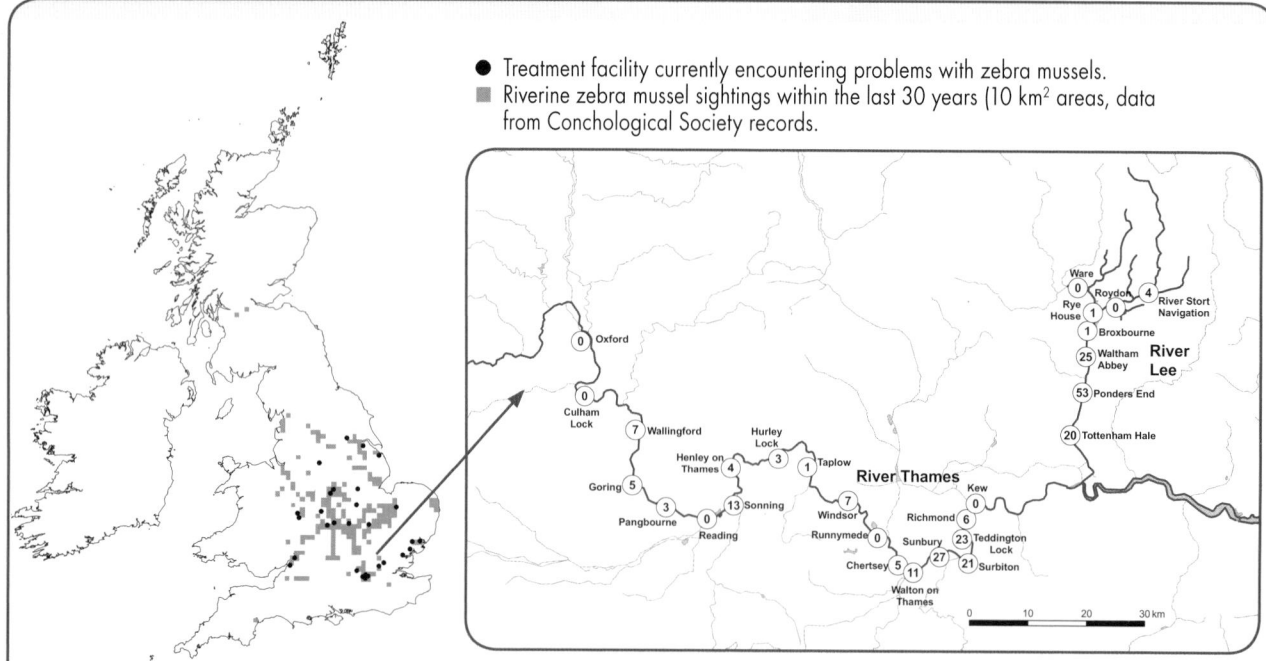

Figure 9.24 Locations occupied by the invasive zebra mussel in UK Openwaters and the distribution of treatment facilities affected by its presence. Enlarged portion of the map shows the effects of zebra mussel distribution along the Rivers Thames and Lean in particular, as revealed by field surveys and interviews with boatyards during April 2002. Numbers in circles indicate the number of zebra mussels collected in five man-minutes. Source: Aldridge *et al.* (2004) Copyright (2004), reproduced with permission from Elsevier; Elliott *et al.* (2005). Reproduced with permission from CIWEM.

the Tweed and the Medway have proved very successful in terms of the local eradication of this species. *Ad hoc* control programmes without coordinated action tend to be less successful as reintroduction from untreated areas in the same catchment often occurs.

Aquatic ecosystem function is usually impaired by the presence of non-native plant species with a high resource demand, resulting in the loss of native species by simple competition, loss of habitat space, and sometimes allelopathic interactions (the production of biochemicals by a species that either positively or negatively affect another species; e.g. New Zealand swamp stonecrop). The absence of suitable control techniques (e.g. loss of appropriate herbicides due to Council Directive 91/414/EEC of 15 July 1991 concerning the placing of plant protection products on the market) and the relatively high cost of mechanical and manual vegetation management in water means that control programmes are limited to areas where the expense of control costs can be justified against the economic use of water (such as income from recreation), or the flood defence risk from not controlling these species. This inevitably leads to the presence of these species in areas where control costs cannot be justified, resulting in a permanent pool for reintroduction to other areas. The recent introduction of biological control for Japanese knotweed could be a good model, both economically and effectively, to follow for other non-native weed species, provided sufficient risk assessment is undertaken.

9.3.16 Climate Change

Lakes, rivers and other wetlands are likely to be among the most sensitive of all habitats to climate change. Temperature and precipitation affect fundamental attributes of aquatic

systems, such as discharge, thermal regimes, stratification, oxygen and solute concentrations. In turn, these effects interact with existing pressures, such as acidification and eutrophication, while also having major consequences for Freshwater organisms that are predominantly cold-blooded (Moss *et al.* 2003; Wilby *et al.* 2006; Ormerod & Durance 2009). As in other parts of the world, temperatures in British Openwaters have increased by about 0.1°C per year over the last 25 years, although trends are winter-biased (Kaushal *et al.* 2010). Trends in discharge are more equivocal because interannual variations are already large (Wilby 2006). Nevertheless, either alone or in combination with natural interannual variations in discharge, temperature changes have already been sufficient to alter species composition in headwaters and alter the abundances of important organisms, including salmonids (Durance & Ormerod 2007; Clews *et al.* 2010). Evidence is also emerging regarding the effects of climate change on water quality (Whitehead *et al.* 2009; Orr *et al.* 2010).

Analysis of the impacts of climate change on Wetlands across Britain (Acreman *et al.* 2009b) suggests that reduced summer rainfall and increased summer evaporation will put stress on Wetland plant communities in late summer and autumn. Bigger impacts are likely to be seen in the south and east of Britain and will be greater on rain-fed Wetlands than on those dominated by river inflows and groundwater. The consequences for ecosystem services, such as water supply, fisheries and energy subsidies for associated ecosystems, have yet to be appraised.

Changes in river flow and in water chemistry associated with the impacts of climate change have been studied by SEPA. These studies provide evidence of major increases in winter peak flows in many rivers since 1961, especially in the west (SEPA 2006). They also show greater flow variability, although less impact has been observed on summer flows.

9.3.17 Wetland Extent

Precise figures for the current extent of the UK's Wetlands are difficult to calculate. According to Natural England's State of the Natural Environment Report (2009), there are an estimated 273,600 ha of coastal and floodplain grazing marsh, fen, lowland raised bog and reedbed in England, making up approximately 2% of England's land area. The majority of this is coastal and floodplain grazing marsh (**Figure 9.25**).

The importance of Wetland habitats is reflected in the fact that they comprise a large proportion of SSSIs in England. Despite this, only 26% of the Wetlands we are considering here are afforded protection by this designation. And while the majority of fen, lowland raised bog and reedbed are designated as SSSIs, only 16% of the coastal and floodplain grazing marsh has been notified (**Table 9.8**). For SSSIs in England, 81% of lowland raised bogs, 87% of fen, marsh and swamp, and 89% of lowland neutral grasslands are in favourable or recovering condition (by area) (statistics provided by Natural England, October 2010). A sample survey of undesignated coastal and floodplain grazing marsh estimated that a similar amount of land (approximately 80%) was in good condition (Dutt 2004). Approximately two-thirds of undesignated fens were not in favourable condition, largely as a result of scrub development, drainage and nutrient enrichment (NWT 2006). It is, therefore, thought that non-statutory Wetlands are generally more likely to be in a poorer condition than SSSIs.

Blanket bog is the most extensive mire habitat in Wales (56,000 ha) and is mainly found in the uplands, although there are significant examples in the lowlands of Gwynedd, Ceredigion and Pembrokeshire (Jones 2009). The relatively small area of lowland blanket bog (1,700 ha) is thought to be a reflection of historic modification and degradation, with current areas of acidic, marshy grassland and wet heath representing former blanket bog. In contrast to the extensive nature of blanket bog, lowland raised bog is confined to just twenty or so scattered sites, including Cors Caron and Cors Fochno, both in mid-Wales. Soligenous (rainwater-fed) fen is widespread and most abundant in the Welsh uplands, while topogeneous (groundwater-fed) fen has a more western

Table 9.8 Wetland Site of Special Scientific Interest (SSSI) designations in England. Source: Natural England (2009).

Wetland habitat	Total resource (hectares)	Area designated SSSI (hectares)	% resources notified
Coastal & floodplain grazing marsh	235,046	37,288	16
Fen	21,927	19,515	89
Lowland raised bog	10,227	8,949	88
Reedbed	6,378	5,388	85
Total	**273,578**	**71,140**	**26**

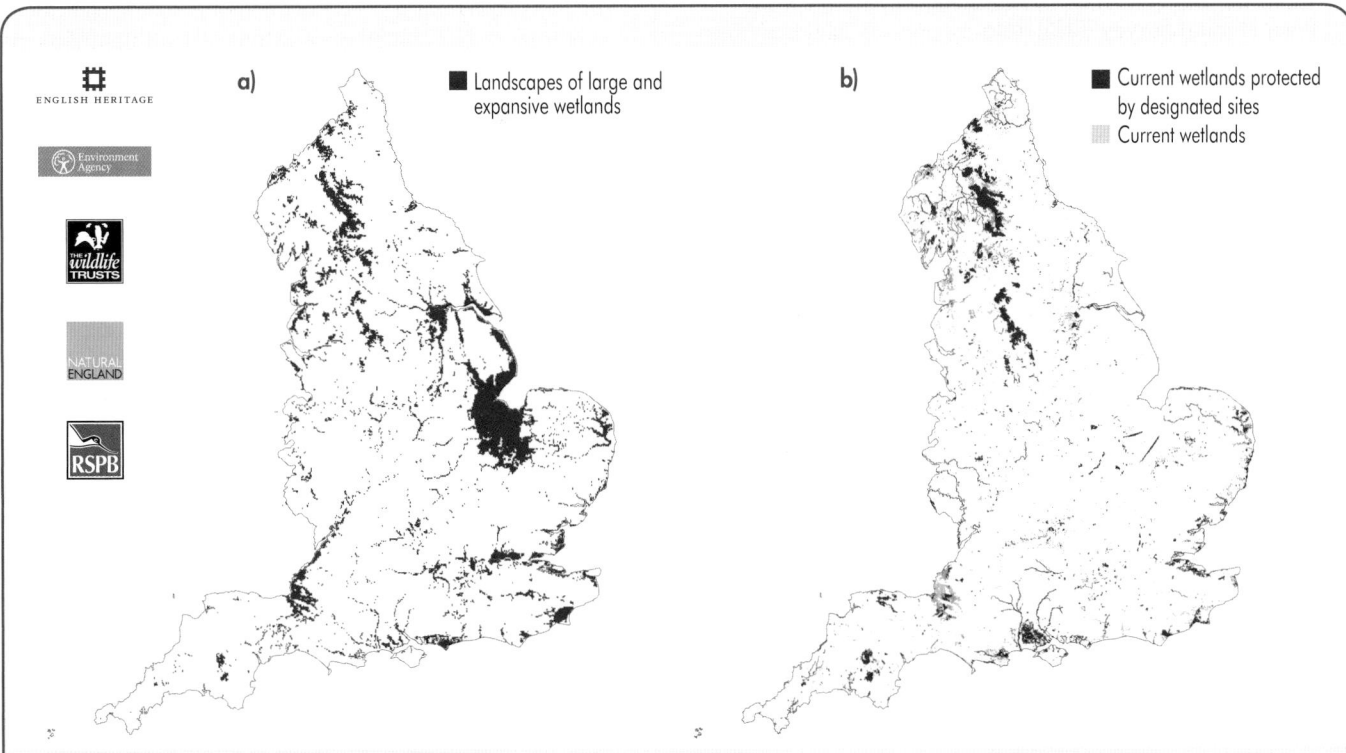

Figure 9.25 Extent of Wetlands in England: a) Historical* maximum extent and b) Current extent of modelled Wetlands.
*Last ten millennia. Source: maps from Hume (2008). ©Wetland Vision, a partnership between Environment Agency, English Heritage, Natural England, RSPB, and The Wildlife Trusts. Derived from data supplied by Natural England ©Natural England 2008. This map is based upon Ordnance Survey material with the permission of Ordnance Survey on behalf of the Controller of Her Majesty's Stationary Office ©Crown Copyright. Unauthorised reproduction infringes Crown copyright and may lead to prosecution or civil proceedings. Natural England 100046223 2008.

lowland distribution; Anglesey is a stronghold for calcareous-rich fen in Wales. Swamp habitat is widespread in Wales (about 1,800 ha in total), but occurs most frequently and extensively along the coast, where reedbeds (about 460 ha) are concentrated (Tyler 1993). The lowland bog inventory of Britain (Lindsay & Immirzi 1996) estimates that the original extent of Welsh lowland bog was around 4,000 ha, but only 1,840 ha have been mapped as such in the more recent field survey of the habitats of Wales (Blackstock *et al.* 2009). The lost Wetland area is concealed by heavily drained, low-lying grassland, with a significant proportion adjacent to extant raised bog near to the Dyfi Estuary. A similar scenario of loss is described for fen habitat: the Welsh Lowland Peatland Survey (Ratcliffe & Hattey 1982) identified 646 probable lowland wetland sites from their analysis of 1,910 maps, but only 289 supported Wetlands in 1978.

Floodplains do not constitute a single habitat type, but may be composed of wet woodland, wet grassland or other habitats, and is, in many cases, a mosaic of habitat types. The River Habitat Survey includes an assessment of Floodplains along with the river channel itself. The data show that, of the UK Floodplains surveyed, around a third are rough pasture and a third improved grassland, with tall herbs (24%), woodland (23%) and scrub (11%) being the next most widespread types (**Table 9.9**). Few Floodplains are reported to have typical Wetland special interest features, with only 0.3% having Openwater (at the time of the survey), 2% having water meadows and 2% supporting fen vegetation.

Table 9.9 Characteristics of Floodplains in the UK from River Habitat Survey (RHS) data. Figures are expressed as a percentage (%) of 1,705 river sites surveyed where the feature is present on at least a third of the right or left bank. Source: Compiled for the UK NEA by the Environment Agency from raw RHS data.

Survey categories	Physical or botanical classes	% site
Banktop land use within 50 m of banktop	Broadleaf/mixed woodland	23.2
	Moorland/heath	9.0
	Scrub	11.3
	Tall herbs	23.7
	Rough pasture	35.9
	Improved grassland	36.0
	Wetland	4.2
Bank profile	Embankments	13.1
	Set-back embankments	6.2
Special interest features of the floodplain	Natural open water	0.3
	Water meadow	0.2
	Fen	0.2
	Bog	0.1
	Carr	0.0
	Marsh	1.0

Statutory agencies, such as Natural England, Scottish Natural Heritage and the Department of the Environment Northern Ireland, compile statistics about Freshwater habitats. However, many statistics are derived for broad habitats, within which, certain Wetlands form a subclass; for example, grazing marsh is included within 'improved grassland' and wet woodland within 'broadleaved mixed and yew woodland'. **Table 9.10** provides a summary of data on Wetland extent from various sources. Estimates vary; for example, the extent of wet woodland is around 50–75,000 ha, while reedbeds cover 6–8,000 ha and grazing marsh 230–300,000 ha. England currently has about 500 ha of intact lowland raised bog, Scotland 2,500 ha, Wales 800 ha and Northern Ireland 2,000 ha. England has about two-thirds of the total area of grazing marsh. The area given for fen in England is likely to be an overestimate since the total habitat area includes other habitats (openwater, woodland habitat) comprising the mosaic within which the fen sits.

In 1996, the Institute of Hydrology calculated the total area of Floodplain land inundated on average once every 100 years. However, the resulting figure of 1,068,000 ha was an estimate of natural Floodplain extent as it did not include any embankments that might separate rivers from their Floodplains. The Environment Agency's ongoing National Flood Risk Assessment includes two datasets related to the 100-year flood zone. The first includes undefended areas (without embankments) and is 963,700 ha, thus defining the actual area of inundated land. The second is a total of both defended and undefended areas and equals 1,658,000 ha. The difference between the two figures provides an estimate of the Floodplain area lost by flood defence embankments. This equates to 694,000 ha or 42% of the former Floodplain extent.

Some idea of the original extent of land naturally and originally affected by waterlogging can be obtained by interpretation of published soil maps. Floodplains associated with alluvial soils occupy long, narrow strips in valley bottoms, most commonly along stream order 4^2 or higher. These sites have been maintained by high groundwater levels, augmented from time to time by periods of flooding from river channels. Unfortunately, soil maps are published at a scale unlikely to show the full extent of these sites. Even at 1:25,000 scale (Harrod 1978), alluvial soils can only be depicted to about a 50 m width margin due to cartographic limitations.

Thus, defining the extent of Wetlands is partly a scale issue, because we lack a systematic inventory. At a national scale, Wetlands can be interpreted from broad soil type, topography and catchment hydrology (flood maps) as was achieved for the Wetland Vision for England (Hume 2008). However, at a local scale, micro-topography, specific soil characteristics and drainage history control precise Wetland extent.

9.3.18 Wetland Condition and Trends

Wetlands are very sensitive to subtle changes in water supply and quality, including acidity, nutrient levels and water table fluctuations (Wheeler & Shaw 2001); they range in acidity from acid (often rain-fed) to base-rich (fed by a chalk aquifer). The requirements of many Wetland plant

2 Stream order is a numerical measure of the branching structure of a river network. At a river's source, the stream has order 1. When two order 1 streams come together, they form an order 2 stream and so on.

Table 9.10 Extent of UK Wetlands. Source: *Natural England 2009; †2008 UK BAP Biodiversity Action Reporting System (BARS 2011); ‡UK BAP priority habitat descriptions; ¶Hume (2008); §Carey *et al.* (2008); **Dutt (2004).

Component habitats	Countryside Survey ('000 ha)§		Priority habitats	UK Historical ('000 ha)	UK Current ('000 ha)	In semi-natural condition ('000 ha)	Trend†
	2007	1990–2007 % change					
Broadleaved mixed/yew woodland			Wet woodland		50–70‡ 62§ (1998) 75§ (2007)		
Semi-natural grassland			Lowland meadow	6,600‡	200‡ (1984)	15‡	
Improved grassland			Grazing marsh	1,200¶ (England)	231† 300‡ (England 235*)	7 (England**)	No clear trend
Fen, marsh, swamp	392	-0.2	Reedbeds	10¶	7.8† 5‡ 6§ (England 6.4*)		Declining slowly
			Fen	310¶ (England)	25.8† (England 21.9*)		
Bog	2,232	8.4	Blanket bog		1,234		
			Lowland raised bog	95‡ 37¶ (England)	37.1‡ (England 17.4, Northern Ireland 8.9, Scotland 8.9, Wales 2.0)	12.9‡ (England 3.7, Northern Ireland 4.5, Scotland 3.3, Wales 1.4)	Fluctuating (probably declining)

communities have been defined along these gradients (Wheeler *et al.* 2002, 2004; **Figure 9.26**).

These distinctions and effects are important as the level of the water table at different times of year determines the viability of different Wetland functions. For example, **Figure 9.26** shows the water table requirements for a mesotrophic wet grassland vegetation community in NVC category MG13. Water levels in the dark green zone are desirable for this community, water levels in the mid-green green zone are tolerable for short periods, but water levels in the light green zone are unacceptable and will lead to the loss of this community.

For most natural and semi-natural UK Wetlands, water tables are above, at or near the land surface during the winter, frequently falling to 40–80 cm in the summer, except where there is emerging groundwater. The seasonal water regime provides a cycle of multiple benefits including wildlife habitat, traditional summer grazing and hay-making. **Figure 9.27** shows the seasonal water table requirements for conservation objectives in the Parrett catchment in Somerset, which would provide a compatible mixture of habitat and agricultural opportunities. If the water table is altered, for example, to enable agricultural use throughout the year, this will be incompatible with some ecosystem services; for instance, it may be too dry in winter for waterbirds and too wet in summer for flood meadow plant communities.

It is even more difficult to estimate the changes in Wetland extent. Various estimates suggest that as much as 90% of the national resource of Wetlands has been lost since Roman times, with 13% of the Floodplain resource degraded or completely disconnected from river channels. In the case of lowland raised bog, the area retaining a largely undisturbed surface has declined by 94% (**Table 9.10**). This national trend is mirrored globally: more than 50% of specific types of Wetlands in parts of North America, Europe, Australia and New Zealand were destroyed during the 20th Century,

and many others in many other parts of the world have been degraded. **Table 9.10** suggests that lowland meadows have declined in the UK from 6,600,000 ha to 200,000 ha, and fens have declined from 310,000 ha to 26,000 ha. On the other hand, reedbeds have only declined from 10,000 ha to 6–8,000 ha as a result of recent restoration efforts; Countryside Survey data from a sample of 591 1x1 km squares, show a small decrease in reedbeds since 1990 (Haines-Young *et al.* 2000). A comprehensive assessment (Hume 2008) has been made of the theoretical historical extent of Wetlands (**Figure 9.25a**) and the current extent (**Figure 9.25b**) in England.

The areal extent of Wetlands is only part of the story since the delivery of their ecosystem services depends on their ecological condition and actual location in the landscape. For designated sites (SSSIs, SPAs, SACs), the statutory authorities maintain information on condition and status, although this is generally not in a form directly

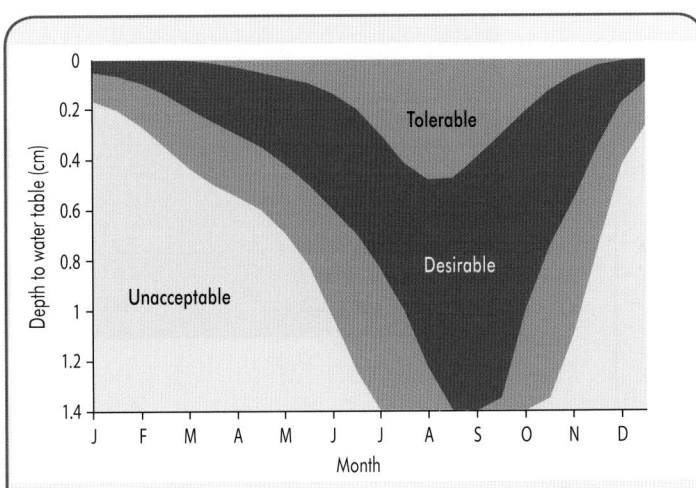

Figure 9.26 Water table regime requirements for MG13 grassland (Midelney Soil). Source: Wheeler *et al.* (2004). Contains Environment Agency information © Environment Agency and database right.

related to ecosystem services. Much more technical data are required for this purpose, which have yet to be collated and applied (Maltby 2009a). Furthermore, we only have limited distributional information for those Wetlands that have been legally designated, and no, or very little, information on undesignated sites; however, most Local Records Centres have some electronic data, and Natural England is currently improving the Wetland habitat inventories. These updated inventories will provide more comprehensive information on the distribution and extent of different Wetland types, and will also provide a baseline from which to monitor changes in the condition of the wider Wetland resource.

Plant species within Wetlands provide one measure of condition; the strongest changes in species recorded by the Countryside Survey between 1990 and 2007 are shown in **Table 9.11** (increases and decreases), together with implications for ecosystem services. In general, UK lowland wetlands are quite small, so are not necessarily well represented by the sampling of 591 grid squares. Although a few species may display trends as a result of altered precision in taxonomic recording, for the majority of species, trends will reflect changes in the habitats that are being monitored. When all the individual trends reported above are assessed together, general trends in Wetland habitats seem to reflect:

- Higher nutrient levels, with a general increase in nutrient-loving plants and a related decline in species requiring nutrient-poor situations.
- A coarsening of the vegetation due to the general eutrophication of the habitats, with lower-growing species declining, especially those which prefer nutrient-poor conditions.
- Increased atmospheric deposition of nitrogen, making soils both more fertile and more acid.

- An expansion of alder and sallow, reflecting the abandonment/lack of cutting or grazing (as sites no longer fit within conventional agricultural systems), increased planting, or more accurate recording of species.
- Altered grazing pressure in parts of the UK—reduced grazing pressure is indexed by a decline in common yellow sedge (*Carex viridula*) and red fescue (*Festuca rubra*), and an increase in creeping willow (*Salix repens*).
- Localised effects, with species such as heath rush (*Juncus squarrosus*) and deer-grass (*Trichophorum cespitosum agg.*) declining in the lowlands, as (wet) heaths and bogs have been drained, enriched or abandoned, but increasing their range in the uplands.
- A large increase in vigorous coarse sedges in Floodplain meadows as a result of increased inundation.

While Scotland, like England, has seen decreases in the extent of important Wetland species and habitats, there are still examples of large areas of key habitats such as the 410 ha of the inner Tay reedbeds (6% of the UK total), and the Insh marshes (300 ha of base-poor fen in the floodplain of the River Spey), as well as concentrations of internationally important smaller fens in the Borders (Magee & Badenoch 2010).

Major restoration and creation efforts have been focused on reedbeds in order to create habitat for rare birds such as bittern and bearded tit (*Panurus biarmicus*). For example, the RSPB has created 190 ha of reed at Ham Wall in Somerset in worked-out peat diggings and 300 ha at Lakenheath in Norfolk on previously arable farmland.

9.3.19 Trends in Bird Populations

A further indicator of Wetland condition is provided by the revised 'Water and Wetland Birds Indicator' for different

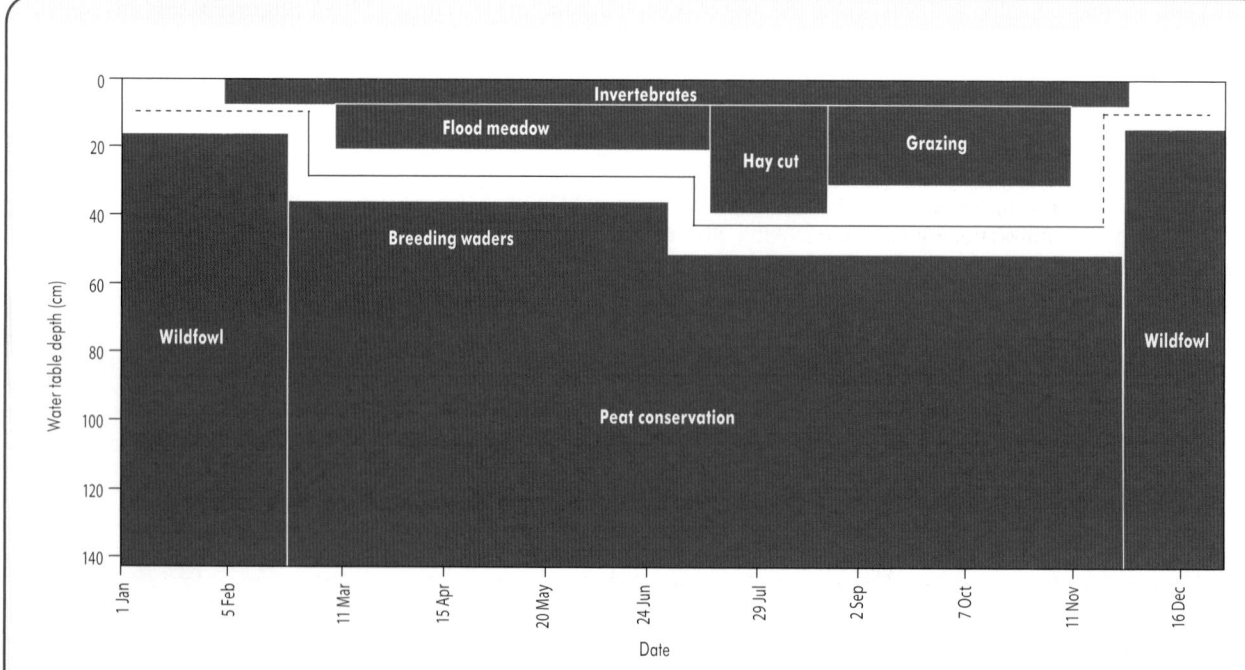

Figure 9.27 Water table requirements for environmental characteristics in the Parrett catchment. The shaded zones represent ranges of water table depth which could potentially be detrimental to the named interest. The uncoloured zone represents an optimal soil-water regime to integrate the requirements of all the objectives at a site. Source: Morris *et al.* (2008a). Copyright (2008), reproduced with permission from Elsevier.

UK National Ecosystem Assessment: Technical Report

habitat types (Smithers *et al.* 2008). Overall, the index comprises an 'All Freshwater Habitats Indicator' covering 26 birds (of which, four are generalists within the wetland environment), backed up by separate indicators for 'Fast-flowing Waters' (four species), 'Slow/standing Waters' (six species), 'Reed Beds' (four species) and 'Wet Meadows' (eight species).

It should be stressed that these indicators do not necessarily provide good information on Wetland habitats and condition in the UK, as the majority of Wetland bird species are migratory and their population levels can be heavily influenced by external factors (Noble *et al.* 2008). For example, the extent and quality of the summer breeding grounds for many waterfowl (often in the Arctic) will influence annual productivity; similarly, the habitat condition of key migration routes will influence survival. The generally more stable All Freshwater Habitats Indicator masks considerable variability among the species making up the indicator. For example, the Fast-moving Waters index has fluctuated at levels about 20% below the 1975 baseline. Despite an initial increase, the Wet Meadows index has shown a marked and steady decline since the early 1980s. The birds of Reed Beds declined from 1975 through to the 1990s, and then increased almost back to the 1975 index (perhaps due to targeted habitat creation work). The trend for birds of Slow/standing Waters has increased to almost double its 1975 baseline.

Migratory Wetland birds, such as yellow wagtail (*Motacilla flava*) and reed and sedge warblers (*Acrocephalus scirpaceus* and *Acrocephalus schoenobaenus*), are affected by factors beyond the UK. Increasing effects of climate change will also influence the future trend of the Index, and an increase in the distribution of several relatively recent arrivals has already been noted (e.g. little egret, *Egretta garzetta*, Cetti's warbler, *Cettia cetti*).

In terms of breeding birds, redshank (*Tringa totanus*), snipe (*Gallingo gallinago*), curlew (*Numenius arquata*) and lapwing (*Vanellus vanellus*) are the most relevant for determining the condition of lowland Wetlands due to their dependence on this habitat, although these species also breed in coastal, upland and arable locations. Breeding populations for all UK Wetland birds have declined since 1982, with increasing severity in recent years (**Table 9.12**). This decline is consistent with estimates of breeding pairs of waders for wet meadows in England and Wales. Many of these species are now concentrated on just a few sites in lowland England, most of which are managed as nature reserves.

The recent decline in redshank numbers has been related to the drainage of farmland (Gibbons *et al.* 1993). Lowland breeding snipe numbers have also declined, with most of the remaining birds becoming highly aggregated on a very small number of nature reserves. Lapwings have also decreased in number, possibly because changes in agricultural practice

Table 9.11 Changes in plant species between 1990 and 2007. Source: derived from results of the Countryside Survey.

Habitat type	Wetland species increasing	Wetland species declining	Possible implications
General	*Alnus glutinosa* (Alder); *Calystegia sepium* (Great Bindweed); *Epilobium parviflorum* (Hoary Willow-herb); *Salix cinerea* (Grey Willow)	*Alopecurus pratensis* (Meadow Foxtail); *Carex dioica* (Dioecious Sedge); *Carex pallescens* (Pale Sedge); *Drosera anglica* (Great Sundew); *Glyceria fluitans* (Floating Sweet-grass); *Juncus bulbosus* (Bulbous Rush); *Pinguicula vulgaris* (Common Butterwort); *Myosotis scorpioides* (Water Forget-me-not); *Salix aurita* (Eared Willow); *Valeriana dioica* (Marsh Valerian)	More nutrient-rich Wetlands Some changes may reflect mechanical disturbance to Wetlands, including planting or abandonment/lack of cutting or grazing as sites no longer fit within conventional agricultural systems.
Neutral grasslands	*Cirsium palustre* (Marsh Thistle); *Glyceria fluitans* (Floating Sweet-grass); *Juncus bulbosus* (Bulbous Rush); *Molinia caerulea* (Purple Moor-grass); *Ranunculus acris* (Meadow Buttercup)	*Alopecurus geniculatus* (Marsh Foxtail); *Leontodon (Scorzoneroides) autumnalis* (Autumnal Hawkbit)	More nutrient-rich Wetlands that are coarser (greater productivity), including some evidence of increased atmospheric deposition of nitrogen resulting in elevated nutrient levels and some soil acidification.
Acid grasslands	*Eriophorum angustifolium* (Common Cotton-grass); *Juncus squarrosus* (Heath Rush); *Trichophorum cespitosum* (Deergrass)	*Carex nigra* (Common Sedge); *Carex pulicaris* (Flea Sedge); *Carex viridula* (Yellow Sedge); *Luzula campestris/multiflora* (Woodrushes); *Juncus bulbosus* (Bulbous Rush)	More nutrient-rich Wetlands that are coarser (greater productivity), including some evidence of increase atmospheric deposition of nitrogen resulting in elevated nutrient levels and some soil acidification.
Woodland	*Cirsium palustre* (Marsh Thistle); *Rumex conglomeratus* (Clustered Dock)	*Agrostis stolonifera* (Creeping Bent); *Luzula campestris/multiflora*; (Woodrushes)	More nutrient-rich Wetlands with coarser growth.
Dwarf shrub heaths	*Carex binervis* (Green-ribbed Sedge); *Carex echinata* (Star Sedge); *Juncus effusus* (Soft Rush); *Salix repens* (Creeping Willow)	*Carex nigra* (Common Sedge); *Carex flacca* (Glaucous Sedge); *Carex viridula* (Yellow Sedge); *Festuca rubra* (Red Fescue)	Further acidification of the Wetland soil, together with some increased fertility.
Bogs	*Agrostis canina* (Velvet Bent); *Epilobium palustre* (Marsh Willow Herb); *Rhynchospora alba* (White Beak-Sedge); *Salix repens* (Creeping Willow)	*Agrostis stolonifera* (Creeping Bent); *Drosera intermedia* (Oblong-leaved Sundew); *Festuca rubra* (Red Fescue); *Triglochin palustre* (Common Arrow-grass)	Further acidification of the Wetland soil (possibly with some increased fertility).

	Table 9.12 Trends in breeding populations of selected Wetland birds. Source: *BTO (2009a); †Wilson et al. (2005); ‡Henderson et al. (2002).						
	All habitats UK*			All habitats England*		Wet meadows England and Wales†	Northern Ireland All habitats‡
	1982–2007	1997–2007	2002–2007	1982–2007	1997–2007	1982–2002	1985–1999
Redshank	-54%	-41%	-27%			-29%	
Curlew	-11%	-31%	-21%			-39%	-60%
Lapwing	-38%	-29%	-21%	-42%	+12%	-36%	-50%
Snipe						-62%	-30%

have led to their breeding productivity dropping below a sustainable level (Galbraith 1988; Hudson et al. 1994; Siriwardena et al. 2000a; Besbeas et al. 2002; Milsom 2005); however, lapwing data for England do show an increase in numbers between 1997 and 2007.

In winter, the UK holds internationally important populations of swans, geese, ducks and wading birds. The Wintering Waterbird Indicator (**Figure 9.28**) shows that numbers rose steadily from the mid-1970s to the late 1990s, stabilised in 2000, but have declined in recent winters (BTO 2009b). Trends in recent colonists due to climate change are evident: breeding by little egrets, for example, was first confirmed in 1996 and, by 2006, there were 600 pairs. Targeted conservation efforts have also had an effect on bird populations and have, for example, led to a rise in the number of bittern from 19 males (heard booming) in 1999 to 75 in 2008.

Development work on Scottish wintering waterbird indicators (by the British Trust for Ornithology for Scottish Natural Heritage) determined that 1975/1976 provided the most reliable baseline for trend analyses (Austin et al. 2007). In contrast to England, the overall index has shown no decline up to the end of 2008, but this masks a persisting decrease in wader numbers which is counterbalanced by large increases in most geese species. Scotland is particularly important for wintering geese, most of which have shown marked increases since the mid-1970s. The population of native Greylag geese has also increased. Of the other waterfowl, whooper (Cygnus Cygnus) and mute swans, teal (Anas crecca), widgeon (Anas penelope) and pintail (Anas acuta) have all increased, whereas mallard (Anas platyrhynchos), shelduck (Tadorna tadorna), pochard (Aythya farina) and goosander (Mergus merganser) are among those that have declined. The dipper (Cinclus cinclus) can be considered an iconic Welsh riverine bird, but the population has declined due to acidification (Lovegrove et al. 2009).

9.3.20 Land Ownership

An additional broad-scale assessment of the condition of, and land management objectives for, Wetlands can be made by analysing ownership. Traditionally, many of the UK's Wetlands were owned or rented by farmers as part of their wider landholding with the aim to maximise their food production function. However, increasingly, land has been acquired by local authorities and NGOs such as The Wildlife Trusts, Wildfowl & Wetlands Trust, The National Trust and the RSPB. These organisations tend to focus on the biodiversity and recreation services of Wetlands. For example, parts of the Floodplain of the Thames between Oxford and Reading are owned by South Oxfordshire District Council. From 2004 to 2009, Wetland land purchases made by the RSPB equalled 4,200 ha in England, 2,345 ha in Scotland, 247 ha in Wales and 45 ha in Northern Ireland for bird reserves.

9.3.21 Environmental Archaeology

Van de Noort (2001) determined the rate of Wetland heritage loss for England between 1950 and 2000 in three broad Wetland types: upland wetlands (predominantly blanket mires), lowland peatlands, and lowland alleviated wetlands. They concluded that the peatlands had suffered the most in the second half of the 20th Century, especially the upland peats, and that up to 50% of the archaeological sites that existed in these areas in 1950 were lost by 2000; the rate of loss of heritage in lowland alleviated wetlands was much less, and also less visible. Assessment of the quality of nine archaeological sites in the Somerset Levels and Moors showed that those in soils with a low pH, and where a significant overburden of peat and/or clay is present, were best preserved (Brunning 2001).

9.3.22 Trends in Ecosystem Services Delivered by Lowland Wetland Priority Habitat Types

The degree of importance of individual ecosystem services delivered by key lowland wetland types, along with the direction of change in the degree to which these services are effectively delivered, is summarised in **Table A9.4.1**

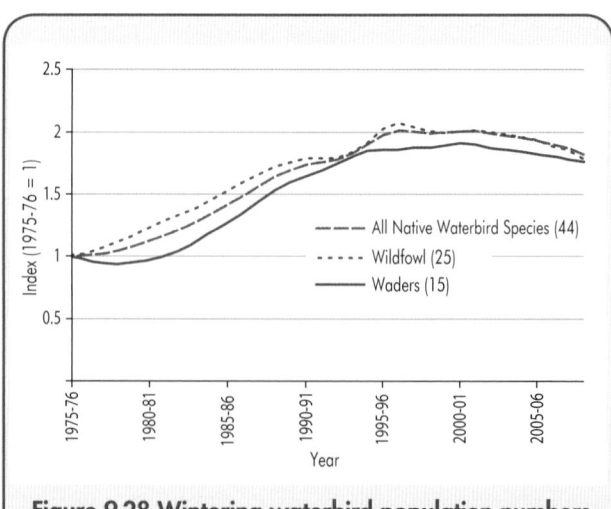

Figure 9.28 Wintering waterbird population numbers for Great Britain. Source: BTO (2009b).

(**Appendix 9.4**). Also shown is the confidence behind this data, based on the amount of evidence in published literature and the extent to which that literature is in agreement. The degree of importance of each service varies among the different Wetland types, with managed Floodplains clearly providing services to a lesser degree overall than any of the other Wetland types. However, this does not necessarily mean that this Wetland type is less valuable and may, in fact, demonstrate the potential for restoring Floodplains to regenerate lost or degraded services. Moreover, across all Wetland types, the degree to which most services are being delivered has deteriorated.

9.4 Drivers of Change

Freshwater habitats—Openwaters, Wetlands and Floodplains—have been affected by a range of drivers that reflect changes in economic development, social preferences, technology and systems governance. Indeed, many of the responses to pressures on the water environment, such as the WFD, have themselves become drivers of change.

9.4.1 Openwaters
The drivers of environmental change for Freshwaters are identified elsewhere in this assessment (Chapter 3). Other past or emerging drivers of change in Freshwaters include: economic development associated with increased abstractions from, and discharges to, the water environment which lead to specific pollution pressures; low flows or groundwater levels; channel modifications; and ecological impacts. Technological development has generated new contamination issues. The changing use of chemicals in domestic and industrial settings is shifting the spectrum of important pollutants from sanitary wastes to emerging contaminants including: endocrine-disrupting chemicals, flame retardants, nanoparticles, personal care products, synthetic biological components, and microelectronics. The drive to achieve 20% of the UK's energy from renewable sources has led to the development of wind turbines, which have an indirect impact on Freshwaters, for example, through peat erosion. In particular, small-scale hydroelectric power generation may have more direct impacts when associated with weirs, diversions and small dams.

These drivers have led to responses to alleviate pressures on Freshwater habitats that have, in turn, become drivers of change themselves. For example, the WFD is the overarching policy regime for freshwater quality in the UK, driving targets for water quality improvement. It subsumes a host of EU directives (and related national laws) such as the Drinking Water Directive, Nitrates Directive, and Habitats Directive. The WFD seeks to achieve good ecological water quality status using cost-effective intervention measures, such as investment in water treatment works or limitations on the use of agrichemicals. The WFD has forced a better understanding of water demand and supply at the catchment-scale, and of the implications for water ecology.

The WFD has also nudged water users with different interests to join together to take collaborative actions. For example, campaigns to use water wisely and a genuine willingness to invest in clean-up and wastewater treatment have led to substantial improvements in some aspects of water quality and quantity (e.g. organic pollution, acid deposition, flows). New approaches by water companies (e.g. United Utilities, Dwr Cymru, Northumbrian Water, South West Water) are progressively leading to considerations of asset protection or upstream thinking. Treatment costs of water supply are being reduced by developments in catchment management that protect supply and deliver other service benefits (reviewed by Everard 2009).

9.4.2 Wetlands
The main drivers of change for Wetlands have been economic factors associated with population growth, economic prosperity, and increased demand for land for intensive agriculture; these drivers have been influenced by actions to protect remaining Wetland sites. The increase in demand for peat in horticulture and gardening since the 1970s is just one driver which has impacted lowland bogs in particular. Wetlands have been strongly influenced by interactions between agricultural and environmental policies (Morris *et al.* 2008b, 2009; Posthumus & Morris 2010).

The period since the Second World War has seen a succession of policy shifts that reflect a changing balance of priorities given to farming and other countryside services, including biodiversity. For example, the post-war period between 1945 and 1980 was characterised by agricultural growth (Chapter 7). Publicly funded flood defence and improved land drainage for agriculture became major features of support for farming in the UK (Robinson & Armstrong 1988; Morris 1992; Johnson *et al.* 2005), and included the reclamation of wet land for agriculture.

The period from 1980 to 2000 marked a transition in agricultural policy from a focus on production to one that addressed growing concerns about agricultural subsidies and the environmental impacts of intensive farming. International agreements (e.g. the Ramsar Convention on Wetlands, 1971) and European legislation (e.g. the EU Birds Directive, 1979) ran parallel with national initiatives such as the UK Wildlife and Countryside Act (1981) (Hodge & McNally 2000). This gave public agencies a duty to consider nature conservation, to designate some Wetlands as SSSIs, and to allow Floodplain and river restoration to begin (Adams *et al.* 2004).

The mid-1980s witnessed the introduction of production quotas and agri-environment schemes. Agricultural and environmental policies were integrated with the designation of Environmentally Sensitive Areas (ESAs) in 1987. This was followed in 1991 by the wider Countryside Stewardship Scheme (CSS). Both of these schemes included options for Wetland and Floodplain sites. They implicitly recognised the publicly valued ecosystem services provided by managed landscapes, even if they were not framed in these terms (Everard & Appleby 2009). However, these payments were voluntary and cooperative action between landowners was not encouraged, so they were not very effective at reducing habitat losses or reversing the decline of Wetlands. About the same time, the Common Agricultural Policy reform partially decoupled subsidies from farm income support and introduced 'set-aside' to take land out of production, unintentionally providing opportunities for environmental benefits.

The period since 2000 has been one of reform, driven by further realignment of agricultural and environmental policy. These include the European Union Common Agricultural Policy (CAP) reform of 2003 and, in 2005, the introduction of the Single (Farm) Payments Scheme whereby income support is no longer linked to production. A new Environmental Stewardship scheme, with options for Wetland habitats and 'inundation grassland', was also introduced at this time. Options currently under consideration for the future of the CAP through to 2020 vary in terms of the type and extent of interventions, and the balance of agricultural, environmental and other priorities (EU 2010).

9.4.3 Floodplains and Flood Risk Management

It is apparent that a combination of extreme rainfall events and changes in land use has made flooding more problematic in the UK, resulting in very significant social, economic and environmental costs (Foresight 2004; Pitt 2008). About six million properties are exposed to some degree of flood risk, mostly from river and coastal flooding (Foresight 2004; Environment Agency 2009a,c). Critical infrastructure and public services can also be affected by flooding, as was demonstrated by the summer floods of 2007 in England (Chatterton *et al.* 2010). For these reasons, the management of flood risks has become an increasing concern for government at both local and national levels, and there has been a three-fold increase in expenditure on flood risk in England since 2004 (Environment Agency 2009d).

During the last decade, however, emphasis has switched from flood defence to flood risk management. Strategies such as the Defra's Making Space for Water (Defra 2005) advocate the creation of wetlands and washlands, river corridor widening and river restoration to alleviate flood risk in downstream urban areas, as well as providing other benefits at the same time (Environment Agency 2003; Morris *et al.* 2004; Defra 2005). However, the emphasis is on appraising, managing and reducing risk not necessarily avoiding Floodplain development.

Thus, rural land use in some Floodplain areas has shifted from intensive farming to uses that need less protection against flooding and can deliver multiple benefits, including flood storage. In this respect, as the name suggests, Catchment Flood Management Plans (Environment Agency 2008b) take a landscape-scale approach to managing flood risk, identifying where increased catchment storage might help. Alongside this, in some areas, the Catchment Sensitive Farming Programme aims to join flood risk management with other objectives such as the control of diffuse pollution from farmland (Defra 2008). Other actions have also promoted this integration of policy areas, such as regulatory measures like habitat protection or limits on nitrogen fertiliser to protect water quality. Economic mechanisms such as agri-environment payments for Wetland management, and/ or voluntary arrangements undertaken by landowners in collaboration with NGOs, such as the Farm and Wildlife Advisory Group (FWAG) and Linking Environment and Farming (LEAF), are other examples. Yet incentives are still piecemeal, and there are no mechanisms for requiring changes to land use or management when and where they are needed in order to achieve other objectives such as those of the WFD. Appraisals of public investment in flood alleviation now recognise the benefits of creating Wetland areas (Defra 2007), and landowners may be paid for the retention and/or storage of floodwater on their land (Defra 2005; JNCC 2008).

In broad terms, the various administrations in the UK now explicitly include conservation objectives in their flood risk management strategies (Werritty *et al.* 2010), seeking the protection of nationally important wildlife sites and the achievement of biodiversity targets (Defra 2005; Environment Agency 2009d). Furthermore, guidance aims to avoid the development of Floodplain land wherever possible, and to provide storage and pathways for floodwaters in urban areas. The Flood Risk Management (Scotland) Act (2009), for example, is leading to a complete shift in the sustainable management of whole catchments and the restoration of Wetlands (Spray *et al.* 2010). This is clear recognition of the role of Floodplains in providing a range of ecosystem services (CLG 2009).

Although priorities appear to have switched in favour of environmental enhancement, there remains a requirement for farmers to maintain land in 'Good Agricultural and Environmental Condition' (Defra 2008). The food shortages and price spikes of 2007/2008, exacerbated by international demand for bioenergy, confirm the relevance of maintaining capacity in reserve. Indeed, in the UK, much of this capacity exists in lowland areas that are almost universally dependent on managed land drainage and, in many cases, on some degree of flood protection. This is endorsed by resurging UK government concerns about food security (Defra 2010). In this respect, it will be increasingly important to achieve the sustainable management of agricultural floodplains, balancing the demand for food and fibre with the protection and enhancement of floodplain landscapes and wildlife (Foresight 2010; 2011), particularly in lowland peatland areas. (Morris *et al.* 2010).

9.5 Trade-offs and Synergies

The quality of Freshwater ecosystems has always been traded-off against the aims of wider landscape management, usually for purposes unconnected with water, but which lead to effects downstream. Examples include using water for wastewater disposal or the inadvertent runoff of agricultural chemicals, both of which affect other services and water users, such as fisheries and anglers. In many cases, ecosystem modifications have been undertaken in order to boost production of one or a few favoured services, while wholly overlooking the implications for other ecosystem services and overall ecosystem integrity. For example, widespread drainage has permitted increased crop yields, but has simultaneously led to the loss or degradation of other ecosystem services ranging from water regulation and soil erosion, to changes in valued landscapes and the loss of habitats for biodiversity. Draining peatlands for agriculture also releases soil carbon to the atmosphere, potentially contributing to global warming.

The key message in the matrix in **Table A9.4.1** (**Appendix 9.4**) is that the only lowland wetland ecosystem that is showing any form of improvement in the degree to which ecosystem services are delivered is managed floodplains. In these, the delivery of provisioning services is increasing, while in all other ecosystems considered, the levels of services are either declining or are unchanged. The degree of knowledge supporting these conclusions is only consistently high for Floodplains, which are the most studied of our Wetlands systems; our knowledge of other systems is generally poor, demonstrating key gaps in our understanding about how other Wetland ecosystems function. It is also apparent that the majority of functions in most lowland wetland ecosystems are considered important, but despite this, they are still deteriorating.

Table A9.4.2 (**Appendix 9.4**) is a trade-off matrix for a 'natural' Floodplain, showing how optimising one ecosystem service affects the delivery of other ecosystem services. The key point demonstrated in this table is that optimisation of the provisioning service of crops, plants and animals results in large decreases in the delivery of all other ecosystem services. This supports the finding of Pilgrim *et al.* (2010) who also identified that maximising agricultural production is one of the most damaging activities to ecosystem services that can be carried out.

Matrices such as **Table A9.4.2.** can assist in the better assessment of scenarios required for meeting desired policy and management objectives. One emerging challenge will be to quantify these potential synergies and trade-offs in economic terms, such as the maintenance of high water table levels for conservation versus flood storage and flood risk reduction. **Figure 9.29** illustrates one such potential management dilemma, where Wetlands may reduce the levels of nitrate flowing from agricultural land into rivers and lakes through denitrification, but if these processes generate nitrous oxide (a highly potent greenhouse gas) rather than nitrogen gas, the result is a contribution to global warming.

The ecosystem approach (Maltby 2006, 2009b; Defra 2007) has done much to promote an appreciation of the value of Wetlands, Freshwater and Floodplains for human welfare (Chapter 22), but also the trade-off and synergies among different ecosystem services. Recent examples include applications in Floodplain management (Everard 2009; Posthumus *et al.* 2010), peat and Wetland management (Turner *et al.* 2008; Bonn *et al.* 2010, Maltby 2010) and the wider countryside (Eigenbrod *et al.* 2009). The ecosystems framework typically uses sets of biophysical and socioeconomic indicators to assess the relative performance of alternative land and water management strategies such as the creation of Wetlands and the ecological restoration of agricultural Floodplains. For example, **Figure 9.30** shows the synergies and trade-offs among ecosystem indicators for alternative land use scenarios that aim to meet different objectives in

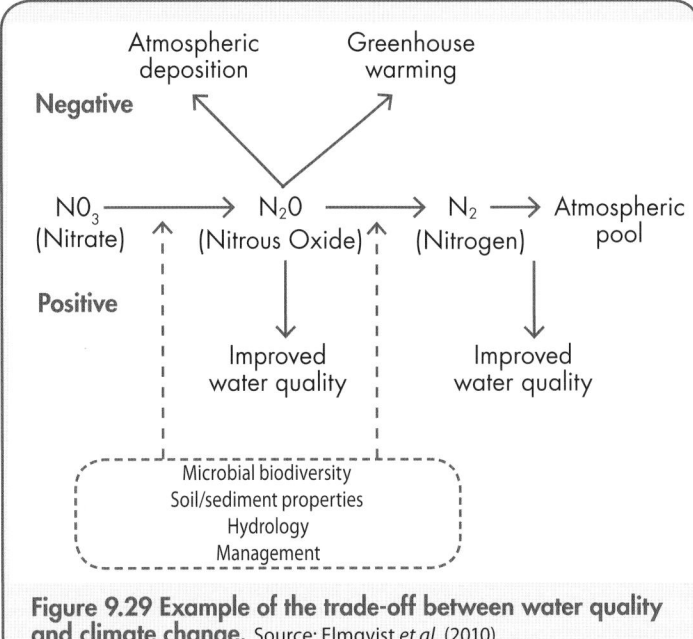

Figure 9.29 Example of the trade-off between water quality and climate change. Source: Elmqvist *et al.* (2010).

Beckingham Marshes—900 ha of Floodplain by the River Trent in Nottinghamshire (Posthumus *et al.* 2010).

For this case, the existing (2006) agricultural land use, maximum flood storage and maximum agricultural production scenarios show similarity and convergence in values for ecosystem indicators. These scenarios score high on agricultural production and floodwater storage, but low on environmental services such as water quality, greenhouse gas balance, habitats and space for water recreation and landscape. By comparison, the agri-environment and biodiversity scenarios show relatively higher values for indicators relating to soil quality, habitats, space for water, recreation and landscape. Controlled flood storage is more compatible with the agricultural land use scenario than the biodiversity scenario for this site. The scores shown here are unweighted, so all the ecosystem services are considered of equal importance; expressing them in monetary terms provides a basis for comparison.

Similar synergies and trade-offs almost certainly vary according to local conditions. Some trade-offs are more obvious than others, such as the draining of peatlands for agriculture and resultant loss of carbon and biodiversity (Bonn *et al.* 2010; Natural England 2010), or the intensification of agriculture and the resultant loss of biodiversity (Eigenbrod *et al.* 2009). But in some situations, the use of Floodplains for storage may be more compatible with agricultural land uses than some types of biodiversity conservation (Posthumus *et al.* 2010). From a management viewpoint, it is critical to understand the potentially diverse impact on ecosystems services associated with interventions, including unintended consequences.

Across Europe, there are many examples (e.g. Skjern catchment in Denmark) of engineers draining the land for intensive agriculture, knowing the gains would be short-term, but without realising the ramifications of what they were doing. This resulted in a decline in the condition of habitats designated as SAC and their dependent species, impacts on water quality and fisheries, and the loss of landscape value. Ultimately, it led to the government

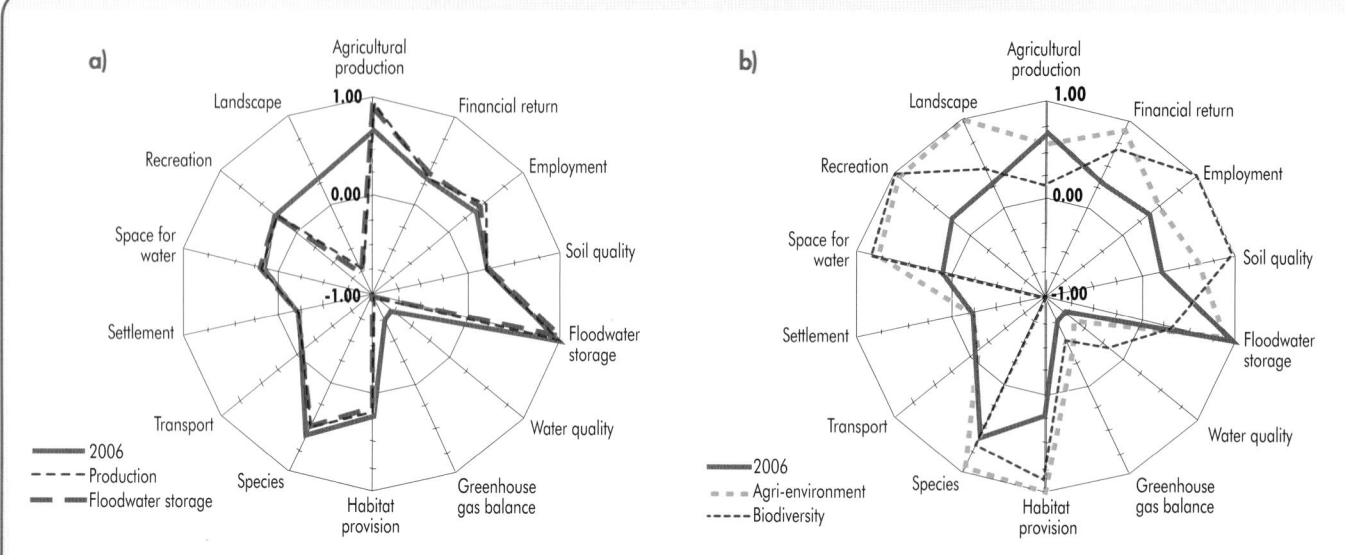

Figure 9.30 Synergies and trade-offs among land use scenarios in the Beckingham Marshes, Nottinghamshire. a) Shows the convergence of existing (2006) agricultural production and flood storage scenarios; **b)** Shows how environmentally oriented scenarios diverge from existing land use. P=production; R=regulation; H=habitat; C=carrier; I=information service. Scale: from -1 (worst performance) to 1 (best performance). Source: Posthumus *et al.* (2010). Copyright (2010), reproduced with permission from Elsevier.

purchasing land for restoration and producing what is now a very popular local amenity and tourism resource.

Qualitative assessments of the ecosystem service outcomes from river habitat enhancement (Everard 2009; 2010) has concluded that the restoration of ecosystem functioning is likely to deliver generally positive benefits to the full range of provisioning, regulatory, cultural and supporting ecosystem services, whereas 'heavy engineering' solutions to optimise only specific benefits were likely to degrade most other ecosystem services (Everard & Kataria 2010).

Tools to appraise the optimisation of such trade-offs and synergies in Freshwaters, particularly in operational forms relevant to day-to-day support for management decisions, require further development.

9.6 Sustainable Management

The sustainable management of all Freshwaters should derive from the recognition of the importance catchment-scale management and the potentially large cost savings that can result from it. Some of the instruments are already available, and involve using existing directives and legislation better (such as the Habitats Directive, WFD, Floods Directive, Water Act, Strategic Environmental Assessment (SEA) and Environmental Impact Assessment (EIA)) to deliver appropriate management measures for good ecological status, beneficial ecosystem services and key species. In Scotland, the requirements of the Flood Risk Management (Scotland) Act (2009) and the provisions in the earlier Water Environment Water Services Act (2003) provide a direct stimulus to progress in this area. Better

focus will require competent authorities to identify sensitive features in Freshwater systems and initiate management to protect them more adequately than they have done before. In smaller water bodies, such as headwaters and ponds, the UK BAP could have greater purchase, although this has, until recently, been a weak driver for improvements and has no linkage to ecosystem services. The England Biodiversity Group has developed a series of Integrated Biodiversity Delivery Areas within which landscape-scale approaches to the delivery of UK BAP objectives for species and habitats will be trialled; this makes a more explicit reference to the need to consider a broader range of ecosystem services. The joint Wetland Vision for England, a partnership project involving statutory agencies and voluntary wildlife groups, is already developing this approach in a number of key regions of Wetland importance across England (www. wetlandvision.org.uk).

More visionary delivery is liable to derive from strengthening links between management of the terrestrial and Freshwater environments through, for example: catchment sensitive farming; agri-environment schemes that link water, carbon and biodiversity (e.g. Glastir) (Cook 2010); integrated 'upstream thinking' rather than paying increased treatment costs; and 'slowing water down' by more sustainable catchment drainage. The reform of the CAP is likely to stimulate more payments for maintaining ecosystem services. Considering both land and water protection at a landscape-scale could hold major benefits in terms of safeguarding water-related ecosystem services and biodiversity simultaneously, while allowing the integrated management of catchments, riparian zones and Floodplains at a reduced cost. Enhancing stakeholder and community involvement, for example, through the current Government's 'Big Society' thinking, are key to this approach, and a range of stakeholder groups are already expressing interest in taking on these roles (e.g. the Association of Rivers Trusts which is now operating throughout the UK).

The dissemination of 'ecosystem services' thinking will be key to valuing Freshwater ecosystems more fully, communicating more clearly their importance to broader sets of stakeholders, and appropriately costing the pressures arising from catchment land use and Freshwater modification. Major synergies could accrue from simultaneous and more cost-effective management for biodiversity, water quality, flood risk and security of supply.

Other key needs include:

i) To better understand the trade-offs between different ecosystem services, as well as the synergies that may arise from novel management approaches. This would support decisions on how to optimise the balance of ecosystem services, taking into account embedded costs (e.g. carbon costs of importing reed from abroad) and wider sustainability, as well as local economics. Where ecosystem-based solutions can be applied to problems, such as Sustainable Urban Drainage Systems (SUDS), Wetland treatment and buffer zoning, it is more likely that win-win outcomes may arise than through traditional, engineered, single-benefit, management solutions.

ii) To improve our understanding of how best to optimise Wetland and Freshwater management to maximise the range of ecosystem services. Sustainable management with minimum intervention often requires a large-scale perspective to enable natural processes to operate as far as possible, and to enable a range of different and, perhaps otherwise, incompatible ecosystem services to be delivered. At the smaller-scale, it is often possible to adopt management approaches which enable more than one outcome to be delivered; for example, increasing the variation in topography in a floodplain grazing marsh to allow for a range of degrees of wetness alongside a flood defence function.

iii) To strengthen the drivers for sustainable Freshwater management incentive payments under agri-environment schemes. These payments are a major potential mechanism for delivering ecosystem objectives and are currently mainly targeted at biodiversity and resource protection (with a significant focus on landscape and access as well). Incentive payments have an increasing future role to play in other areas such as flood risk management and mitigating greenhouse gas production. For some Freshwaters, however (e.g. Wetlands), particular problems with Higher Level Stewardship schemes include: a) incentive payments that are not sufficient to promote restoration or the reversion of land to Wetlands along river corridors for biodiversity and flood risk management; and b) the scale of Freshwater systems requiring farms to coordinate their activities to deliver benefits across a catchment or along a Floodplain. Future constraints are likely to arise from the scale of agri-environment funding under the next revision of the CAP and EU budget post-2013. Nevertheless, recognition of the breadth of benefits arising from sensitive ecosystem management may open up opportunities for 'paying for ecosystem services' (PES) including for benefits such as improvements in local air quality and health through habitat regeneration.

iv) To develop effective monitoring to evaluate sustainable Freshwater and Wetland management and restoration at large scales (while recognising that action at smaller scales may also be important to account for local effects). All major Freshwater and Wetland management or restoration must be accompanied by appropriate monitoring to evaluate success and to guide future steps; hence, it will properly quantify the range of benefits achieved by operating at a large scale and across a range of ecosystem services. Though there are good examples, particularly at plot-scale, there is no consistent approach to monitoring the full range of benefits at a landscape-scale over the long-term.

v) To link land and water management more explicitly to 'slow water down', enhance quality, reduce flood risk and increase security of supply. The water industry is a key stakeholder in land and water management. An essential part of managing Freshwaters is that water be progressively released from catchments, urban areas and Wetlands in ways that overcome tendencies for over-rapid drainage. Gentler and more consistent flows make water easier to treat, protect minimum flows in droughts and allow reservoir water releases to be reduced. South West Water is promoting £10 million worth of capital works for Wetland restoration and farm pollution reduction from 2010 to 2015 on moorland and farmland, none of which is owned by the company. The aim is to achieve "savings on operating costs for water treatment and deferral or avoidance of future costly treatment systems upgrading to meet deteriorating water quality in feeder rivers" (M. Ross *pers comm.*). The cost of this work is met as a levy to customers of about 60p per annum by 2015, compared to a customers' 'willingness to pay' assessment for price setting of £2.50 per annum for environmental enhancements; approval from Ofwat was secured for this more holistic catchment-based approach which has a cost-benefit score of 1:65. The company is working with Defra, Natural England and many other organisations on a 'proof of concept' to identify a 'reward system' for landowners and managers who consistently produce the best quality and quantity of water, thereby reducing the risks to the business and management of extreme events or diffuse pollution.

vi) To engage with all legitimate stakeholders. Valuation of ecosystem services must take into account the range of stakeholder interests in Freshwater ecosystems, and the way ecosystems services are distributed among them (**Table 9.13**) (Rawlins & Morris 2009; Reed *et al.* 2009). Dominant stakeholders pursue their interests through control over property rights, such as farmers holding agricultural tenure for the purpose of agriculture production. Many non-market 'goods' such as flood regulation, carbon sequestration, biodiversity and landscape, and conversely, non-market 'bads', are not the subject of clearly defined entitlements. Valuation and an understanding of distributional aspects can help inform policies to correct for these market failures, including the potential to create 'markets' in ecosystem services.

vii) To develop an integrated policy for Wetland resources. Wetlands are considered only partially within our most comprehensive piece of water policy: the WFD. Sustainable management will require both a policy and

Table 9.13 Links between ecosystems and stakeholder interests in Floodplains and Wetlands. Source: Morris *et al.* (2009).

Function and service	Goods	Stakeholder	Values
Production	Crops, fuel	Farmers, Defra	Economic gains from crop and livestock production
Regulation	Floodwater storage, drainage	Environment Agency-Flood Risk Management, Internal Drainage Boards, farmers, local industry, carbon traders	Avoid damage due to flooding, tradable services
Habitat	Maintenance and enhancement of biodiversity	RSPB, Environment Agency, Natural England, local residents	Contribution to UK BAP targets, Willingness To Pay
Carrier	Transport and settlements	Local residents, local industry, farmers, local authority	Location for housing, roads, local industry. Property and service values, costs of alternatives
Information	Amenity, landscape, recreation, history	RSPB, local residents, local authority	Enjoyment of the countryside and related benefits, Willingness To Pay

legislative framework which recognises the importance of linkages among the diversity of Wetlands, Openwaters and other habitats. Unlike some countries, notably the USA, there is no unifying wetland policy which would strengthen the recognition and perception of the resource as a whole as a priority.

9.7 Knowledge Gaps

Some Freshwaters are well monitored and understood, and provide obvious targets for developing integrated indicators of the delivery of ecosystem services at a catchment-scale. There are, nevertheless, generic gaps in understanding that cross all Freshwater systems. Some of the largest gaps include quantitative links between service provision and ecosystem structure or function, and valuation of those ecosystem services that generate benefits for which there is no obvious market price, such as the value of species whose functional contribution is small (Tallis & Polasky 2009). There is also a major need to improve understanding of how to manage Freshwater sustainably through the ecosystem services paradigm to ensure that shorter-term use does not degrade longer-term capacity. The past focus on the conservation of species and communities needs to be complemented with the maintenance of ecosystem functions if services are to be delivered in the future. We also need to understand the interactions of various different Freshwater and land types within a catchment in order to assess how their processes and functions combine to deliver ecosystem services (Maltby 2009a).

Other specific issues that may arise include how to:
- uncouple the use of Freshwater catchments for food production from negative impacts downstream;
- optimise catchment management effectively as the climate changes to ensure both biodiversity protection and service delivery;
- value the aggregate role of all organisms, including microbes, in ecosystem processes;
- restore processes and functions in degraded catchment ecosystems to optimise service benefits;
- identify factors that maintain resilience and resistance

in Freshwater ecosystems in the face of use and development to deliver services;
- determine the area and distribution patterns of those habitats necessary to provide the appropriate balance of regulatory and productive services in order to meet specified policy objectives;
- model links across Freshwater ecosystems and their functions to enable the reliable assessment of possible future environmental or management changes;
- identify robust, measureable and verifiable indicators of ecosystem changes which lead to alterations in ecosystem service delivery.

In all these respects, there is a pressing need for pilot studies and projects that demonstrate how best to manage Freshwater catchments, and how to guide management operationally.

9.8 Conclusions

This assessment reveals a need to reappraise our view of the importance of Freshwater ecosystems and their critical position in policy, management and a sustainable economy. This involves recognising the multiple benefits, potential cost-benefits and wide range of public and private interests which can be supported simultaneously by Freshwaters through a more holistic approach linked to their pivotal role in delivering ecosystem services. In turn, this recognition will arise from a more practical implementation of the ecosystem approach to integrate the sustainable management of land, water and living resources. Above all other ecosystems, and because of their many linkages through their catchments with terrestrial and marine environments, Freshwaters demonstrate the need for more joined-up thinking across the whole ecological continuum through which ecosystem services are supplied. Of particular significance is the need for integrated policy to bolster the current emphasis on individual priority habitats, which represent often arbitrary and artificial separations of land and water, upland and lowland landscapes, rivers and wetlands, and different segments of the hydrological cycle. We suggest that such approaches would improve the valuation of Freshwaters, while simultaneously improving their integrated management and offering a more effective means for overall conservation.

The wide-ranging benefits derived from Freshwater ecosystems have been largely taken for granted, gone unnoticed, got lost in preference for overriding, single-sector objectives, or at worst, been wilfully abused. Reversing such inadequacies requires better understanding and explanation from the scientific community of how Freshwater condition and management translates into economic, social and conservation benefits through ecosystem service delivery. At the same time, it is essential to recognise that the management of ecosystem services in Freshwaters will increasingly be taking place under highly dynamic and uncertain circumstances—despite recent improvements in quality, Freshwaters will be extremely sensitive to future changes in climate, land use, demographics and water demand. Therefore, a key management aim will be to ensure that Freshwater ecosystems are sufficiently resilient to deliver their most valuable benefits over the longer-term. The associated uncertainties also imply the need to ensure that key functions are maintained even under extreme scenarios. Furthermore, the development and implementation of monitoring, assessment and modelling procedures, which evaluate ecosystem service delivery through time and under different future trajectories, will be immensely important.

Within these broader objectives, a range of more specific needs and near-term policy goals have emerged from this assessment. These include:

1. Strengthening public awareness of the 'ecosystem service perspective' of Freshwaters. There is a need to address concerns in some sectors that this does not replace existing conservation and legislative approaches to Freshwater management, but adds value through the recognition of functions and benefits.

2. Improving understanding of the links between ecosystem structure, species composition, ecosystem functioning, ecosystem services, and economic and non-economic values throughout catchment systems to better inform management and appraise management outcomes. This study has shown the need for improved understanding of the current extent and state of Wetlands across the UK. An improved Wetland inventory will be key to better planning for a range of ecosystem services, especially as the climate changes.

3. Highlighting the practicalities of the 'ecosystem approach' in meeting the combined challenges of climate change, and secure and sustainable food and water supplies. Increasing food production from Freshwater catchments implies an ability to offset or minimise the effects downstream by catchment management actions. Buffer zones and habitat networks (Lawton *et al.* 2010) are one such mechanism, but others will be required to balance productive and protective ecosystem services.

4. Adapting policy and legislation, especially within agri-environment measures, to more fully recognise the links between catchment activities and Freshwaters. Analysis of existing legislation (the WFD, Habitats Directive, Flood and Water Management Act, etc.), strategies (BAPs, the Natural Value Programme in England and the Natural Environment Framework in Wales) and tools (SEA, EIA) to identify how the ecosystem approach can be used more effectively to deliver ecosystem services (e.g. through various WFD 'programmes of measures') will be required.

5. Stimulation of markets and stronger engagement with business and other stakeholders to ensure that: i) opportunities for the 'green economy' are maximised; and ii) those benefiting from the use of catchment services pay appropriate costs to support or protect ecosystems and services that are affected negatively by their actions. This will require exploring the institutional aspects of property rights and entitlements that recognise the support and provision of multiple benefits from Freshwater ecosystems. New collaborative arrangements might include rewards for the provision of ecosystem services by land and water managers where these serve the public good.

6. Partnering with, strengthening and informing local actors (e.g. local authorities, landowners and Rivers Trusts) to consider wider ecosystems (i.e. whole catchments and beyond) in local decisions. Actions need to be supported with the best available guidance, evidence and evaluation to achieve optimal mutual outcomes beneficial to a wide range of stakeholders. A key outcome will be more participatory decision-making.

References

Acreman, M.C., Adams, B., Birchall, B. & Connorton, B. (2000) Does groundwater abstraction cause degradation of rivers and wetlands? *Journal of the Chartered Institution of Water and Environmental Management,* **14**, 200–206.

Acreman, M.C. (2001a) Ethical aspects of water and ecosystems. *Water Policy Journal,* **3**(3), 257–265.

Acreman, M.C. (ed) (2001b) Hydro-ecology: linking hydrology and aquatic ecology. IAHS No. 266. pp. 213.

Acreman, M.C., Booker, D.J. & Riddington, R. (2003) Hydrological impacts of floodplain restoration: a case study of the river Cherwell, UK. *Hydrology and Earth System Sciences,* **7**(1), 75–86.

Acreman, M.C., Fisher, J., Stratford, C.J., Mould, D.J. & Mountford, J.O. (2007) Hydrological science and wetland restoration: case studies from Europe. *Hydrology and Earth System Sciences,* **11**(1), 158–169.

Acreman, M.C. & Mountford, O. (2009) Wetland Management. Handbook of Catchment Management (eds. R.C. Ferrier & A. Jenkins), pp. 19-50. Blackwell Publications, Oxford.

Acreman, M.C., Aldrick, J., Binnie, C., Black, A.R., Cowx, I., Dawson, F.H., Dunbar, M.J., Extence, C., Hannaford, J., Harby, A., Holmes, N.T., Jarrett, N., Old, G., Peirson, G., Webb, J. & Wood, P.J. (2009a) Environmental flows from dams: the Water Framework Directive. *Engineering Sustainability,* **162**, 13–22.

Acreman, M.C., Blake, J.R., Booker, D.J., Harding, R.J., Reynard, N., Mountford, J.O. & Stratford, C.J. (2009b) A simple framework for evaluating regional wetland ecohydrological response to climate change with case studies from Great Britain. *Ecohydrology*, **2**, 1–17.

Acreman, M.C., Harding, R.J., Lloyd, C., McNamara, N., Mountford, J.O., Mould, D., Purse, B.V., Stratford, C.J. & Dury, S.J. (2011) Ecosystem services of the Somerset Levels and Moors peat wetlands. *Hydrological Sciences Journal*, in press.

Adams, W.M., Perrow, M.R. & Carpenter, A. (2004) Conservatives and champions: river managers and the river restoration discourse in the United Kingdom. *Environment and Planning, 36,* 1929–1942.

ADAS UK Ltd and Enviros Consulting Ltd (2008) Monitoring of peat and alternative products for growing media and soil improvers in the UK 2007. Second biennial report to Defra. Defra, London. [online] Available at: <http://archive. defra.gov.uk/evidence/science/publications/documents/ peatAlternatives2007.pdf> [Accessed: 15.06.11].

Adkins, L. & Adkins, R. (1992). A field guide to Somerset archaeology. Wimborne, Dovecote Press.

Aldridge, D.C., Elliott, P. & Moggridge, G.D. (2004) The recent and rapid spread of the zebra mussel (*Dreissena polymorpha*) in Great Britain. *Biological Conservation*, **119**, 253–261.

Alveres, B., Clelland, Z., Johnstonova, A. & E. Commerford (2007). Insh Marshes: its hydrology, multiple uses and economic value. Report to RSPB Scotland, October 2007.

Anon. (2002) Study into Inland and Sea Fisheries in Wales. The National Assembly for Wales, Cardiff.

Aprahamian, M.W., Hickley, P., Shields, B.A. & Mawle, G.W. (2010) Examining changes in participation in recreational fisheries in England and Wales. *Fisheries Management and Ecology, 17,* 93–105.

Aprahamian, M. & Walker, A. (2008) Status of eel fisheries, stocks and their management in England and Wales. *Knowledge and Management of Aquatic Ecosystems*, **90–91**, art. no.-07.

Armstrong, A., Holden, J., Kay, P., Francis, B., Foulger, M., Gledhill, S., McDonald, A.T. & Walker, A. (2010) The impact of peatland drain-blocking on dissolved organic carbon loss and discolouration of water; results from a national survey. *Journal of Hydrology*, **381**, 112–120.

Austin, G.E., Rehfisch, M.M. & Banks, A. (2007) Natural Heritage Trends: developing a Scottish Wintering Waterbird Indicator. Scottish Natural Heritage Commissioned Report No. 227 (ROAME No. F05NB01). [online] Available at: <http:// www.snh.org.uk/pdfs/publications/commissioned_reports/ ReportNo227.pdf> [Accessed: 15.06.11].

Baird, A., Holden, J. & Chapman, P. (2009) A Literature Review of Evidence on Emissions of Methane in Peatlands (Defra Research Report SP0574). School of Geography and Water, Leeds University, Leeds.

BARS (Biodiversity Action Reporting System) (2011). UK Biodiversity Action Reporting System. [online] Available at: <http://ukbars.defra.gov.uk/> [Accessed: 25.07.11].

Baker, C., Thompson, J.R. & Simpson, M. (2009) Hydrological dynamics I: Surface waters, flood and sediment dynamics. The Wetlands Handbook (eds E. Maltby & T. Barker), pp.120–168. Wiley-Blackwells, Chichester.

Barbier, E.B., Adams, W.M. & Kimmeridge, K. (1991) Economic valuation of wetlands benefits, the Hadejia-Jama'are floodplain Nigeria. Paper DP 91-02. IIED, London

Baxter, C.V., Fausch, K.D. & Saunders, W.C. (2005) Tangled webs: reciprocal flows of invertebrate prey link streams and riparian zones. *Freshwater Biology*, **50**, 201–220.

Bennion, H., Duigan, C.A., Haworth, E.Y., Allott, T.E.H., Anderson, N.J., Juggins, S. & Monteith, D.T. (1996) The Anglesey Lakes, Wales, UK – changes in trophic status of three standing waters as inferred from diatom transfer functions and their implications for conservation. *Aquatic Conservation: Marine and Freshwater Ecosystems*, **6**, 81–92.

Besbeas, P., Freeman, S.N., Morgan, B.J.T. & Catchpole, E.A. (2002) Integrating mark–recapture–recovery and census data to estimate animal abundance and demographic parameters. *Biometrics*, **58**, 540–547.

Beven, K.J. & Kirkby (1979) A physically-based variable contributing area model of basin hydrology. *Hydrological Sciences Bulletin, 24,* 43–69.

Beven, K.J., Kirkby, M.J., Schoffield, N. & Tagg, H. (1984) Testing a physically-based flood forecasting model (TOPMODEL) for three UK catchments. *Journal of Hydrology, 69,* 119–143.

Biggs, J., Williams, P., Whitfield, M., Nicolet, P., Bronw, C., Hollism, J., Arnold, D. & Pepper, T. (2007) The freshwater biota of British agricultural landscapes and their sensitivity to pesticides. *Agriculture, Ecosystems and Environment*, **122**, 137–148.

Blackstock, T.H., Howe, E.A., Stevens, J.P., Burrows, C.R. & Jones, P.S. (2009) Habitats of Wales: a comprehensive field survey, 1979–1997. University of Wales Press, Cardiff.

Blackwell, M.S.A., Hogan, D.V., Pinay, G. & Maltby, E. (2009) The role of wetlands as buffer zones for nutrient removal from agricultural runoff. The Wetlands Handbook (eds E.B. Maltby & T. Barker), pp.417–439. Wiley-Blackwells, Chichester.

Boar, R.R., Crook, C.E. & Moss, B. (1989) Regression of *Phragmites australis* reedswamps and recent changes of water chemistry in the Norfolk Broadland, England. *Aquatic Botany*, **35**, 41–55.

Boar, R.R., Kirby, J.J.H. & Leeming, D.J. (1999) Variations in the quality of the thatching reed *Phragmites australis* from wetlands in East Anglia, England. Floodplains: Interdisciplinary Approaches (eds S. Marriott & J. Alexander), pp. 145–151. Geological Society Special Publication, **163**, Bath.

Boitsidis, A.J., Gurnell, A.M., Scott, M., Petts, G.E. & Armitage, P.D. (2006) A decision support system for identifying the habitat quality and rehabilitation potential of urban rivers. *Water and Environment Journal*, **20**, 130–140.

Bonn, A., Holden, J., Parnell, M., Worrall, F., Chapman, P.J., Evans. C.D., Termansen, M., Beharry-Borg, N., Acreman, M.C., Rowe, E., Emmett, B. & Tsuchiya, A. (2010) Ecosystem services of peat – Phase 1 Report. Defra SP0572. Defra, London. [online] Available at: <http://randd.defra.gov.uk/Default.aspx?Menu= Menu&Module=More&Location=None&Completed=0&Project ID=15990> [Accessed: 15.06.11].

Boult, S., Collins, D.N., White, K.N. & Curtis, C.D. (1994) Metal transport in a stream polluted by acid mine drainage – The Afon Goch, Anglesey, UK. *Environmental Pollution*, **84**, 279–284.

Boulton, J., Fenwick, G.D., Hancock, P.J. & Harvey, M.S. (2008) Biodiversity, functional roles and ecosystem services of groundwater invertebrates *Invertebrate Systematics*, **22**, 103–116.

Briers, R.A., Cariss, H.M., Geoghegan, R. & Gee, J.H.R. (2005) The lateral extent of the subsidy from an upland stream to riparian lycosid spiders. *Ecography*, **28**, 165–170.

Britton, J.R., Davies, G.D., Brazier, M. & Pinder, A.C. (2007) A case study on the population ecology of the topmouth gudgeon (*Pseudorasbora parva*) population in the UK and the implications for native fish communities. *Aquatic Conservation Marine and Freshwater Ecosystems,* **17**, 749–759.

Britton, J.R., Davies, G.D. & Harrod, C. (2010a) Trophic interactions and consequent impacts of the invasive fish *Pseudorasbora parva* in a native aquatic foodweb: a field investigation in the UK. *Biological Invasions,* **12**, 1533–1542.

Britton, J.R., Cucherousset, J., Davies, G.D., Godard, M.J. & Copp, G.H. (2010b) Non-native fishes and climate change: predicting species responses to warming temperatures in a temperate region. *Freshwater Biology,* **55**, 1130–1141.

Brookes, A., Gregory, K.J.& Dawson, F.H. (1983). An assessment of river channelization in England and Wales. *Science of the Total Environment,* **27**, 97–112.

Brooks, S. (2003) Commercial Peat Extraction in Scotland. Draft report for Scottish Natural Heritage, Scotland.

Brown, A.G. (2009a) Carbon storage and sequestration in the Somerset Levels, UK. Report for Somerset County Council. UK.

Brown, A.G. (2009b) Colluvial and alluvial response to land use change in Midland England: an integrated geoarchaeological approach. *Geomorphology,* **108**, 92–106.

Brown, C.D., Turner, N., Hollis, J., Bellamy, P., Biggs, J., Williams, P., Arnold, D., Pepper, T. & Maund, S. (2006) Morphological and physico-chemical properties of British aquatic habitats potentially exposed to pesticides. *Agriculture, Ecosystems and Environment,* **113**, 307–319.

Brunke, M. & Gonser, T. (1997) The ecological significance of exchange processes between rivers and groundwater. *Freshwater Biology,* **37**, 1–33.

Brunning, R. (2001) Archaeology and peat wastage on the Somerset Moors. Report to the Environment Agency, Somerset County Council, Taunton.

BTO (British Trust for Ornithology) (2009a) BTO Breeding Birds in the Wider countryside: their conservation status 2009. BTO, Thetford, UK. [online]. Available at: <http://www.bto.org/birdtrends2009/index.htm> [Accessed: 08.04.11].

BTO (British Trust for Ornithology) (2009b) The state of the UK's birds 2008. BTO, Thetford, UK. [online]. Available at: <http://www.rspb.org.uk/Images/SUKB_tcm9-231778.pdf> [Accessed: 08.04.11.].

Bullock, A. & Acreman, M.C. (2003) The role of wetlands in the hydrological cycle. *Hydrology and Earth System Sciences,* **7**(3), 75–86.

Burton, R.G.O. & Hodgson, J.M. (1987) Lowland Peat in England and Wales, Special Survey No. 15. Soil Survey of England and Wales, Harpenden.

Butler, J.R.A., Radford, A., Riddington, G. & Laughton, R. (2009) Evaluating an ecosystem service provided by Atlantic salmon, sea trout and other fish species in the River Spey, Scotland: The economic impact of recreational rod fisheries. *Fisheries Research,* **96**, 259–266.

Butterini, A., Batten, T.J. & Sabater, F. (2000) Nitrification in stream sediment biofilms: the role of ammonium concentration and DOC quality. *Water Research,* **34**, 629–639.

Cadw: Welsh Historic Monuments (1998) Register of Landscapes of Outstanding Historic Interest in Wales. Welsh Assembly Government, Cardiff.

Cadw: Welsh Historic Monuments (2001) Register of Landscapes of Special Historic Interest in Wales. Welsh Assembly Government, Cardiff.

Capita Symonds (2005) UK Biodiversity Action Plan: Lowland Raised Bogs. Identification of sites for remediation in England and options for their remediation. Report to English Nature. Natural England, Peterborough.

Carey, P.D., Wallis, S., Chamberlain, P.M., Cooper, A., Emmett, B.A., Maskell, L.C., McCann, T., Murphy, J., Norton, L.R., Reynolds, B., Scott, W.A., Simpson, I.C., Smart, S.M. & Ullyett, J.M. (2008) Countryside Survey: UK Results from 2007. NERC/Centre for Ecology & Hydrology, 105 pp.

Carlson, J.C., Dyer, L.A., Omlin, F.X. & Beier, J.C. (2009) Diversity cascades and malaria vectors. *Journal of Medical Entomology,* **46**, 460–464.

Chatterton, J., Viavattene, C., Morris, J., Penning-Rowsell, E. & Tapsell, S. (2010) The costs of the summer 2007 floods in England. Environmental Agency, Bristol. Science Project SC070039. [online] Available at: <http://publications.environment-agency.gov.uk/pdf/SCHO1109BRJA-e-e.pdf> [Accessed: 07.03.11].

Church, M. (2002) Geomorphic thresholds in riverine landscapes. *Freshwater Biology,* **47**, 541–557.

Clark, J.M., Chapman, P.J., Adamson, J.K. & Lane, S.N. (2005) Influence of drought-induced acidification on the mobility of dissolved organic carbon in peat soils. *Global Change Biology,* **11**, 791–809.

Clews, E., Durance, I., Vaughan, I. P. & Ormerod, S. J. (2010). Juvenile salmonid populations in a temperate river system track synoptic trends in climate. *Global Change Biology,* **16**, 3271–3283.

CLG (Communities and Local Government) (2009) Planning Policy Statement 25: Development and flood risk practice guide. Department for Communities and Local Government, London. [online] Available at: <http://www.communities.gov.uk/documents/planningandbuilding/pdf/pps25guideupdate.pdf> [Accessed: 07.03.11].

Coles, B. (1990) Archaeology and wetlands: a wealth of evidence: Wetlands: a threatened landscape (ed M. Williams). Institute of British Geographers Special Publication 25. Blackwell, Oxford.

Cook, H.F. (2010) Floodplain agricultural systems: functionality, heritage and conservation. *Journal of Flood Risk Management,* **3**(3), 192–200. DOI:10.1111/j.1753-318X.2010.01069.

Cooper, P. (2007) The Constructed Wetland Association UK database of constructed wetland systems. *Water, Science and Technology,* **50**, 1–6.

Cope, D.W. & Colborne, G.J.N. (1981) Thickness of peat in the Somerset Moors. Map at scale 1:50,000. Soil Survey of England and Wales, Harpenden.

Countryside Survey (2009) Countryside Survey: England Results from 2007. NERC/Centre for Ecology & Hydrology, Department for Environment, Food and Rural Affairs, Natural England, 119pp. (CEH Project Number: C03259).

Couwenberg J., Augustin J., Michaelis, D. & Joosten, H. (2008). Emission reductions from rewetting of peatlands: Towards a field guide for the assessment of greenhouse gas emissions from central European peatlands. Draft report, Duene/Greifswald University.

Danielopol, D.L., Griebler, C., Gunatilika, A. & Notenboom, J. (2003) Present state and future prospects for groundwater ecosystems. *Environmental Conservation,* **30**, 104–130.

D'Arcy, B.J., May, L., Long, J., Fozzard, I.R., Greig, S. & Brachet, A. (2006) The restoration of Loch Leven, Scotland, UK. *Water Science and Technology, 53*, 183–191.

Darby, H.C. (1983) The changing Fenland. Cambridge University Press, Cambridge.

Davies, B., Biggs, J., Williams, P., Whitfield, M., Nicolet, P., Sear, D., Bray, S. & Maund, S. (2008) Comparative biodiversity of aquatic habitats in the European agricultural landscape. *Agricultural Ecosystems and Environment, 125,* 1–8.

Davies, J.J.L., Jenkins, A., Monteith, D.T., Evans, C.D. & Cooper, D.M. (2005) Trends in surface water chemistry of acidified UK Freshwaters, 1988–2002. *Environmental Pollution, 137*, 27–39.

Davis, T.J. (1993) Towards the wise use of wetlands. Ramsar Convention Bureau, Gland Switzerland. 180p.

Dawson, J.J.C., Malcolm, I.A., Middlemas, S.J., Tetzlaff, D. & Soulsby, C. (2009) Is the Composition of Dissolved Organic Carbon Changing in Upland Acidic Streams? *Environmental Science & Technology, 43*, 7748–7753.

Defra (Department for Environment, Food and Rural Affairs) (2005) Making Space for Water. Department for Environment, Food and Rural Affairs, London.

Defra (Department for Environment, Food and Rural Affairs) (2007) Securing a healthy natural environment: an action plan for embedding an ecosystem approach. Department of Environment, Food and Rural Affairs, London.

Defra (Department for Environment, Food and Rural Affairs) (2008) Farming: Single Payment Scheme. Department for Environment, Food and Rural Affairs, London.

Defra (Department for Environment, Food and Rural Affairs) (2010) Food 2030. Department of Environment, Food and Rural Affairs, London.

Denny, P. (1994) Biodiversity and wetlands. *Wetlands Ecology and Management, 3*, 55–61.

Dobson, M., Naura, M. & McElhone, M. (2009) Welsh rivers under threat: Physical factors. The Rivers of Wales – a natural resource of international and historical significance (eds D.D. Williams & C.A. Duigan), pp. 205–222. Backhuys Publishers/ Margraf Publishers, Weikersheim.

Doughty, R., Gardiner, R. & Mills, D. (2003) The return of salmon to cleaner rivers: a Scottish perspective. Salmon at the Edge (eds D. Mills), pp. 175–185. Blackwell Science Ltd, Oxford.

Downing, R.A. (1998) (ed) Groundwater: our hidden asset. Earthwise Popular Science Books. British Geological Survey, Nottingham, UK.

Duff, J.H. & Triska, F.J. (1990) Denitrification in sediments from the hyporheic zone adjacent to a small forested stream. *Canadian Journal of Fisheries and Aquatic Sciences, 47*, 1140–1147.

Dugan, P.J. (1993) Wetland conservation – a review of current issues and required action. IUCN, Gland, Switzerland.

Duigan, C.A. & Haycock, B. (1995) Reserve Focus – The Bosherston Lakes. *British Wildlife, 6*, 231–234.

Duigan, C.A., Reid, S., Monteith, D.T., Bennion, H., Seda, J.M. & Hutchinson, J. (1999) The past, present and future of Llangorse Lake – a shallow, nutrient-rich lake in the Brecon Beacons National Park, Wales, UK. *Aquatic Conservation: Marine and Freshwater Ecosystems, 9*, 329–341.

Duigan, C.A., Kovach, W.L. & Palmer, M.A. (2006) Vegetation communities of British lakes: a revised classification. Joint Nature Conservation Committee, Peterborough.

Duigan, C.A., Kovach, W.L. & Palmer, M.A. (2007) Vegetation communities of British lakes: a revised classification scheme for conservation. *Aquatic Conservation: Marine and Freshwater Ecosystems, 17*, 147–173.

Duigan, C. (2009) Rivers in the Welsh physical and cultural landscape. The Rivers of Wales – a natural resource of international and historical significance (eds D.D. Williams & C.A. Duigan), pp. 5–15. Backhuys Publishers/Margraf Publishers, Weikersheim.

Duigan, C.A., Hatton-Ellis, T., Latham, J., Campbell, S. & Mathews, B. (2009) River Conservation in Wales: A synthesis. The Rivers of Wales – a natural resource of international and historical significance (eds D.D. Williams & C.A. Duigan), pp. 235–268. Backhuys Publishers/Margraf Publishers, Weikersheim.

Dunbar, M.J., Warren, M., Extence, C., Baker, L. Cadman, D., Mould, D.J., Hall, J. & Chadd, R. (2010a) Interaction between macroinvertebrates, discharge and physical habitat in upland rivers. *Aquatic Conservation: Marine Freshwater Ecosyststems, 20*(S1), S31–S44. DOI: 10.1002/aqc.1089.

Dunbar, M.J., Lauge Pedersen, M., Cadman, D., Extence, C., Waddingham, J, Chadd, R. & Larsen, S.E. (2010b) River discharge and local scale habitat influence macroinvertebrate LIFE scores. *Freshwater Biology, 55*, 226–242 DOI:10.1111/j.1365-2427.2009.02306.x

Dunbar, M., Murphy, J., Clarke, R., Baker, R., Davies, C. & Scarlett, P. (2010c) Countryside Survey: Headwater Streams Report from 2007. Technical Report No. 8/07 NERC/Centre for Ecology & Hydrology, 67pp. (CEH Project Number: C03259).

Durance, I. & Ormerod, S.J. (2007) Climate change effects on upland stream invertebrates over a 25 year period. *Global Change Biology, 13*, 942–957.

Dutt, P. (2004) An assessment of habitat condition of coastal and floodplain grazing marsh within agri-environment schemes. Defra, London.

Eigenbrod, F., Anderson, B.J., Armsworth, P.R., Heinemeyer, A., Jackson, S., Parnell, M., Thomas C.D. & Gaston, K.J. (2009) Biodiversity and ecosystem service benefits of contrasting conservation strategies in a human-dominated region. *Proceedings of the Royal Society B, 276*, 2903–2911.

Elliott, P., Aldridge, D.C., Moggridge, G.D. & Chipps, M. (2005) The increasing effects of Zebra mussels on water installations in England. *Water and Environment Journal, 19*, 367–375.

Elmqvist, T., Maltby, E., Barker, T., Mortimer, M., Perrings, C., Aronson, J., De Groot, R., Fitter, A., Mace G., Nurbery, J., Pinto, I.S. & Ring, I. (2010) Biodiversity, Ecosystems and Ecosystem Services. The Economics of Ecosystems and Biodiversity: Ecological and Economic Foundations (ed P. Kumar). Earthscan, London.

Environment Agency (2002) Metal Mine Strategy for Wales. Environment Agency. Bristol.

Environment Agency (2003) River Habitat Survey in Britain and Ireland: Field Survey Guidance Manual. River Habitat Survey Manual: 2003 version, Environment Agency. [online] Available at: <http://www.irpi.to.cnr.it/documenti/RHS%20manual%20 2003.PDF> [Accessed: 07.03.11].

Environment Agency (2006) Fishing for the future. Environment Agency, Bristol.

Environment Agency (2008a) Water Resources in England and Wales: current state and future pressures. Report GEHO1208BPAS-E-E. Environment Agency, Bristol

Environment Agency (2008b) Catchment Flood Management Plans. Environment Agency, Bristol.

Environment Agency (2009a) Flooding in England. Environment Agency, Bristol.

Environment Agency (2009b) The Hyporheic Handbook. A handbook on the groundwater–surface water interface and hyporheic zone for environment managers. Integrated catchment science programme. Environment Agency, Bristol. [online] Available at: <http://www.hyporheic.net/SCHO1009BRDX-e-e.pdf> [Accessed: 07.03.11].

Environment Agency (2009c) Flooding in Wales. Environment Agency, Cardiff.

Environment Agency (2009d) Investing for the Future: Flooding and Coastal Risk Management. Environment Agency, Bristol.

Erlandsson, M., Buffam, I., Fölster, J., Laudon, H., Temnerud, J., Weyhenmeyer, G.A. & Bishop, K. (2008) Thirty-five years of synchrony in the organic matter concentrations of Swedish rivers explained by variation in flow and sulphate. *Global Change Biology*, **14**, 1191–1198.

European Commission (2003) Common implementation strategy for the Water Framework Directive (2000/60/EC) Guidance document No. 12: The role of wetlands in the Water Framework Directive. European Commission, Luxemburg.

EEA (European Environment Agency) (2003) Indicator fact sheet: water exploitation index. EEA, Copenhagen.

EU (European Union) (2010) The CAP Towards 2020; Meeting the Food, Natural Resources and Territorial Challenges of the Future. Communication from the Commission to the European Parliament, The Council, The European Economic and Social Committee and the Committee of the Regions. European Commission, Brussels.

Evans, C.D., Monteith, D.T. & Cooper, D.M. (2005) Long-term increases in surface water dissolved organic carbon: Observations, possible causes and environmental impacts. *Environmental Pollution*, **137**, 55–71.

Everard, M. (2009) Ecosystem services case studies. Environment Agency Science report SCHO0409BPVM-E-E. Environment Agency, Bristol. [online] Available at: <http://publications.environment-agency.gov.uk/pdf/SCHO0409BPVM-E-E.pdf> [Accessed: 03.03.11].

Everard, M. & Appleby, T. (2009) Safeguarding the societal value of land. *Environmental Law and Management*, **21**, 16–23.

Evans, M., Milner, N. & Aprahamian, M. (2009) Life in Welsh rivers: Fishes. The Rivers of Wales – a natural resource of international and historical significance (eds D.D. Williams & C.A. Duigan), pp. 115–140. Backhuys Publishers/Margraf Publishers, Weikersheim.

Everard, M. (2010) Ecosystem services assessment of sea trout restoration work on the River Glaven, North Norfolk. Environment Agency Evidence report SCHO0110BRTZ-E-P. Environment Agency, Bristol.

Everard, M. & Kataria, G. (2010) The proposed Pancheshwar Dam, India/Nepal: A preliminary ecosystem services assessment of likely outcomes. An IES research report.

Everard, M., Gray, J., Victoria Wilkins-Kindemba, K. & Cowx, I.G. (2010) Impacts of invasive species on ecosystem services: the case of the signal crayfish (*Pacifastacus leniusculus*). *Environmental Law and Management*, **21**, 250–259.

Fischer H., Kloep, F., Wilzcek, S. & Pusch, M. (2005) A river's liver – Microbial processes within the hyporheic zone of a large lowland river. *Biogeochemistry*, **72**, 349–371.

Fisher, B., Turner, K., Zylstra, M., Brouwer, R., de Groot, R., Farber, S., Ferraro, Green, R., Hadley, J., Jefferiss, P., Kirby, C., Morling, P., Mowatt, S., Naidoo, R., Paavola, J., Strassburg, B., Yu, D. & Balmford, A. (2008) Ecosystem services and economic theory: integration for policy-relevant research. *Ecological Application*, **18**, 2050–2067.

Fisher, B., Turner, R.K. & Morling, P. (2009) Defining and classifying ecosystem services for decision making. *Ecological Economics*, **68**, 643–653.

Fisher, J. & Acreman, M.C. (2004) Water quality functions of wetlands. *Hydrology and Earth System Sciences*, **8**(4), 673–685.

Foresight (2004) Foresight Flood and Coastal Flooding Project, 2004. Government Office for Science, London.

Foresight (2010). Land Use Futures. Making the most of land in the 21st century. Government Office for Science, London.

Foresight (2011) Global Food and Farming Futures. Government Office for Science, London.

Freeman, C., Evans, C.D., Monteith, D.T., Reynolds, B. & Fenner, N. (2001) Export of organic carbon from peat soils. *Nature*, **412**(6849), 785–785.

Freeman, C., Fenner, N., Ostle, N.J., Kang, H., Dowrick, D.J., Reynolds, B., Lock, M.A., Sleep, D., Hughes, S. & Hudson, J. (2004) Export of dissolved organic carbon from peatlands under elevated carbon dioxide levels. *Nature*, **430**(6996), 195–198.

Freeman, M.A., Turnbull, J.F., Yeomans, W.E. & Bean, C.W. (2010) Prospects for management strategies of invasive crayfish populations with an emphasis on biological control. *Aquatic Conservation: Marine and Freshwater Ecosystems*, **20**, 211–223.

Friedland, K.D., Miller, M.J. & Knights, B. (2007) Oceanic changes in the Sargasso Sea and declines in recruitment of the European eel. *ICES Journal of Marine Science*, **64**, 519–530.

Galbraith, H. (1988) Effects of agriculture on the breeding ecology of lapwings. *Journal of Applied Ecology*, **25**, 487–503

Gaterell M.R., Morse G.K. & Lester J.N. (1995) A valuation of Rutland Water using environmental economics. *Environmental Technology*, **16**, 1073–1082.

Gee, J. & Fowles, A. (2009) Life in Welsh Rivers: Invertebrates. The Rivers of Wales – a natural resource of international and historical significance (eds D.D. Williams & C.A. Duigan), pp. 89–113. Backhuys Publishers/Margraf Publishers, Weikersheim.

Geist, J. & Auerswald, K. (2007) Physicochemical stream bed characteristics and recruitment of the freshwater pearl mussel (*Margaritifera margaritifera*). *Freshwater Biology*, **52**, 2299–2316.

Gibert, J., Stanford, J.A., Dole-Olivier, M-J. & Ward, J.V. (1994) Basic attributes of groundwater ecosystems and prospects for research. Groundwater Ecology. Academic Press (eds J. Gilbert, D.L. Danielopol & J.A. Stanford), pp. 8–42. CA, San Diego.

Gilbert, M., Slingenbergh, J. & Xiao, X. (2008) Climate change and avian influenza. *Revue Scientifique et Technique de l'Office Internationale des Epizooites*, **27**, 459–466.

Gibbons, D.W., Reid, J.B. & Chapman, R.A. (1993) The New Atlas of Breeding Birds in Britain and Ireland: 1988–1991. Poyser, London.

Gilvear, D., Rundle, S. & Griffin, I. (2006) River biodiversity: a preliminary study of the hyporheos of Scottish gravel bed rivers. Scottish Natural Heritage Commissioned Report, 16 (ROAME No. F05AC604).

Gilvear, D.J., Casas-Mulet, R. & Spray, C.J. (2010) Trends and issues in delivery of integrated catchment scale river restoration: lessons learned from a national river restoration survey within Scotland. *River Research and Applications.* DOI: 10.1002/rra.1437.

GHK Consulting Ltd and GFA-Race Partners Ltd (2004) Revealing the Value of the Natural Environment in England. Report to Defra. [online] Available at: <http://www.hm-treasury.gov.uk/d/2%281%29.pdf > [Accessed: 15.06.11].

Gregory, K.J. (2006) The human role in changing river channels. *Geomorphology,* **79**, 172–191.

Gregory, K.J., Benito, G. & Downs, P.W. (2008) Applying fluvial geomorphology to river channel management: Background for progress towards a palaeohydrology protocol. *Geomorphology,* **98**, 153–172.

Gregory, S.V., Swanson, F.J., McKee, W.A. & Cummins, K.W. (1991) An ecosystem perspective of riparian zones. *Bioscience,* **41**(8), 540–551.

Gregory, S.V., Boyer, K.L. & Gurnell, A.M. (Eds) (2003) The ecology and management of wood in world rivers. American Fisheries Society, Bethesda, Maryland.

George, D.G. & Harris, G.P. (1985) The effect of climate on long-term changes in the crustacean zooplankton biomass of Lake Windamere. *Nature,* **316**, 536–539.

Gritten, R.H., Duigan, C.A., Millband, H. (eds) (2003) The ecology, conservation and environmental history of the largest natural lake in Wales. University of Liverpool, Liverpool.

Groundwater Forum (2002) Groundwater: our hidden asset. Groundwater Forum, Wallingford, U.K. 59pp.

Gurnell, A.M., O'Hare, J.M., O'Hare, M.T., Dunbar, M.J. & Scarlett, P.M. (2010) An exploration of associations between assemblages of aquatic plant morphotypes and channel geomorphological properties within British rivers. *Geomorphology,* **116**, 135–144.

Gurnell, A.M. & Petts, G.E. (2002) Island-dominated landscapes of large floodplain rivers, a European perspective. *Freshwater Biology,* **47**, 581–600.

Gurnell A.M. & Petts, G.E (2010) Changing River Channels. Wiley, Chichester.

Gurnell, A.M. & Petts, G.E. (2011) Hydrology and Ecology of River Systems. Treatise on Water Science Vol 2. (ed. P. Wilderer), pp. 237–269. Academic Press, Oxford.

Haines-Young, R.H., Barr, C.J., Black, H.I.J., Briggs, D.J., Bunce, R.G.H., Clarke, R.T., Cooper, A., Dawson, F.H., Firbank, L.G., Fuller, R.M., Furse, M.T., Gillespie, M.K., Hill, R., Hornung, M., Howard D.C., McCann, T., Morecroft, M.D., Petit, S., Sier, A.R.J., Smart, S.M., Smith, G.M., Stott, A.P., Stuart R.C. & Watkins J.W. (2000) Accounting for nature: assessing habitats in the UK countryside. DETR, London ISBN 1 85112 460.

Hanley, N., Colombo, S., Tinch, D., Black, A. & Aftab, A. (2006) Estimating the benefits of water quality improvements under the Water Framework Directive: are benefits transferable? *European Review of Agricultural Economics,* **33**, 391–413.

Hannaford, J. & Marsh, T.J. (2006) An assessment of trends in UK runoff and low flows using a network of undisturbed catchments. *International Journal of Climatology,* **26**(9), 1237–1253. DOI: 10.1002/joc.1303.

Hannaford, J. & Marsh, T.J. (2007) High flows and flood trends in a network of undisturbed catchments in the UK. *International Journal of Climatology,* **28**(10), 1325–1338. DOI: 10.1002/joc.1643.

Hannaford, J. & Harvey, C. (2010) UK seasonal river flow variability in near-natural catchments, regional outflows and long hydrometric records. *Proceedings of the British Hydrological Society International Conference,* 2010, pp. 7.

Harrod, T.R. (1978). Soils in Devon IV: Sheet SS30 (Holsworthy). Soil Survey Record. No.47.

Hastie, L.C., Cooksley, S.L., Scougall, F., Young, M.R., Boon, P.J. & Gaywood, M.J. (2003) Characterization of freshwater pearl mussel (*Margaritifera margaritifera*) riverine habitat using River Habitat Survey data. *Aquatic Conservation: Marine and Freshwater Ecosystems,* **13**, 213–224.

Hatfield, R.G. & Maher, B.A. (2009) Holocene sediment dynamics in an upland temperate lake catchment: climatic and land-use impacts in the English Lake District. *Holocene,* **19**, 427–438.

Hatton-Ellis, T., Blackstock, T. & Orange, A. (2009) Life in Welsh Rivers: Plants. The Rivers of Wales – a natural resource of international and historical significance (eds D.D. Williams & C.A. Duigan), pp. 69–87. Backhuys Publishers/Margraf Publishers, Weikersheim.

Headley, A.D. & Dargie, T. (2004) UK Biodiversity Action Plan – lowland raised bogs: identification of sites for remediation in England. Final report to English Nature. Contract no: EIT 34-01-015.

Henderson, I.G., Wilson, A.M., Steele, D. & Vickery, J.A. (2002) Population estimates, trends and habitat associations of breeding Lapwing *Vanellus vanellus*, Curlew *Numenius arquata* and Snipe *Gallinago gallinago* in Northern Ireland in 1999. *Bird Study,* **49**, 17–25.

Hendry, K., Sambrook, H. & Waterfall, R. (2007) Assessment of salmon stocks and the use of management targets; a case study of the River Tamar, England. *Fisheries Management and Ecology,* **14**, 7–19.

Hewelett, J.D. & Hibbert, A.R. (1966) Factors affecting the response of small watersheds to precipitation in humid areas. International Symposium on Forest Hydrology, pp. 275–2790. Pergamon Press, New York.

Hill, A.R., Labadia, C.F. & Sanmugadas, K. (1998) Hyporheic zone hydrology and nitrógeno dynamics in relation to the stream bed topography of a N-rich stream. *Biogeochemistry,* **42**, 285–310.

Hodge, I. & McNally, S. (2000) Wetland restoration, collective action and the role of water management institutions. *Ecological Economics,* **35**, 107–118.

Holden, J., Kirkby, M.J., Lane, S.N., Milledge, D.G., Brookes, C.J., Holden, V. & McDonald, A.T. (2008) Overland flow velocity and roughness properties in peatlands. *Water Resources Research,* **44**, 1–11.

Holliday, V.J., Warburton, J. & Higgitt, D.L. (2008) Historic and contemporary sediment transfer in an upland Pennine catchment, UK. *Earth Surface Processes and Landforms,* **33**, 2139–2155.

Holman, I.P. (2009) An estimate of peat reserves and loss in the East Anglian Fens. Commissioned by the RSPB. Cranfield University. [online] Available at: <http://www.rspb.org.uk/Images/Fenlandpeatassessment_tcm9-236041.pdf> [Accessed: 15.06.11].

Holmes, N. & Gough, P. (2009) Welsh River Rehabilitation. The Rivers of Wales – a natural resource of international and historical significance (eds D.D. Williams & C.A. Duigan), pp. 223–234. Backhuys Publishers/Margraf Publishers, Weikersheim.

Hooke, J. M. & L. Yorke (2010) Rates, distributions and mechanisms of change in meander morphology over decadal timescales, River Dane, UK. *Earth Surface Processes and Landforms,* **35**, 1601–1614.

Hudson, R., Tucker, G.M. & Fuller, R.J. (1994) Lapwing *vanellus vanellus* populations in relation to agricultural changes a review. The ecology and conservation of Lapwings *Vanellus vanellus* (eds. Tucker, G.M., Davies, S.M. & Fuller, R.J.) pp. 1–33 JNCC, Peterborough.

Hume, C. (2008) Wetland vision technical document: overview and reporting of project philosophy and technical approach. The Wetland Vision Partnership, Sandy, UK.

Immirzi, C.P. & Maltby, E. with Clymo, R.S (1992) The global status of peatlands and their role in carbon cycling. Report for Friends of the Earth. University of Exeter/ Friends of the Earth, London.

Inger, R., McDonald, R.A., Rogowski, D., Jackson, A.L., Parnell, A., Preston, S.J., Harrod, C., Goodwin, C., Griffiths, D., Dick, J.T.A., Elwood, R.W., Newton, J. & Bearhop, S. (2010) Do non-native invasive fish support elevated lamprey populations? *Journal of Applied Ecology,* **47**, 121–129.

Jarvie, H. & King S. (2010) Just scratching the surface? New techniques to show how surface functionality of nanoparticles influences their environmental fate. *Nano Today,* **5**, 248–250.

Jarvie, H.P., Withers, P.J.A., Bowes, M.J., Palmer-Felgate, E.J., Harper, D.M., Wasiak, K., Wasiak, P., Hodgkinson, R.A., Bates, A., Stoate, C., Neal, M., Wickham, H.D., Harman, S.A. & Armstrong, L.K. (2010) Streamwater phosphorus and nitrogen across a gradient in rural-agricultural land use intensity. *Agriculture Ecosystems & Environment,* **135**, 238–252.

Jeffries, M. (2008) The spatial and temporal heterogeneity of macrophyte communities in thirty small, temporary ponds over a period of ten years. *Ecography,* **31**, 765–775.

JNCC (Joint Nature Conservation Committee) (2008) Thorne Moor Natura 2000 Data Form. JNCC, Peterborough.

JNCC (Joint Nature Conservation Committee) (2011) Towards an assessment of the state of UK peatlands. JNCC Report No. 445. JNCC, Peterborough.

Johnes, P.J., Foy, R., Butterfield, D. & Haygarth, P.M. (2007) Land use scenarios for England and Wales: evaluation of management options to support 'good ecological status' in surface freshwaters. *Soil Use and Management,* **23**, 176–194 (Suppl. 1).

Johnsen, B.O. & Jensen, A.J. (1991) The Gyrodactylus story in Norway. *Aquaculture,* **98**, 289–302.

Johnson, A.C., Acreman, M.C., Dunbar, M.J., Feist, S.W., Giacomello, A.M., Gozlan, R.E., Hinsley, S.A., Ibbotson, A.T., Jarvie, H.P., Jones, J.I., Longshaw, M., Maberly, S.C., Marsh, T.J., Neal, C., Newman, J.R., Nunn, M.A., Pickup, R.W., Reynard, N.S., Sullivan, C.A., Sumpter, J.P. & Williams, R.J. (2009) The British river of the future: how climate change and human activity might affect two contrasting river ecosystems in England. *Science of the Total Environment,* **407**, 4787–4798.

Johnson, C.L., Tunstall, S.M. & Penning-Rowsell, E.C. (2005) Floods as catalysts for policy change: historical lessons from England and Wales. *Water Resources Development,* **21**, 561–575.

Jones, P.S. (2009) Mires. Habitats of Wales – a comprehensive field survey 1979–1997 (eds Blackstock, T.H., Howes, E.A., Stevens, J.P., Burrows, C.R. & Jones, P.S.), pp. 138–162. University of Wales Press, Cardiff.

Jones, P., Stevens, D., Latham, J. & Duigan, C. (2009) Habitats in Welsh river floodplains. The Rivers of Wales – a natural resource of international and historical significance (eds D.D. Williams & C.A. Duigan), pp. 35–58. Backhuys Publishers/Margraf Publishers.

Junk, W.J., Bayley, P.B. & Sparks R.E. (1989) The flood pulse concept in river-floodplain systems. *Canadian Journal of Fisheries Aquatic Science,* **106**, 110–127.

Kaldec, R.H. & Knight, R.L. (1996) Treatment wetlands. Lewis Publishers, Boca Raton, Florida, USA.

Kaushal, S.S., Likens, G E., Jaworski, N.A., Pace M. L., Sides, A.M,. Seekell. D., Belt, K.T., Secor, D.H., & Wingate, R.L. (2010) Rising stream and river temperatures in the United States. *Frontiers in Ecology and Environment,* **8**, 461–466. doi:10.1890/090037.

Kay, D., Kershaw, S., Lee, R., Wyer, M.D., Watkins, J. & Francis, C. (2008) Results of field investigations into the impact of intermittent sewage discharges on the microbiological quality of wild mussels (*Mytilus edulis*) in a tidal estuary. *Water Research,* **42**, 3033–3046.

Kay, G. (1794) General view of the agriculture and rural economy of Anglesey with observations on the means of improving it. John Moir, Edinburgh.

Kernan, M., Battarbee, R.W., Curtis, C.J., Monteith, D.T. & Shilland, E.M. (eds) (2010) Recovery of lakes and streams in the UK from the effects of acid rain: UK Acid Waters Monitoring Network 20 year interpretive report. UCL Environmental Change Research Centre, London.

Knight, L.R.F.D. (2008) A survey of groundwater fauna of the Scilly Isles, UK. *Cave and Kast Science,* **35,** 63–68.

Kowalik, R.A., Cooper, D.M., Evans, C.D. & Ormerod, S.J. (2007) Acidic episodes retard the biological recovery of upland British streams from chronic acidification. *Global Change Biology,* **13**, 2439.

Lamb, H.H. (1972) The cold little ice age of about 1550 to 1800. Climate: present, past and future. Methuen, London, 107pp.

Lane, S.N. (2008) Climate Change and the summer 2007 floods in the UK. *Geographical Association,* **93**(2), 91–97.

Larsen, S. & Ormerod, S.J. (2010) Low-level effects of inert sediments on temperate stream invertebrates. *Freshwater Biology,* **55**, 476–486.

Lawlor, A.J. & Tipping, E. (2003) Metals in bulk deposition and surface waters at two upland locations in northern England. *Environmental Pollution,* **121**, 153–167.

Lawton, J.H., Brotherton, P.N.M., Brown, V.K., Elphick, C., Fitter, A.H., Forshaw, J., Haddow, R.W., Hilborne, S., Leafe, R.N., Mace, G.M., Southgate, M.P., Sutherland, W.A., Tew, T.E., Varley, J. & Wynne, G.R. (2010) Making Space for Nature: a review of England's wildlife sites and ecological network. Report to Defra. Defra, London.

Lindsay, R.A. & Immirzi, P. (1996) An inventory of lowland raised bogs in Great Britain. SNH Survey and Monitoring Report 78. Scottish Natural Heritage, Battleby.

Lindsay, R. (2010) Peatbogs and Carbon: A critical synthesis to inform policy development in oceanic peat bog conversation and restoration in the context of climate change. Report for RSPB Scotland, University of East London, Environment Research Group.

Lindsay, S.W. & Thomas, C.J. (2001) Global warming and risk or *Vivax Malaria* in Britain. *Global Change and Human Health,* **2**, 80–84.

Lloyd, C.R. (2006) Annual carbon balance of a managed wetland meadow in the Somerset Levels, UK. *Agriculture and Forest Meteorology*, **138**, 168–179.

Lovegrove, R., Strachan, R., Crawford, A., Tyler, S., Halliwell, L. & Slater, F. (2009) Life in Welsh rivers: Other vertebrate life. The Rivers of Wales – a natural resource of international and historical significance (eds D.D. Williams & C.A. Duigan), pp. 141–162. Backhuys Publishers/Margraf Publishers.

Lyle, A.A. & Smith, I.R. (1994) Standing Waters, The Fresh Waters of Scotland (eds P.S. Maitland, P.J. Boon & D.S. McLusky), pp. 35–50. John Wiley and Sons, Chichester.

MA (Millennium Ecosystem Assessment) (2005) *Ecosystems and Human Well-being*. Island Press, Washington D.C. USA.

Maberly S.C., King L., Dent M.M., Jones R.I. & Gibson C.E. (2002) Nutrient limitation of phytoplankton and periphyton growth in upland lakes. *Freshwater Biology*, **47**, 2136–2152.

Macdonald, D.M.J., Bloomfield, J.P., Hughes, A.G., MacDonald, A.M., Adams, B. & McKenzie, A.A. (2008) Improving the understanding of the risk from groundwater flooding in the UK. Proceedings of Flood Risk 2008, European Conference on Flood Risk Management, Oxford, September 2008. CRC Press, the Netherlands.

Mackey, E.C. & Mudge, G. (2010) Scotland's Wildlife: An assessment of biodiversity in 2010. Scottish Natural Heritage, Scotland.

Macklin, M.G. & Lewin, J. (2008) Alluvial responses to the changing Earth system. *Earth Surface Processes and Landforms*, **33**, 1374–1395.

Magee, M. & Badenoch, C. (2010) Tweed Wetland Strategy. The Tweed Forum, Melrose.

Mainstone, C.P., Dils, R.M. & Withers, P.J.A. (2008) Controlling sediment and phosphorus transfer to receiving waters: a strategic management perspective for England and Wales. *Journal of Hydrology*, **350**, 131–143.

Maitland, P.S., Winfield, I.J., McCarthy, I.D. & Igoe, F. (2007) The status of Arctic charr *Salvelinus alpinus* in Britain and Ireland. *Ecology of Freshwater Fish*, **16**, 6–19.

Malcolm, I.A., Youngson, A.F., Greig, S. & Soulsby, C. (2008) Hyporheic influences on spawning success. Salmon Spawning Habitat in Rivers: Physical Controls, Biological Responses and Approaches to Remediation (eds D. Sear & P. DeVries), pp. 225–248. American Fisheries Society, Bethesda, Maryland, USA.

Malcolm I.A., Middlemas C.A., Soulsby C., Middlemas S.J., Youngson A.F. (2010) Hyporheic zone processes in a canalised agricultural stream: implications for salmonid embryo survival. *Fundamental and Applied Limnology*, **176**(4), 319–336.

Maltby, E. (1986) Waterlogged wealth. Earthscan, London.

Maltby, E., Hogan D.V., Immirzi C.P., Tellam J.H. & van der Peijl M.J. (1994) Building a new approach to the investigation and assessment of wetland ecosystem functioning. Global Wetlands: Old World and New (ed. W.J. Mitsch), pp. 637–658. Elsevier, Amsterdam.

Maltby, E. (2006) Wetland conservation and management: questions for science and society in applying the ecosystem approach. *Ecological Studies*, **191**, 93–116.

Maltby, E. (ed) (2009a) Functional assessment of wetlands. Woodhead Publishing Ltd, Cambridge.

Maltby, E. (2009b) The changing wetland paradigm. The Wetlands Handbook (eds E. Maltby, T. Barker), pp. 3–42. Wiley-Blackwell, Oxford.

Maltby, E. (2010) Effects of climate change on the societal benefits of UK upland peat ecosystems: applying the ecosystem approach. *Climate Research*, **24**, 1–11.

Marsh, T.J. & Hannaford, J. (2008) The 2007 summer floods in England and Wales: a hydrological appraisal. Centre for Ecology & Hydrology, UK. 32pp.

May, L. & Carvalho, L. (2010) Maximum growing depth of macrophytes in Loch Leven, Scotland, United Kingdom, in relation to historical changes in estimated phosphorus loading. *Hydrobiologia*, **646**, 123–131.

May, L., Place, C., O'Malley, M. & Spears, B. (2010) The impact of phosphorus inputs from small discharges on designated freshwater sites. NERC/ Centre for Ecology and Hydrology, pp.125.

Mayes, W.M., Johnston, D., Potter, H.A.B. & Jarvis, A.P. (2009) A national strategy for identification, prioritisation and management of pollution from abandoned non-coal mine sites in England and Wales. I. Methodology development and initial results. *Science of the Total Environment*, **407**, 5435–5447.

Medlock, J. M., Snow, K.R. & Leach, S. (2005) Potential transmission of West Nile virus in the British Isles: an ecological review of candidate mosquito bridge vectors. *Medical and Veterinary Entomology*, **19**, 2–21.

Mermillod-Blondin, F., Creuzé des Châtelliers, M., Gerino, M. & Gaudet, J.P. (2000) Testing the effect of *Limnodrilus* sp. (Oligochaeta, Tubificidae) on organic matter and nutrient processing in the hyporheic zone: a microcosm method. *Archiv für Hydrobiologie*, **149**, 467–487.

Merritt, A. (1994) Wetlands, Industry and wildlife: a manual of principles and practices. The Wildfowl and Wetland Trust, Slimbridge.

Milsom, T.P. (2005) Decline of Northern Lapwing *Vanellus vanellus* breeding on arable farmland in relation to loss of spring tillage. *Bird Study*, **52**, 297–306.

Monteith, D. T. & Evans, C. D. (2005) The United Kingdom Acid Waters Monitoring Network: a review of the first 15 years and introduction to the special issue. *Environmental Pollution*, **137**, 3–13.

Monteith, D.T., Hildrew, A.G., Flower, R.J., Raven, P.J., Beaumont, W.R.B., Collen, P., Kreiser, A.M., Shilland, E.M. & Winterbottom, J.H. (2005) Biological responses to the chemical recovery of acidified fresh waters in the UK. *Environmental Pollution*, **137**, 83–101.

Monteith, D.T., Stoddard, J.L., Evans, C.D., de Wit, H.A., Forsius, M., Høgåsen, T., Wilander, A., Skjelkvåle, B.L., Jeffries, D.S., Vuorenmaa, J., Keller, B., Kopácek, J. & Vesely, J. (2007) Dissolved organic carbon trends resulting from changes in atmospheric deposition chemistry. *Nature*, **450**, 537–540.

Morris, J. (1992) Agricultural land drainage, land use change and economic performance: experience in the UK. *Land Use Policy*, **3**, 185–198.

Morris, J., Hess, T.M., Gowing, D.J.G, Leeds-Harrison, P.B., Bannister, N., Wade M. & Vivash. R.M. (2004) Integrated washland management for flood defence and biodiversity. Research report 598. English Nature, Peterborough.

Morris, J., Bailey, A.P., Lawson, C.S., Leeds-Harrison, P.B., Alsop, D. & Vivash, R. (2008a) The economic dimensions of integrating flood management and agri-environment through washland creation: a case from Somerset, England. *Journal of Environmental Management,* **88**, 372–381.

Morris, J., Hess T.M., & Posthumus, H (2008b) Agriculture's Role in Flood Adaptation and Mitigation – Policy Issues and Approaches. Discussion paper. Organisation for Economic Cooperation and Development publishing, Paris.

Morris, J., Posthumus, H., Hess, T.M., Gowing, D.J.G. & Rouquette, J.R. (2009) Watery land: the management of lowland floodplains in England. What is Land For? The Food, Fuel and Climate Change Debate (eds M. Winter & M. Lobley), pp. 320. Earthscan. ISBN 9781844077205.

Morris J., Graves, A., Angus, A., Hess, T., Lawson, C., Camino, M., Truckell, I. and Holman, I. (2010) Restoration of Lowland Peatland in England and Impacts on Food Production and Security. Report to Natural England. Cranfield University, Bedford.

Moss, B., Balls, H., Booker, I., Manson, K. & Timms, M. (1984) The River Bure, United Kingdom: patterns of change in chemistry and phytoplankton in a slow-flowing fertile river. *Verhandlung Internationale der Vereinigung Theoretische und Angewandte Limnologie,* **22**, 1959–1964.

Moss, B., Balls, H., Booker, I., Manson, K. & Timms, M. (1988) Problems in the construction of a nutrient budget from the River Bure and its Broads (Norfolk) prior to its restoration from eutrophication. Algae and the Aquatic Environment (ed F.E. Round), pp. 326–353. Biopress, Bristol.

Moss, B., Mckee, D., Atkinson, D., Collings, S.E., Eaton, J.W., Gill, A.B., Harvey, I., Hatton, K., Heyes, T. & Wilson, D. (2003) How important is climate? Effects of warming, nutrient addition and fish on phytoplankton in shallow lake microcosms. *Journal of Applied Ecology,* **40**, 782–792.

Natural England (2009) State of the Natural Environment Report 2008. Natural England, Sheffield.

Natural England (2010) England's Peatlands: Carbon storage and Greenhouse Gas Emissions. NE257, Natural England, Sheffield. [online] Available at: <http://naturalengland. etraderstores.com/NaturalEnglandShop/NE257> [Accessed: 07.03.11].

Natural England (2011). Agricultural land classification, England. [online] Available at: <http://magic.defra.gov.uk/datadoc/metadata.asp?dataset=2> [Accessed: 16.03.11].

Natural England & Environment Agency (2011) Invasive shrimp *Dikerogammarus villosus*. Briefing note 3, March 2011. CCW, Environment Agency, Natural England.

Neal, C., Jarvie, H.P., Withers, P.J.A., Whitton, B.A. & Neal, M. (2010) The strategic significance of wastewater sources to pollutant phosphorus levels in English rivers and to environmental management for rural, agricultural and urban catchments. *Science of the Total Environment,* **408**, 1485–1500.

Newbold, J.D., Elwood, J.W., O'Neill, R.V. & Vanwinkle, W. (1981) Measuring nutrient spiralling in streams. *Canadian Journal of Fisheries and Aquatic Science,* **38**(7), 860–863.

Newson, M.D. (2002). Geomorphological concepts and tools for sustainable river ecosystem management. *Aquatic Conservation: Marine and Freshwater Ecosystems,* **12**, 365–379.

Newson, M.D. & Brookes, A. (1995) Sediment-related river maintenance: the role of fluvial geomorphology. *Earth Surface Processes and Landforms,* **20**, 629–647.

Noble, D.G., Everard, M. & Joys, A.C. (2008) Development of wild bird indicators for freshwater wetlands and waterways: provisional indicators. British Trust for Ornithology, Thetford.

Norton, L.R., Murphy, J., Reynolds, B., Marks, S., Mackey, E.C. (2009) Countryside Survey: Scotland Results from 2007. NERC/Centre for Ecology & Hydrology, The Scottish Government, Scottish Natural Heritage, 83pp. (CEH Project Number: C03259).

Nuttall, P.M., Boon, A.G. & Rowell, M.R. (1997) Review of the design and management of constructed wetlands. CIRIA, Westminster, London.

NWT (Norfolk Wildlife Trust) (2006) Norfolk fens assessment 2005-2006. An assessment of non SSSI fen sites outside the Broads. Norfolk Wildlife Trust, Norwich.

Oertli, B., Cereghino, R., Hull, A. & Miracle, R. (2009) Pond conservation: from science to practice. *Hydrobiologia,* **634**, 1–9.

Ormerod, S.J. (2003) Current issues with fish and fisheries: editor's overview and introduction. *Journal of Applied Ecology,* **40**, 204–213.

Ormerod, S.J. & Durance, I. (2009) Restoration and recovery from acidification in upland Welsh streams over 25 years. *Journal of Applied Ecology,* **46**, 164–174.

Ormerod, S. & Jüttner, I. (2009) Pollution effects on Welsh rivers: a damaged past, an uncertain future? The Rivers of Wales – a natural resource of international and historical significance (eds. D.D. Williams & C.A. Duigan), pp. 181–203. Backhuys Publishers/Margraf Publishers.

Orr, H.G. & Carling, P.A. (2006) Hydro-climatic and land use changes in the river lune catchment, North West England, implications for catchment management. *River Research and Applications,* **22**, 239–255.

Orr, H.G., Jacobs, R. & Dunbar, M.J. (2010) Freshwater ecological response to climate change. Environment Agency Science Report.

Owens, P.N. & Walling, D.E. (2002) Changes in sediment sources and floodplain deposition rates in the catchment of the River Tweed, Scotland, over the last 100 years: The impact of climate and land use changes. *Earth Surface Processes and Landforms,* **27**, 403–423.

Peeler, E.J. & Thrush, M.A. (2009) Assessment of exotic fish disease introduction and establishment in the United Kingdom via live fish transporters. *Diseases of Aquatic Organisms,* **83**, 85–95.

Peirson, G., Tingley, D., Spurgeon, J. & Radford, A. (2001) Economic evaluation of inland fisheries in England and Wales. *Fisheries Management and Ecology,* **8**, 415–424.

Petts, G.E. & Gurnell, A.M. (2005) Dams and geomorphology: research progress and future directions. *Geomorphology,* **71**, 27–47.

Petts, G.E. (2009) Instream-flow science for sustainable river management. *Journal of the American Water Resources Association,* **45**, 1071–1086.

Pickup, R.W., Rhodes G., Arnott, S., Sidi-Boumedine, K., Bull, T.J., Weightman, A., Hurley, M. & Hermon-Taylor, J. (2005) *Mycobacterium avium* subsp. *paratuberculosis* in the catchment area and water of the River Taff in South Wales, United Kingdom, and its potential relationship to clustering of Crohn's Disease cases in the City of Cardiff. *Applied and Environmental Microbiology,* **71**, 2130–2139.

Pickup, R.W., Rhodes, G., Bull, T.J., Arnott, S., Sidi-Boumedine, K., Hurley, M. & Hermon-Taylor, J. (2006) *Mycobacterium avium* subsp. *paratuberculosis* in lake catchments, in river water abstracted for domestic use, and in effluent from domestic sewage treatment works: diverse opportunities for environmental cycling and human exposure. *Applied and Environmental Microbiology,* **72**, 4067–4077.

Pilgrim, E.S., Macleod, C.J.A., Blackwell, M.S.A., Hogan, D.V., Bol, R., Cardenas, L., Chadwick, D., Dungait, J., Haygarth P.M., Hobbs, P., Hodgson, C., Jarvis, S.C., Misselbrook, T.H., Murray, P. & Firbank, L.G. (2010) Interactions among agricultural production and other ecosystem services delivered from European grassland systems. *Advances in Agronomy,* **109**, 117–154.

Pitt, M. (2008) Learning Lessons from the 2007 Floods. Cabinet Office, London.

Posthumus, H. & Morris, J. (2010) Implications of CAP Reform for land management and runoff control in England and Wales. *Land Use Policy,* **27** (1), 42-50.

Posthumus, H., Rouquette, J.R., Morris, J., Gowing, D.J.G. & Hess, T.M. (2010) A framework for the assessment of ecosystem goods and services; a case study on lowland floodplains in England. *Ecological Economics,* **69** (7), 1510-1523.

Prior, H. & Johnes, P. J. (2002) Regulation of surface water quality in a Chalk catchment, UK: an assessment of the relative importance of instream and wetland processes. *Science of the Total Environment,* **282–283**, 159–174.

Proudlove, G.S., Wood, P.J., Harding, P.T., Horne, D.J., Gledhill, T. & Knight, L.R.F.D. (2003) A review of the status and distribution of the subterranean aquatic Crustacea of Britain and Ireland. *Cave and Karst Science,* **30**, 53–74.

Ratcliffe, J.B. & Hattey, R.P. (1982) Welsh lowland peatland survey. Nature Conservancy Council.

Raven, P.J., Holmes, N.T.H., Dawson, F.H., Everard, M., Fozzard, I.R. & Rouen, K.J. (1998) River Habitat Quality: the physical character of rivers and streams in the UK and Isle of Man. River Habitat Survey Report No. 2. Environment Agency, Bristol.

Raven, P. & Diamond, M. (eds) (2010) Preface. Recent Developments in Classification, Assessment and Management Strategies for Freshwater Habitats in Britain and Europe. *Aquatic Conservation: Marine and Freshwater Ecosystems (Special Issue),* **20**, S2-S3.

Rawlins, A. & Morris, J. (2009) Social and economic aspects of peatland management in northern Europe: with particular reference to the English case. *Geoderma,* **154**(3–4), 242–251.

Reed, S., Graves, A., Dandy, N., Posthumus, H., Hubacek, K., Morris, J., Pell, C., Quinn, C.H., & Stringer, L.C. (2009) Who is in and why? A typology of stakeholder analysis methods for natural resource management. *Journal of Environmental management,* **90**, 1933–1949.

Rees, S.E. (1997) The historical and cultural importance of ponds and small lakes in Wales, UK. *Aquatic conservation: Marine and Freshwater Ecosystems,* **7**, 133–139.

Robertson, A.L., Smith, J.W.N., Johns, T. & Proudlove, G.S. (2009) The distribution and diversity of stygobites in Great Britain: an analysis to inform groundwater management. *Quarterly Journal of Engineering Geology and Hydrogeology,* **42**, 359–368.

Robertson, A.L. & Wood, P.J. (2010) Ecology of the hyporheic zone: origins, current knowledge and future directions. *Fundamental & Applied Limnology,* **176**, 279–289.

Robinson, M. & Armstrong, A. (1988) The extent of agricultural field drainage in England and Wales. *Transactions of the Institute of British Geographers,* **13**(1), 19–28.

Robinson, M. (1990) The impact of improved land drainage on river flows. Institute of Hydrology Report 113. IH, Wallingford.

Romanowicz, R., Beven, K., Wade, S. & Vidal, J. (2006) Effects of Climate Change on River Flows and Groundwater Recharge, A Practical methodology. Interim Report on Rainfall-Runoff Modelling, UKWIR report CL/04, London.

Rothwall, J.J., Dise, N.B. Taylor, K.G., Allott, T.E.H., Scholefield, P., Davies, H. & Neal, C. (2010) A spatial and seasonal assessment of river water chemistry across North West England. *Science of the Total Environment,* **15**, 841–855.

RSPB (Royal Society for the Protection of Birds) (1994) Reedbed management for bitterns. Sandy, UK.

Salgado, J., Sayer, C., Carvalho, L., Davidson, T. & Gunn, I. (2010) Assessing aquatic macrophyte community change through the integration of palaeolimnological and historical data at Loch Leven, Scotland. *Journal of Paleolimnology,* **43**, 191–204.

Sanders, I.A., Heppell, C.M., Cotton, J.A., Wharton, G., Hildrew, A.G., Flowers, E.J. & Trimmer, M. (2007) Emission of methane from chalk streams has potential implications for agricultural practices. *Freshwater Biology,* **52**, 1176–1186.

Sayer, C.D., Davidson, T.A. & Jones, J.I. (2010) Seasonal dynamics of macrophytes and phytoplankton in shallow lakes: a eutrophication-driven pathway from plants to plankton? *Freshwater Biology,* **55**(3), 500–513.

Snow, L.C., Newson, S.E., Musgrove, A.J., Cranswick, P.A., Crick, H.Q.P. & Wilesmith, J.W. (2007) Risk-based surveillance for H5N1 avian influenza virus in wild birds in Great Britain. *Veterinary Record* **161**, 775-781.

Sear, D.A. & Newson, M.D. (2003) Environmental change in river channels: a neglected element. Towards geomorphological typologies, standards and monitoring. *The Science of the Total Environment,* **310**, 17–23.

SEPA (Scottish Environment Protection Agency) (2006) State of Scotland's Environment 2006. Scottish Environment Protection Agency, Stirling.

Sinclair, C. J., Ramwell, C. T., Lynn, R. & Jowett, V. (2007) Cypermethrin losses from sheep farms. Final Report, CSL Project N3LT. Central Science Laboratories, Sand Hutton, York.

Siriwardena, G.M., Baillie, S.R., Crick, H.P.Q., Wilson, J.D. & Gates, S. (2000) The demography of lowland farmland birds. Ecology and conservation of lowland farmland birds. (eds N.J. Aebischer, A.D. Evans, P.V. Grice & J.A. Vickery), pp. 117–133. BTO, Tring.

Smart, S.M., Allen, D., Murphy, J., Carey, P.D., Emmett, B.A., Reynolds, B.;,Simpson, I.C., Evans, R.A., Skates, J., Scott, W.A., Maskell, L.C., Norton, L.R., Rossall, M.J. & Wood, C. (2009) Countryside Survey: Wales Results from 2007. NERC/Centre for Ecology & Hydrology, Welsh Assembly Government, Countryside Council for Wales, 94pp. (CEH Project Number: C03259).

Smithers, R.J., Cowan, C., Harley, M., Hopkins, J.J., Pontier, H. & Watts, O. (2008) England biodiversity strategy Climate change adaptation principles. Defra, London.

Small, I.F., Rowan, J.S., Duck, R.W., Dyer, T.D., Franks, S.W. & Wyatt, A. (2005) Can reservoir bottom sediments be used in the estimation of long-term catchment sediment budgets? *Sediment Budgets,* **292**, 231–238.

SNH (Scottish Natural Heritage) (2008) The economic impact of Scotland's natural environment. Scottish Natural Heritage Commissioned Report No. 304. SNH, Edinburgh.

Snow, L.C., Newson, S.E., Musgrove, A.J., Cranswick, P.A., Crick, H.Q.P. & Wilesmith, J.W. (2007) Risk-based surveillance for H5N1 avian influenza virus in wild birds in Great Britain. Veterinary Record **161**, 775-781.

Solomon, D.J. & Lightfoot, G. (2007) Climate change and chalk stream salmon. Report to Environment Agency, Salisbury, UK.

Spears, B.M. & Jones, I.D. (2010) Spatial and seasonal variations in the depth of the wave mixed layer in a shallow loch (Loch Leven, Scotland): evidence of climatic forcing. *Hydrobiologia*, **646**, 49–59.

Spillett, P.B., Tagg, A.F., de Garis, Y.S. & Lult, N.W. (2003) Conflicts in river basin management: the example of the Upper River Kennet, UK. Proceedings of the 1st International Yellow River Forum on River Basin Management (ed Shang, H.Q.), pp. 477–485. People's Republic of China.

Spray, C.J., Ball, T. & Rouillard, J. (2010) Bridging the water law, science, policy interface: flood risk management in Scotland. *Journal of Water Law*, **20**(2/3), 165–174.

Spray, C. (2011) The changing nature of Scotland's fresh water environment. The Changing Nature of Scotland. (eds. Marrs, S.J., Foster, S., Hendrie, C., Mackey, E.C. & Thompson, D.B.A.). TSO, Scotland, Edinburgh.

Stapleton, C.M., Wyer, M.D., Crowther, J., McDonald, A.T., Kay, D., Greaves, J. Wither, A. Watkins, J. & Francis, C. (2008) Quantitative catchment profiling to apportion faecal indicator organism budgets for the Ribble system, the UK's sentinel drainage basin for Water Framework Directive research. *Journal of Environmental Management*, **87**, 535–550.

Stratford, C., Duenas, M., Bowes, M., Palmer-Felgate, E. & Mackenzie, S. (2010). 10 Years On: how the nutrient removal performance of a treatment reed bed changes with time. 2nd Irish International Conference on Constructed Wetlands for Wastewater Treatment and Environmental Pollution Control, 1-2 October 2010 (eds Zhao & Babatunde), University College Dublin, Ireland.

Strayer, D.L. (2010) Alien species in fresh waters: ecological effects, interactions and other stressors, and prospects for the future. *Freshwater Biology*, **55**, 152–174, Supplement 1.

Strayer, D.L. & Dudgeon, D. (2010) Freshwater biodiversity conservation: recent progress and future challenges. *Journal of the North American Benthological Society*, **29**, 344–358.

Tallis, H. & Polasky, S. (2009) Mapping and valuing ecosystem services as an approach for conservation and natural-resource management. *Annals of the New York Academy of Sciences*, **1162**, 265–283.

Thackeray, S.J., Jones, I.D. & Maberly, S.C. (2008) Long-term change in the phenology of spring phytoplankton: species-specific responses to nutrient enrichment and climate change. *Journal of Ecology*, **96**, 523–535.

Thomas, P. & Walker, M. (2004). Mosslands of northwest Merseyside, Lancashire & Greater Manchester: state and extent of surviving acid mossland habitats. Unpublished report.

Thorley, J.L., Eatherley, D.M.R., Stephen, A.B., Simpson, I., MacLean, J.C. & Youngson, A.F. (2005) Congruence between automatic fish counter data and rod catches of Atlantic salmon (*Salmo salar*) in Scottish rivers. *ICES Journal of Marine Science*, **62**, 809–817.

Thorp, J.H., Thoms, M.C. & DeLong, M.D. (2008) The riverine ecosystem synthesis: towards conceptual cohesiveness in river science. Academic Press, Amsterdam.

Tockner, K., Malard, F., Ward, J.V. (2000) An extension of the flood pulse concept. *Hydrological Processes*, **14**(16–17), 2861–2883.

Tockner, K. & Stanford, J.A., (2002) Riverine flood plains: present state and future trends. *Environmental Conservation*, **29**, 308–330.

Turner, R.K., Georgiou, S. & Fisher, B. (2008) Valuation of ecosystems services: the case of multi-functional wetlands. Earthscan, London.

Tyler, S.J. (1993) Reed-beds in Wales: their extent and distribution, their birds and the threats facing them. Royal Society for the Protection of Birds. Unpublished Report. Wales.

Van der Noort, R. (2001) Thorne Moors: a contested wetland in north-eastern England. The Heritage Management of Wetlands in Europe (eds B. Coles & A. Olivier), pp.133–140. EAC, Brussels.

Vannote R.L., Minshall, G.W., Cummins, K.W., Sedell, J.R. & Cushing, C.E. (1980) The River Continuum Concept. *Canadian Journal of Fisheries and Aquatic Sciences*, **37**, 130–137.

Vøllestad, L.A., Hirst, D., L'Abée-Lund, J.H. MacLean, J.C. Youngson, A.F. & Stenseth, N.C. (2009) Divergent trends in anadromous salmonid populations in Norwegian and Scottish rivers. *Proceedings of the Royal Society B*, **22**, 1021–1027.

Walling, D.E., Collins, A.L. & McMellin, G.K. (2003) A reconnaissance survey of the source of interstitial fine sediment recovered from salmonid spawning gravels in England and Wales. *Hydrobiologia*, **497**, 91–108.

Ward, J.V. (1998) Riverine landscapes: biodiversity patterns, disturbance regimes and aquatic conservation. *Biological Conservation*, **83**, 269–278.

Webb, J.R., Drewitt, A.L. & Measures, G.H. (2010) Managing for species: Integrating the needs of England's priority species into habitat management. Natural England Research Report, NERR024, Natural England, Sheffield.

Welton, J.S., Beaumont, W.R.C. & Ladle, M. (1999) Timing of migration and changes in age structure of Atlantic salmon, *Salmo salar* L., in the River Frome, a Dorset chalk stream, over a 24-year period. *Fisheries Management and Ecology*, **6**, 437–458.

Werritty, A., Ball, T., Spray, C., Bonell, M., Rouillard, J., Archer, N., Bowles, C. & Moir, H. (2010) Restoration strategy: Eddleston water scoping study. Dundee University, Dundee.

Wheeler, B.D. & Shaw, S.C. (2001). A wetland framework for impact assessment at statutory sites in eastern England. Environment Agency R&D Report W6-068/TR1 and W6-068/TR2. WRC, Medmenham.

Wheeler, B.D., Money, R.P. & Shaw, S.C. (2002). Freshwater Wetlands. Handbook of Ecological Restoration. Volume 2. Restoration in Practice (eds M.R. Perrow & A.J. Davy), pp. 325–354. Cambridge University Press, Cambridge.

Wheeler, B.D., Gowing, D.J.G., Shaw, S.C., Mountford, J.O. & Money, R.P. (2004) Ecohydrological guidelines for lowland wetland plant communities (eds A.W. Brooks, P.V. Jose & M.I. Whiteman). Environment Agency (Anglian Region), Peterborough.

Whitehead, P.G., Wade, A.J. & Butterfield, D. (2009) Potential impacts of climate change on water quality and ecology in six UK rivers. *Hydrology Research*, **40**, 113–122.

Whitehouse, J. (2002) Trawsfynydd, a lake with three lives. *FBA News*, **18**, 1–3.

Wilby, R.L. (2006) When and where might climate change be detectable in UK river flows? *Geophysical Research Letters*, **33**, L19407. DOI: 10.1029/2006GL027552.

Wilby, R.L., Whitehead, P.G., Wade, A., Butterfield, D., Davis, R.J. & Watts, G. (2006) Integrated modelling of climate change impacts on water resources and quality in a lowland catchment? *Journal of Hydrology*, **330**, 204–220.

Williams, E., Firn, J.R., Kind, V., Roberts, M. & D. McGlashen (2003) The value of Scotland's ecosystem services and natural capital. European Environment, **13**, 67-78.

Williams, P., Whitfield, M., Biggs, J., Bray, S., Fox, G., Nicolet, P. & Sear, D. (2004) Comparative biodiversity of rivers, streams, ditches and ponds in an agricultural landscape in Southern England. *Biological Conservation,* **115**, 329–341.

Williams, P., Biggs, J., Crowe, A., Murphy, J., Nicolet, P., Weatherby, A. & Dunbar, M. (2010) Countryside Survey: Ponds Report from 2007. Technical Report No. 7/07 Pond Conservation and NERC/Centre for Ecology & Hydrology, pp. 77 (CEH Project Number: C03259).

Williams, R.J., Keller, V.D.J., Johnson, A.C., Young, A.R., Holmes, M.G.R., Wells, C., Gross-Sorokin, M. & Benstead, R. (2009) A national risk assessment for intersex in fish arising from steroid estrogens. *Environmental Toxicology and Chemistry,* **28**, 220–230.

Wilson, A.M., Vickery, J.A., Brown, A., Langston, R.H.W., Smallshire, D., Wotton, S. & Vanhinsbergh, D. (2005) Changes in the numbers of breeding waders on lowland wet grasslands in England and Wales between 1982 and 2002. *Bird Study,* **52**, 55–69.

Winfield, I.J., Fletcher, J.M. & James, J.B. (2008). The Arctic charr (*Salvelinus alpinus*) populations of Windermere, UK: population trends associated with eutrophication, climate change and increased abundance of roach (*Rutilus rutilus*). *Environmental Biology of Fishes*, **83**, 25-35.

Wiseman, I.M., Rutt, G.P. & Edwards, P.J. (2004) Constructed wetlands for minewater treatment: environmental benefits and ecological recovery. *Journal of the Chartered Institution of Water and Environmental Management*, **18**, 133–138.

Wood, P.J., Hannah, D.M., Agnew, M.D. & Petts, G.E. (2001) Scales of hydroecological variability within a groundwater-dominated chalk stream. *Regulated Rivers: Research and Management*, **17**, 347–367.

Worrall, F. & Burt, T.P. (2007) Trends in DOC concentration in Great Britain. *Journal of Hydrology,* **346**, 81–92.

Worrall, F., Burt, T.P., Jaeban, R.Y. & Shedden, R. (2002) Release of dissolved organic carbon from upland peat. *Hydrological Process,* **16**, 3487–3504.

Worrall, F., Burt, T. & Shedden, R. (2003) Long term records of riverine dissolved organic matter. *Biochemistry,* **64**, 165–178.

Youngson, A.F., Jordan, W.C., Verspoor, E., McGinnity, P., Cross, T. & Ferguson, A. (2003) Management of salmonid fisheries in the British Isles: towards a practical approach based on population genetics. *Fisheries Research,* **62**, 193–209.

Zimmer, I., Medlock, J., Taylor, M., Bell, H., Smith, G.C. & Learmount, J. (2010) Wetlands: disease and nuisance threats to humans and livestock. Draft report to Defra. Defra, London.

Appendix 9.1 Description of Sources of Data

1. State of the Natural Environment Report (Natural England)

This report covers the natural environment (landscapes, flora and fauna, freshwater and marine environments, geology and soils) using existing data.

2. BAP matrix

UK BAP Biodiversity Action Reporting System (BARS) report for 2008. Source: www.ukbap-reporting.org.uk/status/species_habitat.asp

This website provides access to information collated from the UK's four countries charting progress towards UK BAP targets under the quinquennial reporting review in 2008. It includes information on current status (extent and habitat condition) and trends in those characteristics. It contains important caveats over the quality and reliability of data used in the assessment; in particular, habitat inventory information is very unreliable for several priority UK BAP wetland habitats.

3. UK BAP priority habitat descriptions

The species and habitats were selected through the application of criteria based on international importance, rapid decline and high risk. These criteria and their application were then further developed separately for marine biodiversity, terrestrial/freshwater species and terrestrial/freshwater habitats in recognition of the very different forms of information and knowledge available for these three groupings.

4. Wetland Vision for England

Data was defined in three stages: i) Basic conditions that support the current range and extent of wetlands, such as the suitability of soils, topography and relationship to the fluvial or tidal floodplain, generated a baseline for wetland potential; ii) Factors that could support landscape-scale wetlands were summarised by sub-catchment and then weighted; they included: the presence of indicator species, existing priority habitat, statutorily designated wetlands, nature reserves, low extent of urbanisation within floodplains, the grade of agricultural land, and the presence of large contiguous areas; and iii) The Technical Advisory Group (TAG) and stakeholders defined the areas of greatest potential across the country, based on comparing information analysed per sub-catchment (Hume 2008).

5. Countryside Survey 2007

The Countryside Survey is made up of two main parts: a) the Field Survey which focuses on habitats, vegetation, soils (0–15 cm) and freshwater; and b) the Land Cover Map which is a digital map using satellite data from space. The Field Survey covered a total of 591 1x1 km sample squares spread across England, Scotland and Wales, which were representative of the variations in the climate and geology of the three countries. Where appropriate, data are also included from a separate survey of 0.5x0.5 km squares undertaken in Northern Ireland. Not all Field Survey squares contain a suitable stream or pond. Streams and ponds are not surveyed in detail in Northern Ireland. Areas of habitat were mapped within each square and more detailed samples were made of vegetation in a series of plots. Soil (0–15 cm) samples were also collected from five plots in each square, and a stream and a pond were also sampled in many of the squares. The UK Results from the 2007 Report (Carey *et al.* 2008) provide further details of the survey methodology and key results, while the country reports (Countryside Survey

2009; Norton *et al.* 2009; Smart *et al.* 2009) provide results for each country surveyed. Freshwater results are contained in Dunbar *et al.* 2010c (headwater streams) and Williams *et al.* 2010 (ponds).

6. Scottish Environment Protection Agency (SEPA) State of the Environment Report 2006

This report brings together existing information from a variety of sources covering the state of Scotland's air, land and water environments. It also covers key environmental issues: waste and resources, radioactivity, hazardous chemicals, nutrient enrichment and acidification; and three main environmental challenges: human health, biodiversity and climate change.

7. Scotland's Biodiversity: An assessment of biodiversity in 2010. Mackey, E.C. & Mudge, G. (2010) Scottish Natural Heritage

This report, coincident with the start of the International Year of Biodiversity (2010), provides an initial commentary on progress with Scotland's biodiversity targets. It uses data from the 2008 UK assessment biodiversity reporting round, Scotland's biodiversity indicators, protected site condition monitoring outcomes, and progress with Scotland's 2010 targets.

Appendix 9.2 Current Initiatives

In 2008, the Scottish Government commissioned a study to develop the ecosystem approach into a workable methodology, with the development of an outline guidance framework and a model ecosystem framework for a pilot area in Aberdeenshire a key goal (Macaulay report March 2010). There is also particular interest in developing pilot catchment studies, with work being initiated in the Cairngorms National Park (SEPA and Cairngorms National Park Authority) and Eddleston Water in the Borders (SEPA, Tweed Forum & Dundee University) (Werritty *et al.* 2010). This latter project links in to the earlier work done in the Borders by the Tweed Forum to produce the Tweed Wetland Strategy, and focuses on ecosystem services delivered through natural flood management, alongside habitat restoration. Similar examples are now emerging in England (e.g. SCaMP; 'Upstream thinking') and Wales (e.g. Lake Vyrnwy, Pont Bren), and involve partnerships across several sectors.

1. **The WATER Project** (Wetted Land Assessment and Techniques for Restoration) is developing a market-based catchment restoration scheme that will be built on a Payments for Ecosystem Services (PES) model and aims to identify both delivery and funding mechanisms to lever private investment for catchment restoration by:
- Developing a substantive Northern European cooperation network that identifies our shared common

identities and problems and can deliver environmental restoration of wetted land within a river catchment in a cost-effective way.
- Developing a set of five robust cost-benefit guides that demonstrate how investment from private companies in catchment restoration can make a long-term impact on their profitability and competitiveness.

Simply put, the people and businesses that benefit from good ecosystem function will pay the people who deliver good ecosystem functions directly. They will do this because they have a clear understanding of the economic, social and environmental benefits, as demonstrated by the WATER Project.

2. **Natural England** is undertaking studies in three upland catchments to evaluate the ecosystem approach (and benefits from ecosystem services) in practice. The project aims:
- To use the ecosystem approach to define land and water management.
- To demonstrate that investment in the natural environment can result in multiple benefits (carbon, water, biodiversity, recreational and health benefits).
- To work in partnership to deliver a range of ecosystem services in a cost-effective way and link these services to the beneficiaries.

The study is being undertaken in three pilot areas:
- Bassenthwaite Lake catchment, Cumbria
- South Pennines National Character Area, Yorkshire
- Dartmoor and Exmoor, South West England.

Each is being run by stakeholder groups at a regional level, with technical aspects being coordinated nationally.

3. The **West Country Rivers Trust** is heading a project (Wetland Example of Payments for Ecosystem Services) that is part-funded by the Natural England Wetland Vision Fund, and based on a section of historic Floodplain on the River Fal in West Cornwall. The project aims to:
- Reconnect and re-wet 21 ha of extensively grazed and cultivated, disconnected Floodplain, reinstating it as a series of lowland wetland UK BAP habitats.
- Economically evaluate the direct and indirect ecosystem services benefits including carbon sequestration, flood mitigation, nutrient stripping, biodiversity and extensive management (limited grazing, shooting, fishing).
- Identify and sell the most economically beneficial services to local investors.
- Establish with the landowner, and pay for, mechanisms to remove land from long-term intensive production to light-touch extensive management agreements or 1,000-year covenants.
- Evaluate the project's applicability in terms of developing a PES based scheme that ensures long-term protection of other hydrologically important areas within the rest of the Fal catchment.

Appendix 9.3 Summary of Recent Assessments of UK Peatlands

Table A9.3.1 Comparison of the ecosystem service values of different lowland peatland management practices using active non-impacted peatland systems as a baseline. The table indicates how different management practices, when applied to an active lowland peatland, affect delivery of these services*. ↓ shows a decrease in ecosystem service function; ↑ shows an increase in ecosystem service function; ≈ shows no change in ecosystem function. The table is adapted from JNCC (2011); it is based on expert judgement and on review versions of UK NEA chapters reflecting the current state of understanding and is not a definitive assessment of process interactions. Note that even this qualitative analysis is subject to some uncertainties, not least because the scale and direction of ecosystem service delivery is heavily context dependent.

		Afforestation	Abandonment	Peat cutting (fuel)	Peat cutting (horticulture)	Agricultural improvement	Cultivation
	Vegetation produced	Coniferous forestry	Scrub/Woodland	Wet/Dry Heath	Bare	Improved grassland, Grazing marsh	Cropland
	Peatland type most affected	Shallow peat, Raised bog	Raised bog, Fens	Raised bog	Raised bog	Shallow peat, Raised bog, Fen	Raised bog, Fens
	Peat condition	Degraded/Archaic	Degraded	Degraded	Bare	Archaic	Archaic
Provisioning	Crops, livestock & fisheries	↓	↓	≈	≈	↑	↑
	Fuel or horticultural peat	≈	≈	↑	↑	≈	≈
	Timber or building material	↑	↑	≈	≈	≈	≈
	Genetic resources	↓	↑/↓	↓	↓	↓	↓
	Drinking water supply	↓	≈	≈	≈	≈	≈
Regulating	Carbon storage	↓/≈	↓	↓	↓	↓	↓
	Preventing GHG emissions	↑/↓	↓	↓/≈	↓	↓	↓
	Flood prevention	↓/↑	↑	↓/≈	↓	↓	↓
	Disease prevention	≈	≈	≈	↑?	↑	↑
	Detoxification and purification	↓	≈	≈	↓	↓	↓
	Pollination	↓	↑	↓	↓	↓	↓
Cultural	Religion and spirituality	↑	↑	≈	≈	↑?	↑?
	Cultural heritage	↑	↓	↑	↑	↑	↑
	Aesthetics	↓	↓/↑	↑	↓	↓/↑	↓?
	Social Cohesion	≈	↓	↑	↑?	≈/↑	≈/↓
	Tourism and recreation	↑	↓	↑	↓	≈	≈
	Education	↑	↑	↑	↓	↑	↑
Supporting	Soil formation	↓	↓	↓	↓	↓	↓
	Nutrient cycling	≈	↑	↑	↑	↑	↑
	Biodiversity	↓	↑	↓	↓	↓	↓

* An increase or decrease of any given ecosystem service function does not necessarily equate to an improvement or deterioration of the system overall.

Appendix 9.4 Ecosystem Service Delivery for Lowland Wetlands and Trade-off Matrices for Floodplains and Reedbeds

Table A9.4.1 Ecosystem service delivery by key lowland wetland types.

	Service	Floodplains — Natural	Floodplains — Managed	Fens	Reedbeds	Grazing marsh	Lowland raised bogs	Headwater wetlands
Provisioning services	Crops, plants, livestock, fish, etc. (wild and domesticated)	Light grazing, wild game, sedge for thatching ↘2	Intense grazing of livestock (meat and wool) and crop production ↗1	Grazing of livestock, sedge for thatching ↓1	Grazing of livestock, reeds for thatching etc. ↓1	Potentially intense grazing of livestock ↓1	Bulb fibre, sphagnum for hanging baskets ↓1	Managed grouse moors, extensive grazing ↓1
	Trees, standing vegetation and peat	Timber, some peat, other vegetation ↘2	Short-term vegetation for agricultural production ↗1	Natural vegetation, peat ↘4	Some standing vegetation and organic soils ↓1	Maybe some peat/organic soil horizons ↓1	Peat accumulation ↓1	Peatlands ↓1
Provisioning and regulatory services	Water quantity	Natural buffer zone, flood defence by natural flooding regime ↘1	Often embanked to prevent flooding, promotes flooding downstream. Fertiliser inputs etc. degrade water quality ↘2	Provides clean water ↘2	Flood protection, water purification potential ↓2	Flood protection, aquifer recharge ↓1	Provides clean water ↓1	Major source/ shallow aquifer ↘4
	Wild species diversity including microbes	High biodiversity ↘1	Low biodiversity ↘1	Rare and some degree of diverse habitat ↘1	Rare but not particularly diverse habitats ↓1	Grazing restrictions (e.g. July onwards) promotes increased plant diversity ↓1	Rare but not particularly diverse habitats ↓1	Rare habitats ↔4
Regulatory services	Climate regulation	High carbon sequestration ↘1	Low carbon sequestration ↓1	Carbon sequestration (peat soils) ↓1	Carbon sequestration in soils ↓2	Local temperature and humidity regulation ↓2	Carbon sequestration (peat soils) ↓1	Carbon sequestration (peat soils) ↓1
	Hazard regulation: vegetation and other habitats	Natural flooding regime helps prevent downstream flooding ↘1	Does little to prevent flooding or climate stress ↘1	Prevent flooding if on floodplain ↔2	Some erosion protection potential, little flood prevention, some carbon sequestration ↓2	Flood protection potential, aquifer recharge ↓1	Some erosion protection potential, little flood prevention, high carbon sequestration ↓2	Flood protection potential, aquifer recharge ↓4
	Waste breakdown and detoxification	Natural processes can break down wastes ↘1	More likely a source than a sink ↘1	Natural buffer zone system ↘1	Natural buffer zone system ↓2	Breakdown of animal wastes and of contaminants in runoff ↓2	Natural buffer zone system ↓2	Natural buffer zone system ↘4
	Purification	Natural buffer zone ↘1	Buffer zone qualities lost due to intensification/ embankment ↓1	Natural buffer zone system ↘1	Natural buffer zone system ↓2	Breakdown of animal wastes and of contaminants in runoff ↓2	Natural buffer zone system ↓2	Natural buffer zone system ↘4
Cultural services	Meaningful places including green and blue space	Integral components of evolving river systems, diversity of processes, spawning areas for fish species, art, folklore ↘1	Development pressures have been intense due to high productivity, flat topography, proximity to navigable routes and potable water. Biological degradation and isolation of habitats ↓1	Unique self-supporting landscapes created by alliances of humans and nature, 'sense of place', religious significance; folklore and mythology, art, language, place-names, family histories ↘2	Landscape that regularly flood, coastal reedbeds act as natural buffers ↓2	A once common feature, species-rich habitat, support for wide variety of insects and birds; aesthetic and spiritual value ↓2	Unique self-generated landscapes, 'sense of place', religious significance; folklore and mythology, art, language, place-names, family histories ↓2	Unique self-generated landscapes, 'sense of place', religious significance; folklore and mythology, art, language, place-names, family histories ↘4
	Socially valued landscapes and waterscapes	Traditional landscape uses (wet meadows, osier beds, mill leats, fisheries); 'living landscape'— mosaic of habitat created at a landscape scale ↘1	Natural landscape-scale rhythms lost; fragmented habitats, species isolation, increased flood risk due to enhanced 'flashiness' ↓1	Artefacts of the past, traditional water and land-use, traditional medicine and ethno-botany, educational resource ↘2	One of the forgotten crops of the British countryside thatching industry, sedge, constructed reedbeds as environmentally-sensitive water treatment systems' bird habitat (e.g. the bittern) ↓2	Traditional agricultural practices evolved over centuries, flood alleviation, rich source of biodiversity ↓2	Rare but not particularly species-diverse habitats; artefact preservation (trackways, bog people) palaeontological records of environmental and climate change ↓2	Rare but not particularly species-diverse habitats; artefact preservation (trackways, bog people) palaeontological records of environmental and climate change ↘4

Degree of importance of ecosystem service: ■ High level ■ Medium level ☐ Low level
Direction of change: ↑ Improving ↗ Some improvement ↔ Equivocal changes ↘ Some deterioration ↓ Deteriorating
Confidence: 1 – High agreement, high evidence   2 – High agreement, low evidence   3 – Low agreement, high evidence   4 – Low agreement, low evidence

Table A9.4.2 Trade-off matrix for natural Floodplains. The assumption is that the Floodplain is pristine, that is, it is predominantly diverse mixed woodland. This means that for many of the services they are being optimally performed and can not be improved; therefore, the trade-off is neutral as nothing would change. The trade-off is determined by considering how optimisation of the policy lever would affect the responding factor.

Policy lever	Responding factor →	Crops, plants, animals	Trees, standing vegetation, peat	Water quantity	Climate regulation	Hazard regulation	Waste break-down	Wild species diversity	Purification	Meaningful places	Valued landscapes	
	Crops, plants, animals		↓ ***	↓ ***	↓ ***	↓ ***	↓ ***	↓ ***	↓ ***	↓ ***	↓ ***	1
	Trees, standing vegetation, peat	↔		↑ *	↔	↔	↔	↓ *	↓ *	↓ *	↓ *	2
	Water quantity	↔	↔		↔	↔	↔	↔	↔	↔	↔	3
	Climate regulation	↔	↑ *	↔		↔	↔	↓ *	↓ *	↓ *	↓ *	4
	Hazard regulation	↔	↔	↔	↔		↔	↔	↔	↔	↔	5
	Waste breakdown	↓ *	↓ *	↑ *	↓ *	↔		↓ **	↑ *	↓ *	↓ *	6
	Wild species diversity	↑ *	↓ *	↔	↔	↔	↔		↔	↑ *	↑ *	7
	Purification	↓ *	↓ *	↑ *	↓ *	↔	↑ *	↓ **		↓ *	↓ *	8
	Meaningful places	↔	↔	↔	↔	↔	↔	↔	↔		↔	9
	Valued landscapes	↔	↔	↔	↔	↔	↔	↔	↔	↔		10

Direction of change: ↑ Increase ↓ Decrease ↔ No change
Degree to which change would occur: * Low ** Medium *** High

Interpretation:
1. To increase crops etc. natural Floodplain would need to be converted to agriculture, thereby degrading most of the natural functions it is performing.
2. To increase timber production, the natural Floodplain would require afforestation, thereby removing natural habitat, although more carbon may be sequestered.
3. Nothing could really be done to enhance this service—it is already optimally provided (natural buffer zone).
4. Enhancement of climate regulation would probably arise through afforestation, which would increase trees and timber, but have negative effects on some other services.
5. Erosion protection and flood protection are already provided, so no action is required to enhance service delivery. (There is some debate about function of Floodplain woodland, so one possibility is the removal of woodland, but this option is not considered here due to uncertainty).
6. If the Floodplain is used to enhance waste breakdown and detoxification, it is likely to reduce some services due to habitat degradation, but would enhance the provision of potable water. However, this may lead to production of more greenhouse gases.
7. This would probably involve the creation of mixed habitat involving felling of some natural woodland.
8. Same as 6.
9. & 10. It is undetermined as to how these services can be enhanced—natural Floodplains are usually valued and meaningful.

Table A9.4.3 refers to managed reedbeds, used for the production of reed (*Phragmites australis*). Sedge (*Cladium mariscus*) is cut from sedge beds and is also used for roofing. Natural reedbeds and sedge beds are more diverse components of natural Floodplains, where they are successional to carr woodland. Managed reedbeds will succeed to carr woodland if they are not cut regularly and are kept at high water level during summer, but drained down to make cutting (usually every two years) easier in winter, when the dead stems are cut for thatch. Sedge beds are managed much more lightly and kept at high water level throughout the year; the sedge is cut green in summer, usually once every few years. Thus, sedge beds have higher nature conservation value than reedbeds, which are closer to monocultures, and are mainly only valued alongside fen vegetation and natural Floodplains in terms of conservation.

The intention to increase crop production is not relevant as managed reedbeds are already looked after for maximal reed production. Intention to produce timber would mean the complete loss of reed production (indicated in **Table A9.4.3** as ---). Reduced management for reed production will tend to moderately increase the values of other services (indicated in **Table A9.4.3** as ++) because it will mean maintaining water levels higher for longer and less removal of biomass as reed. The most common useful change is to cease cutting for up to a decade or only to cut small areas in a large reed marsh. This, with inevitably increased water levels, will favour characteristic birds like bittern, but essentially means abandonment of crop production and allowing the area to revert to semi-natural Wetland conditions. Complete abandonment of reed production would increase the values of these services even more and result in conversion to a semi-natural reed swamp.

Table A9.4.3 Trade-off matrix for reedbeds.

		Will have the indicated consequences for these other services							
Intention to increase these services		Crops	Timber and wood	Water quantity	Climate regulation	Hazard regulation	Waste breakdown and water purification	Wild species diversity	Meaningful places and valued landscapes
	1. Crops	Not relevant as the prime intention is already crop production							
	2. Timber and wood	---	++						
	3. Water quantity			++					
	4. Climate regulation				++				
	5. Hazard regulation					++			
	6. Waste breakdown and Water purification						++		
	7. Wild species diversity							++	
	8 Meaningful places and Valued landscapes								

Value of ecosystem service:
■ High ■ Medium □ Low
Loss of service - - -   Gain in service ++

Interpretation:
1. Managed reedbeds are specifically managed to produce a crop of reed.
2. Regular cutting precludes succession to scrub then carr, so the habitat would move to the fen category if there was intention to allow it to succeed to woodland.
3. Storage of water in summer may alleviate summer flooding elsewhere. Managed reedbeds are always located on Floodplains, which are then inevitably no longer natural as the water levels are manipulated for reed production. Reedbed management reduces the overall capacity of the Floodplain to store water, while potentially preserving the Floodplain from complete drainage.
4. Carbon storage is minimal under management conditions as the potentially stored carbon is removed to roofs. The half-life of the carbon compounds will be long (decades), but still shorter than if they had been stored as waterlogged peats (millennia).
5. See 3.
6. Reedbeds will denitrify nitrate in summer; indeed, specifically managed, constructed Wetlands are currently used to do this. They may retain heavy metals and other pollutants temporarily, but as the peat builds up, they dry out and cease to function as reedbeds. Digging out or burning to reduce the soil level will obviate this storage.
7. Managed reedbeds provide very little diversity because they are maintained as near monocultures. Cleaning reed of other species to create bundles of thatch is expensive and to be avoided. Birds like bittern (*Botaurus stellaris*), Cetti's warbler (*Cettia cetti*) and bearded tit (*Panurus biarmicus*) are associated with reedbeds, but less so with the commercially managed ones than with those that are components of natural Floodplains.
8. The noise of wind in the reeds, the visual appeal of rural industries, the great swathes of beige-yellow reed stems, and the attractiveness of thatched roofs all contribute to the importance of reedbeds in the landscape to recreational users of these habitats, such as walkers and boaters. Countless calendars and boxes of biscuits and chocolates use photographs on these themes. Tourist Boards in Eastern England regularly use pictures of wind pumps, sailing boats and sunsets within the settings of common reed. Reed areas, however, have declined since the Second World War as reed production demands expensive labour, traditional crafts are declining, and cheaper reed imports come from Eastern Europe. Much of the former managed reedbed resource has succeeded to scrub and alder woodland.

Appendix 9.5 Approach Used to Assign Certainty Terms to Chapter Key Findings

This chapter began with a set of Key Findings. Adopting the approach and terminology used by the Intergovernmental Panel on Climate Change (IPCC) and the Millennium Assessment (MA), these Key Findings also include an indication of the level of scientific certainty. The 'uncertainty approach' of the UK NEA consists of a set of qualitative uncertainty terms derived from a 4-box model and complemented, where possible, with a likelihood scale (see below). Estimates of certainty are derived from the collective judgement of authors, observational evidence, modelling results and/or theory examined for this assessment.

Throughout the Key Findings presented at the start of this chapter, superscript numbers and letters indicate the estimated level of certainty for a particular key finding:

1. *Well established:* high agreement based on significant evidence
2. *Established but incomplete evidence:* high agreement based on limited evidence
3. *Competing explanations:* low agreement, albeit with significant evidence
4. *Speculative:* low agreement based on limited evidence

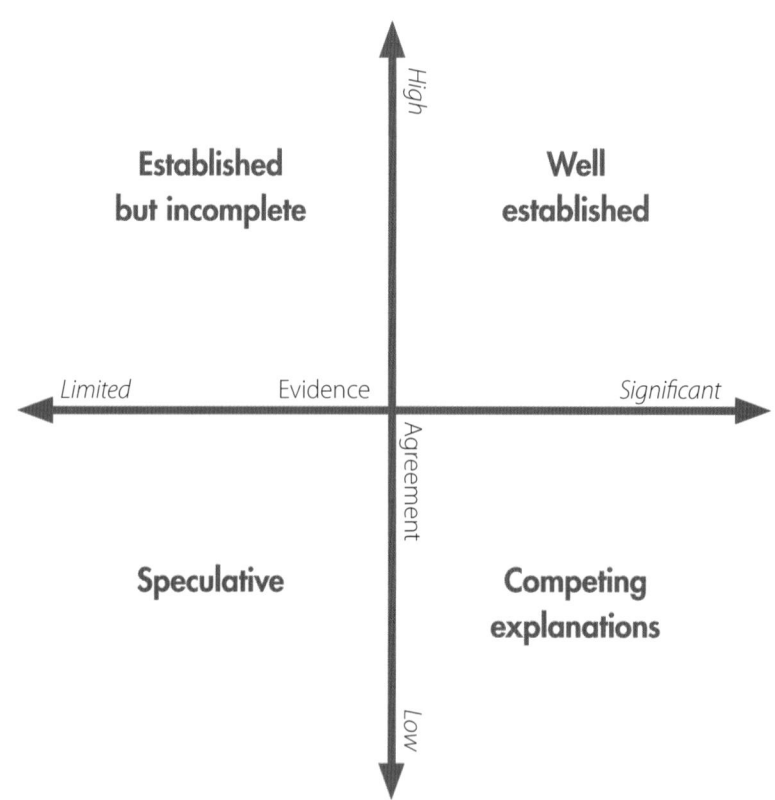

a. *Virtually certain:* >99% probability of occurrence
b. *Very likely:* >90% probability
c. *Likely:* >66% probability
d. *About as likely as not:* >33–66% probability
e. *Unlikely:* <33% probability
f. *Very unlikely:* <10% probability
g. *Exceptionally unlikely:* <1% probability

Certainty terms 1 to 4 constitute the 4-box model, while *a* to *g* constitute the likelihood scale.

Chapter 10:
Urban

Coordinating Lead Author: Linda Davies
Lead Authors: Lester Kwiatkowski, Kevin J. Gaston, Helen Beck, Hope Brett, Michael Batty, Lian Scholes, Rebecca Wade, William R. Sheate, Jon Sadler, Grischa Perino, Barnaby Andrews, Andreas Kontoleon, Ian Bateman and Jim A. Harris
Contributing Authors: Paul Burgess, Nigel Cooper, Simon Evans, Samantha Lyme, Hazel I. McKay, Robert Metcalfe, Kenton Rogers, Lucy Simpson and Jonathan Winn

Key Findings*

The ecosystem goods and services that could potentially be derived from Urban greenspace are substantial. In the past, the importance of these areas for the health and general well-being of society was not appreciated and their potential not realised[2]. It is not just the limited extent and variable quality of greenspaces, but also their spatial distribution, connectivity, functionality and accessibility that currently create barriers to their optimisation.

[2] *established but incomplete evidence*

Access to Urban greenspace is essential for good mental and physical health, childhood development, social cohesion and other important cultural services[1]. More than 6.8% of the UK's land area is now classified as 'urban', with more than 10% of England, 1.9% of Scotland, 3.6% of Northern Ireland and 4.1% of Wales contributing to this habitat. About 80% of the population resides in these areas, where the amount of mean accessible greenspace is 2 hectares (ha) per 1,000 people in England and 16 ha per 1,000 people in Scotland[2]. Deprived areas systematically fare worse in terms of quantity and quality of greenspace[2].

[1] *well established*
[2] *established but incomplete evidence*

During the last three decades of the 20th Century, there was a decline in the condition and accessibility of Urban greenspace in the UK[2]. It is likely that the reduction in funding for public parks, the absence of any statutory parks services, and the sale of playing fields (approximately 10,000 between 1979 and 1997) and allotments (estimated at below 10% of peak levels) have all contributed to this decline. Evidence suggests that there has been some improvement since the work of the Urban Task Force. Local authorities, public bodies and over 4,000 community groups, many with National Lottery funding, have contributed to the refurbishment and renewal of many of these areas.

[2] *established but incomplete evidence*

Greenspace within urban areas is not systematically monitored. Without such basic data the ecosystem services cannot be quantified[2]. There is no regular collection of data or centrally coordinated Urban greenspace database. Responsibilities are spread across a range of organisations, from different government departments and agencies to charities and private sector organisations, which collect extensive amounts of information but often using inconsistent typology at different temporal and spatial scales.

[2] *established but incomplete evidence*

Provisioning services are limited and the majority of goods are imported; but there is evidence of changing attitudes towards urban food production[2]. In the early 1940s, gardens (covering 4% of England) and allotments, over half of which were in urban areas, provided 10% of all food production in the UK (1.3 million tonnes). Today, there is increasing interest in domestic production, with 33% of people now saying they grow their own food[2]. Per household, savings exceeding £1,000 per annum have been reported from allotments.

[2] *established but incomplete evidence*

Many of the supporting and regulating functions that Urban soil could provide have been reduced and restricted[1]. Widespread sealing and degradation have resulted in Urban soil losing function and resilience, and has led to major hazards such as flooding. In London alone, it is currently estimated that 3,200 ha of front gardens have been paved, and, in Leeds, an estimated 75% of the increase in impervious surfaces that has occurred from 1971 to 2004 is attributed to the paving of residential front gardens[2].

[1] *well established*
[2] *established but incomplete evidence*

---

* Each Key Finding has been assigned a level of scientific certainty, based on a 4-box model and complemented, where possible, with a likelihood scale. Superscript numbers indicate the uncertainty term assigned to each finding. Full details of each term and how they were assigned are presented in Appendix 10.1.

Urban air quality has significantly changed over the last 60 years with consequences for clean air that extend far beyond the urban boundary[1]. Improvements in air quality arising from the national decline of sulphur dioxide and black smoke emissions (both have declined by more than 95% in London since 1962) are attributed to good regulation and enforcement, together with cleaner fuels. The growing significance in recent decades of nitrogen oxides, fine particles (PM_{10} and $PM_{2.5}$) and background ozone have largely been driven by changes in energy production and the rise in vehicle ownership.

[1] well established

Species respond differently to increasing urbanisation of a landscape and the form of that urbanisation[2]. Overall, the species that tend to disappear with urbanisation include habitat specialists, more area-demanding species (the patch size of greenspace tends to decline with urbanisation) and species typically associated with more complex vegetation structures such as forests. The species that tend to remain or increase in richness are more likely to be habitat generalists, less area-demanding species and edge specialists.

[2] established but incomplete evidence

Urban ecosystem services could be significantly enhanced to improve climate mitigation and adaptation. Temperatures in cities are higher than in rural areas with consequences for human well-being and the environment[2]. London's maximum daytime and nocturnal Urban Heat Intensity can reach 8.0°C and 7.0°C respectively[2]. The process of urbanisation and development alters the natural energy balance, mainly due to the loss of cooling from vegetated surfaces when they are replaced by impervious materials used in the construction of buildings and roads.

[2] established but incomplete evidence

Trade-offs and synergies in ecosystem goods and services are complex, with scale a major issue in decision-making. As yet, they have not been widely investigated in the Urban environment. For example, increasing vegetation cover in urban areas could reduce surface water runoff, decrease peak temperatures and the temperature-dependent formation of ozone and volatile organic compounds (VOCs)[2]. Conversely, increasing vegetation cover incurs maintenance costs, requires watering, is vulnerable to disease, can produce VOCs and would be expensive in city centres, the place where it would be likely to deliver high levels of ecosystem services and benefits.

[2] established but incomplete evidence

Urban greenspace is fundamental to sustaining urban life and, therefore, should be integral to the way in which it is planned and managed[1]. For example, the Thames Gateway Green Grid Network in South East England demonstrates the effectiveness of integrating multifunctional land use, connectivity, and accessibility using an ecosystem services approach early in the planning process. While in Scotland, sustainable drainage systems (SuDS), which can substantially enhance ecosystem goods and services delivery, have already been incorporated into an estimated 80–90% of all new developments.

[1] well established

10.1 Introduction

The UK NEA Conceptual Framework (Chapter 2) acknowledges the value of the Urban environment in providing ecosystem services by including Urban as one of its eight Broad Habitats. Assessing Urban habitats in the UK poses a number of challenges since they are not systematically monitored and the wide range of organisations collecting data often use inconsistent typology.

There is no international agreement on the defining characteristics of the Urban habitat (McIntyre *et al.* 2000; OECD 2010), nor are there any scientifically accepted criteria by which to identify urban areas and populations (McGranahan *et al.* 2005). Urbanisation is generally defined by the size or density of the human population and the associated geographic boundaries which often vary in extent and ecological diversity. A variety of landscapes (natural and semi-natural environments) and organisms are found within these boundaries, but humans and the built environment form the dominant features.

While recognising the importance of the built environment, this chapter can only attempt to assess the extent, condition and trends of Urban greenspace using available data. In the UK NEA, the term 'greenspace' refers to, and includes, the following Urban subhabitats (mainly land use types): i) natural and semi-natural greenspace (woodlands, Sites of Special Scientific Interest (SSSIs), urban forestry and scrub); ii) street trees; iii) public parks and formal gardens; iv) domestic gardens; v) green corridors; vi) outdoor sports facilities and recreational areas; vii) amenity greenspace; viii) allotments, community gardens and urban farms; ix) cemeteries, churchyards and burial grounds; x) Previously Developed Land (brownfield); xi) water; and xii) peri-urban areas (the urban fringe between the suburbs and the open countryside) (see Section 10.1.4 for further definitions of the urban subhabitats).

Towns and cities can be considered as urban systems, which are characterised by their history, structure and function (including both biotic and abiotic components), and the cycling and conversion of energy and materials. They also have their own spatial organisation and distinctive patterns of change, which influence species behaviour patterns, population dynamics and the formation of communities (Sukopp 2000).

Furthermore, urbanisation can be considered as a human ecosystem framework with three levels: social, biological and physical (Pickett 2008). The interaction between these three components within the Urban environment can be expressed in terms of interacting spheres: abiotic spheres include the atmosphere, hydrosphere, lithosphere and pedosphere; and biotic spheres include the biosphere of urban plants and animals, plus the socioeconomic world of people, known as the anthroposphere (Marzluff *et al.* 2008). Ecosystem assessments incorporate all of these components.

Unlike other habitats, such as Woodlands (Chapter 8) and Coastal Margins (Chapter 11), which primarily generate and supply ecosystem services, Urban habitats are sites of consumption (McGranahan *et al.* 2005). They draw heavily on other habitats for their basic needs (energy and materials), exporting their wastes and accelerating ecological decline on a local and global scale. Conversely, there are substantial benefits from urbanisation, not least the economies of scale it provides; for example, utilities and other essential services are far more efficient in urban than in rural areas. Here, we focus on the ecosystem services and goods arising within Urban habitats.

10.1.1 Urbanisation

The value of ecosystem goods and services arising from the Urban environment is, to a large extent, related to land use—which is the "functional dimension of land for different human purposes or economic activities" (OECD 2010)—and the extent, location, condition, connectivity and accessibility of that land. Each town or city is unique, with proportional provision of the various land types not always scaling with city size. This chapter identifies the main Urban subhabitats (Section 10.1.4) and highlights the main abiotic and biotic processes (air, water and soil) within towns and cities and the ecosystem services and goods arising from them. We review post-war trends in extent and condition of Urban subhabitats, as well as processes and associated drivers of change. Finally, we consider some of the options for sustainable management that could increase the efficiency and functionality of Urban ecosystems, along with some of the constraints.

10.1.2 The Urban Boundary

The Broad Habitats used by the UK NEA have been mapped using data from the UK Land Cover Map 2000 (LCM 2000) project (Fuller *et al.* 2002). However, the Office of National Statistics (ONS 2005) classifies 'urban' as contiguous areas with 10,000 people, which they define as 'physical settlement areas'. These data appear to reflect more closely the extent of urbanisation than the LCM 2000 data and administrative units such as local authority boundaries—the latter of which often include large expanses of sparsely populated open land (Bibby 2009). For the purposes of this report, we illustrate the distribution of urban areas across the UK (**Figure 10.1**) and the extent of urbanisation by country (**Table 10.1**). Note that **Table 10.1** compares urban areas based on population sizes greater than 10,000 people (and associated boundary conditions) to urban areas classified as 'built up areas' by LCM 2000 and clearly shows the difference in extent between the two approaches. It should be understood that the difference between land use classifications can be immense and should not be underestimated when comparing data; in most examples, it is not possible to compare across datasets due to the different approaches and typologies applied.

The proportion of the population living in urban areas was calculated as 79% in 1951 (House of Commons 1999), rising to circa 90% in 1991 (ONS 1998), based on the definition of an urban area as being at least 20 hectares (ha) in size and having a minimum population of 1,000 people. A change in the definition of 'urban' was introduced in 2004 and raised the minimum population size to more than 10,000 for England (Countryside Agency *et al.* 2004), 4,000 for Scotland, 3,000 for Wales and 4,500 for Northern Ireland.

The change also extended the area definition to 'contiguous areas', thus, based on 2001 census data, the proportion of people living in urban areas of the UK is currently estimated at 80% (ONS 2005) which is equivalent to 44 million people. Urban ecosystem goods and services will differ according to the population size, boundary and location of settlements. Villages and small towns (now defined as 'rural') will benefit from many of the goods and services provided by neighbouring Broad Habitats, but may also be subject to some of the disadvantages of more densely populated areas such as increased air pollution.

10.1.3 Overview of Urban Land Use: History and Classification

Up to and during the First World War (WWI), cities were largely composed of dense, urban cores of industry and poor housing, which began to spread out as an increasingly wealthy population, supported by government, aspired to their own homes. The advent of the car enabled people to travel further, but it was not until after the Second World War (WWII), in the 1950s, that suburban development became the predominant mode of urban growth. The creation of new towns, originally designed to ease congestion in large cities by lowering densities, accelerated this trend by housing the overspill population from slum clearances in particular. The development of better road networks facilitated a shift to travelling by car rather than rail, bus and walking, which reinforced suburbanisation. This process of suburbanisation was accompanied throughout the post-war

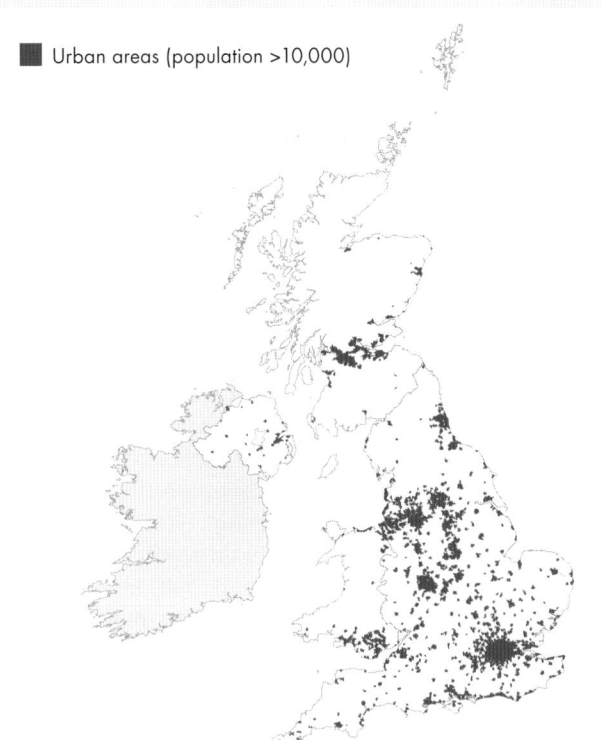

□ Urban areas (population >10,000)

Figure 10.1 UK urban and suburban areas with populations >10,000 people. Source: England, Scotland and Wales data is provided through EDINA UKBORDERS with the support of ESRC and JISC, and uses boundary material which is copyright of the Crown. Northern Ireland population statistics data was provided by Neighbourhood Statistics (NISRA): www.ninis.nisra.gov.uk. Crown copyright material is reproduced with permission of the Controller of HMSO. Northern Ireland spatial data is © Crown copyright and database rights.

Table 10.1 Urban areas: comparison of the extent of urban areas estimated from 'land-use' classification methods with 'population-based' classification methods. Source: data for land-use classification methods derived from the Land Cover Map 2000 (Fuller et al. 2002). Data for population-based area estimates for England, Scotland and Wales is provided through EDINA UKBORDERS with the support of ESRC and JISC, and uses boundary material which is copyright of the Crown. Northern Ireland population statistics data was provided by Neighbourhood Statistics (NISRA): www.ninis.nisra.gov.uk. Crown copyright material is reproduced with permission of the Controller of HMSO. Northern Ireland spatial data is © Crown copyright and database rights.

The LCM 2000 maps all built-up areas* ranging from a single building up to a city, based upon 25 m cells (Fuller et al. 2002). The urban areas zones map areas with populations >10,000[†] and their boundaries include a range of land use types. Although each country has developed mapping of the urban-rural typology (identifying areas with populations >10,000 people) the methods used to create the boundaries of the urban areas differ between the countries. In Northern Ireland mapped settlement zones have been delimited by the Planning Service and closely reflect the edges of the built-up areas of towns and cities. Within England and Wales, the urban-rural typology has been based upon mapped census boundaries named Output Areas (OA). The OA boundaries are designed to include a certain number of households and populations within an area, and differ in size between locations. The OAs range in size from very small areas to hundreds of hectares. Within Scotland, the urban-rural typology has been applied to mapped DataZones; each DataZone is based on a group of approximately five OAs. Due to these methods, the accuracy with which these mapped boundaries capture the perceived extent of urban areas differs between countries. The accuracy of boundary capture is highest in Northern Ireland, declines for England and Wales, and is lowest in Scotland. The result of these differences is such that, in Scotland, large areas of farmland or grassland will be present within areas classified as 'urban'.

It is a known limitation of the OA boundaries that they include significant areas where the boundary extends into the marine areas. The calculations presented here have excluded the areas returned for the extent of marine ecosystem within urban areas.

	Extent of Urban areas ('Built-up Areas')*		Extent of Urban areas (>10,000 population)[†]		Total area of country
	'000 ha	%	'000 ha	%	'000 ha
England	1,384	10.6	1,902	14.6	13,043
Northern Ireland	48	3.4	42	3.0	1,416
Scotland	152	1.9	240	3.0	7,871
Wales	87	4.2	164	7.9	2,081
UK	1,672	6.8	2,348	9.5	24,729

years by a massive restructuring of industry based on the decline of heavy industry and the growth of the services sector (deindustrialisation). By the late 1980s, however, suburbanisation had gradually come to a halt.

In more recent years and, in particular, due to the publication of the Report of the Urban Taskforce (DETR 1999), there has been a focus on urban regeneration within cities, with more than 60% of all new development occurring on Previously Developed Land (PDL, commonly termed 'brownfield'). The process of urban compaction and the designation of the 'Green Belt' in the fight against sprawl, together with housing policies, have increased density quite severely in some parts (DCLG 2010a). New build on all land types in London increased from 47 dwellings per hectare (dph) in 1989 to 121 dph in 2009 (48 dph to 122 dph on PDL). In other regions, increases were more modest, but rises from 23 dph and 21 dph (in 1989) to 43 dph and 34 dph (in 2009) were observed in the North West and East Midlands respectively (26 dph to 49 dph, and 23 dph to 37 dph on PDL (DCLG 2010b)). In addition, during the past decade, many large cities have developed extensive flatted accommodation in inner areas (Bibby 2009), which houses high population densities and provides little greenspace (**Figure 10.2**).

One of the most important distinctions within urban areas relates to spatial variation. The densest urban areas have the least open space, and all open space, including domestic gardens, strongly inversely correlates with density. Generally, there is good provision in the lowest density areas, with less greenspace in intermediate and higher density areas. Recent research has found that wards with fewer than 20 dph have three times as much greenspace

as wards in high density areas (CABE 2010). This issue of spatial variation is illustrated using data for Greater London (**Figure 10.3**).

Since the 1947 Town and Country Planning Acts, which were created over 70 years ago and established a universal planning system, there has been very little focus on the extent and condition of greenspace, although this has started to change in recent years.

Using the Broad Habitat criteria applied in other chapters of the UK NEA, Urban areas extend over approximately 6.8% of the UK, covering 1,672,000 ha (Fuller *et al.* 2002). In England, 10.6% of the land (1,384,000 ha) is classified as Urban, which compares with 4.2% of Wales (87,000 ha), 3.4% (48,000 ha) of Northern Ireland and 1.9% (152,000 ha) in Scotland (**Table 10.1**). The UK NEA classification of Urban areas is based on the LCM 2000 (Fuller *et al.* 2002) and is described as '*Built-up Areas and Gardens*' which includes rural development, roads, railways, waste and derelict ground (including vegetated wasteland), gardens and urban trees. Urban greenspace estimates are, however, hugely variable, ranging from 54% in the Generalised Land Use Database (England only[i]), which does not distinguish agricultural land within urban areas from other greenspace, to 14%, according to the National Audit Office (NAO 2006). This compares with an area of just 6.5% of accessible greenspace in a recent, but incomplete, study using a more detailed classification and consistent typologies (CABE 2010).

There is no single source of Urban greenspace data. It is, therefore, difficult to provide good estimates of extent and condition across the UK. To help illustrate this issue, and to explore the variation in extent data and classification of greenspace, we draw on four different data sources:

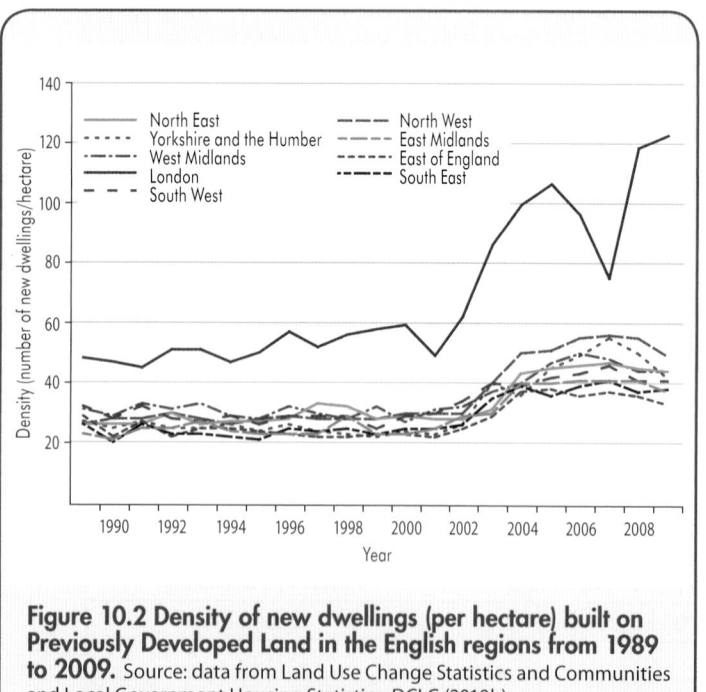

Figure 10.2 Density of new dwellings (per hectare) built on Previously Developed Land in the English regions from 1989 to 2009. Source: data from Land Use Change Statistics and Communities and Local Government Housing Statistics; DCLG (2010b).

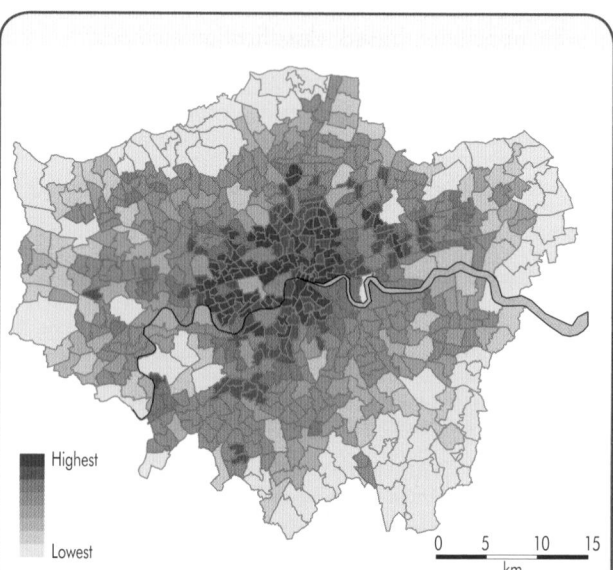

Figure 10.3 Population density in London in 2001. Dark green indicates highest densities and light green indicates lowest densities. Source: based on an analysis by Mike Batty, University College London, using 2001 Census data from the Office of National Statistics (ONS 2002).

1 However, Greenspace Scotland are currently mapping and categorising Scotland's Urban greenspace using aerial photography and have identified different types of greenspace in around two thirds of Scottish authorities. (Greenspace Scotland 2009; Figure 10.4). Plus, in Wales, in 2010, 18 of the 22 local authorities were working on complete assessments of the extent and location of accessible natural greenspace in their Urban areas (Chapter 20).

UK National Ecosystem Assessment: Technical Report

1. Inventory of individual greenspaces by the Commission for Architecture and the Built Environment (CABE 2010)

This inventory includes records for more than 16,000 individual greenspaces, covering 11 categories and using data from numerous sources collected specifically to try to quantify the extent of Urban greenspace (**Table 10.2**). Each record contains an estimate of size and geographic location. Although incomplete, this is the first time that these data have been collated into one database. They provide a useful indication of the extent of the various greenspace subhabitats in England. Calculated *per capita*, mean provision is given as 1.79 ha per 1,000 people, with variation between regions ranging from 2.86 ha per 1,000 people in the South East to 1.24 ha per 1,000 people in London.

2. Greenspace Strategies in England

Local authorities in England are currently required to develop Greenspace Strategies. The typology is not always consistent, and extent is often far lower than estimated by data from the Department of Communities and Local Government who include agricultural land (GLUD 2005) in their classification. However, these data provide an indication of the extent of subhabitats defined by local authorities as public greenspace.

Box 10.1 indicates that Greenspace Strategies for four randomly selected cities classified public greenspace (excluding domestic gardens) as extending over 17–24% of the urban area. The case studies illustrate that land use is highly variable; parks and gardens, natural and semi-natural greenspace, and outdoor sports facilities predominate in these areas.

Greenspace Strategies give an indication of *per capita* greenspace provision across the four chosen cities, but such data are not necessarily indicative of access to greenspace. For example, *per capita* greenspace provision is higher in Newcastle (8.42 ha per 1,000 people) than Coventry (5.68 ha per 1,000 people). Yet the single entity, Newcastle Town Moor, constitutes approximately 20% of total greenspace, and the distribution of the remaining greenspace is much less uniform than within Coventry. So, evenness, location and the implications for access need to be taken into account. Moreover, golf courses and school playing fields are included in the outdoor sports facilities category, but are generally not freely accessible to the public. This is important in an assessment because cultural benefits will largely arise where there is public access.

Local audits asking users for their views on the quality of greenspace in Newcastle and Coventry provide an indication of the variability of greenspace condition between and within greenspace categories. In Newcastle, public parks and cemeteries still open for burials typically achieved the highest quality ratings. Amenity greenspace, outdoor sports facilities and natural and semi-natural greenspace received the lowest scores (Newcastle City Council 2004). In Coventry, the country park and war memorial park achieved high scores, followed by neighbourhood parks. Incidental open spaces (mainly amenity greenspace) achieved the lowest scores (Coventry City Council 2008).

Table 10.2 CABE Space analysis of public Urban greenspace. Source: CABE (2010).

Greenspace type	Count	Area (ha)	Data
Allotments	997	1,356.8	Allotment sites 2004–2005
Cemeteries	1,643	3,679.1	Burial grounds 2006
Community farms	197	472.8	Community gardens and city farms 2004–2005
Country parks	72	5,765.9	Country parks
Doorstep greens	82	140.3	Doorstep greens
Golf courses	361	5,720.6	Golf courses
Grass pitches	10,243	8,170.4	Sport England/Fields in Trust
Millennium greens	91	164.5	Millennium greens
Nature reserves	663	14,308.0	National nature reserves; local nature reserves
Parks	1,770	52,243.2	Registered parks and gardens 2008; Public parks assessment; Green Flag parks 2006–2007
National Trust	128	14,537	National Trust
All types	**16,247**	**106,549.6**	

3. Generalised Land Use Database (GLUD) for England based on urban Output Areas covering nine land cover categories (2005)

According to this database, the extent of greenspace in the urban areas of each English region (54% on average across all regions) far exceeds other land use types (GLUD 2005; **Table 10.3**). However, it should be noted that urban agricultural land is included in the greenspace classification. Domestic gardens account for a further 18% of urban land use, and water accounts for an extra 6.6%; thus, 78.6% of urban areas is designated as natural rather than built. The other land use types are domestic and non-domestic buildings, roads, paths and railways.

At city level, a comparison of six cities reveals that the relative proportions of various types of space are remarkably similar to each other (**Table 10.4**), with an average of 12% buildings and 11% roads constituting 25% of the area. This can be compared with natural areas where domestic gardens average 21%, water 2% (excluding Liverpool which has a disproportionately high area of water due to the local authority boundary) and general greenspace averages 37% (excluding an unusually high 58% in Newcastle because it includes the Newcastle Town Moor). Even allowing for unclassified land and railways and paths, the total greenspace still exceeds 60% of the land cover in these six cities.

4. Greenspace Scotland (2009)

The first analysis of Urban (areas of more than 3,000 people with a 500 m buffer around the settlement area) greenspace extent in Scotland is estimated at 84,870 ha: 30% domestic gardens, 28% natural and semi-natural greenspace, 9% public parks, 15% amenity greenspace, 13% sports areas and 5% other (play spaces, allotments, green corridors, burial grounds and civic spaces) (Chapter 19). Spatial variation (**Figure 10.4**)

Box 10.1 Analysis of greenspace in four urban areas of England. Source: Coventry City Council (2008); Newcastle City Council (2004); Liverpool City Council (2005); Northampton Borough Council (2006). H Raper, Newcastle City Council, pers. comm.; N Barr, pers. comm.

Greenspace Strategies typically include some form of assessment of both the quantity and quality of greenspace within the city boundaries, as well as including recommendations on how Urban greenspace may be enhanced. In line with Planning Policy Guidance Note 17 (PPG17 2002), city councils have classified their Urban greenspace (see below) using locally derived typologies, hence caution should be exercised when making direct comparisons.

a) **Newcastle upon Tyne**
Population (2001 census): 259,536
Total area: 11,300 ha
Total area greenspace: 2,185 ha
Per capita provision: 8.42 ha/1,000

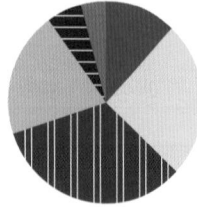

■ Public parks and gardens
□ Natural and semi-natural greenspace
▥ Outdoor sports facilities
▨ Amenity greenspace
▤ Allotments
■ Cemeteries and churchyards

c) **Coventry**
Population (2001 census): 300,848
Total area: 9,864 ha
Total area greenspace: 1,710 ha
Per capita provision: 5.68 ha/1,000

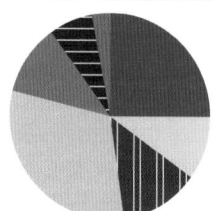

■ Public parks and gardens
□ Natural and semi-natural greenspace
▥ Outdoor sports facilities
▨ Incidental open space
▦ Principal open space
▤ Allotments
■ Cemeteries and churchyards

b) **Northampton**
Population (2001 census): 202,828
Total area: 8,076 ha
Total area greenspace: 1,403 ha
Per capita provision: 6.92 ha/1,000

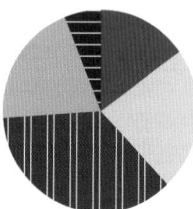

■ Public parks and gardens
□ Natural and semi-natural greenspace
▥ Outdoor sports facilities
▨ Amenity greenspace
▤ Allotments

d) **Liverpool**
Population (2001 census): 439,473
Total area: 11,184 ha
Total area greenspace: 2,648 ha
Per capita provision: 6.02 ha/1,000

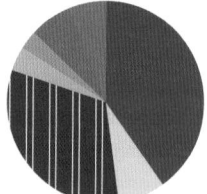

■ Public parks and gardens
□ Natural and semi-natural greenspace
▥ Outdoor sports facilities
▨ Amenity greenspace
▤ Allotments, community gardens and city farms
■ Cemeteries and churchyards
■ Green corridors

Table 10.3 Generalised Land Use Database (GLUD) for England: proportion of urban land by region. Source: data from GLUD (2005).

Region	Domestic buildings %	Non-domestic buildings %	Roads %	Paths %	Rail %	Domestic gardens %	Greenspace %	Water %	Other land %
East Midlands	4.6	2.6	6.9	0.4	0.4	15.9	62.7	1.7	4.7
East of England	4.7	2.4	6.7	0.5	0.4	16.9	59.1	4.3	5.0
London	9.3	5.0	13.0	0.8	1.1	25.4	34.4	2.9	8.0
North East	5.6	3.0	9.4	0.8	0.8	14.3	57.4	3.2	5.5
North West	5.4	3.1	8.9	0.6	0.6	15.9	50.2	9.8	5.5
South East	5.1	2.3	7.5	0.5	0.4	19.9	55.1	4.4	4.8
South West	5.5	2.7	7.6	0.6	0.4	18.4	55.9	3.8	5.4
West Midlands	6.1	3.7	9.1	0.7	0.5	21.8	50.9	1.2	6.2
Yorkshire and The Humber	5.1	3.0	8.5	0.5	0.7	16.3	58.4	2.0	5.5
England: rural and urban combined (Total)	**1.1**	**0.65**	**2.22**	**0.1**	**0.13**	**4.26**	**87.46**	**2.59**	**1.39**

Table 10.4 Proportion of built to greenspace in Urban environments (based on local authority boundaries). Source: data from GLUD (2005).

City	Buildings (domestic & non-domestic) %	Roads %	Domestic gardens %	Greenspace* %	Water %	Other (paths, railways, unclassified) %
Birmingham	14	12	29	34	1	10
London	13	12	24	38	3	10
Newcastle upon Tyne	9	10	13	58	2	8
Northampton	11	11	21	46	3	8
Coventry	12	11	22	44	1	11
Liverpool	10	11	15	23	32	9

* Farmland is included in Urban greenspace classification.

and accessibility are important factors in the provision of greenspace. Inner city greenspace in central Edinburgh is low (2.66 ha per 1,000 people) compared with the whole of Edinburgh (4.25 ha per 1,000 people) and the urban mean (16 ha per 1,000 people). However, 82% of people in the city centre can access a greenspace within 400 m of their home (**Figure 10.5**). Overall, 50–70% of all Urban greenspace in Scotland is considered accessible.

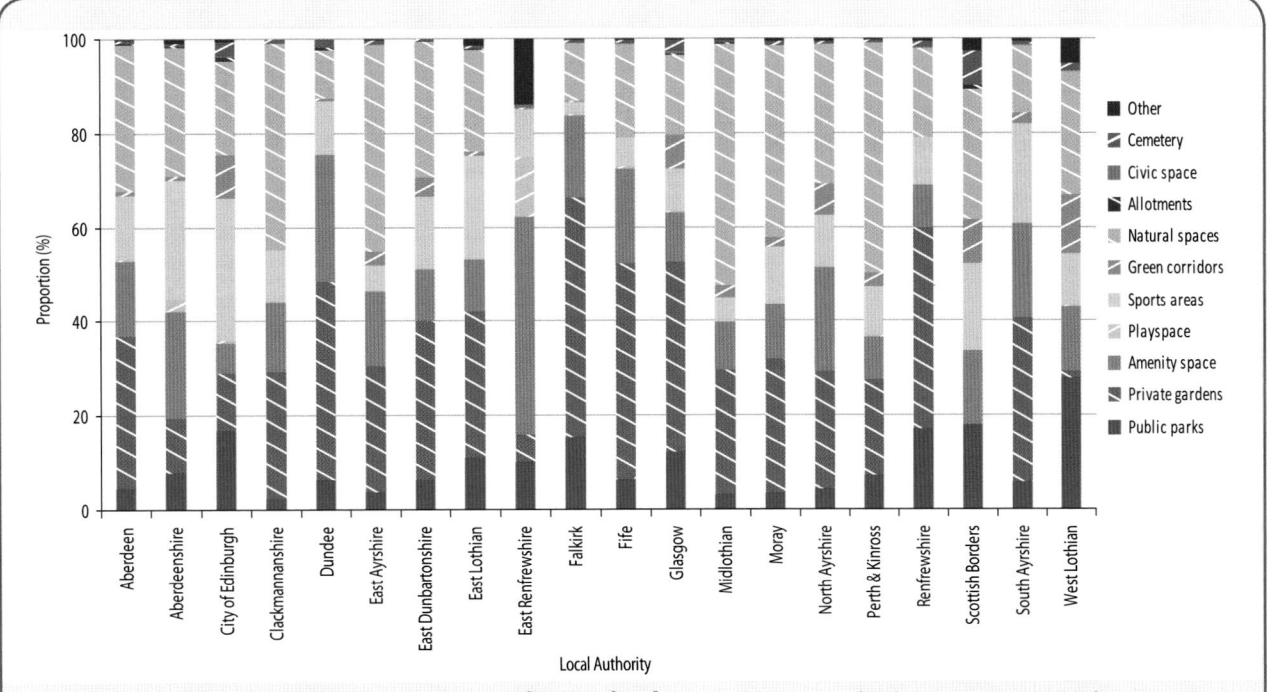

Figure 10.4 Urban greenspace composition within Scotland. The composition of Urban greenspace within 20 reporting local authorities in Scotland has been comprehensively categorised mainly using the Planning Advice Note: PAN 65 Planning and Open Space (PAN 65) typology. This work has shown both the variation in Urban greenspace composition throughout Scotland and the intra-urban heterogeneity of greenspace composition and access (e.g. the dichotomy between central and western Edinburgh's greenspace). Source: reproduced from Greenspace Scotland (2009).

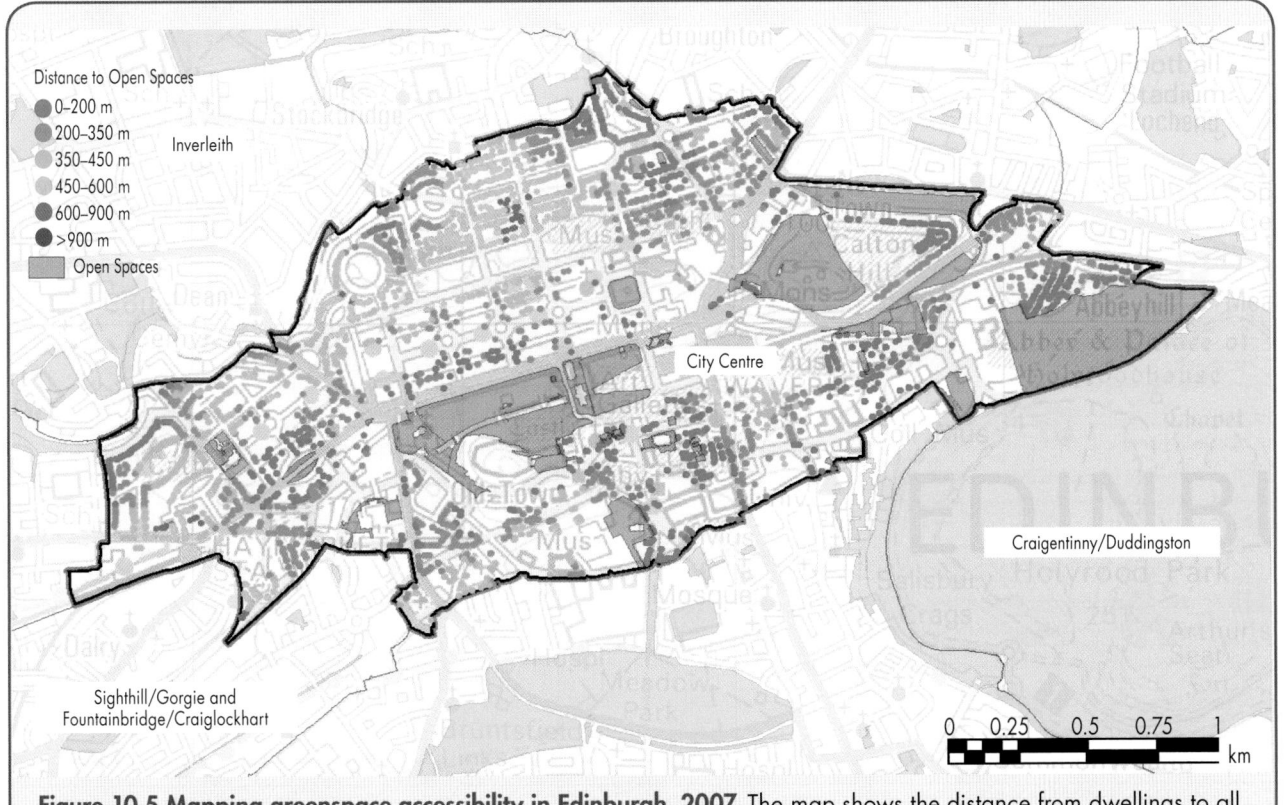

Figure 10.5 Mapping greenspace accessibility in Edinburgh, 2007. The map shows the distance from dwellings to all significant accessible open spaces. Source: reproduced from Greenspace Scotland (2009).

10.1.4 Urban Land Use Classification for the UK NEA

This chapter identifies a range of different Urban land uses, referred to here as Urban subhabitats, that provide ecosystem services (**Table 10.5**). As far as possible, we apply land use typology defined by Planning Policy Guidance Note 17: Planning for Open Space, Sport and Recreation (PPG17 2002), Planning Advice Note: PAN 65 Planning and Open Space (PAN 65 2008) and Planning Policy Statement 8: Open Space, Sport and Outdoor Recreation (PPS8 2004), which categorise open

Table 10.5 Comparison of the Urban subhabitat classification used in the UK NEA (with a focus on provision of ecosystem services) and in local authorities' planning guidance in England and Wales (Planning Policy Guidance Note 17 (PPG17 2002)), in Scotland (Planning Advice Note 65 (PAN 65 2008)) and in Northern Ireland (Planning Policy Statement 8: Open Space, Sport and Outdoor Recreation (PPS8 2004)).

UK NEA Urban subhabitat	What the subhabitat includes	PPG17 (England and Wales)	PAN 65 (Scotland)	PPS8 (Northern Ireland)
Natural and semi-natural greenspace (woodlands, SSSIs, urban forestry, scrub)		**Natural and semi-natural urban greenspaces**—including woodlands, urban forestry, scrub, grasslands (e.g. downlands, commons and meadows), wetlands, open and running water, wastelands and derelict open land, and rock areas (e.g. cliffs, quarries and pits).	**Natural and semi-natural urban greenspaces**—woodland, open semi-natural and open water.	**Natural and semi-natural urban green spaces**—including woodlands, urban forestry, grasslands (e.g. meadows), wetlands, open and running water, and rock areas (e.g. cliffs).
Street trees	Single trees and small areas with scattered trees, often surrounded by paved ground.	*Not listed in PPG17*	*Not listed in PAN 65*	*Not listed in PPS8*
Public parks and formal gardens		**Parks and gardens**—including urban parks, country parks and formal gardens.	**Public parks and gardens**	**Parks and gardens**—including urban parks, country parks, forest parks and formal gardens.
Domestic gardens		*Covered under amenity greenspace.*	**Private gardens or grounds**—private gardens, school grounds and institutional grounds.	*Not listed in PPS8*
Green corridors	Verges and hedges, river and canal banks, cycleways, and rights of way.	Including river and canal banks, cycleways and rights of way.	Green access routes and riparian routes.	Including river and canal banks, amenity footpaths and cycleways.
Outdoor sports facilities and recreational areas	Sports facilities such as golf courses, football pitches, athletics tracks, school and other institutional playing fields, and other outdoor sports facilities (largely grassland).	**Outdoor sports facilities** (with natural or artificial surfaces and either publicly or privately owned)—including tennis courts, bowling greens, sports pitches, golf courses, athletics tracks, school and other institutional playing fields, and other outdoor sports areas. **Provision for children and teenagers**—including play areas, skateboard parks, outdoor basketball hoops, and other more informal areas (e.g. 'hanging out' areas, teenage shelters).	**Playspace for children and teenagers**—playspace. **Sports areas**—playing fields, golf courses, tennis courts, bowling greens and other sports.	**Outdoor sports facilities** (with natural or artificial surfaces and either publicly or privately owned)—including tennis courts, bowling greens, sport pitches, golf courses, athletics tracks, school and other institutional playing fields, and other outdoor sports areas. **Provision for children and teenagers**—including play areas, kickabout areas, skateboard parks and outdoor basketball hoops.
Amenity greenspace	Most commonly, but not exclusively, in housing areas—including informal recreation spaces, greenspaces in and around housing.	Most commonly, but not exclusively, in housing areas—including informal recreation spaces, greenspaces in and around housing, domestic gardens and village greens.	Amenity—residential Amenity—business Amenity—transport	Most commonly, but not exclusively, in housing areas—including informal recreation spaces, communal greenspaces in and around housing, and village greens.
Allotments, community gardens and urban farms	Includes arable farmland and orchards.	**Allotments, community gardens, and city (urban) farms.**	**Allotments and community growing spaces**—allotments and community growing spaces.	**Allotments and community gardens**
Cemeteries, churchyards and burial grounds		**Cemeteries and churchyards**	**Burial grounds**—churchyards and cemeteries.	**Cemeteries and churchyards**
Previously Developed Land (brownfield) but not including domestic gardens	Derelict, contaminated and vacant land.	*Not listed in PPG17*	*Not listed in PAN 65*	*Not listed in PPS8*
Water	Includes natural and artificial e.g. rivers, streams, groundwater, lakes, wetlands, ponds, ditches, canals, reservoirs.	*Covered under natural and semi-natural urban greenspace.*	*Covered under natural and semi-natural urban greenspaces.*	*"Open space is taken to mean all open space of public value, including not just land, but also inland bodies of water such as rivers, canals, lakes and reservoirs which offer important opportunities for sport and outdoor recreation and can also act as a visual amenity" (PPS8 2004)*
Peri-urban		Accessible countryside in urban fringe areas. Green belt.		

space. In order to differentiate between different ecosystem services, it has been necessary to further define some of these definitions; for example, street trees can provide different services from woodlands. It should be noted that the term greenspace is used throughout this chapter to collectively represent the subhabitats, including water.

Ecosystem services arising from the built infrastructure are not quantified, but it is recognised as an important habitat, particularly for birds. It also provides extensive surfaces for vegetation such as roof gardens and window boxes.

10.1.5 Interaction with other UK NEA Broad Habitats

To a greater or lesser extent, all UK NEA Broad Habitats interact with the Urban environment. Enclosed Farmland (Chapter 7), Semi-natural Grassland (Chapter 6) and Woodlands are the most extensive, with the latter constituting a significant part of the peri-urban Green Belt. The lowest interaction occurs with Freshwaters— Openwaters, Wetlands and Floodplains (Chapter 9), which is followed by Coastal Margins (Chapter 11) (LCM 2000). Areas of UK NEA Broad Habitats that are more than 5 km² and fall within urban boundaries are illustrated in **Table 10.6**.

Urban populations draw heavily on external resources for provisioning and other ecosystem services. They export considerable solid and liquid waste (largely contained) and release pollution emissions to air, water and land that extend far beyond the urban boundary (Luck *et al.* 2001). The ecological footprint of urban areas is widely recognised. Urban areas also export visitors to other habitats, giving rise to associated transport pressures (pollution and infrastructure). The ecological footprint of the UK is discussed more fully in Chapter 21.

A large part of Urban and peri-urban greenspace is designated as Green Belt (**Figure 10.6**). The fundamental aim of Green Belt policy is to prevent urban sprawl, and shape patterns of development, by keeping land permanently open. In so doing, Green Belts protect countryside and incidentally help to secure nature conservation interest (Planning Policy Guidance Note 2: Green Belts (PPG2 1995)). Green Belts were first designed to be used in association with growth in large cities and the development of new towns, which were located at some distance from the city, beyond its Green Belt. This was a principle of planning policy in the UK in the mid to late 20th Century, and, in many senses, remnants of that policy still exist today. Current planning policy for England is expressed in Planning Policy Guidance Note 2 as follows (PPG2 1995, amended 2001):

- to check the unrestricted sprawl of large built up areas;
- to prevent neighbouring towns from merging into one another;
- to assist in safeguarding the countryside from encroachment;
- to preserve the setting and special character of historic towns;

Table 10.6 The extent of UK NEA Broad Habitats within Urban areas with a population >10,000. Source: extent of UK NEA Broad Habitats estimated from the Land Cover Map 2000 (Fuller *et al.* 2002). Extent of Urban areas with a population >10,000 for England, Scotland and Wales is provided through EDINA UKBORDERS with the support of ESRC and JISC, and uses boundary material which is copyright of the Crown. Northern Ireland population statistics data was provided by Neighbourhood Statistics (NISRA): www.ninis. nisra.gov.uk. Crown copyright material is reproduced with permission of the Controller of HMSO. Northern Ireland spatial data is © Crown copyright and database rights.

Each country has developed mapping of the urban-rural typology (identifying areas with populations >10,000 people). The methods used to create the boundaries of the urban areas differ between the countries. In Northern Ireland mapped settlement zones have been delimited by the Planning Service and closely reflect the edges of the built up areas of towns and cities. Within England and Wales the urban-rural typology has been based upon mapped census boundaries named Output Areas (OA). The OA boundaries are designed to include a certain number of households and populations within an area, and differ in size between locations. The OAs range in size from very small areas to hundreds of hectares. Within Scotland, the urban-rural typology has been applied to mapped DataZones; each DataZone is based on a group of approx five OAs. The accuracy of boundary capture is highest in Northern Ireland, declines for England and Wales, and is lowest in Scotland. The result of these differences is such that, in Scotland, large areas of farmland or grassland areas will be present within areas classified as 'urban'.

UK NEA Broad Habitat	England Area ('000 ha)	England % of total Urban area	Northern Ireland Area ('000 ha)	Northern Ireland % of total Urban area	Scotland Area ('000 ha)	Scotland % of total Urban area	Wales Area ('000 ha)	Wales % of total Urban area	UK Area ('000 ha)	UK % of total Urban area
Mountains, Moorlands & Heaths	34	1.8	3	6.8	19	7.8	14	8.5	69	2.9
Semi-natural Grasslands	189	10	4	10.1	36	15	26	15.9	256	10.9
Enclosed Farmland	582	30.6	11	25.1	73	30.6	47	28.8	713	30.4
Woodlands	164	8.6	1	3.5	28	11.5	22	13.2	215	9.2
Freshwaters – Open water, Wetlands & Floodplains	13	0.7	0	0.5	2	0.9	1	0.5	16	0.7
Urban	826	43.4	21	49.7	76	31.5	41	25.1	963	41
Coastal Margins	42	2.2	0	0.6	1	0.4	9	5.4	52	2.2

	Areal extent of Green Belt ('000 ha)	Areal extent of country ('000 ha)	% Green Belt in country
England	1,983	13,043	15.2
Northern Ireland	336	1,416	23.7
Scotland	143	7,871	1.8
Wales	3	2,081	0.1
UK	2,465	24,729	10.0

■ Green Belt land

Figure 10.6 Designated Green Belt land in the UK in 2009. Source: data derived from Defra (England), Department of the Environment Northern Ireland (Northern Ireland), Scottish Natural Heritage (Scotland), and Newport Council (Wales). The data for England and Scotland are Copyright Landmark Information Group.

■ and to assist with urban regeneration, by encouraging the recycling of derelict and other urban land.

Green Belts have succeeded in preserving openness and areas of countryside around large cities, as well as providing cultural and provisioning services for urban dwellers (Natural England & CPRE 2010; Scottish Government 2004).

10.1.6 Indicators of Change of the Urban Environment and its Potential for Delivering Ecosystem Services

Existing indicators of relevance to ecosystem goods and services can be classified into five broad groups:

1. Urban population size and other social and demographic data (DCLG: ONS).
2. Land use (DCLG: GLUD).

3. Biodiversity (Sustainability Indicators, e.g. urban bird populations; Countryside Survey, see Carey *et al.* 2008; State of the UK's Birds, see Eaton *et al.* 2010).
4. Regulating Services (DCLG: Sustainability Indicators)
5. Cultural Services (DCLG: GLUD; CABE).

Urban ecosystem-specific indicators can be developed from selected, existing indicator scales (1–5), but will need additional indicators to reflect the special nature of the Urban habitat.

Community interest in the state of the environment could be harnessed through a programme of public recording schemes, drawing on expertise developed through projects such as single species sightings (Harlequin Ladybird Survey 2010), ecological surveys (OPAL 2010; Davies *et al.* 2011) and garden bird and wetland surveys (RSPB 2010; WWT 2010). Community participation data from voluntary services, such as 'Friends of Parks', are also relevant (Thornton 2009).

10.2 Trends and Changes in Urban Subhabitats and Associated Abiotic and Biotic Processes

In this section, we present data from a range of sources on the extent, condition and accessibility of the UK NEA Urban subhabitats (identified in **Table 10.5**), from post-war to the present day. Priority is given to national datasets, which are scarce, so additional examples are drawn from various publications based on regional and local studies. Caution is required in data interpretation due to the broad classifications used by some organisations resulting in overlap and duplication. More importantly, the various approaches applied by the different responsible authorities and charities mean that it is not possible to compare data between Urban subhabitats. Trend data are also uncertain due to boundary changes and the differing typologies used.

Each town and city is unique, so it is difficult to make general statements based on this synthesis of published information. Data provided in this report merely give an indication of the extent and condition of greenspaces and physical processes that collectively form the Urban environment; but some trends have emerged that can help to inform the process of assessment and contribute to the valuation of the essential ecosystem goods and services that Urban habitats deliver.

The main drivers of change are identified at the beginning of each subsection. Social and demographic change and economic development are major forces, with policies on planning, housing and transport having the greatest impact on ecosystem services and goods derived from the Urban environment.

Over the past 60 years, there has been a steady increase in the UK's population, of which, a large percentage now lives in urban areas (ONS 2005). Demographic change, commercial growth, new housing and transport needs greatly contribute to the increasing extent of non-permeable surfaces and pollution, associated with which is the loss of regulating and provisioning services and important cultural benefits (Section 10.3). More recently, climate change has become a major driver. Other drivers include market forces, particularly interest in food provision and organic products which are becoming of increasing importance. Recognition of the impact of urbanisation on other habitats nationally and globally, and policies on sustainable development in particular, are stimulating new schemes within urban areas for recycling, local waste management and renewable energy.

10.2.1 Natural and Semi-natural Greenspaces (Woodlands, SSSIs, Urban Forestry and Scrub)

Following a study of landscape character in the 1990s, deterioration in the condition of woodland in Scotland was attributed to neglect (SNH 2004). In England, however, the principle drivers of woodland condition decline (based on data collected from woodlands classified as SSSIs) are inadequate or inappropriate management, and grazing or browsing by deer (Natural England 2008). In comparison, factors contributing to a decline in the condition of Urban SSSIs are more varied due to the broad range of habitats they encompass and include under-grazing, inappropriate scrub control and coastal squeeze (Natural England 2008).

In the case of woodland SSSIs in London, in particular, deer do not seem to be causing damage at their current density (taking SSSI condition as a proxy measure); nevertheless, deer populations do appear to be growing in Urban habitats and may well become a problem in the future (S. Lyme, Natural England pers. comm.).

The extent of Urban woodland as a percentage of the total urban area is calculated at 11.3% for the whole of the UK, with 8.7% in England, 13.1% in Wales, 11.5% in Scotland and 3.3% in Northern Ireland (LCM 2000). This is not dissimilar to the 12% coverage of Woodland across the entire UK (Chapter 8). Over 15% of people in Scotland have access to a woodland more than 2 ha in size and within 500 m of their home, and around 55% have access to a woodland more than 20 ha in size within 4 km of their home (Woodland Trust 2004). In England, 50% of the population is estimated to have access to a woodland more than 20 ha in size within 4 km of their home (Defra 2006b); the same is true for Northern Ireland (50%), whereas, in Wales, 70% of the population has equivalent woodland access.

Data to assess trends and condition at UK level have not been located, so Urban woodlands are reviewed using two case studies. The first, from Scotland, documents a decline in broadleaved woodland from the 1940s to 1980s (SNH 2001) mainly due to replacement by conifers. Following a landscape character study in the 1990s, and in recognition of the cultural value of woodlands, a government-funded programme of expansion in, or in close proximity to, urban areas was established and has since proved hugely

Box 10.2 The National Forest. Source: the National Forest Company (2010).

Led by the National Forest Company and involving numerous partners, The National Forest is a initiative that is creating a new Forest for the nation across 200 square miles of the Midlands. Woodland creation is enhancing rural, urban and former coalfield landscapes. Tree planting has been particularly successful in and around the Forest's towns: Burton upon Trent, Swadlincote, Ashby de la Zouch and Coalville. This is achieving multi-purpose benefits including landscape and biodiversity enhancement, creating new places for recreation, carbon sequestration and community involvement. Schemes which the National Forest is initiating include:

- Urban Forest Parks—created at Swadlincote Woodlands (30 ha) and Coalville (15 ha) on former derelict land.
- Woodland 'pocket parks'—in residential neighbourhoods and hospital grounds.
- Sponsored woodland—including the Burton Mail Centenary Woodland and Jaguar Lount Woodland, east of Ashby.
- Urban fringe woodlands—created through farm diversification.
- Development-related and roadside tree planting.
- Community projects—including community orchards, school grounds tree planting, plus the National Forest Company's Plant a Tree, Free Trees for Gardens, and Grow a Tree from Seed schemes.

Around 20,000 people and 40,000 school children are involved in the Forest's creation each year. Key challenges to increasing urban woodland include the availability and cost of land, development 'hope value', avoiding underground services, having an effective catalyst to lead activity, and achieving joined-up working between the public, private and voluntary sectors, landowners and civil society.

Environmental education session at Conkers Discovery Centre, Derbyshire. *Photo courtesy of Christopher Beech/National Forest Company.*

successful (Greenspace Scotland 2010). A basic standard was established of one hectare per 500 people living within five miles of the site. The first planting scheme involved 51 community groups in the development and maintenance of 64 sites covering 22,000 ha. Woodlands were mainly located within the urban belt and averaged 58 ha in size.

The second example is from London. Extent data is taken from a survey in 1993 (GLA 2005b) which estimated that there were seven million trees in London, two thirds of which were located within domestic gardens. Of those remaining, 25% were classified as woodland, making up 8% of London's greenspace. A later survey in 2000 (Forestry Commission 2003) recorded 3.9% (6,204 ha) of London as woodland (up from 3.8% in 1993), with 592 small woodlands less than 2 ha in size and 621 more than 2 ha. Broadleaved woodland dominated with oak as the main species. About 70% of London woodlands were owned by local authorities. Dense woodland (more than 40 trees per hectare) tended to be concentrated on the outskirts of the city, with the exception of a few very important SSSIs.

There are about 600 SSSIs (less than 4% of the total number) within or near urban areas in England, covering about 39,000 ha (Natural England 2009). Trends in Urban SSSI condition from 2003 to 2010 suggest that progress towards the England Biodiversity Strategy objective of increasing the proportion of SSSIs in favourable or recovering condition is being made. The September 2003 baseline assessment reported that 67% of the total area of Urban SSSIs were in a favourable or recovering condition; by March 2009, this had increased to 80%, with figures from March 2010 recorded as 83.6% (Natural England 2009, 2010 unpublished).

The term 'urban forest' was not introduced into the UK until the 1980s and was followed by the country's first city-wide urban forestry project—the Forest of London project. Since then, a number of similar projects and Community Forests in metropolitan areas have been established, which aim to provide a broad range of social, environmental and economic benefits to urban communities. Lately, the health and well-being aspects of these benefits are receiving growing interest (O'Brien et al. 2010; see Chapter 23).

More recent initiatives focusing on urban and community forestry include the Black Country Urban Forest in England (BBCWT 2010), the TreeGeneration programme in Wrexham and Flintshire in North East Wales (Forestry Commission 2010), Woodlands in and Around Towns in Scotland (Forestry Commission Scotland 2010), and Northern Ireland's Forest of Belfast partnership (Belfast City Council 2010). One further example is The National Forest in central England (**Box 10.2**), which aims to increase the area of multi-purpose woodland close to towns and cities; it is having very good success in this respect.

10.2.2 Street Trees

Drivers of change in the condition and extent of street trees (not woodlands) are unclear. Tree campaigns that occurred during the 1980s appear to be responsible for the increased plantings at that time, but have not been maintained (DCLG 2008b). Current recognition of the regulatory (particularly climate-based) and cultural services that street trees can provide is generating renewed interest in plantings. Climate change is however also identified as a potential threat to Urban trees through possible increases in pests and diseases (Tubby & Webber 2010).

Data on Urban trees are taken from two surveys carried out in 1992/3 and 2004/5 (DoE 1993; DCLG 2008b). They are distinguished from woodlands, which are covered separately, but some overlap is inevitable. In England, Urban trees are found mainly on private land, with 66% occurring in gardens, schools, churchyards and allotments. A further 20% grow in public parks and open spaces, and 12% are street trees. Town size does not appear to influence tree density (DCLG 2008b). The survey data also provide evidence of temporal trends since 1992, suggesting a regional increase in tree density in South East and South West England, with proportionate increases in street trees in residential areas; there is no obvious explanation for such trends.

Although 70% of Urban street trees surveyed in 2004/5 were in good condition, a comparison with the 1992/3 data suggests that there has been an overall decline in this status; however, there has also been a decrease in the percentage of trees considered poor, dead or dying, so caution is advised when interpreting recent trends in Urban tree condition. It is clear that between 1992 and 2005 there was a relative decline in the quality of trees in town centres, compared to those in surrounding residential areas (DCLG 2008b).

10.2.3 Public Parks and Formal Gardens

Parks and greenspaces are not a statutory service that local authorities are legally obliged to provide. Funding cuts and skills shortages have led to a significant decline in their quality in recent decades (Urban Greenspaces Taskforce 2002). Since the introduction of the Green Flag Awards in England and Wales (1996), and Scotland (2006), and other initiatives to improve parks and the use of greenspace by local communities (NAO 2006; Big Lottery Fund 2008; Heritage Lottery Fund 2008), conditions have improved; however, improvements have not been shared equally (CABE 2010). The main driver of improvements has been recognition of the importance of parks for health and well-being.

The Urban Parks Forum's (UPFOR 2001) Public Park Assessment identified 27,000 parks covering 121,953 ha located in the top 100 deprived areas of the UK, which are predominantly in cities and towns. Of this area, 19,527 ha (16%) were designated as of national historic importance and 19,945 ha (16.3%) as of local historic importance. Of all the parks assessed, 13% were considered to be in poor condition (obvious signs of decay), 69% in fair condition (adequate condition with repairs likely to be made in the near future), and 18% in good condition (thriving and well-managed). A more recent study reported improvements in condition, but observed that more needed to be done (NAO 2006). Deprived areas systematically fare worse in nearly all respects, particular in terms of park quantity, quality and level of use (CABE 2010).

Public parks have been the focus of various studies of Urban biodiversity (Gavareski 1976; Faeth & Kane 1978; Luniak 1981; Sasvári 1984). This continues to be a major theme (Suhonen & Jokimäki 1988; Jokimäki 1999; Morneau et al. 1999; Fernández-Juricic 2000, 2001; Fernández-Juricic & Jokimäki 2001; Platt & Lill 2006), motivated principally by the fact that parks typically constitute the largest continuous areas of greenspace in urban areas, so are important contributors to Urban morphology. By definition, they are readily accessible for purposes of data collection, and represent an important point of interaction between people and biodiversity. They have been likened to a series of valuable 'islands' for biodiversity in a less hospitable landscape, leading to suggestions that island biogeography theory may be relevant. Indeed, some of the principal ecological patterns associated with this theory have been found to apply to Urban parks, with species richness commonly increasing with area (Faeth & Kane 1978; Sasvári 1984; Jokimäki 1999; Fernández-Juricic 2000; Fernández-Juricic & Jokimäki 2001) and patterns of species composition being highly nested (Fernández-Juricic & Jokimäki 2001). However, in most urban areas in England, at least, this viewpoint seems inappropriate for a lot of species groups because the landscape matrix in which Urban parks are embedded comprises extensive networks of other kinds of greenspaces (e.g. allotments, cemeteries and domestic gardens).

Some Urban parks have experienced large temporal changes in species composition; this is an important consideration in understanding how biodiversity changes with their structure. For example, from 1947 to 1994, Pelham Bay Park, the second largest park in New York City, lost 25% of the native plant species, while the number of non-native plant species increased by 40% (DeCandido 2004).

10.2.4 Domestic Gardens

The main drivers negatively affecting the extent of domestic gardens include demographic change leading to an increase in housing demand (more flats and smaller gardens, particularly on PDL), and an increase in the paving of front gardens. An additional pressure arises from the introduction into gardens of invasive species. These can take many forms, but include pests and diseases that can have substantial negative effects. This may be compounded by the fact that climate change is predicted to lead to further increases in pests and diseases (Gates 2002; Wilby & Perry 2006). However, the popularity of gardening, particularly horticulture (including exotic species) and food production, together with the need to provide safe play areas, continue to drive the market for homes with gardens.

The extent of both urban and rural domestic gardens in England was reported at just over 4% (564,500 ha) of total land cover (GLUD 2005; **Table 10.3**). Data from other sources (Bibby 2009) suggest that Urban gardens cover an average of 13% of the Urban landscape. Our case studies (GLUD 2005) show the substantial variability of extent by city: Newcastle 13% (1,500 ha), Northampton 21% (1,700 ha), Coventry 22% (2,200 ha) and Liverpool 15% (2,400 ha). Liverpool gardens cover the largest area, but due to the inclusion of water (37%) within the GLUD classification, the percentage of land designated as garden appears proportionately low. London and Birmingham both averaged 25%. In Scotland, 30% of all Urban greenspace is classified as domestic garden. The size of gardens varies with housing type (Smith et al. 2005) and is associated with the occurrence and extent of different land cover types within their bounds and the occurrence

of different features of relevance to biodiversity (e.g. trees, ponds) (Smith et al. 2005). There is limited available information on the condition of domestic gardens because they are not under local authority control.

The importance of these areas in the provision of habitats for the large numbers of species that they can harbour has long been acknowledged (Davis 1978; Owen 1991). Recent studies have shown that the richness and abundance of garden species respond both to characteristics of the gardens themselves (e.g. area, management) and to the nature of the landscape matrix in which they are embedded (e.g. cover by greenspace, housing density and type of housing) (Davis 1978; Smith et al. 2006a, 2006b, 2006c). The relative weighting of these two sets of factors tends to be determined, in part, by the dispersal characteristics of the species concerned, with better dispersers being more strongly influenced by the broader context in which individual gardens are placed.

The composition of Urban domestic gardens is poorly understood, but survey data from Sheffield estimated that 14.4% contained ponds, 26% had nest boxes, 29% had compost heaps and 48% had trees more than 3 m tall (Gaston et al. 2005). The Garden Bird Watch and Garden Nesting surveys of the British Trust for Ornithology (BTO) are helping to quantify the avian biodiversity of UK gardens (BTO 2010). Although such findings may not be indicative of private gardens throughout the UK, they suggest that this highly heterogeneous Urban subhabitat is likely to provide a wide range of ecosystem-derived goods and benefits that are particularly important for pollination services (Section 10.3). However, gardens also typically comprise a large number of non-native species, some of which may be considered invasive and a potential threat to ecosystem goods and services (Reichard & White 2001).

One particular trend that negatively affects ecosystem services is the increase in paving over front gardens. Aerial photographs from 1971 to 2004 were used to map changes in the impervious cover of a 1.16 km² suburban area of Leeds, England. A 13% increase in impervious surfaces was observed over the 33-year study period. Of the increase in impervious surfaces, 75% was due to paving of residential front gardens (Perry & Nawaz 2008). In London, an estimated 3,200 ha of front gardens have been covered in surfacing other than vegetation (i.e. paving, concrete, bricks and gravel)—this represents a loss of a significant percentage of domestic gardens in the area (based on GLUD 2005 data) in order to enable parking (GLA 2005a) and to provide further housing (infilling). This action has resulted in less percolation and increased runoff. Evidence suggests that the paving of front gardens is highest in North East England and Scotland, where 47% and 31% of front gardens are more than three quarters paved respectively (RHS 2006). Policies have been introduced to curb the trend in paving (e.g. Amendment No. 2 of the Town and Country Planning Act 2008) and to stop infilling. Gardens are no longer classified as PDL and housing density caps have been lifted (Barclay 2010).

10.2.5 Green Corridors

One of the major drivers of change for green corridors has been the recent recognition of their importance as transport links and wildlife dispersal aids. This has led to their integration into planning and conservation policy in 2010 through their inclusion in the UK BAP as Open Mosaic Habitats.

Green corridors are generally poorly quantified by local authorities making their extent and condition difficult to assess. There is evidence of increased use of these ribbons of land in terms of recognising their intrinsic wildlife value and their importance as public pathways that join greenspaces across large regions, thus providing valuable cultural benefits to local people and visitors (Wilby & Perry 2006). In Birmingham, the wildlife conservation strategy, published in 1997 (BCC 1997) was explicitly built around the corridor concept. Since then, the management of wildlife in the city has relied heavily on corridors as strategic planning tools. In London, the South East London Green Chain extends over 40 miles linking 300 open spaces across the area (London Borough of Bexley 2009). Green Grids, networks of attractive and accessible greenspaces that can link inner urban areas to rural areas, are also being used more widely in planning to improve accessibility and promote a broad range of benefits through multifunctional land use, as illustrated by the Thames Gateway Green Grid development in South East England (Section 10.5.1).

Hedges are natural features of green corridors that can provide a route for dispersing wildlife; as such, they are recognised for their habitat importance (Defra 2007a). Data on Urban hedge extent were not located although privet (*Ligustrum* spp.) is identified as the mostly widely planted urban hedge species.

10.2.6 Outdoor Sports Facilities, Recreational Areas and Amenity Greenspace

These subhabitats can include a broad range of greenspaces (**Table 10.5**). Amenity greenspace includes play parks and sports facilities but can also be just small patches of ground. Consistent datasets were not identified. Large areas of grassland (more than 5 km²) are covered under Chapter 6, other grassland areas are covered here under 'playing fields and parks'.

During the 1980s, many playing fields were sold to developers and other land users. But since the importance of

these facilities for good childhood development, education, and community cohesion (cultural benefits) was recognised, the decline in these facilities has generally halted. In recent years, funding from local authorities, charities and the Big Lottery Fund has contributed to improvements in outdoor play provision for young people.

Trends in extent and condition are limited, although it is estimated that 10,000 playing fields were sold between 1979 and 1997 (DCMS 2009). A significant proportion of local authority-designated greenspace is classified as outdoor sports facilities (e.g. Coventry 13%, Liverpool 32%, Newcastle upon Tyne 33% and Northampton 33%), but has variable quality and access. A total of 10,243 sports pitches, covering 8,170 ha, were reported in Urban areas (CABE 2010).

Fields in Trust recently commissioned research to assess the provision of outdoor play and recreational facilities in the UK (FIT & NPFA 2008). The report reviews the attainment of The Six Acre Standard (SAS) of accessibility to outdoor sport and play space by 147 local authorities around the UK, but does not provide extent or condition data. Results from the survey indicate that about 70% of local authorities refer to, use or have adopted the SAS in their plans. This means that, in England, playing pitches are provided within 1.2 km of urban dwellings, other outdoor sport facilities within a 20–30 minute drive, and children's playing spaces within 100–1,000 m walking distance from home (FIT & NPFA 2008). These data are compared with the recommendations in the SAS in **Table 10.7**.

Extensive data from Northern Ireland suggests that provision is significantly lower than England, with a median score of 0.06 ha of equipped playing space per 1,000 of the population and 0.48 ha per 1,000 of playing pitches. Insufficient data were received from Scotland and Wales for assessment.

10.2.7 Allotments, Community Gardens and Urban Farms

There are numerous views on the main drivers of decline for allotments. Suggested drivers include the emergence of the 'affluent society', which reduced the economic necessity of producing personal food supplies to the extent that allotment gardening became recreational. The sale of allotment space for development is also a key factor. Other influences include the absence of any consistent national campaigns to increase allotment uptake. However, the recent growth of 'green markets' is renewing interest. Factors such as an increased interest in organic food, concerns over reliance on importations, desire for a greater sense of self-sufficiency (33% of people in a recent poll say they now grow their own food; Thornton 2009), concerns over food costs, and general worries about food security are driving the increasing pressure on limited allotment space.

On the eve of WWII, there were 110,000 ha of allotments in England and Wales, made up of 740,000 plots. Urban areas provided approximately 55% of these, albeit generally smaller than rural allotments (Thorpe 1969; Crouch 1997). By the end of the 1940s, there were 1.4 million allotments popularised by the WWII 'Dig for Victory' campaign which encouraged people to grow their own food (Hope & Ellis 2009). During WWII, 10% of all UK-produced food came from allotments, private gardens and plots cultivated by service

Table 10.7 Comparison between reported provision of space for outdoor sports and play in England and the recommended Six Acre Standard published in 2001. Source: data extracted from FIT & NPFA (2008).

Type of space for outdoor sports and play	Reported median level provision (% response from local authorities)	Six Acre Standard
	ha/1,000 population	
For playing pitches	1.12 (58%)	1.2
For all outdoor sports facilities (including pitches)	1.32 (29%)	1.6
Casual playing spaces/amenity greenspace	0.7 (31%)	0.4–0.5*

*Based on the 1992 children's playing space standard.

personnel. In 1941, the Ministry of Agriculture assessed the total annual food production from allotments alone as 1.3 million tonnes. Food production in allotments and city farms is discussed in **Box 10.4** (Section 10.3.1).

Over the past 60 years, the extent of allotments has declined, with only 10% of the post-war acreage remaining in England (Campbell & Campbell 2009) and only 211 plots existing in Scotland (45% of these sites are located in Glasgow, Edinburgh, Dundee and Aberdeen) (SAGS 2007). On an annual basis, the number of people on national allotment waiting lists has varied significantly (Crouch 1997). Today, allotment demand is far higher than allotment supply, especially in inner cities (GLA 2006a; SAGS 2007); a total of 997 plots covering just 1,356.8 ha (compared with an estimated 55,000 ha post-war) were recorded in the CABE Inventory (CABE 2010).

10.2.8 Cemeteries, Churchyards and Burial Grounds

The main driver of change in the extent and condition of cemeteries, churchyards and burial grounds relates to the shift from burials to cremations.

There is no comprehensive list of UK burial grounds, but the Wilson report (2004) estimated that there are 16,000–18,000 Church of England burial grounds in England and nearly 2,000 in Wales (**Table 10.8**).

An extensive survey of burial grounds in England and Wales received a total of 9,747 responses (Ministry of Justice 2007). The average size of local authority burial grounds was just over 3 ha with 46%, 19% and 10% of total area located in 'major urban', 'large urban' and 'other urban' areas respectively (75% of the total grounds). In contrast, Church of England-operated burial grounds averaged just under 0.5 ha with only 15%, 6% and 8% of total area located in 'major urban', 'large urban' and 'other urban' areas respectively[2].

The lack of a centralised record of UK burial grounds makes assessment of temporal trends in their extent and quality difficult. Very few churches built since the Edwardian era have incorporated yards for burial (J. Goodchild, Church of England, pers. comm.). The introduction of cremation in the 1870s, and its gradual rise to overtake burial as the principal mode of disposal by 1968, constrained requirements to expand burial facilities (Rugg 2006).

Table 10.8 Estimated total area usable in England for burials, and predicted future period of operation of local authority and Church of England burial grounds, by district rural/urban classification*[†] Source: reproduced from Ministry of Justice (2007).

Region	Estimated total area of burial grounds usable for burials (ha)[‡]	Area occupied by graves		Area occupied by graves more than 100 years old		Area as yet unused		Median predicted period of operation of burial grounds (yrs)[¶§]	Mean predicted period of operation of burial grounds (yrs)[¶§]
		Area (ha)	Percentage of total (%)	Area (ha)	Percentage of total (%)	Area (ha)	Percentage of total (%)		
Local authority burial grounds									
Major Urban	1,773	1,469	83	390	22	305	17	25	49
Large Urban	758	624	82	118	16	134	18	19	32
Other Urban	412	315	77	109	27	97	23	20	32
Significant Rural	450	354	79	91	20	97	21	25	42
Rural-50	314	234	74	43	14	80	26	40	50
Rural-80	244	184	75	51	21	60	25	30	40
Church of England burial grounds									
Major Urban	227	208	92	83	36	19	8	20	37
Large Urban	100	89	89	32	32	11	11	20	32
Other Urban	117	94	80	55	47	23	20	20	32
Significant Rural	261	215	82	97	37	46	18	25	37
Rural-50	309	253	82	118	38	57	18	25	40
Rural-80	533	428	80	195	37	105	20	25	55

* Classes are according to the Defra Classifications of Local Authority districts and Unitary Authorities in England. Does not include burial grounds in Wales. See the Defra website (http://archive.defra.gov.uk/evidence/statistics/rural/documents/rural-defn/LAClassifications_technicalguide.pdf) for more information.
† Data in this table exclude those for which a rural/urban classification could not be identified.
‡ For those burial grounds that were able to provide information on area and occupancy, in hectares, as well as a rural/urban classification.
¶ Predicted period of operation is the expected time before unused land available for burials is filled by interments.
§ Median and mean estimates also exclude: those burial grounds already closed to new burials, those open only to burials in existing graves, and those not providing information on predicted period of operation.

2 Urban classifications are from the Defra-recommended method of urban/rural categorisation (Defra 2010b).

Post-war, most of the churchyards that were no longer used for burial were passed to local authorities to manage. Their condition is highly variable; Highgate Cemetery, London, is recognised for its cultural value through its Grade I listing and designation as a site of Metropolitan Importance for Nature Conservation, yet other cemeteries and churchyards are in a state of neglect. Church grounds in general include a wide range of habitats and provide important urban sites for biodiversity (Cooper 2001).

10.2.9 Previously Developed Land (PDL) (Brownfield)[3]

Previously Developed Land is that which is, or was, occupied by a permanent structure, including the curtilage of the developed land and any associated fixed surface infrastructure (Planning Policy Statement 3: Housing (PPS3 2006)); until 2010, PDL included domestic gardens.

Planning policy has driven the redevelopment of brownfield land to curtail urban sprawl, reduce the need to travel by creating compact developments, and to meet the shortfall in new housing identified by the Barker Review (Barker 2004). In combination, these forces led to the once national target for 60% of new housing to be built on PDL (PPG3 2000; PPS3 2006). A recent report (NHPAU 2010) confirms that policies encouraging this brownfield development, coupled with policies to increase housing density from 30 to 50 dph (with a minimum density of 30 dph)

(PPS3 2006), have been successful. Critics have argued that such targets have driven extensive development of domestic gardens ('garden-grabbing') with negative consequences for Urban areas (Barclay 2010).

From 1980 to 2000, densities for new homes built on PDL were fairly stable, but over the past decade, they have increased substantially in many regions and are up to 122 dph in London, for example (DCLG 2010b). In general, higher densities are associated with a larger share of flats (Bibby 2009). The extent of PDL is illustrated in **Table 10.9**.

A very recent policy change has led to the following changes to PDL (Barclay 2010):

- Private residential gardens are now excluded from the definition of PDL.
- The national indicative minimum density of 30 dph has ceased.

The general decline in extent of genuine Urban brownfield in England and Scotland over the last 10 years has implications for ecosystem service provision. In particular, the loss of permeable brownfield land and site fragmentation are likely to reduce services such as wild species diversity (Harvey 2000; Eyre *et al.* 2003; Angold *et al.* 2006; Schadek *et al.* 2009), climate regulation and flood regulation within the Urban environment. It should be noted that large areas of brownfield may have some degree of contamination. Some areas within PDL are now being recognised as an important

Table 10.9 Previously Developed Land (PDL)			
	England	**Scotland**	**Wales**
Classification system	PDL: i) Vacant or derelict; ii) Developed but with potential for redevelopment.	i) Vacant land within urban areas; ii) Derelict land and buildings within all areas (SVDLS 2008).	
Data availability	Lack of comparative data prior to 2002 (DCLG 2006).	Temporal trends analysed since 2002 (SVDLS 2008).	Very limited information on the extent and characterisation.
Current extent	62,130 ha PDL in 2007 (DCLG 2006). An estimated 33,600 ha was vacant or derelict and 28,520 ha are in use but with potential for redevelopment. 47% of vacant and derelict land and buildings is considered urban and 29% is on the urban fringe. 71% of PDL currently in use is urban, with 18% in the urban fringe and only 11% in rural areas (DCLG 2006).	In 2008, 10,832 ha of derelict and urban vacant land were recorded, of which, 2,630 ha (24%) were urban vacant and 8,203 ha were derelict (76%) (SVDLS 2008).	
Temporal trends	Since 2002, the total amount of PDL has declined by approximately 6%. Significantly, increases in PDL currently in use mask far greater declines in vacant land (-18.9%) and derelict land (-5.8%) (DCLG 2007), both of which are more likely to confer ecosystem services, such as flood regulation, due to a greater proportion of permeable land.	In 2002, there were 2,968 ha of urban vacant land. This figure has fluctuated somewhat in the intermediate period; however, by 2008, it had dropped to 2,630 ha (an overall net decrease of 338 ha). This represents a net fall in levels of urban vacant land in Scotland of 11% (SVDLS 2008).	
Spatial trends	Great regional variation. Former industrial regions of the North West and Yorkshire/Humber contain the highest amounts of PDL (17.6% and 14.7% respectively). In contrast, London and the North East contain only 6.3% and 6.5% respectively (DCLG 2006).	The local authority with the highest amount of derelict and urban vacant land was North Lanarkshire, containing 1,397 ha (13% of Scotland total). Glasgow City had the second highest with 1,325 ha (12% of Scotland total), and North Ayrshire was third with 1,276 ha (12%) (SVDLS 2008).	Up to 50% of reclaimed and derelict land is a result of the coal industry, especially in the valleys of South Wales (Environment Agency 2009).

3 Urban/rural classifications are based on the Department of Communities and Local Government urban settlements Ordnance Survey classification (2001).

biodiversity resource and these areas are now being classified as UK BAP priority habitats.

10.2.10 Water

The subhabitat of water separates out natural from artificial water bodies as these can provide different ecosystem services.

Legislation from the EU and associated policies have been the main drivers influencing the aquatic Urban environment and the subsequent goods and benefits derived from it. The EU Water Framework Directive (WFD) requires all water bodies to meet 'good status' or 'good ecological potential' by 2015 (see Chapter 27). Measures are currently being taken to classify and improve all water bodies in Urban locations. In total, 0.8% of the UK is classified as Urban freshwater (LCM 2000), with an average of 6.6% in England (GLUD 2005). The extent of land classified as water within our Urban

case study is: Liverpool 31% (5,100 ha), Northampton 2.7% (200 ha), Coventry 0.5% (50 ha) and Newcastle 1.8% (200 ha) (GLUD 2005).

The Scottish Environment Protection Agency carried out an evaluation of the current status of all Scottish water bodies as part of their ongoing implementation of the WFD (2000). Of the 29 wholly Urban water bodies identified, 18 are classified as heavily modified water bodies (**Figure 10.7**). The results of analysis for conventional water quality parameters (dissolved oxygen, pH, temperature and soluble phosphorous) indicated that the quality of Scottish Urban waters is relatively good, with values for only three water bodies falling below a classification of moderate (two are related to soluble phosphorus and one to dissolved oxygen) (**Table 10.10**; **Table 10.11**).

The Environment Agency currently classifies 278 (approximately 34%) of Urban river bodies in England and

Table 10.10 Minimum and maximum total concentrations of metals measured in a selection of Urban stream and river sediments (µg/g dry weight). n = number of samples. Values in green exceed the Canadian Sediment Quality Guidelines (2003) (standard not available for nickel). Source: Scholes *et al.* (2008).

	n	Cadmium	Chromium	Copper	Nickel	Lead	Zinc
Scholes *et al.* (1999)	45	**3.0–10**	3–**169**	17–**178**	22–187	33–**332**	21–**1,035**
Rhoads & Cahill (1999)	41		9–**328**	6–**55**	8–244	10–**225**	29–**528**
Wilson & Clarke (2002)	9			**440.6**	80.9		**407.0**
Filgueiras *et al.* (2004)*	33	0.37–0.41	78–**139**	30.5–**55.9**	32.5–60.7	**43.6–91.1**	
Tejeda *et al.* (2006)	32			9–165		12–**64**	38–**1,467**
Thevenot *et al.* (2007)†		**1.70**	**47**	31		**43**	**140**
Samecka-Cymerman & Kempers (2007)	21	0.20–0.58	4.9–**28.5**	2.1–10.6	7.5–15.2	15–57	6.8–**458**
	24	0.24–**1.72**	17–**85.2**	9.5–43.7	14.5–39.0	17–97	22.9–**174**
Walling *et al.* 2003 ‡	51		8–17	33–92		**689–1,471**	**775–1,850**
	52		21–**181**	118–**198**		**90–237**	**274–580**
	17		65–**313**	141–**235**		**199–343**	**397–907**
Carpentier *et al.* 2002	50¶	<**0.8–6**	4–**78**	<5–**172**	<5–30	<5–**278**	39–**563**

* range of values across 11 sites; † estimated average metal contents over the time period 1995 to 2000 of dredged sediments; ‡ range of values reflect average concentrations at multiple sampling points on 3 different rivers sampled approximately bi-monthly over a 12-month period; rivers located close to metal mines (no longer operational); ¶ number of samples analysed for cadmium = 42 and chromium = 32.

Table 10.11 Concentrations of microbiological parameters recorded in a selection of Urban stream and river waters and sediments. Values in green exceed EU Bathing Water Directive values. MPN = most probable number and CFU = colony forming units. Source: Scholes *et al.* (2008).

	Total coliforms		Faecal coliforms	
	Water	Sediment	Water	Sediment
Torres (1997)	**84,000** MPN/100 ml	280,000 MPN/g	1,800 MPN/100 ml	20,000 MPN/g
Crabill *et al.* (1999)			29–527 CFU/100 ml*	100,000–3,000,000 CFU/100 ml†
Snook & Whitehead (2004)	**710,000** CFU/100 ml		**120,000** CFU/100 ml	
Ellis & Yu (1995)‡	3,000–**3,000,000** MPN/100 ml	22,000 MPN/g	800–**800,000** MPN/100 ml	2,800 MPN/g
Miyabara *et al.* (1992)¶	<2,000–**4,900,000** MPN/100 ml		<2,000–**7,900,000** MPN/100 ml	
He *et al.* (2007)§	8,000–**170,000** MPN/100 ml	50,000–130,000 MPN/g	20–1,300 MPN/100 ml	130–5000 MPN/g
EU Bathing Water Directive**	10,000 CFU/100 ml		2,000 CFU/100 ml	

* range in mean annual values across 8 sites; † range in mean annual values across 4 sites; ‡ geometric mean densities across 4 sites; combined sewer overflows discharging into an Urban stream; ¶ range of values reported across 14 Urban rivers; § average of samples collected across approximately one third of 500 sites; ** value for marine waters.

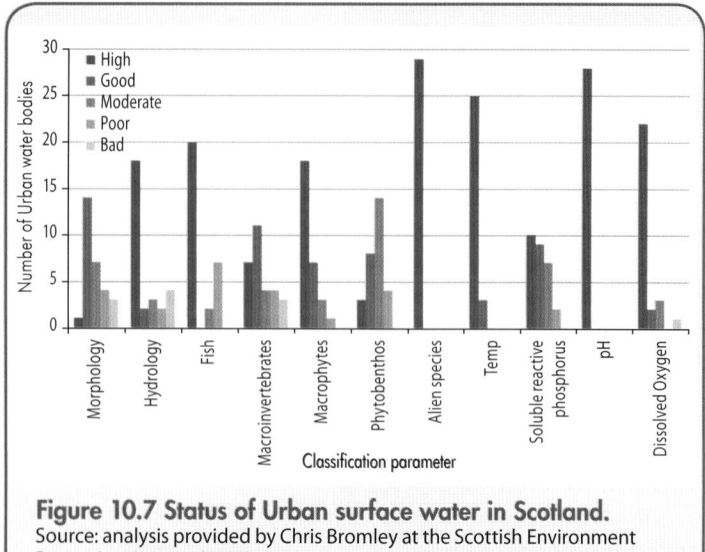

Figure 10.7 Status of Urban surface water in Scotland.
Source: analysis provided by Chris Bromley at the Scottish Environment Protection Agency (2009).

Wales as having an overall status below 'good' and with below 'moderate' status for the parameters: dissolved oxygen, temperature, pH and phosphorus (Jones 2010). Across the UK, there was a general improvement in both the chemical and biological status of rivers and canals between 1990 and 2005. Although the extent to which this trend has occurred in Urban areas in general is difficult to assess, within London the proportion of rivers and canals of 'good' chemical or biological status has more than doubled (ONS 2007).

Urban water bodies are considered by Paul and Meyer (2001) to typically receive polluted inputs from sources that include urban and highway runoff, and cross-connections and overloads from foul to storm sewers (Gasperi *et al.* 2008), resulting in a prevalence of pollution tolerant fauna and flora (Scholes *et al.* 2008). The straightened and modified banks and channels that characterise many Urban streams (Gurnell *et al.* 2007) means that physical habitat variability is low, flow refugia is reduced and a range of other deleterious ecological impacts occur, especially when in association with poor water quality. The water quality of Urban water bodies is also discussed in Chapter 9 and, more generally, in Chapter 14.

Water use can be measured by the amount of water we abstract from natural water resources. The Environment Agency reported little change in the amount of water abstracted (nearly 60,000 megalitres per day) from 2000/01 to 2006/07. In relation to usage *per capita*, between 2002 and 2007, domestic demand varied between 148 and 152 litres per day, indicating that domestic water demand in the UK is fairly stable (Water UK 2008). Policies to reduce water use to 120 litres per day are proposed by the Department for Environment, Food and Rural Affairs as part of its Future Water Strategy (Defra 2008).

10.2.11 Green Belt (Urban Fringe and Peri-urban)

Green Belt land is usually located on the Urban fringe and extends into the countryside, therefore providing accessible greenspace for the urban population who benefit from the additional ecosystem services and goods it provides.

Although the promotion of the reuse of PDL has constrained the demand for housing development elsewhere, this driver has persisted in putting pressure on peri-urban Green Belt (Natural England & CPRE 2010). Since 1989, the annual percentage of new housing built on Green Belt land has fluctuated between 2–4%, stabilising at approximately 2% (DCLG 2010c).

It is estimated that 60% of England's population live in towns and cities surrounded by Green Belt. Between 1997 and 2007, land in England designated as Green Belt is estimated to have increased by 33,000 ha, and as of March 2009, stood at 1,983,000 ha, or 15.2% of the land mass (**Figure 10.6**) (DCLG 2009a). In total, there are 14 separate Green Belts in England varying in size from London (Metropolitan) at 486,000 ha to Burton-upon-Trent and Swadlincote at 700 ha. They include 38 towns and cities with populations over 100,000. Most increases in extent since 2007 have been apportioned to improvements in measurement technology, as opposed to changes due to adopted plans (real changes) (DCLG 2009a).

In Scotland, the Green Belt area is estimated to have fallen by 9% between 2007 and 2009 (Greenspace Scotland 2009), and now only covers 143,000 ha, of which, 34,555 ha is classified as Urban. Wales has just introduced its first Green Belt between Cardiff and Newport at 3,000 ha, but the greatest percentage of designated Green Belt by country is found in Northern Ireland which has 23.7% (336,000 ha) cover.

10.2.12 Urban Biodiversity

Recognition of the importance of Urban biodiversity is the likely future driver of policy change and habitat and species monitoring and protection.

A number of studies have explored the relationship between species assemblage structure and Urban greenspaces other than parks and domestic gardens including: allotments (Luniak 1980); brownfield sites (Davis & Glick 1978; Dickman 1987); cemeteries (Lussenhop 1977; Biadun 1994); ponds (Parris 2006); public squares (Zanette *et al.* 2005); remnant habitat patches (Crooks *et al.* 2004); roundabouts and traffic islands (Whitmore *et al.* 2002; Helden & Leather 2004); and woodland/forest patches (Tilghman 1987; Hobbs 1988; Miyashita *et al.* 1998; Park & Lee 2000, Niemelä *et al.* 2002; Magura *et al.* 2004; Lehvävirta *et al.* 2006; Morimoto *et al.* 2006; Platt & Lill 2006; Sadler *et al.* 2006). The predominant themes have been similar to those for Urban parks and domestic gardens, and include the influence of the size of these spaces, of their isolation, and of surrounding land cover and uses. These are important determinants of patterns of biodiversity across Urban habitats, with species richness typically strengthening with an increased size of area, and with the broader coverage of usable habitat. However, these and related ecological patterns may be weakened, if not entirely masked, by variation in the quality of the greenspace and the profound influence upon quality of the form of management that is (or is not) undertaken. Pollution can also contribute to habitat and species change (e.g. the impact of acidification on lichen diversity) (Davies *et al.* 2007).

Threshold effects have been discussed, including levels of urbanisation that are sufficient to cause marked changes in species richness or composition (Paul & Meyer 2001; Riley *et al.* 2005). But given the important influences of species identity and context on observed responses, such thresholds are unlikely to occur on a wide scale. Values for thresholds would have to be established separately, at least for different broad regions.

Some have argued that urbanisation leads to biotic homogenisation, whereby a few widespread and abundant species replace a more diverse assemblage (Brandes 1995; Jokimäki & Kaisanlahti-Jokimäki 2003; Crooks et al. 2004; McKinney 2006). While perhaps a useful caricature, this is rather simplistic as Urban species assemblages frequently retain some local character, reflecting the fact that they are drawn, in part, from native regional assemblages, not simply from the species that occur ubiquitously. Similarity of species assemblages in Urban habitats may also be a function of the degree of urbanisation and the sizes of towns and cities, increasing with the number of people and the size of the urban area (Jokimäki & Kaisanlahti-Jokimäki, 2003; McKinney 2006).

10.2.12.1. Biodiversity: species richness and abundance

The categorisation of the findings of individual analyses is not always straightforward, but certain studies (few of which have been conducted in the UK) document a variety of trends in biodiversity.

Trends associated with species richness of major taxonomic groups:

- Declines with increased urbanisation—bees and wasps (McIntyre & Hostetler 2001; Zanette et al. 2005); beetles (Niemelä et al. 2002; Ishitani et al. 2003; Venn et al. 2003; Weller & Ganzhorn 2004; Sadler et al. 2006); butterflies (Hardy & Dennis 1999); amphibians (Riley et al. 2005; Rubbo & Kiesecker 2005); birds (Emlen 1974; Hohtola 1978; Beissinger & Osborne 1982; Jokimäki & Suhonen 1993; Clergeau et al. 1998, 2001a, 2001b; Rottenborn 1999; Marzluff 2001; Green & Baker 2003; Melles et al. 2003; Donnelly & Marzluff 2006; Sandström et al. 2006); mammals (Hourigan et al. 2006). This pattern is usually attributed to the loss of suitable habitat and resources as urbanisation increases.
- Peaks at intermediate levels of development—plants (Kowarik 1990; Porter et al. 2001; Zerbe et al. 2003); butterflies (Blair & Launer 1997); lizards (Germaine & Wakeling 2001); birds (Sewell & Catterall 1998; Blair 2001; Clergeau et al. 2001a; Crooks et al. 2004; Marzluff, 2001, 2005). This is often associated with a greater number of land use types in intermediate levels of development, disturbance, and the multiple private ownership of land that leads to variation in management (Zerbe et al. 2003).
- Increases with increased urbanisation—plants (Kühn et al. 2004; Turner et al. 2005; Wania et al. 2006); butterflies (Hardy & Dennis 1999); birds (Marzluff 2001). Generally, this seems to occur because of the relatively high numbers of invasive alien species in more heavily urbanised areas (Kowarik 1990; Germaine et al. 1998; Kent et al. 1999; Roy et al. 1999; Marzluff 2001; Savard et al. 2000; Wittig 2004; Burton et al. 2005; Wania et al. 2006; Zhao et al. 2008). In some cases, numbers of native species have also been shown to be greater (Kühn et al. 2004).

- Other or no pattern with increased urbanisation—plants (Roy et al. 1999); beetles (Niemelä et al. 2002; Magura et al. 2004); birds (Jokimäki et al. 1996; Sewell & Catterall 1998; Mason 2006).

Trends associated with species abundance of major taxonomic groups:

- Declines with increased urbanisation—bees and wasps (McIntyre & Hostetler 2001; Zanette et al. 2005); beetles (Niemelä et al. 2002; Ishitani et al. 2003; Magura et al. 2004); butterflies (Blair & Launer 1997); birds (Marzluff 2001; Sandström et al. 2006). This is usually attributed to the loss of suitable habitat with increasing urbanisation.
- Peaks in moderately urbanised areas—beetles (Niemelä et al. 2002); lizards (Germaine & Wakeling 2001); birds (Sewell & Catterall 1998; Blair 2001; Marzluff 2001).
- Increases with increased urbanisation—earthworms (Steinberg et al. 1997); beetles (Niemelä et al. 2002); birds (Emlen 1974; Beissinger & Osborne 1982; Jokimäki et al. 1996; Mills et al. 1989; Clergeau et al. 1998, 2001b; Marzluff 2001; Green & Baker 2003). This pattern is often associated with the abundance of invasive alien species (Mills et al. 1989; Clergeau et al. 2001b; Niemelä et al. 2002).
- No simple pattern with increased urbanisation—beetles (Venn et al, 2003); birds (Hohtola 1978; Marzluff 2001; Mason 2006).

There are necessary caveats when drawing conclusions from collations of empirical studies of the relationship between the structure of species assemblages (including species richness and overall abundance) and urbanisation (**Table 10.12**). They explain much of the variation between the patterns documented.

Most studies of changes in biodiversity across rural-urban gradients focus on individual towns and cities and their environs. Others have drawn data from wider regions, encompassing multiple urban centres, often with a focus on how levels of urbanisation contribute to broad geographic patterns (Hostetler & Holling 2000; Kühn et al. 2004). This provides much greater generality in the conclusions. However, caution needs to be exercised to avoid confounding effects of other gradients. At broad geographic scales, the number of species in different groups in an area correlates positively with the numbers of people: there is a positive species-human relationship (Luck 2007). In heavily industrialised areas, such relationships seem to persist at quite fine resolutions (10 km; Evans & Gaston 2005). For birds, relationships between species richness and human population density have been shown to be positive up to densities of about 1,000 individuals per km², after which they start to decline markedly (Evans & Gaston 2005, Turner et al. 2003).

Although there are other possibilities (e.g. coincidence, disturbance, extinction filters, geomorphology; Araújo 2003; Kühn et al. 2004), the most generally accepted explanation for this pattern of positive covariance is that species richness and human populations respond positively and independently to levels of environmental energy availability (variously measured in terms of temperature and net primary production). Species numbers often increase with energy

Table 10.12 Methodologies used in Urban biodiversity studies that explain much of the variation between the patterns documented.

Pattern documented	
The range of and position on the rural-urban gradient.	Mazluff *et al.* (2001)
How finely the rural-urban gradient is sampled and its potential for detecting non-linear relationships. There are few studies that sample intensively across the gradient.	
The quality of the rural (e.g. native vegetation, farmland, intensification of agricultural activities) **or less urbanised landscape** with which to compare Urban areas.	
The extent to which sample areas contain heterogeneous land cover or focus on a particular land cover.	Guntenspergen & Levenson (1997) Steinberg *et al.* (1997)
Spatial resolution which is significant because different groups of species may operate, and be managed, across different spatial scales and by different stakeholders (e.g. city councils, developers, individual garden owners).	Hostetler & Holling (2000) Savard *et al.* (2000)
Study plot area which may vary systematically with urbanisation, especially when using habitat patches as the unit of analysis (patch size typically declining with urbanisation), and may be problematic because species richness and abundance may be functions of plot area.	Rosenzweig (1995) Gaston & Matter (2002)
History of urbanisation where the long-term temporal dynamics of the response of species richness, abundance and composition to urbanisation may be marked.	Munyenyembe *et al.* (1989) Morneau *et al.* (1999) Godefroid (2001) Chocholoušková & Pyšek (2003) Pyšek *et al.* (2004) Turner *et al.* (2005)

(the species-energy relationship) at a geographic scale, at least over a wide range of values of energy availability, for a variety of reasons (Evans & Gaston 2005). At broad geographic scales, number and proportions of threatened species tend to increase with the numbers of people in an area (Kerr & Currie 1995; Dobson *et al.* 1997; Kirkland & Ostfeld 1999; McKinney 2001, 2002; Araújo 2003; Chown *et al.* 2003; Luck *et al.* 2004; Vázquez & Gaston 2006).

While urbanisation is a leading cause of species threat in some regions (Czech & Krausman 1997), variable patterns in the number and proportions of threatened species have been reported (Duhme & Pauleit 1998; Zerbe *et al.* 2003; Kühn *et al.* 2004). Presumably, these variations occur because remnant populations have survived the urbanisation process but are at high risk of extinction in their newly developed habitat. In other cases, urbanisation has extirpated these species, and those that remain occur predominantly at lower levels of development.

Due to its high spatio-temporal dynamics, and its transient character, PDL can significantly influence Urban biodiversity (Schadek *et al.* 2009; Angold *et al.* 2006). This land is likely to support higher trophic levels with larger ranges, and high plant and invertebrate diversity has been observed here (Eyre *et al.* 2003; Harvey 2000).

10.2.13 Trends and Changes in Abiotic and Biotic Processes

As described in Section 10.1, the Urban system includes abiotic and biotic processes relating to air, water and soil. This section discusses trends within these processes, covering climate, noise, and air and soil quality. Water is covered in Section 10.2.10 under the Urban subhabitat of water.

10.2.13.1 Climate

Concerns about Urban Heat Intensity (UHI) are driving a range of mitigation and adaptation measures.

Recent temperature increases have most adversely affected urban areas in southern England due to the combination of warmer prevailing conditions and the Urban microclimate (RMetS 2009a). Given the absence of abrupt changes in rainfall over the last few decades, such as those described for temperature, it is not possible to attribute any of the recent UK precipitation trends to anthropogenic warming (Department of Health 2008). However, the 2003 heatwave episode provides an indication of the possible impact to human health from hotter, drier summers (GLA 2010).

Only limited data are available for UK spatial trends on the degree of Urban climate regulation services. The extent of UK Urban 'heat islands' (the warming of the atmosphere and surfaces in towns and cities compared to their rural surroundings) is likely to be synchronous with factors such as city size and percentage and type of greenspace. This dependency has been shown both spatially and temporally for cities such as Atlanta, Georgia, USA (Dixon & Mote 2003), and Singapore (Chow & Roth 2006). In the UK, datasets are less well established, but some urban land use categories, such as storage and manufacturing, are considerably warmer than low density residential areas and farmland (RMetS 2009b). A recent study of the London heat island identified a maximum daytime UHI of 8.9°C in semi-urban (not inner core) areas during partially cloudy periods, while a maximum nocturnal UHI of 8.6°C was found in urban areas during clear sky periods when the wind velocity was below 5 m/s. Among the variables studied, the most critical variable that determines the daytime and nocturnal changes in outdoor air temperature is surface albedo (i.e. the reflectivity of our towns and cities) (Kolokotroni & Giridharan 2008; GLA 2006b).

10.2.13.2 Air quality

Historically, the factors responsible for reductions in acidic atmospheric conditions of the post-war decades were regulation and enforcement, together with cleaner fuels. Anthropogenic alteration of the global nitrogen cycle is now driving change in Urban habitats (Vitousek *et al.* 1997). Reactive nitrogen from transport, industry and heating, as well as nearby intensive agriculture, has led to changes in biodiversity, community structure and the condition of multiple Urban subhabitats, and has also adversely affected human health. The regulatory framework governing air pollution and vehicle standards has been the main driver of change in Urban areas in recent years, offsetting increases in car ownership and distance travelled to an extent. Increasing temperatures and lower levels of nitrogen oxides are contributing to higher background ozone levels.

Changes in atmospheric pollution both within Urban areas and the surrounding countryside have had a profound effect on Urban air quality over the last 60 years. Emissions of black smoke and sulphur dioxide have declined markedly (e.g. in London, annual mean sulphur dioxide and black smoke concentrations have decreased by more than 95% since 1962; AEA 2008), and, more recently, concentrations of lead have also decreased. The dominant source of pollution emissions in Urban environments is now from vehicles (AQEG 2007) and heating. In 2008, 42% of London's nitrogen oxides emissions and 69% of London's PM_{10} (particulate matter of 10μm or less) emissions were attributed to road transport (TfL 2008). This shift from acidic atmospheric conditions to a more eutrophicated environment is clearly illustrated in the change in lichen diversity in London where nitrophytes have replaced acidophytes over a 30-year period (Davies *et al.* 2007; **Box 10.3**). Protective standards for sensitive vegetation do not apply in large conurbations where they are widely exceeded.

Air Quality Management Areas (AQMAs) have to be declared where UK air quality objectives for human health are exceeded (AEA 2009). Despite a substantial decline in nitrogen oxides since the early 1990s, most AQMAs declared for nitrogen dioxide and PM_{10} are located in large conurbations where street canyons inhibit dispersion (Vitousek *et al.* 1997), traffic flow rates are high and traffic speeds are low.

10.2.13.3 Noise
Road traffic is the principal source of noise pollution in the UK (Grimwood 2002). Increases in car ownership and distance travelled (mean has increased from 3,660 miles in 1965 to 6,720 miles in 2001; DfT 2002) are the main drivers that will continue to place increasing pressure on noise regulating ecosystem services. The European Directive on the Assessment and Management of Environmental Noise (END 2002/49) has led to improvements in noise modelling.

Between 1990 and 2000, changes in noise level and exposure in England and Wales were small and trends were subtle, with different indicators showing different changes (Skinner & Grimwood 2002). Average daytime noise levels, measured by L_{Aeq} and L_{A10} indicators, decreased during this period, while average night noise levels, measured by the L_{A90} indicator, increased. For many indicators, over all periods of the day and night, noise levels are significantly higher in Greater London than over the whole of England and Wales (Skinner & Grimwood 2002). Based on current datasets, however, it is not possible to discern the extent to which any trends in Urban noise are the result of altered provision of noise regulation services. Trends in noise regulation are discussed further in Chapter 14.

10.2.13.4. Soil
The importance of soil and the location and extent of permeable surfaces had not been recognised within the planning system until recently. However, recognition in recent years has driven changes that are reflected in Planning Policy Statements PPS3 (Housing; 2006) and PPS7 (Sustainable Development in Rural Areas; 2004), and Planning Policy Guidance 9 (PPG9 Biodiversity and Geological Conservation; 2005). Other drivers of change in

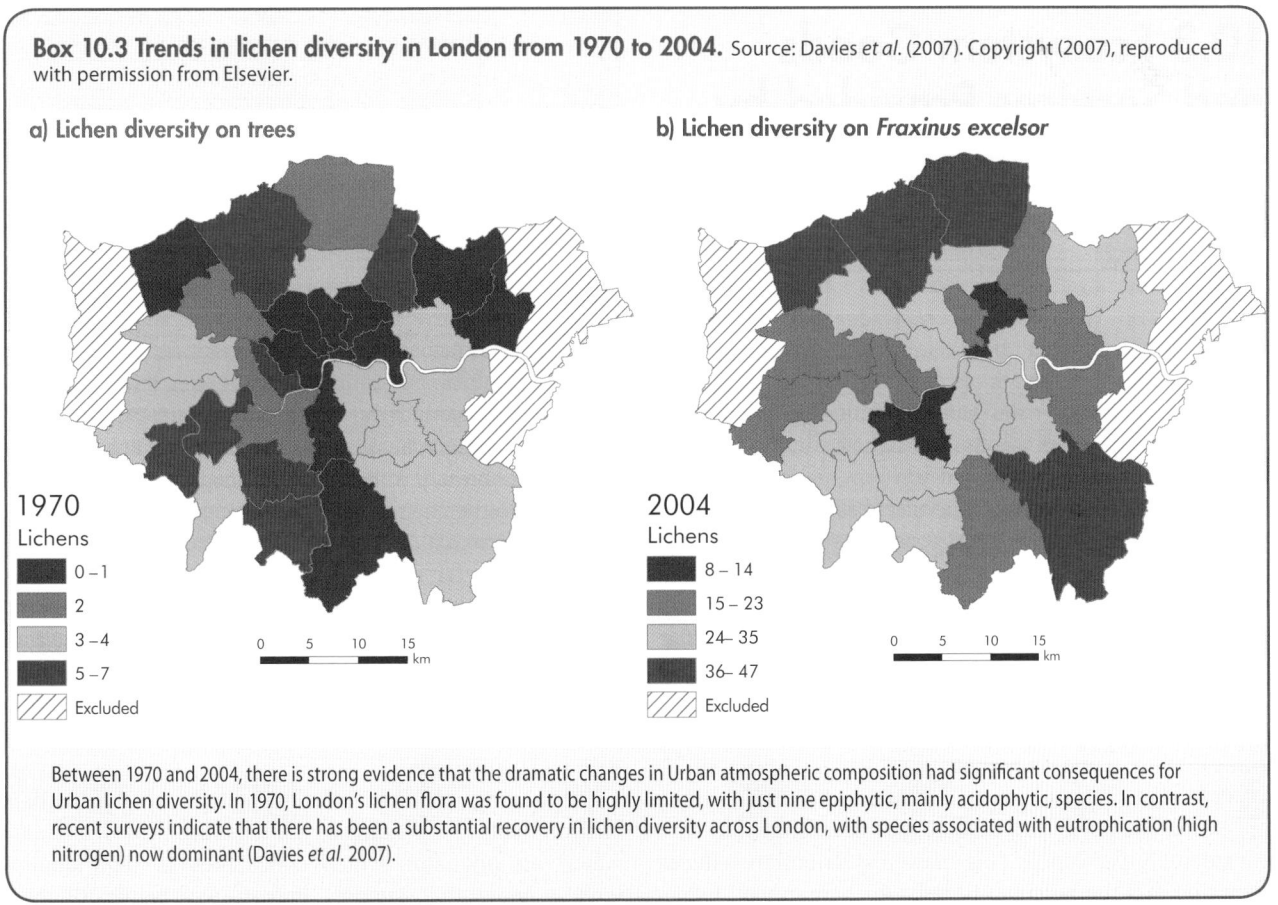

Box 10.3 Trends in lichen diversity in London from 1970 to 2004. Source: Davies *et al.* (2007). Copyright (2007), reproduced with permission from Elsevier.

a) Lichen diversity on trees

b) Lichen diversity on *Fraxinus excelsor*

1970
Lichens
■ 0 – 1
■ 2
■ 3 – 4
■ 5 – 7
▨ Excluded

0   5   10   15
km

2004
Lichens
■ 8 – 14
■ 15 – 23
■ 24 – 35
■ 36 – 47
▨ Excluded

0   5   10   15
km

Between 1970 and 2004, there is strong evidence that the dramatic changes in Urban atmospheric composition had significant consequences for Urban lichen diversity. In 1970, London's lichen flora was found to be highly limited, with just nine epiphytic, mainly acidophytic, species. In contrast, recent surveys indicate that there has been a substantial recovery in lichen diversity across London, with species associated with eutrophication (high nitrogen) now dominant (Davies *et al.* 2007).

soil quality and permeable surfaces include demographic changes and associated housing policy linked to urban regeneration which have driven up housing density in urban areas, reducing garden size. Car ownership has, in part, led to the paving of front gardens, and the use of private and public areas for car standing (with the added benefit of less garden maintenance). Legislation on contaminated land and soil quality should drive new developments in soil remediation and soil quality assessment procedures.

Information about the chemical and physical properties of Urban soil is limited as, historically, these areas have been excluded from soil surveys which focused on rural areas (Fordyce *et al.* 2005). A systematic sampling programme started in the Midlands and has been ongoing since 2005; it confirms that, while the underlying geology is important in determining the elemental composition of Urban soil, the pressures from urbanisation have led to increased levels of pollution (Fordyce *et al.* 2005).

Urban soils are often highly compacted with concomitant structural degradation. Although they retain the ability to support soil flora and fauna, the impacts of anthropogenic activities often mean that many organisms are unable to survive, and opportunities for ecological colonisation can be limited (Wood *et al.* 2005). Basal rates of respiration are commonly elevated in comparison with rural equivalents (Post & Beeby 1996). The implications of the condition of Urban soils in the global carbon cycle (*inter alia*) and on the soils' capacity to sequester atmospheric carbon dioxide remain unclear.

10.3 Ecosystem Goods and Services Provided by the Urban Environment for Human Well-being

In this section, we review the ecosystem services and the subsequent goods and benefits provided by the Urban environment. The definitions of goods, benefits and ecosystem services are described in Chapter 2.

Many of the main goods and benefits available from the Urban environment—which are summarised in **Table 10.13**—arise from cultural services and include good physical and mental health, recreation and community cohesion. Cultural services are particularly important in Urban areas where human population density is higher than it is in all other habitats. The goods and benefits that arise come from the many local and culturally valued landscapes and waterscapes, such as parks and woodlands, playing fields and nature reserves, as well as the many smaller open areas that are found throughout the Urban environment.

Provision of greenspace in towns and cities, while appearing extensive (GLUD 2005), has been shown to vary considerably *per capita*. This uneven distribution reduces provision and the potential benefits for human well-being.

Table 10.13 Main goods and benefits derived from final ecosystem services provided by the Urban environment.

Ecosystem service	Final ecosystem service	Description of the main goods and benefits from the Urban environment
Provisioning	Crops, plants, livestock, fish,	Food: e.g. vegetables, fruit, meat, milk, honey
		Fibre: e.g. compost
		Ornamental: e.g. flowers
		Genetic resources
	Trees, standing vegetation & peat	Trees: e.g. timber, wood chippings
		Fuel
	Water supply	Drinking water
		Industrial use of water
		Energy
Provisioning/ Cultural	Wild species	Wild food: e.g. berries
		Recreation and tourism
Cultural	Environmental settings	Physical and mental health
		Spiritual and religious
		Heritage: includes cultural heritage, aesthetic and inspirational, security and freedom, neighbourhood development, social and environmental citizenship
		Recreation and tourism
		Education
Regulating	Climate	Avoidance of climate stress
		Carbon sequestration
	Hazard	Erosion protection
		Flood protection
		Avoidance of climate stress
	Purification	Clean air
		Clean water
		Clean soil
	Noise	Noise reduction

Effective delivery of these services is determined by many factors including accessibility and condition. For example, inner cities have the lowest provision, thus the value of goods and benefits should be weighted accordingly. Dense, inner city populations tend to have the least accessible greenspace, with small parks, few domestic gardens or allotments, and associated low biodiversity. In areas of Urban fringe, where the extent of greenspace itself is not an issue, poor condition, caused by neglect and poor maintenance, together with poor accessibility due to safety concerns, can often prevent cultural benefits reaching deprived communities.

Regulating services are essential to the Urban environment. For example, purification provides clean water, air and soil, which contributes to high quality environments that support human well-being (Chapter

14). The Urban environment also supports other regulating services associated with climate, hazards and noise.

To a lesser extent, Urban areas supply provisioning services, such as crops and livestock for food, but these tend to be limited to a smaller number of subhabitats. The provision of trees and standing vegetation is one exception, as it is widely delivered across the subhabitats, and supplies both cultural goods (e.g. recreation and tourism) and regulating goods (e.g. avoidance of climate stress and noise regulation).

Biodiversity can be viewed as underpinning all ecosystem services through its role in supporting fundamental ecosystem processes. Some wild species also directly deliver provisioning services, supplying a range of wild food, such as berries, for example. Moreover, wild species diversity is also considered a cultural service, contributing to the spiritual, aesthetic and cultural value of Urban areas (Chapter 2; Chapter 4). The increasing prevalence of certain mammal species in urban and peri-urban areas, such as badgers and deer, means that more people are aware of, and place value on, the presence of such wildlife (Dandy *et al.* 2009).

10.3.1 Provisioning Services

The limited extent of cultivation and the high proportion of impermeable surfaces in urban areas restrict the production of goods, such as food, flowers, timber and fibre (compost), in the Urban environment. Most essential provisions are produced within other Broad Habitats, so urbanisation almost entirely draws on national and global ecosystems.

Nevertheless, there is some production by community farms, domestic gardeners and allotment holders (**Box 10.4**), with the latter estimated to save up to £1,000 per household per annum through reduced food bills (Hope & Ellis 2009) and seen to gain access to goods that might otherwise be unavailable to them due to high supermarket prices (GLA 2006a). Contrary to widely perceived stereotypes, the goods and benefits provided by allotments are delivered by a wide demographic range of society (NSALG 1993). Honey bees have even been shown to produce more honey in the urban areas of cities such as Birmingham than in the surrounding countryside (Memmott 2010).

Trees in Urban areas provide sources of timber and other byproducts, including charcoal, wood chip and compost, but are particularly important in the provision of other goods arising from regulating services, such as clean air, clean water and erosion protection (Gill *et al.* 2007; NUFU 2005). Species composition and age structure of Urban trees are crucial determinants of ecosystem service provision (NUFU 2005).

Other Urban habitats, such as Urban water bodies, supply drinking and irrigation water (both through abstraction and via recharge of groundwater) and a medium for industrial processes, as well as sites for recreational and spiritual activities (Petts *et al.* 2002).

Very little information exists on genetic resources in Urban greenspace. However, domestic gardens, allotments and some formal gardens are particularly important for horticulture and home-grown produce, and so, it is likely that a considerable amount of genetic diversity exists through generations of breeding plants.

Box 10.4 Urban food production.

Urban food production reached its peak during the Second World War. A sharp decline followed, but interest began to revive in the 1970s as evidence of the impact of pesticides and other pollutants was recognised. Interest in home-grown produce has continued to gain popularity, particularly in more recent years, due to increasing environmental awareness and sustainability issues (Howe & Wheeler 1999), the desire for organic food, and the rising costs of provisions. Produce arises from domestic gardens, allotments (**Figure 1**) and larger facilities such as city farms and orchards.

A recent survey of 124 allotment holders (Perez-Vazquez *et al.* 2005) identified the most common crops as: potatoes, spinach, onions, courgettes, runner beans, leeks, Brussels sprouts, tomatoes and cabbage. The average plot had 16 crop species, although species diversity was highly variable and included maize, squashes, callaloo, scallion and a wide range of herbs and flowers. Produce grown on an allotment cannot be sold, hence the lack of data on its economic value. However, the standard allotment plot in England and Wales is the '10-pole plot' (250 m², or one sixteenth of an acre) and the National Society for Allotments and Leisure Gardens estimates that this size of plot, properly husbanded, should feed a family of four for a year (NSALG 1995). Calculations based on current market prices estimate the annual yield value at £1,128.

Figure 1 An allotment in Winshill, Staffordshire. *Photo by Stephen Jones available under a Creative Commons Attribution license.*

In a study of city farms in Leeds and Bradford, annual turnover from food sales was deemed low in absolute and relative terms, with none of the farms exceeding £2,000 in sales per year (excluding animal sales). If animal sales were included, then an approximate peak value of £10,000 worth of animal and vegetable produce was sold annually (Howe & Wheeler 1999), but this represents only a small percentage of a potential estimated revenue of £171,000. Similarly, a farm in Scotland, supported since its beginning by a range of national, district and regional public and private sector funds, and with a turnover of £180,000 a year, generated only 5% of their income from sales of vegetables. Another community farm in Oxford produces vegetables, herbs, soft fruit, top fruit and willow (for basketry), with an estimated 60% of its income coming from statutory bodies and between 15–35% from produce sales (£80 per week) (Garnett 1996).

10.3.2 Regulating Services

The presence of urban heat islands, together with high levels of pollution from transport and commercial and residential heating, mean that the avoidance of climate stress and the ecosystem-derived benefits of clean air, water and soil are extremely pertinent, albeit heavily compromised, in the Urban environment.

10.3.2.1 Air quality

Poor air quality is a major factor influencing health in Urban environments, with the extent of vegetation and open spaces having a large impact on dispersion, deposition and even the formation of certain pollutants (Chapter 23, Section 23.5.1). Epidemiological studies have shown a clear association between human health (including cardiovascular morbidity, decreased lung function, increased hospital admissions and increased mortality) and airborne concentrations of photochemical and particulate pollutants (Kelly 2003). Time-series studies indicating short-term associations between ambient air pollution and mortality are well-established (Stieb *et al.* 2002; Bell *et al.* 2004). Such studies indicate that short-term urban exposure to carbon monoxide, nitrogen dioxide, sulphur dioxide and ozone correlate with varying increases in excess risk of mortality (Stieb *et al.* 2002; Bell *et al.* 2004; Gryparis *et al.* 2004; Defra 2010a). The evidence base linking mortality to long-term exposure to air pollution is increasing (Kelly 2003). In 2005, the estimated cost of the overall health impact from levels of anthropogenic $PM_{2.5}$ (particulate matter of 2.5μm or less) was between £8.6 billion and £20.2 billion (assuming a 6% hazard rate) (Defra 2007c).

Atmospheric processes regulate air pollutant concentrations, including chemistry, atmospheric mixing and deposition. Hydroxyl radical chemistry in the troposphere provides an efficient chemical scavenging mechanism for pollutants. Free radical chain reactions can oxidise pollutants to carbon dioxide and water (Wayne 2000). Pollutants are also dispersed within the atmosphere by diffusion and turbulent mixing.

Pollutants may be removed through dry deposition (where atmospheric elements are settled onto soil, water or plant surfaces) or wet deposition (where constituents are incorporated into precipitation elements, e.g. clouds, rain droplets, aerosols) (Wayne 2000). Within the boundary layer, turbulent mixing brings air parcels into repeated contact with surfaces that enhance deposition. Deposition has the immediate effect of cleansing the atmosphere. Pollutants not deposited within the boundary layer can be incorporated into the free troposphere and transported over potentially large distances with negative national and global consequences. Urbanisation has increased emissions of pollutants, yet resulted in fewer potential sinks for these toxins. Dispersal and formation of pollutants are also influenced by urban heat islands. Overall, these changes have reduced the capacity of the atmosphere to regulate itself.

Greenspaces within the Urban environment can aid the regulation of air quality (biogenic regulation). Vegetation can act as an enhanced deposition sink for gaseous and particulate pollution (Fowler 1989; Freer-Smith *et al.* 1997; Hirano 1996); tree canopies capture particles more effectively than any other vegetation type due to their greater surface roughness (Manning & Feder 1980) which increases turbulent deposition and impaction processes. Within the Urban environment, the interception of particles by vegetation is typically far greater for street trees than for more distant vegetation due to their proximity to high intensities of road traffic (Impens & Delcarte 1979).

Urban trees are said to have reduced atmospheric PM_{10} by 0.4% and 0.72% in Chicago (McPherson *et al.* 1994) and Philadelphia (Nowak *et al.* 1997; Nowak 2006) respectively. More recently, dispersion modelling has predicted potential PM_{10} reduction by increasing tree cover in Glasgow, the West Midlands (McDonald *et al.* 2007) and London (Tiwary *et al.* 2009). Such studies show how Urban trees can contribute to the regulation of air quality (see also Chapter 23).

High rates of transpiration, in addition to shading and pollutant uptake effects, help to reduce localised particulate concentrations by lowering Urban air temperatures. Moll (1996) suggests that up to 12% of air pollution problems in cities are attributable to heat island effects due to the temperature-dependent formation of many pollutants, such as volatile organic compounds (VOCs) and ozone (Nowak *et al.* 1997), and the dynamics of particulate dispersal.

10.3.2.2 Soil quality

There are a variety of both engineered soils and modified natural soils in the Urban environment. Urban soils are moved, mixed, compacted, burned and changed by mineral and chemical additives, and show extreme diversity (Vrscaj *et al.* 2008). The condition, degree of compaction and associated biological activity affects the services they provide (Young & Ritz 2005; Wood *et al.* 2005). Urban soils are often structurally highly degraded, leading to a loss of porosity and a decreased ability to infiltrate and store water; this increases runoff and has consequences for regulating ecosystem services such as flood alleviation, water purification and water storage. In addition, the ability of poor quality soil to support vegetation is reduced (Jim 1998).

10.3.2.3 Water quality

Urban rivers are frequently used as receiving bodies for sewage treatment plant effluents and stormwater discharges. They provide a habitat for a variety of flora and fauna both in-channel and within associated riparian corridors (Petts *et al.* 2002). These riparian corridors are of particular value in Urban areas, providing habitats that can contribute to further regulating services such as pollination, noise regulation and sequestration of carbon. The regulation of water quality is discussed in Chapters 9 and 14.

10.3.2.4 Noise regulation

Aircraft noise alone is estimated to cost the EU £10–40 billion annually, mainly due to impacts on urban areas (Dekkers & van der Straaten 2008); road noise also has major economic costs in urban areas. In terms of its impact on human health, environmental noise has been linked to various non-auditory effects including increased risk of hypertension (Barregard *et al.* 2009; Jarup *et al.* 2008), impaired cognitive development in children (Stansfield & Matheson 2003) and psychological stress (Evans *et al.* 1995, 2001). The negative effects of noise on health and education performance are further discussed in Chapter 14. High noise levels have also been shown to affect bird species adversely (Quinn *et al.* 2006; Habib *et al.* 2007), particularly grassland birds (Forman *et al.* 2002; Green *et al.* 2000). Some species have been shown to modify their signalling behaviour in terms of timing, or increased sound frequency and volume (Slabbekoorn & Ripmeester 2008).

Various Urban subhabitats provide mechanisms for reducing noise pollution. A major factor in the delivery of this service is ground characteristics; for example, soft lawn reduces noise levels by up to 3 dB relative to concrete paving (Bolund & Hunhammar 1999).

10.3.2.5 Climate regulation

Large areas of heat-absorbing surfaces, and high-energy use within city environments, contribute to an increased UHI, which all natural surfaces can help to reduce. Urban water areas level out temperature extremes in summer and winter, strongly influencing Urban microclimates. Vegetation is important as it results in more energy-driving transpiration as opposed to turbulent sensible heat (Grimmond 2009). One large tree can transpire 450 litres of water per day, consuming 1,000 megajoules of heat energy to drive the evaporation process. In this way, city trees can lower summer temperatures (Hough 1989) and, combined with their ability to provide shade and reduce wind speeds, reduce the need for summer air conditioning and winter heating (McPherson *et al.* 1997). A single shade tree in Los Angeles, USA, avoids the combustion of 18 kg of carbon annually, in addition to the 4.5–11 kg it sequesters; therefore, in terms of climate regulation, it is worth 3–5 forest trees (Akbari 2002).

Moisture from soil contributes to climate regulation by facilitating cooling and effective transpiration in vegetation (Wood *et al.* 2005). The role of Urban soils in the global carbon cycle and their capacity to sequester atmospheric carbon dioxide remain largely unclear; however, the flux of carbon to soil in plant residues is highly significant in the carbon cycle (Schlesinger & Andrews 2000). Greenhouse gases are emitted from the soil into the atmosphere, the most significant of which are methane and nitrous oxide. Climate regulation is also discussed in Chapter 14.

10.3.2.6 Hazard regulation (including erosion and flood risk management)

Vegetation roots help to bind and stabilise the soil which, combined with the effect of leaves and branches on reducing the impact of rainstorms, helps to lessen the rate of soil erosion and downstream sedimentation. This physical protection brings significant benefits for highway drainage and wastewater management by restricting sediment loss (Lull & Sopper 1969).

The study of a river catchment in south-east Northumberland estimated the value of existing woodlands for flood alleviation at around £1,200 per ha. This figure is based on savings to the engineering costs of flood risk management (NUFU 2005).

10.3.2.7 Pollination

Pollination potentially has a large impact on regulating the provision of final ecosystem services such as crops (Chapter 14). Gardens play a key role in providing habitats for pollinators, such as solitary and social bees (McFrederick & LeBuhn 2006; Frankie *et al.* 2009), and this is reflected in the subsequent pollination service (Cussans *et al.* 2010). Results of the National Bumblebee Nest Survey 2004 (Osborne *et al.* 2008) indicated that there were much higher densities of bumblebee nests in gardens than in farmland habitats (such as grassland, woodlands, hedgerows and fencelines). And in a single garden in Leicester, 35% of British hoverfly species have been found (Owen *et al.* 1981).

Gardeners are keen to grow long-lasting displays of flowers, so gardens tend to provide a diversity of nectar and pollen resources for flower-visiting insects all year-round (Stelzer *et al.* 2010). They also provide a variety of nesting opportunities for bees. The high density of nests and faster growth rates observed (Goulson *et al.* 2002) are believed to be due to the extent of resources provided and the diversity of habitats afforded by a patchwork of gardens managed in very different ways by different owners (Gaston *et al.* 2007). There is also some evidence that pollination levels of particular plant species are higher in gardens than in arable farmland (Cussans *et al.* 2010), suggesting that the diversity and abundance of bees and other pollinators in suburban habitats provides a strong pollination service compared to agricultural landscapes where pollination can be limiting. In turn, they and the resultant seeds, berries and other fruits are likely to provide important resources for other wildlife (such as small mammals and birds) in Urban areas.

10.3.2.8 Diseases and pests

Diseases and pests affect greenspace in Urban areas and are particularly important during extreme temperatures when vegetation is already under stress, for example from UHI or poor quality soil. Many are invasive species that are unknowingly imported via infected planting stock, and are of particular concern in relation to the extensive planting of newly created areas of greenspace. Prevalence of invasive species is predicted to increase under changing climatic conditions. Steps to reduce the impact of these projected increases have been proposed in relation to trees (Tubby & Webber 2010) and include policies associated with plant health legislation.

10.3.3 Cultural Services

The UK NEA considers the environmental settings provided by the natural environment to be a cultural service that, through people's interactions with it, provides various goods and benefits (Chapter 16). This section explores a range of these goods and benefits in an Urban context.

10.3.3.1 Physical and mental health

The majority of people live in Urban areas where access to greenspace is lower than in any other habitat. Yet an increasing amount of literature supports the view that access to good quality Urban greenspace is essential for physical activity, positive mental well-being and healthy childhood development (Sadler *et al.* 2010). The health benefits of Urban greening are also discussed in Chapter 16 and Chapter 23. Benefits arise from most subhabitats and even the most fragmented green corridors can provide excellent opportunities for physical activity.

Regular physical activity contributes to the prevention and management of over 20 conditions that are major costs to the National Health Service including coronary heart disease, diabetes, obesity and certain types of cancer (Liu *et al.* 2007; Pretty 2004). Epidemiological research has found strong links between health and greenspace in large conurbations (de Vries *et al.* 2003; Maas *et al.* 2006, 2008), with access to walkable greenspace linked to longevity in the elderly (Takano *et al.* 2002; Mitchell & Popham 2008). Living in close proximity to greenspace has been shown to promote physical exercise (Bird 2004). Good quality open spaces encourage people to make short journeys on foot or by bike, and web-based tools, such as Walkit, enable people to avoid areas with poor air quality (Sustrans 2009).

Associations between greenspace and a reduced risk of anxiety and depression are well-documented (Maas *et al.* 2008; Pretty *et al.* 2005; Pretty *et al.* 2004; Grahn & Stigsdotter 2003; Maller *et al.* 2002; Kellert & Wilson 1993; Ulrich *et al.* 1991), with even moderate activity within greenspace improving depression (Natural England 2006). Contact with nature has been shown to promote a better mood (van den Berg *et al.* 2003; Hartig *et al.* 2003) and improve attention (Hartig *et al.* 2003; Ottosson & Grahn 2005). Benefits to cognitive restoration (Kuo 2001; Taylor *et al.* 2002) and self-discipline (Taylor 2009) have also been recorded; these restorative benefits are thought to stem from nature's ability to promote temporary escape and connectedness (Kaplan & Kaplan 1989).

Healthy childhood development is associated with greenspace. Children with access to safe, green areas are more likely to be physically active and less likely to be overweight (Gong 2009; Health Scotland 2008; Wells & Evans 2003). Contact with nature has also been shown to reduce the severity of Attention Deficit Hyperactivity Disorder (ADHD) symptoms in children (Taylor 2009).

Urban rivers have been linked to a variety of mental and physical health benefits, from promoting environmental consciousness and engendering a sense of well-being, to providing increased opportunity for exercise and fresh air (Landrigan *et al.* 2004; Curtis *et al.* 2002; Tapsell *et al* 2001; Environment Agency 2002, 2006; GLA 2004).

Few studies have sought to determine a relationship between the level of biodiversity and human health and well-being in Urban areas (see Chapter 23, Section 23.1.2). One study shows that psychological benefits increase with the species richness of Urban parks (Fuller *et al.* 2007). Botkin and Beveridge (1997) concluded that vegetation is essential for living reasonably within an Urban environment.

10.3.3.2 Heritage

Neighbourhood development and social and environmental citizenship. Good quality greenspace can foster better levels of community cohesion and promote social inclusion (Fredrickson & Anderson 1999). Research has shown that community open space and natural settings enhance social ties and a sense of community in older adults (Kweon *et al.* 1998; Sullivan *et al.* 2004) and can promote social integration within disadvantaged communities (Dines *et al.* 2006). Maas *et al.* (2008) found that having less greenspace in our environment coincided with feelings of loneliness and

perceived shortage of social support. Greenspace may also have the potential to reduce health inequalities between the rich and poor (Mitchell & Popham 2008).

Risbeth (in press) found that the experience of first generation migrants in negotiating the Urban landscape was a key aspect in the process of cultural adaptation and social integration, facilitating feelings of belonging. Several studies have found that the social use of parks by minority ethnic groups tends to be in large family or friendship groups (Worpole & Greenhalgh 1995; Burgess *et al.* 1988). This reflects other research, carried out in rural contexts, which shows that many ethnic minority groups, particularly Asians, connect to the landscape via the focus of food and picnics. Limited studies have suggested that greenspace may enhance feelings of social safety in a neighbourhood and help to reduce aggression and crime (Kuo & Sullivan 2001a, 2001b).

Cultural heritage. In the UK, our environments are all heavily infused with the cultural values and histories of human use. Through their differing heritages, every environmental setting is capable of being interpreted as possessing a distinctive sense of place, including Urban areas. However, while certain versions of national or regional identity have developed around Urban areas and spectacular architectural sites and monuments, sense of place appears to be formed around typically rural landscapes (Weiner 2004).

10.3.3.3 Recreation and tourism, and aesthetic and inspirational benefits

In Urban areas, accessible, high quality environments are used by all ages for informal recreation and community events (CABE 2010). Parks provide multiple, concurrent services to the specific areas within which they are located (CABE 2005a). In England, 48% of the population use these spaces at least once a week (Thornton 2009), and, in Scotland, 42% of adults (16+) use them (Scottish Government 2009); 87% of the population said they used their local parks or open spaces regularly (DCLG 2008a). Survey data reveal that 91% of the public believe that parks and open spaces improve quality of life, and 74% believe that parks and open spaces are important to health and mental and physical well-being (CABE 2004). Such sites are considered critical for allowing experiences of Urban wildlife (Defra 2006a). Many of the tourist attractions in cities and towns are built heritage; nevertheless, they are often in historic parks which contribute to their aesthetic value.

10.3.3.4 Spiritual and/or religious benefits

The primary purpose of churchyards and cemeteries is spiritual and religious service provision, space for quiet contemplation, and historic and symbolic value. In 2006, Church of England average weekly attendances were over one million (Church of England 2007), suggesting that churchyards and burial grounds remain a major component of people's regular interaction with nature.

Habitats that contain water are often used for spiritual contemplation as this element is considered peaceful and symbolic. Urban rivers are considered as remnants of nature (Eden *et al.* 2000) offering Urban communities a chance to reconnect with water in both a spiritual and cultural context.

10.3.3.5 Educational benefits

Outdoor play contributes to positive cognitive development (National Heart Forum 2007) and includes wildlife conservation, biodiversity and environmental education (Leather & Quicke 2009). Ecological knowledge is being lost in wealthier countries (Pilgrim *et al.* 2008), and, in the UK, awareness of local wildlife appears to have declined in recent decades (Bebbington 2005; Cheeseman & Key 2007), especially in children where outside play is presently less favoured than other activities (Valentine & McKendrick 1997). Such trends are particularly relevant in minority ethnic groups whose experience of nature occurs predominantly in Urban contexts (Davies *et al.* 2009; Wong 2007). Loss of ecological knowledge is a loss of substantial economic value as it contributes to a wide range of current and future ecosystem goods and services (Pilgrim *et al.* 2008).

10.3.4 Delivery of Ecosystem Services by the Urban Environment

In recent years, housing density has increased (Bibby 2009), driven by demographic and economic pressure and associated planning, housing and transport policies. Coupled with loss and deterioration of greenspace (e.g. sales of playing fields, poor condition of parks, sale of allotments, reduced tree planting, paving of front gardens, infilling), ecosystem services have been heavily compromised. Where the built environment dominates the landscape, particularly in city centres, it is clear that even the most essential of ecosystem services are ineffective: pollution overwhelms the regulating services, impermeable surfaces make climate and hazard regulation ineffective and affect water quality and water supply, and *per capita* provision of greenspace is at its lowest.

The additional ecosystem services that could potentially be derived from Urban areas appear to be substantial. Their importance to our health and general well-being has not previously been recognised. It is not just the limited extent and variable quality, but also spatial distribution and accessibility, that currently create barriers to optimising existing Urban ecosystem services. Strategic planning and resourcing will be required to take full advantage of opportunities that Urban ecosystems could deliver, but it appears that major advances could be achieved with relatively low investment.

10.3.5 Valuing Urban Greenspace in the UK

Examples of economic analysis of greenspaces are highly variable. In Philadelphia, USA, the park system was valued at $1 billion (Trust for Public Land 2008), while, in England, public parks have been allocated a value as low as £1 (CABE 2009b). An estimate of the value of local trees has been calculated for the Torbay area of Devon, England (**Box 10.5**).

In Chapter 22 of the UK NEA, key ecosystem services provided by Urban greenspace in the UK are valued using the benefit transfer method. These benefits include recreation, aesthetics, physical and mental health, neighbourhood development, noise regulation and air pollution reduction all of which are provided to local residents as a bundled good in relation to the distance of a dwelling from parks and greenspaces. Nevertheless, some important and essential services, like the impact of Urban greenspace on the reduction of downstream flooding risks, are not covered. The values presented should, therefore, be treated as lower bound estimates.

Box 10.5 i-Tree Eco Project in Torbay, Devon.

Introduction: The UK's pilot i-Tree Eco Project was carried out in order to measure the value of the ecosystem services that Torbay's trees provide. The project applied a system (i-Tree Eco) that has been successfully used in other countries, but which had previously not been applied to the UK.

Project aims: i) Complete a pilot i-Tree Eco Project in the UK, providing a specific UK benchmark allowing the system to be applied elsewhere. ii) To quantify the ecosystem services of Torbay's trees and provide monetary values for these services in order to establish a datum point from which to measure future trends and to demonstrate the value of its trees. iii) To demonstrate the benefits of the Urban forest to communities, businesses and policy makers, thereby promoting an ecosystem services approach.

Methods: The UK pilot was delivered as a partnership between Hi-line (project management and field work), Davey Group (i-Tree Eco developers), Forest Research (UK data handling) and Torbay Council (host area), with assistance from Natural England. In the summer of 2010, information on tree cover, size, species, tree health and ground cover was collected by trained arboriculturalists from 250 random plots stratified by land use across Torbay. Region-specific data on climate, hourly pollution and growth rates were also collated and fed into the model.

Results: Torbay's Urban forest contains 818,000 trees representing an estimated structural asset of £280,000,000. These trees provide the equivalent of £345,811 in ecosystem services annually. An estimated 98,100 tonnes (15.4 t/ha) of carbon (C) is stored in Torbay's trees, with an additional gross sequestration rate of 4279 tC/yr. This equates to £1,474,508 in storage and £64,316 in annual sequestration. Contributions to improving air quality of Torbay total over 50 tonnes of pollutants removed every year which equates to an annual estimated value of £281,495 (Rogers *et al.* 2011).

Full results for the project will be made available in a report to be published in 2011. For more information contact: trees@torbay.gov.uk .

i-Tree is a free peer-reviewed software suite (originally The Urban Forest Effects Model (UFORE)) which has been designed by the United States Forest Service. i-Tree has been used to quantify Urban forest structure, function and values in numerous communities throughout the world. For more information visit www.i-treetools.org

Torbay i-Tree Eco Project: Key Findings (population: 134,000; area: 6,375 ha)	
Ecosystem Service	**Value per ha**
Carbon Storage (98,100 tonnes)	£240.00
Carbon Sequestration (4,279 tonnes)	£10.09
Annual Pollution Filtration (50 tonnes)	£44.15
Total Annual benefits	**£54.24**

On average, people living closer to a park typically derive more benefits from its presence than those living further away. There are several reasons for this and include the fact that the fraction of people using the site for recreational purposes decreases with distance from the site (Bateman *et al.* 2006); and some of the non-recreation ecosystem services, such as noise abatement and pollution reduction, tend to be greater the closer people live to the site.

Based on the selected data used in the analysis by Perino *et al.* (2010) (which supports Chapter 22 and has been chosen in relation to distance from parks and a limited set of services and goods arising), Chapter 26 presents the changes in Urban ecosystem services implied by the six UK NEA scenarios (Chapter 25) by 2060. Depending on the scenario, urban households stand to gain (about £8,000 per urban household) or lose (about £-40,000 per urban household) substantial amounts.

A number of additional ecosystem services provided by Urban greenspace are covered in Chapter 22, such as recreational day trips and the amenity value and health benefits derived from domestic gardens that are not included in the values presented above.

10.4 Trade-offs and Synergies Among Urban Goods and Ecosystem Services

In this section, we provide some examples of synergies among ecosystem services and consider possible trade-offs. There are many complex issues to consider, particularly for plantings, where ecosystem assessments could aid decision-making. However, before trade-offs are considered, options for multifunctional use should be explored.

10.4.1 Synergies

Urban vegetation is essential to ecosystem service provision. Trees, grasslands and heaths, as well as water bodies, can have a dramatic impact in reducing UHI effects. Increasing tree cover by 25%, for example was estimated to reduce afternoon air temperatures by between 5–10°C (Zipperer *et al.* 1997; ASLA 2011). With up to 12% of air pollution problems in cities attributable to UHI effects (Moll 1996), lower Urban temperature would be indirectly beneficial. Research by Gill *et al.* (2007) suggests that increasing tree cover in Urban areas by 10% could reduce surface water runoff by almost 6%, and increasing greenspace by 10%, could reduce it by almost 5%. Replacement of mature trees with younger trees typically results in considerable reductions in benefits derived from ecosystem services (NUFU 2005). Therefore, multiple benefits would arise from increasing Urban greenspace through schemes such as tree planting programmes, with the synergistic ecosystem services improving the resilience of cities to climate change (GLA 2010).

Well-planned and managed parks, gardens and squares have a positive impact on the value of nearby properties, attracting inward human and capital investment. Increases in property values range between 0–34%, with a typical increase of about 5% (CABE 2005b). They are also used and appreciated more often, and landscape design is critical to ecosystem service interactions and the cultural importance of these greenspaces (CABE 2010).

Synergies between the goods and services provided by aquatic ecosystems have important implications for Urban management. Leaving rivers in a more natural state enhances local flood attenuation and flood storage capacity, while reducing downstream flooding, and is a cost-effective alternative to traditional engineering (Environment Agency 2002). Urban river restoration can provide multiple benefits similar to sustainable drainage systems (Skinner & Bruce-Burgess 2005), as has been shown where concrete channels have been broken down and rivers re-meandered to allow flows to reduce and to provide access to historic floodplains (Defra 2004; Environment Agency 2005, 2006; **Box 10.6**).

New driveways legislation (e.g. in England, Statutory Instrument No. 2362 (2008) requires that permeable paving be used if garden areas are to be paved over to facilitate drainage, reduce flooding and remove pollution from these surfaces, particularly in high frequency, low magnitude events. Planning permission is now required to cover a front garden with an impermeable material (DCLG 2009b). Tree planting schemes can mitigate the effects of soil-sealing, but their adoption has, so far, been patchy and uncoordinated.

Transport policies to encourage walking and cycling, and support low energy technologies, will benefit ecosystem services. Future market penetration of cleaner vehicle technologies, such as hybrid, fully electric and hydrogen fuel cell vehicles, could significantly contribute to improvements in Urban air quality and reduce greenhouse gas emissions and noise (NAIGT 2008; TfL 2008).

The combined ecosystem services, goods and benefits that good quality, accessible public parks can provide are substantial. Programmes to improve their facilities and encourage greater use will help to improve physical and mental health, childhood development, social cohesion, aesthetics and other important cultural benefits. More parks of different sizes and locations will also contribute substantially to regulating services of air quality including dispersion, mixing and deposition, cooling for climate regulation, water drainage and flood protection. Havens for wildlife and provisioning services further contribute to an under-valued resource.

10.4.2 Trade-offs

A significant and obvious trade-off occurs between the extent of the built environment in comparison to greenspace within an Urban area. Options to use built environment as a surface for plantings or to incorporate improved permeable surfaces within the built areas appear extensive.

Here, we provide selected examples to illustrate some of the conflicts that can arise between options to increase ecosystems services. Few studies have been completed to date. Many trade-offs result from complex interactions between biological systems and other components of the

Box 10.6 Sustainable Drainage Systems (SuDS).

The term sustainable drainage systems (SuDS) (also known as stormwater best management practices: BMPs) covers a wide range of systems, such as constructed wetlands, infiltration trenches, swales and porous paving, which approach the issue of stormwater management from a different perspective to that of conventional systems. Rather than piping stormwater away, SuDS aim to manage stormwater as close as possible to its source, reducing runoff volumes and rates. This is achieved in the first instance by infiltrating, but where this is not possible, by collecting, temporarily storing and subsequently discharging stormwater at a controlled rate to the soil, receiving water or sewer system. In addition to managing water volume, SuDS also mitigate water quality through facilitating the occurrence of a complex interaction of biological, chemical and physical processes (e.g. microbial degradation, photolysis and adsorption), offering opportunities to reduce energy costs associated with mechanised water treatment through the provision of localised passive treatment options. Furthermore, SuDS may also provide social amenity, habitat and recreational benefits through the provision of green infrastructure in Urban environments. According to Scottish Planning Policy (SPP 2010) and English legislation (PPS25 2006), the use of SuDS to manage stormwater is required within all new housing developments before it is discharged into the water environment.

The Ardler Regeneration Project in Dundee, Scotland, is an award-winning case study demonstrating the strategic use of SuDS within urban redevelopment. This public, private, community and voluntary organisation partnership drove the regeneration of a 1960s high and medium density housing estate covering a 58 ha site. Prior to its regeneration, Ardler suffered high levels of anti-social behaviour and its population had fallen by 50%. With the key objective of making Ardler a thriving regional centre, the area was completely remodelled over a 10-year period, with work completed in 2008. As an area prone to flooding, the management of surface water was a priority issue and the decision was taken to disconnect surface water from the main trunk sewer. A suite of SuDS was then used throughout the site to retain and treat surface water flows, which were then discharged into the local watercourse. As well as successfully managing surface water runoff, the use of SuDS has additionally provided a network of greenspace including two ponds, a pocket park combined with a detention basin and a football pitch combined with a flood storage zone, all linked by numerous swales. A key factor in the wider success of this regeneration project is recognised to have been the high level of stakeholder collaboration at project inception, with the development of a combined vision to create a sustainable development and community (Scottish Government 2009b; Greenspace Scotland 2007).

Figure 1 SuDS in Ardler Village, Dundee, Scotland. Source: image by kind permission of Alison Duffy, UWTC, University of Abertay Dundee. Based on Google map © 2009 Infoterrra Ltd & Bluesky, © 2009 Europa Technologies, © 2009 Tele Atlas.

Urban environment. Vegetation, for example, can act as an enhanced deposition sink for gaseous and particulate pollution (Fowler 1989; Freer-Smith 1997; Hirano 1996) and provide many other ecosystem services. However, the value of plantings is partly dependent on species composition and quantity, as well as location. Volatile Organic Compounds generated by oaks (most abundant in London), willows and poplars, for example, can contribute to ozone formation and worsen air quality if present in sufficient densities (Donovan *et al.* 2005), in contrast to species with much lower emissions. Similar trade-offs are found in other systems such as green roofs and roof gardens. The goods and benefits arising from a range of new plantings can be highlighted by ecosystem assessments that will help inform decision-making across this very important area, extending ecosystem service provision.

Resources required for the management and maintenance of greenspaces are an important consideration; for example, plantings require water and regular upkeep and have associated cost implications. The resources that are required will be dependent on the design of each scheme. The creation of greenspaces using landscaping close to semi-natural vegetation typically requires less water than more intensive schemes, and is more beneficial for biodiversity, forming a valuable part of a more widely connected ecosystem. Given climate predictions of greater urban drought stress (GLA 2010), good design for a locale may also benefit from incorporating water capture and storage techniques.

There is widespread channelisation and culverting of Urban water bodies to manage floodwaters (Scholes *et al.* 2008). Although it reduces localised flooding, the flood may simply be shifted to a downstream location. Conversely, the direct discharge of stormwater into receiving waters can have a negative effect. Impacts include the erosion of riverbanks and in-stream sediments, and the addition of an associated stormwater pollutant load (e.g. pollutants from vehicles and microbial organisms,) resulting in the prevalence of pollution-tolerant aquatic and riparian species.

A major conflict between air quality and climate change in Urban areas arises from the use of biomass boilers, which reduce greenhouse gas emissions, but increase nitrogen oxides and PM_{10} emissions. Biomass fuel is a key growth area, driven by the recently published Renewable Energy Strategy (DECC 2009) and the UK's binding target to produce 15% of energy from renewable sources by 2020. Conversely, any urban transport policies that restrict the use of diesel vehicles within city centres, as has occurred in Germany, are likely to benefit air quality at the expense of greater carbon dioxide emissions from less fuel-efficient petrol vehicles.

10.5 Options for Sustainable Management

Options for improving ecosystem service delivery through sustainable management are substantial, but require careful evaluation at appropriate scales. For example, regional tree planting schemes, green bridges, green roofs, roof gardens and green corridors can all increase regulating, supporting and cultural services and improve biodiversity, but there are trade-offs to consider, particularly where drivers such as climate change and air pollution are in conflict. In

Box 10.7 Case study of ecosystem service mapping in the Thames Gateway region. Source: THESAURUS project (2006–2008).

The THESAURUS project, supported by the Department for Environment, Food and Rural Affairs Natural Environment Policy Research Programme Phase II (2006 to 2008), sought to assess the types of ecosystem services provided within Kent Thameside (**Figure 1**), an area undergoing extensive urban regeneration, and how best they could be evaluated within current land use planning and decision-making frameworks (Sheate *et al.* 2008). The area is part of the Government's Thames Gateway Growth Area within the Sustainable Communities Plan and already under some considerable environmental constraints in terms of water resource availability, flood risk, air quality, transport and biodiversity. However, there are extensive areas of brownfield land available in North Kent for new development, resulting from historic quarry and cement works activity, and derelict industrial and ports sites, in particular. The Channel Tunnel Rail Link (CTRL) passes through Kent Thameside and the new CTRL station at Ebbsfleet is also located within the area.

Figure 1 Kent Thameside. *Photo courtesy of William Sheate.*

The project focused on the Kent Thameside Green Grid initiative—an important planning concept designed to improve the environmental perception of the Gateway, enhance environmental assets with a network of greenspaces and corridors, recognise the importance of multifunctional greenspaces for community life, and help ensure that greenspaces can also provide important adaptation tools, for example, in relation to helping with flood relief and in improving quality of life. The project explored ecosystem services delivered by the Green Grid at two different scales—sub-regional and local—and related ecosystem services to land use/land cover categories, rather than simply to habitats, since this approach is more appropriate for spatial planning within an Urban context. To connect land use/land cover categories to the ecosystem services they deliver, the open space categories of PPG17 (Planning Policy Guidance 17: Planning for open space, sport and recreation) were used and a network analysis technique applied to understand the relationship between the typology of ecosystem services developed for Kent Thameside (using stakeholder engagement) and the different open space/Green Grid land use/land cover categories for which a range of geographic information system (GIS) datasets already exist. This relationship allowed the ecosystem services delivered by specific land use/land cover categories to be traced, and consequently made the reverse also possible, i.e. to trace back from desired ecosystem services to the various land use/land cover categories that have the potential to deliver those services. Consequently, it was possible to physically map those services using GIS by combining the appropriate existing datasets relating to land use/land cover, e.g. for potential flood regulation services, or visual aesthetic services, etc. (see **Figure 2**).

Network analysis proved to be a useful technique to engage with stakeholders and to understand the relationships between land use/land cover categories and the ecosystem services they provide. GIS was used to represent the land use/land cover types—and thereby ecosystem services—spatially by combining a range of existing datasets. This geographical representation was not without difficulties, including the problems posed by combining different types of datasets of different quality and scale. Any errors or assumptions contained in datasets can be compounded if combined with other datasets; similarly, by combining good quality data with poor quality data it could result in data of unknown quality and unknown limitations. However, it did prove possible to use existing datasets to represent ecosystem services spatially, most usefully at the strategic level; at the local level, the existing datasets are rarely of a resolution sufficiently fine enough to distinguish the heterogeneity of the local

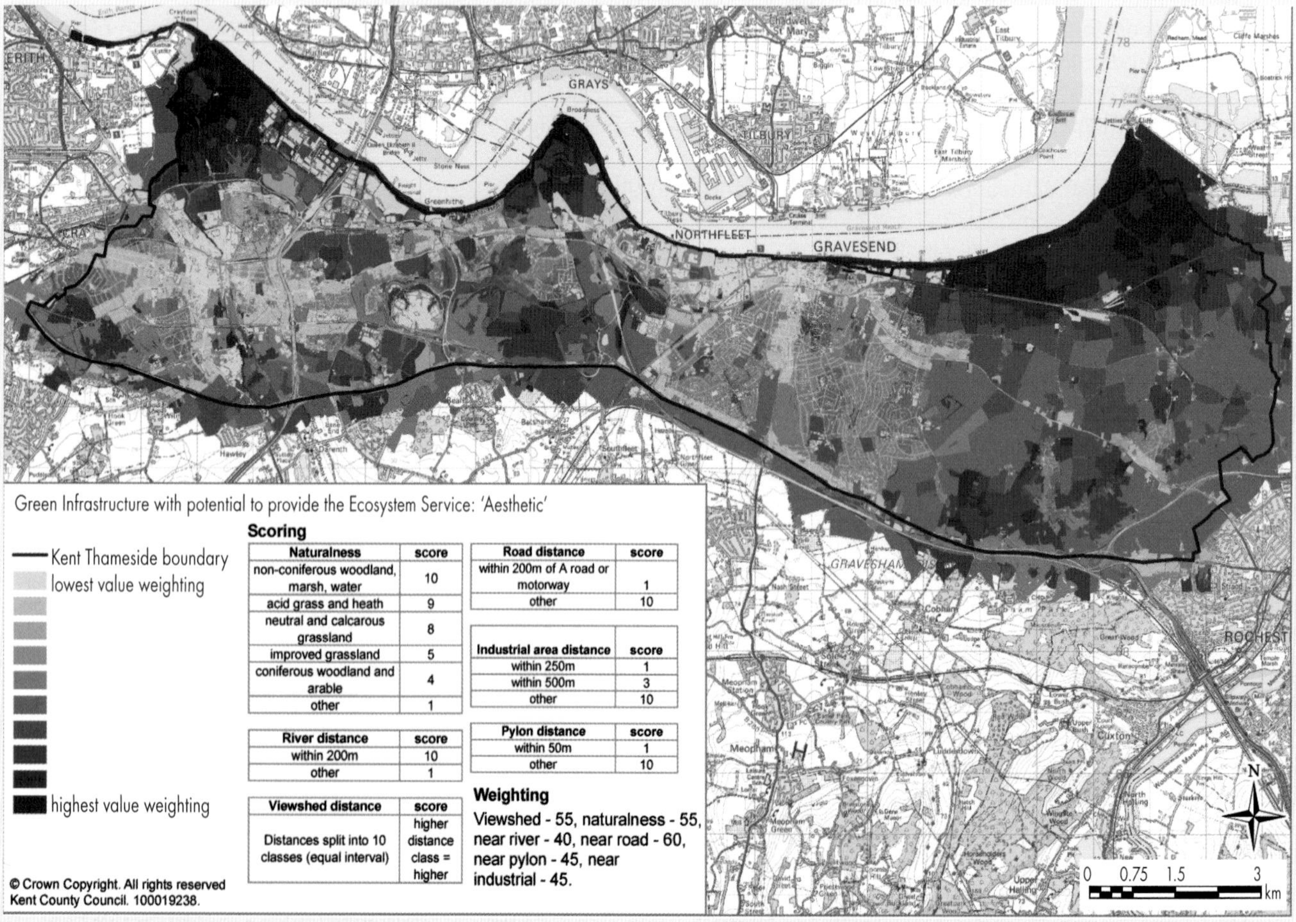

Green Infrastructure with potential to provide the Ecosystem Service: 'Aesthetic'

— Kent Thameside boundary
lowest value weighting

highest value weighting

© Crown Copyright. All rights reserved
Kent County Council. 100019238.

Scoring

Naturalness	score
non-coniferous woodland, marsh, water	10
acid grass and heath	9
neutral and calcarous grassland	8
improved grassland	5
coniferous woodland and arable	4
other	1

River distance	score
within 200m	10
other	1

Viewshed distance	score
Distances split into 10 classes (equal interval)	higher distance class = higher

Road distance	score
within 200m of A road or motorway	1
other	10

Industrial area distance	score
within 250m	1
within 500m	3
other	10

Pylon distance	score
within 50m	1
other	10

Weighting
Viewshed - 55, naturalness - 55, near river - 40, near road - 60, near pylon - 45, near industrial - 45.

0 0.75 1.5 3
km

Figure 2 Green infrastructure with potential to provide the Ecosystem Service: 'Aesthetic'. Source: Sheate *et al.* (2008). © Crown Copyright and/or database right. All rights reserved. License number 100051548.

environment, although even here, the GIS could be useful in identifying areas with potential for multifunctionality. At the local level, a combination of 'ground-truthing', using aerial photography and site visits, and local public consultation proved to be successful in getting a better understanding of the sorts of ecosystem services delivered by local greenspace. Information gathered in this way was readily translated using network analysis into a typology of local-level ecosystem services by tracing possible management interventions through the interaction pathways back to the associated land cover types. Network analysis proved a useful tool to represent the complexity of an ecosystem and the interactions between its various components.

The ability to map ecosystem services in this way offers real benefits to spatial planning, particularly in promoting multifunctionality, by ensuring that Green Grids (or greenspace generally) help to proactively shape development, planning around what exists and its potential, rather than their delivery simply occurring reactively through development. Ecosystem services also provide a different focus for discussion with stakeholders, with the potential to help reduce the common problem of trade-off between different interests through seeking to deliver multiple services and multiple benefits. Such an approach offers the potential to make baseline data in Sustainability Appraisals and Strategic Environmental Assessments much more relevant to the assessment process by combining datasets in a useful way for planners and decision-making. What GIS and network analysis could not do in this project was quantify the amount of an ecosystem service that was present or desirable, i.e. relate ecosystem services to environmental limits. These shortfalls are not insurmountable and point to the need for more research to develop the tools further.

other cases, ecosystem services can be addressed locally through actions such as: replacing impermeable surfaces with porous materials; encouraging better use of domestic gardens; allocating space for allotments; improving conditions and services in public parks; supporting community engagement and social cohesion; and better greenspace provision for young people.

10.5.1 Planning for Multiple Benefits

Issues relating to scale are crucial to inform sustainable management and multifunctional land use; therefore, each development should be considered accordingly. Two case studies illustrate how multifunctional land use can be applied in new developments to maximise ecosystem goods and service provision. One is a recent case study in the Thames Gateway area of South East England (Sheate *et al.* 2008; THESAURUS Project 2008; **Box 10.7**) and the second is from Stoke-on-Trent (**Box 10.8**). They show how ecosystem services can be evaluated within current land use planning frameworks to inform strategic decision-making and encourage a broad range of land uses.

10.5.2 Increasing Surface Permeability, Planting and Creation of Additional Greenspace

Options exist to increase the permeability of a range of surfaces, especially roads, which constitute a significant part of the built environment (12% in London). By limiting the use of non-permeable surfaces and changing the type of building materials, ecosystem services associated with Urban climate, such as temperature and flood regulation, could be substantially increased (GLA 2010; Smith & Levermore 2008).

Allotments, community gardens and outdoor markets are being established on the paved, previously unproductive, surfaces of Urban areas. For example, the Urban Garden Project in Middlesborough has turned unused land, such as roundabouts, into 'makeshift' allotments (One North East 2007). Better use of disused areas, vacant (uncontaminated) PDL, reservoir banks, disused railway lines and urban roofs and walls for gardens, horticulture (**Box 10.9**), and many other community initiatives is already occurring, contributing to enhanced cultural and provisioning services (Pretty 2002, 2004; Mulholland 2008).

Although not classified as an ecosystem, the built environment provides havens for birds and other organisms, offers extensive space for vegetation (**Box 10.9**) for wildlife,

horticulture and food production, as well as opportunities for leisure and recreation, and should be considered as a potential area for substantially enhancing Urban ecosystem services.

Increased tree planting and the creation of additional greenspace offer potential for flood storage (GLA 2010) and reduced UHI effects (Smith & Levermore 2008). Such active policies create more open space (pollution dispersion), shade (cooling), new opportunities for recreation and healthy lifestyles, and improved aesthetic value which contributes to cultural services (Trees in Cities 2010). Protecting existing areas and designating new ones that can provide these services are important, and approaches such as Natural England's Sustainable Alternative Natural Greenspace (SANGs) which was successfully used in relation to the Thames Basin Heaths Special Protection Area (SPA) provides a useful example of such mechanisms.

10.5.3 Mapping and Assessments

Accurate mapping of the Urban environment is crucial if planning is to be used more effectively for ecosystem service delivery. Scottish Natural Heritage has recently analysed aerial photographs to identify different types of greenspace in two thirds of Scottish authorities; this has been digitally mapped for planning purposes. It has enabled the understanding and planning of natural habitat networks, facilitated the creation of positive and appropriate recreation provision, and taken account of natural heritage in inner cities (Greenspace Scotland 2009; CABE 2009a). There are opportunities to plan open space provision around that already in existence, with potential for multifunctional provision rather than *ad hoc* designation of areas of open space as a side effect of development.

Incorporating elements, such as lakes and ponds, street trees, small woodlands and green bridges, into new developments can significantly improve the economic value of developments (TDAG 2008) and the interconnection between Urban habitats (Sheate *et al.* 2008). However, it is essential to understand and map ecosystem service provision at different scales for such spatial planning to be most effective.

Urban ecosystem assessments supported by funded maintenance and management schemes would aid ecosystem service delivery. A national strategy on Urban tree management, for example, could address deterioration in tree condition in inner cities, protect ancient and mature trees, recommend appropriate tree species for new

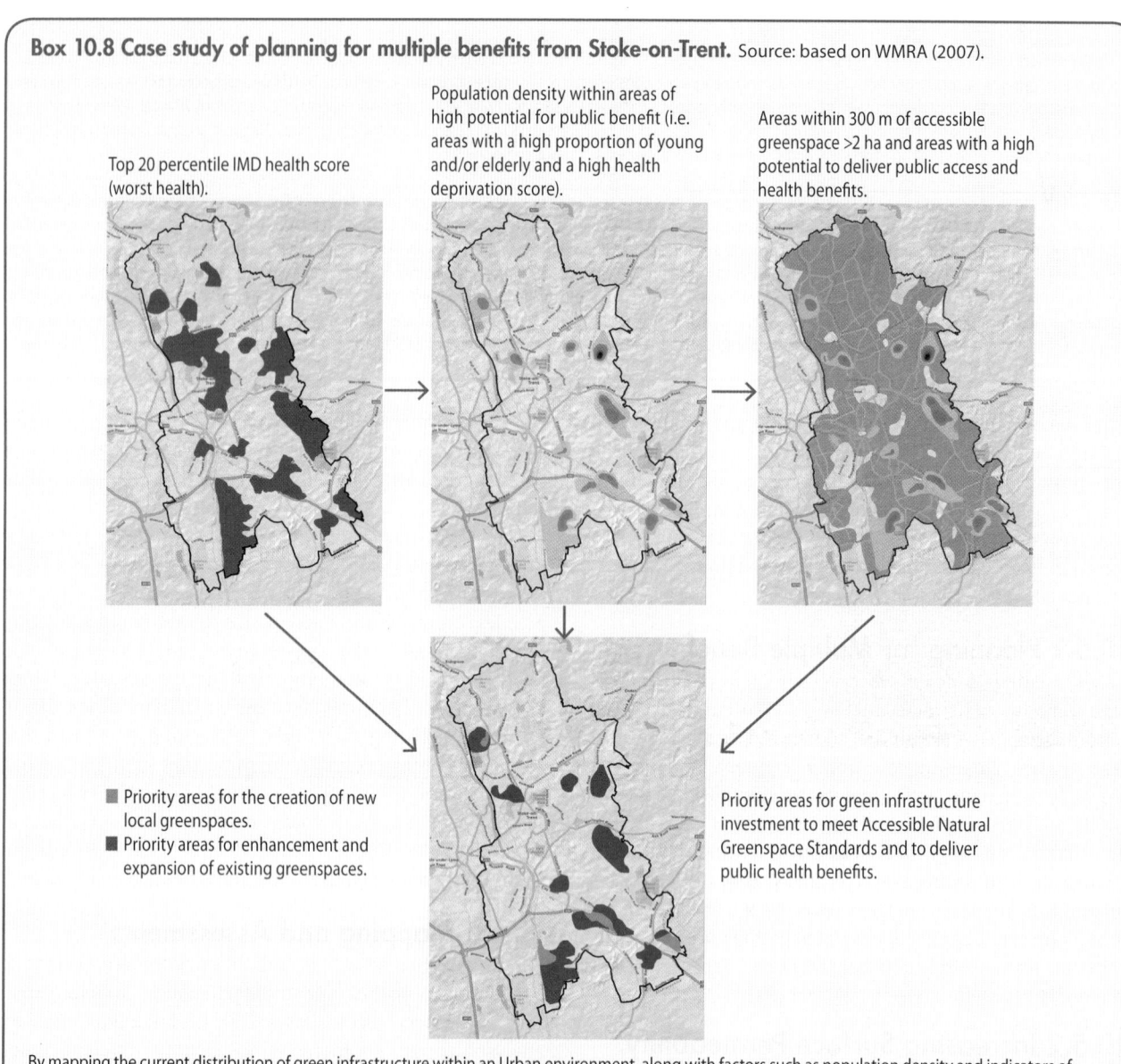

Box 10.8 Case study of planning for multiple benefits from Stoke-on-Trent. Source: based on WMRA (2007).

Top 20 percentile IMD health score (worst health).

Population density within areas of high potential for public benefit (i.e. areas with a high proportion of young and/or elderly and a high health deprivation score).

Areas within 300 m of accessible greenspace >2 ha and areas with a high potential to deliver public access and health benefits.

■ Priority areas for the creation of new local greenspaces.
■ Priority areas for enhancement and expansion of existing greenspaces.

Priority areas for green infrastructure investment to meet Accessible Natural Greenspace Standards and to deliver public health benefits.

By mapping the current distribution of green infrastructure within an Urban environment, along with factors such as population density and indicators of deprivation, the creation and enhancement of greenspaces can be highly strategic.

The example for Stoke-on-Trent illustrates how population density, greenspace accessibility and public health can be incorporated using GIS mapping techniques to inform planning and policy implementation within the Urban area.

plantings, review water and maintenance costs, and support new planting schemes.

There is increasing interest in the feasibility of adopting alternative Urban drainage management techniques. Interest has intensified since the analysis of the 2007 floods, which clearly indicated the pressures on sewage and drainage networks (Water UK 2008).

10.5.4 Conceptual Changes to Influence Management

Interaction with Urban greenspace varies between different social and cultural groups (CABE 2010; Harrison *et al.* 1987; Harrison *et al.* 1995). Recognition of this and the perceived risks different genders and ethnicities associate with Urban subhabitats (Burgess 1998) would allow management practitioners to increase the utilisation of Urban greenspace and its ecosystem services, particularly in relation to cultural benefits to society (CABE 2010).

Funding for public parks and Urban greenspace was significantly reduced between 1979 and 2000 (Urban Greenspaces Taskforce 2002). Many services have not recovered from this under-investment. Local authorities prefer not to assume responsibility for new open spaces unless they come with investment to pay for their long-term maintenance. A potential research question is whether developers, seeking to minimise payments to the local authority, landscape as simply as possible, using lawn as the cheapest option. Such behaviour by developers may be misconceived, however, as there is evidence to suggest that changing to a less intensive management regime, with the aim of creating a more biodiverse and naturalistic landscape, can be cheaper and help to engage the local community with the natural environment (CABE 2006).

The creation and maintenance of good quality greenspace in cities is a major challenge for society and requires innovative leadership, philanthropy, fiscal and other

incentives. Ecosystem services assessment can be used to inform decisions about new and existing developments.

In recent years, tools have been developed to calculate access to public greenspace (Greenspace Scotland 2009; ANGSt 2003; CCW 2006), building on the early work of the Playing Fields Trust and the SAS (FIT 2009). These tools could be applied more widely to encourage and support investment in public areas. New schemes to protect and champion public greenspace are also important. Fields in Trust, for example, has recently launched the Queen Elizabeth II Fields Challenge which, in celebration of the 2012 Diamond Jubilee, gives communities an opportunity to vote for a playing field in the local area to be protected permanently by the scheme (Queen Elizabeth II Fields Challenge 2010).

10.6 Future Research and Monitoring Gaps

Major knowledge gaps remain in terms of Urban land use, extent, condition, location and accessibility.

Many of the processes that determine the quality of Urban water, air and soil remain poorly understood, and degradation continues. While new technology has driven improvements in spatial mapping and process modelling, this review clearly identifies some fundamental problems for Urban ecosystem assessments:

■ Typology is inconsistent and confusing.

■ Various organisations, local, regional and national authorities, government agencies, charities and other bodies collect substantial datasets, but they are often at different temporal and spatial scales and it is not always possible to extract urban-specific information. There is no single body to collate and interpret Urban greenspace data.

■ Monitoring is very limited (only one survey of national public parks in three decades) and collaboration between organisations is unclear.

The Urban habitat needs to be recognised as a unique ecosystem and monitored accordingly.

Progress has been made recently with local authority Greenspace Strategies, an important driver in the mapping of Urban greenspace. There is still a need for a consistent framework for data collection in such strategies, which currently preclude any comparative studies across Urban subhabitats and by country because clear, consistent guidance is not provided nor always compatible with other systems. Local authority greenspace provision is an important aspect of ecosystem services and should not be considered in isolation from other public and private land use, such as domestic gardens, or from air, water and soil processes and biodiversity; these systems are complementary. Urban areas have underperformed in recent decades in relation to the potential ecosystem services, goods and benefits that could be provided. There appears, however, to be significant opportunity for major improvement.

The Urban habitat in the UK has not previously been looked at in terms of ecosystem services, therefore, many knowledge gaps exist in relation to this concept; some of these are detailed below.

10.6.1 Monitoring, Data Collection Methods and Mapping

The lack of systematic monitoring is limiting the present understanding of the Urban environment and its potential for ecosystem service delivery. There is no single inventory in the UK for data on Urban landscape morphology and character, and no harmonisation between existing data sources. Some information is simply not collated or collected; for example, social landlords are responsible for the open spaces of nearly 4 million households, yet such spaces are invisible in national data collection (CABE 2009a). Planning Policy Guidance Note 17 states that local authorities must carry out audits of existing open spaces, taking into account use and access to these areas (PPG17 2002). However, no standardised method of data collection is available, hindering comparability between areas, and the information is not yet collated on a national scale. The Commission for Architecture and the Built Environment (CABE) has assembled a useful, but incomplete, single inventory of public greenspace for English urban authorities by combining data from a wide range of existing data sources (CABE 2010). CABE's research highlights the wide range of organisations involved, and the overlaps, inconsistencies and patchiness of such data (Sadler *et al.* 2010). Sources of information on rural areas are better (MAGIC 2009), probably because they exhibit far less spatial heterogeneity and are, therefore, easier to map.

Natural England has been collating digital map datasets of urban and rural accessible greenspace since 2006. Collation is based on the categories described in PPG17. They have identified 32 datasets and collated 70% of them. Resources are required to review and evaluate the different approaches to, and responsibilities for, Urban greenspace mapping.

The term 'green infrastructure' has been introduced in recent literature to replace greenspace and other similar typologies used to describe the semi-natural environment, as well as terms proposed for assessing connectivity, multifunctionality and ecosystem services. Green infrastructure includes greenspaces and other natural elements, such as rivers and lakes, which are interspersed between, and connect, villages, towns and cities. Individually, these elements are classified as green infrastructure 'assets' and the roles that these play are termed green infrastructure 'functions' (Land Institute 2009). Developing common terminology for use in Urban ecosystem assessment is critical and the green infrastructure system (along with many others) requires urgent review in the broader context in order to establish a consensus among the relevant authorities on the most appropriate way forward.

10.6.2 Developing Datasets to Inform Regulating Services

10.6.2.1 Air and climate

There is a shortage of meteorological stations within most Urban environments, so data on the extent of UHI is limited, although an ongoing national study is attempting to improve the situation (RMetS 2009b). The development of such a dataset would permit greater interpretation of how Urban ecosystems contribute to localised climate regulation, and how the spatial distribution and species composition of Urban vegetation influences cooling effects. Such measurements would contribute to model validation and improve climate predictions and air quality modelling.

Increasing episodes of tropospheric ozone are anticipated due to reductions in nitrogen oxides and the higher temperatures and humidity thought to be associated with elevated atmospheric carbon dioxide (Jacobson 2008). Drought conditions and high temperatures can affect vegetation, shutting down plant stomata and reducing the uptake of ozone, thus enhancing ozone persistence and concentration (ApSimon *et al.* 2009). Such ozone episodes are likely to affect both human health and sensitive vegetation. However, expected reductions in nitrogen dioxide have not been uniform across Urban areas and emission reductions remain challenging.

By 2050, winter river flows are predicted to increase by 10–15% in response to climate change. However, in the late summer and early autumn, flows could fall by over 50%, and by as much as 80% in some catchments. Overall, this could mean a drop in annual river flows of up to 15%, creating huge challenges for water supply. Indications are that climate change may reduce the recharge of aquifers and lower groundwater levels. Climate change may also increase water temperatures and the prevalence of invasive alien species, which will influence aquatic plants and animals. These effects need to be evaluated.

10.6.2.2 Water

A common typology for water services has been developed under the WFD. Action to ensure that the typology is appropriately adopted within the UK will be necessary.

10.6.2.3 Soil

There is a need to find out what soil resources there are in Urban areas, their condition and how they fit into a wider planning context. It is possible to produce spatially explicit (map-based) planning decision support models to assess proposals for new development (with appropriate investment in model development and data acquisition), but it will require the systematic collection and maintenance of high resolution, spatial environmental asset data (Hindmarch *et al.* 2006).

Assessing soil quality is a complex issue. New methods are under development to help prioritise areas where further investigation is necessary, with the potential to complement existing monitoring programmes and to assist in the development and implementation of current and future soil protection legislation (Bone *et al.* 2010; OPAL 2010). Management options that could benefit Urban soil quality are outlined in Chapter 14.

The Environment Agency calculates that around 325,000 sites (300,000 ha) have had some current or previous use that has caused contamination (Environment Agency 2009). Although many PDL sites are important providers of ecosystem services, there remains a currently unquantified risk that may have localised consequences for human health and well-being.

The planning system does not fully recognise the ecosystem services provided by soil. While steps have been taken to address this issue in recent years, more could be done to reduce the widespread sealing and degradation, and subsequent loss of function and resilience, of soil. Raising awareness and providing training for planners on ecosystem services could help address these issues.

10.6.2.4 Noise

While the spatial modelling of noise has increased, actual measurements of noise appear limited. As shown by the UK National Noise Incidence Study of 2000/01 (Skinner & Grimwood 2002), it is useful to be able to compare perceptions of noise with actual measurements.

10.6.3 Understanding the Importance of Urban Biodiversity

Research is required to further the understanding of the importance of Urban biodiversity in general, and the relationship between biodiversity and well-being in particular. It is also important to monetise these benefits as some projects have done (Natural Economy 2010). Most studies of species richness and abundance in Urban areas have been conducted outside the UK. There is a need to investigate trends in Urban areas through case studies, for example, digitising post-war aerial photographs in order to map changes in garden structure and diversity, paving, etc.

10.6.4 Increasing Knowledge Transfer on Ecosystem Services Between Academics and Other Urban Practitioners (e.g. Planners)

There is scope to increase links between academic research groups and delivery organisations in Urban areas to inform parameters for greenspace management and design. A successful example of such collaboration is the Living Roofs project where PhD/MSc research has contributed to design recommendations for biodiverse roofs that support species of conservation concern while providing cooling, water attenuation and, in some cases, amenity (Living Roofs 2010).

10.6.5 Linking Ecosystem Services to Human Well-being

The rise of well-being theory has created an assertion that the best measure of social utility as the basic objective of social policy is creating happiness. The use of subjective well-being as an economic valuation tool, as opposed to revealed and stated preferences, is a technique in its infancy, but it may help evaluate the benefit of ecosystem services to human well-being (Dolan & Metcalfe 2008; Levinson 2009; Luechinger 2009; Chapter 23).

Research programmes in the UK that develop new approaches to Urban development and management, given the pressures of climate change and other drivers, are extensive (e.g. SCORCHIO 2010; LUCID 2010; SUE 2010), but are not reviewed here. It is also recognised that there are numerous examples emerging nationally and internationally of innovation in urban design that reflect the importance of ecological and economic health in Urban planning and their importance to human well-being (WWF 2010).

10.7 References

AEA Energy and Environment (2008) Air Pollution in the UK: 2007. Report number: AEA/ENV/R/2544.

AEA EE (AEA Energy and Environment) (2009) UK Air Quality Archive. [online] Available at: <www.airquality.co.uk/laqm/list.php> [Accessed 21.03.11].

Akbari, H. (2002) Shade trees reduce building energy use and CO_2 emissions from power plants. *Environmental Pollution,* **116**, 119–126.

Angold, P., Sadler, J., Hill, M., Pullin, A., Rushton, S., Austin, K., Small, E., Wood, B., Wadsworth, R. & Sanderson, R. (2006) Biodiversity in urban habitat patches. *Science of the Total Environment,* **360** (1–3), 196–204.

ANGSt (2003) Accessible Natural Green Space Standards in Towns and Cities: A Review and Toolkit for their Implementation. English Nature Research Report No 526. English Nature, Peterborough.

ApSimon, H., Amann, M., Astrom, S. & Oxley, T. (2009) Synergies in addressing air quality and climate change. *Climate Policy,* **9** (6), 669–680.

AQEG (Air Quality Expert Group) (2007) Trends in primary Nitrogen Dioxide in the UK. Defra, London.

Araújo, M.B. (2003) The coincidence of people and biodiversity in Europe. *Global Ecology and Biogeography,* **12** (1), 5–12.

ASLA (American Society of Landscape Architects) (2006) Green infrastructure. [online] Available at: <www.asla.org/ContentDetail.aspx?id=24076> [Accessed: 10.03.11].

Barclay, C. (2010) Housing Density and Gardens. Standard Note, SN/SC/3827. House of Commons Library, London.

Barker, K. (2004) Review of Housing Supply. Delivering Stability: Securing our Future Housing Needs.

Barr, N. (2009) Greenspace development officer, Newcastle City Council. (Personal communication, 1st December 2009).

Barregard, L., Bonde, E. & Ohrstrom, E. (2009) Risk of hypertension from exposure to road traffic noise in a population-based sample. *British Medical Journal,* **66** (6), 410.

Bateman, I. J., Day B., Georgiou, S. & Lake, I. (2006) The aggregation of environmental benefit values: Welfare measures, distance decay and total WTP. *Ecological Economics,* **60**, 450–460.

BCC (Birmingham City Council) (1997) The Birmingham Nature Conservation Strategy. Birmingham City Council, Birmingham.

BBCWT (Wildlife Trust for Birmingham and the Black Country) (2010) The Black Country Urban Forest. [online] Available at: <http://www.wild-net.org/wildbbc/index.aspx?id=502>[Accessed 11.11.10].

Bebbington, A. (2005) The ability of A-level students to name plants. *Journal of Biological Education,* **39**, 63–67.

Beissinger, S.R. & Osborne, D.R. (1982) Effects of urbanisation on avian community organization. *The Condor,* **84**, 75–83.

Belfast City Council (2010) Forest of Belfast [online] Available at: <www.belfastcity.gov.uk/parksandopenspaces/forestofbelfast.asp> [Accessed 11.11.10].

Bell, M.L., McDermott, A., Zeger, S.L., Samet, J.M. & Dominici, F. (2004) Ozone and short-term mortality in 95 US urban communities, 1987–2000. *Jama,* **292** (19), 2372–2378.

Biadun, W. (1994) The breeding avifauna of the parks and cemeteries of Lublin (SE Poland). *Acta Ornithologica,* **29**, 1–13.

Bibby, P. (2009) Land use change in Britain. *Land Use Policy,* **26**, S2–S13.

Bird, W. (2004) Natural Fit: Can Greenspace and Biodiversity Increase Levels of Physical Activity? Royal Society for the Protection of Birds.

Blair, R.B. (1996) Land use and avian species diversity along an urban gradient. *Ecological Applications,* **6**, 506–519.

Blair, R.B. & Launer, A.E. (1997) Butterfly assemblages and human land use: species assemblages along an urban gradient. *Biological Conservation,* **80**, 113–125.

Blair, R.B. (2001) Creating a homogenous avifauna. Avian ecology and conservation in an urbanising world (eds J.M. Marzluff, R. Bowman & R. Donnelly), pp. 459–486. Kluwer Academic, Boston.

BLF (Big Lottery Fund) (2008) Big Lottery Fund Annual Reports and Accounts for the financial year ending 31 March 2008. The Stationary Office, London.

Bolund, P. & Hunhammar, S. (1999) Ecosystem services in urban areas. *Ecological Economics,* **29** (2), 293–301.

Bone, J., Head, M., Barraclough, D., Archer, M., Scheib, C., Flight, D., & Voulvoulis N. (2010) Soil Quality Assessment under Emerging Regulatory Requirements. *Environment International,* **36**: 609–622.

Botkin, D.B. & Beveridge, C.E. (1997) Cities as environments. *Urban Ecosystems,* **1** (1), 3–19.

Brandes, D. (1995) The flora of old town centres in Europe. Urban ecology as the basis of urban planning (eds H. Sukopp, M. Numata & A. Huber), pp. 49–58. SPB Academic Publishing, The Hague.

BTO (British Trust for Ornothology) (2010) Core BTO surveys. [online] Available at: <www.bto.org/survey/core.htm> [Accessed 21.03.11].

Burgess, J., Harrison, C.M. & Limb, M. (1988) People, Parks and the Urban Green: A study of popular meanings and values for open spaces in the city. *Urban Studies,* **25**, 455–473.

Burgess, J. (1998) Not worth taking the risk? Negotiating access to urban woodland. New frontiers of space, bodies and gender (ed R. Ainley), pp. 115–128. Routledge, London.

Burton, M.L., Samuelson, L.J. & Pan, S. (2005) Riparian woody plant diversity and forest structure along an urban-rural gradient. *Urban Ecosystems,* **8**, 93–106.

CABE (Commission for Architecture and the Built Environment) (2004) Public Attitudes to Architecture and Public Space: Transforming neighbourhoods. Unpublished research.

CABE (Commission for Architecture and the Built Environment) (2005a) The Value of Public Space: How high quality parks and public spaces create economic, social and environmental value. CABE, London.

CABE (Commission for Architecture and the Built Environment) (2005b) Does Money Grow on Trees? CABE, London.

CABE (Commission for Architecture and the Built Environment) (2006) Making contracts work for wildlife: how to encourage biodiversity in urban parks. CABE, London.

CABE (Commission for Architecture and the Built Environment) (2009a) The Green Information Gap: mapping the nation's greenspaces. CABE, London.

CABE (Commission for Architecture and the Built Environment) (2009b) Making the Invisible Visible: The real value of park assets. CABE, London.

CABE (Commission for Architecture and the Built Environment) (2010) Urban green nation: Building the evidence basis. CABE, London.

Campbell, M. & Campbell, I. (2009) A survey of allotment waiting lists in England. National Society of Allotment and Leisure Gardeners (NSALG).

Canadian Interim Sediment Quality Guidelines (2003) Canadian Environmental Quality Guidelines – summary table. [online] Available at: <www.ec.gc.ca/> [Accessed 01.08.2005].

Carey, P.D., Wallis, S., Chamberlain, P.M., Cooper, A., Emmett, B.A., Maskell, L.C., McCann, T., Murphy, J., Norton, L.R., Reynolds, B., Scott, W.A., Simpson, I.C., Smart, S.M. & Ullyett, J.M. (2008) Countryside Survey: UK Results from 2007. NERC/Centre for Ecology & Hydrology, 105pp. (CEH Project Number: C03259).

Carpentier, S., Moilleron, R., Beltran, C., Herve, D. & Thevenot, D. R. (2002) Quality of dredged material in the River Seine basin (France). II. Micro-pollutants. *The Science of the Total Environment,* **299**, 57–72.

CCW (Countryside Council for Wales) (2006) Providing Accessible Natural Greenspace in Towns and Cities. A Practical Guide to Assessing the Resource and Implementing Local Standards for Provision in Wales. CCW, Manchester.

CEC (The City of Edinburgh Council) (2009) Edinburgh Open Spaces Audit 2009. CEC, Edinburgh.

Cheeseman, O.D. & Key, R.S. (2007) The extinction of experience: a threat to insect conservation? In Insect Conservation Biology (eds A.J.A. Stewart, T.R. New & O.T. Lewis), pp. 322–348. CABI, Wallingford.

Chocholoušková, Z. & Pyšek, P. (2003) Changes in composition and structure of urban flora over 120 years: a case study of the city of Plzen. *Flora,* **198**, 366–376.

Chow, W. & Roth, M. (2006) Temporal dynamics of the urban heat island of Singapore. *International Journal of Climatology,* **26**(15), 2243–2260.

Chown, S.L., van Rensburg, B.J., Gaston, K.J., Rodrigues, A.S.L. & van Jaarsveld, A.S. (2003) Species richness, human population size and energy: conservation implications at a national scale. *Ecological Applications,* **13**, 1223–1241.

Church of England (CE) (2007) Church Statistics 2006/07. [online] Available at: <www.cofe.anglican.org/info/statistics/churchstats2006/statisticscontent.html> [Accessed 21.03.11].

Clergeau, P., Savard, J-P.L., Mennechez, G. & Falardeau, G. (1998) Bird abundance and diversity along an urban-rural gradient: a comparative study between two cities on different continents. *The Condor,* **100**, 413–425.

Clergeau, P., Jokimaki, J. & Savard, J-P.L. (2001a) Are urban bird communities influenced by the bird diversity of adjacent landscapes? *Journal of Applied Ecology,* **38**, 1122–1134.

Clergeau, P., Mennechez, G., Sauvage, A. & Lemoine, A. (2001b) Human perception and appreciation of birds: A motivation for wildlife conservation in urban environments of France. Avian ecology and conservation in an urbanising world (eds J.M. Marzluff, R. Bowman & R. Donnelly), pp. 70–88. Kluwer Academic, Boston.

Cooper, N. (2001) Wildlife in Church and Churchyard. Plants, animals and their management. 2nd edition, Church House Publishing.

Countryside Agency, Department for Environment, Food and Rural Affairs, Office for National Statistics, Office of the

Deputy Prime Minister & the Welsh Assembly Government (2004) Rural and Urban Area Classification 2004, An Introductory Guide. [online] Available at: <www.statistics.gov.uk/geography/downloads/Rural_Urban_Introductory_Guidev2.pdf> [Accessed on 26.11.10].

Coventry City Council (2008) Greenspace strategy 2008–2018. Coventry City Council, Coventry.

CPRE (Campaign to Protect Rural England) (2007) Major development threats to Green Belt. CPRE.

Crabill, C., Donald, R., & Snelling, J. (1999) The impact of sediment faecal coliform reservoirs on seasonal water quality in Oak Creek, Arizona. *Water Research*, **33**, 2163–2171.

Crooks, K.R., Suarez, A.V. & Bolger, D.T. (2004) Avian assemblages along a gradient of urbanisation in a highly fragmented landscape. *Biological Conservation,* **115**, 451–462.

Crouch, D. (1997) English Allotments Survey: Report of the Joint Survey of Allotments in England. National Society of Allotment and Leisure Gardens Ltd (NSALG) & Anglia Polytechnic University. NSALG, Corby.

Curtis, S., Cave, B. & Coutts, A. (2002). Is urban regeneration good for health? Perceptions and theories of the health impacts of urban change. *Environmental Planning* C, **20**, 517–534.

Cussans, J.W., Goulson, D., Sanderson, R., Goffe, L. & Osborne, J.L. (2010) Two bee-pollinated plant species show higher seed production when grown in gardens compared to arable farmland. *PLoS ONE* **5**: 1–10 e11753.

Czech, B. & Krausman, P.R. (1997) Distribution and causation of endangerment in the United States. *Science,* **277**, 1116–1117.

Dandy, N., Ballantyne, S., Mosely, D. Gill, R. & Quine, C. (2009) The management of roe deer in peri-urban Scotland, Final report, Forest Research. [online] Available at: <www.forestry.gov.uk/fr/INFD-7D4AXC> [Accessed: 09.03.11].

Davies, L., Bates, J., Bell, J., James, P. & Purvis, O. (2007) Diversity and sensitivity of epiphytes to oxides of nitrogen in London. *Environmental Pollution,* **146** (2), 299–310.

Davies, L. (2011) Open Air Laboratories (OPAL) A Community-Driven Research Programme. *Environmental Pollution.* DOI 10.1016/j.envpol.2011.02.053.

Davies, Z.G., Fuller, R.A., Loram, A., Irvine, K.N., Sims, V. & Gaston, K.J. (2009) A national scale inventory of resource provision for biodiversity within domestic gardens. *Biological Conservation,* **142**, 761–771.

Davis, A.M. & Glick, T.F. (1978) Urban ecosystems and island biogeography. *Environmental Conservation,* **5**, 299–304.

Davis, B.N.K. (1978) Urbanisation and the diversity of insects. I. Diversity of insect faunas (eds. Mound, L.A. & Waloff, N.). Blackwell Scientific Publications, Oxford, pp. 126–138.

DCLG (Department of Communities and Local Government) (2006) Previously developed land that may be available for development: England 2005. DCLG, London.

DCLG (Department of Communities and Local Government) (2008a) Place Survey: England. [online] Available at: <www.communities.gov.uk/publications/corporate/statistics/placesurvey2008> [Accessed: 15.12.09].

DCLG (Department of Communities and Local Government) (2008b) Trees in Towns II. DCLG, London.

DCLG (Department of Communities and Local Government) (2009a) Local Planning Authority Green Belt Statistics 2008/09. Department of Communities and Local Government, London, UK. [online] Available at: <www.communities.gov.uk/publications/corporate/statistics/lagreenbelt2008> [Accessed 22.03.11].

DCLG (Department for Communities and Local Government) (2009b) Guidance on the permeable surfacing of front gardens. [online] Available at: <http://www.communities.gov.uk/publications/planningandbuilding/pavingfrontgardens> [Accessed 22.03.11].

DCLG (Department of Communities and Local Government) (2010a) Live Tables on Land Use Change Statistics. [online] Available at: <www.communities.gov.uk/planningandbuilding/planningbuilding/planningstatistics/livetables/landusechange/> [Accessed 11.01.11].

DCLG (Department of Communities and Local Government) (2010b) Live tables on Land Use Change Statistics. Tables 231–232: Land Use Change – Density. [online] Available at: <www.communities.gov.uk/planningandbuilding/planningbuilding/planningstatistics/livetables/landusechange/> [Accessed 11.01.11].

DCLG (Department of Communities and Local Government) (2010c) Live tables on Land Use Change Statistics. Tables 241–246: Land Use Change – Green Belt. [online] Available at: <www.communities.gov.uk/planningandbuilding/planningbuilding/planningstatistics/livetables/landusechange/> [Accessed 11.01.11].

DCMS (Department for Culture, Media and Sport) (2009) The Number of School Playing Fields – Case 101795. DCMS, London.

DeCandido, R. (2004) Recent changes in plant species diversity in urban Pelham Bay Park, 1947–1998. *Biological Conservation,* **120**, 129–136.

DECC (Department of Energy and Climate Change) (2009) The UK Renewable Energy Strategy. DECC, London.

Defra (Department of Environment, Fisheries and Rural Affairs) (2004) Making Space for Water: Developing a New Government Strategy for Flood and Coastal Erosion Risk Management in England. Consultation Exercise. Defra, London.

Defra (Department of Environment, Fisheries and Rural Affairs) (2006a) Working with the grain of nature – taking it forward: volume II, Measuring progress on the England Biodiversity Strategy: 2006 assessment. Defra, London.

Defra (Department of Environment, Fisheries and Rural Affairs) (2006b) England's trees, woods and forests: a consultation document. Defra, London.

Defra (Department of Environment, Fisheries and Rural Affairs) (2007a) Hedgerow Survey Handbook, A standard procedure for local surveys in the UK. Defra, London.

Defra (Department of Environment, Fisheries and Rural Affairs) (2007b) Air Quality Strategy for England, Scotland, Wales and Northern Ireland. Volume 1. Defra, London.

Defra (Department of Environment, Fisheries and Rural Affairs) (2007c) An economic analysis to inform the review of the Air Quality Strategy. Defra, London.

Defra (Department of Environment, Fisheries and Rural Affairs) (2008) Future Water. The Government's water strategy for England. Defra, London.

Defra (Department of Environment, Fisheries and Rural Affairs) (2010a) Air Pollution: Action in a Changing Climate. Defra, London.

Defra (Department of Environment, Fisheries and Rural Affairs) (2010b) Rural definition and local authority classification.

[online] Available at: <http://archive.defra.gov.uk/evidence/statistics/rural/rural-definition.htm> [Accessed 11.05.11].

Dekkers, J. & van der Straaten, W. (2008) Monetary Value of Aircraft Noise. Tinbergen Discussion paper TI 2008-064/3.

Department of Health (2008) Health Effects of Climate Change in the UK 2008: An update of the Department of Health Report 2001/2002. Department of Health, London.

DETR (1999) Towards an Urban Renaissance: Report of the Urban Task Force. HMSO, London.

de Vries, S., Verheij, R.A., Groenewegen, P.P. & Spreeuwenberg, P. (2003) Natural environments – healthy environments? An exploratory analysis of the relationship between greenspace and health. *Environment and Planning A*, **35**, 1717–1731.

DfT (Department for Transport) (2002) National travel survey: revised data for urban and rural areas. [online] Available at: <www.dft.gov.uk/pgr/statistics/datatablespublications/personal/mainresults/nts19962001/> [Accessed: 27.11.09].

Dickman, C.R. (1987) Habitat fragmentation and vertebrate species richness in an urban environment. *Journal of Applied Ecology, 24*, 337–351.

Dines, N., Catell, V. Gesler, W. & Curtis, C. (2006) Public spaces and social relations in East London. Joseph Rowntree Foundation.

Dixon, P.G. & Mote, T.L. (2003) Patterns and causes of Atlanta's urban heat island–initiated precipitation. *Journal of Applied Meteorology, 42* (9), 1273–1284.

Dobson, A.P., Rodriguez, J.P., Roberts, W.M. & Wilcove, D.S. (1997) Geographic distribution of endangered species in the United States. *Science, 275*, 550–553.

DoE (Department of the Environment) (1993) Trees in Towns. DoE, London.

Dolan, P. & Metcalfe, R. (2008) Comparing willingness-to-pay and subjective well-being in the context of non-market goods. Centre for Economic Performance discussion paper series.

Donnelly, R. & Marzluff, J.M. (2006) Relative importance of habitat quantity, structure, and spatial pattern to birds in urbanising environments. *Urban Ecosystems, 9*, 99–117.

Donovan, R. G., Stewart, H. E., Owen, S. M., MacKenzie, A. R. & Hewitt, C. N. (2005) Development and Application of an Urban Tree Air Quality Score for Photochemical Pollution Episodes Using the Birmingham, United Kingdom, Area as a Case Study. *Environ.Sci.Technol, 39* (17), 6730–6738.

Duhme, F. & Pauleit, S. (1998) Some examples of different landscape systems and their biodiversity potential. *Landscape and Urban Planning, 41*, 249–261.

Eaton, M.A., Appleton, G.F., Ausden, M.A., Balmerm, D.E., Grantham, M.J., Grice, P.V., Hearn, R.D., Holt, C.A., Musgrove, A.J., Noble, D.G., Parsons, M., Risely, K., Stroud, D.A. & Wotton, S. (2010) The state of the UK's birds. RSPB, BTO, WWT, CCW, JNCC, NE, NIEA and SNH. Sandy, Bedfordshire.

Eden, S., Tunstall, S. M., & Tapsell, S. M. (2000) Translating nature: river restoration as nature-culture. *Environment Planning D, 18*, 257–273.

Ellis, J. B. & Yu, W. (1995) Bacteriology of urban runoff—the combined sewer as a bacterial reactor and generator. *Water Science & Technology, 31* (7), 303–310.

Emlen, J.T. (1974) An urban bird community in Tucson, Arizona: derivation, structure, regulation. *The Condor, 76*, 184–197.

Environment Agency (2002). River restoration: A stepping stone to urban regeneration highlighting the opportunities in South London. Environment Agency, Reading.

Environment Agency (2005) Introducing river restoration in London: improving the quality of life for Londoners. Environment Agency, Thames Region, NE Area Office, Hatfield.

Environment Agency (2006) Bringing your rivers back to life. A guide to restoring rivers in North London. Environment Agency, Thames Region, NE Area Office, Hatfield.

Environment Agency (2009) Environment Agency statistics on contaminated land [online]. Available at: <http://www.environment-agency.gov.uk/research/planning/33706.aspx> [Accessed: 09.03.11].

European Commission (2000) Directive 2000/60/EC: establishing a framework for Community action in the field of water policy. *Official Journal of the European Communities,* L327, pp. 1–73.

European Commission (2002) Directive 2002/49/EC: relating to the assessment and management of environmental noise. *Official Journal,* L 189.

Evans, G.W., Hygge, S. & Bullinger, M. (1995) Chronic noise and psychological stress. *Psychological Science, 6*, 333–338.

Evans, G.W., Lercher, P., Meis, M., Ising, H. & Kofler, W.W. (2001) Community noise exposure and stress in children. *The Journal of the Acoustical Society of America, 109*, 1023.

Evans, K.L. & Gaston, K.J. (2005) People, energy and avian species richness. *Global Ecology and Biogeography, 14*, 187–196.

Eyre, M., Luff, M. & Woodward, J. (2003) Beetles (Coleoptera) on brownfield sites in England: An important conservation resource? *Journal of Insect Conservation, 7* (4), 223–231.

Faeth, S.H. & Kane, T.C. (1978) Urban biogeography: city parks as islands for Diptera and Coleoptera. *Oecologia, 32*, 127–133.

Fernández-Juricic, E. (2000) Bird community composition patterns in urban parks of Madrid: The role of age, size and isolation. *Ecological Research, 15*, 373–383.

Fernández-Juricic E. (2001) Avian spatial segregation at edges and interiors of urban parks in Madrid, Spain. *Biodiversity and Conservation, 10*, 1303–1316.

Fernández-Juricic, E. & Jokimaki, J. (2001) A habitat island approach to conserving birds in urban landscapes: case studies from southern and northern Europe. *Biodiversity and Conservation, 10*, 2023–2043.

Filgueiras, A.V., Lavilla, I. & Bendicho, C. (2004) Evaluation of distribution, mobility and binding behaviour of heavy metals in surficial sediments of Louro River (Galicia, Spain) using chemometric analysis: a case study. *Science of the Total Environment, 330*, 115–129.

FIT & NPFA (Fields in Trust & National Playing Fields Association) (2008) Planning and Design for Outdoor Sport and Play. FIT & NPFA.

FIT (Fields in Trust) (2009) Fields in Trust. History of King George's Fields Foundation. [online] Available at: <http://fieldsintrust.org/index.php?option=com_content&view=article&id=70:king-george-v-fields&catid=35:what-we-do&Itemid=79> [Accessed: 27.11.09].

Fordyce, F., Brown, S., Ander, E., Rawlins, B., O'Donnell, K., Lister, T., Breward, N.& Johnson, C. (2005) GSUE: urban geochemical mapping in Great Britain. *Geochemistry: Exploration, Environment, Analysis, 5* (4), 325.

Forestry Commission (2002) Health and Well-being Trees, Woodlands and Natural Spaces, Outcomes from expert consultations held in England, Scotland and Wales during 2002. Forestry Commission, Edinburgh.

Forestry Commission (2003) National Inventory of Woodland and Trees, Regional Report for London. Forestry Commission, Edinburgh.

Forestry Commission (2010) TreeGeneration: A review of the urban forestry pilot project for North East Wales [online] Available at: <www.forestry.gov.uk/fr/INFD-7S6BQC> [Accessed 11.11.10].

Forestry Commission Scotland (2010) Woods In and Around Towns (WIAT) programme. [online] Available at: <www.forestry.gov.uk/wiat> [Accessed 11.11.10].

Forman, R.T.T., Reineking, B. & Hersperger, A.M. (2002) Road traffic and nearby grassland bird patterns in a suburbanising landscape. *Environmental Management* **29**, 782–800.

Fowler, D., Cape, J.N., Unsworth, M.H., Mayer, H., Crowther, J.M., Jarvis, P.G., Gardiner, B. & Shuttleworth, W.J. (1989) Deposition of atmospheric pollutants on forests [and Discussion]. *Philosophical Transactions of the Royal Society of London. Series B, Biological Sciences,* **324**, 247–265.

Frankie, G.W., Rizzardi, M., Vinson, S.B. & Griswold T.L. (2009) Decline in Bee Diversity and Abundance from 1972–2004 on a Flowering Leguminous Tree, *Andira inermis* in Costa Rica at the Interface of Disturbed Dry Forest and the Urban Environment. *Journal of the Kansas Entomological Society,* **82** (1), 1–20.

Fredrickson, L.M. & Anderson, D.H. (1999) A qualitative exploration of the wilderness experience as a source of spiritual inspiration. *Journal of Environmental Psychology,* **19**, 21–40.

Freer-Smith, P.H., Holloway, S. & Goodman, A. (1997) The uptake of particulates by an urban woodland: site description and particulate composition. *Environmental Pollution,* **95** (1), 27–35.

Fuller, R.M., Smith, G.M., Sanderson, J.M., Hill, R.A. & Thomson, A.G. (2002) The UK Land Cover Map 2000: construction of a parcel-based vector map from satellite images. *Cartographic Journal,* **39**, 15–25.

Fuller, R.A., Irvine, K.N., Devine-Wright, P., Warren, P.H. & Gaston, K.J. (2007) Psychological benefits of greenspace increase with biodiversity. *Biology Letters,* **3**, 390–394.

Garnett, Y. (1996) Growing food in cities: A report to highlight and promote the benefits of urban agriculture in the UK. National Food Alliance, London.

Gasperi, J., Garnaud, S., Rocher, V. & Moilleron, R. (2008). Priority pollutants in wastewater and combined sewer overflow. *Science of The Total Environment,* **407** (1), 263–272.

Gaston, K.J. & Matter, S.F. (2002) Individuals-area relationships: Comment. *Ecology,* **83**, 288–293.

Gaston, K.J., Warren, P.H., Thompson, K. & Smith, R.M. (2005) Urban domestic gardens (IV): the extent of the resource and its associated features. *Biodiversity and Conservation,* **14** (14), 3327–3349.

Gaston, K.J., Fuller, R.A., Loram, A., MacDonald, C., Power, S. & Dempsey, N. (2007) Urban domestic gardens (XI): Variation in urban wildlife gardening in the UK. *Biodiversity and Conservation,* **16**, 3227–3238.

Gaston, K.J. & Fuller, R.A. (2009) The sizes of species' geographic ranges. *Journal of Applied Ecology,* **46** (1), 1–9.

Gates, P. (2002) Gardening in the Global Greenhouse: The Impacts of Climate Change on Gardens in the UK; Summary Report. UK Climate Impacts Programme.

Gavareski, C.A. (1976) Relation of park size and vegetation to urban bird populations in Seattle, Washington. *The Condor,* **78**, 375–382.

Germaine, S.S., Rosenstock, S.S., Schweinsburg, R.E. & Richardson, W.S. (1998) Relationships among breeding birds, habitat, and residential development in Greater Tucson, Arizona. *Ecological Applications,* **8**, 680–691.

Germaine, S.S. & Wakeling, B.F. (2001) Lizard species distributions and habitat occupation along an urban gradient in Tucson, Arizona, USA. *Biological Conservation,* **97**, 229–237.

Gill, S., Handley, J., Ennos, A. & Pauleit, S. (2007) Adapting cities for climate change: the role of the greenspace. *Built environment,* **33** (1), 115–133.

GLA (Greater London Authority) (2004) The London Plan, Spatial development strategy for London. GLA, London.

GLA (Greater London Authority) (2005a) Crazy paving: The Environmental importance of London's front gardens. GLA, London.

GLA (Greater London Authority) (2005b) Connecting Londoners with Trees and Woodlands. A Tree and Woodland Framework for London. GLA, London.

GLA (Greater London Authority) (2006a) A lot to lose: London's disappearing allotments. GLA, London.

GLA (Greater London Authority) (2006b) London's Urban Heat Island: A Summary for Decision Makers. GLA, London.

GLA (Greater London Authority) (2008) Living roofs and Walls Technical Report: Supporting London Policy Plan. GLA, London.

GLA (Greater London Authority) (2010) The draft climate change adaptation strategy for London, Public Consultation Draft. GLA, London.

GLUD (Generalised Land Use Database) (2005) Physical Environments, Generalised Land Use Database Statistics for England 2005. [online] Available at: <www.communities.gov.uk/publications/planningandbuilding/generalisedlanduse> [Accessed on 25.11.10].

Godefroid, S. (2001) Temporal analysis of the Brussels flora as indicator for changing environmental quality. *Landscape and Urban Planning,* **52**, 203–224.

Gong, Y. (2009) Exploring Children's Movements: An Investigation of GPS Tracking in the Local Environment, unpublished PhD Thesis, Bartlett School, University College London.

Goulson, D., Hughes, W.O.H., Derwent, L.C. & Stout, J.C. (2002) Colony growth of the bumblebee, *Bombus terrestris*, in improved and conventional agricultural and suburban habitats. *Oecologia,* **130,** 267–273.

Grahn, P. & Stigsdotter, U. A. (2003) Landscape planning and stress. *Urban Forestry & Urban Greening,* **2** (1), 1–18.

Green, D.M. & Baker, M.G. (2003) Urbanization impacts on habitat and bird communities in a Sonoran desert ecosystem. *Landscape and Urban Planning,* **63**, 225–239.

Green, R.E., Tyler, G.A. & Bowden, C.G.R. (2000) Habitat selection, ranging behaviour and diet of the stone curlew (*Burhinus oedicnemus*) in southern England. *Journal of Zoology,* **250**, 161–183.

Greenspace Scotland (2007) Demonstrating the links: Action research on Greenspace. Ardler Village, Dundee: A study into the link between the quality of Ardler's greenspace and its use. [online] Available at: <www.greenspacescotland.org.uk/default. asp?page=414> [Accessed 22.12.09].

Greenspace Scotland (2009) State of Scotland's Greenspace 2009. Greenspace Scotland, Stirling.

Greenspace Scotland (2010) Demonstrating the Links Action Research on Greenspaces. A consortium programme for communities funded by Greenspace Scotland and Scottish National Heritage. [online] Available at: <www. greenspacescotland.org.uk/upload/File/BriefingNote1.pdf> [Accessed: 27.08.10].

Grimmond, S. (2009) Climate and Cities. In: Douglas, I. *et al.* An Encyclopaedia of Urban Ecology, Taylor & Francis Books.

Grimwood, C.J. (2002) Trends in environmental noise. *Clean Air*, **30** (1), 15–20.

Gryparis, A., Forsberg, B., Katsouyanni, K., Analitis, A., Touloumi, G., Schwartz, J., Samoli, E., Medina, S., Anderson, H. R. & Niciu, E. M. (2004) Acute effects of ozone on mortality from the Air pollution and health: A European approach project. *American Journal of Respiratory and Critical Care Medicine,* **170** (10), 1080.

Guntenspergen, G.R. & Levinson, J.B. (1997) Understory plant species composition in remnant stands along an urban-to-rural land-use gradient. *Urban Ecosystems,* **1**, 155–169.

Gurnell, A., Lee, M. & Souch, C. (2007) Urban rivers: hydrology, geomorphology, ecology and opportunities for change. *Geography Compass,* **1** (5), 1118–1137.

Habib, L., Bayne, E.M., & Boutin, S. (2007) Chronic industrial noise affects pairing success and age structure of ovenbirds *Seiurus aurocapilla. Journal of Applied Ecology*, **44**, 176–184.

Hardy, P.B. & Dennis, R.L.H. (1999) The impact of urban development on butterflies within a city region. *Biodiversity and Conservation,* **8**, 1261–1279.

Harlequin Ladybird Survey (2010) [online] Available at: <www.harlequin-survey.org> [Accessed: 22.04.10].

Harrison, C.M., Burgess, J. & Limb, M. (1987) Nature in the city: popular values for a living world. *Journal of Environmental Management*, **25**, 347–362.

Harrison, C.M., Burgess, J., Millward, A. & Dawe, G. (1995) *Accessible natural greenspace in towns and cities: a review of appropriate size and distance criteria. Guidance for the preparation of strategies for local sustainability*. English Nature Research Reports, No. 153. English Nature, Peterborough.

Hartig, T., Evans, G. W., Jamner, L. D., Davies, D. S. & Gärling, T. (2003) Tracking restoration in natural and urban field settings, *Journal of Environmental Psychology*, **23**, 109–123.

Harvey, P. (2000) The East Thames Corridor: a nationally important invertebrate fauna under threat. *British Wildlife*, **12** (2), 91–98.

He, L.-M., Lu, J. & Shi, W. (2007). Variability of fecal indicator bacteria in flowing and ponded waters in Southern California: implications for bacterial TMDL development and implementation. *Water Research*, **41**, 3132–3140.

Health Scotland (2008) Health Impact Assessment of Greenspace: A guide. Greenspace Scotland, Scottish Natural Heritage and Institute of Occupational Medicine.

Helden, A.J. & Leather, S.R. (2004) Biodiversity on urban roundabouts – Hemiptera, management and the species-area relationship. *Basic and Applied Ecology*, **5**, 367–377.

Heritage Lottery Fund (2008) Valuing our heritage, Investing in our future, Our Strategy 2008–2013. Heritage Lottery Fund, London.

Hindmarch, C., Harris, J., & Morris, J. (2006) Growth and sustainability: integrating ecosystem services into economics. *The Biologist*, **53** (3), 135–142.

Hirano, T., Kiyota, M. & Aiga, I. (1996) Vegetation in Sakai City, Osaka, as a Sink of Air Pollutants. *Bulletin-University of Osaka Prefecture Series B*, 55–64.

Hobbs, E.R. (1988) Species richness of urban forest patches and implications for urban landscape diversity. *Landscape Ecology*, **1**, 141–152.

Hohtola, E. (1978) Differential changes in bird community structure with urbanisation: a study in Central Finland. *Ornis Scandinavica*, **9**, 94–100.

Hope, N. & Ellis, V. (2009) Can You Dig It? Meeting community demand for allotments. New Local Government Network, London.

Hostetler, M. & Holling, C.S. (2000) Detecting the scales at which birds respond to structure in urban landscapes. *Urban Ecosystems*, **4** (1), 25–54.

Hough, M. (1989) City Form and Natural Process. Routledge, London, 280 pp.

Hourigan, C.L., Johnson, C. & Robson, S.K.A. (2006) The structure of a micro-bat community in relation to gradients of environmental variation in a tropical urban area. *Urban Ecosystems*, **9**, 67–82.

House of Commons (1999) A Century of Change: Trends in UK Statistics since 1900 Research Paper 99/111. [online] Available at: < http://www.parliament.uk/documents/commons/lib/ research/rp99/rp99-111.pdf> [Accessed: 29.12.09].

Howe, J. & Wheeler, P.U. (1999) Urban Food Growing; the experience of two UK cities. *Sustainable Development*, **7**, 13–24.

Impens, R.A. & Delcarte, E. (1979) Survey of urban trees in Brussels, Belgium. *Journal of Arboriculture*, **5**, 169–176.

Ishitani, M., Kotze, D.J. & Niemela, J. (2003) Changes in carabid beetle assemblages across an urban-rural gradient in Japan. *Ecography*, **26**, 481–489.

Jacobson, M.Z. (2008) On the causal link between carbon dioxide and air pollution mortality. *Geophysical Research Letters*, **35** (3).

Jarup, L., Babisch, W., Houthuijs, D., Pershagen, G., Katsouyanni, K., Cadum, E., Dudley, M.L., Savigny, P., Seiffert, I. & Swart, W. (2008) Hypertension and exposure to noise near airports: the HYENA study. *Environmental Health Perspectives*, **116**, 329–333.

Jim, C.Y. (1998) Urban soil characteristics and limitations for landscape planting in Hong Kong. *Landscape and Urban Planning*, 40, 235–249.

Jokimaki, J. & Suhonen, J. (1993) Effects of urbanisation on the breeding bird species richness in Finland: a biogeographical comparison. *Ornis Fennica*, **70**, 71–77.

Jokimaki, J., Suhonen, J., Inki, K. & Jokinen, S. (1996) Biogeographical comparison of winter bird assemblages in urban environments in Finland. *Journal of Biogeography,* **23**, 379–386.

Jokimaki, J. (1999) Occurrence of breeding bird species in urban parks: Effects of park structure and broad-scale variables. *Urban Ecosystems*, **3**, 21–34.

Jokimaki, J. & Kaisanlahti-Jokimaki, M-L. (2003) Spatial similarity of urban bird communities: a multiscale approach. *Journal of Biogeography,* **30**, 1183–1193.

Jones, R. (2010) Policy Advisor, Environment Agency. (Personal communication, 30th June 2010).

Kaplan, R. & Kaplan, S. (1989) The experience of nature: a psychological perspective. Cambridge University Press, Cambridge.

Kellert, S.R. & Wilson, E.O. (1993) The biophilia hypothesis. Island Press, Washington D.C.

Kelly, F. J. (2003) Oxidative stress: its role in air pollution and adverse health effects. *British Medical Journal,* **60** (8), 612–616.

Kent, M., S Stevens, R.A. & Zhang, L. (1999) Urban plant ecology patterns and processes: a case study of the flora of the City of Plymouth, Devon, U.K. *Journal of Biogeography,* **26**, 1281–1298.

Kerr, J.T. & Currie, D.J. (1995) Effects of human activity on global extinction risk. *Conservation Biology,* **9**, 1528–1538.

Kirkland, G.L. & Ostfeld, R.S. (1999) Factors influencing variation among states in the number of federally listed mammals in the United States. *Journal of Mammalogy,* **80**, 711–719.

Kolokotroni, M. & Giridharan, R. (2008) Urban heat island intensity in London: an investigation of the impact of physical characteristics on changes in outdoor air temperature during summer, *Solar Energy,* **82** (11), 986–998.

Kowarik, I. (1990) Some responses of flora and vegetation to urbanisation in Central Europe. Urban ecology: plants and plant communities in urban environments. (eds Sukopp, H., Hejný, S. & Kowarik, I.). SPB Academic Publishing, The Hague, pp. 45–74.

Kuhn, I., Brandl, R. & Klotz, S. (2004) The flora of German cities is naturally species rich. *Evolutionary Ecology Research,* **6** (5), 749–764.

Kuo, F.E. (2001) Coping with poverty: impacts of environment and attention in the inner city. *Environment and Behavior,* **33** (1), 5–34.

Kuo, F.E. & Sullivan, W.C. (2001a) Aggression and violence in the inner city: effects of environment on mental fatigue. *Environment and Behavior,* **33**, 543–571.

Kuo, F.E. & Sullivan, W.C. (2001b) Environment and crime in the inner city: effects of environment on mental fatigue, *Environment and Behavior,* **33**, 343–367.

Kweon, B.S., W.C. Sullivan & Wiley, A. (1998) Green common spaces and the social integration of inner-city older adults. *Environment and Behavior,* **30**, 832–858.

Landrigan, P. J., Kimmel, C. A., Correa, A., & Eskenazi, B. (2004) Children's health and the environment: public health issues and challenge for risk assessment. *Environmental Health Perspectives,* **112**, 257–265.

Landscape Institute (2009) Green infrastructure:connected and multifunctional landscapes. Landscape Institute Position Statement, London. [online] Available at: <www.landscapeinstitute.org/PDF/Contribute/GreenInfrastructurepositionstatement13May09.pdf> [Accessed: 24.08.10].

LCM (2000) Land Cover Map. [online] Available at: <http://www.countrysidesurvey.org.uk/land-cover-map> [Accessed: 21.12.09].

Leather, S.R. & Quicke, D.J.L. (2009) Do shifting baselines in natural history knowledge threaten the environment? *The Environmentalist,* **30**, 1–2.

Lehvävirta, S., Kotze, D.J., Niemelä, J., Mäntysaari, M. & O'Hara, B. (2006) Effects of fragmentation and trampling on carabid beetle assemblages in urban woodlands in Helsinki, Finland. *Urban ecosystems,* **9** (1), 13–26.

Levinson, A. (2009) Valuing public goods using happiness data: The case of air quality. National Bureau of Economic Research working paper 15156.

Liu, G.G., Wilson, J.S., Qi, R. & Ying, R. (2007) Green neighbourhoods, food retail and childhood overweight: differences by population density. *American Journal of Health Promotion,* **21** (4), 317–325.

Liverpool City Council (2005) Liverpool Open Space Study. Liverpool City Council, Liverpool.

Living Roofs (2010) On Green Roofs and Brown Roofs. [online] Available at: <www.livingroofs.org/> [Accessed: 13.08.10].

London Borough of Bexley (2009) South East London Green Chain Walk. [online] Available at: <http://www.bexley.gov.uk/index.aspx?articleid=3904> [Accessed: 27.08.10].

Loram, A., Tratalos, J., Warren, P.H. & Gaston, K.J. (2007) Urban domestic gardens (X): the extent & structure of the resource in five cities. *Landscape Ecology,* **22**, 601–615.

LUCID (2010) The Development of a Local Urban Climate Model and its Application to the Intelligent Design of Cities. [online] Available at: <www.homepages.ucl.ac.uk/~ucftiha/index.html> [Accessed: 15.04.10].

Luck, G.W. (2007) A review of the relationships between human population density and biodiversity. *Biological Reviews,* **82**, 607–645.

Luck, G.W., Ricketts, T.H., Daily, G.C. & Imhoff, M. (2004) Alleviating spatial conflict between people and biodiversity. *Proceedings of the National Academy of Sciences, USA,* **101**, 182–186.

Luck, M.A., Jenerette, G.D., Wu, J. & Grimm, N.B. (2001) The urban funnel model and the spatially heterogeneous ecological footprint. *Ecosystems,* **4** (8), 782–796.

Luechinger, S. (2009) Valuing air quality using the life satisfaction approach. *Economic Journal,* **119** (536), 482–515.

Lull, H.W. & Sopper, W.E. (1969) Hydrologic Effects from Urbanisation of Forested Watersheds in the Northeast, Upper Darby, Pa., U.S. Northeastern Forest Experiment Station.

Luniak, M. (1980) Birds of allotment gardens in Warsaw. *Acta Ornithologica,* **17**, 297–320.

Luniak, M. (1981) The birds of the park habitats in Warsaw. *Acta Ornithologica,* **18**, 335–370.

Lussenhop, J. (1977) Urban cemeteries as bird refuges. *The Condor,* **79**, 456–461.

Maas, J., Verheij, R.A., Groenewegen, P.P., de Vries, S. & Spreeuwenberg, P. (2006) Greenspace, urbanity and health: how strong is the relation? *Journal of Epidemiological Community Health,* **60**, 587–592.

Maas, J., Verheij, R. A., Spreeuwenberg, P. & Groenewegen, P. P. (2008). Physical activity as a possible mechanism behind the relationship between greenspace and health: a multilevel analysis. *BMC Public Health,* **8**, 206.

MAGIC (2009) [online] Available at: <http://magic.defra.gov.uk/> [Accessed on: 21.12.09].

Magura, T., Tóthmérész, B. & Molnár, T. (2004) Changes in carabid beetle assemblages along an urbanisation gradient in the city of Debrecen, Hungary. *Landscape Ecology,* **19**, 747–759.

Maller, C., Townsend, M. & Brown, P. (2002) Healthy parks healthy people: the health benefits of contact with nature in park context. Deakin University and Parks Victoria, Melbourne, Australia.

Manning, W.J. & Feder, W.A. (1980) Biomonitoring Air Pollutants with Plants. Applied Science Publishers, London.

Marzluff, J.M. (2001) Worldwide urbanisation and its effects on birds. Avian ecology and conservation in an urbanising world (eds Marzluff, J.M., Bowman, R. & Donnelly, R.). Kluwer Academic, Boston, pp. 19–47.

Marzluff, J.M. (2005) Island biogeography for an urbanising world: how extinction and colonization may determine biological diversity in human-dominated landscapes. *Urban Ecosystems,* **8**, 157–177.

Marzluff, J.M., Shulenberger, E., Endlicher, W., Alberti, M., Bradley, G., Ryan, C., ZumBrunnen, C. & Simon, U. (2008) Urban Ecology. Springer, New York.

Mason, C.F. (2006) Avian species richness and numbers in the built environment: can new housing developments be good for birds? *Biodiversity and Conservation,* **15**, 2365–2378.

McDonald, A., Bealey, W., Fowler, D., Dragosits, U., Skiba, U., Smith, R., Donovan, R., Brett, H., Hewitt, C. & Nemitz, E. (2007) Quantifying the effect of urban tree planting on concentrations and depositions of PM10 in two UK conurbations. *Atmospheric Environment,* **41** (38), 8455–8467.

McFrederick, Q.S. & LeBuhn, G. (2006) Are urban parks refuges for bumble bees *Bombus* spp. (Hymenoptera: Apidae)? *Biological Conservation,* **129**, 372–382.

McGranahan, G., Marcotullio, P., Bai, X., Balk, D., Braga, T., Douglas, I., Elmqvist, T., Rees, W., Satterthwaite, D., Jacob Songsore J. & Zlotnik, H. (2005) Urban Systems. Millennium Ecosystem Assessment, Ecosystems and Human Well-Being: Current State and Trends. Island Press, Washington D.C.

McIntyre, N.E., Knowles-Yanez, K., Hope, D. (2000) Urban Ecosystems. **4**, 5–24.

McIntyre, N.E. & Hostetler, M.E. (2001) Effects of urban land use on pollinator (Hymenoptera: Apoidea) communities in a desert metropolis. *Basic and Applied Ecology,* **2**, 209–218.

McKinney, M.L. (2001) Role of human population size in raising bird and mammal threat among nations. *Animal Conservation,* **4**, 45–57.

McKinney, M.L. (2002) Why larger nations have disproportionate threat rates: area increases endemism and human population size. *Biodiversity and Conservation,* **11**, 1317–1325.

McKinney, M.L. (2006) Urbanisation as a major cause of biotic homogenization. *Biological Conservation,* **127**, 247–260.

McPherson, E.G., Nowak, D.J., & Rowntree, R.E. (1994) Chicago's Urban Forest Ecosystem: Results of the Chicago Urban Forest Climate Project. U.S. Northeastern Forest Experiment Station, General Technical Report NE-186.

McPherson, E.G., Nowak, D., Heisler, G., Grimmond, S., Souch, C., Grant, R. & Rowntree, R. (1997) Quantifying urban forest structure, function and value: the Chicago Urban Forest Climate Project. *Urban Ecosystems,* **1**, 49–61.

Melles, S., Glenn, S. & Martin, K. (2003) Urban bird diversity and landscape complexity: species-environment associations along a multiscale habitat gradient. *Conservation Ecology,* **7**, 5.

Memmott, J. (2010) Urban pollinators: ecology and conservation. [online] Available at: <www.bbsrc.ac.uk/web/FILES/PreviousAwards/pollinators-memmott.pdf> [Accessed: 16.08.10].

Mills, G.S., Dunning, J.B. Jr & Bates, J.M. (1989) Effects of urbanisation on breeding bird community structure in southwestern desert habitats. *The Condor,* **91**, 416–428.

Ministry of Justice (2007) Burial Grounds: The results of a survey of burial grounds in England and Wales. Ministry of Justice, London.

Mitchell, R. & Popham, F. (2008) Effect of exposure to natural environment on health inequalities: an observational population study, *The Lancet,* **372** (9650): 1655–1660.

Miyabara, Y., Sakata, Y., Suzuki, J. & Suzuki, S. (1994) Estimation of faecal pollution based on the amounts urobilins in urban rivers. *Environmental Pollution,* **84**, 117–122.

Miyashita, T., Shinkai, A. & Chida, T. (1998) The effects of forest fragmentation on web spider communities in urban areas. *Biological Conservation,* **86**, 357–364.

Moll, G. (1996) Using geographic information systems (GIS) to analyse the value of urban ecosystems. In: Urban Trees-Costing The Benefits. Conference Proceedings. Chartered Institute of Water and Environmental Management, London.

Morimoto, T., Katoh, K., Yamaura, Y. & Watanabe, S. (2006) Can surrounding land cover influence the avifauna in urban/suburban woodlands in Japan? *Landscape and Urban Planning,* **75**, 143–156.

Morneau, F., Decarie, R., Pelletier, R., Lambert, D., Desgranges, J-L. & Savard, J-P. (1999) Changes in breeding richness and abundance in Montreal parks over a period of 15 years. *Landscape and Urban Planning,* **44**, 111–121.

Mulholland, H. (2008) Boris Johnson unveils plans to create 2012 new vegetable gardens in London. *The Guardian.* 4 November 2008. [online] Available at: <www.guardian.co.uk/politics/2008/nov/04/boris-london> [Accessed: 21.12.09].

Munyenyembe, F., Harris, J., Hone, J. & Nix, H. (1989) Determinants of bird populations in an urban area. *Australian Journal of Ecology,* **14**, 549–557.

NAIGT (New Automotive Innovation and Growth Team) (2008) An Independent Report on the Future of the Automotive Industry in the UK. [online] Available at: <www.berr.gov.uk/files/file51139.pdf> [Accessed: 04.07.09].

NAO (National Audit Office) (2006) Enhancing Urban Greenspace. The Stationary Office, London.

National Heart Forum (2007) Building Health: Creating and enhancing places for healthy active lives. In partnership with Living Streets and CABE.

Natural Economy (2010) Green Infrastructure reports. [online] Available at: <www.naturaleconomynorthwest.co.uk/resources+reports.php> [Accessed: 13.08.10].

Natural England (2006) Physical Activity and the Natural Environment. Evidence Sheet 3. Natural England.

Natural England (2008) The State of the Natural Environment 2008. Research Report NE85. Natural England, Sheffield.

Natural England (2009) T2 Condition of Sites of Special Scientific Interest (SSSIs) in urban areas in England. [online] Available at: <http://archive.defra.gov.uk/environment/biodiversity/documents/indicator/200905t2.pdf > [Accessed 03.03.11].

Natural England & CPRE (Campaign to Protect Rural England) (2010) Green Belts: a greener future. Natural England and CPRE, Sheffield.

Natural England (2010) Urban SSSI condition statistics. Personal communication (unpublished).

Newcastle City Council (2004) Greenspaces... your spaces, Newcastle's Greenspace Strategy. Newcastle City Council, Newcastle upon Tyne.

NHPAU (National Housing and Planning Advice Unit) (2010) The Implications of Housing Type/Size Mix and Density for the Affordability and Viability of New Housing Supply. NHPAU, Fareham. [online] Available at: <www.communities.gov.uk/documents/507390/pdf/1486173.pdf > [Accessed: 27.08.10].

Niemelä, J., Kotze D.J., Venn S., Penev, L., Stoyanov, I., Spence, J., H Hartley, D. & De Oca, E.M. (2002) Carabid beetle assemblages (Coleoptera, Carabidae) across urban-rural gradients: an international comparison. *Landscape Ecology,* **17**, 387–401.

Northampton Borough Council (2006) Open Space, Sport and Recreation Needs Assessment and Audit. Northampton Borough Council, Northampton.

Nowak, D.J., McHale, P.J., Ibarra, M., Crane, D., Stevens, J.C. & Luley, C.J. (1997) Modelling the effects of urban vegetation on air pollution. 22nd NATO/CCMS International Technical Meeting on Air Pollution Modelling and its Application, pp. 276–282. NATO/CCMS, Brussels.

Nowak, D.J. (2006) Air pollution removal by urban trees and shrubs in the United States. *Urban Forestry & Urban Greening,* **4**, 115–123.

NSALG (National Society of Allotments and Leisure Gardeners) (1993) National Survey of Allotment and Leisure Gardeners, NSALG.

NUFU (The National Urban Forestry Unit) (2005) Trees Matter! Bringing lasting benefits to people in towns. NUFU, Wolverhampton.

O'Brien, L., Williams, K. & Stewart, A. (2010) Urban health and health inequalities and the role of urban forestry in Britain: A review. Forest Research.

OECD (Organisation for Economic Co-operation and Development) (2010) OECD Glossary of Statistical Terms [online] Available at: <http://stats.oecd.org/glossary/index.htm> [Accessed: 26.11.10].

One North East (2007) Middlesbrough sows the seeds of urban farming. *One North East*. 23 May 2007 [online] Available at: <www.onenortheast.gov.uk/page/news/article.cfm?mode=search&articleId=2285> [Accessed: 21.12.09].

ONS (Office for National Statistics) (1998) Differences in urban and rural populations. (eds Denham C. & White I.). Population Trends 91. HMSO. [online] Available at: <www.statistics.gov.uk/articles/population_trends/urbrurdif_pt91.pdf> [Accessed: 24.11.10].

ONS (Office of National Statistics) (2002) Census 2001. [online] Available at: <www.statistics.gov.uk/census2001/census2001.asp> [Accessed 24.01.11].

ONS (Office of National Statistics) (2005) The UK's Major Urban Areas. (ed) Pointer, G. Focus on People and Migration. [online] Available at: <www.statistics.gov.uk/downloads/theme_compendia/fom2005/03_FOPM_UrbanAreas.pdf> [Accessed: 26.11.10].

ONS (Office of National Statistics) (2007) Focus on London 2007. ONS, London.

ONS (Office of National Statistics) (2009) Office of National Statistics Geography Glossary. [online] <www.statistics.gov.uk/geography/glossary/u.asp> [Accessed: 24.11.10].

OPAL (2010) Open Air Laboratories. [online] Available at: <www.opalexplorenature.org/> [Accessed: 21.04.10].

Osborne, J.L., Martin, A.P., Shortall, C.R., Todd, A.D., Goulson, D., Knight, M.E., Hale, R.J. & Sanderson, R.A. (2008) Quantifying and comparing bumblebee nest densities in gardens and countryside habitats. *Journal of Applied Ecology,* **45**, 784–792.

Ottosson, J. & Grahn, P. (2005) A comparison of leisure time spent in a garden with leisure time spent indoors on measures of restoration in residents in geriatric care, *Landscape Research,* **30** (1), 23–55.

Owen, J., Townes, H. & Townes, M. (1981) Species diversity of Ichneurnonidae and Serphidae (Hymenoptera) in an English suburban garden. *Biological Journal of the Linnean Society,* **16** (4), 315–336.

Owen, J. (1991) The ecology of a garden: the first fifteen years. Cambridge University Press, Cambridge.

PAN 65 (2008) Planning Advice Note, PAN 65 Planning and Open Space. Scottish Government, Edinburgh.

Park, C-R. & Lee, W-S. (2000) Relationship between species composition and area in breeding birds of urban woods in Seoul, Korea. *Landscape and Urban Planning,* **51**, 29–36.

Parris, K.M. (2006) Urban amphibian assemblages as metacommunities. *Journal of Animal Ecology,* **75**, 757–764.

Paul, M.J. & Meyer, J.L. (2001) Streams in the urban landscape. *Annual Review of Ecology and Systematics,* **32**, 333–365.

Perez-Vazquez, A., Anderson, S., Rogers, A.W. (2005) Assessing benefits from allotments as a component of urban agriculture in England. Agropolis: the social, political and environmental dimensions of urban agriculture (ed Mougeot, L. J.A.). Earthscan, London.

Perino, G., Andrews, B., Kontoleon, B. & Bateman, I.J. (2010) Economic Assessment of Ecosystem Services provided by UK Urban Habitats. The Economics Team of the UK National Ecosystem Assessment, University of East Anglia, Norwich.

Perry, T. & Nawaz, R. (2008) An investigation into the extent and impacts of hard surfacing of domestic gardens in an area of Leeds, United Kingdom, *Landscape and Urban Planning,* **86** (1), 1–13.

Petts, G.E., Heathcote, J. & Martin, D. (eds.) (2002) Urban rivers: our inheritance and future. IWA Publishing.

Pickett, S.T.A. (2008) Urban Ecological Systems: Linking Terrestrial Ecological, Physical and Socioeconomic Components of Metropolitan Areas. Urban Ecology. (eds Marzluff, J.M., Shulenberger, E., Endlicher, W., Alberti, M., Bradley, G., Ryan, C., ZumBrunnen, C., Simon, U.) Springer, New York.

Pilgrim, S.E., Cullen, L.C., Smith, D.J. & Pretty, J. (2008) Ecological knowledge is lost in wealthier communities and countries, *Environmental Science and Technology,* **42** (4), 1004–1009.

PPG2 (1995) Planning Policy Guidance Note 2: Green Belts, Office of the Deputy Prime Minister. [online] Available at: <www.communities.gov.uk/planningandbuilding/planningsystem/planningpolicy/planningpolicystatements/> [Accessed 15.02.11].

PPG3 (2000) Planning Policy Guidance Note 3: Housing, Office of the Deputy Prime Minister, London. [online] Available at: <www.communities.gov.uk/planningandbuilding/planningsystem/planningpolicy/planningpolicystatements/> [Accessed 15.02.11].

PPG9 (2005) Planning Policy Statement 9: Biodiversity and Geological Conservation. Office of the Deputy Prime Minister, London. [online] Available at: <www.communities.gov.uk/planningandbuilding/planningsystem/planningpolicy/planningpolicystatements/> [Accessed 15.02.11].

PPG17 (2002) Planning Policy Guidance 17: Planning for open space, sport and recreation. Office of the Deputy Prime Minister, London. [online] Available at: [Accessed 15.02.11].

PPS3 (2006) Consultation on Planning Policy Statement 3: Housing (PPS3) – A summary of responses and key issues Planning Policy Statement. Department for Communities and Local Government, London. [online] Available at: [Accessed 15.02.11].

PPS7 (2004) Planning Policy Statement 7: Sustainable Development in Rural Areas. Office of the Deputy Prime Minister, London. [online] Available at: [Accessed 15.02.11].

PPS9 (2005) Planning Policy Statement 9: Biodiversity and Geological Conservation. Office of the Deputy Prime Minister, London. [online] Available at: <www.communities.gov.uk/planningandbuilding/planningsystem/planningpolicy/planningpolicystatements/> [Accessed 15.02.11].

Platt, A. & Lill, A. (2006) Composition and conservation value of bird assemblages of urban 'habitat islands': Do pedestrian traffic and landscape variables exert an influence? *Urban Ecosystems*, **9**, 83–97.

Porter, E.E., Forshner, B.R. & Blair, R.B. (2001) Woody vegetation and canopy fragmentation along a forest-to-urban gradient. *Urban Ecosystems*, **5**, 131–151.

Post, R. & Beeby, A. (1996) Activity of the microbial decomposer community in metal-contaminated roadside soils. *Journal of Applied Ecology,* **33** (4), 703–709.

Pretty, J. (2002) Agri-Culture: Reconnecting People, Land and Nature. Earthscan, London.

Pretty, J. (2004) How nature contributes to mental and physical health. *Spirituality & Health International,* **5** (2), 68–78.

Pretty, J., Peacock, J., Sellens, M. & Griffin, M. (2005) The mental and physical health outcomes of green exercise. *International Journal of Environmental Health Research,* **15** (5), 319–337.

Pyšek, P., Chocholoušková, Z., Pyšek, A., Jarošík, V., Chytrý, M. & Tichý, L. (2004) Trends in species diversity and composition of urban vegetation over three decades. *Journal of Vegetation Science,* **15**, 781–788.

Queen Elizabeth II Fields Challenge. (2010) Queen Elizabeth II Fields Challenge. [online] Available at: <www. qe2fields.com/default.aspx> [Accessed: 01.09.10].

Quinn, J.L., Whittingham, M.J., Butler, S.J. & Cresswell, W. (2006) Noise, predation risk compensation and vigilance in the chaffinch *Fringilla coelebs. Journal of Avian Biology* **37**, 601–608.

Raper, H. (2009) Recreation Development Officer, Newcastle City Council. (Personal communication, 7th December 2009).

Rawlins, B., Lark, R., O'Donnell, K., Tye, A. & Lister, T. (2005). The assessment of point and diffuse metal pollution of soils from an urban geochemical survey of Sheffield, England. *Soil Use and Management,* **21** (4), 353–362.

Reichard, S.H. & White, P. (2001) Horticulture as a pathway of invasive plant introductions in the United States, *Bioscience,* **51** (2), 103–113.

Rhoads, B.L. & Cahill, R.A. (1999) Geomorphological assessment of sediment contamination in an urban stream system. *Applied Geochemistry*, **14**, 459–483.

RHS (Royal Horticultural Society) (2006) Front Gardens: Are we parking on our gardens? Do driveways cause flooding? Gardening Matters, Royal Horticultural Society.

Riding, A., Critchley, N., Wilson, L. & Parker, J. (2010) Definition and mapping of open mosaic habitats on previously developed land: Phase 1 Final Report to Defra. [online] Available at: <http://randd.defra.gov.uk/Document. aspx?Document=WC0722_9022_FRP.pdf > [Accessed: 27.08.10].

Riley, S.P.D., Busteed, G.T., Kats, L.B., Vandergon, T.L., Lee, L.F.S., Dagit, R.G., Kerby, J.L., Fisher, R.N. & Sauvajot, R.M. (2005) Effects of urbanisation on the distribution and abundance of amphibians and invasive species in southern California streams. *Conservation Biology*, **19**, 1894–1907.

RMetS (Royal Meteorological Society) (2009a) Urban Heat Island Information. [online] Available at: <http://www. metlink.org/weather-climate-resources-teenagers/what-is-weather/urban-heat-islands/urban-heat-island-background. html> [Accessed: 03.03.11].

RMetS (Royal Meteorological Society) (2009b) Manchester's Urban Heat Island on March 6th 2009. [online] Available at: <http://www.metlink.org/weather-climate-resources-teenagers/what-is-weather/urban-heat-islands/urban-heat-island-manchester.html> [Accessed: 03.03.11].

Rogers, K., Hansford, D., Sunderland, T., Brunt, A., & Coish, N. (in press) Measuring the ecosystem services of Torbay's trees The Torbay i-Tree Eco pilot project. Paper submission for the ICF – Urban Tree Research Conference 2011 April 13–14th.

Rosenzweig, M.L. (1995) Species diversity in space and time. Cambridge University Press, Cambridge.

Rottenborn, S.C. (1999) Predicting the impacts of urbanisation on riparian bird communities. *Biological Conservation,* **88**, 289–299.

Roy, D.B., Hill, M.O. & Rothery, P. (1999) Effects of urban land cover on the local species pool in Britain. *Ecography,* **22**, 507–515.

RSPB (The Royal Society for the Protection of Birds) (2009) Nature Count Results. [online] Available at: <www.rspb. org.uk/naturecount/> [Accessed: 03.03.11].

RSPB (The Royal Society for the Protection of Birds) (2010) Big Garden Birdwatch. [online] Available at: <www.rspb. org.uk/birdwatch/results/> [Accessed: 22.04.10].

Rubbo, M.J. & Kiesecker, J.M. (2005) Amphibian breeding distribution in an urbanized landscape. *Conservation Biology*, 19, 504–511.

Rugg, J. (2006) Lawn cemeteries: the emergence of a new landscape of death. *Urban History*, **33**, 213–233.

Sadler, J.P., Small, E.C., Fiszpan, H., Telfer, M.G. & Niemela, J. (2006) Investigating environmental variation and landscape characteristics of an urban-rural gradient using woodland carabid assemblages. *Journal of Biogeography*, **33**, 1126–1138.

Sadler, J.P., Bates, A.J. & Hale, J. (2010) Bringing cities alive: the importance of urban greenspaces for people and biodiversity. Urban Ecology (ed. K.J. Gaston). Cambridge University Press, Cambridge.

SAGS (Scottish Allotments and Gardens Society) (2007) Finding Scotland's Allotments. SAGS.

Samecka-Cymerman, A. & Kempers, A.J. (2007) Heavy metals in aquatic macrophytes from two small rivers polluted

UK National Ecosystem Assessment: Technical Report

by urban, agricultural and textile industry sewages SW Poland. *Archives of Environmental Contamination and Toxicology,* **53**, (2), 198–206.

Sandström, U.G., Angelstam, P. & Mikusinski, G. (2006) Ecological diversity of birds in relation to the structure of urban greenspace. *Landscape and Urban Planning,* **77**, 39–53.

Sasvari, L. (1984) Bird abundance and species diversity in the parks and squares of Budapest. *Folia Zoologica,* **38**, 249–262.

Savard, J-P.L., Clergeau, P. & Mennechez, G. (2000) Biodiversity concepts and urban ecosystems. *Landscape and Urban Planning,* **48**, 131–142.

Schadek, U., Strauss, B., Biedermann, R. & Kleyer, M. (2009) Plant species richness, vegetation structure and soil resources of urban brownfield sites linked to successional age. *Urban Ecosystems,* **12** (2), 115–126.

Schlesinger, W.H. & Andrews, J.A. (2000) Soil respiration and the global carbon cycle. *Biogeochemistry,* **48** (1), 7–20.

Scholes, L., Faulkner, H.P., Tapsell, S. & Downward, S. (2008). Urban rivers as pollutant sinks and sources: a public health concern to recreational river users? *Water, Air and Soil Pollution: FOCUS,* **8**, 543–553.

SCORCHIO (2010) Sustainable Cities: Options for Responding to Climate cHange Impacts and Outcomes (SCORCHIO). [online] Available at: <http://www.sed.manchester.ac.uk/research/cure/research/scorchio/> [Accessed: 15.04.10].

Scottish Government (2004) Review of Green Belt Policy in Scotland. Scottish Government, Edinburgh.

Scottish Government (2009a) Scotland's People Annual report: results from 2007/2008 Scottish Household Survey. Scottish Government, Edinburgh.

Scottish Government (2009b) Designing Streets: Consultation Draft. Case Study G9: Ardler Village. [online] Available at: <www.scotland.gov.uk/Publications/2009/01/27140909/13> [Accessed 01.03.11].

SEPA (Scottish Environment Protection Agency) (2008) Water Framework Directive Classification of Urban Rivers. [online] Available at: <www.sepa.org.uk/default.aspx> [Accessed: 27.08.10].

Sewell, S.R. & Catterall, C.P. (1998) Bushland modification and styles of urban development: their effects on birds in south-east Queensland. *Wildlife Research,* **25**, 41–63.

Sheate, W., Eales, R., Daly, E., Murdoch, A., Hill, C. (2008) Case study to develop tools and methodologies to deliver an ecosystem-based approach: Thames Gateway Green Grids, Project report NR0109. Defra, London. [online] Available at: <http://randd.defra.gov.uk/Default.aspx?Menu=Menu&Module=More&Location=None&Completed=0&ProjectID=14753#Description> [Accessed 03.03.11].

Skinner, C.J. & Grimwood, C.J. (2002) The UK National Noise Incidence Survey 2000/2001. Noise Forum Conference 20 May 2002. Building Research Establishment, Watford.

Skinner, K.S. & Bruce-Burgess, L. (2005) Strategic and project-level river restoration protocols-key components for meeting the requirements of the water framework directive (WFD). *Water and Environment Journal,* **19** (2), 135–142.

Slabbekoorn, H. & Ripmeester, E.A.P. (2008). Birdsong and anthropogenic noise: implications and applications for conservation. *Molecular Ecology,* **17**, 72–83.

Smith, C. & Levermore, G. (2008). Designing urban spaces and buildings to improve sustainability and quality of life in a warmer world. *Energy Policy,* **36**(12), 4558–4562.

Smith, R.M., Gaston, K.J., Warren, P.H. & Thompson, K. (2005) Urban domestic gardens (V): relationships between landcover composition, housing and landscape. *Landscape Ecology,* **20**, 235–253.

Smith, R.M., Gaston, K.J., Warren, P.H. & Thompson, K. (2006a) Urban domestic gardens (VIII): environmental correlates of invertebrate abundance. *Biodiversity and Conservation,* **15**, 2515–2545.

Smith, R.M., Thompson, K., Hodgson, J.G., Warren, P.H. & Gaston, K.J. (2006b) Urban domestic gardens (IX): composition and richness of the vascular plant flora, and implications for native biodiversity. *Biological Conservation,* **129**, 312–322.

Smith, R.M., Warren, P.H., Thompson, K. & Gaston, K.J. (2006c) Urban domestic gardens (VI): determinants of variation in invertebrate biodiversity. *Biodiversity and Conservation,* in press.

SNH (Scottish Natural Heritage) (2001) Natural Heritage Trends – Forest and Woodlands: an Overview. Information and Advisory Note Number 137. [online] Available at: <http://www.snh.org.uk/publications/on-line/advisorynotes/137/137.htm> [Accessed on 27.04.10].

Snook, D.L. & Whitehead, P. G. (2004) Water quality and ecology of the River Lee: mass balance and a review of temporal and spatial data. *Hydrology and Earth System Science,* **8**, 636–650.

Soltis, D. (1997) Loss of trees increase stormwater runoff in Atlanta, *Water Engineering and Management,* **144**, 6.

Stansfield, S. & Matheson, P. (2003) Noise Pollution: Non-Auditory Effects on Health. *British Medical Bulletin,* **68**: 243–257.

Statutory Instrument (2008) No. 2362. Town and Country Planning, England. The Town and Country Planning (General Permitted Development) (Amendment) (No. 2) (England) Order 2008.

Steinberg, D.A., Pouyat, R.V., Parmelee, R.W.& Groffman, P.M. (1997) Earthworm abundance and nitrogen mineralization rates along an urban-rural land use gradient. *Soil Biology and Biochemistry,* **29**, 427–430.

Stelzer, R.J., Chittka, L. Carlton, M. & Ings, T.C. (2010) Winter Active Bumblebees (*Bombus terrestris*) Achieve High Foraging Rates in Urban Britain. *PLoS ONE* **5** (3): e9559.

Stieb, D.M., Judek, S. & Burnett, R.T. (2002) Meta-analysis of time-series studies of air pollution and mortality: effects of gases and particles and the influence of cause of death, age, and season. *Journal of the Air & Waste Management Association,* **52** (4), 470–484.

SUE (Sustainable Urban Environment) (2010) The Sustainable Urban Environments Programme. [online] Available at: <http://www.urbansustainabilityexchange.org.uk/ISSUESSueProgramme.htm? [Accessed: 28.04.10].

Suhonen, J. & Jokimäki, J. (1988) A biogeographical comparison of the breeding bird species assemblages in twenty Finnish urban parks. *Ornis Fennica,* **65**, 76–83.

Sukopp, H. (2002) On the early history of urban ecology in Europe. *Preslia,* **74**: 373–393.

Sullivan, W.C., Kuo, F.E., Depooter, S.F. (2004) The fruit of urban nature: vital neighbourhood spaces. *Environment and Behavior,* **36**, 678–700.

Sustrans (2009) Related academic research. [online] Available at: <http://www.sustrans.org.uk/resources/research-and-monitoring/related-academic-research> [Accessed on 22.12.09].

SVDLS (Scottish Vacant and Derelict Land Survey) (2008) Scottish Vacant and Derelict Land Survey. Communities Analytical Services Division, Scottish Government, Edinburgh.

Takano, T., Nakamura, K. & Watanabe, M. (2002) Urban residential environments and senior citizens' longevity in megacity areas: the importance of walkable greenspaces. *Journal of Epidemiological Community Health,* **56**, 913–918.

Tapsell S., Tunstall S., House M., Whomsley, J. & Macnaghten, P. (2001) Growing Up with Rivers? Rivers in London Children's Worlds. *Area,* **33** (2), 177–189.

Taylor, F., Kuo, F.E. & Sullivan, W. (2002) Views of nature and self discipline: evidence from inner city children. *Journal of Environmental Psychology,* **22**, 49–63.

Taylor, F. (2009) Children with attention deficits concentrate better after walk in the park, *Journal of Attention Disorders,* **12** (5), 402.

TDAG (Trees and Design Action Group) (2008) Trees in the Urban Realm. TDAG.

Tejeda, S., Zarazua-Ortega, G., Avila-Perez, P., Garcia-Mejia, A., Carapia-Morales, L. & Diaz-Delgado, C. (2006). Major and trace elements in sediments of the upper course of Lerma river. *Journal of Radioanalytical and Nuclear Chemistry,* **270** (1), 9–14.

TfL (Transport for London) (2008) Transport for London Environmental Report. Greater London Authority, London. [online]. Available at: <www.tfl.gov.uk/assets/downloads/corporate/environment-report-2008.pdf> [Accessed: 04.12.09].

THESAURUS Project (2008) Thames Gateway Ecosystem Services Assessment Using Green Grids and Decision Support Tools for Sustainability, Collingwood Environmental Planning/GeoData Institute (2006–08). [online] Available at: <http://www.cep.co.uk/THESAURUS.htm> [Accessed: 22.12.09].

Thévenot, D.R., Moilleron, R., Lestel, L., Gromaire, M.C., Rocher, V., Cambier, P., Bonté, P., Colin, J.L., de Pontevès, C. & Meybeck, M. (2007) Critical budget of metal sources and pathways in the Seine River basin (1994–2003) for Cd, Cr, Cu, Hg, Ni, Pb and Zn. *Science of the Total Environment,* **375**, 180–203.

Thornton, A. (2009) Public attitudes and behaviours towards the environment – tracker survey: A report to the Department for Environment, Food and Rural Affairs. TNS. Defra, London.

Thorpe, H. (1969) Departmental Committee of Inquiry into Allotments. HMSO.

Tilghman, N.G. (1987) Characteristics of urban woodlands affecting breeding bird diversity and abundance. *Landscape and Urban Planning,* **14**, 481–495.

Tiwary, A., Sinnett, D., Peachey, C., Chalabi, Z., Vardoulakis, S., Fletcher, T., Leonardi, G., Grundy, C., Azapagic, A. & Hutchings, T.R. (2009) An integrated tool to assess the role of new planting in PM10 capture and the human health benefits: A case study in London. *Environmental Pollution,* **157** (10), 2645–2653.

Torres, M.J. (1997) Effects of lead and cadmium on the survival of faecal coliforms in sediments of constructed wetlands. Unpublished internal report, Middlesex University, London.

Trees in Cities (2010) Annual Report 2008–09. Trees in Cities.

Trust for Public Land (2008) How Much Value Does the City of Philadelphia Receive from its Parks and Recreation System? Trust for Public Land Center for City Park Excellence, Philadelphia.

Tubby, K.V. & Webber, J.F. (2010) Pests and diseases threatening urban trees under a changing climate. *Forestry,* **83**, 451–459.

Turner, W.R. (2003) Citywide biological monitoring as a tool for ecology and conservation in urban landscapes: the case of the Tucson Bird Count. *Landscape and Urban Planning,* **65**, 149–166.

Turner, K., Lefler, L. & Freedman, B. (2005) Plant communities of selected urbanized areas of Halifax, Nova Scotia, Canada. *Landscape and Urban Planning,* **71**, 191–206.

Ulrich, R.S., Simons, R.V., Losito, B.D., Fiorito, E., Miles, M.A. & Zelson, M. (1991) Stress recovery during exposure to nature and urban environments. *Journal of Environmental Psychology,* **11**, 201–230.

UPFOR (Urban Parks Forum) (2001) Public Park Assessment. A survey of local authority owned parks focusing on parks of historic interest. Urban Parks Forum, Caversham.

Urban Greenspaces Taskforce (2002) Greenspaces, Better Places: Final report of the Urban Greenspaces Taskforce. DTLR, London.

Valentine, G. & McKendrck, J. (1997) Children's outdoor play: exploring parental concerns about children's safety and the changing nature of childhood, *Geoforum,* **28** (2), 219–235.

Vázquez, L.B. & Gaston, K.J. (2006) People and mammals in Mexico: conservation conflicts at a national scale. *Biodiversity & Conservation,* **15**, 2397–2414.

van den Berg, A.E., Koole, S.L., & van der Wulp, N.Y. (2003) Environmental preference and restoration: (How) are they related? *Journal of Environmental Psychology,* **23** (2), 135–146.

Venn, S.J., Kotze, D.J. & Niemela, J. (2003) Urbanisation effects of carabid diversity in boreal forests. *European Journal of Entomology,* **100**, 73–80.

Vitousek, P.M., Aber, J.D., Howarth, R.W., Likens, G.E., Matson, P.A., Schindler, D.W., Schlesinger, W.H. & Tilman, D.G. (1997) Human alteration of the global nitrogen cycle: sources and consequences. *Ecological Applications,* **7** (3), 737–750.

Vrscaj, B., Poggio, L. & Marsan, F.A. (2008) A method for soil environmental quality evaluation for management and planning in urban areas. *Landscape and Urban Planning,* **88** (2–4), 81–94.

Wackernagel, M. & Rees, W. (1996) Our Ecological Footprint: Reducing Human Impact on the Earth. New Society Publishers.

Walling, D.E., Owens, P.N., Carter, J., Leeks, G.J.L., Lewis, S., Meharg, A.A. & Wright, J. (2003) Storage of sediment-associated nutrients and contaminants in river channel and floodplain systems. *Applied Geochemistry,* **18** (2), 195–220.

Wania, A., Kühn, I. & Klotz, S. (2006) Plant richness patterns in agricultural and urban landscapes in Central Germany – spatial gradients of species richness. *Landscape and Urban Planning,* **75**, 97–110.

Water UK (2008) Sustainable Water. State of the Water Sector Report. Water UK, London.

Wayne, R.P. (2000) Chemistry of Atmospheres. Clarendon Press, Oxford.

Weiner M.J. (2004) English culture and the decline of the industrial spirit 1850–1980 (2nd Edition). Cambridge University Press, Cambridge.

Weller, B. & Ganzhorn, J.U. (2004) Carabid beetle community composition, body size, and fluctuating asymmetry along an urban-rural gradient. *Basic and Applied Ecology,* **5**, 193–201.

Wells, N.M. & Evans, G.W. (2003) Nearby nature: a buffer of life stress among rural children. *Environment and Behavior,* **35**(3), 311.

WMRA (West Midlands Regional Assembly) (2007) Greenspace for the West Midlands Region: Technical Mapping Paper, A guide to the spatial mapping and assessment of Greenspace for public and wildlife benefit. TEP, Warrington.

WFD (2000) EU Water Framework Directive 2000/60/EC. [online] Available at: <http://ec.europa.eu/environment/water/water-framework/index_en.html> [Accessed 03.03.11].

Whitmore, C., Crouch, T.E. & Slotow, R.H. (2002) Conservation of biodiversity in urban environments: invertebrates on structurally enhanced road islands. *African Entomology,* **10**, 113–126.

Wilby, R.L. & Perry, G.L.W. (2006) Climate change, biodiversity and the urban environment: a critical review based on London, UK. *Progress in Physical Geography*, **30**, 73–98.

Wilson, B. & Robson, J. (2004) Cemeteries and their management, Home Office online report 1/04, 2004.

Wilson, C. & Clarke, R. (2002). Persistent pollutants in freshwater sediments. Unpublished SEPA report for SEPA Diffuse Pollution Initiative. December 2002. Edited version available as DPI Report No. 7, from SEPA Diffuse Pollution Initiative, Edinburgh.

Wittig, R. (2004) The origin and development of the urban flora of Central Europe. *Urban Ecosystems*, **7**, 323–339.

Wong, J.L. (2007) Culture, heritage and access to open spaces. Open Space: People Space (eds. Ward Thompson, C., & Travlou, T.). Taylor & Francis Inc.

Wood, G.A., Kibblewhite, M.G., Hannam, J.A., Harris, J.A. & Leeds-Harrison, P.B. (2005) Soil-based Services in the Built Environment. A report for the Defra published by National Soil Resources Institute, Cranfield University.

The Woodland Trust (2004) Space for People: Targetting action for woodland access. Woodland Trust Publications.

Worpole, K. & Greenhalgh, L. (1995) Park Life: Urban Parks and Social Renewal. Comedia and Demos, London.

Wright, I. (2008) House of Commons Debate on the 7th May 2008.

WWF (2010) Reinventing the City – Three Prerequisites For Greening Urban Infrastructures. [online] Available at: <http://assets.panda.org/downloads/wwf_reinventing_the_city_final_3_low_resolution.pdf> [Accessed: 15.12.10].

WWT (The Wildfowl and Wetlands Trust) (2010) Wetlands In My Back Yard (WIMBY). [online] Available at: <www.wwt.org.uk/our-work/conservation-projects/wetlands-in-my-back-yard-wimby> [Accessed: 06.08.10].

Young, I.M. & Ritz, K. (2005) The habitat of soil microbes. Biological Diversity and Function in Soils (eds. Bardgett, R.D., Usher, M.B. & Hopkins, D.W). Cambridge University Press, Cambridge.

Zanette, L., Martins, R. & Ribeiro, S. (2005) Effects of urbanisation on Neotropical wasp and bee assemblages in a Brazilian metropolis. *Landscape and Urban Planning,* **71** (2–4), 105–121.

Zerbe, S., Maurer, U., Schmitz, S. & Sukopp, H. (2003) Biodiversity in Berlin and its potential for nature conservation. *Landscape and Urban Planning*, **62**, 139–148.

Zhao, S., Da, L., Tang, Z., Fang, H., Song, K. & Fang, J. (2008) Ecological consequences of rapid urban expansion: Shanghai, China. *Frontiers in Ecology and the Environment*, **4**: 341–346.

Zipperer, W.C., Foresman, T.W., Sisinni, S.M. & Pouyat, R.V. (1997) Urban tree cover: an ecological perspective. *Urban Ecosystems*, **1**, 229–247.

Appendix 10.1 Approach Used to Assign Certainty Terms to Chapter Key Findings

This chapter began with a set of Key Findings. Adopting the approach and terminology used by the Intergovernmental Panel on Climate Change (IPCC) and the Millennium Assessment (MA), these Key Findings also include an indication of the level of scientific certainty. The 'uncertainty approach' of the UK NEA consists of a set of qualitative uncertainty terms derived from a 4-box model and complemented, where possible, with a likelihood scale (see below). Estimates of certainty are derived from the collective judgement of authors, observational evidence, modelling results and/or theory examined for this assessment.

Throughout the Key Findings presented at the start of this chapter, superscript numbers and letters indicate the estimated level of certainty for a particular key finding:

1. *Well established:*   high agreement based on significant evidence
2. *Established but incomplete evidence:*   high agreement based on limited evidence
3. *Competing explanations:*   low agreement, albeit with significant evidence
4. *Speculative:*   low agreement based on limited evidence

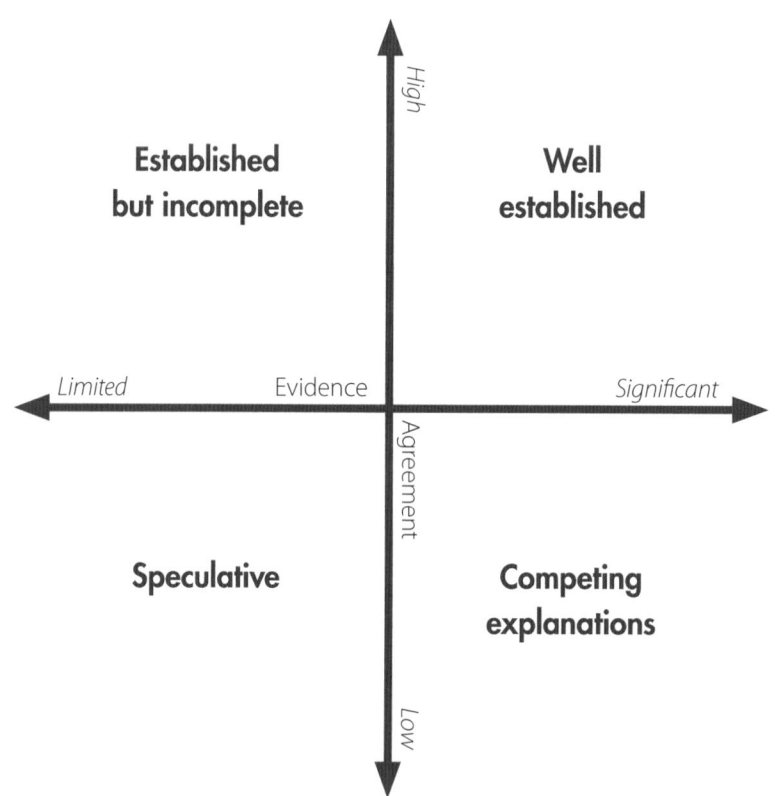

a. *Virtually certain:*   >99% probability of occurrence
b. *Very likely:*   >90% probability
c. *Likely:*   >66% probability
d. *About as likely as not:*   >33–66% probability
e. *Unlikely:*   <33% probability
f. *Very unlikely:*   <10% probability
g. *Exceptionally unlikely:*   <1% probability

Certainty terms 1 to 4 constitute the 4-box model, while *a* to *g* constitute the likelihood scale.

Chapter 11:
Coastal Margins

Coordinating Lead Author: Laurence Jones
Lead Authors: Stewart Angus, Andrew Cooper, Pat Doody, Mark Everard, Angus Garbutt, Paul Gilchrist, Jim Hansom, Robert Nicholls, Kenneth Pye, Neil Ravenscroft, Sue Rees, Peter Rhind and Andrew Whitehouse

Key Findings*

The six Coastal Margin habitats (Sand Dunes, Machair, Saltmarsh, Shingle, Sea Cliffs and Coastal Lagoons) make up only 0.6% of the UK's land area, but are far more important to society than their small area might suggest. The total value of the ecosystem services provided by the UK's coast is estimated at £48 billion (adjusted to 2003 values), equivalent to 3.46% of Global National Income (GNI). As an island nation, coastal landscapes are part of our cultural heritage and sense of identity. The Coastal Margins are an interface between land and sea, and directly provide ecosystem services to adjacent terrestrial and marine habitats. The ecosystem services of greatest financial value are tourism and leisure (cultural) and coastal defence (regulating), but the relative importance of these services differs according to location.

Sand Dunes, Saltmarsh and Machair make up the greatest area of Coastal Margin habitats: approximately 70,000 hectare (ha), 45,000 ha and 20,000 ha respectively. However, except for protected areas, basic data on the extent of these habitats is lacking; for some, estimates of their total area vary by up to 50%. Overall, Coastal Margin habitats have declined by an estimated 16% since 1945[2] due to development and coastal squeeze, but this is poorly quantified. All habitats have been affected by coastal development for industry, housing and tourism. Sand Dunes and Saltmarsh have also been affected by agricultural development (including forestry). Although the introduction of greater statutory protection in the 1980s has slowed the rate of loss and fragmentation of many sites, Coastal Margin habitats are still being lost today[2].

[2] established but incomplete evidence

Habitat losses due to sea-level rise have been relatively small so far, estimated at 2% over the past 20 years for Sand Dunes and 4.5% for Saltmarsh[2]. However, habitat losses are projected to reach 8% by 2060. Steepening of the intertidal coastal profile on soft coasts has been observed across the UK. Future losses will increase throughout the UK as storm erosion events increase in magnitude and sea-level rise further outstrips isostatic readjustment[2,b]; this issue is of particular concern where coastal squeeze operates, preventing land-ward migration of these habitats in response to sea-level rise.

[2] established but incomplete evidence

[b] very likely

The quality of Coastal Margin habitats has declined since 1945[2]. Sediment supply has fallen and natural dynamics have been reduced due to decreased availability of post-glacial sediment, widespread installation of artificial sea-defence structures, and increased armouring of soft cliffs[1]. The proportion of early successional habitats has fallen—by up to 90% in some dune systems—while scrub and grassland have increased. This reduces the Coastal Margins biological and conservation interest, and may indirectly alter ecosystem service provision. It also restricts their capacity to adapt to climate change and sea-level rise. The principal causes of these changes include a decline in traditional forms of management, such as grazing (particularly in the south and east), an increase in nitrogen deposition speeding up plant growth and soil development, and early conservation efforts which often focused on stabilising these naturally dynamic systems.

[1] well established
[2] established but incomplete evidence

---

* Each Key Finding has been assigned a level of scientific certainty, based on a 4-box model and complemented, where possible, with a likelihood scale. Superscript numbers and letters indicate the uncertainty term assigned to each finding. Full details of each term and how they were assigned are presented in Appendix 11.1.

Cultural ecosystem services provided by the coast are very important to the UK[2], with seaside tourism valued at £17 billion. The public values the coast highly: as living space; as a symbol of identity; for its scenery and wildlife; and for activities like walking, birdwatching, boating and outdoor sports. More than 250 million visits are made to the UK's coast per year, of which, around one-third are to natural habitats. Tourism patterns have changed in recent years, with day trips replacing overnight visits[1]. Overnight trips to the UK's seaside were worth £4.8 billion in 2009, while day visits were worth £3.9 billion in 2002. Moreover, overnight stays at the seaside exceed overnight stays in the rest of the UK's countryside and villages combined. These economic benefits are particularly significant in more remote areas. In Wales, in 2005, seaside tourism accounted for 42% of domestic tourism spend, supporting nearly 100,000 jobs and contributing £5 billion to income; the value of tourism to the Western Isles of Scotland is £49.9 million per year.

[1] well established
[2] established but incomplete evidence

Coastal defence is the most important regulating service provided by Coastal Margins[1]. All habitats contribute to coastal defence either directly by dissipating or attenuating wave energy or indirectly through regulating sediment. Sand Dunes and Shingle provide direct protection as a barrier, while Saltmarsh primarily attenuates wave energy. Up to 50% of wave energy is attenuated in the first 10–20 m of vegetated Saltmarsh, reducing the size needed for landward defences; 70% of Essex seawalls rely upon fronting Saltmarsh to maintain defence integrity[1]. Sand Dunes protect residential areas and high quality farmland, particularly in North West England and along the Norfolk Broads, while Shingle protects parts of the south and south-east coasts[2]. The soft coasts provide an estimated £3.1–£33.2 billion worth of capital savings in sea-defence costs in England alone.

[1] well established
[2] established but incomplete evidence

Carbon sequestration rates are high in Saltmarsh, Sand Dunes and Machair due to rapid soil development or sediment accumulation[2]. Sand Dunes on the west coast of the UK store 0.58 to 0.73 tonnes carbon/hectare/year (t C/ha/yr), while Saltmarsh stores 0.64 to 2.19 t C/ha/yr. However, the net benefit to the UK is small due to the low total area of these habitats. Carbon stocks in Coastal Margin habitats are (conservatively) estimated to be at least 6.8 megatonnes of carbon. Provisioning services generally play a minor role in Coastal Margins, although Saltmarsh-grazed lamb and beef are premium products.

[2] established but incomplete evidence

Coastal Margin habitats have high biodiversity and support a wide range of specialist and rare species[1]. This is reflected in the number of coastal sites designated for their biological importance. This diversity is partly dependent on natural dynamics forming a mosaic of habitats of different ages. This biological diversity contributes to the coast's cultural services and directly supports some regulating services; for example, Saltmarsh provides nursery grounds for many fish species including commercially important species such as sea bass (*Dicentrarchus labrax*) and herring (*Clupea harengus*). Coastal Margins provide important habitats for many bird species which provide a focus for nature-oriented visits to the coast[1]; at just four RSPB reserves, for example, such visits are worth £1.2 million. Sand Dunes, Machair, Saltmarsh, Shingle and Sea Cliffs support a wide range of natural pollinators, which, together with ground predators and parasitoids, may provide services of pollination and pest control to adjacent arable fields[4]. This may be of considerable local importance but, at the UK scale, the extent of this service is likely to be small.

[1] well established
[4] speculative

The principal conflicts in Coastal Margin habitats occur between services associated with disturbance and those associated with stability. In general, the disturbance resulting from processes such as erosion and sediment transport provide essential dynamics in natural coastal systems. However, pressure for land, fixed human assets, and management requirements to maintain coastal infrastructure, such as ports, mean that this natural dynamism is often deemed unacceptable. Conflicts can also occur between biodiversity interest and use of these habitats for leisure and recreation. Nonetheless, there is potential to identify 'win-win' combinations of services. Synergies are complex and may not occur in the same place or time, for example: sediment transport benefits coastal defence down the coast; pollination benefits other Broad Habitats; and erosion may cause serious short-term loss, but benefit habitat creation in the longer-term.

Sustainable management of Coastal Margin habitats must be holistic, taking into account physical, chemical and biological processes, spatial and temporal scales, drivers of change, and cultural elements. Most large Coastal Margin sites are designated as Special Areas of Conservation (SACs) under the Habitats Directive, or are Sites of Special Scientific Interest (SSSIs); therefore, the protection and maintenance of the biodiversity, natural processes and geomorphological interest remain primary objectives. However, appropriate management may enhance both biodiversity and other services. Sustainable management options include:

- Allowing Coastal Margin habitats room to migrate inland with rising sea levels in order to mitigate coastal squeeze ('managed realignment'). In Saltmarsh, this has shown additional ecosystem service benefits compared with a 'hold the line' strategy, but the principles can be applied to the other Coastal Margin habitats too.
- Managing sediment supply by allowing erosion to contribute new sediment to the coast, and allowing natural transport processes to proceed where possible.
- Maintaining or encouraging natural formation of early successional habitats where these are threatened or have disappeared.

Implications for policy include:
- The Coastal Margin habitats are of high financial and cultural value to the UK, yet they often fall into the policy no-man's land between marine and terrestrial interests.
- There remain major knowledge gaps for Coastal Margins, including basic data such as extent and trends, particularly in Scotland. This needs to be addressed by unified and strategic data gathering across the UK to detect change in coastal sediments and habitats in order to inform adaptation strategies. Coastal Margins face major threats in the coming decades, particularly from sea-level rise and climate change, as well as pollution and continuing development pressures. These threats are exacerbated by the linear nature of the habitat, with pressures on every edge and very little safe, core habitat, except on the largest sites. Threats from sea level rise will be most acute on coasts where habitats are constrained by artificial sea defences.
- Coastal Margins need to be managed holistically, maintaining natural dynamics where possible and acknowledging the interdependence with other habitats, including the Marine environment.

11.1 Introduction

The coastline of the UK is 32,086 km long with the inclusion of major islands (Frost 2010; Chapter 12). The coastline incorporates urban areas and a wide range of other natural and semi-natural habitats, but this chapter focuses on the six main habitats which are considered primarily coastal: Sand Dunes, Machair, Shingle, Saltmarsh, Sea Cliffs, and Coastal Lagoons (**Figure 11.1**). Small islands are considered within Sea Cliffs; sand and shingle beaches are included under Sand Dunes and Shingle respectively. The main linkages with other UK National Ecosystem Assessment (UK NEA) Broad Habitats are shown in **Table 11.1**, and the following habitats are considered elsewhere: coastal grasslands are included under Semi-natural Grassland (Chapter 6); mudflats, rocky shores and estuaries are covered under Marine (Chapter 12); and coastal urban areas are covered under Urban (Chapter 10). Within this Coastal Margin chapter, common issues across habitats are discussed first, followed by additional habitat-specific text where appropriate.

The habitats of the Coastal Margin provide some unique ecosystem services and drivers of change due to their location. Coastal Margin habitats generally form a transition zone between marine and terrestrial systems, with influences from both directions. Many are dependent on an active sediment supply (e.g. Sand Dunes, Machair, Saltmarsh, Shingle), and are governed to a large extent by marine-mediated geomorphological processes such as coastal erosion (of beaches, dunes and cliffs, for example) and alongshore sediment transport to down-drift shores and lagoons. Salt-spray, nutrient inputs and high wind speeds from the sea influence the vegetation of these habitats. Plant propagules arrive both from the sea and the land, while other natural and human influences occur from both directions and include succession, land use change, alterations in sediment supply and coastal development. Transitions and gradations also occur between Coastal Margin habitats.

The following text describes the properties of the main Coastal Margin habitats which underpin the goods and ecosystem services described later. **Figure 11.2** shows the UK distributions of these habitats.

11.1.1 Sand Dunes

Coastal Sand Dunes occur all around the UK (**Figure 11.2a**). They are formed from sand (0.2–2 mm grain size) that is blown inland from the beach, and are usually stabilised by vegetation (Packham & Willis 1997). Typically, phases of mobility and natural coastal dynamics lead to a sequence of dune ridges, which increase in stability the further away from the sea they are. As environmental stresses, such as wind speed, sand mobility and salt-spray, decrease further

Figure 11.1 The Coastal Margin habitats. a) Sand Dunes*, b) Machair†, c) Saltmarsh*, d) Shingle†, e) Coastal Lagoons†, f) Sea Cliffs*. *Photos courtesy of L. Jones* and J.P. Doody†.*

inland, pioneer plant species are replaced by more diverse vegetation communities and soil development advances. In the wake of migrating dunes, or on accreting coasts, wind can scour bare sand down to the water table; the exposed damp sand is colonised by a different set of plant species, creating low-lying dune slacks: a (usually) seasonal wetland, flooded in winter and often with high botanical diversity. The main vegetation types are dry dune grassland and dune slacks, with dune heath on some acidic sites; all have the potential for succession to woodland over time (Provoost et al. 2010). Therefore, Sand Dunes provide a highly diverse mix of habitats and services—often on the same site—due

Table 11.1 Linkages between Coastal Margin and other UK National Ecosystem Assessment (UK NEA) habitats.
✓ denotes a link; relevant habitat components are listed; - indicates not applicable.

Coastal Margin habitat	Other UK NEA Broad Habitats						
	Mountains, Moorlands & Heaths	Semi-natural Grassland	Enclosed Farmland	Woodlands	Freshwaters – Open waters, Wetlands and Floodplains	Urban	Marine *
Sand Dunes	✓ dune heath	✓ dune grassland	-	✓ afforested dunes	✓ dune slacks	✓ sandy beaches	✓ sediment
Machair	-	✓ machair grassland	✓ cultivated machair	-	✓ machair lochs	-	✓ sediment
Saltmarsh	-	✓ saltmarsh grassland	✓ enclosed saltmarsh	-	-	-	✓ sediment & water
Shingle	-	-	-	-	-	✓ shingle beaches	✓ sediment
Sea Cliffs	-	-	-	-	-	✓ soft cliffs	✓ sediment
Coastal lagoons	-	-	-	-	✓ lagoon water bodies	✓ lagoons	✓ sediment & water

* There are many links, principal exchanges are listed here but all are described in the text.

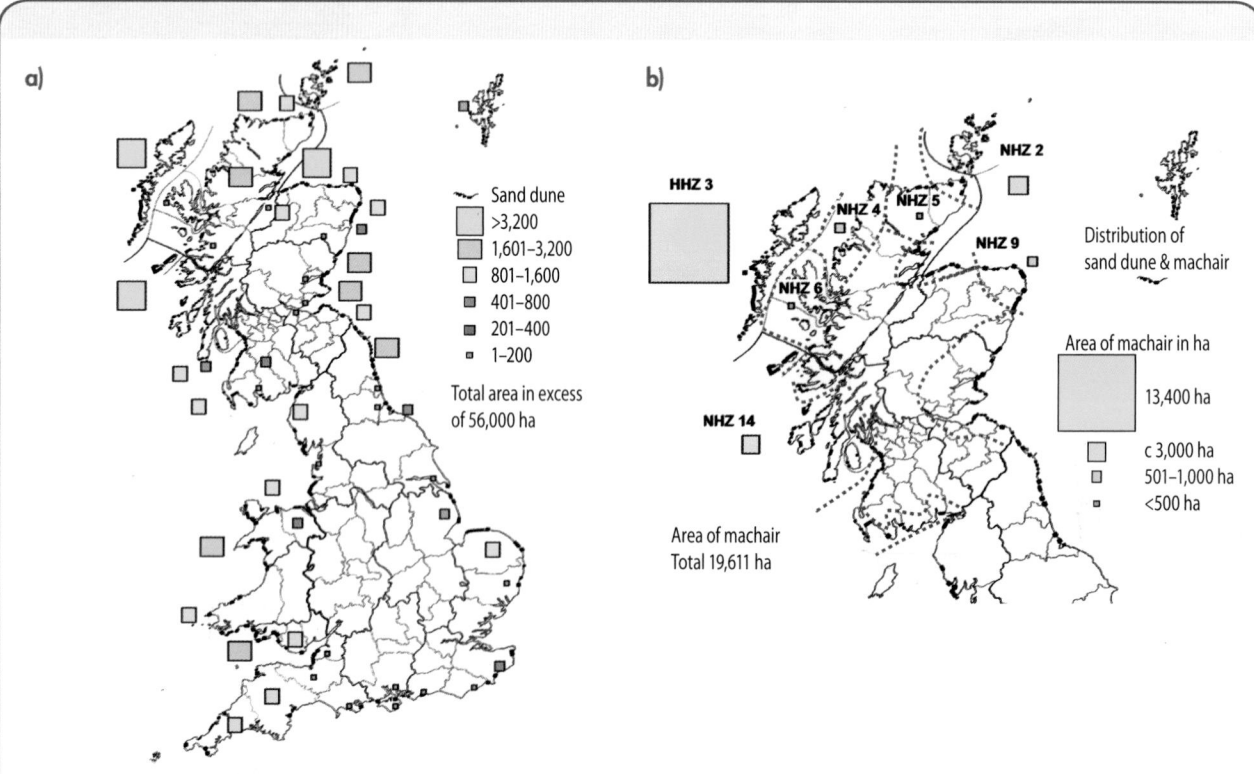

Figure 11.2 Distributions and approximate extent of Coastal Margin habitats in GB, by county based on JNCC data circa 1990: a) Sand Dunes, b) Machair in Scotland, c) Saltmarsh, d) Shingle, e) Sea Cliffs (more than 20 m high), f) Coastal Lagoons. Note: figures (ha and km) are based on 1:50,000 maps and are meant to facilitate comparisons. Field surveys since they were drawn up have greatly increased our knowledge of the resource which is bigger than indicated by the figures. Source: all maps provided by J.P. Doody; Coastal Lagoons map includes data from Barne et al. (1995–1998).

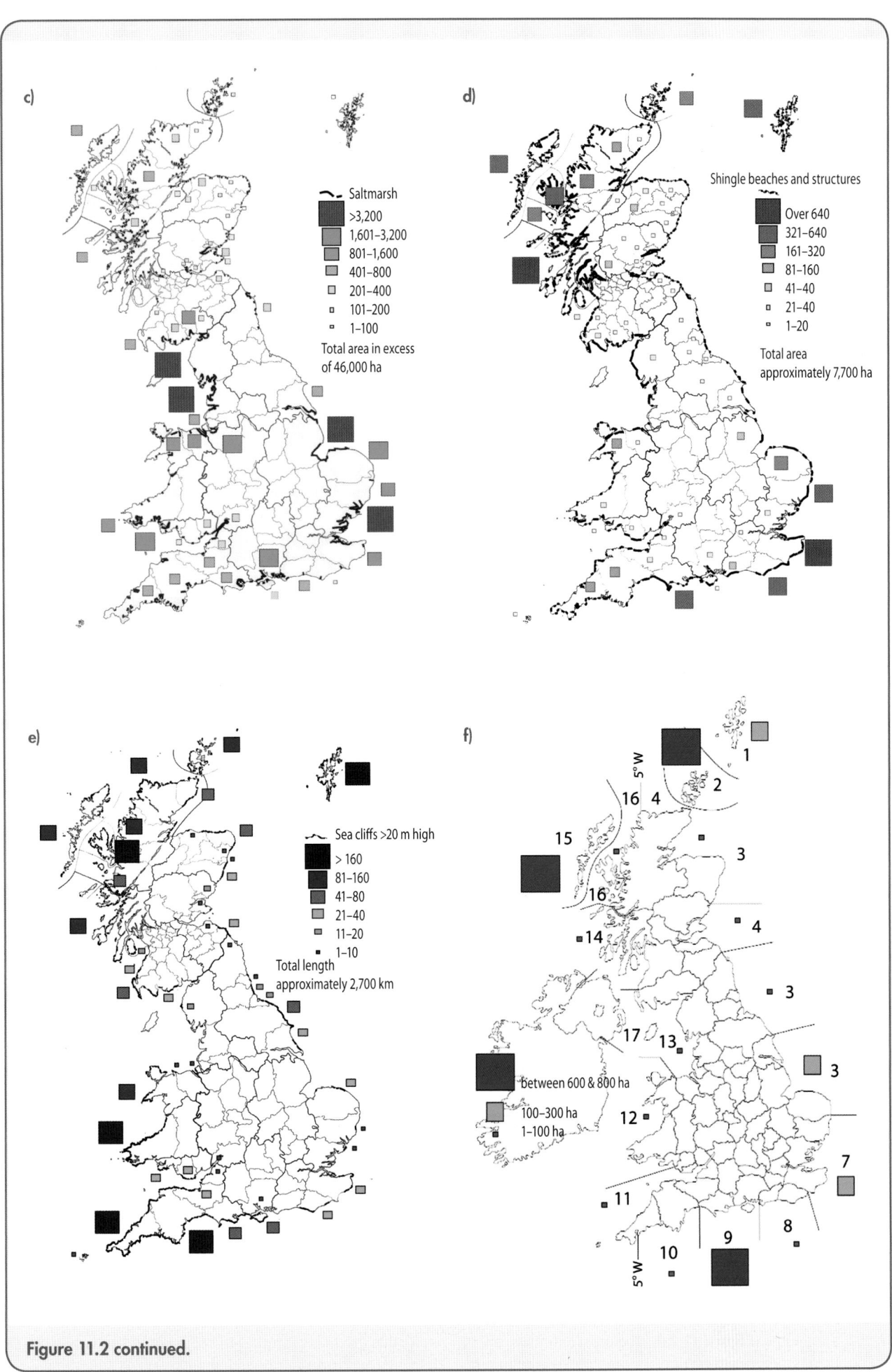

c)

Saltmarsh
>3,200
1,601–3,200
801–1,600
401–800
201–400
101–200
1–100

Total area in excess
of 46,000 ha

d)

Shingle beaches and structures
Over 640
321–640
161–320
81–160
41–40
21–40
1–20

Total area
approximately 7,700 ha

e)

Sea cliffs >20 m high
> 160
81–160
41–80
21–40
11–20
1–10

Total length
approximately 2,700 km

f)

between 600 & 800 ha
100–300 ha
1–100 ha

Figure 11.2 continued.

to differences in successional age, soil pH, local disturbance, management history, the steepness and aspect of slopes, groundwater chemistry and the hydrological regime in dune slacks (Everard *et al.* 2010).

11.1.2 Machair

Sharing many of the characteristics and processes found in Sand Dunes, Machair is a unique form of dune system, found nowhere else on Earth other than on the north-western seaboards of Scotland and Ireland (**Figure 11.2b**). Machair is a gently sloping and undulating (often inland-sloping) coastal dune-plain formed by depositional recycling of wind-blown calcareous shell-sand from the beach. There is usually a dune cordon seaward and species-rich grassland (managed by traditional low-intensity agriculture in the Uists Islands, Scotland), wetland, loch and peatland (with sand/peat admixtures) to the landward. Machair is characteristically lime-rich, subject to strong, moist, oceanic winds, and affected by current or historic human interference via grazing, cultivation, the addition of seaweed fertiliser and artificial drainage. The term 'machair' has both geomorphological and cultural meaning, much of its spatial extent mapping with Gaelic language and culture (Hansom & Angus 2001). All machair habitats have similarities in their land use history and their present distribution owes as much to cultural factors as it does to biotic and abiotic influences.

11.1.3 Saltmarsh

Saltmarsh is widely distributed around the UK (**Figure 11.2c**). The most extensive areas occur along estuaries in the counties of Hampshire, north Kent, Essex, Norfolk, Lincolnshire and Lancashire (May & Hansom 2003). Saltmarshes generally occur between mean high water spring tides and mean high water neap tides at temperate latitudes. The development of saltmarshes is largely controlled by physiography: fine sediments accumulate in relatively low-energy environments where wave action is limited. Consequently, salt tolerant vegetation develops where there is an accumulation of mud in estuaries, inlets, behind barrier islands or spits, and occasionally via marine inundation of low-lying ground. Four physical factors, sediment supply, tidal regime, wind-wave climate, and the movement of relative sea-level, primarily govern the character and dynamic behaviour of saltmarshes (Boorman 2003). The composition of saltmarsh flora and fauna is determined by complex interactions between the frequency of tidal inundation, salinity, suspended sediment content and particle size, slope, and herbivory. In general, total species-richness increases with elevation, leading to a characteristic zonation of the vegetation (Doody 2008). Transitions to mudflat occur at the seaward limit, while in the upper elevations of saltmarshes there may be further transitions to brackish, freshwater marsh, dune vegetation or vegetation overlying shingle structures.

11.1.4 Shingle

Shingle beaches and structures occur around the whole of the UK's coastline (**Figure 11.2d**). The most extensive are in the south-east where sediment of a suitable size is abundant, or has been in the past, and where there are rising sea levels. The more exposed and storm prone areas of north-west Scotland also have, mainly small, shingle beaches, including those raised above high water by isostatic uplift.

The term 'shingle' applies to any sediment with a mean grain size of between 2 and 200 mm (Randall 1977), which define thresholds for wind and wave transport. Sediment availability is crucial and comes from three sources. In order of importance these are:

1. Offshore Pleistocene glacial sediments reworked by storms and rising sea levels;
2. Rivers transporting shingle to the coast; and
3. Active erosion of existing 'soft rock' coastal cliffs and bluffs.

The first two of these sources are much reduced from former levels of supply in the UK, but although minor, the third is increasing in importance due to enhanced erosion, particularly in the south and east of England.

Shingle habitats most often occur as fringing beaches deposited at, or near, the limit of high tide. In exposed areas with abundant sediment they can develop into more permanent stony banks (shingle structures), often occurring as sequences of ridges which reflect the prevailing direction of alongshore drift and storms (Pye 2001). Vegetated shingle communities are uncommon and depend on substrate stability, moisture and nutrient availability. Two broad communities occur:

1. On dynamic beaches where species survive periodic disturbance and salt-spray; and
2. Away from the shore, in more stable conditions, allowing mature grassland, lowland heath, moss and lichen communities, or scrub to develop.

11.1.5 Sea Cliffs

Hard cliffs are widely distributed along the UK's exposed coasts, occurring principally in the north and west, but also in the south-west and south-east of England as 'hard' chalk cliffs. Soft cliffs are more restricted, occurring mainly on the east and central south coasts of England and in Cardigan Bay, Wales (**Figure 11.2e**). The UK Biodiversity Action Plan (UKBAP) for maritime cliffs and slopes (www.ukbap.org.uk/UKPlans.aspx?ID=27) defines them as "sloping to vertical faces on the coastline where a break in slope is formed by slippage and/or coastal erosion". The cliff-top zone can extend landward to at least the limit of maritime influence (i.e. the limit of salt-spray deposition), which in some exposed situations may continue for up to 500 m inland. Under this definition, cliffs may comprise entire islands or headlands, depending on their size. On the seaward side, they extend to the limit of the supralittoral zone (Chapter 12), and so, include splash zone lichens and other species occupying this habitat. Where the underlying geology of the cliffs is predominately soft rocks, such as clays, they are classified as soft cliffs. Such cliffs are often characterised by slips or areas of slumped cliff face that gradually become vegetated. Hard and soft cliffs under pressure from erosion behave differently and provide different functions: hard cliffs provide little sediment, while soft cliffs are major sources of sediment to sand and shingle beaches and to fine-grained habitats such as saltmarsh.

11.1.6 Coastal Lagoons

'Saline lagoon' (**Figure 11.2f**) is a term that is applied loosely in the UK to cover a wide range of coastal water bodies of varying salinity from nearly freshwater to fully marine (www.ukbap.org.uk/ukplans.aspx?id=42#8). The key characteristics of saline lagoons are that they are shallow, quiet water bodies, adjacent to the sea but sheltered from its direct effects. They exhibit great diversity of form (Barnes 1988; 1989a,b), ranging from fully natural water bodies enclosed by gravel or sandy barriers, or rock outcrops, through systems exhibiting varying degrees of human alteration, to wholly artificial water bodies impounded by human structures (Conlan *et al.* 1992). There is a broad geographical variation in their form, with rock basins dominant in western Scotland, natural bar-built lagoons in England, Wales, Orkney and Shetland, and artificial impoundments dominant in Northern Ireland (NIHAP 2003). They are categorised according to the mechanism of water exchange with the sea (Smith & Laffoley 1992; Downie 1996; Bamber *et al.* 2001).

Coastal Lagoons exhibit great diversity in substrate (bedrock, sand, gravel, mud), salinity, depth and stratification, and marginal habitats. They range in size from over 800 hectares (ha), such as the Loch of Stenness in Orkney, to less than 1 ha. They exchange water with the sea via seepage through barriers, overtopping, and direct discharge through permanent or temporary surface water connections that may be artificial or natural.

Depending on salinity, the dominant fringing vegetation type ranges from reeds (e.g. *Phragmites* species) to saltmarsh species (e.g. *Puccinellia maritima*). There is often a diverse submerged aquatic plant community as well, ranging from water lilies to seagrasses (e.g. *Ruppia maritima*); macrophytes can root on lagoon floors because of low current speeds. The fauna tends to reflect the species pool in neighbouring waters (Bamber *et al.* 2001), but lagoon specialists can occur (Ivell 1979; Barnes 1989b).

11.2 Trends and Changes in Coastal Margins

Coastal Margin habitats are naturally dynamic, as are the coastal environments in which they sit. They have responded to climate change and long-term geomorphological trends as the coast has adjusted to the higher sea levels of the Holocene Period. Human influences, such as land-claim, harbour construction and the expansion of coastal towns, have also been shaping the coast for the last 2,000 years. Since the 1960s, protective legislation has reduced many of the direct human pressures on Coastal Margin habitats. However, important drivers of change remain, and some, such as climate change and sea-level rise, are expected to intensify significantly during the coming decades. The text here describes some of the drivers common to Coastal Margins as a whole, followed by habitat-specific sections detailing changes in extent and quality of habitats over time, and the drivers that influence these.

11.2.1 Sediment Supply

Sedimentary coastal habitats are built from a supply of mobile sediment of varying grain size (Chapter 12). The natural supply of sediment was much larger in the early Holocene when sea levels were rising rapidly, and the erosion and reworking of sediment was widespread (Hansom 2001). Under the more stable sea levels of the late Holocene this supply has declined. Cliff erosion is a locally important source of sediment, such as on the southern and eastern coasts between the Exe and the Tees, while elsewhere, reworking of existing sediments dominates. In the last century, sediment supply has declined dramatically due to cliff protection and other armouring of the shore (Clayton 1989; Dickson *et al.* 2007), while dredging for navigation has reconfigured many estuaries and has often led to the significant export of sediment via spoil disposal. An important indicator of sediment loss is the widespread occurrence of intertidal steepening in the UK, with low water marks migrating landward faster than high water marks (Taylor *et al.* 2004; Hansom 2010). The loss of sediment supply to beaches causes beach-lowering and frontal erosion, and reduces their protective function, allowing erosion and reworking of backshore sediments. For other sedimentary environments, these effects are less well quantified, but in qualitative terms, the loss of sediment supply will have similar effects, although compare with Nicholls *et al.* (2000).

Looking to the future, sea-level rise and climate change are expected to promote erosion and sediment reworking (Pye & Saye 2005). However, without new supplies of sediment, these changes are expected to be adverse and cause significant reconfiguration, relocation and decline of coastal sedimentary intertidal and supratidal habitats (Orford *et al.* 2007).

Coastal engineering often causes a decline in sediment supply, for example, due to cliff protection. However, it can also locally, and even regionally, cause large increases in supply as sediment is imported for beach nourishment (Hanson *et al.* 2002); the largest scheme to date is the Lincshore project which covers beaches from Mablethorpe to Skegness. The beneficial use of dredge spoil may see similar trends for finer-grained sediments. In future, the development of offshore renewable energy may also alter sediment supply. Hence, sediment supply is increasingly linked to certain policy drivers, such as shoreline management, described in Section 11.2.7.

11.2.2 Climate Change

Climate change will have a range of impacts on Coastal Margins, which are discussed by habitat in Section 11.2.8. Changing temperature and rainfall patterns may lead to shifts in distributions of coastal species (Harrison *et al.* 2001; Berry *et al.* 2005), with local extinctions of species that are unable to disperse to suitable habitat or compete with incoming species. Changing rainfall will have big impacts on water table dependent habitats. Changing storm climates will impact on the rate of erosion (Lozano *et al.* 2004), and on the quantity and frequency of sediment exchanges between habitats. Increasing storminess may deepen the wave-base, remobilising sediment previously out of circulation, and altering threshold-dependent processes such as sea-defence functions in saltmarsh (Möller *et al.* 1999; Möller 2006).

11.2.3 Sea-level Rise

Predicted rates of eustatic sea-level rise will greatly exceed isostatic readjustment on all UK coasts (**Box 11.1**) and will impact all Coastal Margin habitats. The most recent UKCP09 sea-level rise projections for the UK (Lowe *et al.* 2009) (incorporating the results of the Fourth IPCC Scientific Assessment) provide 'central estimate' increases in mean sea level by 2095 that range from 23.4 cm (Edinburgh, low emissions scenario) to 53.1 cm (London and Cardiff, high emissions scenario). A maximum increase of 1.9 m under a high plus emissions scenario is considered possible. Tide gauge trends over the last 15 years in Scotland suggest that present rates are now equivalent to the high plus emissions scenario of UKCP09 (Rennie & Hansom 2011). The UK NEA Scenarios analyses (Chapter 25) have also incorporated the effects of sea-level rise on different habitats, including Coastal Margins.

The main implications will be inundation of low-lying coastal areas and islands, accelerated erosion of beaches, dunes and soft cliffs exposed to significant wave action, more frequent coastal flooding and saline intrusion (both surface and sub-surface). Coastal squeeze will occur where natural habitats, such as dunes and saltmarshes, are constrained by steeply rising ground or coastal defences on their landward side, preventing natural landward translation (coastal plain or estuary 'rollover') (Pethick 2001; Halcrow 2002; Pye *et al.* 2007; Saye & Pye 2007). Sea-level rise will

also cumulatively disengage the wave base from the seabed, so that waves impact with more of their energy (Angus *et al.* 2011). Therefore, sea-level rise will put increased pressure on the sea-defence role of Coastal Margin habitats, making careful consideration of shoreline planning essential.

11.2.4 Air Pollution

Atmospheric pollution from nitrogen, sulphur and ozone influences the vegetation and soils of Coastal Margin habitats. To date, their influence has generally been greater on southern and eastern UK coasts due to the location of pollution sources and the prevailing south-westerly winds. Sulphur deposition has declined dramatically since the 1970s (NEGTAP 2001; RoTAP 2011), but nitrogen deposition increased rapidly between 1940 and 1990 (Fowler *et al.* 2004), and remains high today (RoTAP 2011). Both nitrogen and sulphur contribute to soil acidification which negatively affects biological and conservation interest on acidic or weakly buffered soils, and has caused a decline in base-loving dune slack species in the Netherlands, for example (Sival & Strijkstra-Kalk 1999). However, soil acidification has limited influence on other ecosystem services.

In addition to its acidifying effect, nitrogen causes eutrophication, resulting in declines in species-richness and increasing rates of vegetation succession and soil development in dunes (Jones *et al.* 2004, 2008; Remke *et al.* 2009). Nitrogen deposition enhances productivity for

---

Box 11.1 Rates of sea-level rise and isostatic adjustment.

Analysis of sedimentary sea-level index points (Shennan *et al.* 2009) and results of geophysical modelling (Lambeck 1995) show that different parts of the UK have experienced very different sea-level histories during the Holocene, reflecting spatially varying patterns of isostatic and hydro-isostatic readjustment following melting of the last British ice sheet. At many locations, the tide gauge records indicate that high waters have been rising faster than low waters and mean sea level, with a resulting slight increase in tidal range (Woodworth *et al.* 1991; Pugh 2004).

Changes in the level and frequency of high waters are potentially of greater significance than changes in mean sea level, as it is extreme events that are mainly responsible for episodes of rapid coastal erosion, barrier-breaching and coastal flooding (Pye & Blott 2008, 2009).

Table 1 Central estimates of relative sea-level changes (cm) with respect to 1990, under high, medium and low emissions scenarios. Source: extracted from Lowe *et al.* (2009).

Year	London			Cardiff		
	High	Medium	Low	High	Medium	Low
2000	3.5	3.9	2.5	3.5	2.9	2.5
2030	16.0	13.5	11.4	15.9	13.4	11.4
2060	31.4	26.3	22.2	31.4	26.3	22.2
2095	53.1	44.4	37.3	53.1	44.4	37.3

Year	Edinburgh			Belfast		
	High	Medium	Low	High	Medium	Low
2000	2.2	1.6	1.2	2.3	1.7	1.3
2030	10.7	8.2	6.1	11.1	8.6	6.6
2060	22.1	71.1	13.0	22.9	17.8	13.7
2095	39.2	30.5	23.4	40.3	31.6	24.5

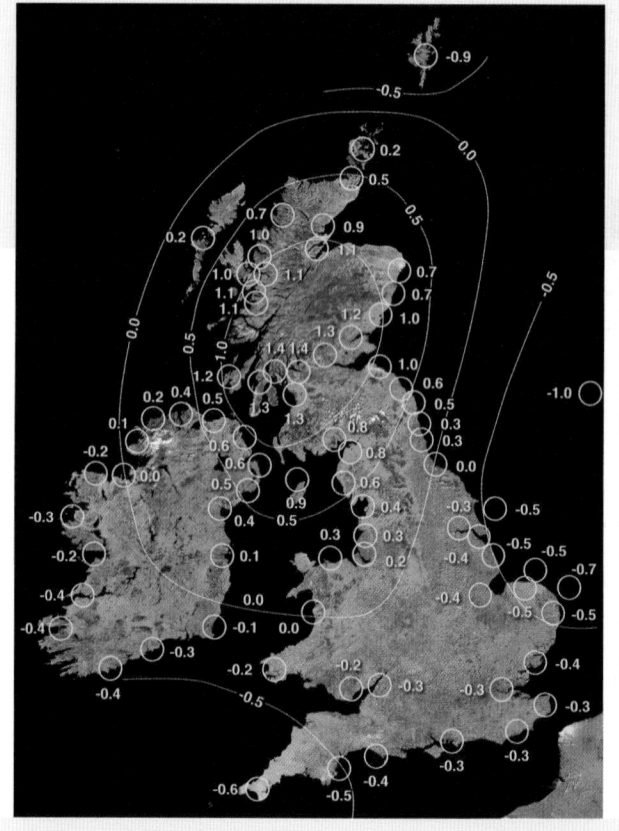

---

marginal agriculture and contributes to ecosystem services which benefit from stabilisation, but acts to the detriment of services dependent on early successional systems which are particularly sensitive to eutrophication due to their nutrient- and organic-poor soils. Saltmarsh is highly productive but is still regarded as nitrogen-limited and, therefore, susceptible to the impacts of nitrogen deposition (van Wijnen & Bakker 1999), with similar effects on vegetation growth and rates of succession. Direct deposition of atmospheric nitrogen to Coastal Lagoons is low, but runoff, groundwater and surface waters contribute to eutrophication issues in both Coastal Lagoons and Saltmarsh. The eutrophication impacts of nitrogen may be lower where other nutrients, such as phosphorus, become limiting.

11.2.5 Tourism

Tourism is both a driver of change and a beneficiary of social, cultural and biodiversity services (Section 11.3.3). Almost all of the population of the UK lives within 100 km of the coast (Cooper 2009), so tourism has been a major driver of change at the coast. Tourism patterns and their impact have changed over the last 60 years. Resort tourism dominated from the 1940s to the 1960s (Walton 2000), resulting in high visitor pressure at relatively few coastal locations, primarily located near beaches. As long seaside holidays have declined due to increasing overseas travel (Cooper 1997; Williams & Shaw 1997), and car ownership has increased, coastal tourism is increasingly dominated by day trips (Williams & Shaw 2009), dispersing visitor pressure more widely along coasts within a few hours' drive of major urban areas. More recently, interest in nature- and outdoor-oriented attractions and specialist sports have further dispersed visitor pressure to more remote locations and a wider range of coastal habitats. At low to moderate levels, tourism benefits Coastal Margin economies. However, excessive tourism levels can put pressure on resources, such as water or waste treatment, increase land-claim for infrastructure development, damage sensitive ecosystems, cause pollution, and have adverse social impacts, particularly when tourist numbers are strongly seasonal or greatly exceed the local population. Current trends indicate that long-stays at the coast will remain static or decline slightly in the future, while day visits and short-stays will continue to increase (VisitWales 2008; Williams & Shaw 2009). Trends in tourism as a cultural ecosystem service are discussed in more detail in Section 11.3.4 and Chapter 16.

11.2.6 Coastal Development

Development pressure is high at the coast. Historically, land-claim, harbour construction and the expansion of coastal towns and infrastructure have all been taking place for the last 2,000 years, but have intensified greatly since the mid-19th Century (French 1997; May & Hansom 2003). Seaside resorts were the fastest growing British towns in the first half of the 19th Century, and their expansion for tourism continued until after the Second World War (WWII) (Walton 1983, 2000). Fourteen seaside resorts trebled their census population between 1881 and 1911 (Walton 1983), with further growth in many resorts between 1911 and 1951, bringing the resort population in England and Wales from 1.6 million in 1911 to nearly 2.5 million in 1951 (Walton 1997). Development pressures since 1945 have differed by habitat, with industrial and agricultural expansion the most common pressure on Saltmarsh, while housing and tourism infrastructure were the dominant pressure on Sand Dunes and Shingle (Section 11.2.8.1 and 11.2.8.4, respectively).

Demographics and residential preference also drive coastal development. There is strong net in-migration to coastal towns of people of working age and people choosing to retire by the sea (Beatty & Fothergill 2003; Chapter 3).

11.2.7 Policy Drivers

Policy influences all the major drivers affecting Coastal Margins. Devolution has resulted in different coastal policy approaches across the UK, although all are influenced by European legislation, such as the Habitats Directive, the Water Framework Directive and the Floods Directive, as well as the EU Recommendation on Integrated Coastal Zone Management (ICZM) (McKenna et al. 2008).

11.2.7.1 Sea defence and shoreline management planning

Historically, the response to flooding and erosion has been sea defence and coastal protection respectively. While these measures deal with the immediate and local problem, they often have adverse consequences down-drift, and into the future, as they may export problems of erosion and hence degrade natural defences. They may also reduce the natural capacity of the coast to respond to changing conditions.

The current policy for coastal management in England and Wales is based on Shoreline Management Plans (SMPs) (Leafe et al. 1998; MAFF et al. 1995; Defra 2006), with some limited application of SMPs in Scotland (Hansom et al. 2004). Northern Ireland lacks a strategic approach to shoreline management. The emphasis of SMPs is on reducing the risk of flood and coastal erosion through an integrated portfolio of measures which work more closely with natural processes and include a move from hard defences to soft protection, beach nourishment and managed realignment (Klein et al. 2001). With current knowledge there is a greater appreciation of the relationship between cliff erosion and sediment supply to beaches and intertidal zones, and, as a consequence, we have a better understanding of erosion and flood risk (Dawson et al. 2009). In particular, the English coastline currently has the greatest rates of relative sea-level rise in the UK, so initiatives in the last decade have moved away from simple cost-benefit considerations to a multi-criteria approach that takes account of environmental, social and technological elements.

Shoreline Management Plans take a strategic perspective over a 100-year timeframe. Essentially, they choose between four options:

- Advance the line
- Hold the line
- Managed realignment (adaptive management)
- No active intervention

The SMP process explicitly considers the full range of options, including managed realignment at sites that have previously been defended. Managed realignment is becoming a key tool in coastal management, providing sustainable flood risk management, potential long-term economic benefits and possible climate change mitigation (**Box 11.2**; Section 11.5.1.2). Addressing a series of 'epochs', SMPs may move from one policy to another over time in recognition of the fact that a particular policy may not be sustainable over the full 100-year period. Many plans currently adopt a 'hold the line' policy, which is due, in part, to the possibility of a managed realignment option being locally unpopular, but also suggests that the full economic and ecosystem benefits that can be obtained from managed realignment are not well appreciated or understood (Andrews *et al.* 2006; Turner *et al.* 2007).

Box 11.2 Alkborough Flats: a managed realignment case study highlighting multiple benefits across all ecosystem service categories. Source: Everard (2009).

Figure 1 Alkborough Flats. *Photo courtesy of M. Everard.*

Managed realignment was one of the options at Alkborough Flats (**Figure 1**) on the Humber, England, setting back the defence and allowing 400 hectares of 'reclaimed' arable land to flood and to form saltmarsh, mudflat, reedbed and other intertidal habitat. It addressed multiple objectives including reducing flood risk, as well as providing compensation for habitat lost elsewhere in the estuary. The Environment Agency case study sought to evaluate benefits across the full suite of ecosystem services in the Millennium Ecosystem Assessment classification (i.e. provisioning, regulating, cultural and supporting services; MA 2005).

The biggest surprise was evidence overturning an unstated assumption that 'provisioning services' were being traded-off to boost 'regulatory services' (particularly flood risk) and 'supporting services' (habitat for wildlife). The annual loss of food production (£28,075 calculated by the loss of arable production partly offset by livestock-grazing), was compensated by the higher value of fibre (£26,820 greater value from wool production relative to prior straw production) and the sale of rare breed genetic stock sheep and cattle (£3,000). The recruitment of fish of commercial and recreational importance was acknowledged as a research gap with potentially significant value.

Regulatory services were enhanced by an estimated annual value of £14,553 from carbon sequestration, in addition to a total flood risk management benefit (over 100 years) of £12.26 million. Research gaps thwarted valuation of the regulation of air quality, microclimate and erosion.

Enhancements to cultural services included an estimated £164,830 uplift to (formal) recreation and tourism, and £5,000 from protection of navigation. The supporting services were understandably harder to value, but included a significant annual benefit of £749,438 from habitat for wildlife and a further £8,160 estimated for enhanced primary productivity. Care was taken not to double-count services.

Cumulatively, and relative to the initial £10.2 million investment, the net lifetime benefit-to-cost ratio was 3.22. This confirms that ecosystem restoration, rather than technological solutions, can offer substantial value across the full range of ecosystem services. It also demonstrates that environmentally sensitive innovations can result in win-win solutions, and need not be a trade-off between benefit types and beneficiaries. The managed realignment scheme was officially opened in September 2006.

11.2.7.2 Conservation policy

Conservation policy affects the degree of statutory protection for coastal sites, how that protection is enforced and, at a local scale, how individual sites are managed. While the majority of large sites are protected under Special Area of Conservation (SAC) designations, a number only have Area/ Site of Special Scientific Interest (ASSI/SSSI) or National Nature Reserve (NNR)/Local Nature Reserve (LNR) status, and, therefore, a lower level of legal protection. In terms of area protected, only around 20% of Sand Dunes and Machair, 50% of Saltmarsh and Coastal Lagoons, and 58% of Shingle are under SAC protection (calculated from area under SAC (JNCC 2007) and habitat area in **Table 11.2**). The statutory protection of sites of biological, geological or other interest (for example, Everard *et al.* 2010) has been a major factor in slowing land-claim or agricultural intensification of Coastal Margin habitats. At the regional scale, a smaller proportion of sites have statutory protection in Scotland and in Northern Ireland. Piecemeal development continues on unprotected sites, but even sites protected by SSSI status are not immune, for example, the sand dunes at Menie in Aberdeenshire, Scotland, partly within the Foveran Links SSSI, were recently purchased for golf and leisure development.

11.2.7.3 Coastal access

The length and accessibility of coastal paths is increasing all the time, but the issue in England and Wales of legal access to Coastal Margin habitats, many of which are in private ownership, remains. Scotland has its own access legislation which allows responsible public access to all land except Ministry of Defence land and private dwellings and their curtilages. Through its 'Enterprise Neptune' programme, the National Trust has acquired approximately one-third of the coast of England and Wales, and has been instrumental (often in partnership with local authorities) in developing coastal paths that allow people to view and experience these habitats without causing damage. A new legal right of access to all the coast of England has been created by the Marine and Coastal Access Act 2009, which will provide a linear route along the coast, with access from this route to the water or cliff edge. For the first time, this will allow people direct access to many coastal habitats that were previously forbidden lands. Saltmarshes have been excluded from the provisions of the Act, largely on the grounds of public health and safety.

11.2.7.4 The Coastal and Marine Access Act

Under this act, the Marine Management Organisation (MMO) was created. The MMO will prepare marine plans on behalf of the marine planning authorities in UK territorial waters, and be the regulator of most activities in the marine environment including new development. A number of the activities the MMO regulates have direct relevance to Coastal Margins, including coastal dredging, aggregate extraction and the laying of submarine cables. The MMO will also be a key advisor on marine issues to other bodies taking decisions affecting the marine area. The Act requires the designation of Marine Conservation Zones (MCZs) as part of a wider UK network of Marine Protected Areas (MPAs). Some MPAs will be based on existing national and international nature conservation designations such as SSSIs and Special Protection Areas (SPAs).

11.2.8 Overview of Trends and Changes in Coastal Margin Habitats

The Coastal Margin habitats described in this chapter (excluding Sea Cliffs) have declined in area by an estimated 16.8% over the last 60 years, mainly through development pressures for residential, tourism and industrial use, and agricultural intensification; habitat quality has also deteriorated (Williams 2006). **Table 11.2** summarises the areal extent and trends over the last 10 years for each habitat, and the changes in habitat quality. In the future, habitat loss due to coastal erosion, compounded by sea-level rise and reduced sediment supply, will increase, with a total loss of a further 8% of current habitat projected. These trends are discussed in detail for each habitat in Section 11.2.8.1 and 11.2.8.6. The trends in habitat area from 1945 to the present day, and future projections up to 2060 (estimated from the literature), are summarised in **Figure 11.3**.

11.2.8.1 Sand Dunes

In the UK there are more than 70,000 ha of Sand Dunes (excluding Machair), the greatest resource of which is in Scotland (**Table 11.2a**), and more than a fifth of which (around 15,000 ha) falls within protected SACs (**Table 11.2b**) (JNCC 2007). Although estimates differ depending on survey methodology and scope, it is thought that the UK has lost 30% of its dune area since 1900 (Delbaere 1998; **Figure 11.4a**). After the 1960s, the rate of loss slowed due to statutory protection of most of the larger, high quality sites. However, habitat loss or deterioration from development pressures, such as caravan parks, industry, residential homes and golf courses, will continue to occur on those sand dunes lacking full legal protection (Packham & Willis 1997). Sympathetic management of links golf courses where the dunes have SSSI status can benefit conservation (Simpson *et al.* 2001), but this is by no means the case at every site. Future losses

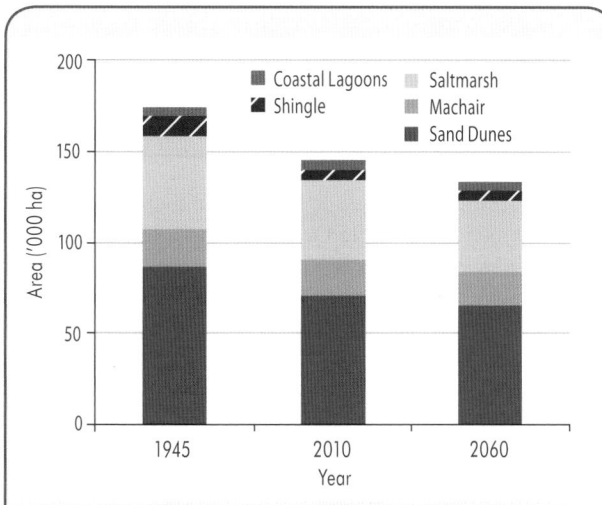

Figure 11.3 Past, present and projected future area of Coastal Margin habitats (excluding Sea Cliffs). Data sources discussed by habitat in Section 11.2.8. Estimated declines: 1945 to 2010 (16.8%); 2010 to 2060 (8.1%).

Table 11.2 Extent, trends and condition in Coastal Margin habitats. There remains considerable uncertainty about some of these estimates of area, primarily as most reporting focuses on sites with statutory protection (Special Area of Conservation, SAC; Site/Area of Special Scientific Interest, SSSI/ASSI) and ignores the smaller sites, but also due to the variety of habitat definitions and mapping protocols/techniques used. Two tables are shown: **a) Extent data deemed most reliable, together with reported trends.** Trends: = stable, ↓ weak decline, ↓↓ strong decline, ↔ trend equivocal, ? trend unknown. Source: JNCC (www.jncc.gov.uk), except Sand Dune and Machair for Scotland (Dargie 2000), Shingle and Sea Cliffs for Northern Ireland (NIEA; www.doeni.gov.uk/niea/). 'Sea Cliffs' are assumed to be comparable to JNCC habitat class 'Maritime Cliffs and Slopes', and 'Coastal Lagoons' comparable to JNCC 'Saline Lagoons'. Note: totals may not match sum of country estimates due to different update years. **b) Area and trends in area from Article 17 of the Habitat Directive reporting on habitats within SAC and SSSI.** Limited extrapolation to UK resources; UK-level data only. Trends: = stable, ↓ weak decline, ↓↓ strong decline, ↔ trend equivocal, ? trend unknown. Source: JNCC (2007). Current condition based on condition monitoring of SACs and SSSI/ASSIs, reported by Natura 2000 habitat types. Note, these are not easily summarised to Coastal Margin habitats for Sand Dunes or Saltmarsh. For an explanation of Natura 2000 codes, see JNCC (2007).

a)

	Sand Dune (ha) Good quality survey data, 1980s to 1990s, 2000		Machair (ha)		Saltmarsh (ha) Old survey data		Shingle (ha) Only vegetated shingle		Sea Cliffs (km) Incomplete data, 1990s		Coastal Lagoons (ha) Mostly recent data up to 2005	
England	11,897	↓	0	n/a	32,462	↓↓	5,023	↓	1,082	?	1,205	=
Northern Ireland	1,571	↓	0	n/a	250	=	50 n/a	n/a	500	?	42	=
Scotland	50,000	?	19,698	↔	6,000	↔	670	?	2,450	?	3,900	=
Wales	8,101	↓	0	n/a	5,800	↓	109	↓	522	↓	37	=
UK	71,569	?	19,698	↔	44,512	↓↓	5,852	?	4,554	?	5,184	=

b)

	Sand Dune (ha)*		Machair (ha)		Saltmarsh (ha)†		Shingle (ha)‡		Sea Cliffs (ha)¶		Coastal Lagoons (ha)	
Trend period	1950/1994–2006		1994–2006		1973/1987–1998/1999		1994–2006		1994–2006		1994–2006	
Area (ha) and trend	28,762	↔	13,300	=	31,805	↓ (1% p.a.)	5,160	↓ (1% p.a.)	22,000	=	5,480	=
Current condition of SACs which were assessed (% of those assessed), 1998–2006												
Unfavourable	66		70		57		76		50		7§	
Favourable	34		30		43		24		50		93§	
Current condition of strongly indicative SSSI/ASSIs (% of those assessed)												
Unfavourable	-		53		-		46		34		-	
Favourable	-		47		-		54		66		-	

* Covers Natura 2000 habitats: H2110, H2120, H2130, H2140, H2150, H2160, H2170, H2190, H2250. Current condition summarised for H2120, H2130, H2190 only (92% of UK resource).
† Covers Natura 2000 habitats: H1310, H1320, H1330, H1420. Current condition summarised for H1310, H1330 only (99% of UK resource).
‡ Covers Natura 2000 habitats: H1210, H1220. Current condition reported only for H1220.
¶ Area assumes 50 m width x 4,066 km length.
§ Trend period 1998–2005 only.

will also occur through sea-level rise and increased coastal erosion, which are predicted to contribute a further 2% loss in area between 1999 and 2020 at the UK scale (www.ukbap. org.uk/ukplans.aspx?ID=28). Impacts will vary by region depending on the rate of sea-level rise and local sediment supply, as well as exposure to storm wave activity (Saye & Pye 2007). Many large dune sites in England, Wales and Scotland have shown steepening of the beach profile over the last 100 years, which will cause further losses in area (May & Hansom 2003; Saye & Pye 2007).

The character of the UK's Sand Dunes has changed markedly over the last 60 years. In the mid-1940s, many UK dune systems had a high proportion of bare sand (Dargie 2000); for example, bare sand at Newborough Warren in Anglesey declined from 75% to just 6% today, which is a decrease of

more than 90% of its original extent (Rhind *et al.* 2001, 2008; Jones *et al.* 2010a). Although successional development from bare sand to full vegetation cover and soil development is a natural process, its rate is slowed by disturbance (both natural and man-made), but hastened by artificial stabilisation, reduced sediment supply, eutrophication and climate change (Jones *et al.* 2004, 2008; Provoost *et al.* 2010). In a minority of sites, large-scale disturbance due to military activity during WWII (e.g. Braunton Burrows) or tourism pressure (Ranwell & Boar 1986) temporarily kept succession at bay. However, there has been a consistent trend towards increased vegetation cover and over-stabilisation in the UK, and across north-west Europe (Jones *et al.* 2010a; Provoost *et al.* 2010), resulting in the loss of specialised species (Howe *et al.* 2010) and loss of the dynamic and open character of dunescapes. A few sites have managed to buck this trend, and continue to show considerable mobility (e.g. Sands of Forvie, Scotland and Morfa Dyffryn, Wales), but this is mainly where sediment supply remains high.

Climate change may shift species distributions northwards, but this is unlikely to impact much on ecosystem service provision in the Coastal Margin habitat. However, future decreases in rainfall and altered seasonality of rainfall are predicted to lower dune water tables by up to 1 m by 2080 (Clarke & Sanitwong 2010). The associated drying out of dune slacks will result in a loss of many rare species, and may cause release of stored soil carbon due to faster decomposition. Furthermore, dune soils develop faster in the wetter regions of the UK, but warmer temperatures due to climate change may speed up soil development in other areas too (Sevink 1991; Jones *et al.* 2008), leading to successional change.

Invasive species, such as sea buckthorn (*Hippophae rhamnoides*) which is considered non-native around most of the UK, except in some sites in Lincolnshire and Norfolk where it is classed as native, and garden escapees, such as Japanse Rose (*Rosa rugosa*), can change the character of dune vegetation and significantly impact on native species,

causing a decline in dune biodiversity (Binggeli *et al.* 1992; Edmondson 2009).

The intensity of grazing by managed stock and by natural grazers is important in governing the balance between stability and mobility, and therefore impacts on the ecosystem services provided. Since WWII, managed grazing of dunes has declined, particularly in the south and east (Section 11.3.1).

11.2.8.2 Machair

The world extent of Machair is about 30,000–40,000 ha, of which, around 67% is found in Scotland and 33% in the Republic of Ireland. The UK total is estimated at 19,698 ha (**Table 11.2**). Of the Scottish Machair, around 4,000 ha are covered by SAC protection and around 6,300 ha are SSSIs (Hansom & Angus 2001). In general, Machair sand budgets have been negative for a substantial period of time (Hansom 2010) and Machair erosion losses are not balanced by Machair gains. The most extensive Machair occur in the Uists, where the average recession rates over the past 100 years have been about 0.5 m per year: this represents a loss of 1.2 ha/km of coast over the period 1945 to 2010 (Hansom 2010). Over the past 15 years, rates of sea-level rise in the

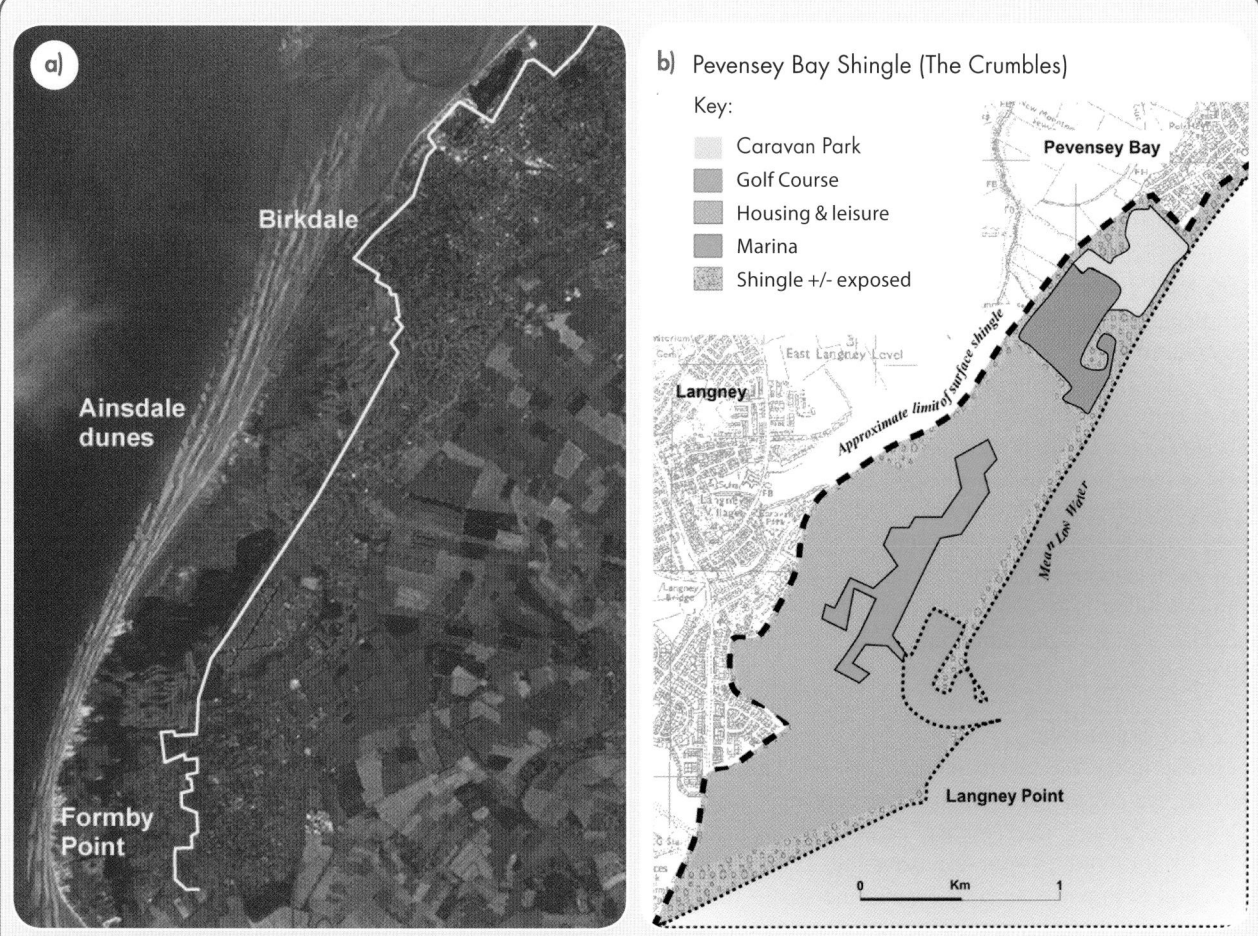

Figure 11.4 Examples of habitat loss: a) Sand Dunes on the Sefton coast, north-west England, lost to urbanisation, forestry and golf courses; and b) almost complete loss of Shingle due to development pressures at The Crumbles, East Sussex. The white line shows seaward limit of urban extent in 1945. Note the subsequent development at Ainsdale and Formby. Golf courses and afforestation of dunes pre-date 1945. Source: a) ArcGIS World Imagery Map: ESRI, i-cubed, USDA FSA, USGS, AEX, GeoEye, Getmapping, Aerogrid, IGP; urban extent courtesy of Sefton Borough Council. b) Map courtesy of J.P. Doody.

Western Isles have almost tripled from 2.2 mm/yr (before 1992) to 5.7 mm/yr. This is due to land subsidence (not emergence), faster global sea-level rise (Rennie & Hansom 2011), increased storm wave activity and reductions in sediment supply over the last century because of coastal steepening (Taylor *et al.* 2004; Hansom 2010). Therefore, it is likely that future losses will exceed the rates predicted elsewhere in UK: 6% over the next 60 years. Nevertheless, the likely extent of future Machair loss is unknown.

Given the remoteness of most Machair, development pressures are reduced, yet much of the transport infrastructure of the Scottish islands (roads, airports and bridges/causeways), military land and many crofting townships are located on Machair. There have been recent disputes over the extent of traditional grazing rights between Machair crofters and golf course developers in the Uists.

Changes in the character of Machair occur both naturally and through anthropogenic influences. Machair development relies upon exhumed and recycled sands eroded from older dunes or Machair, so ongoing aeolian activity is essential to the future health of the system. At present, aeolian erosion of Machair is minimal, and Machair surfaces are now more stable than they have been in the past (Angus & Elliott 1992). Machair supports much of the transport infrastructure in the outer Isles, so human responses to erosion events are a driver in themselves as decisions can often exacerbate erosion on site and/or export the erosion elsewhere.

Agricultural practices have changed over time in Machair areas; from the mid-1970s to 2009, there has been a 60% reduction in arable land use across five townships on the Uists and Benbecula, for instance. In Lewis and Harris, sheep have gradually replaced cattle over the past 50 years, with negative impacts on Machair biodiversity (Hansom & Angus 2001).

An additional grazing pressure on almost all the Machair islands comes from rabbits that were introduced in the Outer Hebrides in the late 18th Century and are now widespread. Their grazing pressure has resulted in problems in areas already heavily grazed by livestock. Although less evidence exists to fully determine the effects of burrowing and scraping, it is thought that these actions may initiate erosion (Angus & Elliott 1992) and that, combined with grazing, they may also lead to significant changes in vegetation (Dargie 2000).

11.2.8.3 Saltmarsh

Saltmarsh in the UK covers about 45,000 ha (**Table 11.2**), with the five largest sites (Wash, Inner Solway, Morecambe Bay, Burry Estuary, Dee Estuary) accounting for one-third of the UK total (Burd 1989). Approximately 22,000 ha are in SACs, and Common Standards Monitoring shows that 58% of saltmarsh features assessed are in favourable condition (JNCC 2007).

Prior to the 1980s, major losses of Saltmarsh occurred due to widespread, large-scale reclamation of land for agriculture or development (Morris *et al.* 2004). In the Wash, 3,000 ha of marsh were reclaimed in the 20th Century alone (Doody 2008). Extensive marshes once existed in the Forth

Estuary but, over the last 4,000 years, some 50% of the former intertidal area has been claimed for agriculture and development, 33% of this decline occurring during the past 150 years (Hansom *et al.* 2001). Currently, major losses in Saltmarsh extent are occurring in the south-east of England. Between 1973 and 1998, over 1,000 ha were lost (Cooper *et al.* 2001). In the Solent the total Saltmarsh resource declined from 1,700 to 1,080 ha between the 1970s and 2001 (Baily & Pearson 2001), with further losses in Poole Harbour (Born 2005). Losses also occur due to erosion, which takes a number of different forms, but most commonly includes the landward retreat of the seaward edge, either as a cliff or steep 'ramp', or as an expanding internal dissection of the marsh by the widening creeks. Erosion predominantly affects lower marsh communities which are more vulnerable to wave action.

There have been some gains in Saltmarsh extent, particularly on the larger, west-coast marshes (e.g. the Dee, Ribble, Solway Firth and Morecambe Bay), which is largely accounted for by the expansion of lower marsh transitional plant communities over intertidal mud and sand flats, and by the expansion of common cord-grass (*Spartina anglica*). Managed realignment also contributes to new habitat creation; nonetheless, Saltmarsh losses continue to exceed gains (Rupp-Armstrong & Nicholls 2007) and estimates of net losses vary in range from 4.5% over 20 years (French 1997) up to 2% per year (Nottage & Robertson 2005).

The non-native common cord-grass is the result of hybridisation between an introduced American cord-grass and a native British species. It was extensively planted along British coasts to stabilise mudflats, but became invasive. The expansion of common cord-grass onto previously bare upper mudflats is considered to have negative impacts on shorebird and wildfowl feeding areas, benthic invertebrate habitat and seagrass (*Zostera* species) populations (Doody 1984). Common cord-grass has expanded onto beaches at Southport (Ribble Estuary) and Cleethorpes (Humber Estuary) causing possible changes in their amenity value. However, in some areas, dieback of common cord-grass has occurred for unknown reasons, preventing the need for artificial control; in the late 19th and early 20th Centuries, for example, widespread dieback occurred on many southern sites (Lacambra *et al.* 2004).

Wind-wave climate has the most influence on the horizontal extent of Saltmarshes, while relative sea-level rise has a major influence on their vertical growth and on their medium- and long-term evolution (Allen & Pye 1992). Evidence from Holocene sedimentary sequences suggests that vertical saltmarsh accretion is able to keep pace with projected rates of mean sea-level rise, with the essential sediment supply being provided by the accelerated erosion of soft cliffs, beaches and the seaward edge of the marshes themselves (Pye & French 1992). However, in some larger estuaries there may be insufficient sediment available to maintain the areas of saltmarshes and tidal flats at current levels and, particularly where saltmarshes are backed by embankments for coastal defence, they may suffer coastal squeeze. Even where accretion is able to keep pace with sea-level rise, the loss of fronting saltmarsh will lessen coastal defence services.

Agricultural operations may cause unfavourable Saltmarsh condition. Cessation of grazing or over-grazing can lead to a loss of biodiversity. Over-grazing may reduce the wave attenuation function, but it may also raise erosion thresholds through soil compaction—although there is little evidence on the impacts of grazing to date.

11.2.8.4 Shingle

Vegetated Shingle covers approximately 5,800 ha in the UK (**Table 11.2**), mostly in England. Of this total, 3,382 ha are in SACs (JNCC 2007). Areas of undisturbed Shingle have declined dramatically over time, but this is not well quantified. The principle pressures have been infrastructure development; for instance, during the 1980s, almost all of the 160 ha of Shingle at 'The Crumbles', East Sussex, were lost to housing, gravel extraction, caravan sites and a new marina (**Figure 11.4b**). Dungeness is the largest shingle structure in Great Britain, with 1,700 ha of exposed Shingle. Yet gravel extraction has taken place there since the 1940s, affecting some 40% of its surface (Fuller 1985), although there is currently minimal shingle extraction from the main shingle structures as they are now mostly designated as an SSSI. At Rye Harbour, East Sussex, most of the 375 ha of Shingle are damaged through gravel extraction and disturbance. Losses of Shingle landforms in England were predicted to total 200 ha (1.6%) between 1992 and 2010 (French 1997), but are yet to be verified.

Infrastructure development has been a major driver of change for Shingle, particularly for facilities requiring remote locations (such as those for military uses) or a nearby source of cooling water, such as nuclear power stations (such as those in Dungeness). However, these developments have largely ceased, and in the recent Department of Energy and Climate Change (DECC) consultation relating to the provision of new nuclear power stations, Dungeness is specifically excluded because its development would impact adversely on its internationally important nature conservation sites. On the other hand, there is a continuing threat to the site from an extension to Lydd airport. Orford Ness, another large Shingle structure on the south-east coast, is now owned and managed by the National Trust, so is unlikely to be damaged further by large infrastructure developments.

Climate is the major variable affecting community distribution and species range of Shingle vegetation (Farrell & Randall 1992); for example, Oysterplant (*Mertensia maritima*), which has a northern distribution, has disappeared from several more southern localities in the UK and Republic of Ireland due to the warming climate (Randall 2004). Because of the skeletal soils, high porosity and low water-retention of shingle, predicted reductions in summer precipitation in the south and east will have a negative effect on plant survival. Warmer temperatures also favour invasive species, especially garden escapees, which threaten many native species (Doody & Randall 2003a).

Disturbance, both natural and human-induced, affects Shingle vegetation. A few specialised plants are able to survive periodic movement of shingle beaches, but increasing storm frequency and intensity will destroy most vegetation. This will be particularly significant for mature, stable vegetation on stony banks as re-establishment takes a long time (although restoration is possible) (Walmsley & Davy 1997, 2001). On the most mature shingle structures, even relatively small incursions, such as those made into the surface layer by vehicles, may remain visible for many years. Regular disturbance as a result of re-profiling for sea defence has significant adverse effects on vegetation at some sites. For example, at Cuckmere Haven, Sussex, the western part is highly managed and devoid of vegetation, whereas the eastern side is unmanaged and, despite high visitor numbers, shows good vegetation cover (Smith 2009).

11.2.8.5 Sea Cliffs

Approximately 4,500 km of the UK's coastline has been classified as Sea Cliff (**Table 11.2**). The Joint Nature Conservation Committee (JNCC) estimates the area of cliffs as 22,000 ha, of which, 8,482 ha are in SACs (JNCC 2007). There has been no national survey of maritime cliffs and slopes in the UK, but 'desktop' inventories exist for England and Wales (Hill 2002; Tantram & Dargie 2005) and the Department of the Environment (DOE) in Northern Ireland has an online Maritime Cliffs and Slopes Habitat Action Plan (HAP). Without a national survey, it is not possible to provide a meaningful account of the status of this habitat, or discuss national trends in terms of its conservation value. However, unpublished evidence suggests that large stretches of maritime cliff vegetation are in sub-optimal condition, with coastal slopes dominated by rank, coarse grasses, bramble, bracken and scrub (Oates 1999). Traditional grazing of cliff slopes is now far less prevalent than it was in the late 1800s, but it is still practised on a local scale in places such as north and west Wales (Oates 1999).

According to the JNCC (2007), the main pressures affecting maritime cliffs are:

- Modification of cultivation practices
- Over- and under-grazing
- Abandonment of pastoral systems
- Urbanised areas (human habitation)
- Continuous urbanisation
- Walking
- Horse riding and non-motorised vehicles
- Air pollution
- Sea defence and coast protection works
- Erosion
- Invasion by unwanted species.

A major concern has been the loss of habitat due to agricultural encroachment, urban or industrial development, and holiday accommodation. In some places, cliff-top vegetation has been reduced to a narrow strip with most of the natural zonation destroyed. This prevents cliff-top biological communities from retreating in response to cliff erosion, subjecting them to a form of coastal squeeze.

Erosion is a highly significant factor in soft cliffs. However, this does not imply a loss of the cliff resource, either in geological or biological terms, as erosion is vital for constantly renewing geological exposures and recycling the botanical succession of this habitat.

Coastal protection systems have been built on many soft cliff coasts in order to slow or stop the rate of erosion, and thus protect capital assets behind the cliff line. Cliff faces may also be drained, re-profiled and sown with hardy grasses of little value for nature conservation. All such works have the effect of stabilising the cliff face, resulting in geological exposures being obscured, bare soil and early pioneer stages being progressively overgrown, and wet flushes drying out. Additional effects of defences include accelerated erosion and sediment starvation at coastal sites down-drift of defended sites. Taking into account cliff protection works over the past 100 years, it has been estimated that sediment inputs may have declined by as much as 50% (Clayton 1989). In 1994, a Ministry of Agriculture, Fisheries and Food (MAFF; now Defra) survey identified more than 90 km of new cliff protection works likely to be needed in the following ten years, which was estimated at the time to incur a 36% loss of the remaining soft cliff resource. The actual loss from these works has yet to be quantified.

In the traditional low-intensity grazing systems that prevailed before WWII, livestock were grazed on cliff grasslands where they maintained open, maritime grassland vegetation. But post-war intensification of agriculture has led to maritime grassland on more level terrain being ploughed out, while that on sloping ground has been abandoned and, where not maintained by exposure, is frequently overgrown by scrub. In addition, localised eutrophication can be caused by fertiliser runoff from arable land nearby.

The siting of holiday accommodation on cliff-tops not only reduces the landscape value of a site, but can also cause heavy, localised erosion and disturbance to nesting birds. A rise in the number of walkers and dogs along some coastal footpaths has increased livestock-worrying and forced a number of farmers to remove their stock from these sites. Consequently, some of the sites are now suffering from a lack of appropriate grazing, and scrub encroachment is likely to become a problem.

Predators, such as rats, can have a significant impact on populations of cliff- or burrow-nesting seabirds, particularly on island sites. The spread of alien, invasive plants, such as hottentot fig (*Carpobrotus edulis*), can have a devastating impact through smothering indigenous maritime plant communities.

11.2.8.6 Coastal Lagoons

Saline lagoon habitat has been reported in terms of the number of individual systems and the areal extent of the lagoonal habitat. Due to the ongoing debate on the classification of lagoons, these figures are subject to revision. **Table 11.2** gives the areal extent of lagoons as an estimated 5,184 ha, of which, around 2,600 ha are in SACs (JNCC 2007). Symes and Robertson (2004) present tabulated data on the numbers of saline lagoons in Great Britain broken down according to type and country. The lagoons of Northern Ireland have not been categorised, but are few in number. Lagoons were indicated in a 2005 Biodiversity Action Plan (BAP) report to be stable in all UK regions. However, earlier work by Bamber *et al.* (2001) estimated that some 30–40 lagoons were lost in England alone during the 1980s. In 1992, it was estimated that about 120 ha of Coastal Lagoons in England (10% of the existing English resource) would be lost over the subsequent 20 years, mainly as a consequence of sea-level rise (Smith & Laffoley 1992), with an estimate of

net loss of 500 ha from SAC/SSSI/Ramsar sites in England and Wales over a 50 year period (Lee 2001).

Many lagoons have been altered by coastal defences or infilling associated with waterfront development, and this threat will continue. Lagoons are also created artificially and extensive human interference in their geomorphology is often advocated to maintain habitat (Symes & Robertson 2004). In addition to direct impacts on natural barriers, the interruption of sediment supply through coastal engineering works can cause changes in barrier morphology and sedimentology, altering porosity, inlet persistence and dimensions.

Saline lagoons with natural barriers are likely to migrate landwards with rising sea levels by barrier 'over-washing' and the transfer of sediment from the front to the rear of the barrier. Associated with this, the landward margins of the lagoon will be flooded, and the marginal habitats will migrate over terrestrial environments. The patterns of barrier evolution are highly site-specific and dependent on the rate of sea-level rise, sediment supply, transport modes (along-shore/cross-shore) and the surrounding topography. The various scenarios for barrier evolution are outlined by Carter *et al.* (1987). Barriers may breach, accrete, break down, or migrate, according to local circumstances. There are obvious differences in the responses of the back-barrier lagoon to each of these changes. Natural lagoons with rock sills are likely to experience increased saline influence with rising sea levels and a landward shift in the marginal habitats. Artificial lagoons, however, are entirely dependent on continued human intervention.

Geomorphological evolution of natural lagoons is often inhibited by infrastructure and human activities. Many are likely to experience coastal squeeze as a result of defences on their landward margins: the barrier migrates landward, but the lagoon margins are fixed. Conversely, artificial lagoon habitats are likely to be maintained and may even increase in area. In addition, managed realignment schemes in SMPs often include provision for the creation of new artificial lagoons, which is likely to increase the extent of such habitat.

Increased summer temperatures as a result of climate change may lead to an increased level of desiccation in the intertidal area, restricting the distribution of intertidal species (NIHAP 2003), and increased water temperatures may affect lagoon specialists with limited dispersal ability. Changes in the volume and timing of freshwater discharge due to climate change have the potential to alter lagoon salinity regimes. The salinity regimes of lagoons are subject to natural change as succession leads to freshening of the water and eventually to vegetation such as fen carr. Thus some formerly saline sites are now freshwater lagoons. In contrast, the regime of Porlock lagoon in Somerset is shifting in the opposite direction since artificial maintenance of the gravel barrier halted. Since a breach of the barrier in 1998, it has transformed into a more saline system (Orford *et al.* 2001; **Figure 11.5**).

Pollution, in particular nutrient enrichment leading to eutrophication, can have major detrimental effects on lagoons, including species loss, although studies in the Fleet lagoon in Dorset demonstrate that a distinctive ecosystem can be maintained under such conditions (Weber *et al.* 2006). Regulation of freshwater inputs and artificial manipulation of seawater input through inlet/outlet control can impact on salinity, residence time and water quality.

Johnson & Gilliland (2000) list the following impacts on water quality of saline lagoons:

- nutrient enrichment: including direct metabolic effects on species (for example foxtail stonewort (*Lamprothamnium papulosum*), which most frequently occurs at sites where soluble reactive phosphate is below 10 micrograms per litre; an increase in growth of epiphytic, floating, ephemeral, benthic and phytoplanktonic algae and associated competition with lagoonal vegetation of conservation interest; and indirect effects on lagoonal fauna;
- turbidity: including an increase in light attenuation and smothering, or inhibition of feeding of lagoonal invertebrates;
- toxic contamination: suggested contaminants of concern from studies outside lagoons include heavy metals, herbicides/pesticides and chronic oil pollution. These potentially impact on the suitability of lagoons as habitats, and the exploitation of their living resources;
- organic enrichment: likely to be of limited concern given that lagoonal sediments are naturally high in organic material.

Coastal defence policy affects natural and artificial lagoons both directly and indirectly. Holding the line will require that the elevation of the barrier be raised, while allowing the barrier to migrate will mean flooding of adjacent land or, if that is defended, a reduction in lagoon area. Holding the line in an adjacent coastal area can reduce the sediment supply to a lagoon barrier. The main policy driver for Coastal Lagoons is the Water Framework Directive which requires water bodies to achieve at least 'good' ecological status. Those Coastal Lagoons fronted by shingle or sand barriers are subject to the implications of SMPs that affect the barrier.

11.3 Ecosystem Goods and Services Provided by Coastal Margins for Human Well-being

Ecosystem services provided by the UK's Coastal Margins are many and varied (**Figure 11.6**), and have substantial value, being estimated at £48 billion (adjusted 2003 values—3.46%

Figure 11.5 Porlock in Somerset: a Shingle ridge breached in a storm (at point arrowed) has become a tidal inlet with the grazing land behind reverting to Saltmarsh (Doody & Randall 2003b). *Photo courtesy of J.P. Doody (September 2005).*

of UK Global National Income—by a study which applied the ecosystem service economic values of Constanza *et al.* (1997) to coastal biomes in Europe (COREPOINT 2007; Firn Crichton Roberts 2000). This section discusses the main goods and ecosystem services provided by the Coastal Margin, using the set of services and definitions of the UK NEA Conceptual Framework (Chapter 2). Goods and benefits provided by the identified 'Final Ecosystem Services' for each Coastal Margin habitat, and an indication of their importance, are summarised in **Table 11.3**.

Goods relating to *provisioning services* in the Coastal Margins are relatively minor; the most important are meat and wool from Saltmarsh, and timber from afforested Sand Dunes, while seaweed-gathering from the beach, used as fertiliser, and fodder crops are both locally important on Machair. Non-food provisioning services include the use of easily engineered flat land for development, the use of cooling water for nuclear power stations, and the use of land for military exercises.

Sea defence is the most important *regulating service*, with all habitats contributing either directly by energy absorption or dissipation, or indirectly through sediment supply. Goods and benefits linked to wild species diversity are very important in these habitats, particularly fish nursery

Figure 11.6 Some of the ecosystem services provided by Coastal Margin habitats. a) sea defence*, b) leisure and amenity[¶], c) crops[†], d) meat and wool*, e) biodiversity (puffin[‡]; orchid[†]; moth[†]), f) military use*, g) personal space*, h) industry use*, i) sense of place*, j) education* and k) health and recreation*. *Photos courtesy of J.P. Doody[*]; L. Jones[‡] and P. Jones[‡]; photo used under Creative Commons from J.D. Champion[¶].*

grounds in Saltmarsh, and ecological niche provision for birds in all habitats.

Goods and benefits relating to *cultural services* are very numerous in Coastal Margins, and are primarily linked to tourism and recreation, but also to cultural, social, historical, artistic, and physical and mental health benefits to society. The specific services and how they provide these goods, together with their interactions are described in Sections 11.3.1 to 11.3.5. The inter-relationships between services provided by Coastal Margins are shown in **Figure 11.7**, and the text describes how the goods and benefits listed in **Table 11.3** are derived from these services.

11.3.1 Provisioning Services

11.3.1.1 Production livestock

Provision of wool and meat from livestock-grazing (sheep and cattle) occurs on the older, well-established grasslands of Sand Dunes and Machair, on cliff-tops and on the higher elevation Saltmarsh grasslands where the soils are sufficiently developed to support richer vegetation. Productive Saltmarsh-grazing produces distinctive-tasting, specialist products, such as saltmarsh lamb and beef, which are sold at a premium: on average 100% more than mass-produced meat. An evaluation of the benefits arising from

Table 11.3 Goods and benefits provided by final ecosystem services from Coastal Margin habitats. ⊚ denotes high, and ⊙ denotes some importance of each good/benefit; superscript numbers indicate which goods/benefits are relevant to each habitat; * denotes locally important; † denotes historical use; P = Provisioning service, R = Regulating service, C = Cultural service, S = Supporting service.

Service Group	Final ecosystem service	Goods/Benefits	Sand Dunes ‡	Machair ¶	Saltmarsh	Shingle §	Sea Cliffs **	Coastal Lagoons
P	Crops, plants, livestock, fish, etc. (wild and domesticated)	Crops: vegetables, cereals, animal feed	-	⊙	-	-	-	-
		Meat: sheep/cattle[1], rabbits[2†], fish/shellfish[3]	⊚ 1, 2 *	⊚ 1	⊚ 1 *	-	⊙ 1 *	⊙ 3 *
		Wild food: Mushrooms[4], Salicornia[5], other plants/berries[6], fish/shellfish[7], wildfowl[8]	⊙ 4, 6	⊙ 4, 6, 7	⊙ 5, 6, 8	⊙ 6	⊙ 6	⊙ 7
		Wool: sheep	⊙ *	⊚ *	⊙ *	-	-	-
		Genetic resources of rare breeds[9], crops[10]	⊙ 9	⊙ 9, 10	⊙ 9	-	⊙ 9 *	-
P	Trees, standing vegetation & peat/other resources	Reed/grass for thatching†, mats & basket weaving†	⊙	⊙	-	-	-	⊙
		Timber for wood pulp, furniture	⊙ *	-	-	-	-	-
		Turf/peat cutting	-	⊙	⊙ *	-	-	-
		Seaweed gathering for fertiliser	-	⊙	-	-	-	-
		Extraction of sand[11], gravel[12]	⊙ 11	⊙ 11	-	⊙ 12	-	-
		Military use	⊙	⊙	⊙	-	⊙	-
		Industrial use: pipeline landfall/energy generation	⊙	⊙	⊙	-	-	-
R	Climate regulation	Carbon sequestration	⊙	⊙	⊙	⊙	⊙	⊙
P R	Water quantity	Water for irrigation, drinking	⊙ *	⊙ *	-	⊙ *	-	-
R	Hazard regulation—vegetation & other habitats	Sea defence	⊚	⊚	⊚	⊚	⊚ Indirect	⊙
		Preventing soil erosion	-	-	-	-	⊙	-
R	Waste breakdown & detoxification	Immobilisation of pollutants	-	-	⊚	-	-	⊙
P	Wild species diversity including microbes	High diversity, or rare/unique plants, animals and birds, insects	⊚	⊚	⊚	⊚	⊚	⊙
		Ecosystem-specific protected areas	⊚	⊙	⊚	⊚	⊚	⊙
		Nursery grounds for fish	-	⊚	⊚	-	-	⊚
R		Breeding, over-wintering, feeding grounds for birds	⊚ *	⊚	⊚	⊚	⊚	⊙

Table 11.3 continued. Goods and benefits provided by final ecosystem services from Coastal Margin habitats. ◉ denotes high, and ⊙ denotes some importance of each good/benefit; superscript numbers indicate which goods/benefits are relevant to each habitat; * denotes locally important; † denotes historical use; P = Provisioning service, R = Regulating service, C = Cultural service, S = Supporting service.

Service Group	Final ecosystem service	Goods/Benefits	Sand Dunes‡	Machair¶	Saltmarsh	Shingle§	Sea Cliffs**	Coastal Lagoons
R	Purification	Water filtration: groundwater[13], surface flow[14], seawater[15]	⊙ 13	⊙ 13, 14, 15	⊙ 14	⊙ 13		⊙ 14, 15
C	Environmental Settings: Religious/spiritual + Cultural heritage & media	Sites of religious/cultural significance; World Heritage Sites; folklore; TV & Radio programmes & Films	⊙	◉	⊙	⊙	◉	⊙
C	Environmental Settings: Aesthetic/inspirational	Paintings, sculpture, books	◉	⊙	◉	◉	◉	⊙
C	Environmental Settings: *Enfranchisement + Neighbourhood development*	Beach cleaning/litter picking	⊙	⊙	-	⊙	⊙	⊙
C	Environmental Settings: *Recreation/tourism*	Many opportunities for recreation: incl. sunbathing, walking, camping, boating, fishing, birdwatching etc.	◉	◉	◉	◉	◉	◉
C	Environmental Settings: *Physical/mental health + Security and freedom*	Opportunities for exercise, local meaningful space, wilderness, personal space	◉	◉	⊙	◉	◉	⊙
C	Environmental Settings: *Education/ ecological knowledge*	Resource for teaching, public information, scientific study	◉	◉ *	◉	⊙	◉	⊙

‡Includes sandy beaches; ¶Includes fringing beaches, dunes, machair lochs; §Includes shingle beaches; **Includes small islands.

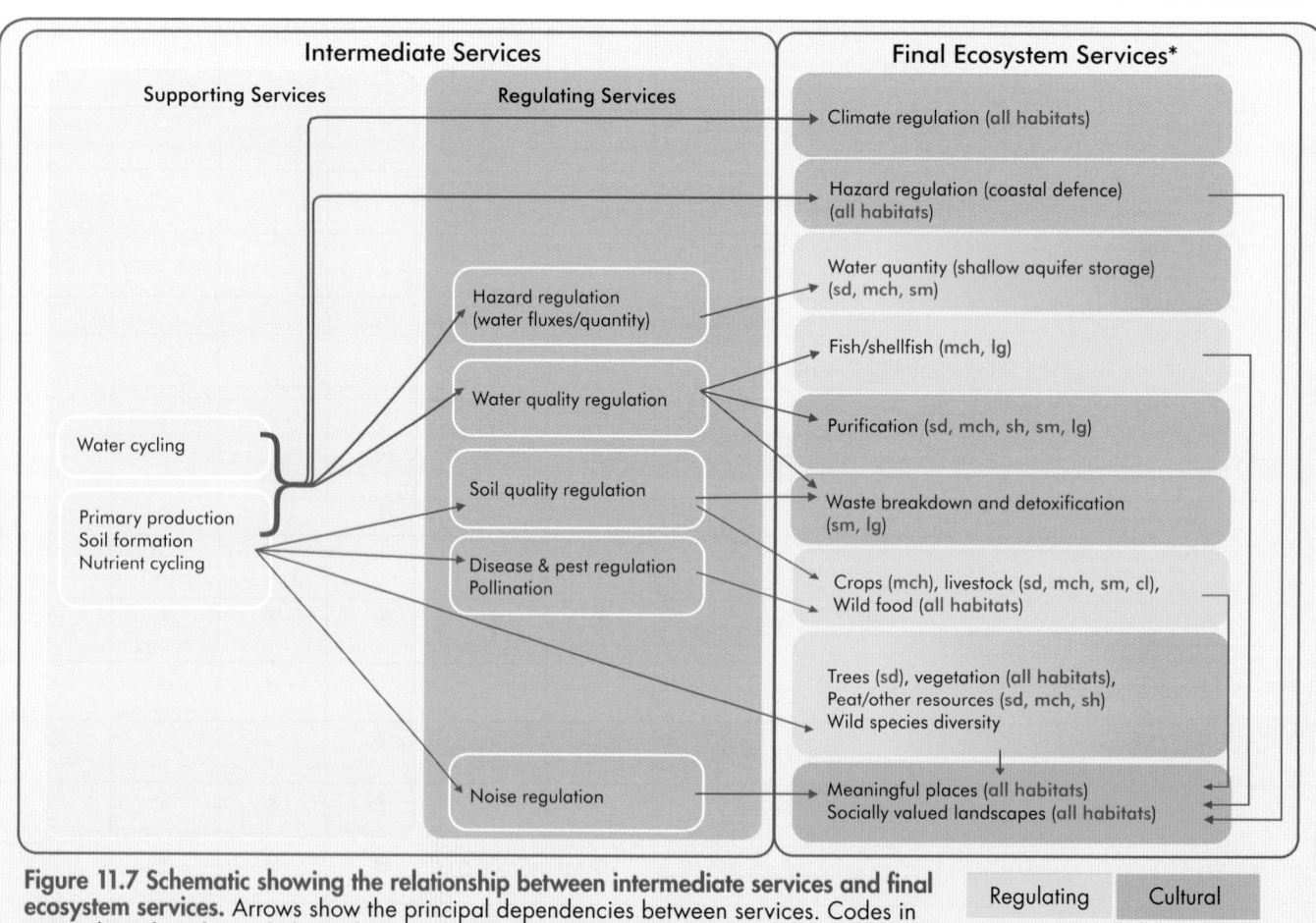

Figure 11.7 Schematic showing the relationship between intermediate services and final ecosystem services. Arrows show the principal dependencies between services. Codes in green show the relevant habitats for each final service: **sd**=Sand Dunes, **mch**=Machair, **sm**= Saltmarsh, **sh**=Shingle, **cl**=Sea Cliffs and **lg**=Coastal Lagoons. *Final ecosystem services can include those from the provisioning, regulating and cultural services.

the 440 ha Alkborough Flats Saltmarsh restoration project on the Humber estuary, England, estimated that an annual yield from sheep was £19,500 and from cattle was £21,000 (Everard 2009).

Apart from Saltmarsh, the herbage quality of Coastal Margin grasslands is poor, and most stock are hardy breeds or traditional varieties: cattle breeds include Welsh Black, Dexter, Galloway, Highland and North and South Devon; and sheep breeds include Herdwick, Scottish Blackface, Swaledale and White Welsh Mountain, as well as ancient breeds like Hebridean and Soay. Agricultural stock numbers on UK Sand Dunes have declined since 1945 and are now very low, with a rough estimate of 4,000 cattle and 13,000 sheep currently grazing this habitat (estimated from data in Boorman 1989; Boorman & Boorman 2001; Burton 2001), predominantly in north-west England (Burton 2001) and Scotland. In some Machair crofting townships, sheep and cattle are winter-grazed on the Machair grassland. This traditional cattle-based land management, which includes the growing of winter fodder on Machair during the summer, is an important element in maintaining the high biodiversity of Machair. Historically, cliff-tops were valued for summer grazing because grass under coastal bracken often remains green during hot dry spells and coastal slopes have a low incidence of sheep ticks. Today, rare breeds or hardy varieties of ponies, sheep and cattle are now used at many sites primarily for conservation grazing (Radley 1994; Oates *et al.* 1998) and have minimal direct agricultural value; however, preservation of their genetic diversity is an important service.

Crops. Of the Coastal Margin environments, Machair probably provides the most extensive and unique provisioning service in the UK in the form of crop production. In contrast to the acidic, poorly drained and hilly land of the west coast of Scotland and Ireland, the calcium-rich flatlands of Machair offer agricultural opportunities in an otherwise resource-poor periphery. In the past, the inland sectors of the dry Machair, and the seaward sectors of the wet Machair, were extensively cultivated. A traditional rotation involving two or more years fallow following cropping was used to produce black oats, rye and bere barley for animal feed; today, this practice is now largely restricted to the Uists.

Wild foods. A wide range of plant and animal species are gathered in small quantities for use as 'wild food' throughout the UK, but these have minor economic importance. They include mushrooms from Sand Dunes, wildfowl from Saltmarshes, miscellaneous edible plants and berries from all habitats, fish/shellfish from Coastal Lagoons, and small-scale, recreational (and commercial in Norfolk) harvesting of common samphire (*Salicornia* species) from Saltmarsh which is sold as a luxury item at around £3.50/ kg. Saltmarshes are also important nursery grounds for commercial fish species (Section 11.3.3).

Household goods, building materials and fertilisers. Uses of plant material were historically important, but now have only minor economic importance. For instance, dune grasses such as Marram grass (*Ammophila arenaria*) and Lyme grass (*Leymus* species) were used in the past for animal bedding, thatching, and mat- and basket-weaving (Ranwell 1959; Jones *et al.* 1993; Angus 2001), while wave-torn tangle seaweed (*Laminaria hyperborea*) was, and is still, used as an organic fertiliser and sand-binding agent on Machair. In fact, the character of Machair occurs, in part, because of soil-improvement through the addition of seaweed as fertiliser, and because of shallow tilling for the small-scale cultivation of crops.

Other historical uses. Historically, the well-drained sandy soils of older Sand Dune grasslands were used for rabbit-warrening, grazing or were reclaimed for growing crops such as asparagus (Jones *et al.* 1993). Seabirds and their eggs were harvested from cliffs and islands, but this tradition has largely died out, except on Lewis in the Western Isles, as lifestyles have changed and protective legislation has come into force.

Aquifers. Provision of other resources dependent on Coastal Margin habitats includes coastal aquifers. Sand Dunes, Machair and Shingle with a reasonable depth or extent of substrate form a shallow aquifer of clean water, which is used for small-scale local abstraction such as golf course watering. In Shingle habitats, this often overlies saline water and fluctuates with the tide (Burnham & Cook 2001); Dungeness is the only Shingle site which provides a local source of drinking water.

Biochemical and pharmaceutical products. From a provisioning perspective, the flora of Coastal Margin habitats has some biochemical or pharmaceutical potential, for example, sea holly (*Eryngium maritimum*) is being investigated for its anti-inflammatory properties (Küpeli *et al.* 2006; Meot-Duros *et al.* 2008). The diversity, conservation interest and rarity of much of the UK's coastal flora and fauna are of interest to many people, and, as such, our wildlife is a resource providing educational and cultural benefits; this is discussed further under Section 11.3.6.

11.3.1.2 Other provisioning services

The following provisioning services are also provided to some extent by the soft coastal habitats (Sand Dunes, Machair, Saltmarsh and Shingle), but are generally considered detrimental to the continued natural function of these habitats.

Afforestation. Uniquely among the Coastal Margin habitats, some Sand Dunes were afforested intermittently from the late 19th Century to the 1960s. Widespread planting occurred between 1922 and 1966, with approximately 8,000 ha (approximately 14% of UK dune area) now afforested (Doody 1989). During the 1940s, there was some clearance of sites, such as Ainsdale in Merseyside (Sturgess & Atkinson 1993), and there has been limited clear felling subsequently at a number of sites to restore functionality of dune processes, but further tree removal is unlikely to be undertaken at a large-scale. The timber produced from this afforestation is used for wood pulp and, after strengthening, furniture and construction. Afforestation also served a sand-stabilising function. However, on the relatively poor sand dune soils, timber is generally of low quality, and harvesting is currently not economically viable. Instead, recreational and amenity uses predominate.

Soil and aggregate removal. Turf-cutting is practised on Saltmarsh in north-west England. Aggregate extraction of sand from beaches and dunes for the glass industry, and from dunes and machair for local agricultural, horticultural and construction use (Jones *et al.* 1993; Radley 1994; Dargie 1995; Hansom & Comber 1996) has substantially declined. Aggregate extraction from Shingle has been considerable in the past (Fuller 1985) and has led to environmental degradation. Some benefits arise through the creation of new habitat, such as flight ponds for wildfowl, once extraction has ceased, but these are generally not considered sustainable practices.

Military use. There are also some industrial uses considered under provisioning services that are potentially reversible. The relative inaccessibility and uncompromising terrain of Sand Dunes, Machair, Saltmarsh and Sea Cliffs make these coastal habitats ideal for military activities including firing ranges and training (Radley 1994). Large-scale military use occurs on more than ten UK Sand Dune systems, most of which are under SAC protection (Doody 1989). Saltmarsh is used as 'over-shoot' protection areas for small arms fire or, when adjacent to tidal flats, on bombing ranges. Undulating Machair and Sand Dunes also lend themselves to military use, as occurs on South Uist (rocket range), Barry Buddon, Angus (military exercises) and at Balnakeil, Sutherland (air bombardment).

Energy production. In terms of energy needs, the development of oil and gas facilities and pipeline construction and their landfall at the coast have occurred in Sand Dunes (Ritchie & Gimingham 1989), such as at St Fergus in Aberdeenshire, Sinclairs Bay in Caithness, and Talacre in North Wales, and have also been built across Saltmarsh, such as at Morrich More in Ross-shire. Ready availability of cooling water and remote locations mean that nuclear power stations are also primarily sited on the coast.

Golf courses. Finally, golf courses are a largely non-reversible use, but sympathetic management can preserve stable dune communities (Simpson *et al.* 2001), albeit in a fragmented state, removed from most natural dune processes.

11.3.2 Regulating Services

11.3.2.1 Hazard regulation

Of the regulating services, hazard regulation is arguably the most important service provided by Coastal Margins; this includes protection from erosion, storm and wave damage and coastal flooding. **Table 11.4** shows the extent of the UK coastline affected by coastal erosion, ranging from 12% in Scotland to 30% in England. Coastal defence is provided by all the Coastal Margin habitats to a greater or lesser extent. In Saltmarsh, vegetation attenuates wave energy: pioneer Saltmarsh has been shown to reduce incident wave energy by 82%, compared with 29% over bare tidal flats (Möller *et al.* 1999). However, under storm conditions, it is likely that water depth thresholds exist that may lower the efficiency with which vegetated surfaces reduce wave energy (Möller *et al.* 1999). Under average tidal inundation depths, up to 50% of wave energy is dissipated in the first 10–20 m of a vegetated Saltmarsh surface (Möller 2006), while an 80 m strip can reduce the height of a seawall needed for landward defences from 12 m to only 3 m (King & Lester 1995). King and Lester (1995) estimated that an 80 m saltmarsh width results in capital cost savings of £2,600–4,600 per metre of seawall

(1994 prices). More recent Environment Agency guideline average costs of building seawalls are £1,522 per metre (Environment Agency 2007); scaling this figure by coastline length of Saltmarsh, rather than area, gives a capital cost saving of £2.17 billion on sea defence for England. Beaumont *et al.* (2006), showed that scaling King & Lester values by Saltmarsh area give capital cost savings of £13–32 billion, and annual maintenance cost savings of £0.3 billion for sea defence in England. For areas such as Essex, where 431 km of seawalls provide coastal defence, fronting Saltmarsh helps maintain defence integrity along 70% (300 km) and provides huge cost savings (Lester & King 1995).

In contrast to Saltmarsh, Sand Dunes and Shingle provide direct protection, often replacing the need for artificial sea defence structures providing the dune or shingle system is wide enough, or the primary dune ridge is large enough. Sand and shingle beaches are dissipaters of energy, absorbing, rather than reflecting, wave attack. Shingle provides important natural defence structures, such as those at Chesil Beach, Hurst Spit and Pevensey in England, and at Spey Bay in Scotland. Many of these features are now maintained by artificial nourishment, re-shaping or recycling

Table 11.4 Summary of the length of UK coastline with erosion and protection. Source: Gatliff *et al.* (2010).

Region	Coast length*	Length of coast eroding	Coast length with defence works and artificial beaches	
	km	km	%	km	%
North-east England	297	80	26.9	111	37.4
North-west England	659	122	18.5	329	49.9
Yorkshire and Humber	361	203	56.2	156	43.2
East Midlands	234	21	9.0	234	100.0
East England	555	168	30.3	382	68.8
South-east England	788	244	31.0	429	54.4
South-west England	1,379	437	31.7	306	22.2
England	4,273	1,275	29.8	1,947	45.6
Northern Ireland	456	89	19.5	90	19.7
Wales	1,498	346	23.1	415	27.7
Scotland	11,154	1298	11.6	733	6.6
Northern Ireland	456	89	19.5	90	19.7
UK	17,381	3008	17.3	3,185	18.3

*Coastline length is highly dependent on the scale of the data from which it is measured. Therefore the length of coastline presented in this table differs from that in Chapter 12 due to the different techniques and sources on which these measurements are based.

to retain shingle in front of human assets; **Figure 11.8** gives a striking example of loss of this protective function. Sand Dunes provide a recognised sea defence function around the UK, particularly for residential areas, and for high quality farmland in north-west and eastern England and in north Wales (Everard *et al.* 2010). Vegetation cover and root mass bind the substrate, promote sand deposition and help build wider and higher dunes. Scaled by coastline length and accounting for costs of maintaining natural habitats (Environment Agency 2007), dunes and shingle are estimated to provide £0.52 billion and £0.79 billion sea defence value in England respectively. A more conservative estimate for dunes alone, taking into account only those dunes protecting high value land and those lacking any artificial defence structures (Pye *et al.* 2007), gives a sea defence value of £173.7 million in England and £54.2 million in Wales. With 'room to move' and adequate sediment, dunes and shingle 'roll-over' in response to sea-level rise, retaining a similar shape and therefore similar sea defence properties. This makes them an ideal and sustainable sea defence. Dynamic shingle beaches provide material for new ridges, which have the potential to build up along the shore and create new protective structures elsewhere. Sea Cliffs are, in themselves, a barrier to the sea, but they also support the sea defence role of down-drift Coastal Margin habitats, such as beaches and dunes, via the sediment they supply when they are allowed to erode naturally (Dickson *et al.* 2007; Dawson *et al.* 2009). Vegetation may alter the stability of slopes directly and indirectly through controls on water infiltration. The barriers which form Coastal Lagoons provide a buffer to wave action for the enclosed water body and surrounding environments and are, therefore, a natural sea defence. Additionally, in Machair, some brackish lagoons are connected to the land drainage system and perform a flood control function under normal conditions, but, conversely, may also exacerbate the area of impact of coastal flooding under extreme events. Including the lower and upper estimates for Sand Dunes and Saltmarsh, the sea defence value of soft coast habitats in England ranges from £3.1–£33.2 billion.

11.3.2.2 Climate regulation

A degree of climate regulation is provided by those habitats where rapid soil development or sediment accumulation occurs (primarily Sand Dune, uncultivated Machair and Saltmarsh). Rates of carbon (C) sequestration are high in both dry dune (0.58 ±0.26 tonnes per hectare per year [t C/ha/yr]) and wet slack (0.73 ±0.22 t C/ha/yr) habitats (Jones *et al.* 2008) as they are early successional systems. Rates in uncultivated Machair may be similar to older dune grasslands, at the lower end of the range for dunes. Rates of carbon sequestration within UK Saltmarshes are even higher, storing 0.64–2.19 t C/ha/yr (Cannell *et al.* 1999). In accreting systems, Saltmarshes have the potential for long-term storage of carbon (Shepherd *et al.* 2007). These three habitats may also emit greenhouse gases to an unknown extent. In Saltmarsh, methane emissions are thought to be negligible due to sulphate inhibition of methanogenesis, but nitrous oxide emissions may be important (Andrews *et al.* 2006). In Coastal Lagoons, Mitchell *et al.* (2007) demonstrated

Figure 11.8 Disastrous consequences of losing a protective Shingle beach. Hallsands village, South Devon, in 1894—a postcard by Valentine and Sons. The beach protects the village from erosion. The loss of the beach followed shingle removal offshore. 1904—the village after a series of storms. The house indicated by the arrow was inhabited in 1994 when the third picture was taken. Today there is no public access to what remains of the houses for safety reasons. *Photos courtesy of J.P. Doody; www. hallsands.org.uk/*

the role of salinity stratification on the trapping of sediments at the muddy tidal limits of Pagham Harbour, Sussex. The net effect on climate regulation is likely to be beneficial; however, the contribution to climate regulation is probably small at the UK scale due to the low total area of these habitats. Coastal Margin vegetation and soils (to 15 cm) are estimated to hold at least 7.24 million tonnes of carbon (CEH unpublished), but this figure considerably underestimates the carbon storage component in Saltmarsh soils where soil depth remains largely unquantified.

11.3.2.3 Water quality regulation
This occurs through the purification of groundwater by Sand Dunes, Machair and Shingle, and the purification of surface waters by Saltmarsh and Coastal Lagoons. Sand Dunes are used for water purification in the Netherlands (van Dijk 1989), and similar natural filtration processes almost certainly remove nutrients from groundwater in the UK, thus reducing diffuse pollution to the marine environment; however, this is not well studied. Physical, chemical and biological processing in Saltmarsh (Andrews *et al.* 2006; Andrews *et al.* 2008; Boorman 2009) and saline Coastal Lagoons (Mitchell *et al.* 2007) removes nutrients from seawater, river water, groundwater and land-derived flows from agricultural land. Some lagoon systems (for example, the Fleet), have been overloaded with nutrients for some time (at least 140 years for nitrogen), but the ecosystem has adjusted to this eutrophic condition (Weber *et al.* 2006).

11.3.2.4 Soil quality regulation
This is provided by those habitats where soil development, and, therefore, the accumulation of soil organic matter, is rapid. However, since these are often dynamic environments, localised destruction of established soils also occurs. Where more fertile soils occur on Sand Dunes, Saltmarsh and Machair, they can support low intensity agriculture; today, this type of farming is often maintained by agri-environment schemes. Traditional mixed agriculture is possible on Machair by striking a fine balance between the rates of recycled sand deposition, the application of seaweed fertiliser and the cropping regime (Angus 2009). Cliff-top vegetation plays an important role in preventing surface soil erosion (Brenner-Guillermo 2007), and probably acts as a buffer in the prevention of erosion of adjacent agricultural land, especially where this inclines towards the sea.

11.3.2.5 Air quality regulation
Taller vegetation types scavenge more particulates and aerosols from the atmosphere than short vegetation, partly due to their greater leaf area index (Petroff *et al.* 2008); on a local scale, this acts to regulate and improve air quality. The Coastal Margin habitats are oligotrophic (nutrient-poor) and are generally a sink for ammonia (Loubet *et al.* 2009). However, agricultural stock grazing on Saltmarsh, Sand Dunes and Machair may be a low-level local source of ammonia, and some ammonia emissions may also occur from seaweed spreading on Machair.

11.3.2.6 Waste breakdown and detoxification
This service is primarily provided by Saltmarsh, where processes in the water column, sediment-trapping by vegetation and high rates of sediment accumulation all contribute to the immobilisation of heavy metals and other pollutants. This storage is not permanent and they can be remobilised as sediment is reworked, and may enter the food chain. In 54 ha of Saltmarsh in the Humber Estuary, 90 tonnes of zinc, 46 tonnes of lead, 16 tonnes of arsenic and 19 tonnes of copper have been recorded (Andrews *et al.* 2008).

11.3.2.7 Pollination, pest control, nursery grounds
Sand Dunes, Machair, Saltmarsh, Shingle and Sea Cliffs support a wide range of natural pollinators. Dunes and cliffs in particular support a high diversity of aculeate hymenoptera, including parasitoids (Whitehouse 2007; Howe *et al.* 2010). Together with ground predators, these may be of local importance in providing services of pollination and pest control to adjacent arable fields. However, the extent of these services is not well known and depends on the proximity of crop fields to these Coastal Margin habitats. Another biotic function which may be considered a regulating service is that of nursery grounds for fish species, provided by Coastal Lagoons with a good tidal exchange (Johnston & Gilliland 2000) and Saltmarsh, including managed realignment sites (Colclough *et al.* 2004). In a study on Essex Saltmarshes, commercially important species, such as herring (*Clupea harengus*) and sea bass (*Dicentrarchus labrax*), comprised 45.5% of the 14 species caught (Green *et al.* 2009). Lastly, certain characteristics of Coastal Margin habitats are key to their importance as breeding, feeding, migratory stopover sites or overwintering grounds for a wide range of bird species including wildfowl, several species of passerine and breeding shorebirds, seabirds and birds of prey. These characteristics include: relatively unimproved habitats; linear habitats with good connectivity which aids migrating species; frequent wetlands and damp pasture; bare, open ground for ground-nesting species; inaccessible rock ledges for cliff-nesting species; and islands uncolonised by ground predators. Machair, in particular, with its mosaic of crops, different stages of fallow and a lack of herbicides, provides a highly varied habitat for invertebrates and breeding birds.

11.3.2.8 Noise regulation
Direct regulation of noise pollution is provided by a varied topography, particularly in Sand Dunes and along coasts with Sea Cliffs. The exposure and subsequent high wind speeds in many of the habitats produce natural 'white noise' of wind over vegetation and the sound of the sea. These natural sounds are usually considered pleasant and contribute to the wilderness appeal of these habitats.

11.3.3 Cultural Services

11.3.4.1 Reasons for visiting the coast
A large part of the attraction to the coast hinges on its juxtaposition between land and sea. In the UK, human settlement is thought to have been based around the coastline, and the first Mesolithic peoples exploited the coastal environment for fish and shellfish (Gregory *et al.* 2005). Our view of the coast is shaped by history and cultural memories (explored in the television series 'Coast'), which are themselves partially dependent on other ecosystem services: provisioning (fish/shellfish, livestock/crops/wildfood, timber and biodiversity); and regulating (hazard/flood regulation, noise regulation). As an island nation, the coast has an important place in our national psyche—

negative associations include the threats of invasion, flooding and sea-level rise, while positive connotations include an empire based on naval strength, livelihoods such as fishing, and seaside holidays. The coast is highly valued by the public as: living space for coastal communities; a symbol of identity; a place for rest and relaxation; somewhere that provides a sense of freedom; a place where people can enjoy scenery and wildlife; and a site for specific activities including boating, swimming, walking, birdwatching, climbing and wildfowling (Ipsos Mori 2006). In 2005, there were around 250 million visits to the UK coast, of which, around one-third were to natural habitats such as beaches, sand dunes, shingle and cliffs (UKTS 2006; VisitBritain 2007). For 32% of visitors to the seaside in 2005, the key draw was sunbathing and paddling in the sea; eating and drinking came second by attracting 28% of visitors, and seaside towns and cities also drew 16% of visitors (VisitBritain 2007). Visitors to the Welsh seaside in 2006 were most interested in walking (69%), putting cultural and heritage interests second (32%) and shopping and entertainment third (25%), but closely followed by active land- and water-based sports (23%); wildlife-watching also attracted a number of visitors (5%) (VisitWales 2008). Tourists in Scotland rated seashores as representing the most freedom of use of all countryside destinations (TNS 2005); as a comparison, **Box 11.3** provides data on tourist-use of different coastal habitats in north Norfolk. The UK coast has many iconic landmarks, particularly related to Sea Cliffs, and is a focus for art, literature and creativity, for example, Anthony Gormley's sculptures in north-west England (**Figure 11.9**). Remote coastlines and islands have also been a focus for shrines, monastic settlements and holy sites for Christianity and earlier religions (e.g. Bardsey, Iona, Lindisfarne).

11.3.3.1 Economic value (and trends) in coastal tourism

Coastal areas generate substantial economic benefits. Pugh and Skinner (2002) valued coastal activities within the UK marine sector; most important was recreation and tourism: £19.2 billion, of which, seaside tourism revenue was £17 billion. In 2006, British residents took 27.1 million overnight seaside trips, of which, 22.5 million were holidays. The latter generated a tourism spend of £4.2 billion (£3.3 billion in England, £0.6 billion in Wales and £0.29 billion in Scotland). An additional 270 million day trips to the coast generated £3.1 billion in spending (www.britishresorts.

Box 11.3 Tourism case studies.

a) The Sefton Coast
The Sefton coast, north of Liverpool, has 4.5 million visits per year, generating £62.7 million towards the economy (Steward 2001). Of those visits, 26% came specifically to visit the beach. Information from a visitor survey at Ainsdale Sand Dunes National Nature Reserve (NNR) suggested that most people come to walk, relax and enjoy the scenery (one in five visitors mentions 'nature' as a reason for the visit). Annual visitor numbers at the principal Sand Dune nature reserves are 340,000 at Formby (National Trust), and 55,000 at Ainsdale Sand Dunes NNR.

b) Visitor spend on seabird-watching
Visitor spend was estimated at four Royal Society for the Protection of Birds (RSPB) seabird reserves around the UK (RSPB 2010; **Table 1**). Combined visitor numbers in 2009 at the four sites were 145,000, spending an estimated £1.2 million. The opportunity to watch seabirds was the main reason for visiting Bempton Cliffs, while it was just one of the reasons for visiting the other three sites.

Table 1 Visitor spend at seabird Royal Society for the Protection of Birds (RSPB) reserves around the UK. Source: RSPB (2010).

	Visitors in 2009	Estimated spend (£)
Bempton Cliffs, England	67,500	750,000
South Stack, Wales	44,000	223,000
Mull of Galloway, Scotland	19,000	126,000
Rathlin Island, Northern Ireland	14,500	115,000
Totals	**145,000**	**1,214,000**

c) The North Norfolk Coast
Holkham and Cley are coastal nature reserves forming part of the North Norfolk Coast SAC. Holkham is a wide sandy beach, fronting sand dunes and saltmarsh, receiving 500,000 visitors per year (English Nature 2003). Cley is a narrow, shingle beach, fronting saltmarsh and mudflats, receiving 25,000–100,000 visitors per year (Klein & Bateman 1998).

Visitor use and preferences were studied over 18 months by Coombes and Jones (2010). Dog walking was the predominant activity at these sites (**Table 2**), followed by walking. Birdwatching, relaxing/sunbathing and playing/paddling were minor activities. Remoteness was scored highly by all groups except those playing/paddling. Habitat preferences (Likert scores) were strongest for

Table 2 Visitor use and preferences. Source: based on Coombes & Jones (2010). Copyright (2010) reproduced with permission from Elsevier.

	Dog walkers	Walkers	Bird watchers	Relaxing or sunbathing	Playing or paddling
Major activity	57%	22%	14%	6%	1%
Habitats most used	Dunes	Dunes	Sand/shingle	Sand/shingle	Sand/shingle
Mean Likert preference scores by habitat (highest in bold):					
Sand	**1.3**	**1.2**	0.8	**1.1**	**1.3**
Rocks/rock-pools	0.0	0.4	0.6	0.6	0.0
Sand dunes	**1.3**	**1.2**	1.1	1.0	1.0
Saltmarsh	0.6	0.4	**1.4**	0.3	0.1
Cliffs	0.1	0.6	0.7	0.2	0.4

sand or sand dunes in all groups except birdwatchers who valued saltmarsh highest. At these sites, facilities such as tea rooms/large car parks were given low preference scores, although toilets scored slightly higher. All visitor activities were predicted to increase under climate change, despite beach fore-shortening under coastal erosion.

---

co.uk/tourismfacts.aspx) (Cooper 2009). The coastal share of domestic tourism is greatest in Wales (43%), somewhat lower in England (24%), but very low in Scotland (13%) (UKTS 2009). In Wales, the overall economic impact of the coastal environment equated, in 2005, to nearly 100,000 direct and indirect jobs, nearly £5 billion per annum income to businesses, and a contribution of £1.5 billion to Wales' Gross Domestic Product (GDP; Valuing our Environment Partnership 2006).

Coastal tourism is highly significant in the more remote areas of the UK where it can form a major source of employment and economic activity. In the Western Isles, tourist activity is mainly coastal in distribution, and, between 1999 and 2002, saw a 9% growth in tourist numbers and a 20% growth in value to £40 million per annum (Macpherson Research 2003), much of this strongly biased towards ecotourism. This value had increased to around £50 million per annum by 2006 (Taylor *et al.* 2010).

Coastal tourism in the UK increased during the early 1800s, a trend which continued after 1945, and peaked in the 1970s (Walton 2000). Since that peak, the number of tourism bed-nights at the coast has declined consistently (**Figure 11.10**), reflecting national trends for the population increasingly taking their main holiday abroad (Cooper 1997; Williams & Shaw 1997), but also reflecting the decline in the seaside share of domestic tourism in favour of cities and large towns (Williams & Shaw 2009). The downward trend in long stays is consistent in all regions (**Figure 11.11a**), but is not the whole picture, and is partially offset by an increase in short stays and day visits (**Figure 11.11b**), facilitated by rising private car ownership (Williams & Shaw 2009). In Wales, day visits increased from 1 million in 1993 to 2.2 million in 2006 (Welsh Assembly Government 2008). Long-term trends in tourism as a pressure are discussed in Section 11.2.5.

The seaside still remains a more popular destination in the UK than the countryside/villages for overnight stays, both in number of visits and in expenditure: in 2009, 24% (worth £4.8 billion) of UK overnight tourism expenditure occurred at the seaside compared with 18% (worth £3.4 billion) at the countryside (UKTS 2009). The value of overnight stays (**Figure 11.11c**) shows a further offset in the decline as rising disposable income means greater spend per visit. The value of day visits to the GB seaside in 2002 (**Figure 11.11d**), was £3.1 billion (GB Leisure Day Visits 2004). In England, seaside visits were worth £2.2 billion in 2005, and comprised 7% of the market share. This was roughly half the value of overnight stays and less than the value of visits to the countryside (worth £4 billion, 16% of market share) (VisitBritain 2007). However, people were prepared to travel for considerably longer on day trips to coastal areas, with a mean journey time of 3.4 hours to the seaside compared with 2 hours to the countryside (VisitBritain 2007). Although long-term trends in tourism patterns and spend are apparent, they are difficult to quantify. Since 2005, a consistent methodology has been applied through the United Kingdom Tourism Survey to estimate overnight stays, but no such survey exists to quantify day visits. Prior to 2005, sporadic data collection, changing survey methodologies and incomplete sampling across the UK preclude accurate quantification of national trends.

Figure 11.9 'Another Place' coastal art installation by Anthony Gormley. One hundred life-sized cast-iron figures exploring man's relationship with nature. Crosby Beach, north-west England, 2006. *Photo courtesy of L. Jones.*

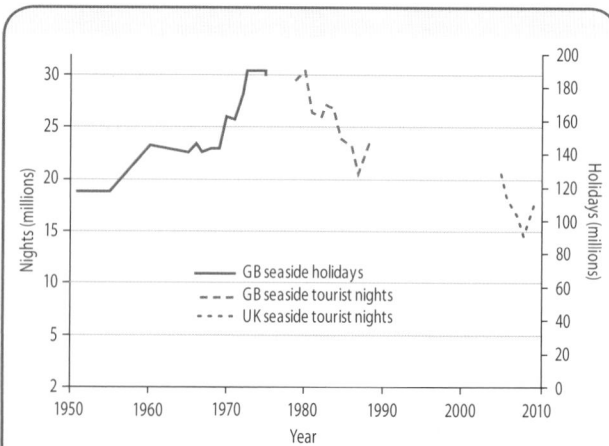

Figure 11.10 Coastal tourism, showing long-term trends in the number of seaside holidays (primary axis) in GB, 1951 to 1974*, seaside holiday nights (secondary axis) in GB, 1979 to 1988†, and UK, 2005 to 2009‡. Number of seaside holidays assumes seaside market share of 75% of GB main holidays in 1968 (British Travel Association 1968). Source: data from British National Travel Survey (1976), reported in Demetriadi (1997)*; Wales Tourist Board (1992), reported in Cooper (1997)†; UKTS (2009)‡.

UK National Ecosystem Assessment

Projections for coastal tourism are that long, main holidays by UK residents are likely to be static in volume or decline, but growth in short breaks and additional holiday markets will be sustained. Specialised activities for the elderly, the active and environmentally aware are likely to increase (VisitWales 2008; Williams & Shaw 2009). Visitor numbers are likely to be higher in warmer summers under climate change, despite reductions in beach area due to sea-level rise (Coombes & Jones 2010).

In contrast to the trend of a general decline in overnight leisure visits to the coast, over the last decade, the demand for specialist activities that require specific habitats has increased. These include coastal hiking, birdwatching, whale-watching and extreme sports such as cliff-climbing, sand-yachting and coasteering (Mintel 2005, 2008). The biodiversity, landscapes and wildness of coastal habitats make them a focus for statutory protection as nature reserves, or for management by Non-governmental Organisations (NGOs) such as the National Trust, the Royal Society for the Protection of Birds (RSPB) and The Wildlife Trusts. There are five coastal National Parks and 26 coastal Areas of Outstanding Natural Beauty (AONBs) in England, Wales and Northern Ireland. England and Wales have 45 Heritage Coasts covering 1,500 km of coastline. The National Trust owns 900 km of coast in England, Wales and Northern Ireland. Scotland has 415 coastal SSSIs covering 290,000 ha and 33 NNRs covering 41,000 ha (Cooper 2009). These underline the importance that society attaches to coastal habitats and the biodiversity they support. The text below discusses specific habitat characteristics underlying the cultural services described above.

11.3.3.2 Sand Dunes

Everard *et al.* (2010) discuss in detail the ecosystem services provided by dunes. Sand Dunes are a very distinctive landscape, with some form of dunes backing many of the sandy beaches in the UK. Dunes and beaches are a major part of the reason for visiting the coast, including seaside towns (VisitBritain 2007; Coombes & Jones 2010). The Sefton Coast, north of Liverpool, has 4.5 million visits per year, generating £62.7 million towards the economy (Steward 2001; **Box 11.3**). As well as tourism and leisure, the cultural services provided by dunes include archaeological (heritage) interest, aesthetic value and artistic inspiration (e.g. poems by Robert Frost and Carl Sandburg) (Everard *et al.* 2010). Dunes and sandy beaches also provide a wide range of amenity uses and activities including playing, paddling, sunbathing, walking, dog walking, cycling, horse riding, athletics training, orienteering and nudism (VisitBritain 2007; VisitWales 2008; Coombes & Jones 2010; Everard *et al.* 2010). Dunes modified by afforestation or by golf courses can provide amenity and recreation of significant financial value. Golf courses in Scotland have an estimated gross value added (GVA) figure of £120 million, but the proportion attributable to courses on dunes is not known. The unique biodiversity and ecology of dunes provides a focus for education (understanding succession theory, for example: Cowles 1899; Clements 1916; Connell & Slatyer 1977) and for encouraging membership of conservation organisations. Along with beaches, they are probably the semi-natural habitat directly experienced by the greatest number of people in the UK.

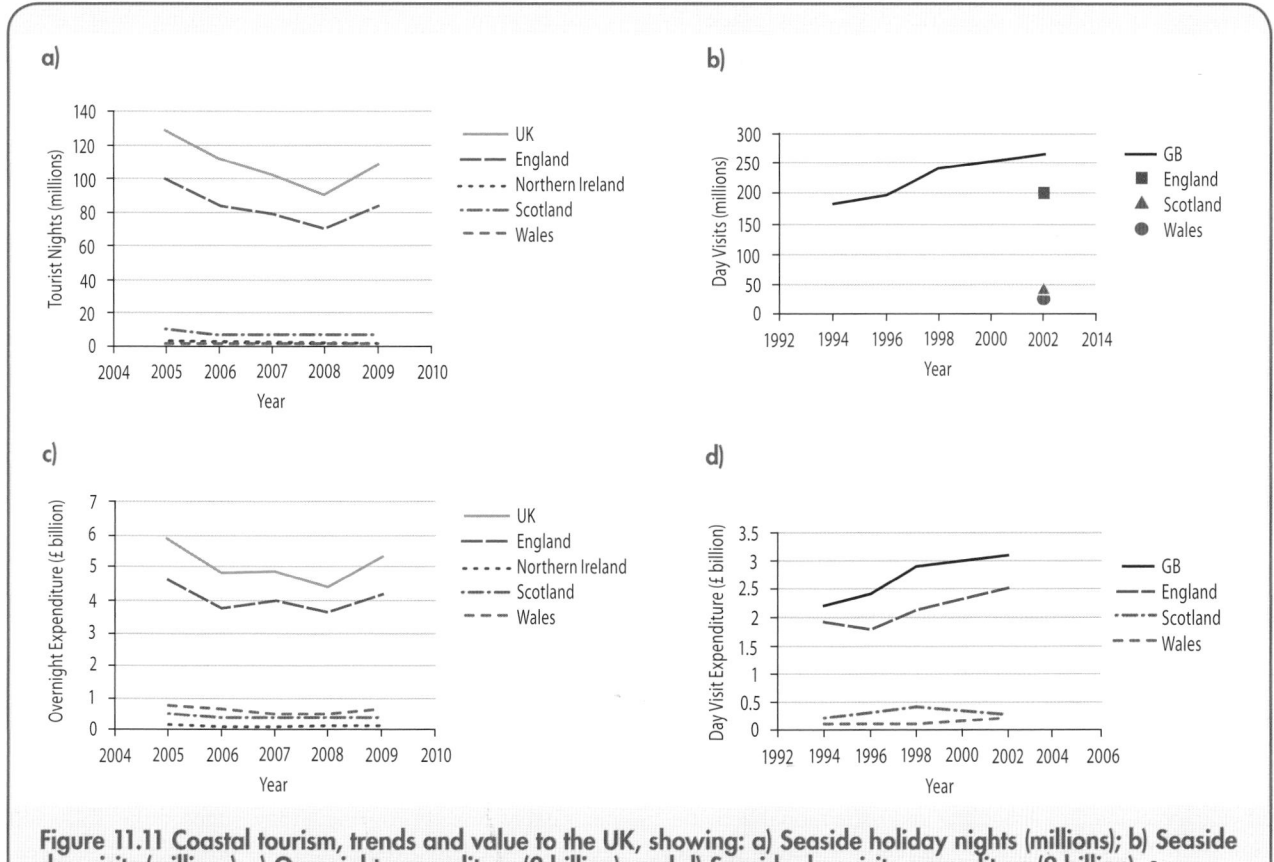

Figure 11.11 Coastal tourism, trends and value to the UK, showing: a) Seaside holiday nights (millions); b) Seaside day visits (millions); c) Overnight expenditure (£ billion); and d) Seaside day visits expenditure (£ billion). Source: data from a) UKTS (2009); b) GB Leisure Day Visits (2004); c) UKTS (2009) and d) GB Leisure Day Visits (2004).

11.3.3.3 Machair

The cultural services provided by Machair are extensive and deeply rooted within Gaelic culture. The flatlands of the sea remain interwoven within a storytelling and song tradition that extends back into legend (Angus 2001). Indeed, most modern and archaeological burial sites in the Western Isles are on Machair. Thus this 'wild' landscape has strong historical and cultural connotations for both communities and visitors because of the overpowering sense that Machair has been 'lived in'—shaped by past generations of Gaels whose traditions remain. There even exists a BBC ALBA television soap called Machair! Partly for these cultural reasons, and partly for the isolation and perceived emptiness of hectares of grass and meadow plants fronted by sweeps of brilliant white shell-sand beaches, coastal tourism is very important to Machair communities. Much of the ecotourism expansion of recent years is Machair-based, providing a wide range of amenity uses and activities including ornithology, walking, surfing, angling, cycling, horse riding, caravanning and wild camping. A few golf courses exist on Machair but these are neither extensive nor numerous.

11.3.3.4 Saltmarsh

Saltmarshes are wild places, creating iconic landscapes depicted in art and literature. There is a long history of landscape art depicting saltmarshes, usually associated with wild geese and ducks and hunting; some of the most famous examples are by Sir Peter Scott. In literature, *The Snow Goose* by Paul Gallico was one of the most popular fiction/natural history crossover books of the last century, inspired by the Saltmarsh landscapes of south-east England.

Access to Saltmarsh is restricted in many places by coastal defences and/or adjacent agricultural land, with designated nature reserves receiving the majority of visitors. Visitors are generally dominated by those with natural history interest and remain near the landward edges of the habitat. The UK's estuaries (including mudflats; Chapter 12) are internationally important for their vast numbers of overwintering waterbirds (Cayford & Waters 1996; Rehfisch *et al.* 2003), attracted by a combination of productive wetlands and relatively mild winters. Many are designated SSSI/ASSI, SPA or Ramsar sites specifically for wildfowl. A new nature reserve created in 2002 provided public access to The Wash; it attracted more than 50,000 visits in its second year of opening, with visitors spending an estimated £500,000 locally on food and services (Manly 2004). Hunting wildfowl is a traditional sport, still practised on all the major Saltmarsh complexes in the UK. There may be adverse health implications of stored pollutants transferred via Saltmarsh food products, but this is not well studied.

11.3.3.5 Shingle

Shingle structures provide landscapes that reflect the power of the sea. Their dynamic nature can inspire wonder. They provide excellent examples of coastal processes and are often used for outdoor education. Shingle beaches also provide locations for sunbathing and recreational activities (Spurgeon 1999). Estimates of recreational value for Cley Marshes (a site with shingle, saltmarsh and mudflats) ranged from £40,000–£480,000 per annum (Klein & Bateman 1998).

Other recreational and cultural values include stark and remote coastal landscapes used in advertising, provision of access to the sea, areas for boat-mooring, and a local amenity for walking (Coates *et al.* 2001). Some areas are not only remote, but also have a significant historical value, e.g. Orford Ness due to its association with wartime activities, weapons testing and use of radar. Coastal gravel pits, once restored, can be important birdwatching areas; some also provide opportunities for sailing and windsurfing.

11.3.3.6 Sea Cliffs

In addition to having important value for nature conservation in their near natural state (Howe 2002; Whitehouse 2007; Howe *et al.* 2008), Sea Cliffs often have tremendous aesthetic (heritage) value, such as the iconic coastal 'cliffscapes' of The White Cliffs of Dover in England, Stockpole Head in Wales, the Old Man of Hoy in Scotland and the Giants Causeway in Northern Ireland. They are widely recognised for their geological or geomorphological interest and the majority are notified as geological SSSIs, with some having higher status as Geological Conservation Review (GCR) sites (May & Hansom 2003). However, their ecological importance, and in particular their invertebrate interest, is less well known. They support much of the length of the UK's numerous coastal paths and provide a human interest focus due to dramatic scenery and clear views. High seabird densities on cliffs and islands provide opportunities for birdwatching, with UK coasts supporting around 8 million breeding seabirds every year (RSPB 2010). Visitor spend to watch seabirds on cliffs at four RSPB reserves was estimated at more than £1.2 million in 2009 (RSPB 2010; **Box 11.3**). Cliffs also facilitate specific activities such as whale-watching, walking, coasteering, climbing, and fossil collecting, particularly along the Jurassic Coast in Dorset and in north-east England; the East Devon and Dorset coast is, in fact, a World Heritage Site. In addition, the inaccessibility of most islands is a key part of their allure, and also their nature conservation potential since disturbance by humans is minimal.

11.3.3.7 Coastal Lagoons

Cultural services are provided through the aesthetic value of lagoons. There is a diverse range of contemporary recreational activities. In resort towns they are used as boating lakes and natural swimming pools, and can become intensively developed around their shorelines with waterfront properties, marinas, jetties and quays. Other lagoons are important for scientific research, education and activities such as birdwatching, wildfowling and fishing. Between 1997 and 2002, visitor numbers to the Porlock Visitor Centre averaged 40,000–50,000 per year (Jennings 2004); Abbotsbury Swannery (www.dorsetforyou.com/index.jsp?articleid=332842) attracted around 100,000 visitors per year between 1999 and 2002.

11.3.4 Supporting Services

Primary production, nutrient cycling and soil formation are inextricably linked. Together, they support the soil- and vegetation-mediated regulating and provisioning services. Water cycling, combined with the first three services, helps to maintain those regulating services involving water and the provisioning services which are dependent on water flows/quality/biota, as well as soils and vegetation. These supporting services are common to all UK NEA Broad Habitats and are discussed in Chapter 13. However, sediment supply and transport, discussed elsewhere in this chapter (Section 11.2.1), could also be considered a physical supporting service as it is fundamental to the existence of the Coastal Margin habitats and to the delivery of a wide range of ecosystem services.

Coastal Margins often provide supporting functions to other margin, marine or terrestrial habitats, or are supported by them. The fringing cordon of Sand Dunes provides coastal defence for Machair. Shingle is a significant part of the wider coastal ecosystem, providing the basis for services associated with Sand Dunes, Saltmarsh and Mudflats. Shingle can form the backbone of sand dune spits and bars, and provide shelter for lagoons and for the sedimentation of tidal mudflats and the growth of saltmarshes (**Figure 11.5**). Erosion of soft cliffs provides a source of sediment, maintaining other Coastal Margin

habitats which are linked by sediment transport (Dawson *et al.* 2009). Sediment storage and transport occurs in both the marine and terrestrial zones, with the greatest exchange between beaches and adjacent dunes and shingle structures during storms. Saltmarsh provides nutrient and silica exchanges with the sea between the marsh itself and the water column, providing resources for primary production in nearshore communities (Boorman *et al.* 1996; Andrews *et al.* 2006; Struyf *et al.* 2006; Shepherd *et al.* 2007).

11.3.5 The Role of Wild Species Diversity

The Coastal Margin contains a very wide diversity of ecological niches (Howe 2002; Whitehouse 2007; Howe *et al.* 2008; Everard *et al.* 2010). The dynamic nature of these habitats means that they provide among the best examples of early successional environments in the UK. They support a wide range of highly specialised and distinctive species due to the harsh environmental gradients associated with their proximity to the sea (**Box 11.4**). Their general unsuitability for agricultural development means that they

---

Box 11.4 Wild species diversity in Coastal Margin habitats.

Sand Dunes

Sand Dune habitats in the UK support a wide range of species, including more than 680 Red Data Book or Nationally Rare/Scarce invertebrate species alone (Howe *et al.* 2010). These include the vernal sand-mining bee (*Colletes cunicularius*), dune tiger beetle (*Cicindela maritima*) and various spiders (e.g. wolf spider *Arctosa cinerea*) (Archer 1994; Houston 2008). Red Data Book vertebrate species include the natterjack toad (*Epidalea calamita*), and sand lizard (*Lacerta agilis*) (Brooks & Agate 2001; Denton *et al.* 2003). Plant species of conservation importance include fen orchid (*Liparis loeselii*) (Jones 1998) and the Annex II-listed liverwort *Petalophyllum ralfsii* (petalwort).

Machair

The following UK BAP priority species have significant populations on Machair: skylark (*Alauda arvensis*), corncrake (*Crex crex*), corn bunting (*Miliaria calandra*), the beetle *Protapion ryei,* great yellow bumble bee (*Bombus distinguendu*), northern colletes (*Colletes floralis*), slender naiad (*Najas flexilis*), and Shetland pondweed (*Potamogeton rutilus*).

Saltmarsh

The following UK BAP priority species have significant populations on Saltmarsh: the eyebright (*Euphrasia heslop-harrisonii*), ground beetles *Amara strenua* and *Anisodactylus poeciloides*, natterjack toad, narrow-mouth whorl snail (*Vertigo angustior*) and endemic sea-lavenders (*Limonium* species).

Shingle

Mobile and stable Shingle provides habitats for a unique and fascinating flora and invertebrate fauna. At least 11 shingle-specialist taxa occur in the UK, of which four are endemic (Shardlow 2001). Neon pictus, a rare spider, has only one site in the UK, which is on Shingle. Breeding terns, plovers and oystercatchers rely on bare shingle.

Sea Cliffs

Maritime cliffs and slopes support 26 priority species, with a further 59 priority species using the habitat (Simonson & Thomas 1999). Nine UK BAP priority invertebrates are restricted to, or strongly associated with, soft cliffs including Luccombe click beetle (*Anostirus castaneus*), large mason bee (*Osmia xanthomelana*), chalk carpet moth (*Scotopteryx bipunctaria*), and Glanville fritillary butterfly (*Melitaea cinxia*) (Whitehouse 2007). Around 8 million seabirds from 26 species, including gannets, terns, and puffins, breed in the UK. The UK and Ireland support 90% of the world's Manx shearwaters (*Puffinus puffinus*) and 68% of the world's northern gannets (*Morus bassanus*).

Coastal Lagoons

Lagoon specialists include lagoon cockle (*Cerastoderma glaucum*) (Ivell 1979) and the snail *Hydrobia/Ventrosia ventrosa*. Some 36 species (of algae, vascular plants, Cnidaria, Bryozoa, Polychaeta, Mollusca, Crustacea, Coleoptera, Diptera and birds) are particularly associated with saline lagoons. Of these, 25 rely entirely on lagoonal habitats, and 20 are Red Data Book listed (Barnes 1989b; Symes & Robertson 2004).

North Wales coast. *Photo courtesy of L Jones.*

---

form important refugium habitats for species lost from other lowland habitats. This biological diversity supports a number of services. Directly, these habitats supply wild food and commercially harvestable resources, and provide living space to charismatic species like puffins or orchids which are a strong focus for many cultural services and can provide significant economic value through visitor spend (RSPB 2010). Indirectly, they modify the ecosystem level processes underlying the regulating services including sea defence, pest control and pollination. Their biological diversity forms part of the reason why so much of the UK coastline is under statutory protection.

11.4 Trade-offs and Synergies Among Coastal Margins Goods and Ecosystem Services

A large proportion of the area of Coastal Margin habitats has SAC protection under the Habitats Directive, is protected within SSSIs, or comes under other designations such as AONBs. Therefore, protection and maintenance of the biodiversity, geomorphological interest and unspoilt character remain primary objectives. Evaluation of the likely synergies and trade-offs for Sand Dunes (**Table 11.5**) are typical for most of the Coastal Margin habitats and show the potential for clear synergies between different services, allowing the identification of 'win-win' combinations. Synergistic services are clearly linked to similar geomorphological and ecological processes, with disturbance and natural dynamics promoting one set of services, while natural and artificial stability promote another set. This dichotomy also defines the principal conflicts: in general, the disturbance resulting from natural processes provides the essential dynamics in a healthy system which is usually beneficial for biodiversity, but may place constraints on other services. Therefore, a balance is required, particularly if there is insufficient room to allow natural processes to operate, or where there is conflict with fixed assets or infrastructure such as ports. By contrast, some natural processes like succession also promote stability. The optimum balance between disturbance and stability differs according to the habitat characteristics and the requirements of society. Other conflicts occur between those services causing deterioration of other services, for example excessive water abstraction, or altered water quality; those services promoting single use of land versus multi-functional uses; and those services which enhance or maintain the coastal margin 'character' versus those which replace it with characteristics available elsewhere.

Timescales of use and extent of use are both relevant issues. For example, small-scale turf-cutting or aggregate extraction are damaging but may create new habitat in the long-term. Synergies are, therefore, complex, and depend on the intensity of use and the timescales over which benefits are assessed.

11.4.1 Sand Dunes

Table 11.5 lists the main trade-offs and synergies for dunes, with key points discussed here. Land uses which involve major change to the functioning of dunes, such as forestry, golf courses and sand extraction, are incompatible with maintaining a characteristic dune landscape, although some are more multi-functional than others.

Forestry on dunes increases carbon stocks in soils (Hill & Wallace 1989) and above-ground, but it reduces recharge to dune aquifers (Clarke & Sanitwong 2010), potentially threatening the conservation status of adjoining dune slack habitat. Forestry adds to amenity value by providing a diversity of possible activities, but these are generally forest-related and not specific to the Coastal Margin habitat. Forest replaces natural dune habitat, although a few dune rarities persist and can thrive in forest, for example, dune helleborine (*Epipactis leptochila* var. *dunensis*) in the plantation at Newborough Warren. However, the net effect of dune forestry on wild species diversity is negative. Invertebrate diversity at Newborough Warren is far higher in the dunes than in the forest. The dunes support around 80% of over 900 beetle species found within the SAC (Loxton 2010), despite covering a similar area to the plantation forest. Red squirrels (*Sciurus vulgaris*) have been re-introduced into the dune conifer plantation at Newborough Warren (Ogden *et al.* 2005), and there is a population in the dune plantations at Ainsdale and Formby on the Sefton coast. Interactions between dune (coniferous) forestry and dune habitats, and the relative proportions of each, remain contentious in the UK, particularly within the context of UK BAP targets to restore 1,000 ha of degraded dunes by 2010 and to create Atlantic Dune Woodland at two sites by 2015.

High groundwater levels are undesirable for golf and some golf courses abstract water for irrigation; however, if water tables are lowered, potential conflicts with dune slack biodiversity may arise. Replacement of natural dune habitat, fertilisation, minimising natural erosion processes and the control of rabbit populations on golf courses are all activities which occur to the detriment of most dune species, although sensitive management of the roughs can protect older dune habitats such as acid dune grassland and dune heath (Simpson *et al.* 2001) and can retain some open dunescapes (i.e. landscape as well as habitats).

Disturbance caused by military use interrupts soil carbon accumulation, but at low levels, disturbance benefits wild species diversity by promoting the area of early successional habitats (Baker 2001). The restricted public access on golf courses, industrial and military sites limits amenity-related cultural services.

Large-scale but largely non-destructive uses, such as grazing, water abstraction and amenity use, also impact on other services. Grazing prevents invasion of scrub and benefits plant diversity (van Dijk 1992; Plassmann *et al.* 2010), and, through small-scale disturbance, benefits some vertebrate, invertebrate and fungal diversity (Howe *et al.* 2010). Surprisingly, it has negative effects on a number of other services: stock are incompatible with forestry, golf and sand-extraction; the public are often fearful of large livestock, dogs can worry animals, and fencing hinders public access; and disturbance to soils disrupts carbon accumulation.

Over-abstraction of groundwater impacts on wild species diversity in dune slacks, and may reduce carbon accumulation rates which are faster in wet slacks than dry grassland (Jones *et al.* 2008). This may become more of an issue where water scarcity is increased due to climate change and rising demand.

Maintaining dunes as a coastal defence on all but the largest sites involves maintaining a continuous vegetated foredune ridge, which reduces wind speeds and sand supply to the rest of the dune system and promotes stabilisation. This benefits commercial grazing and carbon accumulation,

Table 11.5 Trade-offs and synergies for final ecosystem services in Sand Dunes. = No effect, - Minor negative or net negative if mixed, -- Strong negative, + Minor positive or net positive if mixed, ++ Strong positive, +/- Balanced positive/negative. Note: scores should not be summed due to potential double-counting across services. P=Provisioning service, R=Regulating service, C=Cultural service. Waste breakdown not relevant to dunes.

			Livestock related	Wild food	Forestry	Sand extraction	Military; pipelines	Climate regulation	Water quantity	Hazard regulation –vegetation & other habitats	Waste breakdown & detoxification	Wild species diversity including microbes	Purification	Environmental Settings: Meaningful places inc. green & blue space	Golf courses	Other amenity activities
			P		P			R	P R	R	R	P R	R	C	C	
P	Crops, plants, livestock, fish, etc. (wild and domesticated)	Livestock related		=	-*	--	=	-	=	=		++	- †	- ‡	--	- ‡
		Wild food			±	--	=	=	=	=		++	=	+	=	+
P	Trees, standing vegetation & peat	Forestry				--	±¶	+	-	+		-	=	+	--	+
		Sand extraction					--	--	-	--		±§	=	-	--	--
		Military; pipelines						-	=	=		++	- †	-	--	-
R	Climate regulation								=	++		--	=	-	+	-
P R	Water quantity									=		=	+	=	±	=
R	Hazard regulation –vegetation & other habitats											-	=	±	++	±
R	Waste breakdown & detoxification															
P R	Wild species diversity including microbes												=	+	±	+
R	Purification													=	- †	=
C	Environmental Settings: places (inc. green & blue space)														- **	++
C	Environmental Settings: landscapes and waterscapes	Golf courses														- **
		Other amenity activities														

* Stock damage young trees; trees limit grazing; † Potential faecal/chemical contamination of water; ‡ People are afraid of stock, fences hinder access; ¶ Woodland neutral for military use, but restricts pipeline laying; § Sand extraction removes habitat, but creates early successional habitat afterwards; ** Golf courses restrict access, management options and modify the natural dune landscape.

but is detrimental to wild species diversity. Where a continuous, high, frontal dune is not maintained, dunes still provide coastal defence, but this function may vary spatially and the level of protection is less predictable (Lee, 2001).

The interaction of amenity uses with other services depends on their intensity. At low intensity, most uses are compatible with other services, while at high intensity amenity uses can conflict with each other (e.g. horse riding and walking) and with other services. Limited disturbance may benefit wild species diversity in over-stabilised systems, but excessive disturbance disrupts carbon accumulation and wild species diversity, and may reduce the effectiveness of coastal defence since pressure is concentrated on particular areas such as beach access through the foredune (Doody 1989; Coombes & Jones 2010).

11.4.2 Machair
Many of the trade-offs and synergies that affect Sand Dunes also affect Machair. Services involving major land use change, such as golf courses and sand extraction, are incompatible with maintaining a characteristic Machair landscape and usage, although golf courses are more multi-functional than other uses. The few golf courses that exist on Machair (e.g. at Askernish, South Uist and Sanday, Orkney) tend to be managed in a traditional and conservation-friendly fashion, and promote the grazing of fairways by sheep (but not cattle). However, this has not prevented crofters viewing such developments as impinging on their rights of common grazing to deploy cattle onto the Machair, and has resulted in their mounting challenges to development. Limited military disturbance benefits wild species diversity (Baker 2001) in much the same way that cattle-grazing promotes disruption of the turf cover and favours biodiversity.

Removal of sand from Machair for local constructional activity also creates trade-offs. Importing sand from the mainland to the islands, or even to remoter parts of the mainland, is cost-prohibitive. But since the only source of economically viable construction sand is contained within the extensive Machair systems, this sand is viewed as an exploitable resource (Merritt & Cavill 1993). Machair habitat and species conservationists recognise the critically important role played by crofting in maintaining Machair biodiversity, and also that the skilled, active crofting that delivers biodiversity must be an integral part of a healthy socioeconomic system. Any blanket prohibition of sand removal threatens the viability of local building and so the viability of the crofting communities themselves.

Machair is part of a highly complex system of mutually supportive ecosystem services: readily available seaweed supplies both reverse nutrient deficiencies in the Machair soils and provide a contribution to coast protection, while still retaining the natural mobility of the system.

11.4.3 Saltmarsh
The intensity of grazing by livestock and other herbivores (such as migratory geese and brown hares) produces trade-offs between meat production, biodiversity, conservation, climate regulation and coastal defence. Grazing impacts on vegetation structure and species-composition, both directly through feeding, and indirectly through habitat modification

as a result of trampling and soil compaction (Bos *et al.* 2005). Soil compaction impacts on processes relating to carbon cycling, some of which have conflicting implications for climate regulation. High intensity livestock-grazing reduces litter deposition, and organic matter returned as faeces rapidly decomposes; collectively, these factors depress carbon storage. On the other hand, the absence of grazing or low intensity grazing can lead to the domination of the plant community by productive grass species with decreased biodiversity value, faster decomposition rates and, therefore, lower carbon accumulation. Hence grazing intensity can be an effective regulator of biodiversity, with intermediate levels usually producing the most diverse assemblages and structure.

Vegetation structure also impacts on the ability of saltmarshes to trap sediment and, therefore, store nutrients and pollutants, and adjust to changing sea levels. Although saltmarsh width remains the most important variable, the potential for grazing to influence coastal protection is important. High intensity grazing reduces shore zonation, transforming plant communities with a variable structure into homogenous lawns dominated by short grass, which reduces the ability of the marsh to dissipate wave energy. Low grazing intensity increases vegetation patchiness and overall plant height, creating increasing wave friction. Saltmarsh biodiversity, coastal protection and climate regulatory services exist in trade-off against meat production. High diversity assemblages are often more productive, which would be expected to lead to greater below-ground biomass and carbon sequestration. Very low grazing pressure may, however, lead to higher biomass and the greatest wave attenuation.

There are trade-offs to be made between the protection of material assets and infrastructure on the coast and the services Saltmarshes provide. Assets worth about £120 billion are currently at risk from flooding and coastal erosion in England and Wales. The UK governmental budget for managing flood risk and coastal erosion for 2009–2010 is £800 million (Defra 2009).

11.4.4 Shingle
So long as the Shingle beach or structure has room to move, then the goods and services will remain largely unimpaired. However, sea defence requirements and shingle reprofiling may prevent this movement, resulting in a loss of natural values such as the "Annual vegetation of drift lines": a key element for designating Shingle SACs (JNCC 2007). Rising sea levels, increasing costs and a more enlightened approach to the value of the 'natural' environment for coastal defence are shifting this paradigm, and artificial coastal defences are no longer sacrosanct. This is important since there is currently a shortage of sediment in many coastal cells and an increasing risk of over-washing and breaching (Orford *et al.* 2001). As a result, other, more environmentally friendly, 'soft' approaches, such as beach nourishment, have less impact and may help create conditions for shingle beach vegetation to develop. However, this will require more sediment material, putting pressure on the diminishing supplies offshore and on land-based resources.

Solutions that are more radical can involve a trade-off between different habitats. At Cley, on the North Norfolk coast, reprofiling of a shingle ridge complex for sea defence purposes adversely affected shingle beach vegetation forming part of an SSSI and SAC. Following detailed appraisal of alternatives, a £7 million management scheme to create a new defence inland was dropped in favour of a modified scheme involving 'limited intervention'. This will result in the gradual reduction of grazing marsh and reedbed as the ridge moves landward. More frequent overtopping by the sea will help recreate saline lagoons, saltmarsh and shingle wash-over fans (www.eclife.naturalengland.org.uk/). This occurred despite reservations about the trade-off between maintenance costs (£20,000–£30,000 per annum) and an estimated loss in recreational value (£40,000–£120,000, assuming 25,000 visits per year) to a popular freshwater nature reserve (Klein & Bateman 1998).

There is also a significant trade-off with gravel extraction. This replaces stable and often undisturbed vegetated shingle ridges with areas of open water. Man-made gravel pits can develop a significant interest, especially for waterbirds, and some may become nature reserves in their own right. However, the new habitat and coastal bird populations that colonise these areas, and the opportunity for water-based sports activities, do not represent an acceptable trade-off for the loss of rare coastal vegetated Shingle from a nature conservation perspective.

At Dungeness, water abstraction has lowered the water table and saline intrusion threatens the water supply. This has resulted in changes in species composition of some of the low-lying fresh water 'open pits' of high nature conservation value. Reducing water abstraction in the face of rising sea levels may be required.

Walking with or without dogs is a significant activity affecting Shingle beaches (Coombes & Jones 2010). Often the crest of the beach is the most attractive. Unfortunately, it is here that some of the more important plants such as sea pea (*Lathyrus japonicus*), or lichens on Scottish gravel complexes, occur. Trampling causes significant disturbance, with the loss of sea pea in some areas. Trampling also affects ground-nesting terns and ringed plover (*Charadrius hiaticula*) on Shingle. In many places, especially on the east coast, nesting areas are roped-off to avoid such damage.

11.4.5 Sea Cliffs

The fundamental trade-offs occur between services requiring a stable coastline (agriculture, built infrastructure and, to a certain extent, amenity and recreation use of footpaths) and services requiring natural dynamics (erosion, sediment supply for natural coastal defence structures, biological diversity). Since Sea Cliffs are such a narrow, linear habitat, the greatest conflicts occur between services provided by cliffs and those provided by the adjacent non-cliff habitats—primarily agriculture, but some built infrastructure. Likewise, attempts to control cliff erosion affect sediment supply to other Coastal Margin habitats (Dawson *et al.* 2009), as well as negatively impacting the biodiversity and amenity services provided by cliffs themselves.

11.4.6 Coastal Lagoons

Because of their accessibility, Coastal Lagoons have historically experienced a range of demands on their ecosystem services. The fact that they still exist as functioning ecosystems indicates that some uses are compatible with a healthy ecosystem. Yet there are clearly other activities that are incompatible. The regulating service provided by lagoons for terrestrial pollutants compromises the lagoon ecosystem. The construction of dwellings and infrastructure adjacent to lagoons to take up their aesthetic services, damages those services themselves. In addition, there are potential conflicts between permanent developments and infrastructure sited adjacent to lagoons, and the ability of the lagoon to adapt to sea-level rise. Protection of these developments is often likely to be in conflict with the natural operation of the lagoon. Similarly, artificial regulation of water levels to prevent flooding of adjacent lands alters lagoon hydrography.

11.5 Options for Sustainable Management

11.5.1 Overview

In general, sustainable management should enhance or maintain the specific characteristics of the Coastal Margin habitat, rather than replicate services provided better elsewhere. It should also take into account the uniqueness and irreplaceability of services. The synergies and trade-offs show that win-win combinations of services can be achieved by identifying complementary services within the context of sustainable management of these largely natural systems. In this context, maximising economic value, or maximising diversity of service provision may not be appropriate. Two particular issues are pertinent to the sustainable management of coastal erosion and sea-level rise at all Coastal Margin habitats: sediment supply and managed realignment.

11.5.1.1 Sediment supply

Historically, sediment supply and sediment budgets have not been considered (Hansom 2001; Hansom & McGlashan 2004), or worse have been seen as a problem. However, the importance of the links between Coastal Margin habitats through sediment supply and transport are increasingly recognised. The principle of 'working with natural processes' in the EU recommendation on ICZM is fraught with problems due to different interpretations of the concept (Cooper & McKenna 2008). In the future, active sediment management is required within shoreline management planning. Sites with significant beach nourishment are already following this path using techniques like bypassing (Section 5.11.5.5) or re-nourishment, as are some estuaries, such as the Humber. In others, shoreline management planning will need to avoid interfering with natural sediment budgets. Due regard for sediment budgets needs to become universal to maximise the multiple benefits for all coastal habitats.

11.5.1.2 Managed realignment or roll-back

Managed realignment has primarily been applied to Saltmarshes; however, the principles are relevant to all the

Coastal Margin habitats, including Sea Cliffs and Coastal Lagoons (Lee, 2001). It has the potential to give them room to migrate inland with rising sea levels, and use their sea defence characteristics to reduce the cost of hard defences which can be set back behind the natural habitat if required. Although individual beneficiaries change, managed realignment is often a win-win situation if the wider set of ecosystem services are considered (**Box 11.2**). Managed realignment schemes in the Humber and Blackwater Estuaries pass the economic efficiency test, i.e. aggregate benefits outweigh the costs. However, sites or zones in which significant numbers of people, property and other cultural assets are potentially at risk present complex social decision-making contexts. In such circumstances, cost benefit analysis (CBA) will provide useful, but not necessarily decisive, information on trade-offs (Turner et al. 2007). The latest examples of managed realignment are multi-objective schemes developed in partnership with local organisations (www.abpmer.net/wallasea/). It is recognised that the land required for realignment must come from some other land use but, unless this occurs, the main loser will be the coastal habitats with their high biological diversity and high social and economic value.

11.5.2 Sand Dunes

While most large dune systems are designated SACs under the Habitats Directive, or are SSSIs, appropriate management may enhance both biodiversity and ecosystem services. Sympathetic management is particularly important for those sites lacking legal protection, where biodiversity may not be seen as a primary objective. Management for sea-level rise may include beach nourishment or roll-back options (Lee, 2001), and these requirements for sustainability need to be included in planning consents. Beach nourishment provides extra sediment to the system, bolstering the foredune and, therefore, coastal defence, and creating an element of sand mobility, providing new bare-sand habitat for early successional species. Allowing roll-back onto land purchased immediately inland of dune systems maintains dune area and the sea defence role of the dunes, and can create successionally young habitat. Passive roll-back measures would allow space for natural processes to create dune habitat over time, yet, given current climatic constraints (Jones et al. 2010a), natural processes are unlikely to achieve large-scale mobility. Therefore, active roll-back measures to restore or create dune habitat (for example, by topsoil inversion (Rhind et al. 2008; Jones et al. 2010b) or remobilisation schemes (Arens et al. 2004; Arens & Geelen 2006)) would be necessary. These measures will also benefit biodiversity in over-stabilised systems. Turf-cutting and dune slack reprofiling (Rhind et al. 2008) may protect biodiversity, and its related cultural services, against the drying out of dune slacks under climate change. This would not be necessary in a dynamic system where new slacks would form naturally, but intervention is required in over-stabilised systems.

With reference to **Table 11.5** showing trade-offs and synergies, maximising ecosystem services generally means avoiding large, single-use services, such as forestry and golf courses, and maximising the diversity of habitats. On the other hand, some services are scale-dependent and service provision is better within a larger area. Sea defence can be provided by a single foredune ridge, but the resilience of the system is improved if it is backed by a larger dune hinterland, providing a range of habitats for biodiversity, space for other ecosystem services and reducing the exposure of inland areas to coastal flooding (Everard et al. 2010).

The local meaningful value of dunes is largely independent of their character; generally, it is sudden change (such as forest felling or dune remobilisation) which affects this cultural service. Sustainable management needs to achieve buy-in for these activities through stakeholder involvement as part of the decision-making process.

11.5.3 Machair

Most Machair systems are designated SAC under the Habitats Directive, or are SSSI, and so, protection and maintenance of biodiversity and geomorphological interest remain primary conservation objectives. A conundrum facing managers of Machair is that any engineered protection measures to reduce frontal erosion of the coastal edge and conserve habitat, risks cutting-off the erosional recycling of sand that is the lifeblood of that habitat. The accepted position on coastal protection and resilience is that, if backed by a dune system larger than a single cordon, exposure of inland areas to coastal flooding is reduced. However, in many cases this grassland has a negative landward gradient and erosion of the frontal dune cordon can result in wave overtopping, accelerated frontal erosion and salinisation of the backslope habitat, with potential for lateral flooding of low-lying areas from a breach (Angus et al. 2011). Present management focuses on the hard protection of a few sites (e.g. Balivanich airport, short stretches of roadway), as well as allowing roll-back in undeveloped areas. Future options could include beach nourishment to allow sediment delivery while slowing erosion, although sourcing sufficient sand is an issue. Any roll-back on to land immediately inland of the Machair dune cordon systems would replace or stabilise the dune area lost to coastal erosion. Intervention to allow remobilisation of dune sand is not needed on the already highly dynamic Machair.

There is an intensity of integration between human activity, biodiversity and the natural heritage in Machair management, which is now rare in the UK; this positive interaction is not only pivotal to the international value of the habitat, but is critical to its future. Sustainable management of Machair landform and habitat depends on policies that acknowledge the wider sediment-machair system and fully embrace the socioeconomic and cultural dimension of Machair. As agriculture, economy and culture are inextricably interlinked with the landform and habitat of Machair itself, management strategies aimed at sustainable stewardship of the resource need to fully engage the people who live there.

Conservationists encourage the use of tangle seaweed as fertiliser on Machair crops in preference to artificial fertiliser, as it is believed that it promotes wider wild flower diversity in the crop. It is important to leave at least some seaweed on eroding coastlines to provide a binding agent and nutrients for strandline plant growth, and crofters recognise the importance of maintaining the dune cordon. Moreover, the role of tangle beds in wave energy reduction is now fully recognised to the extent that no application for commercial tangle-cutting to the west of the Uists is likely to obtain consent.

Most conservationists also recognise that even traditional agricultural management must be able to evolve, and some aspects of change might be damaging, but essential, if crofting is to continue in any meaningful way. This compromise results in the erection of buildings and the compartmentalisation of formerly open common land into fenced 'apportionments'. Without such compromises, it is possible that cattle-rearing could be reduced or even locally abandoned. Likewise, new, more economic technology has resulted in the increased use of local agricultural contractors for ploughing and harvesting, and the practical amalgamation of crop areas and entire crofts to ease management. Despite the legal constraint on the amalgamation of crofts (the croft will always be a discrete legal and land tenure unit), its physical boundaries will become difficult to identify on the ground due to such merged management (Angus 2009).

11.5.4 Saltmarsh

Saltmarsh area is declining: to maintain its 1992 extent, 2,240 ha of Saltmarsh need to be created between 1999 and 2015 in the UK, primarily through managed realignment. Broadly speaking, managed realignment schemes in the UK have shown that, with relatively minimal pre-treatment and/or management of the area, allowing tidal ingress through a simple, relatively small breach of the existing seawall onto low-lying agricultural land will quickly produce intertidal mudflats which are subsequently colonised by Saltmarsh plants (French et al. 2000; Wolters et al. 2005). Research into flood risk management benefits established the flood defence benefits of seawalls with an area of Saltmarsh in front to attenuate wave energy—if there was a wide Saltmarsh, seawalls could be lower (and therefore less expensive) than if there were no Saltmarsh (King & Lester 1995; Möller et al. 2001). Experience to date has shown that managed realignment sites are sinks of sediment and, given time and the appropriate elevation, recognisable plant, invertebrate and bird communities can develop (Garbutt et al. 2006), although these do not always match exactly the surrounding saltmarsh (Atkinson et al. 2004). Nonetheless, there is growing evidence that restored Saltmarsh can perform many of the ecosystem services provided by natural systems including coastal defence and the storage of pollutants. High intertidal parts of managed realignment sites have also been found to be important nursery areas for fish, and Colclough et al. (2004) give recommendations for the design of habitat creation and survey methods. Where Saltmarsh regenerates on former agricultural land, and where grazing is not introduced, there may be a transfer in services from provisioning services (e.g. farmed food and fibre), towards regulatory services (e.g. flood risk), supporting services (e.g. biodiversity) and cultural services (e.g. amenity). Cultural services, in particular, can benefit from this regeneration (**Box 11.2**).

11.5.5 Shingle

Maintaining natural dynamics where possible is key to the sustainable management of Shingle. Under 'natural' conditions, Shingle moves in response to sea-level change and storms. For example, between 1978 and 1991, the Shingle beach at Kessingland in Suffolk had migrated several kilometres to the north, covering a groyne field with sand and shingle (Rees 2005; **Figure 11.12**).

Adopting a flexible approach to managing Shingle beaches and structures is likely to be more sustainable and should enhance or maintain the specific characteristics of that habitat. Allowing the habitat to move inland in response to storms and, in the longer-term, sea-level rise, will be the best option. The replacement of some valuable habitats may occur, but others may develop in their place, helping to maintain the ecosystem services—as seen at Porlock on the north Somerset coast (Jennings et al. 1998; Doody & Randall 2003a,b; **Figure 11.5**).

Engineering approaches to coastal protection have been, and in many places still represent, the preferred solution to problems of flooding and erosion, especially where high quality agricultural land, life or property are threatened. In the south and south-east, the trend is for nourishment schemes involving Shingle bypassing (e.g. Shoreham harbour) and recycling (e.g. Dungeness). The Dungeness nuclear power stations initially required the annual transport of 30,000 m^3 of shingle (subsequently increased to 67,000 m^3) from east (down-drift) of the station to be inserted west (up-drift) of the station in order to maintain the coastal protection function of the fronting beaches (Hansom 1988; Doody 2001).

In recent years, there has been greater recognition of the value of Shingle habitats for landscape, nature conservation and recreation. This is reflected in a number of local authority and research initiatives. On the south coast, several projects seek to create a better understanding of the value of Shingle as a habitat for rare plants and animals, improving conservation measures. In Sussex, Shingle is one of the key habitats included in the Sussex Biodiversity Action Plan (www.biodiversitysussex.org/habitats/vegetated-shingle). In East Sussex, there is a Vegetated Shingle Management Plan (www.eastsussex.gov.uk/environment/conservation/shingleplants/download.htm), and the Channel Beaches at Risk programme (2003–2008) included Shingle beach management (www.geog.susx.ac.uk/BAR/home.html). Shingle vegetation can be successfully restored by appropriate conservation measures, as at Sizewell in Suffolk (Walmsley & Davy 1997, 2001). Opportunities exist even in built-up Shingle areas to highlight the importance of the Shingle habitat and to promote demonstration Shingle habitats in show-home gardens.

11.5.6 Sea Cliffs

Coastal soft cliffs are amongst the most natural habitats in the UK: on many sites, active human intervention or management is not required to maintain the habitat and species diversity. However, due to a lack of recognition for their nature conservation interest, much of the UK resource has been altered or lost behind coastal protection schemes, or degraded through inappropriate management of cliffs and slopes and their immediate surroundings.

The ecological and geomorphological benefits of soft cliffs are intrinsically linked to the rate of erosion. Armouring and stabilisation measures should, therefore, not be considered routine, and the nature conservation interest and sediment supply role of coastal soft cliffs must be

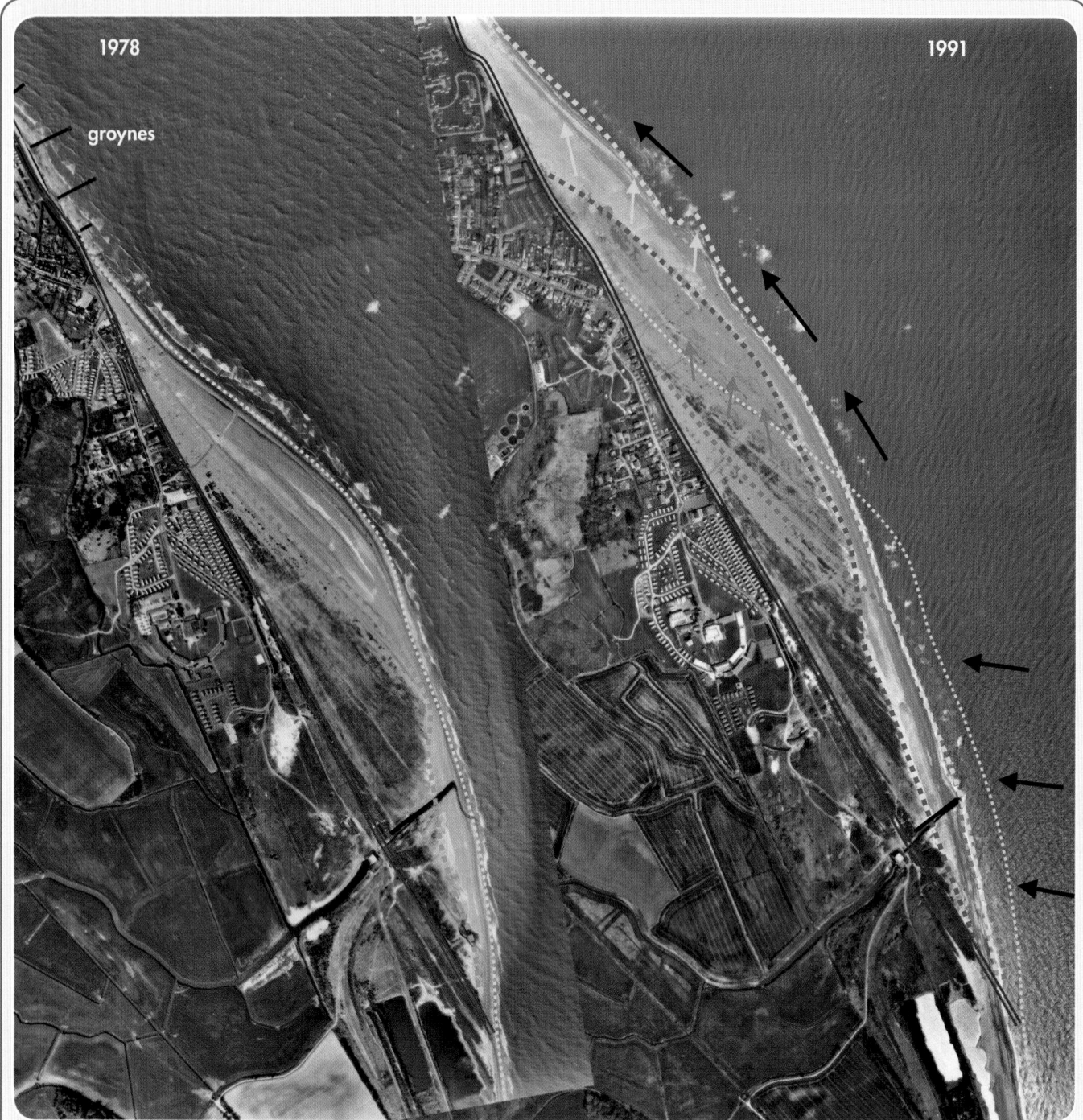

Figure 11.12 Lateral migration of Shingle. Aerial photographs of Kessingland Beach, Suffolk, south-east England, showing approximate position of the sandy shoreline (yellow, thin line) and shingleness (orange thin line) in 1978, and changes to 1991 (thicker dotted yellow and red lines). Black arrows show where the beach has eroded in the south and accreted in the north to cover the groynes (hard sea defences). Source: courtesy of J.P. Doody (January 2011).

given full consideration in the SMP process where relevant. Any proposed changes to coastal management must be assessed in terms of their impact on soft cliff faunal and floral assemblages, and on sediment supply. Where this data is not available, surveys must be included as part of a full environmental assessment.

Water abstractions within the catchment of soft cliff sites, and altered drainage near cliffs, may affect seepages and other hydrological features of high value to invertebrates, and may affect rates of erosion. Appropriate cliff-top management can provide a range of resources

for invertebrates of the cliff slope, seed sources for plant colonisation of slumped or eroded areas, and ecological linkages between isolated or fragmented soft cliff sites.

There remain many opportunities for enhancing and protecting sites through effective targeting of agri-environment schemes to revert arable and intensive grazing management of cliff-tops to herb-rich semi-natural cliff-top grassland. One approach is through the use of cliff-top buffer strips designed to accommodate the natural retreat ('roll-back') of the cliff-top and promote the development of semi-natural vegetation. Buffer strips provide opportunities for combining new and improved coastal access for people, alongside the enhancement of biodiversity on soft cliff sites.

11.5.7 Coastal Lagoons

Management of lagoons poses some dilemmas. Many are natural systems that experience long-term processes of evolution such that they may change their state quite dramatically in terms of salinity and connection with the sea. Attempting to maintain the current conditions in such lagoons would, in effect, be resisting their natural patterns of evolution, and would be inconsistent with policies of non-intervention such as those contained in the Department for Environment, Food and Rural Affairs (Defra) 'Making Space For Water' (Defra 2005). Maintaining the conditions in artificial lagoons is likely to be the only option for such systems, but these will be affected by changing external environmental conditions such as sea-level rise. In Natura 2000 sites likely to experience change, creation of compensatory habitat is one option for management.

In Scotland, management currently concentrates on maintaining existing levels of marine water exchange and on minimising catchment enrichment, but there is a need to become more actively involved in advising on new or upgraded infrastructure that often uses lagoon impoundment ridges and sills.

Sea-level rise may present opportunities for creation of new lagoonal habitat where sea water inundates low-lying land and freshwater areas. Managed realignment schemes often include provision for the creation of lagoons. Managed realignment has also been applied directly to Anne's Point—a small lagoon in Strangford Lough, Northern Ireland—where the National Trust and Northern Ireland's River's Agency agreed to breach the sea defences. A benefit of the enhanced salinities that resulted was the reappearance of a rare snail, *Hydrobia acuta*.

Artificial lagoon creation can also be achieved through direct engineering works. In Belfast Lough, for example, a decision to discontinue landfill on the foreshore led to the transformation of artificial impounds into saline lagoons, as did the construction of a motorway across the foreshore. The likely total cost, in England and Wales, of replacing freshwater and brackish habitat predicted to be lost due to sea-level rise "on a hectare-for-hectare basis, is estimated to be in the order of £50–£60 million, including site purchase, set-up and on-going management costs" (Lee 2001).

11.6 Future Research and Monitoring Gaps

Key knowledge gaps in the Coastal Margins are:
1. *Basic information on extent and trends*: Estimates of the area of Sand Dunes, Saltmarsh and Shingle vary by up to 50% depending on methodology. There is still no definitive classification of saline lagoons, different interpretations of Machair exist and the habitats of UK cliffs are only

partially surveyed. A consistent and thorough survey methodology for each habitat would allow accurate estimates of change in extent and habitat condition over time (Article 17 reporting only covers Natura 2000 i.e. SAC sites, and assessment methodologies of conservation status differ by region).
2. *A national picture of the likely effects of climate change*: Coastal Margin habitats are among the most sensitive to climate change, being affected by sea-level rise, increased storminess, changing rainfall and temperature. However, there is no national picture of the likely impacts on them with respect to: loss of area; geomorphological responses to sea-level rise; direct and indirect impacts on species; and consequent impacts on ecosystem services, particularly the role of sea defence. Data from Scotland and Northern Ireland are especially lacking. There is a clear need to identify priorities for a national strategic monitoring programme.
3. *Information on the management options required to respond to sea-level rise*: In particular, how to apply roll-back or managed realignment to the other Coastal Margin habitats as well as Saltmarsh. More research is needed on any habitat restoration measures needed to make this feasible.
4. *Basic quantification of many of the ecosystem services of Coastal Margins*: This is difficult, in part because some are shared with the Marine environment, but also because the Coastal Margins constitute a narrow zone of land, are not a distinct habitat and data gathering does not differentiate between certain aspects, for example, coastal farms and inland farms. Particular services that merit more attention are: a) the value of Coastal Margin habitats in providing or contributing to 'soft' sea defences, including system thresholds which govern this role; b) the realised pollination and pest control services provided by Coastal Margin insects to agriculture; and c) greenhouse gas emissions from coastal wetland habitats and carbon storage.
5. *Understanding how to achieve trade-offs between competing Coastal Margin uses*: Cultural and societal benefits from the Coastal Margins are large. This can create tensions between different societal services, such as solitude and wildness versus increasing recreational use of the coast, but also between societal and environmental services, particularly the role of biodiversity. Understanding how to accommodate multiple uses of this environment is important.

References

Allen, J.R.L. & Pye K. (1992) Coastal saltmarshes: their nature and significance. Saltmarshes: Morphodynamics. Conservation and Engineering Significance (eds J.R.L. Allen & K. Pye) pp.1–19. Cambridge University Press, Cambridge.

Andrews, J.E., Burgess, D., Cave, R.R., Coombes, E.G., Jickells, T.D., Parkes, D.J. & Turner, R.K. (2006) Biogeochemical value of managed realignment, Humber estuary, UK. *Science of the Total Environment,* **371**, 19–30.

Andrews, J.E., Samways, G. & Shimmield, G.B. (2008) Historical storage budgets of organic carbon, nutrient and contaminant elements in saltmarsh sediments: Biogeochemical context for managed realignment, Humber estuary, UK. *Science of the Total Environment*, **405**, 1–13.

Angus, S. & Elliott, M.M. (1992) Problems of erosion in Scottish machair with particular reference to the Outer Hebrides. Coastal dunes: geomorphology, ecology and management for conservation (eds R.W.G. Carter, T.G.F. Curtis & M.J. Sheehy–Skeffington) pp. 93–112. A.A. Balkema, Rotterdam.

Angus, S. (2001) The Outer Hebrides: moor and machair. White Horse Press, Cambridge.

Angus, S. & Hansom, J.D. (2004) Tir a' Mhachair, Tir nan Loch? Climate change scenarios for Scottish Machair systems: a wetter future? Delivering Sustainable Coasts: connecting science and policy (eds D.R. Green, S. Angus, D. Bailey, M. Eleveld, K. Furmanczyk, J. Hansom, R.A. Longhorn, R. Paskoff, N.P. Psuty, R. Randall, W. Ritchie, A. Salman, J. Taussik, F.T. Pinto, & H. Wensink), pp. 565–569. 7th International Symposium, Littoral 2004, (EUROCOAST-EUCC), Aberdeen, Scotland.

Angus, S. (2009) De tha cearr air a'mhachaire? Biodiversity issues for Scottish machair: an initial appraisal. *The Glasgow Naturalist*, **25**, 53–62.

Angus, S., Hansom, J. & Rennie, A. (2011) Oir-thirean na h-Alba ag atharrachadh: habitat change on Scotland's coasts. The Changing Nature of Scotland (eds S.J. Marrs S. Foster, C. Hendrie, E.C. Mackey, & D.B.A. Thompson). TSO, Edinburgh.

Archer, M.E. (1994) Survey of Aculeate Wasps and Bees (Hymenoptera) on the Sand Dune Systems of South Wales. Countryside Council for Wales, Bangor.

Arens, S.M., Slings, Q. & de Vries, C.N. (2004) Mobility of a remobilised parabolic dune in Kennemerland, The Netherlands. *Geomorphology*, **59**(1–4), 175–188.

Arens, S.M. & Geelen, L. (2006) Dune landscape rejuvenation by intended destabilisation in the Amsterdam water supply dunes. *Journal of Coastal Research*, **22**(5), 1094–1107.

Atkinson, P.W., Crooks, S., Dixon, M. Drewitt, M. Grant, A., Rehfisch, M.M., Sharpe, J. & Tyas, C. (2004) Managed Realignment in the UK – the first five years of colonisation by birds. *Ibis*, **146**(S1), 101–110.

Baily, B. & Pearson, A.W. (2001) Change detection mapping of saltmarsh areas of south England from Hurst Castle to Pagham Harbour. Department of Geography, university of Portsmouth report to Posford Haskoning consultants, English Nature and Environment Agency.

Baker, J. (2001) Military land use, sand dunes and nature conservation in the UK. Coastal Dune Management: Shared experience of European Conservation Practice. (eds J.A. Houston, S.E. Edmondson & P.J. Rooney), pp. 99–205. Liverpool University Press, Liverpool.

Bamber, R., Gilliland, P. & Shardlow, M. (2001) Saline lagoon guide: A guide to their management and creation (ISBN 1 85716 573 X).

Barnes, R.S.K. (1988) The faunas of landlocked lagoons: chance differences and problems of dispersal. *Estuarine and Coastal Shelf Science*, **26**, 309–18.

Barnes, R.S.K. (1989a) The coastal lagoons of Britain. An overview and conservation appraisal. *Biological Conservation*, **49**, 295–313.

Barnes, R.S.K. (1989b) What, if anything, is a brackish-water fauna? *Transactions of the Royal Society of Edinburgh, Earth Sciences*, **80**, 235–240.

Barne, J.H. *et al.* 1995–1998. *Coasts and Seas of the United Kingdom, the Coastal Directories Project: Regions 5–11 & 13*. UK Joint Nature Conservation Committee, Peterborough [online] Available at: <http://www.jncc.gov.uk/page-2157> [Accessed 09.02.11].

Beatty, C. & Fothergill, S. (2003) The Seaside Economy. Centre for Regional Economic and Social Research, Sheffield Hallam University, Sheffield.

Beaumont N., Townsend M., Mangi S., Austen M.C. (2006) Marine Biodiversity. An economic valuation. Building the evidence base for the Marine Bill. Defra, London, July 2006.

Berry, P.M., Harrison, P.A., Dawson, T.P. & Walmsley, C.A. (eds) (2005) Modelling Natural Resource Responses to Climate Change (MONARCH): A Local Approach. UKCIP Technical Report, Oxford.

Binggeli, P., Eakin, M., Macfadyen, A., Power, J. & McConnel, J. (1992) Impact of the alien sea buckthorn (*Hippophae rhamnoides* L.) on sand dune ecosystems in Ireland. Coastal dunes (eds R.W.G. Carter, T.G.F. Curtis & M.J. Sheehy-Skeffington) Geomorphology, Ecology and Management for Conservation. Proceedings of the third European dune congress. Galway/Ireland. Balkema, Rotterdam, Galway.

Boorman, L.A. (1989) The grazing of British sand dune vegetation. *Proceedings of the Royal Society Edinburgh*, **96B**, 75–88.

Boorman, L.A., Pakeman, R. J., Garbutt, R.A. & Barratt, D. (1996) The effects of environmental exchange on European salt marshes: structure, functioning and exchange potentialities with marine coastal water, Report to the European Union, Volume 5. University of Rennes, France.

Boorman L.A. & Boorman M.S. (2001) The spatial and temporal effects of grazing on the species diversity of sand dunes. Coastal Dune Management: shared experience of European conservation practice (eds J.A. Houston S.E. Edmondson & P.J. Rooney) pp. 161–167. Liverpool University Press, Liverpool.

Boorman, L. (2003) Saltmarsh review: and overview of coastal saltmarshes, their dynamic and sensitivity characteristics for conservation and management. JNCC Report 334. Peterborough.

Boorman, L.A. (2009) The role of freshwater flows on salt marsh growth and development. Coastal Wetlands: An Integrated Ecosystem Approach (eds G.M.E. Perillo, E. Wolanski, D.R. Cahoon, M.M. Brinson) pp. 493–514. Elsevier Science, Amsterdam.

Born, K. (2005) Predicting habitat change in poole harbour using aerial photography. The Ecology of Poole Harbour (eds J. Humphreys & V.J. May), pp. 239–253. Elsevier B.V., Amsterdam.

Bos, D., Loonen, M., Stock, M., Hofeditz, F., van Der Graff, A. & Bakker, J. (2005) Utilisation of Wadden Sea salt marshes by geese in relation to livestock grazing. *Journal for Nature Conservation*, **13**, 1–15.

Brenner-Guillermo, J. (2007) Valuation of ecosystem services in the Catalan coastal zone. Doctorate Dissertation. Laboratori d'Enginyeria Maritima, Universtat Politecnica de Catalunya.

BTA (British Travel Association) (1968) British National Travel Survey. British Travel Association, London.

Brooks A. & Agate E. (2001) Sand dunes. Pp. 109. BTCV. ISBN 0 946752 32 X.

Burd, F. (1989) The Saltmarsh Survey of Great Britain. An Inventory of British Saltmarshes. Research & survey in nature conservation, 17, Nature Conservancy Council, Peterborough.

Burnham, C.P. & Cook, H.F. (2001) Hydrology and soils of coastal shingle with specific reference to Dungeness. Ecology & Geomorphology of Coastal Shingle (eds. J.R. Packham, R.E. Randall, R.S.K. Barnes & A. Neal), pp. 107–131. Westbury Academic & Scientific Publishing, Otley, West Yorkshire.

Burton, P. (2001) Grazing as a management tool and the constraints of the agricultural system: a case study of grazing on Sandscale Haws Nature Reserve, Cumbria, northwest England. Coastal dune management: Shared experience of European Conservation Practice (eds J.A. Houston, S.E. Edmondson, P.J. Rooney), pp. 80–84. Proceedings of the European Symposium Coastal Dunes of the Atlantic Biogeographical Region Southport, northwest England, September 1998. Liverpool University Press, Liverpool.

Cannell, M.G., Milne, R., Hargreaves, K.J., Brown, T.A., Cruickshank, M.M., Bradley, R.I., Spencer, T., Hope, D., Billett, M.F., Adger, W.N. & Subak S. (1999) National Inventories of Terrestrial Carbon Sources and Sinks: The UK Experience. *Climate Change,* **42**(3) 505–530.

Carter, R.W.G., Orford, J.D., Forbes, D.L. & Taylor, R.P. (1987) Gravel barriers, headlands and lagoons: an evolutionary model. Proceedings Coastal Sediment 1987, New Orleans, LA, USA, May 12–14, 1987. American Society of Civil Engineers: 1776–1792.

Cayford, J. & Waters, R. (1996) Population estimates for waders (Charadrii) wintering in Great Britain, 1987/88–1991/92. *Biological Conservation,* **77**, 1–17.

Clarke, D. & Sanitwong na Ayutthaya, S. (2010) Predicted effects of climate change, vegetation and tree cover on dune slack habitats at Ainsdale on the Sefton Coast, UK. *Journal of Coastal Conservation,* **14**, 115–125.

Clayton, K.M. (1989) Sediment input from the Norfolk cliffs, Eastern England – a century of coast protection and its effects. *Journal of Coastal Research,* **5**, 433–442.

Clements, F.E. (1916) Plant succession: an analysis of the development of vegetation. Carnegie Institution of Washington, Washington.

Coates, T.T., Brampton, A.H., Powell, K.A. (2001) Shingle Beach Recharge in the Context of Coastal Defence: Principles and Problems. Ecology & Geomorphology of Coastal Shingle (eds J.R. Packham, R.E. Randall, R.S.K. Barnes & A. Neal) pp. 394–401. Westbury Academic & Scientific Publishing, Otley.

Colclough, S., Fonseca, L., Astley, T., Thomas, K. & Watts, W. (2005) Fish utilisation of managed realignments. *Fisheries Management and Ecology* **12**(6), 351–360.

Conlan, K., White, K.N. & Hawkins, S.J. (1992) The hydrography and ecology of a redeveloped brackish water dock. *Estuarine Coastal and Shelf Science,* **35**, 435–452.

Connell, J.H. & Slatyer, R.O. (1977) Mechanisms of succession in natural communities and their role in community stability and organization. *American Naturalist,* **111**, 1119–1144.

Costanza, R., d'Arge, R., de Groot, R., Farber, S., Grasso, M., Hannon, B., Limburg, K., Naeem, S., O'Neill, R.V., Paruelo. J., Raskin, R.G., Sutton, P. & van den Belt, M. (1997) The value of the world's ecosystem services and natural capital. *Nature,* **387**, 253–260.

Coombes, E.G. & Jones, A.P. (2010) Assessing the impact of climate change on visitor behaviour and habitat use at the coast: A UK case study. *Global Environmental Change,* **20**, 303–313.

Cooper, C. (1997) Parameters and indicators of the decline of the British seaside resort. The Rise and Fall of British Coastal Resorts: cultural and economic perspectives (eds G. Shaw & A. Williams), pp. 79–101. Pinter, London.

Cooper, N.J., Cooper, T. & Burd, F. (2001) 25 years of salt marsh erosion in Essex: Implications for coastal defence and nature conservation. *Journal of Coastal Conservation,* **9**, 31–40.

Cooper, J.A.G. & McKenna, J. (2008) Working with natural processes: the challenge for Coastal Protection Strategies. *Geographical Journal,* **174**, 315–331.

Cooper, J.A.G. (2009) Coastal economies and people review in Marine Climate Change Ecosystem Linkages Report Card 2009 (eds J.M. Baxter, P.J. Buckley & M.T. Frost) pp. 18. Online science reviews. [online] Available at: <www.mccip.org.uk/elr/coasts> [Accessed 20.01.11].

COREPOINT (Coastal REsearch POlicy INTegration) (2007) Quantification of the economic benefits of natural coastal systems. Coastal research and policy integration. EU-Interreg IIIb project report.

Cowles H.C. (1899) The Ecological Relations of the Vegetation on the Sand Dunes of Lake Michigan. *Botanical Gazette,* **27**(3), 167–202.

Dargie, T.C.D. (1995) Sand dune vegetation survey of Great Britain. A national inventory. Part 3: Wales, Joint Nature Conservation Committee.

Dargie, T.C.D. (2000) Sand dune vegetation survey of Scotland: national report. Scottish Natural Heritage Report.

Dawson, R.J., Dickson, M.E., Nicholls, R.J., Hall, J.W., Walkden, M.J.A., Stansby, P., Mokrech, M., Richards, J., Zhou, J., Milligan, J., Jordan, A., Pearson, S., Rees, J., Bates, P., Koukoulas, S. & Watkinson, A. (2009) Integrated analysis of risks of coastal flooding and cliff erosion under scenarios of long term change. *Climatic Change,* **95**(1–2), 249–288.

Defra (Department for Environment, Food and Rural Affairs) (2005) Making space for water. Taking forward a new Government strategy for flood and coastal erosion risk management in England. March 2005. [online] Available at <http://archive.defra.gov.uk/environment/flooding/documents/policy/strategy/strategy-response1.pdf> [Accessed 10.02.11].

Defra (Department for Environment, Food and Rural Affairs) (2006) Shoreline management plan guidance. Volume 2: Procedures. March 2006. [online] Available at: <http://archive.defra.gov.uk/environment/flooding/documents/policy/guidance/smpguide/volume2.pdf> [Accessed 09.02.11].

Defra (Department for Environment, Food and Rural Affairs) (2009) Flood and Water Management Bill Impact Assessment – Flood and Coastal Erosion Risk Management Funding Provisions. September 2009. [online] Available at <http://archive.defra.gov.uk/environment/flooding/documents/policy/fwmb/fwmiafunding.pdf> [Accessed 10.02.11].

Delbaere, B.C.W. (1998) Facts and figures on European biodiversity; state and trends 1998-1999. European Centre for Nature Conservation. Tilburg, the Netherlands.

Demetriadi, J. (1997) The golden years: English seaside resorts 1950-1974. The Rise and Fall of British Coastal Resorts: cultural and economic perspectives. (eds G. Shaw & A. Williams) pp. 49–78. Pinter, London.

Denton, J.S., Hitchings, S.P., Beebee, T.J.C. & Gent, A. (2003) A Recovery Program for the Natterjack Toad (*Bufo calamita*) in Britain. *Conservation Biology*, **11**(6), 1329–1338.

Dickson, M.E., Walkden, M.J.A. & Hall, J.W. (2007) Systemic impacts of climate change on an eroding coastal region over the twenty-first century. *Climatic Change*, **84**(2), 141–166.

Doody, J.P. (1984) Spartina in Great Britain (Focus on nature conservation no. 5). Nature Conservancy Council Report, Attingham, UK.

Doody, J.P. (1989) Management for nature conservation. *Proceedings of the Royal Society of Edinburgh*, **96B**, 247–265.

Doody, J.P. (2001) Coastal Conservation and Management: an Ecological Perspective. Conservation Biology Series, 13, Kluwer, pp.306. Academic Publishers, Boston, USA.

Doody, J.P. & Randall, R.E. (2003a) A Guidance Document for the Management of Vegetated Shingle, Contract No. MAR 05-03-002 English Nature.

Doody, J.P. & Randall, R.E. (2003b) A Guidance Document for the Management of Vegetated Shingle, Contract No. MAR 05-03-002 English Nature. Annex 01 Porlock.

Doody, J.P. (2008) Saltmarsh conservation, management and restoration. Coastal Systems and Continental Margins Series. Springer, USA.

Downie, A.J. (1996) Saline lagoons and lagoon-like saline ponds in England. English Nature, Peterborough.

Edmondson, S.E. (2009) Non-native plants on the Sefton Coast sand dunes. Proceedings of the Sefton Natural Coast Conference, Southport.

English Nature (2003) National Nature Reserves in Norfolk. Pp. 28. Report produced by English Nature, Norwich, UK.

Environment Agency (2007) Flood risk management Estimating Guide. Unit cost database.

Everard, M. (2009) Ecosystem services case studies. Science Report SCHO0409BPVM-E-E. Environment Agency, Bristol.

Everard, M., Jones, M.L.M. & Watts, B. (2010) Have we neglected the societal importance of sand dunes? An ecosystem services perspective. *Aquatic Conservation: Marine and Freshwater Ecosystems*, **20**, 476–487.

Farrell, L. & Randall, R.E. (1992) The distribution of *Mertensia maritima* (L.) Gray, Oyster Plant, in Ireland. *Irish Naturalist's Journal*, **24**, 135–140.

Firn Crichton Roberts Ltd (2000) An assessment of the socio-economic cost & benefits of Integrated Coastal Zone Management, Contract NO: B4-3040/99/134414/MAR/D2. Final report to the European Commission. Firn Crichton Roberts Ldt and Graduate Schools of Environmental Studies, Scotland.

Fowler, D.O., Donoghue, M., Muller, J.B.A., Smith, R.I., Dragosits, U. & Skiba, U. (2004) A chronology of nitrogen deposition in the UK between 1900 and 2000. *Water Air Soil Pollution Focus*, **4**, 9–23.

French, P.W. (1997) Coastal and Estuarine Management (Routledge Environmental Management Series). Pp. 251. Routledge, London.

French, C.E., French, J.R., Clifford, N.J. & Watson, C.J. (2000) Sedimentation-erosion dynamics of abandoned reclamations: the role of waves and tides. *Continental Shelf Research*, **20**, 1711–1733.

Frost, M. (2010) Overall Assessment. Charting Progress 2: Healthy and Biologically Diverse Seas Evidence Group Feeder Report (ed M. Frost), UK Marine Monitoring and Assessment Strategy, Defra. [online] Available at: <http://chartingprogress.defra.gov.uk/chapter-3-healthy-and-biologicaly-diverse-seas> [Accessed 19.01.11].

Fuller, R.M. (1985) An assessment of the damage to the shingle beaches and their vegetation. Dungeness: ecology and conservation (eds B. Ferry & S. Waters), pp. 25–42. Focus on nature conservation, No. 12. Nature Conservancy Council, Peterborough.

Garbutt, R.A., Reading, C.J., Wolters, M., Gray, A.J. & Rothery, P. (2006) Monitoring the development of intertidal habitats on former agricultural land after the managed realignment of coastal defences at Tollesbury, Essex, UK. *Marine Pollution Bulletin*, **53**, 155–164.

Gatliff, R., Prior, A., Mason, T., Wolf, J., Pepper, J., Osborne, M., Spillard, R., Stoker, M., Long, D., Stevenson, A., Cotterill, C., Cooper, R. & Hobbs, P., (2010). Sedimentary Processes and Morphology. Charting Progress 2 Feeder Report: Ocean Processes (ed. J. Hunthnance), pp. 211-252. UK Marine Monitoring and Assessment Strategy (UKMMAS), Defra. [online] Available at: <http://chartingprogress.defra.gov.uk/ocean-processes-feeder-report> [Accessed 15.01.11].

GBLDV (GB Leisure Day Visits) (2004) Report of the 2002–03 Great Britain Day Visits Survey.

Gregory, R.A., Murphy, E.M., Church, M.J., Edwards, K.J., Guttmann, E.B. & Simpson, D.D.A. (2005) Archaeological evidence for the first Mesolithic occupation of the Western Isles of Scotland. *The Holocene*, 15, 944–950.

Green, B.C., Smith, D.J., Earley, S.E., Hepburn L.J. & Underwood G.J.C. (2009) Seasonal changes in community composition and trophic structure of fish populations of five salt marshes along the Essex coastline, United Kingdom. *Estuarine, Coastal and Shelf Science*, **85**(2), 247–256.

Halcrow (2002) Futurecoast: Future coastal evolution around England and Wales. Report to DEFRA, London (available on CD).

Hansom, J.D. (1988) *Coasts*. Pp. 96. Cambridge University Press, Cambridge.

Hansom, J.D. & Comber, D. (1996) Eoligarry (Barra) SSSI, site documentation and management. pp. 73. Scottish Natural Heritage Commissioned Report Series, Edinburgh. ISSN 1350-3103.

Hansom, J.D. (2001) Coastal Sensitivity to Environmental Change: a view from the beach. *Catena*, **42**, 291–305.

Hansom, J.D. & Angus, S. (2001) Tir a' Mhachair (Land of the Machair): sediment supply and climate change scenarios for the future of the Outer Hebrides machair. Earth Science and the Natural Heritage (eds J.E. Gordon & K.F. Lees), pp. 68–81. The Stationery Office, Edinburgh.

Hansom, J.D., Lees R. G., Maslen J., Tilbrook, C. & McManus, J. (2001) Coastal dynamics and sustainable management: the potential for managed realignment in the Forth estuary. Earth Science and the Natural Heritage (eds J.E. Gordon & K.F. Lees) pp. 148–160. The Stationery Office, Edinburgh.

Hansom, J.D. & McGlashan, D.J. (2004) Scotland's coast: understanding past and present processes for sustainable management. *Scottish Geographical Journal*, **120**(1), 99–116.

Hansom, J.D., Lees, G., McGlashan, D.J. & John, S. (2004) Shoreline Management Plans and coastal sediment cells in Scotland: *Coastal Management*, **32**, 227–242. DOI:10.1080/08920750490448505.

Hansom, J.D. (2010) Coastal steepening around the coast of Scotland: the implication of sea level changes. Scottish Natural Heritage Commissioned Report Series, Edinburgh.

Hanson, H., Brampton, A., Capobianco, M., Dette, H.H., Hamm, L., Laustrup, C., Lechuga A. & Spanhoff R. (2002) Beach nourishment projects, practices and objectives – a European overview. *Coastal Engineering*, **47**, 81–112.

Harrison, P.A., Berry, P.M. and Dawson, T.P. (eds) (2001) Climate Change and Nature Conservation in Britain and Ireland: Modelling natural resource responses to climate change (the MONARCH project). UKCIP Technical Report, Oxford.

Hill, M.O. & Wallace, H.L. (1989) Vegetation and Environment in Afforested Sand Dunes at Newborough, Anglesey. *Forestry,* **62**(3), 249–267.

Hill, C., Ball, J.H., Dargie, T., Tantram, D. & Boobyer, G. (2002) Maritime cliff and slope inventory. English Nature Research Report, No. 426.

Houston J.A. (2008) Management of Natura 2000 habitats. 2130 Fixed coastal dunes with herbaceous vegetation ('grey dunes'). European Commission.

Howe, M.A. (2002) A review of the coastal cliff resource in Wales, with particular reference to its importance for invertebrates. CCW Natural Science Report. 02/5/1. Countryside Council for Wales, Bangor.

Howe, M.A., Whitehouse, A.T., Knight, G.T. (2008) Life on the edge – key coastal soft cliffs for invertebrates in England and Wales. *British Wildlife,* **19**(3), 172–181.

Howe, M.A., Knight, G.T. & Clee, C. (2010) The importance of coastal sand dunes for terrestrial invertebrates in Wales and the UK, with particular reference to aculeate Hymenoptera (bees, wasps & ants). *Journal of Coast Conservation,* **14**(2), 91–102.

Ipsos Mori (2006) Coastal Access in England (Ipsos Mori – Report prepared for Natural England).

Ivell, R. (1979) Biology and ecology of a brackish lagoon bivalve, *Cerastoderma glaucum* Bruigiere in an English lagoon, the Widewater, sussex. *Journal of Molluscan Studies,* **45**, 383–400.

Jennings, S. (2004) Coastal tourism and shoreline management. *Annals of Tourism Research,* **31**, 899–922.

Jennings, S.C., Orford, J.D., Canti, M., Devoy, R.J.N. & Straker, V. (1998) The role of relative sea-level rise and changing sediment supply on Holocene gravel barrier development; the example of Porlock, Somerset, UK. *The Holocene,* **8**, 165–181.

JNCC (Joint Nature Conservation Committee) (2007) Second Report by the UK under Article 17 on the implementation of the Habitats Directive from January 2001 to December 2006. Joint Nature Conservation Committee, Peterborough. [online] Available at: <www.jncc.gov.uk/article17> [Accessed 20.01.11].

Johnston, C.M. & Gilliland, P.M. (2000) Investigating and managing water quality in saline lagoons based on a case study of nutrients in the Chesil and the Fleet European marine site. English Nature. (UK Marine SACs Project).

Jones, C.R., Houston, J.A., Bateman, D. (1993) A history of human influence on the coastal landscape. The Sand Dunes of the Sefton Coast (eds D. Atkinson & J.A. Houston), pp.3–20. Liverpool Museum, Liverpool.

Jones, M.L.M., Wallace, H.L., Norris, D., Brittain, S.A., Haria, S., Jones, R.E., Rhind, P.M., Reynolds, B.R. & Emmett, B.A. (2004) Changes in vegetation and soil characteristics in coastal sand dunes along a gradient of atmospheric nitrogen deposition. *Plant Biology,* **6**(5), 598–605.

Jones, M.L.M., Sowerby, A., Williams, D.L. & Jones, R.E. (2008) Factors controlling soil development in sand dunes: evidence from a coastal dune soil chronosequence. *Plant and Soil,* **307**(1–2), 219–234.

Jones, M.L.M., Sowerby, A. & Rhind, P.M. (2010a) Factors affecting vegetation establishment and development in a sand dune chronosequence at Newborough Warren, North Wales. *Journal of Coastal Conservation,* **14**(2), 127–137.

Jones, M.L.M., Norman, K., Rhind, P.M. (2010b) Topsoil inversion as a restoration measure in sand dunes, early results from a UK field-trial. *Journal of Coastal Conservation,* **14**(2), 139–151.

Jones, P.S. (1998) Aspects of the population biology of *Liparis loeselii* (L.) Rich. var. ovata Ridd. ex Godfery (Orchidaceae) in the dune slacks of South Wales, UK. *Botanical Journal of the Linnean Society,* **126**, 123–139.

King, S.E. & Lester, J.N. (1995) Pollution Economics. The value of salt marshes as a sea defence. *Marine pollution bulletin,* **30**, 180–189.

Klein, R.J.T. & Bateman, I.J. (1998) The recreational value of Cley Marshes Nature Reserve: an argument against managed retreat? *Journal of the Chartered Institution of Water and Environmental Management,* **12**, 280–285.

Klein, R.J.T., Nicholls, R. J., Ragoonaden, S., Capobianco, M., Aston, J., Buckley, E.N. (2001) Technological options for adaptation to climate change in coastal zones. *Journal of Coastal Research,* **17**(3), 531–543.

Küpeli, E., Kartal, M., Aslan, S. & Yesilada, E. (2006) Comparative evaluation of the anti-inflammatory and antinociceptive activity of Turkish Eryngium species. *Journal of Ethnopharmacology,* **107**(1), 32–7.

Lacambra, C., Cutts, N., Allen, J., Burd, F. & Elliott, M. (2004). *Spartina anglica*: a review of its status, dynamics and management. *English Nature Research Reports* No. 527. English Nature, Peterborough.

Lambeck, K. (1995) Late Devensian and Holocene shorelines of the British Isles and the North Sea from models of glacio-hydro-isostatic rebound. *Journal of the Geological Society, London,* **152**, 437–448.

Leafe, R., Pethick, J. & Townend, I.H. (1998) Realizing the benefits of shoreline management, *The Geographical Journal,* **164**(3), 282–290.

Lee, M. (2001) Coastal Defence and the Habitats Directive: Predictions of Habitat Change in England and Wales. *The Geographical Journal,* **167**(1), 39–56.

Loubet, B., Asman, W.A.H., Theobald, M.R., Hertel, O., Tang, S., Robin, P., Hassouna, M., Dammgen, U., Genermont, S., Cellier, P., Sutton, M.A. (2009) Ammonia deposition near hot spots: processes, models and monitoring methods. (eds M.A. Sutton, S. Reis & S.M.H. Baker) pp. 71–86. Atmospheric Ammonia: Detecting emission changes and environmental impacts. Results of an Expert Workshop under the Convention on Long-range Transboundary Air Pollution. Springer, UK.

Lowe, J.A., Howard, T.P., Pardaens, A., Tinker, J., Holt, J., Wakelin, S., Milne, G., Leake, J., Wolf, J., Horsbaugh, K., Reeder, T., Jenkins, G., Ridley, J, Dye, S. & Bradley, S. (2009) UK Climate Projections Science report: Marine and Coastal Projections. Met Office Hadley Centre, Exeter, UK.

Loxton, R.G. (2010) Records of invertebrates at Newborough Forest, Newborough Warren NNR and Llandwyn Island during 2009 with a discussion of the number of insect species exploiting the conifers. Pp.24. Report to CCW and Forestry Commision.

Lozano, I., Devoy, R.J.N., May, W., Andersen, U. (2004) Storminess and vulnerability along the Atlantic coastlines of Europe: analysis of storm records and of a greenhouse gases induced climate scenario. *Marine Geology,* **210**, 205–225.

Luisetti T., Turner, R.K., Bateman, I.J., Morse-Jones, S., Adams, C. & Fonseca, L. (2010) Coastal and marine ecosystem services valuation for policy and management: managed realignment case studies in England, Ocean and Coastal Management. DIO:10.10.16/j.ocecoaman.2010.11.003

MA (Millennium Ecosystem Assessment) (2005) Ecosystems and human wellbeing: synthesis. Island Press, Washington, D.C.

Macpherson Research (MR) (2003) Western Isles Tourism Facts & Figures Update Review of 2002 Season Final Report for Western Isles Enterprise & Western Isles Tourist Board

MAFF (Ministry of Agriculture, Fisheries and Food) (1995) Shoreline management plans – a guide for coastal defence authorities. May 1995.

Manly, A. (2004) Freiston Shore Visitors' Survey. RSPB Market Research Team Internal Report, November 2004.

May, V.J. & Hansom, J.D. (2003) Coastal Geomorphology of Great Britain. Geological conservation Review Series, No. 28, Joint Nature Conservation Committee, Peterborough.

McKenna, J., Cooper, J.A.G. & O'Hagan, A.M. (2008) Managing by principle: a critical assessment of the EU principles of ICZM. *Marine Policy*, **32**, 941–955.

Meot-Duros, L., Le Floch, G. & Magné, C. (2008) Radical scavenging, antioxidant and antimicrobial activities of halophytic species. Journal of *Ethnopharmacology*, **116**(2) 258–62.

Merritt, J. W. & Cavill, J .E. (1993) Supply and demand of sand and gravel in the Western Isles, Scotland. British Geological Survey Onshore Geology Series TECHNICAL REPORT WA/93/59R. Natural Environment Research Council.

Mintel (2005) Extreme Sports – UK, [online] Available at <http://oxygen.mintel.com/index.html> [Accessed 10.02.11]

Mintel (2008) Wildlife Tourism – International. [online] Available at <http://oxygen.mintel.com/index.html> [Accessed 10.02.11]

Mitchell, S.B., Theodoridou, A. & Pope, D.J. (2007) Influence of freshwater discharge on nutrient distribution in a macrotidal lagoon, West Sussex, UK. *Hydrobiologia,* **588**, 261–270.

Möller, I., Spencer, T., French, J.R., Leggett, D.J. & Dixon, M. (1999) Wave transformation over salt marshes: A field and numerical modelling study from North Norfolk, England. *Estuarine, Coastal and Shelf Science,* **49**, 411–426.

Möller, I., Spencer, T., French, J.R., Leggett, D.J., Dixon, M. (2001) The sea-defence value of salt marshes – a review in the light of field evidence from North Norfolk. *Journal of the Chartered Institution of Water and Environmental Management,* **15**, 109–116.

Möller, I. (2006) Quantifying saltmarsh vegetation and its effect on wave height dissipation: Results from a UK east coast saltmarsh. *Estuarine and Coastal Shelf Science,* **69**, 337–351.

Morris, R.K.A., Reach, I.S., Duffy, M.J., Collins, T.S. & Leafe, R.N. (2004) On the loss of salt marshes in south-east England and the relationship with *Nereis diversicolor. Journal of Applied Ecology,* **41**, 787–791.

NEGTAP (National Expert Group on Transboundary Air Pollution) (2001) Transboundary Air Pollution: Acidification, Eutrophication and Ground-Level Ozone in the UK. ISBN 1 870393 61 9.

Nicholls, R.J., Dredge, A. & Wilson, T. (2000) Shoreline change and fine-grained sediment input: Isle of Sheppey Coast, Thames Estuary, UK. Coastal And Estuarine Environments: Sedimentology, Geomorphology And Geoarchaeology Book Series: Geological Society Special Publication Volume: 175 Pages: 305–315

NIHAP (Northern Ireland Habitat Action Plan) (2003) Saline lagoons. Final Draft April 2003. [online] Available at: <http://www.ni-environment.gov.uk/saline_lagoon_web_version_april_03.pdf> [Accessed 20.01.11].

Nottage, A.S. & Robertson, P.A., (2005) The saltmarsh creation handbook: a project managers guide to the creation of saltmarsh and intertidal mudflat. The RSPB, Sandy & CIWEM, London, UK.

Oates, M., Harvey, H. J., Glendell, M. (1998) Grazing sea cliffs and dunes for nature conservation. The National Trust, Estates Department, Cirencester.

Oates, M. (1999) Sea cliff slopes and combes – their management for nature conservation. *British Wildlife,* **10**(6), 394–403.

Ogden, R., Shuttleworth, C., McEwing, R. & Cesarini, S. (2005) Genetic management of the red squirrel, Sciurus vulgaris: a practical approach to regional conservation. *Conservation Genetics,* **6**, 511–525.

Orford, J.D., Jennings, S.C. & Forbes, D.L. (2001) Origin, development, reworking, and breakdown of gravel dominated coastal barriers in Atlantic Canada: future scenarios for the northwest European coast. *Ecology & Geomorphology of Coastal Shingle*, (eds J.R. Packham, R.E. Randall, R.S.K. Barnes & A. Neal) pp. 23–55.Westbury Academic and Scientific Publishing, Otley, West Yorkshire.

Orford, J.D., Pethick, J.S. & McFadden, L. (2007) Reducing the vulnerability of natural coastal systems – A UK perspective. *Managing coastal vulnerability.* (eds McFadden, L., Nicholls, R.J. & Penning-Rowsell, E) pp. 177–194. Elsevier Publishing, Amsterdam.

Packham, J.R. & Willis, A.J. (1997) Ecology of dunes, salt marsh and shingle. Chapman and Hall, London.

Pethick J.S. (200)1 Coastal management and sea-level rise. *Catena,* **42**, 07–22.

Petroff, A., Mailliat, A., Amielh, M. & Anselmet, F. (2008) Aerosol dry deposition on vegetative canopies. Part I: Review of present knowledge. *Atmospheric Environment,* **42**, 3625–3653.

Plassmann, K., Jones, M.L.M. & Edwards-Jones, G. (2010) Effects of long-term grazing management on sand dune vegetation of high conservation interest. *Applied Vegetation Science,* **13**, 100–112.

Provoost, S., Jones, M.L.M. & Edmondson, S.E. (2010) Changes in landscape and vegetation of coastal dunes in northwest Europe: a review. *Journal of Coastal Conservation.* [online] DOI: 10.1007/s11852-009-0068-5.

Pugh, D. & Skinner, L. (2002) A new analysis of marine related activities in the UK economy with supporting science and technology. IACMST Information Document, No. 10. Pp. 48.

Pugh, D.T. (2004) Changing Sea Levels. Pp. 265. Cambridge University Press, Cambridge.

Pye, K. & French, P.W. (1992) Targets for Coastal Habitat

Recreation. English Nature Science Series No. 17, English Nature, Peterborough.

Pye, K. (2001) The nature and geomorphology of coastal shingle. Ecology & Geomorphology of Coastal Shingle (eds J.R. Packham, R.E. Randall, R.S.K. Barnes & A. Neal), pp. 2–22. Westbury Academic and Scientific Publishing, Otley, West Yorkshire.

Pye, K. & Saye, S.E. (2005) The Geomorphological Response of Welsh Sand Dunes to Sea Level Rise Over the Next 100 Years and the Management Implications for SAC and SSSI Sites. CCW Contract Science Report 670, Countryside Council for Wales, Bangor.

Pye, K., Saye, S.E. & Blott, S.J. (2007) Sand Dune Processes and Management for Flood and Coastal Defence. Parts 1 to 5. Joint DEFRA/EA Flood and Coastal Erosion Risk Management R & D Programme, R & D Technical Report FD1 1302/TR.

Pye, K. & Blott, S.J. (2008) Decadal-scale variation in dune erosion and accretion rates: an investigation of the significance of changing storm tide frequency and magnitude on the Sefton coast, UK. *Geomorphology*, **102**, 652–666.

Pye, K. & Blott, S.J. (2009) Progressive breakdown of a gravel-dominated barrier system, Dunwich–Walberswick, Suffolk, UK. *Journal of Coastal Research*, **25**, 589–602.

Radley, G.P. (1994) Sand dune vegetation survey of Great Britain. A national inventory. Part 1: England, Joint Nature Conservation Committee.

Randall, R.E. & Sneddon, P. (2001) Initiation, development and classification of vegetation on British shingle beaches: a model for conservation management. Ecology & Geomorphology of Coastal Shingle (eds. J.R. Packham, R.E. Randall, R.S.K. Barnes & A. Neal), pp. 202–223. Westbury Academic & Scientific Publishing, Otley, West Yorkshire.

Randall, R.E. (1977) Shingle foreshores. *The Coastline* (ed R.S.K., Barnes), pp. 49–61. Wiley, London.

Randall, R.E. (2004) Management of coastal vegetated shingle in the United Kingdom. *Journal of Coastal Conservation*, **10/1**, 159–168.

Ranwell, D.S. (1959) Newborough Warren, Anglesey 1: the dune system and dune slack habitat. *Journal of Ecology*, **47**, 571–601.

Ranwell, D.S. & Boar, R. (1986) Coast dune management guide. Institute of Terrestrial Ecology, Norwich.

Rees, S.M. (ed) (2005) Coastal Evolution in Suffolk: an evaluation of geomorphological and habitat change. English Nature Research Reports No. 647. English Nature, Peterborough.

Rehfisch, M.M., Austin, G.E., Armitage, M.J.S., Atkinson, P.W., Holloway, S.J., Musgrove, A.J. & Pollitt, M.S. (2003) Numbers of wintering Waterbirds in Great Britain and the Isle of Man (1994/1995–1998/1999): II. Coastal waders (Charadrii). Biological Conservation, **112**, 329–341.

Remke, E., Brouwer, E., Kooijman, A., Blindow, I., Esselink, H. & Roelofs, J.G.M. (2009) Even low to medium nitrogen deposition impacts vegetation of dry, coastal dunes around the Baltic Sea. Environmental Pollution, **157**, 792–800.

Rennie, A.F. & Hansom, J.D. 2011. Sea level trend reversal: Land uplift outpaced by sea level rise on Scotland's coast. *Geomorphology*. 125, 193–202.

Rhind, P.M., Blackstock, T.H., Hardy, H.S., Jones, R.E., Sandison, W. (2001) The evolution of Newborough warren dune system with particular reference to the past four decades. Coastal dune management, shared experience of European conservation practice (eds J. Houston, S.E. Edmondson, P.J. Rooney), pp. 345–379. Liverpool University press, Liverpool.

Rhind, P.M., Jones, R., Jones, M.L.M. (2008) Confronting the impact of dune stabilisation and soil development on the conservation status of sand dune systems in Wales. Proc. International conference on management and restoration of coastal dunes, Santander, Spain (ICCD 2007). Universidade de Cantabria, pp. 143–152.

Ritchie, W. & Gimingham C.H. (1989) Restoration of coastal dunes breached by pipeline landfalls in north-east Scotland. Coastal sand dunes (eds W. Ritchie, C.H. Gimmingham, B.B. Willets, A.J. Willis), pp. 231–245. Proceedings of the Royal Society of Edinburgh, Edinburgh.

RoTAP (Review Of Transboundary Air Pollution) (2011) Review of Transboundary Air Pollution: Acidification, Eutrophication, Ground Level Ozone and Heavy Metals in the UK. Contract Report to the Department for Environment, Food and Rural Affairs. Centre for Ecology & Hydrology.

RSPB (Royal Society for the Protection of Birds) (2010) The Local Value of Seabirds: Estimating spending by visitors to RSPB coastal reserves and associated local economic impact attributable to seabirds. The RSPB, Sandy, UK.

Rupp-Armstrong, S. & Nicholls, R.J. (2007) Coastal and Estuarine Retreat: A Comparison Of The Application Of Managed Realignment In England And Germany. *Journal of Coastal Research*, **23**(6), 1418–1430.

Saye, S.E. & Pye, K. (2007) Implications of sea level rise for coastal dune habitat conservation in Wales, UK. *Journal of Coastal Conservation*, **11**, 31–63.

Sevink, J. (1991) Soil development in the coastal dunes and its relation to climate. *Landscape Ecology*, **6**, 49–56.

Shardlow, E.A. (2001) A review of the conservation importance of shingle habitat for invertebrates in the United Kingdom (UK). Ecology & Geomorphology of Coastal Shingle, (eds J.R. Packham, R.E. Randall, R.S.K. Barnes, & A. Neal), pp. 355–377. Westbury Academic and Scientific Publishing.

Shennan, I., Milne, G. & Bradley, S.L. (2009) Late Holocene relative land – and sea-level changes: providing information for stakeholders. *GSA Today.* **19**:52–53.

Shepherd, D., Burgess, D., Jickells, T., Andrews, J., Cave, R., Turner, R.K., Aldridge, J., Parker E.R. & Young, E. (2007) Modeling the effects and economics of managed realignment on cycling and storage of nutrients, carbon and sediments in the Blackwater estuary, UK. *Estuarine Coastal and Shelf Science,* **73**, 355–367.

Simonson, W. & Thomas, R. (1999) Biodiversity: Making the links. English Nature, Peterborough.

Simpson, D.E., Rooney, P.J., Houston, J.A. (2001) Towards best practice in the sustainable management of sand dune habitats: Management for golf and nature on the Sefton Coast. Coastal dune management: shared experience of European conservation practice (eds J.A. Houston, S.E. Edmondson, P.J. Rooney) pp. 271–280. Liverpool University Press, Liverpool.

Sival, F.P. & Strijkstra-Kalk, M. (1999) Atmospheric deposition of acidifying and eutrophicating substances in dune slacks. *Water Air and Soil Pollution*, **116**, 461–477.

Smith, B.P. & Laffoley, D. (1992) Saline lagoons and lagoon-like habitats. English Nature Science No. 6. English Nature, Peterborough.

Smith, T. (2009) East Sussex Vegetated Shingle Management Plan Source. [online] Available at: <http://www.

eastsussex.gov.uk/NR/rdonlyres/04C8BD90-8E98-4DB7-87CA-47AA0BA94E4A/0/shingle_mgmt_plan.pdf> [Accessed 03.02.11].

Spurgeon, J. (1999) The Socio-Economic Costs and Benefits of Coastal Habitat Rehabilitation and Creation. *Marine Pollution Bulletin*, **37/8**, 373–382.

Steward, H. (2001) Quality of Coastal Towns. Merseyside Coast Visitor Research 2000. Formby Council Offices, Formby.

Struyf, E., Dausse, A., Van Damme, S. Bal, K., Gribsholt, B, Boschker, H.T.S. Middelburg, J.J. & Meire, P. 2006. Tidal marshes and biogenic silica recycling at the land–sea interface, *Limnology and Oceanography*, **51**(2), 838–846.

Sturgess, P. & Atkinson, D. (1993) The clearfelling of sanddune plantations: soil and vegetational processes in habitat restoration. *Biological Conservation*, **66**, 171–183.

Symes, N.C. & Robertson, P.A. (eds) (2004) A Practical Guide to the Management of Saline Lagoons. The RSPB, Sandy.

Tantram, D. & Dargie, T. (2005) Maritime Cliff and Slope Inventory for Wales. Contract Science Report. Countryside Council for Wales, Bangor.

Taylor, J.A., Murdock, A.P., & Pontee, N.I. (2004) A macroscale analysis of coastal steepening around the coast of England and Wales, *The Geographical Journal*, **170**(3), 170–188.

Taylor, W.A., Bryden, D.B., Westbrook, S.R., & Anderson, S. (2010) Nature Based Tourism in the Outer Hebrides. Scottish Natural Heritage Commissioned Report No. 353 (Tender 29007).

Turner, R.K., Burgess, D., Hadley, D., Coombes, E.G. & Jackson, N. (2007) A cost–benefit appraisal of coastal managed realignment policy. *Global Environmental Change*, **17**, 397–407.

TNS (2005) Scottish Recreation Survey: annual summary report 2003/04. Scottish Natural Heritage Commissioned Report No. 105 (ROAME No. F02AA614/2).

UKTS (United Kingdom Tourism Statistics) (2006) United Kingdom Tourism Statistics 2006. Tourism volumes and values in 2006. [online] Available at: <http://tourisminsights. info/STATISTICS/UKTS.htm> [Accessed 09.02.11].

UKTS (United Kingdom Tourism Statistics) (2009) United Kingdom Tourism Statistics 2009. Tourism volumes and values in 2009. [online] Available at: < http://www.visitengland. org/insight-statistics/major-tourism-surveys/overnightvisitors/ index.aspx> [Accessed 09.02.11].

VEP (Valuing our Environment Partnership) (2006) The economic impact of the coastal and marine environment of Wales. [online] Available at: < http://www.nationaltrust.org.uk/ main/w-wales-valuing_our_environment-marine-english.pdf> [Accessed 09.02.11].

van Dijk, H.W.J. (1989) Ecological impact of drinking-water production in Dutch coastal dunes. Perspectives in coastal dune management. Proceedings of the European Symposium Leiden, September 7–11, 1987 (eds F. van der Meulen, P.D. Jungerius, J. Visser), pp. 163–182. SPB Academic Publishing, The Hague.

van Dijk, H.J.W. (1992) Grazing domestic livestock in Dutch coastal dunes: Experiments, experiences and perspectives. Coastal dunes: Geomorphology, ecology and management for conservation. Proceedings of the third European Dune Congress, Galway, Ireland, 17–21 June 1992. (eds R.W.G. Carter, T.G.F. Curtis, M.J. Sheehy-Skeffington), pp. 235–250. Balkema, Rotterdam.

van Wijnen, H.J. & Bakker, J.P. (1999) Nitrogen and phosphorus limitation in a coastal barrier salt marsh: the implications for vegetation succession. *Journal of Ecology*, **87**, 265–272.

VisitBritain (2007) England Tourism Day Visits 2005. VisitBritain, London.

VisitWales (2008) Coastal Tourism Strategy (2008). Published by Visit Wales, the Tourism and Marketing Division of the Welsh Assembly Government.

WTB (Wales Tourist Board) (1992) Prospects for coastal resorts – a Paper for Discussion. Wales Tourist Board, Cardiff.

Walmsley, C.A. & Davy, A.J. (1997) The restoration of coastal shingle vegetation; effects of substrate composition on the establishment of seedlings. *Journal of Applied Ecology*, **34**, 143–153.

Walmsley, C.A. & Davy, A.J. (2001) Habitat creation and restoration of damaged shingle communities. Ecology & Geomorphology of Coastal Shingle (eds J.R. Packham, R.E. Randall, R.S.K. Barnes & A. Neal), pp. 409–420. Westbury Academic and Scientific Publishing.

Walton, J.K. (1983) The English Seaside Resort: a Social History 1750–1914. Leicester.

Walton, J.K. (1997) The seaside resorts of England and Wales, 1900 – 1950: growth, diffusion and the emergence of new forms of coastal tourism. The Rise and Fall of British Coastal Resorts: cultural and economic perspectives (eds G. Shaw & A. Williams), pp. 21–48. Pinter, London.

Walton J.K. (2000) The British Seaside: Holidays and Resorts in the Twentieth Century. Manchester University Press, Manchester.

Weber, G.J., O'Sullivan, P.E. & Brassley, P. (2006) Hindcasting of nutrient loadings from its catchment on a highly valuable coastal lagoon: the example of the Fleet, Dorset, UK, 1866–2004. *Saline Systems*, **2**, 15.

WAG (Welsh Assembly Government) (2008) Coastal Tourism Strategy. Visit Wales, the Tourism and Marketing Division of the Welsh Assembly Government, Cardiff.

Whitehouse, A.T. (2007) Managing coastal soft cliffs for invertebrates. Buglife – The Invertebrate Conservation Trust, Peterborough.

Williams, J.M. (ed) (2006) Common Standards Monitoring for Designated Sites: First Six Year Report. JNCC, Peterborough.

Williams, A. & Shaw, G. (1997) Riding the big dipper: the rise and decline of the British seaside resort in the twentieth century. The Rise and Fall of British Coastal Resorts: cultural and economic perspectives (eds G. Shaw & A. Williams). Pinter, London.

Williams A.M. & Shaw, G. (2009) Future play: tourism, recreation and land use. *Land Use Policy*, **26S**, S326–S335.

Wolters, M., Garbutt, A. & Bakker, J.P. (2005) Salt-marsh restoration: evaluating the success of de-embankments in north-west Europe. *Biological Conservation*, **123**, 249–268.

Woodworth, P.L., Shaw, S.M. & Blackman, D.L. (1991) Secular trends in mean tidal range around the British Isles and along the adjacent European coastline. *Geophysical Journal International*, **104**, 593–609.

Appendix 11.1 Approach Used to Assign Certainty Terms to Chapter Key Findings

This chapter began with a set of Key Findings. Adopting the approach and terminology used by the Intergovernmental Panel on Climate Change (IPCC) and the Millennium Assessment (MA), these Key Findings also include an indication of the level of scientific certainty. The 'uncertainty approach' of the UK NEA consists of a set of qualitative uncertainty terms derived from a 4-box model and complemented, where possible, with a likelihood scale (see below). Estimates of certainty are derived from the collective judgement of authors, observational evidence, modelling results and/or theory examined for this assessment.

Throughout the Key Findings presented at the start of this chapter, superscript numbers and letters indicate the estimated level of certainty for a particular key finding:

1. *Well established:*   high agreement based on significant evidence
2. *Established but incomplete evidence:* high agreement based on limited evidence
3. *Competing explanations:*   low agreement, albeit with significant evidence
4. *Speculative:*   low agreement based on limited evidence

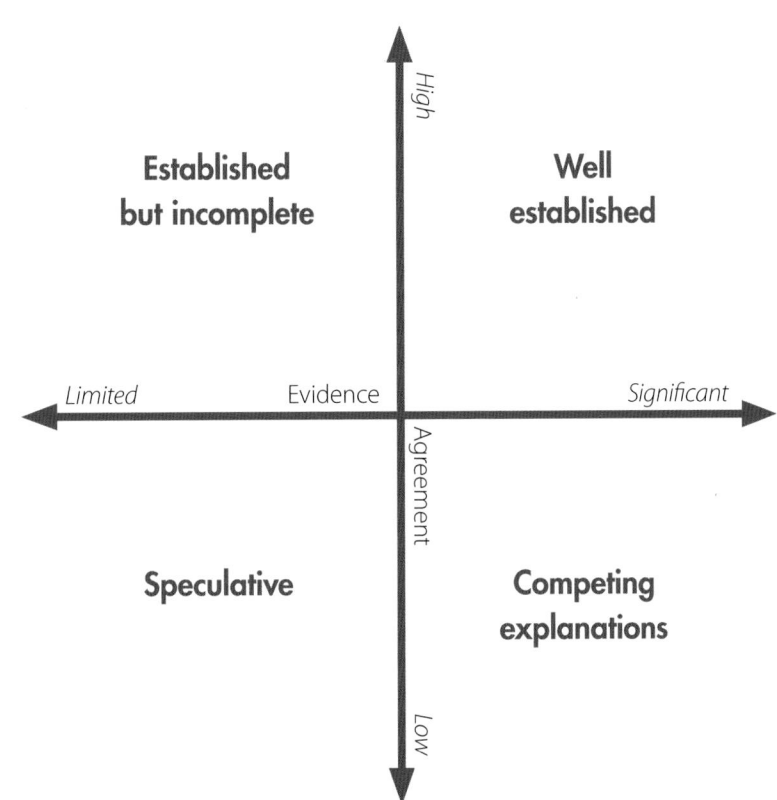

a. *Virtually certain:*   >99% probability of occurrence
b. *Very likely:*   >90% probability
c. *Likely:*   >66% probability
d. *About as likely as not:*   >33–66% probability
e. *Unlikely:*   <33% probability
f. *Very unlikely:*   <10% probability
g. *Exceptionally unlikely:*   <1% probability

Certainty terms 1 to 4 constitute the 4-box model, while *a* to *g* constitute the likelihood scale.

Chapter 12:
Marine

Coordinating Lead Authors: Melanie C. Austen and Stephen J. Malcolm
Lead Authors: Matthew Frost, Caroline Hattam, Stephen Mangi and Grant Stentiford
Contributing Authors: Stephen Benjamins, Michael Burrows, Momme Butenschön, Callan Duck, David Johns, Gorka Merino, Nova Mieszkowska, Alison Miles, Ian Mitchell, Eunice Pimm and Tim Smyth

Key Findings*

The diversity of organisms in Marine habitats provide a range of ecosystem services and benefits of significant value to UK society[1]. The benefits include food (fish, shellfish); reduction of climate stress (carbon and other biogas regulation); genetic resources (for aquaculture); blue biotechnology (e.g. biocatalysts, natural medicines); fertiliser (seaweed); coastal protection; waste detoxification and removal and disease and pest control; tourism, leisure and recreation opportunities; a focus for engagement with the natural environment; physical and mental health benefits; and cultural heritage and learning experiences. Energy from waves and tides and biofuels from macro- and microalgae are likely to be provided in the near future. Many of the benefits are accrued directly by coastal dwellers and visitors, but also indirectly by much of the UK's society[1,a].

[1] *well established*
[a] *virtually certain*

Changes in sea temperature are likely to be affecting most Marine ecosystem services. These changes are already affecting food production, wildlife populations, such as seabirds, and possibly human health through the increase in optimum environmental conditions for outbreaks of pathogens[c]. Yet at the same time, climate change could bring increased benefits for the marine leisure and recreation industries because of the potential for warmer summers. Some of the effects of increases in sea temperature and those of heavy fisheries exploitation are difficult to distinguish from each other and are likely to have synergistic effects[c].

[c] *likely*

Climate change is changing species distribution. This is particularly evident in coastal intertidal species, plankton and fish, where long-term data is richest. Comparison of historic (since the 1950s) and present distribution and abundance of over 60 indicator species in the UK has shown some of the fastest changes in the abundance, range and population structures of species in the world. These changes have been related to recent, rapid climatic warming. In particular, several southern species of warm water intertidal invertebrates and macroalgae have considerably extended their ranges northwards along the Welsh and Scottish coastlines, and eastwards along the English Channel. Northern cold water species have shown a modest contraction in range and significant declines in abundance at sites close to their southern limits. These species-specific rates of change are driving alterations of community structure and function[1,a].

[1] *well established*
[a] *virtually certain*

Human activities that affect the seafloor damage regulating and supporting services. Human activities that have a physical impact on the seafloor (e.g. trawl fishing, building offshore windfarms, aggregate extraction, coastal defences, ports and coastal developments) damage the benthic biota (species which live on the seabed) and their communities, and affect the regulating and supporting services that they provide. Usually the impacts are quite localised, but seabed trawl fishing activity, the most widespread of these activities, has the greatest impact[1,a].

[1] *well established*
[a] *virtually certain*

Increasing activity in several economic sectors in the Marine environment is putting extra pressure on all sea shelf, coastal and estuarine habitats[1,c]. These sectors include marine renewable energy development, expansion in recreation and leisure activities, and port activities. Their impacts vary in spatial extent and importance, but are compounded by climate change. Human contamination of marine waters with a range of hazardous substances has been reduced through reductions in industrial effluent and improvements in sewage treatment infrastructure[1,a]; however, there are now concerns about more recently introduced chemicals, such as nanoparticles and pharmaceuticals, which pass through sewage treatment plants[c].

[1] *well established*
[a] *virtually certain*
[c] *likely*

---

* Each Key Finding has been assigned a level of scientific certainty, based on a 4-box model and complemented, where possible, with a likelihood scale. Superscript numbers and letters indicate the uncertainty term assigned to each finding. Full details of each term and how they were assigned are presented in Appendix 12.1.

The quantity of wild fish caught in UK waters is insufficient to meet the UK demand for this food. Landings into UK ports of fish and other seafood declined steadily from 1.2 million tonnes wet weight in 1948 to 0.5 million tonnes in 2000, but have remained steady since then. Since 1945, there has been an increased demand for fish in the human diet leading to the rise of aquaculture, particularly of finfish in Scottish waters and shellfish in English, Welsh and Northern Irish waters. There has also been a 46% increase in the volume of fish imported from overseas between 1998 and 2008[1,a].

[1] *well established*
[a] *virtually certain*

The sustainability of food provision from Marine Habitats is threatened by overexploitation of fisheries; fishing is also damaging other Marine ecosystem services. Over the last 50 years, fishing activity has put significant pressure on living resources and habitats. Several fish stocks in the North Sea and Irish Sea are overexploited and are subject to recovery plans. Out of 18 indicator finfish stocks in UK waters, only 50% were considered to have full reproductive capacity and to be harvested sustainably in 2008, but this is an improvement from 10% or less in the early 1990s[1,a].

[1] *well established*
[a] *virtually certain*

Water purification and breakdown of waste by ecosystems appears to be keeping pace with inputs in open shelf waters, although localised contamination and some eutrophication problems persist[1,a]. The waste processing and purification services widely provided by Marine habitats generally ensure that food provided by the sea is safe to eat and the water is clean enough to use for recreation, such as swimming, angling, scuba diving, and surfing[c]. In some coastal waters, such as estuaries, local contamination by diffuse pollution (e.g. agricultural fertiliser, urban runoff and synthetic chemicals) still exceeds the capacity of the ecosystem to remediate or assimilate it[c].

[1] *well established*
[a] *virtually certain*
[c] *likely*

The UK's seas are important to people's quality of life but are less well protected than terrestrial environments[a]. The UK population has a strong affinity for the sea and has always derived inspiration from it. More people are using the sea for leisure and recreation, education, research and health benefits. Despite this, protection of the Marine environment falls short of that on land. For example, there are only 81 marine Special Areas of Conservation (SACs) out of a total of 621 designated under the Habitats Directive, and very few marine Sites of Special Scientific Interest (SSSIs). The Marine and Coastal Access Act (2009) signals an increasing awareness of how important Marine Habitats are to UK culture and society and will foster greater biodiversity protection[a].

[a] *virtually certain*

Marine microbial organisms play a key role in cycling nutrients that are essential for other marine organisms and the services and benefits they provide[1,a]. Microbial processing of nutrients in the sediment depends on invertebrates disturbing and irrigating the sediment[2]. Without this recycling, most nutrients would be lost from the ecosystem to the seabed as they would sink from the water column and then be buried[a]. In open water, planktonic coccolithophores make a major contribution to the global carbon sink[a]. Climate change may affect internal nutrient cycling by changing nutrient exchange processes between the open waters and the open ocean and altering water stratification, but the likely direction and extent of these changes is still poorly understood[c].

[1] *well established*
[2] *established but incomplete evidence*
[a] *virtually certain*
[c] *likely*

Many organisms create living habitats such as reefs and seagrass meadows. These can provide essential feeding, breeding and nursery space that can be particularly important for commercial fish species[1,c]. Such habitats play a critical role in species interactions and the regulation of population dynamics, and are a prerequisite for the provision of many goods and services[c]. Fishing at the seabed with trawl nets and dredging fishing gears severely damages living reefs and deep-sea corals, which are very slow-growing and, consequently, take a long time to recover[a]. Boat anchoring, propeller scarring and channel dredging can damage shallow water and intertidal habitats[c]. However, building coastal defences and offshore structures, such as wind turbines, oil platforms and reefs, provides artificial habitats which can have positive impacts, particularly for species usually associated with rocky environments[b].

[1] *well established*
[a] *virtually certain*
[b] *very likely*
[c] *likely*

Marine ecosystem services are strongly interlinked[2,c]. Very similar ecosystem functions and biological activity underpin waste regulation, climate regulation and nutrient cycling. These functions also underpin cultural services, such as leisure and recreation, which depend on clean, functioning seas. Attractive seascapes, inshore fishing boats, and the local seafood provide enhanced local tourism and cultural services. Yet fishing also affects other components of the ecosystem, damaging food webs and seabed habitats. Hence, the provisioning service of fishing can negatively affect delivery of other services. For instance, seabirds and mammals are important for tourism and recreation, but compete with humans for fish as food or are trapped in fishing nets; this indicates a trade-off between food provision, cultural services and conservation[a].

[2] *established but incomplete evidence*
[a] *virtually certain*
[c] *likely*

Farmland food production and urban waste disposal may conflict with the delivery of ecosystem services and benefits in estuarine and coastal waters[2,c]. Fertiliser use can increase food production, but excess nutrients run off the land into estuarine and coastal waters. These waters also receive significant amounts of other agrochemicals (e.g. pesticides, artificial growth hormones), microorganisms and urban surface waste water, thereby providing a cleansing regulating service for farmlands and urban habitats. However, excessive enrichment of water by nutrients can reduce the flow of oxygen and nutrients to the seabed, with a deleterious effect on the water quality and other organisms. The major pressures occur in the east, south and north-west of England. Here, some estuarine areas are nutrient-enriched and are at risk from, or currently affected by, eutrophication. Nevertheless, UK marine waters as a whole do not suffer from eutrophication[1,a].

[1] *well established*
[2] *established but incomplete evidence*
[a] *virtually certain*
[c] *likely*

The development of Marine Plans and designation of Marine Conservation Zones will incorporate the explicit objectives of sustaining and increasing ecosystem services and managing the use of marine resources sustainably. It is imperative that these plans consider the components of Marine habitats not only in terms of biodiversity and habitats, but also with regards to ecosystem functioning and the provision of ecosystem services and benefits. The use of monetary and non-monetary valuation of ecosystem services will aid the process of considering the impacts and benefits of development on Marine habitats[a].

[a] *virtually certain*

The characteristics and biodiversity of a large proportion of UK subtidal Marine habitats is still unknown and not mapped; Marine ecosystem services are poorly quantified. We need to understand and measure the links between Marine biodiversity, ecosystem function and provision of ecosystem goods and services, and the effects of human impacts on these links. Although recent national assessments (e.g. Charting Progress 2, State of Scotland's Seas) have gathered a lot of evidence, extensive data gaps remain. Such knowledge would support more effective marine planning and licensing of activity in UK waters for the sustainable use of Marine habitats and the maintenance of clean, healthy, productive and biologically diverse seas[a].

[a] *virtually certain*

12.1 Introduction[1]

"How inappropriate to call this planet Earth, when it is quite clearly Ocean." Arthur C. Clarke

The broad marine habitat covers all UK areas that are either permanently immersed in seawater or are inundated with saline water at some stage in the tidal cycle. This includes estuaries, beaches, coasts and all subtidal habitats out to the limit of the UK's marine area (**Figure 12.1**). The seas of the UK extend to some 867,400 km^2, which is more than three and a half times the land area. Mainland Britain has over 17,820 km of coastline (based on ordnance survey digital measurements of 1:10,000 maps using the high water line, www.ordnancesurvey.co.uk/; **Table 12.1**) and the widest range of marine habitats of any European country with an Atlantic border (Hiscock 1996). These habitats support a high diversity of animals and plants, and are ranked as one of the highest in Europe (Defra 2005) with approximately 8,500 marine species (Hiscock & Smirthwaite 2004). This number only refers to multi-cellular species, however, and molecular techniques are now enabling documentation of the vast diversity of microbes that are naturally present in the oceans. One drop (one millilitre) of seawater can contain 10 million viruses, 1 million bacteria and about 1,000 small protozoans and algae (Heip *et al.* 2009). Estimates of marine biodiversity for the UK will, therefore, continue to be revised upward as the diversity of the microbial component is elucidated.

At phyletic levels marine diversity is higher than diversity on land or in freshwater. There are 14 exclusively marine phyla and only one exclusively terrestrial phylum. Recorded multi-cellular species diversity is lower in the marine environment than it is on land and in freshwater.

12.1.1 Charting Progress

The underlying data on the description of marine habitats and species and their current status and recent trends (Sections 12.1.2, 12.1.3, 12.2) draws heavily on the information collated for the Charting Progress (CP) reports prepared by the UK Marine Monitoring and Assessment Strategy (UKMMAS) Community for the UK Government and the Devolved Administrations (Scottish Government, Welsh Assembly Government, and the Department of the Environment, Northern Ireland). These reports show the extent of progress towards the UK Government and Devolved Administrations vision of "clean, safe, healthy, productive and biologically diverse oceans and seas". The first report was published in 2005 (Defra 2005) and the latest report, Charting Progress 2, was published in July 2010 (UKMMAS 2010). Charting Progress 2 (CP2) focuses on the state of components of the

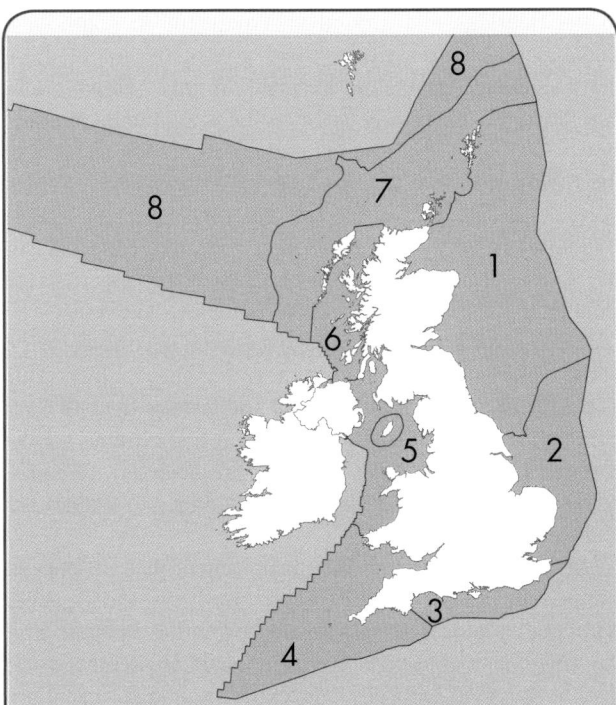

Figure 12.1 UK Regional Seas and boundaries.
1) Northern North Sea; 2) Southern North Sea; 3) Eastern Channel; 4) Western Channel and Celtic Sea; 5) Irish Sea; 6) Minches and Western Scotland; 7) Scottish Continental Shelf; 8) Atlantic North-West Approaches, Rockall Trough and Faeroe/Shetland Channel. Source: map based on UKMMAS (2010). Coastline: World Vector Shoreline@National – Geospatial Intelligence Agency. Source: NOASS, NGDC.

Table 12.1 Length of coastline for Great Britain and Northern Ireland*. Lengths given with and without principal islands and derived from 1:10,000 Ordnance Survey maps.
Source: adapted from Frost (2010), where GB data is derived from the British Cartography Society (www.cartography.org.uk/default. asp?contentID=749) and Northern Ireland data is provided by the Agri-Food & Biosciences Institute AFBI.

Coastline	Approximate Length (km)
England	8,982
England + Principal Islands (Isle of Wight, Lundy, Scilly Isles)	10,077
Scotland	6,718
Scotland + Principal Islands (Arran, Islay and Jura, Shetland and Orkney, Western Isles)	18,588
Wales	2,120
Wales + Principal Islands (Anglesey and Holyhead)	2,740
Northern Ireland	686
Northern Ireland + Principal Islands (Rathlin)	718
Total Mainland GB	**17,820**
Total GB + Principal Islands	**31,368**
Total UK (GB + Northern Ireland + Principal Islands)	**32,086**

* Coastline length is highly dependent on the scale of the data from which it is measured. Therefore the length of coastline presented in this table differs from that in Chapter 11 due to the different techniques and sources on which these measurements are based.

1 Section 12.1 has been reproduced (with minor modifications) with permission from Frost (2010).

marine environment including marine habitats and ranging from microbes through to higher trophic levels such as seals, cetaceans and turtles. It also provides information on trends in these components, along with the pressures and drivers of change. This chapter includes a summary of the relevant sections of CP2 and the supporting Feeder Reports (see Sections 12.1.2, 12.1.3, 12.2). For more information please visit the CP2 website: http://chartingprogress.defra.gov.uk

12.1.2 Marine Habitats[2]

The UK marine seabed was categorised into six component habitat types (**Figure 12.2**) for the CP2 assessment (Benjamins et al., 2010). These categories (**Table 12.2**) have also been used in this and other assessments such as the Marine Climate Change Impacts Partnership (MCCIP) report card.

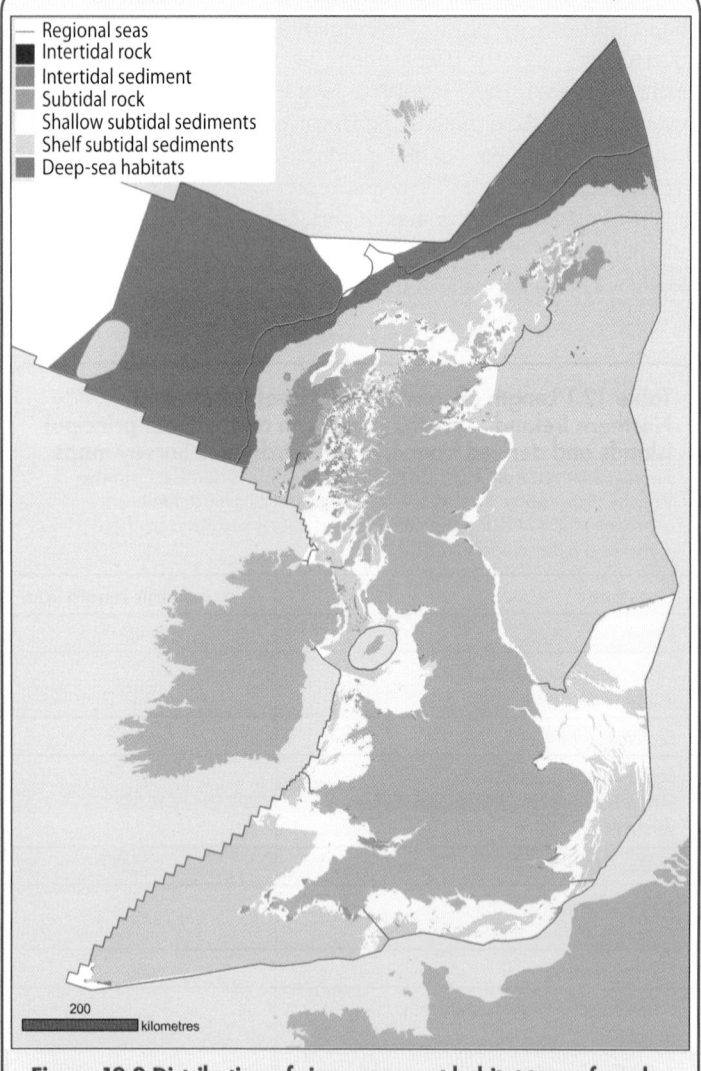

Legend:
— Regional seas
- Intertidal rock
- Intertidal sediment
- Subtidal rock
- Shallow subtidal sediments
- Shelf subtidal sediments
- Deep-sea habitats

200 kilometres

Figure 12.2 Distribution of six component habitat types found throughout UK marine waters. Subtidal and deep-sea habitat types are derived from modelling; intertidal habitat types are derived from survey data. Any white space in the map indicates where there are insufficient data to model the habitats. Source: data from JNCC and reprinted with permission from UKMMAS (2010). Map © JNCC 2010. World Vector Shoreline © US Defense Mapping Agency. Seabed habitats derived from UKSeaMap 2010 predictive map and survey data © JNCC and UKSeaMap funding partners and © MESH 2010, respectively.

Intertidal Rocky habitats are widespread throughout the UK, with the exception of the south-eastern and north-western coasts of England where they are almost completely absent and the intertidal zone is dominated by sandy beaches or intertidal mudflats. Intertidal Sediment habitats are most common in England and Wales, making up large stretches of coastline, as opposed to Scotland where lengths of Intertidal Sediment coastlines are interrupted by rocky promontories and headlands. Nearly 25% of all Intertidal Sediments occur within estuaries (Wyn et al. 2006) where muddy sediments are particularly prevalent. Saltmarshes also typically occur within estuaries, usually landward of intertidal muds.

In the subtidal zone, sedimentary habitats, such as sand, gravel, muds and mixed sediments, cover almost all of the continental shelf around the UK as well as coastal habitats such as sea lochs and lagoons. Shallow Subtidal Sediment habitats, which can be regularly disturbed by surface waves, are widespread in the Irish Sea, the Eastern Channel and the Southern North Sea; they also occur in coastal lagoons, particularly in southern England and western Scotland. Shelf Subtidal Sediment habitats are only rarely disturbed by surface waves because of their greater water depth and, therefore, support more stable communities. They occur throughout offshore areas of most regional seas, but also much closer to coasts where the water deepens rapidly such as around most of Scotland, Northern Ireland and Cornwall.

Subtidal Rock habitats are relatively uncommon. The largest expanses occur in Scotland (particularly to the west of the Hebrides and around Shetland) and in south-west England and Wales where there are significant offshore reefs. Biogenic reefs are included in this category and can be quite extensive, such as beds of horse mussels (*Modiolus modiolus*), or small and isolated, such as reefs of the tubeworm (*Serpula vermicularis*), both of which have a northern distribution in the UK. The ross worm (*Sabellaria spinulosa*) is very widespread and common, especially in the south-east of England, but occurs mostly as crusts or isolated individuals, only rarely forming low-lying reefs.

Deep-sea habitats occur below 200 m, beyond the edge of the continental shelf. Within UK waters they mainly occur to the north and west of Scotland and west of Rockall islet, although there are also small areas in the extreme south-western Celtic Sea. Most of these are sediment habitats, with rocky habitats and reefs largely confined to seamounts and similar structures.

In addition, the marine environment has a pelagic component which is the water overlying the seabed. Additional physical factors influence marine habitats and the organisms that live in them including: temperature, tidal flows, wind-induced wave exposure and stratification. These physical factors are influenced by the structure of the coastline. For example, headlands entrain high tidal current flows. The degree of wave exposure of coastlines is dependent on the predominant wind direction and the amount of fetch. Marine organisms are also affected by the degree of light penetration and turbidity and salinity of the water in which they live—the latter of which depends on the freshwater inflow as in estuaries, for example see Section 12.1.4.

2 Section 12.1.2 has been reproduced (with some minor modification) with permission from Benjamins (2010).

Table 12.2 Component and sub-component habitats assessed in the Charting Progress 2 report. Each component habitat corresponds to one or more high-level European Nature Information System (EUNIS) habitat codes. This includes a diversity of underlying, more specific, EUNIS habitat sub-component categories which are also included in the component habitat type, except where indicated.

Component Habitat	Definition	Sub-component Habitat
Intertidal Rock	All rocky habitats and biogenic reefs between Highest Astronomical Tide mark and Lowest Astronomical Tide mark	Intertidal rock
		Intertidal biogenic reefs
Intertidal Sediment	All sediment habitats (muds, sands, gravels and mixed sediments) between Highest Astronomical Tide mark and Lowest Astronomical Tide mark	Saltmarshes
		Intertidal muds
		Intertidal sands and muddy sands
		Intertidal coarse and mixed sediment
		Intertidal seagrass beds
Subtidal Rock	All rocky habitats and biogenic reefs from Lowest Astronomical Tide mark outward to 200 m depth (typically the edge of the continental shelf)	Infralittoral rock
		Circalittoral rock
		Subtidal biogenic reefs
Shallow subtidal Sediment	All sediment habitats (muds, sands, gravels and mixed sediments) from Lowest Astronomical Tide mark down to the wave-base depth (between 50–70 m depth around much of the UK)	Shallow muds
		Shallow sands and muddy sands
		Shallow coarse and mixed sediment
		Macrophyte-dominated sediment (seagrasses, maerl, seaweeds)
Shelf Subtidal Sediment	All sedimentary habitats (muds, sands, gravels and mixed sediments) from the wave-base depth outward to 200 m depth (typically the edge of the continental shelf)	Shelf muds
		Shelf sands and muddy sands
		Shelf coarse and mixed sediment
Deep-sea Habitats	All habitats occurring in waters deeper than 200 m depth (typically beyond the edge of the continental shelf)	Deep-sea rock
		Deep-sea bioherms
		Deep-sea sediments

12.1.3 Marine Fauna

Charting Progress 2 focused on the indicators of change affecting the major and/or more distinctive taxonomic marine groups (thus reflecting important changes to the marine environment) where there is a significant amount of data or the species or groups have conservation status. These include plankton, fish, seals, cetaceans, birds, and turtles. The invertebrate fauna which dominate the biomass within sediments are useful as indicators of change, but are not systematically monitored in either time or space in UK waters. However, in CP2 a variety of studies were used to determine the status of intertidal, subtidal and deep-sea sediment habitats (see Benjamins *et al.* 2010).

The plankton component of the UK marine ecosystem includes bacteria, archaea, viruses and many protists (microbes). The CP2 assessment highlights the importance of microbes for the functioning of the oceans; for example, viruses help to sustain the balance and diversity of life because of their involvement in nutrient cycling (Schroeder 2010). However, there is not enough information to be able to provide any assessment of status or trend for the UK's microbial community (Schroeder 2010). Photosynthesis by phytoplankton makes up at least 50% of primary production in UK marine waters, and plankton, along with the smaller microbial community, are the basis of the food supply for all higher trophic levels (Reid *et al.* 2010).

More than 330 fish species inhabit the shelf seas surrounding the British Isles, ranging from species commonly found in coastal waters or in estuaries, to those present in deep-sea and offshore oceanic waters (Pinnegar *et al.* 2010). Fish represent an important link in marine food webs, both as predators (sometimes 'top predators') and as prey for marine mammals and seabirds, as well as sustaining important commercial fisheries.

Two species of seal are found in the UK: grey seals (*Halichoerus grypus*) and harbour (or common) seals (*Phoca vitulina*) (Duck 2010), each of which makes up 36% and 4% of the world's population of these species, respectively. Grey seals are found all around the UK, however 90% of the UK's population is found in Scotland. Eighty percent of harbour seals are also found in Scotland. Harbour seals are also found in the south and south-west of England but here they are very sparse (Duck 2010).

In UK waters there are 28 species of cetacean (whales, dolphins and porpoises), of which, 11 appear regularly (Pinn 2010). The greatest diversity occurs off the continental shelf, particularly in waters to the north and west of Scotland and in the south-west towards the Bay of Biscay. Cetaceans are mobile and wide-ranging, so most of the animals found in UK waters are part of much larger and more widespread biological populations (Pinn 2010). The five species most abundant in UK waters are considered to have a favourable conservation status assessment. The status of a further six species is unknown due to a lack of suitable abundance estimates. The remaining 17 species are considered rare or vagrant and their conservation status in UK waters cannot be assessed (Pinn 2010).

The UK's marine environment supports internationally important numbers of birds. More than 100 species regularly use the marine areas of the UK. The majority of these species are waterbirds, such as waders, herons, egrets, ducks, geese, swans, divers and grebes, and seabirds, such as petrels, gannets, cormorants, skuas, gulls, terns and auks (Mitchell 2010). Most of the evidence of status and trends in birds is collected near to land, that is in estuaries and coastal areas. Less is known about bird populations that do not live in the intertidal zone or close inshore due to difficulties in gathering data in offshore areas (Mitchell 2010).

The leatherback turtle (*Dermochelys coriacea*) is the most common of the four turtles occasionally reported in UK waters (Marubini 2010). It is a wide-ranging species, migrating throughout the Atlantic; UK waters represent a small peripheral part of its summer foraging habitat (Marubini 2010). There is currently not enough evidence to be able to assess population trends.

12.1.4 Linkages with Other UK National Ecosystem Assessment Habitats

Specific marine habitats occur at the interface with freshwater (river) and coastal habitats. In these marine habitats, usually estuaries, sea lochs or sometimes lagoons, the salinity of the water can be reduced and spatially or temporally variable depending on the amount of freshwater inflow, the physical structure of the terrestrial boundary, and the extent of tidal inflow from the sea.

The marine ecosystem, especially coastal estuarine, sea loch and coastal shelf habitats, directly interacts with terrestrial habitats, particularly Coastal Margins (Chapter 11), coastal and estuarine urban habitats and freshwater (through runoff into estuaries and coasts). The division between Coastal Margin habitats and Marine habitats is usually rather indistinct. For example, many Coastal Margin habitats are inundated with saline water during extreme weather events.

There is also a freshwater catchment to coast connection between all of the terrestrial habitats that are further inland and the marine habitat, via the freshwater flows that link them.

12.2 Trends and Changes in Marine Habitats

This section includes a discussion of the trends and changes in component habitats (extent and status) included in this assessment and their associated fauna. The major drivers of change are also identified.

12.2.1 Intertidal Rock[3]

Although Intertidal Rock habitats are generally in good condition, the harvesting of edible shellfish and the occurrence of non-native species are adversely affecting some local communities. In addition, species composition of intertidal rocky communities in the Channel and Celtic Seas is already impacted by warmer waters. Recorded occurrences of non-native species are increasing around the UK coastline, but the impacts on native communities are still poorly understood. The pressures on this habitat have increased over the last ten years (**Box 12.1**).

12.2.2 Intertidal Sediments

Human pressures have adversely affected moderate to large areas of Intertidal Sediment habitats, notably mudflats and saltmarshes, in most of the UK's seas apart from northern and western Scotland. Historical land-claim from the sea and the construction of coastal defences and other structures have caused widespread habitat loss, particularly in England. Such structures also affect these habitats by changing water current patterns and sediment distribution. In the Southern North Sea and Eastern Channel, the spread of non-native species, such as common cordgrass (*Spartina anglica*), has led to changes in saltmarshes and mudflats. Although water quality levels have improved overall, there are still some small inshore areas (particularly within the North Sea and Irish Sea) where pollution and nutrient enrichment are a problem. Beach litter levels remain high and have been increasing in almost all areas except the eastern English Channel. The pressure on this habitat has increased over the last ten years.

12.2.3 Subtidal Rock and Other Hard Substrata

Overall, only limited areas of subtidal rocky habitat appear to be directly impacted by human activity. Some have, however, been permanently damaged by mobile fishing gear such as bottom trawling. This has had a particular impact on fragile biogenic reefs such as horse mussel beds. Locally, particularly near some large ports around England and Wales, subtidal rocky habitat has also been lost because of construction, coastal infrastructure or the disposal of dredged materials. The pressure on this habitat has not changed over the last ten years.

12.2.4 Shallow and Shelf Subtidal Sediments

In most regions, large areas of subtidal sediments have been adversely affected by mobile fishing gears, such as bottom trawls and dredges, but there have been less severe impacts on the Scottish Continental Shelf and the Eastern Channel. Locally, the extraction of aggregates has altered the seabed in the Eastern Channel, Southern North Sea, Bristol Channel and Irish Sea. While there is increasing demand for marine aggregate, the area impacted is relatively small, and is likely to remain so. There is also pressure from windfarm developments, particularly on shallow sandbanks, which is likely to increase in the future. Some estuaries and subtidal coastal habitats along the south coast of England and in the Irish Sea continue to experience nutrient enrichment and hazardous substances pollution. In most regions, non-native species are spreading in the subtidal coastal areas. The picture on pressures for these habitats over the last

3 Sections 12.2.1–12.2.5 have been reproduced (with some minor modification) with permission from Benjamins (2010).

Comparison of historic and present distribution and abundance of over 60 indicator species has provided evidence of some of the fastest changes in the abundance, range and population structures of species globally, and related these changes to recent rapid climatic warming. In particular, several southern species of warm water intertidal invertebrates and macroalgae have considerably extended their range northward along the Welsh and Scottish coastlines, and eastward along the English Channel. Northern cold water species, meanwhile, have shown a modest contraction in range, and significant declines in abundance, at sites close to their southern limits during the same period (Mieszkowska *et al.* 2006, Hawkins *et al.* 2008). Contractions and expansions of geographic range edges due to global environmental change are resulting in species both being lost from, and introduced to, assemblages. Such changes are initially being recorded at the periphery of the geographic ranges in Britain where organisms are often already experiencing temperatures close to their thermal limits. However, MarClim data has also identified local and regional heterogeneity within the geographic range of several species, as evidenced by environmental hotspots or physical/hydrographic barriers occurring inside the distributional limits of sessile invertebrates.

Laboratory and field experiments have shown that many of the changes in the southern species have occurred as a result of increased reproductive output and juvenile survival close to northern range edges in response to increased warming, particularly shorter, milder winters (Mieszkowska *et al.* 2006, 2007; Herbert *et al.* 2007). This data has also highlighted the role of the North Atlantic Oscillation (NAO)—an index describing large-scale climatic changes—in larval transport and subsequent recruitment success. Dispersal of intertidal invertebrate larvae is primarily influenced by NAO-induced variability in oceanic circulation, whereas recruitment is mainly impacted by atmospheric effects (Broitman *et al.* 2008). Annual monitoring at approximately 150 key sites around the British coastline has continued since the completion of the MarClim report. The time-series data shows continued temperature-

Figure 1 Lower shore at Mothecombe. *Photo courtesy of Nova Mieszkowska, Marine Biological Association.*

induced changes in intertidal rocky communities (an example of which is displayed in **Figure 1**), including increased abundance of non-native species, such as the Pacific oyster (*Crassostrea gigas*), the increase in which has resulted in declines in local biodiversity in regions where it has established natural populations. In addition, the role of artificial hard structures (e.g. for coastal defence) as stepping stones allowing the expansion of species linked to rock habitats has been highlighted (Moschella *et al.* 2005; Herbert *et al.* 2007). All of these factors influence the outcomes of species' interactions including competition, facilitation and predation, ultimately altering the structure of communities and ecosystem processes within British intertidal ecosystems (Coleman *et al.* 2006; Poloczanska *et al.* 2008; Burrows *et al.* 2009).

ten years is different across the regions; in general, there has been improvement in the southern North Sea, but for most other regions, there has been no change or there is not enough evidence to assign a trend.

12.2.5 Deep-sea Habitats

Deep-sea habitats are similar to other subtidal habitats in their vulnerability to the impacts of some types of mobile fishing gears. Although this represents the main pressure on these habitats, their current status varies by region, with large areas of habitat impacted in the Scottish Continental Shelf area and only limited areas known to be impacted further offshore. The fishing pressure on this habitat has increased over the last ten years.

12.2.6 Plankton[4]

Over the past two decades, there has been a large increase in phytoplankton biomass in offshore waters around, and to the west of, the British Isles. There have been large changes (a 'regime shift') in the plankton community in UK waters particularly in the North Sea. In recent studies, climatic variability and water transparency have been shown to be more important than nutrient concentration to phytoplankton production at offshore regional scales, at least for the North Sea. Warming water has caused many

phytoplankton taxa to change their seasonality (i.e. spring blooms are occurring earlier), resulting in their availability as seasonal food for zooplankton and fish larvae being out of synchrony (**Figure 12.3**). Since the 1950s, the abundance of total copepods has reduced considerably in UK waters with implications for the fish that feed on them. There has also been a marked shift from a cold boreal community dominated by plankton that spend all their time in the water column, to one characterised by warm temperate species. Since the mid-1980s, there has been a large increase in the abundance of planktonic larvae of benthic animals in the North Sea, but the causes are not clear.

Over the last 50 years, there has been a progressive shift northward in warmer water zooplankton and a retreat to the north of colder water species. The relative proportions of the cold water indicator copepod (*Calanus finmarchicus*) and its warmer water sister species (*C. helgolandicus*), which is said to have lower nutritional value, have shown a similar northward movement. The increasing sea temperature since the 1980s is the key driver linked to these changes.

12.2.7 Fish[5]

The CP2 report provides an integrated assessment of the status of fish populations over the last 20 years, with a specific focus on the past five years, using a range of data

4 Section 12.2.6 has been reproduced (with some minor modification) with permission from Reid & Edwards (2010).
5 Section 12.2.7 has been reproduced (with some minor modification) with permission from Pinnegar *et al.* (2010).

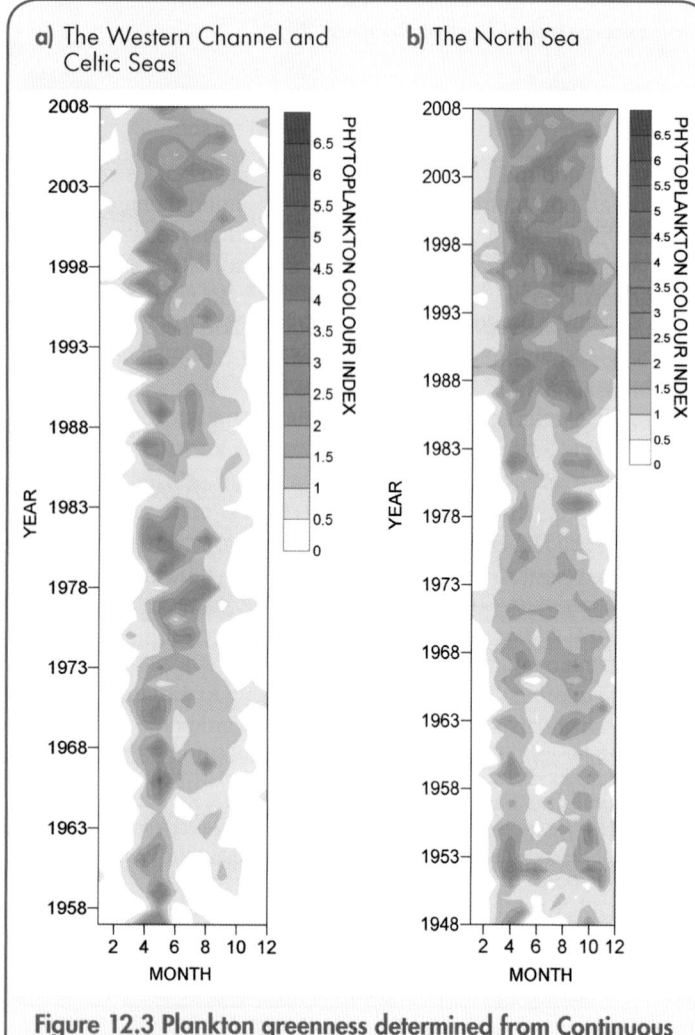

a) The Western Channel and Celtic Seas

b) The North Sea

Figure 12.3 Plankton greenness determined from Continuous Plankton Recorder data in a) the Western Channel and Celtic Seas, and b) the North Sea. Source: data provided by David Johns, Sir Alister Hardy Foundation for Ocean Science (SAHFOS) (2010).

sources from non-commercial monitoring programmes. It has shown improvements since the first Charting Progress report (Defra 2005). It is more challenging to compare current state and trends with respect to historical conditions (fish communities and populations from 50, or 100 to 120 years ago, before the onset of industrialised steam trawling) as only piecemeal data exists.

The diversity and overall abundance of demersal (bottom-dwelling) fish have improved around the UK during the past five years. This probably reflects a decrease in fishing, although life-history traits, such as average size and age-at-maturity, typically show little or no change and seem to respond more slowly to reductions in human pressures. This reduction in fisheries pressure has been largely associated with a combination of EU controls on Total Allowable Catches and the large-scale decommissioning of fishing vessels in the UK.

However, demersal fish populations are, today, severely depleted when compared with those of 50 or 100 years ago, and there has been a long-term trend in overexploitation impacting fish communities as a whole. Interpretation of the limited data that exists for earlier periods suggests that, although fish are smaller on average than previously reported, species diversity may have increased in some areas of the UK compared to historic data. The Southern North Sea, the Western Channel and Celtic Sea are considered to have shown the most deterioration from historic data (1880 to 1900) due to the impact of fishing. All other areas of the UK have shown a less severe deterioration, but fishing is still acting as the main pressure and driver of change. Surveys throughout the UK have revealed a gradual increase in estuarine fish diversity and overall numbers, probably linked to the fact that many estuaries have become significantly cleaner in recent years. The numbers of adult salmon (*Salmo salar*) and sea trout (*Salmo trutta*) returning to rivers have increased on many rivers, though there have also been declines in a number of rivers. The number of eel (*Anguilla anguilla*) juveniles has fallen in many areas, reflecting an Atlantic-wide downturn in the numbers of elvers returning to rivers. Causes of this decline are unclear, but suggestions include changes in oceanic conditions, overexploitation, freshwater habitat destruction, contaminants and the introduction of the parasite *Anguillicola crassus* from Asia.

Although the general situation for most estuarine and marine fish communities seems to have improved in recent years, certain vulnerable fish have continued to deteriorate. This includes many deep-water fish species, sharks, rays and skates, and transitional/diadromous species that move between fresh- and saltwater, such as the European eel and sturgeon.

Commercial fisheries continue to exert a significant pressure on target and non-target fish populations, but there are improvements in the proportion of stocks being harvested sustainably. However, as the seas become busier, other anthropogenic pressures are also becoming increasingly apparent. These include the impact of new on- and offshore infrastructure such as: the release of endocrine-disrupting substances from sewage works; pesticides and plastics manufacturing; the extraction of sand and gravel; the loss of coastal habitats; and the extraction of water from, or alteration of river flows in, estuaries. Climate change is also beginning to have a detectable impact on fish populations, with marked changes in distribution, the timing of migration, overall reproductive output (recruitment) and growth rates.

12.2.8 Seals[6]

After decades of increase, total grey seal pup production now appears to be levelling off in the UK and is rising at only a small number of colonies. This reduction in the rate of increase is probably because of density dependent factors affecting the population as a whole, for example, competition for space and food. In contrast, harbour seal numbers have dramatically declined by more than 50% in Shetland, Orkney and the east coast of Scotland since 2001. There has been a smaller decline in the Outer Hebrides, but numbers on the west coast of Scotland have remained relatively stable. The causes of these declines are not yet known. Contributing factors could be either natural, anthropogenic, or both, and include: competition with grey seals, predation by killer whales (in the Northern Isles), unregulated shooting (in local

6 Section 12.2.8 has been reproduced (with some minor modification) with permission from Duck (2010).

areas), declines in important prey species (such as sand eels) and disease (Phocine Distemper Virus outbreaks). As a charismatic species, harbour seals are often highly valued, for example, by the local tourist industry. Therefore, even when populations are very small such as in the southern part of England, pressure on these individuals is considered significant.

12.2.9 Cetaceans[7]

Abundance estimates exist for a few cetacean species over a large geographic and temporal scale, whilst for other species the information is restricted to a more local, limited geographic scale. Harbour porpoise (*Phocoena phocoena*), bottlenose dolphin (*Tursiops truncatus*), white-beaked dolphin (*Lagenorhynchus albirostris*), minke whale (*Balaenoptera acutorostrata*) and fin whale (*Balaenoptera physalus*) are the five most abundant cetacean species in UK waters. Their abundance in North Sea and adjacent waters has not changed and they, therefore, have a favourable conservation status assessment. The status of white-sided dolphin (*Lagenorhynchus acutus*), Risso's dolphin (*Grampus griseus*), short-beaked common dolphin (*Delphinus delphis*), killer whale (*Orcinus orca*), sperm whale (*Physeter macrocephalus*) and long-finned pilot whale (*Globicephala melas*) is unknown due to a lack of suitable abundance estimates. Other species in UK waters are considered to be rare or vagrant, so their conservation status in UK waters cannot be assessed.

12.2.10 Birds[8]

Seabird and waterbird populations in the UK have increased in size over the last century as a direct result of increased protection from hunting and persecution in the UK. But since around the mid-1990s, declines in numbers of both wintering waterbirds and breeding seabirds indicate that pressure is once again being exerted on marine bird populations.

12.2.10.1 Seabirds

The number of seabirds breeding in the UK increased from around 4.5 million in the late 1960s to 7 million by the end of the 1990s. Between 2000 and 2008, the total number of breeding seabirds decreased by around 9%, although changes in breeding numbers have varied greatly between individual species (JNCC 2009). Of the seabird species breeding in the UK, only northern gannet (*Morus bassanus*) and great skua (*Stercorarius skua*) sustained a positive trend in population size since 1969 when comprehensive monitoring of breeding numbers began. Conversely, herring gull (*Larus argentatus*) and roseate tern (*Sterna dougallii*) numbers have declined the most since 1969: by approximately 70% and 90% respectively. In 2004, 2005 and 2007, the mean breeding success of a sample of 21 seabird species was at its lowest levels since monitoring began in the mid-1980s. These falls in breeding success have been most acute in black-legged kittiwakes (*Rissa tridactyla*) and other species, such as common guillemot (*Uria aalge*), that rely on sandeels. There is strong evidence that climate-driven changes in the food chain have had acute negative impacts on seabird breeding success, particularly on Britain's North Sea coast. However, it is important to note that, although the impact of climate change on seabirds is considered to be high, much of the evidence for this is correlative rather than demonstrably causal. Other impacts affecting seabirds include fisheries reducing sandeel and other key prey species availability and quality, and reducing their discards, which is potentially linked to the reduced abundance of scavenging species such as great skua and northern fulmar (*Fulmarus glacialis*). The introduction of non-indigenous species (e.g. brown rats and mink on offshore islands that prey on ground-nesting seabirds such as storm-petrels and Atlantic puffins) has caused considerable damage to colonies in the past. However, more recent control measures have led to increases in numbers and breeding success at some seabird colonies, and to the complete recovery of others (e.g. Craik 1997, 1998).

Due to difficulties in gathering data in offshore areas, less is known about seabird populations outside the breeding season when they spend the majority of their time offshore and are not tied to particular intertidal or inshore coastal locations.

12.2.10.2 Waterbirds

Average numbers of waterbirds wintering in, or migrating through, marine areas in the UK doubled between the mid-1970s and the mid-1990s (Chapter 9). Since then, average numbers have declined slightly, but in the winter of 2006–2007, they were still 85% higher than in the mid-1970s when coordinated monitoring began. However, some species of diving duck and estuarine wader have recently declined more substantially: in 2006–2007 there were 43% fewer goldeneye (*Bucephala clangula*), 54% fewer dunlin (*Calidris alpina*) and 28% fewer bar-tailed godwit (*Limosa lapponica*) than in 1975–1976.

Five pressures were identified as being the most significant for UK waterbird populations: contamination by hazardous substances (waterbirds such as seaduck, divers and grebes have a low resistance to the effects of contamination by surface pollutants like oil); removal of species (leading to reduced food availability); habitat damage; habitat loss; and climate change. Climate change may already be contributing to recent declines in numbers of some species, including bar-tailed godwit, grey plover (*Pluvialis squatarola*), dunlin and ringed plover (*Charadrius hiaticula*), by encouraging a north-eastwards shift in their distribution. As a result, more birds are now wintering on the east coast of Britain and fewer birds are wintering in the south-west. Total numbers of waders wintering in the UK may be starting to decline as more birds move east and spend winter along the coasts of mainland Europe. The other impacts described are also thought to be contributing to changes in numbers and distributions of waterbirds. Visual disturbance from offshore renewable energy development could lead to the loss of foraging habitat for inshore feeders, such as terns, and is likely to increase in the future as the UK and Devolved Governments strive to meet their targets for renewable energy production (Mitchell 2010).

---

7 Section 12.2.9 has been reproduced (with some minor modification) with permission from Pinn (2010).
8 Section 12.2.10 has been reproduced (with some minor modification) with permission from Mitchell (2010).

12.2.11 Summary of Pressures Causing Change in Marine Habitats and their Biodiversity

Climate change is rapidly altering species distribution, a fact which is becoming particularly evident in those marine communities and populations where long-term data is available: coastal rocky intertidal species, plankton and fish. These changes have been related to recent rapid climatic warming, with southern species extending their range northward and northern cold water species undergoing a modest contraction in range, and significant declines in abundance, at sites close to their southern limits. Climate change will also facilitate outbreaks of non-native species in the future and different species-specific rates of change are already driving alterations of community structure and function.

Human activities that have a physical impact on the seafloor (e.g. trawl fisheries, aggregate extraction, construction of offshore windfarm developments, coastal defences, ports and coastal developments) adversely affect the species and communities (benthos) which live on the seabed. Usually the impacts are quite localised, but seabed trawl fishing activity is the most widespread activity and has the greatest impact of all human activities.

There is an increase and diversification of human activity in the marine environment which is creating additional pressures on all shelf sea, coastal and estuarine habitats. These include marine renewable energy development, expansion in recreation and leisure activities, port activities and aggregate extraction, as well as land reclamation and urban development at the coast. Human contamination of marine waters with hazardous substances has been reduced through improvements in sewage treatment infrastructure and reductions in industrial effluent, but there are now concerns about emerging environmental contaminants and chemicals, such as nano-particles and pharmaceuticals, which pass through sewage treatment (Readman 2006; Guitart & Readman 2010).

12.3 Ecosystem Goods and Services Provided by Marine Habitats for Human Well-being

Marine habitats and their diversity of organisms provide a wide range of ecosystem goods, services and benefits of significant value to the UK's society (**Figure 12.4**). These benefits include: food such as fish and shellfish, the reduction of climate stress by regulating carbon and other biogases; genetic resources for aquaculture; industrial inputs for blue biotechnology such as biocatalysts, natural medicines; fertiliser (seaweed); coastal protection; waste breakdown and detoxification leading to pollution control, waste removal and waste degradation; disease and pest control; tourism, leisure and recreation opportunities; a focus for engagement with the natural environment; physical and mental health benefits; and cultural heritage and learning experiences. Energy provision is likely to be an increasingly important marine ecosystem service. The technology for energy extraction from the physical component of marine habitats, such as wave and tidal power, is being developed and biofuels from macro and microalgae are likely to be provided by their biomass in the near future. The benefits accrue directly to coastal dwellers and visitors, and also

Figure 12.4 Examples of the goods, services and benefits from Marine habitats provided to human well-being. Source: adapted from Hiscock *et al.* (2006) and Beaumont *et al.* (2006); drawings by Jack Sewell and Tim Holleyman.

indirectly to much of the UK's society. The following sections explore each of these services, and the benefits that society obtains from them, both within the UK and overseas.

12.3.1 Provisioning Services

The provisioning services provided by UK seas, such as finfish and shellfish stocks, seaweed and other raw materials, benefit people both within the UK and abroad. The benefits include: fish and shellfish for consumption both from wild capture and aquaculture; fishmeal and fish oil as inputs for aquaculture and food supplements; algae and seaweed as inputs into pharmaceuticals and biofuels; and bait used during sea angling. Although the industry built around the provisioning of fish is declining in importance in terms of its contribution to Gross Domestic Product, it still remains an important socio-economic activity in coastal regions. This is especially so in remote coastal communities in Scotland, Wales and south-west England where it provides employment through fishing, aquaculture farms, fish processing, and associated industries such as boat building and maintenance, gear supply, markets and transportation. This section focuses on trends in production and consumption of fisheries resources from the UK's marine habitats.

Official statistics for catch landings by UK and foreign vessels into the UK are used as a proxy for the volume and value of the provision of fish for consumption. It is important to note that, although these statistics are incomplete estimates of the total provisioning services provided by marine habitats in UK waters, alternative technology now available, may improve future estimates (**Box 12.2**).

Not all fishing vessels registered in the UK are obliged to land all their UK catch in the UK, and similarly vessels registered in other countries can land some of their non-UK catch in the UK should they choose to do so. The Sea Around Us project estimates that more than 75% of the volume of fish caught in UK seas in 2006 was captured by non-UK vessels, notably by French, Danish, Norwegian and Dutch fishing fleets. It is also difficult to relate specific landings to the actual location where they were caught. Currently, technology allows catches to be attributed to areas of the oceans, usually referred to as ICES (International Council for the Exploration of the Sea) rectangles (0.5° Latitude x 1° Longitude), but this has not always been the case and many of the rectangles include both UK and non-UK waters. For example, UK vessels catch fish from the west of Scotland, Irish Sea, Norwegian Coast, Bear Island and Spitzbergen, Faroe Islands, North Sea, Rockall, Barents Sea, south and west of Ireland, English Channel, Bristol Channel, Bay of Biscay, east and west of Greenland, and Labrador, amongst other areas. The most important areas are the west of Scotland, Irish Sea, North Sea, south and west of Ireland, Celtic Sea and the English Channel. Finally, there is no defined relationship between landings of fish by UK boats and consumption of fish by UK citizens, so the benefits obtained from fish consumption caught by UK and foreign vessels landing into UK waters must be assumed to be obtained both within the UK and by the UK's export markets (e.g. Netherlands, France and Russia).

The remainder of this section draws on historical data collated from the UK Sea Fisheries Statistics. Unfortunately,

it is difficult to attribute this data in a strict sense to marine ecosystems that lie within the boundaries of the UK, but it is currently the best data available, for the time period covered by the UK National Ecosystem Assessment (UK NEA).

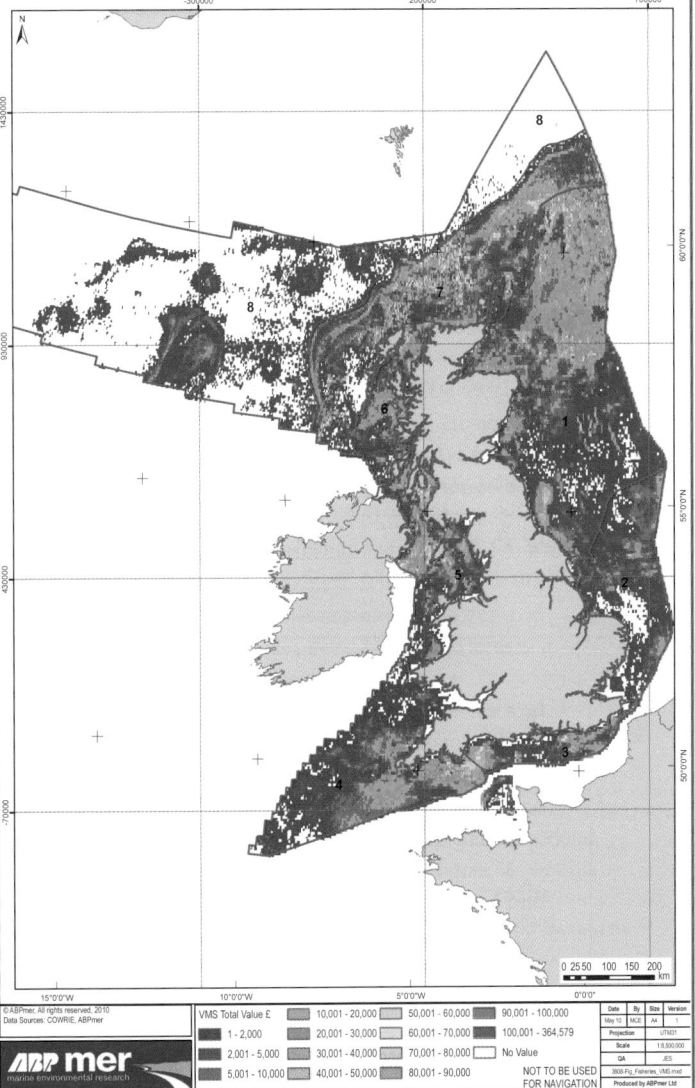

Box 12.2 Using position data and catch value to illustrate spatial dimension of catch value. An alternative approach to quantifying and valuing food provisioning from UK seas is to use spatial effort data based on satellite-derived Vessel Monitoring System (VMS) position data of vessels over 15 m, and plot this together with catch value as shown in **Figure 1** (Saunders *et al.* 2010). At present, this data is only available for 2004 to 2007 and does not distinguish between species caught. Nevertheless, it provides a highly resolved spatial dimension to catch data and demonstrates the patchy nature of catch value by area. It also illustrates the importance of coastal areas around the mainland and offshore islands; these areas tend to have the highest value, reflecting the dominance of shellfisheries for lobster, crabs, nephrops (scampi or langoustine) and scallops. Other areas of value include the shelf-edge of northern Scotland and the northern half of the North Sea; demersal species are particularly important targets for the Scottish fleet in these areas, as are nephrops.

Figure 1 Spatial distribution of the annual mean value of all UK fish landings in 2004–2007 based on VMS position data and ICES rectangle data on catch value for VMS vessels. Source: map reproduced with permission from Dunstone (2008).

12.3.1.1 Production

Finfish and shellfish from marine ecosystems. Landings of fish are divided into three separate fisheries statistics categories: 1) demersal fish species which live on or near the seabed including cod, haddock, plaice, whiting, pollack, and soles; 2) pelagic fish species, such as herring and mackerel, which are typically found in mid and upper waters; and 3) shellfish including scallops, oysters, mussels, cockles, octopus, squid, cuttlefish, prawns, crabs, and lobsters.

Total landings of demersal, pelagic and shellfish species combined into the UK increased from 1.1 million tonnes per year in 1938 to 1.2 million tonnes per year in 1948, after which they declined steadily to 0.5 million tonnes in 2000 (MMO 2010). Thereafter, total landings have remained stable (**Figure 12.5**). The value of total landings on the other hand, increased rapidly from around £17 million in 1938 to £464 million in 1990, and has shown a gradual increase since then. However, if these figures are adjusted using the Retail Price Index (RPI) to be equivalent to 2008 values (**Figure 12.5**), the total value of the fish catch shows a similar decline to that of volume caught. The decline in landings has not been consistent across all landing categories. Landings of demersal and pelagic species have declined over time, while landings for shellfish increased from 34,090 tonnes in 1966 to 144,986 tonnes in 2008 (**Figure 12.6a**). Landings of shellfish have now overtaken both demersal and pelagic species in terms of value (**Figure 12.6b**), but they remain the smallest in terms of volume. Demersal species still constitute the largest proportion of total landings, but they are much reduced since the Second World War (WWII) as a result of declining stock sizes, reduced quotas and imposed fishing effort reductions in the North Sea, eastern English Channel, west of Scotland and Irish Sea.

From 1956 to 2008 there have been declines in landings of demersal and pelagic finfish and shellfish in all regions of the UK (**Figure 12.7a**), but declines have been most dramatic in England and Wales. Pelagic landings have shown instability across the countries throughout the whole of this period (**Figure 12.7b**), while shellfish landings have increased for all (**Figure 12.7c**).

The trends in demersal and pelagic finfish landings can be attributed to a number of factors including: declining fish stocks due to fishing and environmental change; catch quotas; restrictions on the number of days allowed at sea; a shift to shellfish harvesting; and latterly, decommissioning schemes that have seen reductions in the size of the overall fishing fleet.

For certain species, such as cod and herring, there have been substantial declines in landings during this period following stock crashes. Reporting on the mackerel fishery in the English Channel and Celtic Sea, Lockwood and Johnson (1976) state that between 1926 and 1966 mackerel catch fluctuated between 12,000 and 40,000 tonnes; by 1970 this had increased to 60,000 tonnes, and in 1975 it was more than 300,000 tonnes. They report that similar increases were seen in the North Sea. The mackerel catch has since declined and, in 2008, approximately 90,000 tonnes were harvested (MMO 2010). The North Sea herring fishery has also had mixed fortunes; overfishing since WWII led to a stock collapse and a complete moratorium on herring fishing between 1978 and

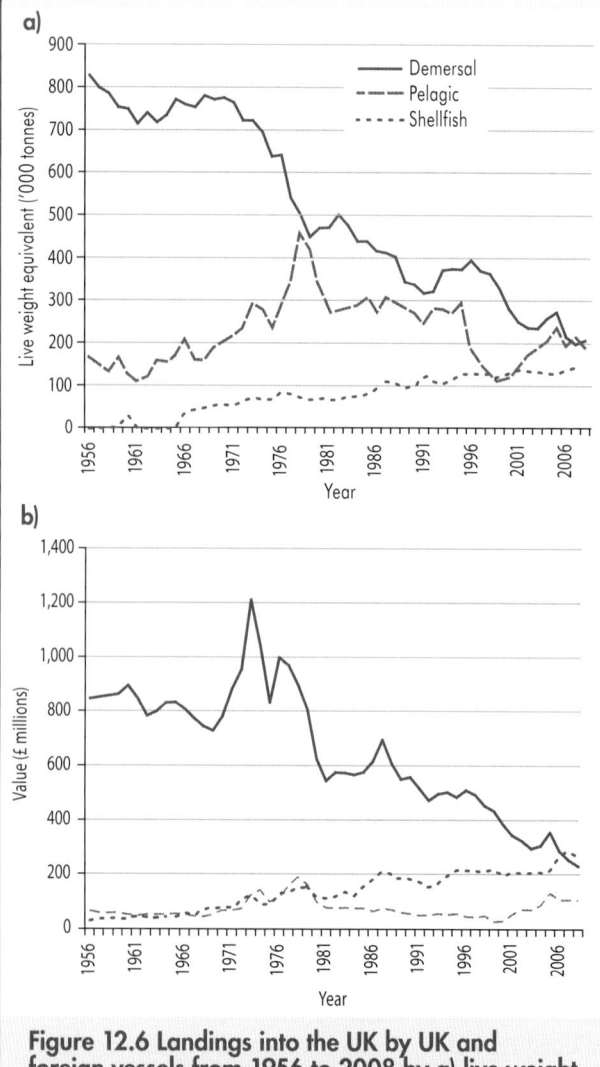

Figure 12.6 Landings into the UK by UK and foreign vessels from 1956 to 2008 by a) live weight equivalent, and b) value, of three categories of landings: demersal, pelagic and shellfish. Values were adjusted to 2008 prices using the Retail Price Index. Source: data extracted from MMO (2010).

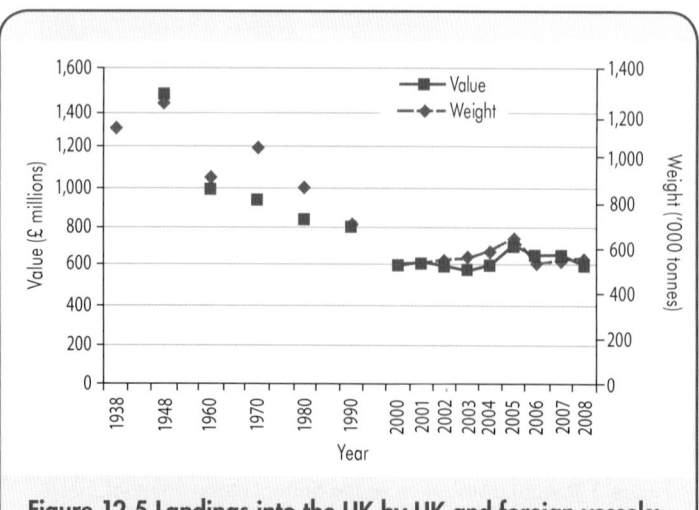

Figure 12.5 Landings into the UK by UK and foreign vessels: 1938 to 2008 adjusted to 2008 prices using the Retail Price Index. Source: data extracted from MMO (2010).

1982. Herring biomass has subsequently recovered and the fishery is now considered to be within safe biological limits (Pinnegar *et al.* 2006).

Shellfish landings, especially of scallops and Norway lobster (*Nephrops* species), have increased since 1966. The increase in scallop fishing is partly due to stringent quotas being placed on demersal and pelagic fish species, but also the ease by which boats fitted for demersal trawling can be converted to activities such as scallop dredging. In addition, most shellfish species are not under quota restrictions (quotas are only in place for *Nephrops* species and the northern prawn *Pandalus borealis*).

The recorded declines in landings do not necessarily reflect the size of the fish stocks in UK waters. Out of 18 indicator finfish stocks in UK waters, the proportion of stocks being harvested sustainably rose from 5–15% in the early 1990s to around 50% in 2008 (Armstrong & Holmes 2010). The proportion of stocks with full reproductive capacity (when spawning stock biomass is at, or above, the ICES-defined precautionary reference point at the start of each year) declined until the late 1990s, but since 2000, has started to increase again. However, the majority of stocks continue to be fished at rates well above the values expected to provide the highest long-term yield (Saunders 2010).

To fully understand the importance of food provisioning services from the marine environment, it is necessary to consider the effort expended in catching the fish and other secondary services associated with marine fishing. In 1948, there were 39,380 regular fishermen in the UK, by 2008, this number had fallen to 10,242 (**Figure 12.8**). England and Wales have constantly had the highest number of regular fishermen compared to Scotland and Northern Ireland. The capacity of the Scottish fleet, however, is much greater than that of the English, Welsh and Northern Irish fleets (**Table 12.3**), reflecting the greater proportion of boats over 10 m-long in the Scottish fleet.

In recent years, there has been a decline in fishing effort in the demersal whitefish fleet in the cod recovery zones. The

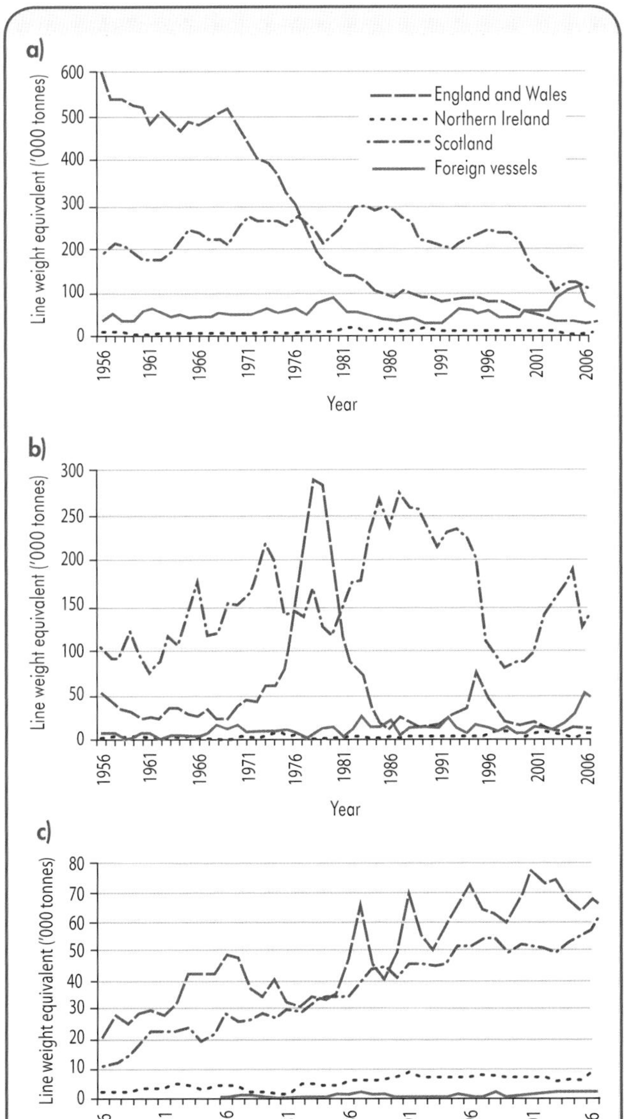

Figure 12.7 Landings (live weight equivalent in tonnes) of a) demersals (1956 to 2008), b) pelagics (1956 to 2008), and c) shellfish (1966 to 2008) into England and Wales, Scotland and Northern Ireland by UK vessels and by foreign vessels into the UK.
Source: data extracted from MMO (2010).

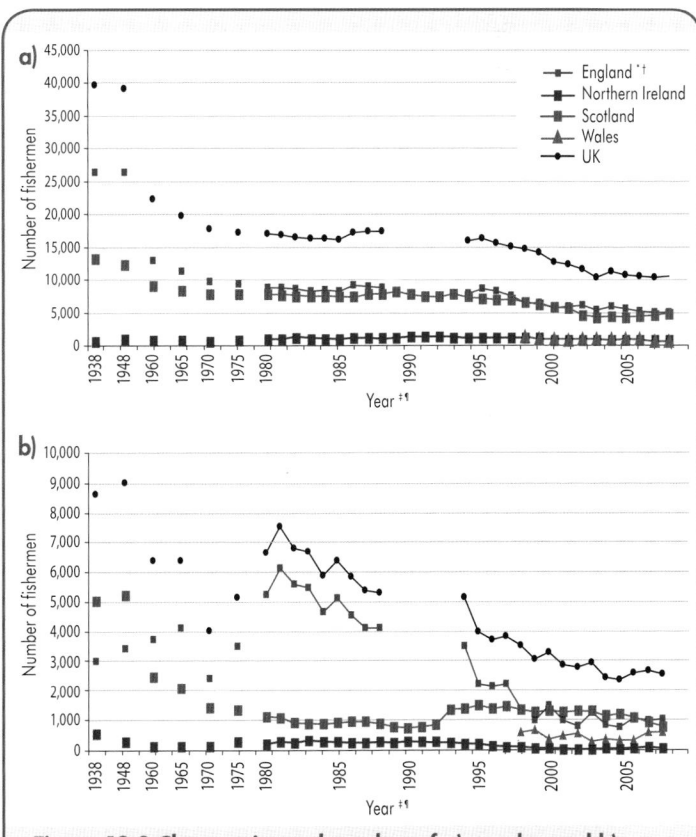

Figure 12.8 Changes in total number of a) regular and b) part-time fishermen for each nation of the UK. No data is available for England and Wales between the years 1989 to 1993. *Prior to 1952 figures were based on information supplied by the Registrar General of Shipping and Seamen. Since 1952 figures have been supplied by the District Fishery Officers of Defra. †From 1966 these figures exclude 'hobby' fishermen, i.e. fishermen who do not fish commercially. The corresponding figures for Scotland and Northern Ireland have never included 'hobby' fishermen. ‡1987 figures include those from 1986 for Newlyn and Plymouth. ¶The apparent increase in fisherman in Scotland 1993 reflected the licensing of 10 m and under vessels, when more information became available on the numbers of such active vessels. Source: data extracted from MMO (2010).

Table 12.3 Fleet capacity in 2008 by country. Source: data extracted from MMO (2010).			
Country	Number of Vessels	Capacity (gross tonnage)	Engine power (kilo watts)
England	3,200	59,974	306,450
Northern Ireland	351	12,734	52,828
Scotland	2,213	126,794	419,984
Wales	470	5,606	32,803

UK fleet has been heavily altered by both decommissioning and vessels switching from demersal fish to *Nephrops* fishing. Restrictions on the number of days allowed at sea, introduced by the Scottish Parliament in 2003 for the North Sea and Irish Sea and west of Scotland cod recovery zones, are also limiting the number of fishing days of certain segments of the UK fleet. In addition, decommissioning schemes run between 1997 and 2007 have led to a reduction in fleet size which has resulted in a 12% decrease in fish landed. As a consequence of fleet contraction, the Scottish demersal fleet is now considered to be in line with catch opportunity (Baxter *et al.* 2008).

A number of secondary services are also supported by the provision of fish, both up and down the supply chain. The fishing industry is dependent upon boat builders and repairers, gear merchants, and suppliers of boxes and ice, amongst other items. At the same time, the industry supplies numerous fish processors and food industries, and the UK has around 480 fish processing sites that employ around 15,000 people (Seafish 2009). Furthermore, the seafood service sector covers a range of outlets including fish and chips shops, and hotels and restaurants, and hence, is beneficial to millions of workers and consumers. There are also around 280 ports, harbours and creeks around the UK where finfish and shellfish are landed. The major fishing ports in the UK in terms of value of fish landed are Peterhead, Fraserburgh and Lerwick (all in Scotland). In 2005, the combined employment level in the catching, processing and aquaculture sector in the UK was 31,633 people, representing 3.5% of the total employment in all maritime industries in the UK, including leisure and recreation (Pugh 2008).

Fishing impacts on the marine environment. The removal of fish from marine environments has a number of impacts on marine ecosystems which may affect the delivery of other ecosystem services. Food web changes occur when the abundance of a species is severely reduced. Physical impacts are also common, especially from the use of bottom-trawls and dredging methods. The impacts of beam and demersal trawls on benthic communities are well understood. They are known to affect the biomass and production of benthic invertebrate communities (Jennings & Kaiser 1998) which are an important food source of many commercially exploited fish species. Disturbance of these benthic communities may also interfere with supporting ecosystem services such as nutrient cycling (Widdicombe *et al.* 2004).

Aquaculture. Aquaculture is the farming or culturing of aquatic organisms (fish, molluscs, crustaceans and algae) using techniques designed to increase the production of the organisms in question, for example, through regular stocking, feeding and protection from predators (ONS 2007). The majority of marine aquaculture in the UK is related to salmon and shellfish (including mussels, oysters, clams and scallops) farming. Farming of seaweed is a growing part of this sector although there is very little information about its likely future importance or impact.

As catches of wild fish have declined over time, so the demand for farmed fish has increased. The aquaculture sector in the UK has increased dramatically: the economic contribution from fish and shellfish farming increased by 132% over the period 2000 to 2006 (CEFAS 2008). In 2007, Scottish production of marine finfish represented over 99% of UK cultured marine finfish, producing approximately 130,000 tonnes (FRS 2009). Production was dominated by Atlantic salmon (*Salmo salar*), making Scotland the largest salmon producer in the EU and the third largest globally after Norway and Chile (Baxter *et al.* 2008). In 2007, turnover from finfish farming in the UK was £327 million, while shellfish farming generated £23 million (CEFAS 2008).

Trends in Scottish salmon production show a nine-fold increase from 17,952 tonnes in 1988 to 169,736 tonnes in 2003 (**Figure 12.9**). Between 2002 and 2005, salmon production varied, but since then, it has remained stable. At the same time, employment in the salmon aquaculture farms has decreased from 1,309 total staff in 1998 to 949 staff in 2008 (FRS 2009; **Figure 12.10**). Mean productivity per person, however, has been increasing; for Atlantic salmon it increased from 132.4 tonnes per person in 2005 to 151.4 tonnes per person in 2006 (Baxter *et al.* 2008).

In England and Wales, there were 518 registered fish and shellfish farms in 2008, of which, 197 were trout and other finfish farms (marine and freshwater fish are not separated) and 128 were shellfish farms; the remainder were coarse fish farms. Shellfish farm production in England and Wales has been gradually rising (**Figure 12.11**). A total of 15,686 tonnes were produced in 2008 comprised primarily of mussels (15,025 tonnes) and oysters (642 tonnes). In England it was worth £4.5 million in 2007, and was mainly mussels with small quantities of Pacific oyster (*Crassostrea gigas*) and native oyster (*Ostrea edulis*), and very small quantities of clam and cockle (Saunders 2010). In Wales, shellfish production was almost entirely mussels and was worth £7.5 million. In Northern Ireland there were 84 licensed fish farms in 2007 (CEFAS 2009) which were dominated by mussels, with some oyster and clam production. It was estimated to be worth £5.8 million in 2007 (Saunders 2010). Shellfish production in Scotland in 2007 involved 170 shellfish production companies operating on 336 sites and was worth £5.1 million. Total production in 2007 was 5,053 tonnes, and was dominated by mussels (4,806 tonnes), followed by Pacific oysters (208 tonnes), native oysters (22 tonnes), queen scallops *Aequipecten opercularis* (15 tonnes) and scallops *Pecten maximus* (2 tonnes) (FRS 2008).

Marine aquaculture contributes 21.4% of the finfish and shellfish supplied to the fish processing sector (Seafish 2009). Provisional data for 2007, released by the Office for

National Statistics, shows that total sales (turnover) by the UK fish processing sector were £2,567 million, compared with total inputs of £2,077 million, resulting in a GVA (Gross Value Added) of £490 million. Based on the proportion of aquaculture product supplied to the fish processing sector, it is estimated that £105 million of the GVA was related to aquaculture.

Aquaculture impacts on the marine environment. The CP2 Productive Seas Evidence Group Feeder Report (Saunders 2010) describes a number of impacts of both finfish and shellfish aquaculture on the marine environment. Finfish production often has a greater environmental footprint due to:

- The dependence on wild species as fish feed (e.g. sandeeels, herring and anchovy), the removal of which may impact on seabird breeding success.
- The organic enrichment of areas beneath fish cages leading to the deoxygenation of seabed sediments.
- Increased inputs of nitrogen and phosphorus from fish faeces which may contribute to phytoplankton growth and eutrophication.
- Introductions of non-indigenous species and interbreeding of escaped farm species with the wild population.
- Increased densities of larval sea lice which can be transferred from farmed fish to wild fish.
- Contamination by synthetic compounds (e.g. disinfectant antibiotics) and non-synthetic compounds (e.g. heavy metals).
- The introduction of microbial pathogens.
- Changes in habitat structure, water flow and wave exposure due to the presence of infrastructure both underwater and around the aquaculture site.
- Management of other species, such as seals, that may impact on aquaculture.

Shellfish aquaculture is often considered relatively sustainable, especially where spat collection results as a consequence of natural settlement (as is the case of many mussel farms) and where harvesting is based on hand-collection or raking. Where bottom cultivation is used and harvesting (including spat collection) is undertaken by dredging (e.g. for mussels and oysters), there are concerns over the impacts of physical damage to the environment. Other concerns over shellfish aquaculture include localised depletion of phytoplankton where overstocking has occurred and the introduction of non-indigenous species.

Fishmeal and fish oil. Fishmeal is produced almost exclusively from small, bony species of pelagic fish which generally live in the surface waters or middle depths of the sea, and for which there is a limited market for human consumption, for example, sandeel, herring, capelin and sprat (**Figure 12.12**). Fishmeal production also provides a major outlet for recycling trimmings from the food-fish processing sector, which would otherwise be dumped at extra cost to the environment and the consumer. The UK imports around four times as much fishmeal as it produces (FAO 2008).

Seaweed (macroalgae). Seaweeds play a wide and varied role in modern life as they are increasingly being exploited as a food resource and a source of industrial

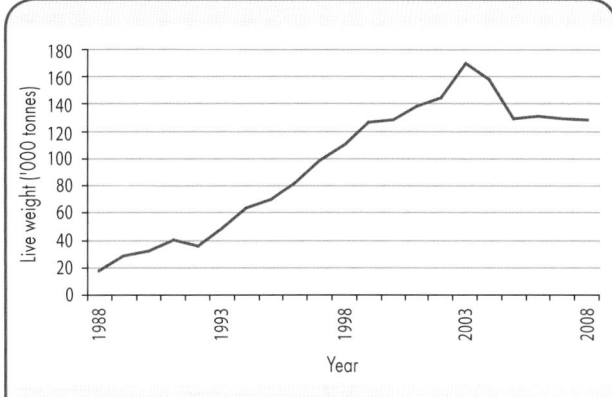

Figure 12.9 Annual production of Atlantic salmon (live weight equivalent in tonnes) from the Scottish aquaculture sector between 1988 and 2008. Source: data extracted from FRS (2009).

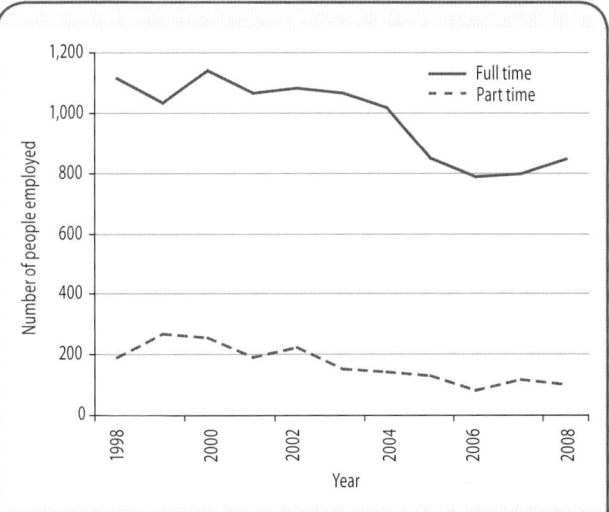

Figure 12.10 Number of people employed in Scottish salmon farms between 1988 and 2008. Source: data extracted from FRS (2009).

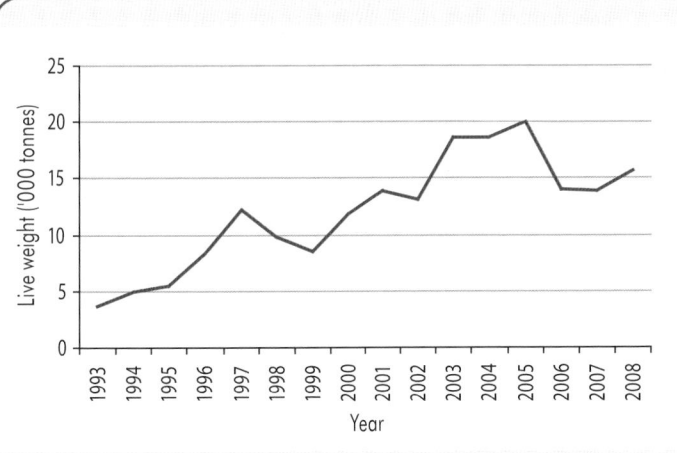

Figure 12.11 Farmed shellfish production (live weight equivalent in tonnes) in England and Wales from 1993 to 1998, including the production of oysters, mussels, clams, cockles and scallops Source: data extracted from CEFAS (2009).

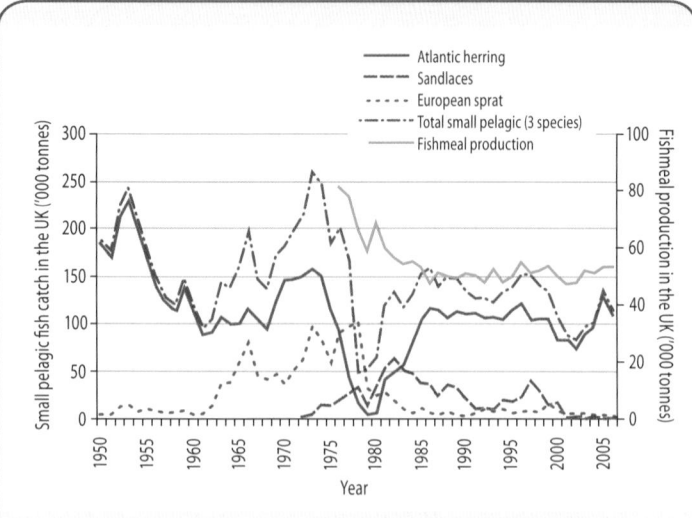

Figure 12.12 Yearly small pelagic fisheries and fishmeal production in the UK. The species used to produce fishmeal are herring, sprat, sandeels and capelin (following the International Fishmeal and Fish Oil Organization). Source: data from the Food and Agriculture Organization (FAO) FishStat statistical collections for fish production in the UK (FAO 2008).

and pharmaceutical chemicals. Gelatinous extracts include alginate, agar and carrageenan, which are used as food additives. Seaweeds are marketed for consumption as sea vegetables, beauty and health products, and land fertilisers. The UK coastline harbours a large array of seaweeds, a small number of which are exploited for commercial gain. Around 3,000–4,000 tonnes (wet weight) per year of *Ascophyllum* are harvested in Scotlands' Uist Islands (see The Minch Project; www.cne-siar.gov.uk/minch/seaweed/seaweed. htm), along with *Laminaria* species, principally *L. hyperborea*, cast ashore during the winter months; some 35 people are involved in its collection. In 2006, three commercial seaweed harvesting companies were identified in Northern Ireland, although small-scale collection is also seasonally customary (McLaughlin *et al.* 2006). Twelve species of seaweed were commercially harvested as fresh vegetation or drift, beach-cast seaweed. Collection was carried out largely by non-mechanical means: harvesters use boats for shore access, vehicles for the transportation of the harvest, and diving and cutting equipment. The international seaweed industry value exceeds US $6 billion annually (McLaughlin *et al.* 2006; equivalent to approximately £3.6 billion), which is an important driving factor for the UK seaweed industry.

Bait. Estimates of sea angling in the UK currently suggest that at least 1,000 tonnes of bait worms are used every year (Fowler 1999). Bait collection or provision activity is rarely recorded or declared, but market surveys indicate that some 500–700 tonnes of bait worms are dug for personal use and 300–500 tonnes of worms from commercial (including 'black economy') sources enter the retail trade. Bait worms entering the retail market are derived from wild-dug and farmed sources in the UK. The commercial value of the main bait species (e.g. ragworms (*Neanthes* (*Nereis*) *virens*, *Hediste* (*Nereis*) *diversicolor*, *Nephtys* species), lugworms (*Arenicola marina*, *A. defodiens*) and peeler crabs (*Carcinus maenus*)) in the UK is between £25–£30 million per annum (Fowler 1999).

12.3.1.2 Consumption

Supplies of seafood to the UK can be divided into four categories: landings by UK and foreign vessels, aquaculture, and imports. In 2008, consumers in the UK bought over 385,000 tonnes of fresh, frozen and canned seafood at retail outlets, together worth over £2.73 billion (Seafish 2009). The UK consumes an average of 23.6kg of fish products per person per year, and predictions have suggested that this is set to rise (Pinnegar *et al.* 2010). The UK human population is anticipated to rise from 61 million to 77 million by the year 2051 (Office for National Statistics 2010). This equates to a total UK demand for fish products of 1.8 million tonnes, suggesting that indigenous and global fish resources will come under increasing pressure in the future.

UK exports of fish and shellfish rose from 377,000 tonnes (£355 million) in 1998 to 480,000 tonnes (£891 million) in 2003 (Saunders *et al.* 2010). Exports subsequently declined in weight to 431,000 tonnes in 2007, although the value increased to £944 million in 2006 before declining to £909 million in 2007. Exports are mainly the pelagic fish mackerel and herring, as well as salmon.

The UK is becoming increasingly reliant on imports. Import volumes have increased by 46% between 1998 and 2008. In 1998, 533,000 tonnes (£1,066 million) were imported, rising to 754,000 tonnes (£1,922 million) in 2006 (MFA 2008), making the UK a net importer of fish. The main species imported are cod, haddock, tuna, shrimps and prawns. For some key demersal species, such as cod and haddock, imports currently are well in excess of exports. Whereas in the pelagic fishing sector, exports of herring and mackerel are larger than imports. Most imports in 2007 were from European countries. These figures are part of the total landings into the UK.

12.3.1.3 Pressures

The provision of fish and other ecosystem services are being impacted through non-sustainable rates of fishing mortality (related to fishing effort and fishing gear selectivity) leading to changes in age structure, spawning stock biomass, species compositions and distribution of fish stocks. In addition, some fishing practices, such as trawling and dredging, have a negative impact on the marine environment which, in turn, reduces the environment's ability to provide food. Climatic factors have been shown to alter fish community structure through changes in distribution, migration, recruitment and growth (Pinnegar *et al.* 2010; Pinnegar & Heath 2010).

Profitability of fishing operations has also varied widely due to factors such as increases in fuel prices, quota trading, and first-sale prices following the introduction of buyers and sellers regulations in 2006. For instance, the demersal fisheries in the North Sea, west of Scotland and Irish Sea have experienced a shift away from offshore fishing for finfish species, towards valuable fisheries for Norway lobster and other shellfish, along with mixed demersal species in inshore waters (Saunders *et al.* 2010). The shift away from offshore demersal finfish has resulted partly from long-term declines in many stocks and associated fishing restrictions, particularly those aimed at cod recovery, and partly from the perceived economic opportunities in other fisheries.

The Common Fisheries Policy (CFP) has been the dominant regulatory influence on the behaviour of fishermen.

The restrictive influences of this policy have intensified in recent years with a combination of catch quotas, gear restrictions and limits on days at sea all seeking to reduce fishing effort and catches to more sustainable levels. The fishing industry has also continued to innovate, and there have been marked technological developments to increase catch efficiency. However, Thurstan *et al.* (2010) propose that the landings of fish (in tonnes) per unit of fishing power may have declined by 94% over the last 118 years (1889 to 2007). It seems obvious that declining stocks of many fish have resulted in reduced catches. Climate change is also a factor and is to be included alongside fishing pressure in the current ongoing review of the CFP to cover the two main drivers of fish stocks in the north-east Atlantic.

12.3.2 Regulating Services

12.3.2.1 Waste breakdown and detoxification

There is a long history of the use of rivers, estuaries and coastal water for disposal of various types of waste materials by humans. The waste results from industrialisation and the need to dispose of toxic and non-toxic materials, and urbanisation requiring the need to remove human waste products through sewerage systems. This use of the water system solved immediate health problems for humans, but created environmental problems. Yet the environment has a natural capacity to detoxify some substances and to degrade others to less toxic forms (although sometimes more toxic forms are produced). Marine ecosystems that receive human waste materials are, therefore, providing a waste breakdown and detoxification service. The capacity of the marine environment to cope with such loads has been overwhelmed at times, resulting in pollution.

The development of sewerage systems resulted from the need to dispose of human waste away from populations to allow improvements in human health and hygiene; with relatively low population levels at the time, this proved successful. The subsequent growth in population resulted in a gross overloading of many estuarine and coastal waters, and led to the introduction of different levels of technical treatment over time. Primary treatment, involving the settling of solid material and its subsequent disposal to agricultural land as soil conditioner and fertiliser, or the disposal of solid material to designated coastal sites, was effective for many years. However, this resulted in many waters being contaminated with faecal bacteria and caused local changes to the ecosystem at designated sites. After WWII (during which the sewerage infrastructure had been severely damaged in many places), the needs of the developing population were met by no, or only primary, treatment of solid material prior to its discharge to coastal waters. By the end of the 1980s, however, it was apparent that there was a need for change, and the EC Urban Waste Water Treatment Directive came into force requiring a minimum of secondary treatment generally using aerobic biological processes to degrade the biological content of the sewage (derived from, for example human waste, food waste, soaps and detergent) before discharge. Hence, the pressure on the environment's capacity to process the sewage effluent reduced. Although the human population continues to grow, technical treatment has reduced our need to make use of the capacity of the ecosystem to degrade sewage waste. There still remain local issues, however, where the presence of human faecal bacteria and pathogens is affecting other uses of the coastal seas.

The deleterious effects of recently introduced and less well studied environmental contaminants and chemicals, such as nano-particles and pharmaceuticals, which pass through sewage treatment plants is of concern, and the capacity of ecosystems to breakdown and detoxify these products is largely unknown (Readman 2006; Celiz *et al.* 2009).

Sewage contains significant quantities of the nutrients nitrogen and phosphorous. Add to this the significant use of compounds of nitrogen and phosphorus in agriculture as fertilisers, manures and slurries and there is considerable risk of eutrophication, especially in estuaries and coastal waters, if nutrient enrichment leads to an increase in the growth of algae and other plant life and subsequently causes an undesirable disturbance to the balance of organisms and water quality. To prevent this happening, many discharges of sewage to freshwaters are now given further treatment to remove nitrogen and phosphorus. In England and Wales, for example, secondary treatment was applied to the waste from 63 million population equivalents (a measure of the load from sewage and industrial waste expressed in human population terms) in 2009, which is about 99.4% of the total; of this, 16 million population equivalents were subject to tertiary treatment including the reduction of nutrient concentration (Environment Agency pers. comm.). As a result of such treatments, eutrophication has become a localised problem. The fact that the seas around the UK are dynamic and well-oxygenated—a requirement of the bacteria that help to breakdown the organic materials in sewage—also means that further treatment of sewage is often not necessary. Wetlands, particularly around estuaries, can be very effective at absorbing nutrients and further reducing the load on the sea. This capacity is under threat from construction for flood and coastal protection and, though mostly in the past, through land reclamation. Some of this capacity is being redeveloped as part of managed realignment schemes improving natural flood defences, but it requires careful management to deliver the service (Andrews *et al.* 2006; Shepherd *et al.* 2007; Chapter 11).

Since WWII there has been a rapid growth in chemical industries and industries that make use of a wide range of chemicals. This has resulted in the discharge of substantial quantities of substances to the seas which have caused various degrees of pollution; now, all significant industrial discharges are subject to permits designed to protect the environment. However, there still is a legacy today of certain substances that are persistent, toxic and liable to bio-accumulate, and these materials will be present in the environment for some time. To some extent, and for some substances, burial in sediments and dispersion will reduce the threat that these substances pose—providing a service of storage and removal from the environment. In some circumstances, activities that disturb sediments, such as bottom trawling or dredging and disposal operations in ports, can interfere with this service.

We use the environment to degrade all contaminants on a shorter or longer timescale by bacterial action, hydrolysis, photolytic degradation and metabolism within animals. Anything which is readily biodegradable or which hydrolyses rapidly would take a shorter time to degrade (e.g. organophosphate insecticides); anything that is persistent (e.g. polychlorinated biphenyl's (PCBs), particularly CB138, CB153 and CB180) would take longer to degrade. But over varying periods of time, the majority are eventually transformed to less toxic compounds. There can be problems with this service, for example, alkylphenol ethoxylates are readily degraded, but to alkylphenols which are both more persistent and more toxic. While it may be desirable to ensure that discharges of hazardous substances to the sea are as low as we can reasonably achieve, we should also aim to avoid damaging the plants and animals in the sea—making appropriate use of the capacity of the sea to degrade and detoxify will help us to achieve this.

Some of the most high profile, and often accidental, discharges are those of oil (hydrocarbons) into the sea. The oil and shipping industries release small quantities of oil during routine operations which, together with natural oil seeps on the seabed, provide a background level of hydrocarbons in the seas. Populations of bacteria which can degrade hydrocarbons are present in the sea. Therefore, there is an effective natural cleansing service in the seas for hydrocarbons, except in the case of large spills from shipping accidents. Even in the case of large spills, the oil is eventually degraded, although it can take some time to return to pre-existing levels due to a combination of factors; more often than not, it takes the oil too long to degrade to prevent disruption to other ecosystem services.

Growth of organisms on structures and vessels in the sea is known as fouling and can be a serious problem reducing the performance and strength of these economically important maritime appliances. The widespread use of Tributyltin (TBT) as an anti-foulant on ships and structures during the 1970s and 1980s dealt with the problem very effectively. However, a well-documented side-effect of TBT is the severe impact it has on certain molluscs (Gibbs *et al.* 1991; Vos *et al.* 2000). Following restrictions on the use of TBT due to its detrimental effects on marine life, and coupled with the fact that TBT does degrade in the seabed as a result of bacterial activity, there is good evidence that the problems it causes will disappear after a few years. Since the ban on the use of TBT, several new synthetic anti-foulants have been brought onto the market. Some, including Irgarol, are compounds which have been shown to have deleterious impacts on non-target benthic organisms living in the vicinity of marinas, ports and harbours (Hall *et al.* 1999; Chesworth *et al.* 2004).

12.3.2.2 Climate regulation

The chemical composition of the atmosphere and ocean is maintained through a series of biogeochemical processes regulated by living marine organisms. The maintenance of a healthy, habitable planet is dependent on processes such as the regulation of the volatile organic halides, ozone, oxygen and dimethyl sulphide, and the exchange and regulation of carbon, by marine organisms. For example, marine organisms play a significant role in climate control through their regulation of carbon fluxes, by acting as a reserve or sink for carbon dioxide in living tissue, and by facilitating burial of carbon in seabed sediments. Of all the carbon dioxide captured in the world by photosynthesis and stored as living or dead material of biological origin, over half (55%) is captured by living marine organisms (Nellemann *et al.* 2009). However, there is no readily available data for the UK that quantifies total living biomass in marine and estuarine sediments or the water column.

Shelf sea systems make a significant contribution to the carbon budget (Nellemann 2009), and marine phytoplankton productivity in UK ocean, shelf and coastal waters has been used as an indicator of the climate regulation service (Beaumont *et al.* 2008). Large-scale marine primary production can be determined by remote sensing methods to quantify the concentration of photosynthetic pigments (Joint & Groom 2000). Production can then be calculated using the photosynthesis model of Smyth *et al.* (2005). This model was applied to earth observation data collected between 1998 and 2009 (www.neodaas.ac.uk) to calculate planktonic primary productivity for an area slightly larger than UK territorial waters (47°–63°N; 15°W–9°E). The average annual primary production (carbon sequestered by phytoplankton) was 0.371 ±0.020 billion tonnes of carbon per year (Gt C/yr ±95% confidence interval; Smyth unpublished). This is about 0.75% of the widely accepted value of around 50 Gt C/yr for global marine production based on global primary production models (Behrenfeld & Falkowski, 1997; Field *et al.* 1998; Carr *et al.* 2006). Values for the 12-year period are quite variable with no clear patterns evident (**Figure 12.13a**). These surface water figures are an underestimate for total primary production. They do not include primary production from the significant quantities of macroalgae on the intertidal seashore and the shallow subtidal rocks, nor from the significant levels of benthic micro-algal production on intertidal sand and mudflats, especially within estuaries. They also do not indicate how much of the fixed carbon is then subsequently sequestered either by removal offshore sinking into deep water and sediments, or by burial in shallow water sediments.

Another approach that is being developed by various research projects (e.g. Natural Environment Research Council (NERC) Oceans 2025, EU Marine Ecosystem Evolution in a Changing Environment (MEECE)) is coupled, hydrodynamic ecosystem modelling of the last 50 years in the north-east Atlantic and north-west European shelf seas. A 3D simulation model hindcast (ERSEM-POLCOMS and developments (Allen *et al.* 2001; Holt *et al.* 2005)) forced by the ECMWF-ERA (climate) re-analysis produces estimates of annual biomass of carbon in the pelagic components of bacteria, phytoplankton and zooplankton (Butenschön unpublished, **Figure 12.13b**). Similar to the 12-year phytoplankton production time-series, there is considerable annual variation in the modelled biomass outputs and no signal of a clear trend in change over the period from 1960 to 2004.

Changes in marine biodiversity influence the biogeochemical cycling of carbon and nutrients within seabed sediments, in the overlying water column, and at the interfaces between sediment and water. This can ultimately result in changes in the capacity of the marine environment

UK National Ecosystem Assessment: Technical Report

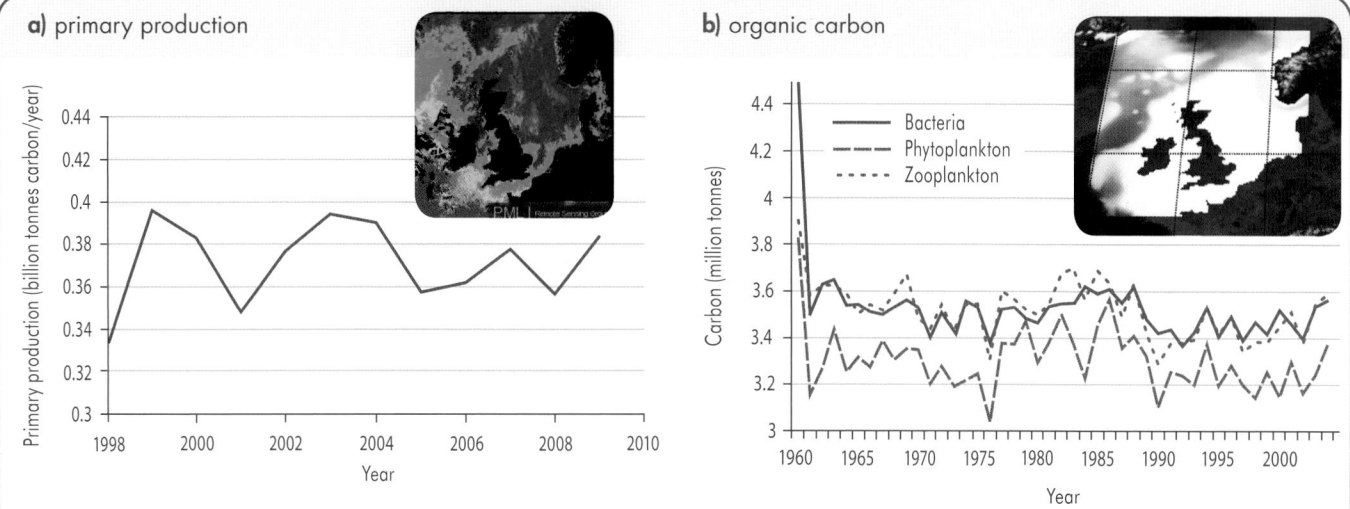

Figure 12.13 Carbon regulation in UK waters: a) using the indicator of annual marine phytoplankton productivity in ocean, shelf and coastal waters for an area slightly larger than UK territorial waters (47°–63°N; 15°W–09°E). Large-scale marine primary production was determined by applying remote sensing methods for data collected between 1998 and 2009 (www.neodaas.ac.uk) to quantify the concentration of photosynthetic pigments (Joint & Groom 2000) and then calculating primary production using the photosynthesis model of Smyth *et al.* (2005); **b)** using hindcast ecosystem modelling (ERSEM-POLCOMS and developments (Allen *et al.* 2001; Holt *et al.* 2005)) forced by the ECMWF-ERA (climate) re-analysis of annual biomass of carbon in the pelagic components of bacteria, phytoplankton and zooplankton (Butenschön unpublished). Map insets show domain area which is used to generate data.

to act as a carbon sink and has a strong feedback on the atmosphere and the climate (Legendre & Rivkin 2005). The surface water primary production of carbon by phytoplankton that is exported as organic and inorganic carbon to the deeper ocean waters is termed the 'biological carbon pump'. The global ocean has taken up approximately one third of accumulated emissions of the greenhouse gas carbon dioxide since the industrial revolution (Sabine *et al.* 2004; Sabine & Feeley 2007). This has had the benefit of slowing the rate of build-up in the atmosphere, but the accumulation in the ocean reduces seawater pH making it more acidic. This high rate of reduction of pH, known as ocean acidification, may lead to ecosystem damage and functional changes in the future (Widdicombe *et al.* 2009; Hopkins *et al.* 2010) with possible impacts on ecosystem services including changes in shellfish yields and fish productivity, changes in wildlife resources, such as deep-water corals and genetic resources for biotechnology, and negative feedbacks on climate regulation. Research is underway to assess the impacts of ocean acidification.

12.3.2.3 Flood, storm and coastal protection

Living marine flora and fauna can play a valuable role in the defence of coastal regions by dampening environmental disturbances (Beaumont *et al.* 2007, 2008; Chapter 11). A diverse range of species bind and stabilise sediments and create natural sea defences, for example biogenic reefs, seagrass beds, mudflats and saltmarshes. The presence of these organisms in the front line of sea defence can dissipate energy and, therefore, dampen and prevent the impact of tidal surges, waves, storms and floods (Brampton 1992; Möller *et al* 1999; Widdows & Brinsley 2002). This is a critical service, particularly as the risk of flooding, both in terms of severity and frequency, has been accentuated in recent years by the onset of climate change. The impacts of

global sea level rise (Boorman 2003) climate related changes in shoreline erosion, and human influence on shoreline structure are causing a loss of saltmarsh in the UK of 2% per year (Nottage & Robertson 2005). This loss of wetland has contributed to an increase in flood risk and subsequent investment in flood defence (Dixon *et al.* 1998).

Many types of flora can contribute to the reduction in wave energy in UK coastal zones. Seagrasses (Fonseca & Cahalan 1992) and halophytic (salt tolerant) reeds (Coops *et al.* 1996) play a minor role in the UK due to their small spatial scale; the major contribution to disturbance prevention is from saltmarshes (Paramor & Hughes 2004). With respect to alleviating flood risk to coastal communities, estuarine and coastal wetlands not only attenuate wave energy, but also play a role in reducing erosion of the coastline. Mudflats dissipate tidal and wave energy to a level low enough to permit net sediment deposition and this allows colonisation by saltmarsh or reedbed vegetation on the upper intertidal zone (Nottage & Robertson 2005). This coupled system is maintained through sediment exchange aided by the alternating dominance of bio-stabilisers and bio-destabilisers, controlled by climatic factors (Widdows & Brinsley 2002). Although saltmarshes are often inundated with marine water, especially during high spring tides, their role in disturbance prevention is addressed in detail in Chapter 11.

Subtidal and intertidal biogenic reefs are habitats that are under threat (Section 12.2.3). They are also likely to dampen energy in waves and tidal surges but the contribution that they make to disturbance prevention has not been quantified.

12.3.3 Cultural Services

The population of the UK is often cited as having a strong affinity for the sea, as much of our heritage is linked to maritime activities. Reminders of this maritime heritage are still in existence today: fishing villages, fish and chips, the large navy, lighthouses and museums, and literature on smuggling. In a UK-wide poll undertaken by The Wildlife Trusts in 2007, 78% of respondents stated that the UK's seas are important to their personal quality of life (The Wildlife Trusts 2007). While the majority of the UK population no longer obtains its livelihood from the sea, the fact that many people consider the sea to be important for their quality of life suggests that they obtain other benefits from it that include cultural ones.

It is difficult, however, to disentangle the cultural benefits society derives from the marine environment from those it obtains from the coastal terrestrial fringes as it is from the coast that most people experience the sea (Chapter 11 & 16). Few people, other than divers, ever interact with the underwater seascapes around the UK. Fishermen, who are dependent upon the sea for their livelihoods, and commercial and recreational boat users do not experience the underwater world in the same way as one would a terrestrial environment. The sense of place associated with sites on land is rarely experienced for sub-marine sites (Rose *et al.* 2008). Furthermore, while the coast is often thought of as a place of beauty and with a sense of nostalgia, the sea and undersea are considered quite differently, often in negative terms such as barren, cold and dark (KSBR Brand Futures 2008).

The relationship with the marine environment is also distinct because of the way property rights are defined. The Crown Estate owns the seabed out to the 12 nautical mile (nm) territorial limit, but they do not own the water column or the rights for navigation or for fishing. In some cases, fishing rights are heritable (for example, some coastal salmon fisheries in Scotland are owned by the operators as heritable titles) or informal agreements exist between fishermen (for example, crab potting areas are allocated to particular boats), but in general, marine waters are open access; the sense of ownership is, therefore, missing.

12.3.3.1 Environmental settings: education, research and development opportunities

The marine environment presents a number of educational opportunities; school trips to the beach and/or aquaria are common particularly in coastal communities, although people living some distance away from the coast are also able to learn about marine life through visits to aquaria and sealife centres throughout the UK (e.g. Birmingham and Alton Towers) (**Figure 12.14**). A number of environmental non-governmental organisations (NGOs) and environmental education businesses also offer educational facilities to schools. For example, the Marine Conservation Society (MCS), through its Cool Seas programme, has visited more than 400 schools in the UK, reaching over 120,000 school children since its inception in 2006. Surfers Against Sewage also have a schools programme, as do many aquaria: for example, the National Marine Aquarium (NMA) in Plymouth received 27,166 educational visitors during 2008–2009. Recognising their educational potential, the NMA offers a number of educational experiences linked to the national curriculum. The Marine Biological Association runs both The Shore Thing, a climate change shore project linked to the national curriculum, and

educational events at beaches designated as part of the BBC Breathing Places national educational programme. The Aggregates Levy Sustainability Fund has also supported an outreach programme, Explore the Sea Floor, which reached over 500 schools between 2005 and 2008, and has distributed more than 9,000 interactive educational CD-ROMs, amongst other activities (Murphy 2008).

In recent years, the development of new technologies (such as remotely operated underwater vehicles, deep-sea sampling equipment, remote sensing and improved diving equipment) and investment in marine research have led to greater understanding of the marine environment. An indication of how marine research and development in the UK has changed is given by Pugh & Skinner (2002). Between surveys in 1988–1989, 1994–1995 and 1999–2000 they report an approximate 10% increase in public sector research funding (e.g. NERC, Department for the Environment, Food and Rural Affairs (Defra), university), with researcher numbers fluctuating around 2,000. Some funding levied from marine industries, such as aggregate extraction, is used to support a broad range of marine research (**Box 12.3**). The top four marine-related university course disciplines in 1999–2000 were marine biology, physical and chemical ocean environment, the coastal zone and ship design. The proportion of research that is focused entirely on UK seas is unknown.

The private sector, particularly pharmaceuticals and 'blue' biotechnology industries, are growth areas that are also known to invest substantial sums into marine-related research and development. For example, Aquapharm Biodiscovery Ltd, Oban, secured £4 million in 2007 to support its work on anti-infective drug discovery and the development of novel ingredients for food additives and cosmetics such as anti-ageing creams (www.aquapharm. co.uk/news_archive.html); it has subsequently obtained a further £4.2 million in 2010 to continue this work (www. aquapharm.co.uk/news.html). Other centres of blue biotechnology strength include the Marine Biodiscovery

Figure 12.14 Educational trips to the seashore are becoming increasingly popular amongst schools, especially those located near the coast. Gara rocks near East Prawle in South Devon. *Photo courtesy of MarLIN.*

UK National Ecosystem Assessment: Technical Report

Centre, Aberdeen; Plymouth Marine Laboratory; Glycomar, based together with Aquapharm within the European Centre for Marine Biotechnology, Oban; and the University of Newcastle's School of Marine Technology and Science. Detailed statistics that disaggregate the marine related component are not available to assess how these industries have changed over time.

12.3.3.2 Environmental settings: leisure and recreation

The most obvious cultural benefit that society receives from the marine environment is the opportunity for leisure and recreational activities. The UK Leisure Day Visits Survey (2002–2003[9]) reports 267 million visits to the seaside during that year, approximately 5% of all UK leisure day visits. This is an increase from previous surveys: in 1994, seaside visits accounted for only 3.5% of all UK day leisure visits (although this figure varies across England, Scotland and Wales: in 2002–2003 4% of day visits in England were to the seaside, compared to 9% in Scotland and 12% in Wales). Expenditure at the seaside as a proportion of all expenditure on leisure day visits has remained more or less constant at around 4% between 1994 and 2002–2003, although the actual amount has increased over this period from £2.2 billion to £3.2 billion.

It is difficult to account for the contribution of the marine environment to these figures, but the draw of the sea must be assumed to play a part, especially given the opportunity it provides for water-based recreational activities and wildlife-watching. Anecdotal evidence suggests that wildlife-watching is an increasingly popular activity at the coast, yet the sector has still to be documented quantitatively (Curtin & Wilkes 2005) and only a small number of focused studies currently exist. The 2002 UK Tourism Survey data suggests that of all UK tourism trips (trips away from home lasting one night or more), 17.1% involved wildlife-watching/nature study; up from 14.8% in 2000 and 15.4% in 2001 (these statistics have not been collected in subsequent years). It is unclear what proportion of these are marine wildlife-watching activities, but there appears to be a growing number of tour operators offering trips to see whales, sharks, dolphins, seals and seabird colonies around the UK coast. In Scotland, all forms of wildlife-watching tourism have been estimated to generate £156 million in income and 7,446 jobs (Scottish Government Social research 2010). Of this, £36 million and 1,705 jobs (Full Time Employment (FTE) equivalent) are attributable to marine wildlife tourism, and £56 million and 2,681 jobs are generated by coastal wildlife tourism. In a like-minded study, the Royal Society for the Protection of Birds (RSPB 2010) has attempted to estimate the value of seabird colonies through the analysis of visitor expenditure across four case study sites: Bempton

---

Box 12.3 Marine aggregate extraction support for marine research.

Support for marine research comes from a diverse range of sources, for example, the Aggregates Levy Sustainability Fund (ALSF) which is a research levy imposed on the industry (MALSF 2010). By March 2011, the Marine ALSF will have provided about £25 million to marine research associated with aggregate extraction (MEPF Secretariat 2010). While much of the research it funds focuses on environmental and ecosystem impacts of aggregate extraction (**Figure 1**) and the recovery of extraction sites, some £7 million is dedicated to the characterisation of the seabed environment (for example, Regional Environmental

Characterisation (REC) projects to enable broad-scale characterisation of the seabed habitats, their biological communities and potential historic environment assets within the regions); development of techniques for locating seabed historic objects, their management and conservation (**Figure 2**); and knowledge transfer. One such example is the Historic Seascape Characterisation programme supported jointly through the ALSF and English Heritage. The programme is developing an approach for mapping the historic seascapes of England's waters in an attempt to better understand the historical and cultural development of the present marine, intertidal and coastal areas.

Figure 1 Operational trailer suction hopper dredger.
Photo courtesy of HR Wallingford.

Figure 2 Divers photograph the wooden hull structure of the 'Mystery Wreck', Eastern Solent. *Photo courtesy of Hampshire & Wight Trust for Maritime Archaeology and D. McElvogue.*

---

9 More recent statistics are available from the 2005 survey, but the surveys were carried out independently for each country within the UK and the method of data collection changed making comparison difficult.

Cliffs nature reserve, East Yorkshire; South Stack Cliffs nature reserve, Anglesey; Mull of Galloway nature reserve, Dumfries and Galloway; and Rathlin Island, County Antrim. They estimate that between 3–9% of day-tripper spend and 5–16% of holidaymaker spend (those staying overnight) is attributable to seabirds in the four locations. In 2009, this equated to £754,190 from Bempton; £222,822 from South Stack; £114,848 from the Mull of Galloway; and £115,629 from Rathlin. Given the isolated nature of these locations, the reserves make an important contribution to the local economies. The RSPB has also calculated that certain iconic bird species make substantial contributions to local economies through the attraction of visitors (Dickie *et al.* 2006). For example, white-tailed eagles (*Haliaeetus albicilla*) bring between £1.4 million and £1.6 million annually to the Isle of Mull, and the small family of choughs (*Pyrrhocorax pyrrhocorax*) on the Lizard, Cornwall, brought £118,000 in 2004.

Statistical evidence is available for water-based recreational activities for 2005 to 2008 from a consortium of the British Marine Federation (BMF), Maritime and Coastguard Agency (MCA), Royal National Lifeboat Institution (RNLI) and Royal Yachting Association (RYA) (BMF *et al.* 2005–2008). They estimate that more than 50% of all small sail boat activities, wind surfing, use of personal water craft, motor boats/cruising, yacht cruising, power-boating, yacht racing, surfing, kite surfing, angling from a boat, outdoor swimming, and sub-aqua activities in the UK occur at the coast where they are dependent on the marine environment. In many instances, over 75% of activities occur at the coast (e.g. yacht cruising and racing, power-boating and the use of personal water craft), with this figure rising to 94% for kite surfing and 100% for surfing. In 2005, water-based activities accounted for 36.7 million coastal visits[10]

(52.2% of all water-based visits), rising to 47.1 million coastal visits in 2007 (55.2%). In 2008, like all water based activities, coastal visits fell to 35.6 million although as a proportion of total water-based activities they rose to 60%. Since the survey began distinguishing between coastal and inland waters (2005), participation in most activities has remained quite consistent. Only angling from boats and sub-aqua diving have shown any real change, with a large increase in participants in the last two years.

Recreational sea angling is a popular and relatively well-studied activity. It is comparatively well-quantified in terms of number of participants, their expenditure and the jobs associated with this leisure industry (**Box 12.4**).

12.3.3.3 Environmental settings: health goods (mental and physical)

Angling and many other activities that occur at sea bring with them extra cultural benefits, in addition to the activity itself. For example, drawing from an internet survey of the social and community benefits of angling, Stolk (2009) reports high levels of club membership by anglers (49% for sea anglers). Respondents stated that club membership brings a number of benefits including connecting people, building relational networks, enabling intergenerational socialisation and providing routes into volunteering. Almost a quarter of respondents also reported involvement in environmental or aquatic habitat conservation projects, helping to engage local communities and raise awareness of conservation issues.

In addition, spending time by the sea and coast has long been recognised for its benefits for health and well-being. For example, Victorian doctors often prescribed visits to the coast to hasten recovery after long illnesses. It is only recently, however, that the links between the environment

---

Box 12.4 Recreational sea angling.

In Scotland, 125,188 adults and 23,445 children participated in sea angling in 2008, equating to 1,540,206 sea angling days and a total expenditure of approximately £141 million (Radford *et al.* 2009). The industry is thought to directly support 3,148 jobs (FTE), supporting a Scottish household income of approximately £70 million through wages, self-employment income, rents and profits.

The most recent Defra figures for England and Wales indicate that, in 2003, 1.1 million households in England and Wales contained one or more members who partook in sea angling and the mean number of sea angling days per year was 11.3 (Crabtree *et al.* 2004). The industry was estimated to have a value of £538 million per year and to support 18,889 jobs (FTE). Estimates from the South West alone suggest that 240,000 residents participate in sea angling, plus an additional 750,000 angling days are engaged in by visitors (Cappell & Lawrence 2005). The value of the industry is estimated at £165 million and supports more than 3,000 jobs.

All of these studies found that the majority of anglers fished within 50 miles of their homes. Visiting anglers, however, make a considerable contribution to the total angling expenditure. Crabtree *et al.* (2004) estimated this as £192 million per year or 35% of the total for 2002. This equates to 1% of all tourism spend in 2002 for England and Wales (UK Tourism Survey 2002).

Although exact figures are unavailable, the evidence suggests that the population of sea anglers has either stabilised or shown a small increase since the early 1990s. The mean number of days spent angling, however, has decreased from 36 days per

year in the 1970s, to 12 days per year in 1992 (Dunn & Potten 1994) and to 11.3 days per year in 2002 (Crabtree *et al.* 2004). These figures hide the fact that shore anglers (**Figure 1**) are much more active than those fishing from a charter boat: 13.6 days per year compared to 4.96 days per year respectively (Crabtree *et al.* 2004).

Figure 1 An angler watches waves in Whitby, North Yorkshire. *Photo © ronfromyork, 2011. Used under license from Shutterstock.com*

---

10 These figures do not include those for cliff-climbing, coastal walking and general leisure time at the beach.

and health and well-being have been medically documented. This has mainly occurred for the green environment (Bird 2007) and has demonstrated how interaction with nature can help reduce stress, increase physical activity and create stronger communities. Effort is now turning to the blue environment, and in 2009 the Blue Gym project was initiated by the Peninsula Medical School[11] (Universities of Exeter and Plymouth) to examine the health benefits that can be gained by spending time in coastal environments (Depledge & Bird 2009).

12.3.3.4 Environmental settings: heritage goods

Aesthetic and inspirational properties. Even though much of the marine environment is hidden from view, it has captured the imagination of many over the centuries leading to a wealth of literature, for example Coleridge's *The Rime of the Ancient Mariner*, Wordsworth's *By the Sea*, John Masefield's *Sea Fever* and Neil Gunn's *The Silver Darlings*; works of art, such as Pocock's sea battles and Turner's coastal views; and schools of artists, including The Newlyn and St. Ives Schools. The sea continues to be drawn upon as a source of inspiration with any number of craft fairs and galleries exhibiting art work using driftwood, shells and other marine themes. In addition, it inspires underwater documentaries, such as 'The Blue Planet', and has always permeated through children's cartoons, for example 'Popeye' and 'Captain Pugwash', the incidence of which has increased in the last five to ten years with films like 'Finding Nemo', 'Shark Tale' and 'SpongeBob SquarePants'.

Cultural heritage. Advancements in understanding the marine environment have led to a corresponding increase in public interest about underwater heritage resources (Kaoru & Hoagland 1994) and wider marine issues. To date, no assessment of the heritage value of the marine environment in UK waters has been undertaken, but a growing number of marine sites are receiving protected status because of their importance to UK history. Protection is offered for a number of reasons including the presence of ancient monuments, important wrecks and war graves (through the Protection of Wrecks Act, 1973; the Protection of Military Remains Act, 1986; and the Ancient Monuments and Archaeological Areas Act, 1979). Approximately 93 marine sites have been protected (MCA 2010), but this represents only a small proportion of the 44,000 wrecks that have been mapped and catalogued by Shipwrecks UK (www.shipwrecks.uk.com/info1_2.htm) around the coast of Great Britain and Ireland (the number which is growing as more wrecks are discovered). The level of protection for such sites has increased since 2002 when English Heritage, Cadw, Historic Scotland and Northern Ireland Environment Agency took over responsibility for marine archaeology in UK waters.

Currently, protection of the marine environment falls short of that on land. For example, there are only 83 inshore and nine offshore Special Areas of Conservation (SACs) out of a total of 621 designated under the Habitat's Directive

in the UK. And there are only 107 Special Protection Areas (SPAs) designated under the Bird's Directive (out of 262 across the UK) in coastal areas, of which, only three are entirely marine (Bae Caerfyrddin/Carmarthen Bay, the Outer Thames Estuary and Liverpool Bay; www.jncc.gov.uk/page-1414); some of these sites are also protected under the OSPAR Convention. Although there are a small number of Sites/Areas of Special Scientific Interest (SSSIs/ASSIs)[12] below the low water mark (mean low spring water in Scotland), such as The Wash and Morecombe Bay, many coastal SSSIs/ASSIs do not offer protection to subtidal marine life (JNCC 2010). Furthermore, there are only two marine nature reserves (Skomer Island and Strangford Lough) and they are considered limited in their scope; although a former marine nature reserve has recently been made into the first Marine Conservation Zone (MCZ) designated under the Marine and Coastal Access Act (2009). This relative absence of protection of marine habitats results from the land-based focus of much existing conservation legislation and a probable lack of understanding of the value of marine ecosystems. For example, the Wildlife and Countryside Act, 1981, through which SSSIs are designated, made no provision for SSSIs in the marine environment (Defra 2009); SACs can only be selected according to the presence of four marine habitats (sandbanks always slightly covered with water, reefs, submarine structures with leaking gases, submerged or partially submerged sea cave); only four marine species appear in Annex II of the Habitats Directive (common and grey seals, bottlenose dolphin and harbour porpoise[13]).

It is also important to note that not all protected areas are protected by statutory designations. The RSPB, for example, owns a number of nature reserves around the UK coast which provide protection for important seabird colonies (e.g. Ramsey Island, Noup Cliffs, Rathlin); The Wildlife Trusts also own a number of coastal nature reserves. Neither of these organisations has dedicated marine reserves, however, largely because of the inability to purchase the seabed and designate it as a reserve.

Protection of the marine environment, however, will see a number of changes in the near future due to requirements written into the UK Marine and Coastal Access Act (2009) and the Marine (Scotland) Act 2010 (Section 12.5).

Enfranchisement and neighbourhood development. Concern over marine issues unites people in a number of ways, contributing to social and environmental citizenship and neighbourhood development. For example, the NGO Surfers Against Sewage originally formed in 1990 and has grown into an organisation with 10,000 members (Surfers Against Sewage 2010). They campaign on a number of issues, particularly those relating to the health of recreational water users and rights of access. They are also involved in beach litter picks, in association with MCS's Adopt-a-Beach programme, and in outreach activities within schools in Cornwall. The MCS initiated its beach clean and litter survey activities through its Beachwatch programme in 1993. In

---

11 Recently renamed as the Peninsula College of Medicine and Dentistry.
12 SSSI is a conservation designation denoting a protected area in GB. ASSI is a conservation designation denoting a protected area in Northern Ireland.
13 Although other species listed in Annex II of the Habitats Directive do occur in UK waters, it is unlikely that areas away from the coast can be identified as essential to their life and reproduction.

1994, Beachwatch involved 2,062 volunteers and covered 173 beaches, equating to 204 km of coast. By 2008, these numbers had grown to 374 beaches and 5,219 volunteers, but with a slight reduction in coastal length surveyed to 175.1 km. The increase in interest in beach-cleaning led MCS to develop the Adopt-a-Beach programme in 1999 to help its members to carry out more regular beach cleans and litter surveys.

12.3.4 Supporting Services

12.3.4.1 Nutrient cycling

There is substantial input of nutrients into UK marine waters through exchange with offshore waters (North Atlantic, English Channel inflow), rivers, groundwater and atmospheric inputs (Jickells 1998). However, the storage, cycling and maintenance of this supply of nutrients and micronutrients, for example, carbon, nitrogen, phosphorus, sulphur and metals, is essential for living marine organisms and supports all of the other marine ecosystem services.

Nutrient cycling encourages productivity, including fisheries productivity, by making the necessary nutrients available to all levels of food chains and webs. Nutrient cycling is undertaken in many components of the marine environment: within seabed sediments, particularly intertidal and subtidal muds, where bacterial processing of nutrients (e.g. nitrification and denitrification) is facilitated by the physical feeding, burrowing and irrigation activity, known as 'bioturbation', of invertebrates (Covich et al. 2004; Olsgard et al. 2008); within the water column where bacterial nutrient cycling is facilitated via food web links with phytoplankton and zooplankton and also fish (Proctor et al. 2003; Blackford 1997); between trophic levels and in the course of bacterial breakdown of detritus (mainly dead algal and plant material) in macroalgal beds and in saltmarshes. Without recycling at the sediment-water interface, most nutrients would be lost from the ecosystem, sinking and becoming buried in the sediments that cover much of the seabed.

Nutrient concentrations are seasonally and annually variable (Butler 1979; Jordan & Joint 1997; Gowen & Stewart 2005). For example, water column nitrate and phosphate concentrations measured at an English Channel station between 1923 and 1987 show a wide range in the nitrate:phosphate ratio (Jordan & Joint 1998). Since the late 1950s and early 1960s, enrichment of the Irish Sea with anthropogenic nutrients has increased winter levels of dissolved inorganic nitrogen and phosphorus (Gowen & Stewart 2005).

Climate change may alter nutrient exchange processes between the open waters and the open ocean, and also alter water stratification, therefore affecting internal nutrient cycling, but the likely direction and extent of changes are still poorly understood (MCCIP 2008). Threats to nutrient cycling in the estuarine and saltmarsh areas principally arise from increasing loss of saltmarshes and intertidal mudflats due to land reclamation. A further threat has been excess nutrient loading through river runoff exceeding capacity for storage and recycling, although, as stated in Section 12.3.2.1 this threat is diminishing.

12.3.4.2 Biologically mediated habitat

Many organisms provide structured space or living habitat for other organisms through their normal growth, for example, reef-forming invertebrates, meadow-forming seagrass beds, marine algae forests and networks of burrows and holes in the sediment (Beaumont et al. 2007). These 'natural' marine habitats can provide essential feeding, breeding (spawning grounds) and nursery space for other plants and animals, which can be particularly important for the continued recruitment of commercial and/or subsistence fish and shellfish species. Such habitat can also provide a refuge for plants and animals including places to hide from predators. Living habitat plays a critical role in species' interactions and regulation of population dynamics, and is a pre-requisite for the provision of many goods and services. In the UK, examples of living habitat include kelp and seagrass beds, maerl grounds (calcified red seaweed), mussel patches and cold water coral reefs.

Maerl grounds are predominantly found on the west coasts, but are also patchily distributed around the UK. They support a large number of species (Jackson et al. 2004) through their provision of refuge and food for juvenile life stages of commercially important shellfish, such as the queen scallop (*Aequipecten opercularis*) (Kamenos et al. 2004), and juvenile gadoid fish such as Atlantic cod (*Gadus morhua*), saithe (*Pollachius virens*) and pollack (*Pollachius pollachius*) (Hall-Spencer et al. 2003). Seagrass has only a patchy distribution in the UK, but provides both refuge and nursery habitat for a number of commercial fish species (Murphy et al. 2000) including Atlantic cod, halibut (*Hippoglossus hippoglossus*), flounder (*Platichthys flesus*) and plaice (*Pleuronectes platessa*) (Gotceitas et al. 1997), and also commercial shellfish (Davidson & Hughes 1998). Kelp and many other species of marine macrophytes are widely distributed in UK coastal waters (Birkett et al. 1998), support a diverse range of species (Orth et al. 1984; Norderhaug et al. 2002) and provide refuge for fish species such as juvenile Atlantic cod (Cote et al. 2002).

Mussel patches, both living and dead shells, can be used as substratum for colonisation by some species and provide refuge from predation for others (Gutiérrez et al. 2003). Intertidal mussel beds reduce the harsh effects of temperature, wave action and light, providing favourable conditions for a wide range of associated fauna (Seed & Suchanek 1992; Lintas & Seed 1994).

Cold water corals can occur in deep water, for example, *Lophelia pertusa* is found off the UK coast from north of the Shetland Islands into the north-east Atlantic (Wilson 1979). This species, and several others, can form colonies which aggregate over time into reef structures. Cold-water reefs, like their tropical counterparts, provide habitats for various species of invertebrate (Bett 2001; Gage 2001). Fish are present in significantly higher densities in cold water coral reefs than the background environment (Bett & Jacobs 2000).

Seabed fishing with trawl nets and dredging fishing gears is particularly destructive to living reefs which take a long time to recover since deep-sea corals can be particularly slow-growing. In 2003, evidence that trawl fishing was damaging cold water coral reefs in the deep-sea Darwin Mounds off the west coast of Scotland resulted in legislation under the Common Fisheries Policy to protect them. Shallow water and intertidal living habitats are vulnerable to invasive macroalgae species (Milneur *et al.* 2008) as well as smothering by opportunistic algae, such as *Ulva* species, particularly in nutrient enriched areas (Fletcher 1996); at a more local level they can be damaged by boat anchoring, propeller scarring, and channel dredging.

12.3.5 Wild Species Diversity

12.3.5.1 Flagship species

Flagship species are "popular charismatic species that serve as symbols and rallying points to stimulate conservation awareness and action" (Leader-Williams & Dublin 2000). Walpole & Williams (2002) state that to be a flagship species "they need only operate in the public relations and fundraising spheres". Marine flagship species are mainly the large megafauna, such as turtles, seals and cetaceans (whales, dolphins and porpoises), as well as smaller species such as seabirds and seahorses.

Scientists and conservationists will often consider a wide range of species and habitats as having flagship status as they are considered to be health indicators for the marine environment. For example, WWF lists 16 marine flagship species/habitats for UK waters: harbour porpoise; leatherback turtle; Atlantic salmon; Atlantic cod; long-snouted seahorse; basking shark; common skate; fan mussel; native oyster; pink seafan; saltmarsh; seagrass beds; maerl beds; horse mussel beds; deep-water mud habitats and deep-water reefs (Hiscock *et al.* 2005).

The significance of flagship species is that their importance goes beyond their ecological function and is related primarily to their appeal to the wider public. For example, relatively small populations of harbour seals on the south and west coasts of England and Wales (in some cases less than 10 individuals) may not have a huge impact from an ecological perspective. However, the populations are well known to locals and popular with tourists, thus providing a significant boost to the local economy. Even single individuals, such as straying migratory whales, can generate media interest and a short-term boost in tourism activity. In Looe, south-east Cornwall, a single grey seal (named Nelson due to only having one eye) was such a popular draw for locals and tourists that when it died in 2003, after 20 years of inhabiting the local area, a statue was erected in its honour (www.bbc.co.uk/cornwall/content/articles/2008/01/23/aboutcornwall_nelsontheseal_feature.shtml).

On a larger scale, the economic benefits of well-established populations of flagship species are derived from a wide range of activities linked to their presence including diving and snorkelling, rock-pooling, boat trips (e.g. whale- and dolphin-watching, shark-spotting and visits to seal colonies) and aquarium visits. Seabirds are also hugely popular and a major factor in encouraging wildlife tourism. Spectacular seabird 'cities' and particular species, such as the Atlantic puffin (*Fratercula arctica*), draw many visitors and are important sources of income for local economies (RSPB 2010; Mitchell *et al.* 2010).

Flagship species can also play a part in encouraging membership of societies that promote marine conservation. Many organisations promoting a scientific or conservation interest in the sea (e.g. NGOs, conservation agencies and learned societies) adopt a 'charismatic species' as a logo. The value of UK wildlife is partially reflected in membership of marine wildlife-related charities. There are at least 10 in the UK that are either entirely, or strongly, focused on marine life, with some specifically related to whales, dolphins, seabirds, seals and seahorses. A significant example is the RSPB which plays an important role in championing marine conservation; of its 200 reserves, 53 can be classified as being in habitat category 'Cliffs, beaches and estuary' providing protection for a number of important seabird colonies.

12.3.5.2 Sentinels of human health

Wild species can act as important sentinels of human health for chemicals (**Box 12.5a**), pathogens and harmful algal blooms (**Box 12.5b**). Consumption of microbe or biotoxin contaminated shellfish has the potential for significant impacts on individual and population human health. Recent studies have highlighted the relatively high disease and hospitalisation risk of consuming seafood. Between 1996 and 2000, the estimated annual impact of seafood-borne illness in England and Wales was approximately 116,000 cases, 77,000 of which were associated with the consumption of shellfish. These shellfish cases led to approximately 13,000 visits to General Practitioners, 3,600 hospital days and 16 deaths (Adak *et al.* 2005). The total cost of indigenous food-borne illness in 2008 was estimated by the Food Standards Agency for England and Wales at approximately £1.48 billion (using the 'value of fatality prevention index'). Only a small proportion of this would be attributable to contaminated shellfish consumption. While little historic evidence is available for incidence of shellfish-associated food-borne illness, it is assumed that monitoring of UK shellfish harvesting sites using the approach outlined (**Box 12.5a,b**) has led to a reduction in food-borne illnesses associated directly with shellfish consumption. However, specific data to substantiate this assumption is not available.

12.3.5.3 Blue biotechnology

Since the 1960s, many pharmaceutical compounds have been produced from a diverse range of marine bacteria. Marine micro-organisms continue to be a productive and successful focus for natural products research. Emerging products include new medicines, enzymes, and chemicals with applications in human health and manufacturing, as well as new additives and colourants for the food industry. The marine environment is viewed as an increasingly important source of novel antimicrobial metabolites. For example, marine biotechnology forms a significant part of research activities in the European Centre for Marine Biotechnology at the Scottish Association for Marine Science (SAMS), in the newly opened Marine Biodiscovery Centre at Aberdeen University, and at PML within its trading subsidiary PML Applications. At these research centres, scientists are exploiting their expertise in the biology and chemistry of a wide variety of marine organisms to produce novel pharmaceutical products, biomedical research tools, anti-foulants, catalysts, high-value extracts for nutritional

Box 12.5

Box 12.5a Wild species as sentinels of the environmental impact of chemicals on human health and well-being.

Several so-called 'biological effects markers' are widely measured in sentinel marine animals, such as fish, to measure exposure to, and effect of, man-made chemical pollutants. In this instance, the sentinels are employed to indicate potential effects of similar exposures of human populations to water and products arising from polluted areas. In the UK, liver cancer is measured in sentinel marine and estuarine flatfish to indicate exposure to carcinogenic chemicals (**Figure 1**). The prevalence of these cancers differs between sites and ranges from baseline (less than 1%) to high (more than 20%) at given locations. Due to the migratory behaviour of fish (many species move between feeding and breeding grounds) and the slow formation of cancers (over a year or more), it has been somewhat problematic to link cancer prevalence directly with man-made chemical pollutants, particularly at offshore sites. However, strong evidence exists for this relationship in other heavily polluted waterways of the world, and the pattern of prevalence is very repeatable in UK waters, suggesting a clear basis for cause (Stentiford et al. 2009).

Other markers utilised in UK waters include the measurement of the egg yolk protein vitellogenin (VTG) in the blood of male fish. This protein is known to occur in male fish exposed to endocrine disrupting chemicals (EDCs) and is elevated in some UK estuaries (Kirby et al. 2004) and even offshore (Scott et al. 2007). In both areas, elevated VTG has been associated with the occurrence of so-called 'intersex' fish at these sites. In these cases, the male testis is partially replaced with a female ovary which most likely indicates an exposure to EDCs during crucial early life stages (Stentiford et al. 2003, 2005). The linkage between freshwater and estuarine inputs of EDCs and the effects seen in the marine environment is currently unstudied.

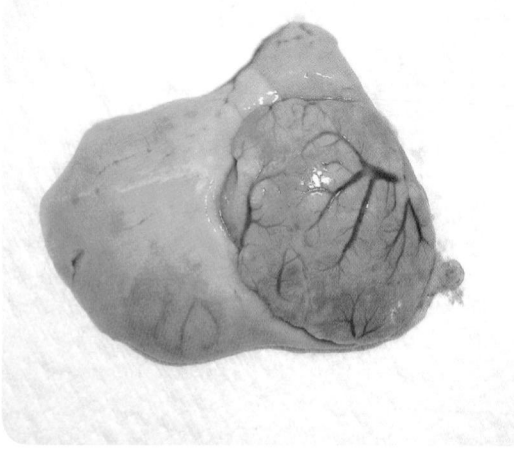

Figure 1 Liver cancer (on right of picture) in marine flatfish from UK waters. *Photo Crown Copyright 2010, reproduced with permission from CEFAS.*

Box 12.5b Wild species as sentinels of the environmental impacts of pathogens and harmful algal blooms on human health and well-being.

Pathogenic microbial contamination and the presence of harmful algal blooms are important issues in waters used for potable water supplies, recreation and for the protection and propagation of fish, shellfish and wildlife. Pathogenic microbes are present in faecal inputs into terrestrial, freshwater and marine environments, and include viruses, bacteria and parasites. Sources are broad-ranging and include farmed and wild mammalian and avian faecal matter, and human faecal matter in various states of treatment. The traceability of these sources has been highlighted as a problem (Simpson et al. 2002; Baker-Austin et al. 2009). Pathogens of concern to human health can remain viable and in large quantities in the environment for long periods of time (e.g. *Escherichia coli* O157:H7). Filter-feeding shellfish, such as clams and mussels (**Figure 2**), may concentrate bacteria and viruses from their growing waters. Because they are frequently consumed raw or only lightly cooked, shellfish contaminated with these pathogens have the potential to cause human disease.

In the UK, considerable effort is expended in the direct and indirect monitoring of pathogenic microbes from faecal sources, mainly through detection and quantification in farmed and fished molluscan shellfish. These pathogens are monitored under a framework of EU food health regulations, and so, exceeding agreed levels of contamination can lead to cessation of the harvest of shellfish in affected zones. Thus, in very specific circumstances, the presence of microbial biodiversity can be viewed as an antagonistic problem, reducing the marine food provisioning service. The measurement of microbial contaminants in water and in sentinel shellfish provides a direct indicator of health risk to human consumers and demonstrates the complex association of terrestrial, freshwater and marine habitats in governing this level of risk in specific geographic locations.

Harmful Algal Blooms (HABs) are caused by massive and prolonged overgrowth of algae and other plant-like organisms such as dinoflagellates, diatoms and cyanobacteria. Natural links have been made between the occurrence of HABs and eutrophication in riverine, estuarine and coastal waters, and the management of nutrient inputs to the watershed can lead to significant reductions in HABs (Heisler et al. 2008). The issues surrounding the presence of HABs, and the toxins associated with them, in the marine environment are broadly similar in scope and effect to those described for the microbial contaminants of bivalve molluscs and controls are included in the same regulatory framework on food hygiene across Europe. Essentially, these toxins can bioaccumulate, particularly within filter-feeding molluscan shellfish, and can cause harm to human consumers. Due to perceived increases in HAB occurrence and severity, and the known acute and chronic toxicity to animals, plants and humans, HABs, and their associated effects, have emerged as a worldwide concern.

The measurement of toxins associated with the formation of HABs in sentinel shellfish provides a direct indicator of health risk to human consumers and, as described for microbial contaminants of shellfish, particularly demonstrates the complex interactions between terrestrial, freshwater and marine habitats that govern the level of risk in specific geographic marine locations.

Figure 2 Mussel beds in Exmouth. *Photo courtesy of Rob Ellis, Plymouth Marine Laboratory.*

supplements and personal care products. In its current manifestation, blue biotechnology development makes use of only very small amounts of sampled material, with further development for products being predominantly laboratory based.

12.3.6 Delivery of Marine Ecosystem Services by Different Components of the Marine Habitat and Associated Fauna

We considered the delivery of services and benefits from each of the six CP2 habitats: Intertidal Sediment, Intertidal Rock, Shallow Subtidal Sediment, Subtidal Rock, Shelf Subtidal Sediment, and Deep-sea habitats; as well as additional habitats which could be considered to have distinct biodiversity and biogeochemical properties that might affect provision of ecosystem services: estuarine (transitional) waters, pelagic mixed water column and pelagic stratified water column and shelf subtidal rock. The same services tend to be delivered by different habitat types (i.e. sediment, rock or pelagic) regardless of where they are (i.e. intertidal, coastal shelf, transitional waters, deep-sea). The organisms and their biological activity and functions differ between these habitats and locations, but most marine environments deliver most marine ecosystem services. The ecosystem processes and intermediate services that underpin benefits are similar for provisioning (Chapter 15), regulating (Chapter 14) and cultural services (Chapter 16). However, the amount of service, and hence the benefit derived, will vary according to the habitat/location. This is the key point for quantifying ecosystem service delivery, but most of the ecosystem service and benefit data is not available at the disaggregated level of marine habitat/location type in the UK.

Consideration of three key marine communities—pelagic microbial communities (including phytoplankton and zooplankton), benthic bioturbators (organisms living in seabed sediments whose physical activities, such as feeding, burrowing and irrigation, disturb the sediment), and fish—suggests that the number of final benefits delivered by a community or assemblage is not always equivalent to their contribution in terms of underpinning intermediate and final ecosystem services (**Figure 12.15**). For example, this encapsulates the concerns about future ocean acidification impacts since there is building evidence that these are likely to affect pelagic microbial communities and benthic organisms in particular (Widdicombe *et al.* 2009; Turley *et al.* 2010). Potentially, although we get fewer direct benefits from these organisms, all of the underpinning ecosystem processes and functions, and intermediate services they provide, could be impacted, with catastrophic effects. The impacts on fish may also be large, but the ecosystem impacts might not be so catastrophic.

12.3.7 Ecosystem Service Interactions with other UK NEA Broad Habitats

The ecosystem services and benefits of the Coastal Margins (Chapter 11) are largely shared with, and often derived from, the access and proximity to marine habitats. Examples include: bathing waters adjacent to sand dunes and sandy beaches; marine wildlife-watching (seabirds

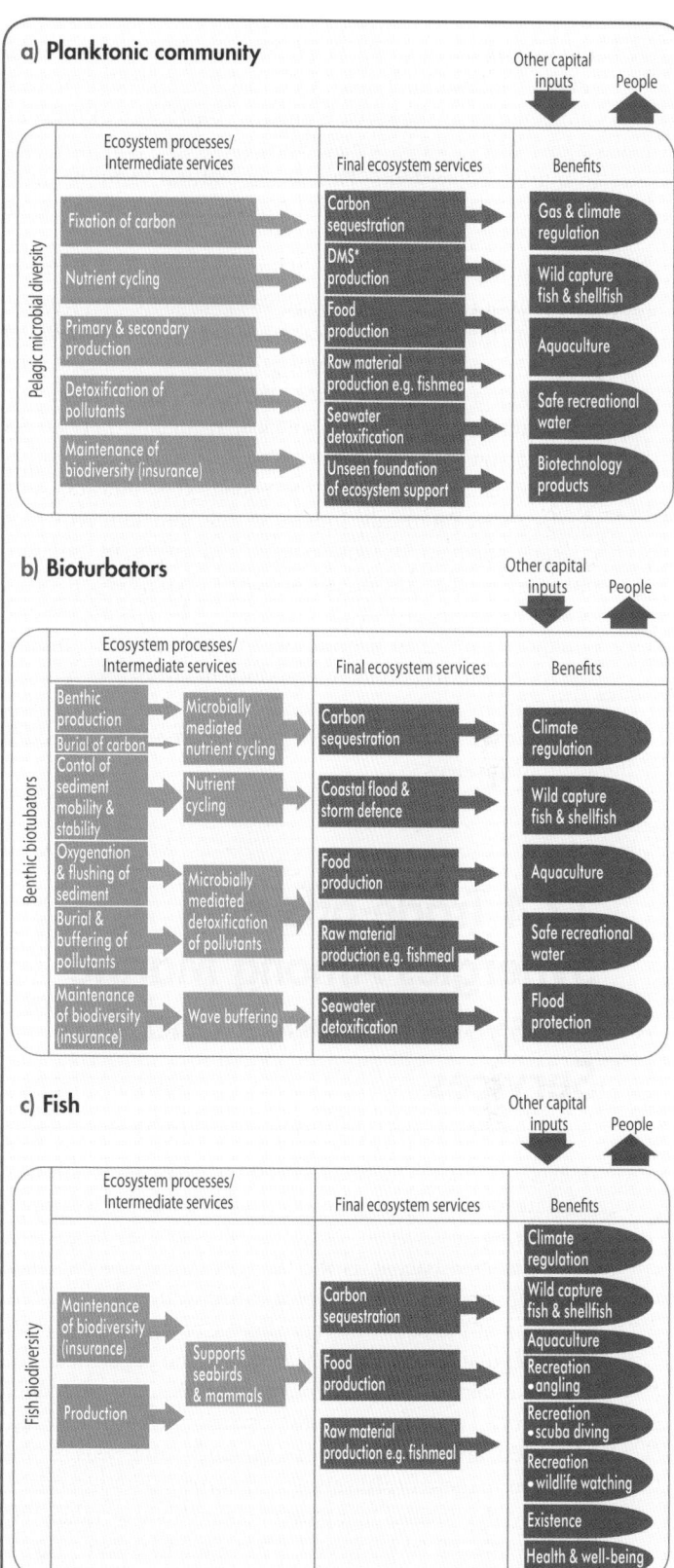

Figure 12.15 Schematic diagram of a selection of ecosystem processes and/or intermediate ecosystem services from three key marine communities to illustrate how ecosystem processes are linked to final ecosystem services and the benefits they generate for people: a) pelagic planktonic community; b) benthic bioturbators; and c) fish. Schematic follows the philosophy of the UK NEA Conceptual Framework (Chapter 2), and is adapted from Fisher *et al.* (2008). *DMS is dimethyl sulphide which is a climate regulating gas (Charlson *et al.* 1987; Liss *et al.* 1997).

and mammals); boating; and habitat and food provision for seabirds in intertidal areas (e.g. beaches and saltmarshes) inundated with seawater. Similarly, coastal urban habitats enjoy many of these benefits through access and proximity to marine ecosystems. Part of the cultural value of these terrestrial habitats is derived from locally caught food of marine origin.

In turn, marine ecosystems receive much of the diffuse waste from terrestrial and freshwater habitats, for example, via river runoff, treated sewage effluent, urban stormwater overflow, and excess nutrient runoff from farmland and air pollution in coastal cities. Therefore, they provide an important, but largely unquantified, regulating service for these habitats of waste removal and degradation.

Another linkage is that the aquatic medium acts as a carrier for economically important eels and salmon which migrate between oceans, coasts and rivers in different phases of their lifecycle. As juveniles, eels migrate from the oceans via coastal waters into rivers, where they grow to adulthood, and then migrate back to the sea to reproduce again. In contrast, salmon reproduce in rivers and migrate as juveniles to the sea, where they grow to adulthood, returning to the rivers where they spawned to reproduce again themselves.

12.4 Trade-offs and Synergies Among Marine Ecosystem Goods and Services

Delivery of many marine ecosystem services is strongly interlinked and synergistic, as would be expected when considering ecosystem services in such a large and interconnected habitat as the UK's estuarine, coastal, shelf and deep-sea waters. The biological activity and ecosystem functions of the same, or very similar, organisms underpin waste regulation and detoxification, climate regulation, and nutrient cycling in the water column or in the sediment seabed (Section 12.3.6). In turn, cultural services, such as leisure and recreation, are dependent on clean, functioning seas, so the functions of these organisms also underpin cultural services. Similarly, the habitats that prevent disturbance by mitigating the hazards of flooding and wave damage also provide supporting habitat for other species, and are constituent parts of habitats for leisure and recreation. Generally, the flagship wild species are those which underpin wildlife-watching activities and pertain to marine cultural benefits. Regionally based fisheries providing food also support local tourism and, therefore, cultural services.

Yet excessive fish extraction is unsustainable and impacts on other components of the ecosystem by affecting trophic (food web) structure and damaging seabed habitats. Hence, excessive fishing potentially negatively affects delivery of the other services. Trade-offs occur, to a greater or lesser extent,

between many marine ecosystem services and food provision by fisheries. For example, birdwatching is a popular leisure activity and public engagement with seabirds and mammals is evident (Section 12.3.5), but there has been a conflict with fisheries overexploitation. Commercial fisheries for small fish species, such as sandeels, may reduce food availability for seabirds (Frederiksen et al. 2004; Frederiksen et al. 2007; Wanless et al. 2005), marine mammals and predatory fishes (MacLeod et al. 2007). Poor breeding success at many seabird colonies has been related to a lack of sandeel prey resources, although it is likely that climate change is also contributing to a reduction in the number and quality of prey fish (Mitchell et al. 2010).

In the waters off south-east Scotland, a sandeel fishery that operated in the 1990s significantly depressed adult survival and breeding success of black-legged kittiwakes at adjacent colonies compared with years prior to the fishery opening and after it was closed. Since 2000 there has been a ban on sandeel fishing off eastern Scotland and north-east England. If fishing is resumed to levels that significantly reduce local sandeel stock, it would potentially exacerbate reductions in breeding success and survival that are probably now being caused by increases in sea surface temperature as a result of climate change (Mitchell et al. 2010).

At the same time, fisheries were benefiting some seabirds by providing them with food as discharged offal and discarded undersize fish, and thus, supported populations of scavenging species (e.g. great skua, northern fulmar) above levels that natural food sources could sustain. However, overfishing and the introduction of measures to conserve fish stocks have reduced the amount of discards which may have contributed to a population downturn of northern fulmars and other offshore surface-feeders since the mid-1990s (Mitchell et al. 2010).

Bottom trawling fisheries and some shellfisheries cause habitat damage and hence substantial changes to marine ecosystems including the disturbance of the seafloor leading to mortality of benthic organisms, changes in benthic community composition and re-working of sediment (Frid et al. 1999; Kaiser et al. 2006). This changes the levels of supporting services, such as nutrient cycling and habitat provision (Percival et al. 2005; Bremner et al. 2005; Olsgard et al. 2008; Cesar & Frid 2009), and there is evidence that these changes have taken place over the last 60 years (Frid et al. 2000). Changes in marine benthic communities can lead to a reduction in the food available to waterbirds, which has probably resulted in changes in numbers and distribution of seaducks, divers and waders (Mitchell et al. 2010).

Seals and cetaceans, such as dolphins, are popular with wildlife-watchers, making an important contribution to cultural services, as well as being flagship wild species. However, they are viewed by fishermen as competitors for fish stocks for human consumption, and can be trapped and damaged by nets. Similarly, recreational angling is sometimes viewed as competing for resource with commercial fisheries for food provision. Some recreational fishermen consider that overexploitation by commercial fisheries has reduced the overall size of trophy fish that they target.

Marine habitats are strongly linked to inland and coastal habitats including farmland, coastal urban cities and freshwater (Section 12.1.4). Application of fertilisers and livestock manure on farmland promotes increased terrestrial food provision, but excess nutrients and also nutrient-rich effluent from the storage of silage are conveyed, via freshwater runoff, into estuarine and coastal areas. For example, on an annual basis freshwaters contribute about 50% of the total external supply of dissolved inorganic nitrogen to the Irish Sea (Gowen *et al.* 2005). The enrichment of marine water by nutrients causes accelerated growth of macroalgae and microalgae. In shallow coastal and intertidal waters, the macroalgae can smother the soft sediments, impeding the flow of oxygen and nutrients to and from the sediment, and affecting marine life living within the sediment. When the microalgae and macroalgae die, their decomposition by microbial communities can further deplete oxygen in the sediment and overlying water, causing hypoxia and even anoxia, which have a deleterious effect on the water quality.

Eutrophication is one of the major threats to the health of estuarine, coastal and marine ecosystems around the world. The major pressures in the UK occur in the east, south and north-west of England where inputs of nutrients of anthropogenic origin (notably nitrate and phosphate from agriculture, but also urban wastewater sources) have resulted in nutrient enrichment of coastal waters (Chapter 4 in UKMMAS 2010). UK marine waters as a whole do not suffer from eutrophication problems, but some estuarine areas are nutrient enriched and are at risk from, or currently affected by, eutrophication.

Eutrophication can reduce and change marine biodiversity through the mortality of fish, shellfish and invertebrates, which will impact on most marine ecosystem services. It also encourages macro and micro algal blooms, which may be visually unattractive and reduce leisure and recreation benefits. Eutrophication can potentially increase blooms of harmful toxin-producing algae (harmful algal blooms; HABs), which can accumulate in filter-feeding shellfish or humans through consumption of contaminated shellfish, thus impacting on the human health benefits of marine food provision (see **Box 12.5a,b**). However, recent studies (Gowen *et al.* 2009) indicate that the abundance of HAB species that occur in the UK and Irish coastal waters is not related to anthropogenic nutrient enrichment. If poisoned shellfish are consumed, either because of a screening failure or unregulated harvesting, the human consequences can be severe, ranging from diarrhoea, to memory loss, paralysis and death. Harmful algal blooms may harm fish through food chain effects: fish may consume contaminated algae either directly or indirectly by eating prey that have consumed contaminated algae. This can impact food provision through reduced catches in the case of direct kills (e.g. fish and shellfish) or through closure of wild and aquaculture shell-fisheries when accumulated toxins have rendered the harvested shellfish unfit for human consumption.

The use of the marine ecosystem for waste disposal and detoxification services can also impact on food provision when it leads to bioaccumulation of pollutants, such as heavy metals and organic compounds, through the food chain. This impacts on sealife but also potentially on human health when fish and shellfish are consumed.

12.5 Options for Sustainable Management

A common paradigm amongst scientists discussing marine management has been that we do not manage marine ecosystems; rather we manage human activities within them. However, fundamentally we rarely understand the biodiversity or ecosystem implications of management decisions, let alone the impacts on ecosystems services. It is arguable whether, with the exception of fisheries, we manage any activity in the marine environment with respect to the provision of ecosystem services and their benefits. In the case of fisheries, it is only very recently that our management strategies are showing even slight signs of success.

The biodiversity and habitats of 80–90% of the UK's marine seabed remains unmapped and is known only via interpolation from the sites that have been surveyed and sampled: we do not know in detail what the characteristics of the seabed are in terms of sediment or rock habitat, what organisms live there, or how they change temporally. We need a much more comprehensive evidence base to properly quantify ecosystem services in a meaningful way that supports policy and new marine legislation.

12.5.1 Policy and Legislation

Currently, this is a time of massive change in EU and UK legislation with respect to marine ecosystems due to the recent introduction and forthcoming implementation of the EU Marine Strategy Framework Directive (MSFD), the UK Marine and Coastal Access Act (2009) and the Marine (Scotland) Act. The MSFD seeks to put in place measures to achieve good environmental status in EU waters by 2020. The EU and national legislation recognise that there are increasing commercial and leisure uses of marine ecosystems, for example, a growth in shipping for transport, marine renewable energy production, gas pipe and cable-laying, recreational boating, fishing, scuba diving and wildlife-watching, as well as traditional activities such as fishing (**Figure 12.16**). UK marine waters are viewed as

Figure 12.16 The marine environment is becoming increasingly busy, sometimes causing conflict in the use of space. Plymouth Sound. *Photo courtesy of Trevor Burrows Photography, Plymouth Marine Labratory.*

becoming increasingly crowded, but unlike on land, there are few, if any, defined property rights regarding the water column and the seabed beyond 12 nm, so management has only recently become spatially oriented. Within the new legislation the ecosystem and its biodiversity is viewed as being of sufficient importance that it must be considered equally with economic and social issues to be managed (as embodied by the ecosystem approach).

12.5.2 Conservation, Protected Areas and Fisheries Management

Protection within the marine environment around the UK will see dramatic change in the near future. The Marine and Coastal Access Act (2009) and the Marine (Scotland) Act 2010 (and the forthcoming Northern Ireland Marine Bill) require the designation of an ecologically coherent network of (MCZs), or Marine Protected Areas (MPAs) in Scotland, by 2012. This is also a requirement under the EU Marine Strategy Framework Directive. The MCZs will protect nationally important marine wildlife, habitats, geology and geomorphology, and will focus on all marine wildlife, not just threatened species; while the Scottish MPAs will focus on marine biodiversity and nationally important marine historic assets.

There are also calls from some scientists and NGOs to implement closed area networks to fulfil the same function for fish stocks. The EU Common Fisheries Policy is about to be revised and it is hoped that it will become more harmonious with the aspirations of the MSFD. Important progress is being made in UK fisheries management to improve the status of commercial fish stocks; for example, real-time closures, such as the voluntary closures in the North Sea to avoid areas of high cod abundance (www.scotland.gov.uk/ Topics/marine/Sea-Fisheries/17681/closures), and changes to gear, such as the use of square-meshed escape panels in nets to help non-target species escape.

Some inshore areas around the UK are now closed to towed gear through fisheries bylaws. For example, no fishing is allowed out to three nautical miles at Whitby, north-east England and some sea lochs in Scotland are closed to benthic trawls to protect deep mud sediments. Other areas that are closed through conservation designations to protect slow-growing features include a SAC designated near Arisaig, western Scotland to protect mearl beds, and 60 nm² of Lyme Bay in south-west England which has been closed to benthic trawls and scallop dredging to protect fragile reefs.

It is not yet known whether these measures will lead to significant reductions in the levels of physical disturbance to seabed habitats. It is unlikely that the status of impacted benthic habitats will improve without further directed management measures to protect the seabed, particularly where they support long-lived, fragile and/or functionally important species.

The UK has direct control of inshore fisheries (within 6 nm of the coast) that mainly utilise small vessels of less than 15 m in length. New Global Positioning System (GPS) tracking technologies to monitor fishing vessel effort (see **Box 12.2**) should be implemented widely on these vessels with a view to strengthening management strategies and measures.

12.5.3 Management of Human Activities and Future Environmental Change

The development of marine planning, as proposed in the Marine and Coastal Access Act (2009) and the Marine (Scotland) Act, should be an important mechanism to help maintain or improve the quality of marine habitats, integrating the needs for sustainable use by industry with environmental protection objectives. They should enable proactive management of marine ecosystems. It is imperative that such plans consider not only the components of marine ecosystems in terms of biodiversity and habitats, but also in terms of ecosystem functioning and the provision of ecosystem services. The use of monetary and non-monetary techniques for the valuation of ecosystem services will aid the process of considering the impacts on, and also benefits for, ecosystems of marine development within marine plans.

With the extent of human activity in the marine environment increasing, it is likely that stronger governance will be needed including increased stakeholder involvement, improved enforcement of legislation and possibly reconsideration of property rights.

The marine environment is a dynamic and changing habitat, not least because of the rapid impacts of climate change and the anticipated onset of the impacts of ocean acidification. It is also highly interconnected. Planning will need to consider not only the current spatial impacts of different human uses of, and activities in, the marine environment, but also the future implications. This is particularly important with respect to deciding on the locations of protected or conservation areas, and of permanent structures such as wind turbines and other renewable energy devices. Spatially resolved modelling tools are likely to be able to assist in this process.

Links between deep-sea, shelf, coastal, estuarine, freshwater and terrestrial systems must be considered in these plans. A further complication is that most relevant legislation divides the UK marine area into inshore and offshore parts. This is because international and EU law usually places different rights and obligations on states in respect of their territorial waters (0–12 nm). There is a need to re-invigorate integrated coastal zone management in the light of the new marine legislation so that coastal management and marine management are fully aligned.

12.6 Future Research and Monitoring Gaps

Although recent National reports (Charting Progress 2 in 2010, State of Scotland's Seas in 2011) have gathered a lot of evidence, the characteristics and biodiversity of many UK marine habitats, particularly those which are subtidal, are still unknown and unmapped, and marine ecosystem services are poorly quantified. We need to understand and quantify the ecological links between marine biodiversity, ecosystem function and provision of ecosystem goods and services, and to understand the effects of human impacts on these links. Such knowledge would support more effective marine planning and licensing of activity in UK waters, encouraging the sustainable use of marine habitats and the maintenance of clean, healthy, productive and biologically diverse seas.

A list of gaps in knowledge was prepared by Austen *et al.* (2008) and many of the issues are still relevant, particularly with respect to the need to support marine spatial planning for sustainable management:

- ■ *Spatial and temporal ecology of marine systems*— information is needed on the scales at which underlying marine ecosystem processes occur, how these relate to the scales at which services are delivered, and what the linkages are between them. Marine landscape ecology still needs considerable research effort if it is to reach the level of understanding we have for terrestrial ecosystems.
- ■ *Improved understanding of non-coastal and sub-tidal marine ecosystems*—empirically derived theory concerning the nature of marine biodiversity-ecosystem functioning relationships needs to be tested under natural conditions and in a wide variety of marine habitats, particularly non-coastal and subtidal.
- ■ *Relationship between function (and/or biodiversity), process and provision of services*—a diversity of ecological processes underpin the provision of marine ecosystem services, but the relationships between them needs to be quantified and the key processes and elements of biodiversity determined.
- ■ *Development of modelling and predictive tools to link biodiversity to function, provision of service and value*—a predictive capacity to anticipate the impacts of human activity on the provision of marine ecosystem services and benefits is required to support policy and management. Models of marine systems exist but they need to better incorporate biodiversity and ecosystem services, and they need to be made operational.
- ■ *The role of biodiversity in providing resilience in the provision of ecosystem services*—the extent to which marine biodiversity facilitates resistance to change in the delivery of marine ecosystem services, as well as the ability of marine biodiversity to recover and restore delivery of services, needs to be understood.
- ■ *Limitations ('tipping points') of marine biodiversity*— there may be a uniform relationship between biodiversity and the provision of marine ecosystem services or there may be crucial non-linearities and tipping points at which delivery is no longer possible. These relationships, and the limits at which marine biodiversity can still provide a service, need to be defined.
- ■ *Defining the best mechanisms to afford the protection of goods and services*—the species, habitats and functions that are critical to maintain and enhance the delivery of marine ecosystem services need to be identified. This will help to define and prioritise management mechanisms and policy strategies for their protection and restoration. Knowledge that can inform such management priorities is particularly limited in subtidal zones.
- ■ *Development and application of technology to support research*—some underwater technology is already available but has not been fully utilised. For

example, there are technologies to support underwater habitat-mapping where data is remotely collected, yet much of the seabed remains unmapped. Consequently, we do not know what the characteristics of the seabed are or what organisms live there.

- ■ *Building environmental accounts for the services associated with marine systems*—to support policy and management we need to clearly describe and quantify the processes that impact upon marine ecosystem services, the benefits they generate and their value.

References

Adak, G.K., Meakins, S.M., Yip, H., Lopman, B.A. & O'Brien, S.J. (2005). Disease risks from foods, England and Wales, 1996–2000. *Emerging Infectious Diseases,* **11** (3), pp. 365–372.

Allen, J.I., Blackford, J.C., Ashworth, M.I., Proctor, R., Holt, J.T. & Siddorn, J.R. (2001) A highly spatially resolved ecosystem model for the north–west European continental shelf. *Sarsia,* **86,** 423–40.

Andrews, J. E., Burgess, D., Cave, R.R., Coombes, E.G., Jickells, T.D., Parkes, D.J. & Turner, R.K. (2006) Biogeochemical value of managed realignment, Humber estuary, UK. *Science of the Total Environment,* **371,** 19–30.

Armstrong, M. & Holmes, I. (2010) An indicator of sustainability for marine fin-fish stocks around the UK: 1990–2008, Centre for Environment, Fisheries and Aquaculture Science, Lowestoft.

Austen, M.C., Burrows, M., Frid, C., Haines-Young, R., Hiscock, H., Moran, D., Myers, J., Paterson, D.M. & Rose, P. (2008) Marine biodiversity and the provision of goods and services: identifying the research priorities. Report to the UK Biodiversity Research Advisory Group.

Baxter, J.M., Boyd, I.L., Cox, M., Cunningham, L., Holmes, P. & Moffat, C.F. (eds) (2008) Scotland's Seas: Towards Understanding their State. pp. 174. Fisheries Research Services, Aberdeen.

Beaumont, N.J. & others (2006) Identification, definition and quantification of goods and services provided by Marine Biodiversity. MarBEF Theme 3 working paper. [online] Available at: <www.MarBEF.org> [Accessed 19.01.11].

Beaumont, N.J., Austen, M.C., Mangi, S.C. & Townsend, M. (2008) Economic Valuation for the Conservation of Marine Biodiversity. *Marine Pollution Bulletin,* **56,** 386–396.

Beaumont, N.J., Austen, M.C., Atkins, J., Burdon, D., Degraer, S., Dentinho, T.P., Derous, S., Holm, P., Horton, T., van Ierland, E., Marboe, A.H., Starkey, D.J., Townsend, M. & Zarzycki, T. (2007) Identification, definition and quantification of goods and services provided by marine biodiversity: Implications for the Ecosystem Approach. *Marine Pollution Bulletin,* **54,** 253–265.

Behrenfeld, M.J. & Falkowski, P.G. (1997) Photosynthetic rates derived from satellite-based chlorophyll concentration. *Limnology and Oceanography,* **42,** 1–20.

Benjamins, S. (2010) Benthic Habitats. Charting Progress 2 Feeder Report: Healthy and Biologically Diverse Seas. UK Marine Monitoring and Assessment Strategy (UKMMAS) (ed M. Frost). Defra, London. [online] Available at: <http://chartingprogress. defra.gov.uk/chapter-3-healthy-and-biologicaly-diverse-seas> [Accessed 19.01.11].

Benwell, Y. (2004) Research into the Economic Contribution of Sea Angling. Final report to the Department for Environment, Food and Rural Affairs, London.

Bett, B.J. (2001) UK Atlantic Margin Environmental Survey: introduction and overview of bathyal benthic ecology. Continental *Shelf Research*, **21**, 917–956.

Bett, B.J. & Jacobs, CL. (2000) RRS Charles Darwin cruise 119C leg B, 13 August–24 September 1999. White Zone WhiZ Environment survey: Seabed survey of the deep waters to the north and west of Shetland. Southampton Oceanography Centre Cruise report. Report to the department of Trade and Industry.

Bird, W.J. (2007) Natural Thinking: Investigating the Links Between the Natural Environment, Biodiversity and Mental Health. Royal Society for the Protection of Birds.

Birkett, D.A., Maggs, C. & Dring, M.J. (1998) Maerl volume V An overview of dymanics and sensitivity characteristics for conservation management of marine SACs, pp. 116. Scottish Assoiciation for Marine Science UK Marine SACs Project.

Blackford, J.C. (1997) An analysis of benthic biological dynamics in a North Sea ecosystem model. *Journal of Sea Research*, **38**, 213–230.

BMF, MCA, RNLI, RYA & YBW (2005–2008) Watersports and Leisure Participation Surveys. Arkenford Market Research. [online] Available at: <http://www.britishmarine.co.uk/publications.aspx?category=StatisticsandMarketResearch> [Accessed 26.01.11].

Boorman, L.A. (2003) Saltmarsh Review. An overview of coastal saltmarshes, their dynamic and sensitivity characteristics for conservation and management. JNCC Report, No. 334. JNCC, Peterborough, p114. [online] Available at: < http://www.jncc.gov.uk/pdf/jncc334.pdf> [Accessed 06.06.10].

Brampton, A.H. (1992) Engineering Significance of British Saltmarshes. Saltmarshes Morphodynamics, Conservation and Engineering Significance (eds J.L.R. Allen & K. Pye), pp. 115–122. Cambridge University Press, Cambridge UK.

Bremner, J., Frid, C.L.J. & Rogers, S.I. (2005) Biological traits of the North Sea benthos: Does fishing affect benthic ecosystem function? *Benthic Habitats and the Effects of Fishing*, **41**, 477–489.

Broitman, B., Mieszkowska, N., Helmuth, B.T. & Blanchette, C. (2008) Climate and recruitment of rocky shore intertidal invertebrates in the eastern north Atlantic. *Ecology*, **89**(Supplement 06), 81–90.

Burrows, M.T., Harvey, R., Robb, L., Poloczanska, E.S., Mieszkowska, N., Moore, P., Leaper, R., Hawkins, S.J. & Bennedetti-Cecci, L. (2009) Spatial scales of variance in distributions of intertidal species on complex coastlines: effects of region, dispersal mode and trophic level. *Ecology*, **90**(5), 1242–1254.

Butler, E.I. (1979) Nutrient balance in the Western English Channel. *Estuarine and Coastal Marine Science,* **8**, 195–197.

Cappell, R. & Lawrence, R. (2005). The motivation, demographics and views of south west recreational sea anglers and their socio-economic impact on the region. Invest in Fish South West Report. 118pp.

Carr, M.E., Friedrichs, M.A.M., Schmeltz, M., Aite, M.N., Antoine, D., Arrigo, K., Asanuma, I, Aumont, O., Barber, R., Behrenfeld, M., Bidigare, R., Buitenhuis, E., Campbell, J., Ciotti, A., Dierssen, H., Dowell, M., Dunne, J., Esaias, W., Gentili, B., Groom, S.B., Hoepffner, N., Hishisaka, J., Kameda, T., Le Quere, C., Lohrenz, S., Marra, J., Melin, F., Moore, K., Morel, A., Reddy, T., Ryan, J., Scardi, M., Smyth, TJ, Turpie, K., Tilstone, G, Waters, K. & Yamanaka, Y. (2006) A comparison of global estimates of marine primary production from ocean color. *Deep Sea Research II*, **53**, 741–770.

CEFAS (Centre for Environment, Fisheries & Aquaculture Science) (2008) Shellfish News 26, Autumn/Winter 2008. Centre for Environment, Fisheries and Aquaculture Science. [online] Available at: <http://www.cefas.co.uk/publications/shellfish-news/shellfish-news-issue-no-26,-autumnwinter-2008.aspx> [Accessed 19.01.11].

CEFAS (Centre for Environment, Fisheries & Aquaculture Science) (2009) Shellfish News 27, Spring/Summer 2009. Centre for Environment, Fisheries and Aquaculture Science [online] Available at: <http://www.cefas.co.uk/publications/shellfish-news/shellfish-news-issue-no-27,-springsummer-2009.aspx> [Accessed 19.01.11].

Cesar, C.P. & Frid, C.L.J. (2009) Effects of experimental small-scale cockle (Cerastoderma edule L.) fishing on ecosystem function. *Marine Ecology-an Evolutionary Perspective*, **30**, 123–137.

Charlson, R. J., Lovelock, J. E., Andreae, M. O. & Warren, S. G. (1987). Oceanic phytoplankton, atmospheric sulphur, cloud albedo and climate. *Nature* **326**: 655–661.

Chesworth, J.C., Donkin, M.E. & Brown, M.T. (2004) The interactive effects of the antifouling herbicides Irgarol 1051 and Diuron on the seagrass *Zostera marina* (L.). *Aquatic toxicology*, **66**, 293–305.

Coleman, R., Underwood, A., Benedetti-Cecchi, L., Åberg, P., Arenas, F., Arrontes, J., Castro, J., Hartnoll, R., Jenkins, S., Paula, J., Santina, P. & Hawkins, S. 2006: A continental scale evaluation of the role of limpet grazing on rocky shores. *Oecologia,* **147**, 556–564.

Coops, H., Geilen, N., Verheij, H.J., Boeter, R. & van der Velde, G. (1996) Interactions between wave, bank erosion and emergent vegetation: an experimental study in wave tanks. *Aquatic Botany*, **53**, 187–198.

Cote, D., Ollerhead, L.M.N., Gregory, R.S., Scruton, D.A. & McKinley, R.S. (2002) Activity patterns of juvenile Atlantic cod *Gadus morhua* in Buckley Cove, Newfoundland. *Hydrobiologia*, **483**,121–127.

Covich, A.P., Austen, M.C., Bärlocher, F., Chauvet, E., Cardinale, B.J., Biles, C.L., Inchausti, P., Dangles, O., Statzner, B., Solan, M., Moss, B.R. & Asmus, H. (2004) The role of biodiversity in the functioning of freshwater and marine benthic ecosystems: review of current evidence and future research needs. *Bioscience*, **54**, 767–775.

Crabtree, B., Willis, K., Powe, N., Carman, P., Rowe, D., Macdonald, D. & Usher-Benwell, Y. (2004) Research into the Economic Contribution of Sea Angling. Final report to the Department for Environment, Food and Rural Affairs, London.

Craik, J.C.A. (1997). Long-term effects of North American Mink *Mustela vison* on seabirds in western Scotland. *Bird Study* **44**, 303–309.

Craik, J.C.A. (1998). Recent mink-related declines of gulls and terns in west Scotland and the beneficial effects of mink control. *Argyll Bird Report*, **14**, 98–110.

Curtin, S. & Wilkes, K. (2005) British Wildlife Tourism Operators: Current Issues and Typologies. *Current Issues in Tourism*, **8**, 455–478.

Davidson, D.M. & Hughes, D.J. (1998) Zostera Biotopes Volume I. An overview of dynamics and sensitivity characteristics for conservation management of marine SACs. Scottish Association for Marine Science (UK Marine SACs Project).

Depledge, M.H. & Bird, W.J. (2009) The Blue Gym: health and wellbeing from our coasts. *Marine Pollution Bulletin*, **58**(7), 947–948.

Defra (2005) Charting Progress—an Integrated Assessment of the State of UK Seas. Defra Report (Crown copyright). [online] Available at: <http://chartingprogress.defra.gov.uk/feeder/chartingprogress.pdf > [Accessed 21.02.11].

Defra (2009) Draft guidance on SSSIs and National Nature Reserves in the subtidal area (Note 4) [online] Available at: <http://www.defra.gov.uk/environment/biodiversity/marine/documents/guidance-note4.pdf **>** [Accessed 21.02.11].

Dickie, I., Hughes, J. & Esteban, A. (2006) Watched Like Never Before... the local economic benefits of spectacular bird species. The RSPB, Sandy, UK.

Dixon, A.M., Leggett, D.J. & Weight, R.C. (1998) Habitat creation opportunities for landward coastal re-alignment : Essex case studies. *Journal of the Chartered Institution of Water and Environment*, **12**, 107–112.

Duck, C. (2010) Seals. Charting Progress 2 Feeder Report: Healthy and Biologically Diverse Seas. UK Marine Monitoring and Assessment Strategy (UKMMAS) (ed. M. Frost). Defra, London. [online] Available at: <http://chartingprogress.defra.gov.uk/chapter-3-healthy-and-biologicaly-diverse-seas> [Accessed 19.01.11].

Dunn, M.R. & Potten, S.D. (1994) National Survey of Bass Angling. Report to MAFF. CEMARE, University of Portsmouth.

Dunstone, D. (2008) Development of spatial information layers for commercial fishing and shellfishing in UK waters to support strategic siting of offshore wind farms. Cowrie Ltd., 2008. [online] Available at: <www.offshorewind.co.uk> [Accessed 20.02.11].

FAO (Food and Agriculture Organization of the United Nations) (2008) Fishery Statistical Collections, Global Capture Production [Online] Available at: <http://www.fao.org/fishery/statistics/global-capture-production/en> [Accessed 26.01.11].

Field, C.B., Behrenfeld, M.J., Randerson, J.T. & Falkowski, P. (1998) Primary production of the biosphere: Integrating terrestrial and oceanic components. *Science*, **281**, 237–240.

Fisher, B., Turner, K., Zylstra, M., Brouwer, R., de Groot, R., Farber, S., Ferraro, P., Green, R., Hadley, D., Harlow, J., Jefferiss, P., Kirkby, C., Morling, P., Mowatt, S., Naidoo, R., Paavola, J., Strassburg, B., Yu, D. & Balmford, A. (2008) Ecosystem services and economic theory: integration for policy-relevant research. *Ecological Applications*, **18**, 2050–67.

Fletcher, R.L. (1996) The occurrence of "green tides" – a review. Marine Benthic Vegetation: Recent Changes and the Effects of Eutrophication (eds W. Schramm, P.H. Nienhuis, P.H.), pp. 7–43. Springer, Berlin, Heidelberg, New York.

Fonseca, M.S. & Cahalan, J.A. (1992) A preliminary evaluation of wave attenuation by four species of seagrass. Estuarine. *Coastal and Shelf Science,* **35**, 565–576.

Fowler, S.L. (1999) Guidelines for managing the collection of bait and other shoreline animals within UK European marine sites. 132p. Peterborough: English Nature.

Frederiksen, M., Furness, R.W. & Wanless, S. (2007) Regional variation in the role of bottom-up and top-down

processes in controlling sandeel abundance in the North Sea. *Marine Ecology Progress Series*, **337**, 279–286.

Frederiksen, M., Harris, M.P., Daunt, F., Rothery, P. & Wanless, S. (2004) The role of industrial fisheries and oceanographic change in the decline of North Sea black-legged kittiwakes. *Journal of Applied Ecology*, **41**, 1129–1139.

Frid, C.L.J., Hansson, S., Ragnarsson, S.A., Rijnsdorp, A. & Steingrimsson, S.A. (1999) Changing levels of predation on benthos as a result of exploitation of fish populations. *Ambio*, **28**, 578–582.

Frid, C.L.J., Harwood, K.G., Hall, S.J. & Hall, J.A. (2000) Long-term changes in the benthic communities on North Sea fishing grounds. *Ices Journal of Marine Science*, **57**, 1303–1309.

Frost, M. (ed) (2010) Charting Progress 2 Feeder Report: Healthy and Biologically Diverse Seas. UK Marine Monitoring and Assessment Strategy (UKMMAS). Defra, London. [online] Available at: <http://chartingprogress.defra.gov.uk/chapter-3-healthy-and-biologicaly-diverse-seas> [Accessed 19.01.11].

FRS (Fisheries Research Services) (2008) Scottish Shellfish Farm Production Survey 2007. Fisheries Research Services, Aberdeen.

FRS (Fisheries Research Services) (2009) Scottish Fish Farms Annual Production Survey, 2007. Fisheries Research Services, Aberdeen.

Gage, J.D. (2001) Deep-sea benthic community and environmental impact assessment at the Atlantic Frontier. *Continental Shelf Research*, **21**, 957–986.

Gibbs, P.E., Bryan, G.W. & Pascoe, P.L. (1991) TBT-induced imposex in the dogwhelk, *Nucella lapillus*: Geographical uniformity of the response and effects. *Marine Environmental Research,* **32**, 79–87.

Gotceitas, V., Fraser, S. & Brown, J.A. (1997) Use of eelgrass beds Zostera marina by juvenile Atlantic cod Gadus morhua. *Canadian Journal of Fisheries and Aquatic Sciences*, **54**, 1306–1319.

Gowen, R.J. & Stewart, B.M. (2005) The Irish Sea: nutrient status and phytoplankton. *Journal of Sea Research*, **54**, 36–50.

Gowen, R., Tett, P., Bresnan, E., Davidson, K., Gordon, A., McKinney, A., Millligan, S., Mills, D., Silke, J. & Crooks, A.M. (2009) Anthropogenic Nutrient Enrichment and Blooms of Harmful Micr-Algae. Report to Defra, London.

Guitart, C. & Readman, J.W. (2010) Critical evaluation of the determination of pharmaceuticals, personal care products, phenolic endocrine disrupters and faecal steroids by GC/MS and PTV-GC/MS in environmental waters. *Analytica Chimica Acta*, **658**, 32–40.

Gutiérrez, J.L., Jones, C.G., Strayer, D.L. & Iribarne, O.O. (2003) Molluscs as ecosystem engineers: the role of shell production in aquatic habitats. *Oikos,* **101**, 79–90.

Hall, L.W., Giddings, J.M., Solomon, K.R. & Balcomb, R. (1999) An ecological risk assessment for the use of Irgarol 1051 as an algaecide for antifoulant paints. *Critical Reviews in Ecotoxicology,* **29**, 367–437.

Hall-Spencer, J.M., Grall, J. & Moore, P.G. (2003) Bivalve fishing and maerl-bed conservation in France and the UK – retrospect and prospect Atkinson. *Aquatic Conservation: Marine and Freshwater Ecosystems*, **13**, S33–S41.

Hawkins, S.J., Moore, P.J., Burrows, M.T., Poloczanska, E., Mieszkowska, N., Herbert, R.J.H., Jenkins, S.R., Thompson, R.C., Genner, M.J. & Southward, A.J. (2008) Complex interactions in a rapidly changing world: responses of rocky shore communities to recent climate change. *Climate Research*, **37**, 123–133.

Heip, C., Hummel, H., van Avesaath, P., Appeltans, W., Arvanitidis, C., Aspden, R., Austen, M., Boero, F., Bouma, T.J., Boxshall, G., Buchholz, F., Crowe, T., Delaney, A., Deprez, T., Emblow, C., Feral, J.P., Gasol, J.M., Gooday, A., Harder, J., Ianora, A., Kraberg, A., Mackenzie, B., Ojaveer, H., Paterson, D., Rumohr, H., Schiedek, D., Sokolowski, A., Somerfield, P., Sousa Pinto, I., Vincx, M., Wesławski, J.M. & Nash, R. (2009) Marine Biodiversity and Ecosystem Functioning. Printbase, Dublin, Ireland. ISSN 2009-2539.

Heisler, J., Glibert, P.M., Burkholder, J.M., Anderson, D.M., Cochlan, W., Dennison, W.C., Dortch, Q., Gobler, C.J., Heil, C.A., Humphries, E., Lewitus, A.J., Magnien, R., Marshall, H.G., Sellner, K., Stockwell, D.A., Stoecker, D.K. & Suddleson, M. (2008) Eutrophication and harmful algal blooms: A scientific consensus. *Harmful Algae, 8*, 3–13.

Herbert, R.J.H., Southward, A.J., Sheader, M. & Hawkins, S.H. (2007) Influence of recruitment and temperature on distribution of intertidal barnacles in the English Channel. *Journal of the Marine Biological Association of the United Kingdom*, **87**(2), 487–499.

Hiscock, K. (1996) Marine Nature Conservation review: Rationale and Methods. Joint Nature Conservation Committee, Peterborough.

Hiscock, K., Sewell, J. & Oakley, J. (2005) Marine Health Check 2005. A report to gauge the health of the UK's sea-life. Godalming, WWF-UK.

Hiscock, K. & Smirthwaite, J. (2004) Marine Life Topic Note. Marine Biodiversity. Marine Life Information Network. Marine Biological Association, Plymouth.

Hiscock, K., Marshall, C., Sewell, J. & Hawkins, S.J. (2006). The structure and functioning of marine ecosystems: an environmental protection and management perspective. Report to English Nature from the Marine Life Information Network (MarLIN). Marine Biological Association of the UK, Plymouth. English Nature Research Reports, ENRR No. 699.

Holt, J.T., Allen, J.I., Proctor, R. & Gilbert, F. (2005) Error quantification of a high-resolution coupled hydrodynamic-ecosystem coastal-ocean model: Part 1 model overview and assessment of the hydrodynamics. *Journal of Marine Systems*, **57**, 167–88.

Hopkins, F.E., Turner, S.M., Nightingale, P.D., Steinke, M., Bakker, D. & Liss, P.S. (2010) Ocean acidification and marine trace gas emissions. *Proceeding of the National Academy Of Sciences*, **107**, 760–765.

Jackson, C.M., Kamenos, N.A., Moore, P.G., Young, M. (2004) Meiofaunal bivalves in maerl and other substrata; their diversity and community structure. *Ophelia*, **581**, 49–60.

Jennings, S. & Kaiser, M.J. (1998) The effects of fishing on marine ecosystems. *Advances in Marine Biology*, **34**, 201–352.

Jickells, T.D. (1998) Nutrient biogeochemistry of the coastal zone. *Science*, **281**, 217–222.

JNCC (Joint Nature Conservation Committee) (2009). UK Seabirds in 2008, ISBN 978 1 86107 611 3.

JNCC (Joint Nature Conservation Committee) (2010). Different types of Marine Protected Areas leaflet. [online] Available at: <http://www.jncc.gov.uk/pdf/MPAsInfoDoc_v2_2. pdf> [Accessed 04.02.11].

Joint, I. & Groom, S.B. (2000) Estimation of phytoplankton production from space: current status and future potential of satellite remote sensing. *Journal of Experimental Biology and Ecology, 250*, 233–255.

Jordan, M.B. & Joint, I.R. (1998) Seasonal variation in nitrate: phosphate ratio in the English Channel 1923–1987. *Estuarine and Coastal Shelf Science*, **46**, 157–164.

Kaiser, M.J., Clarke, K.R., Hinz, H., Austen, M.C., Somerfield, P.J. & Karakassis, I. (2006) Global analysis of the response and recovery of benthic biota to fishing. *Marine Ecology Progress Series*, **311**, 1–14.

Kamenos, N.A., Moore, P.G. & Hall-Spencer, J.M. (2004) Nursery-area function of maerl grounds for juvenile queen scallops *Aequipecten opercularis* and other invertebrates. *Marine Ecology Progress Series, 274*, 183–189.

Kaoru, Y. & Hoagland, P. (1994) The value of historic shipwrecks: Conflicts and management. *Coastal Management*, **22**(2), 195–213.

Kirby, M.F., Allen, Y.T., Dyer, R.A., Feist, S.W., Katsiadaki, I., Matthiessen, P., Scott, A.P., Smith, A., Stentiford, G.D., Thain, J.E., Thomas, K.V., Tolhurst, L. & Waldock, M.J. (2004) Surveys of plasma vitellogenin and intersex in male flounder (*Platichthys flesus*) as measures of endocrine disruption by oestrogenic contamination in UK estuaries: Temporal trends 1996–2001. *Environmental Toxicology and Chemistry*, **23**, 748–758.

KSBR Brand futures (2008) Marine Protected Areas. Qualitative Value Modes Research. Report prepared for Natural England.

Leader-Williams, N. & Dublin, H.T. (2000) Charismatic megafauna as 'flagship species'. Priorities for the conservation of mammalian diversity: has the panda had its day? (eds A. Entwhistle & N. Dunstone), pp. 53–81. Conservation Biology Series, Cambridge University Press, Cambridge.

Legendre, L. & Rivkin, R.B. (2005) Integrating functional diversity, food web processes, and biogeochemical carbon fluxes into a conceptual approach for modelling the upper ocean in a high CO_2 world. *Journal of Geophysical Research*, **110**, C09S17.

Lintas, C. & R. Seed. (1994) Spatial variation in the fauna associated with *Mytilus edulis* on a wave-exposed rocky shore. *Journal of Molluscan Studies*, **60**, 165–174.

Liss P.S., Hatton A.D., Malin G., Nightingale P.D. & Turner S. (1997) Marine sulphur emissions. *Philosophical Transactions of the Royal Society London B*, **352**, 159–169.

Lockwood, S.J. & Johnson, P.O. (1976) Mackerel research in the South-West of England. Laboratory Leaflet Number 32, Ministry of Agriculture, Fisheries and Food, Directorate of Fisheries Research, Lowestoft.

MacLeod, C., Santos, M., Reid, R.J., Scott, B. & Pierce, G.J. (2007) Linking sandeel consumption and the likelihood of starvation in harbour porpoises in the Scottish North Sea: could climate change mean more starving porpoises? *Biology Letters*, **3**, 185–188.

MALSF (Marine Aggregate Levy Sustainability Fund) (2010) Achievements and Challenges for the Future – March 2010. [online] Available at: <http://www.alsf-mepf.org.uk/downloads. aspx> [Accessed 18.02.11].

Marubini, F. (2010) Turtles. Charting Progress 2 Feeder Report: Healthy and Biologically Diverse Seas. UK Marine Monitoring and Assessment Strategy (UKMMAS)(ed. M. Frost). Defra, London. [online] Available at: <http://chartingprogress. defra.gov.uk/chapter-3-healthy-and-biologicaly-diverse-seas> [Accessed 24.01.11].

MCA (Maritime and Coastguard Agency) (2010) Receiver of Wreck. [online] Available at: <http://www.mcga.gov.uk/c4mca/mcga07-home/emergencyresponse/mcga-receiverofwreck/mcga-protectedwrecks.htm> [Accessed 26.01.11].

MCCIP (Marine Climate Change Impacts Partnership) (2008) Marine Climate Change Impacts Annual Report Card 2007–2008. Scientific Review – Nutrient Enrichment.

McLaughlin, E., Kelly, J., Birkett, D., Maggs, C. & Dring, M. (2006) Assessment of the Effects of Commercial Seaweed Harvesting on Intertidal and Subtidal Ecology in Northern Ireland. Environment and Heritage Service Research and Development Series. No. 06/26.

Mieszkowska, N., Hawkins, S.J., Burrows, M.T. & Kendall, M.A. (2007) Long-term changes in the geographic distribution and population structures of some near-limit populations of Osilinus lineatus in Britain and Ireland. *Journal of the Marine Biological Association of the United Kingdom,* **87**(2), 537–545.

Mieszkowska, N., Kendall, M.A., Hawkins, S.J., Leaper, R., Williamson, P., Hardman-Mountford, N.J. & Southward, A.J. (2006) Changes in the range of some common rocky shore species in Britain—a response to climate change? *Hydrobiologia,* **555**, 241–251.

Milneur, F., Johnson, M.P. & Maggs, C.A. (2008) Non-indigenous marine macroalgae in native communities: a case study in the British Isles. *Journal of the Marine Biological Association of the United Kingdom,* **88**, 693–698.

Mitchell, P.I. (2010) Marine Birds. Charting Progress 2 Feeder Report: Healthy and Biologically Diverse Seas. UK Marine Monitoring and Assessment Strategy (UKMMAS) (ed. M. Frost). Defra, London. [online] Available at: <http://chartingprogress.defra.gov.uk/chapter-3-healthy-and-biologicaly-diverse-seas> [Accessed 24.01.11].

MMO (Marine Management Organisation) (2010) United Kingdom Sea Fisheries Statistics Archive. [online] Available at: <http://www.marinemanagement.org.uk/fisheries/statistics/annual_archive.htm> [Accessed 12.11.10].

Möller, I., Spencer, T., French, J.R., Leggett, D.J. & Dixon, M. (1999) Wave transformation over saltmarshes: a field and numerical modelling study from North Norfolk, England. *Estuarine Coastal Shelf Science,* **49**, 411–426.

Moschella, P.S., Abbiati, M, Åberg, P., Airoldi, L., Anderson, J.M., Bacchiocchi, F., Bulleri, F., Dinesen, G.E., Frost, M., Gacia, E., Granhag, L., Jonsson, P.R., Satta, M.P., Sundelöf, A., Thompson, R.C. & Hawkins, S.J. (2005). Low-crested coastal defence structures as artificial habitats for marine life: Using ecological criteria in design. *Coastal Engineering,* **52**, (10–11): 1053–1071.

Murphy, L. (2008) Explore the Sea Floor Education and Outreach Programme 2007–2008 report. Welsh Assembly Government. [online] Available at: < http://www.cefas.co.uk/media/462179/mepf-07-05-final-report08small.pdf> [Accessed 26.01.11].

Murphy, M.L., Johnson, S.W. & Csepp, D.J. (2000) A comparison of fish assembalges in Eelgrass and adjacent subtidal habitats near Craig, Alaska. *Alaskan Fishery research Bulletin,* **7**, 11–21.

Nellemann, C., Corcoran, E., Duarte, C.M., Valdés, L., De Young, C., Fonseca, L., Grimsditch, G. (eds) (2009) Blue Carbon. A Rapid Response Assessment. United Nations Environment Programme, GRID-Arendal. [online] Available at: <www.grida.no> [Accessed 26.01.11].

Norderhaug, K.M., Christie, H. & Rinde, E. (2002) Colonisation of Kelp imitations by epiphyte and holdfast fauna; a study of mobility patterns. *Marine Biology,* **141**, 965–973.

Nottage, A.S. & Robertson, P.A. (2005) The saltmarsh creation handbook: a project managers guide to the creation of saltmarsh and intertidal mudflat. The RSPB, Sandy & CIWEM, London.

Olsgard, F., Schaanning, M.T., Widdicombe, S., Kendall, M.A., Austen, M.C. (2008) Effects of bottom trawling on ecosystem functioning. *Journal of Experimental Marine Biology and Ecology,* **366**, 123–133.

ONS (Office for National Statistics) (2007) The UK Standard Industrial Classification of Economic Activities 2007 (SIC 2007), Structure and explanatory notes.

ONS (Office for National Statistics) (2010) National population projections: 2008-based. ONS Series PP2 no. 27. [online] Available at: <http://www.statistics.gov.uk/downloads/theme_population/pp2no27.pdf> [Accessed 26.01.11].

Orth, R.J., Heck, K.L. & van Montfrans, J. (1984) Faunal communities in seagrass beds: a review of the influence of plant structure and prey characteristics on predator-prey relationships. *Estuaries,* **7**(4a), 339–350.

Paramor, O.A.L. & Hughes, R.G. (2004) The effects of bioturbation and herbivory by the polychaete *Nereis diversicolor* on the loss of saltmarsh in south-east England. *Journal of Applied Science,* **41**, 449–463.

Percival, P., Frid, C. & Upstill-Goddard, R. (2005) The impact of trawling on benthic nutrient dynamics in the North Sea: Implications of laboratory experiments. *Benthic Habitats and the Effects of Fishing,* **41**, 491–501.

Pinn, E. (2010) Cetaceans. Charting Progress 2 Feeder Report: Healthy and Biologically Diverse Seas. UK Marine Monitoring and Assessment Strategy (UKMMAS) (ed. M. Frost). Defra, London. [online] Available at: <http://chartingprogress.defra.gov.uk/chapter-3-healthy-and-biologicaly-diverse-seas> [Accessed 26.01.11].

Pinnegar, J.K., Viner, D., Hadley, D., Dye, S., Harris. M., Berkout, F. & Simpson, M. (2006) Alternative future scenarios for marine ecosystems: technical report. Centre for Environment, Fisheries and Aquaculture Science, Lowestoft.

Pinnegar, J.K. & Heath, M. (2010) Fish. Marine Climate Change Impacts Partnership. Annual Report Card 2010–11, MCCIP Science Review. [online] Available at: <www.mccip.org.uk/arc> [Accessed 26.01.11].

Pinnegar, J., Greenstreet, S., Fraser, H. & Greathead, C. (2010). Fish. Charting Progress 2 Feeder Report: Healthy and Biologically Diverse Seas. UK Marine Monitoring and Assessment Strategy. Defra, London. [online] Available at: <http://chartingprogress.defra.gov.uk/chapter-3-healthy-and-biologicaly-diverse-seas> [Accessed 26.01.11].

Poloczanska, E.S., Hawkins, S.J., Southward, A.J. & Burrows, M.T. (2008) Modelling the response of populations of competing species to climate change. *Ecology,* **89**, 3138–3149.

Proctor, R., Holt, J., Allen, J.I. & Blackford, J. (2003) Nutrient fluxes and budgets for the North West European Shelf from a three dimensional model. Science of the Total Environment, **314**, 769–785.

Pugh, D. (2008) Socio-economic indicators of marine-related activities in the UK economy. The Crown Estate.

Pugh, D.T. & Skinner, L. (2002) A New Analysis of Marine-Related Activities in the UK Economy with Supporting Science and Technology. Inter-Agency Committee on Marine Science and Technology Information, Document No.10. [online] Available at: <http://www.marine.gov.uk/publications/NEWMARSURVACRO.PDF> [Accessed 26.01.11].

Radford, A., Riddlington, G. & Gibson, H. (2009) Economic Impact of Recreational Sea Angling in Scotland. Scottish Government Report. [online] Available at: <http://www.scotland.gov.uk/Publications/2009/07/31154700/0> [Accessed 26.01.11].

Readman, J.W. (2006) The world's waters: a chemical contaminant perspective. An Introduction to Pollution Science (ed R.M. Harrison), pp. 77–121. Royal Society of Chemistry publications.

Reid, P.C. & Edwards, M. (2010) Plankton. Charting Progress 2 Feeder Report: Healthy and Biologically Diverse Seas. UK Marine Monitoring and Assessment Strategy (UKMMAS) (ed. M. Frost). Defra, London. [online] Available at: <http://chartingprogress.defra.gov.uk/chapter-3-healthy-and-biologicaly-diverse-seas> [Accessed 26.01.11].

Rose, C., Dade, P. & Scott, J. (2008) Qualitative and Quantitative Research into Public Engagement with the Undersea Landscape in England. Natural England Research Reports, NERR019.

RSPB (Royal Society for the Protection of Birds) (2010) The Local Value of Seabirds: Estimating spending by visitors to RSPB coastal reserves and associated local economic impact attributable to seabirds. The RSPB, Sandy, UK.

Sabine, C.L., Feely, R.A., Gruber, N., Key, R.M., Lee, K., Bullister, J.L., Wanninkhof, R., Wong, C.S., Wallace, D.W.R., B. Tilbrook, B., Millero, F.J., Peng, T.H., Kozyr A., Ono, T. & Ríos, A.F. (2004) The oceanic sink for anthropogenic CO_2. Science, **305**, 367–371.

Sabine, C.L. & Feely, R.A. (2007) The oceanic sink for carbon dioxide. Greenhouse Gas Sinks (ed D. Reay, N. Hewitt, J. Grace & K. Smith), pp. 31–49. CABI Publishing, Oxfordshire.

SAS (Surfers Against Sewage) (2010) Surfers Against Sewage. [online] Available at: <www.sas.org.uk> [Accessed 26.01.11].

Saunders, J. (ed) (2010) Charting Progress 2 Feeder Report: Productive Seas. UK Marine Monitoring and Assessment Strategy (UKMMAS). Defra, London. [online] Available at: <http://chartingprogress.defra.gov.uk/productive-seas-feeder-report-download> [Accessed 26.01.11].

Scott, A.P., Sanders, M., Stentiford, G.D., Reese, R.A. & Katsiadaki, I. (2007) Evidence for oestrogenic endocrine disruption in an offshore flatfish, the dab (*Limanda limanda* L.). *Marine Environmental Research*, **64**(2), 128–148.

Schroeder, D. (2010) Microbes. Charting Progress 2 Feeder Report: Healthy and Biologically Diverse Seas. UK Marine Monitoring and Assessment Strategy (UKMMAS) (ed. M. Frost). Defra, London. [online] Available at: <http://chartingprogress.defra.gov.uk/chapter-3-healthy-and-biologicaly-diverse-seas> [Accessed 26.01.11].

Seafish (2009) Facts about sea food from SEAFISH. [online] Available at: <www.seafish.org> [Accessed 26.01.11].

Seed, R. & Suchanek, T.H. (1992) Population and community ecology of *Mytilus*. The Mussel *Mytilus*: ecology, physiology, genetics and culture (ed E.M. Gosling), pp 87–168. Elsevier Press, Amsterdam.

SGSR (Scottish Government Social Research) (2010) The Economic Impact of Wildlife Tourism in Scotland. Report prepared by the International Centre for Tourism and Hospitality Research, Bournemouth University. [online] Available at: <www.scotland.gov.uk/socialresearch> [Accessed 26.01.11].

Shepherd, D., Burgess, D., Jickells, T., Andrews, J., Cave, R., Turner, R.K., Aldridge, J., Parker, E.R. &Young, E. (2007) Modelling the effects and economics of managed realignment on the cycling and storage of nutrients, carbon and sediments in the Blackwater estuary UK. *Estuarine Coastal and Shelf Science*, **73**, 355–367.

Smyth, T.J., Tilstone, G.H. & Groom, S.B. (2005) Integration of radiative transfer into satellite models of ocean primary production. *Journal of Geophysical Research*, **110**, C10014. DOI:10.1029/2004JC002784.

Stentiford, G.D., Longshaw, M., Lyons, B.P., Jones, G., Green, M. & Feist, S.W. (2003) Histopathological biomarkers in estuarine fish species for the assessment of biological effects of contaminants. *Marine Environmental Research*, **55**, 137–159.

Stentiford, G.D. & Feist, S.W. (2005) First case of intersex (ovotestis) in the flatfish species, dab (*Limanda limanda*): Dogger Bank, North Sea. *Marine Ecology Progress Series*, **301**, 307–310.

Stentiford, G.D., Bignell, J.P., Lyons, B.P. & Feist, S.W. (2009) Site-specific disease profiles in fish and their use in environmental monitoring. *Marine Ecology Progress Series*, **381**, 1–15.

Stolk, P. (2009) The Social and Community Benefits of Angling. Research Task 1: Angling Participation Interim Report, Manchester. [online] Available at: <http://www.anglingresearch.org.uk/sites/anglingresearch.org.uk/files/Research_Task_1_Angling_Participation.pdf> [Accessed 26.01.11].

The Wildlife Trusts (2007) Marine Opinion Poll. [online] Available at: <http://www.wildlifetrusts.org/index.php?section=marinebill:opinionpoll> [Accessed 26.01.11].

Thurstan, R.H., Brockington, S. & Roberts, C.M. (2010) The effects of 118 years of industrial fishing on UK bottom trawl fisheries. *Nature Communications*, **1**(15), 1–6. DOI: 10.1038/ncomms1013.

Turley, C., Eby, M., Ridgwell, A.J., Schmidt, D.N., Findlay, H.S., Brownlee, C., Riebesell, U., Fabry, V.J., Feely, R.A. & Gattuso, J.P. (2010) The societal challenge of ocean acidification. *Marine Pollution Bulletin*, **60**, 787–792.

UKLDVS (UK Leisure Day Visits Survey) (2004) Report of the 2002–03 GB Day Visits Survey. [online] Available at: <http://www.naturalengland.org.uk/ourwork/enjoying/research/monitor/leisuredayvisits/default.aspx> [Accessed 04.02.11].

UKMMAS (UK Marine Monitoring and Assessment Strategy) (2010) Charting Progress 2: The State of UK Seas. Published by the Department for Environment, Food and Rural Affairs on behalf of UKMMAS. TSO, London. 166pp. ISBN 9780112432937. Available at: <http://chartingprogress.defra.gov.uk/resources> [Accessed 06.06.10].

UKTS (UK Tourism Survey) (2002) Activities Undertaken by Domestic Tourists 2000–03. [online] Available at: <http://www.enjoyengland.com/Images/Activities%20undertaken%20by%20domestic%20tourists%2C%202000-3_tcm21-171031.pdf> [Accessed 26.01.11].

Vos, J.G., Dybing, E., Greim, H.A., Ladefoged, O., Lambre, C., Tarazona, J.V., Brandt, I. & Vethaak, A.D. (2000). Health effects of endocrine-disrupting chemicals on wildlife, with special reference to the European situation. *Critical Reviews in Toxicology*, **30**, 71–133.

Walpole, M.J. & Leader-Williams, N. (2002) Tourism and flagship species in conservation. *Biodiversity and Conservation*, **11**(3), 543–547.

Wanless, S., Harris, M.P., Redman, P. & Speakman, J.R. (2005) Low energy values of fish as a probable cause of a major seabird breeding failure in the North Sea. *Marine Ecology Progress Series*, **294**, 1–8.

Widdicombe, S., Austen, M.C., Kendall, M.A., Olsgard, F., Schaaning, M.T., Dashfield, S.L. & Needham, H.P. (2004) The importance of bioturbators for biodiversity maintenance: the indirect effects of fishing disturbance. *Marine Ecology Progress Series,* **275**, 1–10.

Widdicombe, S., Dashfield, S.L., McNeill, C.L., Needham, H.R., Beesley, A., McEvoy, A., Oexnevad, S., Clarke, K.R. & Berge, J.A. (2009) Impact of CO_2 induced seawater acidification on sediment diversity and nutrient flux. *Marine Ecology Progress Series*, **379**, 59–75.

Widdows, J. & Brinsley, M. (2002) Impact of biotic and abiotic processes on sediment dynamics and the consequences to the structure and functioning of the intertidal zone. *Journal of Sea Research*, **48**, 143–156.

Wilson, J.B. (1979) The distribution of the coral *Lophelia pertusa* L. [*L. prolifera* Pallas] in the North East Atlantic. *Journal of the Marine Biological Association of the UK*, **59**, 149–164.

Wyn, G., Brazier, P., Birch, K., Bunker, A., Cooke, A., Jones, M., Lough, N., McMath, A. & Roberts, S. 2006. Handbook for marine intertidal Phase 1 biotope mapping survey. Countryside Council for Wales. ISBN: 1 86169 144 0.

Appendix 12.1 Approach Used to Assign Certainty Terms to Chapter Key Findings

This chapter began with a set of Key Findings. Adopting the approach and terminology used by the Intergovernmental Panel on Climate Change (IPCC) and the Millennium Assessment (MA), these Key Findings also include an indication of the level of scientific certainty. The 'uncertainty approach' of the UK NEA consists of a set of qualitative uncertainty terms derived from a 4-box model and complemented, where possible, with a likelihood scale (see below). Estimates of certainty are derived from the collective judgement of authors, observational evidence, modelling results and/or theory examined for this assessment.

Throughout the Key Findings presented at the start of this chapter, superscript numbers and letters indicate the estimated level of certainty for a particular key finding:

1. *Well established:*   high agreement based on significant evidence
2. *Established but incomplete evidence:* high agreement based on limited evidence
3. *Competing explanations:*   low agreement, albeit with significant evidence
4. *Speculative:*   low agreement based on limited evidence

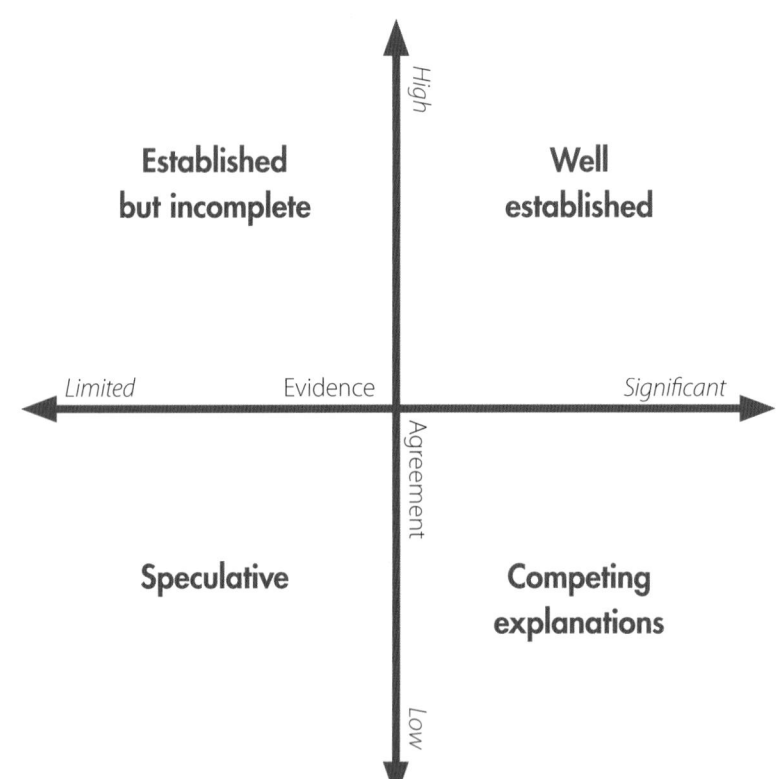

a. *Virtually certain:*   >99% probability of occurrence
b. *Very likely:*   >90% probability
c. *Likely:*   >66% probability
d. *About as likely as not:*   >33–66% probability
e. *Unlikely:*   <33% probability
f. *Very unlikely:*   <10% probability
g. *Exceptionally unlikely:*   <1% probability

Certainty terms 1 to 4 constitute the 4-box model, while *a* to *g* constitute the likelihood scale.

Chapter 13:
Supporting Services

Coordinating Lead Author: Richard D. Bardgett
Lead Authors: Colin D. Campbell, Bridget A. Emmett, Alan Jenkins and Andrew P. Whitmore

Key Findings*

Supporting services underpin the delivery of all other ecosystem services. Therefore, understanding their response to key drivers, such as climate change, land use and nutrient enrichment, is vital for the sustainable management of the UK's land and water resource. Supporting services include the ecological status of soil and water, and processes that drive the formation of soils, cycling of nutrients and fixation of carbon by plants. These are all strongly interrelated and, in many cases, underpinned by a vast array of physical, chemical and biological interactions. Our understanding of the ways that these interactions influence supporting services, and of the relative contribution of biological, chemical and physical factors, is generally limited.

The soils of the UK are diverse and relatively young as most of Britain was under ice or peri-glacial conditions until 10–15,000 years ago. Soils form slowly, but can be quickly degraded and lost[1]. Soil formation rates in the UK are 0.04–0.08 mm per year for mineral soils, which is less than 1 cm per century, although there is still a lack of data with which to formulate a truly accurate picture[2]. In actively growing bogs of good habitat status, peat formation is approximately 0.8 mm/yr, which is equivalent to a carbon accumulation rate of 0.5 tonnes carbon/hectare/year (t C/ha/yr). However, the average is probably closer to 0.1 t C/ha/yr given that many peatlands are not of good status[2]. Threats to soil formation include organic matter loss due to climate warming, inundation of coastal soils due to sea-level rise, erosion and compaction caused by intensive agriculture, and soil-sealing due to urbanisation[1]. There are many consequences of loss of soil for supporting, regulating and provisioning services.

[1] well established
[2] established but incomplete evidence

The last 50 years have witnessed substantial changes in the nutrient status and pH of waters and soils, with likely consequences for the delivery of both regulating and provisioning services. One of the most dramatic trends in nutrient cycling has been the enrichment of terrestrial and aquatic habitats with nitrogen due to the use of nitrogen fertilisers to increase food production[1]. This has resulted in substantial changes in plant productivity, plant species diversity and composition, and an accelerated rate of nitrogen cycling[1]. Another major change in soils and waters is the recent decrease in acidity of surface soils and acid-sensitive waters due to a substantial decline in sulphate deposition and an increase in rainfall pH since the late 1970s[1].

[1] well established

Recent evidence suggests that there may have been a widespread decline in the availability of phosphorus across terrestrial and aquatic systems over the last decade. Across UK terrestrial systems, extractable phosphorus in soils has apparently declined by an average of 25% between 1998 and 2007[1]. The reasons for this are not understood and require further investigation. There is evidence of decreasing phosphate concentrations in rivers across the UK which is linked to a reduction in the application of phosphorus fertiliser to land[1].

[1] well established

---

* Each Key Finding has been assigned a level of scientific certainty, based on a 4-box model and complemented, where possible, with a likelihood scale. Superscript numbers and letters indicate the uncertainty term assigned to each finding. Full details of each term and how they were assigned are presented in Appendix 13.1.

Spatial variation in rainfall and runoff is exceptionally high across the UK and few general trends in precipitation and annual runoff have been identified. However, a change in rainfall seasonality has been observed, with wet winters being more common in the last 30 years[1]. A gradual increase in annual average evaporation loss from 500 mm to 550 mm during the period 1980 to 2005 has been observed[1]. This probably reflects an increase in average temperatures across the UK of around 1.0°C over the last 30–40 years.

[1] *well established*

There is significant inter- and between-year variation in terrestrial primary production that is driven primarily by weather patterns, such as those which occurred during the summer drought of 2003[1]. There is mounting evidence that climate change will impact on primary production and community composition across all UK habitats, but there is an even greater risk of dramatic changes occurring as a result of extreme weather events[2]. Changes in primary production resulting from climate change will have significant implications for provisioning and regulating services.

[1] *well established*
[2] *established but incomplete evidence*

In agricultural and forestry systems, improvements in land management have had a major impact on primary production due to nutrient input, technological developments and genetic selection[1]. This is reflected in a ten-fold increase in yields in some agricultural systems over the last century. In semi-natural systems, atmospheric nitrogen deposition has increased primary productivity[2]. In lakes, streams and coastal waters, nutrient inputs of nitrogen and phosphorus from sewage and fertiliser runoff have caused major increases in primary production, in some cases eliminating seasonal patterns and causing undesirable hypoxia[1].

[1] *well established*
[2] *established but incomplete evidence*

In general, there is much uncertainty about the mechanisms that underpin supporting services, and our knowledge of how these services will be affected by current and future drivers, including climate change, is limited. However, it is clear that the mechanisms that underpin supporting services vary greatly across habitats, and the effects of key drivers, such as climate change, land use and nitrogen deposition, will impact on supporting services differently across UK habitats. Research is urgently needed to develop sustainable options for the management of UK supporting services and the regulating and provisioning services that they underpin.

13.1 Supporting Services and Human Well-being

Supporting services provide the basic infrastructure of life, including the capture of energy from the sun, the formation and maintenance of soils for plant growth, and the cycling of water and nutrients in terrestrial and aquatic ecosystems. In other words, supporting services are those that are required for the production of all other ecosystem services (i.e. regulating (Chapter 14), provisioning (Chapter 15) and cultural services (Chapter 16)), and include ecosystem functions of primary production, decomposition and nutrient cycling, water cycling and the formation of soils (EASAC 2009). Supporting services differ from other ecosystem services in that their impacts on human well-being are indirect and mostly long-term in nature; in the context of the UK NEA conceptual framework, they are the primary and intermediate services that underpin the final ecosystem services that are more directly linked to goods (Chapter 2). For example, soil formation involves changes in the physical, chemical and biological properties of soil over decades, centuries and even millennia (Jenny 1941), and its impacts on human well-being are mostly indirect, influencing regulating and provisioning services. Likewise, nutrient cycling is driven by many abiotic and biological factors that operate over both short and long timescales (Chapin et al. 2002; Vaughan et al 2009), and its impact on human well-being is indirect, affecting regulating and provisioning services.

Supporting services are all strongly interrelated and, in many cases, they are underpinned by a vast array of physical, chemical and biological interactions (**Figure 13.1**; Acreman et al. 2009; Bardgett & Wardle 2010). For instance, primary production both influences, and is influenced by, the supporting services of nutrient cycling, water cycling and soil formation. Moreover, although primary production is strongly regulated by external nutrient inputs and various environmental pressures (e.g. land use, climate change and atmospheric pollution), it is also dependent, in part, on the biological composition of communities and biotic interactions, for example between plants, plants and soil organisms, and between plants, herbivores and their consumers (Bardgett and Wardle 2010). Indeed, the last two decades have witnessed an explosion of interest in the roles that species and their interactions play in ecosystems, to the extent that this topic is now a dominant theme in ecology. This has been motivated by many factors, including a growing recognition of the roles that organisms and their interactions play in driving ecosystem processes (Grime 1979; Lawton and Jones 1995; Wardle et al. 2004; Bardgett & Wardle 2010), and a vast research effort aimed at connecting biodiversity, in terms of species richness and composition, to ecosystem functioning (Hooper et al. 2005; Naeem et al. 2009). Furthermore, the growing interest in predicting how species' responses to global change influence supporting services, such as decomposition, nutrient cycling and primary production, has generated much interest in the concept of functional classification and, in particular, the role of species traits in ecosystem functioning (Diaz et al. 2007; De Deyn et al. 2008). Supporting services are also strongly affected by geodiversity, namely the variety of rocks, minerals, fossils, landforms, sediments and soils in a place (Chapter 2). Not only does geodiversity support the provision of basic raw materials upon which supporting services, such as soil formation, are based, but it also influences biodiversity and its spatial variation at the habitat and landscape scale (Chapter 2).

Despite the above, our understanding of the mechanisms by which ecological interactions influence ecosystem processes and the delivery of supporting services is limited, as is our knowledge of their contribution relative to abiotic factors as drivers of supporting services at the landscape scale (Bardgett & Wardle 2010). The picture is complicated further by the knowledge that the effects of ecological interactions on supporting services, such as plant production and nutrient cycling, are strongly context dependent. For example, a number of studies indicate that the effects of biodiversity on ecosystem processes in terrestrial and aquatic ecosystems vary depending on environmental context (Fridley 2002; Covich et al. 2004; Wardle & Zackrisson 2005). There are also indications that the influence of biotic

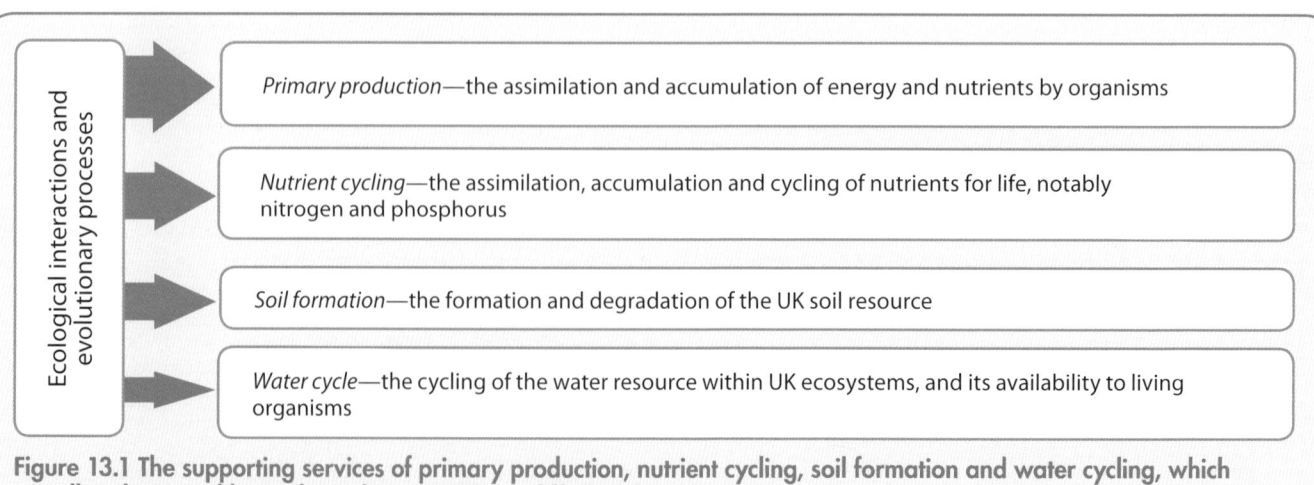

Figure 13.1 The supporting services of primary production, nutrient cycling, soil formation and water cycling, which are all underpinned by ecological interactions to differing degrees. The size of the arrows represents the extent that each supporting service is regulated by biotic/ecological interactions.

drivers (e.g. herbivory) on ecosystem processes varies along environmental gradients of climate, nutrient availability and topography (Olff *et al.* 2002; Bardgett & Wardle 2003; Anser *et al.* 2009). Given that such biological interactions and their relationship with the abiotic environment underpin the delivery of supporting services (**Figure 13.1**), we consider them as an integral part of our evaluation.

In this chapter, we provide an overview of the trends, past, present and future, which are evident in supporting services provided by the broad habitats of the UK, and consider what the main drivers are for these trends. We also evaluate what is known about the consequences of these trends and consider options for the sustainable management of supporting services in the future. Finally, we identify knowledge gaps regarding the delivery of supporting services in the UK.

13.2 Soil Formation

13.2.1 Condition, Status and Trends

Soils are formed by the weathering of rocks and minerals and the accumulation of organic materials, which often takes hundreds to thousands of years (**Box 13.1**). Soil formation is a continuous process and its speed and nature is affected by several factors (Jenny 1941) including the parent material, climate, topography, biota (including plants, animals and microorganisms) and land management. Rates of soil formation for mineral soils vary greatly, but they typically lay in the range 0.04–0.08 mm/yr; this would create soil at a rate of less than 1 cm per century (EASAC 2009). The loss of soil by erosion is also a natural process, but it can be very rapid and accelerated by land use. Moreover, rates of soil loss can be much greater than formation; hence, soils should be treated as a non-renewable resource. Data for rates of soil loss by erosion in the UK are few, although estimates of 0.02–1.27 tonnes/hectare/year for mineral soils, and as much as 10 t/ha/yr for tillage erosion from arable fields have been reported (Verheijen *et al.* 2009). Based on global literature, Wilkinson & McElroy (2007) estimated an average natural erosion rate of 0.4 t/ha/yr over 542 million years of the Phanerozoic, with a peak of 1.4 t/ha/yr in the Tertiary period.

A combination of soil processes and soil-forming factors is responsible for the formation of different soil types. On well-drained soils, humus formation, leaching, weathering, clay migration and clay alteration lead to the formation of podzols. On poorly drained soils, the mobilisation and precipitation of iron gives rise to gley soil; whereas low rates of organic matter decomposition, caused by waterlogging and low temperatures, leads to the formation of peats. In the UK, most areas have greater precipitation than evaporation and, as a consequence, leaching is a dominant soil process. However, slower processes of weathering are also of importance, as a primary source of essential elements (e.g. trace elements and base cations) for plants and soil organisms whose actions (mixing, dissolution, physical disruption) promote further weathering. For example, biological weathering occurs via roots which penetrate and

crack open rocks, and via mycorrhizal fungi which form extensive hyphal networks in soil and so play a significant role in weathering minerals. The release of base cations from chemical weathering is also of importance because it replenishes those which are lost through leaching or biological uptake. Soil is also the primary natural source of essential trace elements in animals and man, although trace element concentrations depend strongly upon soil parent material, being lowest in soils derived from acid igneous rocks and sands. Hence, in soils derived from sedimentary and base rich rocks commonly found in England and Wales, approximately 5% of agricultural soils have low trace element status compared to 30% of agricultural soils in Scotland where soils are derived from igneous and metamorphic rocks and sands (Sinclair & Edwards 2008).

The interaction of so many soil-forming factors, which vary simultaneously in space and time, means that the UK has many diverse soil types (**Box 13.2**; **Figure 13.2**). Also, the combination of the maritime climate of the UK (with cool temperatures and relatively wet conditions) and the predominantly hard rock resistant to weathering, has given rise to soils that are much younger, contain more organic carbon (C) and experience more leaching and poorer natural drainage, than soils in eastern and southern Europe. This pedological youthfulness is due to the presence of ice sheets and periglacial conditions that only retreated from most of Britain 10,000–15,000 years ago. There is a marked contrast across Britain between the mineral soil types, which primarily form in the lowlands, and the soils in the uplands which have surface horizons rich in organic matter. The balance in terms of provisioning economically valued ecosystem services is often juxtaposed to important regulating services that have uncertain or no market value. For example, the uplands harbour most of the UK's organic soils which store most of the nation's carbon, compared to lowland areas where mineral soils of much lower organic

---

Box 13.1 Definition of Soil

Soil forms a thin mantle over the Earth's surface and acts as the interface between the atmosphere and lithosphere, the outermost shell of the Earth. Soil is a biologically active and complex mixture of weathered minerals, organic and inorganic compounds, living organisms, air and water, which provides the foundation for life in terrestrial ecosystems. Soil is not merely the sum of these parts; rather, it is a product of interactions between these components, and the formation of soil is dependent on these interactions. The rate at which these processes occur typically decreases with depth, high latitudes and altitudes. The depth at which these processes cease or become insignificant varies, but in mid–latitudes, it is generally between 1–2 m below the ground surface.

Within any landscape there is an incredible range of soils, resulting from almost infinite variation in the soil-forming factors of parent material, climate, biota, relief and time (Jenny 1941). These are highly interactive, all playing a part in the development of a particular soil. A specific combination of these factors leads to the development of a unique soil type, with a relatively predictable series of horizons (layers) that constitute the soil profile. Of most relevance for ecosystem service delivery, are those horizons that are at, or close to, the soil surface; this is where most microbes and animals live, and where most root growth and nutrient recycling occurs. These horizons are referred to as the surface organic O horizon, derived from decomposing plant and animal material, and the uppermost A horizon, composed largely of mineral material, but also intimately mixed with organic matter derived from the surface O horizon.

carbon content support most of the UK's agricultural production.

Data on the status of soils in the UK is generally lacking and we know little about trends with respect to future drivers. Two highly relevant issues for ecosystem service delivery are: a) the formation and loss of peat soils, largely due to their great importance as a carbon sink; and b) the loss of soil to urbanisation, which is considered in Section 13.2.2 of this chapter and in Chapter 10.

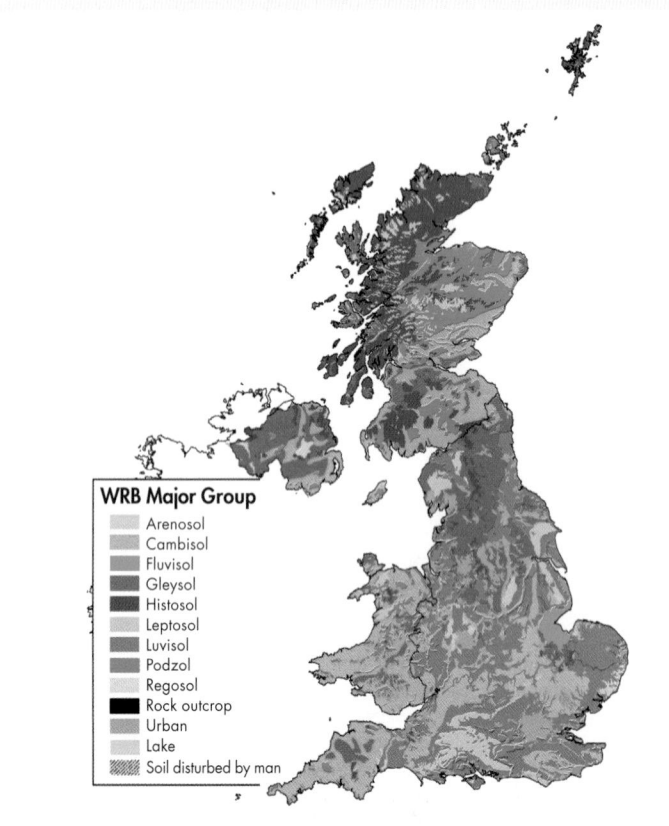

WRB Major Group
- Arenosol
- Cambisol
- Fluvisol
- Gleysol
- Histosol
- Leptosol
- Luvisol
- Podzol
- Regosol
- Rock outcrop
- Urban
- Lake
- Soil disturbed by man

Figure 13.2 Principal Soil Types in the UK according to the World Reference Base for Soil Resources (FAO-IUSS-ISRIC 2006). Source: EU 1:1000000 soil map (European Soil Database (v 2.0), European Soil Bureau Network and the European Commission, EUR 19945 EN, March 2004).

Peatlands are a distinctive ecosystem associated with deep peat soils, which began to form in the UK 3,000–9,000 years ago following the retreat of the last ice sheet and the subsequent cool and wet period. Peat soils have developed to become over 10 m deep in places, although the mean depth, at least in Scotland, is 2 m (Chapman *et al.* 2009). The depth of peat soils is estimated to increase at a rate of 0.8 mm/yr in actively growing bogs of good habitat status, which is equivalent to a carbon accumulation rate of 0.5 tonnes of carbon/hectare/year. However, the average is probably closer to 0.1 tC/ha/yr given that many peatlands are not of good status (Joosten & Clarke 2002). The total peatland carbon stocks in Scotland and Wales have been estimated to be 1,620 megatonnes of carbon (MtC) and 116 MtC, respectively (Chapman *et al.* 2009; Smith *et al.* 2007), whereas in England and Northern Ireland C stocks have been estimated at 296 MtC and 90 MtC, respectively (Bradley *et al.* 2005) but only to a depth of 1m. This estimate therefore does not include the unknown stock of carbon below 1m depth for England and Northern Ireland. The current rate of carbon fixation for all UK peatland is difficult to determine, but a conservative estimate based upon the above figures gives 0.27 MtC/yr; others have estimated 0.7 MtC/yr (Cannell *et al.* 1999), assuming that the peatlands are in good condition. In practice, many areas have been subjected to draining, agriculture and peat cutting, and losses have been estimated at 1 MtC/yr (Cannell *et al.* 1999). Other peatlands have been subjected to afforestation, burning, overgrazing, atmospheric pollution and extensive erosion (**Figure 13.3**). Much of the carbon is lost as carbon dioxide to the atmosphere, but a significant proportion is lost to water as dissolved organic carbon (DOC) and particulate organic matter (POM), the ultimate fate of which is largely unknown. Total UK fluvial losses of carbon in the form of DOC and POM have been estimated at 1 MtC/yr (Cannell *et al.* 1999) with much of this arising from peat soils and having significant consequences for water quality (Chapter 14).

Figure 13.3 Peat erosion within highland landscape of Ladder Hills, Scotland. *Photo © A.J. Nolan / Macaulay Land Use Research Institute.*

13.2.2 Drivers of Change

In the UK, humans have been managing and interacting with soils for over 5,000 years. This long-term relationship has contributed to the diversity of the soils found here and the uniqueness of the British landscape. Furthermore, because UK soils are well-fed by rainwater and well-endowed with organic matter, they are often considered to be more fertile and resilient than soils elsewhere in Europe, especially southern Europe, where erosion is more intense and water is in short supply. Indeed, recent status reports conclude that UK soils are generally in good health, although there are significant potential threats such as carbon loss, erosion, compaction and contamination (Environment Agency 2004; Towers *et al.* 2006). Here, we identify the main drivers of change in soil formation and associated threats to UK soils.

13.2.2.1 Land use

Land use is a major driver of change in soil formation through soil erosion and the accumulation or loss of soil organic matter. Rates of soil formation are slow, yet anthropogenic interventions and management can significantly change the properties of surface soil in only a few years. In the last 50 years, UK agricultural soils have been subject to significant change, particularly through increased mechanisation and use of agrochemicals and synthetic fertilisers, and through the introduction of new crop varieties. Increased frequency and depth of tillage, reductions in land under forage crops, and continuous use of grain cereals have all led to major concerns about declines in soil organic matter, with significant losses of top soil carbon in some circumstances (Johnson *et al.* 2009). For example, the ploughing, liming and fertilising of podzols in lowland England over the last 30 years, has transformed them into brown podzolic soils of lower soil surface carbon content. Changes may also be occurring in the uplands; the growth of birch on heather moor can change the soil from a carbon sequestering peaty podzol to a brown podzolic in less than 40 years (Mitchell *et al.* 2007). In addition, increased grazing pressure and associated land improvement in the uplands (e.g. liming and fertiliser application) over the last few decades have led to the widespread conversion of semi-natural grassland on brown podzlic soils into species-poor improved grassland with brown earths of lower carbon content (Bardgett *et al.* 2001; Grayston *et al.* 2004).

Over the next 50 years, potential changes including the introduction of biofuel crops, increased recycling of organic wastes and by-products to land, and reductions in fertiliser application in response to higher oil and energy costs, could have significant impacts on UK soils. Moreover, the UK intends to increase its amount of forested land. If significant new planting of trees on agricultural soils occurs, this could greatly influence soil formation because trees root deeper and accumulate litter and organic matter at the surface, with likely consequences for physical properties and nutrient cycling (Carroll 2004).

13.2.2.2 Climate change

The changing climate is one of the greatest threats to UK soils, although its impact will vary with soil type and other pressures placed on soils. Major changes or damage to soil due to climate change is anticipated in the coastal zones, such as the machairs (fertile low-lying grassy plains found on some of the north-west coastlines of Ireland and Scotland) and Links soils of Scotland which are directly under threat from sea-level rises (Angus *et al.* 2010; Rennie & Hansom in press). The formation of montane soils, where freezing cycles are an important soil-forming process, is also likely to diminish if the climate warms. Current trends indicate that winters will become warmer and wetter, and summers drier. These changes will affect rates of soil weathering and could increase both water and wind erosion. Warming of organic soils is likely to exacerbate loss of soil carbon through accelerated decomposition of organic matter (Dorrepaal *et al.* 2009). Increased drought and drying in wetlands and peatlands, which will lower the water table and introduce oxygen into previously anaerobic soil, will create more favourable conditions for microbial activity and, therefore, cause carbon loss (Freeman *et al.* 2004). Also, long-term climate change experiments in upland heathland have demonstrated the potential for cumulative effects of repeated summer drought on soil carbon dioxide flux, which increased year on year to be 40% greater than the control after six years (Sowerby *et al.* 2008). These findings demonstrate the risk of peatlands and wetlands being degraded under climate change, with implications for the global carbon cycle.

Climate change may also alter the magnitude, frequency, rate and nature of soil-forming processes, resulting in enhanced rates of process activity, including less recovery time between extreme events. Some of the most dramatic impacts are likely to be in coastal areas where the effects of climate change will be compounded by sea-level rise (Rennie & Hansom in press). This, in turn, will impact on coastal landforms, habitats and soils, resulting in issues such as enhanced coastal retreat and steepening, coastal squeeze (where landward migration of landforms and habitats is impeded) and enhanced landslide activity on susceptible coasts (Angus *et al.* 2010). In some cases, rates of change may exceed those seen in the last 7,000 years or more (Orford & Pethick 2006; Rennie & Hansom in press), leading to widespread reorganisation and disturbance of coastal landforms, habitats and soils (Angus *et al.* 2010; **Figure 13.4**).

Figure 13.4 Variation in coastal morphology at Culbin Sands Moray. *Photo © P. & M. Macdonald/Scottish Natural Heritage.*

While The Intergovernmental Panel on Climate Change's (IPCC 2007) projections of future sea-level rise cover a wide range, they are considered to be conservative in the light of observational data and because the dynamic responses of ice sheets have not been accounted for (Pfeffer *et al.* 2008; Rahmstorf 2007). Sea-level rise will not only influence the tidal immersion of coastal habitats, but also rates of erosion, sediment transport and accretion. Sea-level rise will also increase brackish water encroachment on lowland coastal areas, leading to localised risk of soil, habitat and groundwater salinisation (Orford & Pethick 2006). This will impact on several coastal Sites of Special Scientific Interest (SSSIs) and other protected habitats (Angus *et al.* 2010). Climate change scenarios suggest that some land-forming processes that are also hazardous, such as coastal flooding and erosion, flash floods and landslides, are likely to occur more frequently (Orr *et al.* 2008). The response to hazards often results in expensive site-by-site geotechnical solutions, but many of these approaches are unsustainable and may exacerbate or transfer the problem elsewhere in the catchment or along the coast, with additional impacts (Prosser *et al.* 2010).

13.2.2.3 Urbanisation

When land is used for built infrastructures, such as houses, roads and industrial structures, the loss of soil as a resource in itself is complete and, in most cases, irreversible within our lifetime. Often, urban expansion takes over good agricultural land because population centres were historically established in close proximity to food supplies. Data on the conversion of land primarily in agricultural use to urban development (**Figure 13.5**) shows that, in England, the net conversion of agricultural land to urban use amounted to between 5,000 and 6,000 ha/yr between 1989 and 2003 although it has fallen markedly in more recent years, whereas in Scotland it was 1,200 ha/yr between 1995 and 2002 (Towers *et al.* 2006). Given the huge difference in population between the two countries and, by implication, the demand for new housing, roads and development projects, the loss in Scotland is surprisingly large, although there may be differences in the definition of 'sealed land'. In Northern Ireland, a net conversion rate of agricultural land to urban (both urban and suburban) of 1,000 ha/yr was found for the period 1970 to 1990 (Cannell *et al.* 1999). One target for development in England is that 60% of new housing should be built on previously developed and/or abandoned industrial land ('Brownfield sites'); this has been attained every year since 2000. In the Countryside Survey, the area of 'Built-up areas and Gardens Broad Habitat' in Wales was estimated to have increased by 14,700 ha between 1998 and 2007 (Smart *et al.* 2009).

13.2.3 Consequences of Change

There are multiple consequences of loss of soil, or change in soil formation rate, for all other supporting services, and the regulating and provisioning services that they underpin. Even partial loss or reorganisation of soil surface horizons has significant consequences for the delivery of other ecosystem services. For example, a total or partial loss of soil represents a loss of nutrient supply capacity with knock-on consequences for primary production and the provisioning and regulation of the quantity and quality of water. Also, total or partial loss of soil can reduce our capacity to produce food and fibre, which is dependent on the maintenance of soil fertility. For example, if the loss of 1,200 ha/yr in Scotland continued for seven years, and all

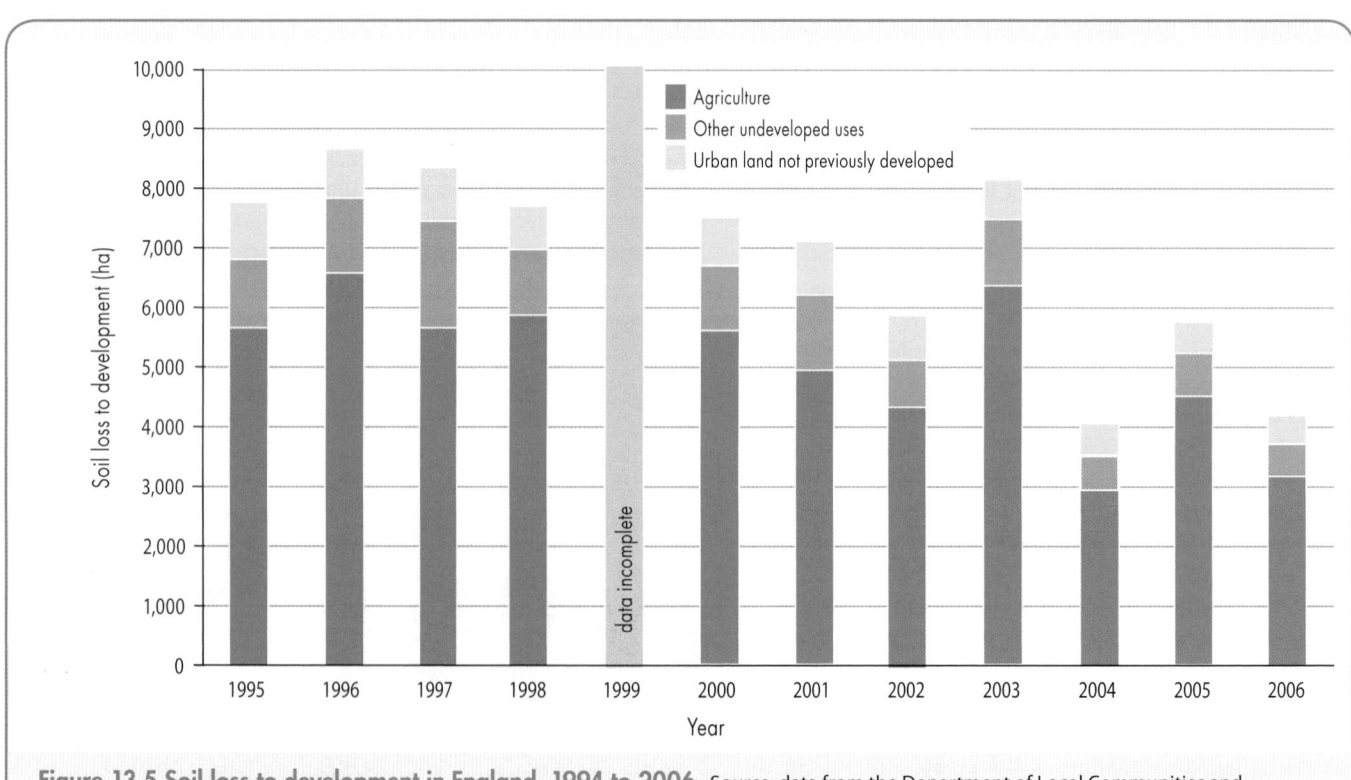

Figure 13.5 Soil loss to development in England, 1994 to 2006. Source: data from the Department of Local Communities and Government (DLCG 2010).

this land was good agricultural land, it would be equivalent to losing 1.5%, 1.4% and 1.25% of the national production of spring barley, wheat and potatoes respectively. Soil loss affects the regulation of soil fertility and climate because soil acts as a major sink for carbon and source for greenhouse gases (Chapter 14). It has been estimated that around 2.2 million tonnes of top soil is eroded annually in England and Wales, affecting agricultural production and nutrient availability (Quinton *et al.* 2010), and also water quality (Environment Agency 2004), with the total annual costs being around £45 million, including £9 million in lost production (Environment Agency 2007). This also causes a loss of soil biodiversity and the ecosystem services that it underpins, which has been estimated at approximately $3 trillion worldwide (Pimentel *et al.* 1997) excluding the economic benefits of primary production.

The depth of soil to the parent material represents the total amount of soil available for performing functions and ecosystem services, and the soil column is differentiated into soil horizons whose individual properties and characteristics control many of the environmental interactions. Pimentel and Pimentel (2000) suggested a minimal soil depth of 15 cm was required for agricultural production. The depth of some soils can be as low as 10 cm, while some peat soils are over 10 m deep. However, depth alone is not an indicator of the status or age of soil; the rate of soil formation can be significantly reduced under harsh climatic conditions, such as those found on mountains, where soils may show well-differentiated and fully functional soil horizons of only a few centimetres in depth.

Using depth and bulk density values it is possible to estimate stocks in various currencies. The total mass of soil in the UK is 200,000 Mt, which contains 10,000 Mt of carbon, 440 Mt of nitrogen and 120 Mt of phosphorus (**Table 13.1**). It can also be estimated that, when fully saturated, UK soils store 130 billion m³ of water (**Table 13.1**). To put this into perspective, the amount of water stored in soil in Scotland alone (42 billion m³) is more than all the fresh water found in Scottish lochs. Given the importance of soil carbon for other ecosystem services, and especially climate regulation (Chapter 14), using organic matter accumulation as a proxy for soil formation is a useful way of valuing soil formation in terms of the full social costs as there are established prices structures in different markets. Of the 10 billion tonnes of carbon stored in UK soils (Smith *et al.* 2007) most is found in organic soils in semi-natural montane, moor and woodland habitats (including peat soils), and carbon is lower under enclosed agricultural land and settlements (Bradley *et al.* 2005).

13.2.4 Options for Sustainable Management

There are several management options for enhancing soil formation and minimising soil loss. New soil strategies in the UK and EU (Defra 2009; European Commission 2002, 2006a and 2006b; Scottish Government 2009) recognise soil as a finite resource and the need to protect it from carbon loss, compaction and contamination, setting out measures for more sustainable management. The appropriate use of bulky organic fertilisers, such as manures and composts,

Table 13.1 Estimates of total mass of soil, soil carbon (C), nitrogen (N), phosphorus (P), calcium (Ca), magnesium (Mg), potassium (K) and volume of water in saturated soil for the UK. Values were calculated for Scotland using the Scottish Knowledge and Information Base and extrapolated to UK by area.

	Total Mass in top 1 m (millions of tonnes)							Volume of water (billion m³)
	Soil	C	N	P	Ca	Mg	K	
Scotland	64,000	3,000	142	40	45	9	3.5	42
Total for UK	200,000	10,000*	440	120	140	27	11	130

*Smith *et al.* (2007)

will enhance the accumulation of soil organic matter. Similarly, different crop rotations with ley crops and the use of cover crops can increase organic matter and help to minimise erosion losses. In the arable sector, minimal tilling and seed-bed preparation help to minimise direct loss of soil from erosion. Certain crops which require intensive cultivation, such as potatoes, can be confined to relatively gentle slopes and contour ploughing, although this is not widely practiced. Inappropriate grazing pressure can also exacerbate soil loss, notably on vulnerable, highly organic soils. And forestry management now encourages much less destructive forms of site preparation prior to planting, minimising disturbance to soils.

Management strategies aimed at maintaining, or enhancing, the accumulation of soil organic matter can have multiple synergies for provisioning, supporting and regulating services (Lal 2008; Smith *et al.* 2008a; Woodward *et al.* 2009). For example, an increase in soil organic matter content can afford benefits for soil fertility such as improved soil structure and water-holding capacity, greater complexity and diversity of the soil food web, binding and transforming pollutants that might otherwise enter the food chain or water supplies, and increased storage and retention of nutrients and water (Lal 2008; Woodward *et al.* 2009). Increased soil organic matter accumulation can also have synergies with biodiversity conservation: planting of high-diversity mixtures of native grassland perennials on degraded, low organic matter content soils can yield advantages over monocultures in terms of productivity, reduced greenhouse gas emissions and carbon storage (Tilman *et al.* 2006), with additional benefits for wildlife conservation. Positive effects of plant diversity for soil carbon sequestration have also been reported in grasslands, although this has been attributed to the presence of particular plant functional groups, most notably legumes, rather than diversity *per se* (Fornara & Tilman 2008; Steinbeiss *et al.* 2008; De Deyn *et al.* 2009).

Soils take a long time to form, but a short time to degrade. This has led many to call for a long-term land use strategy that considers the appropriate time-scales of soil formation and accounts for the complex synergy between soil-forming processes. For example, planning policies used to guard against building on prime agricultural land, but this protection was lost during the 1980s. With food security a key issue and the realisation of soil loss rates to building, some soil strategies are suggesting this protection of prime land should be reinstated (Scottish Government 2009).

13.2.5 Knowledge Gaps

Despite an historical interest in the study of soil formation, our understanding of the mechanism and rates of soil formation and soil loss for key soil types is limited. There are few models of soil formation, in contrast to the many models available for predicting soil loss by erosion. Our understanding of erosion processes in organic soils and the role of biodiversity in soil formation is limited. However, there is increasing recognition that approaches based on plant functional diversity (i.e. the range, type and relative abundance of plant functional traits) offer potential for understanding the impact of biodiversity on supporting services, including soil formation and carbon accumulation (Díaz *et al.* 2007; De Deyn *et al.* 2008).

Soil is also an ecosystem in its own right and changing its formation process will impact on the habitat of soil biota, as well as interact with above-ground biodiversity. Therefore, the sensitivity and responses of habitats to climate change and sea-level rise will depend, in part, on how the underlying soil processes respond. Climate change will lead to changes in land use and land management practices as a result of changes in the suitability of land for agriculture, forestry and renewable energy production, along with indirect pressure from population growth (such as food policies) and displacement (planning development away from flood-prone areas). The consequences for soil formation of such increased pressures on the land are poorly understood.

Changes in the rate of accumulation or loss of organic matter in UK soils are of central importance for ecosystem service delivery, as discussed above. Two large-scale surveys which have monitored change in soil carbon have been completed, but they have found contrasting results: Bellamy *et al.* (2005) reported significant losses, whereas the Countryside Survey (2010) found no change. (The difference between the two monitoring schemes remains unresolved and is the subject of continuing studies.) As with most studies of soil carbon, both surveys were conducted on surface horizons, but future studies need to understand the distribution and dynamics of carbon in deeper soil horizons, including that below the plough layer (Neff *et al.* 2002). This is because significant quantities of carbon can be found in deep horizons and the soil processes that regulate the turnover of this carbon are quite different from those that operate in superficial layers. The depth of soil and its spatial variation is difficult to measure, but such an assessment of soil carbon stocks in relation to depth is of fundamental importance in determining the natural capital stock of our soil resource, the soil organic carbon and nutrients required to support ecosystem services, and the links to human well-being.

13.3 Nutrient Cycling

13.3.1 Condition, Status and Trends

Although data on nutrient cycling in different UK habitats is sparse, several national surveys have provided information on key trends, including the Countryside Survey (2010), the

UK Environmental Change Network (ECN), which since 1992 has been monitoring soil chemistry at 12 locations throughout the UK as well as water quality in 16 lakes and 29 rivers, and the Review of Transboundary Air Pollution (RoTAP 2011), which has reported on the extent and impact of nitrogen (N) deposition across the UK. Here, we identify some of the main trends in nutrient cycling that have emerged from these surveys and other studies.

13.3.1.1 Nitrogen

The mineralisation of nitrogen—the process by which soil microbes break down organic nitrogen and convert it into inorganic forms—is of critical importance because, in many habitats, it determines the availability of nitrogen for primary production. There are major differences in amounts of nitrogen and rates of nitrogen mineralisation in top soils (0–15cm) across UK terrestrial habitats, which broadly relate to the total amount of organic matter present and whether soils have been agriculturally improved (Emmett *et al.* 2010; **Figure 13.6a,b**). For example, total amounts of nitrogen in topsoil of habitats that have had no fertiliser added, such as coniferous woodland and wetlands (approximately 4 tN/ha), is lower than in grassland soils, especially those which have been improved for intensive agriculture (approximately 6 tN/ha). On the other hand, rates of nitrogen mineralisation vary with organic matter content: arable soils, which contain relatively little organic matter, mineralise far more nitrogen per unit of organic matter than upland or woodland soils,

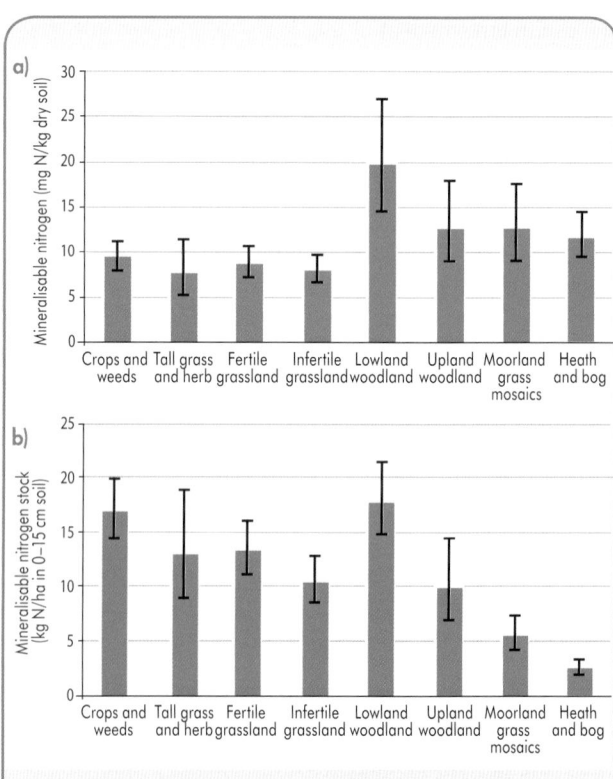

Figure 13.6 Mean (+/- one standard error) nitrogen stock and availability in soils (0–15 cm) in aggregate vegetation classes: a) mineralisable nitrogen concentration in soil organic matter (mg N/kg loss-on-ignition); and b) stock of total mineralisable nitrogen (kg N/ha). Source: reproduced from Emmett *et al.* (2010). Countryside Survey data owned by NERC – Centre for Ecology & Hydrology.

and indirectly by altering the productivity and composition of plant communities (Bardgett et al. 2008; Bardgett & Wardle 2010). For example, warming and changes in moisture conditions can directly impact on the activity of heterotrophic microbes involved in nutrient cycling, as can changes in the frequency of extreme weather events, such as drought, waterlogging and freezing (Schimel et al. 2007; Bardgett et al. 2008; Whitmore & Whalley 2009). Also, changes in vegetation growth and composition can indirectly influence the abundance and activity of soil organisms, thereby impacting on rates of nutrient cycling and primary production. As an example of this, elevated atmospheric carbon dioxide can increase plant photosynthesis and growth which, in turn, increases the flux of carbon to roots, their symbionts and free-living soil organisms (Bardgett et al. 2008). Elevated atmospheric carbon dioxide and changes in weather patterns might also cause shifts in the composition of terrestrial plant communities, with consequences for nutrient cycling (Bardgett et al. 2008). Long-term climate change experiments do provide evidence of potential change, with decoupling of carbon and nitrogen cycling (Beier et al. 2008), enhanced soil carbon loss (Sowerby et al. 2008) and shifts in soil biological activity (Toberman et al. 2008) being reported from a long-term climate change experiment in an upland heathland habitat.

Warming has also caused changes in marine fauna generating potential knock-on effects for nutrient and carbon cycling. Warming of water, for example, has caused large changes in the plankton community of deep-sea habitats; many taxa have moved forward their seasonality (i.e. earlier spring blooms) and there has been a progressive shift northward in warmer water zooplankton over the last 50 years (Chapter 12). Also, ocean acidification, which is caused by rising atmospheric carbon dioxide concentrations that drive changes in seawater carbonate chemistry and reduce pH, could affect many marine organisms, with likely consequences for carbon and nutrient cycling. As identified in Chapter 12 there is much uncertainty in this area; however, a recent global meta-analysis suggests that the biological effects of ocean acidification are generally large and negative, but that the variation in sensitivity amongst organisms will have important implications for ecosystem responses (Kroeker et al. 2010).

There is much uncertainty about how climate change has, and will continue to, influence nutrient cycling in terrestrial and aquatic habitats due to incomplete knowledge of the mechanisms involved. The impacts of climate change will also vary across UK terrestrial habitats depending on a range of factors, such as vegetation type, soil fertility, soil water conditions and soil type, and in aquatic habitats depending on pre-existing levels of eutrophication. The situation is further complicated in aquatic habitats where long-term nutrient fluctuations are strongly affected by the North Atlantic Oscillation (NAO) and Gulf Stream. For example, long-term (1961 to 1997) inter-annual variations in concentrations of dissolved reactive phosphorus in Blelham Tarn in the Lake District were found to be strongly linked to NAO, mediated through changes in rainfall (George 2002). Likewise, decadal cycles in salinity of the Irish Sea have also been found to be linked to NAO (Evans et al. 2003).

13.3.3 Consequences of Change

Nutrient cycling in natural, unpolluted habitats is largely regulated by biological processes; nutrient inputs generally represent only a small fraction of the quantity of nutrients that cycle internally, leading to a relatively closed system maintained by myriad ecological interactions (Bardgett & Wardle 2010). For example, nutrient cycling in natural terrestrial habitats is dependent on an intimate partitioning of nitrogen between the plants and soil microbes over the seasons (Bardgett et al. 2005). And, in many habitats, plant nutrient acquisition is strongly dependent on mycorrhizal fungi which associate with the roots of most terrestrial plant species (Smith & Read 2008). Nutrient cycling in rivers and soils is also regulated by detritivore communities which break down dead organic matter (Gessner et al. 2010), and by faunal consumers of microbes which regulate nutrient cycling by altering the balance between microbial immobilisation and mineralisation and, therefore, the availability of nutrients for plant uptake (Bardgett & Wardle 2010). As discussed in Chapter 12, nutrient cycling occurs in many components of the marine habitat. In seabed sediments, bacterial processing of nutrients (e.g. nitrification and denitrification) is facilitated by the physical feeding, burrowing and irrigation activity of invertebrates (Covich et al. 2004; Olsgard et al. 2008), whereas, within the water column, bacterial nutrient cycling is facilitated via food web links with phyto- and zooplankton and fish (Blackford 1997; Proctor et al. 2003). Likewise, nutrient cycling takes place between trophic levels and, in the course of bacterial breakdown of detritus (mainly dead algal and plant material), in macroalgal beds and salt marshes. Any disruption of such ecological interactions, for example, through nitrogen enrichment, disturbance or pollution, is likely to have consequences for nutrient cycling in that habitat, although the magnitude of such potential responses is uncertain. Moreover, changes in nutrient cycling that lead to the loss of nutrients to waters and the atmosphere will have consequences for regulating services, as discussed in Chapter 14.

A consequence of enhanced nutrient cycling is a change in the composition and diversity of the terrestrial plant community. Most natural and semi-natural plant communities are nitrogen limited, so increased availability of nitrogen (e.g. through nitrogen deposition or fertiliser addition) will substantially alter their structure and productivity, favouring productive, fast-growing species that are best able to use this added resource at the expense of slower-growing, less competitive species. The implications of this for plant species diversity in UK grasslands are clear from the study of Stevens et al. (2004). These authors reported that long-term nitrogen deposition across Britain (ranging from 5–to–35kg N/ha/yr) has significantly reduced species-richness in grassland and that species-richness has declined as a linear function of the rate of nitrogen deposition, with a reduction of 1 species per 4 m² for every 2.5kg nitrogen deposited per ha per yr. However, in gradient studies of this kind, there is potential for other factors, such as climate and sulphur deposition, to play role, and it has been argued that the largest changes in plant species composition occurred in the UK in the early part of the 20th Century (Emmett 2007). Indeed, no major changes in plant species composition were detected in a series of long-term nitrogen addition experiments across the UK, which was attributed to most nitrogen sensitive plant species being already lost prior to the start of the experimental work, i.e. prior to 1990 (Emmett 2007). Nitrogen enrichment can also impact on the diversity and composition of soil biological communities (Bardgett & Wardle 2010), potentially altering rates of decomposition and nutrient cycling, and the ecosystem services that these processes underpin. Indeed, it is well-known that nitrogen enrichment can negatively impact on saprophytic fungi (Donnison *et al.* 2000; Treseder 2008) and the activity of certain extracellular enzymes involved in decomposition processes (Craine *et al.* 2007; Allison *et al.* 2008). It can also change the structure of mycorrhizal fungal communities (Egerton-Warburton & Allen 2000; Frey *et al.* 2004) with unknown consequences for nutrient cycling.

In contrast to conservative or 'closed' systems, provisioning systems exploit nutrient cycling and remove nutrients in products. Agricultural soils are characterised by a high supply of nutrients per unit of organic matter, so it is difficult to farm without loss of nutrients (Goulding 2000). However, enhanced nutrient cycling in provisioning ecosystems could yield additional benefits for regulatory services, especially carbon sequestration. For instance, the application of fertiliser nitrogen could enhance soil carbon storage through increasing plant production and carbon return to soil and by suppressing microbial decomposition of recalcitrant organic matter (Conant *et al.* 2001; Craine *et al.* 2007). Evidence for this is mixed, however, as studies also show that nitrogen fertilisation of agricultural soils can enhance soil organic matter decomposition (Shevtsova *et al.* 2003; Khan *et al.* 2007), and the long-term application of nitrogen to some forests has been shown to have no net effect on soil carbon stocks (Harding & Jokela 2003; Magill *et al.* 2004). There is also a risk that emissions of other greenhouse gases (i.e. nitrous oxide and methane) may increase with nitrogen enrichment, thereby offsetting benefits of enhanced carbon dioxide uptake (Liu & Greaver 2009). In view of this uncertainty, it is not yet possible to make sweeping statements about how soil carbon sinks will respond to nitrogen enrichment (Reay *et al.* 2008).

The consequences of ocean acidification for nutrient cycling are uncertain (Chapter 12). But the consequence of the reduction of acidity and the decline in phosphorus content of freshwaters will be an improvement in water quality due to reduced eutrophication. This will not only lead to reduced treatment costs for downstream users, but it will also increase amenity value of waters due to reductions in toxic algal blooms and physical blocking of waterways. In terrestrial habitats such as grasslands, high soil phosphorus concentrations can constrain the restoration of plant diversity (Smith *et al.* 2008b); hence, widespread reductions in soil phosphorus could, in some habitats, yield added benefits for biodiversity conservation.

13.3.4 Options for Sustainable Management

A key goal for sustainable management of semi-natural and natural habitats is the protection of ecological interactions that contribute to 'closed' systems of nutrient cycling, characterised by efficient use of nutrients by plants and microbes, and low levels of nutrient loss to waters and the atmosphere. Following on from this, a key goal for sustainable management of provisioning systems, such as agricultural land, is to develop management strategies that enhance reliance on natural processes of nutrient cycling and plant nutrient acquisition, and which minimise nutrient loss to waters and the atmosphere. Several management options could help achieve this goal including more efficient use of fertilisers, greater use of perennial crops, legumes and crop mixtures, and the use of intercropping, which has been found to reduce losses of nitrogen from systems (Whitmore & Schröder 1997). In addition, the exploitation of deep-rooting plants capable of retaining or capturing nutrients, or those which can obtain phosphorus via acid exudation or by means of mycorrhizal fungi, offers potential in terms of the sustainable management of nutrients. Management strategies that enhance the abundance of fungi relative to bacteria in soil, such as no-till agriculture and reduced fertiliser use, also offer the potential to improve the efficiency of nutrient cycling, including the retention of nitrogen and phosphorus in soil (de Vries *et al.* 2006; Gordon *et al.* 2008). In general, our understanding of the mechanisms by which plant-soil interactions regulate nutrient cycling is limited. Hence, new research is needed to better exploit the potential for different plants to access nutrients efficiently from soil via their interactions with soil organisms, and to develop management strategies that increase reliance on soil biological processes for the provision of available plant nutrients for crop growth.

Finally, the contribution of soil erosion to nutrient cycling and the transfer of nutrients to lakes, rivers and the ocean are not widely appreciated. Soil erosion contributes greatly to nutrient loss from land, especially phosphorus, and to the transport of nutrients to the ocean (Quinton *et al.* 2010). It was recently estimated that the amount of nitrogen moved by erosion globally is in the order of 37–75 Tg N/yr, which is of the same order of magnitude as the 98 Tg N/yr nitrogen applied to agricultural land as chemical fertilisers (Quinton *et al.* 2010). Also, soil erosion-driven fluxes of phosphorus have been estimated to be similar in magnitude to the amount of fertiliser phosphorus added to agricultural land per year (Quinton *et al.* 2010). Management strategies aimed at preventing soil erosion will therefore have major implications for nutrient cycling and the regulating and provisioning services that it underpins.

13.3.5 Knowledge Gaps

Although there have been significant advances in our mechanistic understanding of nutrient cycling and the response of nutrient cycles to various environmental and management drivers, significant gaps remain. One of the biggest challenges concerns the need to better understand the biological mechanisms that regulate nutrient cycling in different habitats and the role that biodiversity plays in nutrient cycling in soil and water. In particular, the contribution of soil microbes to the functioning of ecosystems is still poorly understood, largely because more than 95% of microbes are unable to be cultured on conventional media (Van der Heijden *et al.* 2008; Singh *et al.* 2010). And so, our understanding of the functional consequences of changes in the diversity and composition of complex soil communities remains poor (Bardgett & Wardle 2010). Such an understanding is essential for developing future land management strategies aimed at enhancing reliance on natural processes of nutrient cycling and plant nutrient acquisition, and for minimising nutrient loss from land to waters and the atmosphere.

Another major gap in understanding concerns the impact of climate change and other drivers (e.g. nitrogen deposition) on nutrient cycles. In particular, much remains to be learned about the response of nutrient cycles to climate change which involves many direct and indirect mechanisms operating differently across habitats. A particular gap in understanding concerns the effects of climate change-driven alterations in the allocation of carbon to roots, and the transfer of plant carbon to soil, which can stimulate the abundance and activity of soil microbes, enhancing the mineralisation of both recent and old soil organic carbon (i.e. priming), and therefore increase carbon loss from soil (Bardgett *et al.* 2008). Indeed, several free-air carbon dioxide enrichment (FACE) experiments have shown that elevated carbon dioxide can lead to substantial increases in root biomass and soil respiration (Pritchard *et al.* 2008; Jackson *et al.* 2009), and that, in general, below-ground responses to elevated carbon dioxide are often greater than above-ground responses in the same systems (Jackson *et al.* 2009). Mycorrhizal fungi also act as a significant sink for recent plant photosynthate (Högberg & Read 2006), and increased supply of photosynthate carbon to these fungi under elevated carbon dioxide can stimulate their growth, especially under conditions of low nutrient availability (Klironomos *et al.* 1997; Staddon *et al.* 2004), with unknown consequences for nutrient cycling. It is important to note that drivers other than climate change can strongly affect organisms involved in nutrient cycles. As a consequence, it is becoming increasingly apparent that our ability to predict future responses of nutrient cycles to global change requires a greater understanding of the simultaneous effects of multiple drivers (Tylianakis *et al.* 2008; Bardgett *et al.* 2008). Thus, understanding how multiple drivers acting simultaneously affect nutrient cycles represents a major research challenge for the future.

Many gaps in understanding exist concerning the fate and transfer of anthropogenic nitrogen in terrestrial and aquatic habitats, and its impact on nutrient cycles and other ecosystem services. For instance, little is known about the mechanisms involved in the retention of anthropogenic nitrogen in soils, although it is evident that microbes can act as a major sink for nitrogen and that they can regulate the transfer of nitrogen to soil organic matter, plants and aquatic habitats. Also, nitrogen enrichment can impact on other ecosystem services, especially carbon sequestration, although much remains unknown about the mechanisms involved and how the effects of nitrogen on carbon cycling vary across habitats. Our understanding of phosphorus cycling is also limited, especially with regards to how plants and microbes interact to access soil phosphorus, and how both nitrogen and phosphorus cycling are coupled. In general, there been relatively few studies on the interactions between nutrients or between environmental stresses and nutrient cycling. Thus, the mechanisms involved in the widespread decline in phosphorus availability across UK

habitats, and the implications for other ecosystem services, are poorly understood.

13.4 The Water Cycle

13.4.1 Condition, Status and Trends

In terms of supporting ecosystem services, the water cycle is most appropriately considered with respect to the major water fluxes (rainfall, evapotranspiration, river flow) and the major water storages (soil, groundwater, lakes) that combine to determine the availability of water in time and space. Fluxes and pathways that move water between the major storages are also important, as is the issue of water quality—poor chemical and/or microbiological quality can render the water effectively unavailable for supporting some services. Hydro-meteorological monitoring in the UK allows assessments of both rainfall and runoff (**Table 13.2**) to be made with reasonable accuracy (Marsh & Sanderson 2006).

Spatial variation in average rainfall across the UK is exceptionally high: annual totals can exceed 5,000mm in parts of the western Highlands of Scotland, whilst totals in the driest parts of lowland England can be an order of magnitude less (**Figure 13.12**). National rainfall assessments for England and Wales are available back to 1766 (**Figure 13.13a**) and, although rainfall for the last 30 years modestly exceeds the average for the preceding record, there is no overall trend (Alexander & Jones 2001). For Scotland, precipitation has increased substantially since a notably dry episode in the early 1970s; over the last 30 years, it is around 5% greater than the preceding average (**Figure 13.13b**) as a result of increased winter precipitation, particularly in the western Highlands. A change in rainfall seasonality has also been observed, with wet winters (November to April) more common during the last 30 years than during much of the 19th Century when summer rainfall totals (May to October) were generally higher.

Estimation of the flux of water lost in gaseous form as evapotranspiration (ET) largely represents rainfall minus runoff (**Table 13.2**). The flux is highly variable over the scale of a few metres and depends on factors such as plant cover and surface wetness. The long-term catchment experiment at Plynlimon is the best record of rainfall and runoff available

Table 13.2 UK water balance (mm), 1971–2000.
Source: rainfall data based on data from the Met Office National Climate Information Centre.

	Rainfall	Runoff	Rainfall-Runoff
GB	1,086	650	436
England and Wales	896	455	441
Scotland	1,440	1,100	340
Northern Ireland	1,111	679	432

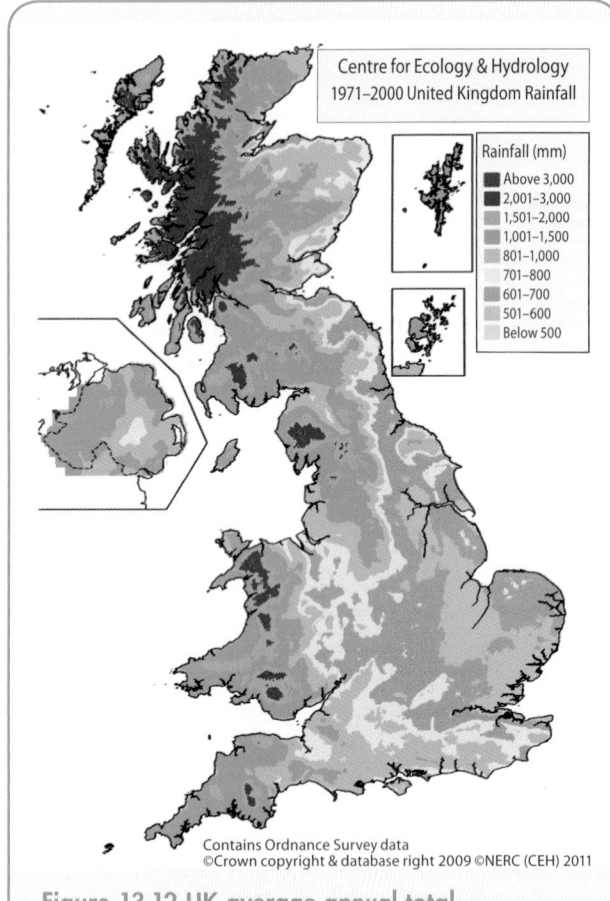

Figure 13.12 UK average annual total precipitation, 1971 to 2000. Source: data from Met Office National Climate Information Centre.

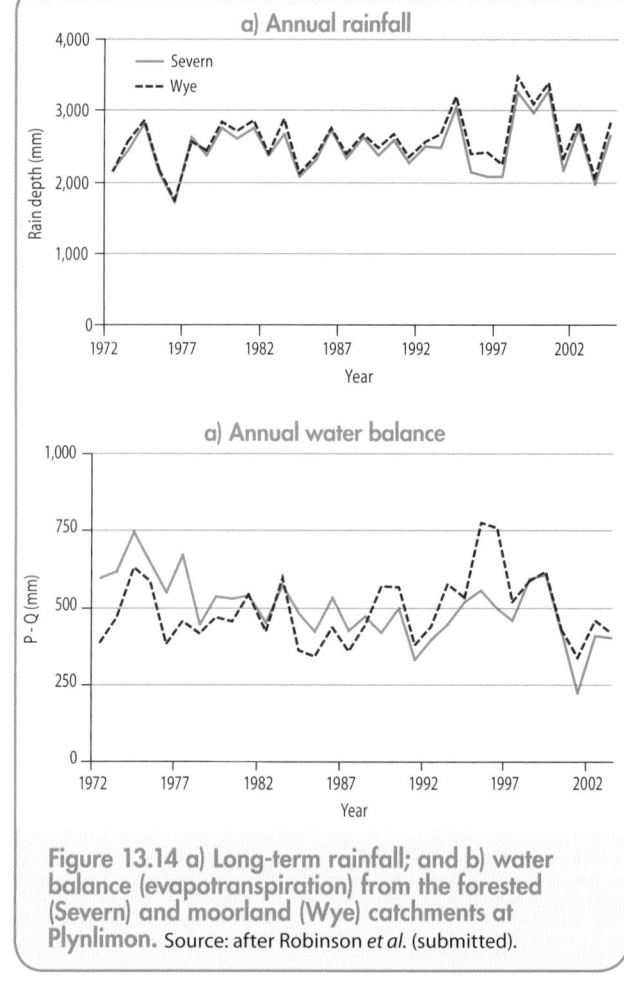

Figure 13.14 a) Long-term rainfall; and b) water balance (evapotranspiration) from the forested (Severn) and moorland (Wye) catchments at Plynlimon. Source: after Robinson et al. (submitted).

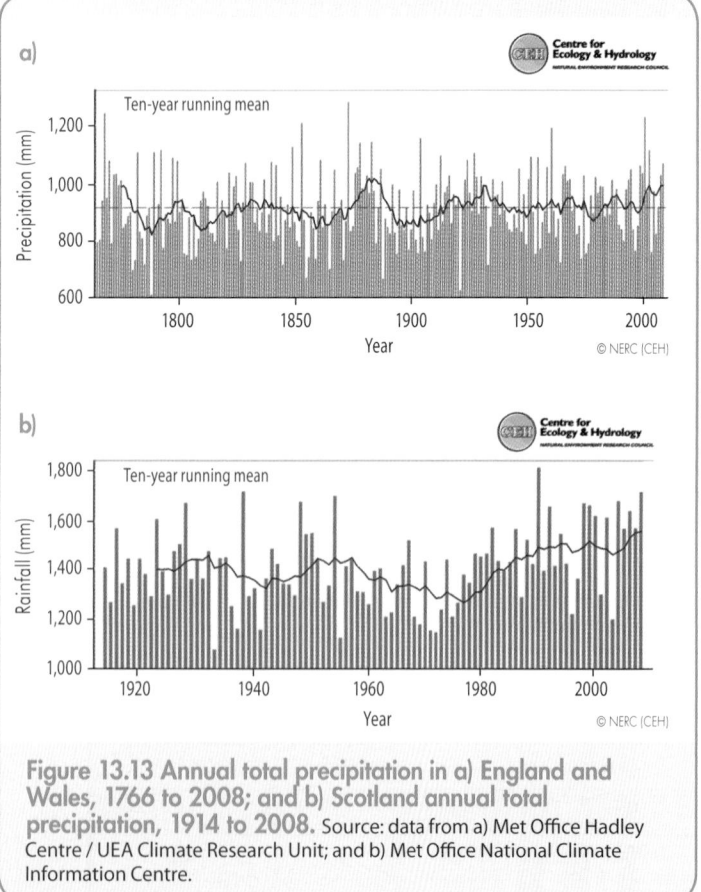

Figure 13.13 Annual total precipitation in a) England and Wales, 1766 to 2008; and b) Scotland annual total precipitation, 1914 to 2008. Source: data from a) Met Office Hadley Centre / UEA Climate Research Unit; and b) Met Office National Climate Information Centre.

(**Figure 13.14**) and shows the impact of a maturing pine forest plantation promoting increased evaporative losses relative to a nearby moorland (Marc & Robinson 2007). The UK's Met Office Rainfall and Evaporation Calculation System (MORECS) provides assessments of potential (**Figure 13.15a**) and actual (**Figure 13.15b**) evaporative losses for 40 km squares throughout Great Britain. These assessments indicate that, on average, over 40% of UK rainfall is lost to evaporation, although the proportion varies greatly regionally, reaching around 80% in the driest parts of the English Lowlands (Hough & Jones 1997).

River flows integrate the precipitation and evaporation interactions at the basin scale and, therefore, measured runoff represents the most appropriate variable upon which to assess overall water resources and hydrological variability in space and time. Many UK river flow regimes, however, are profoundly affected by artificial influences such as abstractions and river regulation. Given the limited length of most river flow records and the climatic volatility of the last 30 to 40 years, the presence or absence of hydrological trends can be very sensitive to the length of record under review. There exists little indication of trend in total annual runoff from England and Wales between 1961 and 2008, although the recent past has been characterised by notable year-on-year variability (Hannaford & Marsh 2006). For Scotland, runoff has increased markedly following the early 1970s, but with limited change over the last 25 years (Hannaford & Marsh 2006).

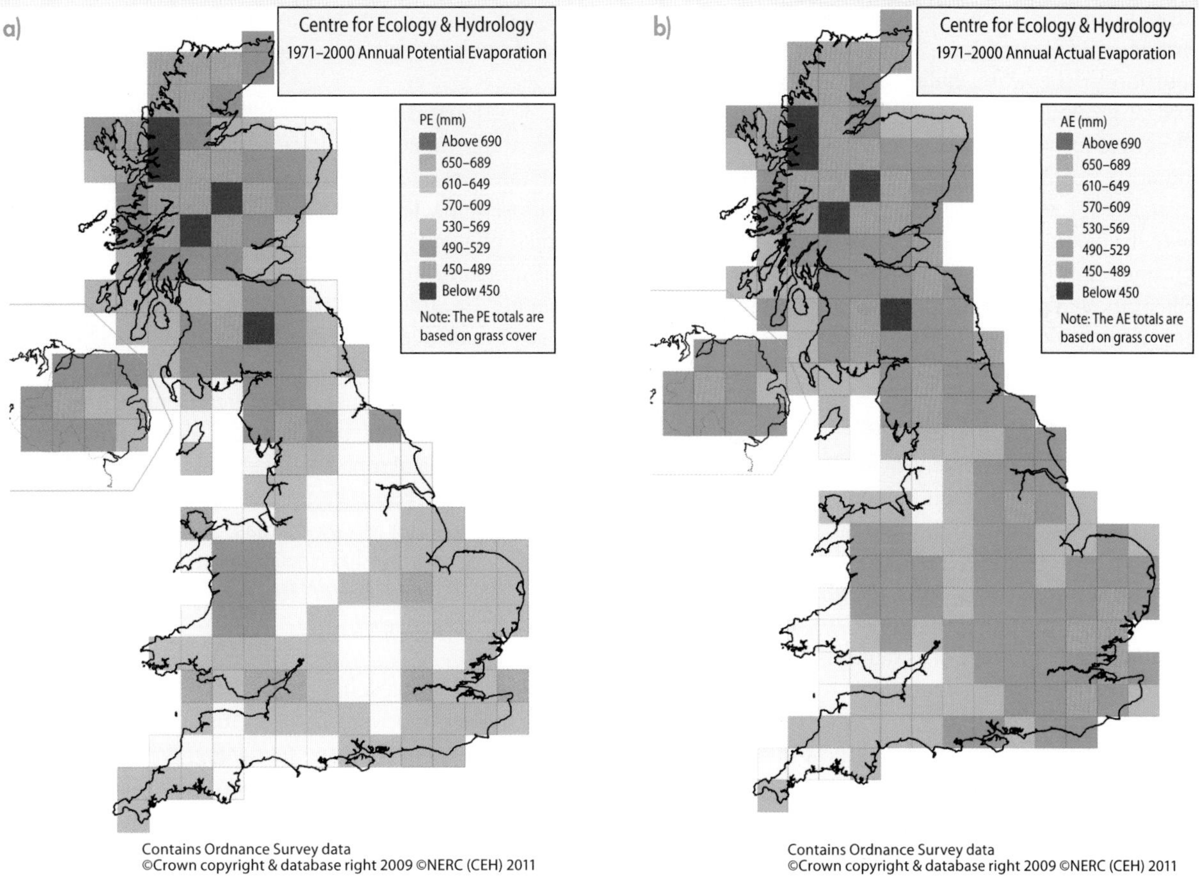

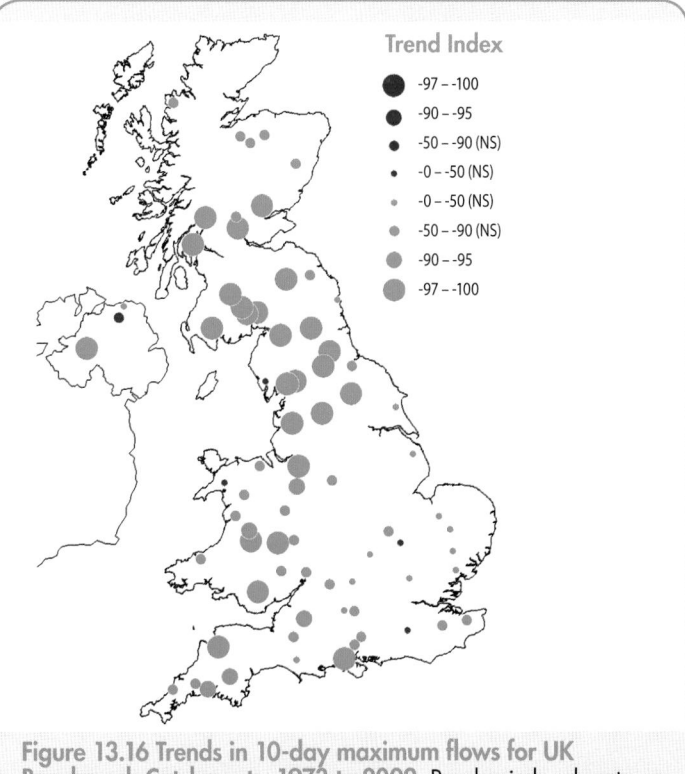

Figure 13.15 Great Britain average a) annual Potential Evaporation (PE); and b) Actual Evaporation (AE) totals, 1971 to 2000. Source: Met Office Rainfall and Evapotranspiration Calculation System.

Regional variations in runoff patterns across the UK are notably large, reflecting the diversity of the UK in terms of its climate, geology, land use and water utilisation patterns. The network of UK Benchmark Catchments (Hannaford & Marsh 2006) allows spatial responses to be assessed from the early 1970s, although particular caution needs to be exercised when interpreting trends over the last 30 to 40 years since the 1970s were a quiescent period in hydrological terms, while the period 1998 to 2002 is the wettest five-year sequence on record. Trend analysis of annual runoff over the period 1973 to 2002 at the UK Benchmark Catchments indicates significant increases in runoff (Hannaford & Marsh 2008) for a number of northern and western rivers (**Figure 13.16**). Corresponding analyses for the limited number of river flow time series over 70 years in length suggest that such trends are considerably less compelling as the time-span examined increases. Nonetheless, a modest tendency towards recent increase in runoff can be recognised. Low flows (30-day minima) at the Benchmark Catchments over the period 1973 to 2002 indicate little evidence of a decrease in low flows across the UK (Hannaford & Marsh 2006).

Groundwater storage (i.e. water located beneath the ground surface) provides a significant component of water resources used in the UK. Aquifers are generally replenished by winter rainfall when soil moisture deficits are negligible, although intense rainfall events can lead to localised recharge at any time of the year. Groundwater levels within aquifers represent a dynamic balance between

Figure 13.16 Trends in 10-day maximum flows for UK Benchmark Catchments, 1973 to 2002. Purple circles denote negative trends, turquoise circles positive trends, with graduated symbols representing statistical significance. Source: Hannaford & Marsh (2008). Copyright © 2007 Royal Meteorological Society. Reproduced with permission of Blackwell Publishing Ltd.

natural recharge, discharge to rivers and the sea, and anthropogenic abstractions, which often represent a large proportion of the water balance. The longest continuous record of groundwater level in the UK dates back to 1838 at Chilgrove in West Sussex. A drought index, representing cumulative departures from mean monthly levels, shows no consistent trends over this period, but distinct patterns of activity or quiescence at decadal scales exists. Trends in groundwater levels over decadal timescales most often result from changes in historical abstraction, for instance commencement or cessation of pumping for public supply, industry or mine dewatering.

13.4.2 Drivers of Change

The water cycle is extremely dynamic and sensitive to a range of drivers: impacts on any one major water store or flux can lead to significant changes propagating throughout the system. The major driver of long-term changes in the quantity of water in rivers, soils and groundwater is human activity such as changes in land use (including sealing due to urbanisation), drainage of agricultural land, development of impoundments and supply structures, and structural changes to rivers and water abstraction. In addition, acute or short-term changes are largely driven by cyclical changes in weather over a period of several years (e.g. The North Atlantic Oscillation). Extreme weather events, such as droughts (lasting one or two years) and floods (lasting days or weeks), can also have long-lived impacts on the water environment and water resource availability.

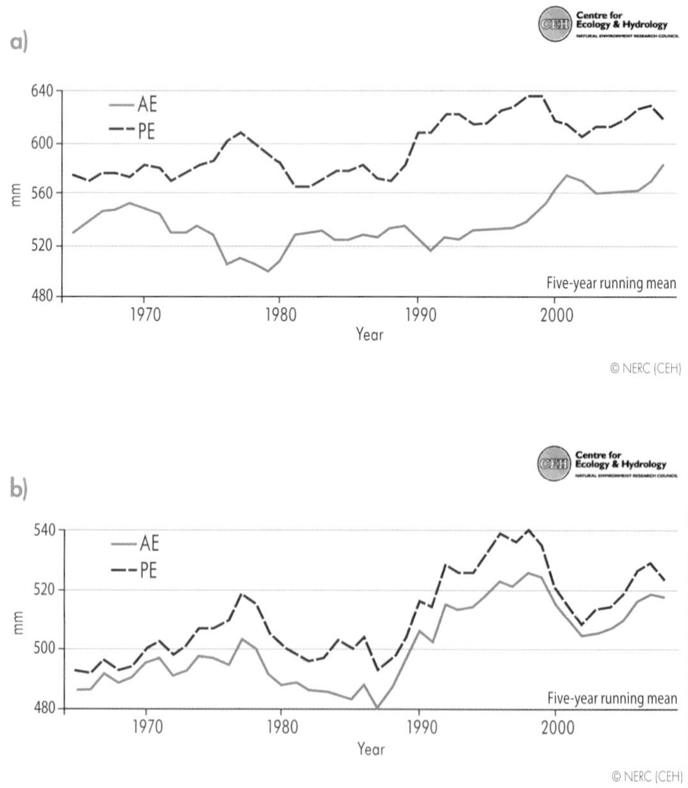

13.4.2.1 Land use and climate

The importance of future drivers will differ between habitats. For example, the water cycle in mountain habitats is most impacted by changes in temperature and rainfall which influence rates of evapotranspiration and, therefore, soil moisture and river flow regime. It is also impacted by changes in atmospheric deposition, especially of nitrogen. In semi-natural grassland areas, river flows and soil moisture regimes reflect changes in precipitation and temperature, but significant land use change can engulf this signal. In farmlands, pressures from increased abstraction for irrigation and agrochemical runoff are likely to have the greatest impact on the water cycle. The impacts of increasing populations in currently water stressed areas, such as the south-east of England, are further likely to promote increased competition for the available water resource between human and environmental needs.

13.4.2.2 Climate change

All of the above drivers are likely to be amplified in the future as the UK adapts to an increasing population, changing energy mix (e.g. increased importance of biofuels, hydro-power) and future climate change. Climate change alone is predicted to influence patterns of water movement both spatially and temporally, including greater frequency of extreme events and long-term changes in precipitation and evaporation. Climate change may also amplify effects of other drivers such as agriculture, with potentially more water resources required for irrigation and the replacement of conventional crops with dedicated energy crops. Such crops will result in increased evaporation rates, but reduced risk to water quality due to low inputs of agrochemicals. As an example, annual average evaporation loss for England and Wales has been observed to have gradually increased from around 500 to 550 mm over the period 1980 to 2005. This reflects an increase in average temperatures across the UK of around 1.0°C over the last 30 to 40 years (**Figure 13.17a,b**).

13.4.3 Consequences of Change

The consequences of future climate change in the UK are predicted to have a profound effect on the timing and magnitude of rainfall and runoff patterns. On average, the UK is likely to experience warmer, drier summers, and warmer, wetter winters (UKCP09). This will cause changes in annual river flow, although changes will be catchment-specific and will depend upon topography, soils, land use and geology. In addition, it is predicted that seasonal changes in the duration and intensity of rainfall will promote an increased occurrence of extreme floods, yet there is no clear understanding about change in size, or even direction, of flood-flow magnitudes in the UK. Changes in flood flows will also be catchment-specific, being driven by hydrological variables, such as geology, and the seasonal distribution of rainfall (Reynard *et al.* 2007). With respect to low-flows and drought periods, the projected increase in mean precipitation in winter and decrease in summer

Figure 13.17 Annual Potential Evaporation (PE) and Actual Evaporation (AE) totals in a) England and Wales; and b) Scotland. Source: Met Office Rainfall and Evapotranspiration Calculation System.

months may lead to an increase in frequency of short-term summer drought in most water resource regions, except Scotland and Northern Ireland. However, the uncertainty associated with such changes is immense (Blenkinsop & Fowler 2007).

Assessing the consequences of climate change on the availability and flux of freshwater in response to future climate change, however, is more complex than simply quantifying changes in rainfall, evapotranspiration and runoff. In most UK river catchments, human activities have historically driven significant changes to the water cycle through increased abstraction for water supply, agriculture, industry, and to sustain an increasing human population, and through changes in drainage in urban areas and for navigation management, flood defence and re-alignment (Ferrier *et al.* 2010). The water cycle is conventionally managed with the catchment as a central concept in water resource planning. The available water resources must support all demand within the catchment, and often outside the catchment area as well, including potable supply, irrigation, cooling and for ecosystem services. Activities and decisions made within catchment systems and relating to any one resource demand, will ultimately impact on the nature and function of downstream waterbodies, be they groundwaters, lakes, rivers, wetlands, estuaries or coastal zones. Traditionally, water resource management systems have been operated under the assumption of stationarity, where the statistical distribution (i.e. mean, standard deviation, etc.) of observations do not change over time. Hydrologists now face a future where assumptions about key parameters can no longer be based on historical records (Milly *et al.* 2008), making the consequences of change more difficult to predict and to manage.

13.4.4 Options for Sustainable Management

The sustainable management of water relies fundamentally upon the assessment of equitable allocation of available resources to all sectors requiring them. Protecting and providing for the water requirement for potable supply, industry and agriculture have conventionally formed the basis of management legislation, whilst water for ecosystem services has not been formally quantified. As a result, the ecosystem gets what resource remains. Of course, this can lead to problems for the provision of ecosystem services in areas of high anthropogenic water demand, particularly at times of water shortage, usually during the summer or prolonged drought periods.

The Water Framework Directive (WFD; EU 2000) provides a legislative platform upon which to base a more holistic approach to the water cycle, including the maintenance of ecological quality. Its objectives are: to protect and, where necessary, to improve the quality of all inland and coastal waters, groundwater and associated wetlands; to promote the sustainable use of water; to enhance protection and improvement of the aquatic environment; and to lessen the effects of flooding and drought. A key concept underlying the WFD is that of integration of environmental objectives, combining quality, ecological and quantity objectives, and all water uses, functions and values, into a common policy framework. This basically translates as water for the environment, water for health and human consumption, water for economic sectors, transport and leisure, and water as a social good. Conflicts in management of water resources, however, are common and are likely to become more commonplace in a future where rainfall totals are decreased, demand for water increases and water resources are scarcer.

Managing flooding presents further conflicts for holistic water management. For example, it is widely recognised that raising water levels in floodplain wetlands can have generally positive outcomes for ecosystem services such as carbon sequestration. However, it may also have detrimental effects, for instance, on flood storage. It has been calculated, for example, that for the North Drain catchment in the Somerset Levels and Moors, raising ditch and drain water levels to field level would remove 3.6 million m^3 of floodwater storage. This is equivalent to about 84% of the median annual maximum flood for the North Drain catchment (Acreman *et al.* 2007).

13.4.5 Knowledge Gaps

In general, our understanding of the water cycle is well advanced, and this has provided the basis for the establishment of predictive models capable of describing the spatial and temporal variation in the water cycle, and for predicting future changes in the water cycle in response to key drivers. When tested against observations of river discharge over time, however, hydrological models are often incapable of accurately simulating both the extreme storm-flow and base-flow of a catchment. This implies the need to elaborate the flow paths between groundwater, soil water and river channels within catchments. Such an understanding requires very detailed measurements of water stores and fluxes in space and time. The necessity for such a development lies in the link between ecosystem function and water; this is unlikely to relate to either simple high or low flow extremes, or to simple mean flows over a time period, but rather to periods of time for which critical flows are exceeded. These critical flows may also vary for different seasons of the year.

Soil water remains perhaps the most elusive store to quantify because measurements are sparse and tend to relate only to individual points within a catchment. Again, models have filled this gap, but without appropriate data for testing them, how applicable they are remains uncertain. Therefore, future studies need to better understand the dynamics of soil water and the influence of various drivers, such as climate change and land use, on soil water fluxes. Such an understanding also has implications for nutrient cycling, since most biological processes that govern nutrient and carbon cycling are strongly affected by soil moisture.

Another challenge concerns the need to reduce uncertainty, and increase resolution of, hydrological models and their outputs. This is crucial because our ability to predict future variability in the water cycle in space and time relies on the hydrological models being coupled to climate models capable of producing rainfall fields at an appropriate scale and time resolution. This is an area where further research is required.

13.5 Primary Production

13.5.1 Condition, Status and Trends

Primary production is the fixation by photosynthesis of either atmospheric or aquatic carbon dioxide, or its assimilation as organic compounds by plants and algae. Only a proportion of carbon dioxide fixed by photosynthetic organisms is retained; the rest is lost through the respiration processes that are required to maintain existing biomass. The overall amount of organic carbon fixed is described as gross primary production (GPP), whilst the amount retained after respiration is defined as net primary production (NPP). It is NPP that is of most relevance for ecosystem service delivery: it is available for food and timber harvesting in managed systems, provides the foundation of food webs in semi-natural and natural ecosystems, and underpins climate regulation by removing carbon dioxide from the atmosphere.

Major controls on primary production include light, temperature and water, the availability of nutrients (especially nitrogen and phosphorus), community diversity and composition, and the intensity of management to which vegetation is subjected. Response functions vary for each of these controls. For example, too little or too much water results in reduced rates of plant primary production in terrestrial systems, whilst there is typically a humpback relationship between plant productivity and diversity, and between disturbance and diversity (Grime 1979; Al Mufti *et al.* 1979). The relative importance of different factors that control primary production will also differ across habitats. For example, land management is the primary control on primary production in agricultural habitats, whilst water table height might be the primary control of primary production in wetland habitats. In marine habitats, most primary production is carried out by microbial communities in the phytoplankton, which include diatoms, coccolithophores and cyanobacteria.

Quantifying the status and trends of primary production is problematic because it is not possible to measure it directly, other than at local scales. As a consequence, data on the status and trends of primary production in the UK is limited. Particular problems include our inability to quantify production. Hence, knowledge is lacking about the amount of fixed carbon that is allocated below-ground to roots, which varies greatly across habitats (Jackson *et al.* 1996). This plays a significant role in soil carbon sequestration which is one of the main services derived from primary production (De Deyn *et al.* 2008). There is also a lack of information about the fate of organic and inorganic carbon fluxes to surface waters, which, if not included, can lead to major underestimations of primary production in aquatic systems (Evans *et al.* 2005). Finally, incomplete knowledge of response functions to different climate, soil, ecological and management variables, both singly and in combination and across all habitats, limits our ability to upscale primary production estimates in both time and space. These problems have led to a range of approaches and surrogate measures being employed, either singly or in combination, to provide estimates of primary production at a range of scales from plot to catchment, regional to national levels. These approaches include: net ecosystem exchange of carbon dioxide (NEE), which is the balance between net uptake of carbon dioxide by photosynthesis and its loss by respiration; net ecosystem productivity (NEP); plant standing biomass or biomass increments; crop, herbage and timber yields (Jenkinson *et al.* 1994); carbon accumulation rates; chlorophyll *a* concentrations and remotely sensed absorption by plants and algae. These approaches often include many assumptions and yield estimates often with limited justification (Lovett *et al.* 2006).

The earliest attempts to estimate primary production were made by geographers based on regressions of temperature data computed to a simple annual measure of actual evapotranspiration (AET), which was then regressed to field measurements of standing plant biomass (Running *et al.* 2004). This type of measurement can provide clear links to climate variables such as that demonstrated in biomass changes in a 20-year record of road verge vegetation by Willis *et al.* (1995) (**Figure 13.18**). These authors found that total vegetation productivity of above-ground vegetation was positively correlated with minimum spring temperature and that, in general, those plant species favoured by environmental stress or disturbance were promoted following warm dry springs and summers, whereas those preferring more productive conditions were promoted following a wet growing season (Willis *et al.* 1995). In the UK's longest record of herbage yields, the Park Grass Continuous Hay experiment at Rothamsted, climate variables explained between 12–21% of variability in grass yield in both unfertilised and fertilised plots over a 100-year time period (Jenkinson *et al.* 1994).

In forests, annual stem increment data, plus litter fall and assumptions for below-ground root production, are often used in combination with remotely sensed plant biomass data to derive net primary production values. Forest management aims at maximising timber yields and trees are harvested when rates of growth start to decline due to maturation; this typically occurs between 40 to 50 years for

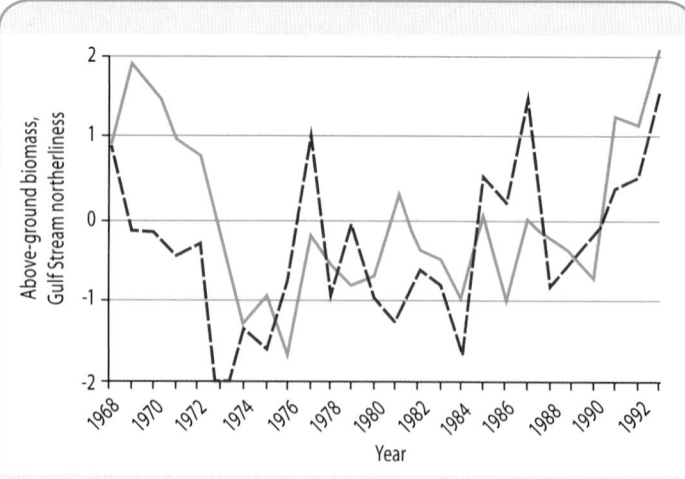

Figure 13.18 Standardised mean annual variations in above-ground biomass in road-verges in Bibury, Gloucestershire (solid line) and Gulf Stream northerliness index in the previous spring–summer months (dashed line). Source: Willis *et al.* (1995). Copyright © 2005 Nordic Society Oikos. Reproduced with permission of Blackwell Publishing Ltd.

monoculture softwoods such as spruce. Native woodlands are often less intensively managed to enhance other services such as biodiversity and recreation. Current forestry production rates in the UK have recently been estimated to be responsible for removing 15 Mt of carbon dioxide from the atmosphere every year with a total stock of carbon of 790 Mt of carbon in trees and forest soils (Read *et al.* 2009; Chapter 8 and Chapter 15).

The use of eddy-covariance in terrestrial habitats to measure the total exchange of carbon dioxide (i.e. NEE) has been employed to estimate landscape-scale spatial and temporal patterns of primary production. For example, work on ecosystem carbon dioxide exchange in forests across Europe identified the clear negative impact of the summer drought in 2003 on NPP. This trend was also observed for other habitats using remotely sensed radiation measures and country-level crop yields (Ciais *et al.* 2005). However, these measurements omit DOC, POC and inorganic carbon fluxes to aquatic systems (as highlighted above) and, therefore, underestimate primary production.

Earth observation provides another tool to estimate primary production based on the amount of photosynthetically active radiation available, the fraction of photosynthetically active radiation absorbed, estimated using the Normalised Difference Vegetation Index (NDVI), the amount of leaf area present to absorb solar energy, and a conversion efficiency factor (Running *et al.* 2004). The use of NDVI at the UK scale has identified the complex spatial pattern of leaf area that is required for primary production and how it is driven by a range of inherent landscape properties including soil type, topography and altitude, as well as land management practices. In marine systems, the patterns of primary production of coastal waters can be determined as a product from Earth observation methods and the spatial and temporal patterns of primary production can be identified in UK marine waters (**Figure 13.19**). The images indicate how the spring blooms of primary productivity start on the shelf and then move into deeper waters in the ocean. The Plymouth Marine Laboratory (PML) produces estimates of net primary production for the seas around the UK (daily estimates) and globally (monthly estimates). These use inputs of satellite-derived chlorophyll *a* and sea-surface temperature, and measured or modelled irradiance. The estimates of primary production use the model of Smyth *et al.* (2005) which is forced by phytoplankton chlorophyll *a* which absorbs light for photosynthesis, temperature which affects the rate of growth of the phytoplankton, and irradiance on the sea-surface and its attenuation with depth, which depends on the optical constituents in the water. The current model allows for in-water absorption by water, phytoplankton and its associated by-products, including co-varying coloured dissolved organic matter (CDOM). However, the model does not account for the effects of suspended particulate matter (notably in the Thames Estuary, southern North Sea, Bristol Channel) nor CDOM from riverine sources (such as in the Baltic outflow along the Norwegian coast or in Liverpool Bay). In these areas, primary production is likely to be overestimated. Work at the Plymouth Marine Laboratory is aiming to improve these coastal estimates.

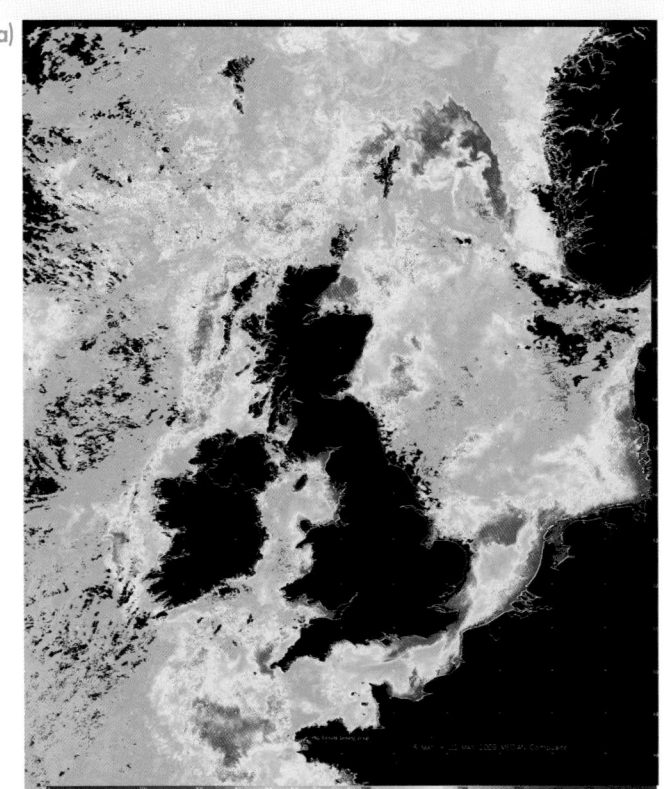

300   600   1,000   3,000
milligrams of carbon production/square metre/day

Figure 13.19 Seven day 'composites' produced from the NASA MODIS Aqua instrument received at NEODAAS-Dundee and processed at NEODAAS-Plymouth for a) 16–22 May; and b) 5–11 June 2009. The estimates of primary production use the model of Smyth *et al.* (2005) and are probably overestimated close to the coast in the southern North Sea.

In freshwaters, primary production is estimated from the surrogate phytoplankton chlorophyll *a* concentration. Primary productivity in most freshwater systems was thought to be primarily phosphorus limited but, as discussed previously, there is now strong evidence that nitrogen limitation, and nitrogen and phosphorus co-limitation, is widespread, especially in UK upland environments (Maberly *et al.* 2002). Long-term historical trends of 36 years are available for four lakes in the Lake District; here there is some evidence of suppression of chlorophyll *a* concentration with higher rainfall in small lakes with shorter residence times, but there was no overall trend in chlorophyll *a* concentrations (George *et al.* 2004).

As can be seen above, modelling provides a valuable tool to upscale and integrate measurements. It can also be used to test our current understanding of controls of primary production in the UK and forecast changes under different climate, pollution and management scenarios. For example, the JULES model (The Joint UK Land Environment Simulator) can produce a range of outputs, including primary production. However, a great deal of testing and development of the JULES model is required before its outputs can be used with any confidence. Models are also used in the marine environment, for example, ERSEM (European Regional Seas Ecosystem Model) coupled with the hydrographic model POLCOMS (The Proudman Oceanographic Laboratory Coastal Ocean Modelling System), which is now being used by the Met Office to provide marine system forecasting (www.ncof.co.uk/Coastal-Seas-Modelling.html).

13.5.2 Drivers of Change

In addition to intended modifications of primary production for food and fibre production, human activities have also had unintended effects on primary production through:

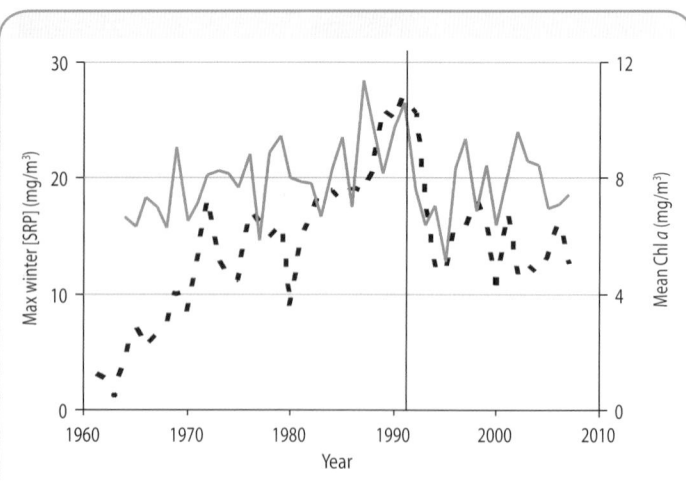

Figure 13.20 Long-term changes in the maximum winter concentration of soluble reactive phosphorus (SRP, dotted line) and annual mean concentration of phytoplankton chlorophyll *a* (solid line) in the South Basin of Windermere, Cumbria. The vertical line show the start of tertiary P-removal in 1992 at the two wastewater treatment works that discharge directly into Windermere. Source: data © NERC (CEH), © FBA (Freshwater Biological Association).

(i) climate change; (ii) change in light levels due to reduced sulphur emissions and aerosol formation; (iii) various aspects of air quality including continued elevated reactive nitrogen in the atmosphere, reduced acidity and increased ozone; and (iv) nutrient release into aquatic systems (**Figure 13.20**).

13.5.2.1 Land use

The main driver of change of terrestrial primary production has been, and continues to be, the production of specific food and fibre products and an associated increase in overall productivity through land use and management. This has been highly successful, resulting in an exponential rise in food production over the last 150 years, particularly through the development and widespread use of nitrogenous fertilisers in combination with new crop varieties (Goulding *et al.* 2008; **Figure 13.21**). Other successful management practices include a wide range of activities in different habitats, such as improved grazing management, genetics and crop improvements, fertiliser use, liming and drainage. For much of the second half of the 20th Century, subsidies often dominated over economic market forces in ensuring continued focus on food production, although more recent policies directed at biodiversity conservation have led to extensification of management and reduced productivity in some habitats, such as agriculturally improved grassland. As discussed in Section 13.1, changes in land use, for instance increased grazing and fertiliser use, can also instigate plant-soil feedbacks that promote nutrient cycling and, therefore, plant production by altering the composition of the soil microbial community (Bardgett & McAlister 1999; Smith *et al.* 2008b).

13.5.2.2 Nitrogen deposition

Atmospheric nitrogen deposition is thought to be a major driver of change in primary productivity in UK semi-natural habitats. But evidence of its importance is contradictory, with no trends in primary productivity being observed for the longest agricultural herbage record at Rothamsted (Jenkinson *et al.* 1994), but increased primary productivity being measured or modelled in many forest systems (de Vries *et al.* 2009). Some soils appear to have a very high capacity to accumulate and retain nitrogen in stable organic matter pools, thereby reducing nitrogen export and the harmful effects of pollution. Indeed, most mineral nitrogen entering soils, whether from deposition or fertilisers, is rapidly immobilised by soil microbes and, in strongly nitrogen limited habitats, is subsequently transferred to plants and/or stable, non-microbial organic matter pools (Zogg *et al.* 2000; Bardgett *et al.* 2003). Indeed, the primary control on nitrogen retention and leaching to freshwaters appears to be the potential for vegetation uptake (e.g. high in an aggrading forest) and relative and absolute amounts of carbon and nitrogen in soil, which determines its capacity to sequester more nitrogen (Emmett 2007). Despite the above, long-term changes in vegetation diversity and composition across UK habitats in response to nitrogen deposition have been detected, for instance, in montane heath in the Highlands of Scotland (Van der Wal *et al.* 2003), in UK grasslands (Stevens *et al.* 2004) and in UK habitats as a whole (Maskell *et al.* 2010); such changes in vegetation alter the amount and quality of organic matter entering soil as plant litter and root exudates, which, in turn, affects the abundance and activity of soil organisms involved in nutrient cycling and the subsequent liberation of nutrients for plant growth (Bardgett & Wardle 2010). However, few, if any, changes in plant species composition and production have been observed in a series of long-term nitrogen addition experiments across the UK, suggesting than many terrestrial systems are no longer nitrogen limited and changes to both production and composition occurred during the early or mid-part of the 20th Century (Emmett 2007; RoTAP 2011). In many situations, increasing rates of recovery and restoration of the original plant community is now a major challenge for agri-environmental policy (Smith *et al.* 2008b).

Nitrogen enrichment may also have direct and indirect effects on soil biological communities that regulate plant nutrient supply and primary production including bacteria, saprophytic fungi (Donnison *et al.* 2000; Treseder 2008) and mycorrhizal fungi (Egerton-Warburton & Allen 2000; Frey *et al.* 2004). There is much uncertainty, however, about the relative effects on soil communities and primary production of acute large-dose fertiliser and chronic deposition of atmospheric nitrogen, and little is known about how responses vary between different habitat types. Ozone pollution can act against the promoting effect of nitrogen on plant productivity, which is an issue that is expected to increase; despite the decline of peak levels of ozone, background concentrations are increasing due to the continuing industrialisation of developing countries (RoTAP 2011).

There is also evidence that eutrophication can strongly impact on the phytoplankton community and fish populations of freshwater lakes (Moss *et al.* 2003; Moran *et al.* 2010). And in marine habitats, eutrophication can reduce and change marine biodiversity through mortality of fish, shellfish and invertebrates, which will impact on primary production and related ecosystem services (Chapter 12). It also encourages macro and microalgal blooms, which impact on primary production and may also harm fish through food chain effects, as discussed in Chapter 12. In shallow coastal and intertidal waters, the macroalgae can smother the soft sediments, impeding the flow of oxygen and nutrients to and from the sediment and affecting marine life and primary production (Chapter 12).

13.5.2.3 Climate change

Climate change will be a major driver of primary productivity in future years, with UK-level changes in temperature and precipitation regimes having potentially marked effects on vegetation productivity and composition of many broad habitats. For example, climate envelope models (which are based on species' environmental preferences) predict severe loss of biodiversity due to climate warming (Thuiller *et al.* 2006), with likely consequences for primary productivity. Moreover, climate change can cause shifts in species' distributions in terrestrial and aquatic habitats, causing changes in primary productivity. It can also affect species' phenology and interaction strengths, which can lead to mismatches in the life histories of consumers and their resources (Beaugrand

et al. 2003; Post & Forchhammer 2008) and the decoupling of trophic interactions on which they rely (Visser & Both 2005; Memmott *et al.* 2007). As discussed for nutrient cycling, direct and indirect effects of climate change on soil microbial communities and mineralisation-immobilisation dynamics (via changes in carbon supply to soil) will influence plant nutrient supply; hence affecting the productivity of plant communities (Bardgett *et al.* 2008). Within individual habitats, drivers of change vary in their importance and can interact. For example, the potential enhancement of photosynthesis and primary production through elevated carbon dioxide will be limited by nitrogen availability in nitrogen limited and low-pollution areas (Hungate *et al.* 2003; Luo *et al.* 2004). Freshwaters are particularly vulnerable to climate change because: (i) many species within these fragmented habitats have limited abilities to disperse as the environment changes; (ii) water temperature and availability are climate-dependent; and (iii) many systems are already exposed to numerous anthropogenic stressors (Woodward *et al.* 2010). Likewise, effects of climate change on marine primary productivity are likely to be exacerbated due to ocean acidification, which is caused by increasing levels of carbon dioxide absorption by the oceans and the consequent changes to marine chemistry (Chapter 12).

In general, a large number of experiments, done under field and glasshouse conditions, highlight the complexity of responses to climate change and the need to include the effects of changing rainfall patterns, extreme events

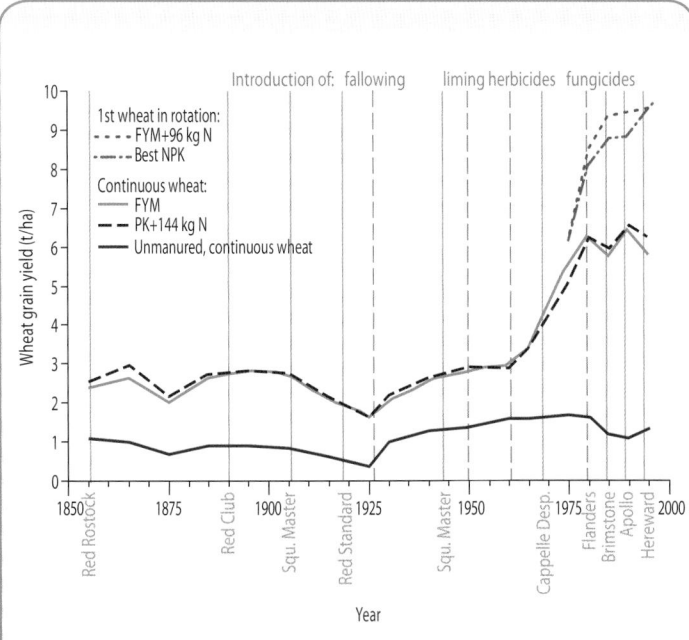

Figure 13.21 Yields of winter wheat (grain only, t/ha) on selected plots of the Broadbalk Wheat Experiment showing changes over time in varieties of wheat along the x-axis and changes in farming practice along the top of the graph. As a driver, this diagram illustrates the intensification of agriculture during the last few years which may be expected to continue. Less obviously, the increases in yield have been achieved by using more and more nutrients which have inevitably found their way into other ecosystems, terrestrial, freshwater and marine. Source: reprinted from Goulding *et al.* (2008).

and the interactive effects of different climate, pollution and management drivers. For example, a study of outdoor, shallow, freshwater mesocosms revealed that both warming and nutrient loading had a strong negative impact on sticklebacks, but combined, they resulted in extinction of this population (Moran *et al.* 2010). Studies of climate change impacts on primary productivity of heathland across a European climatic gradient also reveal contrasting effects of repeated summer drought on wet and dry sites; even within sites there are differential effects on plant species and nutrient cycles (Beier *et al.* 2008). In general, there is much uncertainty about the response of primary production to climate change and how responses vary across UK habitats, both terrestrial and aquatic, and in combination with other drivers of change. Future studies are needed which simultaneously vary two or more change drivers to determine their influence on primary production and other ecosystem services across a range of UK habitats. Such studies need to be linked to ecosystem models which provide an important tool for integrating this complex set of drivers on ecosystem processes (including primary production), and for making future projections about responses to climate change.

13.5.3 Consequences of Change

Primary production is the amount of carbon gained by vegetation, including new plant biomass, but also roots exudates and carbon transfer to symbionts. Therefore, any change in primary production will have significant consequences for all ecosystem services, including supporting services that depend on, or are affected by, the availability and rate of carbon accumulation (Smart *et al.* 2010). For instance, changes in primary production will have significant consequences for soil carbon sequestration in terrestrial habitats, given that the amount of carbon stored in soil is a function of carbon input by primary production and carbon loss through decomposition and plant respiration (De Deyn *et al.* 2008; Chapter 14). Changes in primary production also have far reaching consequences for terrestrial biodiversity conservation. Peak above-ground diversity commonly occurs at intermediate productivity (Al Mufti *et al.* 1977; Grime 1979; Grace 1999), with declining diversity at higher levels of productivity being due to competitive exclusion. Also, primary production acts as a major driver of below-ground communities and the processes that they drive, such as decomposition and nutrient cycling (Bardgett & Wardle 2010). Therefore, changes in primary production caused by drivers such as climate change and/or nitrogen enrichment are likely to have significant consequences for the biodiversity of above-ground and below-ground communities and the ecosystem services that they drive.

Primary production also regulates energy flow through food webs. Therefore, changes in primary production will cascade through both terrestrial and aquatic food webs, potentially altering their structure and function, their contribution to the delivery of ecosystem services (provisioning, regulating and cultural) and the goods and benefits that they provide. There is much uncertainty in this area, but one example of this concerns the North Sea where

climate-driven changes in plankton communities have been shown to exert a strong control on cod stocks, complicating the management of this species (Beaugrand *et al.* 2003; Beaugrand & Kirby 2010). In terrestrial ecosystems, changes in primary production can affect herbivore populations and their consumers, but in turn, these changes can potentially modulate the effects of drivers such as climate change on primary production in the future (Bardgett & Wardle 2010). The Countryside Survey (2010) provides a capability to explore trade-offs and synergies between primary production and carbon sequestration which contribute to climate regulation and other intermediate and final ecosystem services such as water quality regulation and provision of habitat for wild species.

13.5.4 Options for Sustainable Management

Sustainable management of primary production in semi-natural and natural habitats, including rivers, lakes and oceans, is dependent on the maintenance of a complex set of physical, chemical and biological interactions that regulate the supply of growth-limiting resources like light, nutrients and water. Any disruption of this state, whether on land or water, will have knock-on effects for primary production and the regulating and provisioning services that they underpin. As highlighted above, a key driver of change in primary productivity in most habitats is nutrient enrichment (nitrogen and phosphorus). While this has reaped rewards in terms of provisioning services, for instance, increased crop production, it can have significant, detrimental effects on regulating services, such as water quality, and on the biological diversity that underpins the delivery of supporting, regulating and cultural services. Therefore, future management strategies need to be aimed at the better exploitation of these valuable resources to ensure efficient utilisation for provisioning services, whilst preventing transfers to aquatic systems or terrestrial habitats valued for their cultural, regulating or supporting services. Furthermore, given that long-term nutrient enrichment has already impacted significantly on UK vegetation production and contributed to observed declines in plant diversity, future management needs to be directed at reversing these effects through appropriate restoration management. For example, a key objective of UK agri-environment policy and Environmental Stewardship is the restoration of biodiversity in agricultural systems with potential benefits, albeit over long timescales, for other ecosystem services such as carbon storage and nutrient retention. However, restoration of habitats to deliver a full range of ecosystem services is very challenging. Research is needed to better understand the synergies between different ecosystem services (including primary production) and how management systems might be designed to reap multiple rewards for supporting, regulating and provisioning services.

Managing for the effects of climate change is problematic because impacts on primary production and related ecosystem services (e.g. nutrient cycling) are poorly understood and effects of climate change are often habitat-specific. In addition, whilst the role that primary production plays in the carbon cycle is well appreciated, there is much uncertainty about the links between primary production and carbon cycling, especially in the soil. As a result, several gaps in understanding need to be tackled before sustainable management strategies aimed at climate change mitigation—for instance, through carbon sequestration on land and in waters—can be developed and implemented. Such linkages will also be affected by other drivers, such as nitrogen deposition; hence, future studies aimed at sustainable management of primary production and carbon sequestration need to consider responses to multiple, rather than just single, drivers of change.

13.5.5 Knowledge Gaps

As previously mentioned, data on the status and trends of primary production across UK habitats is limited. For terrestrial habitats, when data is available, it is mostly incomplete due to a lack of information about the amount of fixed carbon that is allocated below-ground to roots, which varies greatly across habitats (Jackson *et al.* 1996). This represents a significant gap in understanding, especially given the important roles that roots play in the delivery of terrestrial ecosystem services, including carbon sequestration, soil formation, nutrient cycling and the provisioning of food. There is also much uncertainty about the fate of land-derived fluxes of organic and inorganic carbon to surface waters, which can lead to major underestimations of primary production in aquatic systems. And there is little understanding of the effects of different land management regimes on soil carbon sequestration, despite them being proposed as effective means of mitigating greenhouse gas emissions. In inshore marine systems or intertidal areas, where water is shallow and visibility is often low due to suspended sediment, the contribution of macro and microalgae to seabed primary production is likely to be more significant. However, measurement of phytoplankton primary production via remote sensing in these areas is unreliable, and the extent of macro- and micro-algae in the UK is poorly mapped and quantified. This means the necessary data are missing to fully quantify UK marine primary production.

Another important gap concerns our understanding of how present or future changes in vegetation diversity and composition caused by land use and/or climate change, for example, influence primary production in UK habitats. Many experimental studies have explored how variations in species or functional group richness influence ecosystem processes, and several of these have found positive effects of diversity on primary production (Balvanera *et al.* 2006; Cardinale *et al.* 2006). But the interpretation and mechanistic basis underlying the results of these studies continues to be debated (Hooper *et al.* 2005). Indeed, many past diversity-function experiments have been based on randomly constructed plant assemblages that are artificial in nature and often immature, and while they have yielded a deeper mechanistic understanding of diversity-productivity relationships, their relevance to conservation management is debatable (Leps 2004; Bullock *et al.* 2007). Furthermore, the importance of species richness as a driver of productivity varies greatly among, and even within, studies (Fridley 2002; Hooper & Dukes 2004), and may be only minor in some

habitats when compared to other biotic and abiotic factors (Grace *et al.* 2007). There is an urgent need for studies which explore the consequences of real scenarios of non-random changes in plant species diversity and composition on primary production and other related ecosystem services across UK habitats.

A related challenge concerns the role of soil biodiversity in regulating primary production. As discussed previously, soil biodiversity is known to be highly sensitive to a range of drivers (e.g. land use, climate change and nitrogen deposition), but the consequences of reductions in soil biodiversity for primary production, and the services that it underpins, are poorly understood (Bardgett & Wardle 2010). Another key challenge concerning primary production involves its role in the exchange of carbon dioxide with the atmosphere, and how NEE is controlled by abiotic, biotic and management factors (Wohlfart *et al.* 2008). In general, our understanding of how land use and other drivers (e.g. nitrogen deposition) influence NEE is limited, although evidence is emerging to suggest that factors such as grazing can trigger short-term shifts in NEE in grassland systems (Wohlfarht *et al.* 2008). For example, long-term grazing by sheep in a UK peatland has been shown to increase NEE and, hence, ecosystem carbon sink strength due to an increase in photosynthesis relative to respiration (Ward *et al.* 2007). Also, while year-to-year variation in NEE is mostly attributed to climatic variability, grazing has been shown to alter the impact of climate on land-atmosphere carbon fluxes (Polley *et al.* 2008). These findings indicate that predictive models need to accommodate biotic factors such as grazing in order to accurately simulate the dynamics of carbon dioxide fluxes in UK terrestrial ecosystems.

Finally, as also highlighted for nutrient cycling, it is becoming increasingly apparent that our ability to predict future responses of UK habitats to global change requires a greater understanding of the simultaneous effects of multiple global change drivers on primary production and other ecosystems services. There is much potential for interactions between global change drivers to amplify, suppress or even neutralise climate change-driven effects on the primary production and NEE, with likely consequences for the ability of UK habitats to provide ecosystem services. Studies in this area are still few and far between, and there is an urgent need for experiments which simultaneously vary two or more change drivers to determine their influence on primary production and other ecosystem services across a range of UK habitats.

13.6 Conclusions

Supporting services underpin the delivery of all other ecosystem services (i.e. regulating, provisioning and cultural services). Hence, understanding their response to key drivers such as climate change, land use and nitrogen enrichment is of fundamental importance for future sustainable management of the UK's land and water resource. In this Chapter, we have identified a number of key trends in supporting services which have major implications for the delivery of other ecosystem services both now and in the future. First, while UK soils have taken thousands of years to develop (an average of <1 cm per century soil depth), there are concerns about the loss of soil by erosion under intensive agriculture, as well as the loss of organic matter from peat soils due to climate warming. Such soil loss has major implications for nutrient and carbon cycling in terrestrial and aquatic habitats, and for the delivery of regulating and provisioning services. Moreover, given that rates of soil loss can be much greater than formation, soils are essentially a non-renewable resource. Second, with regards to nutrient cycling, there is evidence of a widespread reduction in phosphorus available to plants in UK soils, which is possibly associated with increased primary production stimulated by increased atmospheric nitrogen deposition and climate warming. Also, nutrient cycles and primary production across all UK habitats have been, and continue to be, affected by anthropogenic inputs of nitrogen. In many UK habitats this has caused reductions in species diversity with uncertain implications for other ecosystem services such as carbon sequestration. In lakes, streams and coastal waters, it is well established that nutrient inputs of nitrogen and phosphorus from sewage, fertiliser runoff and soil erosion has caused major increases in primary production, again with uncertain implications for regulating and provisioning services. Warming has also caused changes in marine fauna, with potential knock-on effects for nutrient and carbon cycling, and ocean acidification could affect many marine organisms with uncertain consequences for supporting services. Finally, there have been few trends in the water cycle, but in the last 30 years, milder winters have been associated with increasing winter rainfall.

Although several key trends have been identified, our understanding of the mechanisms that underpin supporting services is limited, as is our knowledge of how these services will be affected by current and future drivers including climate change. It is also apparent that the mechanisms that underpin supporting services, such as plant production and nutrient cycling, are strongly context dependent. For example, studies indicate that the effect of plant species richness and community composition on ecosystem processes varies under different environmental conditions; likewise, drivers such as climate change, land use and nitrogen deposition will impact on supporting services differently across UK habitats. As a consequence, we identify many knowledge gaps concerning the need to better understand the mechanisms that underpin supporting services and their response to key drivers such as climate change. In addition, we highlight the urgent need for studies which explore the consequences of real scenarios of changes in biodiversity (i.e. species diversity and composition) on supporting services, and for experiments which simultaneously vary two or more key drivers of change to determine their influence on supporting and other ecosystem services across a range of UK habitats. Such studies are needed in order to develop sustainable options for the management of UK supporting services and the regulating, provisioning, and cultural services that they underpin.

References

Aber, J.D., Nadelhoffer, J.K., Steudler, P. & Melillo, J.M. (1989) Nitrogen saturation in northern forest ecosystems. *BioScience,* **39**, 378–386.

Acreman, M.C, Blake, J.R., Booker, D.J., Harding, R.J., Reynard, N., Mountford, J.O. & Stratford, C.J. (2009) A simple framework for evaluating regional wetland ecohydrological response to climate change with case studies in Great Britain. *Ecohydrology,* **2**, 1–17.

Acreman, M.C., Fisher, J., Stratford, C.J., Mould, D.J. & Mountford, J.O. (2007) Hydrological science and wetland restoration: case studies from Europe. *Hydrology and Earth System Sciences,* **11**, 158–169.

Alexander, L.V. & Jones, P.D. (2001) Updated precipitation series for the U.K. and discussion of recent extremes. *Atmospheric Science Letters,* **1** (2) 142–150.

Allison, S.D., Czimczik, C.I. & Treseder, K.K. (2008) Microbial activity and soil respiration under nitrogen addition in Alaskan boreal forest. *Global Change Biology,* **14**, 1156–1168.

Al-Mufti, M.M., Sydes, C.L., Furness, S.B., Grime, J.P. & Bond, S.R. (1977) A quantitative analysis of shoot phenology and dominance in herbaceous vegetation. *Journal of Ecology,* **65**, 759–791.

Angus, S., Hansom, J.D. & Rennie, A.F. (2010) Oir-thirean na h-Alba ag atharrachadh: habitat change on Scotland's coasts. The Changing Nature of Scotland (eds. S.J. Marrs, S. Foster, C. Hendrie, E.C. Mackey, & D.B.A. Thompson) TSO, Edinburgh.

Anser, G.P., Levick, S.R., Kennedy-Bowdoin, T., Knapp, D.E., Emerson, R., Jacobson, J., Colgan, M.S. & Martin, R.E. (2009) Large-scale impacts of herbivores on the structural diversity of African savannas. *Proceedings of the National Academy of Sciences, U.S.A.,* **106**, 4947–4952.

Aulakh, M.S., Garg, A.K. & Kabba, B.S. (2007) Phosphorus accumulation, leaching and residual effects on crop yields from long-term applications in the sub-tropics. *Soil Use and Management,* **23**, 417–427.

Balvanera, P., Pfisterer, A.B., Buchmann, N., He, J.S., Nakashizuka, T., Raffaelli, D. & Schmid, B. (2006) Quantifying the evidence for biodiversity effects on ecosystem functioning and services. *Ecology Letters,* **9**, 1146–1156.

Bardgett, R.D., Speir, T.W., Ross, D.J., Yeates, G.W. & Kettles, H.A. (1994) Impact of pasture contamination by copper, chromium and arsenic timber preservative on soil microbial properties and nematodes. Biology and Fertility of Soils, **18**, 71–79.

Bardgett, R.D. & McAlister, E. (1999) The measurement of soil fungal: bacterial biomass ratios as an indicator of ecosystem self-regulation in temperate meadow grasslands. *Biology and Fertility of Soils,* **29**, 282–290.

Bardgett, R.D., Jones, A.C., Jones, D.L., Kemmitt, S.J., Cook, R. & Hobbs, P.J. (2001) Soil microbial community patterns related to the history and intensity of grazing in sub-montane ecosystems. *Soil Biology and Biochemistry,* **33**, 1653–1664.

Bardgett, R.D. & Wardle, D.A. (2003) Herbivore mediated linkages between above-ground and below-ground communities. *Ecology,* **84**, 2258–2268.

Bardgett, R.D., Streeter, T.C. & Bol, R. (2003) Soil microbes compete effectively with plants for organic nitrogen inputs to temperate grasslands. *Ecology,* **84**, 1277–1287.

Bardgett, R.D. (2005) The Biology of Soil: A Community and Ecosystem Approach. Oxford University Press, Oxford.

Bardgett, R.D., Freeman, C. & Ostle N.J. (2008) Microbial contributions to climate change through carbon-cycle feedbacks. *The ISME Journal,* **2**, 805–814.

Bardgett, R.D. & Wardle, D.A. (2010) Aboveground-Belowground Linkages: Biotic Interactions, Ecosystem Processes, and Global change. Oxford Series in Ecology and Evolution, Oxford University Press.

Beaugrand, G. Brander, K.M., Lindley, J.A., Souissi, S. & Reid, P.C. (2003) Plankton effect on cod recruitment in North Sea. *Nature,* **426**, 661–664.

Beaugrand, G. & Kirby, R.R. (2010) Climate, plankton and cod. *Global Change Biology,* **16**, 1268–1280.

Beier, C., Emmett, B.A., Peñuelas, J., Schmidt, I.K., Tietema, A., Estiarte, M., Gundersen, P., Llorens, L., Riis-Nielsen, T., Sowerby, A. & Gorissen, A. (2008) Carbon and nitrogen cycles in European ecosystems respond differently to global warming. *Science of the Total Environment,* **407**, 692–697.

Bellamy, P.H., Loveland, P.J., Bradley, R.J, Lark, R.M. & Kirk, G.J.D. (2005) Carbon losses from all soils across England and Wales 1978–2003. *Nature,* **437**, 245–248.

Blackford, J.C. (1997) An analysis of benthic biological dynamics in a North Sea ecosystem model. *Journal of Sea Research,* **38**, 213–230.

Blenkinsop, S. & Fowler, H.J. (2007) Changes in drought frequency, severity and duration for the British Isles projected by the PRUDENCE regional climate models. *Journal of Hydrology,* **342**, 50–71.

Bradley, R.I., Milne, R., Bell, J., Lilly, A., Jordan, C., & Higgins, A. (2005) A soil carbon and land use database for the United Kingdom. *Soil Use and Management,* **21**, 363–369.

BSFP (2009) British Survey of Fertiliser Practice: Fertiliser use on farm crops for crop year 2008. [online] Available at: <http://www.defra.gov.uk/evidence/statistics/foodfarm/enviro/fertiliserpractice/documents/2008.pdf> [Accessed 16.12.10].

Bullock, J.M., Pywell, R.F. & Walker, K.J. (2007) Long-term enhancement of agricultural production by restoration of biodiversity. *Journal of Applied Ecology,* **44**, 6–12.

Cannell, M.G.R., Milne, R., Hargreaves, K.J., Brown, T.A.W., Cruickshank, M.M., Bradley, R.I., Spencer, T., Hope, D., Billett, M.F., Adger, W.N. & Subak, S. (1999) National inventories of terrestrial carbon sources and sinks: The UK experience. *Climatic Change,* **42**, 505–530.

Cardinale, B.J., Srivastava, D.S., Duffy, J.E., Wright, J.P., Downing, A.L., Sankaran, M. & Jouseau, C. (2006) Effects of biodiversity on the functioning of trophic groups and ecosystems: A meta-analysis. *Nature,* **443**, 989–992.

Carroll, Z.L., Bird, S.B., Emmett, B.A., Reynolds, B. & Sinclair, F.L. (2004) Can tree shelterbelts on agricultural land reduce flood risk? *Soil Use and Management,* **20**, 357–359.

Chapin, F.S., Matson, P.A. & Mooney, H.A. (2002) Principles of Terrestrial Ecosystem Ecology. Springer-Verlag, New York.

Chapman, S.J., Bell, J., Donnell, D. & Lilly, A. (2009) Carbon stocks in Scottish peatlands. *Soil Use and Management,* **25**, 105–112.

Ciais, P., Reichstein, M., Viovy, N., Granier, A., Ogée, J., Allard, V., Aubinet, M., Buchmann, N., Bernhofer, C., Carrara, A., Chevallier, F., De Noblet, N., Friend, A.D., Friedlingstein, P., Grünwald, T., Heinesch, B., Keronen, P., Knohl, A., Krinner, G., Loustau, D., Manca, G., Matteucci, G., Miglietta, F., Ourcival, J.M., Papale, D., Pilegaard, K., Rambal, S., Seufert, G., Soussana, J.F., Sanz, M.J., Schulze, E.D., Vesala, T. & Valentini, R. (2005) Europe-wide reduction in primary productivity caused by the heat and drought in 2003. *Nature,* **437**, 529–533.

Combs Jr., G.F. (2001) Selenium in global food systems. *British Journal of Nutrition,* **85**, 517–547.

Conant, R.T., Paustian, K. & Elliott, E.T. (2001) Grassland management and conversion into grassland: effects on soil carbon. *Ecological Applications,* **11**, 343–355.

Cordell, D., Drangert, J.O. & White, S. (2009) The story of phosphorus: Global food security and food for thought. *Global Environmental Change,* **19**, 292–305.

Countryside Survey (2010) Reports from Countryside Survey in 2007. [online] Available at: <http://www.countrysidesurvey.org.uk/reports-2007> [Accessed 16.12.10].

Covich, A.P., Austen, M.C., Barlocher, F., Chauvet, E., Cardinale, B.J., Biles, C.L., Inchausti, P., Dangles, O., Statzner, B., Solan, M., Moss, B.R. & Asmus, H. (2004) The role of biodiversity in the functioning of freshwater and marine benthic ecosystems: review of current evidence and future research needs. *Bioscience,* **54**, 767–775.

Craine, J.M., Morrow, M. & Fierer, N. (2007) Microbial nitrogen limitation increases decomposition. *Ecology,* **88**, 2105–2113.

De Deyn, G.B., Cornelissen, H.C. & Bardgett, R.D. (2008) Plant functional traits and soil carbon sequestration in contrasting biomes. *Ecology Letters,* **11**, 516–531.

De Deyn, G.B., Quirk, H., Zho, Y., Oakley, S., Ostle, N.J. & Bardgett, R.D. (2009) Vegetation composition promotes carbon and nitrogen storage in model grassland communities of contrasting soil fertility. *Journal of Ecology,* **97**, 864–875.

De Vries, F.T., Hoffland, E., van Eekeren, N, Brussaard, L. & Bloem, J. 2006. Fungal/bacterial ratios in grassland with contrasting nitrogen management. *Soil Biology and Biochemistry,* **38**, 2092–2103.

de Vries, W., Solberg, S., Dobbertin, M., Sterba, H., Laubhann, D., van Oijen, M., Evans, C., Gundersen, P., Kros, J., Wamelink, G.W.W., Reinds, G.J. & Suttong, M.A. (2009) The impact of nitrogen deposition on carbon sequestration by European forests and heathlands. *Forest Ecology and Management,* **258**, 1814–1823.

Defra (Department for Environment, food and Rural Affairs) (2009) Safeguarding our soils: A strategy for England. Defra, London. [online] Available at: <http://www.archive.defra.gov.uk/environment/quality/land/soil/documents/soil-strategy.pdf> [Accessed: 16.12.10].

Díaz, S., Lavorel, S., de Bello, F., Quétier, F., Grigulis, K. & Robson, T.M. (2007) Incorporating plant functional diversity effects in ecosystem service assessments. *Proceedings of the National Academy of Sciences, USA,* **104**, 20684–20689.

DCLG (Department of Local Communities and Government) (2010) Land Use Change Statistics. Table P261. [online] Available at: <http://www.communities.gov.uk/documents/planningandbuilding/xls/1658136.xls> [Accessed 13.12.10].

Donnison, L.M., Griffith, G.S. & Bardgett, R.D. (2000) Determinants of fungal growth and activity in botanically diverse haymeadows: effects of litter type and fertiliser additions. *Soil Biology and Biochemistry,* **32**, 289–294.

Dorrepaal, E., Toet, S., van Logtestijn, R.S.P., Swart, E., van de Weg, M.J., Callaghan, T.V. & Aerts, R. (2009) Carbon respiration from subsurface peat accelerated by climate warming in the subarctic. *Nature,* **460**, 616–619.

Downing, J.A., Osenberg, C.W. & Sarnelle, O. (1999) Meta-analysis of marine nutrient-enrichment experiments: variation in the magnitude of nutrient limitation. *Ecology,* **80**, 1157–1167.

Dowrick, D.J., Hughes, S., Freeman, C., Lock, M.A., Reynolds, B. & Hudson, J.A. (1999) Nitrous oxide emissions from a gully mire in mid-Wales UK, under simulated summer drought. *Biogeochemistry,* **44**, 151–162.

Egerton-Warburton, L.M. & Allen, E.B. (2000) Shifts in arbuscular mycorrhizal communities along an anthropogenic nitrogen deposition gradient. *Ecological Applications,* **10**, 484–496.

Elser, J.J., Marzolf, E.R. & Goldman, C.R. (1990) Phosphorus and nitrogen limitation of phytoplankton growth in the freshwaters of North America: a review and critique of experimental enrichments. *Canadian Journal of Fisheries and Aquatic Sciences,* **47**, 1468–1477.

Elser, J.J., Bracken, M.E.S., Cleland, E.E., Gruner, D.S., Harpole, W.S., Hillebrand, H., Ngai, J.T., Seabloom, E.W., Shurin, J.B. & Smith, J.E. (2007) Global analysis of nitrogen and phosphorus limitation of primary producers in freshwater, marine and terrestrial ecosystems. *Ecology Letters,* **10**, 1135–1142.

Emmett, B.A. (2007) Nitrogen saturation of terrestrial ecosystems: some recent findings and their implications for our conceptual framework. *Water Air and Soil Pollution,* **7**, 99–109.

Emmett, B.A., Reynolds, B., Chamberlain, P.M., Rowe, E., Spurgeon, D., Brittain, S.A., Frogbrook, Z., Hughes, S., Lawlor, A.J., Poskitt, J., Potter, E., Robinson, D.A., Scott, A., Wood, C. & Woods, C. (2010) Countryside Survey: Soils Report from 2007. NERC/Centre for Ecology & Hydrology, 192pp. (CS Technical Report No. 9/07, CEH Project Number: C03259).

Environment Agency (2004) The State of Soils in England and Wales. 32pp, Environment Agency, Bristol.

Environment Agency (2007) The Total External Environmental Costs and Benefits of Agriculture in the UK. [online] Available at <http://www.environment-agency.gov.uk/static/documents/Research/costs_benefitapr07_1749472.pdf> [Accessed 16.12.10].

Environment Agency (2008) [online] Similar data available at: <http://www.environment-agency.gov.uk/research/library/data/58820.aspx> [Accessed 16.12.10]. Contact enquiries@environment-agency.gov.uk for more details.

EU (European Union) (2000) Directive 2000/60/EC of the European Parliament and the Council of 23 Oct. 2000 establishing a framework for Community action in the field of water policy. *Official Journal of the European Communities,* L327, 1–72.

EASAC (European Academies Science Advisory Council) (2009) Ecosystem Services and Biodiversity in Europe. The Royal Society, Clyvedon Press, Cardiff.

European Commission (2002) Towards a thematic Strategy for Soil Protection – COM(2002) 179 final, 16.4.2002 (Brussels).

European Commission (2006a) Thematic Strategy for Soil Protection Communication (COM(2006) 231).

European Commission (2006b) Proposal for a Directive of the European Parliament and of the Council establishing a framework for the protection of soil and amending Directive 2004/35/ EC. Directive (COM(2006) 232).

Evans, C.D., Monteith, D.T. & Cooper, D.M. (2005) Long-term increases in surface water dissolved organic carbon: Observations, possible causes and environmental impacts. *Environmental Pollution,* **137**, 55–71.

Evans, G.L., Williams, P.J. & Mitchelson-Jacob, E.G. (2003) Physical and anthropogenic effects on observed long-term nutrient changes in the Irish Sea. *Estuarine, Coastal and Shelf Science,* **57**, 1159–1168.

Fan, M.S., Zhao, F.J., Poulton, P.R. & McGrath, S.P. (2008) Historical changes in the concentrations of selenium in soil and wheat grain from the Broadbalk experiment over the last 160 years. *Science of the total Environment,* **389**, 532–538.

Ferrier, R.C., Jenkins, A. & Blackstock, K. (2010) The future for catchment management. Handbook of Catchment Management (eds R.C. Ferrier & A. Jenkins), pp. 501–516. Wiley-Blackwell.

FAO (Food and Agriculture Organization) (2006) World Reference Base for international classification, correlation and communication. World Soil Resources Reports 103. FAO, Rome.

Fornara, D. & Tilman, D. (2008) Plant functional composition influences rates of soil carbon and nitrogen accumulation. *Journal of Ecology,* **9**, 314–322.

Francoeur, S.N. (2001) Meta-analysis of lotic nutrient amendment experiments: detecting and quantifying subtle responses. *Journal of the North American Benthological Society,* **20**, 358–368.

Freeman, C., Fenner, N., Ostle, N.J., Kang, H., Dorwick, D.J., Reynolds, B., Lock, M.A., Sleep, D., Hughes, S. & Hudson, J. (2004) Export of dissolved organic carbon from peatlands under elevated carbon dioxide levels. *Nature,* **430**, 195–198.

Frey, S.D., Knorr, M., Parrent, J.L. & Simpson, R.T. (2004) Chronic nitrogen enrichment affects the structure and function of the soil microbial community in temperate hardwood and pine forests. *Forest Ecology and Management,* **196**, 159–171.

Fridley, J.D. (2002) Resource availability dominates and alters the relationship between species diversity and ecosystem productivity in experimental plant communities. *Oecologia,* **132**, 271–277.

George, D.G. (2002) Regional-scale influences on the long-term dynamics of lake phytoplankton. Phytoplankton Productivity-Carbon Assimilation in Marine and Freshwater Ecosystems (eds P.J. le B. Williams, D.N. Thomas & C.S. Reynolds), pp. 265–290, Oxford University Press.

George, D.G., Maberly, S.C. & Hewitt, D.P. (2004) The influence of the North Atlantic Oscillation on the physical, chemical and biological characteristics of four lakes in the English Lake District. *Freshwater Biology,* **49**, 760–774.

Gessner, M.O., Swan, C.M., Dang, C.K., McKie, B.G., Bardgett, R.D., Wall, D.H. & Hättenschwiler, S. (2010) Diversity meets decomposition. *Trends in Ecology and Evolution,* **25**, 372–380.

Giller, K.E., McGrath, S.P. & Hirsch, P.R. (1989) Absence of nitrogen fixation in clover grown on soil subject to long-term contamination with heavy metals is due to survival of only ineffective *Rhizobium. Soil Biology and Biochemistry,* **21**, 841–848.

Giller, K.E., Witter, E. & McGrath, S.P. (1998) Toxicity of heavy metals to soil microorganisms and microbial processes in agricultural soils: A review. *Soil Biology and Biochemistry,* **30**, 1389–1414.

Gordon, H., Haygarth, P.M. & Bardgett, R.D. (2008) Drying and rewetting effects on soil microbial community composition and nutrient leaching. *Soil Biology and Biochemistry,* **40**, 302–311.

Goulding, K.W.T. (2000) Nitrate leaching from arable and horticultural land. *Soil Use and Management*, **16**, 145–151.

Goulding, K.W.T., Jarvis, S.C. & Whitmore, A.P. (2008) Optimising nutrient management for farm systems. *Philosophical Transactions of the Royal Society series* B, **363**, 667–680. doi:10.1098/rstb.2007.2177

Gowen, R.J., Hydes, D.J., Mills, D.K., Stewart, B.M., Brown, J., Gibson, C.E., Shammon, T.M., Allen, M. & Malcolm, S.J. (2002) Assessing Trends in Nutrient concentrations in Coastal Shelf Seas: a Case Study in the Irish Sea. *Estuarine, Coastal and Shelf Science*, **54**, 927–939.

Grace, J.B. (1999) The factors controlling species density in herbaceous plant communities: an assessment. *Perspectives in Plant Ecology, Evolution, and Plant Systematics*, **2**, 1–28.

Grace, J.B., Anderson, T.M., Smith, M.D., Seabloom, E., Andelman, S.J., Meche, G., Weiher, E., Allain, L.K., Jutila, H., Sankaran, M., Knops, J., Ritchie, M. & Willig, M.R. (2007) Does species diversity limit productivity in natural grassland communities? *Ecology Letters*, **10**, 680–689.

Grayston S.J., Campbell, C.D., Bardgett, R.D., Mawdsley, J.L., Clegg, C.D., Ritz, K., Griffiths, B.S., Rodwell, J.S., Edwards, S.J., Davies, W.J. & Elston, D.J. (2004) Assessing shifts in soil microbial community structure across a range of grasslands of differing management intensity using CLPP, PLFA and community DNA techniques. *Applied Soil Ecology*, **25**, 63–84.

Grime, J.P. (1979) Plant Strategies and Vegetation Processes. John Wiley, Chichester, UK.

Hannaford, J. & Marsh, T.M. (2006) An assessment of trends in UK runoff and low flows using a network of undisturbed catchments. *International Journal of Climatology*, **26**, 1237–1253.

Hannaford, J. & Marsh, T.M. (2008) High-flow and flood trends in a network of undisturbed catchments in the UK. *International Journal of Climatology*, **28**, 1325–1338.

Harding, R.B. & Jokela, E.J. (2003) Long-term effects of forest fertilisation on site organic matter and nutrients. *Soil Science Society of America Journal*, **58**, 216–221.

Högberg, P. & Read, D.J. (2006) Towards a more plant physiological perspective on soil ecology. *Trends in Ecology and Evolution*, **21**, 548–554.

Hooper, D.U. & Dukes, J.S. (2004) Overyielding among plant functional groups in a long-term experiment. *Ecology Letters*, **7**, 95–105.

Hooper, D.U., Chapin, F.S., Ewel, J.J. Hector, A., Inchausti, P., Lavorel, S., Lawton, J.H., Lodge, D.M. Loreau, M., Naeem, S., Schmid, B., Setälä, H., Symstad, A.J., Vandermeer, J. & Wardle, D.A. (2005) Effects of biodiversity on ecosystem functioning: a consensus of current knowledge and needs for future research. *Ecological Monographs*, **75**, 3–35.

Hough, M.N. & Jones, R.J.A. (1997) The United Kingdom Meteorological Office rainfall and evaporation calculation system: MORECS version 2.0 and overview. *Hydrology and Earth Systems Science*, **1**, 227–239.

Howarth, R.W. (1988) Nutrient limitation of net primary production in marine ecosystems. *Annual Reviews of Ecology and Systematics*, **19**, 89–110.

Howarth R.W. & Marino, R. (2006) Nitrogen as the limiting nutrient for eutrophication in coastal marine ecosystems: Evolving views over three decades. *Limnology and Oceanography*, **51**, 364–376.

Hungate, B.A., Dukes, J.S., Shaw, M.R. & Field, C.B. (2003) Nitrogen and climate change. *Science*, **302**, 1512–1513.

Jackson, R.B., Canadell, J., Ehleringer, J.R., Mooney, H.A., Sala, O.E. & Schulze, E.D. (1996) A global analysis of root distributions for terrestrial biomes. *Oecologia*, **108**, 389–411.

Jackson, R.B., Cook C.W., Pippen, J.S. & Palmer, S.M (2009) Increased belowground biomass and soil CO_2 fluxes after a decade of carbon dioxide enrichment in a warm-temperate forest. *Ecology*, **90**, 3352–3366.

Jenkinson, D.S., Potts, J.M. Perry, J.N., Barnett, V., Coleman, K. & Johnston, A.E. (1994) Trends in herbage yields over the last century on the Rothamsted Long-term Continuous Hay Experiment. *The Journal of Agricultural Science*, **122**, 365–374.

Jenny, H. (1941) Factors of Soil Formation. McGraw Hill, New York.

Jewell, P.L., Käuferle, D., Berry, N.R., Berry, N.R., Kreuzer, M. & Edwards, P.J. (2007) Redistribution of phosphorus by cattle on a traditional mountain pasture in the Alps. *Agriculture, Ecosystems and Environment*, **122**, 377–386.

Johnston, A.E., Poulton, P.R. & Coleman, K. (2009) Soil organic matter: its importance in sustainable agriculture and carbon dioxide fluxes. *Advances in Agronomy*, **101**, 1–57.

Joosten, H. & Clarke, D. (2002) Wise Use of Mires and Peatlands – Background and principles including a framework for decision-making. International Mire Conservation Group and International Peat Society.

Jordon, M.B. & Joint, I. (1998) Seasonal variation in nitrate: phosphate ratios in the English Channel 1923–1987. *Estuarine, Coastal and Shelf Science*, **46**, 157–164.

Khan, S.A., Mulvaney, R.L., Ellsworth, T.R. & Boast, C.W. (2007) The myth of nitrogen fertilisation for soil carbon sequestration. *Journal of Environmental Quality*, **36**, 1821–1832.

Kirk, G.J.D., Bellamy, P.H. & Lark, R.M. (2010) Changes in soil pH across England and Wales in response to decreased acid deposition. *Global Change Biology*, **16**, 3111–3119.

Kirby, K.J., Smart, S.M., Black, H.I.J., Bunce, R.G.H., Corney, P.M. & Smithers, R.J. (2005) Long term ecological change in British woodland (1971–2001). A re-survey and analysis of change based on the 103 sites in the Nature Conservancy 'Bunce 1971' woodland survey. English Nature Research Reports No 653 [online] Available at <http://naturalengland.etraderstores.com/NaturalEnglandShop/product.aspx?ProductID=28082251-db96-462c-87ac-ce547f587d1c> [Accessed 16.12.10].

Klironomos, J.N., Rillig, M.C., Allen, M.F., Zak, D.R., Kubiske, M. & Pregitzer, K.S. (1997) Soil fungal-arthropod responses to *Populus tremuloides* grown under enriched atmospheric CO_2 under field conditions. *Global Change Biology*, **3**, 473–478.

Kroeker, K.J., Kordas, R.L., Crim, R.N. & Singh, G.G. (2010) Meta-analysis reveals negative yet variable effects of ocean acidification on marine organisms. *Ecology Letters*, **13**, 1419–1434. DOI: 10.1111/j.1461-0248.2010.01518.x

Lal, R. (2008) Carbon sequestration. *Philosophical Transactions of the Royal Society B*, **363**, 815–830.

Lavelle, P., Dugdale, R., Scholes, R. (2005). *Nutrient Cycling*. Ecosystems and Human Well-being: Current State and Trends (pp.333–351). Island Press, Washington D.C.

Lawton, J.H. & Jones, C.G. (1995) Linking species and ecosystems – organisms as ecosystem engineers. Linking Species and Ecosystems (eds. C.G. Jones, & J. H. Lawton), pp. 141–150. Chapman and Hall, New York.

Liu, L. & Greaver, T.L. (2009) Review of nitrogen enrichment effects on three biogenic GHGs: the CO_2 sink may be largely offset by stimulated N_2O and CH_4 emission. *Ecology Letters,* **12**, 1103–1117.

Lovett, G.M., J.J. Cole & M.L. Pace. (2006) Is net ecosystem production equal to ecosystem carbon accumulation? *Ecosystems,* **9**, 1–4.

Luo, Y., Su, B., Currie, W.S., Dukes, J.S., Finzi, A.C., Hartwig, U., Hungate, B., McMurtrie, R.E., Oren, R., Parton, W.J., Pataki, D.E., Shaw, M.R., Zak, D.R. & Field, C.R. (2004) Progressive nitrogen limitation responses to rising atmopsheric carbon dioxide. *BioScience,* **54**, 731–739.

Maberly, S.C., King, L., Dent, M.M., Jones, R.I. & Gibson, C.E. (2002) Nutrient limitation of phytoplankton and periphyton growth in upland lakes. *Freshwater Biology,* **47**, 2136–2152.

Magill, A.H., Aber, J.D., Currie, W.S., Nadelhoffer, K.J., Martin, M.E., McDowell, W.H., Melillo, J.M. & Steudler, P. (2004) Ecosystem response to 15 years of chronic nitrogen additions at the Harvard Forest LTER, Massachusetts, USA. *Forest Ecology and Management,* **196**, 7–28.

Marc, V. & Robinson, M. (2007) The long-term water balance (1972–2004) of upland forestry and grassland at Plynlimon, mid Wales. *Hydrology and Earth System Sciences,* **11**, 44–60.

Marsh, T.J. & Sanderson, F.J. (2006) Revised method to assess the water balance and overall water resources for the UK, England & Wales, Scotland and Northern Ireland. Report to Defra, 8 pages.

Maskell, L.C., Smart, S.M., Bullock, J.M., Thompson, K. & Stevens, C.J. (2010) Nitrogen deposition causes widespread loss of species richness in British Habitats. *Global Change Biology,* **16**, 671–679.

Messiga, A.J., Ziadi, N., Plenet, D., Parent, L-E. & Morel, C. (2010) Long-term changes in soil phosphorus status related to P budgets under maize monoculture and mineral P fertilisation. *Soil Use and Management,* **26**, 354–364.

Memmott, J., Craze, P.G, Waser, M.N. & Price, M.V. (2007). Global warming and the disruption of plant–pollinator interactions. *Ecology Letters,* **10**, 710–717.

Milly, P.C.D., Benancourt, J., Falkenmark, M., Hirsch, R.M., Kundzewicz, Z.W., Lettenmaier, D.P. & Stouffer, R.J. (2008) Stationarity is dead: whither water management? *Science,* **319**, 573–574.

Mitchell, R.J., Campbell, C.D., Chapman, S.J., Osler, G.H.R., Vanbergen, A.J., Ross, L.C., Cameron, C.M. & Cole, L. (2007) The cascading effects of birch on heather moorland: a test for the top-down control of an ecosystem engineer. *Journal of Ecology,* **95**, 540–554.

Moran, R., Harvey, I., Moss, B., Feuchtmayr, H., Hatton, K., Heyes, T. & Atkinson, D. (2010) Influence of simulated climate change and eutrophication on three-spined stickleback populations: a large scale mesocosm experiment. *Freshwater Biology,* **55**, 315–325.

Morecroft, M.D., Bealey C.E., Beaumont, D.A., Benham, S., Brooks, D.R., Burt, T.P., Critchley, C.N.R., Dick, J., Littlewood, N.A., Monteith, D.T., Scott, W.A., Smith, R.I., Walmsley, C. & Watson, H. (2009) The UK Environmental Change Network: Emerging trends in the composition of plant and animal communities and the physical environment. *Biological Conservation,* **142**, 2814–2832.

Moss, B., Mckee, D., Atkinson, D., Collings, S.E., Eaton, J.W., Gill, A.B., Harvey, I., Hatton, K., Heyes, T. & Wilson, D. (2003) How

important is climate? Effects of warming, nutrient addition and fish on phytoplankton in shallow lake microcosms. *Journal of Applied Ecology,* **40**, 782–792.

Nadelhoffer, K.J., Emmett, B.A., Gundersen, P., Kjonaas, O.J., Koopmans, C.J., Schleppi, P., Tietema A. & Wright, R.F. (1999) Nitrogen deposition makes a minor contribution to carbon sequestration in temperate forests. *Nature,* **398**, 145–148.

Naeem, S., Bunker, D.E., Hector, A., Loreau, M. & Perrings, C. (Editors). (2009) Biodiversity, Ecosystem Functioning, and Human Wellbeing: An Ecological and Economic Perspective. Oxford University Press, Oxford.

Neff, J.C., Townsend, A.R., Gleixner, G., Lehman, S.J., Turnbull, J. & Bowman, W.D. (2002) Variable effects of nitrogen additions on the stability and turnover of soil carbon. *Nature,* **419**, 915–917.

Olff, H., Ritchie, M.E. & Prins, H.H.T. (2002) Global environmental controls of diversity in large herbivores. *Nature,* **415**, 901–904.

Olsgard, F., Schaanning, M.T., Widdicombe, S., Kendall, M.A. & Austen, M.C. (2008) Effects of bottom trawling on ecosystem functioning. *Journal of Experimental Marine Biology and Ecology,* **366**, 123–133.

Orford, J.D. & Pethick, J. (2006) Challenging assumptions of future coastal habitat development around the UK. *Earth Surface Processes and Landforms,* **31**, 1625–1642.

Orr, H.G., Wilby, R.L., McKenzie-Hedger, M. & Brown, I. (2008) Climate change in the uplands: a UK perspective on safeguarding regulatory ecosystem services. *Climate Research,* **37**, 77–98.

Pfeffer, W.T., Harper, J.T. & O'Neel, S. (2008) Kinematic Constraints on Glacier Contributions to 21st-Century Sea-Level Rise. *Science,* **321**, 1340.

Phoenix, G.K., Booth, R.E., Leake, J.R., Read, D.J., Grime, J.P. & Lee, J.A. (2004) Effects of enhanced nitrogen deposition and phosphorus limitation on nitrogen budgets of semi-natural grasslands. *Global Change Biology,* **9**, 1309–1321.

Pimentel, D., Wilson, C., McCullum, C., Huang, R., Dwen, P., Flack, J., Tran, Q., Saltman, T. & Cliff, B. (1997) Economic and environmental benefits of biodiversity. *BioScience,* **47**, 747–757.

Pimentel, D. & Pimentel, M. (2000) Feeding the world's population. *BioScience,* **50**, 387–387.

Polley, H.W., Frank, A.B., Sanabria J. & Phillips R.L. (2008) Interannual variability in carbon dioxide fluxes and flux-climate relationships on grazed and ungrazed northern mixed-prairie. *Global Change Biology,* **14**, 1620–1632.

Post, E. & Forchhammer, M.C. (2008) Climate change reduces reproductive success of an Arctic herbivore through trophic mismatch. *Philosophical Transactions of the Royal Society B-Biological Science,* **363**, 2369–2375.

Pritchard, S.G., Strand, A.E., McCormack, M.L., Davis, M.A., Finzi, A.C., Jackson, R.B., Matamala, R., Rogers, H.H. & Oren, R. (2008) Fine root dynamics in a loblolly pine forest are influenced by Free-Air-CO_2-enrichment: a six year minirhizotron study. *Global Change Biology,* **14**, 588–602.

Proctor, R., Holt, J., Allen, J.I. & Blackford, J. (2003) Nutrient fluxes and budgets for the North West European Shelf from a three dimensional model. *Science of the Total Environment,* **314**, 769–785.

Prosser, C.D., Burek, C.V., Evans, D.H., Gordon, J.E., Kirkbride, V., Rennie, A.F. & Walmsley, C.A. (2010) Conserving geodiversity sites in a changing climate: management challenges and responses. *Geoheritage,* **2**(3–4): 123–136.

Quinton, J.N., Govers, G., Van Ooost, K.V. & Bardgett, R.D. (2010) The impact of agricultural soil erosion on biogeochemical sampling. *Nature Geoscience*, **3**, 311–314.

Rahmstorf, S. (2007) A semi-empirical approach to projecting future sea level rise. *Science*, **315**, 368–370.

Read, D.J., Freer-Smith, P.H., Morison, J.I.L., Hanley, N., West, C.C. & Snowdon, P. (Editors) (2009) Combating climate change – a role for UK forests. An assessment of the potential of the UK's trees and woodlands to mitigate and adapt to climate change. The synthesis report. The Stationery Office, Edinburgh.

Reay, D.S., Dentener, F., Smith, P., Grace, J. & Fely, R.A. (2008) Global nitrogen deposition and carbon sinks. *Nature Geoscience*, **1**, 430–437.

Rennie, A.F. & Hansom, J.D. (In press) Sea level trend reversals: end of the isostatic honeymoon of the Scottish coast? *Geomorphology.*

Reynard, N.S., Kay, A.L. & Crooks, S.M. (2007) Flood risk in the UK: current and future. *WIT Transactions on Ecology and the Environment*, **104**, 299–310.

Robinson, M., Rodda, J.C. & Sutcliffe, J.V. (submitted) Origins of the Plynlimon research catchments and lessons for the future. *Transactions of the Institute of British Geographers.*

RoTAP (Review of Transboundary Air Pollution) (2011) Review of Transboundary Air Pollution: Acidification, Eutrophication, Ground Level Ozone and Heavy Metals in the UK. Contract Report to the Department for Environment, Food and Rural Affairs. Centre for Ecology & Hydrology.

Running, S.W., Ramkrishna, R., Nemani, F.A.H., Maosheng, Z., Reeves, M. & Hirofumi, H. (2004) A continuous satellite-derived measure of global terrestrial primary production. *Bioscience.* **54**, 547–5650.

Schimel, J., Balser, T.C. & Wallenstein, M. (2007) Microbial stress-response physiology and its implications for ecosystem function. *Ecology*, **88**, 1386–1394.

Schindler, D.W. (1977) Evolution of phosphorus limitation in lakes. *Science*, **195**, 260–262.

Scottish Government (2009) The Scottish Soil Framework. [online] Available at: <http://scotland.gov.uk/Publications/2009/05/20145602/13> [Accessed 16.12.10].

SEPA (Scottish Environment Protection Agency) (2009) Trends in Scottish River Water Quality [online] <www.sepa.org.uk/scotlands_environment/data_and_reports/water/scottish_river_water_quality.aspx#totalphosphorus> [Accessed: 16.12.10].

Shevtsova, L., Romanenkov, V., Sirotenko, O., Smith, P., Smith, J.U., Leech, P., Kanzyvaa, S. & Rodionova, V. (2003) Effect of natural and agricultural factors on long-term soil organic matter dynamics in arable soddy-podzolic soils—modelling and observation. *Geoderma*, **116**, 165–189.

Simard, S.W., Jones, M.D. & Durall, D.M. (2002) Carbon and nutrient fluxes within and between mycorrhizal plants. Mycorrhizal Ecology (eds M.G.A. Van der Heijden & I. R. Sanders), pp. 33–74. Ecological Studies 157. Springer Verlag, Heidelberg.

Sinclair, A.H. & Edwards, A.C. (2008) Micronutrient deficiency problems in agricultural crops in Europe. Micronutrient Deficiencies in Global Crop Production (ed B.J. Alloway), pp. 225–244. Springer.

Singh, B.K., Bardgett, R.D., Smith, P. & Reay, D.S. (2010) Microorganisms and climate change: terrestrial feedbacks and mitigation options. *Nature Reviews Microbiology*, **8**, 779–790.

Smart, S., Dunbar, M.J., Emmett, B.A., Marks, S., Maskell, L.C., Norton, L.R., Rose, P. & Simpson I.C. (2010) An Integrated Assessment of Countryside Survey data to investigate Ecosystem Services in Great Britain. Technical Report No. 10/07 NERC/Centre for Ecology & Hydrology 230pp. (CEH Project Number: C03259).

Smart, S.M., Robinson, J.C., Shield, E.J. & van de Poll, H.M. (2003) Locating eutrophication effects across British vegetation between 1990 and 1998. *Global Change Biology*, **9**, 1763–1774.

Smart, S.M., Ashmore, M.R., Scott, W.A., Hornung, M.H., Dragosits, U., Fowler, D., Sutton, M.A., Famulari, D. & Howard, D.C. (2004) Detecting the large-scale signal of atmospheric N deposition across British ecosystems. *Water, Air and Soil Pollution: Focus*, **4**, 269–278.

Smart, S.M., Allen, D., Murphy, J., Carey, P.D., Emmett, B.A., Reynolds, B., Simpson, I.C., Evans, R.A., Skates, J., Scott, W.A., Maskell, L.C., Norton, L.R., Rossall, M.J. & Wood, C. (2009) Countryside Survey: Wales Results from 2007. NERC/Centre for Ecology & Hydrology, Welsh Assembly Government, Countryside Council for Wales, pp. 94 (CEH Project Number: C03259).

Smith, P., Martino, D., Cai, Z., Gwary, D., Janzen, H., Kumar, P., McCarl, B., Ogle, S., O'Mara, F., Rice, C., Scholes, B., Sirotenko, O., Howden, M., McAllister, T., Pan, G., Romanenkov, V., Schneider, U., Towprayoon, S., Wattenbach, M. & Smith, J. (2008a) Greenhouse gas mitigation in agriculture. *Philosophical Transactions of the Royal Society B*, **363**, 789–813.

Smith, P., Smith, J., Flynn, H., Killham, K., Rangel-Castro, I., Foereid, B., Aitkenhead, M., Chapman, S., Towers, W., Bell, J., Lumsdon, D., Milne, R., Thomson, A., Simmons, I., Skiba, U., Reynolds, B., Evans, C., Frogbrook, Z., Bradley, I., Whitmore, A. & Falloon, P. (2007). ECOSSE—Estimating carbon in organic soils sequestration and emissions, 2007. Edinburgh, Scottish Executive Environment and Rural Affairs Department.

Smith, R.S., Shiel, R.S., Bardgett, R.D., Corkhill, P., Evans, P., Quirk, H., Hobbs, P.J. & Kometa, S. (2008b) Long-term change in vegetation and soil microbial communities during the phased restoration of traditional meadow grassland. *Journal of Applied Ecology*, **45**, 670–679.

Smith, S.E. & Read, D.J. (2008) Mycorrhizal Symbiosis. 3rd Edition. Academic Press. London.

Smythe, T.J., Tilstone, G.H. & Groom, S.B. (2005) Integration of radiative transfer into satellite models of ocean primary production. *Journal of Geophysical research – Oceans*, **110**, C10014.

Sowerby, A., Emmett, B.A., Tietema, A. & Bier, C. (2008) Contrasting effects of repeated summer drought on soil carbon efflux in hydric and mesic heathland soils. *Global Change Biology*, **14**, 2388–2404.Staddon, P.L., Jakonsen, I. & Blum, H. (2004) Nitrogen input mediates the effects of free-air CO_2 enrichment on mycorrhizal fungal abundance. *Global Change Biology*, **10**, 1687–1688.

Steinbeiss, S., Bessler, H., Engels, C., Temperton, V.M., Buchmann, N., Roscher, C., Kreutziger, Y., Baade, J., Habekost, M. & Gleixner, G. (2008) Plant diversity positively affects short-term soil carbon storage in experimental grasslands. *Global Change Biology*, **14**, 2937–2949.

Stevens, C.J., Dise, N.D., Mountford, J.O. & Gowing, D.J. (2004) Impact of nitrogen deposition on the species richness of grasslands. *Science*, **303**, 1876–1879.

Thuiller, W., Lavorel, S., Araújo, M.B., Sykes M.T. & Prentice I.C. (2006) Climate change threats to plant diversity in

Europe. *Proceedings of the National Academy of Sciences*, **102**, 8245–8250.

Tilman, D., Hill, J. & Lehman, C. (2006) Carbon-negative biofuels from low-input high-diversity grassland biomass. *Science*, **314**, 1598–1600.

Toberman, H., Evans, C.D., Freeman, C., Fenner, N., White, M., Emmett, B.A. & Artz, R.R.E. (2008) Summer drought effects upon soil and litter extracellular phenol oxidase activity and soluble carbon release in an upland *Calluna* heathland. *Soil Biology & Biochemistry*, **40**, 1519–1532.

Towers, W., Grieve, I.C., Hudson, G., Campbell, C.D., Lilly, A., Davidson, D.A., Bacon, J.R., Langan, S.J. & Hopkins, D.W. (2006) Scotland's Soil Resource – Current State and Threats. Report to Scottish Executive. [online] Available at: <http://www.scotland.gov.uk/Publications/2006/09/21115639/> [Accessed 16.12.10].

Treseder, K.K. (2008) Nitrogen additions and microbial biomass: a meta-analysis of ecosystem studies. *Ecology Letters*, **11**, 1111–1120.

Tylianakis, J.M., Didham, R.K., Bascompte, J. & Wardle, D.A. (2008) Global change and species interactions in terrestrial ecosystems. *Ecology Letters*, **11**, 1351–1363.

UKCP09 (United Kingdom Climate Projections) [online] Available at: <http://ukclimateprojections.defra.gov.uk/> [Accessed: 16.10.12].

Van der Heijden, M.G.A., Bardgett, R.D. & van Straalen, N.M. (2008) The unseen majority: soil microbes as drivers of plant diversity and productivity in terrestrial ecosystems. *Ecology Letters,* **11**, 296–310.

Van der Wal, R., Pearce, I.S.K., Brooker, R., Scott, D., Welch, D. & Woodin, D.J. (2003) Interplay between nitrogen deposition and grazing causes habitat degradation. *Ecology Letters,* **6**, 141–146.

Vaughan, I.P., Diamond, M., Gurnell, A.M., Hall, K.A., Jenkins, A., Milner, N.J., Naylor, L.A., Sear, D.A., Woodward, G. & Ormerod, S.J. (2009) Integrating ecology with hydromorphology: a priority for river science and management. *Aquatic Conservation: Marine and Freshwater Ecosystems*, **19**, 113–125.

Verheijen, F., Jones, R. Rickson, R. & Smith, C. (2009) Tolerable versus actual soil erosion rates in Europe. *Earth-Science Reviews*, **94**, 23–38.

Visser, M.E. & Both, C. (2005) Shifts in phenology due to global climate change: the need for a yardstick. *Proceedings of the Royal Society B- Biological Sciences,* **272**, 2561–2569.

Ward, S.E., Bardgett, R.D., McNamara, N.P., Adamson, J.K. & Ostle, N.J. (2007) Long-term consequences of grazing and burning on northern peatland carbon dynamics. *Ecosystems*, **10**, 1069–1083.

Wardle, D.A. & Zackrisson, O. (2005) Effects of species and functional group loss on island ecosystem properties. *Nature*, **435**, 806–810.

Wardle, D.A., Bardgett, R.D., Klironomos, J.N., Setälä, H., van der Putten, W.H. & Wall, D.H. (2004) Ecological linkages between aboveground and belowground biota. *Science*, **304**, 1629–1633.

Whitmore, A.P. & Whalley, W.R. (2009) Physical effects of soil drying on roots and crop growth. *Journal of Experimental Botany*, **60**, 2845–2857.

Wilkinson, B.H. & McElroy, B.J. (2007) The impact of humans on continental erosion and sedimentation. *The Geological Society of America Bulletin*, **119**, 140–156.

Willis, A.J., Dunnett, N.P., Hunt, R. & Grime, J.P. (1995) Does Gulf Stream position affect vegetation dynamics in Western Europe? *Oikos,* **73**, 408–410.

Wohlfarht, G., Anderson-Dunn, M., Bahn, M., Balzarolo, M., Berninger, F., Cambell, C., Carrara, A., Cescatti, A., Christensen, T., Dore, S., Eugster, W., Friborg, T., Furger, M., Gianelle, D., Gimeno, C., Hargreaves, K., Hari, P., Haslwanter, A., Johansson, T., Marcolla, B., Milford, C., Nagy, Z., Nemitz, E., Rogiers, N., Sanz, M.J., Siegwolf, R.T.W., Susiluoto, S., Sutton, M., Tuba, Z., Ugolini, F., Valentini, R. Zorer, R. & Cernusca, A. (2008) Biotic, abiotic, and management controls on the net ecosystem CO_2 exchange of European mountain grassland ecosystems. *Ecosystems,* **11**, 1338–1351.

Woodward, F.I., Bardgett, R.D., Raven, J.A. & Hetherington, A.M. (2009) Biological approaches to global environment change mitigation and remediation. *Current Biology*, **19**, R615–R623.

Woodward, G., Perkins, D.M. & L.E. Brown. (2010) Climate change and freshwater ecosystems: impacts across multiple levels of organisation. *Philosophical Transactions of the Royal Society B- Biological Sciences*, **365**, 2093–2106.

Zhao, F.J., McGrath, S.P., Blake-Kalff, M.M.A., Link, A. & Tucker, M. (2002) Crop responses to sulphur fertilisation in Europe. Proceedings No. 504. International Fertiliser Society. York.

Zogg, D.G., Zak, D.R., Pregitzer, K.S. & Burton, A.J. 2000. Microbial immobilisation and the retention of anthropogenic nitrate in a northern hardwood forest. Ecology, **81**, 1858–1866.

Appendix 13.1 Approach Used to Assign Certainty Terms to Chapter Key Findings

This chapter began with a set of Key Findings. Adopting the approach and terminology used by the Intergovernmental Panel on Climate Change (IPCC) and the Millennium Assessment (MA), these Key Findings also include an indication of the level of scientific certainty. The 'uncertainty approach' of the UK NEA consists of a set of qualitative uncertainty terms derived from a 4-box model and complemented, where possible, with a likelihood scale (see below). Estimates of certainty are derived from the collective judgement of authors, observational evidence, modelling results and/or theory examined for this assessment.

Throughout the Key Findings presented at the start of this chapter, superscript numbers and letters indicate the estimated level of certainty for a particular key finding:

1. *Well established:*   high agreement based on significant evidence
2. *Established but incomplete evidence:* high agreement based on limited evidence
3. *Competing explanations:*   low agreement, albeit with significant evidence
4. *Speculative:*   low agreement based on limited evidence

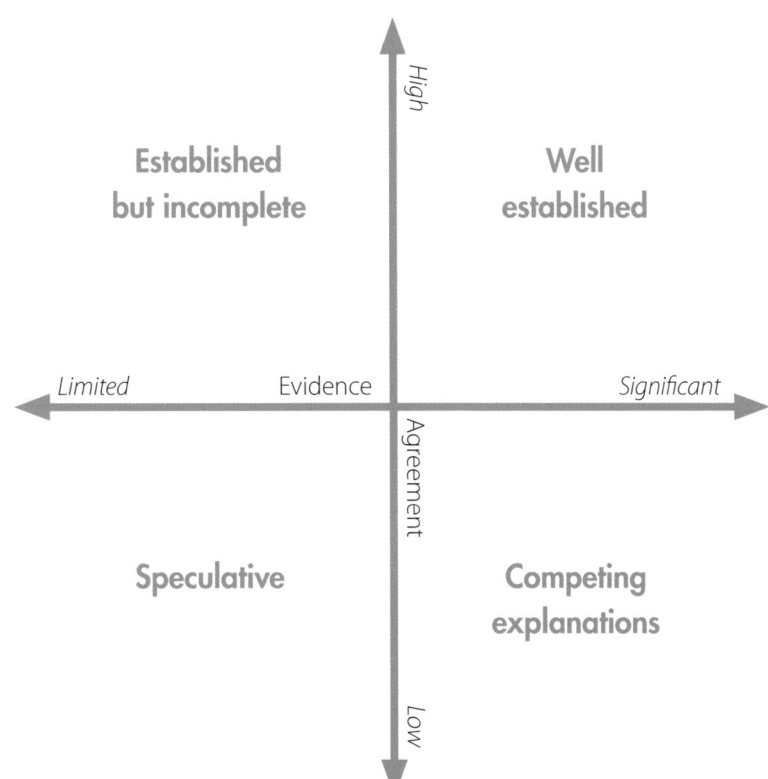

a. *Virtually certain:*   >99% probability of occurrence
b. *Very likely:*   >90% probability
c. *Likely:*   >66% probability
d. *About as likely as not:*   >33–66% probability
e. *Unlikely:*   <33% probability
f. *Very unlikely:*   <10% probability
g. *Exceptionally unlikely:*   <1% probability

Certainty terms 1 to 4 constitute the 4-box model, while *a* to *g* constitute the likelihood scale.

Chapter 14:
Regulating Services

Coordinating Lead Author: Pete Smith
Lead Authors: Mike Ashmore, Helaina Black, Paul Burgess, Chris Evans, Rosemary Hails, Simon G. Potts, Timothy Quine and Amanda Thomson
Contributing Authors: Koos Biesmeijer, Tom Breeze, Mark Broadmeadow, Robert Ferrier, Jim Freer, Jim Hansom, Phil Haygarth, Helen Hesketh, Kevin Hicks, Andrew Johnson, David Kay, William Kunin, Allan Lilly, Linda May, Jane Memmott, Harriet Orr, Roger Pickup, Beth Purse and Geoff Squire

Key Findings*

The regulating services provided by ecosystems are extremely diverse. Their status and trends, drivers and consequences of change, effective management, and knowledge gaps differ greatly There are differences even among indicators within individual regulating services, as can be observed, for example, with the various components of water quality including acidity, pollutants and sediment. The services are, therefore, reported independently, although relevant interactions (particularly between air, soil and water quality regulation) are noted.

Ecosystems regulate climate by: i) providing sources or sinks of greenhouse gases (affecting global warming) and sources of aerosols (affecting temperature and cloud formation); and ii) their physical characteristics which can regulate local and regional climate. The UK has large amounts of carbon 'locked up' in its forests, peatlands and soils (114 megatonnes Carbon (Mt C) in vegetation; 9,838 ± 2,463 Mt C in soils)[1]. Projected changes in emissions (under a 'business as usual' scenario) from the land use and forestry sector over the next ten years could switch this sector from being a net sink of carbon dioxide to a source[c]. The effects of a failure in climate regulation services globally would be particularly pronounced in urban areas, and would exacerbate climate stress for large numbers of people. There are a wide range of sustainable management options to improve climate regulation services, which would also benefit other ecosystem services. Our main knowledge gaps concern the effects of land use management (rather than land use change) on greenhouse gas emissions and removals, and the quantification of the climate regulation provided by urban, coastal and marine ecosystems around the UK.

[1] well established
[c] likely

The capacity to regulate water, nutrient, pollutant and sediment transfer from the land surface continues to be compromised by soil degradation[2] and contributes to fluvial flood risk. The ability of the soft landforms of the UK coast to regulate erosion (17% currently eroding) and mitigate flood and storm damage is threatened by sea-level rise, changes in the frequency and severity of storms, and low sediment availability[2]. Assessment of the current and future delivery of hazard regulation is limited by our knowledge of coast and upland condition; our understanding of rates and pathways of recovery from degradation; and the need to quantitatively understand the effects of extreme events.

[2] established but incomplete evidence

Ecosystems regulate pests and diseases, but this service is under threat. Agricultural intensification, human population growth, accidental introduction of pest and pathogen organisms and land and wildlife management are currently important drivers of disease and pest incidence. Changes in climate are likely to become more important over the next few decades, as recently witnessed for vector-borne diseases. For example, relatively innocuous weeds at the base of the arable food web have declined due to the more frequent use of broader spectrum herbicides, with likely impacts on wider biodiversity[1]. The inadvertent import of fungal plant pathogens via live plant material is arguably one of the most significant loopholes in terms of biosecurity[d]. Understanding how to better manage ecosystems to control pests and pathogens requires detailed longitudinal field studies to describe host-pest and host-pathogen interactions and to understand how these alter in response to environmental changes.

[1] well established
[d] about as likely as not

Both managed pollinators (honey bees) and wild pollinators (primarily non-managed bees and hoverflies) have been in severe decline for the past 30 years and it is very likely that this trend will continue[1]. Twenty percent of the UK cropped area comprises pollinator-dependent crops, and a high proportion of wild flowering plants depend on insect pollination for reproduction. However, the overall extent of pollination limitation in crops and wildflowers has not been quantified in the UK. The value of pollinators to UK agriculture is conservatively estimated to be £430 million per annum. There are multiple drivers of pollinator loss including loss of semi-natural habitat, the introduction of pathogens, inappropriate use of agrochemicals and climate change[2].

[1] well established
[2] established but incomplete evidence

---

* Each Key Finding has been assigned a level of scientific certainty, based on a 4-box model and complemented, where possible, with a likelihood scale. Superscript numbers and letters indicate the uncertainty term assigned to each finding. Full details of each term and how they were assigned are presented in Appendix 14.1.

Noise, or unwanted sound, can have a negative effect on human well-being[1] and certain bird species[2], but can be regulated by ecosystems. Actual spatial measurements of noise are very limited, but national models consistently suggest that noise and visual intrusion has increased[a] as urbanisation, including road traffic, has increased. Ecosystems adjacent to roads (created by tree planting and the use of soil bunds) can reduce some of the effects of road traffic noise[2]. Sounds produced and moderated by ecosystems can also be considered as a cultural service: some natural sounds, such as bird song, are considered positively[2]. In this context, noise can be considered a "disservice".

[1] *well established*
[2] *established but incomplete evidence*
[a] *virtually certain*

Soil quality is linked to almost all other regulating services (e.g. nutrient cycling, biomass production, water quality, climate regulation, pollination, etc.) through the soil's capacity to buffer, filter and transform. Soil quality in all UK NEA Broad Habitats has been degraded by human actions over the last 50 years[1], primarily by atmospheric pollution and inappropriate management practices[b]. Ecosystems are involved in regulating soil quality at all scales. If soil quality is degraded, then soils' capacity to buffer, filter and transform chemical substances is reduced[2]. The trends[2] indicate that recovery from, and remediation of, both diffuse and point source pollution is in progress[c]. There is insufficient and speculative knowledge regarding the recovery of soils under a changing climate; uppermost among these are the competing explanations for the changes in, and vulnerability of, UK's soil carbon stocks and the role of soil in purifying water resources.

[1] *well established*
[b] *very likely*
[2] *established but incomplete evidence*
[c] *likely*

Ecosystems can have positive effects on air quality, primarily through interception, deposition and removal of pollutants. However, if the rate of deposition of pollutants exceeds critical thresholds, there may be adverse effects on a range of other ecosystem services. Emissions to the atmosphere from ecosystems can also directly and indirectly degrade air quality. Although there have been significant improvements in UK air quality over recent decades, current concentrations and deposition rates still exceed thresholds for effects on human health, crop and forest production, and biodiversity over significant areas of the country[1b]. The national improvements in air quality are primarily due to reduced anthropogenic emissions from the transport and energy sectors[1b]. In contrast, the main drivers of changes in the ecosystem service of air quality regulation over recent decades are likely to have been those changes in land use and management which influence deposition and emission of pollutants. It is likely that there are local benefits of tree planting for air quality in urban areas and close to point sources of pollution; these benefits have been quantified for individual air pollutants[2]. However, the overall national benefits of ecosystem regulation for air quality, and for its health and ecological impacts, are very uncertain.

[1] *well established,*
[b] *very likely*
[2] *established but incomplete evidence*

Since the 1980s, water quality has improved in the uplands because lower atmospheric pollution levels in these areas enable terrestrial ecosystems to buffer lakes and streams against acidification and nitrate leaching[1]. In the lowlands, water quality improvements have largely been driven by better control of point source pollution, rather than improved ecosystem regulation of diffuse pollutants[1]. Widespread increases in upland dissolved organic carbon concentrations have had negative consequences for water treatment, but appear linked to soil recovery from acidification[3]. The key regulating service of pollutant dilution by water flow is maximised by land management that increases infiltration rates; this also reduces phosphorous, sediment and faecal pollutant losses via overland flow[1]. However, these ecosystem services are likely to be degraded in the future by more extreme droughts and high flows due to climate change.

[1] *well established*
[3] *competing explanations*

While there are a number of synergies between regulating services (e.g. tree planting can improve air quality, reduce noise and sequester carbon for climate regulation), there are also a number of trade-offs (e.g. improvements in soil buffering of water quality as a result of decreased acid deposition may cause more carbon to be released from upland soils).

---

* Each Key Finding has been assigned a level of scientific certainty, based on a 4-box model and complimented, where possible, with a likelihood scale. Superscript numbers indicate the uncertainty term assigned to each finding. Full details of each term and how they were assigned is presented in Appendix 14.1.

14.1 Regulating Services and Human Well-being

A number of regulating services either act as final ecosystem services, such as climate regulation and hazard regulation, or contribute significantly to final ecosystem services, such as water quantity (which is also a provisioning service), detoxification and purification (arising from air, water and soil quality). Other regulating services are primary or intermediate ecosystem services, such as the effects of pollination and pests and diseases on regulating the provision of crops, other plants and livestock.

In this chapter, we focus on eight regulating services which map on to the Millennium Ecosystem Assessment (MA) (2005) regulating services, as supplemented by further ecosystem service research frameworks in the EU and the UK[1]. These are discussed in detail in Chapter 2. The regulating services considered in this assessment are as follows:

Climate regulation is a final ecosystem service. It provides goods and services that regulate climate so that adverse impacts on human well-being and biodiversity are avoided. Ecosystems regulate climate through biogeochemical effects and biophysical effects (MA 2005; **Table 14.1**). Biogeochemical effects operate at the regional or global scale, while biophysical effects operate at the local or regional scale. Local effects in particular assist in the avoidance of climate stress. Climate regulation has strong links with the other regulating services and with provisioning services.

Hazard regulation is a final ecosystem service that provides the following goods and services: coastal protection, erosion protection, flood protection, and to a lesser extent,

the avoidance of climate stress. The regulating ecosystem services associated with individual hazards are defined in **Table 14.2**. This framework of services is used to consider the capacity for regulation of the associated hazards.

Disease and pest regulation is an intermediate ecosystem service which directly affects human health and well-being (in the case of human pests and diseases) and has a potentially large impact on regulating the provision of final ecosystem services, such as crops, other plants and livestock, which deliver food and fibre, amongst other things. This regulating service largely relates to the role of ecosystems in regulating the incidence and spread of insect pests of crops and pathogens of consequence to humans, livestock, crops and ecosystems.

Pollination is a primary or intermediate ecosystem service which has a potentially large impact on regulating the provision of final ecosystem services, such as crops and other plants, which deliver food and fibre. This regulating service largely relates to the role of ecosystems in regulating the incidence and spread of wild and managed insect pollinators. The honeybee is the only species of pollinator that is widely managed; the majority of pollination services are provided by wild bees and other insects. Diversity within wild communities of pollinators provides resilience against environmental change and can be supported through the provision of natural and semi-natural habitats, including agri-environment schemes, which provide a range of flower communities.

Noise regulation is considered as a final regulating ecosystem service in this report. However, the sounds produced and moderated by ecosystems could also be considered as a 'cultural service' as some natural sounds are considered beneficial. Noise, i.e. unwanted sound, can be considered a 'disservice'.

Soil quality regulation is a primary or intermediate regulating service which has a pivotal role in delivering regulating services through the storage and degradation of organic

Table 14.1 Biogeochemical and biophysical mechanisms through which ecosystems regulate climate.

Biogeochemical effects	Sources or sinks of GHGs affect radiative forcing and leads to climate warming
	Sources of aerosols that can reflect or trap solar radiation (warming or cooling effect) and affect cloud formation
Biophysical effects	**Local**
	Provision of shade from heat and UV light
	Provision of shelter from wind and precipitation
	Regulation of temperature
	Regulation of humidity and precipitation
	Regional/global
	Surface albedo—affects radiative forcing and temperature
	Evapotranspiration—affects radiative forcing, cloud formation and precipitation
	Surface roughness—affects winds

Table 14.2 The regulating ecosystem services associated with individual hazards.

Hazard	Ecosystem Service (how ecosystems reduce the hazard)
Mass movements, coastal erosion and flooding	The service is the maintenance of the integrity of landsurfaces (regolith and landforms)
Soil erosion	The service is soil retention on the land surface that is evident in two further services: i) maintenance of 'intact' soil cover while allowing for gradual evolution (on timescales of natural soil formation); ii) maintenance of low suspended sediment loads in fluvial systems
Runoff generation and flooding	The service is water retention and storage and delayed release from the land surface and attenuation of peaks as floodwater passes through river networks

1 http://naturalengland.etraderstores.com/NaturalEnglandShop/R701; www.ecosystemservices.org.uk

matter, mediating exchange of gases to the atmosphere, storing, degrading and transforming materials such as nutrients and contaminants, and regulating the flow of water. This regulating service largely relates to the role of ecosystems in regulating soil quality, and contributes significantly to other final ecosystem services, such as climate regulation, detoxification and purification, as well as the provision of crops and other plants (delivering, for example, food and fibre), trees, standing vegetation and peat.

Air quality regulation is a primary or intermediate regulating service that influences the atmospheric concentrations of air pollutants and their deposition to land and water surfaces. Nationally, the most significant pollutants are particles, ozone, nitrogen oxides, ammonia, and nitrogen and sulphur, the deposition of which can lead to ecosystem acidification and eutrophication. Ecosystems contribute to air quality because they remove pollutants from the atmosphere: gases and particles are deposited to ecosystem (primarily plant) surfaces, and pollutant gases enter leaves through stomata. The extent of this removal depends on a number of factors, including the turbulence of the air above the ecosystem (taller vegetation has a greater efficiency), the duration of leaf cover (evergreen tree species are more effective than deciduous species), and the stomatal aperture of the vegetation (deposition may decrease under drought conditions). However, this deposition or uptake into the leaf can have negative effects on other ecosystem services if critical thresholds are exceeded. The deposited or absorbed pollutants may be detoxified (e.g. ozone), assimilated by plants or microbial activity (e.g. nitrogen oxides and ammonia), or simply accumulate within the ecosystem (e.g. lead and other metals). The detoxification process may occur at the expense of utilising resources for plant growth, therefore, decreasing production, while assimilation may differentially increase the growth of different plant species, changing competition and leading to a loss of less competitive species. Ecosystems can also have negative effects on air quality due to emissions to the atmosphere, which increase air concentrations either directly or indirectly through chemical reactions in the atmosphere. Therefore, ecosystems contribute to final ecosystem services such as detoxification and purification. Because this regulatory service affects the concentrations and deposition of air pollutants, it may, in turn, affect the provision of final ecosystem services such as the production of crops and the growth and biomass of trees.

Water quality regulation is a primary or intermediate regulating service determined primarily by catchment processes. It is, therefore, intimately linked to other ecosystem services addressed in this section (e.g. soil and air quality, climate regulation) and elsewhere in the report (e.g. nutrient cycling (Chapter 13)). Key ecosystem processes regulating water quality include plant and microbial nutrient uptake, pollutant sequestration in soil and sediment organic matter, breakdown of organic pollutants, acidity buffering and denitrification. These processes contribute to final ecosystem services including detoxification and purification, drinking water and fisheries provision, and recreation (e.g. bathing waters).

Numerous cultural services (Chapter 16) are also supported by ensuring good water, air and soil quality, including physical health, mental health, ecological knowledge, cultural heritage and mediated natures, and aesthetic and inspirational.

In the following sections, we examine each regulating service in turn and describe: i) the condition, status and trends; ii) drivers of change; iii) consequences of change; iv) knowledge gaps, and v) sustainable management for each regulating service. We conclude with a section summarising the key synergies and trade-offs between different regulating services, and between key regulating services and other ecosystem services. And we consider how regulating services might be managed to promote synergies and minimise trade-offs.

14.2 Climate Regulation

14.2.1 Trends in Climate Regulating Services

The biosphere, and the ecosystems within it, regulate climate by controlling the flux of GHGs (principally carbon dioxide, but also methane and nitrous oxide), sources of aerosols and the transfer of heat, moisture and momentum (Burroughs 2001; Houghton 2004; Beaumont *et al.* 2007; Bonan 2008; Fowler *et al.* 2009). Ecosystems also regulate microclimate, dampening temperature extremes and providing shade and shelter. The processes involved in climate regulation include:

- Photosynthesis which is the fundamental process affecting levels of carbon dioxide in the atmosphere. Through negative feedback, the biosphere can also act as a temporary sink for additional carbon dioxide entering the atmosphere from fossil fuel combustion.
- Marine organisms acting as a carbon sink in the ocean and facilitating carbon burial in seabed sediments.
- Evapotranspiration from soil and plants which controls the amount of water vapour entering the atmosphere, regulating cloud formation and the radiative properties of the atmosphere.
- The albedo values of different land surfaces (i.e. the proportion of incoming solar radiation that is reflected from the Earth's surface). A change in albedo, through a change in vegetation for example, can have a cooling or heating effect on the surface climate and may affect precipitation.
- The production of aerosols by ecosystems from soil erosion or vegetation, and the regulation of aerosols through vegetation scavenging, which affects radiative heating of the atmosphere and surface albedo (Bonan 2008; Section 14.8).

Nearly 10 billion tonnes of carbon is stored in UK soils (Dawson & Smith 2007): over half of this occurs in organic soils (Smith *et al.* 2007) predominantly in Scotland and Wales (**Figure 14.1**). Soil carbon densities are greatest under semi-natural habitats (Mountains, Moorlands and Heaths, Semi-natural Grasslands, wetlands) and Woodland habitats (including those with peat soils) and lower under Enclosed Farmland and Urban habitats (**Figure 14.2**). There are significant biomass carbon stocks in the forest plantations planted during the 20th Century (150 million tonnes). Soil carbon densities and storage can be high in Coastal Margin habitats, but they are limited in extent. There will be considerable carbon stores in the Marine habitats around the UK but these have yet to be quantified. The marine ecosystem balances and maintains the chemical composition of the atmosphere and oceans (Beaumont *et al.* 2008).

The management of ecosystems can result in emissions of GHGs through the cultivation of previously undisturbed soils, peat extraction or the production of methane by ruminant livestock, amongst other things. Or it can counter emissions through removals, for example, via forest planting and the removal of land from cultivation (**Box 14.1**). Ecosystem products such as timber and biomass crops, can also store carbon or replace other products with higher emission costs. Peat bogs are the only major soil source of methane in the UK, but the soil sink for methane is insignificant in this country (Fowler *et al.* 2008).

Setting aside existing long-term carbon stores, UK ecosystems have produced an increasing net sink of carbon dioxide since 1990, as reported in the Land Use, Land Use Change and Forestry (LULUCF) sector of the UK Greenhouse Gas (GHG) Emissions Inventory (Jackson *et al.* 2009; MacCarthy *et al.* 2010).This sector is projected to become a net source by 2014 under a 'Business As Usual' scenario (Thomson *et al.* 2010) as afforestation rates have slowed and large areas of conifer plantations are reaching maturity, leading to a declining rate of net carbon uptake by UK forests. The Cropland and Settlement land use categories are net sources, while the Forest Land and Grassland categories are net sinks. Among the countries of the UK, England is a net source of carbon dioxide (although this has diminished from 1990 to 2007), whereas Scotland, Wales and Northern Ireland are net sinks. Methane emissions from ruminant livestock are a major source of GHGs from agriculture, but have reduced by 13% since 1990 in line with livestock numbers (Jackson *et al.* 2009; MacCarthy *et al.* 2010). Nitrous oxide emissions from agricultural soils arise from nitrogen application, leaching of fertiliser and manure to ground and surface water, ploughing in crop residues, atmospheric deposition of ammonia and nitrogen oxides, cultivation of highly organic soils and biological fixation in improved grass. These sources are the largest contributors to nitrous oxide emissions across the UK, from 64% in England to 81% in Northern Ireland. They contribute 3–9% of the total 2007 GHG emissions in each country. But overall, nitrous oxide emissions have decreased by 23% since 1990, a decline driven by a fall in synthetic fertiliser application and reduced livestock numbers. Enclosed agricultural land has the greatest nitrous oxide emissions, with woodlands, mountains, moorlands and heaths contributing less than 5% to the total soil emissions (Sozanska *et al.* 2002).

The status and trends in climate regulation by habitat are summarised in **Table 14.3**. More detail is given in Chapters 5 to 12.

14.2.2 Drivers of Change

The direct drivers of change in climate regulation and their effects are summarised in **Table 14.4**. Full descriptions of these drivers and the related indirect drivers of change are given in Chapter 3. Land use drivers are the most immediately important in the ecosystem context, but over

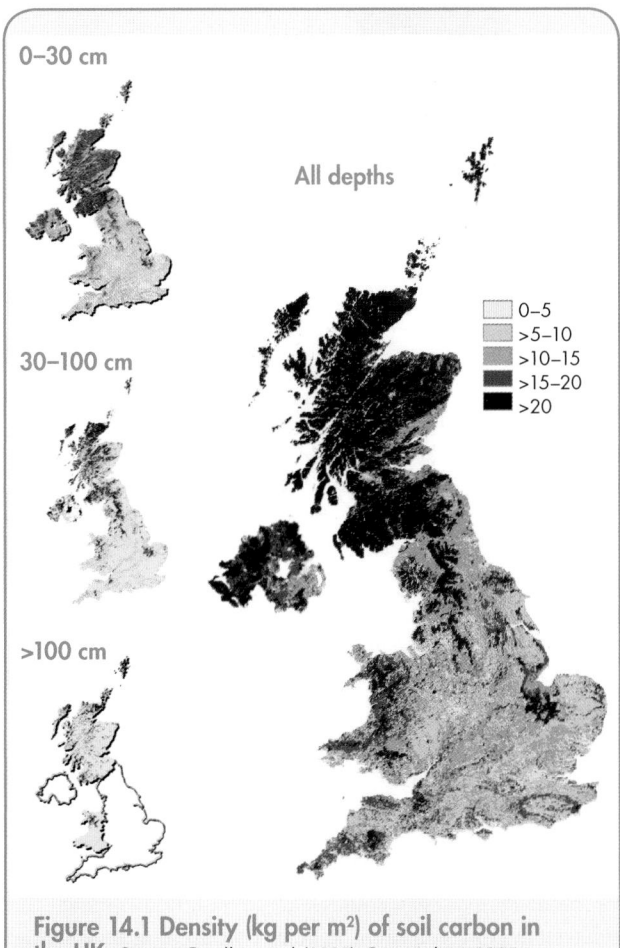

Figure 14.1 Density (kg per m²) of soil carbon in the UK. Source: Bradley *et al.* (2005). Copyright © 2005 British Society of Soil Science. Reproduced with permission of Blackwell Publishing Ltd.

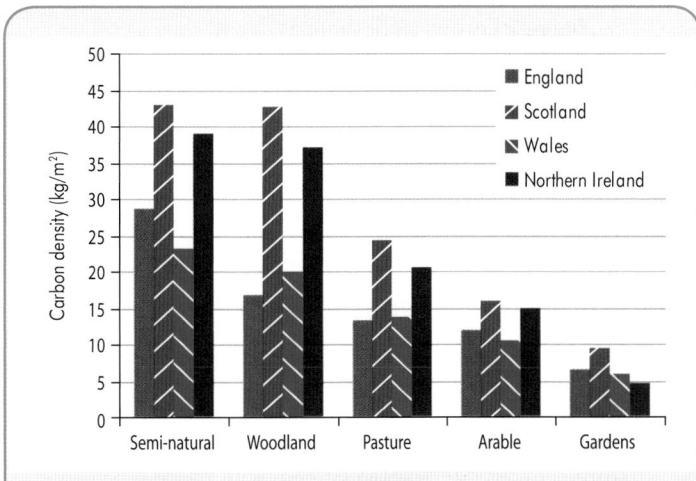

Figure 14.2 Soil carbon density 0–100 cm under different land use types in the UK. Source: data from Bradley *et al.* (2005) and Smith *et al.* (2007). Copyright © 2005 British Society of Soil Science. Reproduced with permission of Blackwell Publishing Ltd.

Box 14.1 The UK greenhouse gas inventory.

The UK produces annual inventories and projections of GHG emissions. These help monitor progress on reducing emissions for international and national targets, e.g. the Kyoto Protocol of the UN Framework Convention on Climate Change and targets in the UK Climate Change Act. The national inventory (MacCarthy *et al.* 2010) has six sectors:

- Energy
- Industrial Processes
- Solvent and Other Product Use
- Agriculture
- Land Use, Land Use Change and Forestry (LULUCF)
- Waste

It follows the methods developed by the Intergovernmental Panel on Climate Change. Emissions are reported for 1990 to the present, and projections to 2020.

The LULUCF sector reports carbon stock changes of carbon dioxide (can be emissions or removals) and emissions of methane and nitrous oxide from land use activities (Figure 1 and Figure 2). The broad categories for reporting are:

- Forestry
- Cropland
- Grassland
- Settlements

Wetland areas are included under Grassland. Emission estimates are made using models driven by activity data from government agencies, such as the Forestry Commission.

More information is available at: www.edinburgh.ceh.ac.uk/ukcarbon

Figure 1 UK LULUCF emissions and removals in Gigagrams of carbon dioxide (Gg CO₂) from 1990 to 2008. Source: reproduced from MacCarthy et al. (2010) © NERC (CEH).

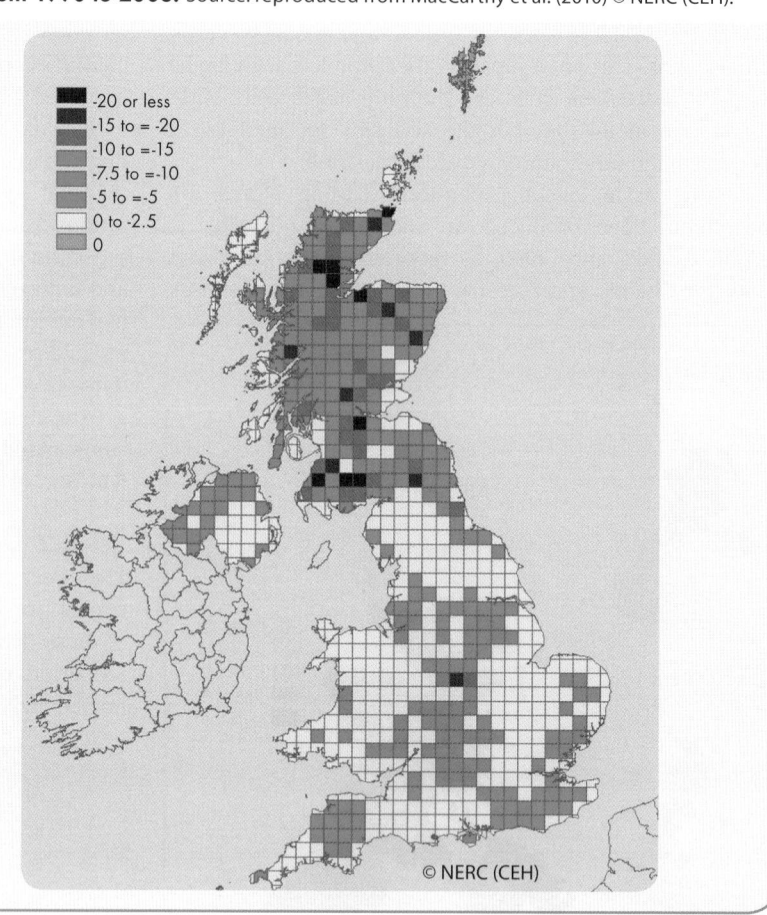

Figure 2 Carbon stock changes due to Article 3.3 Afforestation in the UK from 1990 to 2007. Carbon stock changes modelled on planting data from the Forestry Commission. Source: reproduced from Dyson *et al.* (2009).

---

the longer term, climate change will also feedback to climate regulation services (Schröter *et al.* 2005).

14.2.3 Consequences of Change

The increased levels of GHGs in the atmosphere as a result of human action (burning fossil fuel and land use change) during the past 200 years are resulting in climate change on a global scale (IPCC 2007a). Global climate change threatens all human populations, with those most affected often having contributed least to the problem (IPCC 2007b). Ecosystem services that regulate GHGs can affect the whole atmosphere, not just that above a specific region, so national policies have global consequences.

The effects of climate regulation are particularly pronounced in urban areas. A reduction in climate regulation services could exacerbate climate stress for large numbers of people, reducing well-being and increasing death rates (for example, through higher summer temperatures). Urban areas in southern England are probably at greatest risk.

Changes in temperature and moisture regimes will shift ecosystem boundaries and have consequences for biodiversity. This could lead to potential changes in ecosystem composition as species that are operating at the edges of their climatic range lose or gain ground. Under a warmer climate this could particularly affect biodiversity in the Mountain, Moorlands and Heaths (Chapter 5),

Table 14.3 The status and trends in climate regulation by UK NEA Broad Habitat. The status includes UK NEA uncertainty terms.

UK NEA Broad Habitat	Status		Trends in climate regulation
Mountains, Moorlands and Heaths	+	Positive (extensive carbon stores, few other GHG emissions) (*established but incomplete, very likely*).	Losses of carbon storage potential in past (particularly in England) but this trend is potentially reversing with increased focus on peatland restoration.
Semi-natural Grasslands	− / +	Mixed. Significant carbon stores under acid grasslands (*established but incomplete, likely*), but also GHG emissions from livestock, nitrogen fertilisation and liming.	Probably stable. Loss of carbon storage capacity has occurred in the past but not recently (according to Carey *et al.* 2007).
Enclosed Farmland	−	Overall negative impact on with high emissions of GHGs from agricultural management and low carbon stocks in soils (*well established, very likely*).	Continuing loss of carbon storage capacity in soils. Loss of shelter from degradation of hedgerows and shelterbelts. Reduced methane emissions due to reductions in livestock numbers.
Woodlands	+	Positive (extensive stores and sequestration of carbon in vegetation and soils), provision of shade and shelter (*well established, very likely*).	Increasing trend over time due to extensive tree planting in past 50 years.
Freshwaters—Openwaters, Wetlands and Floodplains	+	Positive (extensive carbon stores) (*well established, very likely*). Also affect regional climate (cooling effect, reduced evaporation, modifies cloud cover).	Losses of carbon storage potential in past but this trend is potentially reversing with increased focus on wetland restoration.
Urban	−	Overall negative impact: the urban heat island effect increases climate stress, but there can be significant quantities of carbon stored in vegetation and soils in urban areas (*competing explanations*). Urban greenspace can have high levels of GHG emissions due to the use of fertilisers and drainage.	Negative trend over time.
Coastal Margins	+	Positive, can have high rates of carbon sequestration but total area is small (*established but incomplete*).	Decrease in area has led to loss of carbon storage in the past but managed realignment may increase area of saltmarshes (and carbon storage capacity).
Marine	+	Positive (extensive carbon stores and uptake of atmospheric carbon dioxide), also affect regional climate (weather patterns).	Continuing uptake of carbon dioxide but ocean acidification may lead to functional changes in the future.

Table 14.4 Direct drivers of change in climate regulation and their effects.

Driver category	Driver of change	Effect on climate regulation	UK NEA Broad Habitats most affected
Habitat change: Land and sea use	Productive area: expansion, conversion, abandonment (agriculture, forestry)	Affects carbon sinks and existing stores, GHG emissions, albedo and evapotranspiration, shade and shelter	Semi-natural Grassland Enclosed Farmland Woodlands Freshwaters Marine
	Mineral and aggregate extraction (peat)	Affects soil carbon stores, GHG emissions	Mountains, Moorlands and Heaths Freshwaters
	Urbanisation and artificial sealed surfaces	Affects soil carbon stores, albedo, shade, shelter, local temperatures and humidity	Urban
Pollution and nutrient enrichment	Pollution emissions and deposition	Affects aerosol sources (soot)	Urban
	Nutrient and chemical inputs	Affects GHG emissions	Enclosed Farmland
Harvest levels/resource consumption	Livestock stocking rates	Affects GHG emissions	Semi-natural Grasslands Enclosed Farmland
Climate variability and change	Temperature and precipitation	Affects existing carbon stores, evapotranspiration	All
	Carbon dioxide and ocean acidification	Affects existing carbon stores, GHG emissions, aerosol sources	Marine
	Sea-level change	Affects existing carbon stores	Coastal Margins

and Coastal Margin (Chapter 11) habitats. Rising sea temperatures are already affecting species distributions in the marine environment (Chapter 12).

Threats to the integrity of the UK's carbon stores (particularly deep peats) have the potential to release massive amounts of carbon dioxide into the atmosphere—the carbon equivalent of five years' worth of England's annual carbon dioxide emissions is stored in English peatlands alone (584 million tonnes of carbon) (Natural England 2010). Habitat restoration of degraded ecosystems with deep peats (Chapter 5) could also enhance their carbon sink potential and counter other emissions. However, in some cases, restoration achieved through raising water levels in deep peats may result in methane release through other mechanisms, resulting in a net GHG source in the short-term (10–30 years), although the long-term balance will be positive due to increased carbon sequestration.

Changes in carbon sinks may affect other ecosystem services: for example, land use change may initiate erosion, affecting soil, water or air quality and/or increasing vulnerability to hazards like flooding (although these are avoidable if change is sensitively undertaken). Conversion of semi-natural habitats to agricultural land uses can result in losses of both carbon stocks and biodiversity: a lose-lose situation. Some changes which have produced a net carbon sink, such as the widespread planting of non-native conifers, have had adverse effects on biodiversity (a win-lose situation) with area lost from Mountains, Moorlands and Heaths and Semi-natural Grassland habitats as well as broadleaved woodland.

14.2.4 Options for Sustainable Management

There are already efforts in place to encourage the biogeochemical aspects of climate regulation that will reduce GHG emissions and enhance GHG sinks. The UK has international commitments under the terms of the Kyoto Protocol, as well as domestic targets for reducing emissions, and each of the devolved administrations is in the process of developing national targets and climate change strategies (HM Government 2009; DECC 2009; Scottish Government 2009; WAG in press). Responsibility for agriculture and forestry is devolved to individual countries where sector emission reduction targets are still being developed; for example, English farmers have an emission reduction target of 6% below current predictions by 2020 under the Low Carbon Transition Plan (HM Government 2009; CCTF 2010). Management options for UK forestry are reviewed in Read *et al.* (2009), and each country has developed its own forestry strategy: the Strategy for England's Trees, Woods and Forests, the Scottish Forestry Strategy, Woodlands for Wales, and Northern Ireland's Department of Agriculture and Rural Development Forest Service Strategy for Sustainability and Growth. Sustainable management affecting sources or sinks of GHGs include the maintenance of existing carbon sinks, and the reduction of emissions or the increase in carbon storage as a result of human activities (**Table 14.5**).

Implementation of sustainable management strategies should include a complete assessment of all potential GHG losses and savings over the short- and long-term (Nayak *et al.* 2008; Six *et al.* 2004) and the repercussions for other

ecosystem services. For example, wetland restoration through plantation removal may actually result in net emissions in the short-term if non-carbon dioxide losses and loss of carbon sequestration in forest biomass are taken into account, but a net sink over the long-term as the carbon sink capacity of the peat is restored. There are also biodiversity benefits to such restoration. However, it is important to ensure that reducing emissions in one instance does not directly result in greater emissions globally through displacement abroad ('leakage').

Sustainable management can also enhance local climate regulation, particularly in urban areas where it will have direct benefits to most of the human population. Tree planting and the creation or restoration of urban greenspaces can increase shade and shelter, reduce the urban heat island effect, improve water retention in soils and reduce runoff (reducing flood hazard risks), and reduce pollution loads (through scavenging by vegetation). Such management also benefits cultural services by making urban areas more pleasant places to live and work, and provisioning services, for example, through allotments and improved water management. Hard impermeable surfaces sealing the soil, such as asphalt car parks, could be replaced with semi-permeable surfaces, such as honeycomb structures, which retain soil functions including heat absorption and water retention. The continued planting of farm woodland will increase the provision of shade and shelter for livestock and other animals in rural areas, reducing climate stress from higher temperatures and more frequent storms. There are also indications that the planting of shelterbelts on upland grassland can enhance carbon storage (Marshall *et al.* 2009; Chapter 6).

14.2.5 Knowledge Gaps

The biogeochemical aspects of climate regulation (i.e. fluxes of GHGs and sources of aerosols) are widely studied and work is underway to address knowledge gaps in most cases. There are a number of approaches to estimating fluxes of GHGs (Smith *et al.* 2008). While it is possible to measure GHG fluxes directly at regional and national scales by sensors on tall towers, aircraft (Fowler *et al.* 2008) and satellites (e.g. SCIAMACHY), the techniques to apportion fluxes between sources are still being developed (Bousquet *et al.* 2006). At the ecosystem level there are large natural fluxes of carbon dioxide, methane and nitrous oxide, both to and from the atmosphere, which can be highly variable over time (Randerson *et al.* 1997). Assessing the potential of natural carbon sinks or the contribution of human-induced fluxes (from land use practices) to total emissions requires the use of process-based models. There are knowledge gaps in both the information used to parameterise such models and our understanding of the processes underpinning them (Smith *et al.* 2008).

There is a body of knowledge on the carbon stored in the uppermost layers of soils across the UK (Bellamy *et al.* 2005; Bradley *et al.* 2005; Emmett *et al.* 2010) and, in recent years, there has been a focus on the carbon stores in peat soils in particular (Smith *et al.* 2007). Carbon storage in urban areas is less studied (even though green space may make up more than 40% of settlement area) and little is known about

Table 14.5 Sustainable management affecting sources or sinks of greenhouse gases include the maintenance of existing carbon sinks (M), and the reduction of emissions (R) or the increase in carbon storage (I) as a result of human activities.

Management option	Effect	UK NEA Broad Habitats affected	Effects on other ecosystem services
Enhanced protection of soils with high carbon contents that are at risk of degradation through management, land use conversion or erosion.	M	Mountains, Moorlands and Heaths Semi-natural Grassland Enclosed Farmland Freshwaters Coastal Margins	Soil quality (+) Hazard regulation (+)
Restoration of the water table in deep peats through the reduction or removal of drains and plantations.	M, R, I	Mountains, Moorlands and Heaths Woodlands Freshwaters	Water quality (+)
Conversion of organic soils under agricultural cultivation to natural vegetation cover.	M, I	Enclosed Farmland	Provisioning services (-) Pollination (+?)
Reduction of soil disturbance through minimal tillage practices (M, R), and the promotion of perennial cropping (e.g. biomass crops).	I, R	Enclosed Farmland	Soil quality (+)
Return more agricultural residues to the soil.	I	Enclosed Farmland	Soil quality (+)
Improved fertiliser practices to reduce the total applied and minimise losses.	R	Enclosed Farmland	Water quality (+) Air quality (+)
Modify livestock diet and housing, convert animal manures into energy.	R	Enclosed Farmland	Water quality (+) Air quality (+)
Managed coastal realignment (conversion to saltmarsh will reduce overall area losses and possibly enhance carbon sequestration).	M	Coastal Margins Marine	Hazard regulation (+) Water quality (+) Supporting services (+) Cultural services (+) Provisional services (-)
Shifting forest management to longer rotations or continuous cover practices.	M, I over long-term	Woodlands	Provisioning services (+,-) Cultural services (+)
Take opportunities to improve forest product utilisation and management practices that deliver wood fuel and material substitution.	R	Woodlands	Provisioning services (+)
Reduction of urban development on greenfield sites, particularly woodland	R	Enclosed Farmland Woodlands Freshwaters	Provisioning services (+) Soil quality (+)

carbon stores and GHG fluxes in fluvial and coastal habitats in a UK context.

There is less detailed understanding of the impact of different land management practices (which do not result in land use change) on total soil carbon and, therefore, potential emissions and removals. Some of these practices, for example minimum tillage, are thought to have the potential to sequester soil carbon, although this has been challenged by Baker *et al.* (2007). Not enough is known about their potential in a UK context or the permanence of such carbon sequestration (Ogle *et al.* 2005; Manley *et al.* 2005). There is a need for specific measurement and monitoring of emissions from land under such practices. When agricultural policy encourages such practices (see ClimSoil, 2008, for an analysis of European policies affecting soil carbon), especially for their potential to ameliorate climate change, there should be monitoring of actual take-up. The contribution of improved agricultural management cannot be shown in emissions inventories if there is no data on where and when it is happening. There is also a requirement for improved country-specific GHG emission factors for agricultural activities, which will be addressed by the Agricultural Inventory Research Platform recently funded by the Department for Environment, Food and Rural Affairs (Defra) and the Devolved Administrations.

Mountain, Moorland and Heath habitats (Chapter 5), in addition to their existing carbon stores, can either be sources or sinks of carbon dioxide and methane depending on location, management, prevailing climate and season. Information on GHG fluxes from deep peats is, at present, too patchy to make consistent, robust calculations at the UK scale. Understanding of the effect of peat habitat restoration on GHG fluxes could also be improved (Baird *et al.* 2009), and is currently the focus of ongoing research projects funded by Natural England, the Forestry Commission and Defra.

While there is sufficient knowledge of nitrous oxide emissions from agricultural practices to make estimates at a national scale (MacCarthy *et al.* 2010), there are still serious knowledge gaps about emissions from soil under different land uses and under different management practices, largely due to the temporal and spatial heterogeneity of nitrous oxide emissions (Reis *et al.* 2009).

There is also a need for improved modelling of long-term future scenarios and integration of emissions models with socio-economic models. Land use policy aimed at reducing emissions or conserving carbon sinks does not exist in a vacuum and may have wider implications; for example, returning cultivated land to semi-natural habitats might reduce emissions in the LULUCF sector but also increase dependence on imported food and increase transport emissions. The impact of climate change on land-based carbon stores and sinks, particularly soils, is also an issue of concern.

The biophysical effects of climate regulation at the regional scale are poorly quantified: how do changes in habitat and vegetation structure (e.g. plantation versus open-structured forest) affect regional albedo and exchanges of energy with the atmosphere driving temperatures and rainfall? Will this work to exacerbate or mitigate the effect of global climate change in the UK?

14.3 Hazard Regulation

14.3.1 Trends in Hazard Regulating Services

14.3.1.1 Maintenance of the integrity of landforms

Rates of geomorphic change in the UK's landscape are typically relatively modest and the integrity of landforms is rarely threatened. However, there are two significant exceptions.

Firstly, the beaches, dunes and saltmarshes of the UK's coastline (Chapter 11) are wasting assets that have a declining capacity to provide hinterland protection from erosion and flooding, particularly in the south and east (Pye & French 1993). It is estimated that 17% of the UK's coast (30% in England; 23% in Wales; 20% in Northern Ireland; 12% in Scotland) is experiencing erosion (Masselink & Russell 2008). Furthermore, erosion of these areas represents a significant loss of important habitat. The exceptions are locations such as river exits and estuaries where coastal sediment is locally available, but even here, the erosion and flooding hazard is increasing, compounded by a rise in fluvial flooding. Widespread frontal erosional loss of estuarine saltmarsh and habitat is the norm, particularly in the south. Similarly, in dune systems, the proportion of embryo dune and new dune slack is minimal as a result of declining volumes of sand being fed in from fronting beaches.

Secondly, in the uplands, the last half century has seen increased *reporting* and *impact* of landslides, debris flows and peat-slides. These events are believed to be driven by hydrology, although the precise mechanisms are not well understood (Ballantyne 2004; Warburton *et al.* 2004). Most landslides are linked to intense rainfall events affecting steep slopes with shallow regolith (soil and unconsolidated rock) cover, and most peat-slides are associated with convective summer thunderstorms, rapid snowmelt or intense winter rainfall. Therefore, if climate change results in an increased frequency of extreme rainfall events, then the hazards of mass movements and associated flooding are likely to escalate.

14.3.1.2 Maintenance of soil cover

In the absence of human activity, most of the land surface of the UK would be characterised by full vegetation cover. This would be expected to result in minimal threat to the maintenance of soil cover and low suspended sediment concentrations. However, the capacity for maintenance of soil cover has been reduced by human activity over millennia and, more significantly, over the last 50 years (evidenced by sediment accumulation in dry valleys and lakes). UK uplands are considered to be in a poor condition (Sites of Special Scientific Interest (SSSI) assessments; **Table 14.6; Table 14.7**) with large areas of bare organic soils (McHugh *et al.* 2002), gullying in peatlands (Evans & Warburton 2005) and high sediment export (Holden *et al.* 2007a). The increasing loss of carbon from upland peat soils in the forms of dissolved and particulate organic carbon (DOC and POC, respectively) has been identified (Worrall *et al.* 2003, 2007), the cause of which may include drought frequency or local management and recovery from acidification (DOC only), although no consensus has been achieved (Worrall *et al.* 2007; Orr *et al.* 2008). Reversal of these trends without deliberate

Table 14.6 Soil erosion in upland England and Wales, based on field measurements in 1999 at 399 circular sites each of radius 50 m. Source: adapted from McHugh *et al.* (2002). Copyright © 2002 John Wiley & Sons Ltd. Reproduced with permission of Blackwell Publishing Ltd.

	Volume (m³)	Area (m²)		
	All sites with evidence of erosion (206 sites)	All sites with evidence of erosion (206 sites)	Bare soil exposed (198 sites)	Eroded area revegetated (85 sites)
Total	88,962	77,212	39,186	38,026
Site mean	432	375 (4.8%)	198 (2.5%)	447 (5.7%)
Range	0.04–1,1750	0.16–7,854 (0–100%)	0.02–4,712 (0–60%)	0.1–7,124 (0–91%)

Table 14.7 Soil erosion in upland Scotland. Derived from 1988–1999 aerial photography by Grieve *et al.* (1995) based on 144 tiles (each 5x5 km). Copyright © 1995 John Wiley & Sons Ltd. Reproduced with permission of Blackwell Publishing Ltd.

Erosion type	Percentage of total sampled area	Ranges amongst 16 regions (% of sampled area)
Eroded peat	6.02	0.47–20.43
Gullied area	4.69	0.00–15.40
Debris flow/cone	0.61	0.00–6.80
Landslide	0.08	0.00–0.35
Sheet erosion	0.61	0.00–2.71

	Density (m/km)	Ranges amongst 16 regions (m/km²)
Linear gullies	80	0–236
Footpaths	5	0–72
Vehicle tracks	40	0–183

management is improbable; however, measures have been undertaken to improve condition such as reseeding, blocking grips (artificial drains), reducing grazing and managing burning. The effectiveness of these measures is as yet uncertain, and their full effect may take years to be realised (Holden *et al.* 2007b; Orr *et al.* 2008; Bonn *et al.* 2009). In uplands, semi-natural grassland and pasture there has been some evidence of an increased frequency of localised loss of vegetation cover and exposure of subsoil. Such losses have been attributed to recreational impacts, such as footpath erosion, and high grazing density (**Table 14.7**). In contrast, on some lowland heathland, reduced grazing pressure and nitrogen deposition can result in successional change that is considered undesirable with respect to biodiversity, but the identification of optimum management has proved elusive (Newton *et al.* 2009). Furthermore, some mobility in dune systems is necessary for both coastal defence and habitat diversity; one exception being machair where centuries of seaweed application has promoted deep soil development and a distinctive habitat.

On arable land, water, wind and tillage erosion have accelerated over the last 50 years, but the quantification of these processes at a regional or national scale remains a challenge (**Table 14.8**).

Water erosion is increasingly being observed and local rates of water erosion have also risen significantly (Boardman & Evans 2006).These fluxes have been attributed to changes in the management of agricultural land leading to prolonged surface exposure to erosive agents (Section 14.3.2). Accelerated water erosion occasionally results in very high suspended sediment loads ('muddy flows');indeed, there is some suggestion that the frequency of muddy flows has increased and is likely to continue to do so if the frequency of extreme rainfall events rises in response to climate change. However, evidence for a more general increase in suspended sediment concentrations is less clear. This may reflect the high capacity for storage of sediment within agricultural landscapes between the site of erosion and the fluvial system.

Wind erosion becoming a more common problem, especially where high organic content soils in areas with a high potential for desiccation are subject to cultivation (for example, East Anglia).

Advances in the measurement of soil redistribution have revealed that tillage erosion (the net differential movement of soil by tillage implements) has been responsible for rates of erosion and deposition in fields equal to or higher in magnitude than those caused by water erosion. Tillage erosion is also extremely common on sloping agricultural land (Van Oost *et al.* 2006; Van Oost *et al.* 2007, 2009). This is resulting in the development of high spatial variability in soils on sloping agricultural land, with shallow, impoverished soils on spurs and shoulders, and deep soils in hollows (Quine & Zhang 2002; Quine & Van Oost 2007).

14.3.1.3. Water retention, storage and delayed release (flood risk regulation)

The changes to the landscape that promote water erosion (discussed in Section 14.3.1.2) also promote lower water retention and storage, and a reduction in the mediation of water release. This has the consequence of promoting more rapid runoff and a greater potential for flooding. Furthermore, increases in soil surface compaction and a concomitant reduction in infiltration on grasslands have been attributed to changes to the intensity of grazing. These are associated with small increases in sediment yield and more significant increases in runoff and the rate of pollutant and nutrient transfer from the land surface. Assessing

Table 14.8 Soil erosion on arable land in England and Wales. There is a significant difference between erosion rates derived using caesium-137 (^{137}Cs), which represents all erosion processes, and landscape-scale estimates of water erosion rates. The simulated rates of tillage erosion are of a similar magnitude to the ^{137}Cs-derived rates and it is probable that the difference between the ^{137}Cs-derived rates and typical water erosion rates is due to the contribution to total erosion and deposition made by tillage erosion. This is consistent with analysis of the relative contributions of water and tillage erosion to total erosion in individual detailed field-scale studies (Quine & Zhang 2002).

Erosion process	Method	Area sampled or analysed (soil association code)	Erosion rate (tonnes/ha/year)				Source
			Median gross	Mean gross	Mean gross eroded area	Net	
Rill erosion	Aerial/field survey	1,700 fields					Boardman & Evans (2006)
		92 fields, 2 counties (343)	0.4–0.6	1.0–1.1			
		112 fields, 2 counties (411)	0.3–0.7	0.6–1.4			
		212 fields, 3 counties (541)	0.4–2.1	1.1–4.8			
		516 field, 4 counties (551)	0.5–1.1	1.1–3.2			
		348 fields, 5 counties (571,2)	0.7–1.6	1.3–5.5			
		45 fields, 1 county (581)	0.2	0.9			
Tillage erosion	Simulation	Arable area England & Wales		3.7	7.4		Quine *et al.* (2006)
Root crops	Simulation	Root crop fields		1		0.8–2	Quine *et al.* (2006)
All	^{137}Cs	248 fields	6.6	8.4	10.6	6.7	Walling & Zhang (in press)

changes in land use, Carroll *et al.* (2004) found that the introduction of tree shelterbelts in the Pontbren catchment in mid-Wales increased the overall infiltration capacities by up to 60 times, which implies that rapid surface runoff could be reduced. The effects of such interventions on the overall flood magnitudes in the catchment were evaluated by Wheater *et al.* (2008), who concluded that interventions in land management in the Pontbren significantly reduced peak runoff. In the uplands, changes in flood frequency have been attributed to the creation of rapid flow pathways through the use of grips to drain moorland (Longfield & Macklin 1999; Evans *et al.* 2004, 2008). Recognition of this has led to the management changes outlined in Section 14.3.1.2. Changes in flood frequency and magnitude have been analysed with respect to climate change, but a clear link has not been identified. However, Robson (2002) has suggested that trends towards protracted high flows over the last 50 years could be accounted for by climatic variation. Robson (2002) found that, for the UK, there were clear flood-rich and flood-poor periods, but extremes were seldom shown to be increasing over the last 100 years (Wilby *et al.* 2008). Possible increases in winter precipitation associated with climate change may lead to an increase in flooding (Hulme & Dessai 2008).

14.3.1.4 Climate change trends

Climate change might lead to an intensification of the hydrological cycle and an increase in floods in many parts of the world (Huntington 2006). In the UK, for example, a possible increase in winter precipitation may lead to an increase in flooding (Hulme & Dessai 2008). Growing confidence surrounds the prediction of mean and seasonal changes in rainfall total. Nevertheless, there is significant uncertainty associated with the identification of an increase in frequency of extreme rainfall events (which drive flooding and erosion episodes) in both observed historical records and climate change projections. Wilby *et al.* (2008) discuss many of the issues at length, highlighting various studies, the evidence used, and their conclusions. In summary, evidence of increases in extremes for some studies may have been the result of shorter time periods incorrectly characterising the postulated current UK and European flood-rich period. Projections of extremes, therefore, are still poorly understood, and a greater emphasis needs to be placed on the capability of climate models to be fit for purpose to estimate changes to some types of extreme events.

14.3.2 Drivers of Change

14.3.2.1 Maintenance of stable land surfaces

The drivers of landslides, mass movements and fluvial flooding are those that permit hydrological thresholds to be exceeded. These may include:

- Changed frequency of convective summer thunderstorms, rapid snowmelt or intense winter rainfall.
- Changes to hydrology that increase the probability of ground saturation.
- Land drainage schemes and river training works aimed at rapid evacuation of water, enhancing the probability of flooding and floodplain inundation within the lower catchment.

The principal drivers of enhanced coastal erosion and flooding are:

- Sea level rise (1993 to 2007 satellite altimetry indicates 3.36 ± 0.41 mm/yr (Beckley *et al.* 2007)).
- Frequency and severity of storms (North Atlantic storm wave heights have increased by 1–3 mm/yr over the last 30 years (Gulev & Hasse, 1999)).
- Expansion of coastal development and attempts at restricting coastal erosion and flooding (French 2001; McManus 2010), both of which often have unforeseen negative impacts on landforms and habitats.
- A chronic lack of sediment supply to beaches caused by near exhaustion of the sediment transported to the coastal zone during the last glacial period and exacerbated by attempts to control cliff erosion. Over the last century, the reductions in sediment supply have been manifest in coastal steepening (Taylor *et al.* 2004; Hansom 2010).

14.3.2.2 Maintenance of soil cover and low suspended sediment

The main drivers that have promoted failure in this ecosystem service are those that threaten the integrity of the vegetation cover, prolong the exposure of unprotected soil to wind and water, or lead to direct redistribution of soil (tillage erosion). In the uplands these include:

- Increased slope to channel connectivity due to drainage including moorland grips.
- Overgrazing by domesticated stock.
- Sporting endeavours, such as grouse moor burning—a substantial past driver of heather monoculture that has recently increased, along with its attendant need for burning (Ramchunder *et al.* 2009), new roads and tracks on upland peat.
- Windfarms and associated infrastructure.
- Tourism including the concentrated erosion of popular footpaths and the increased risk of fire (Cavan *et al.* 2006).
- Plantation forestry, specifically forest operations and transport network.

In grasslands, heathlands, sand dunes and machair:
- Overgrazing (including intensive winter grazing) of grasslands by domesticated stock and wild animals (Bilotta *et al.* 2007) resulting in the loss of vegetation cover and increased soil compaction. However, it is noted that 'undergrazing' in lowland heaths, resulting in undesirable habitat loss and stabilisation of soil cover in some dune systems, may reduce their protective function and habitat value.
- Intensive winter grazing.
- Frontal coastal erosion of dunes and enhanced sand blow.

In arable landscapes (Boardman & Evans 2006):
- Increase in arable area.
- Change from spring-sown to winter-sown cereals.
- Increase in row crops (maize, beet, etc.).
- High-powered equipment allowing cultivation in wetter conditions and on steeper slopes.
- Deeper, more rapid tillage on sloping ground.

- Soil compaction as a result of numerous passes of heavy machinery.
- Removal of hedges and other boundary features, and increased hydrological connectivity between fields and the fluvial system.

At a more fundamental level, the drivers of many of these changes can be found in the policy environment, especially that of UK and European Agricultural Policy. Events such as outbreaks of disease including Foot and Mouth have brought about temporary reversals of the grazing density driver.

14.3.2.3 Water retention, storage and delayed release

In addition to those drivers that threaten soil cover and low suspended sediment content, changes in water retention, storage and delayed release, evident in flooding, have been attributed to (Evans *et al.* 2004, 2008):

- an increase in impermeable areas of catchments (urbanisation, extension and increased connectivity of road networks);
- land use change that leads to reduced roughness of catchment surfaces (removal of hedgerows, overgrazing);
- isolation of rivers from their floodplains and development on floodplains;
- changes to river networks, including canalisation, that promote rapid transfer of water downstream and also increase the risk of downstream flooding and floodplain inundation;
- climate change;
- and alterations to hydrology in response to changing power demands (hydro, biofuels, etc.).

However, there are a large number of physical controls on fluvial flooding, including catchment area, topography, precipitation rates, infiltration rates, pre-existing surface and groundwater conditions, and characteristics of the river system itself. In turn, these factors are affected by climate, season, ground conditions, vegetation, land use, geology, soil structure and the existence (or not) of flood protection infrastructure, to name a few of the more important influences. The controlling processes may vary in both space and time, making floods a very complicated phenomenon to understand, capture in models and to forecast for specific scenarios.

14.3.3 Consequences of Change

14.3.3.1 Failure of maintenance of coastal land surfaces

Beaches, dunes and saltmarshes provide a sea defence role and have always been subject to evolution, but two important current changes have significant consequences. Firstly, rapid erosion, coastal flooding and landward movement of beaches, dunes and saltmarsh landforms and habitats is likely (Pye & French 1993), compromising their sea defence role. Secondly, there is now a greater concentration of human infrastructure and tangible assets at the coast and the effects of increased erosion and flooding are, therefore, more keenly felt. Assuming the present patterns continue

to be reinforced by enhanced fluvial flooding, the main erosional losers will be the landforms and habitats of the outer coast, the main gainers being landforms and habitats recreated further landward and within the inner reaches of estuaries (French 1997; Valiela 2006; Defeo *et al.* 2009). The loss of the protection provided by coastal and estuarine landforms and habitats is highly significant. Over 5 million people in England and Wales inhabit properties that are at risk of river or coastal flooding, and indicative flood maps for river and coastal flooding in the UK show large areas at risk (Environment Agency 2010; SEPA 2010a).

14.3.3.2 Failure of maintenance of sloping land surfaces and soil cover

Landslides and peatslides, although infrequent, can have catastrophic consequences as is clear from the historic record (e.g. the Aberfan disaster 1966), increased incidences of infrastructure disruption due to recent landslides in the Scottish Highlands (Winter *et al.* 2005) and the event at Dooncarton, County Mayo, Ireland, in September 2003 (Warburton *et al.* 2004); impacts of the latter included loss of all soil from large areas, loss of buried farmland, livestock, houses and a graveyard. Less dramatic, but more widespread, the loss of peatlands due to gully erosion and downwasting represents significant impacts on local biodiversity, losses of carbon storage that are unlikely to be replaceable over sub-century timescales, and the loss of sources of DOC and POC to fluvial systems. Although landslides are infrequent in the more densely populated lowlands, when muddy flows resulting from intensive rainfall on erodible soils occur, they often pass through areas of human habitation, and there have been several instances of extensive damage to civic and domestic property on large scales (Boardman *et al.* 2003). These have significant direct, indirect and intangible costs.

The continued productivity of agricultural soils does not appear to be threatened by current rates of water and wind erosion. However, the ubiquitous nature and high rates of tillage erosion may have a more deleterious impact than the more visible erosion processes (**Table 14.8**). Furthermore, the failure of the regulating services of soil retention has wider consequences; for example, fine sediment deposition in river channels, and its ingress into gravels, has been identified as a potential cause of decline in reproductive success of Salmonids. Increased sediment, nutrient and pathogen loads associated with the erosion of, and runoff from, organic and mineral soils reduce water quality and increase water treatment costs. Moreover, future changes to intensification of both plant and animal production have the potential to increase diffuse pollutant burdens.

14.3.3.3 Failure of maintenance of water retention, storage and delayed release

The Environment Agency (2009a) determined that 5.2 million homes (approximately one in six properties) in England are built on a floodplain, near a river or where there is a risk of surface water flooding during heavy rainfall. Of those properties, 490,000 are estimated to be at 'significant risk' of flooding, meaning they have a greater than one in 75 chance of being flooded in any year. In Scotland, 158,195 homes and 12,826 businesses are at risk of flooding, river flooding alone causing around £32 million worth of damage annually (Evans *et al.* 2004; Scottish Government 2010). The costs of structural intervention (e.g. flood prevention schemes, sea walls, armoured revetments and gabions) have increased, in part because development and mitigation measures have prevented the natural landforms along rivers (floodplains and saltmarshes) and coasts (saltmarshes, wetlands, barrier beaches and dune systems) from performing their protective functions including absorbing flood waters and maintaining coastal barriers.

14.3.4 Options for Sustainable Management

14.3.4.1 Coastal protection and flood prevention

Human attempts to prevent coastal erosion and flooding have resulted in short-term success at the protection site at the expense of the long-term stability of other sites, since eroded sediments are prevented from supplying beaches, dunes and saltmarshes elsewhere and thereby sustaining their protective function. Faced with chronic negative impacts of sediment deficit and sea level rise, along with further projected changes, it is clear that the future coast cannot be accommodated within the confines of the current coastal zone and that adaptive management (managed realignment) should be pursued to allow landform and habitat to respond dynamically to the changing climate (Townend & Pethick 2002). Flooding and erosion of vulnerable, low-lying coasts puts in jeopardy the ecosystem services provided by mudflats, saltmarshes and sand dunes, so adaptive management seeks to recreate these environments landward of existing ones, allowing the coast to move in a sustainable fashion. The potential of this strategy for ecosystem services management is demonstrated by the success of the 23 coastal realignment schemes in England (Dixon *et al.* 2008) and three in Scotland. These are mostly saltmarsh recreation schemes, but there is a clear imperative to extend adaptive management to other coastal situations. Such management of ecosystem services to regulate hazard is likely to continue to be an important strategy for erosion and flood mitigation at the coast.

Similarly, in order to reduce the risk of damaging flooding within river catchments, there is a real need for adaptive management to allow river courses to move more freely and reconnect to their undeveloped floodplains. Upper catchment landforms and land uses are critical in determining the rate of transfer of water and sediment through the fluvial system to the channels and floodplains of the lower catchment. For example, there is clear evidence of the benefits of wetland management and forestry, as well as shelterbelts on agricultural land (Carroll *et al.* 2004), all increasing infiltration and reducing rapid runoff (Marshall *et al.* 2009). Such habitat recreation methods have an important role in flood risk management for the whole catchment (O'Connell *et al.* 2004; Jackson *et al.* 2006).

In relation to river flooding, the Pitt review in 2008 (an assessment of the 2007 floods) concluded that major improvements were needed at local and national level. In fact, it identified 92 recommendations that spanned all aspects of flood mitigation, adaptation, parliamentary acts,

infrastructure needs, planning, prediction and forecasting needs, emergency services, and risk assessment and prediction. Subsequent reports have addressed: national assessments of flood risk (Environment Agency 2009a, 2009b); flood and coastal risk management (Environment Agency 2009c, 2010); and guidance notes for flood preparation in Scotland (SEPA 2010b).

14.3.4.2 Erosion reduction

Sustainable management to maintain soil cover in upland areas requires an emphasis on low-intensity land use, including reducing grazing pressure and actively managing livestock. The removal of grips to re-establish wet heath and reduce the rates of water transfer to fluvial networks is expected to have significant biodiversity benefits, as well as reducing flood peak magnitude. Although the basis of this restoration measure is well-established, detailed analysis of the changes consequent to grip-blocking is required. For example, the greater potential for water storage in wet heaths may result in the quicker onset of runoff generation (due to saturation) when there is a short interval between storms, and the full effect at catchment-scale of such potential changes is uncertain. Slowing the rate of water transfer from land to fluvial systems in lowlands will be beneficial in terms of plant productivity (helping to avoid moisture shortages), processing and retention of nutrients and pathogens, reducing soil loss and reducing peak river flow (O'Connell *et al.* 2004). On grassland, the management of grazing intensity to reduce soil compaction is expected to yield benefits and the use of farm ponds and wetlands to separate and filter dirty water may reduce pathogen load and potentially enhance habitat and biodiversity (Bilotta *et al.* 2007). On arable lands, precision farming and nutrient management can reduce nutrient losses, while additions of organic matter, including on-farm products, those from civic recycling schemes and possibly biochar (Collison *et al.* 2009), can be beneficial for soil structure, reducing erosion and runoff and enhancing crop production. Contour tillage can reduce the probability of overland flow generation. Similarly, changes in tillage practice to conservation or no-till systems are likely to have benefits in terms of increasing soil quality and reducing water erosion, and would certainly reduce tillage erosion. In addition, the carbon-poor eroded elements of the landscape offer significant potential for carbon sequestration under such changed management strategies. Management of the riparian zone can alleviate some of the diffuse pollution burden—reducing nutrient, pathogen, persistent chemical and sediment delivery—and expansion of wet woods and riparian woodlands also increases habitat diversity.

14.3.5 Knowledge Gaps

14.3.5.1 Coastal erosion and flooding

It is surprising that a full assessment has not yet been undertaken of the effect that coastal change in the UK will have on erosion and flooding. For example, there remains an assumption that isostatic emergence of the Scottish coast will negate the impact of rising sea levels, whereas tide gauge data over the last 15 years shows that, in line with global estimates, all of the Scottish coast is actually subject to a 2–5 mm/yr sea level rise (Woodworth *et al.* 2009). The availability of UK wave data is spatially patchy, as is an analysis of how enhanced wave heights, storm surges and storm frequency actually force erosion and flood-related change at the coast. Similarly, the impact of adaptive management schemes (Adger *et al.* 2005) on future tide prisms and flooding within estuaries is not yet fully understood, although there are clear habitat recreation benefits. In this context, a systematic assessment of the past and present changes to coastal landforms and habitats is crucial to better inform decision-makers about the nature of future impacts.

14.3.5.2 River flooding

Over the past 20 years there has been an explosion of risk, uncertainty and hazard-related research activity addressing flood hazards. However, hydrological risks are characterised by extreme events, for which observational data are often very limited. Even where data exist, they are rarely sufficient to characterise the behaviour of events in detail. A rigorous estimate of the possible increase in flood hazard is, therefore, a crucial task for planning future climate adaptation strategies, but our understanding of this change in risk is currently limited. Furthermore, there is limited capacity to predict propagation of flood impacts through catchments, and to mitigate them, due to the lack of multi-scale, catchment-wide monitoring and modelling (O'Connell *et al.* 2004).

14.3.5.3 Land surface stability and soil cover

In the uplands, there is a lack of systematic mapping of upland condition, although Natural England is starting to address this within its remit. Systematic monitoring could usefully address:

- GHG fluxes and carbon budgets of peatlands;
- vegetation change as an indicator of the impacts of climate change on biodiversity;
- and upland water quality, especially the concentration of phosphorus.

Although there is still much to understand about rates of ecosystem degradation, there is also a pressing need for understanding the rates and pathways of recovery from degradation:

- In relation to acidification, what are the time lags to recovery? Is there hysteresis?
- In relation to erosion-induced soil heterogeneity, how rapid is the refilling of depleted soil carbon stores and recovery of soil productivity in response to conservation measures?
- In relation to land use change for carbon sequestration (e.g. afforestation), what are the concomitant changes with respect to biodiversity, soil recovery and water quality?
- How might ongoing climate change offset or derail patterns of recovery?

There remain key uncertainties concerning residence times of soil, sediment, nutrients and pathogens passing from source to sink, and hamper understanding of the potential for their processing in temporary stores, including colluvial deposits, in-channel sediments, floodplains, wetlands and estuaries.

Neither the full biogeochemical budgets nor the optimum management of the cycles can be achieved without improved understanding of both the timescales and the processes.

14.4 Disease and Pest Regulation

14.4.1 Trends in Disease and Pest Regulation

Pathogens and pests in the UK will each be regulated or maintained below harmful levels by a specific combination of: i) biotic factors, such as predators, pathogens, competitors and hosts; ii) abiotic factors, such as climate and agricultural and urban land use; and iii) socio-economic factors, such as disease or pest management. Abiotic conditions, including fluctuating temperatures, changes in humidity or ultra-violet light (which degrades DNA), are likely to have the largest influence on pathogens that spend a large proportion of their lifecycle outside their hosts, such as vector-borne or water-borne pathogens. Biotic processes, such as genetic diversity, are particularly likely to impact multi-host pathogens and pests, especially where wild species are involved in life- or transmission cycles. Thus, the management of ecosystems and landscapes can influence the regulation of pests and diseases. As explained in Chapter 4, monitoring data are scarce for species, such as pests and pathogens, which have low cultural value. The relative role of abiotic, biotic, and socio-economic factors in regulating specific pest and pathogen systems is largely unknown, making it difficult to evaluate the importance of UK ecosystems in regulation. Here, we examine changes in incidence of pathogens and pests, and whether these changes have occurred concurrently with changes in potential drivers, in order to provide initial indications of the ecosystem components involved in their regulation and to highlight knowledge gaps.

Case studies discussed here include insect pests, and weeds of crops and pathogens of importance to humans, livestock, crops and ecosystems. Examples are restricted to those for which incidence or impacts have been altered by anthropogenic ecological changes, and which are either currently circulating in UK habitats or have a high likelihood of establishing in the medium- to long-term. An emerging disease is defined as one which has recently increased in incidence, impact, geographic or host range. Both emerging and established pests and diseases are of importance in the UK, and examples are chosen to illustrate themes in subsequent sections.

14.4.1.1 The role of biodiversity in regulating diseases and pests

Different components of biodiversity may be involved in the processes that regulate pests and pathogens in the UK: examples are presented in **Table 14.9**. Establishing these links is essential for designing intervention strategies that alter ecosystem components to enhance or reduce ecosystem processes as required.

Due to the temperate climate there are relatively few agricultural insect pests in the UK compared to continental Europe, the main group being aphids. Of the approximately 4,400 known species, around 250 feed on agricultural and horticultural crops (Blackman & Eastop 2006), to which they can cause significant damage and transmit viruses. Barley Yellow Dwarf Virus transmitted principally by *Rhopalosiphum padi* in the south of England and *Sitobion avenae* in the Midlands and north of England, causes significant crop loss in cereals (Plumb 2002). Natural enemies, such as predators, parasitoids and pathogens, are key regulators of aphids (Völkl *et al.* 2007). Exclusion of predators and parasitoids can result in reduced crop yields (Östman *et al.* 2003; Schmidt *et al.* 2003). Entomopathogenic fungi are known to cause dramatic episodes of disease in aphid populations in some years (Pell *et al.* 2001), but these are sporadic and records are infrequent.

Meta-analyses have shown that, on average, increasing the diversity of natural enemies generally strengthens pest suppression (Stiling & Cornelissen 2005; Cardinale *et al.* 2006). A greater number of predator species was found to increase aphid suppression (Snyder *et al.* 2006), and complementary effects of parasitoids and hoverflies significantly reduced aphid population growth rates (Powell *et al.* 2004). Habitat diversity at the landscape-scale is associated with an increased diversity and abundance of polyphagous predators such as beetles (MacLeod *et al.*, 2004) and especially spiders (Schmidt-Entling & Döbeli 2009). Landscapes with more field margins and perennial crops were associated with low pest establishment (Östman *et al.* 2001; **Table 14.9**). However, specific examples do not always follow this pattern; for instance, in a study of organic and conventional farms, it was observed that, overall, parasitoid

diversity was greater on the organic farms, but that this did not translate into greater pest regulation (Macfadyen *et al.* 2009a). In south-west England specifically, there was no difference between organic and conventional fields in the level of cereal aphid mortality due to parasitoids, the levels of primary parasitism, hyperparasitism and multiparasitism or parasitoid diversity (Macfadyen *et al.* 2009b). Other studies have also found that species-rich parasitoid communities do not result in higher parasitism rates than species-poor communities (Rodriguez & Hawkins 2000).

Despite their importance, data on changes in the abundance of natural enemies of aphids is rare; in their study, Potts *et al.* (2006) found no significant change in natural enemies of aphids, except for Syrphidae which have been increasing since the mid-1980s, whilst MacLeod *et al.* (2004) demonstrated a maintenance of carabid diversity over seven years in a managed refuge. The status of natural enemies in providing a regulating service is, therefore, well established, but there is little information about trends over time at a landscape-scale.

One hypothesis that has been promoted is that ecosystems with greater biodiversity are more resistant to disease (Pelly 2009). Since disease outcomes result from the interactions between pathogens, vectors, hosts and the environment, the capacity of ecosystems to regulate pathogens and pests is likely to depend on several different components of biodiversity rather than simply species richness *per se*. For vector-borne diseases, one mechanism of disease reduction could be the 'dilution effect'. This is where the contact rates between vectors and competent reservoirs are reduced in a community with high host diversity either directly, due to deflection of vector meals to alternative hosts, or indirectly, because abundance of the competent reservoirs is regulated

Table 14.9 Components of biodiversity involved in regulating key pathogens and pests in the UK.

Component of biodiversity involved	Mechanism that produced the effect	Evidence from UK case studies
Habitat diversity within the landscape	Landscapes with abundant field margins and perennial crops associated with low pest establishment.	*Rhopalosiphum padi*, Östman *et al.* (2001)
	Diversity and density of natural enemies increase with perennial habitats at the landscape scale.	Spiders, Schmidt-Entling & Döbeli (2009)
	Density and species richness of natural enemies increase with provision of wildflower strips at edge of crops.	Haenke *et al.* (2009)
	Diversity and density of epigeal natural enemies increases with provision of beetle banks.	Cereal aphids, Collins *et al.* (2002)
Species richness	Greater number of predator species increases pest suppression.	Aphids, Snyder *et al.* (2006)
Host or vector population density	Increase in abundance and distribution of deer, increasing abundance of ticks (vectors).	*Lyme borreliosis*, Scharlemann *et al.* (2008), Gilbert (2009)
	Mast years increase rodent populations (reservoir species).	Hantavirus, Klempa (2009), Piechotowski *et al.* (2008)
Niche invasion or shifts in host or vector species susceptibility	Successful invasion of a sporulating host predisposing invasion of woodland and heath by pathogen.	*Phytophora ramorum* and *P. kernoviae*, Anon (2009), Webber *et al.* (2009)
		Bluetongue Virus (BTV)
Genetic diversity including human-driven genetic changes	Use of antibiotics	Antibiotic-resistant bacteria
	Vaccination	Novel strains of BTV produced by re-assortment with vaccine strains, Batten *et al.* (2008)

by competition and predation (Keesing 2006). In empirical tests, however, indices of species diversity and richness are uncorrelated (Loss 2009) or only weakly correlated with patterns in disease prevalence (LoGiudice 2008), and are less important than other components of biodiversity such as host community composition or absolute abundance of competent hosts and vectors.

Specific components of biodiversity may be responsible for the regulation of disease. An example is provided by one of the commonest tick-borne infections in the northern hemisphere, *Lyme borreliosis*: a tick-borne spirochaete infection, caused by the bacterium *Borrelia burgdorferi s.l.,* that produces viral-like meningitis and non-specific flu-like symptoms in humans. The principle vector in the UK is the sheep tick *Ixodes ricinus* which also feeds on a range of wild vertebrates. The incidence of Lyme Disease has increased dramatically over the last decade (**Table 14.10**), with the Scottish Highlands being particularly affected. Deer numbers have been positively associated with tick vector abundance as deer are key reproductive hosts for ticks (Gilbert 2009; Scharlemann *et al.* 2008).

Alternatively, specific components of biodiversity may act as a reservoir of disease, so providing 'an ecosystem disservice'. Bovine Tuberculosis (bTB) caused by *Mycobacterium bovis* is a disease which inflicts substantial economic costs on the cattle industry in the UK and could potentially affect public health. In the 1970s, infection rates had been reduced to very low levels, but they have been rising since the mid-1990s (Krebs *et al.* 1997). Human-to-human transmission is rare, with the first case being reported relatively recently (Evans *et al.* 2007). The European badger (*Meles meles*) has been implicated as an important wildlife reservoir (Woodroffe *et al.* 2006) and, in this sense, the ecosystem is providing a 'disservice'. The disease is rare or absent in many cattle-raising areas where there are no major wildlife reservoirs of disease (Krebs *et al.* 1997). In contrast, the west of England—a patchwork of agriculture, woodland, recreational countryside and residential areas—is a hotspot where protective legislation has led to an increase in badger numbers (Bourne *et al.* 2005; 2006). The distribution of the incidence of bTB in cattle has spread substantially over the last two decades, now encompassing most of the south and mid-west of England and south and east Wales.

14.4.1.2 Possible regulatory breakdown when novel pathogens invade the UK

The importance of biodiversity in regulating pathogens is perhaps best illustrated by the high prevalence and rapid spread of exotic pathogens invading new ecosystems, indicating that the usual regulatory mechanisms (predators, competitors and pathogens) have broken down. Examples include fungal plant pathogens which have changed the UK's landscape in recent years. The prime example is *Ophiostoma novo-ulmi*, or Dutch Elm Disease, responsible for killing some 30–50 million elms in the UK (Braiser 1996). Other examples include *Phytophora* species, arguably the world's most destructive group of plant pathogens; *P. ramorum* infects a broad range of plant species, including oaks, causing 'sudden oak death'. It was first detected in the UK in 2002 and has since increased in incidence in north and south-west England, although phytosanitary measures are now thought to have contained spread between nurseries, but not from nurseries to adjacent semi-natural habitats (Xu *et al.* 2009). *P. kernoviae* has more recently been detected on *Vaccinium myrtillus,* and other heathland species are known to be susceptible, leading to the suggestion that this is a potential threat for UK heathland (Beales *et al.* 2009). Since the 1990s, a stream of invasive fungal plant pathogens which are potentially damaging to trees, natural ecosystems and horticulture have been entering the UK (Brasier 2008). An agricultural example of a potential future threat is provided by *Dickeya dianthicola* (formerly *Erwinia chrysanthemi*), which causes a form of soft rot in potatoes (**Table 14.10**).

14.4.2 Drivers of Change

Over the past 60 years, land use change, specifically urban expansion and agricultural intensification (including the accidental and deliberate introduction of pest and disease organisms into natural habitats), has been the major driver of change in pest and disease incidence and, therefore, changes in their regulation. Further shifts towards the abundance of a few inimical species in the typical weed community are likely to occur while arable production is dominated by a few crops and chemical herbicides. That small changes in weed control can systematically shift the composition of weed communities, sometimes with unintended results, is shown by field experiments on Genetically Modified (GM) herbicide-tolerant winter oilseed rape in the Farm Scale Evaluations (Bohan *et al.* 2005; Squire *et al.* 2009). The herbicide used in this instance, glufosinate ammonium, encouraged grass weeds that would be detrimental to cereal crops in future years, and discouraged broadleaf weeds that support much of the arable food web. More generally, the weed flora in the UK have been resistant to the ingress of new non-crop species since seedbank records began over 100 years ago, but changes in cropping patterns and in the crop varieties grown have altered the weed flora. Crops themselves are now a common feature of seedbanks, and so, become weeds in subsequent crops. Notably, oilseed rape (**Table 14.10**) has become among the most common arable weeds since the recent rise of the crop in the 1980s (Squire *et al.* 2005). Its most prominent role might be that of an impurity in oilseed rape harvest rather than as a yield-reducing weed (Andersen *et al.* 2010).

Agricultural intensification has altered pest and disease incidence, in part because plants and animals are kept in high densities of homogenous host genotypes that favour the spread (Matson *et al.* 1997) and evolution of pathogenic strains (Slingenbergh 2004). The drive to increase the short-term profitability of milk production, for example, led to the use of ruminant-derived meat and bone-meal in animal feed and ultimately to the emergence of Bovine Spongiform Encephalopathy (BSE). The rapid spread of Foot and Mouth Disease (FMD) illustrated the large distances over which many livestock are routinely moved for trading and slaughter (Gibbens *et al.* 2001). Fish farming, if improperly managed, can increase the incidence of fish pathogens and parasites, to the extent that disease spreads to wild fish (Krkosek *et al.* 2007; Ford & Myers 2008). However, other intensive practices

Table 14.10 Status and trends of a selection of diseases of humans, livestock, honeybees and plants and weeds of crops. Values are for the UK unless otherwise specified. Honeybee sections compiled by Mike Brown, Gay Marris and Giles Budge, all of the Food and Environmental Research Agency's (Fera's) National Bee Unit.

Pathogens

Disease (Hosts)	Transmission routes	Current Incidence	Past trends	Future trends	References
Lyme Disease (Humans, deer, hare, rodents, birds)	Vector: Tick (*Ixodes* species) Broad spectrum of competent vertebrate hosts.	2007: 1.49 per 100,000, (1.34 indigenously acquired)	Five-fold increase in England and Wales, with a higher rate of increase in Scotland.	Vectors and reservoir hosts are increasing. Defra estimates up to 3,000 cases per annum, mostly undiagnosed.	Defra (2007) Kirby et al. (2005) Scharlemann et al. (2008) Health Protection Agency Milner et al. (2009)
Bovine Tuberculosis (bTB) (Cattle, badgers and other wildlife, humans)	Between badgers and cattle, and between cattle. Other reservoir hosts include deer.	2008: 4.9% of herds tested were confirmed as new incidents. 40,000 cattle slaughtered due to bTB in 2008.	Average annual rise of 10–11% per annum in herd incidents over the last four years. A near six-fold increase in the number of confirmed bTB reactor cattle over the 1998–2008 period.	It is thought likely that the increase in incidence in cattle will continue, probably until efficacious badger and/or cattle vaccines are developed.	www.defra.gov.uk/foodfarm/farmanimal/diseases/atoz/tb/stats/county.htm EFSA (2007)
Bluetongue (Ruminants including cattle, sheep and deer)	Vector: *Culicoides* midges	2007: 137 premises in England	First confirmed in UK in September 2007.	Vector susceptibility and population dynamics are climate mediated – therefore likely to increase in the future.	Carpenter et al. (2009) Purse et al. (2005, 2007)
Avian influenza (Wild birds, poultry)	Direct contact but can persist outside the host in water-bodies.	Prevalence in domestic birds ranges from 2% (ducks) to 50% (turkeys).	Seven outbreaks in UK poultry since 2006. One to three farms infected per outbreak.	Restoration of wetlands could potentially increase contact rates between wild and domestic birds.	Snow et al. (2007) Gilbert et al. (2008)
Chikungunya Virus	Vector: Mosquitoes with *Aedes aegyptii* being the major vector in northern Italy.	Absent in the UK	Outbreak in Italy 2007. Single mutation in the envelope protein adapted this virus to *A. albopictus*, a container breeding mosquito that has undergone a rapid spread across Europe.	Entry of Chikungunya Virus (through travel of people from endemic areas) and the vector, *A. albopictus*, into the UK in the medium term is likely. A greater frequency of warm, humid summers could facilitate establishment.	Bonilauri (2008) Knudsen (1995) Tsetsarkin et al. (2007) ECDC (2006) Medlock et al. (2006)
Gastrointestinal bacteria from farm animals (humans, farm animals)	Use of slurry on farmland, contaminated food and water, direct contact with animals, bathing in contaminated water.	*Campylobacter*: 2007: 57,590 cases Crohn's Disease: 1.6–14.7 per 100,000 people. E. coli O157 approx. 1,000 cases per annum. Weil's Disease (*Leptospirosis*): stable at around 50 cases a year.	*Campylobacter* has risen over the last 25 years, but has been stable over last 10 years. Incidence of Crohn's Disease is increasing worldwide (and by 4,000–8,000 people per annum in the UK), particularly in children, thought to be linked to infection with the potentially zoonotic pathogen (*Mycobacterium avium* subspecies *paratuberculosis*) which is responsible for Johne's Disease in animals. E. coli stable over last 10 years (rising trend in previous decade). Weil's Disease—no trend of increase in cases for the UK. Incidence decreasing in other Western	Possible increases in incidence in all cases if warm, stormy summers increase in frequency with knock-on increases in rodent populations and recreational use of fresh water but empirical associations have not been made.	EFSA (2007) Economou et al. (2009) Young et al. (2007) Rangel et al. (2005) Mourato et al. (2003) Pickup et al. (2006) Defra (2008a) Baranton et al. (2006)

	Dispersal/driver	Current incidence	Past trends	Future trends	References
Giardia / *Cryptosporidium*	Contaminated food and water, direct contact with diarrhoeic human, infected pets/livestock animals. Person to person spread within families common (Caccio et al. 2005). Swimming in infected water for *Cryptosporidium*.	*Giardia*: 33,431 cases in England and Wales between 1995 and 2001 (compared with 31,655 cases of *Cryptosporidiosi*); 300–400 cases a year in Scotland (Pollock et al. 2005). *Cryptosporidium*: 3,074 cases England and Wales (2007)—average of 4,500 cases per year; 525 Scotland.	European countries over the last decades attributed to rodent control and improved hygiene. *Giardia* stable incidence since 1988 for Scotland (Pollock et al. 2005). But evidence of recent decline in cases across GB in the early 2000s (Ellam et al. 2008; Pollock et al. 2005). *Cryptosporidium* higher incidence occurring in spring and early autumn. The spring peak has been identified as predominantly C. parvum cases and has declined since 2001 as a result of improved drinking water quality (Lake et al. 2007).	*Giardia*: increased detection rates due to improved diagnostic tools but should also benefit from water quality regulations implemented for *Cryptosporidium*. *Cryptosporidium*: continued reduction in case numbers if drinking water quality regulations are maintained and public awareness of the risks of contact with livestock is increased.	Defra (2008a) HPA (2009) Hunter et al. (2005) Caccio et al. (2005) Lake et al. (2007) Smith et al. (2006)
Phytophthora ramorum and *P. kernoviae* (many species of shrubs and trees (>130) including *Fagus sylvatica, Quercus robur, Rhododendron ponticum*)	Splash dispersal, movement of infected material, aerial dispersal, water-borne dispersal. Spread between plants of economic and aesthetic importance aided by invasion of *Rhododendron ponticum*, a sporulating host.	*P. ramorum* has declined from 164 sites (2003) to 41 sites (2006). *P. kernoviae* first detected in heathland vegetation in 2007.	*P. ramorum* newly described in 2001. First UK record 2002. Initial spread of *P. ramorum* from garden centres probably contained by phytosanitary measures. *P. kernoviae* first described 2005.	Potential threat for UK heathland now that *Vaccinium myrtillus* infected by *P. kernoviae* has been detected in the wild, and other heathland species are susceptible.	Defra (2008b) Werres et al. (2001) Brasier et al. (2005) Beales et al. (2009) Xu et al. (2009)
Dickeya dianthicola (formerly *Erwinia chrysanthemi*) causing soft rots in potato (*Solanum tuberosum*)	Listed as a quarantine organism. Transmission via infected host, soil, water and possible alternative hosts, traced to imports of potato.	Uncertain, but probably spreading in the UK.	First reported in Netherlands in 1970s, now spreading in countries importing seed potatoes, including England and Wales; first found in English seed potatoes in 2001.	Seed certification measures as they stand may be insufficient to ensure containment; potential severe threat to UK seed potato industry, which is mainly in Scotland.	Council Directive 2000/29/EC EPPO A-2 (2009) Toth & Elphinstone (2009)

Weeds

Weed	Dispersal/driver	Current incidence	Past trends	Future trends	References
Increasing abundance and frequency of grass weeds in cereals	Seed return, dispersal; increase of cereal crops in which grasses are difficult to control.	Most arable fields	Continuing trend of increase in a range of grass species, of which *Poa annua* is now the most abundant weed in most fields.	Uncertain, depends on relative changes in phenology of weeds and crops; can be averted by varying rotations and management.	Marshall et al. (2001, 2003) Squire et al. (2005)
Herbicide resistance of grass weeds	Very high selection pressure due to use of same type of herbicide in same crop (e.g. winter wheat).	Many arable fields in the south of the UK, but recently, resistant blackgrass (*Alopecurus myosuroides*) found in Scotland.	Large increase in the UK mirrors the global trend in herbicide resistance due to large arable areas sprayed with very few herbicides (e.g. the 'glyphosate belt' in the USA).	Trend will continue unless averted by new herbicides or else more varied rotations and cropping patterns.	http://www.pesticides.gov.uk/rags.asp?id=714.; http://www.weedscience.org/In.asp
Volunteer oilseed rape—a potential impurity in oilseed rape; a crop weed; a secondary host of *Erwinia* pathogen (blackleg in potato)	Seed drop from crops, secondary dormancy and seed persistence in soil; similar niche to annual broadleaf arable weeds; seed dropped outside farm from farm vehicles and seed transporters.	Volunteer oilseed rape in the top 10 most common arable weeds 2000–2005; established as a feral of rural landscapes across northern Europe, where it is often the commonest wayside crucifer.	Increase, from being undetected in 1970s to become commonplace as a volunteer and feral plant since the late 1980s.	Will likely be correlated with broadleaf ruderal assemblage e.g. *Capsella bursa pastoris* and *Sinapis arvensis*; long-term existence without replenishment from oilseed rape crops still uncertain.	Debeljak et al. (2008) for oilseed rape in arable seedbanks in the UK. Squire et al. (2005) for oilseed rape in the list of common weed species. Anderson et al. (2009) for examples of volunteer persistence.
Epilobium species as arable weeds	Wind dispersed, wide range of phenology, highly plastic.	Several species and hybrids now prevalent; but not yet regarded widely as a major agricultural weed.	Some types arrived in the UK about 100 years ago, but records show they were uncommon in agricultural seedbanks until recently.	Causes of spread not certain so unable to predict future trend.	Records from the Farm Scale Evaluations of GM herbicide tolerant crops.

Table 14.10 continued, Honeybees

Disease (hosts)	Transmission routes (before arrival and after arrival)	Infection route	Current UK Incidence	Past UK trends	Future UK trends	References
Varroa destructor mite (honey bees)		Direct contact (bee to bee). Adult honey bees are highly mobile hosts.	Most honeybee colonies are now classified as endemic. In some isolated areas (e.g. of Scotland) the mite may still be absent.	Confirmed in England and Wales in 1992.	Expected to remain ubiquitous but increasingly difficult to manage e.g. due to resistance and lack of effective medicines.	NAO (2009) www. nationalbeeunit.com
Tropilaelaps mite (honey bees)	Parasitic mite carried on adult bees via swarming, drifting, robbing, migratory beekeeping, and imports. Also exchange of combs and equipment and other beekeeping practices etc.	Direct contact (bee to bee). Adult honey bees are highly mobile hosts.	Apparently absent	Surveillance programme in place: Apparently absent.	Remains a high risk, two species pose risks for *Apis mellifera*. (*T. mercedesae* and *T. clareae*.) As climate warms, risks likely to increase. Formal Pest Risk Assessment in prep.	NAO (2009) www. nationalbeeunit.com Anderson & Morgan (2007)
Other parasitic mites e.g. *Varroa jacobsoni* Papua New Guinea		Direct contact (bee to bee). Adult honey bees are highly mobile hosts.	Apparently absent	Apparently absent	High risk	Anderson (2009) www. nationalbeeunit.com Pettis & Wilson (1996)
Other parasitic mites, tracheal mites		Direct contact	Widespread	Trends not monitored	Normally not high risk but synergistic effects with other pests and pathogens unknown.	
European Foulbrood (EFB) (honey bees)	Carried by adult bees via swarming, drifting, robbing, migratory beekeeping, and imports. Also exchange of combs and equipment and other beekeeping practices etc.	Larvae ingesting bacteria that are present in their food.	Approximately 4.18% of inspected apiaries in England (2008)	Trends monitored by NBU inspectorate for England and Wales. Relatively stable since 1999 (fluctuating between 2.7–4.4%).	Expected to remain stable through controls and monitoring (Statutory Notifiable disease). Large and newly detected outbreaks found in Scotland in 2009.	NAO 2009 www. nationalbeeunit.com Fera (2009)
American Foulbrood (AFB) (honey bees)		Larvae ingesting spores that are present in their food.	Approximately 0.76% of inspected apiaries (2008)	Trends monitored by NBU inspectorate for England and Wales. Relatively stable since 1999 (fluctuating between 0.1–1.2%).		

do not necessarily lead to increased disease risk; for instance, the rearing of poultry confined to indoor sheds prevents contact with wildfowl and so reduces the risk of Avian Influenza (HPAI). The increase in incidence of bTB represents another area of conflict between wildlife management (the protective legislation that has led to an increase in badger numbers) and agriculture (Bourne *et al.* 2005).

Climate change scenarios of 2°C could translate into an extra five generations a year for aphids and two to three generations for Hymenoptera—natural enemies of many pests including aphids (Yamamura & Kiritani 1998). The potential for the control of pests with natural enemies under such conditions may be variable; for example, the consumption rate of aphids by ladybirds increases more rapidly with temperature than the reproductive rate of aphids (Harrington 2002), but an asynchrony between parasitoid and host phenology could lead to a reduction in parasitism (Hassell *et al.* 1993). The extent to which this will translate into overall changes in regulatory control of

aphids will depend partly on how the phenology of their crop hosts changes (including planting date), and partly on how external conditions affect the top-down control of herbivores by predators and parasitoids (Hawes *et al.* 2009). In the case of annual spring planted crops, planting dates depend greatly on soil condition in spring, which is affected by winter and spring rainfall. There is much more uncertainty over future patterns of rainfall than there is over temperature, making predictions difficult. In the case of potatoes and sugar beet in the UK, planting dates are not advancing as fast as aphid first flight dates. If this continues to be the case, aphids may arrive when crops are at an earlier and more susceptible growth stage (Harrington *et al.* 2007). Encouraging natural enemies at this time is a prerequisite for successful pest suppression by restricting early pest population increases (Landis & van der Werf 1997). Predicting the overall impact of climate change on the regulation of pests requires an integration of all these factors. A summary of possible changes in pest status due to a changing climate are presented in **Table 14.11**.

Disease (hosts)	Transmission routes (before arrival and after arrival)	Infection route	Current UK Incidence	Past UK trends	Future UK trends	References
Predatory: Small hive beetle (honey bees)	As above but also imports of produce (fruit), imported plants (in the soil) contaminated heavy machinery and potentially in imported bumble bees.	Adults highly mobile	Apparently absent	Surveillance programme in place: Apparently absent	Remains a high risk, formal Pest Risk Assessment in prep	www.nationalbeeunit.com Cuthbertson *et al.* (2008) Neumann & Elzen (2004)
Predatory Asian hornets e.g. *Vespa velutina nigrithorax*	Imported products e.g. garden pots.	Adults highly mobile	Apparently absent	Apparently absent	Perceived to be high risk, formal Pest Risk Assessment in prep.	Chauzat & Martin (2009)
Fungal pathogens: *Nosema* species *Nosema ceranae* *Nosema apis*	Carried by adult bees via swarming, drifting, robbing, migratory beekeeping, and imports. Also exchange of combs and equipment and other beekeeping practices etc	Horizontal/Vertical (faecal/oral; genetic?)	Widespread throughout England and Wales.	Not Statutory Notifiable, trends not monitored for, but screening has shown these to be common and widespread. 35% current honey imports positive for *Nosema* species.	Unknown and under evaluation, but reported *N. ceranae* associated with losses in Spain.	www.nationalbeeunit.com Fera (2009)
Fungal pathogen Chalk brood		Direct contact; ingestion of spores.	Widespread throughout England and Wales.	Not Statutory Notifiable, trends not monitored for but screening has shown these to be common and widespread.	Impact believed to be low.	Fera (2009)
Israeli Acute Paralysis Virus (IAPV)	Carried in diseased adult bees, and by their parasitic mites, via swarming, drifting, robbing, migratory beekeeping, and imports.	Horizontal/Vertical (faecal/oral; genetic?)	Apparently absent	Not Statutory Notifiable, trends not monitored for but screening has shown apparently absent.	Remains high risk – implicated as a significant risk indicator of colony collapse disorder in the USA.	www.nationalbeeunit.com
Other honey bee viruses e.g. Deformed Wing Virus (DWV), Black Queen-Cell Virus (BQCV), Chronic Bee Paralysis Virus (CBPV)	Generally carried by adult bees and parasitic mites; therefore risk of transmission via swarming, drifting, robbing, migratory beekeeping, and imports.	Horizontal/Vertical	Widespread throughout England and Wales.	Not Statutory Notifiable, trends not monitored for, but screening has shown these to be common and widespread.	DWV correlates with poor colony health; and clear association between CBPV and colony losses in England and Wales.	www.nationalbeeunit.com

It is widely predicted that climate change will increase the incidence and intensity of diseases transmitted by arthropod vectors, such as insects and ticks (Martens & Moser 2001), but direct evidence is lacking (perhaps with the exception of Bluetongue Virus (BTV) as discussed below). Instead, there is a growing recognition that other biological and socio-economic factors may drive changes in incidence (Sumilo *et al.* 2007). Land use change is likely to have driven the increase in Lyme Disease, for example, alongside high rates of recreational use of those parts of the countryside where *Lyme borreliosis* occurs. Expansion of scrub and woodland habitat, together with milder winters and earlier springs (affecting food availability), has driven an increase in numbers of deer which are key reproductive hosts for adult ticks (Scharlemann *et al.* 2008; Gilbert 2009).

Even though climate change impacts have been detected for only a few pest and disease systems up to now, there is potential for more significant impacts in the future (Department of Health 2008). The recent succession of relatively mild winters is thought to have contributed to the increase in Lyme Disease by allowing greater tick survival. Differences in tick abundance with elevation also suggest that future climate warming could lead to further increases in tick abundance and, therefore, incidence of Lyme Disease and other tick-borne pathogens (Gilbert 2009). Evidence also indicates that the emergence of BTV—a devastating midge-borne RNA orbivirus of livestock—in southern Europe at the end of the 20th Century was climate-mediated. Non-climatic factors, such as changes in host densities and movements and agricultural land use, could not account for the spatial pattern of spread, particularly since *Culicoides* midges are generalists in their habitat and feeding preferences (Purse *et al.* 2005). Regional warming is thought to have increased the susceptibility of European midge species, widespread in the

UK, to orbivirus infection. Transmission by European midge vectors has subsequently facilitated the establishment of the disease in cooler and wetter areas in Europe (Purse *et al.* 2007). Thus, further climate change could facilitate the establishment and persistence of BTV and closely-related orbiviruses, such as African Horse Sickness Virus, in the UK.

Anthropogenic intervention has also played a significant role in suppressing pests and diseases. Typically, five to ten of the 300 or so plant species in arable seedbanks are considered noxious, economically damaging weeds (Marshall *et al.* 2001, 2003; Squire *et al.* 2005), and are usually suppressed by management (e.g. cultivation, rotations and spraying). The perennial broadleaf weed species proscribed in the various 'weed acts', such as the Weed Act 1959 and Ragwort Control Act 2003, are still sometimes injurious in grazed land, but are no longer the most damaging to

arable production, probably having been suppressed by the increased frequency of soil disturbance. The main shift in arable weed flora in recent decades has been towards grass species, probably as a result of the increasing prevalence of cereal crops that leave fewer opportunities in the cropping cycle for the control of grasses. In addition, the evolution of resistance to certain chemical herbicides has tended to increase the predominance of certain grass weeds (**Table 14.10**). During the past 25 years, the number of herbicide applications has also increased, and the active ingredients applied act upon a broader range of target species (Marshall *et al.* 2001, 2003). Consequently, most of the innocuous weed species, including those supporting the arable food web (Hawes *et al.* 2009), have declined.

Disease management has also had a substantial impact on the origin and incidence of new strains of BTV into Europe. Some live attenuated vaccines induce viraemia and

Table 14.11 Examples of insects which may increase in pest status in the UK (unless stated otherwise) under changing climatic conditions.

Pest	Potential changes	Consequence	Reference
Aphids	Increased number of generations per year, phenological shifts with earlier activity. Increased fecundity in some cases under elevated carbon dioxide.	Increased pesticide use e.g. prophylactic spraying for *S. avenae* control in autumn cereals to reduce Barley Yellow Dwarf Virus incidence. Increased risk of defoliation in spruce plantations e.g. green spruce aphid (*Elatobium abietinum*) in Sitka spruce.	Awmack *et al.* (1997) Evans *et al.* (2001) Holland & Oakley (2007) Harrington (2003) Zhou *et al.* (1995)
Lepidoptera			
Diamond back moth (*Plutella xylostella*); Silver Y moth (*Autographa gamma*)	Migrants that may be able to overwinter under warmer conditions.	Increased pesticide use resulting in increased resistance.	Cannon (1998)
Turnip moth (*Agrotis segetum*)	Increased survival of water-intolerant larval stages under drought conditions.	Increased pesticide use.	Collier *et al.* (2008)
European corn borer (*Ostrinia nubilalis*) Mediterranean corn borer (*Sesamia nonagrioides*)	Increased range into UK (in 2006 survey, restricted to South East England) from Europe as maize cropping increases.	Regular use of pesticides and/or adoption of insect resistant maize varieties.	Cannon (1998) Gianessi *et al.* (2003) Porter (1994)
Coleoptera			
Western corn rootworm (*Diabrotica virgifera*)	Increased range in UK with establishment from European base as maize cropping increases.	Increased pesticide use.	MacLeod *et al.* (2007)
Pollen beetle (*Meligethes aeneus*)	Earlier migration into crops.	Increased pesticide use and development of resistance (already seen on continent).	Holland & Oakley (2007)
Asian long-horn beetle (*Anoplophora glabripennis*) Southern pine beetle (*Dendroctonus frontalis*)	Warmer temperatures may allow establishment in Europe and may make UK forests susceptible.	Felling of diseased trees.	Ungerer *et al.* (1999) (modelling work from United States)
Pine weevil (*Hylobius abietis*)	Increased populations under warmer temperatures.	Death of re-stocked conifer plantations.	Broadmeadow & Ray (2005)
Thysanoptera			
Thrips	Warmer temperatures may allow establishment in UK.	Currently resistant to pyrethroids – increased pesticide use may increase resistance.	Defra (2006)
Diptera			
Cabbage root fly (*Delia radicum*)	Spring emergence earlier and less synchronized but total number of generations may not increase.	Increased pesticide use.	Holland & Oakley (2007) Collier *et al.* (1991)

even clinical cases of disease and can be transmitted by midges (Veronesi *et al.* 2005; Ferrari *et al.* 2005). The recent strains of BTV-6 and BTV-11 identified in the Netherlands, Belgium and Germany are closely related to such vaccine strains (Carpenter *et al.* 2009) and, since BTV is multi-segmented, may have been produced by re-assortment.

Finally, the global trade in plants and animals provides a mechanism by which pests, pathogens and vectors can enter new areas (Tatem *et al.* 2009). A lack of biosecurity, particularly in the international trade in plants, has already driven the emergence of a number of invasive pathogens in the UK, and could lead to the emergence of other diseases in the future. The potato pathogen *D. dianthicola* appears to be an example of a pathogenic organism that has been imported into the UK despite the existence of quarantine and plant health procedures. *Phytophora* species are thought to have been brought in on infected plant material, and represent one set of a number of plant pathogens which could present a threat to UK ecosystems (Brasier 2008; **Table 14.10**).

14.4.3 Consequences of Change

Any increase in pest diversity or abundance will require increased control measures; an increase in pesticide applications may be expected due to increased aphid problems, for example. As a result of a mild winter during 1988–1989, the grain aphid *S. avenae* emerged as a significant overwintering vector of Barley Yellow Dwarf Virus. In turn, this has resulted in the adoption of a prophylactic approach to autumn aphid control on cereals (Holland & Oakley 2007). Increased insecticide use may lead to increased pest resistance (Devonshire *et al.* 1998; Anstead *et al.* 2007), so integrated pest management utilising alternative strategies may become more important (Cook & Denholm 2008). A consequence of the change in the species composition of weed communities following greater use of broad spectrum herbicides is the loss of relatively innocuous weeds which play an important role supporting farmland biodiversity (Hawes *et al.* 2009).

One of the consequences of the aspiration to increase access to the countryside for recreation will be an increase in contact rates between humans and wildlife reservoirs of disease. Further trade-offs may arise with the restoration of wetlands, which could potentially augment contact zones between wild and domesticated birds. There have been seven outbreaks of the Avian Influenza Virus H5N1, and contact with wild birds has been implicated as a plausible route of entry.

The movement of plants and their products between different biogeographical zones by humans is accepted to be the primary mode by which novel pests and pathogens are introduced to new regions. If the potato pathogen *D. dianthicola* became established within the potato industry, its spread would be hard to manage and it could have a severe economic impact, particularly on the seed potato industry of Scotland. It has been argued that the current international plant health protocols are exacerbating rather than alleviating the problem, with *P. ramorum* being symptomatic of the issues. Only listed species are regulated, yet most pathogens are unknown until they have escaped their centre of origin, where they are likely to be benign, and

caused significant damage elsewhere. The consequences of leaving this particular gate open could be severe for the UK's natural environment, changing the landscape in the way that Dutch Elm Disease did in the last few decades. Change may not be fast and dramatic either—weak pathogens can contribute to declines over longer periods of time, or interact with other environmental stresses, such as climate change, (Jönsson 2004) with knock-on impacts for dependent species, amenity value and carbon storage. For example, the current death of alders due to a *Phytophora* species is damaging riparian ecosystems, destabilising riverbanks and affecting shelter for wildlife (Brasier 2008). Spread of the *Phytophthora* diseases to native heathland could have significant impacts on heathland biodiversity. The Government target of ensuring that 95% of heathland is in 'good' condition by 2010 would be jeopardised by *Phytophthora* outbreaks (Defra 2008b).

There are significant economic consequences arising from human infections acquired directly or indirectly from animals. It is difficult to estimate working days lost through gastrointestinal infections due to underreporting by patients and GP non-referrals (www.wales.nhs.uk). However, estimates from England and Wales lead to around 500,000 to 600,000 working days lost per annum (Zia *et al.* 2003; EFSA 2007). Such infections tend to be short-lived and do not need multiple drugs, apart from Crohn's Disease which is a life-long debilitating illness requiring heavy medication—the latter is estimated at costing Europe 1.6 billion Euros per year. Human health risks of bTB are relatively small due to routine milk pasteurisation and milk inspection. However, the Government spent some £108 million on control of bTB in 2008/09 (Defra 2009b), and this spend looks set to continue to increase until alternative control strategies are employed.

14.4.4 Options for Sustainable Management

Alternative agricultural management options may be required to combat any change in weed, insect pest or crop disease incidence or profile. Options are available for achieving a balance between the traits in the weed flora that reduce yield and those that support the food web. Tillage is frequently practiced to control weeds but is also responsible for loss of soil carbon, although alternatives may be sought to achieve a better balance. The arrival of novel pests may result in changes in crop varieties, for example, corn borers could be controlled by the use of Genetically Modified Insect Resistant (GMIR) maize. The limited adoption of GMIR maize in the EU is estimated to have reduced pesticide use by 53,000 kg per year (Gianessi *et al.* 2003), and evidence suggests that GMIR crops have lower impacts on natural enemies than conventional crops managed with pesticides (Marvier *et al.* 2007). Biological control as a conservation measure aims to enhance or restore indigenous populations of natural enemies through habitat management (Haenke *et al.* 2009). Although empirical evidence demonstrates the relationship between natural enemy diversity and biological control is context dependent (Straub *et al.* 2008), in general, the conservation of natural enemy biodiversity and biological control is compatible. Similarly, elements of agri-environment schemes aim to restore or preserve non-crop habitats to exploit the positive relationship that is considered to exist between plant diversity in uncropped habitats and the diversity of natural enemies (Dennis & Fry 1992).

The development of disease risk reduction strategies, including culling of wildlife reservoirs, vaccination of susceptible hosts, reduced movement, and general management of the contact network, could form part of an organised strategy to reduce disease risk. Vaccination has been used successfully in the control of Salmonella (Mastroeni et al. 2001) and the 2007 BTV outbreak in England (outbreak was restricted to 137 premises (Carpenter et al. 2009)). But vaccination proves problematic for some other diseases of livestock, such as FMD, as it is not possible to distinguish vaccinated from recovered animals that would be routinely destroyed (Mackay et al. 2004). Vaccination is unlikely to be effective when wildlife reservoirs may maintain the cycle of infection (as in the case of Louping Ill and sheep, when the cycle is maintained by grouse and hares) unless these reservoirs can also be vaccinated, e.g. Lyme Disease (Tsao et al. 2004).

In the early part of the 20th Century, a large proportion of cattle herds in Great Britain were found to be infected with M. bovis. As a result, a compulsory test-and-slaughter scheme was introduced in 1950 and eventually led to the whole of GB becoming 'attested' in 1960: each cattle herd was certified as being subject to regular tuberculin testing with immediate slaughter of any reactors. A very low incidence of reactor herds was maintained throughout the 1960s and 1970s, resulting in the incidence of bTB reaching a historical low in the late 1970s and early 1980s. However, the progressive reduction in bTB incidence stalled in the mid-1980s. Since then, bTB herd incidence has remained about three times higher in parts of South West England than in the rest of GB, despite retaining an annual (and occasionally more frequent) tuberculin testing regime in those areas. The difficulties in resolving these final bTB hotspots, and the identification of a wild badger infected with M. bovis on a Gloucestershire farm in 1971, turned attention to the badger as a possible wildlife reservoir of infection. From 1973 to 1998, the cattle test-and-slaughter regime was complemented by a succession of culling strategies aimed at reducing badger populations in the areas where bTB remained endemic. But in the absence of experimental controls, it was not possible to know whether the observed fall in breakdowns was due to badger removal or some other factor.

Following a review by Professor John Krebs, an Independent Scientific Group (ISG) was set up in 1998 to oversee a Randomised Badger Culling Trial (RBCT) to investigate the effectiveness of badger culling (ISG 2007). As a result of work carried out in association with the RBCT it was concluded that localised culling of badgers influences their spatial organisation, disrupting territorial behaviour and increasing intraspecific transmission rates (Woodroffe et al. 2006). The consequence is that, while bTB incidence (confirmed cattle herd breakdowns) may be reduced within the culled area by approximately 23% (95% CI: 12.4% decrease to 32.7% decrease), it is increased in the surrounding 2 km ring by approximately 25% (95% CI: 0.6% decrease to 56.0% increase). Higher prevalence of TB among badgers may offset reduced densities achieved by culling. The end result is that badger culling has the potential to either reduce or increase

TB incidence in cattle depending on how it is carried out, its extent and its intensity (Woodroffe et al. 2006). The ISG's conclusion was that, to be effective, culling would have to be carried out at a landscape-scale which is unlikely to be socially acceptable, practical or economically viable (ISG 2007). There is evidence that transmission occurs from cattle to badgers, and between cattle, and that improved cattle controls might yield benefits (Jenkins et al. 2007); indeed, the ISG concluded that rigid application of cattle-based controls alone could prevent the rising incidence of the disease and control its geographical spread (ISG 2007). However, a consideration of this report by the then Government Chief Scientific Adviser, Sir David King, concluded that badger removal (alongside controls on cattle) remained an option for TB control if it was conducted under certain conditions, e.g. alongside hard geographical boundaries that prevent badger migration (King et al. 2007).

More recent analyses suggest that the negative effects of culling on disease prevalence may disappear over time (Jenkins et al. 2008, 2010), decreasing the landscape-scale over which the activity would need to be applied, which also changes the economic case. While badger culling remains controversial, the evidence suggests that when done on a sufficient geographical scale, in a widespread, coordinated and efficient way, and over a sustained period of time, it is likely to reduce the incidence of bTB in cattle in high incidence areas. Other control measures targeted at the transmission between badgers and cattle include the development and use of efficacious vaccines for badgers and/or cattle. An injectable badger vaccine is now licensed and is being used in a field deployment project (www.defra.gov.uk/foodfarm/farmanimal/diseases/atoz/tb/vaccination/index.htm). As a result of trade and regulatory controls, a vaccine for cattle is still considered to be some years away. It is important to note, however, that there is no single solution to tackling bTB—a comprehensive package of both cattle and badger controls, and biosecurity measures are required to effectively tackle the disease.

The movement of living plants, especially rooted nursery stock, between continents is a high risk business, and it has been argued that current biosafety protocols are insufficient (Brasier 2008). Eradication once a pathogen has arrived and established is extremely difficult and costly, so the emphasis should be on preventing pathogen introduction in the first place. Monitoring of plant material, even by molecular methods, is unlikely to be successful, due to the high quantities involved, and the lack of knowledge about which fungal isolates may be present or pathogenic. The most effective way would be to limit plant imports to licensed material: treated seeds and tissue culture only, to be propagated and tested before release (Brasier 2008). Such stringent measures would reduce, but not eliminate, the risk.

The education of health workers and GPs to recognise the most likely diseases of the future should be a priority. The Health Protection Agency estimate that most cases of Lyme Disease go undiagnosed (**Table 14.10**). Efforts to educate the public about the risk of Lyme Disease should continue, particularly in areas of relatively high incidence. Improved public awareness is also desirable for activities involving children and animals.

Horizon scanning exercises should be undertaken regularly to determine the probability of known risks from outside the UK, and combined with disease surveillance and emergency planning (HPA 2008).

14.4.5 Knowledge Gaps

The assumptions that agri-environment schemes are effective in protecting biodiversity and that enhanced biodiversity delivers enhanced pest regulation have rarely been tested (Kleijn & Sutherland 2003), although a review of Environmental Stewardship schemes suggests 87% have the potential to support biodiversity (Defra 2009b). Current empirical evidence indicates improved biocontrol of pests in some cases and negligible differences in others under Environmental Stewardship in the UK (Holland & Oakley 2007). Further data is required; natural enemy studies have predominately concentrated on parasitoids, carabid beetles and coccinellids. There is incomplete knowledge of other important natural enemies such as insect pathogens (Vega *et al.* 2009). The utility of practices such as conservation biological control could have significant positive impacts on pathogen and arthropod natural enemies (Gurr *et al.* 2004), and requires continued investigation.

The trade-offs in weed management are difficult to predict, largely because the biology of these important organisms is little known and, apart from in studies such as the Farm Scale Evaluations referred to earlier, is not prioritised by research funding bodies. For example, in the UK, the spray-area of the herbicide glyphosate rose during the 1990s at rate of about 17% per year to become the most widely applied herbicide in some regions. The impacts of this on the yield and economy of crops, weed flora and food webs, the overall profile of pesticides in water, and on the carbon footprint of arable cropping, are poorly understood, necessitating comprehensive studies on the management of weeds and other arable pests.

The identity and life history of many future pathogens are unknown to science. For example, it is estimated that only 7–10% of fungal pathogens have been identified and that 90% of pathogens are currently unknown (Hawksworth 2001). There are a large number of poorly characterised mosquito-borne viruses circulating in wild vertebrates, which could lead to emerging diseases, such as Kyansur Forest Disease, Sin Nombre Viris and Nipah, as climate and land use changes (Arinaminpathy & McLean 2009).

Recent problems with managing pathogens in the UK and Europe have arisen where the role of indigenous hosts, pathogens and vectors in the transmission cycle has not been fully explored. To forecast the likelihood of pathogen establishment, laboratory studies of host (e.g. heathland plants to *P. ramorum* and *P. kernoviae*) and vector (e.g. species within the *C. obsoletus* and *C. pulicaris* groups for BTV) species' susceptibility must be combined with detailed longitudinal field studies to understand the role of abiotic and biotic drivers in disease regulation. Certainly in the case of agricultural crop pathogens, the emphasis of research has been on epidemiology within the crop, to the neglect of biology and life history outside the crop host. This lack of fundamental knowledge makes it difficult to develop sustainable management strategies.

Obtaining information on the current distribution of infectious diseases in the UK and combining it with other spatial data on hosts, vectors and environmental conditions is currently difficult, making it hard to quantify disease changes or understand underlying processes. A previous UK Department of Health report (Kovats 2008) on the impacts of climate change on vector-borne diseases recommended the following actions:

- Create a database against which to monitor change in incidence.
- General Practitioners to report centrally on any insect-associated conditions, e.g. wasp/bee stings, rashes from caterpillars, tick bites.
- Any significant change in incidence should be the alert for focused research.
- Map the distribution and abundance of key vector species in the UK.

This should be broadened to include other pathogens with natural transmission cycles and the mapping of key domestic and wildlife hosts and other components of biodiversity involved in regulation. The European Centre for Disease Control is currently sponsoring initiatives to combine epidemiological, ecological and environmental data across Europe to understand patterns in diseases.

Another consistent feature of the case studies we have described is how landscape changes and human behavioural changes have interacted to alter the overlap between humans, hosts and vectors and the resulting contact rates between humans and pathogens. Use of key UK habitats by people, hosts, and vectors must be investigated within the same landscape framework, incorporating the work of ecologists, epidemiologists and social scientists to understand the processes underlying abrupt changes in disease incidence.

14.5 Pollination

14.5.1 Trends in Pollination

Pollination is either abiotic, primarily by wind, or biotic, primarily by bees and other insects. Pollinator-dependent crops which are restricted to enclosed agricultural land, such as oilseed rape, apples, pears and strawberries, comprised 20% of the total UK cropped area in 2007 (England: 23%, Northern Ireland: 5%, Scotland: 8%, Wales: unknown). This coverage has increased by 38% since 1989 (BHS 1999, 2008; Defra 2009c). UK consumers are highly dependent upon overseas pollination services contributing to imported foodstuffs; the UK only produces a small proportion of its own pollinator-dependent crop products (e.g. 30% of apples, 18% pears and 57% of strawberries) (Defra 2008c). Some biofuels, such as oilseed crops, require insect pollination and may become more widespread in the future if demand increases.

Using the methods of Gallai *et al.* (2009), the production function value of biotic pollination as a contribution to crop market value in 2007 was £430 million (England: £364 million, Northern Ireland: £19 million, Scotland: £47 million, Wales:

unknown), which is approximately 8% of the total value of the market (Defra 2008c, 2009b; BHS 2008; **Table 14.12**).

Wildflowers are primarily found in semi-natural grasslands, mountains, moors and heathlands, woodlands, coastal margins and some urban habitats, such as parks, gardens and roadside verges. Most wildflowers are directly dependent on insect pollination, and a high proportion of studied species (62–73%) have populations that are pollination limited (Burd 1994; Ashman *et al.* 2004). Since 1980, animal-pollinated plants have declined in the UK more than self- or wind-pollinated species (Biesmeijer *et al.* 2006), and 76% of bumblebee forage plants have decreased in frequency (Carvell *et al.* 2007).

The value of pollinators and pollination services to wildflowers and for recreational and other cultural services is unknown, but is expected to be significant. Several studies indicate that diverse, visible assemblages of wildflowers make important contributions to the aesthetic qualities of whole landscapes and roadside verges within the UK (Willis & Garrod 1993; Akbar 2003; Natural England 2009).

In the UK, honeybees (*Apis mellifera*) are the most commonly managed species of pollinator, though most beekeepers are 'hobby beekeepers' primarily interested in honey production rather than providing pollination services.

Between 1985 and 2005, managed colony numbers went into serious decline (England: -54%, Northern Ireland: unknown, Scotland: -15%, Wales: -23%) and this trend is expected to continue in the short-term (Potts *et al.* 2010a; **Figure 14.3**). Feral honeybees are now almost extinct in Europe (Jaffé *et al.* 2009).

Some crops, such as strawberries, tomatoes and peppers, are mainly pollinated by managed bumblebees which are imported commercially. Though honeybees are widely managed, they are not as effective at pollinating some crops (e.g. field beans, apples, raspberry) as wild pollinators (Free 1993; Willmer *et al.* 1994; Vicens & Bosch 2000). Based on the area of crops needing insect pollination (Defra 2009b) and the recommended densities of hives needed to pollinate these crops (Free 1993), the number of registered hives in the

UK is only sufficient to supply up to a third of the pollination services, with the remainder of the services being supplied by wild pollinators. The extent to which wild pollinators contribute to wildflower pollination remains to be quantified, but is likely to be high, as species other than honeybees constitute the majority of visitors in plant-pollinator webs (Memmott 1999). Several wild pollinators are UK Biodiversity Action Plan (BAP) listed: these include 20 from a total of about 250 other species of bee, 24 from a total of 56 species of butterflies, 7 of 250 species of hoverflies and many other insects. Since 1980, wild bee diversity has declined in most landscapes, with habitat and diet specialist species suffering greater losses than more generalist species (Biesmeijer *et al.* 2006); hoverflies showed both increases and decreases in diversity for the same time period, but again specialists fared poorly. Butterflies, though rarely pollinators in the UK, have also undergone major range and population shifts (Asher *et al.* 2001).

14.5.2 Drivers of Change

Current knowledge for the UK primarily relates to the drivers of pollinators rather than the service *per se*. While global honeybee stocks have increased by approximately 45% (except in the UK where they have declined), the proportion of crops dependent upon pollination has increased much more rapidly by about 300%, meaning that demand for pollination services could outstrip the supply of honeybee hives (Aizen & Harder 2009). The drivers of the decline of managed honeybees in the UK and Europe remain poorly understood, but it is expected that a combination of pressures may be responsible (Potts *et al.* 2010a). The ectoparasitic mite (*Varroa destructor*) has contributed to the loss of most wild and feral honeybee colonies in Europe (Jaffé *et al.* 2009), and remains a major pressure on managed colonies in the UK, to the extent that it is considered impossible to eradicate (NAO 2009; **Table 14.10**). Incidences of two notifiable diseases, European Foul Brood and American Foul Brood, have remained stable since 1999 (NAO 2009; **Table 14.10**). A wide variety of other diseases are recorded for honeybees including several viruses, fungi and protozoa (**Table 14.10**). Outside the UK, no single disease can alone be attributed to recent severe colony losses (ICCL 2008), but comprehensive studies investigating colony losses across England and Wales indicate that specific organisms may be involved (www.nationalbeeunit.com); moreover, there is a trend that smaller, weaker colonies contain a greater number of disease agents. Though prevalent elsewhere, the small hive beetle (*Aethina tumida*), *Tropilaelaps* mites and Asian hornets (*Vespa velutina*) are not currently found in the UK, but remain serious threats (NAO 2009; **Table 14.10**).

Data on diseases of wild bees is lacking, but it is likely that honeybee viruses are able to invade multiple host species and thus able to infect non-*Apis* wild bees and *vice versa* (Eyer *et al.* 2009).

The loss of natural and semi-natural habitat is thought to be a major driver of wild bee declines (Winfree *et al.* 2009), but urban areas (Carré *et al.* 2009) and mass-flowering crops (Westphal *et al.* 2003) may provide important resources for some bee guilds. Semi-natural features, such as woodlands and semi-natural grasslands, have been shown to provide

Table 14.12 Crop dependencies on pollinators and annual value of pollination in 2007.		
Crop	Dependence on Pollinators (%)	Value per annum (£ millions)
Oilseed rape	25	106
Strawberries	45	72
Dessert apples	85	44
Culinary apples	85	43
Raspberries	45	39
Cucumbers	65	22
Tomatoes	25	21
Runner beans	85	16
Plums	65	6
Pears	65	5
Others	5–85	54
Total		Approx. £430 million

a spill-over of pollinators into farmland and can increase pollination services (Kremen *et al.* 2007; Ricketts *et al.* 2008). Many important bee habitats are being lost; from 1990 to 1998, 19.8% of calcareous grasslands and 12.0% of acid grasslands have been lost from the UK (Howard *et al.* 2003). Habitat fragmentation *per se*, though not well studied, has been found to have mixed impacts on bees (Winfree *et al.* 2009). Case studies have shown that habitat degradation can be a driver of pollinator loss. Some pesticides are known to have lethal and sub-lethal effects on bees (Morandin *et al.* 2005), and intense field applications of some pesticides can cause local shifts in bee communities (Brittain *et al.* 2010). With current research to date, neonicotinoid pesticides alone appear to have no (Nguyen *et al.* 2009) or low impact on pollinators (Faucon *et al.* 2005), although no consensus across studies has been reached; most of the highly publicised cases of bee mortality are associated with spillage or incorrect use of neonicotinoids. Floral food resource availability can be reduced by herbicide use, however (Gabriel & Tscharntke 2007).

Invasive plants can have positive (Stout 2007) or negative (Traveset & Richardson 2006) impacts on native pollinators through resource supplementation and competition with native plants respectively. However, the impact of invasive plants is probably relatively minor compared to the replacement of semi-natural habitats by cereals and improved grasslands following agricultural expansion and intensification of management.

Climate change is predicted to result in declines in European bee species richness (Dormann *et al.* 2008); though expected shifts in the UK are not projected, disruption of plant-pollinator networks may be expected (Memmott *et al.* 2007). Bumblebee declines in the UK have been related to climatic niche shifts (Williams *et al.* 2007).

Drivers of pollinator declines have been studied in isolation, but they are likely to interact in such a way that one sub-lethal driver may increase the severity of impact of another driver, and it is this that is most likely to explain the patterns of pollinator declines in the UK (Potts *et al.* 2010b).

14.5.3 Consequences of Change

Relatively little information is currently available on the direct consequences of changes in pollination services, so consequences related to changes in pollinators are reported here. Continued declines, or total loss of one or more pollinator functional groups, would be expected to have direct and short-term consequences for agricultural producers and consumers and wide-ranging and longer-term impacts on wild plant communities and wider ecosystem functions.

Total pollinator loss for UK agriculture would translate into an annual loss of £430 million (using data from Defra 2008c, 2009b; BHS 2008). However, this estimate fails to take into account the contribution of pollinators to: forage crops, such as clover, which support livestock; small-scale agriculture, such as allotments and gardens; ornamental flower production; and seed production for agricultural crop planting. While on the one hand this is a conservative estimate of total loss value, it is an unrealistic scenario as complete pollinator collapse in the UK is improbable. Nevertheless, the calculation serves as a guide to the relative importance of insect pollination for food production. Several studies have demonstrated that locally depauperate pollinator communities can lead to reduced crop yield and/ or quality (Ricketts *et al.* 2008).

Decreases in pollination services would, therefore, result in short-term economic losses for famers, at least until alternative wind- and self-pollinating crops replaced insect-pollinated crops, or supplemental services could be brought in through managed pollinators. It would also force a change in food choice and security in that UK consumption would either have to shift away from pollinator-dependent products, or a greater reliance would have to be placed on imported pollinator-dependent foods. Foods particularly affected would be many fruits and vegetables (e.g. raspberries, apples, pears, cucumbers and beans) and processed and derived products.

As the majority of wild flowering plants depend upon insect pollination, decreases in pollinators will result in a reduced seed/fruit set and may ultimately lead to the local extinction of plant species (Ashman *et al.* 2004; Aguilar *et al.* 2006). Species which obligately outcross are particularly vulnerable to pollinator loss (Biesmeijer *et al.* 2006) as no compensation mechanism (e.g. self-pollination) is available. Loss of flowering plants will reduce the availability of resources for pollinators, which, in turn, will reduce insect pollination services for plants in a positive feedback loop (Bascompte *et al.* 2006). Wild plants form key nodes in many food webs, and pollinator products, such as seeds and fruit, support a wide array of taxa including many invertebrates, mammals and birds. Loss of wild plants could, therefore, have wide-ranging impacts on multiple trophic levels and also negatively impact on other ecosystem services reliant on plant communities such as soil health, water quality and pest regulation. Obligately outcrossed insect-pollinated plants generally have showy flowers, and so, also enhance aesthetic values, and contribute directly to quality of life and indirectly to tourism and other rural livelihoods.

14.5.4 Options for Sustainable Management

Three complementary approaches can be taken to sustainably manage pollination services: a) manage the wider landscape to enhance wild pollinator populations; b) improve the health of existing managed pollinators, i.e. honeybees; and c) develop and deploy alternative managed pollinators.

a) Protection of existing, and provision of additional, high quality pollinator habitats in the wider landscape will enable more diverse and resilient pollinator communities to be supported. Key instruments include: a) pollinator-targeted options within national agri-environment schemes, such as pollen and nectar mixes for field margins (Carvell *et al.* 2007, Pywell *et al.* 2007, Potts *et al.* 2009; Chapter 6), and the Campaign for the Farmed Environment; b) cross-sectoral spatial planning to provide better landscape connectivity by allowing agri-environment scheme options to be placed strategically with respect to protected areas and other semi-natural features of the landscape; c) regulation of pesticide approval through Directive 91/414 (to be replaced by Regulation 1107/2009); and iv) continued

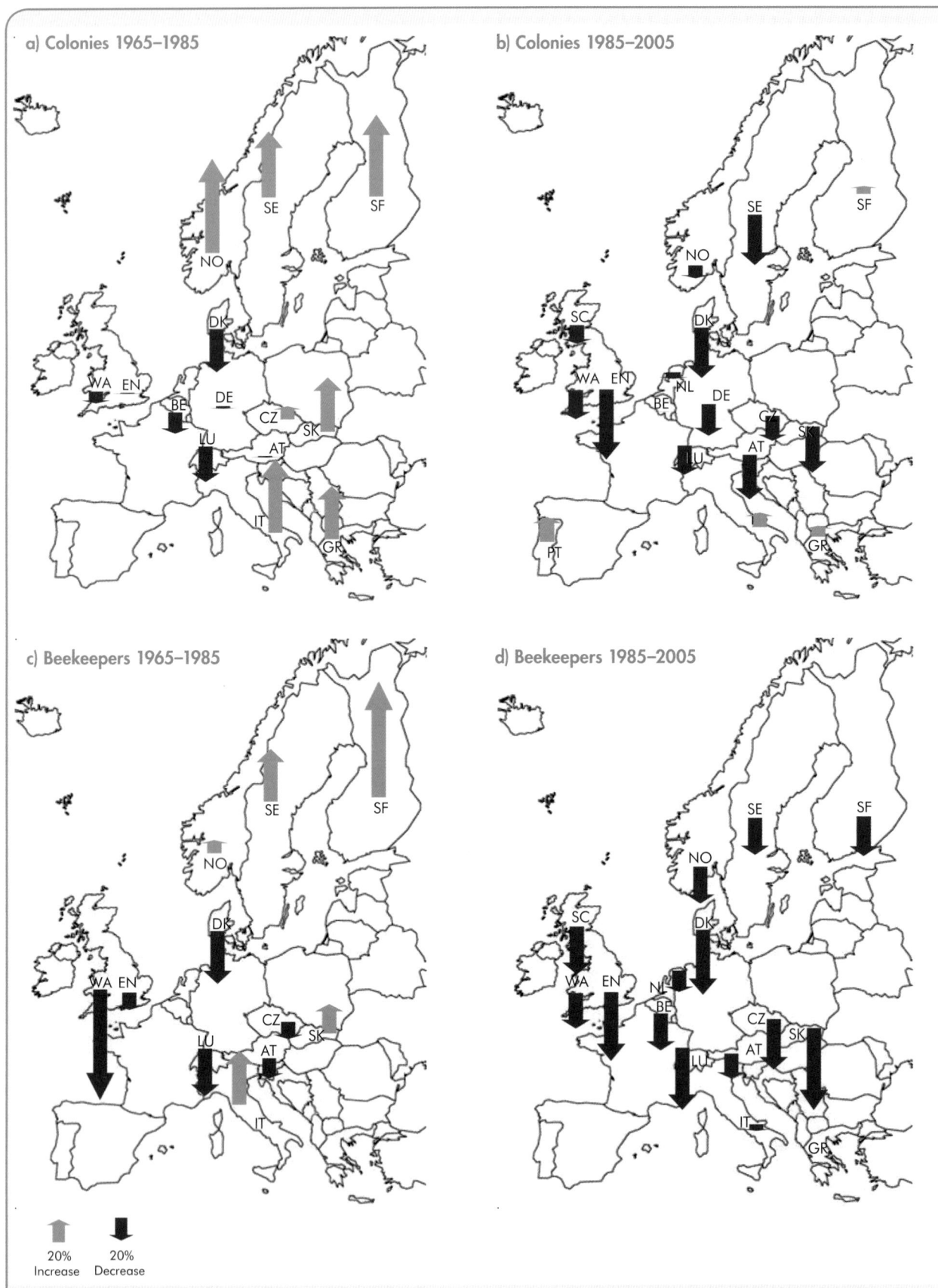

a) Colonies 1965–1985

b) Colonies 1985–2005

c) Beekeepers 1965–1985

d) Beekeepers 1985–2005

20% Increase   20% Decrease

Figure 14.3 Graphical summary of the net proportional changes (%) in: a) total numbers of honey bee colonies between 1965 and 1985, and b) 1985 and 2005; c) total numbers of beekeepers between 1965 and 1985, and d) 1985 and 2005*. Maroon arrows indicate decreases, green arrows indicate increases, and the height of the arrow is proportional to the percentage change with reference arrows provided in legends. Source: reproduced from Potts *et al.* (2010a) with permission from the International Bee Research Association.

*Austria (AT); Belgium (BE); Czech Republic (CZ); Denmark (DK); England (EN); Finland (SF); Germany (DE); Greece (GR); Italy (IT); Luxembourg (LU); Netherlands (NL); Norway (NO); Portugal (PT); Scotland (SC); Slovakia (SK); Sweden (SE); Wales (WA).

support from the UK BAP, targeting actions to protect priority pollinator species and pollinator habitats. Other opportunities to support pollinators include the management of hedgerows, riverbanks, gardens and urban greenspaces to provide pollinator habitats, and the widespread adoption of pollinator-friendly practices for the application of pesticides.

b) The health of honeybee colonies can be increased through: a) improved inspection regimes including a greater proportion of colonies; b) better diagnosis of colony losses; c) a greater understanding of the drivers of honeybee loss; d) and the teaching and implementation of best practice. This requires further support for the National Bee Unit inspection programmes, and training for beekeepers. Continued stringent screening of imported queens needs maintaining to reduce the risk of small hive beetle or other new pathogens entering the UK.

c) To reduce the risks of pollination service loss we need to identify wild pollinators that can potentially be developed into managed pollinators to supplement pollination services. Reliance on a single species, honeybees, as a management solution is a high risk strategy given the increasing threats faced by this species. In addition, while honeybees are currently widely used for fruit production, pollination is often effected by forcing bees onto flowering plants by saturating the local area with hives, whereas other wild bees can be much more efficient and effective as pollinators (Willmer *et al.* 1994, Vicens & Bosch 2000). Candidate pollinators for management include several bumblebee species, the red mason bee (*Osmia rufa*) and the mining bee (*Andrena flavipes*), the latter two having been shown to be excellent pollinators of apples and pears. Until recently, the only commercial bumblebee pollinator in the UK was a European sub-species of *B. terrestris*, which, being non-native, is only available for use in enclosed systems (e.g. glasshouses). From the spring of 2010, producers have started to supply the UK with other subspecies in limited commercial volumes for use in open-pollination systems. However, due to small production runs, these have a significant price premium. Development management of alternative pollinators requires additional funding for research in to new species, and enterprise support for species already established but requiring commercial development.

14.5.5 Knowledge Gaps

We lack national or regional monitoring schemes for both pollinators and pollination services; consequently, most of our evidence for status and trends comes from data collected for other purposes, and we have no baseline against which to compare future changes.

Basic data on the capacity of different habitats and floral resources to support pollinator communities is missing, making it difficult to model and map pollinator distributions based on land cover. Similarly, we have no generic models allowing us to predict the extent of pollinator services delivered from a given pollinator community, except in cases where a small number of well-studied species are involved.

The pollination requirements and levels of pollination limitation of many crop varieties and wild plants are poorly documented or unknown. The relationship between pollinators and service delivery is not well understood, but the few available studies indicate that pollinator diversity is linked to greater crop yield, resilience and stability (Hoehn *et al.* 2008; Winfree & Kremen 2009).

While many case studies have looked at single driver impacts on pollinators, the interactions of multiple drivers is poorly understood, yet this is likely to be crucial in understanding patterns of pollinator loss (Potts *et al.* 2010b). Particular needs include a better understanding of the interaction between pesticides and pathogens, and competition between managed honeybees and wild pollinators.

For honeybees, it is difficult to diagnose honeybee colony deaths with existing practices, and there are major gaps in the registration of honeybee keepers (NAO 2009); both contribute to the difficulties in identifying the causes of recent colony losses.

The combined lack of knowledge about pollinator-habitat relationships and drivers of pollinator shifts make it difficult to model future projections. Consequently, it is almost impossible to predict the likely impacts for crop and wildflower pollination, except to scope out the likely maximum impacts of total pollinator loss, which is an unrealistic scenario.

14.6 Noise Regulation

14.6.1 Trends in Noise Regulation

Sound, like light and odour, can be experienced by humans and other animals at a distance from the source. Sounds can be physically described in terms of their loudness (L), frequency and duration, but they can also have emotional and aesthetic effects (TQL 2008). Some sounds, for example bird songs, are generally perceived as pleasant and can be associated with specific ecosystems. Conversely, unwanted natural and human-derived sounds, often associated with traffic and urbanisation, are commonly termed as 'noise'. Such noise can be regulated by ecosystems by altering the sound itself or by adsorbing or reflecting the sound before it reaches the hearer.

Quantification of the status and trend of noise in the UK requires an appropriate means of measurement. Physical measurements of loudness are made on a decibel (dB) scale starting at a nominal minimum level of human hearing (0 dB). The logarithmic nature of the scale means that, for example, a sound at 60 dB is ten-times louder than a sound at 50 dB. Because human perceptions of loudness vary with sound frequency, measures of loudness are usually given an A-weighting (L_A). When the noise is discrete, such as a single aeroplane, loudness is often expressed as a maximum level (L_{Amax}). The loudness of continuous sounds, such as road traffic, may be expressed as the mean equivalent level over a period of time (L_{Aeq}).

Within the UK, major surveys of actual noise levels have been restricted to urban areas. A survey of 24-hour urban noise levels outside 1,000 dwellings in England and Wales was conducted in 1990, and a similar study (including Scotland and Northern Ireland) was completed in 2000 (Skinner & Grimwood 2002). In both studies, daytime levels of noise were typically 8–9 dB higher than during the night (**Table 14.13**). In a comparison of sites measured in both 1990 and 2000, there was a significant decrease in daytime noise levels from 57.1 to 56.5 dB, and the level of night-time noise was stable (**Table 14.13**).

In rural areas, noise studies have been integrated with visual impact, and the studies are typically based on models where noise is related to the proximity of features such as transport corridors and population centres. The proportion of England that suffers from some degree of noise or visual disturbance has been estimated to have increased from 25% in the early 1960s, to 50% in 2007 (**Table 14.14; Figure 14.4**).

A similar trend has also been observed in Wales (WAG 2009). The effect has not been related to specific habitats.

14.6.2 Drivers of Change

Road traffic is considered to be the main source of noise in the UK (Grimwood 2002). Engine noise dominates at low speeds, whereas noise from tyres and the road surface dominates at high speeds (>50 km/h). The main driver for the modelled increase in disturbance has been the increase in population, transport and urban development. The UK's population increased from 52.8 million in 1961 to 61.4 million in 2008. The mean distance travelled per person per year increased from 3,660 miles in 1965 to 6,720 miles in 2001 (DfT 2002). These trends are expected to continue: the Department of Transport (2004) predicts a 40% increase in road traffic in England by 2025 compared to 2000 levels. The Department of Transport also predicts a two- to three-fold increase in the demand for air flights over the same period.

14.6.3 Consequences of Change

A higher proportion of people in the UK than in any other EU country identify noise pollution as one of the top five environmental issues (European Commission 2008). Noise levels can have negative effects on health, educational performance and wildlife. However, sound can also have a positive effect on human well-being.

14.6.3.1 Negative effects on health and educational performance

Exposure to noises louder than 120 dB for children and 140 dB for adults, or prolonged exposure to levels above 75 dB, can cause hearing impairment (WHO 2002). High levels of noise also reduce the intelligibility of speech, reduce cognitive performance, disrupt sleep and create hypertension. The World Health Organization (WHO 2002) also suggest that noise above 80 dB can reduce social cohesion and increase aggressive behaviour. A study in the UK has indicated that 10% of respondents 'were annoyed' when night-time noise levels exceeded 55 dB (Skinner & Grimwood 2002). Because of the increased sensitivity of humans to noise while sleeping, The World Health Organization (WHO 2002) recommends that A-weighted noise levels outside dwellings should not exceed 55 dB during the daytime and 45 dB at night. It is estimated that 54% and 67% of UK homes exceed these levels during the day- and at night respectively (**Table 14.15**).

14.6.3.2 Wildlife

While there have been various studies of the effects of noise on marine mammals and fish, the effects of noise on terrestrial biodiversity has largely focused on birds. High noise levels have been shown to decrease the food intake of some species because of the increased need for visual

---

Table 14.13 Mean day-time and night-time noise levels (dB) outside of paired-samples (n = 680) of dwellings in 1990 and 2000. Source: data from Skinner & Grimwood (2002).

	1990	2000	
Day-time L_{Aeq} (07.00–23.00 hrs)	57.1	56.5	Significant (<0.05) decrease
Night-time L_{Aeq} (23.00–07.00 hrs)	48.3	48.2	No significant change

---

Table 14.14 Predicted proportion (%) of each region in England disturbed by noise or visual intrusion for three selected years. Source: data from CPRE & LUC (2007).

	Early 1960s	Early 1990s	2007
North East	24.5	30.5	34.7
South West	14.6	30.1	42.5
Yorkshire & Humberside	24.0	37.1	45.9
North West	30.5	41.5	48.6
West Midlands	28.1	42.9	49.2
Eastern	21.8	38.6	49.6
East Midlands	25.8	40.9	50.2
South East & London	37.8	59.0	69.2
England	25.5	40.6	49.9

Table 14.15 Estimated proportions (%) of the population in England and Wales in 1990 and 2000, and in the UK in 2000–2001 living in dwellings exposed to levels exceeding the World Health Organization's guideline levels. Source: Skinner & Grimwood (2002).

Indicator	WHO guideline level (dB)	Proportion exceeding level (%)		
		England & Wales (1990)	England & Wales (2000)	UK (2000–2001)
Day-time L_{Aeq}, 16 hr	55	60 ± 3	55 ± 3	54 ± 3
Night-time L_{Aeq}, 8 hr	45	66 ± 3	68 ± 3	67 ± 3

scanning for predators (Quinn *et al.* 2006). In a Canadian study, industrial noise has also been related to a 17% reduction in the breeding success of a migrant bird species (Habib *et al.* 2007). Although the effect of road traffic occurs across a range of habitat types, there is particular evidence of the sensitivity of grassland birds. In the USA, Forman *et al.* (2002) related the decline in grassland birds to the increase in traffic. Likewise, Green *et al.* (2000) found that stone curlews (*Burhinus oedicnemus*) in southern England were most likely to breed in fields over 3 km away from the nearest major road. There is evidence that species vary in their response to noise, as some species can modify their signalling behaviour in terms of timing, or increased sound frequency and volume (Slabbekoorn & Ripmeester 2008).

14.6.3.3 Natural sounds and positive effects on well-being

Because most of the UK population lives in an environment of high mental stimulation, it is important that people allow for "restorative periods of cognitive quiet" or "tranquillity" (Pheasant *et al.* 2008). In the national Survey of Public Attitudes towards the Environment, tranquillity is consistently ranked as an important reason for valuing green space, along with fresh air, open space, scenery and plants and wildlife (Defra 2009d). It should be noted that tranquil spaces are not necessarily places of total silence, as tranquillity is enhanced by elements of 'soft fascination', such as a stream or a tree, which provide a pleasing level of sensory input with minimal cognitive effort (Pheasant *et al.* 2008). Similar results were derived from a national participatory appraisal which related tranquillity to both the presence of positive visual and aural factors, and the absence of negative factors (Jackson *et al.* 2008). Hearing birdsong and peace and quiet were seen as positive; hearing traffic was negative (**Table 14.16**). Using these results, and appropriate weightings for 44 indicators, relative tranquillity maps for England (500 m x 500 m resolution) have been developed (Jackson *et al.* 2008; CPRE 2009). The emphasis given to both positive and negative features means that the new tranquillity maps differ from the noise and visual intrusion maps described in **Figure 14.4.**

14.6.4 Options for Sustainable Management

Tranquillity is an important reason why people value green spaces and the countryside (Defra 2009d). Research has shown that people are willing to pay significant sums of money for reductions in the level of noise, and hence, noise should be a feature of the cost-benefit analysis of changes in transport infrastructure (Nellthorp *et al.* 2007). Such noise can be significant even beyond the narrow zone close to the road or railway (Countryside Agency & CPRE 2006). Methods to reduce the impact of noise in relation to traffic can focus on reducing the number of journeys, the noise per journey, or the effect of the emitted noise (**Table 14.17**). Many of these interventions act in the same way as methods to address other environmental issues such as the reduction of GHG emissions.

Table 14.16 The weighting (%) given to the top six factors (out of 44) contributing to and detracting from tranquillity as determined by 1,347 people.
Source: data from Jackson *et al.* (2008).

What is tranquillity?		What is not tranquillity?	
Seeing a natural landscape	6.6	Hearing constant noise from road transport	11.0
Hearing bird song	4.9	Seeing lots of people	7.8
Having peace and quiet	3.3	Seeing urban development	4.5

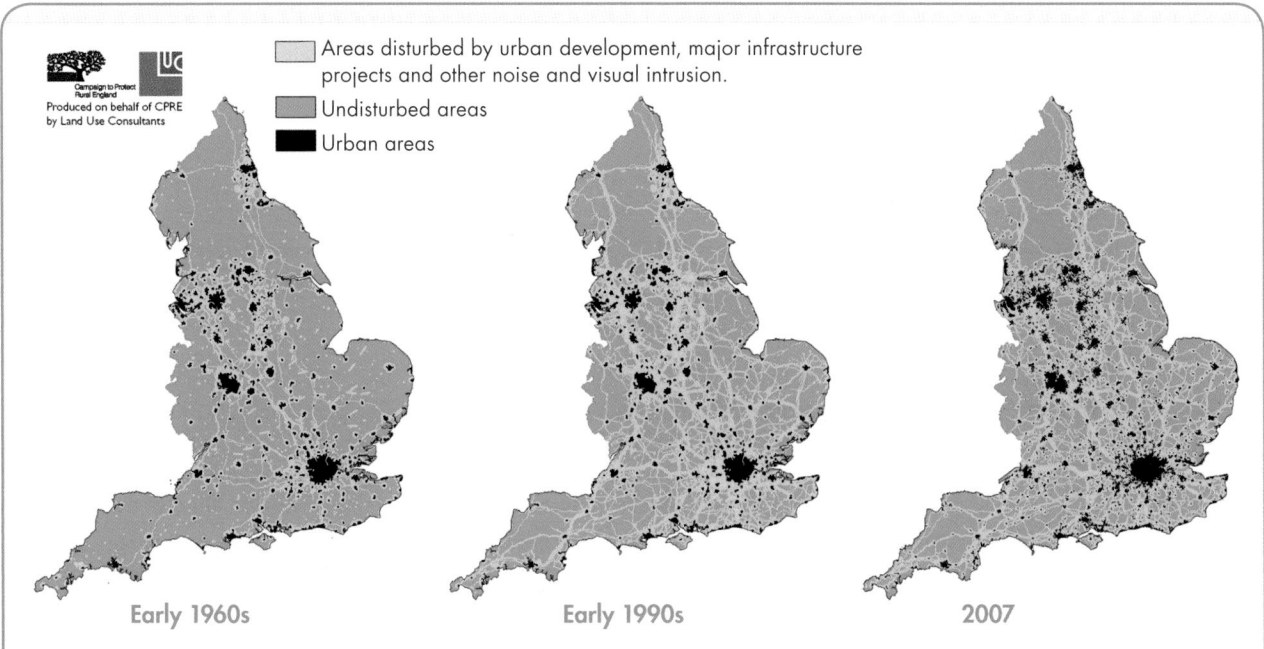

Figure 14.4 Noise and visual intrusion map for England for the early 1960s, early 1990s, and 2007. Source: maps reproduced with permission from the Campaign for the Protection of Rural England (CPRE & LUC 2007). Crown copyright 2007. Produced by Land Use Consultants 2007. Licence No. 100019265.

Ecosystem noise regulation can be linked to changes in land form, the lateral interception of noise by vegetation, and the reduced reflection of noise by porous surfaces. Hence, the effect of noise from roads can be regulated by reducing the height of the road relative to the surrounding environment, or by constructing angled soil bunds to reflect noise upwards (Highways Agency 2008). The construction of 3–5 m-tall noise barriers, typically constructed from concrete and wood, can reduce noise levels by 8 dB(A) (Huddart 1990). Trees and other vegetation are often planted in front of such barriers to improve the visual impact. In a major review, Huddart (1990) also examined how vegetation can reduce traffic noise directly. When planted close to a road, a dense 10 m-deep row of trees was able to reduce noise levels by 8 dB(A) and 5 dB(A) compared to hard ground and grass respectively. For a 20 m-deep row, the corresponding reductions were 10 and 6 dB(A). Although requiring more space, these are similar to the reductions achieved with constructed barriers. Huddart (1990) reported that tree foliage was particularly effective at regulating high frequency sounds (>2,000 Hz), and that soft, wet, and porous surfaces were effective at reducing the reflection of low frequency sounds (<1,000 Hz). Fang and Ling (2005) reported that the greatest noise reductions occurred when the height of the tree row was at least three times that of the noise source and receiver, and when the distance between the source and receiver was less than eight times the tree height.

14.6.5 Knowledge Gaps

Spatial modelling of noise has increased substantially in response to the implementation of the 2002/49 European Directive on the Assessment and Management of Environmental Noise (END) in the UK. In 2006, maps of predicted noise levels in England were developed for 23 urban areas with populations greater than 250,000, and major roads, railways and airports (Defra 2009e). Similar maps have also been created for Scotland (Scottish Government 2007), Wales and Northern Ireland. The Directive requires the relevant authority to draw up action plans to "reduce noise where necessary" and "maintain environmental noise quality where it is good".

While spatial modelling of noise has increased, actual measurements of noise seem very limited. As shown by Skinner and Grimwood (2002), it is useful to be able to compare perceptions of noise with actual measurements. In particular, there is minimal information on the actual sound environment in rural areas. The British Government Panel on Sustainable Development (1999) also highlights a lack of a national structure for monitoring complaints regarding traffic noise. Lastly, Payne *et al.* (2009) have highlighted the need for interdisciplinary research as the perception of noise depends on more than one sense, and there is a need to rigorously assess which interventions work and to link this with design and planning practice.

14.7 Soil Quality Regulation

14.7.1 Trends in Soil Quality

Although not explicitly mentioned in the MA, soil quality has a pivotal role in regulating services, along with air and water quality. We are reliant upon our soils to capture and release carbon, nutrients and water, detoxify pollutants, purify water, and suppress soil-dwelling pests and pathogens (Janvier 2007). The capacity of soil for regulation is determined by the interaction of its chemical composition, physical integrity and the structure and activity of soil biodiversity. Different soil types (Chapter 13) have different inherent regulating capacities. For example, certain soils are more suppressive of plant pathogens than others (Thuerig *et al.* 2009), while others provide better buffers against atmospheric pollutants (Hornung *et al.* 1995). This information is widely communicated as indicators of soil quality which are used to report on status and trends in land use, management practices and wider policy interventions. For instance, the capacity for soils to buffer against atmospheric deposition has been used to establish critical loads of atmospheric pollutants for UK habitats (**Figure 14.5**). The United Nations Economic Commission for Europe (UNECE) Convention on Long-range Transboundary Air Pollution is using information such as this to reduce emissions of air pollutants and, therefore, reduce risks to humans and the environment.

Unlike air and water quality, there is no legislation to specifically protect soil quality to maintain regulating services, although much legislation targets environmental protection *per se* and soil quality is included. The protection of soil quality is encouraged, for example, by the 2010 Soil Protection Review and associated 2010 Soil Cross Compliance Guidance, and the 2009 Defra Code for Good Agricultural Practice.

Table 14.17 Methods of reducing the emission and effects of transport noise. Source: adapted from Wright (2007) and Girvin (2009).

Means of transport	Reduce traffic flow	Reduce noise per journey	Reduce effect of noise
Road	Noise impact assessments on new roads; tolls, congestion charges; bus and high-occupancy-vehicle lane initiatives.	Speed restrictions; restrictions on engines; quieter road surfaces; tyre design.	Noise barriers; sound-proofing buildings; use of vegetation; building dwellings away from roads.
Rail	Reduced train journeys could increase road and aircraft transport.	Maintenance and repair of rolling stock.	Reduce amplification on structures.
Air	Taxes on air fuel, high occupancy initiatives.	Noise-restrictions and taxes; quiet aircraft technology; modified flight patterns.	Property acquisition around airports; timing and routing of flights; noise barriers.

Furthermore, statutory limits exist for concentrations of certain pollutants in soils to protect human health, and there are national headline indicators of soil organic matter for the Sustainable Food and Farming Strategy in England and Wales in recognition of its importance to a range of ecosystem services. Indicators of soil quality relevant to regulating services have been extensively reviewed for the purposes of UK monitoring and to aid policy decisions (Environment Agency 2006; Aalders et al. 2009), along with designs for a fully integrated trans-UK soil monitoring scheme. Until such a scheme is established, assessments of soil quality status and trends depend on data from large-scale and long-term surveys and experiments (Kirby et al. 2005; McDonald et al. 2007; Kirk et al. 2009; Emmett et al. 2010).

14.7.1.1 Retention, detoxification and degradation of pollutants, nutrients and carbon

Soil carbon acts as a surrogate measure for Soil Organic Matter (SOM) content which is vital for regulation. As well as binding and buffering the release of chemicals, SOM affects water retention and infiltration. Since the 1970s, the carbon content of topsoil has shown no significant change in soils under most semi-natural habitats, but small declines in arable soils (Kirby et al. 2005; Bellamy et al. 2005; Carey et al. 2008). There is increasing evidence that a significant proportion of arable soils are close to, or below, the critical threshold for SOM (Emmett et al. 2010). It remains to be determined whether exceedance of SOM levels can be linked to observed changes in soil compaction (Batey 2009), which is associated with reduced water infiltration and soil erosion from fields. In contrast to arable soils (which are generally mineral-derived) these surveys report conflicting trends in SOM and carbon for organic soils in various semi-natural habitats. These differences may reflect different sampling and analytical approaches. Given the significance of organic matter to regulating, and other, services, it is important that these issues are resolved. Forthcoming results from Scotland and the forestry sector's BioSoil Survey may help as they aim to assess trends in soil carbon data to greater depths.

Concentrations of heavy metal pollutants in soils reflect historical and current pressures alongside natural conditions. The recent UK Soil and Herbage Survey (UKSHS) (Environment Agency 2007) indicates that concentrations of copper, lead, mercury, nickel, zinc and tin are higher in urban and industrial soils than rural soils. In the main, these reflect inputs from industry and transport. Elevated levels of tin in soils of Scotland and Northern Ireland reflect local geology (Environment Agency 2007; Emmett et al. 2010). Recent trends in GB-wide topsoil metal concentrations from the Countryside Survey are summarised in **Table 14.18**. In general there have been relatively small changes in metal concentrations between 1998 and 2007. It is not clear what may be causing these trends—they may reflect reductions in atmospheric pollution, changes to farming practice or even reductions in SOM (as a binding agent) in arable soils. Increases within bog habitats may reflect the continued and undisturbed capture of atmospheric pollutants by organic matter.

Countryside Survey results also indicate that concentrations of heavy metals in rural soils are generally below regulatory limits, although zinc poses the most significant risk to soil organisms. Concentrations in grassland soils probably reflect sewage sludge applications, while concentrations in organic soils suggest retention of pollutants from atmospheric deposition (Spurgeon et al. 2008). Recent studies suggest that soil microorganisms responsible for nitrogen fixation (rhizobia) are sensitive to zinc concentrations below current statutory limits (McDonald et al. 2007; Defra 2009f).

The UKSHS results (Environment Agency 2007) indicate that soil concentrations of polychlorinated biphenyls in urban and industrial areas are about 1.5 times those in soils of rural areas. However, the concentrations of polychlorinated biphenyls in soil have fallen approximately 800-fold since the mid-1970s, reflecting changes to industrial production restrictions. Concentrations of total polycyclic aromatic hydrocarbons and benzo(a)pyrene in urban and industrial soils are around five to seven times those in rural areas. Regional differences in polycyclic aromatic hydrocarbon concentrations have been attributed to differences in industrial processes, fossil fuel use (e.g. coal burning and traffic) and historical agricultural inputs (Heywood et al. 2006). Soil dioxin levels increased between 1850 and 1980

Table 14.18 Trends from 1998 to 2007 in topsoil concentrations of heavy metals (0–15 cm) in broad habitats of GB. Arrows indicate significant increases (↑) or decreases (↓) during this period. Source: data from Emmett et al. (2010). Countryside Survey data owned by NERC – Centre for Ecology & Hydrology.

Broad habitat	Cadmium	Copper	Chromium	Nickel	Lead	Zinc
Broadleaved, mixed and yew woodland			↓	↓		
Coniferous woodland						
Arable and horticulture			↓	↓		↓
Improved grassland		↑	↓		↑	
Neutral grassland			↓	↓		↓
Dwarf shrub heath		↑			↑	
Fen, marsh and swamp						
Bog		↑	↑	↑		↑
All habitats		↑				

due to industrial processes, but results from the UKSHS indicate that levels have since dropped by approximately 70%. Across the UK, concentrations of dioxins in urban and industrial soils are two to three times greater than rural soils. Therefore, results indicate that UK soils are maintaining a capacity to detoxify and degrade organic pollutants. However, there is no information to indicate whether this capacity has changed in recent years, for example, through changes to soil pH and SOM.

Long-term atmospheric deposition of sulphur ('acid rain') has compromised the detoxifying and degrading capacity of UK soils with a historical lowering of soil pH throughout the country. This will have influenced the capacity to maintain other aspects of regulation such as metal retention, water purification and nutrient retention, as well as habitat integrity (**Figure 14.5**). Results from several surveys indicate that soils are now recovering from acidification, with significant increases in soil pH since the late 1970s and early 1980s

across most broad habitats (Kirby *et al.* 2005; Kirk *et al.* 2009; Emmett *et al.* 2010). These broad-scale increases reflect successful reductions in acid rain from emissions abatement (NEGTAP 2001). There are concerns that this recovery may be short-lived since continued atmospheric deposition of nitrogen will reinitiate acidification. In contrast, sulphur deficiency is being re-established in certain soils, particularly in South East England, with corresponding additional agrochemical inputs required to maintain crop production (McGrath & Zhao 1995).

Many broad habitats are now displaying nutrient enrichment through agricultural inputs and from atmospheric deposition, both point source and diffuse, which is reflected in extensive exceedance of broad habitat critical loads for nitrogen (RoTAP 2011), eutrophication issues for water quality (Section 14.7.1.2) and, more recently, changes to above-ground plant communities (Smart *et al.* 2003) and soil microbial communities (Smith *et al.* 2003).

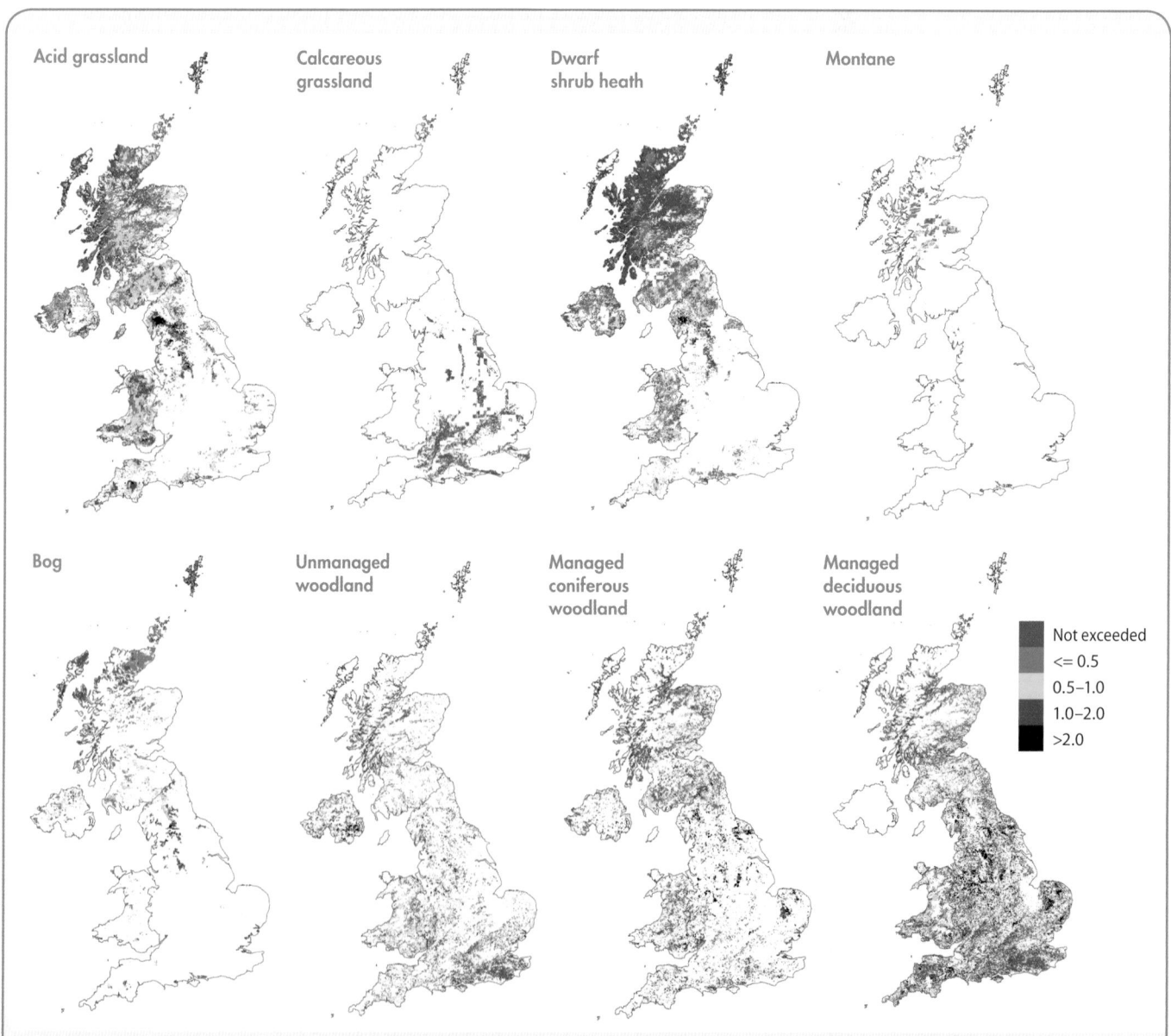

Figure 14.5 Exceedance of the critical loads of acidity for UK broad habitats by acid deposition for 2006–2008. The critical loads of acidity are determined by the buffering capacity of the dominant soil type in each 1x1 km square and habitat-specific parameters. Source: Centre for Ecology and Hydrology; Hall *et al.* (2003, 2004, 2008, 2009); http://cldm.defra.gov.uk)

These above-ground trends are not reflected in results from the Countryside Survey where topsoil nitrogen and Olsen phosphorus have both declined in almost all broad habitats from 1998 to 2007.

Historical local discharges and transboundary pollution from atom bomb-testing and nuclear incidents (e.g. Chernobyl) have resulted in elevated soil concentrations of radionuclides across the UK. Geographical patterns reflect sources as well as regional weather patterns and soil binding capacity. Soil radionuclide levels have declined in recent decades as pollutants decay and releases to the environment are reduced, with only a few locations continuing to have restricted land use from the Chernobyl fallout. These restrictions are based on a critical load approach to account for the transfer of radionuclides from soils to humans through the food chain and, more recently, for the protection of species and habitats under Natura 2000 (Environment Agency 2001).

14.7.1.2 Regulating the exchange of gases with the atmosphere

Model development and experimental studies indicate that poorly drained soils in agricultural use, in particular intensive dairy, are major sources of nitrous oxide, while organic soils with high water content are primary sources of methane (e.g. bogs and moorlands). See Section 14.2.1 for trends in GHGs in relation to land use change. There is no data on long-term trends in the capacity of soils to regulate gas exchange. Raising water tables in organic soils, as part of habitat restoration, will significantly increase methane release and should be balanced against any overall ecosystem carbon gains.

14.7.1.3 Suppressing pests and pathogens

There are distinct differences in the capacities of UK soils to suppress pathogens and pests (Section 14.5) which reflect the structure and activities of soil micro-organisms and soil chemico-physical conditions. There is no information on the current status or trends in soil suppression, which may or may not correspond to changes in the incidence of gastro-intestinal diseases involving transfers from livestock to humans via the soil.

14.7.1.4 Regulating the release of water

Regional changes to soil moisture deficits over the last 30 years reflect changing rainfall patterns (Defra 2003; Brown *et al.* 2009). However, there is a lack of information in habitat-level trends in water release from soils (Section 14.4) or in the aspects of soil quality which determine flows. Circumstantial evidence suggests that soil water retention capacity may be at risk. Results on soil bulk density from the Countryside Survey indicate that many soils in agriculture and horticulture are showing signs of reduced aeration which may influence water flow (Carey *et al.* 2008). Experimental studies indicate that reduced SOM in arable soils makes these soils more susceptible to structural damage. Evidence of localised soil compaction in agricultural soils is associated with changes in water runoff from agricultural land and in the built environment, and with increased erosion of organic soils.

14.7.2 Drivers of Change

There are numerous drivers of change in soil quality which reflect practices and objectives on many levels from local to international. For example, in direct management, farmers apply lime to alter soil buffering capacity and nutrient availability, while international regulations to control air pollution indirectly change soil quality by reducing the levels of pollutant inputs to soils from trans-boundary sources. The significance and extent of these drivers on soil quality are determined by geographical location (reflecting climate), land use, management within habitats and the resilience of individual soils to change. Soils, unlike air and water, are highly resistant to change and it can take several years or even decades for drivers of change to cause damage to soil quality, particularly where drivers are of relatively low, but repeated, intensity e.g. atmospheric inputs. There is considerable uncertainty over the timescales in, and success of, achieving recovery of soil quality for regulating services.

14.7.2.1 Agriculture and forestry

As major UK land uses, management practices within agriculture and forestry have a significant influence on all aspects of soil quality, with corresponding consequences for air and water quality (Angus *et al.* 2009; Burgess & Morris 2009). There are numerous policies, codes of practice and guidance to maintain soil quality in these land uses. Most are targeted at maintaining water or air quality or biomass production rather than soil quality *per se* (Kibblewhite *et al.* 2008). Common management practices include:

- *Liming:* Given the acidic nature of most UK soils, liming has been a fundamental input to agricultural soils for many centuries in order to maintain an appropriate pH for biomass production and improve soil structure and suitability for metal additions. There are recognised trade-offs with liming between the maintenance of biodiversity in species-rich grassland and demands for agricultural productions. It has yet to be established whether broad-scale increases in soil pH, from reduced acid rain, is influencing the application of lime to agricultural and forest soils.
- *Mechanisation and tillage practices:* The continuing trend for larger and heavier field machinery increases the risk of soil compaction, leading to reduced infiltration and storage of water and, potentially, increased soil erosion. Impacts of mechanisation can be minimised by use of tramlines, tracked vehicles or low pressure tyres, and corrected through cultivation and sub-soiling. Minimal cultivation systems have been proposed as an option to increase soil carbon, but there are important trade-offs to consider with soil compaction, weed control, GHG releases and yield maintenance.
- *Drainage:* Post World War II agricultural and forestry expansion led to extensive drainage to improve soil structure and workability for crop production. It is not clear what impact this, or the subsequent removal of drainage subsidies in the 1970s, may have had on soil quality.
- *Use of manure and artificial fertiliser:* The impacts of these on soil quality are widely documented. Technology and management tools to match fertiliser additions to soil type

and crop requirements can help minimise application rates and losses through leaching and volatilisation.

- *Simplification of cropping rotations*: A reduction in ley-arable rotations and increasing use of monocultures can influence potential pollutant levels, the suppression of pests, pathogen and weeds, and SOM levels. There is insufficient information to determine the beneficial or detrimental impacts of different cropping systems on soil quality for regulating services in the UK.

14.7.2.2 Semi-natural habitats

Drivers of change in semi-natural habitats consist mainly of the following:

- *Inappropriate burning of heather* to support game leaves soil exposed, can degrade SOM and release pollutants from the soil store to air and water.
- *Removal of historical drainage* is being used to restore regulating services in organic soils. This drainage was often installed as a precursor to land use change to forestry or agricultural intensification.
- *Restoration of vegetation.* A significant proportion of broad habitats are in poor ecological condition. Above-ground restoration activities are rather localised, but will have consequences below-ground.
- *Peat harvesting* for horticultural and fuel use. Losses of soil stock have obvious implications for soil quality
- *Recreation activities* are generally localised, but are an increasing driver in rural areas.

14.7.2.3 Universal extent

The follow drivers of change occur across all habitats:

- *Climate change, with associated policies and targets*: Although climate change has been identified as the primary threat to soils and soil quality across the UK (Towers *et al.* 2006; Defra 2009f), there are significant uncertainties over the likely responses of soils, particularly SOM and consequences for regulating services. Potential changes to the extent and management of habitats, in particular agricultural land, will have major consequences for soil quality.
- *National and EU Policy objectives:* Implementation of the Water Framework Directive and Common Agricultural Policy (CAP) cross-compliance should lead to improved soil quality for regulating services. Within England, soil policy is working to halt the decline of SOM by 2025 in arable, grassland and semi-natural habitats through improved management practices and reductions in peat-cutting. Targets for habitat restoration, particularly for the restoration of degraded bogs and heaths, will also lead to changes in soil quality. In all instances, there needs to be careful consideration of how changes to soil quality for regulating services may alter the soils' capacity to deliver other services.
- *Pollution emissions abatement:* The application of national and international regulations to limit releases of pollutants from point and diffuse sources is having considerable impacts on pollutant levels in UK soils. It is widely acknowledged that atmospheric nitrogen pollution will have to be lowered further to reduce future risks to soils, waters and habitats.

- *Soil-sealing* through rural developments, such as wind farms, and the expansion of urban and industrial areas, is recognised as a major threat to soils. For example, about 18,000 ha of previously undeveloped land were developed in England between 2001 and 2003 (Defra 2009f). Development typically removes the upper soil layers with a total loss in inherent soil quality for all services. This soil loss has been linked to increased runoff and flooding in urban areas. In recognition of this, planning and development are increasingly utilising and benefiting from the buffering and storage capacity of soils in order to deliver effective urban drainage systems. New standards have been introduced to guide the replacement of topsoil on development sites and reconstruct a more typical soil to support a range of ecosystem services.
- *Remediation of contaminated land* with targets to reduce risk from, and extent of, contaminated land will continue to improve soil quality in urban and industrial areas.
- *Rural drainage systems:* There is increasing evidence that septic tank systems from domestic dwellings are a significant source of pollutant and nutrient loadings to soils, with increasing risk of transfer to waters.
- *Overgrazing or inappropriate livestock densities* influence soil compaction, soil erosion, pathogen loadings and soil nutrient inputs. Guidance on good agricultural practice serves to limit the impact of stocking on soil quality in farmed land.

14.7.3 Consequences of Change

UK soils are already exceeding their capacity to adequately buffer ecosystems from atmospheric pollution, with well-documented consequences for air and water quality and habitat condition. This capacity has been exceeded for the majority of Broad Habitats although exceedance for individual Broad Habitats differs with geographical location; for instance, organic soils associated with bog habitats are at greater risk from atmospheric pollution in northern England than in the north of Scotland. This reduced capacity for soil buffering is linked to reductions in water quality (Section 14.7.4) and to reductions in some fungal species. There is clearly potential to improve aspects of soil quality to restore and enhance regulating services, for example, through judicious increases in SOM content and improvement in soil structural integrity. The potential benefits are clearly laid out through current estimates of the economic and environmental consequences of soil quality degradation, as illustrated below.

In the UK, the financial costs of soil carbon lost to cultivation have recently been estimated at £82 million per annum. In upland semi-natural habitats, large increases in the release of dissolved organic carbon (DOC) from organic soils since the 1980s represent a major operational cost to the water industry. The restoration of organic soils in north-west England is anticipated to save up to £2.4 million per year in avoided water treatment costs. Degradation of organic soils can also lead to losses of biodiversity, archaeological remains and paleo-climatic records, and can speed up the flow of water across the landscape, potentially increasing the risk of flooding downstream. Restoring the soil's capacity to retain carbon will make an important contribution to climate change mitigation.

Heavy metals have the potential to irreversibly alter the soil's capacity to support ecosystems, habitats and biodiversity, and may be a risk to human health. Metal concentrations in soils are exceptionally difficult to lower once the metal has been introduced. Metals, especially zinc, affect soil respiration rates, the soil microbial community and fixation of atmospheric nitrogen. Threshold levels only exist for farmed and developed land. Ingestion by grazing animals is considered to be the pathway which holds the greatest risk of Persistent Organic Pollutants (POPs) entering the food chain. The acidification of soils can lead to detrimental effects on ecosystems, plant growth and community structure, and soil biodiversity.

The annual cost of flooding due to soil degradation is difficult to assess, with estimates ranging from £29 million to £128 million (2004/05 prices) for England and Wales alone. This does not include the impact of flooding on health, well-being and quality of life. Soil-sealing can increase rainwater runoff by as much as 50% and increases the risks of urban flooding and costs in insurance claims. Compaction decreases the infiltration capacity of the soil and increases the risk of runoff leading to flooding. It can also increase the risk of soil erosion, affect crop yields, and have a negative impact on both above-ground and below-ground biodiversity. Estimated annual costs of soil degradation are summarised in **Table 14.19**.

14.7.4 Options for Sustainable Management

UK governments and land use sectors are committed to protecting and improving soil quality for regulating and other services (Scottish Government 2009; Defra 2009g). There is a wealth of guidance on management requirements to maintain, improve or remediate soil quality for regulating services (Kibblewhite *et al.* 2008). In this context, key objectives of sustainable management practices are generally targeted at improving SOM content, improving soil structural integrity, removing or reducing pollutant loadings and toxicity levels, and retaining and utilising the soil stock. All land use sectors will increasingly need to consider how climate change will influence soil quality (e.g. soil moisture deficits, rates of soil biological processes) and management options for adaptation.

Table 14.19 Annual cost of soil degradation based on evidence presented in the Soil Strategy For England (Defra 2009f) (where values are available, but excluding contaminated land identification and remediation). Source: Defra (2009g).

Annual cost of soil degradation (£ millions)	
Soil erosion due to agriculture	45
Loss of soil carbon due to cultivation	82
Flooding due to structural damage to soil	29–128
Sediment in urban drainage systems	50–60
Total	**206–315**

14.7.4.1 Agriculture and forestry

The UK has a wealth of information and guidance for soil management in the agricultural and forestry sectors (Cranfield University 2007), and there are a multitude of management options for land managers to improve and restore soil quality. Key targets are to retain and halt the loss in SOM content and improve soil structure (Defra 2009g), with obvious benefits to regulating services. Economic drivers, alongside water quality and climate change policies, are pointing towards greater nutrient efficiencies and alternative nutrient sources which could be used to reduce nutrient and GHG transfers along with providing biodiversity benefits. Therefore, there will clearly be a need to develop alternative management strategies. Sustainable management of soil quality in the agricultural and forestry sectors now requires careful evaluation of current and alternative practices to assess the benefits and trade-offs of changing land use or practices. Lifecycle analysis and multi-criteria evaluation offer tools to explore options for balancing soil quality to maintain regulating and production services, and to ensure that management changes do not result in pollution swapping (e.g. increased GHG emissions instead of nutrient leaching) or detrimental losses to other ecosystem services.

14.7.4.2 Semi-natural habitats

In habitats of conservation interest, management strategies will be looking to reduce soil nutrient loadings to minimise impacts of eutrophication on habitats and waters. However, without further significant reductions in atmospheric nitrogen deposition, it may be impossible to achieve current conservation goals. In the short-term, therefore, site-level management will be dependent upon reliable information on current soil quality status to determine what management strategies will be feasible and achievable. Recent research has highlighted that improving the retention and storage of SOM in many habitats, in particular peatlands, will be reliant upon practices which can effectively restore soil microbial community structure (Artz *et al.* 2007). In this context, there is a need to determine how effective habitat and vegetation restoration practices (such as grip-blocking, planting, etc.) are at restoring below-ground functions, and over what timescales soil function can be restored to acceptable levels.

14.7.4.3 Urban and industrial areas

There is increasing awareness that sustainable soil use and management can benefit planning and development. Benefits to urban soil quality will be achieved through the uptake and use of the revised standards for topsoil use in developments, while retention of soil stock is recognised as an increasingly important resource for sustainable urban drainage (Defra 2009f). In parallel, there are opportunities to support expansion of allotments and urban gardens through continued practices to reduce the extent and levels of soil contamination.

Sustainable management of soils for regulating services will require consideration of the investment needed to maintain and achieve improvements in soil quality. Who bears the cost of achieving benefits if the benefits are derived off-field or off-site? Catchment management and river basin plans for water quality improvements are going some way in dealing with this issue. Successes here demonstrate that the success of, and challenges to, sustainable management of soil quality for benefits to regulating services are the effective integration and evaluation of multiple management objectives to ensure that the outcomes are complementary and do not result in conflicting outcomes for environmental, economic and social endpoints at different spatial and temporal scales.

14.7.5 Knowledge Gaps

Compatible soil monitoring is required across the UK to provide the information necessary to assess status and trends in soil quality for regulating services. The suitability of numerous indicators of soil quality have been widely reviewed and assessed (Aalders *et al.* 2009; Defra 2009f), demonstrating recognised gaps in suitable indicators of physical soil quality (addressing soil structural changes and water transfer) and in the need for soil profile assessments. Updated information can be used to review our current interpretations of how soils are maintaining capacities to filter, buffer, transform and degrade.

Although various soil quality indicators have been identified for regulating services, data is still limited on optimal ranges, thresholds or trigger values for soil quality in individual Broad Habitats. This information will be required by land managers or other stakeholders to plan and assess the effectiveness of current or future management options to improve soil quality. The critical loads approach for atmospheric pollution has clearly demonstrated that a sound scientific understanding of the buffering capacity of soils can lead to the development of effective risk assessment and mitigation strategies at a range of spatial and temporal scales.

It is crucial that discrepancies in recent results for topsoil soil carbon across the UK are resolved. The UK is relatively rich in soils information and, with the experiences of several large-scale soil surveys, well-placed to resolve globally significant issues regarding the effective monitoring of soil carbon stocks and in improving our understanding of the sensitivity of soil carbon to climate change and other drivers.

Soil organic matter is fundamental to soil quality which underpins the role of soils in regulating services. The potential mechanisms for, and benefits of, increasing SOM in agricultural soils (and thereby reducing GHGs from soils) should be evaluated. With a significant proportion of organic soils in semi-natural habitats in a degraded state, there is a major opportunity to increase soil carbon stocks. This will require evaluation of the techniques for protecting and enhancing SOM stores over decades.

Guidance, policy and regulation will need to be evolved to provide more integrated protection to soil quality for regulating and other services, pollutants, and other pressures and drivers. This will require improvements in our capacity to predict the acceptable ranges or thresholds for pollutant loadings within individual habitats which reflect the range of services required. Site-level critical loads and the radiological Environmental Risk from Ionising Contamination (ERICA) approach are examples of how information could be used to

improve soil quality and habitat condition. In parallel, there remain key uncertainties in the mechanism transferring certain pollutants and pathogens from soils to waters.

A major challenge for protecting soil quality will be to disentangle the relative importance of direct and indirect drivers, in particular management practices, atmospheric pollution and climate change. Given the ubiquity of soils, the diversity of drivers of change and the multiple consequences of degradation in soil quality, novel approaches are now required to understand the consequences of multiple drivers across spatial and temporal scales and to keep a watching brief on emerging issues including new wastes and nanotechnologies. This will require better knowledge on the responsiveness or resilience of different soils within individual Broad Habitats in different geographical locations.

14.8 Air Quality Regulation

14.8.1 Trends in Air Quality

The main air pollutants of concern, which are considered under the national Air Quality Strategy (Defra 2007) and in international policy evaluation, are particles (PM), ozone, nitrogen oxides, ammonia and the deposition of nitrogen and sulphur. **Table 14.20** provides an overview of the major effects and trends for these air pollutants (based primarily on Defra (2007) and RoTAP (2011), and summarises the main mechanisms of ecosystem regulation.

There have been significant improvements in UK air quality over recent decades, but these have largely been driven by reductions in anthropogenic emissions such as those from transport or power generation (Defra 2007; RoTAP 2011). However, current concentrations and deposition rates still exceed thresholds for negative effects on human health and ecosystem services over significant areas of the UK. Although planned measures will further reduce emissions, substantial areas of exceedance of critical loads and critical levels (which are set as thresholds for adverse effects on sensitive ecosystems) will remain in 2020 (RoTAP 2011).

Ecosystem regulation can influence concentrations and deposition of air pollutants in four major ways. These four effects of ecosystems can be considered in terms of the impact of local anthropogenic sources, such as roads or intensive livestock units, or in terms of the transport, deposition and impacts of pollutants from a range of national and trans-boundary sources.

1. *Ecosystems remove pollutants from the atmosphere, reducing local and regional air pollutant concentrations.* Tree species are particularly effective at capturing pollutant particles and gases (Fowler *et al.* 1989; Beckett *et al.* 1998). Increasing urban tree planting and green space (Chapter 10) will, therefore, tend to increase the deposition of particulate and gaseous pollutants, and improve air quality. Recent modelling exercises provide some indication of the potential benefits. McDonald *et al.*

(2007) estimate that the current 7% tree cover in the West Midlands region reduces mean air concentrations of PM_{10} (particles above 10 μm) by 4%, and that increasing this to a theoretical maximum of 54% would reduce mean PM_{10} concentrations by 26%. The equivalent figures for Glasgow were lower, only 2% for current tree cover and 7% for maximum cover, primarily because the space available for tree planting in the city centre, where the greatest emissions and concentrations occur, is lower. The health implications of these reductions in concentrations have not been fully evaluated, although Tiwary *et al.* (2009) used a similar modelling approach to estimate the benefits of increasing urban greenspace in a 10 km grid square of East London. They calculated that two deaths and two hospital admissions would be averted each year as a result.

2. *Ecosystems contribute directly to emissions to the atmosphere.* The major contributor is the agricultural sector which is responsible for over 90% of UK emissions of ammonia. While a significant proportion of this is emitted from animal housing, mainly intensive pig and poultry units, the remainder is associated with grazing animals (primarily cattle), manure spreading and fertiliser use. These national ammonia emissions rose to a peak in 1990, but have subsequently declined, primarily because of a reduction in animal numbers and nitrogen use in fertilisers (RoTAP 2011).

3. *Emissions from ecosystems contribute indirectly to air pollution levels via chemical processing in the atmosphere.* The most important of these effects is the emission of reactive volatile organic compounds (VOCs), such as isoprene, which contribute significantly to the formation of ozone, especially during the summer (AQEG 2009). As anthropogenic emissions of VOCs fall, this source will become increasingly important. National inventories of biogenic emissions exist, but past and future trends are uncertain (AQEG 2009), although the high variation in

emission rates between species means that trends in land cover are likely to influence national emissions.

4. *Measures to reduce emissions to, or deposition from, the atmosphere can increase the potential for air quality regulation by ecosystems.* This is primarily because any pollutant deposited or absorbed from the atmosphere by ecosystems is more likely to have adverse effects on those ecosystems when concentrations or deposition rates are high. An important trend in recent decades is the effect of reduced anthropogenic emissions leading to decreased urban concentrations of smoke and sulphur dioxide, which has allowed increased urban planting of conifer species. In turn, this increases interception and deposition of air pollution, hence further improving air quality. At a national scale, there is evidence that the UK landscape has become a more efficient absorber of sulphur dioxide as concentrations have fallen, further decreasing air concentrations (RoTAP 2011).

In addition to chemical pollutants, ecosystems alter air quality through the release of allergens and, in particular, pollen spores. The area affected depends on the pollen spore size; tree pollen is generally larger and travels smaller distances than grass pollen, which has a regional impact. Long-term records provide some evidence of a trend of greater and earlier tree pollen counts, but little evidence of a consistent trend in grass pollen (Spieksma *et al.* 2003).

14.8.2 Drivers of Change
The main drivers of change in air quality over recent decades have been changes in anthropogenic emissions. In terms of ecosystem regulation of air quality, two main drivers can be identified.

4.8.2.1 Land use and management
Local planting of trees and other vegetation in urban areas, especially in areas with high rates of pollutant

Table 14.20 Summary of air quality effects, trends and impacts of ecosystem regulation.

Air pollutant	Major effects	Trend since 1990	Major impacts of ecosystem regulation
Particulate Matter (PM)	Human health	Decreased concentrations	Deposition to plant surfaces, reducing air concentrations, and hence impacts on health. Emissions during fire events. Production of pollen.
Ozone	Human health Reduced crop and forest yield. Changes in species composition.	Decrease in peak concentrations. Increase in background concentrations.	Deposition, through surface deposition and stomatal uptake, reducing air concentrations and hence impacts on health and other ecosystem services. Emission of volatile organic compounds that can contribute to ozone formation.
Nitrogen oxides Ammonia Nitrogen deposition	Human health (nitrogen oxides in urban areas). Ecosystem eutrophication Ecosystem acidification	Decrease in emissions, especially of nitrogen oxide, but only small reduction in nitrogen deposition.	Deposition, reducing air concentrations and hence impacts on health and other ecosystem services. Deposition above critical thresholds can affect sensitive aquatic and terrestrial habitats. Emissions from livestock and from use of manure and fertilisers.
Sulphur deposition	Ecosystem acidification	Decreased deposition	Deposition, reducing air concentrations and hence impacts on health and other ecosystem services. Deposition above critical thresholds can affect sensitive aquatic and terrestrial habitats.

emission, improves air quality by increasing interception and deposition (Beckett *et al.* 1998). It can also have benefits in terms of local climate and noise regulation. Tree planting around pollution sources, and more widely across the UK countryside, likewise increases removal of pollutants from the atmosphere. However, increased tree cover can have adverse effects of pollutant deposition on soils and freshwaters in sensitive catchments (RoTAP 2011) and, depending on species, may increase biogenic VOC emissions. Changes in livestock numbers, fertiliser application rates and methods of manure application will all change ammonia emission rates, and changes in land cover and grassland management can affect rates of pollen release.

4.8.2.2 Climate

Climate directly affects air quality, through changes in wind direction, atmospheric dispersal and atmospheric photochemistry. It also has indirect effects through ecosystem regulation (AQEG 2007). The most important of these effects are seen in hot dry summers. Such conditions increase the frequency of forest fires, mainly outside the UK, which can contribute to episodes of high particulate concentrations. Warmer spring weather has also led to earlier pollen release for some species, and a longer pollen season (van Vliet *et al.* 2002; Emberlin *et al.* 2002). Warmer soil temperatures can increase ammonia emissions, and also increase methane fluxes which contribute to regional ozone production. Emissions of biogenic VOCs, which lead to ozone formation, are highly temperature dependent, for example, isoprene emissions increase by a factor of four between 20–30°C (Guenther *et al.* 1993). Decreased soil water availability will close stomata and, therefore, decrease the removal of air pollutants, such as ozone and ammonia, through stomatal uptake. For instance, in the heatwave of 2003, a decrease in deposition from the atmosphere because of decreased soil water is thought to have contributed to an increase in ozone concentrations of about 20% (AQEG 2007). A further factor is the increase in atmospheric carbon dioxide concentrations. A doubling of atmospheric carbon dioxide concentrations was predicted by Sanderson *et al.* (2007) to significantly increase ozone concentrations over Europe (with adverse effects on human health) because carbon dioxide reduces the uptake of ozone through plant stomata. However, this reduced stomatal uptake by vegetation may, in turn, decrease the impact of ozone on ecosystems, including effecting crop yields and forest growth (Ashmore 2005).

14.8.3 Consequences of Change

Current levels of air pollution in the UK have significant effects on human health, crop and forest production, built materials, and biodiversity. Changes in air quality regulation can, therefore, have significant consequences for human welfare. However, the contribution of ecosystem air quality regulation to these consequences is uncertain, variable and difficult to quantify.

In terms of human health, the Air Quality Strategy (Defra 2007) estimates that the life expectancy of people in the UK is reduced, on average, by 7–8 months due to poor air quality,

although this is expected to decline to five months by 2020. These effects are mainly due to particulates; although the air quality objectives for ozone are exceeded extensively (AQEG 2009), the implications of this for human health critically depend on what threshold for effects is assumed.

Seasonal allergic rhinitis (hayfever) and other allergic diseases are directly linked to pollen levels in the atmosphere. However, while the prevalence of hayfever has apparently increased over recent decades, the levels of grass pollen have not, and hence, factors other than ecosystem regulation are likely to be involved.

In summer and winter smog episodes in particular, visibility can be decreased significantly by high concentrations of aerosols. The ecological effects of this degradation in visibility are uncertain, but the human experience of ecosystems could lose value under these conditions.

High concentrations of ozone can reduce forest growth and crop yield—losses of wheat yield in southern Britain due to ozone were estimated to be 7% in the summer of 2000, for example—and critical levels of ozone for effects on species composition are exceeded over much of the UK (RoTAP 2011).

Many sensitive lakes and streams in the UK have been significantly acidified over the last 50 to 100 years, with implications for invertebrate communities and fisheries. Chemical and biological recovery has occurred over the last two decades at non-forested sites, but evidence of recovery is more limited in forested catchments (RoTAP 2011). Although many aspects of forest management can influence acidification, afforestation is a particularly important factor as it increases interception and deposition of acidifying pollutants (Fowler *et al.* 1989).

Many terrestrial habitats are characterised by low nitrogen status. Significant reductions in total plant species diversity and the frequency of sensitive plant species have been seen in habitats with high rates of nitrogen deposition. Planned emission reductions will only reduce the area of sensitive terrestrial habitats in which critical loads for nitrogen deposition, set to prevent these effects, are exceeded from 60–49% by 2020 (RoTAP 2011). Nitrogen deposition also has wider impacts on the provision of ecosystem services (Hicks *et al.* 2008). Dry deposition of ammonia, makes a greater contribution to these adverse effects than other forms of nitrogen deposition (RoTAP 2011). Although a significant proportion of this ammonia is emitted from intensive livestock units, the remainder is mainly associated with grazing, manure and fertiliser inputs, and so, is linked to ecosystem management.

14.8.4 Options for Sustainable Management

Based on the analysis in previous sections, sustainable management for air quality regulation should maximise the removal and deposition of pollutants from the atmosphere, while ensuring that any additional deposition does not have adverse effects on other ecosystem services provided by the managed system. Management should also aim to minimise the contribution to atmospheric emissions from ecosystems. The balance between these different aims, and the links to other regulating services, may need careful consideration. There are six priority areas for sustainable management:

1. In urban areas, tree planting can increase deposition of pollutants and improve local air quality (Beckett *et al.* 1998; McDonald *et al.* 2007; Tiwary *et al.* 2009). It also has other important benefits, such as climate and noise regulation. Ideally species should be evergreen, resistant to the pollutant loads that they intercept and efficient in intercepting particles and gases. An additional important criterion is that species should not contribute significantly to VOC emissions and, therefore, to increased ozone concentrations. Examples of species that are thought to meet these criteria include maples, birches, larches and pines, but not oaks, willows and poplars, which have high rates of VOC emission (AQEG 2009).

2. In rural areas, tree planting can also play a role in reducing the transport of pollutants from ground-level point sources, such as ammonia emissions from intensive livestock units, to sensitive local targets. Dragosits *et al.* (2006) identified that planting tree belts between large ammonia sources and sensitive sites would be beneficial in significantly reducing deposition to small, sensitive, protected sites. This planting would be more beneficial if it was located around the protected site rather than around the source.

3. Wider-scale rural tree planting will also increase the deposition of pollutants from the atmosphere, reducing air pollutant concentrations. However, in regions with sensitive catchments, it is important that the deposition of sulphur and nitrogen from the atmosphere to soils (and through leaching into freshwaters), does not exceed critical loads. Similarly, future tree planting at a UK scale needs to carefully consider the implications for VOC emissions as several species considered for short-rotation forestry (such as poplars and willows), are high emitters of VOCs which contribute significantly to ozone production.

4. In arable, improved and semi-natural grassland habitats, sustainable management is needed to reduce ammonia emissions to the atmosphere without leading to adverse effects on other ecosystem services, for example, increasing nitrate leaching into waters. This might involve management measures such as the rapid incorporation of manure and slurry applications into arable soils, replacement of urea fertilisers with ammonium nitrate, and changes in cattle diets to reduce nitrogen excretion (Misselbrook *et al.* 2009). Management at a local level can also be used to protect sensitive sites; Dragosits *et al.* (2006) identified the value of local buffer zones of low-emission agriculture around sensitive sites in reducing ammonia deposition.

5. Sustainable management measures that increase water conservation and reduce fire risks will have benefits in terms of air quality regulation, especially in minimising the negative impacts of warmer, drier summers. Such climatic conditions will lead to a decreased deposition to land surfaces and higher atmospheric concentrations of pollutants such as ozone, as well as an increased likelihood of fires, leading to increased particle concentrations (AQEG 2007).

6. Grassland management, in particular the timing of cuts and the intensity of grazing, and the choice of seed mix, can play a significant role in reducing levels of grass pollen in the atmosphere (Emberlin *et al.* 1999).

14.8.5 Knowledge Gaps

In general terms, we understand the basic mechanisms whereby ecosystems influence and regulate air quality. Modelling tools have been developed to quantify these effects at a local or urban level for individual pollutants, and their response to planned or unplanned interventions. However, we lack the modelling tools to provide an integrated assessment for all the major pollutants at a national scale, and hence, an overall assessment of the value of air quality regulation. Furthermore, methods of linking the impacts of ecosystem air quality regulation on local and regional air quality to the impacts of air quality on human health, crop and forest production, carbon sequestration and ecosystem integrity need to be developed for a full evaluation to be made.

Specific knowledge gaps that need to be addressed in addition to these broad objectives include:

- *The regulation of different particle sizes:* The deposition velocity of particulate matter to vegetation is strongly dependent on the particle size distribution, with deposition of very coarse and ultra-fine particles being greatest. While air quality standards to protect human health are set on the basis of concentrations of PM_{10}, there is increasing evidence that ultra-fine particles, which can penetrate deeper into the lung and may cross into the blood stream, are more closely related to health effects. Deposition to vegetation is more efficient for fine particles (smaller than 1 μm) than for particles with a diameter in the size range 1–10 μm (Freer-Smith *et al.* 2005). Hence, the benefits of tree planting in urban areas may have been underestimated by studies to date which have focused only on PM_{10}. Therefore, more detailed evaluation is needed of the local and national benefits of ecosystem regulation for different particle sizes.

- *Knowledge of natural emissions of VOC*: Knowledge in this area is not adequate for the modelling and assessment of ground-level ozone as estimates are only available of annual totals (Royal Society 2008). Improved, spatially and temporally disaggregated, emission inventories and parameterisations for these compounds from UK vegetation need to be developed (RoTAP 2011).

- *Better description of the deposition of ozone:* The stomatal and non-stomatal deposition of ozone to terrestrial surfaces exerts a strong control on ground-level concentrations, especially in peak ozone episodes. Better description of these deposition processes, and their effects on concentrations, are needed for air quality assessment models (RoTAP 2011). In particular, the significance and control of non-stomatal deposition of ozone, and whether it is due to thermal decomposition (Fowler *et al.* 2001) or reactions with biogenic VOC emissions (Goldstein *et al.* 2004), needs better understanding.

14.9 Water Quality Regulation

14.9.1 Trends in Water Quality

Water quality is determined primarily by catchment processes including plant and microbial nutrient uptake, pollutant accumulation in SOM and adsorption on to mineral surfaces, acidity buffering, organic pollutant breakdown, and denitrification. If the capacity of plants and micro-organisms to assimilate, buffer or process pollutants, or of soils to sequester them, is exceeded, water quality is degraded. Drainage systems themselves can dilute pollutants (e.g. from point sources) to safe levels; process or assimilate them (e.g. in lakes and wetlands); or simply transfer pollutants from one ecosystem (the land) to another (the ocean).

There is little, if any, direct long-term monitoring of the ecosystem processes which regulate water quality (Chapter 9). Water quality monitoring data have, therefore, been used to provide inferences regarding these processes. Most monitoring by national environmental agencies is targeted at rivers draining larger, mixed catchments, which are strongly influenced by direct pollutant inputs. Chemical General Quality Assessments, which measure organic pollution, showed that 79% of English, 95% of Welsh and 74% of Northern Irish rivers, by length, were of good chemical quality in 2008, compared to only 55%, 86% and 44%, respectively, in 1990 (Defra 2009h). Although Scottish data cannot be compared directly, a combined chemical, biological and aesthetic assessment classified 88% of rivers as good condition in 2008. Concentrations of phosphates were high (>0.1 mg phosphorus/litre) in 52% of rivers, by length, in England, 23% in Northern Ireland, 4% in Scotland, and 8% in Wales. Nitrates, which cause eutrophication in coastal waters and can impair drinking water quality, showed a similar pattern, with high concentrations (>30 mg nitrate/l) in 32% of English rivers, by length, compared to ≤3% elsewhere in the UK.

The Harmonized Monitoring Scheme (HMS), comprising 230 large river sites, provides the best available long-term perspective on water quality trends in large British rivers. Organic pollution indicators (biological oxygen demand and ammoniacal nitrogen) have declined everywhere since the 1980s, leading to increased dissolved oxygen concentrations (**Figure 14.6**). Phosphate concentrations have fallen substantially in most areas since the mid-1990s, while nitrate has shown little change. Concentrations of heavy metals have generally declined. Monitored pesticides are below detection limits in most samples and clear trends cannot be discerned, but three pesticides (isoproturon, mecoprop and diuron) were above 0.1 μg/l (an arbitrary threshold) in >10% of Environment Agency samples from 1995 to 2004. Faecal indicator organisms (FIOs) are measured routinely at bathing waters which are predominantly coastal. Coastal waters complying with mandatory standards set by the EC Bathing Water Directive increased from 74% in the period 1988 to 1991 to 98% in 2004 to 2007. The stricter Guideline Standards, which indicate excellent bathing water quality, were met in 37% of waters in 1994 to 1997, rising to 73% in 2004 to 2007.

Water quality is more strongly linked to ecosystem processes in the uplands than in the lowlands, but upland waters are poorly represented by standard agency monitoring regimes. While less impacted by agriculture, upland waters are subject to other environmental pressures and are important aquatic habitats (they include many of the UK's lakes) and a major source of clean drinking water. Being relatively unpolluted, water draining the uplands performs a key regulatory service by diluting pollution that enters river systems further downstream. Many upland waters were damaged by acidification during the 1960s to 1980s, but partial recovery is now evident, with pH increasing and toxic aluminium concentrations declining (AWMN 2009; **Figure 14.7a**). Waters draining peaty soils are high in dissolved organic carbon (DOC), and concentrations have risen across the UK in the last 20 to 30 years (Evans et al. 2005a; Worrall & Burt 2007; **Figure 14.7b**). Suspended sediment levels are elevated in areas of active soil erosion, notably downstream of eroding peatlands such as those of the South Pennines (Evans et al. 2006). Upland waters are typically low in nutrients, although nitrate concentrations are higher in areas receiving elevated atmospheric deposition (Allott et al. 1995). Since the 1980s, there have been no clear trends in upland nitrate concentrations (Curtis et al. 2005).

14.9.2 Drivers of Change

In lowland catchments, by far the dominant driver of water quality change over the last 30 years has been regulation of pollutant inputs, rather than changes in ecosystem regulating processes. The greatest improvements are associated with regulation of large point sources, such as waste water treatment works (WWTWs), whilst small point source and diffuse inputs remain comparatively high. Point sources of phosphorus are still considered to provide the greatest risk of eutrophication in rivers, even in rural areas (Jarvie et al. 2006; Arnscheidt et al. 2007). Since 1984, phosphorus fertiliser applications have fallen by 53%, and nitrogen applications by 32% (Defra 2009h). Nitrate concentrations have not decreased, however (**Figure 14.6**), suggesting that the capacity of agricultural ecosystems to retain excess nitrogen has, if anything, declined over the period.

Discharge rates are key to water quality. Low flows reduce effluent dilution capacity and can lead to ten-fold increases in nutrient and organic pollutant concentrations. During summer droughts, 25–33% of flow in some rivers in central and south-east England can be comprised of sewage effluent. High flows mobilise and transport bacterial pollutants from agricultural sources and combined sewage overflows, as well as suspended sediments and associated pollutants. Discharge is affected by climate, particularly the frequency and amount of precipitation, abstraction and land management. Rising water temperatures may accelerate biological activity and nutrient cycling, and exacerbate poor water quality at low flows by reducing dissolved oxygen. Future climate change projections suggest that the frequency of algal blooms will increase, with 70–100% higher pollutant concentrations (Johnson et al. 2009).

The dominant driver of changes in upland water quality in the past has been atmospheric deposition. Sulphur emissions from fossil fuel burning, the primary agent of acidification, have decreased by 90% since 1970, and should fall further by 2020 (RoTAP 2011). In many areas, acid loadings are now less than the buffering capacity provided by base cation weathering, leading to freshwater recovery. However, the historic depletion of soil base status, and remobilisation of accumulated sulphur and nitrogen, continue to constrain this recovery in peatland and slow-weathering upland areas of northern England, Wales, southern Scotland and south-east Northern Ireland.

The impacts of atmospheric nitrogen pollution on upland water quality (acidification and eutrophication) is strongly mitigated by plant and microbial uptake and long-term

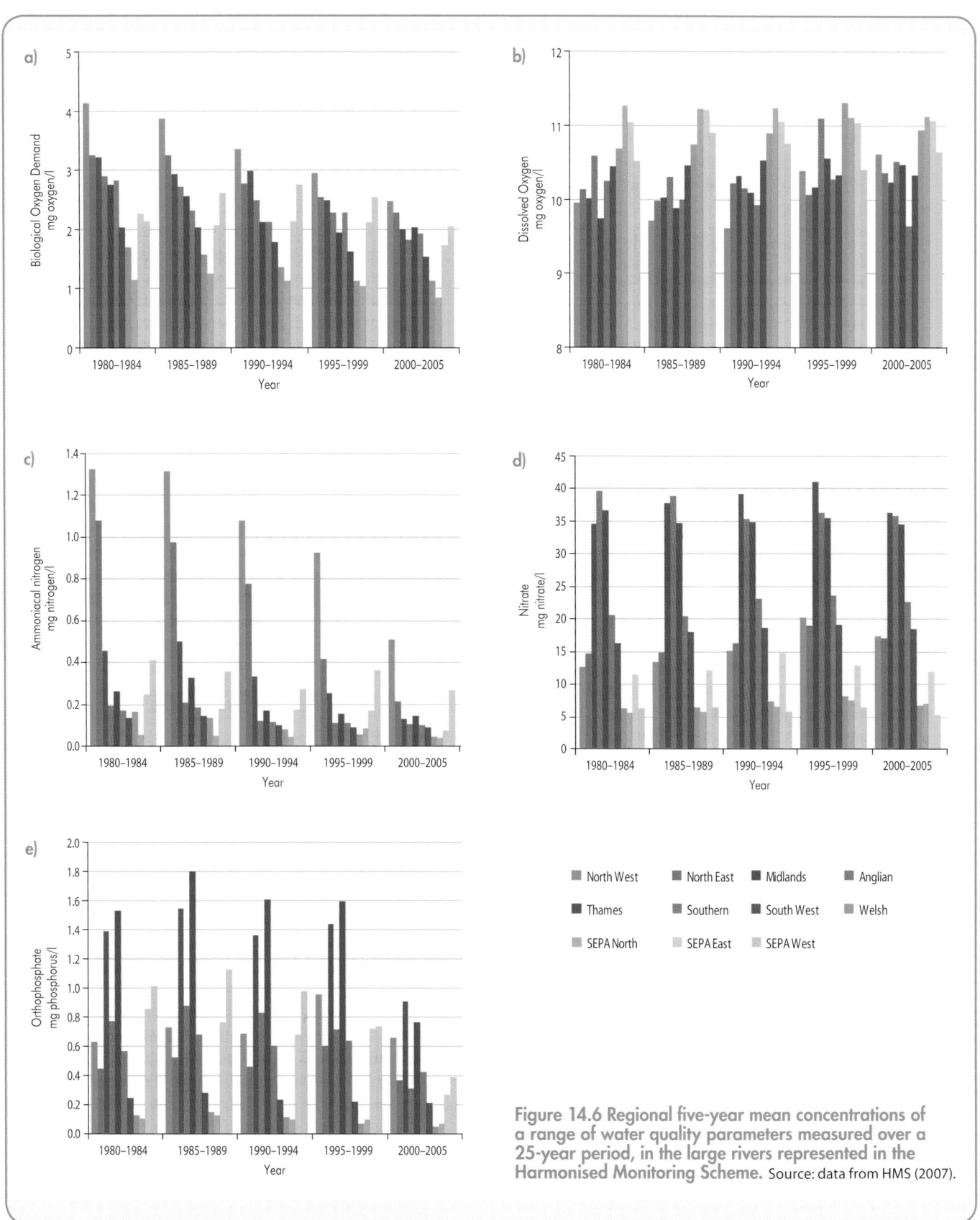

Figure 14.6 Regional five-year mean concentrations of a range of water quality parameters measured over a 25-year period, in the large rivers represented in the Harmonised Monitoring Scheme. Source: data from HMS (2007).

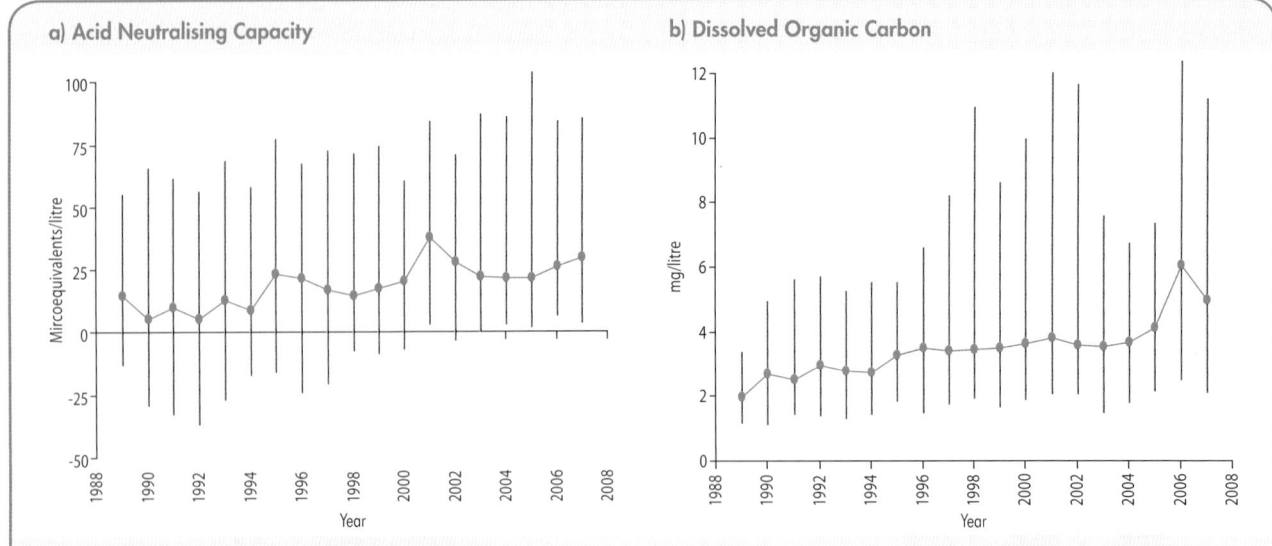

Figure 14.7 Median and 10th–90th percentile range of annual mean concentrations of a) Acid Neutralising Capacity, and b) Dissolved Organic Carbon in the 22 upland lakes and streams of the UK Acid Waters Monitoring Network. Source: Evans *et al.* (2005b); www.ukawmn.ucl.ac.uk.

soil accumulation. With nitrogen emissions expected to remain high, the sustainability of this ecosystem service is uncertain, as semi-natural ecosystems become more nitrogen-enriched (RoTAP 2011). Widespread post-war upland conifer afforestation has had detrimental impacts on water quality, amplifying the effects of acid deposition, and increasing nitrate and sediment losses (Reynolds 2004).

Dissolved organic carbon increases are believed to be linked to recovery from acidification, via increases in SOM solubility (Monteith *et al.* 2007), although climatic factors may also have contributed. Moorland burning and peatland drainage appear to be locally significant (Yallop *et al.* 2010). With atmospheric deposition stabilising at lower levels, climate and land management may be the main determinants of future DOC change. Particulate organic carbon levels are strongly affected by land management; peat erosion in the South Pennines is believed to have been triggered by a combination of historic air pollution, overgrazing and wildfire.

14.9.3 Consequences of Change

Water quality regulates many ecosystem services, and degraded water quality can lead to a breakdown in their function. Eutrophication causes excessive accumulation in the biomass of aquatic plants or algae, resulting in increased treatment costs for downstream users, loss of amenity value due to toxic algal blooms, and the physical blocking of waterways. Under certain conditions, breakdown of accumulated organic matter can lead to deoxygenation of the water, which kills associated fish. Organic pollutants have the same impact, but incidences of this are becoming less frequent. High levels of FIOs lead to increased health risks associated with bathing waters and shellfish beds, which must ultimately be closed as a result. Rising water temperatures may affect ecosystem structure, resulting in the loss of cold water species while favouring the increased success of potentially invasive species.

Over recent decades, acidification led to widespread ecological damage, including biodiversity and fisheries loss

resulting in negative consequences for recreational and provisioning services. This damage is now being reversed in many areas. Rising DOC levels are affecting drinking water provision, adding to treatment costs, and having potential health risks due to formation of halogenated organic compounds during treatment (Singer 1999). Other consequences include the transport of contaminants from soils in soluble organic complexes, and reduced light penetration into the water column, reducing the depth of macrophyte growth but protecting aquatic invertebrates from ultra-violet radiation. Increased particulate export from eroding peatlands also contributes to heavy metal mobilisation (Rothwell *et al.* 2005), and to sediment accumulation and decreased water storage capacity in reservoirs (Yeloff *et al.* 2005).

14.9.4 Options for Sustainable Management

Recent research has indicated that agriculture may be responsible for about 70% of nitrates and 40% of phosphates in UK waters, for 75% of the sediment load to at-risk rivers, and for 36% of bathing beaches and 75% of shellfish waters failing water quality targets (Defra 2009h). The potential for enhanced management of water quality through better land management is thus high, with freshwater-oriented agri-environment schemes, such as the Catchment Sensitive Farming Initiative, providing an implementation mechanism. Specific measures to enhance ecosystem mitigation of diffuse pollutants include: riparian protection and reduced stocking densities; restrictions on timing and loading of fertiliser and manure applications (e.g. within Nitrate Vulnerable Zones); buffer strips to reduce runoff of nutrients and sediment; and the planting of shelter belts to increase water infiltration rates (Kay *et al.* 2007, 2008a, 2010). Constructed wetlands, for example on farms, have potential to purify or de-toxify point source as well as diffuse inputs. Within the drainage network system itself, management options include: riparian wetland restoration (including saltmarshes in the intertidal zone); restoring channelised rivers to more natural courses in order to increase water residence time and in-channel retention; floodplain reconnection to increase overbank retention; and riparian shading to reduce rates of phytoplankton growth (Withers & Jarvie 2008).

Opportunities also exist to enhance ecosystem regulation of upland water quality. Transition from clear-fell to continuous-cover forestry, riparian protection and improved harvesting practice can all reduce sediment losses, nitrate peaks and other detrimental water quality changes downstream of plantations (Reynolds 2004). In peatlands, reduced stocking levels, limited burning and, in some areas, active restoration can minimise suspended sediment losses. The re-establishment of peat-forming vegetation in degraded areas can also enhance sulphur and nitrogen retention (Bonn et al. 2010). The blocking of peat drains and reduced burning may also reduce DOC losses, although significant uncertainty remains in this area (Armstrong et al. 2010).

The relationship between river flows and water quality will be of critical importance over the next 50 to 100 years due to a combination of climate change predictions of longer low-flow periods punctuated by intensive storm events, projected population growth, increasing water consumption per head, and increased demands for food and bioenergy production. These changes could put unprecedented pressures on the capacity of UK river systems to regulate water quality via dilution, particularly in the south and east. Urban drainage systems are also vulnerable to extreme rainfalls, such as organic pollutant discharges from combined sewer overflows (Kay et al. 2008b; Stapleton et al. 2008). Management of rural and urban land to maximise water infiltration rates will have benefits both in terms of flood mitigation and for maintaining low flows, in order to reduce pollutant pressures on aquatic ecosystems and water supplies.

14.9.5 Knowledge Gaps

Most UK water quality monitoring takes place in large rivers, downstream of human habitations. This may be appropriate for identifying gross diffuse and point source pollution from agricultural and urban areas, but provides limited information on sensitive environments such as upland streams and oligotrophic lakes. The HMS network largely comprises tidal limit sites, providing large-scale integration and flux estimates. Monitoring at this scale, however, is less useful for process understanding, especially relating to linkages between terrestrial and freshwater ecosystems. A recent study showed that 90% of the total river length in Sweden lay within (sub)catchments of <15 km^2 (the minimum threshold for monitoring) and concluded that a major component of the aquatic ecosystem was being overlooked (Bishop et al. 2008). In the UK, monitoring of upland headwater catchments is limited to the UK Acid Waters Monitoring Network, Environmental Change Network, and a number of individual catchment studies. Small lowland catchments are also poorly represented in national monitoring schemes, as are relatively unaffected standing waters.

Routine monitoring under-represents water quality extremes associated with high-flow events. These are responsible for most sediment, phosphorus and microbial pollutant transport into rivers, lakes and estuaries, as well as acid episodes in headwater streams. As such, they have high ecological impacts. The development and deployment of a coordinated network of continuous water quality sensors would dramatically improve understanding of these short-duration processes, which are likely to become more frequent and/or severe under a changing climate. Future changes in

Table 14.21 Interactions between regulating services, other ecosystem services, habitat types and cross-cutting issues. The shade of colour indicates the level of interaction, from dark indicating strong interaction, mid-tone = moderate interaction, to light = limited interaction; blank indicates the interaction is not of particular relevance.

	Climate regulation	Hazard regulation	Disease and pest regulation	Pollination	Noise regulation	Soil quality	Air quality	Water quality
UK NEA Broad Habitat types								
Mountains, Moorlands and Heaths								
Semi-natural Grasslands								
Enclosed Farmlands								
Woodlands								
Freshwaters—openwaters, wetlands and floodplains								
Urban								
Marine and Coastal Margins								
Ecosystem services								
Cultural services								
Supporting services								
Provisioning services								
Cross cutting issue								
Biodiversity								

water temperature are also likely to impact significantly on water quality, but current data are patchy and largely limited to spot-sampling. More formal monitoring may be required to manage extreme events, ideally linked to continuous water quality sampling.

Scientific uncertainties persist in relation to the capacity of terrestrial ecosystems to buffer water quality, including microbial and nutrient retention in wetlands and riparian strips, retention of atmospheric nitrogen by semi-natural ecosystems, and controls on DOC leaching. Understanding of the complex mechanisms by which climate change will impact on water quality in rivers and lakes is incomplete.

Emerging water quality issues include the discharge from the human population of organic and other micro-contaminants, such as synthetic nanoparticles (Ju-Nam & Lead 2008), from sources including pharmaceuticals, and personal care and cleaning products. While not necessarily toxic, these may be ecologically disruptive. For example, up to a third of wild fish living in proximity to sewage effluents have been shown to have endocrine disruption effects (Jobling *et al.* 2006) associated primarily with the contraceptive pill, ethinyloestradiol. Nanosilver, which is used in suntan lotions and clothing, has antimicrobial properties, and so, is treated as a pesticide in the United States (Bardsley *et al.* 2009). The ecological impacts of micro-contaminants are highly variable, and in many cases uncertain, but exposure of British surface waters to such chemicals is probably higher than in most other European nations (Williams *et al.* 2009). At present there is no system in place to identify, monitor or detect the effects on wildlife of organic micro-contaminants, and there is little information available on how these pollutants may be cycled within, or removed from, aquatic ecosystems.

14.10 Trade-offs and Synergies

A number of regulating services either act as final ecosystem services or contribute significantly to final ecosystem services, whilst others are primary or intermediate ecosystem services. There are strong interactions between different regulating services (e.g. water, soil and air quality), and between the regulating services and other ecosystem services. Whilst some regulating services have greater relevance to some habitats types more than others, collectively, regulating services underpin many of the goods and services provided by all habitats. The interactions between the different regulating services and other ecosystem services and habitat types are given in **Table 14.21**.

For water, air and soil quality, human well-being and numerous cultural services are also supported through high quality environments including physical health, mental health, ecological knowledge, cultural heritage and mediated natures, and aesthetic and inspirational.

References

Aalders, I., Ball, B., Black, H.I.J., Campbell, C.D., Griffiths, B., Hopkins, D., Hough, R.L., Lilly, A. Mckenzie, B., Rees, R.M.,
Sinclair, A., Towers, W. & Watson, C. (2009) Considerations for Scottish soil monitoring in the European context. *European Journal of Soil Science*, **60**, 833–843.

Adger, W.N., Hughes, T.P., Folke, C., Carpenter, S.R. & Rockström, J. (2005) Social-Ecological Resilience to Coastal Disasters, *Science*, **309**, 1036–1039. DOI: 10.1126/science.1112122.

Aguilar, R., Ashworth, L., Galetto, L. & Aizen, M.A. (2006) Plant reproductive susceptibility to habitat fragmentation: review and synthesis through a meta-analysis. *Ecology Letters*, **9**, 968–980.

Aizen, M.A. & Harder, L.D. (2009) The Global Stock of Domesticated Honey Bees Is Growing Slower Than Agricultural Demand for Pollination. *Current Biology*, **19**, 915–918.

Akbar, K.F., Hale, W.H.G. & Headley, A.D. (2003) Assessment of scenic beauty of the roadside vegetation in northern England. *Landscape and Urban Planning*, **63**, 139–144.

Allott, T.E., Curtis, C.J., Hall, J., Harriman, R. & Battarbee, R.W. (1995) The impact of nitrogen deposition on upland surface waters in Great Britain: A regional assessment of nitrate leaching. *Water, Air and Soil Pollution*, **85**, 297–302.

Andersen, N.S., Rasmussen, J. & Jorgensen, R.B. (2010) You reap what you sow—or do you?—volunteers in organic row sown and broadcast sown oilseed rape fields. *European Journal of Agronomy*, **32**, 121–126.

Anderson, D.L. (2009) Editorial notes. *Australasian Beekeeper*, **110**(7), 225–226.

Anderson, D.L. & Morgan, M.J. (2007) Genetic and Morphological variation of bee-parasitic Tropilaelaps mites (Acari: Laelapidae): new and redefined species. *Experimental and Applied Acarology*, **43**(1), 1–24.

Angus, A., Burgess, P.J., Morris, J. & Lingard, J. (2009) Agriculture and land use: demand for and supply of agricultural commodities, characteristics of the farming and food industries, and their implications for land use in the UK. *Land Use Policy*, **26S**, S230–S242.

Anon (2009) Risk Analysis of *Phytophthora ramorum*, a Newly Recognised Pathogen Threat to Europe and the Cause of Sudden Oak Death in the USA. EU Sixth Framework Project, Contract Number 502672.

Anstead, J.A., Mallet, J. & Denholm, I. (2007) Temporal and spatial incidence of alleles conferring knockdown resistance to pyrethroids in the peach-potato aphid, *Myzus persicae* (Hemiptera: Aphididae), and their association with other insecticide resistance mechanisms. *Bulletin of Entomological Research*, **97**, 243–252.

AQEG (Air Quality Expert Group) (2007) Air Quality and Climate Change: a UK Perspective. Report of the Air Quality Expert Group. Defra, London.

AQEG (Air Quality Expert Group) (2009) Ozone in the United Kingdom. Report of the Air Quality Expert Group. Defra, London.

Arinaminpathy, N. & McLean, A.R. (2009) Evolution and emergence of novel human infections. *Proceedings of the Royal Society of London, Series B-Biological Sciences*, **276**, 3937–3943.

Armstrong, A., Holden, J., Kay, P., Francis, B., Foulger, M., Gledhill, S., McDonald, A.T. & Walker, A. (2010) The impact of peatland drain-blocking on dissolved organic carbon loss and discolouration of water; results from a national survey. *Journal of Hydrology*, **381**, 112–120.

Arnscheidt, J., Jordan, P., Li, S., McCormick, S., McFaul, R. McGrogan, H.J., Neal, M. & Sims, J.T. (2007) Defining the sources of low-flow phosphorus transfers in complex catchments. *Science of the Total Environment*, **382**, 1–13.

Artz, R.R.E., Anderson, I.C., Chapman, S.J., Hagn, A., Schloter, M., Potts, J. & Campbell, C.D. (2007) Changes in fungal community composition in response to vegetational succession during the natural regeneration of cutover peatlands. *Microbial Ecology*, **54**, 508–522.

Asher, J., Warren, M., Fox, R., Harding, P., Jeffcoate, G. & Jeffcoate, S. (2001) The Millennium Atlas of Butterflies in Britain and Ireland. Oxford University Press, Oxford, UK.

Ashman, T-L., Knight, T.M., Streets, J.A., Amarasekare, P., Burd, M., Cambell, D.R., Dudash, M.R., Johnston, M.O., Mazer, S.J., Mitchell, R.J., Morgan, M.T. & Wilson, W.G. (2004) Pollen limitation of plant reproduction: ecological and evolutionary causes and consequences. *Ecology*, **85**, 2408–2421.

Ashmore, M.R. (2005) Assessing the future impacts of ozone on vegetation. *Plant Cell and Environment*, **28**, 949–964.

Awmack, C.S., Harrington, R. & Leather, S.R. (1997) Host plant effects on the performance of the aphid *Aulacorthum solani* (Kalt.) (Homoptera : Aphididae) at ambient and elevated CO_2. *Global Change Biology*, **3**, 545–549.

AWMN (Acid Waters Monitoring Network) (2009) Acid Waters Monitoring Network 20 year review. Defra (in prep.)

Baird, A.J., Belya, L.R., Comas, X., Reeve, A.S. & Slater, L.D. (eds) (2009) Carbon cycling in northern peatlands. AGU Geophysical Monograph Series, Volume 184, American Geophysical Union, Washington D.C., USA.

Baker, J.M., Ochsner, T.E., Venterea, R.T. & Griffis, T.J. (2007) Tillage and soil carbon sequestration—what do we really know? *Agriculture, Ecosystems and Environment*, **118**, 1–5.

Ballantyne, C.K. (2004) Geomorphological changes and trends in Scotland: Debris Flows. Scottish Natural Heritage Commissioned Report, F00AC107A, 27pp.

Bardsley, S., De Lurio, J. & Webb, S. (2009) Strategic responses to emerging technologies: Late lessons and regulatory steps for nanomaterials and synthetic biology. *Environmental Scientist*, **18**, 41–46.

Baranton, G. & Postic, D. (2006) Trends in leptospirosis epidemiology in France. Sixty-six years of passive serological surveillance from 1920 to 2003. *International Journal of Infectious Diseases*, **10**, 162–170.

Bascompte, J., Jordano, P. & Olesen, J.M. (2006) Asymmetric coevolutionary networks facilitate biodiversity maintenance. *Science*, **312**, 431–433.

Batten, C.A., Maan, S., Shaw, A.E., Maan, N.S. & Mertens, P.P.C. (2008) A European field strain of bluetongue virus derived from two parental vaccine strains by genome segment reassortment. *Virus Research*, **137**, 56–63.

Beales, P.A., Giltrap, P.G., Payne, A. & Ingram, N. (2009) A new threat to UK heathland from *Phytophthora kernoviae* on *Vaccinium myrtillus* in the wild. *Plant Pathology*, **58**, 393–393.

Beaumont, N.J., Austen, M.C., Mangi, S.C. & Townsend, M. (2008) Economic Valuation for the Conservation of Marine Biodiversity. *Marine Pollution Bulletin*, **56**, 386–396.

Beaumont, N.J., Austen, M.C., Atkins, J., Burdon, D., Degraer, S., Dentinho, T.P., Derous, S., Holm, P., Horton, T., van Ierland, E., Marboe, A.H., Starkey, D.J., Townsend, M. & Zarzycki, T. (2007) Identification, definition and quantification of goods and services provided by marine biodiversity: Implications for the Ecosystem Approach. *Marine Pollution Bulletin*, **54**, 253–265.

Beckett, K.P., Freer-Smith, P.H. & Taylor, G. (1998) Urban woodlands: their role in reducing the effects of particulate pollution. *Environmental Pollution*, **99**, 347–360.

Beckley, B.D., Lemoine, F.G., Luthcke, S.B., Ray, R.D. & Zelensky, N.P. (2007) A reassessment of global and regional mean sea level trends from TOPEX and Jason-1 altimetry based on revised reference frame and orbits, *Geophysical Research Letters*, **34**, L14608. DOI:10.1029/2007GL030002.

Bellamy, P., Loveland, P.J., Bradley, R.I., Lark, R.M. & Kirk, G.J.D. (2005) Carbon losses from all soils across England and Wales. *Nature*, **437**, 245–248.

BGPSD (British Government Panel on Sustainable Development) (1999) A review of the extent to which domestic legislation and policy provides effective remedies to noise nuisance.

BHS (Basic Horticultural Statistics) (1999) Basic Horticultural Statistics for the United Kingdom, 1999. [online] Available at:<http://archive.defra.gov.uk/evidence/statistics/foodfarm/landuselivestock/bhs/index.htm>.

BHS (Basic Horticultural Statistics) (2008) Basic Horticultural Statistics for the United Kingdom, 2008. [online] Available at: <http://archive.defra.gov.uk/evidence/statistics/foodfarm/landuselivestock/bhs/index.htm>.

Biesmeijer, J.C., Roberts, S.P.M., Reemer, M., Ohlemüller, R., Edwards, M., Peeters, T., Schaffers, A.P., Potts, S.G., Kleukers, R., Thomas, C.D., Settele, J. & Kunin W.E. (2006) Parallel declines in pollinators and insect-pollinated plants in Britain and the Netherlands. *Science*, **313**, 351–354.

Bilotta, G.S., Brazier, R.E. & Haygarth, P.M. (2007) The impacts of grazing animals on the quality of soils, vegetation, and surface waters in intensively managed grasslands. *Advances in Agronomy*, **94**, 237–280.

Bishop K., Buffam I., Erlandsson M., Fölster J., Laudon H. & Temnerud J. 2008. The Unknown Headwaters. *Hydrological Processes*, **22,** 1239–1242.

Blackman, R.L. & Eastop, V.F. (eds) (2006) Aphids on the World's Herbaceous Plant and Shrubs, John Wiley & Sons, New York.

Boardman, J. & Evans, R. (2006) Britain. In Soil Erosion in Europe (eds J. Boardman & J. Poesen), John Wiley & Sons, 439–453.

Boardman, J., Evans, R. & Ford, J. (2003) Muddy floods on the South Downs, southern England: problem and responses. *Environmental Science & Policy*, **6**, 69–83.

Bohan, D.A., Boffey, C.W.H., Brooks, D.R., Clark, S.J., Dewar, A.M., Firbank, L.G., Haughton, A.J., Hawes, C., Heard, M.S., May, M.J., Osborne, J.L., Perry, J.N., Rothery, P., Roy, D.B., Scott, R.J., Squire, G.R., Woiwod, I.P. & Champion, G.T. (2005) Effects on weed and invertebrate abundance and diversity of herbicide management in genetically modified herbicide-tolerant winter-sown oilseed rape. *Proceedings of the Royal Society of London, Series B-Biological Sciences*, **272**, 463–474.

Bonan, G. (2008) Ecological climatology: Concepts and applications. 2nd edition. Cambridge, Cambridge University Press.

Bonilauri, P., Bellini, R., Calzolari, M., Angeflni, R., Venturi, L., Fallacara, F., Cordioli, P., Angelini, P., Venturolli, C., Merialdi, G. & Dottori, M. (2008) Chikungunya virus in Aedes albopictus, Italy. *Emerging Infectious Diseases*, **14**, 852–854.

Bonn, A., Allott, T., Hubacek, K. & Stewart, J. (2009) Drivers of environmental change in uplands. Routledge.

Bonn, A., Holden, J., Parnell, M., Worrall, F., Chapman, P.J., Evans. C.D., Termansen, M., Beharry-Borg, N., Acreman, M.C., Rowe, E., Emmett, B. & Tsuchiya, A. (2010) Ecosystem services of peat—Phase 1. Defra Project code: SP0572, 137 pp.

Bourne, F.J., Donnelly, C.A., Cox, D.R., Gettinby, G., McInerney, J.P., Morrison, W.I. & Woodroffe, R. (2006) TB policy and the badger culling trials. *The Veterinary Record,* **158**, 671–672.

Bourne, J., Donnelly, C.A., Cox, D.R., Gettinby, G., McInerney, J.P., Morrison, I. & Woodroffe, R. (2005) Bovine tuberculosis: Towards a future control strategy. *Cattle Practice,* **13**, 289–294.

Bousquet, P., Ciais, P., Miller, J.B., Dlugokencky, E.J., Hauglustaine, D.A., Prigent, C., Van der Werf, G.R., Peylin, P., Brunke, E.-G., Carouge, C., Langenfelds, R.L., Lathière, J., Papa, F., Ramonet, M., Schmidt, M., Steele, L.P., Tyler, S.C. & White, J. (2006) Contribution of anthropogenic and natural sources to atmospheric methane variability. *Nature,* **433**, 439–443.

Bradley, R.I., Milne, R., Bell, J., Lilly, A., Jordan, C. & Higgins, A. (2005) A soil carbon and land use database for the United Kingdom. *Soil Use and Management,* **21**, 363–369.

Brasier, C.M. (1996) *Phytophthora cinnamomi* and oak decline in southern Europe. Environmental constraints including climate change. *Annales Des Sciences Forestieres,* **53**, 347–358.

Brasier, C.M. (2008) The biosecurity threat to the UK and global environment from international trade in plants. *Plant Pathology,* **57**, 792–808.

Brasier, C.M., Beales, P.A., Kirk, S.A., Denman, S. & Rose, J. (2005) Phytophthora kernoviae sp nov., an invasive pathogen causing bleeding stem lesions on forest trees and foliar necrosis of ornamentals in the UK. *Mycological Research,* **109**, 853–859.

Brittain, C.A., Vighi, M., Bommarco, R., Settele, J. & Potts, S.G. (2010) Impacts of a pesticide on pollinator species richness at different spatial scales. *Basic and Applied Ecology,* **11**, 106–115.

Broadmeadow, M. & Ray, D. (2005) Climate change and British Woodland. Forestry Commission Information Note, no. 69.

Brown, I., Towers, W., Rivington, M., Black, H.I.J. (2009) Influence of climate change on agricultural land-use potential: adapting and updating the land capability system for Scotland. *Climate Research* **37**(1) 43–57.

Burd, M. (1994) Bateman's principle and reproduction: the role of pollinator limitation in fruit and seed set. *The Botanical Review,* **60**, 83–139.

Burgess, P.J. & Morris, J. (2009) Agricultural technology and land use: the UK case. *Land Use Policy.* **26S**, S222–S229.

Burroughs, W.J. (2001) Climate change. A multidisciplinary approach. Cambridge, Cambridge University Press.

Caccio, S.M., Thompson, R.C.A., McLauchlin, J. & Smith, H.V. (2005) Unravelling Cryptosporidium and Giardia epidemiology. *Trends in Parasitology,* **21**, 430–437.

Cannon, R.J.C. (1998) The implications of predicted climate change for insect pests in the UK, with emphasis on non-indigenous species. *Global Change Biology,* **4**, 785–796.

Cardinale, B.J., Srivastava, D.S., Duffy, J.E., Wright, J.P., Downing, A.L., Sankaran, M. & Jouseau, C. (2006) Effects of biodiversity on the functioning of trophic groups and ecosystems. *Nature,* **443**, 989–992.

Carey, P.D., Wallis, S., Chamberlain, P.M., Cooper, A., Emmett, B.A., Maskell, L.C., McCann, T., Murphy, J., Norton, L.R., Reynolds, B., Scott, W.A., Simpson, I.C., Smart, S.M. & Ullyett,

J.M. (2008) Countryside Survey: UK Results from 2007. NERC/Centre for Ecology & Hydrology, 105pp.

Carpenter, S., Wilson, A. & Mellor, P.S. (2009) Culicoides and the emergence of bluetongue virus in northern Europe. *Trends in Microbiology,* **17**, 172–178.

Carré, G., Roche, P., Chifflet, R., Morison, N., Bommarco, R., Harrison-Cripps, J., Krewenka, K., Potts, S.G., Roberts, S.P.M., Rodet, G., Settele, J., Steffan-Dewenter, I., Szentgyörgyi, H., Tscheulin, T., Westphal, C., Woyciechowski, M. & Vaissière, B.E. (2009) Landscape context and habitat type as drivers of bee diversity in European annual crops. *Agriculture Ecosystem and Environment,* **133**, 40–47.

Carroll, Z.L., Bird, S.B., Emmett, B.A., Reynolds, B. & Sinclair, F.L. (2004) Can tree shelterbelts on agricultural land reduce flood risk? *Soil Use Management,* **20**, 357–359.

Carvell, C., Meek, W. R., Pywell, R. F., Goulson, D. & Nowakowski, M. (2007) Comparing the efficacy of agri-environment schemes to enhance bumble bee abundance and diversity on arable field margins. *Journal of Applied Ecology,* **44**, 29–40.

Cavan, G., Handley, J. F., Aylen, J., Albertson, K., McMorrow, J., Lindley, S. & McEvoy, D. (2006) Climate change and the visitor economy in the uplands. *International Journal of Biodiversity Science and Management,* **2**, 1–4.

Chauzat, M.P. & Martin, S.J. (2009) A foreigner in France: Biological information on the Asian hornet *Vespa velutina,* a recently introduced species. *Biologist,* **56**, 86–91.

Climate Change Task Force (2010) Cimate Change: everyone's business. CBI [online] Available at: <http://climatechange.cbi.org.uk/reports/climate-change-everyones-business> [Accessed 15.03.11].

ClimSoil (2008) Review of existing information on the interrelations between soil and climate change. ClimSoil Final Report.

Collier, R.H., Finch, S., Phelps, K. & Thompson, A.R. (1991) Possible impact of global warming on cabbage root fly (*Delia radicum*) activity in the UK. Annals of Applied Biology, 118, 261–271.

Collier, R.H., Fellows, J., Adams, S., Semenov, M. & Thomas, B. (2008) Vulnerability of horticultural crop production to extreme weather events. *Aspects of Applied Biology,* **88**, 3–13.

Collins, K.L., Boatman, N.D., Wilcox, A., Holland, J.M. & Chaney, K. (2002) Influence of beetle banks on cereal aphid predation in winter wheat. *Agriculture, Ecosystems and Environment,* **93**, 337–350.

Collison, M., Collison, L., Sakrabani, R., Tofiled, B. & Wallage, Z. (2009) Biochar and Carbon Sequestration: A Regional Perspective, Low Carbon Innovation Centre, University of East Anglia 124pp.

Cook, S.M. & Denholm, I. (2008) Ecological approaches to the control of pollen beetles in oilseed rape. *EPPO/OEPP Bulletin,* **38**,110–113.

Countryside Agency & CPRE (Campaign to Protect Rural England) (2006) Beyond Transport Infrastructure: Lessons for the Future from Recent Road Projects, pp. 109.

CPRE & LUC (Campaign to Protect Rural England and Land Use Consultants) (2007) Developing an Intrusion Map of England. [online] Available at: <http://www.cpre.org.uk/library/results/intrusion> [Accessed 12.01.11].

CPRE (Campaign to Protect Rural England) (2009) National and Regional Tranquility maps. [online] Available at:

<http://www.cpre.org.uk/resources/countryside/tranquil-places/item/1790-> [Accessed 12.01.11].

Cranfield University (2007) A Guide to Better Soil Structure. National Soil Resources Institute. 19 pp. [online] Available at: <http://www.soil-net.com/legacy/downloads/resources/structure_brochure.pdf> [Accessed 12.01.11].

Curtis, C.J., Evans, C.D., Helliwell, R.C. & Monteith, D.T. (2005) Nitrate leaching as a confounding factor in chemical recovery from acidification in UK upland waters. *Environmental Pollution*, **137**, 73–82.

Cuthbertson, A.G.S., Mathers, J.J., Blackburn, L.F., Wakefield, M.E., Collins, L.E., Luo, W. & Brown, M.A. (2008) Maintaining *Aethina tumida* (Coleoptera: Nitidulidae) under quarantine laboratory conditions in the UK and preliminary observations on its behaviour. *Journal of Apicultural Research*, **47**, 192–193.

Dawson, J.J.C. & Smith, P. (2007) Carbon losses from soil and its consequences for land-use management. *Science of the Total Environment*, **382**, 165–190.

Debeljak, M., Squire, G.R., Demšar, D., Young, M.W., & Džeroski, S. (2008) Relations between the oilseed rape volunteer seedbank, and soil factors, weed functional groups and geographical location in the UK. *Ecological Modelling*, **212,** 138–146.

DECC (Department of Energy and Climate Change) (2009) The UK's Fifth National Communication under the United Nations Framework Convention on Climate Change. Department of Energy and Climate Change. [online] Available at: <http://www.decc.gov.uk/publications/> [Accessed 12.01.11].

Defeo, O., McLachlan, A., Schoeman, D.S., Schlacher, T.A., Dugan, J., Jones, A., Lastra, M. & Scapini, F. (2009) Threats to sandy beach ecosystems: A review. *Estuarine, Coastal and Shelf Science*, **81** 1–12.

Defra (Department for Environment, Food and Rural Affairs) (2002) Origin of the UK foot and mouth disease epidemic in 2001, Defra. [online] Available at: <http://www.defra.gov.uk/foodfarm/farmanimal/diseases/atoz/fmd/documents/fmdorigins1.pdf> [Accessed 12.01.11].

Defra (Department for Environment, Food and Rural Affairs) (2003) Re-assessing drought risks for UK crops using UKCIP02 climate change scenarios—CC0368., Defra.

Defra (Department for Environment, Food and Rural Affairs) (2006) Evaluating the response of UK strains of Thrips tabaci to deltamethrin, Defra. [online] Available at: <http://randd.defra.gov.uk/Document.aspx?Document=PS2710_4711_FRP.doc> [Accessed 12.01.11].

Defra (Department for Environment, Food and Rural Affairs) (2007) The Air Quality Strategy for England, Scotland, Wales and Northern Ireland, Volume 1, Defra. [online] Available at: <http://www.official-documents.gov.uk/document/cm71/7169/7169_i.pdf> [Accessed 12.01.11].

Defra (Department for Environment, Food and Rural Affairs) (2008a) Zoonoses Report, UK 2007.

Defra (Department for Environment, Food and Rural Affairs) (2008b) Impact assessment on future management of risks from *Phytophthora ramorum* and *Phytophthora kernoviae* (ed. by Welsh Assembly Government, Defra, Forestry Commission) [online] Available at: <http://archive.defra.gov.uk/corporate/consult/phytophthora-ram-kern/impact-assessment.pdf> [Accessed 15.03.11].

Defra (Department for Environment, Food and Rural Affairs) (2008c) Overseas Trade Data System (MOTS): UK trade data in food, feed and drink including indigeneity and degree of processing, Defra, London.

Defra (Department for Environment, Food and Rural Affairs), Forestry Commission and Welsh Assembly Government (2008) Impact assessment on future management of risks from *Phytophthora ramorum* and *Phytophthora kernoviae*. [online] Available at: <http://archive.defra.gov.uk/corporate/consult/phytophthora-ram-kern/impact-assessment.pdf> [Accessed 15.03.11].

Defra (Department for Environment, Food and Rural Affairs) (2009a) Bovine TB. [online] Available at: <http://www.defra.gov.uk/foodfarm/farmanimal/diseases/atoz/tb/index.htm> [Accessed 13.01.11].

Defra (Department for Environment, Food and Rural Affairs) (2009b) Provision of ecosystem services through the Environmental Stewardship scheme, Defra. Project code NRO 121. [online] Available at: <http://randd.defra.gov.uk/Default.aspx?Menu=Menu&Module=More&Location=None&Completed=0&ProjectID=15901> [Accessed 13.01.11].

Defra (Department for Environment, Food and Rural Affairs) (2009c) June survey of agriculture and horticulture, Defra. [online] Available at: <http://www.defra.gov.uk/statistics/foodfarm/landuselivestock/junesurvey/> [Accessed 28/01/11].

Defra (Department for Environment, Food and Rural Affairs) (2009d) Survey of public attitudes and behaviours towards the environment, Defra. [online] Available at: <http://www.defra.gov.uk/statistics/environment/public-attitude/> [Accessed 12.01.11].

Defra (Department for Environment, Food and Rural Affairs) (2009e) Noise Mapping England, Defra. [online] Available at: <http://services.defra.gov.uk/wps/portal/noise> [Accessed 12.01.11].

Defra (Department for Environment, Food and Rural Affairs) (2009f) Safeguarding our soils; a strategy for England, Defra. [online] Available at: <http://archive.defra.gov.uk/environment/quality/land/soil/sap/> [Accessed 28.01.11].

Defra (Department for Environment, Food and Rural Affairs) (2009g) Soil strategy for England supporting evidence paper. Defra, London.

Defra (Department for Environment, Food and Rural Affairs) (2009h) River Water Quality Indicator for Sustainable Development – 2008 results. Statistical Release Ref. 203/09. [online] Available at: <www.defra.gov.uk/statistics/environment/inland-water/> [Accessed 12.01.11].

Dennis, P. & Fry, G.L.A. (1992) Field margins: can they enhance natural enemy population densities and general arthropod diversity on farmland? *Agriculture, Ecosystems & Environment*, **40**, 95–115.

Department of Health (2008) Health effects of climate change in the UK 2008. An update of the Department of Health report 2001/2002, Crown.

Devonshire, A.L., Field, L.M., Foster, S.P., Moores, G.D., Williamson, M.S. & Blackman, R.L. (1998) The evolution of insecticide resistance in the peach-potato aphid, *Myzus persicae. Philosophical Transactions of the Royal Society B–Biological Sciences*, **353**, 1677–1684.

DfT (Department for Transport) (2002) National Travel Survey: revised Data for Urban and Rural Areas.

DfT (Department for Transport) (2004) The Future

of Transport: a network for 2030. London: Department of Transport.

Dormann, C.F., Schweiger, O., Arens, P., Augenstein, I., Aviron, S., Bailey, D., Billeter, R., Bugter, R., Bukácek, R., Burel, F., Cerny, M., Cock, R.D., De Blust, G., DeFilippi, R., Diekötter, T., Dirksen, J., Durka, W., Edwards, P.J., Frenzel, M., Hamersky, R., Hendrickx, F., Herzog, F., Klotz, S., Koolstra, B., Lausch, A., Le Coeur, D., Liira, J., Maelfait, J.P., Opdam, P., Roubalova, M., Schermann-Legionnet, A., Schermann, N., Schmidt, T., Smulders, M.J., Speelmans, M., Simova, P., van Wingerden, W. & Zobel, M. (2008) Prediction uncertainty of environmental change effects on temperate European biodiversity. *Ecology Letters*, **11**, 235–244.

Dragosits, U., Theobald, M.R., Place, C.J., ApSimon, H.M. & Sutton, M.A. (2006) The potential for spatial planning at the landscape scale to mitigate the effects of atmospheric ammonia deposition. *Environmental Science and Policy*, **9**, 626–638.

Dyson, K.E., Thomson, A.M., Mobbs, D.C., Milne, R., Skiba, U., Clark, A., Levy, P.E., Jones, S.K., Billett, M.F., Dinsmore, K.J., van Oijen, M., Ostle, N., Foeried, B., Smith, P., Matthews, R.W., Mackie, E., Bellamy, P., Rivas-Casado, M., Jordan, C., Higgins, A., Tomlinson, R.W., Grace, J., Parrish, P., Williams, M., Clement, R., Moncrieff, J., Manning, A. (2009) Inventory and projections of UK emissions by sources and removals by sinks due to land use, land use change and forestry. Annual report July 2009. Edinburgh, UK, CEH, 279pp. (CEH Project Number: C03116, DEFRA Contract GA01088).

ECDC (European Centre for Disease Prevention and Control) (2006). Consultation Chikungunya risk assessment for Europe. Stockholm, 30 March 2006. [online] Available at: <http://ecdc.europa.eu/en/publications/Publications/0603_MER_Chikungunya_Risk_Assessment_for_Europe.pdf> [Accessed 12.01.11].

Economou, M., Zambeli, E. & Michopoulos, S. (2009) Incidence and prevalence of Crohn's disease and its etiological influences. *Annals of Gastroenterology*, **22**, 158–167.

EFSA (European Food Safety Authority) (2007) Trends and sources of zoonoses and zoonotic agents in humans, foodstuffs, animals and feedingstuffs.

Ellam, H., Verlander, N.Q., Lamden, K., Cheesbrough, J.S., Durband, C.A. & James, S. (2008) Surveillance of giardiasis in Northwest England 1996–2006: impact of an enzyme immunoassay test. *Euro surveillance*, **13**(37), 1–5.

Emberlin, J., Mullins, J., Corden, J., Jones, S., Millington, W., Brooke, M. & Savage, M. (1999) Regional variations in grass pollen seasons in the UK, long-term trends and forecast models. *Clinical and Experimental Allergy*, **29**, 347–356.

Emberlin, J., Detandt, M., Gehrig, R., Jaeger, S., Nolard, N. & Rantio-Lehtimaki, A. (2002) Responses in the start of the Betula (birch) pollen seasons to recent changes in spring temperatures across Europe. *International Journal of Biometeorology*, **46**, 159–170.

Emmett, B.A., Reynolds, B., Chamberlain, P.M., Rowe, E., Spurgeon, D., Brittain, S.A., Frogbrook, Z., Hughes, S., Lawlor, A.J., Poskitt, J., Potter, E., Robinson, D.A., Scott, A., Wood, C. & Woods, C. (2010) Countryside Survey: Soils Report from 2007. Technical Report No. 9/07 NERC/Centre for Ecology & Hydrology 192pp. (CEH Project Number: C03259).

Environment Agency (2001) Impact Assessment of Ionising Radiation on Wildlife. R&D Publication 128, Environment Agency, Bristol, 221 pp.

Environment Agency (2006) The development and use of soil quality indicators for assessing the role of soil in environmental interactions. Bristol: Environment Agency (Science report SC030265).

Environment Agency (2007) UK Soil and Herbage Pollutant Survey. UKSHS Report No. 4. Soil property and radiometric analytical methods. [online] Available at: <www.doeni.gov.uk/niea/txt/uk_soil_herbage_pollutant_survey_report4.pdf> [Accessed 12.03.11].

Environment Agency (2009a) Flooding in England: A national assessment of flood risk. Bristol: Environment Agency.

Environment Agency (2009b) Flooding in Wales: A national assessment of flood risk. Cardiff:-Environment Agency.

Environment Agency (2009c) Investing for the Future: flood and coastal risk management in England – a long-term investment strategy. Bristol: Environment Agency.

Environment Agency (2010) Future Flooding in Wales: flood defences – possible long-term investment scenarios. Cardiff:-Environment Agency.

European Commission (2008) Attitudes of European Citizens towards the Environment. [online] Available at: <http://ec.europa.eu/public_opinion/archives/ebs/ebs_295_en.pdf> [Accessed 12.01.11].

Evans, C.D., Monteith, D.T. & Cooper, D.M. (2005b) Long-term increases in surface water dissolved organic carbon: Observations, possible causes and environmental impacts. *Environmental Pollution*, **137**, 55–71.

Evans, E.P., Ashely, R., Hall, J., Penning-Rowsell, E., Sayers, P., Thorne, C. & Watkinson, A. (2004) Foresight Future Flooding, Volume I and Volume II. Office of Science and Technology, London.

Evans, E.P., Simm, J.D., Thorne, C.R., Arnell, N.W., Ashley, R.M., Hess, T.M., Lane, S.N., Morris, J., Nicholls, R.J., Penning-Rowsell, E.C., Reynard, N.S., Saul, A.J., Tapsell, S.M., Watkinson, A.R. & Wheater, H.S. (2008) An update of the Foresight Future Flooding 2004 qualitative risk analysis. Cabinet Office, London.

Evans, H.F., Straw, N.A. & Watt, A.D. (2001) Climate change: implications for forest insect pests. *UK Forestry Commission Bulletin*, **125**, 99–118.

Evans, J.T., Smith, E.G., Banerjee, A., Smith, R.M.M., Dale, J., Innes, J.A., Hunt, D., Tweddell, A., Wood, A., Anderson, C., Hewinson, R.G., Smith, N.H., Hawkey, P.M. & Sonnenberg, P. (2007) Cluster of human tuberculosis caused by Mycobacterium bovis: evidence for person-to-person transmission in the UK. *Lancet*, **369**, 1270–1276.

Evans, M.G. & Warburton, J. (2005a) Sediment budget for an eroding peat-moorland catchment in northern England. *Earth Surface Processes & Landforms*, **30**, 557–577.

Evans, M.G., Warburton, J. & Yang, J. (2006) Eroding blanket peat catchments: global and local implications of upland organic sediment budgets. *Geomorphology*, **79**, 45–57.

Eyer, M., Chen, Y.P., Schäfer, M.O., Pettis, J. & Neumann, P. (2009) Small hive beetle, *Aethina tumida*, as a potential biological vector of honeybee viruses. *Apidologie*, **40**, 419–428.

Fang, C.-F. & Ling, D.-L. (2005) Guidance for noise reduction provided by tree belts. *Landscape and Urban Planning*, **71**, 29–34.

Faucon, J.P., Aurieres, C., Drajnudel, P., Mathieu, L., Ribiere, M., Martel, A.C., Zeggane, S., Chauzat, M.P. & Aubert, M.F.A. (2005) Experimental study on the toxicity of imidacloprid given in syrup to honey bee (*Apis mellifera*) colonies. *Pest Management Science*, **61**, 111–125.

Fera (The Food and Environment Research Agency) (2009) Foul Brood Diseases of Honey Bees and other Common Brood Disorders. Leaflet B0030/0809.

Ferrari, G., De Liberato, C., Scavia, G., Lorenzetti, R., Zini, M., Farina, F., Magliano, A., Cardeti, G., Scholl, F., Guidoni, M., Scicluna, M.T., Amaddeo, D., Scaramozzino, P. & Autorino, G.L. (2005) Active circulation of bluetongue vaccine virus serotype-2 among unvaccinated cattle in central Italy. *Preventive Veterinary Medicine*, **68**, 103–113.

Ford, J.S. & Myers, R.A. (2008) A global assessment of salmon aquaculture impacts on wild salmonids. *PLoS Biology*, **6**, 411–417.

Forman, R.T., Sperling, D., Bissonette, J.A., Clevenger, A.P., Cutshall, C.D., dale, V.H., Fahrid, L., France, R., Goldman, C.R., Heanue, K., Jones, J.A., Swanson, F.J., Turrentine, T., & Winter, T.C. (2003) Road Ecology: Science and Solutions. Washington DC: Island Press.

Fowler, D., Skiba, U., Moncrieff, J.B. & Polson, D. (2008) Greenhouse gas emissions, inventories and validation. Land Management in a Changing Environment (eds K. Crichton & R. Audsley), pp. 134–151. SAC and SEPA Biennial Conference, SAC.

Fowler, D., Pilegaard, K., Sutton, M.A., Ambus, P., Raivonen, M., Duyzer, J., Simpson, D., Fagerli, H., Fuzzi, S., Schjoerring, J.K., Grainer, C., Neftel, A., Isaksen, I.S.A., Laj, P., Maione, M., Monks, P.S., Burkhardt, J., Daemmgen, U., Neirynck, J., Personne, E., Wichink-Kruit, R., Butterbach-Bahl, K., Flechard, C., Tuovinen, J.P., Coyle, M., Gerosa, G., Loubet, B., Altimir, N., Gruenhage, L., Ammann, C., Cieslik, S., Paoletti, E. Mikkelsen, T.N., Ro-Poulsen, H., Cellier, P., Cape, J.N., Horvath, L., Loreto, F., Niinemets, U., Palmer, P.I., Rinne, J., Misztal, P., Nemitz, E., Nilsson, D., Pryor, S., Gallagher, M.W., Vesala, T., Skiba, U., Brueggemann, N., Zechmeister-Boltenstern, S., Williams, J., O'Dowd, C., Facchini, M.C., de Leeuw, G., Flossman, A., Chaumerliac, N. & Erisman, J.W. (2009) Atmospheric composition change: Ecosystems-Atmosphere interactions. *Atmospheric Environment*, **43**(33) 5193–5267.

Forman, R.T.T., Reineking, B. & Hersperger, A.M. (2002) Road traffic and nearby grassland bird patterns in a suburbanising landscape. *Environmental Management*, **29**, 782–800.

Fowler, D., Cape, J.N. & Unsworth, M.H. (1989) Deposition of atmospheric pollutants on forests. *Philosophical Transactions of the Royal Society B-Biological Sciences*, **324**, 247–265.

Fowler, D., Flechard, C., Cape, J.N., Storeton-West, R.L. & Coyle, M. (2001) Measurements of ozone deposition to vegetation, quantifying the flux and the stomatal and non-stomatal components. *Water Air and Soil Pollution*, **130**, 63–74.

Free, J.B. (1993) Insect Pollination of Crops. Academic Press, San Diego, CA.

Freer-Smith, P.H., Beckett, K.P. & Taylor, G. (2005) Deposition velocities to *Sorbus aria, Acer campestre, Populus deltoids x trichocarpa* 'Beaupre', *Pinus nigra* and *Cupressocyparis leylandii* for coarse, fine and ultra-fine particles in the urban environment. *Environmental Pollution*, **133**, 157–167.

French, P.W. (1997) Coastal and Estuarine Management. Routledge, London.

French, P.W. (2001) Coastal defences: processes, problems and solutions. Routledge, London.

Gabriel, D. & Tscharntke, T. (2007) Insect pollinated plants benefit from organic farming. *Agriculture Ecosystem and Environment*, **118**, 43–48.

Gallai, N., Salles, J.-M., Settele, J. & Vaissière, B.E. (2009) Economic valuation of the vulnerability of world agriculture confronted with pollinator Decline. *Ecological Economics*, **68**, 810–821.

Gianessi, L., Sankula, S. & Reigner, N. (2003) Plant Biotechnology: potential impact for improving pest management in European Agriculture. National Centre for Food and Agricultural Policy, Washington, D.C.

Gibbens, J.C., Sharpe, C.E., Wilesmith, J.W., Mansley, L.M., Michalopoulou, E., Ryan, J.B.M. & Hudson, M. (2001) Descriptive epidemiology of the 2001 foot-and mouth disease epidemic in Great Britain: the first five months. *The Veterinary Record*, **149**, 729–743.

Gilbert, L. (2009) Altitudinal patterns of tick and host abundance: a potential role for climate change in regulating tick-borne diseases? *Oecologia*, **162**(1), 217–255.

Gilbert, M., Slingenbergh, J. & Xiao, X. (2008) Climate change and avian influenza. *Revue Scientifique Et Technique-Office International Des Epizooties*, **27**, 459–466.

Girvin, R. (2009) Aircraft noise-abatement and mitigation strategies. *Journal of Air Transport Management*, **15**, 14–22.

Goldstein, A.H., Mckay, M., Kurpius, M.R., Schade, G.W., Lee, A., Holzinger, R. & Rasmussen, R.A. (2004) Forest thinning experiment confirms ozone deposition to forest canopy is dominated by reactions with biogenic VOCs. *Geophysical Research Letters*, **31**, L22106.

Green, R.E., Tyler, G.A. & Bowden, C.G.R. (2000) Habitat selection, ranging behaviour and diet of the stone curlew (*Burhinus oedicnemus*) in southern England. *Journal of Zoology*, **250**, 161–183.

Grieve, I.C., Davidson, D.A. & Gordon, J.E. (1995) Nature, extent and severity of soil erosion in upland Scotland. *Land Degradation and Rehabilitation*, **6**, 41–55.

Grimwood, C.J. (2002) Trends in environmental noise. *Clean Air*, **30**(1), 15–20.

Guenther, A., Hewitt, C.N., Erickson, D., Fall, R., Geron, C., Graedel, T., Harley, P., Klinger, L., Lerdau, M., McKay, W.A., Pierce, T., Scholes, B., Steinbrecher, R., Tallamraju, R., Taylor, J. & Zimmerman, P. (1993) A global model of natural volatile organic compound emissions. *Journal of Geophysical Research*, **100**, 8873–8892.

Gulev, S.K. & Hasse, L. (1999) Changes of wind waves in the North Atlantic over the last 30 years. *International Journal of Climatology*, **19**, 1091–1117.

Gurr, G.M., Wratten, S.D. & Altieri, M.A. (2004). Ecological engineering for pest management: advances in habitat manipulation for arthropods. CABI Publishing, Wallingford.

Habib, L., Bayne, E.M. & Boutin, S. (2007) Chronic industrial noise affects pairing success and age structure of ovenbirds *Seiurus aurocapilla*. *Journal of Applied Ecology*, **44**, 176–184.

Haenke, S., Scheid, B., Schaefer, M., Tscharntke, T. & Thies, C. (2009) Increasing syrphid fly diversity and density in sown flower strips within simple vs. complex landscapes. *Journal of Applied Ecology*, **46**, 1106–1114.

Hall, J., Ullyett, J., Heywood, L., Broughton, R., Fawehinmi, J. & 31 UK experts. (2003) Status of UK critical loads: Critical loads methods, data and maps. February 2003. Report to Defra

(Contract EPG 1/3/185). [Online] Available at: <http://critloads.ceh.ac.uk>; <http://cldm.defra.gov.uk> [Accessed 12.03.11].

Hall, J., Ullyett, J., Heywood, L., Broughton, R. and 12 UK experts. (2004) Update to: The Status of UK Critical Loads–Critical Loads Methods, Data and Maps. February 2004. Report to Defra (Contract EPG 1/3/185). [Online] Available at: <http://critloads.ceh.ac.uk>; <http://cldm.defra.gov.uk> [Accessed 12.03.11].

Hall, J. (2008) Status of UK critical loads and exceedances. June 2008. Report to Defra under CLDMII (Defra Project Code AQ0801). [Online] Available at: <http://cldm.defra.gov.uk> [Accessed 12.03.11].

Hall, J. (2009) Updates to UK critical loads and exceedances. September 2009. Report to Defra under CLDMII (Defra Project Code AQ0801). [Online] Available at: <http://cldm.defra.gov.uk> [Accessed 12.03.11].

Hansom, J. D. (2010) Coastal Steepening around the coast of Scotland. Scottish Natural Heritage Commissioned Report, in press.

Harrington, R. (2002) Insect pests and global environmental change. Causes and consequences of global environmental change (ed I. Douglas), Vol. 3. John Wiley & Sons, Inc. Chichester.

Harrington, R. (2003) Turning up the heat on pests and diseases: a case study for Barley yellow dwarf virus. Proceedings of the British Crop Protection Council International Congress: Crop Science and Technology 2003, November 10–12 2003, Glasgow British Crop Protection Council, Alton. Proceedings, Vol 2, 1195–200.

Harrington, R., Clark, S.J., Welham, S.J., Verrier, P.J., Denholm, C.H., Hulle, M., Maurice, D., Rounsevell, M.D., Cocu, N. & European Union Examine Consortium (2007) Environmental change and the phenology of European aphids. *Global Change Biology*, **13**, 1550–1564.

Hassell, M.P., Godfray, H.C.J. & Comins, H.N. (1993) Effects of global change on the dynamics of insect host-parasitoid interactions. Biotic interactions and global change (ed. by P.M. Kareiva, J.G. Kingsolver & R.B. Huey), pp. 402–423. Sinauer Associates, Sunderland, Mass.

Hawes, C., Haughton, A.J., Bohan, D.A. & Squire, G.R. (2009) Functional approaches for assessing plant and invertebrate abundance patterns in arable systems. *Basic and Applied Ecology*, **10**, 34–42.

Hawksworth, D.L. (2001) The magnitude of fungal diversity: the 1.5 million species estimate revisited. *Mycological Research*, **105**, 1422–1432.

Heywood, E., Wright, J., Wienburg, C.L., Black, H.I.J., Long, S.M., Osborn, D. & Spurgeon, D.J. (2006) Factors influencing the national distribution of polycyclic aromatic hydrocarbons and polychlorinated biphenyls in British soils. *Environmental Science & Technology*, **40** (24), 7629–7635.

Hicks, W.H., Morrissey, T., Ashmore, M.R., Raffaelli, D., Sutton, M., Smart, J., Ramwell, C., Heinemeyer, A., Bealey, B. & van den Berg, L. (2008) Towards an Ecosystems Approach for Ammonia—Embedding an Ecosystem Services Framework for Air Quality Policy Policy on Agricultural Ammonia Emissions. Final report to Defra, contract NR0120.

Higes, M., Martin, R. & Meana, A. (2006) *Nosema ceranae*, a new microsporidian parasite in honeybees in Europe. *Journal of Invertebrate Pathology*, **92** (2), 93–95.

Highways Agency (2008) Design Manual for Road and Bridges, Volume 11, Section 3, part 7 HA213/08. Noise and Vibration. [online] Available at: <http://www.standardsforhighways.co.uk/dmrb/vol11/section3/ha21308.pdf> [Accessed 12.01.11].

HM Government (Her Majesty's Government) (2009) The UK Low Carbon Transition Plan. National strategy for climate and energy. Department for Energy and Climate Change. [online] Available at: <http://www.decc.gov.uk/en/content/cms/what_we_do/lc_uk/lc_trans_plan/lc_trans_plan.aspx> [Accessed 13.03.11].

HMS (The Harmonised Monitoring Scheme) (2007). Defra e-Digest of Environmental Statistics 2007. [online] Available at: <http://archive.defra.gov.uk/evidence/statistics/environment/inlwater/iwhmsdb.htm> [Accessed 20.03.11].

Hoehn, P., Tscharntke, T., Tylianakis, J. M. & Steffan-Dewenter, I. (2008) Functional group diversity of bee pollinators increases crop yield. *Proceedings of the Royal Society B-Biological Sciences,* **275,** 2283–2291.

Holden, J., Gascoign, M. & Bosanko, N.R. (2007a) Erosion and natural revegetation associated with surface land drains in upland peatlands, *Earth Surface Processes and Landforms*, **32**, 1547–1557.

Holden, J., Shotbolt, L., Bonn, A., Burt, T.P., Chapman, P.J., Dougill, A.J., Fraser, E.D.G., Hubacek, K., Irvine, B., Kirkby, M.J., Reed, M.S., Prell, C., Stagl, S., Stringer, L.C., Turner, A. & Worrall, F. (2007b) Environmental change in moorland landscapes. *Earth-Science Reviews*, **82** 75–100.

Holland, J.M. & Oakely, J. (2007) Importance of arthropod pests and their natural enemies in relation to recent farming practice changes in the UK. HGCA Research Review No. 64.

Hornung, M., Bull, K.R., Cresser, M., Hall, J., Langan, S., Loveland, P. & Smith, C. (1995) An empirical map of critical loads of acidity for soils in Great Britain. *Environmental Pollution*, **90**, 301–310.

Houghton, J. (2004) Global warming. The complete briefing. Cambridge, Cambridge University Press.

Howard, D.C. (2003) Estimating the extent and change in Broad Habitats in Great Britain. *Journal of Environmental Management*, **67**, 219–227.

HPA (Health Protection Agency) (2008) The human animal infections and risk surveillance (HAIRS) group. First report 2004-2007. [online] Available at: <http://www.hpa.org.uk/Publications/InfectiousDiseases/InfectionControl/0810HumanAnimalInfectionsandRiskSurveillanceHAIRS/> [Accessed 12.03.11]

HPA (Health Protection Agency) (2009) Health Protection Weekly report, Vol. 3, No. 1, Jan 2009.

Huddart, L. (1990) The use of vegetation for traffic noise screening. Department for Transport, TRL Research Report RR238, Transport Research Laboratory, Crowthorne.

Hulme, M. & Dessai, S. (2008) Negotiating future climates for public policy: a critical assessment of the development of climate scenarios for the UK. *Environmental Science & Policy*, **11** (1): 54–70.

Hunter, P.R. & Thompson, R.C.A. (2005) The zoonotic transmission of Giardia and Cryptosporidium. *International Journal for Parasitology*, **35**, 1181–1190.

Huntington, T.G. (2006) Evidence for intensification of the global water cycle: Review and synthesis. *Journal of Hydrology*, **319** (1–4), 83–95.

ICCL (Imperial College Consultants Ltd) (2008) Honeybee health (risks) in England and Wales. Report to the National Audit Office.

IPCC (Intergovernmental Panel on Climate Change) (2007a) Climate Change 2007: The Physical Science Basis. Contribution of Working Group I to the Fourth Assessment Report of the Intergovernmental Panel on Climate Change. Cambridge, Cambridge University Press.

IPCC (Intergovernmental Panel on Climate Change) (2007b) Climate Change 2007: Impacts, Adaptation and Vulnerability. Contribution of Working Group II to the Fourth Assessment Report of the Intergovernmental Panel on Climate Change. Cambridge, Cambridge University Press.

ISG (Independent Scientific Group) (2007) Bovine TB; The Scientific Evidence. Final Report of the Independent Scientific Group on Cattle TB.

Jackson, B.M., Wheater, H.S., McIntyre, N.R. & Francis, O.J. (2006) The impact of upland management on flooding: preliminary results from a multi-scale modelling programme. *BHS 9th National Hydrology Symposium*, 73–78.

Jackson, J., Li, Y., Murrells, T., Passant, N., Sneddon, S., Thomas, J., Thistlethwaite, G., Dyson, K. & Cardenas, L. (2009) Greenhouse Gas Inventories for England, Scotland, Wales and Northern Ireland: 1990–2007 AEAT/ENV/R/2873.

Jackson, S., Fuller, D., Dunsford, H., Mowbray, R., Hext, S., MacFarlane, R. & Haggett, C. (2008) Tranquillity Mapping: Developing a Robust Methodology for Planning Support. Report to the Campaign to Protect Rural England. Northumbria University, Bluespace Environments and University of Newcastle.

Jaffé, R., Dietemann, V., Allsopp, M.H., Costa, C., Crewe, R.M., Dall'Olio, R., De La Rúa, P., El-Niweiri, M.A.A., Fries, I., Kezic, N., Meusel, M.S., Paxton, R.J., Shaibi, T., Strolle, E. & Moritz, R.F.A. (2009) Estimating the density of honeybee colonies across their natural range to fill the gap in pollinator decline censuses. *Conservation Biology*, in press. DOI: 10.1111/j.1523-1739.2009.01331.x.

Janvier, C. (2007) Soil health through soil disease suppression: Which strategy from descriptors to indicators? *Soil Biology & Biochemistry* **39** (1), 1–23.

Jarvie, H.P., Neal, C. & Withers, P.J.A. (2006) Sewage-effluent phosphorus: A greater risk to river eutrophication than agricultural phosphorous? *Science of the Total Environment*, **360**, 246–253.

Jenkins, H.E., Woodroffe, R., Donnelly, C.A., Cox, D.R., Johnston, W.T., Bourne, F.J., Cheeseman, C.L., Clifton-Hadley, R.S., Gettinby, G., Gilks, P., Hewinson, R.G., McInerney, J.P. & Morrison, W.I. (2007) Effects of culling on spatial associations of Mycobacterium bovis infections in badgers and cattle. *Journal of Applied Ecology*, **44**, 897–908.

Jenkins, H.E., Woodroffe, R. & Donnelly, C.A. (2008) The effects of annual widespread badger culls on cattle tuberculosis following the cessation of culling. *International Journal of Infectious Disease*, **12**, 457–465.

Jenkins, H.E., Woodroffe, R. & Donnelly, C.A. (2010) The duration of the effects of repeated widespread badger culling on cattle tuberculosis following the cessation of culling. PLoS One, **5**(2), e9090: 1–7.

Jobling, S., Williams, R.J., Johnson, A.C., Taylor, A., Gross-Sorokin, M., Nolan, M., Tyler, C.R., van Aerle, R., Santos, E. & Brighty, G. (2006) Predicted exposures to steroid estrogens in UK rivers correlate with widespread sexual disruption in wild fish populations. *Environmental Health Perspectives,* **114**, 32–39.

Johnson, A.C., Acreman, M.C., Dunbar, M.J., Feist, S.W., Giacomello, A., Gozlan, R.E., Hinsley, S.A..,Ibbotson, A.T., Jarvie, H.P., Jones, J.I., Longshaw, M., Maberly, S.C., Marsh, T.J., Neal, C., Newman, J.R., Nunn, M.A., Pickup, R.W., Reynard, N.S., Sullivan, C.A., Sumpter, J.P. & Williams, R.J. (2009) The British river of the future: How climate change and human activity might affect two contrasting river ecosystems in England. *Science of the Total Environment,* **407**, 4787–4798.

Jönsson, U. (2004) Phytophthora species and oak decline—can a weak competitor cause significant root damage in a nonsterilized acidic forest soil? *New Phytologist*, **162**, 211–222.

Ju-Nam, Y. & Lead, J.R. (2008) Manufactured nanoparticles: an overview of their chemistry, interactions and potential environmental implications. *Science of the Total Environment*, **400**, 396–414.

Kay, D., Aitken, M., Crowther, J., Dickson, I., Edwards, A.C., Francis, C., Hopkins, M., Jeffrey, W., Kay, C., McDonald, A.T., McDonald, D., Stapleton, C.M., Watkins, J., Wilkinson, J. & Wyer, M. (2007) Reducing fluxes of faecal indicator compliance parameters to bathing waters from diffuse agricultural sources, the Brighouse Bay study, Scotland. *Environmental Pollution*, **147**, 139–149.

Kay, D., Crowther, J., Fewtrell, L., Francis, C., Hopkins, M., Kay, C., McDonald, A.T., Stapleton, C.M., Watkins, J., Wilkinson, J. and Wyer, M.D. (2008a) Quantification and control of microbial pollution from agriculture: a new policy challenge? *Environment Science and Policy*, **11**, 171–184.

Kay, D., Kershaw, S., Lee, R., Wyer, M.D., Watkins, J. & Francis, C. (2008b) Results of field investigations into the impact of intermittent sewage discharges on the microbiological quality of wild mussels (*M. edulis*) in a tidal estuary. *Water Research*, **42**, 3033–3046.

Kay, D., Crowther, J., Ferguson, C., Stapleton, C.M., Wyer, M.D., Kay, C., McDonald, A.T., Watkins, J. & Wilkinson, J. (2010) Transport Interventions: microbial pollution attenuation by best management practices in agricultural catchments. Animal Waste, Water Quality and Human Health: WHO—Emerging Issues in Water and Infectious Disease series. International Water Association and WHO (eds R. Bos & J. Bartram), London.

Keesing, F., Holt, R.D. & Ostfeld, R.S. (2006) Effects of species diversity on disease risk. *Ecology Letters*, **9**, 485–498.

Kibblewhite, M.G., Ritz, K. & Swift, M.J. (2008) Soil health in agricultural systems. *Philosophical Transactions of the Royal Society B-Biological Sciences*, **363**, 685–701.

King, D., Roper, T.J., Young, D., Woolhouse, M.E.J., Collins, D.A. & Wood, P. (2007). Bovine tuberculosis in cattle and badgers: a report by the Chief Scientific Advisor, Sir David King. [online] Available at: <http://www.bis.gov.uk/assets/biscore/corporate/migratedD/ec_group/44-07-S_I_on> [Accessed 13.01.11].

Kirby, K.J., Smart, S.M., Black, H.I.J., Bunce, R.G.H., Corney, P.M. & Smithers, R.J. (2005) Long term ecological change in British woodland (1971–2001). English Nature Research Report 653. Peterborough: English Nature.

Kirk, G.J.D., Bellamy, P.H. & Lark, R.M. (2009) Changes in soil pH across England and Wales in response to decreased acid deposition. *Global Change Biology,* **16**(11), 1365–2486.

Kleijn, D. & Sutherland, W.J. (2003) How effective are European agri-environment schemes in conserving and promoting biodiversity? *Journal of Applied Ecology*, **40**, 947–969.

Klempa, B. (2009) Hantaviruses and climate change. *Clinical Microbiology and Infection*, **15**, 518–523.

Kovats, S. (Ed.) (2008) Health Effects of Climate Change in the UK 2008. An update of the Department of Health report 2001/2002. Department of Health, Document 285576 1p 0.2k Feb08 (FMP.) [online] Available at: <www.dh.gov.uk/publications> [Accessed 12.03.11].

Knudsen, A.B. (1995) Global distribution and continuing spread of *Aedes albopictus. Parassitologia*, **37**, 91–97.

Krebs, J.R., Anderson, R., Clutton Brock, T., Morrison, W.I., Young, D.B., Donnelly, C.A., Frost, S. & Woodroffe, R. (1997) Bovine tuberculosis in cattle and badgers—An independent scientific review. PB3423, MAFF (London).

Kremen, C., Williams, N.M., Aizen, M.A., Gemmill-Herren, B., LeBuhn, G., Minckley, R., Packer, L., Potts, S.G., Roulston, T, Steffan-Dewenter, I., Vázquez, D.P., Winfree, R., Adams, L., Crone, E.E., Greenleaf, S.S., Jeitt, T.H., Klein, A.-M., Regetz, J. & Ricketts, T.H. (2007) Pollination and other ecosystem services produced by mobile organisms: a conceptual framework for the effects of land use change. *Ecology Letters*, **10**, 219–314.

Krkosek, M., Ford, J.S., Morton, A., Lele, S., Myers, R.A. & Lewis, M.A. (2007) Declining wild salmon populations in relation to parasites from farm salmon. *Science*, **318**, 1772–1775.

Lake, I.R., Nichols, G., Bentham, G., Harrison, F.C.D., Hunter, P.R. & Kovats, R.S. (2007) Cryptosporidiosis decline after regulation, England and Wales, 1989–2005. *Emerging Infectious Diseases*, **13**, 623–625.

Landis, D.A. & Van der Werf, W. (1997) Early-season predation impacts the establishment of aphids and beet yellows virus in sugar beet. *BioControl*, **42**, 499–516.

LoGiudice, K., Duerr, S.T.K., Newhouse, M.J., Schmidt, K.A., Killilea, M.E. & Ostfeld, R.S. (2008) Impact of host community composition on Lyme disease risk. *Ecology*, **89**, 2841–2849.

Longfield, S.A. & Macklin, M.G. (1999) The influence of recent environmental change on flooding and sediment fluxes in the Yorkshire Ouse Basin. *Hydrological Processes*, **13**, 1051–66.

Loss, S.R., Hamer, G.L., Walker, E.D., Ruiz, M.O., Goldberg, T.L., Kitron, U.D. & Brawn, J.D. (2009) Avian host community structure and prevalence of West Nile Virus in Chicago, Illinois. *Oecologia*, **159**, 415–424.

MacCarthy, J., Thomas, S., Choudrie, S., Passant, N., Thistlethwaite, G., Murrells, T., Watterson, J., Cardenas, L. & Thomson, A. (2010) UK Greenhouse Gas Inventory, 1990 to 2008: Annual Report for submission under the Framework Convention on Climate Change AEAT/ENV/R/2978.

Macfadyen, S., Gibson, R., Polaszek, A., Morris, R.J., Craze, P.G., Planque, R., Symondson, W.O.C. & Memmott, J. (2009a) Do differences in food web structure between organic and conventional farms affect the ecosystem service of pest control? *Ecology Letters*, **12**, 229–238.

Macfadyen, S., Gibson, R., Raso, L., Sint, D., Traugott, M. & Memmott, J. (2009b) Parasitoid control of aphids in organic and conventional farming systems. *Agriculture Ecosystems & Environment*, **133**, 14–18.

Mackay, D., Parida, S., Paton, D. & Anderson, J. (2004) Making a vaccinate-to-live policy a reality in foot-and-mouth disease. *Developments in Biologicals*, **119**, 261–266.

Mackey, E.C., Shewry, M.C. & Tudor, G.J. (1998). Land cover change: Scotland from the 1940s to the 1980s. Edinburgh, The Stationery Office.

MacLeod, A., Wratten, S.D., Sotherton, N.W. & Thomas M.B. (2004). 'Beetle banks' as refuges for beneficial arthropods in farmland: long-term changes in predator communities and habitat. *Agricultural and Forest Entomology*, **6**, 147–154.

MacLeod, A., Baker, R.H.A., Cheek, S., Eyre, D. & Cannon, R.J.C. (2007) Pest risk analysis for western corn rootworm (*Diabrotica virgifera virgifera*), Central Science Laboratory, Sand Hutton, York, UK.

Manley, J., van Kooten, G., Moeltner, K. & Johnson, D. (2005) Creating Carbon Offsets in Agriculture through No-Till Cultivation: A Meta-Analysis of Costs and Carbon Benefits. *Climatic Change*, **68**(1–2), 41–65.

Marshall, E.J.P., Brown, V.K., Boatman, N.D., Lutman, P.J.W. & Squire, G.R. (2001) The impact of herbicides on weed abundance and biodiversity. Report no. PN0940. UK Pesticides Safety Directorate.

Marshall, E.J.P., Brown, V.K., Boatman, N.D., Lutman, P.J.W., Squire, G.R. & Ward, L.K. (2003) The role of weeds in supporting biological diversity within crop fields. *Weed Research*, **43**, 77–89.

Marshall, M.R., Francis, O.J., Frogbrook, Z. L., Jackson, B. M., McIntyre, N., Reynolds, B. Solloway, I., Wheater, H.S., Chell, J. (2009) The impact of upland land management on flooding: results from an improved pasture hillslope. *Hydrological Processes*, **23**, 464–475.

Martens, P. & Moser, S.C. (2001) Health impacts of climate change. *Science*, **292**, 1065–1066.

Marvier, M., McCreedy, C., Regetz, J. & Kareiva, P. (2007). A meta-analysis of the Effects of Bt Cotton and Maize on non-target invertebrates. *Science*, **316**, 1475–1477.

Masselink, G. & Russell, P. (2008) Coastal erosion and coastal geomorphology, Marine Climate Change Impacts Partnership. [online] Available at: <http://www.mccip.org.uk/arc/2007/erosion.htm> [Accessed 13.01.11].

Mastroeni, P., Chabalgoity, J.A., Dunstan, S.J., Maskell, D.J. & Dougan, G. (2001) Salmonella: Immune responses and vaccines. *Veterinary Journal*, **161**, 132–164.

Matson, P.A., Parton, W.J., Power, A.G. & Swift, M.J. (1997) Agricultural intensification and ecosystem properties. *Science*, **277**, 504–509.

McDonald, A,G., Bealey, W.J., Fowler, D., Dragosits, U., Skiba, U., Smith, R.I., Donovan, R.G., Brett, H.E., Hewitt, C.N. & Nemitz, E. (2007) Quantifying the effect of urban tree planting on concentrations and deposition of PM_{10} in two UK conurbations. *Atmospheric Environment*, **41**, 8455–8467.

McGrath, S.P., Zhao, F.-J. (1995) A risk assessment of sulphur deficiency in cereals using soil and atmospheric deposition data. *Soil Use and Management*, **11**, 110–114.

McHugh, M., Harrod, T. & Morgan, R. (2002) The extent of soil erosion in upland England and Wales, Earth Surface Processes and Landforms, **27**, 99–107.

McManus, J. (2010) Trends of change in coastal landforms and processes. Scottish Natural Heritage Commissioned Report, in press.

Medlock, J.M., Avenell, D., Barrass, I. & Leach, S. (2006) Analysis of the potential for survival and seasonal activity of Aedes albopictus (Diptera : Culicidae) in the United Kingdom. *Journal of Vector Ecology*, **31**, 292–304.

Memmott, J. (1999) The structure of a plant-pollinator food web. *Ecology Letters*, **2**, 276–280.

Memmott, J., Craze, P.G., Waser, N.M & Price, M.V. (2007) Global warming and the disruption of plant-pollinator interactions. *Ecology Letters*, **10**, 710–717.

Milner, R.M., Mavin, S., Ho-Yen, D.O. (2009) Lyme borreliosis in Scotland during two peak periods. *Journal of the Royal College of Physicians of Edinburgh,* 39, 196–199.

Misselbrook, T.H., Dore, A.J., Dragosits, U., Tang, Y.-S., Sutton, M.A., Hall, J., Reis, S., Anthony, S.G. & Dore, C. (2009) Underpinning evidence for development of policies to reduce ammonia emissions. Final report on Defra, project AQ0602.

Monteith, D.T., Stoddard, J.L., Evans, C.D., de Wit, H., Forsius, M., Høgåsen, T., Wilander, A., Skjelkvåle, B.L., Jeffries, D.S., Vuorenmaa, J., Keller, B., Kopácek, J. & Vesely J. (2007) Rising freshwater dissolved organic carbon driven by changes in atmospheric deposition. *Nature*, **450**, 537–540.

Morandin, L.A., Winston, M.L., Franklin, M.T. & Abbott, V.A. (2005) Lethal and sub-lethal effects of spinosad on bumble bees (*Bombus impatiens* Cresson). *Pest Management Science*, **61**, 619–626.

Mourato, S., Georgiou, S., Ozdemiroglu, E., Newcombe, J. & Howarth, A. (2003) Bathing water revisions: what are the benefits to England and Wales? A stated preference study. CSERGE Working Paper ECM 03-12. University of East Anglia. Pp. 39.

NAO (National Audit Office) (2009) The health of livestock and honeybees in England. Available online at: < http://www. nao.org.uk/publications/0809/the_health_of_livestock.aspx > [Accessed 28.01.11].

Natural England (2009) Experiencing Landscapes: Capturing the 'cultural services' and 'experiential qualities' of landscape. Natural England, Report NECR024.

Natural England (2010) England's peatlands. Carbon storage and greenhouse gases. Natural England, Report NE257.

Nayak, D.R., Miller, D., Nolan, A., Smith, P. & Smith, J. (2008) Calculating carbon savings from wind farms on Scottish peat lands—a new approach. Research report funded by RERAD, Scottish Government, Science Policy and Coordination Division.

NEGTAP (National Expert Group on Transboundary Air Pollution) (2001) Transboundary Air Pollution: Acidification, Eutrophication and Ground-Level Ozone in the UK. ISBN 1 870393 61 9.

Nellthorp, J., Bristow, A.L. & Day, B. (2007) Introducing willingness-to-pay for noise changes into transport: an application of benefit transfer. *Transport Reviews*, **27**, 327–353.

Neumann, P. & Elzen, P.J. (2004) The biology of the small hive beetle (*Aethina tumida*, Coleoptera: Nitidulidae): Gaps in our knowledge of an invasive species. *Apidologie*, **35**, 229–247.

Newton, A.C., Stewart, G.B., Myers, G., Diaz, A., Lake, S., Bullock, J.M. & Pullin, A.S. (2009) Impacts of grazing on lowland heathland in north-west Europe. *Biological Conservation*, **142**, 935–947.

Nguyen, B.K., Saegerman, C., Pirard, C., Mignon, J., Widart, J., Tuirionet, B., Verheggen, F.J., Berkvens, D., De Pauw, E. & Haubruge, E. (2009) Does Imidacloprid Seed-Treated Maize Have an Impact on Honey Bee Mortality? *Journal of Economic Entomology*, **102**, 616–623.

O'Connell, P.E., Beven, K.J., Carney, J.N., Clements, R.O., Ewen, J., Fowleer, H., Harris, G.L., Hollis, J., Morris, J., O'Donnell, G.M., Packman, J.C., Parkin, A., Quinn, P.F., Rose, S.C., Shepherd, M. & Tellier, S. (2004) Review of the impacts of rural land use and management of flood generation R&D Technical report FD2114. Defra, London.

Ogle, S., Breidt, F. & Paustian, K. (2005) Agricultural management impacts on soil organic carbon storage under moist and dry climatic conditions of temperate and tropical regions. *Biogeochemistry*, **72**(1), 87–121.

Orford, J.D. & Pethick, J. (2006) Challenging assumptions of future coastal habitat development around the UK. Earth Surface Processes and Landforms, **31**, 1625–1642.

Orr, H.G., Wilby R.L., McKenzie—Hedger, M. & Brown, I. (2008) Climate change in the uplands: a UK perspective on safeguarding regulatory ecosystem services. *Climate Research*, **37**, 77–98. DOI: 10.3354/cr00751.

Östman, O., Ekbom, B., Bengtsson, J. & Weibull, A.C. (2001) Landscape complexity and farming practice influence the condition of polyphagous carabid beetles. *Ecological Applications*, **11**, 480–488.

Östman, O., Ekbom, B. & Bengtsson, J. (2003). Yield increase attributable to aphid predation by ground-living polyphagous natural enemies in spring barley in Sweden. *Ecological Economics*, **45**, 149–158.

Payne, S.R., Davies, W.J. & Adams, M.D. (2009) Research into the practical and policy applications of soundscape concepts and techniques in urban areas (NANR 2000). Pp. 100, Report to Defra. [online] Available at: < http://www.defra.gov.uk/ environment/quality/noise/research/> [Accessed 28.1.01].

Pell, J.K., Eilenberg, J., Hajek, A.E. & Steinkraus, D.C. (2001) Biology, ecology and pest management potential of Entomophthorales. Fungi as biocontrol agents, progress, problems and potential. (eds T.M. Butt, C. Jackson, N. Magan), pp. 71–153. CABI Publishing, Wallingford.

Pelley, J. (2009) Biodiversity is good for your health. *Frontiers in Ecology and the Environment*, **7**, 347–347.

Pettis, J.S. & Wilson, W.T. (1996) Life history of the honey bee tracheal mite *Acarapis woodi* (Acari: Tarsonemida). *Annals of the Entomological Society of America*, **89**, 368–374.

Pheasant, R., Horoshenkov, K., Watts, G. & Barrett, B. (2008) The acoustic and visual factors influencing the construction of tranquil space in urban and environments tranquil spaces-quiet places. *Journal of the Acoustic Society of America*, **123**, 1446–1457.

Pickup, R.W., Rhodes, G., Bull, T.J., Arnott, S., Sidi-Boumedine, K., Hurley, M. & Hermon-Taylor, J. (2006) *Mycobacterium avium* subsp *paratuberculosis* in lake catchments, in river water abstracted for domestic use, and in effluent from domestic sewage treatment works: Diverse opportunities for environmental cycling and human exposure. *Applied and Environmental Microbiology*, **72**, 4067–4077.

Piechotowski, I., Brockmann, S.O., Schwarz, C., Winter, C.H., Ranft, U. & Pfaff, G. (2008) Emergence of hantavirus in South Germany: rodents, climate and human infections. *Parasitology Research*, **103**, S131–S137.

Plumb, R.T. (2002) Viruses of Poaceae: a case history in plant pathology. *Plant Pathology*, **51**, 674–682.

Pollock, K.G.J., Smith, H.V., Young, D., Ramsay, C.N. & Reilly, W.J. (2005) Giardia surveillance in Scotland, 1988–2003. *European Journal of Clinical Microbiology & Infectious Diseases*, **24**, 571–573.

Porter, J.H. (1994) Some implications of climate change for *Ostrinia nubilalis* in Europe. Pest control and sustainable agriculture (eds S.A. Corey, D.J. Dall & W.M. Milne), pp. 417–420. CSIRO, Canberra.

Potts, G.R., Ewald, J.A. & Moreby, S.J. (2006) Biodiversity in a cereal ecosystem 1968–2004: a 38 year study of the cereal fields on the Sussex downs. Part two: the invertebrates. Report for the Leverhulme Trust (Unpublished).

Potts, S.G., Roberts, S.P.M., Dean, R., Marris, G., Brown, M., Jones, R. & Settele, J. (2010a) Declines of managed honeybees and beekeepers in Europe. *Journal of Apicultural Research,* **49**, 15–22.

Potts S.G., Biesmeijer J.C., Kremen C., Neumann P., Schweiger O. & Kunin W.E. (2010b) Global pollinator declines: trends, impacts and drivers. *Trends in Ecology and Evolution,* **25,** 345–353.

Potts, S.G., Woodcock, B.A., Roberts, S.P.M., Tscheulin, T., Ramsay, A.J., Pilgrim, E., Brown, V.K. & Tallowin, J.R. (2009) Enhancing pollinator biodiversity in intensive grasslands. *Journal of Applied Ecology,* **46**, 369–379.

Powell, W., A'Hara, A., Harling, R., Holland, J.M., Northing, P., Thomas, C.F.G. & Walters, K.F.A. (2004) Managing biodiversity in field margins to enhance integrated pest control in arable crops ('3-D Farming' Project). Project Report No. 356 Part 1, pp. 1–80, HGCA Reports.

Purse, B.V., McCormick, B.J.J., Mellor, P.S., Baylis, M., Boorman, J.P.T., Borras, D., Burgu, I., Capela, R., Caracappa, S., Collantes, F., De Liberato, C., Delgado, J.A., Denison, E., Georgiev, G., El Harak, M., De La Rocque, S., Lhor, Y., Lucientes, J., Mangana, O., Miranda, M.A., Nedelchev, N., Nomikou, K., Ozkul, A., Patakakis, M., Pena, I., Scaramozzino, P., Torina, A. & Rogers, D.J. (2007) Incriminating bluetongue virus vectors with climate envelope models. *Journal of Applied Ecology,* **44**, 1231–1242.

Purse, B.V., Mellor, P.S., Rogers, D.J., Samuel, A.R., Mertens, P.P.C. & Baylis, M. (2005) Climate change and the recent emergence of bluetongue in Europe. *Nature Reviews Microbiology,* **3**, 171–181.

Pye, K. & French, P.W. (1993) Targets for coastal habitat recreation. Research and Survey in Nature Conservation no. 13. English Nature, Peterborough.

Pywell, R.F., Meek, W.M., Carvell, C., Hulmes, L. & Nowakowski, M. (2007) The Buzz project: biodiversity enhancement on arable land under the new agri-environment schemes. In: Boatman *et al.*, N. (ed.) *Delivering Arable Biodiversity.* Wellesbourne, Association of Applied Biologists, 61–68. *Aspects of Applied Biology*, 81, 81.

Quine, T.A. & Zhang, Y. (2002) An investigation of spatial variation in soil erosion, soil properties, and crop production within an agricultural field in Devon, United Kingdom. *Journal of Soil and Water Conservation,* **57**, 55–65.

Quine, T.A. & Van Oost, K. (2007) Quantifying carbon sequestration as a result of soil erosion and deposition: retrospective assessment using caesium-137 and carbon inventories. *Global Change Biology,* **13**, 2610–2625.

Quine, T.A., Van Oost, K., Walling, D.E. & Owens, P.N. (2006) DEFRA project SP08007: Scoping study of soil loss through wind erosion, tillage erosion and soil co-extracted with root vegetables; Objective 2 deliverable: Development and application of GIS-based models to estimate national rates of soil erosion by tillage, wind and root crop harvest, Final Report.

Quinn, J.L., Whittingham, M.J., Butler, S.J. & Cresswell, W. (2006) Noise, predation risk compensation and vigilance in the chaffinch *Fringilla coelebs. Journal of Avian Biology,* **37**, 601–608.

Ragwort Control Act (2003) [online] Available at: <http://www.opsi.gov.uk/acts/acts2003/ukpga_20030040_en_1)> [Accessed 13.01.11].

Ramchunder, S.J., Brown, L.E. & ad Holden, J. (2009) Environmental effects of drainage, drain blocking and prescribed vegetation burning in UK upland peatlands. *Progress in Physical Geography*, **33**, 49–79.

Randerson, J.T., Thompson, M.V., Conway, T.J., Fung, I.Y. & Field, C.B. (1997) The Contribution of Terrestrial Sources and Sinks to Trends in the Seasonal Cycle of Atmospheric Carbon Dioxide. *Global Biogeochemical Cycles*, **11**(4), 535–560.

Rangel, J.M., Sparling, P.H., Crowe, C., Griffin, P.M. & Swerdlow, D.L. (2005) Epidemiology of Escherichia coli O157 : H7 outbreaks, United States, 1982–2002. *Emerging Infectious Diseases*, **11**, 603–609.

Read, D.J., Freer-Smith, P.H., Morison, J.I.L., Hanley, N., West, C.C. & Snowdon, P. (2009) Combating climate change—a role for UK forests. An assessment of the potential of the UK's trees and woodlands to mitigate and adapt to climate change. The Stationery Office, Edinburgh.

Reis, S., Pinder, R.W., Zhang, M., Lijie, G. & Sutton, M.A. (2009) Reactive nitrogen in atmospheric emission inventories. *Atmospheric Chemistry and Physics*, **9**, 7657–7677.

Reynolds B. (2004) Continuous cover forestry: possible implications for surface water acidification in the UK uplands. *Hydrology and Earth System Sciences*, **8**, 306–313.

Ricketts, T.H., Regetz, J., Steffan-Dewenter, I., Cunningham, S.A., Kremen, C., Bogdanski, A.,Gemmill-Herren, B., Greenleaf, S.S., Klein, A.M., Mayfield, M.M., Morandin, L.A., Ochieng, A., Potts, S.G. & Viana, B.F. (2008) Landscape effects on crop pollination services: are there general patterns? *Ecology Letters*, **11**, 499–515.

Robson, A.J. (2002) Evidence for trends in UK flooding. *Philosophical Transactions of the Royal Society A—Mathematical, Physical & Engineering Sciences,* **360**, 1327–1343.

Rodriguez, M.A. & Hawkins, B.A. (2000) Diversity, function and stability in parasitoid communities. *Ecology Letters*, **3**, 35–40.

Rothwell, J.J., Robinson, S.G., Evans, M.G., Yang, J. & Allott, T.E.H. (2005) Heavy metal release by peat erosion in the Peak District, southern Pennies, UK. *Hydrological Processes*, **19**, 2973–2989.

RoTAP (Review of Transboundary Air Pollution) (2011) Review of Transboundary Air Pollution: Acidification, Eutrophication, Ground Level Ozone and Heavy Metals in the UK. Contract Report to the Department for Environment, Food and Rural Affairs. Centre for Ecology & Hydrology.

Royal Society (2008) Ground Level Ozone in the 21st Century: Future Trends, Impacts and Policy Implications. The Royal Society, London.

Sanderson, M.G., Collins, W.J., Hemming, D.L. & Betts, R.A. (2007) Stomatal conductance changes due to increasing carbon dioxide levels: projected impact on surface ozone levels. *Tellus B*, **59**, 404–411.

Scharlemann, J.P.W., Johnson, P.J., Smith, A.A., MacDonald, D.W. & Randolph, S.E. (2008) Trends in ixodid tick abundance and distribution in Great Britain. *Medical and Veterinary Entomology*, **22**, 238–247.

Schmidt, M.H., Lauer, A., Purtauf, T., Thies, C., Schaefer, M. & Tscharntke, T. (2003) Relative importance of predators and parasitoids for cereal aphid control. *Proceedings of the Royal Society of London, Series B-Biological Sciences*, **270**, 1905–1909.

Schmidt-Entling, M.H. & Döbeli, J. (2009) Sown wildflower areas to enhance spiders in arable fields. *Agriculture Ecosystems & Environment*, **133**, 19–22.

Schröter, D., Wolfgang, C., Leemans, R., Prentice, I.C., Araújo, M.B., Arnell, N.W., Bondeau, A., Bugmann, H., Carter, T.R., Gracia, C.A., de la Vega-Leinert, A.C., Erhard, M., Ewert, F., Glendining, M., House, J.I., Kankaanpää, Klein, R.J.T., Lavorel, S., Lindner, M., Metzger, M.J., Meyer, J., Mitchell, T.D., Reginster, I., Rounsevell, M., Sabaté, A. Sitch, S., Smith, B., Smith, J., Smith, P., Sykes, M.T., Thonicke, K., Thuiller, W., Tuck, G., Zaehle, S. & Zierl (2005) Ecosystem service supply and vulnerability to global change in Europe. *Science*, **310**, 1333–1337.

Scottish Government (2007) Scottish Noise Mapping. [online] Available at: <http://www.scottishnoisemapping.org/public/view-map.aspx> [Accessed 13.01.11].

Scottish Government (2009) Climate Change Delivery Plan. Meeting Scotland's statutory climate change targets. [online] Available at: <http://www.scotland.gov.uk/Resource/Doc/276273/0082934.pdf> [Accessed 13.01.11.]

Scottish Government (2010) Climate Change: Flooding Occurrences Review. [online] Available at: <www.scotland.gov.uk/cru/kd01/lightgreen/ccfo-00.asp> [Accessed 13.01.11]

SEPA (Scottish Environment Protection Agency) (2010a) Flooding. [online] Available at: <http://www.sepa.org.uk/flooding/flood map.aspx> [Accessed 13.01.11].

SEPA (Scottish Environment Protection Agency) (2010b) Flooding Publications. [online] Available at: <http://www.sepa.org.uk/flooding/flooding_publications.aspx> [Accessed 13.01.11].

Singer, P.C. (1999) Humic substances as precursors for potentially harmful disinfection byproducts. *Water Science and Technology*, **40**, 25–30.

Six, J., Ogle, S.M., Breidt, F.J., Conant, R.T., Mosiers, A.R. & Paustian, K. (2004) The potential to mitigate global warming with no-tillage management is only realised when practised in the long term. *Global Change Biology*, **10**, 155–160.

Skinner, C.J. & Grimwood, C.J. (2002) The UK National Noise Incidence Study 2000/2001. Noise Forum Conference 20 May 2002. BRE, Watford.

Slabbekoorn, H. & Ripmeester, E.A.P. (2008) Birdsong and anthropogenic noise: implications and applications for conservation. *Molecular Ecology*, **17**, 72–83.

Slingenbergh, J., Gilbert, M., DeBalogh, K. & Wint, W. (2004) Ecological sources of zoonotic diseases. In Emerging zoonoses and pathogens of public health concern. *Revue Scientifique et Technique de l'Office Internationale des Epizooties*, **23**, 467–484.

Smart, S.M., Robertson, J.C., Shield, E.J. & van de Poll, H.M. (2003) Locating eutrophication effects across British vegetation between 1990 and 1998. *Global Change Biology,* **9**(12), 1763–1774.

Smith, H.V., Caccio, S.M., Tait, A., McLauchlin, J. & Thompson, R.C.A. (2006) Tools for investigating the environmental transmission of Cryptosporidium and Giardia infections in humans. *Trends in Parasitology*, **22**, 160–167.

Smith, P., Smith, J.U., Flynn, H., Killham, K., Rangel-Castro, I., Foereid, B., Aitkenhead, M., Chapman, S., Towers, W., Bell, J., Lumsdon, D., Milne, R., Thomson, A., Simmons, I., Skiba, U., Reynolds, B., Evans, C., Frogbrook, Z., Bradley, I., Whitmore, A.,

Falloon, P. (2007) ECOSSE: Estimating Carbon in Organic Soils – Sequestration and Emissions. Final Report, pp. 166, SEERAD Report. ISBN 978 0 7559 1498 2.

Smith, P., Nabuurs, G.-J., Janssens, I.A., Reis, S., Marland, G.,Soussana, J.-F., Christensen, T.R., Heath, L., Apps, M., Alexeyev, V., Fang, J., Gattuso, J.-P., Guerschman, J.P., Huang, Yao, Jobbagy, E., Murdiyarso, D., Ni, J., Nobre, A., Peng, C., Walcroft, A., Wang, S.Q., Pan, Y & Zhou, G.S. (2008). Sectoral approaches to improve regional carbon budgets. *Climatic Change*, **88**, 209–249.

Smith, R.S., Shiel, R.S., Bardgett, R.D., Millward, D., Corkhill, P., Rolph, G., Hobbs, P.J. & Peacock, S. (2003) Soil microbial community, fertility, vegetation and diversity as targets in the restoration management of a meadow grassland. *Journal of Applied Ecology*, **40**(1), 51–64.

Snow, L.C., Newson, S.E., Musgrove, A.J., Cranswick, P.A., Crick, H.Q.P. & Wilesmith, J.W. (2007) Risk-based surveillance for H5N1 avian influenza virus in wild birds in Great Britain. *Veterinary Record*, **161**, 775–781.

Snyder, W.E., Snyder, G.B., Finke, D.L. & Straub, C.S. (2006) Predator biodiversity strengthens herbivore suppression. *Ecology Letters*, **9**, 789–796.

Sozanska, M., Skiba, U. & Metcalfe, S. (2002) Developing an inventory of N_2O emissions from British soils. *Atmospheric Environment*, **36**(6), 987–998.

Spieksma, F.T.M., Corden, J.M., Detandt, M., Millington, W.M., Nikkels, H., Nolard, N., Schoenmakers, C.H.H., Wachter, R., de Weger, L.A., Willems, R. & Emberlin, J. (2003) Quantitative trends in annual totals of five common airborne pollen types (Betula, Quercus, Poacae, Urtica, and Artemisia), at five pollen-monitoring sites in western Europe. *Aerobiologia*, **19**, 171–184.

Spurgeon, D.J., Rowland, P., Ainsworth, G., Rothery, P., Long, S. & Black, H.I.J. (2008) Geographical and pedological drivers of distribution and risks to soil fauna of seven metals (Cd, Cu, Cr, Ni, Pb, V and Zn) in British soils. *Environmental Pollution*, **153**(2), 273–283.

Squire, G.R., Hawes, C., Begg, G.S. & Young, M.W. (2009) Cumulative impact of GM herbicide-tolerant cropping on arable plants assessed through species-based and functional taxonomies. *Environmental Science and Pollution Research*, **16**, 85–94.

Squire, G.R., Hawes, C., Bohan, D.A., Brookes, D.R., Champion, G.T., Firbank, L.G., Haughton, A.J., Heard, M.S., May, M.J., Perry, J.N. & Young, M.W. (2005) Biodiversity effects of the management associated with GM cropping systems in the UK. Defra, London.

Stapleton, C.M., Wyer, M.D., Crowther, J., McDonald, A.T., Kay, D., Greaves, J., Wither, A., Watkins, J., Francis, C., Humphrey, N. & Bradford, M. (2008) Quantitative catchment profiling to apportion faecal indicator organism budgets for the Ribble system, the UK's sentinel drainage basin for Water Framework Directive research. *Journal of Environmental Management*, **87**, 535–550.

Stiling, P. & Cornelissen, T. (2005) What makes a successful biocontrol agent? A meta-analysis of biological control agent performance. *Biological Control*, **34**, 236–246.

Stout, J.C. (2007) Reproductive biology of the invasive exotic shrub, *Rhododendron ponticum* L. (Ericaceae). Botanical Journal of the Linnean Society, **155**, 373–381.

Straub, C.S., Finke, D.L. & Snyder, W.E. (2008) Are the conservation of natural enemy biodiversity and biological control compatible goals? *Biological Control*, **45**, 225–237.

Sumilo, D., Asokliene, L., Bormane, A., Vasilenko, V., Golovljova, I. & Randolph, S.E. (2007) Climate change cannot explain the upsurge of tick-borne encephalitis in the Baltics. *PLoS ONE,* **2**, e500.

Tatem, A.J. (2009) The worldwide airline network and the dispersal of exotic species: 2007–2010. *Ecography,* **32**, 94–102.

Taylor, J.A., Murdock, A.P. & Pontee, N.I. (2004) A macroscale analysis of coastal steepening around the coast of England & Wales, *The Geographical Journal,* **170**, 179–188.

Thomson, A.M. (ed.) (2010) Inventory and Projections of UK Emissions by Sources and Removals by Sinks due to Land Use, Land Use Change and Forestry, Annual Report, July 2010. Centre for Ecology & Hydrology and, Forest Research. [online] Available at: <http://ecosystemghg.ceh.ac.uk/reports.htm. [Accessed: 28.01.11].

Thuerig, B., Fließbacha, A., Bergera, N., Fuchsa, J.G., Krausa, N., Mahlberg, N., Nietlispacha, B. & Tamm, L. (2009) Re-establishment of suppressiveness to soil- and air-borne diseases by re-inoculation of soil microbial communities. *Soil Biology and Biochemistry,* **41**(10), 2153–2161.

Tiwary, A., Sinnett, D., Peachey, C., Chalabi, Z., Vardoulakis, S., Fletcher, T., Leonaride, G., Grundy, C., Azapagic, A. & Hutchings, T.R. (2009) An integrated tool to assess the role of new planting in PM_{10} capture and the human health benefits: a case study in London. *Environmental Pollution,* **157**, 2645–2653.

TQL (Transport for Quality of Life) (2008) Traffic Noise in Rural Areas: Personal Experiences of People Affected. Pp. 196. [online] Available at: <http://www.eta.co.uk/files/Traffic%20 Noise%20Report%202008.pdf> [Accessed 13.01.11].

Traveset, A. & Richardson, D.M. (2006) Biological invasions as disruptors of plant reproductive mutualisms. *Trends in Ecology and Evolution,* **21**, 208–216.

Toth, I. & Elphinstone, J. (2009) *Erwinia chrysanthemi* (Dickeya spp.)—the facts. [online] Available at: <http://www.scri. ac.uk/scri/file/PiP/Erwinia.pdf> [Accessed 13.01.11].

Towers, W., Grieve, I.C., Hudson, G., Campbell, C.D., Lilly, A., Davidson, D.A., Bacon, J.R., Langan , S.J. & Hopkins, D.A. (2006) Scotland's soil resource—current state and threats. [online] Available at: <http://www.scotland.gov.uk/Resource/ Doc/149337/0039742.pdf> [Accessed: 13.01.11].

Townend, I. & Pethick, J. (2002) Estuarine flooding and managed retreat. *Philosophical Transactions of the Royal Society A- Mathematical, Physical & Engineering Sciences,* **360**, 1477–1495.

Tsao, J.I., Wootton, J.T., Bunikis, J., Luna, M.G., Fish, D. & Barbour, A.G. (2004) An ecological approach to preventing human infection: Vaccinating wild mouse reservoirs intervenes in the Lyme disease cycle. *Proceedings of the National Academy of Sciences of the United States of America,* **101**, 18159–18164.

Tsetsarkin, K.A., Vanlandingham, D.L., McGee, C.E. & Higgs, S. (2007) A single mutation in chikungunya virus affects vector specificity and epidemic potential. *Plos Pathogens,* **3**, 1895–1906.

Ungerer, M.J., Ayres, M.P. & Lombardero, M.J. (1999) Climate and the northern distribution limits of Dendroctonus frontalis Zimmermann (Coleoptera : Scolytidae). *Journal of Biogeography,* **26**, 1133–1145.

Valiela, I. (2006) Global Coastal Change. Blackwell, Oxford.

Van Oost, K., Govers, G., de Alba, S. & Quine, T.A. (2006) Tillage erosion: a review of controlling factors and implications for soil quality. *Progress in Physical Geography,* **30**, 443–466.

Van Oost, K., Quine, T.A., Govers, G., De Gryze, S., Six, J., Harden, J.W., Ritchie, J.C., McCarty, G.W., Heckrath, G., Kosmas, C., Giraldez, J.V., da Silva, J.R. Marques, Merckx, R. (2007) The impact of agricultural soil erosion on the global carbon cycle. *Science,* **318**, 626–629.

Van Oost, K., Cerdan, O. & Quine, T.A. (2009) Accelerated sediment fluxes by water and tillage erosion on European agricultural land. *Earth Surface Processes and Landforms,* **34**, 1625–1634.

Van Vliet, A.J.H., Overeem, A., de Groot, R.S., Jacobs, A.F.G., & Spieksma, F.T.M. (2002) The influence of temperature and climate change on the timing of pollen release in the Netherlands. *International Journal of Climatology,* **22**, 1757–1767.

Vega, F.E., Goettel, M.S., Blackwell, M., Chandler, D., Jackson, M.A., Keller, S., Koike, M., Maniania, N.K., Monzon, A., Ownley, B.H., Pell, J.K., Rangel, D.N. & Roy, H.E. (2009). Fungal entomopathogens: new insights into their ecology. *Fungal Ecology,* **2**, 149–159.

Veronesi, E., Hamblin, C. & Mellor, P.S. (2005) Live attenuated bluetongue vaccine viruses in Dorset Poll sheep, before and after passage in vector midges (Diptera : Ceratopogonidae). *Vaccine,* **23**, 5509–5516.

Vicens, N. & Bosch, J. (2000) Pollinating efficacy of *Osmia cornuta* and *Apis mellifera* (Hymenoptera : Megachilidae, Apidae) on 'red Delicious' apple. *Environmental Entomology,* **29**, 235–240.

Völkl, W., Mackauer, M., Pell, J.K. & Brodeur, J. (2007) Predators, parasitoids and pathogens. In Aphids as crop pests. (ed. by H.F. van Emden & R. Harrington), pp. 187–234. CABI, Wallingford, UK.

WAG (Welsh Assembly Government) (2009) State of the Environment. [online] Available at: <http://www.statswales. wales.gov.uk/tableviewer/document.aspx?ReportId=10293> [Accessed 12.03.11].

WAG (Welsh Assembly Government) (2010) Wales Climate Change Strategy. <http://wales.gov.uk/topics/ environmentcountryside/climatechange/tacklingchange/ strategy/walesstrategy/?lang=en> [Accessed: 13.01.11].

Walling, D.E. & Zhang, Y. (in press) A national assessment of soil erosion based on caesium-137 measurements, Catena-Verlag special publication.

Warburton, J., Holden, J. & Mills, A.J. (2004) Hydrological controls of surficial mass movements on peat. *Earth Science Reviews,* **67**, 139–156.

Weeds Act (1959) Weeds Act 1959, Chapter 54 7 and 8 Eliz 2. [online] Available at: <http://www.opsi.gov.uk/ RevisedStatutes/Acts/ukpga/1959/cukpga_19590054_en_1> [Accessed: 13.01.11].

Werres, S., Marwitz, R., Veld, W., De Cock, A., Bonants, P.J.M., De Weerdt, M., Themann, K., Ilieva, E. & Baayen, R.P. (2001) *Phytophthora ramorum* sp nov., a new pathogen on Rhododendron and Viburnum. *Mycological Research,* **105**, 1155–1165.

Westphal, C., Steffan-Dewenter, I. & Tscharntke, T. (2003) Mass flowering crops enhance pollinator densities at a landscape scale. *Ecology Letters,* **6**, 961–965.

Wheater, H.S., Reynolds, B., McIntyre, N., Marshall, M.R., Jackson, B.M., Frogbook, Z., Solloway, I., Francis, O.J. & Chell, J. (2008) Impacts of upland land management on flood risk: Multi-scale modelling methodology and results from the Pontbren experiment. Report: FRMRC Research Report UR 16.

WHO (World Health Organization) (2002) Guidelines for Community Noise (ed. B. Berglund, T. Lindvall & D.H. Schwela). Geneva: World Health Organization.

Wilby, R.L., Beven, K.J. & Reynard, N.S. (2008) Climate change and fluvial flood risk in the UK: more of the same? *Hydrological Processes*, **22**, 2511–2523.

Williams, P.H., Araujo, M.B. & Rasmont, P. (2007) Can vulnerability among British bumblebee (Bombus) species be explained by niche position and breadth? *Biology Conservation*, **138**, 493–505.

Williams, R.J., Keller, V.J.D., Johnson, A.C., Young, A.R., Holmes, M.G.R., Wells, C., Gross-Sorokin, M. & Benstead, R. (2009) A national risk assessment for intersex in fish arising from steroid estrogens. *Environmental Toxicology and Chemistry*, **28**, 220–230.

Willis, K.G. & Garrod, G.D. (1993) Valuing landscape—a contingent valuation approach. *Journal of Environmental Management*, **37**, 1–22.

Willmer, P.G., Bataw, A.A.M. & Hughes, J.P. (1994) The superiority of bumblebee to honeybees as pollinators—insect visits to raspberry flowers. *Ecological Entomology*, **19**, 271–284.

Winfree, R., Aguilar, R., Vázquez, D.P., LeBuhn, G. & Aizen, M.A. (2009) A meta-analysis of bees' responses to anthropogenic disturbance. *Ecology*, **90**, 2068–2076.

Winter, M.G., Macgregor, F. & Shackman, L. (2005) Scottish Road Network Landslides Study, Scottish Executive. ISBN 0 7559 4649 9. [online] Available at: <http://www.scotland.gov.uk/Publications/2005/07/08131738/17395> [Accessed 17.01.11].

Withers, P.J.A. & Jarvie, H.P. 2009 Delivery and cycling of phosphorous in rivers: A review. *Science of the Total Environment*, **400**, 379–395.

Woodroffe, R., Donnelly, C.A., Jenkins, H.E., Johnston, W.T., Cox, D.R., Bourne, F.J., Cheeseman, C.L., Delahay, R.J., Clifton-Hadley, R.S., Gettinby, G., Gilks, P., Hewinson, R.G., McInerney, J.P. & Morrison, W.I. (2006) Culling and cattle controls influence tuberculosis risk for badgers. *Proceedings of the National Academy of Sciences*, **103**, 14713–14717.

Woodworth, P.L., Teferle, F.N., Bingley, R.M., Shennan, I. & Williams, S.D.P. (2009) Trends in UK mean sea level revisited, *Geophysical Journal International*, **176**, 19–30. doi: 10.1111/j.1365-246.

Worrall, F. & Burt, T. (2007) Trends in DOC concentration in Great Britain. *Journal of Hydrology*, **346**, 81–92.

Worrall, F., Reed, M., Warburton, J. & Burt, T. (2003) Carbon budget for a British upland peat catchment, *The Science of the Total Environment*, **312**, 133–146.

Wright, M. (2007) Managing transportation noise reductions. *Acoustics Bulletin*, **32**(4) 23–27.

Xu, X.M., Harwood, T.D., Pautasso, M. & Jeger, M.J. (2009) Spatio-temporal analysis of an invasive plant pathogen (*Phytophthora ramorum*) in England and Wales. *Ecography*, **32**, 504–516.

Yallop, A.R., Clutterbuck, B. & Thacker J. (2010) Increases in humic dissolved organic carbon export from upland peat catchments: the role of temperature, declining sulphur deposition and changes in land management. *Climate Research*, **45,** 43–56.

Yamamura, K. & Kiritani, K. (1998) A simple method to estimate the potential increase in the number of generations under global warming in temperate zones. *Applied Entomology and Zoology*, **33**, 289–298.

Yeloff, D.E., Labadz, J.C., Hunt, C.O., Higgit, D.L. & Foster, I.D.L. (2005) Blanket peat erosion and sediment yield in an upland reservoir catchment in the southern Pennines, UK. *Earth Surface Processes and Landforms,* **30**, 717–733.

Young, K.T., Davis, L.M. & DiRita, V.J. (2007) Campylobacter jejuni: molecular biology and pathogenesis. *Nature Reviews Microbiology*, **5**, 665–679.

Zhou, X.L., Harrington, R., Woiwod, I.P., Perry, J.N., Bale, J.S. & Clark, S.J. (1995) Effects of temperature on aphid phenology. *Global Change Biology*, **1**, 303–313.

Zia, S., Wareing, D., Sutton, C., Bolton, E., Mitchell, D. & Goodacre, J.A. (2003) Health problems following Campylobacter jejuni enteritis in a Lancashire population. *Rheumatology*, **42**, 1083–1088.

Appendix 14.1 Approach Used to Assign Certainty Terms to Chapter Key Findings

This chapter began with a set of Key Findings. Adopting the approach and terminology used by the Intergovernmental Panel on Climate Change (IPCC) and the Millennium Assessment (MA), these Key Findings also include an indication of the level of scientific certainty. The 'uncertainty approach' of the UK NEA consists of a set of qualitative uncertainty terms derived from a 4-box model and complemented, where possible, with a likelihood scale (see below). Estimates of certainty are derived from the collective judgement of authors, observational evidence, modelling results and/or theory examined for this assessment.

Throughout the Key Findings presented at the start of this chapter, superscript numbers and letters indicate the estimated level of certainty for a particular key finding:

1. *Well established:*   high agreement based on significant evidence
2. *Established but incomplete evidence:*   high agreement based on limited evidence
3. *Competing explanations:*   low agreement, albeit with significant evidence

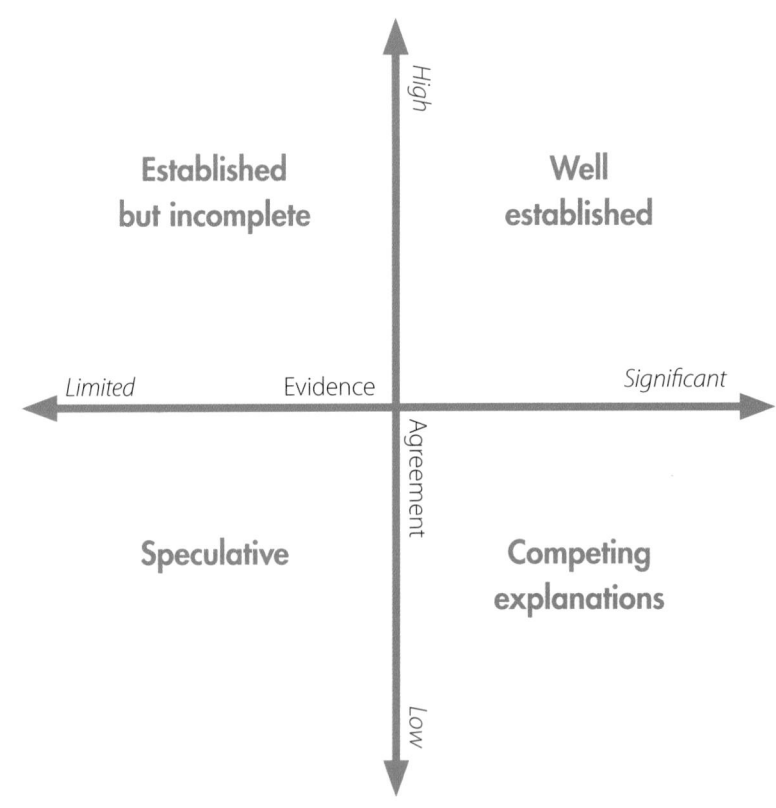

4. *Speculative:*   low agreement based on limited evidence
a. *Virtually certain:*   >99% probability of occurrence
b. *Very likely:*   >90% probability
c. *Likely:*   >66% probability
d. *About as likely as not:*   >33–66% probability
e. *Unlikely:*   <33% probability
f. *Very unlikely:*   <10% probability
g. *Exceptionally unlikely:*   <1% probability

Certainty terms 1 to 4 constitute the 4-box model, while a to g constitute the likelihood scale.

Chapter 15:
Provisioning Services

Coordinating Lead Author: Gareth Edwards-Jones
Contributing Authors: Paul Cross, Nicola Foley, Ian Harris, Mike Kaiser, Lewis Le Vay, Mark Rayment, Matt Scowen and Paul Waller

Key Findings*

Over the last 60 years, production from owned and managed resources has grown, but production from wild resources has declined. Policy, technology and market forces have all played a role, but policy has had the greatest impact. Its goal has sometimes been to maximise production (e.g. Common Agricultural Policy) and sometimes been to prevent overexploitation (e.g. Common Fisheries Policy). Some policies, such as agri-environment schemes, have aimed to reduce the environmental impacts of production.

[1] well established

It is unlikely that declines in environmental quality have reduced agricultural production levels, but overexploitation has harmed marine fish populations and some game species[1].

Over the last decade, the UK has produced more food per year from crops than at any other time in history. The area of land under crops increased in England from 3 million hectares (ha) in 1940 to 4.2 million ha in 2009, but crop areas declined in other regions of the UK: in Wales, for example, there was a 66% decrease over the same time period. The area of wheat trebled in England between 1940 and 2000, while crops such as oats, flax, turnips and vetches declined. Increases in the cropped area were driven by financial returns to farmers[1], partially derived from the Common Agricultural Policy and partially from the market. The changes were facilitated by technologies such as more effective pesticides, mechanisation, varietal improvement and increased fertiliser use. Large increases in the productivity of all crops occurred between 1940 and 2008, as exemplified by average UK wheat yields which increased from 2.5 tonnes/hectare (t/ha) to 8 t/ha.

[1] well established

Livestock productivity has increased, while animal numbers have fluctuated over time. Average milk yields increased from 3,500 litres/cow/year in 1960 to 7,000 litres/cow/year by 2009, and the average dressed carcass weight for steers increased from 267 kg in 1980 to 316 kg in 2003. These productivity gains have been accomplished through enhanced breeding and improved feeding regimes. Numbers of beef cattle peaked at 1.9 million in 1999, dairy cattle at 3.4 million in 1980 and sheep numbers peaked at 45 million in 2000. Numbers have fallen since these times. In 2009, the UK dairy herd comprised 1.8 million dairy cattle, while the national sheep flock was 33 million in 2008. Sheep numbers have fluctuated according to levels of financial support, while numbers of dairy cattle have been affected by market conditions for milk[1]. There has been a large increase in numbers of broiler chickens, largely due to the changed consumption patterns of UK consumers.

[1] well established

The provision of food from marine fisheries is lower now than at any time in the last century. Landings into UK ports were around 1.2 million tonnes in 1948 and declined slightly to just over 1 million tonnes in 1970. The total weight of landings has declined steadily since that time and, in 2008, landings were only 538,000 tonnes. Large declines have been recorded in demersal species, and smaller declines in pelagic species. Pressure from fishing has reduced the size of fish stocks[1]; the development of new technology for finding and harvesting fish has enabled fishers to maintain higher catch rates and exploit new grounds. Production from aquaculture has increased over the last 20 years, especially in Scotland. In 1988, Scotland produced 18 tonnes of salmon from aquaculture, but by 2008, this had increased seven-fold to 128 tonnes.

[1] well established

---

* Each Key Finding has been assigned a level of scientific certainty, based on a 4-box model and complemented, where possible, with a likelihood scale. Superscript numbers and letters indicate the uncertainty term assigned to each finding. Full details of each term and how they were assigned are presented in Appendix 15.1.

Some game species have shown major declines in numbers, while others have become more abundant and widespread. There were declines in the bags of red grouse and partridges between 1940 and 2009, but bags of pheasant increased. Changes in the management of farmland had a major impact on partridge numbers[1]. Deer are now more widespread than during the 1940s, and harvests have not shown any evidence of decline. After 1970, the numbers of wild caught salmon fell in Scotland to a low of less than 100,000 fish in 2006. Yet, in 2007, there was suggestion of an upturn when 91,053 salmon were caught by rod and line, which was the third largest catch by that method since 1952. Catches in England and Wales also declined from 1988, and, in 2006, less than 40,000 fish were caught by all methods. Capture at sea and estuarine netting have been largely responsible for declining numbers of spawning salmon[2].

[1] *well established*
[2] *established but incomplete evidence*

Overall provision of timber has increased over the last 40 years, but major increases in softwood harvests mask declines in the harvest of hardwoods. The production of softwoods in the UK has increased steadily over the last 40 years. The total harvest of softwood was 8.6 million cubic metres (m³) in 2008, compared with less than 400,000 m³ of hardwood. Typically, around 60% of the softwood harvest is derived from Scotland. The increased harvest of softwood reflects the levels of deliberate and extensive planting that began on the national forest estate in the early part of the 20th Century. These were driven by policy needs and, later in the century, were reinforced by financial aid to landowners. The different trends in softwood and hardwood reflect the fact that softwoods are derived from plantation forests, while most hardwoods are derived from managed semi-natural woodlands. The total area of land used for peat extraction fell from 14,980 ha in 1994 to 10,690 ha in 2009. At a Great Britain scale, 1.6 million m³ of peat were sold in 1999 and 760,000 m³ in 2008.

The amount of water taken from ecosystems by the public water supply in the UK declined between 1990 and 2009. In 1990, 20 billion litres/day were taken by the public water supply in the UK. By 2008, this had declined to about 17 billion litres/day. The greatest declines occurred in England and Wales, with hardly any declines occurring in Scotland and Northern Ireland. Total levels of abstractions in England and Wales stayed more or less constant between 1995 and 2007. In Scotland, abstractions decreased between 2002–2003 and 2007–2008 by 4.5% to 2,387 megalitres/day in 2007–2008. Leakage was approximately 41% in Scotland in 2007–2008, but only 16% in England and Wales—down from 23% in the late 1990s. Decreased leakage in England and Wales is related to the privatisation of water supply and its associated legislative requirements[c]. Water demand has decreased due to reduced demand from heavy industry[1].

[1] *well established*
[c] *likely*

15.1 Introduction

Although it may not be as apparent now as in earlier periods of human history, the whole of the human economy is driven by the goods and services provided by ecosystems and natural resources. Minerals are derived from geological deposits. Gas, coal and oil come from ancient deposits of vegetative matter, while peat, biomass and wood fuel are derived from living and less ancient plants. Water for human consumption and industry is extracted from rivers and lakes, and timber comes from forests. Food and fibre are derived from managed agricultural ecosystems and are, to some extent, still harvested from more natural ecosystems.

The role that an ecosystem plays in providing any one of these goods is termed a 'provisioning service', and nowhere is the relationship between ecosystem services and human well-being more apparent than when considering provisioning services. Moreover, because of the direct relationship between the provision of food and fibre and its impact on the environment, nowhere is the risk of damage to ecosystems greater than when deriving provisioning services from nature. These impacts have tended to increase over time as the intensity of extraction from, and management of, ecosystems has increased. On some occasions, the introduction of new technologies has mitigated these impacts, for example, drip irrigation systems save water and reduce emissions of greenhouse gases from soils (Sanchez-Martin *et al.* 2008), while low ground pressure vehicles reduce soil compaction (Tijink *et al.* 2000). However, there have also been occasions when the introduction of new technologies has had adverse impacts on ecosystems, such as the excessive use of some pesticides (Cade *et al.* 1971; Potts *et al.* 2010). Unfortunately, it tends to be difficult to identify these adverse impacts before the technology is introduced as their use and impact is mediated by humans. As a result, there is a lag between introducing a technology, identifying a problem, and then undertaking action to reduce the problem. Thus the provision of food, fuel and fibre is a relationship between ecosystems and three sets of human actors: producers, consumers and regulators; and the dynamics of these relationships are mediated by politics, policy, technology and markets.

In this chapter, we are concerned with documenting the trends in supply of the goods provided by the UK's ecosystems from 1945 to 2009, and in understanding how this provision has interacted with ecosystems and UK NEA Broad Habitats. The supply of these goods is dependent on many of the supporting and regulating services discussed elsewhere in this assessment (Chapter 13; Chapter 14). In addition, because of the historical and social aspects of producing food and fibre, there are also close links between provisioning and cultural services (Chapter 16). These include experiences with nature, landscapes and community, and also the sensory and social experiences of consumption (Laplace 2006; Chen 2009).

This chapter presents data on the provision of the following goods: food from agriculture; wild caught food (i.e. fish, honey, game); timber; fibre; peat; ornamental goods; genetic resources; and water. We are not concerned with either fossil fuels or resources that are derived from mining or the provision of renewable energy. While some individuals may argue these resources are also supplied by ecosystem processes and should, therefore, be considered here, we decided that these were basically physical processes that do not interact sufficiently with extant plant and animal species to warrant inclusion in this ecosystem assessment (where ecosystems are defined as being an interaction of living and non-living entities).

15.1.2 Data Use and Interpretation

Much of the data presented here are derived from surveys undertaken by government and industry over many years. The use of such data in modern Britain presents several challenges. Firstly, there is a need to consider the provision of goods from all four countries in the UK. Secondly, there is a need to be aware of the limitations of the data that are available. While all four countries in the UK currently run separate administrations for many elements of government, e.g. agriculture and nature conservation, this has not always been the case. For this reason, individual, long-term data sets do not necessarily exist on all issues separately for all four countries, and there has been a need to use some form of aggregate data on some occasions. Also, not all four countries have put equivalent efforts into collecting, analysing and publishing data on all items of concern, and so, there are differences in the quality and quantity of data available for each country. Finally, even where long-term data are available on the supply of particular goods, there may have been changes in the way data were collected and/or analysed over the term of data collection. So while we seek to present the best available data on trends in the supply of goods, there are inevitably some deficiencies in the data presented here.

For the purposes of description, the amount of provisioning goods and services produced by the UK's ecosystems are reported at the point of production and not at the point of processing or final use, i.e. yields of wheat are reported in tonnes/hectare (t/ha) and not in bags of flour or loaves of breads produced or purchased. The units used to describe levels of production vary between products, so for crops it is t/ha, for livestock it is numbers, while for bottled water it is litres. The historical trends in each service are presented first, followed by a discussion of the drivers of change for that service. The chapter concludes with a discussion of trade-offs, synergies and options for sustainable management of productive ecosystems, and a review of knowledge gaps relevant to the future delivery of provisioning services.

15.2 Food, Fibre and Energy from Agriculture

This section presents an historical perspective on food supply before considering trends in key agricultural outputs separately. Several of the topics discussed here are also discussed in other chapters in this assessment. Some issues of grazing and grassland management are discussed in Chapters 5, 6 and 7, while Chapter 7 also considers the interaction of crop production and natural ecosystems.

15.2.1 Historical and Global Perspective on Food Supply

Several factors interact when considering the supply of food over time. Firstly, it is necessary to consider the amount of land that is utilised to produce a particular food item. Secondly, it is necessary to consider the amount of that food item that is produced per unit of land, i.e. yield. Thirdly, the quality of the food item may vary nutritionally over time; therefore, the actual nutritional value of a food item in 1945 may not be exactly as it was in 2011 (Davis *et al.* 2004). Fourthly, the financial value of food items will vary over time. This is a function of inflation and real price changes brought about through variations in supply and demand, and occasionally through the impacts of policy (Harrison *et al.* 2010). Finally, it is important to remember that the production of food in the UK does not directly relate to the consumption of food by UK citizens. Some food items are produced in the UK and exported (such as Welsh lamb and Scotch whisky), while other foodstuffs consumed in the UK are produced overseas such as tropical fruits (Edwards-Jones *et al.* 2009).

The balance between domestic supply and demand has varied over time (**Figure 15.1**). Before the industrial revolution, the UK was largely self-sufficient in food; however, as the population grew during the 19th Century, a greater proportion of the UK's food was imported, largely from countries within the British Empire, and this situation continued into the early part of the 20th Century (Defra 2006). After the Second World War (WWII), our self-sufficiency steadily increased once again, reaching its current level of about 70% in temperate foods (and 60% of all foods). When viewed from an historical context, the UK is currently feeding more people from home-grown food than at any other time in history. Thus the food provisioning service of UK ecosystems is currently greater than at any other time

in recorded history. However, the provision of this food largely depends on natural resources derived from outside the UK, such as metals, phosphates and fossil fuels, which are available to the UK through the global trade network (Plassmann & Edwards-Jones 2009). The contribution of these resources to the production of food in the UK is not considered quantitatively here, but their importance must not be overlooked.

15.2.2 Crops

The increased provision of food in the UK has occurred through three main processes: land use change; technological improvements; and system changes. For example, in England in 1940, there were just over 3 million ha of land allocated to the growing of crops, of which, 673,984 ha were allocated to wheat and 732,066 to oats (**Table 15.1**). By 2009, the total amount of cropped land had increased to 4.2 million ha, of which, 1.7 million ha was under wheat and 102,000 ha

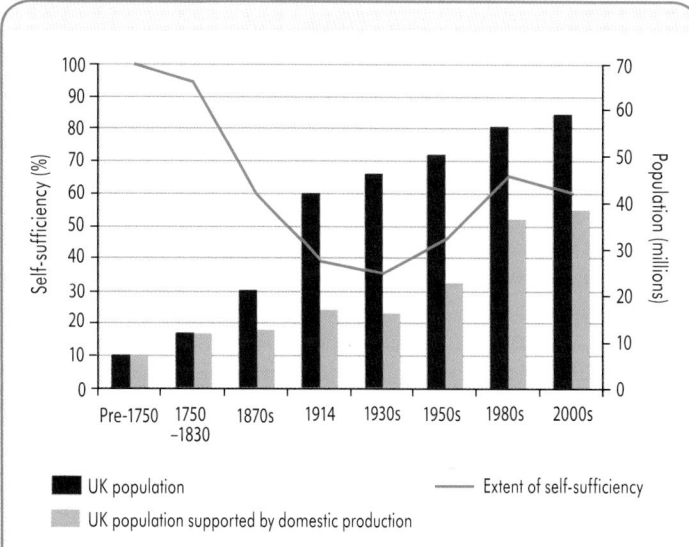

Figure 15.1 Indicative UK self-sufficiency rates during different historic periods. Source: data on self-sufficiency from Defra (2006).

Table 15.1 Changes in area of crops in the UK between 1940 and the most recent June census results available in 2010. Note: although the June agricultural census occurs annually, not all countries make the results available at the same time. Source: June census records from Defra, Department of Agriculture and Rural Development (DARD), Scottish Government and Welsh Assembly Government; data available at www.defra.gov.uk/evidence/statistics/foodfarm/landuselivestock/junesurvey/index.htm.

Country	Crop type	Year									
		1940	1950	1960	1970	1980	1990	2000	2007	2008	2009
England	Cereals	1,980,729	2,554,505	2,488,419	3,096,749	3,290,458	3,075,725	2,811,256	2,393,073	2,729,606	2,595,800
	Other crops	1,089,226	1,396,820	1,019,743	996,285	921,020	1,215,362	1,175,735	1,316,323	1,300,688	1,626,000
Wales	Cereals	157,428	182,115	88,225	82,559	74,345	56,039	45,252	36,522	46,000	48,000
	Other crops	40,470	79,321	54,635	33,590	28,467	18,369	21,901	30,520	29,000	35,000
Scotland	Cereals	453,868	480,663	418,590	456,899	508,176	481,918	450,047	403,898	447,840	448,783
	Other crops		217,051	231,630	204,014	134,207	109,158	132,978	112,719	119,257	115,661
Northern Ireland	Cereals						45,920	40,726	34,206	40,399	39,240
	Other crops						17,471	13,360	16,950	17,950	18,476

was under oats. One reason for the reduction in the amount of oats being grown in 2009, compared to 1940, relates to the transition from horses to tractors as the main source of agricultural power. Up until the widespread adoption of tractors in the late 1940s and 1950s, horses were used both as working animals on the farm and as transport for many rural families. This required that a considerable area of land be given to the production of oats and other crops suitable for their feed. As numbers of horses declined, so the land previously used to grow oats could be switched to other crops such as wheat.

The yields of cereals increased steadily from the 1940s onwards. Average UK wheat yields in 1940 were about 2.5 t/ha, while in 2008 they were approaching 8 t/ha (**Figure 15.2**). All other major crops also had higher yields in 2008 than in 1940, but few had as great a proportional rise as those observed for wheat (Defra 2010a).

While rises in crop yields occurred across the UK, not all regions showed similar increases in the amount of cropped area during this period (**Table 15.1**). In Wales, the area of cereals and other crops dropped significantly from 198,000 ha in 1940 to 83,000 in 2009, while similar, but less severe, declines were observed in Scotland from around 671,000 ha in 1940 to 564,000 ha in 2009. These land use changes probably reflected the switch from horse to tractor power (as noted in previous paragraph), and also the increasing ease with which citizens and farmers in outlying areas of these countries could access sources of both bought-in food and animal feed.

Interestingly, in England, there was a greater area of vegetables grown in open fields in 2009 than there was in 1940 (Defra 2009a). As vegetable yields will have increased over the last 60 years, this means that there was a far greater vegetable crop available for home consumption in 2009 than in previous years. The area of orchards was more or less stable between 1940 and 2000; however, the area of soft fruit in England fell dramatically from around 102,000 ha in 1940 to just under 26,000 ha in 2000. The area of hops and small fruit (redcurrants, blackcurrants and gooseberries) showed a similar decline, and these trends were echoed in Wales and Scotland, albeit from a lower baseline. Despite this, there has been a large growth in the area of fruit grown under some form of protection (i.e. glass or polytunnels) in recent years: between 1998 and 2008, the value of production for soft fruit increased from just over £100 million to more than £300 million (Spedding 2010).

While the area given over to some traditional crops, such as oats, turnips, mangolds and vetches, declined between 1940 and 2009, several crops are now widely grown that were not grown at all in 1940s and 1950s. Most notable amongst these are maize (used as cattle feed), which was first grown in the late 1960s, and oilseed rape, which was first grown in significant quantities in the early 1970s (Marks 1989). By 2009, these crops were substantial components of the landscape, with 550,000 ha of oil seed rape and 148,000 ha of forage maize being grown in England, and 33,740 ha of oil seed rape being grown in Scotland. (Note: Substantial amounts of forage maize are also grown in Scotland, Wales and Northern Ireland, but the exact figures are not readily available). A final point worthy of note is that the amount of bare fallow declined markedly in the latter half of the 20th Century. In 1940, over 120,000 ha of land were recorded in England as being in bare fallow (i.e. not being used for any productive purpose), although it was probably part of an active crop rotation. This amount of land constituted 2.3% of the total crop area, whereas, by 2000, this amount had fallen to 25,000 ha, just 0.36% of England's crop land.

15.2.3 Livestock

Between 1940 and 2009, the number of livestock kept in the UK varied substantially and in a non-linear manner. In 1940, there were relatively few individuals of all main livestock types

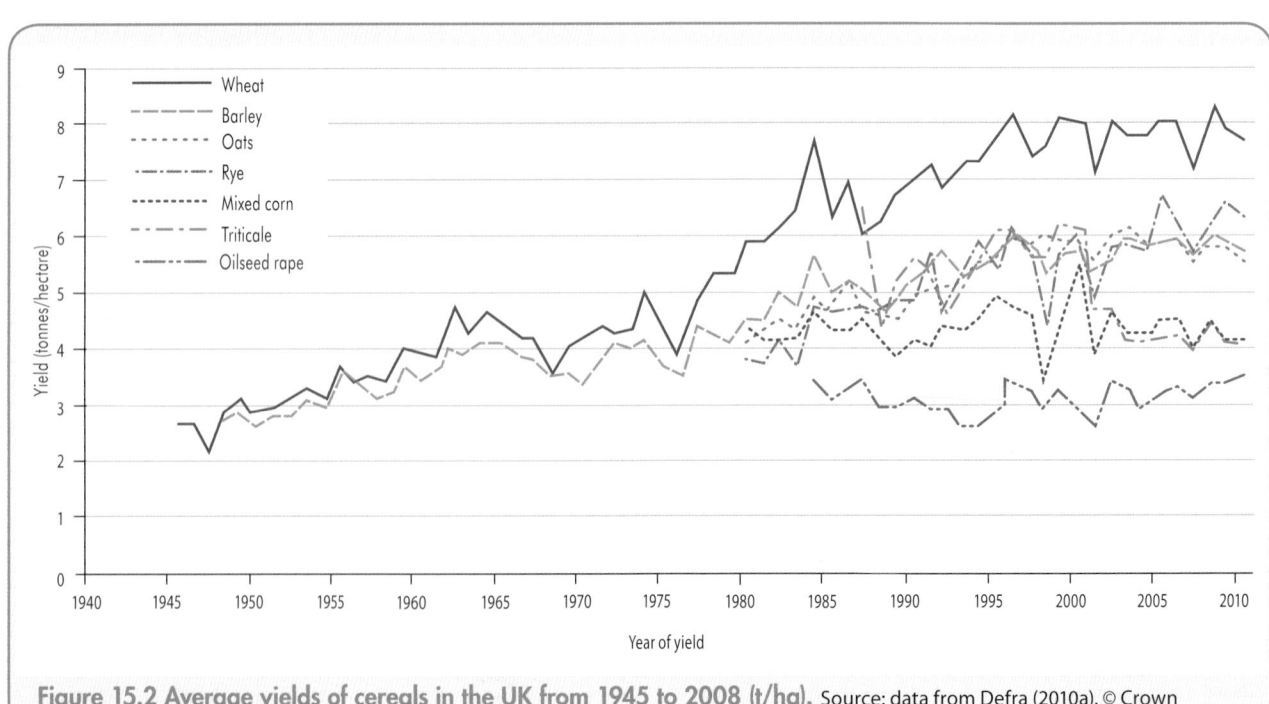

Figure 15.2 Average yields of cereals in the UK from 1945 to 2008 (t/ha). Source: data from Defra (2010a). © Crown Copyright, 2010.

(cattle, sheep and pigs), probably due to the active engagement of the UK in WWII. Numbers of these livestock grew in all four countries of the UK until the late 1980s and early 1990s, but have declined since then (**Table 15.2**). The exact patterns and reasons for these declines vary with species, and are discussed in subsequent sections.

During the latter half of the 20th Century, developments in livestock and cropping systems resulted in major changes to the UK's grassland habitats. Of particular note is the reduction in the overall level of grasslands in the UK, and the apparent shift in grassland between rotational grassland (i.e. lasts less than five years) and cropland, and also some large declines in

rough grazing that occurred in England, Scotland and Wales. For example, in Wales there were 730,079 ha of rough grazing in 1940, but only 393,000 ha in 2009 (**Table 15.3**). The decline in Scotland was less dramatic, shifting from 4.2 million ha in 1940 to 4 million ha in 2008. It would seem most likely that some of this grazing land was afforested, while other areas would have been 'improved' though draining, fertilisation and re-seeding, and would then be classified as 'permanent grassland'.

Associated with the recent development of livestock systems is the shift from conserving winter forage as hay, towards conserving it as silage. This trend began in the 1970s; it quickly became the accepted way of conserving

Table 15.2 Changes in numbers of livestock in the UK between 1940 and most recent results available in 2010. Note: although the June agricultural census occurs annually, not all countries make the results available at the same time. Source: June census records from Defra, Department of Agriculture and Rural Development, Scottish Government and Welsh Assembly Government; data available at www.defra.gov.uk/evidence/statistics/foodfarm/landuselivestock/junesurvey/index.htm.

Country	Livestock type	Year									
		1940	1950	1960	1970	1980	1990	2000	2007	2008	2009
England	Total cattle & calves	6,157,447	7,002,668	7,601,303	7,677,784	8,055,620	7,097,436	6,155,762	5,597,559	5,486,477	5,484,000
	Total sheep & lambs	13,169,707	8,506,327	13,031,632	11,627,455	14,554,451	20,775,878	19,144,345	15,436,577	15,535,215	14,984,000
	Total pigs	3,155,419	2,096,287	4,139,386	6,166,926	6,476,211	6,308,324	5,442,468	3943444	3,854,388	3,872,000
Wales	Total cattle & calves	843,553	1,011,218	1,167,975	1,349,919	1,408,400	1,362,900	1,273,000	1,164,427	1,143,000	1,130,000
	Total sheep & lambs	4,512,823	3,869,962	5,333,340	599,2318	801,3800	10,935,300	11,192,200	8,987,035	8,518,000	8,238,000
	Total pigs								23,812	21,000	22,000
Scotland	Total cattle & calves	1,360,123	1,616,390	2,002,824	2,233,720	2,383,185	2,106,237	2,029,330	1,898,538	1,854,749	1,812,416
	Total sheep & lambs	7,782,532	7,337,269	8,407,026	7,493,866	7,719,565	9,933,721	9,186,968	7,491,287	7,104,688	6,919,860
	Total pigs	271,489	250,830	402,630	611,282	468,043	451,757	558,100	456,669	435,903	396,057
Northern Ireland	Total cattle & calves						1,625,906	1,676,479	1,643,458	1,622,541	1,599,025
	Total sheep & lambs						2,824,527	2,740,586	2,023,978	1,973,593	1,896,722
	Total pigs						687,147	413,480	410,450	402,414	433,539

Table 15.3 Changes in the area of grasslands in the UK between 1940 and the recent results available in 2010. Note: although the June agricultural census occurs annually, not all countries make the results available at the same time. Source: June census records from Defra, Department of Agriculture and Rural Development, Scottish Government and Welsh Assembly Government; data available at www.defra.gov.uk/evidence/statistics/foodfarm/landuselivestock/junesurvey/index.htm.

Country	Grassland type	Year									
		1940	1950	1960	1970	1980	1990	2000	2007	2008	2009
England	Rotational							628,580	642,843	635,956	637,400
	Permanent	5,075,959	3,647,762	3,657,841	3,261,469	3,154,927	3,106,890	2,863,552	3,372,771	3,428,949	3,439,100
	Rough grazing							624,611	555,719	578,369	1,018,200
Wales	Rotational	93,486	174,426	208,016	182,520	164,400	148,600	133,253	95,034	87,000	88,000
	Permanent	764,883	599,765	704,987	738,982	843,275	903,712	933,008	1,001,081	1,017,000	1,027,000
	Rough grazing	730,079	743,839	684,752	628,904	538,398	516,230	441,753	389,808	380,000	393,000
Scotland	Rotational	566,350	583,434	761,817	676,105	490,230	424,862	321,234	316026	300,450	
	Permanent	592,145	481,170	364,067	412,154	576,546	704,889	865,638	919123	917,720	
	Rough grazing	4,236,530	4,421,054	5,068,698	4,547,006	4,384,299	4,286,463	3,982,589	4,001,634	4,027,520	
Northern Ireland	Rotational						195,302	141,554	122,108	117,236	120,787
	Permanent						600,650	687,883	671,940	672,412	669,894
	Rough grazing						186,818	156,543	146,517	147,050	141,926

forage, and was almost universal by the 1980s (Marks 1989). The main agricultural benefit of silage is that it provides a high quality feed which is less weather dependent than hay. The environmental impacts of this switch relate to the earlier and repeated cutting of silage fields, when compared to hay, which has had a significant impact on some farmland species (Green 1996; Vickery *et al.* 2001).

15.2.3.1 Dairy

All commercial dairy enterprises currently occur on improved grasslands. Production is concentrated in the wetter west of the UK, where conditions for grass growth are good. However, this has not always been the case—historically, nearly every farm in the UK would have kept some dairy cattle in order to supply their own needs and those of the local market.

Numbers of dairy cattle in England increased from 2.8 million in 1940 to a peak of 3.4 million in 1980, and then fell to 1.8 million in 2009 (Defra 2009a). Simultaneous to this shift in numbers has been a massive increase in the milk yield of the average cow. In the pre-industrial times of the 17th Century, one cow may have produced 900 litre per year (l/yr). Yields increased substantially over the following 200 years, and, in 1960, average yields were 3,500 l/cow/yr. Yields have continued to increase over recent years: in 1995, average yields were 5,500 l/cow/yr; while in 2009, the average was 7,000 l/cow/yr (although yields of 10,000 l/cow/yr were not uncommon) (Capper *et al.* 2009). The reasons for these increases are related to better genetics, nutrition (Ferris *et al.* 2001; Sutton *et al.* 1996) and management. Management issues that affect dairy cow performance include health management, the status of buildings, herdsmanship, pasture management and the treatment of dry cows. Many components of milk yield are heritable (Ojango & Pollott 2002; Swali & Wathes 2006), but yields also vary between breeds. Because of this, during the 30 years following WWII, most farmers switched from low input/low output breeds, such as Dairy Shorthorn (and their crosses), to high input/high output cows like the Holstein. This change occurred as farms became more specialised in producing one product, and, as a result, herds got larger and greater yields were needed to maintain profit. In addition to the genetic improvements in the UK herd, scientific understanding of nutrition and reproduction in the dairy cow has helped enhance the management of cattle, and also their pastures. Both of these factors have helped to increase yields. Furthermore, the composition of cattle feed has changed over time from one based on cereals and wastes from the food chain, to a more specialised feed based on imported products such as soya.

In 1984, the Common Agricultural Policy (CAP) of the European Union (EU) effectively put a cap on the production of milk by introducing national level quotas of milk across the community (Harris & Swinbank 1997). These quotas were passed down to individual farmers and provided a financial incentive not to increase milk production further. As a result, farmers tended to maintain levels of overall yield, while cutting costs. The increasing milk yields per cow enabled them to achieve this, and dairy cow numbers began to fall during the mid-1980s. However, it was the first few years of the 21st Century that saw major reductions in the national dairy herd due to financial reasons. At this time, most milk was purchased by supermarkets, but they imposed low buying-prices on farmers which were often below the price of production. As a result of several years of low prices, many farmers withdrew from milk production, which had a major impact on the size of the national herd (DairyCo 2009). In 2009, the national herd was lower than it was in 1940, but it produced much more milk than at that time.

15.2.3.2 Beef

Beef production is not the sole enterprise on many farms in the UK; in fact, beef is often undertaken in combination with dairy, arable and/or sheep production. For this reason, there are no typical 'beef systems' in the UK, instead they tend to vary with the location and management of individual farms. However, most systems can be classified as one of three main types: suckler, outdoor reared, and finished and indoor finished.

Suckler systems are composed of breeding cattle and their calves. The calves stay with their mother until they are 6–9 months old, at which point they are either kept for finishing prior to sale, or sold onto other farms for finishing. Prior to finishing, suckler beef cattle tend to be largely grass-fed, and, because suckler cattle are often from traditional breeds, they tend to occur on poor land in the hills and uplands, and on moorlands (i.e. in the Less Favoured Areas (LFAs)). Animals in these systems will spend much of their time outdoors, although they may be kept indoors in winter and fed grains and other feed while being finished.

In outdoor rearing and finishing systems the animals are reared for slaughter and spend some time grazing. During winter or at times of intensive finishing, however, they will be kept in cattle houses and fed grains and silage. This type of system varies greatly and may be found in the uplands where farmers who are predominantly sheep farmers may keep 10–30 beef cattle as well. These cattle will graze the same pastures as the sheep in the summer, and will be housed in winter. Alternatively, they may be kept alongside dairy enterprises where the farmer has chosen to cross the dairy cows with a beef bull in order to produce animals for the beef system. In this system, the beef cattle will graze the same improved pastures as the dairy cattle. Finally, some systems keep beef animals housed in sheds or pens for their entire lives, feeding them silage and feed until they reach slaughter weight. This type of system is not common in the UK.

Because of the differences in the structure and location of these different systems, they have been influenced in different ways by changes in policy and prices. Between 1940 and the 1970s, the number of beef animals in the UK showed a slight increase. Over that period, as discussed previously, dairy farming became more specialised and tended to select specialist dairy breeds, as opposed to the dual purpose breeds that would have been commoner in earlier times. This probably had little impact on the suckler beef herd, which would always have used hardy stock, but it did mean that it was no longer possible to produce profitable beef from dairy cattle. For this reason, there was a growth in the use of more specialist beef breeds such as Charolais and Belgian Blue.

The UK beef breeding herd increased substantially during the last 20 years of the 20th Century. The number of beef cows was 1,478,000 in 1980, and grew to a peak of 1,924,000 in 1999. Increases in the English beef herd were particularly noticeable, with numbers increasing by 45% between 1981 and 1995. However, the overall number of animals marketed for beef between 1980 and 2005 fell by nearly 50%, although the average dressed carcass weight for steers increased from 267 kg in 1980 to 316 kg in 2003 (Mead 2003).

The decline in the number of animals marketed for beef seen during this period was a result of the decline in the dairy herd, which had, until that time, provided over 40% of beef. As with the beef herd, the dairy herd was affected by policies relating to the control of Bovine Spongiform Encephalitis (BSE) and the impact of Foot and Mouth Disease in 2001 (Chapter 14). Following the BSE outbreak, export markets for UK beef were closed. As a result, both demand and prices fell and a high proportion of dairy cross calves, which had previously gone for beef production, were disposed of on-farm. In addition, a related policy, the Over Thirty-Month Scheme (OTMS), required that no cattle over 30 months entered the human food chain, removing many cattle that may have otherwise gone into beef production.

Subsequently, the continued decline in dairy cow numbers has reduced the production of calves that can enter the beef herd. In addition, recent changes in the CAP have reduced the profitability of many suckler beef herds, causing a decline in their numbers. However, in some areas, the extent of these shifts has been counteracted by the support available under agri-environment schemes for grazing by traditional breeds on mountains, moorlands and some coastal regions (Defra 2010b).

15.2.3.3 Sheep

In 1940, there were about 26 million sheep and lambs recorded in the UK (approximately 13 million in England, 4–5 million in Wales, 8 million in Scotland and an unrecorded number in Northern Ireland). This number declined a little during the 1950s, but had again reached 26 million by 1970. Numbers increased rapidly during the following 20 years, reaching 46 million by 1990 (21 million in England, 11 million in Wales, 10 million in Scotland and 3 million in Northern Ireland) (**Table 15.2**). Until 2001, the UK's sheep population stayed at around 40 million, but numbers have been declining steadily ever since, falling to about 32 million in 2009 (**Figure 15.3**).

The financial subsidies provided by the CAP was one of the main drivers that caused the increase in sheep numbers seen after 1970 (Acs *et al.* 2010; Brouwer & van Berkum 1996). For much of the 20 years after the UK joined the EU in 1973, these subsidies were related to the number of sheep a farmer kept, and the payments were of a sufficient amount to provide a significant incentive for farmers to increase the size of their flocks. The subsequent rise in sheep numbers occurred over much of the UK, but the greatest increases were seen in the upland areas of Wales, northern England, the Peak District, Exmoor, Dartmoor and some areas of the Scottish borders (Fuller & Gough 1999). The increase in sheep numbers in the Enclosed Farmlands of lowland England was of a lesser magnitude than in these upland areas.

There is a large variation in the size of individuals of different sheep breeds, with the lowland breeds, such as Border Leicester (ewe weight of 100 kg) and Wensleydale (113 kg), tending to be larger than upland breeds like Welsh Mountain (45–48 kg) and Blackface (50 kg). There is also some suggestion that the size of sheep has varied over time, being larger in the early part of the 20th Century than at its end. Because of these differences in size, both between breeds and over time, it is not possible to make simple generalisations about the long-term impact of sheep on the environment. However, it is well established that, in the uplands, increased levels of sheep-grazing can affect the composition of vegetation (Welch & Scott 1995; Oom *et al.* 2008), and, conversely, a reduction in grazing pressure also brings ecological change in upland habitats (Hope *et al.* 1996; Smith *et al.* 2003; Chapters 5–7).

15.2.3.4 Pigs and poultry

During the 1940s, many farmers and other householders kept pigs and poultry for subsistence use. Over the following decades these sectors became more specialised and larger units developed where greater numbers of pigs or poultry were kept indoors and fed specialised diets. These developments saw the number of pigs in the UK rise from just under 2 million in 1945 to around 7 million between by 1980. By 2009, this number had fallen to 4.7 million, the majority of which were reared in England (3.87 million in 2009) largely due to the proximity of ready sources of feed (**Table 15.2**). There are also some large pig businesses in Scotland, principally in the eastern areas, but after early increases in the 1960s and 1970s, numbers of pigs declined slightly from 468,000 in 1980 to 396,000 in 2009. The reasons for the recent declines in pig numbers in the UK have been related to a combination of policy and market conditions that have put the sector through periods of very low profitability. During these periods, some producers have reduced stock, while others have gone out of business. The principal policy drivers for this decline were welfare reforms for housed animals, which have been applied in the UK, but not necessarily applied in other pig-exporting countries (CIWF 2010); this has potentially placed UK producers at a competitive disadvantage (Bornet *et al.* 2003). In addition,

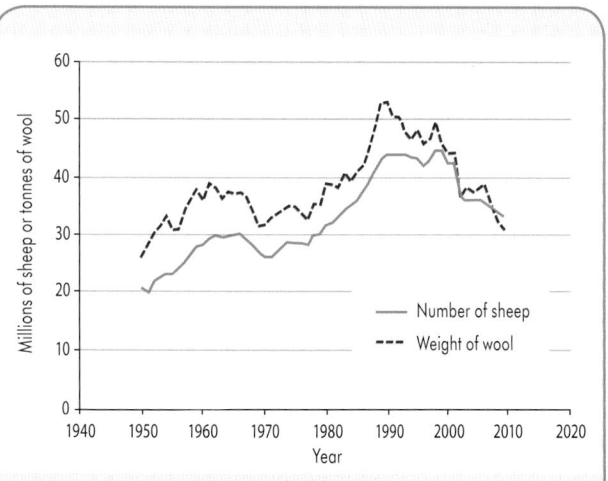

Figure 15.3 Numbers of sheep in the UK between 1945 and 2008, and the total weight of wool harvested in each year. Source: data from British Wool Marketing Board (2010).

fluctuations in the exchange rate and the price of animal feed and energy can have large impacts on the profitability of pigs and poultry (de Lange 1999), and it is well established that there are economies of scale to be gained in the pig sector. As a result, recent increases in the prices of inputs have adversely affected smaller producers in particular.

The poultry industry has followed a very similar pattern to that of the pig industry, moving from a population of 60 million birds in 1945 to 166 million in 2008 (Defra 2009a). In 2008, about 30 million birds were kept for laying, which produced about 868 million eggs in that year. The majority of the remainder are chickens kept for meat, but there are also about 12 million head of other poultry types in the UK such as geese, ducks and turkeys.

The poultry sector is comprised of some very large enterprises which specialise in raising either broilers (poultry for meat) or eggs, and some smaller ones which tend to offer the highest welfare standards and sell their produce for a premium. Although there has typically been a preponderance of poultry enterprises in the east of the England and Scotland, a significant number of poultry are also bred in both Wales and Northern Ireland.

Generally, large-scale pig and poultry units have little interaction with the natural environment, apart from the production of odours and waste disposal (Nicholson et al. 2002). The disposal of wastes from both pigs and poultry can be problematic, but uses for these wastes are currently being researched and include using chicken manure in composts (White 2000) and using pig and chicken manure in aerobic and anaerobic energy systems (Boersma et al. 1981; Tait et al. 2009). However, in recent years, there has been an increase in the number of pigs that are kept outside for at least some of their lives. These enterprises tend to do best on well-drained soils, such as sand and chalk, and, in cases where pigs are kept on a field for a year or two, can be viewed as part of the arable rotation. The environmental impact of such pig units is not well studied, but they may have negative interactions with soil and water quality (Worthington et al. 1992; Haygarth et al. 2009).

15.2.4 Fibre from Agriculture
In the UK, fibre for textiles and ropes has traditionally been derived from wool, flax and hemp. Historically, hemp was used to make ropes and flax was used to make linen, but modern uses focus more on their potential as components of building materials and plastics (Dimmock et al. 2005; Yates 2006). Nearly 11,000 ha of flax were grown in England in 1940, but, by the early 21st Century, plantings of this crop had dropped to almost nothing. In 2000, more than 11,000ha of flax were once again reported growing (Defra 2009a). However, this revival was short-lived as no flax was reported to be grown in 2009.

Hemp for industrial use has been grown in England and Wales since the mid-1990s (Dimmock et al. 2005). Up until that time, the growing of hemp had been banned in the UK under the Misuse of Drugs Act 1971. Varieties of hemp with low levels of THC (Tetrahydrocannabinol: the psychoactive drug in Cannabis) were developed in Europe, and, in 1993, legal agreement was given to grow low-THC hemp in the UK. Currently, UK hemp is processed and used in a range of agricultural and industrial products.

The surge in area of flax and hemp grown in the late 1990s and early 2000s reflected both the development of processing facilities in the UK and active financial support for these crops from the CAP. This level of support was subsequently removed from these crops, resulting in a reduction in growing area in the UK.

Sheep's wool can be used for making clothes, carpets, felt, tweeds, furniture and insulation. In 2009, the UK was the seventh largest producer of wool in the world, responsible for about 2% of global production and exporting considerable amounts of wool. The amount of wool harvested in the UK is closely related to the number of sheep in the country. For this reason, the amount of wool harvested in 1950 was 26 million kg (from about 20 million sheep), while in 1998 it was 49 million kg from 44 million sheep (British Wool Marketing Board website; www.britishwool.org.uk). However, the quality of the wool varies between breeds. Some breeds, such as the Blue Faced Leicester, have fine wool, while others, such as some of the more hardy breeds typical of mountainous areas, produce only a small amount of poor quality wool. The financial returns from wool are relatively low, and few UK farmers would consider sheep wool as a major product. However, some of the specialist farmers of fine wool from other species, such as goats and Angora rabbits, may consider their fleeces as major products.

15.2.5 Biomass and Bioenergy
At the turn of the 20th Century, almost no biomass crops were grown commercially in the UK. Yet, in 2005, 436 ha of short-rotation coppice willow were recorded in the UK, and, by 2007, this had increased five-fold (**Table 15.4**). Similar increases were noted in *Miscanthus* and reed canary grass over the same time-scale, both of which are grown for biomass. However, the most commonly grown crop for bioenergy is oilseed rape, with the area planted in the UK increasing from 10,863 ha in 2004 to 240,032 ha in 2007 (**Table 15.3**).

Plantings for biomass and bioenergy have largely been driven by a combination of market opportunity and policy. Relevant policies are not necessarily agricultural, but contain incentives for energy generators to include a certain proportion of renewable materials in their feed stocks, and for some large establishments to have biomass boilers. This demand has led energy providers to offer contracts to farmers to supply biomass. As transport costs can be substantial for biomass crops, such schemes tend to stimulate farmers in the immediate locality of the power plant, rather than benefiting all farmers across the nation.

15.2.6 Drivers of Change in Agriculture
Agricultural production has typically been driven by three main factors: market price, the policy environment and technological change. For much of the period between 1945 and 1960, the predominant policy was to increase food output in order to provide adequate supplies to the UK's population during the post-war years. At the same time, new technologies were becoming available, such as chemical pesticides, mechanisation and new crop varieties, enabling farmers to realise increased yields. This trend continued through the 1960s, and was further energised in

Table 15.4 Area (ha) of energy crop production on non-set-aside land between 2001 and 2007, identified through the Energy Aid Payment Scheme (UK) and the Energy Crop Scheme (England). Source: data from National Non-Food Crops Centre (2009).

Scheme	Crop	2001	2002	2003	2004	2005	2006	2007
Energy Aid Payment Scheme (UK)	Oilseed rape				10,862	39,865	75,155	240,032
	Short rotation coppice				0	436	1,317	2,085
	Miscanthus				0	0	1,959	2,073
	Linseed				0	0	56	0
	Reed canary grass				0	0	2	0
	Barley				0	0	0	2
	High oleic acid rapeseed				0	0	0	261
Energy Crop Scheme (England)	Miscanthus (new plantings)	0	52	0	302	658	2,345	2,413
	Short rotation coppice (new plantings)	233	65	94	106	290	392	500

the 1970s when the UK joined the EU and farmers became formally involved in the CAP, which offered greater levels of direct subsidy than had previously been available. The twin drivers of direct subsidies and further enhanced technology drove up yields in the 1970s and also encouraged clearance of marginal lands for agricultural production. The drive for production started coming to an end in the 1980s, and the introduction of the first agri-environment scheme in 1987 (Environmentally Sensitive Areas) was a major landmark in the history of agriculture (Bunce *et al.* 1998; Hodge & McNally 1998). Since that date, the amount of land entered into some form of agri-environment scheme has increased steadily in all four countries of the UK: by 2008, more than 4 million ha of land were under an agri-environment agreement (**Table 15.5**). It is unclear what factors have driven this uptake of agri-environment schemes: it may be related to an enhanced awareness of environmental

issues amongst farmers; yet other hypotheses are more related to the financial aspects of these agreements which help farmers diversify their income streams and may offer an acceptable financial return on land to some farmers. This latter hypothesis will be tested if market returns for agricultural produce increase at a faster rate than financial returns from agri-environment schemes.

The expansion of agri-environment schemes throughout the 1990s was consistent with the overall policy environment which sought to make agricultural activities more 'environmentally friendly'. The policy environment changed in 2003 when the CAP was reformed in order to break the link between levels of production and levels of financial support. As a result, agricultural support in the first decade of the 21st Century is paid on an area basis, in accordance to complex national-level formulae. The impacts of this reform are perhaps easiest to see in the sheep sector: numbers

Table 15.5 Area of land (millions of hectares) under agri-environment schemes in the UK from 1992 to 2008. Agri-environment schemes are classed as either 'higher level' or 'entry level' schemes. Note: the first agri-environment scheme, the Environmentally Sensitive Areas scheme, was announced in 1987. Source: data from JNCC (2010).

Scheme type	Country	Year								
		1992	1994	1996	1998	2000	2002	2004	2006	2008
Higher level schemes *	England	0.18	0.42	0.53	0.63	0.81	1.01	1.22	1.18	1.236
	Wales	0.01	0.05	0.07	0.09	0.27	0.29	0.29	0.43	0.394
	Scotland	0.12	0.15	0.37	0.54	0.84	0.98	1.07	1.35	1.070
	Northern Ireland	0.00	0.00	0.12	0.15	0.15	0.20	0.24	0.46	0.437
	Total	**0.31**	**0.62**	**1.10**	**1.41**	**2.08**	**2.48**	**2.82**	**3.42**	**3.137**
Entry level schemes †	England	..	..	..	..	..	..	0.03	3.92	5.024
	Wales	..	..	..	..	..	..	..	0.22	0.293
	Scotland	..	..	..	..	..	..	..	..	..
	Northern Ireland	..	..	..	..	..	..	..	..	..
	Total	**0**	**0**	**0**	**0**	**0**	**0**	**0.03**	**4.14**	**5.317**

* The following agri-environment schemes by country have been defined as higher level schemes and included here are: England: Environmentally Sensitive Areas (ESA), Countryside Stewardship, and new Higher Level Stewardship (HLS); Scotland: ESA, countryside premium, rural stewardship and land management contracts; Wales: ESA, Tir Cymen, and Tir Gofal; Northern Ireland: ESA, countryside management. Higher level schemes have stricter criteria for qualification than other agri-environment schemes. In England, the new HLS was introduced in 2005 and will gradually replace ESA and Countryside Stewardship schemes which are being phased out. Criteria for qualifying for the old and new schemes are different, and membership of the old schemes does not mean land will automatically qualify for the new scheme.
† The following agri-environment schemes by country have been defined as entry level schemes and included here are: England: Entry Level Stewardship (ELS) and Organic ELS; Wales: Tir Cynnal.

declined between 2000 and 2009 despite the existence of relatively good market prices for lamb (**Table 15.2**).

Outbreaks of livestock disease and zoonoses, such as Salmonella, BSE, Newcastle Disease, Bovine Tuberculosis (bTB) and Foot and Mouth, have also had impacts on the livestock sector throughout the last 60 years. While outbreaks of Foot and Mouth Disease were relatively common during the first 60 years of the 20th Century (Woods 2004), perhaps the most important outbreaks occurred in 1966 and 2001. The former was a large outbreak that, in many ways, spurred some farmers in the dairy sector to modernise their systems and enhance the genetic potential of their stock. The second outbreak was important for at least two reasons: firstly, it raised the level of public debate about the social acceptability of different disease control mechanisms, specifically culling versus vaccination; and secondly, it showed that the economic benefits of the countryside were more dependent on tourism and recreation than previously thought (Donaldson *et al.* 2002; Phillipson *et al.* 2004).

It has been well established that these disease outbreaks, or 'food scares' as the media dubbed them, had relatively large impacts on agriculture and the food processing industry, principally through the introduction of policies aimed at reducing risk to humans. However, the social impact of these disease outbreaks has also been significant (Millstone 2009; Jackson 2010), and, along with concern over new technologies, such as Genetic Modification, has served to fuel a growing interest in various forms of alternative agriculture such as organics (Burton *et al.* 2001; Dreezen *et al.* 2005; Saher *et al.* 2006) and 'local food' (Edwards-Jones 2010). Between 1997 and 2002, the area of land in the UK that was certified organic increased massively. The amount of land in conversion or fully certified was 741,200 ha in 2002 and 743,500 ha in 2008, which suggests some sort of plateau may have been reached (**Table 15.6**). In the future, it will be interesting to see how the increasing concern about food security will interact with social and political pressures to support 'environmentally friendly farming' in all its forms. To some extent, trends in both the adoption of agri-environment schemes and organics are suggesting equilibrium has been reached; if food prices increase in the future, it may be a challenge to avoid declines in the areas of land under these forms of management (Tranter *et al.* 2007).

In summary, the main drivers of change in the UK's agricultural sector over the last 60 years have been policy and technology. Since the reform of the CAP in 2003, market conditions have had an increasing influence on levels of production, and, in some sectors, farmers respond quickly to price signals (e.g. wheat in 2007/08). However, when considered over a longer time span, market conditions have not had a major impact on levels of overall outputs, although they have impacted some sectors more than others such as horticulture, pigs and dairy. During the period 1990 to 2010, the consolidation of buying power into fewer supermarkets has impacted the structure and performance of supply chains (Cotterill 2006; Smith 2006). While some producers may complain about the absence of contracts and poor prices, many of the innovations introduced by the supermarkets have served to reduce the direct environmental impact of agriculture (Dreschler *et al.* 2009; Asfaw *et al.* 2010; Cooper & Wrath 2010). There is almost no evidence to suggest that declines in environmental quality have had a direct and negative impact on levels of agricultural production. This does not mean that agriculture does not impact on the environment, but rather that any impacts it does cause have not had direct and lasting effects on overall levels of production to date.

15.3 Food from Marine Ecosystems

This section begins with a brief discussion about the problems of assigning fisheries catch data to a fixed territory

Table 15.6 Changes in fully organic and in-conversion organic land areas (ha) between 2002 and 2008. Source: Organic Certifier Bodies collated by Defra Statistics; Defra (2009a). © Crown Copyright, 2010.

Country	Status	Year						
		2002	**2003**	**2004**	**2005**	**2006**	**2007**	**2008**
England	In conversion	67,800	36,800	28,800	53,200	66,500	89,000	91,100
	Fully organic	184,000	220,200	229,600	238,400	229,900	258,700	284,000
Wales	In conversion	13,700	8,000	8,600	12,800	15,400	30,900	49,500
	Fully organic	41,400	50,200	55,600	58,000	63,500	65,100	75,100
Scotland	In conversion	121,300	20,400	13,700	16,700	35,200	34,800	6,200
	Fully organic	307,300	351,900	331,600	231,200	200,100	193,100	225,100
Northern Ireland	In conversion	1,500	800	1,600	3,200	4,000	3,200	2,300
	Fully organic	4,100	6,600	5,000	6,300	5,100	7,300	10,100
Total UK	**In conversion**	204,300	66,000	52,700	86,000	121,100	157,900	141,900
	Fully organic	536,900	629,000	621,800	533,900	498,600	524,300	594,400
Total Organic Land UK		741,200	695,000	674,500	619,900	619,800	682,200	743,500

such as the UK. It then proceeds to consider trends in landings from 1940 to 2009. These topics overlap a little with Chapter 12, which provides a detailed analysis of the relationship between fisheries and marine ecosystems.

15.3.1 Data Constraints

There are some difficulties in examining the statistics of marine fisheries in the context of the UK NEA. These arise because fishing vessels that are registered in the UK are not obliged to land all of their catch in the UK, and, similarly, vessels registered in other countries can land some of their catch in the UK should they choose to do so. Generally, vessels choose a landing venue according to the relative market conditions in different ports. Fortunately, national fisheries statistics do seek to represent both of these situations, as discussed below. However, it can be difficult to decide how to allocate fish caught in the open ocean to specific nations. Since 1913, records of catches in Northern Europe have been attributed to statistical areas known as ICES (International Council for the Exploration of the Sea) rectangles (0.5° Latitude by 1° Longitude) (Engelhard 2005). Yet these statistical rectangles transcend national boundaries at sea which can complicate the attribution of catches to national waters. As a result, it is difficult to attribute catches to ecosystems that lie within the boundaries of the UK.

It should also be noted that we do not have complete historical records from the inshore fleet that fishes within 12 nautical miles from the coast. At present, vessels less than 15m long are not legally obliged to report their catches either nationally or to the European Commission, and most inshore vessels are below this length. Some data on inshore catches are now available from Sea Fisheries committees and from voluntary logbook schemes in certain sub-samples of the inshore fleet, but these are not included in the historical records discussed below.

Finally, it is not possible to relate the contemporary landings of fish by UK boats to the consumption of fish by UK citizens; for example, more than 90% of cod consumed in the UK is now imported from areas such as Iceland and Greenland. The lack of a direct relationship between domestic consumption and catches by the UK fishing fleet reflects the changing status of that fleet over time. Prior to 1983, the UK was a net exporter of fish, but since then the UK has become a net importer. To some extent, the switch from being a net exporter to a net importer is related to the removal of the UK's 'distant water fleet' from water around Norway and Iceland in the 1970s following the so-called 'cod wars'. Despite being an overall net importer of fish products, the UK is an active exporter of premium species such as Norway lobster (*Nephrops norvegicus*), blue mussels (*Mytilus edulis*), live edible crab (*Cancer pagurus*) and whole scallops.

15.3.2 Trends in Landings

In 1948, the total landings of 1.2 million tonnes from all ships into the UK were the highest recorded since 1888. Landings have fallen consistently after that date, barring a short-lived upsurge in the 1970s (**Table 15.7**). By 2008, total landings were 538,000 tonnes, which was the second lowest amount recorded since 1948. Interestingly, landings made only by UK-registered vessels into both UK and foreign ports were recorded at 409,000t in 2008, which is the lowest peacetime catch recorded since 1890 (i.e. outside the years of the two world wars) (Cracknell 2009).

The pattern of decline in landings has not been consistent across all fish species and types, and it is apparent that the three main groups, demersal fish, pelagic fish and shellfish, have responded differently during the last 60 years. Demersal fish species, such as cod (*Gadus morhua*), plaice (*Pleuronectes platessa*) and haddock (*Melanogrammus aegletinus*), live on or near the seabed, and it is in this group that declines have been most severe. Landings of demersal fish into the UK fell from 923,000 tonnes in 1948 to 206,000 tonnes in 2008 (**Table 15.7**). Landings of pelagic fish species which are typically found in mid and upper-waters, such as herring (*Clupea harengus*) and mackerel (*Scomber scombrus*), were 287,000 tonnes in 1948 and had fallen to 186,000 tonnes by 2008.

Landings of shellfish have shown a very different pattern to that of the finfish discussed above (**Table 15.7**). Total landings were just below 29,000 tonnes in 1948, and have increased steadily since then, totalling 97,500 tonnes in 1990 and reaching 145,000 tonnes in 2008—their highest value for 60 years. One of the main reasons for this rise in shellfish landings has been increased catches of Norway lobster, commonly known as 'scampi'. Interestingly, the increasing prevalence of scampi in UK ecosystems may be related to the removal of key predators such as cod and haddock (Dubuit 1995; Bjornsson & Dombaxe 2004).

Approximately 30% of landings by UK vessels are recorded as having occurred in England and Wales in both 1994 and in 2008, while 68% and 63% occurred in Scotland, respectively. The majority of the UK's landings of pelagic fish occurred in Scotland in both years, while more than 50% of the UK's shellfish landings occurred in England and Wales (**Table 15.8**).

The recorded declines in landings do not necessarily reflect the size of the fish population in UK or EU waters; rather, they are the combined outcome of the results of stock assessments and the subsequent management measures designed to control the fishery-related mortality of fish (Chapter 12). In addition, it is important to consider the effort expended in catching the fish and also the policy conditions affecting the fishing fleet. In 1948, there were 13,300 registered fishing vessels in the UK. By 2008, this number had fallen to 6,573, which itself was a 10% reduction on the number registered a decade earlier (Cracknell 2009). However, the number of vessels is not necessarily a good indicator of fishing effort: larger vessels which utilise the latest technologies for finding and catching fish may be able to catch many more fish in a given time period than a larger number of less efficient, smaller boats. For example, a UK beam trawling vessel working in the first decade of the 21st Century is 100 times more effective at catching plaice than a sailing trawler that operated in the early part of the 20th Century (Englehard 2005). In order to move away from a simple consideration of vessel numbers, other variables like total fleet tonnage (GT) and power (kW) are used as indicators of the effort a fleet can expend in catching fish. These are basically an expression of the catching capacity of the fleet. In 1996, 8,667 vessels had a total tonnage of 274,532 GT and used 1,054,927 kW of power. By 2008, 6573 UK vessels

Table 15.7 Landings of finfish and shellfish into the UK by UK and foreign vessels from 1938 to 2008. Source: data from MMO (2010a).

Year	Fishery							
	Demersal		Pelagic		Shellfish		Total	
	Quantity ('000 tonnes)	Value (£million)	Quantity ('000 tonnes)	Value (£million)	Quantity ('000 tonnes)	Value (£million)	Quantity ('000 tonnes)	Value (£million)
1938	807.82	14.63	295.05	2.03	32.06	0.49	1,134.92	17.16
1948	923.50	46.41	287.63	6.00	28.65	1.43	1,239.78	53.84
1960	758.82	51.98	127.81	2.98	28.09	2.08	914.72	57.05
1970	778.61	67.50	204.01	5.80	56.44	6.73	1,039.06	80.03
1980	484.25	194.42	319.16	30.14	70.24	34.47	873.65	259.03
1990	336.71	327.66	267.85	32.09	97.47	105.09	702.03	464.75
2000	280.54	305.75	117.99	22.32	127.74	154.47	526.27	482.54
2001	249.58	277.19	143.53	42.49	136.91	168.38	530.01	488.06
2002	235.80	265.91	169.83	57.93	132.26	166.22	537.90	490.06
2003	234.44	249.53	185.02	58.26	137.86	181.67	557.31	489.46
2004	257.38	265.49	198.35	74.48	128.05	176.24	583.77	516.21
2005	272.69	317.85	239.78	116.47	126.30	186.09	638.77	620.40
2006	214.76	263.33	194.37	97.77	135.30	240.78	544.43	601.88
2007	197.88	243.57	209.48	102.23	142.23	274.99	549.58	620.79
2008	206.82	231.38	186.17	104.44	144.99	260.33	537.98	596.15

Table 15.8 Fish landings by the UK fleet (thousands of tonnes) into the UK and abroad in 1994 and 2008. Percentages relate to the proportion of total UK landings in that class. Results for separate parts of the UK are made by department of administration. Islands are Isle of Man and Channel Isles. Source: data from MMO (2010b).

Region		1994		2008	
		Total landings	% UK landings	Total landings	% UK landings
UK	Total	874.9		588.3	
	Demersal	371.6		189.9	
	Pelagic	388.9		247.9	
	Shellfish	114.4		150.5	
England & Wales	Total	248.3	28.38	184.5	31.36
	Demersal	115.7	31.14	63.1	33.23
	Pelagic	72.0	18.51	52.8	21.30
	Shellfish	60.6	52.97	68.6	45.58
Scotland	Total	596.6	68.19	371.7	63.18
	Demersal	242.9	65.37	123.6	65.09
	Pelagic	308.0	79.20	183.0	73.82
	Shellfish	44.8	39.16	65.1	43.26
Northern Ireland	Total	27.4	3.13	29.9	5.08
	Demersal	12.1	3.26	2.9	1.53
	Pelagic	8.0	2.06	12.1	4.88
	Shellfish	7.37	6.44	14.9	9.90
Islands	Total	2.6	0.30	2.2	0.37
	Demersal	0.9	0.24	0.2	0.11
	Pelagic	-	0.00		0.00
	Shellfish	1.7	1.49	2.0	1.33

had a total tonnage of 207,423 GT and 836,485 kW of power. This indicates that the size and power of the remaining vessels has not fully compensated for the reduction in vessel number. The policy environment and the untenable state of many fish stocks may partly explain why there has not been more compensation of power and size for numbers in recent years. Under the Common Fisheries Policy of the EU an increasing number of restrictions have been placed on fleets fishing waters around the UK, many of which have been aimed at stock conservation (e.g. restrictions in permissible days at sea, closed areas and gear restrictions) (Frost & Andersen 1996; Laurec & Armstrong 1997; Hadjimichael *et al.* 2010). In particular, declines in landings over the last decade are likely to reflect the impact of these policies, along with a reduction in the amount of fisheries subsidies that are provided to domestic fleets.

15.3.3 Drivers of Change in Marine Fisheries

Since joining the EU the community's fisheries policy has been the dominant influence on the behaviour of fishers. The restrictive influences of this policy have intensified in recent years, with a combination of catch quotas, gear restrictions and limits on days at sea all seeking to reduce catches to more sustainable levels. In spite of these policies, the fishing industry has continued to innovate, and there have been marked developments in technology in recent years. In parallel to these policy and technological trends, it is virtually certain that declining stocks of many fish have resulted in reduced catches. As a result, the trends in the industry are a spiralling and interacting function of a profitable industry investing in technology which causes further declines in stock, and policy makers responding to these two drivers by implementing new regulations.

In addition, certain fishing practices (e.g. beam-trawling, scallop-dredging) can have negative impacts on the marine environment that directly affect the productivity of the system and have subsequent negative consequences for fish populations (Hinz *et al.* 2009; Benn *et al.* 2010; but see also Hiddink *et al.* 2008 for a different viewpoint). Observed changes in ecological communities and the size of animals that occur in areas without fishing disturbance demonstrate the magnitude of the negative impacts fishing can have on marine environments (Kaiser *et al.* 2006).

15.4 Food from Aquaculture

The major finfish products of aquaculture in the UK are the Atlantic Salmon (*Salmo salar*) in coastal waters and rainbow trout (*Oncorhynchus mykiss*) in freshwater. Several shellfish species are also produced, of which, mussels (*Mytilus edulis*) and oysters (two species are grown in UK; the Pacific oyster *Crassostrea gigas* and the European flat oyster, *Ostrea edulis*) are the dominant species. Aquaculture occurs across the UK, but Scotland is responsible for 80% of the UK's aquaculture production, largely due to the scale of the salmon industry (Defra 2009c).

The production of salmon through aquaculture began in Scotland in the 1970s, and, since then, has grown almost exponentially at times (Marine Scotland 2009a). In 1988, Scotland produced 17,951 tonnes of fish, but by 2008, production had increased seven-fold to 128,606 tonnes (**Table 15.9**). The production of salmon is focused in the rural north and west of the country, bringing economic and employment benefits to these areas. However, these benefits have not come without environmental impact, and concerns have been raised over several issues during the past 30 years including: nutrient enrichment of the waters around the fish cages caused by the release of uneaten food and faeces; chemical pollution through the use of pesticides; the impacts of escaped fish on wild salmon populations; and the visual impacts of aquaculture in sensitive landscapes. These issues have been well researched and considerable effort has been expended by government and industry to mitigate their impacts (Navarro *et al.* 2008; Peel & Lloyd 2008; Mayor *et al.* 2010).

In 2008, Scottish production was comprised of Atlantic salmon (128,606 t), rainbow trout (7,670 t), cod (1,822 t), brown trout/sea trout (*Salmo trutta*; 311 t) and halibut (*Hippoglossus hippoglossus*; 206 t). Shellfish production included mussels (5,869 t), Pacific oyster (3,785 t), native oysters (250 t), queen

Table 15.9 Annual production of Atlantic salmon (tonnes) from the Scottish aquaculture sector between 1988 and 2008 (projected production for 2009). Source: Marine Scotland (2009a).

Year	Tonnes	% difference
1988	17,951	41
1989	28,553	59
1990	32,351	13
1991	40,593	25
1992	36,101	-11
1993	48,691	35
1994	64,066	32
1995	70,060	9
1996	83,121	19
1997	99,197	19
1998	110,784	12
1999	126,686	14
2000	128,959	2
2001	138,519	7
2002	144,589	4
2003	169,736	17
2004	158,099	-7
2005	129,588	-18
2006	131,847	2
2007	129,930	-1.4
2008	128,606	-1
2009	133,027*	

* Farmers' estimate of projected tonnage based on stocks currently being on-grown.

scallops (*Aequipecten opercularis*; 687 t) and king scallops (*Pecten maximus*; 15 t) (Marine Scotland 2009ab). However, both the production of cod and Arctic charr (*Salvelinus alpinus*) had ceased by 2010.

In England and Wales, there were 518 registered fish and shellfish farms in 2008: 193 coarse fish farms, 197 trout and other finfish farms and 128 shellfish farms. Of the total 8,127 tonnes of finfish produced in England and Wales in 2006, the majority was rainbow trout (7,294 t). In 2006, there was also production of brown trout (441 t), carp (*Cyprinus carpio*; 175 t) Atlantic salmon (63 t), turbot (*Psetta maxima*; 63.5 t), barramundi (*Lates calcarifer*; 45 t) and tilapia (33 t). Farm-produced shellfish totaled 15,449 tonnes in 2006, with the main species cultivated being mussels (14,553 t) and Pacific and native oysters (880 t) (Defra 2009c).

There were 84 licensed fish farms in Northern Ireland in 2007. Fifty of these were licensed for the cultivation of shellfish (mussels, Pacific oysters, native oysters and clams) and 34 for the cultivation of finfish (salmon, rainbow trout and brown trout). In 2007, production totalled 8,400 tonnes of shellfish and more than 999 tonnes of finfish.

15.4.1 Drivers of Change in Aquaculture

As catches of sea-caught fish have declined over time, so the demand for farmed fish has increased. The industry has adapted technology developed in other countries and has expanded rapidly, mainly in Scotland. However, constraints of the technology require that sea-based fish farms have particular bio-physical requirements. Furthermore, the growth of the industry has been a function of planning restriction and market demand. New technologies may permit some of the future growth in the sector to move further offshore, and the declines in stocks of marine fish will result in price increases, which should, in turn, raise demand for competitively priced products from aquaculture. Thus constraints on future growth in this sector will be a function of environmental regulation and technological developments.

15.5 Game and Food Collected from the Wild

Game species are those species of wild animals, birds, or fish hunted for food and/or sport. Within the UK, the main terrestrial game species are red deer (*Cervus elaphus*), roe deer (*Capreolus capreolus*), fallow deer (*Dama dama*), brown hare (*Lepus europaeus*), mountain hare (*Lepus timidus*), pheasant (*Phasianus colchicus*), grey partridge (*Perdix perdix*), red-legged partridge (*Alectoris rufa*), and red grouse (*Lagopus lagopus scoticus*). In addition, duck like mallard (*Anas platyrhynchos*) and fish species like salmon and trout (*Salmo trutta*) may also be classed as game. Many of these game species are hunted for pleasure; despite this, the majority of game animals that are killed in the UK will enter the human food chain in some form, either by being eaten by their hunter or after being sold to consumers, retailers or game dealers. However, not all game animals are killed explicitly for consumption; instead, some may be culled because of their nuisance value or their role as pests. Species hunted in this way may include deer, hares, rabbits (*Oryctolagus cuniculus*) and wood pigeons (*Columba palumbus*) (note: the latter two species are not typically classed as game animals, but they are hunted for sport and have traditionally been eaten by humans).

Although game species are technically wild animals, many are subject to management of some form. For example, heather moorlands are managed to enhance the numbers of red grouse they support; some agricultural land is managed for partridge and pheasants (e.g. conservation headlands and gamebird cover); and some woodlands are managed to provide opportunities to shoot deer and pheasants. In addition, some game species have their natural populations enhanced through the deliberate release of animals reared domestically prior to the shooting season (especially pheasant, red-legged partridge and mallard). Finally, the predators of game species are often actively culled. For example, the number of foxes (*Vulpes vulpes*) killed on estate land (i.e. land managed for game) increased from about 0.5 fox/100 ha of estate land in 1961 to 3/100 ha of estate land in 2005 (GWCT 2009). The other major predators that are actively controlled include weasels (*Mustela nivalis*), stoats (*Mustela erminea*), brown rats (*Rattus norvegicus*), American mink (*Neovison vison*), carrion crows (*Corvus corone*), hooded crows (*Corvus cornix*) and magpies (*Pica pica*).

15.5.1 Gamebirds

Several species of bird are shot for game and trends in bag sizes have shown variation over time (**Figure 15.4a–d**). For example, annual bags of red grouse shot on upland moors varied around a consistent mean for much of the period during 1900 and 1940. Bags then fell during the war years of 1940 to 1945, increased steadily up to 1970, and declined again through to 2007. The causes of these declines have been the subject of much speculation (Barnes 1987; Sotherton *et al.* 2009). The high bags of the early 20th Century probably reflect the active and intense management of grouse moors and associated fauna. Changes in the structure of large estates in the middle of the 20th Century, however, reduced the availability of labour for undertaking moorland management; while long-term changes in land use and management in the uplands, such as afforestation and increased sheep numbers, very likely served to reduce the quality of grouse habitat and enabled the impacts of predator populations to increase (Thirgood *et al.* 2000).

Contrary to trends seen in red grouse, the numbers of pheasant shot per 100 ha of estate land increased steadily from 1960 to 2007 (**Figure 15.4b**). These increased bags largely reflect the greater number of pheasants reared and released specifically for hunting; in 2004, for example, 35 million pheasants were released in the UK (PACEC 2006).

Interestingly, the average bags of woodcock (*Scolopax rusticola*) during the last few decades of the 20th Century were very similar to those obtained in the first few decades of that century. In contrast, bags of snipe (*Gallinago gallinago*) showed an increase up to the 1940s, followed by a rapid and continued decline throughout the latter half of the 20th Century (National Gamebag Census, GWCT 2009).

Unfortunately, the trends in the bags of another lowland gamebird, the grey partridge have been in decline since the 1940s and 1950s (**Figure 15.4c**). The grey partridge is typically a bird of lowland grassland and arable habitats, and considerable scientific enquiry has gone into understanding the causes of its decline (Potts 1986; Aebischer 1997; Aebischer & Ewald 2010). As a result, it has been well established that changes in the management of arable fields caused a decrease in nesting, brood-rearing and winter habitat for adults partridges, and a scarcity of invertebrate food for the chicks. But the introduction of conservation headlands and other habitats on arable fields has partly ameliorated this decline.

In a converse pattern to that observed for the grey partridge, bags of the red-legged partridge, which was introduced from continental Europe as a game species, have increased from almost zero in 1970 to about 30/100 ha in 2005 (**Figure 15.4d**). Simultaneously, there has been a large increase in the number of red-legged partridge released into the UK countryside: 6.5 million were released in 2004, of which, 2.6 million were shot (PACEC 2006).

15.5.2 Deer

Several species of deer are shot as game and trends in their numbers and distribution are described in the following paragraphs.

The density of red deer shot in the Scottish Highlands remained roughly constant from 1960 to 2000, typically being in the range of 0.1–1 deer shot/100 ha. However, shooting densities increased to more than 1 deer/100 ha in the central Highlands in the 1990s. During the period 1960 to 2000, shooting gradually increased in south-west Scotland, north-west England, East Anglia and south-west England. No red deer were shot in Wales, the Midlands or south-east England between 1960 and 2000. The amount of red deer culled in Scotland on an annual basis between 1996 and 2006 fluctuated between a low of 53,950 in 1996/97 to a high of 71,536 in 1998/99. Over the next five years, numbers shot declined from this level and 63,568 deer were culled in 2005/06 (Deer Commission for Scotland 2006).

During the 1960s, bags of roe deer were restricted to Scotland, north-east England and some southern counties of England. Over the next few decades, the deer spread across

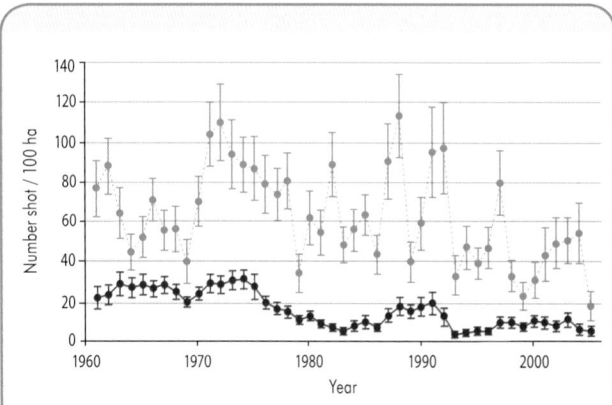

Figure 15.4a Numbers of red grouse (*Lagopus lagopus scoticus*) annually shot per 100 ha of moorland in England (upper line) and Scotland (lower line) from 1961 to 2005. Error bars represent 95% confidence intervals. Source: National Gamebag Census (GWCT 2009).

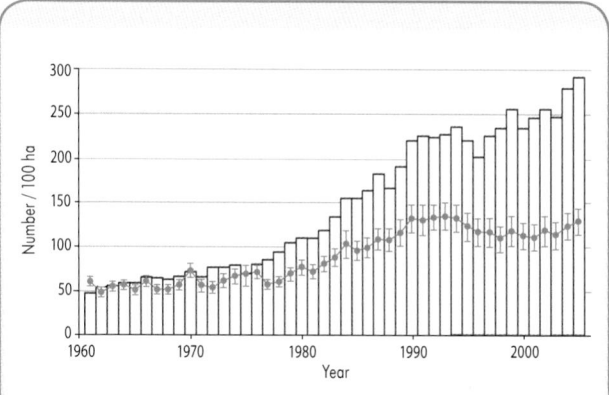

Figure 15.4b Numbers of pheasants (*Phasianus colchicus*) annually shot (solid line) and released (open bars) per 100 ha of total estate area in the UK from 1961 to 2005. Error bars represent 95% confidence intervals. Source: National Gamebag Census (GWCT 2009).

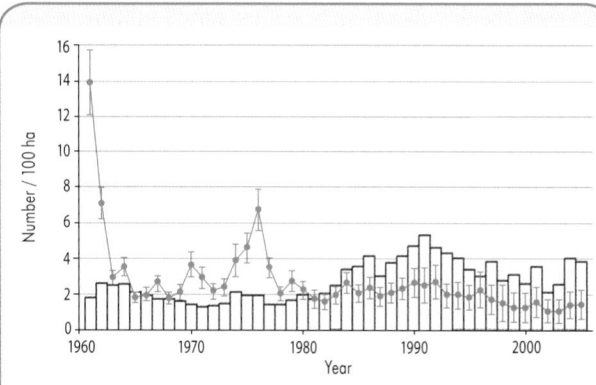

Figure 15.4c Numbers of grey partridges (*Perdix perdix*) annually shot (solid line) and released (open bars) per 100 ha of total estate area in the UK from 1961 to 2005. Error bars represent 95% confidence intervals. Source: National Gamebag Census (GWCT 2009).

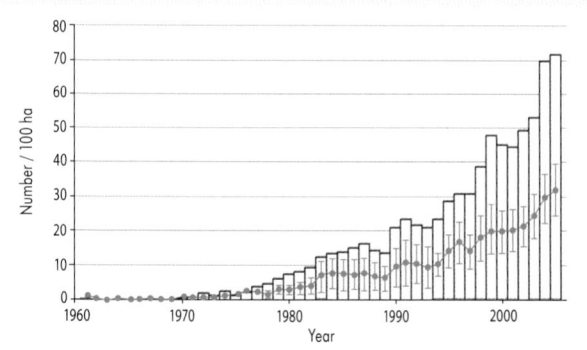

Figure 15.4d Numbers of red-legged partridges (*Alectoris rufa*) annually shot (solid line) and released (open bars) per 100 ha of total estate area in the UK from 1961 to 2005. Error bars represent 95% confidence intervals. Source: National Gamebag Census (GWCT 2009).

much of England, and in southern England bag densities exceeded 1 deer/100 ha in the 1990s. Few roe deer were shot in Wales or the English Midlands during the period 1960 to 2000, although a low level of shooting was recorded in Powys in the 1990s and has continued into the 21st Century.

During the 1960s, fallow deer were only shot in a few localities in the UK. By the 1980s, however, they were being shot across much of southern England and were first shot in Wales. During the 1990s, the densities shot were greater than 1/100 ha in Gloucestershire. In Scotland, fallow deer were shot in Tayside in every decade between 1960 and 2000. They were first shot in Dumfries and Galloway in the 1970s and in the western Highlands in the 1980s.

15.5.3 Salmon and Migratory Trout in Estuaries and Freshwaters

Fishing for salmon with fixed engines and nets and cobles has been undertaken for hundreds of years. Between 1950 and 1970, numbers caught by these methods were constant in Scotland and increased in England. After 1970, the numbers of fish caught by these methods fell in Scotland, and, in 2009, less than 13,000 fish were caught by these methods (Marine Scotland 2010). Catches by rod and line in Scotland were

more or less constant from 1950 to 1988, after which they declined until 2007 (**Figure 15.5**). However, in 2009, 24,228 wild salmon and grilse were caught and killed by rod and line, while a further 48,367 were reported to have been caught but released back into the water. The total rod catch for 2009 (killed plus released) was 106% of the average over the period since 1952. In 2009, catches by rod and line constituted 85% of the total Scottish catch, compared with just 11% in 1952. However, it must be noted that numbers caught by rod and line are not necessarily a reliable indicator of the total returning population of salmon as fishing effort and fishing conditions can have a large influence on catch size.

From 1988, catches in England and Wales also declined, and by 2006 less than 40,000 fish were caught by all methods (**Figure 15.6**). The amount of salmon caught by fixed engines has declined substantially since 2002, being exceeded by the number of salmon caught by rod and line during the following six years. These are the only years this has occurred since records began in 1956 (Cefas & Environment Agency 2009).

Salmon are not the only migratory fish caught in freshwater; sea trout are also fished both commercially and for recreational purposes. Catches of sea trout were steady in England, Wales and Scotland between 1975 and 1988, but they have declined in all regions since that time. This decline is particularly marked in Scotland.

15.5.4 Drivers of Change in Harvesting Game Species

In the UK, mammals and birds are hunted primarily for pleasure, and secondarily for consumption and/or pest management. During the last 30 years of the 20th Century, harvests of gamebirds declined. However, it is not clear how much the harvests recorded in late Victorian and Edwardian eras were a function of very intense ecosystem management aimed solely at enhancing population densities of game animals. If this is the case, it could be argued that the observed declines are due to changes in agricultural landscapes and habitat management, rather than overharvesting. Therefore, the future of game may depend more on the future management of agricultural landscapes than on any activity of the hunters themselves. Also, social attitudes to game species, and those who hunt them, will have a large impact on policies related to game conservation (Ward 1999; Anderson 2006). Should negative attitudes prevail, it will be difficult to justify public funds being spent on game management and conservation. The loss of wild-caught game would have minimal impacts on food security as any loss of inputs to the food chain could be replaced by domestically reared animals.

Traditionally, fixed nets across river mouths, fixed nets in tidal waters and an inshore fleet were all used to catch salmon in estuaries and coastal margins. Recent policy, driven by government and private interests, has sought to remove these interceptor nets through a series of buy-outs and through regulation. As a result, the number of returning fish entering rivers for spawning has increased in recent years, and catches on rod and line have been maintained and even enhanced. Future investments in improving salmon habitats will depend on the economic returns from angling, which may themselves be a function of wider economic factors.

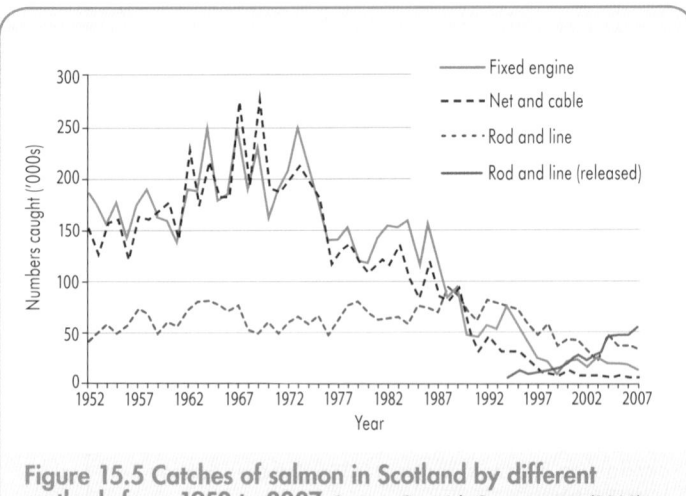

Figure 15.5 Catches of salmon in Scotland by different methods from 1952 to 2007. Source: Scottish Government (2009).

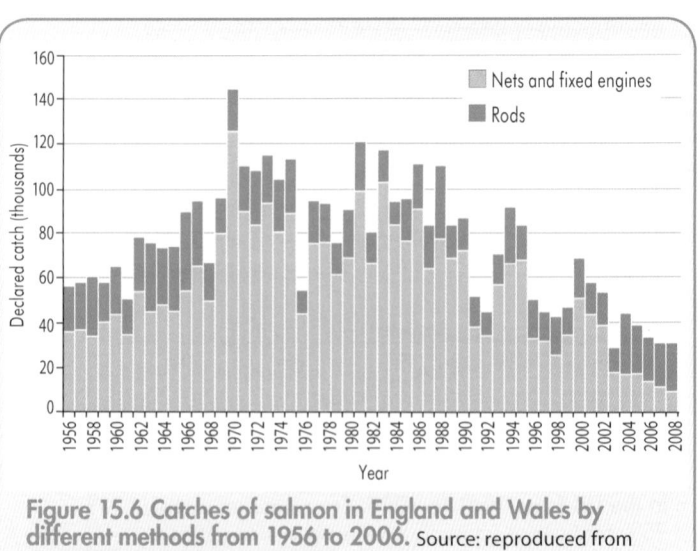

Figure 15.6 Catches of salmon in England and Wales by different methods from 1956 to 2006. Source: reproduced from Cefas & Environment Agency (2009).

15.6 Honey

There was an upsurge in the popularity of bee-keeping in post-war Britain as a response to the severe economic food shortages prevailing at that time, in particular the lack of sugar. The numbers of beekeepers and colonies reached their highest point in 1949 with 87,000 keepers and 465,000 colonies (5.3 colonies per keeper) reported for England (Showler 1996). There was a subsequent and gradual decline in popularity of bee-keeping owing to the increased availability of sugar on the open market, culminating in 1953 with the ending of sugar-rationing. By this time, beekeeper numbers had declined to approximately 80,000 beekeepers with 396,000 colonies (5 colonies per keeper) (**Figure 15.7**), and this decline continued over the next two decades.

In 1970, the number of beekeepers in England and Wales was recorded at 32,000, with 158,000 colonies between them (five colonies per keeper) (Showler 1996). Twenty years later, in 1990, numbers were showing just a slight increase with 33,744 beekeepers and 163,822 colonies (4.85 colonies per keeper). However, the numbers of beekeepers increased sharply during the first decade of the 21st Century, and it is estimated that there were 40,000 beekeepers and 200,000 colonies in the UK during 2009 (five colonies per keeper) (Fera 2011). Of these, approximately 300 commercial beekeepers managed 40,000 colonies between them.

The early 1990s marked a watershed in British bee-keeping for two reasons. Firstly, from 1990 onwards, there was an increase in the number of new beekeepers recorded in the UK (Showler 1996). Secondly, the mite *Varroa destructor* was first recorded in the UK in 1992 (British Beekeepers' Association 2009). This mite enters hives and increases the bees' susceptibility to harmful diseases thereby increasing bee mortality and decreasing honey production (Berthoud *et al.* 2010; Bowen-Walker & Gunn 2001). In order to minimise the impact of *Varroa* on honey production, beekeepers have changed hive management practices by using chemical controls and altering the feeding regimes of the bees.

There are no reliable figures for annual UK honey yields. Based on honey production of 11 kg/hive/yr (Jones 2004) and the number of maintained bee colonies, estimates suggest that the amount of honey produced in the UK in 2009 was about 60% of that produced in 1949, all other things being equal (**Figure 15.8**).

15.6.1 Drivers of Change in Honey Production

Current prices would suggest that there is an underlying and strong demand for honey: average prices rose from £5.00/kg in 2004 to £8.31/kg in 2009. Weather permitting, national honey productivity should continue to rise as long as the number of beekeepers increases and adequate sources of pollen are available. There appears to be increased demand for premium UK-harvested bee products, repeating the pattern of Manuka honey from New Zealand which is used for dermatological and post-surgical treatment.

Future challenges to the industry will relate to global warming, disease and landscape change. For example, honey

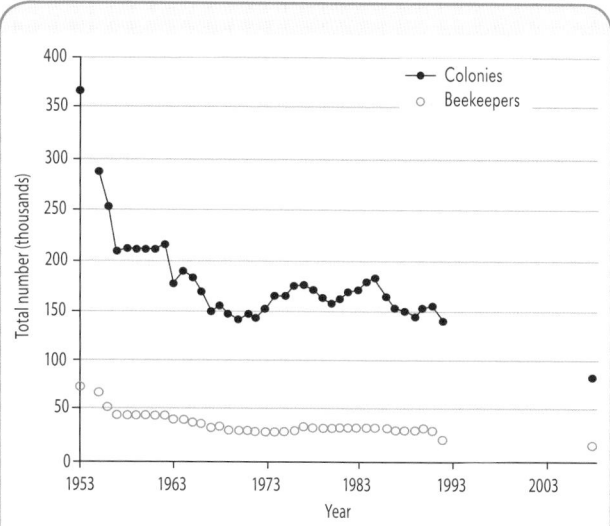

Figure 15.7 Number of beekeepers and colonies in England between 1953 and 1993. Source: reproduced from Potts *et al.* (2010b) with permission from the International Bee Research Association.

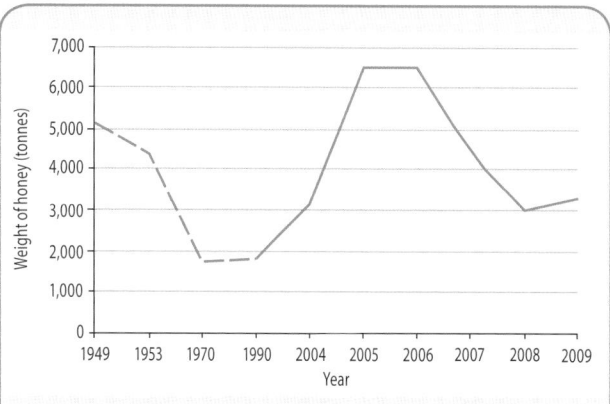

Figure 15.8 Honey production in England and Wales. Data for years 1949 to 1990 is estimated by multiplying the average honey production per hive/yr (11 kg) (Jones 2004) by the number of colonies for that year.

production is tightly linked to the prevalent weather of a given flying season. Wet summers (even if warmer than average) are likely to lead to increased problems for honey bees as they may reduce flying time and hence nectar/pollen collection, and they may also increase the chance of fungal infections.

15.7 Timber and Forest Products

Trees provide a range of goods that are useful to humans. Timber of suitable quality can be used as the main structural material in buildings, while timber with other characteristics can be used in constructing other elements of buildings that do not bear structural loads, such as panels and window frames, and can also be used to craft furniture, utensils and ornaments. Wood products can be used to manufacture paper, cardboard, Medium-density Fibreboard (MDF) and other fibrous products, and can be used as a fuel for heating buildings via logs or wood pellets constructed from wood waste. The focus in this chapter is on the use of produce from forests and woodlands; Chapter 8 provides a more holistic discussion of woodlands and their management.

15.7.1 Timber

Wood products can be divided into softwoods (generally from conifers) and hardwoods (from deciduous trees), both of which have different qualities and uses. Softwood is easier to work, and, because of the growth form of commercial conifers, it is possible to obtain long spans of intact timber from these trees. Until relatively recently, hardwoods were principally obtained from tropical trees such as teak and mahogany. These woods are of greater density than softwoods and can be used for products that require such density or longer lifespans such as musical

instruments, some furniture and window frames. Concern about overexploitation of forests in tropical countries has reduced the supply of these goods to UK markets, and there is now increased interest in deriving products from UK-grown hardwoods. This poses some problems as poor management of the growing trees reduces the quality of the timber available (Siry *et al.* 2004; Thurkettle 1997).

The amount of hardwood harvested in the UK has declined over the past 40 years, and there is no sign of any reverses in this decline for most uses (**Figure 15.9**). The vast majority of hardwoods are produced in England (88% of 2008 harvest). However, there has been a steady decline in English production since the late 1970s despite a surge between 1988 and 1992, which was probably related to the major storms that affected parts of England in 1987 and 1992. Levels of production in Wales (4%) and Scotland (8%) are relatively small, and have both declined over the last 30 years. There are no records of harvested hardwoods in Northern Ireland (**Figure 15.10**). Interestingly, the use of hardwoods for wood fuel has increased in the last five years, perhaps as a response to concerns over use of fossil fuels for heating.

In contrast to the decline in hardwoods, the production of softwoods in the UK has increased steadily over the last 40 years (**Figure 15.11**). The total harvest of softwood was nearly 8,600,000 m³ in 2008, compared with less than 400,000 m³ of hardwood. To a large extent the increased levels of harvested softwood reflect the levels of deliberate and extensive planting that began in the early part of the 20th Century. Since the mid-1990s, the vast majority of the softwood harvest has been derived from Scotland (63% of 2008 harvest), although prior to that date the harvest levels were equivalent between England (21% of 2008 harvest) and Scotland. Northern Ireland has tended to produce a small but constant harvest (5%), while the harvest in Wales has increased three-fold over the last 30 years (11% of 2008 harvest) (**Figure 15.12**). Just over half the softwoods harvested in 2008 were from the Forestry Commission estate (52%), while only 10% of hardwoods were from the Forestry Commission estate.

Although softwood production has steadily increased over the last half-century and hardwood production has steadily declined, these trends are not directly related, i.e. softwood production has not been at the expense of hardwood production. Softwood production has increased largely through the introduction of forest stands, established by the Forestry Commission in the first half of the 20th Century to create a strategic timber reserve for the UK. While the original stands have now been harvested (as part of a 40–50-year rotation), replanting of this land, combined with incentives for an increase in private plantations after WWII, has contributed to the recent surge in softwood harvest.

In the latter half of the 20th Century, policy mechanisms, such as financial incentivisation of private investment, played a significant role in increasing the UK's forest estate. Many of these incentives were aimed at single-objective forestry for softwood timber production; although, there were financial incentives to plant broadleaved woodlands in the 1980s, and to plant native woodlands from the mid-1990s onwards. As a consequence of these incentives, only a small proportion of the UK's forest estate is managed for hardwood production—the bulk of hardwood supplied is the result of arboricultural

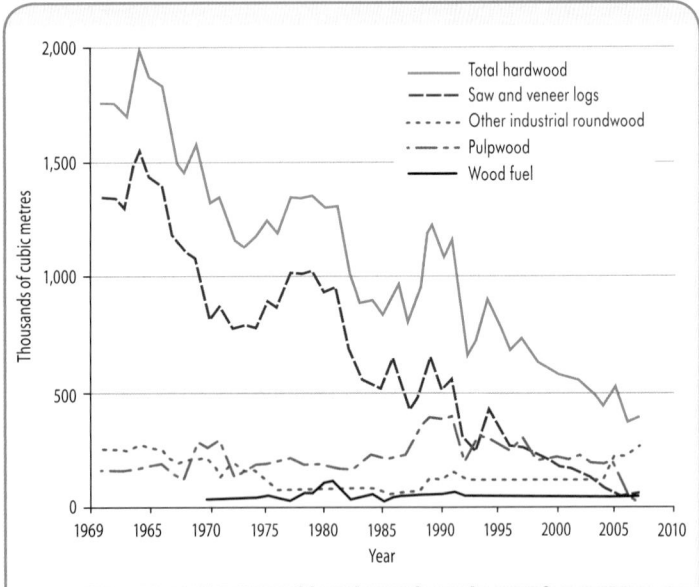

Figure 15.9 Production of hardwoods in the UK from 1961 to 2007. Source: Forestry Commission; data available from www.forestry.gov.uk/forestry/infd-7aql5b.

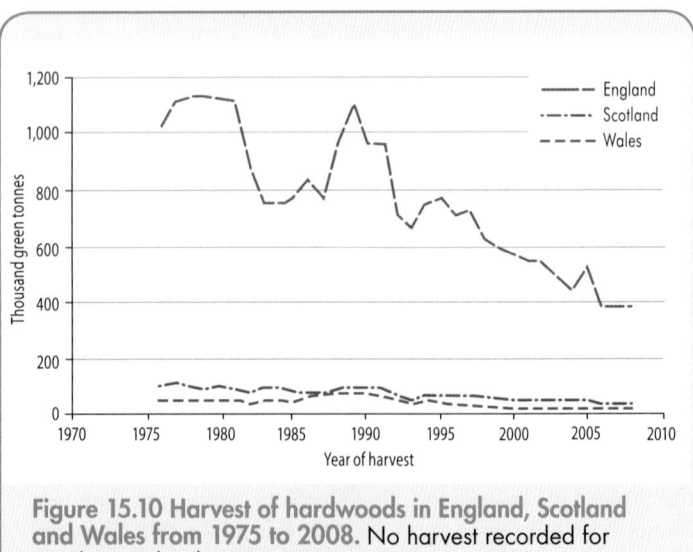

Figure 15.10 Harvest of hardwoods in England, Scotland and Wales from 1975 to 2008. No harvest recorded for Northern Ireland. Source: Forestry Commission (2010).

rather than forestry activity. Although the softwood production industry is a relatively small component of UK industrial output, and softwood imports carry a significant economic advantage, there is no indication that there will be any change to the UK's expectation that at least some domestic softwood production should remain. However, at the regional scale, the importance of softwood provisioning services from forests and woodland are set to decline over most of England and Wales, with production being concentrated in Scotland and north-east England. This decline is a reflection of the increased emphasis on other forestry/woodland ecosystem services, notably recreation, habitat provision and flood mitigation, where hardwood species are favoured over conifers. Further discussion of forests and woodland policy is presented in Chapter 8.

15.7.1.1 Proportion of domestic supply of wood products from UK sources

Around 85% of the 50 million m³ of timber, paper, boards and other wood products used in the UK each year are imported (Forestry Commission 2010). Despite this, there is an active timber processing sector in the UK, and the supply of roundwood to UK sawmills is dominated by UK-grown timber and accounts for 97% of the softwood and 76% of the hardwood processed in 2008. For panel mills, the proportion of UK-grown timber that is processed is higher, being close to 100%. The proportion of total sawn wood produced domestically is somewhat lower, but increasing. In 2008, around 68% of sawn timber was imported; this was a marked drop below 2007 levels (73% imported), and continues a declining trend in imports of sawn wood of around 1% per annum. Exports of UK-grown sawn wood are small (around 8% in 2008) and declining.

15.7.2 Christmas Trees

Sales of UK-grown Christmas trees amount to around 7.5 million trees per annum from a growing stock of around 70 million trees. The value of these trees at the farm gate is around £140 million, with the estimated value at retail outlets being around twice this figure. The majority of these trees are cut, with pot-grown trees amounting to only around 5% of the total. Imported trees represent around 12% of total retail sales, and are largely restricted to species that grow less well in UK conditions than in those of near neighbours (e.g. noble fir (*Abies procera*) imported from Ireland and nordman fir (*Abies nordmanniana*) imported from Belgium). Over the past 20 years, the market has increased by around 100,000 trees per year, but still only represents one live tree for every three UK households (British Christmas Tree Growers Association pers. comm.)

15.7.3 Edible Non-Timber Forest Products

In Scotland, the wild mushroom industry has grown rapidly over the past two decades. In particular, chanterelle (*Cantharellus cibarius*), cep (*Boletus edulis*) and hedgehog mushrooms (*Hydnum repandum*) have become sought-after foodstuffs. In 2000, the total mushroom harvest from both natural and plantation forests, principally in the Scottish Highlands, was worth approximately £406,000/annum. A total of 20 jobs were directly attributable to the harvest and

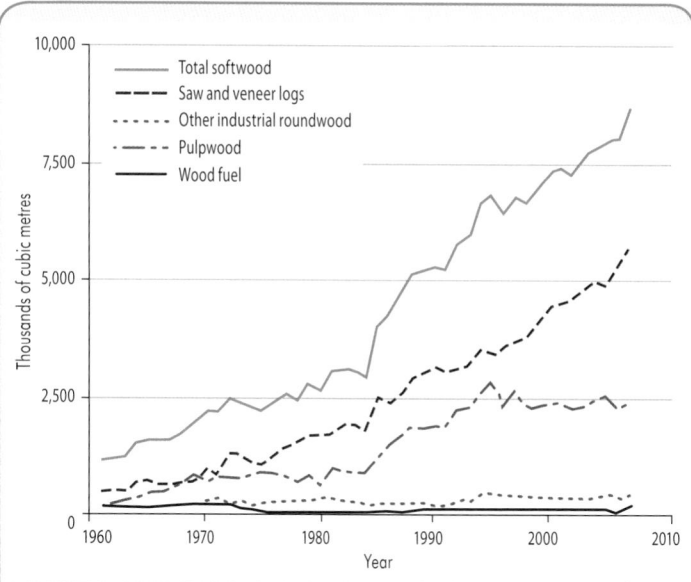

Figure 15.11 Production of softwoods in the UK from 1961 to 2007. Source: Forestry Commission; data available at www.forestry.gov.uk/forestry/infd-7aql5b.

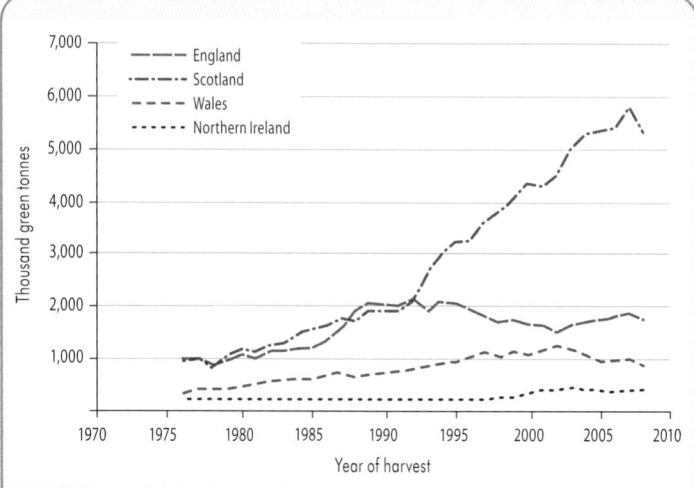

Figure 15.12 Harvest of softwoods in England, Scotland, Northern Ireland and Wales from 1975 to 2008. Source: Forestry Commission; data available at www.forestry.gov.uk/forestry/infd-7aql5b.

approximately 350 pickers benefited from casual earnings (averaging £28.70/week) (Dyke & Newton 1999).

15.7.4 Drivers of Change in Timber and Forest Products

Drivers for change in the forestry sector are discussed in detail in Chapter 8. To a large extent, government policy has driven investments in forestry in the UK throughout the period between 1945 and 2009. These policies have been aimed at a range of targets which include enhancing timber supply through increasing the size of the state forest, increasing private ownerships through financial incentives, and improving the quality of forests for biodiversity and recreation. However, recent concerns about mitigating climate change offer new drivers for forest policy. These are three-fold and relate to potentially increased plantings in order to sequester carbon, the use of timber as a sustainable substitute for other goods, and the use of timber and wood wastes as a fuel for heat.

For example, in recent years, rising energy prices and renewable energy commitments have steadily increased demand for fuel for both domestic and industrial wood-burners. This, combined with steady wood fuel availability, is likely to increase the cost of this commodity, at least in the short-term. As the value of wood fuel increases, it is likely that woodland owners will be increasingly motivated to bring small, unmanaged, private woodlands into management, increasing the wood fuel output from these ecosystems. Large-scale increases in wood fuel production, however, may well be constrained by the high transport costs associated with low energy density fuels, particularly when increased demand is itself driven by increasing fuel costs.

Furthermore, as wood processing and utilisation technologies improve, and embedded energy costs are included in competing raw materials, it is likely that wood products will again become a mainstay of building construction. Increasingly, bio-composites will take the place of oil-derived plastics, and many of these will have a forest-industries precursor. As the range of products (e.g. timber, wood fuel, bio-materials) extracted from forests and woodlands increases, the opportunities for income generation from woodlands will increase, and this will, in turn, increase the finance available for management operations both in small, privately-owned woodlands and the publicly owned forest estate. As a consequence, there is likely to be a gradual improvement in the productive state of forests and woodland, for example, where economic constraints have delayed planned thinning operations in high-density plantations (although, in many cases, thinning may not be possible without incurring major wind-throw losses). Similarly, neglected broadleaved woodlands may benefit from the removal of over-mature trees, increasing their age-diversity and habitat provision, as well as increasing their landscape and amenity value. Therefore, it is likely that escalating investment in management interventions will lead to an increase in sustainable woodland and forest management practices. While from the perspective of provisioning services this increased management is to be welcomed, care will need to be taken to ensure that this increased level of management does not have adverse impacts on biodiversity and ecosystem functioning.

The most significant threat to the future supply of provisioning services from woodlands lies in the spectre of pests and diseases. For example, over the course of the last century, Dutch Elm Disease (caused by the fungus *Ophiostoma novo-ulmi* and spread by the beetles of *Scolytus* species) has severely reduced the abundance and geographic distribution of elms in the UK. Another example of the importance of diseases is Sudden Oak Death, where the fungus *Phytophthora ramorum* can cause the sudden death of both native oak species. In addition, the last decade has witnessed a gradual increase in oak mortality, attributed to Acute Oak decline, although whether this is a single virulent disease, a combination of low-virulence diseases, or a combination of disease and climate change, is subject to ongoing research. Similarly, Red Band Needle Blight (caused

by the fungus *Dothistroma septosporum*) has, over the last couple of decades, dramatically reduced timber yields in infected plantation pine forests (Anon 2008). These are just a few of the pests and diseases that have damaged native and plantation trees in recent decades, and there remains the potential for other introduced pests and diseases to have similar, or even greater, impacts in the future.

15.8 Peat

Peat has been used as a resource by humans in the UK since Neolithic times. In the 19th Century, peat was used as stable litter and fuel to heat houses. The demand for peat fell in the middle of the 20th Century as the number of horses declined and other sources of domestic fuel, such as coal, became more widely available. The ancient right of turbary bestows on individuals or households the right to extract peat for use as a fuel, with specific restrictions. These rights were still in existence in parts of Northern Ireland and Scotland in 2010, although there is evidence from Northern Ireland that fewer people are taking up the these rights than in the previous 30 years (a 95% decrease in 2006 compared to 1983) (Jordan & Tomlinson 2007).

The use of peat in horticulture as a growing medium constituent (other than for acid-loving plants) began in the 1930s with the development and publication of the John Innes compost formulae. These were designed for professional growers to improve crop quality and reliability and employed a potting mixture of seven parts loam, two parts sand and three parts peat by volume (i.e. 25% peat). By the 1960s, it was recognised that a more reliable and consistent medium could be produced without stripping and preparing loam and, instead, using peat alone (or with sand, perlite, vermiculite, etc.). These new formulae had the added advantages of producing crops quicker, having lower shipping weights and a lower overall cost. These products began to be commercialised in the mid-1960s and led to an expansion of peat-harvesting once again. By the 1970s, peat composts had been introduced to the amateur gardener; the market grew rapidly, displacing John Innes, and the demand for peat rose. By 1997, the average peat content of growing media sold in the UK peaked at 96% of market share. However, just ten years later, under government pressure to reduce peat usage and with heavy investment in alternatives, the average peat content in growing media was cut to 81% and 72% in professional and retail products, respectively. During this time, peat use as a soil improver was almost completely eliminated, accounting for just 2% of sales by volume in 2007. The total volume of peat used in UK horticulture in 2007 was just over 3 million m³, of which, less than half (1.3 million m³) was sourced from within the UK.

In addition to its use in horticulture, peat is still sold for fuel in the form of briquettes and remains important in the whisky industry—peat is used to fuel the fires that dry damp malt. Some of the smoke from the burning peat enters the malting barley. The amount of smoke in the malt has an impact on the taste of the whisky, giving rise to different, and consistent, tastes of malt whiskies. In some areas, there may have been over-extraction for the whisky industry, but more recently this industry has taken steps to reduce its use of peat.

The total area of land used for peat extraction has fallen from 14,980 ha in 1994 to 10,690 ha in 2009. The area of land used for extractions does not necessarily reflect the amount of peat extracted from that land in a given period. For example, at a GB scale, 1,616,000 m^3 of peat were sold in 1999 (392,000 m^3 derived in Scotland, 316,000 from north-east England and 249,000 m^3 from north-west England), while, in 2008, this figure had fallen to 760,000 m^3 (265,000 m^3 from Scotland and 416,000 m^3 from north-west England). No commercial exploitation of peat has occurred in Wales in recent times.

The control of commercial peat extraction lies with local authorities who hold information on extent, site location and after-use of extraction sites. In 2003, Scottish Natural Heritage commissioned a review of commercial peat extraction in Scotland which listed sites, areas, planning conditions and relation to nearby protected sites (Special Areas of Conservation (SACs) or Sites of Special Scientific Interest (SSSIs) which intersect or lie within one kilometre of the extraction area) (Scottish Government 2009). At that time, 72 peat extraction consent sites were recorded in Scotland (20 active, 16 expired, three pending, the remaining 33 awaiting confirmation). After-use for sites was varied and included wetland creation, forestry and agriculture (Scottish Government 2009).

Seventeen raised bogs in England and 24 in Scotland have permission for peat extraction, 12 of which have been (at least partly) notified as SSSIs. Local authorities could rescind permission to extract from a site, but this may require the government to pay compensation to owners of the peat extraction rights as occurred in the cases of Hatfield and Thorne Moors and Bolton Fell Moss.

15.8.1 Drivers of Change in Peat Extraction

The combination of policy and demand will determine the amount of peat that is extracted from UK sources in the future. If consumer demand for peat is reduced, i.e. by further adoption of non-peat composts, then there will be less call for peat to be extracted. Similarly, if consumers send strong signals to commercial growers that they do not want to purchase products grown in peat, demand would also be reduced. However, as a lot of peat is currently imported into the UK from countries such as Ireland and the Baltic states, the relationship between demand for peat and UK extraction is not simple. In addition to changing consumer demands, policy could also lessen peat extraction through a reduction in extraction licences.

15.9 Ornamental Resources

Ecosystems provide a number of resources that humans use for ornamental purposes. These include: plants and flowers used in gardens and for indoor decoration; animal resources, such as skins, heads and horns, used in taxidermy and as throws and wall mountings; minerals used as ornaments in gardens (e.g. river cobbles, limestone and slate) and as smaller, indoor decorations (e.g. polished stones); mollusc shells and fossils used in garden and indoor decoration; and driftwood and other pieces of timber used for various purposes. Unfortunately, there are very limited data on the use and production of these resources from UK, but data are available on the production of flowers and shrubs for ornamental purposes.

Some flowers are produced in open fields in the UK (4,578 ha grown in England in 2006), including daffodils and narcissi (3,871 ha)—many of which are produced in the Isles of Scilly, Cornwall, Pembrokeshire, Lincolnshire and south-west Scotland—and gladioli (252 ha) and pinks (56 ha). The area dedicated to these flowers has declined in recent years as retailers have tended to source flowers from producers in Europe and Africa.

Many flowers are also produced under glass; there are large enterprises in Lincolnshire and the south of England producing a range of flowers, such as 1,000 tonnes of narcissi for cut flowers, 84 million tulip bulbs, 151.5 million bulbs of irises and lilies, 566 ha of bedding plants and 56 ha of chrysanthemums. In addition, 45.6 million units of pot plants are produced for indoor use each year, including 11.9 million units of primroses and polyanthus, 1.9 million units of poinsettia and 3.7 million units of begonia. The relationship between glasshouse-produced flowers and ecosystems is limited, although glasshouse enterprises do require resources such as growing media, water and minerals. They also produce waste that needs to be disposed of off-site.

The economic importance of this sector is evidenced by data suggesting that, in 2002, the ornamental sector was worth around £674 million annually, having increased its total value by 50% during the 1990s. The largest ornamental sector was hardy nursery stock, which accounted for 49% of total production and a total value of £284 million. Between them, shrubs, roses and ornamental trees accounted for one third of the sector's value. The UK fresh-cut flower and indoor plant market was worth over £1.45 billion at the retail level, while exports of ornamentals were valued at around £39 million in 2000 (NFU 2002).

15.9.1 Drivers of Change in the Ornamental Sector

Although there are no long-term data available on the production of flowers in the UK, it is very likely that the increased wealth and house ownership that occurred in the latter half of the 20th Century served to increase the demand for shrubs, flowers and pot plants. Supporting evidence for this postulation comes from data on the total area of outdoor flowers and hardy nursery stock grown in England which increased from 6,921 ha in 1940 to 12,775 ha in 2000. If rising wealth is a driver of demand for ornamentals, then further increases will result in greater demand for these goods in the future. However, the opposite is also true: reduced spending by individuals and government in the future may reduce overall demand for ornamentals.

15.10 Genetic Resources

Genes are a resource to humans as the offer potential to meet future needs. Within-species genetic variation provides a range of building blocks which can be used to enhance the desirable traits and characteristics of species that already provide goods to humans, e.g. crops and livestock. Other species, which are closely related to existing crop and livestock species, can also provide genes that can enhance the benefits provided by their domesticated conspecifics. Thus desirable genes from wild relatives of domesticated plants can be transferred into crops through natural breeding or molecular techniques. At another level, the chemicals within animals, plants and microbes may themselves be useful to humans, such as in pharmaceuticals. In essence, it could be argued that all species are potentially beneficial to humans, and, as we do not know what our future needs will be, a prudent strategy would be to ensure that all extant species survive into the future. While there is some merit in this argument, it is also possible to identify some genetic resources that are more likely to be useful than others in the short-term.

One such group of resources is contained within the existing breeds and varieties of current livestock and crops. Commercial production of food tends to rely on relatively few breeds and varieties, which have been selected because of their productivity under current farming systems. However, many other breeds and varieties exist which are not commercially competitive in modern food production systems. It is a challenge to maintain viable populations of non-commercial breeds and varieties. Maintaining varieties of plants, such as wheat or apples, is relatively easy as seed banks provide a reliable long-term store of genetic material. Maintaining animal breeds is more difficult as they need constant care and attention (although long-term storage of semen and ova is becoming more viable). Some of the 'rare livestock breeds', such as Large Black pigs, are kept commercially as they offer niche food products, while others are kept as hobbies. Yet despite best efforts, it has been estimated that 26 native livestock breeds were lost from the UK between 1900 and 1973 (RBST 2010).

A second group of genetic resources is held in the wild relatives of crops and livestock. There are few truly wild relatives of livestock in the UK, as even the most feral goats and sheep are managed to some extent. Wild deer are perhaps the closest example of a wild livestock relative in the UK, but it could also be argued that brown trout, sea trout and wild salmon are also wild relatives of domesticated food animals. There are many more wild relatives of crops in the UK; Maxted *et al.* (2007) suggest that there are 413 genera and 195 species that have close genetic relationships with UK-grown crop plants. Of these, 85% are wild relatives of medicinal and aromatic plants, 82% of agricultural and horticultural crops, 15% of forestry plants and 30% of ornamentals. Although wheat is the most economically important crop in the UK, it has no wild relatives in this country. Consequently, the UK genus of highest economic importance as a crop wild relative is *Brassica*; this is because

of the several crop species of this genus grown here and their numerous wild relatives (Maxted *et al.* 2007). These data highlight both the potential importance of many plant species for future human welfare, and also the international dimension of any conservation effort aimed at maintaining these resources.

15.10.1 Drivers of Change for Genetic Resources

The breeding of new varieties of crops and livestock is a continuous process, and so, there is an ever-growing list of varieties that may warrant conservation. Such conservation is not without cost, and while maintaining rare breeds of animals may offer some income generation opportunities through sale of products and/or leisure experiences, seed banks are costly to build and maintain. For these reasons, the future conservation of many rare breeds and varieties depends upon governmental and societal preferences for spending money on these resources. Although industry may also benefit financially from the use of genetic resources in the future, it is hard to envisage a practical system whereby they would pay now for potential benefits they may accrue in the future. The conservation of crop wild relatives in the field is easier to achieve and these species could be conserved through ongoing habitat conservation initiatives and agri-environment schemes.

15.11 Water

Since the 1940s, the population of the UK has grown, introducing a greater demand for potable water. In addition, although private water supplies are still in use in many rural areas across the UK, there has generally been a movement towards greater connectivity to the central mains water supply. Not only do more people now access water from the mains supply, but the potable water supply also receives far greater levels of treatment than in previous decades, thereby reducing risks to human health. All the same, the amount of water put into the public water supply in England and Wales declined between 1990 and 2009. This trend was not evident in Scotland or Northern Ireland (**Figure 15.13**).

This decline in the water supply of England and Wales may be due to reduced demand from industry during that period. However, another factor that could affect this trend is the privatisation of the water industry in England and Wales in 1989; something that did not happen in Scotland or Northern Ireland. In addition, there is a far higher incidence of water meters in domestic premises in England and Wales (approximately 36% of homes) than in Scotland. The difference in uptake of water meters could be related to the differences in the cost of installation; in England and Wales installation is free to homeowners, while in Scotland the homeowner must bear the cost of installation.

In a similar vein, the total levels of abstractions in England and Wales stayed more or less constant between 1995 and 2007 (**Table 15.10**). Abstractions increased from 1995 to

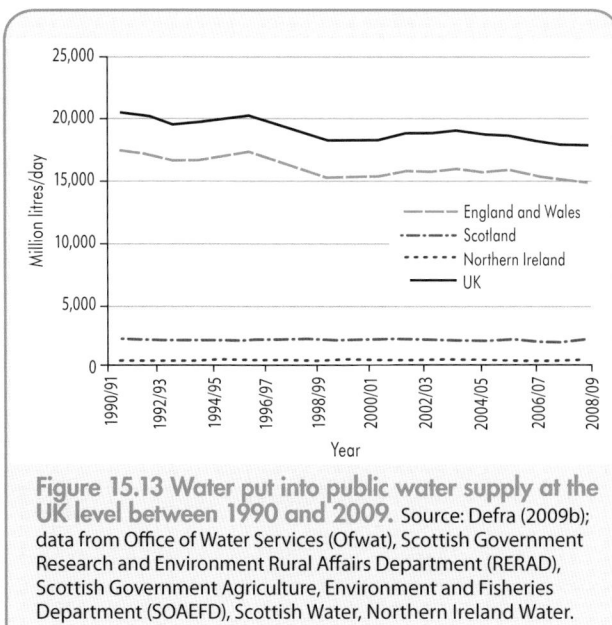

Figure 15.13 Water put into public water supply at the UK level between 1990 and 2009. Source: Defra (2009b); data from Office of Water Services (Ofwat), Scottish Government Research and Environment Rural Affairs Department (RERAD), Scottish Government Agriculture, Environment and Fisheries Department (SOAEFD), Scottish Water, Northern Ireland Water.

1998, largely due to abstraction rise in use for electricity supply and industry, and have declined since then, again in line with abstractions for electricity supply. The abstractions for agriculture have declined since 1996, and in 2007 they represented 0.01% of total abstractions.

Abstractions in Wales were 40% greater in 2007 than 1995, and were 42% greater in England. The major sources of abstraction in Wales related to electricity supply, amounting to 71% of all abstractions for this purpose in England and Wales, and representing 75% of total Welsh abstractions. Abstractions for the water supply represented 18% of Welsh abstractions in 2007, which had increased over 1995 levels. Not all of the water abstracted for this use in Wales is consumed in Wales as there are considerable transfers to English regions.

In Scotland, the management of water resources is shared between Scottish Water and the Scottish Environment Protection Agency under the Water Resource Planning and River Basin Management Processes. Between 2002/03 and 2009/10, estimated water abstractions decreased by 13% to 2,165 million l/d. Over the same period, domestic consumption increased by 8.5%, while non-domestic consumption fell by 15%. Although overall consumption rose, there was a reduction in the production of treated water which was largely achieved by a decrease in leakage. Leakage remains a major element of total demand in Scotland: approximately 38% of treated water was lost in 2009/10, compared with leakage rates of 16% in England & Wales (down from 23% during the late 1990s) (**Figure 15.14**). The differences in leakage rates could be due to differences in management in a privatised and non-privatised industry. However, the large size of the water supply network in Scotland, and the rural nature of much of the population served by the network, could also partly explain the higher leakage rates. See Chapter 9 for a more holistic discussion about water resources and their interaction with other ecosystems.

15.11.1 Bottled Water

There was a dramatic increase in the consumption of bottled water in the UK between 1976 and 2009 (**Figure 15.15**). Total UK consumption increased from 20 million litres in 1976 to 2.09 billion litres in 2009. Most of this water is bottled from springs (88% of the UK market), although some originates from treated mains water (12% of the UK market) (Zenith International 2009). Not all bottled water consumed in the UK is sourced from the UK, and the environmental costs of trade in bottled water have not been well studied (Parag & Roberts 2009).

15.11.2 Drivers of Change for Water Use

Drivers for change can be split into demand-led drivers and policy-led drivers. Demand-led drivers will vary on a

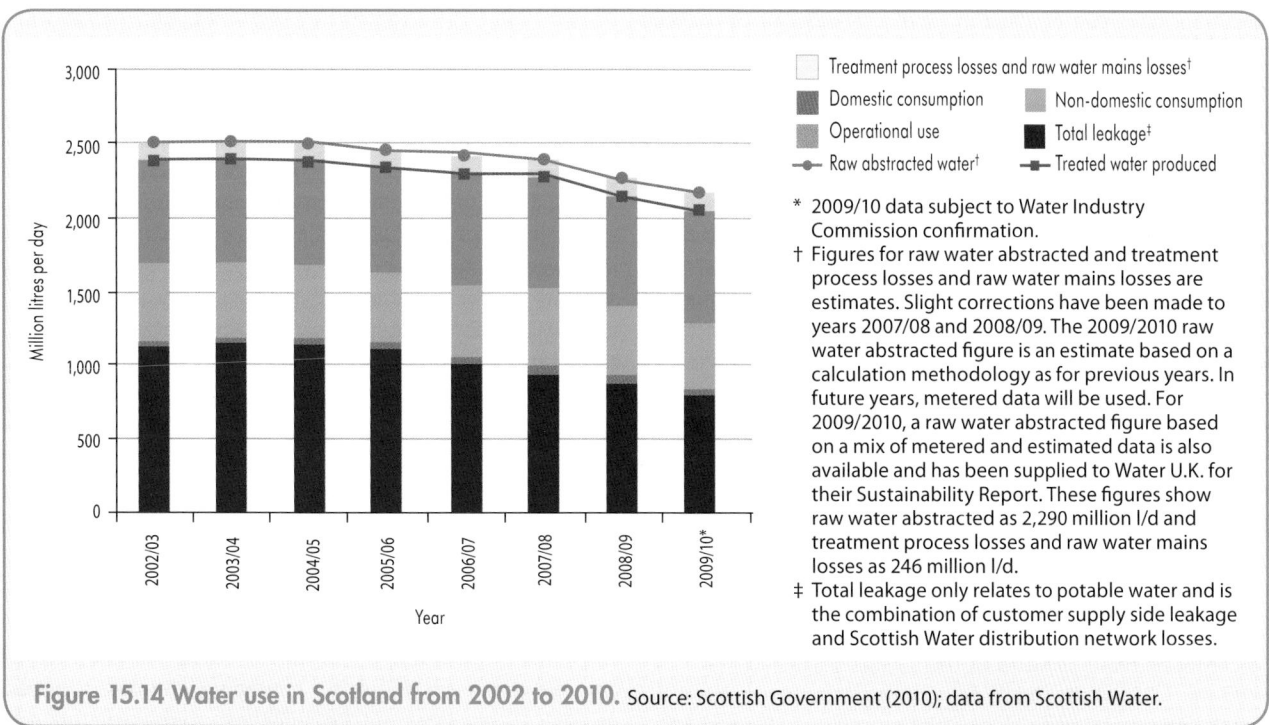

* 2009/10 data subject to Water Industry Commission confirmation.
† Figures for raw water abstracted and treatment process losses and raw water mains losses are estimates. Slight corrections have been made to years 2007/08 and 2008/09. The 2009/2010 raw water abstracted figure is an estimate based on a calculation methodology as for previous years. In future years, metered data will be used. For 2009/2010, a raw water abstracted figure based on a mix of metered and estimated data is also available and has been supplied to Water U.K. for their Sustainability Report. These figures show raw water abstracted as 2,290 million l/d and treatment process losses and raw water mains losses as 246 million l/d.
‡ Total leakage only relates to potable water and is the combination of customer supply side leakage and Scottish Water distribution network losses.

Figure 15.14 Water use in Scotland from 2002 to 2010. Source: Scottish Government (2010); data from Scottish Water.

Year	Public water supply	Spray irrigation	Agriculture (excl. spray)	Electricity supply	Other industry	Mineral washing [b]	Fish farming, etc.	Private water supply [c]	Other	Total
1995 d	17,346	351	103	8,224	2,325	261	4,268	98	220	33,196
1996 d	17,453	368	136	9,435	3,245	247	4,338	171	528	35,920
1997 d	16,820	291	107	11,909	2,862	295	4,210	162	408	37,065
1998 d	16,765	281	111	15,980	2,485	220	5,495	175	286	41,799
1999	16,255	325	142	12,927	4,939	..	4,867	91	518	40,063
2000	16,990	291	152	13,918	4,440	..	4,709	102	556	41,157
2001	16,231	258	108	15,361	3,594	..	4,657	92	103	40,404
2002 f	16,938	248	119	15,146	3,443	..	3,215 n	54	77	39,240
2003 e	16,920	315	131	12,173	4,631	..	3,077 n	60	86	37,394
2004 g h	17,208	225	122	11,573	4,558	..	4,068	30	77	37,860
2005 i j	17,370	226	60	9,998	4,194	..	3,654	26	60	35,588
2006 k l	17,004	277	47	10,364	3,729	..	3,622	37	86	35,166
2007 m	16,381	161	72	10,304	2,736 n	..	3,412	29	113	33,208

a Some regions report licensed and actual abstractions for financial rather than calendar years. As figures represent an average for the whole year expressed in daily amounts, differences between amounts reported for financial and calendar years are small. From 01/04/2008 return requirements were standardised across all the regions and returns are now requested on financial years;
b In 1999, mineral washing was not reported as a separate category. Licences for mineral washing are contained in 'Other industry';
c Private abstractions for domestic use by individual households;
d Under-estimate of actual abstraction due to licences being assigned as industrial cooling rather than electricity supply (North East Region);
e Three licences re-assigned to other industry from electricity supply (Midlands Region);
f No returns received for private water supply licence in 2002 and 2003 led to over-estimate in figures (Midlands Region);
g Increased number of returns received for fish farming licences in South Wessex Area (South West Region);
h Reduced abstraction at Dinorwig and Ffestiniog Power Stations (hydropower) (Wales);
i Reduced hydropower abstraction (North East and Midlands Region);
j Reduction in agricultural abstraction due to deregulation of licences as of 1 April 2005;
k Several licences changed from surface water to tidal (North East Region);
l Increased hydropower abstraction (Wales);
m Decrease in actuals for spray irrigation due to wet summer in 2007;
n Estimate requires further investigation and should be treated with caution.

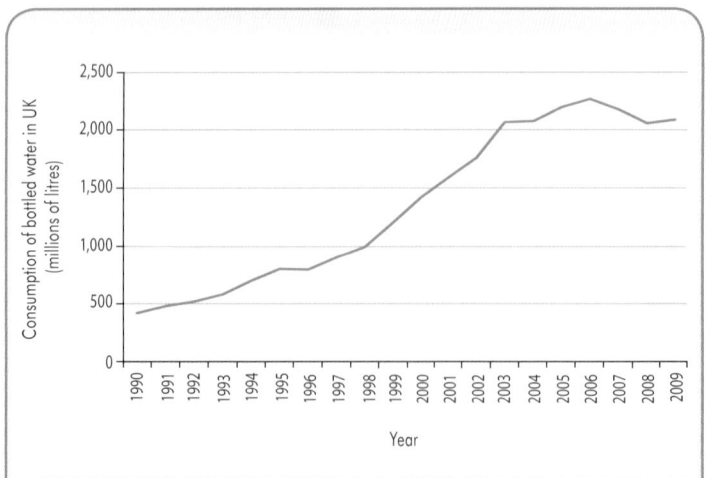

Figure 15.15 Volume of bottled water consumed in the UK (millions of litres) from 1990 to 2009. Source: data from British Bottled Water (2010).

catchment basis. In many largely urban catchments, rising populations and their increased use of water per capita have driven increases in demand. In some catchments, the use of water for industry will also have increased, although the small-scale use of water in traditional industry (e.g. via mills) may have reduced in some areas. Use of water by agriculture remains relatively small in many areas of the UK. Greatest concern is in south-east England where demand is high and supply is low, and in some catchments use for irrigation has increased during the last 20 years (Weatherhead & Knox 2000). This increase has largely occurred on horticultural crops which have not been in receipt of subsidies, and so, any increased water demand has been in response to market demands (Knox *et al.* 2010).

In addition, policies such as the Water Framework Directive (WFD) and the Bathing Water Directive (BWD) could potentially have a large influence on the management of the UK's freshwaters in future years. The WFD introduces new ways of assessing water quality which relate to broad ecological objectives and, through these, to the structure and function of aquatic ecosystems themselves. These objectives are to be met through a river basin management planning system which will seek to deliver integrated management of ground, fresh and coastal waters. The BWD seeks to monitor and improve bathing water quality around the coasts of EU members. In order to achieve this, the EU has set limits for physical, chemical and microbiological parameters, and national authorities must ensure that these limits are not exceeded. Agriculture and land use clearly play important roles in delivering high quality water resources, and, as a result of these new policies, there may be greater pressure on landowners to reduce the amount of chemical and biological pollutants entering water bodies. Several studies highlight problems associated with meeting the required standards (Kay *et al.* 2007; Howden *et al.* 2009), while others suggest that compliance may be financially costly for individual businesses (Fezzi *et al.* 2008).

15.12 Trade-offs, Synergies and Options for Sustainable Management

Detailed discussions of trade-offs and synergies for many of the habitats that provide provisioning services are provided in Chapters 5–9 and 11–12; in order to prevent repetition, this section provides a summary overview of some of the key issues in sustainable management of habitats and ecosystems for the supply of provisioning services.

The provision of food and fibre has large and significant interactions with many ecosystems. Indeed, much of the UK's land and sea is managed to provide these services. Because of this, the trade-offs and synergies are many. Generally, if management is intensive, there is a greater impact on the environment, but the delivery of provisioning services may also be enhanced, for example, increased yield in intensive compared to organic wheat. There are occasions where management can be made less intensive, for example, when a farmer offers a niche product from an extensive farm system, however, it is not apparent that all of society's needs can be met from such 'extensive but niche' systems.

Some foods and fibre are harvested from less intensively managed ecosystems, e.g. game, sea fish and timber from broadleaved woodland. In these ecosystems, there are trade-offs between harvest method, size of harvest, price and long-term supply of the goods. If regulated properly, such harvests can be truly sustainable; however, it is unclear how many of our needs for food and fibre can be met from such systems.

Within more intensive production systems there are many known options for introducing management that can enhance one dimension of sustainability at a time. For example, levels of farmland biodiversity can be enhanced by removing land from agricultural production and enabling re-establishment of natural habitats, as promoted by some

agri-environment schemes (Carvell *et al.* 2007; Walker *et al.* 2007). Similar events have also happened at the large scale when private organisations, such as the Royal Society for the Protection of Birds and National Trust, buy agricultural land and then manage it for biodiversity. In both cases, however, somebody has to pay for the environmental enhancement. In the former case, it is the tax payer, and in the latter case it is the charities' memberships. These systems raise some questions about fairness of payment and distribution of benefits; for instance, should all tax payers contribute to agri-environment payments that increase biodiversity on private land that they will never see? Or is it fair for charity members to support biodiversity which potentially benefits more people than themselves? Are the general public free-riding on the actions of those charity members?

Similar tensions occur in marine fisheries, and, to a large extent, much of recent fisheries policy has been trading-off short-term sector profitability against longer-term stock protection. While fisheries policy has tried to regulate fisheries activities though imposing close seasons for certain stock and restricting the number of days that trawlers may actively fish, perhaps the best examples of trade-offs relate to gear restrictions and closed areas. Gear restrictions seek to limit the types of fishing gear that can be used in certain locations and/or for catching certain fish species: these are known as 'technical measures'. Technical measures can be used to achieve a range of management objectives. For example, minimum mesh sizes may be used to encourage the release of under-sized or juvenile fish, while the use of separator panels or square mesh codends may eliminate the catching of species for which the fishers have no quota or that would be taken as by-catch.

Biodiversity can also be enhanced by extensification of production practices. These may include reduction in inputs to crops, wider planting densities in crops and reduced stocking rates of grazing animals. Similarly, in forestry and fisheries it is possible to develop techniques that provide 'more space for nature', for example, more broadleaved trees in conifer plantations and 'no-take zones' in sea fisheries. Although such activities enhance biodiversity, they may not enhance either levels of food/fibre provision or the incomes of landowners and rural communities. Furthermore, they may not necessarily serve to reduce the emissions of greenhouse gases from production activities. For example, low stocking rates of suckler beef herds may offer biodiversity benefits to upland and marginal habitats, but the slow growth rates of stock in these systems results in greater levels of lifetime methane emissions than in some other beef production systems. Unfortunately, this argument is complicated by the fact that some extensive grazing systems serve to protect extensive carbon stocks in soils, while others may even be able to enhance carbon sequestration on farms (Taylor *et al.* 2010).

Thus the challenge for sustainable management is to find options that offer advances in more than one dimension of sustainability at a time. Can we devise food/fibre production systems that protect biodiversity and reduce greenhouse gas emissions, while still maintaining incomes and cultural values? There are few examples of such win:win management changes available at the moment. So the question that must be asked is: which elements of the sustainability agenda are most important to achieve, and which are least important? If society can define this, then there are options for enhancing sustainability on one or two dimensions simultaneously. However, if demand for provisioning services continues to increase, society will face some very hard choices: to date, there are few examples of provisioning services which meet the highest standards of environmental and social sustainability while simultaneously being highly productive and profitable.

15.13 Key Questions and Knowledge Gaps

The specific knowledge gaps and research needs relating to many of the habitats discussed in this chapter are presented in Chapters 5–9 and 12, the purpose here is to present some of the common and overarching questions and gaps relevant to provisioning services from all habitats.

15.13.1 How Should We Spatially Allocate Productive and Environmental Management Activities?

There is a debate in agriculture about how to spatially integrate productive and environmental management activities (Fischer *et al.* 2008; Ewers *et al.* 2009; Hodgson *et al.* 2010). One option is to separate these two activities and to prioritise production in some areas and environmental conservation in others. A second option is to encourage production and environmental management to occur at the same spatial scale. This debate is relevant at several spatial scales. For example, within a field there could be intensively managed crops in the centre and a wide field margin managed for wildlife at the edge. Alternatively, the whole field could be managed less intensively with lower seed rates, reduced use of agrochemicals and gaps for wildlife, such as skylark scrapes (Smith *et al.* 2009), being present throughout the crop. At larger spatial scales there is potential to have some fields on a farm managed intensively for production and to allocate other areas of the farm for environmental purposes. While at the landscape-scale there is potential to have some larger areas of land dedicated to production and others dedicated to environmental purposes (e.g. reserves of some type).

Similar debates are relevant to fisheries and forestry. Within forestry, the questions are similar to those within agriculture: should commercial forests focus solely on maximising timber production, or should they include areas for wildlife and recreation (e.g. open areas, areas of non-commercial broadleaved species, wide forest rides, etc.) (Hale *et al.* 2009; Tomkins 1990)?

In marine fisheries, debate centres around whether areas of the sea should be designated as marine reserves or no-take zones, while others are left for production (Lorenzen *et al.* 2008; Richardson *et al.* 2006), or whether fishers should be asked to undertake environmentally sustainable activities in all areas. At the extreme, we could ask if increased use of intensive aquacultural activities would serve to reduce fishing pressure on the open ocean.

The environmental and economic costs and benefits of applying these options at various scales are poorly understood, and the balance of costs and benefits will change over time as demand for food and fibre fluctuates. We need a better understanding of the environmental, economic and social aspects of applying these alternative strategies in different locations on land and at sea. Related to this is a need to understand how the best overall option could be implemented in an efficient and effective manner.

15.13.2 What Level of Species Redundancy is There in Productive Ecosystems?

This question is related to the question set out in Section 15.13.1 but focuses more on the levels of biodiversity we should aim to see in productive ecosystems. It could be argued that some of the biodiversity observed on UK farms has little impact on the productive potential of that farm. Advocates of the view that some biodiversity is irrelevant to production could point to the increased trends in wheat yields observed over the last 50 years in the UK and the simultaneous decline in farmland birds (Newton 2004; Fuller & Ausden 2008). They would argue that if farmland birds really were crucial to the health of the productive ecosystem then yields would have decreased at the same time as the populations of farmland birds declined. Indeed, advocates of such a view may point more widely to global trends and highlight the fact that, despite species going extinct at an unprecedented rate (Pimm *et al.* 1995), levels of agricultural production tend to be increasing; this suggests that, at a global level, many species are not that important to production-related activities. There are many counter arguments to this viewpoint (Bell *et al.* 2005; Bunker *et al.* 2005; Chapin *et al.* 2000; Hector *et al.* 2007; Loreau *et al.* 2001), and, as Ehrlich & Ehrlich (1981) pointed out, species loss is analogous to losing rivets from an aircraft wing. You can afford to lose a few rivets without any worry, but you never know when losing another rivet will lead to the loss of the wing, and thereby the loss of all life on the aircraft.

If, in the future, we do need to increase the levels of food and fibre produced from our ecosystems, then it would be useful to understand which species really are crucial to maintaining the productive ability of the ecosystems, and which are effectively redundant from a production point of view. Such information would ensure that managers of farms, forests and fisheries do not accidentally cause loss of species vital to the functioning of their productive ecosystems. It would also enable conservation strategies to be developed for those species that are functionally redundant.

15.13.3 How Can We Predict When Environmental Pressures Will Serve to Reduce Future Flows of Provisioning Services in Given Ecosystems?

All systems which provide food and fibre are vulnerable to two broad classes of factors which could render them unsustainable in the long-term: intrinsic and extrinsic effects. Intrinsic effects can be defined as the impact of activities that arise within that production system upon itself. Extrinsic effects can be defined as the impact of activities outside the production system on that system. An example of an intrinsic effect would include the over-cultivation of some soils which leads to extreme soil erosion and prevents the further use of that land for crop production. An example of an extrinsic effect would be the impact of a distant pollution event on the ability of a piece of land to produce some provisioning services (e.g. the impact of radioactivity from the Chernobyl explosion on sheep production in some areas of the UK).

As described earlier in this chapter, the output of services (per unit area of land) and labour (measured in terms of weight and calories from UK agriculture) increased between 1945 and 2009 in nearly all areas of crop and livestock production. It is also evident that the production of food from agriculture has had wide and varied impacts on the environment; for example, overgrazing on the hills and mountains, pesticide-poisoning of raptors in the 1950 and 1960s, water pollution from phosphorus and nitrogen, and cropping system impacts on populations of farmland birds (Cade *et al.* 1971; Newton 2004; Haygarth *et al.* 2009; Potts *et al.* 2010a). However, the fact that more food is produced in the UK now than in 1940s suggests that the environmental impacts of agriculture have not yet reduced its own productive capacity. In other words, the productive activities of agriculture have not had long-term and lasting intrinsic effects on its ability to provide provisioning goods and services.

The situation in sea fisheries is very different; there have been continued declines in catches of fish over the period 1945 to 2009. The main hypothesised cause for these declines relates to overharvesting of the fish resource (Cook *et al.* 1997; Hutchings 2000; Pauly *et al.* 1998). In effect, the activities of fishers themselves had had a long-term impact on the level of provisioning services provided by the UK's marine ecosystems.

It would be useful to develop indicators that would alert managers to the risk of intrinsic effects decreasing their productive activities in the future. This would enable them to alter their management regimes and, hopefully, ensure the long-term flow of provisioning services from their systems. However, while the development of some indicators may be relatively straightforward at a biophysical level, it may be more difficult to ensure that managers act on the signals they provide. For example, it was evident for many years that the total catch and catch per unit effort of many species of sea fish were in decline (both of which may be indicators of the stock's long-term health), but neither policy makers nor fishers acted effectively on this information. Similarly, in some areas of the world, soil salinity was identified as a problem for cropping systems but no effective action was taken to effectively manage salinity levels; as a result, these areas have now been abandoned (Edwards-Jones 2003).

The reasons why managers may not act on such indicators are complex and varied. Some resource users may not have any options for changing their management regimes, and/or science may not be able to suggest viable alternative management systems to farmers and fishers.

There may also be dispute over the cause of an observed change in the indicator, for example, some people may argue that reduced fish stocks are not related to overfishing, but to other causes instead, such as climate change (Brander 2010; Halliday & Pinhorn 2009). Finally, other factors may serve to obscure the signal provided by the indicator. For instance, technology that enables production to increase despite the impact of declining environmental quality may serve to mask underlying trends in the productive capacity of the ecosystem; new crop varieties may offer enhanced yields despite deteriorating soil quality; and better management of inputs may serve to maintain yields despite declines in natural predators of pests.

Several questions which are relevant to the future management of the UK's productive ecosystems arise from a consideration of the impact of intrinsic and extrinsic factors on these systems:

a) Can we rely on the continued investment in agricultural science and technology to ensure that negative intrinsic effects will not affect the continued flow of provisioning goods and services?

b) How should society balance the impacts of intrinsic and extrinsic effects of production?

c) Are there any early indicators that intrinsic effects are starting to have negative impacts on the ability of production systems to provide a flow of provisioning goods and services?

d) In the future, are the flows of provisioning services from the UK more likely to be interrupted by intrinsic or extrinsic factors?

e) Can the flow of provisioning services from production systems, such as sea fisheries and forestry, be enhanced by altered patterns of investment in science and technology?

15.13.4 How Can We Enhance Resource Efficiency and Reduce Levels of Waste and Pollution?

Natural resources are finite, yet nearly all of human activity depends upon the use of these resources. Recently, there has been much focus on the quantities of oil that remain to be mined (Charpentier 2002; Verbruggen & Marchohi 2010), but many other inputs to production systems are derived from non-renewable sources such as metals, phosphorus and other minerals (Edwards-Jones & Howells 2001). Technological improvements in mining and related industries, combined with increased prices for some non-renewable materials due to increased scarcity, make it more economically viable to access previously untapped pockets of many resources. But this does not remove the fact that these resources are ultimately finite, and it would be a wise long-term strategy to minimise their use.

Similarly, it would seem wise to reduce the amount of waste and pollution that productive activities cause. This is particularly relevant in the context of climate change. Currently, there is much interest in reducing greenhouse gas emissions from agriculture (Burney *et al.* 2010; Huang & Tang 2010; Smith *et al.* 2010), but there remains a considerable challenge in achieving real and meaningful reductions in overall levels of emissions, particularly in levels of greenhouse gases per unit of production.

For these reasons, a very real and immediate challenge across agriculture, fisheries and forestry is to increase the resource efficiency of production by developing systems of production that use fewer non-renewable resources (including water) per unit of production, while simultaneously producing lower levels of pollution per unit of production. This task can only be achieved by the active and positive interaction of scientists, engineers and industry. Recent multi-disciplinary research initiatives and partnership between academia and industry offer some hope for progress in this field. However, the relevant research questions are very applied in nature, and to date many of state funders of research have struggled to divert substantial funds to such applied fields. Developing suitable mechanisms to fund the necessary applied multi-disciplinary research presents a challenge for government and the research community.

References

Acs, S., Hanley, N., Dallimer, M., Gaston, K.J., Robertson, P., Wilson, P. & Armsworth, P.R. (2010) The effect of decoupling on marginal agricultural systems: Implications for farm incomes, land use and upland ecology. *Land Use Policy, 27*, 550–563.

Aebischer, N.J. (1997). Gamebirds: management of the grey partridge in Britain. Conservation and the Use of Wildlife Resources (ed. M.Bolton), pp. 131-151. Chapman & Hall, London.

Aebischer, N.J. & Ewald, J.A. (2010) Grey Partridge *Perdix perdix* in the UK: recovery status, set-aside and shooting. *Ibis* **152**, 530–542.

Anderson, A. (2006) Spinning the rural agenda: The countryside alliance, fox hunting and social policy. *Social Policy & Administration, 40*, 722–738.

Anonymous (2008) New Research Note: Red band needle blight. *Scottish Forestry, 62*, 30.

Asfaw, S., Mithofer, D. & Waibel, H. (2010) Agrifood supply chain, private-sector standards, and farmers' health: evidence from Kenya. *Agricultural Economics, 41*, 251–263.

Barnes, R.F.W. (1987) Long term declines of red grouse in Scotland. *Journal of Applied Ecology, 24*, 735–741.

Bell, T., Newman, J.A., Silverman, B.W., Turner, S.L. & Lilley, A.K. (2005) The contribution of species richness and composition to bacterial services. *Nature, 436*, 1157–1160.

Berthoud, H., Imdorf, A., Haueter, M., Radloff, S. & Neumann P. (2010) Virus infections and winter losses of honey bee colonies (*Apis mellifera*). *Journal of Apicultural Research, 49*, 60–65.

Benn, R., Weaver, P.P., Billet, D.S.M., van den Hove, S., Murdock, A.P., Doneghan, G.B. & Le Bas, T. (2010) Human Activities on the Deep Seafloor in the North East Atlantic: An Assessment of Spatial Extent. *PLoS One, 5*: Article No.: e12730 Art No. 2010.

Bjornsson, B. & Dombaxe, M.A.D. (2004) Quality of Nephrops as food for Atlantic cod (*Gadus morhua* L.) with possible implications for fisheries management. *ICES Journal of Marine Science, 61*, 983–991.

Boersma, L., Gasper, E., Oldfield, J.E. & Cheeke, P.R. (1981) Methods for the recovery of nutrients and energy from swine manure. 1. Biogas. *Netherlands Journal of Agricultural Science, 29*, 3–14.

Bornett, H.L.I., Guy, J.H. & Cain, P.J. (2003) Impact of animal welfare on costs and viability of pig production in the UK. *Journal of Agricultural & Environmental Ethics, 16*, 163–186.

Bowen-Walker, P.L. & Gunn, A. (2001) The effect of the ectoparasitic mite, *Varroa* destructor on adult worker honeybee (*Apis mellifera*) emergence weights, water, protein, carbohydrate, and lipid levels. *Entomologia Experimentalis et Applicata, 101*, 207–217.

Brander, K.M. (2010) Cod *Gadus morhua* and climate change: processes, productivity and prediction. *Journal of Fish Biology, 77*, 1899–1911.

British Beekeepers' Association (2009) *Honey Bee Health Research Concepts,* January 2009.

British Bottled Water (2010) Water's vital statistics: industry data. [online] Available at <http://www.britishbottledwater.org/vitalstats2.html> [Accessed 07.03.11].

Brouwer, F.M. & van Berkum, S. (1996) CAP and environment in the European Union: Analysis of the effects of the CAP on the environment and assessment of existing environmental conditions in policy. Wageningen Pers, The Netherlands pp vii+171p ISBN: 90-74134-39-4.

Bunce, R.G.H., Bell, M. & Farino, T. (1998) The environmentally sensitive area legislation in the United Kingdom and its potential application to the Picos de Europa mountains in north-west Spain. *Environmental Conservation, 25*, 219–227.

Bunker, D.E., DeClerck, F., Bradford, J.C., Colwell, R.K., Perfecto, I., Phillips, O.L., Sankaran, M. & Naeem, S. (2005) Species loss and aboveground carbon storage in a tropical forest. *Science, 310*, 1029–1031.

Burney, J.A., Davis, S.J. & Lobell, D.B. (2010) Greenhouse gas mitigation by agricultural intensification. *Proceedings of the National Academy of Sciences of the United States of America, 107*, 12052–12057.

Burton, M., Rigby, D., Young, T. & James, S. (2001) Consumer attitudes to genetically modified organisms in food in the UK. *European Review of Agricultural Economics, 28*, 479–498.

Cade, T.J., Lincer, J.L., White, C.M., Roseneau, D.G. & Swartz, L.G. (1971) DDE residues and eggshell changes in Alaskan Falcons and hawks. *Science, 172*, (3986), 955–1971.

Capper, J.L., Cady, R.A. & Bauman, D.E. (2009) The environmental impact of dairy production: 1944 compared with 2007. *Journal of Animal Science, 87*, 2160–2167.

Carvell, C., Meek, W.R., Pywell, R.F., Goulson, D. & Nowakowski, M. (2007) Comparing the efficacy of agri-environment schemes to enhance bumble bee abundance and diversity on arable field margins. *Journal of Applied Ecology* **44**, 29–40.

Cefas (Centre for Environment, Fisheries and Aquaculture Science) & Environment Agency (2009) Annual Assessment of Salmon Stocks in England and Wales 2008. Preliminary assessment prepared for ICES, March 2009. Environment Agency & Cefas, 117 pp.

Chapin, F.S., Zavaleta, E.S., Eviner, V.T., Naylor, R.L., Vitousek, P.M., Reynolds, H.L. & Hooper, D.U., Lavorel, S., Sala, O.E. Hobbie, S.E. Mack, M.C., Diaz, S. (2000) Consequences of changing biodiversity. *Nature, 405*, 234–242.

Charpentier, R.R. (2002) Hubbert's peak – The impending world oil shortage. *Science, 295*, 1470–1470.

Chen, J.S. (2009) Food oral processing – A review. *Food Hydrocolloids,* **23**, 1–25.

CIWF (Compassion in Wild Farming) (2010) Pigs in Europe still suffering says Compassion. [online] Available at: <http://www.ciwf.org.uk/news/pig_farming/pigs_in_europe_still_suffering.aspx> [Accessed 16.10.10].

Cook, R.M., Sinclair, A. & Stefansson, G. (1997) Potential collapse of North Sea cod stocks. *Nature,* **385**, 521–522.

Cooper, M.D. & Wrathall, J.H.M. (2010) Assurance schemes as a tool to tackle genetic welfare problems in farm animals: broilers. *Animal Welfare,* **19**, 51–56.

Cotterill, R.W. (2006) Antitrust analysis of supermarkets: global concerns playing out in local markets. *Australian Journal of Agriculltural and Resource Economics,* **50**, 17–32.

Cracknell, R. (2009) *Sea fisheries statistics.* House of Commons Library Standard Note: SN/SG/2788 16pp.

DairyCo (2009) Confidence key to halting decline in milk supply. [online] Available at: <http://www.dairyco.org.uk/news/press-archive/january-2009/confidence-key-to-halting-decline-in-milk-supply.aspx> [Accessed 07.03.11].

Davis, D.R., Epp, M.D. & Riordan, H.D. (2004) Changes in USDA food composition data for 43 garden crops, 1950 to 1999. *Journal of the American College of Nutrition,* **23**, 669–682.

de Lange, K. (1999) Feeding growing-finishing pigs for profit – Main concepts and new opportunities. (Ed. Ball, R.) Advance in Pork Production, 10123–144, 28th Banff Pork Seminar, Banff, Canada.

Defra (Department for Environment, Food and Rural Affairs) (2006) Food Security and the UK: An Evidence and Analysis Paper. Food Chain Analysis Group, Defra, 87pp. [online] Available at: <http://archive.defra.gov.uk/evidence/economics/foodfarm/reports/documents/foodsecurity.pdf>.

Defra (Department for Environment, Food and Rural Affairs) (2009a) Agriculture in the UK 2009 Report. [online] Available at: <http://www.defra.gov.uk/statistics/2010/03/18/auk-2009/> [Accessed 07.03.11].

Defra (Department for Environment, Food and Rural Affairs) (2009b) Environmental and Wildlife Statistics – Inland water. [online] Available at: <http://www.defra.gov.uk/evidence/statistics/environment/> [Accessed: 28.04.11].

Defra (Department for Environment, Food and Rural Affairs) (2009c) Strategic Review of Aquaculture Potential England. [online] Available at: <http://archive.defra.gov.uk/foodfarm/fisheries/documents/aquaculture-report0904.pdf> [Accessed 07.03.11].

Defra (Department for Environment, Food and Rural Affairs) (2010a) Yield and production time series. [online] Available at: <http://www.defra.gov.uk/statistics/foodfarm/food/cereals/cerealsoilseed/> [Accessed 07.03.11].

Defra (Department for Environment, Food and Rural Affairs) (2010b) Environmental Stewardship. [online] Available at: <http://www.defra.gov.uk/food-farm/land-manage/> [Accessed 16.10.10].

Dimmock, J.P.R.E., Bennett, S.J., Wright, D., Edwards-Jones, G. & Harris, I.M. (2005). Agronomic evaluation and performance of flax varieties for industrial fibre production. *Journal of Agricultural Science,* **143**, 299–309.

Dittirch, P., Senser, M. & Frielinghaus, J. (1989). Comparative study on the turnover of quinic acid and shikimic acid and its derivaties in the needles of Norway Spruce, *Picea abies* (L) Karst affected by Waldsterben syndrome. *Forstwissenschaftliches Centralblatt,* **108**, 103–110.

Donaldson, A., Lowe, P. & Ward, N. (2002) Virus-crisis-institutional change: The foot and mouth actor network and the governance of rural affairs in the UK. *Sociologica Ruralis,* **42**, 201–214.

Dreezens, E., Martijn, C., Tenbult, P., Kok, G. & de Vries, N.K. (2005) Food and the relation between values and attitude characteristics. *Appetite,* **45**, 40–46.

Dubuit, M.H. (1995) Food and feeding of cod (*Gadus morhua* L) in the Celtic Sea. *Fisheries Research,* **22**, 227–241.

Dyke, A. & Newton, A. (1999) Commercial harvesting of wild mushrooms in Scottish forests: is it sustainable? *Scottish Forestry,* **53** (2) 77–85.

Edwards-Jones, G. (2003) Agricultural policy and environment in Syria: The cases of rangeland grazing and soil management. *Syrian Agriculture at the Crossroads,* FAO Agricultural Policy and Economic Development Series. No 8. Rome pp 117–133.

Edwards-Jones, G. (2010) Are eating local food and increasing national levels of self-sufficiency good for the health of the environment and consumers? *Proceedings of the Nutrition Society,* **69**, 582–591.

Edwards-Jones, G. & Howells, O. (2001) The origin and hazard of inputs to crop protection in organic farming systems: Are they sustainable? *Agricultural Systems,* **67**, 31–47.

Edwards-Jones, G., Plassmann, K., York, E.H., Hounsome, B., Jones, D.L. & Milà i Canals, L. (2009) Vulnerability of Exporting Nations to the Development of a Carbon Label in the United Kingdom. *Environmental Science and Policy,* **12**, 479–490.

Ehrlich, P.R. & Ehrlich, A.H. (1981) Extinction: the Causes and Consequences of the Disappearance of Species. Random House, New York, NY.

Engelhard, G.H. (2005) Catalogue of Defra historical catch and effort charts: six decades of detailed spatial statistics for British fisheries. Sci. Ser. Tech. Rep., Cefas Lowestoft, No. 128: 42pp.

Ewers, R.M., Scharlemann, J.P.W., Balmford, A. & Green, R.E. (2009) Do increases in agricultural yield spare land for nature? *Global Change Biology,* **15**,1716–1726.

Fera (Food and Environment Research Agency) (2011) *Honey bees.* [online] Available at: <http://www.fera.defra.gov.uk/plants/beeHealth/> [Accessed 25.01.11].

Ferris, C.P., Gordon, F.J., Patterson, D.C., Kilpatrick, D.J., Mayne, C.S. & McCoy, M.A. (2001) The response of dairy cows of high genetic merit to increasing proportion of concentrate in the diet with a high and medium feed value silage. *Journal of Agricultural Science,* **136**, 319–329.

Fezzi, C., Rigby, D., Bateman, I.J., Hadley, D. & Posen, P. (2008) Estimating the range of economic impacts on farms of nutrient leaching reduction policies. *Agricultural Economics,* **39**, 197–205.

Fischer, J. Brosi, B. Daily, G.C., Ehrlich, P.R., Goldman, R., Goldstein, J., Lindenmayer, D.B., Manning, A.D., Mooney, H.A., Pejchar, L., Ranganathan, Jai. & Tallis, H. (2008) Should agricultural policies encourage land sparing or wildlife-friendly farming? *Frontiers in Ecology and the Environment,* **6**, 380–385.

Forestry Commission (2010) Timber Sales. [online] Available at: <http://www.forestry.gov.uk/forestry/INFD-7BADDP> [Accessed 07.03.11].

Frost H. & Andersen, P. (2006) The Common Fisheries Policy of the European Union and fisheries economics. *Marine Policy*, **30** (6) 737–746.

Fuller, R.J. & Ausden, M. (2008) Birds and habitat change in Britain Part I: a review of losses and gains in the twentieth century. *British Birds*, **101**, 644–675.

Fuller, R.J. & Gough, S.J. (1999) Changes in sheep numbers in Britain: implications for bird populations. *Biological Conservation*, **91**,73–89.

Green, R.E. (1996) Factors affecting the population density of the corncrake *Crex crex* in Britain and Ireland. *Journal of Applied Ecology*, **33**, 237–248.

GWCT (Game & Wildlife Conservation Trust) (2009) National GameBag Census. [online] Available at: <http://www.gwct.org.uk/research__surveys/wildlife_surveys/national_gamebag_census/trends_in_game_bags/default.asp> [Accessed 07.03.11].

Hadjimichael, M., Edwards-Jones, M. & Kaiser, M.J. (2010) Distribution of the burden of fisheries regulations in Europe: The north/south divide. *Marine Policy*, **34**,795–802.

Hale, S.E., Edwards, C., Mason, W.L., Price, M. & Peace, A. (2009) Relationships between canopy transmittance and stand parameters in Sitka spruce and Scots pine stands in Britain. *Forestry*, **82**, 503–513.

Halliday, R.G. & Pinhorn, A.T. (2009) The roles of fishing and environmental change in the decline of Northwest Atlantic groundfish populations in the early 1990s. *Fisheries Research*, **97**, 163–182.

Harris, S. & Swinbank, A. (1997). The CAP and the Food Industry. The Common Agricultural Policy (Eds. C Ritson & D R Harvey). CAB, Wallingford UK.

Harrison, M., Lee, A., Findlay, M., Nicholls, R., Leonard, D. & Martin, C. (2010) The increasing cost of healthy food. *Australian and New Zealand Journal of Public Health*, **34**, 179–186.

Haygarth, P.M., ApSimon, H., Betson, M., Harris, D., Hodgkinson, R. & Withers, P.J.A. (2009) Mitigating Diffuse Phosphorus Transfer from Agriculture According to Cost and Efficiency. *Journal of Environmental Quality*, **38**, 2012–2022.

Hector, A. & Bagchi, R. (2007) Biodiversity and ecosystem multifunctionality. *Nature*, **448**,188–U6.

Hinz, H. Prieto, V. & Kaiser, M.J. (2009) Trawl disturbance on benthic communities: chronic effects and experimental predictions. *Ecological Applications*, **19**, 761–773.

Hodge, I. & McNally, S. (1998) Evaluating the environmentally sensitive areas: the value of rural environments and policy relevance. *Journal of Rural Studies*, **14**, 357–367.

Hodgson, J.A., Kunin, W.E., Thomas, C.D., Benton, T.G. & Gabriel, D. (2010) Comparing organic farming and land sparing: optimizing yield and butterfly populations at a landscape scale. *Ecology Letters*, **13**, 1358–1367.

Hope, D., Picozzi, N., Catt, D.C. & Moss, R. (1996) Effects of reducing sheep grazing in the Scottish Highlands. *Journal of Range Management*, **49**, 301–310.

Howden, N.J.K., Bowes, M.J., Clark, A.D.J., Bowes, M.J., Clark, A.D.J., Humphries, N. & Neal, C. (2009) Water quality, nutrients and the European union's Water Framework Directive in a lowland agricultural region: Suffolk, south-east England. *Science of the total Environment*, **407**, 2966–2979.

Huang, Y. & Tang, Y.H. (2010) An estimate of greenhouse gas (N₂O and CO₂) mitigation potential under various scenarios of nitrogen use efficiency in Chinese croplands. *Global Change Biology*, **16**, 2958–2970.

Hutchings, J.A. (2000) Collapse and recovery of marine fishes. *Nature*, **406**, 882–885.

Jackson, P. (2010) Food stories: consumption in an age of anxiety. *Cultural Geographies*, **17**, 147–165.

JNCC (Joint Nature Conservation Committee) (2010) 8. Area of land under agri-environment scheme management. [online] Available at: <http://www.jncc.gov.uk/default.aspx?page=4243> [Accessed 07.03.11].

Jones, R. (2004) European beekeeping in the 21st century: strengths, weaknesses, opportunities, threats. *Bee World*, **85**:77–80.

Jordan, C. & Tomlinson, R.W. (2007) Soil carbon and peat extraction in Northern Ireland. Inventory and projections of UK emissions by sources and removals by sinks due to land use, land use change and forestry (Eds: A.M. Thomson & M. van Oijen). Annual Report, June 2007. Defra: Climate, Energy, Science and Analysis Division.

Kaiser, M.J., Clarke, K.R., Hinz, H., Austen, M.C.V., Somerfield, P.J. & Karakassis, I. (2006) Global analysis and prediction of the response of benthic biota and habitats to fishing. *Marine Ecology Progress Series*, **311**, 1–14.

Kay, D., Aitken, M. & Crowther, J. (2007) Reducing fluxes of faecal indicator compliance parameters to bathing waters from diffuse agricultural sources: The Brighouse Bay study, Scotland. *Environmental Pollution*, **147**, 138–149.

Knox, J.W., Kay, Rodriguez-Diaz, J.A., Weatherhead, E.K. & Kay, M.G. (2010) Development of a water strategy for horticulture in England and Wales. *Journal of Horticultural Science and Biotechnology*, **85**, 89–93.

Laplace, J.P. (2006) Farming and food. Crossed perspectives. *Cahiers Agricultures*, **15**, 375–378.

Laurec, A., & Armstrong, D. (1997) The European Common Fisheries Policy and its evolution. Global trends: fisheries management (Ed. Pikitch, E.K., Huppert, D.D., & Sissenwine, M.P.). American Fisheries Society Symposium, 20. Bethesda, Maryland. pp. 61–72.

Loreau, M., Naeem, S., Inchausti, P., Bengtsson, J., Grime, J.P., Hector, A., Hooper, D.U., Huston, M.A., Raffaelli, D., Schmid, B., Tilman, D. & Wardle, D.A. (2001) Ecology – Biodiversity and ecosystem functioning: Current knowledge and future challenges. *Science*, **294**, 804–808.

Lorenzen, K., Steneck, R.S., Warner, R.R., Parma, A.M., Coleman, F.C. & Leber, K.M. (2008) The spatial dimensions of fisheries: putting it all in place. *Bulletin of Marine Science*, **86**, 169–177.

Marine Scotland (2009a) Scottish Fish Farms Annual Production Survey 2008. Marine Scotland, Scottish Government.

Marine Scotland (2009b) Scottish Shellfish Production Survey 2008 Report. Marine Scotland, Scottish Government.

Marks, H.F. (1989) A hundred years of British Food and Farming. A statistical Survey. Taylor & Francis, London, 275 pp.

Maxted, N., Scholten M, Codd R & Ford-Lloyd B (2007) Creation and use of a national inventory of crop wild relatives. *Biological Conservation*, **140**, 142–159.

Mayor, D.J., Zuur, A.F., Solan, M., Paton, G.I. & Kilham, K. (2010) Factors Affecting Benthic Impacts at Scottish Fish Farms. *Environmental Science & Technology*, **44**, 2079–2084.

Mead, S.J.H. (2003) An analysis of trends in the UK beef industry and key dynamics of change for 2015. *Journal of the Royal Agricultural Society of England* 164.

Millstone, E. (2009) Science, risk and governance: Radical rhetorics and the realities of reform in food safety governance. *Research Policy, 38*, 624–636.

MMO (Marine Management Organisation) (2010a) UK Sea Fisheries Statistics 2009, Table 3.3 [online] Available at: <http://www.marinemanagement.org.uk/fisheries/statistics/annual2009.htm> [Accessed 28.01.11].

MMO (Marine Management Organisation) (2010b) UK Sea Fisheries Statistics Archive [online] Available at: <http://www.marinemanagement.org.uk/fisheries/statistics/annual_archive.htm> [Accessed 28.01.11].

National Non-Food Crops Centre (2009) Area Statistics for Non-food crops. [online] Available at: <http://www.nnfcc.co.uk/metadot/index.pl?id=2179;isa=Category;op=show> [Accessed 28.01.11].

Navarro, N., Leakey, R.J.G. & Black, K.D. (2008) Effect of salmon cage aquaculture on the pelagic environment of temperate coastal waters: seasonal changes in nutrients and microbial community. *Marine Ecology Progress Series, 361*, 47–58.

Newton, I. (2004) The recent declines of farmland bird populations in Britain: an appraisal of causal factors and conservation actions. *Ibis, 146*, 579–600.

NFU (National Farmers Union) (2002) Growing Great Britain: Horticulture Facts and Figures. NFU Public Affairs, August 2002.

Nicholson, R.J., Webb, J. & Moore, A. (2002) A review of the environmental effects of different livestock manure storage systems, and a suggested procedure for assigning environmental ratings. *Biosystems Engineering, 81*, 363–377.

Ojango, J.M.K. & Pollott, G.E. (2002) The relationship between Holstein bull breeding values for milk yield derived in both the UK and Kenya. *Livestock Production Science, 74*, 1–12.

Oom, S.P., Sibbald, A.M., Hester, A.J., Miller, D.R. & Legg, C.J. (2008) Impacts of sheep grazing a complex vegetation mosaic: Relating behaviour to vegetation change. *Agriculture, Ecosystems & Environment, 124*, 219–228.

PACEC (Public and Corporate Economic Consultants) (2006) The Economic and Environmental Impact of Sporting Shooting in the UK. Public and Corporate Economic Consultants. PACEC, London.

Parag, Y. & Roberts, J.T. (2009) A Battle Against the Bottles: Building, Claiming, and Regaining Tap-Water Trustworthiness. *Society & Natural Resources, 22*, 625–636.

Pauly, D., Christensen, V., Dalsgaard, J., Froese, R. & Torres, F. (1998) Fishing down marine food webs. *Science, 279*, 860–863.

Peel, D. & Lloyd, M.G. (2008) Governance and planning policy in the marine environment: regulating aquaculture in Scotland. *Geographical Journal, 174*, 361–373.

Phillipson, J., Bennett, K., Lowe, P. & Raley, M. (2004) Adaptive responses and asset strategies: the experience of rural micro-firms and Foot and Mouth Disease. *Journal of Rural Studies, 20*, 227–243.

Pimm, S.L., Russell, G.J., Gittleman, J.L. & Brooks, T.M. (1995) The future of biodiversity. *Science, 269*, 347–350.

Plassmann, K. & Edwards-Jones, G. (2009) Where does the carbon footprint fall? Developing a carbon map of food production. IIED London, pp34.

Potts, G.R. (1986) The Partridge: Pesticides, Predation and Conservation. Collins, London.

Potts, G.R., Ewald, J.A. & Aebischer, N.J. (2010a) Long-term changes in the flora of the cereal ecosystem on the Sussex Downs, England, focusing on the years 1968–2005. *Journal of Applied Ecology, 47*, 215–226.

Potts, S.G., Roberts, S.P.M., Dean, R., Marris, G., Brown, M.A., Jones, R., Neumann, P. & Settele, J. (2010b) Declines of managed honey bees and beekeepers in Europe. *Journal of Apicultural Research, 49*, 15–22.

RBST (Rare Breeds Survival Trust) (2010) Welcome to the Rare Breeds Survival Trust. [online] Available at: <www.rbst.co.uk> [Accessed 07.03.11].

Richardson, E.A., Possingham, H.P., Kaiser, M.J. & Edwards-Jones, G. (2006) Sensitivity of marine reserve design to the spatial resolution of socioeconomic data. *Conservation Biology, 20*, 1191–1202.

Saher, M., Lindeman, M. & Hursti, U.K.K. (2006) Attitudes towards genetically modified and organic foods. *Appetite, 46*, 324–331.

Sanchez-Martin, L., Arce, A., Benito, A., Garcia-Torres, L. & Vallejo, A. (2008) Influence of drip and furrow irrigation systems on nitrogen oxide emissions from a horticultural crop. *Soil Biology & Biochemistry, 40*, 1698–1706.

Scottish Government (2009) Key Scottish Environment Statistics. [online] Available at: <http://www.scotland.gov.uk/Publications/2009/08/26112651/52> [Accessed 2.11.10].

Scottish Government (2010) Key Scottish Environment Statistics. [online] Available at: <http://www.scotland.gov.uk/Publications/2010/09/08094058/0> [Accessed 07.03.11].

Showler, K. (1996) The development of national beekeeping associations in England. Study two: 1940–1990. *Bee World, 77*, 16–25.

Siry, J.P., Robison, D.J. & Cubbage, F.W. (2004) Economic returns model for silvicultural investments in young hardwood stands. *Southern Journal of Applied Forestry, 28*, 179–184.

Smith, B., Holland, J., Jones, N., Moreby, S., Morris, A.J. & Southway, S. (2009) Enhancing invertebrate food resources for skylarks in cereal ecosystems: how useful are in-crop agri-environment scheme management options? *Journal of Applied Ecology, 46*, 692–702.

Smith, P., Bhogal, A., Edgington, P., Black, H., Lilly, A., Barraclough, D., Worrall, F., Hillier, J. & Merrington, G. (2010) Consequences of feasible future agricultural land-use change on soil organic carbon stocks and greenhouse gas emissions in Great Britain. *Soil Use and Management, 26*, 381–398.

Smith, R.L. (2006) The Australian grocery industry: a competition perspective. *Australian Journal of Agricultural and Resource Economics, 50*, 33–50.

Smith, R.S., Charman, D., Rushton, S.P., Sanderson, R.A., Simkin, J.M. & Shiel, R.S. (2003) Vegetation change in an ombrotrophic mire in northern England after excluding sheep. *Applied Vegetation Science, 6*, 261–270.

Sotherton, N., Tapper, S. & Smith, A. (2009) Hen harriers and red grouse: economic aspects of red grouse shooting and the implications for moorland conservation. *Journal of Applied Ecology, 46*, 955–960.

Spedding, A. (2010) Horticultural Production in England. Briefing Note 1040. [online] Available at: <http://www.nationalrural.org/upload/rusource/1040.pdf> [Accessed 07.03.11].

Sutton, J.D., Aston, K., Beever, D.E. & Dhanoa, M.S. (1996) Milk production from grass silage diets: Effects of high-protein concentrates for lactating heifers and cows on intake, milk production and milk nitrogen fractions. *Animal Science, 62*, 207–215.

Swali, A. & Wathes, D.C. (2006) Influence of the dam and sire on size at birth and subsequent growth, milk production and fertility in dairy heifers. *Theriogenology, 66*, 1173–1184.

Tait, S., Tamis, J., Edgerton, B. & Batstone, D.J. (2009) Anaerobic digestion of spent bedding from deep litter piggery housing. *Bioresource Technology, 100*, 2210–2218.

Taylor, R.C., Jones, A.K. & Edwards-Jones, G. (2010) Measuring holistic carbon footprints for lamb and beef farms in the Cambrian Mountains Initiative. Report for Countryside Council of Wales. 57 pp.

Thirgood, S.J., Redpath, S.M., Haydon, D.T., Rothery, P., Newton, I. & Hudson, P.J. (2000) Habitat loss and raptor predation: disentangling long- and short-term causes of red grouse declines. *Proceedings of the Royal Society B, 267*, 651–656.

Thurkettle, V. (1997) The marketing of British hardwoods. *Forestry, 70*, 319–325.

Tijink, F.G.J. & van der Linden, J.P. (2000) Engineering approaches to prevent subsoil compaction in cropping systems with sugar beet (Eds. Horn, R., VandenAkker, J.J.H & Arvidsson, J.). Subsoil Compaction: Distribution, processes and consequences, 32442–452 International Workshop on Subsoil Compaction, March 1999, Kiel, Germany.

Tomkins, J. (1990) Recreation and the Forestry Commission – the case for multiple use resource-management within public forestry in the UK. *Journal of Environmental Management, 30*, 79–88.

Tranter, R.B., Holt, G.C. & Grey, P.T. (2007) Budgetary implications of, and motives for, converting to organic farming: Case study farm business evidence from Great Britain. *Biological Agriculture & Horticulture, 25*, 133–151.

Verbruggen, A. & Al Marchohi, M. (2010) Views on peak oil and its relation to climate change policy. *Energy Policy, 38*, 5572–5581.

Vickery, J.A., Tallowin, J.R., Feber, R.E., Asteraki, E.J., Atkinson, P.W., Fuller, R.J. & Brown, V.K. (2001) The management of lowland neutral grasslands in Britain: effects of agricultural practices on birds and their food resources. *Journal of Applied Ecology, 38*, 647–664.

Walker, K.J., Critchley, C.N.R., Sherwood, A.J., Large, R., Nuttall, P., Hulmes, S., Rose, R. & Mountford, J.O. (2007) The conservation of arable plants on cereal field margins: An assessment of new agri-environment scheme options in England, UK. *Biological Conservation 136*, 260–270.

Ward, N. (1999) Foxing the nation: the economic (in) significance of hunting with hounds in Britain. *Journal of Rural Studies, 15*, 389–403.

Weatherhead, E.K. & Knox, J.W. (2000) Predicting and mapping the future demand for irrigation water in England and Wales. *Agricultural Water Management, 43*, 203–218.

Welch, D. & Scott, D. (1995) Studies in the grazing of heather moorland in northeast Scotland. 6. 20-year trends in botanical composition. *Journal of Applied Ecology, 32*, 596–611.

White, P.F. (2000) The effect of covering compost with paper on yield of the cultivated mushroom Agaricus bisporus (Lange) Imbach. *Journal of Horticultural Science & Biotechnology, 75*, 667–671.

Woods, A. (2004) A Manufactured Plague: The History of Foot-and-mouth Disease in Britain. Earthscan.

Worthington, T.R. & Danks, P.W. (1992) Nitrate Leaching and intensive outdoor pig production. *Soil Use and Management, 8*, 56–60.

Yates, T. (2006) The use of non-food crops in the UK construction industry. *Journal of the Science of Food and Agriculture, 86*, 1790–1796.

Zenith International (2009) Water's vital statistics: industry data. [online] Available at: <http://www.britishbottledwater.org/vitalstats2.html> [Accessed: 16.10.10].

Appendix 15.1 Approach Used to Assign Certainty Terms to Chapter Key Findings

This chapter began with a set of Key Findings. Adopting the approach and terminology used by the Intergovernmental Panel on Climate Change (IPCC) and the Millennium Assessment (MA), these Key Findings also include an indication of the level of scientific certainty. The 'uncertainty approach' of the UK NEA consists of a set of qualitative uncertainty terms derived from a 4-box model and complemented, where possible, with a likelihood scale (see below). Estimates of certainty are derived from the collective judgement of authors, observational evidence, modelling results and/or theory examined for this assessment.

Throughout the Key Findings presented at the start of this chapter, superscript numbers and letters indicate the estimated level of certainty for a particular key finding:

1. *Well established:*   high agreement based on significant evidence
2. *Established but incomplete evidence:* high agreement based on limited evidence
3. *Competing explanations:*   low agreement, albeit with significant evidence
4. *Speculative:*   low agreement based on limited evidence

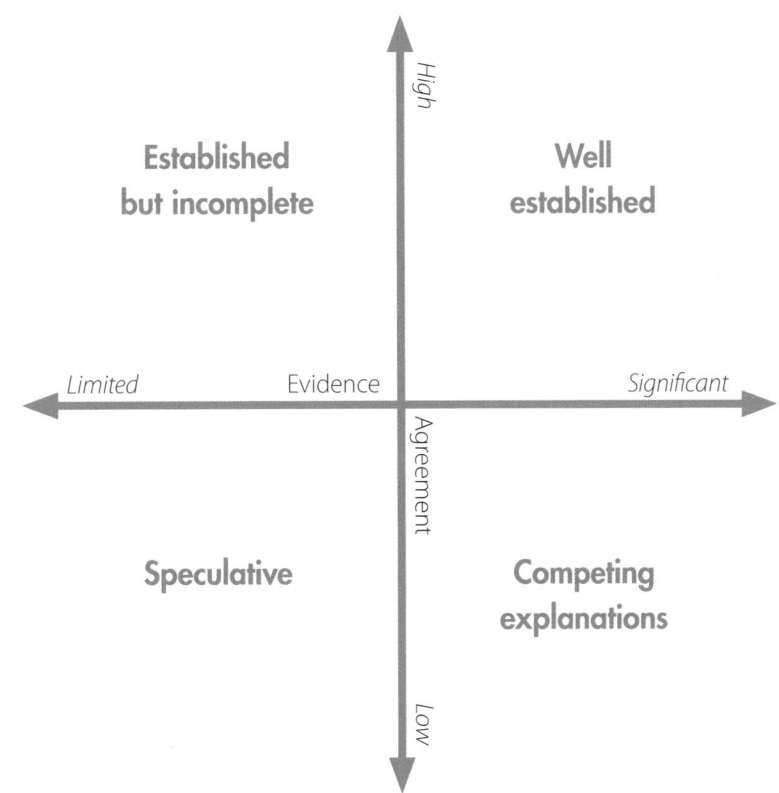

a. *Virtually certain:*   >99% probability of occurrence
b. *Very likely:*   >90% probability
c. *Likely:*   >66% probability
d. *About as likely as not:*   >33–66% probability
e. *Unlikely:*   <33% probability
f. *Very unlikely:*   <10% probability
g. *Exceptionally unlikely:*   <1% probability

Certainty terms 1 to 4 constitute the 4-box model, while *a* to *g* constitute the likelihood scale.

Chapter 16:
Cultural Services

Coordinating Lead Authors: Andrew Church, Jacquelin Burgess and Neil Ravenscroft
Contributing Authors: William Bird, Kirsty Blackstock, Emily Brady, Michael Crang, Robert Fish, Pyrs Gruffudd, Susana Mourato, Jules Pretty, Divya Tolia-Kelly, Kerry Turner and Michael Winter

Key Findings*

Ecosystem cultural services are the environmental settings that give rise to the cultural goods and benefits that people obtain from ecosystems. Over millennia these environmental settings have been co-produced by the constant interactions between humans and nature. They are inscribed with not only natural features but also the legacies of past and current societies, technologies, and cultures. The continual change in these settings involves a range of complex cultural practices, such as the development of institutions, the application of capital, and human processes involving memories, emotions, the senses, and aesthetic appreciation.

There are many environmental settings where people interact with nature including the domestic garden, informal green and blue spaces, formal green/blue spaces, the nearby and wider countryside and national landscapes. People's engagement with environmental settings is contingent, context specific, fluid and mutable[1,a]. Frameworks of interpretation and social practices associated with the production and uses of environmental settings are dynamic: meanings, values and behaviours change over time in response to economic, technological, social, political and cultural drivers. Change can be rapid and far-reaching in its implications. One particularly noticeable characteristic of UK cultural practice, however, is the depth and breadth of engagement with nature and wildlife[1,c].

[1] *well established*
[a] *virtually certain*
[c] *likely*

Ecosystem cultural services make a significant contribution to achieving people's key needs. In the 21st Century the cultural life of the UK is diverse and dynamic. Yet **encounters with the natural world maintain their fascination for very substantial numbers of people,** as reflected for example, in the membership of a very wide range of civil society organizations embracing landscape and nature interests, the numbers of people who use urban parks and green-spaces on a daily basis, and the massive popularity of gardening across the UK. **Daily contact with nature is part, still, of being human.** This is illustrated by the Human-Scale Development Matrix (H-SDM) developed by Manfred Max Neef, which indicates how both existence needs (being, having, doing, interacting) and value needs (subsistence, protection, affection, understanding, participation, creation, leisure, identity and freedom) can be met through nature[1,a]. Evidence suggests that contemporary consumption practices are not satisfying our human needs adequately. Happiness research in economics, and policy initiatives to measure levels of happiness among populations reflects statistical evidence that, although people are far better off in material terms than they have ever been, rates of depression, mental illness, obesity and family breakdown are also increasing[1,b].

[1] *well established*
[a] *virtually certain*
[b] *very likely*

The discipline of ecolinguistics appeared in the 1990s[2,c]. It brought together research from a number of academic disciplines interested in the ways in which scientific, professional, amateur and popular knowledge about the natural world was constructed; how different media shaped the environmental messages being communicated, and the politicisation of environmental issues associated with the rise of non-governmental organisations and pressure groups from the late 1960s. Whether humankind is regarded as a part of nature or as separate from it continues to be a fault line between different philosophical, moral, ethical

[2] *established but incomplete evidence*
[c] *likely*

---

* Each Key Finding has been assigned a level of scientific certainty, based on a 4-box model and complemented, where possible, with a likelihood scale. Superscript numbers indicate the uncertainty term assigned to each finding. Full details of each term and how they were assigned are presented in Appendix 16.1.

and communicative traditions. **One distinctive feature of language relating to the environment appears to be that reference to agency is avoided and there is a strong tendency not to identify who did what when discussing environmental change.** This is achieved in a number of ways, such as using the passive rather than active voice or omitting the grammatical subject and using the object instead, for example, the habitat was destroyed rather than the developer destroyed the habitat. Thus **there is frequently a choice of syntax that obscures agency and, thereby, responsibility for negative changes in environmental conditions.**

Since 1945 there have been some significant changes in people's interactions with environmental settings. The growth of urban settlements means that more people have a set of local environmental settings with urban characteristics. At the same time, however, increased mobility has allowed more people to travel longer distances nationally and internationally to environmental settings for tourism and recreation purposes[1,b]. In more local environmental settings data limits the interpretations of changes in domestic gardens. Marked changes did occur, however, in certain countryside settings of the UK during the second half of the last century especially those in and around large urban areas, although the characteristics of other environmental settings have remained more static. Declines in numbers and/or the quality of certain local/green blue spaces, such as playing fields, allotments and parks in deprived areas, have occurred over past decades but have been arrested in the last few years[2,c].

[1] *well established*
[2] *established but incomplete evidence*
[b] *very likely*
[c] *likely*

Since 1945 a large number of protection schemes instigated by UK and European Union government have been implemented to conserve certain socially and culturally significant environmental settings[1,a]. National Parks, National and Local Nature Reserves, Sites of Special Scientific Interest, Special Protection Areas (SPAs), Ramsar sites, Local Nature Reserves (LNRs) and land owned by bodies such as The National Trust all play a role in managing cultural services in specific landscapes and local places.

[1] *well established*
[a] *virtually certain*

A driver of people's changing relationships with environmental settings has been associated with a desire for self-determination, responsibility and security (of self and environment)[1,c]. This has led to **a small but increasing number of people making new productive connections to environmental settings.** This includes an increasing demand for allotment gardening, increasing membership of community farms, and whilst many people relocate to rural environments for amenity reasons, more people are doing so to run smallholdings or to engage in other forms of 'pro-environmental' lifestyle.

[1] *well established*
[c] *likely*

Environmental settings have been one of the most enduringly popular locations for recreation, leisure and tourism[2,c]. They offer generic opportunities to walk, run or cycle; specific opportunities only available in a few habitats, to ski, swim or sail, for example; and unique settings that offer opportunities to achieve specific benefits, related for example to seeing particular fauna and flora, or being able to climb particular crags. **Three quarters of the population in England consider local greenspace to be a very important part of the local environment, and 50% visit it at least once a week.** Access to environmental settings for recreation, leisure and tourism is highly differentiated, throughout the UK. A number of measures have been implemented to address this, including Natural England's

[2] *established but incomplete evidence*
[c] *likely*

Accessible Natural Greenspace Standard (ANGSt), which provides a set of benchmarks for ensuring access to places near to where people live. Recent legislative changes have contributed to improving access to some settings, with the Countryside and Rights of Way Act 2000 providing access to uplands, downs and commons and the Marine and Coastal Access Act 2009 promising to do the same for access to the coast. Economic studies have highlighted the benefits and monetary value that arise from being able to access environmental settings for recreation, leisure and tourism. Secondary analysis conducted for UK NEA of the English Leisure Visits Survey 2005 estimated that the total recreational value of the 4 billion visits to different habitats generated a value of between £2.2 and £3 billion per annum. A national park designation can raise house prices in proximate locations.

Environmental settings can contribute to a wide range of health goods often by providing places where people can undertake physical activity and interact with nature[2,b]. Levels of interaction/engagement of 'green space' have been linked with longevity and decreased risk of mental ill-health, and that vitamin D obtained from sunshine whilst being in environmental settings plays a role in long-term health. **The presence of urban nature has been associated with improved cognitive functioning, aesthetic inspiration and reduced levels of crime and aggression as well providing an outdoor classroom.** 'Green exercise', defined as any physical activity taking place in the presence of nature, is predicted to lead to positive health outcomes, as well as promoting ecological knowledge, fostering social bonds and influencing behavioural choices.

[2] *established but incomplete evidence*
[b] *very likely*

Open green space and access to nature is important for children[2,c]. The quality of their environmental exposure is inextricably linked to their wellbeing. Children's relationship with nature is a fundamental part of their development, allowing opportunities for self-discovery and natural environmental experience. The outdoor environment is perceived as a social space which influences their choice of informal play activities and promotes healthy personal development. Nature allows unstructured play, generating a sense of freedom, independence and inner strength which children can draw upon when experiencing future incidents of stress.

[2] *established but incomplete evidence*
[c] *likely*

Through their differing heritages, every environmental setting is capable of being interpreted as possessing a distinctive sense of place which can contribute to a range of human value needs[2,a]. The intricacies and contingent nature of the relationship between needs, environmental settings and the past creates analytical challenges but is fundamental to understanding heritage goods. **There is a very diverse range of heritage goods that are linked to ecosystem services, ranging in scale and ease of identification from perceived national landscapes through territorially demarcated National Trust land to the subtle and personal historical meanings people may attach to some urban commons.** Environmental settings also function as a generator of a vast range of local identities based around a more local and everyday sense of heritage. Heritage goods, therefore, can be a source of community empowerment as well as potential conflict between different interests and can contribute to a sense of identity, place, freedom and understanding.

[2] *established but incomplete evidence*
[a] *virtually certain*

The complex emotional and personalised characteristics of heritage goods mean that identifying their value to society is problematic[1,b]. Indeed, a recent survey identified that almost every feature in an environmental setting will connote personal memories and attachments

[1] *well established*
[b] *very likely*

for someone. Despite the highly personal and context-specific nature of heritage, it is widely felt that it should be preserved to be passed on to future generations, as a means of providing both children and adults with an understanding of their history and identity. In addition, **several million people across the UK actively support a wide range of civil society organizations dedicated to conserving and enhancing particular landscapes and places, wildlife and habitats through membership fees and, to a lesser extent, volunteering their time.**

Environmental settings are valuable surroundings for outdoor learning where engaging with nature can lead to enhanced connectedness to nature and increased ecological knowledge[2,c]. Ecological knowledge has been defined as 'accumulated knowledge about nature' and can be acquired through contact with different natural environments, directly or indirectly. **The economic value of ecological knowledge, generated formally in schools and less formally elsewhere, is considered to be substantial.** However, there are significant complexities associated with estimating this economic value, with a recent study undertaken as part of UK NEA using an investment in human capital approach to investigate the value of ecological learning experiences of children in the formal educational system. Benefits of this investment in ecological knowledge include a possible boost in lifetime earnings as well as possibly enhanced quality of life through more productive use of leisure opportunities. Whilst this approach may be appropriate for ecological knowledge acquired in school it is difficult to ascribe a gain in knowledge to a specific trip or location. The approach to the latter therefore involved examining travel costs and resource costs in order to estimate investment costs over and above those involved in gaining knowledge in a classroom situation.

[2] established but incomplete evidence
[c] likely

Environmental settings play a positive role in religious practice and faith but more general evidence on their spiritual and religious role is limited[4]. Religious and spiritual goods are clearly linked to our existence need for being, but the extent to which religious encounters with specific environmental settings are synergistic satisfiers for value needs such as participation and identity resides in the character and qualities of belief. The importance of ecosystems in religious terms had almost certainly increased in the post-war period in Britain, notwithstanding secularisation and the decline of conventional religious observance. There has, apparently, been an increase in the incidence of both pilgrimage and of religious retreats although it is extremely difficult to identify any quantitative measures of this trend. It is extremely hard to pin-point evidence of particular landscapes or ecosystems being conducive to religious experiences. The configuration of Marine and Coastal Habitats which appear to contribute to spiritual/religious experiences at the holy islands of Iona, Lindisfarne and Bardsley have to be seen in the context of other highly popular sites of pilgrimage that are inland and not characterised by dramatic landscape/ ecological characteristics, such as Walsingham in North Norfolk.

[4] speculative

New evidence gathered as part of the UK NEA indicates that **people clearly benefit from a range of environmental settings proximate to their homes and that the presence of certain settings can increase residential house prices[2,c].** A new hedonic price analysis shows that the house market in England reveals substantial amenity value attached to a number of habitats, designations, private gardens and local environmental amenities. In particular, protected areas (National Parks, National Trust land and metropolitan green

[2] established but incomplete evidence

belt), local environmental settings (domestic gardens, local green spaces, rivers) and several habitats (such as woodland, farmland and freshwater) are a statistically significant factor in explaining higher house prices. A new well-being survey analysis also reveals that **people who visit non-countryside green spaces such as urban parks at least once a month, and those who spend time in their own gardens at least once a week, have higher life satisfaction than those who do not.** Survey respondents who used domestic gardens and local green spaces at least once a month also showed better self-reported health, measured by physical functioning and emotional well-being, compared to those who do not.

[c] likely

There are knowledge gaps related to ecosystem cultural services, specifically in data collection and the uneven monitoring of change in different environmental settings[2,c]. An ecosystem services approach to understanding culture-nature interactions is a relatively new perspective and consequently many key sources of social, economic and environmental data are not designed to examine key aspects of cultural services and goods. Recent initiatives, such as the Countryside Quality Counts analysis and the new Master Map digital inventories, are leading to improvements, but a lot remains to be done, particularly to provide consistent data suitable for economic analyses. Further research is required, particularly longitudinal studies, to understand the social and physiological processes involved in people acquiring mental and physical health benefits from engagement with environmental settings and nature so that management of environmental settings for long term behaviour change can be more effective. Further studies are needed to examine people's exercise habits and understand what proportion of exercise is a direct consequence of the provision of green spaces. A key knowledge gap regarding education and ecological knowledge goods concerns the processes by which adults acquire ecological knowledge, their participation in nature-based educational activities and how knowledge acquisition is influenced by engagement with environmental settings as a form of cultural service. For religious and spiritual goods the knowledge gaps are particularly notable. There is a marked lack of evidence on the numbers of people for whom religious/spiritual experience and wellbeing is related to experiences of nature. We do not know how many people in Britain go on pilgrimage or make retreats or for whom contact with nature is an intrinsic part of their religious/spiritual lives. There is also limited evidence on detailed wildlife viewing figures for species other than birds, benefits of TV and radio programmes about nature, nature-based art markets (paintings, arts and crafts, photography), social cohesion and neighbourhood benefits associated with nature and non-use values of environmental settings at a national scale not already reflected in legacies.

[2] established but incomplete evidence
[c] likely

Addressing these knowledge gaps will require the regular and consistent collection of quantitative data at the national scale[1,b]. Many of the gaps, however, require an understanding of the complex ways individuals and groups of people engage with environmental settings, the cultural goods/ benefits that may arise and the inequalities associated with cultural goods/benefits. Recent guidance published by Defra emphasises that the **cultural goods linked to ecosystem services cannot just be understood in monetary terms but in future their shared and non-monetary value will need to be understood** using a range of participatory and deliberative techniques such as multi-criteria analysis that require the use of both quantitative and qualitative methods[3,c].

[1] well established
[3] competing explanations
[b] very likely
[c] likely

16.1 The Characteristics of Cultural Services

16.1.1 Ecosystem Assessment and Cultural Services

Humans are an inseparable component of the world's ecosystems and all ecosystem services are influenced by human actions. Understanding and respecting the world's natural environments, while harnessing nature's benefits, requires a rigorous approach to analysing how human cultures interact with nature (Pilgrim & Pretty 2010). The concepts of 'cultural services' and 'cultural goods' are designed to provide a framework for understanding human benefits from nature and the consequent social, economic and environmental changes that arise. This chapter seeks to advance the understanding of ecosystem services by developing an analytical framework for assessing cultural services and goods.

The Millennium Ecosystem Assessment (MA) described cultural services as "the non-material benefits people obtain from ecosystems through spiritual enrichment, cognitive development, reflection, recreation and aesthetic experiences" (MA 2005a p.29); it acknowledged the challenge of producing a coherent assessment of such services at a global scale because cultural benefits are clearly country and/or context specific. In order to address this difficulty, the cultural services assessment was largely based on differences between universalised, formal knowledge produced through the theory and practice of science, and informal knowledge (often called 'traditional knowledge') associated with people's everyday experiences, customs, practices and beliefs in particular places. The MA's assessment emphasised the influences of globalisation—especially economic development and consumption pressures—on traditional communities and its impact on specific cultural services. At the same time, the MA's approach to cultural services struggled to find a consistent theoretical and methodological framework to match that underpinning other areas of the assessment. There was little quantitative data beyond measures of volumes of global tourism, leading the MA to conclude that whilst difficult to measure the loss of cultural services are significant for many people (MA 2005a).

Every national assessment of the cultural component of ecosystem services faces similar problems with data, partly because the 'subjective' elements of human-nature relationships—supposedly captured in the concept of 'non-material benefits'—have not, to date, been of central concern either to the natural sciences or to economics. Fisher *et al.* (2008) argue that "couching ecosystem service research within economic theory gives us one way to move to a more structured engagement between biophysical science, social science research, and policy". One important challenge is how to develop a conceptual and/or methodological approach which allows the humanities and more interpretive social science disciplines to make their distinctive contributions to the assessment in such a way as to strengthen the integration of scientific, economic, cultural and socio-political evidence for policy.

A key aim of this chapter is to introduce an approach to cultural services that draws on novel thinking in the humanities, and social and natural sciences regarding human-nature relationships. The chapter seeks to assess the status, trends, drivers and knowledge gaps relating to cultural services and goods. The remainder of Section 16.1 outlines the rationale and characteristics of the conceptual approach to ecosystem services. A discussion of human values, the nature of culture, and an analysis of the distinctive forms of language used for 'environmental talk' across the UK is followed by a discussion of the cultural services conceptual approach adopted in the UK NEA. Recognising the importance of finding a value-based framework which supports some level of integration with economic and ecological valuation, we have worked with the Human-Scale Development Matrix (H-SDM) devised by Max-Neef (1989; 1992). Using the framework as a structuring device (which will need substantial field-testing in future work), the chapter examines how components of the UK's habitats and ecosystems acquire cultural meaning and significance because they are able to satisfy human needs for a 'good life'. We argue for a final cultural ecosystem service as being a 'series of environmental settings' which provide locations and places where people interact with each other and with nature.

Section 16.2 assesses the status and trends of these different environmental settings. Section 16.3 discusses a number of cultural goods that emerge from human-nature interactions in environmental settings. Further discussion of the selected cultural goods can be found in Chapters 5–12 and 17–20. Cultural goods arising from people's engagement with all four ecosystem services help to shape the social and economic value of changes in ecosystem services and habitats. In this chapter, we include an assessment of the social and economic value of cultural goods in order to highlight their contribution to human well-being.

16.1.1.1 Cultural services and values

Over the last 30 years, environmental and ecological economists have worked alongside natural and social scientists to develop more robust, defensible estimates of the monetary value of certain aspects of the natural environment that are now termed 'ecosystem services' and the contributions they make to improving human welfare. However, in making a distinction between anthropocentric, instrumental and intrinsic values (Chapter 2), environmental philosophers argue that societies maintain a range of beliefs about the 'ethical' basis of people's relationships with nature—what constitutes right and proper conduct towards the non-human world—and also make 'aesthetic judgements' about what is beautiful or significant in terms of landscapes, species and natural processes (O'Neill 1993; Sagoff 2004).

Ethical concerns and aesthetic judgements are always context-specific: they are outcomes of local circumstances, of specific times and particular places. Values for nature change over time; they are expressed in different ways by different groups of people in different societies; and they give rise to different kinds of formal and informal institutions. Academic research in the fields of ethical concerns and aesthetic judgements for nature, place and landscape tends to rely on a wide range of methods. Often the goal is 'hermeneutic', i.e. the production of sophisticated descriptive interpretations based on reasoned argument and the weighing of many different sources of quantitative and qualitative evidence (Chapter 2).

Some argue that these three dimensions of human-environment relations—utility, ethics, and aesthetics—are basic principles guiding human behaviour and, as such, are incommensurable: ethical and aesthetic principles cannot be meaningfully expressed in financial terms (Vatn & Bromley 1994; O'Neill 1997; Holland 2002; Vatn 2009; Chapter 2). At the same time, environmental decision-makers do have to make choices which require trade-offs to be made between them (Fisher & Turner 2008). What is important in such cases is that the decision-making process is seen to be reliable, credible and legitimate. Current reviews of academic and policy literatures suggest decision-makers would benefit from deliberative tools, such as participatory multi-criteria analysis, to help them integrate the different kinds of quantitative and qualitative information needed to strengthen the ecosystem approach in policy appraisal processes (Fish *et al.* 2011; Dryzek 2002; Wilson & Howarth 2002; Gregory *et al.* 2005; Renn 2006). These issues are discussed in more detail in Chapter 24. In the rest of this section, we introduce some of the key terms that are important in discussions about cultural ecosystem services in the UK.

16.1.2 Culture, Nature, Ecosystems

In his seminal book, *Keywords: a vocabulary of culture and society*, Raymond Williams traced the ways in which the meanings of 'keywords' in the English language had altered as historical contexts changed (Williams 1976). He asserted that "culture' is one of the two or three most complicated words in the English language". He identified three stages in the transformation of the meaning of this word into its modern usage. Coming from the Latin *cultura*, 'culture' was the noun first associated with the tending of plants and animals (*agri-culture, horti-culture, silvi-culture,* etc. (Pretty 2002)). From the 16th Century, the notion of propagation came to be linked with the idea of education producing 'cultured' individuals with sensibilities able to appreciate the products of human knowledge and creativity which, very often, embraced the natural world. The third set of meanings, emerging in the 19th century, uses 'culture' to classify the distinctive practices and ways of life of different human groups. This latter sense structures the discussion of cultural services in the MA with its distinction between, for example, cultural landscapes in different parts of the world. In the MA scenarios assessment, therefore, culture is primarily portrayed as conditioning individuals, influencing what they consider important and stimulating courses of action by individuals that are appropriate and inappropriate in terms of their impacts on ecosystems (MA 2005b).

In the UK, the study of culture has a rich, multidisciplinary intellectual tradition, embracing the biological sciences, social sciences (such as anthropology, geography, sociology, cultural and media studies), and humanities (including history, literature, philosophy and the fine arts). For the majority of these disciplines, culture is not understood as a causal determinant of individual perception and behaviour amenable to experimental research such as that associated with the analysis of landscape preferences. Rather, research is based on an understanding of culture as an interpretive, qualitative endeavour focused on the communicative production of 'shared meanings' within and between different social groups, and the 'particularities of their everyday practices' including individual behaviours and social institutions in different places. Within this framing, cultures are emergent processes, products and practices, while individuals are 'social individuals' living their lives embedded in many different kinds of social groups (Lorimer & Lund 2003; Milbourne 2003; Shove & Pantzar 2005).

Exploring the cultural dimensions of human-environment relations requires attention to be paid to the two key issues of communications and social practices. How people, as members of different social groups, communicate their feelings, experiences and shared knowledge about the natural world is a vital source of evidence for understanding the cultural significance of nature. Understanding how the natural world is significant in what people do (social practices) provides evidence of cultural shifts in environmental meanings and values, and produces tangible changes in the environment. In summary:

> "It is participants in a culture who give meaning to people, objects and events. Things 'in themselves' rarely if ever have any one, single, fixed and unchanging meaning. Even something as obvious as a stone can be a stone, a boundary marker or a piece of sculpture depending on *what it means*—that is, within a certain context of use, within what the philosophers call different 'language games' (i.e. the language of boundaries, the language of sculpture, and so on). It is by our use of things, and what we say, think and feel about them—how we represent them—that we *give them a meaning*. In part, we give objects, people and events a meaning by the frameworks of interpretation which we bring to them. In part, we give things meaning by how we use them, or integrate them into our everyday practices." (Hall 1997 p.9).

16.1.2.1 Ecosystem services and human-nature relationships in the UK

The evidence presented in this section indicates that, in the UK, that the term 'ecosystem services' is not a meaningful framework for the interpretation of human-environment relationships for the vast majority of people; yet it has gained recent traction in policy (Hall 1997). Culturally, the concepts which have most meaning are those of 'nature', 'place' and 'landscape'. These are the products of cultural communications and practices which, despite the homogenising forces associated with multinational forms of consumer capitalism and communications media, still vary across different regions of the UK. The landscapes of the UK are characterised by a diversity of scenery and habitat, created and maintained through the activities of countless generations of people and institutions (The Countryside Agency 2005). Equally, literary and artistic endeavours, ranging from the glowing miniatures depicting medieval practices in the margins of the Holkham Bible (Brown 2007) to Ian McEwan's (2010) novel *Solar* exploring human frailties in the face of climate change, create a reservoir of ideas and images which represent human relations with the living world (Williams 1980; Cosgrove & Daniels 1988). Representations communicate the meanings, values and practices of their historical period, offering potential both for stability and comfort in maintaining some interpretive frameworks, and for re-interpretation as times, places and the natural world change over generations. One particularly noticeable characteristic of UK cultural practice is the depth and breadth of engagement with nature and wildlife dating back to a tradition of amateur naturalists in late 18th and 19th Centuries—many of whom were clergymen, such as Gilbert White (1977)—and which continues to flourish (Rackham 1986; Mabey 1996; Macfarlane 2007; Pretty 2007; Marren & Mabey 2010; Pretty 2011).

Research evidence to support these assertions comes from two recent studies. The first study involved qualitative research carried out for the Department for Environment, Food and Rural Affairs and the Central Office for Information (Defra 2007a) and used a stratified socio-demographic sampling strategy to recruit people for eight focus groups which were led through discussions about the ecosystems approach. The second study, commissioned especially for the UK NEA, is entitled *Corpus linguistics analysis of ecosystems vocabulary in the public sphere* (CLAEVIPS, Wild & McCarthy 2010). It is discussed in more detail in the next section below and provides a quantitative linguistic analysis of the use in public discourse of words and phrases related to 'ecosystems'.

The first study used qualitative methods and found that 'ecosystem services' "was a completely unfamiliar term, and proved to be baffling for most due to the lack of awareness of the term *ecosystem*" (Defra 2007a, p.40). 'Nature', on the other hand, meant a lot. The focus group participants in this study had diverse social backgrounds but shared a common language and understanding of the word 'nature'

as summarised in **Figure 16.1**. The report concludes that everyone in the study talked about nature as 'other' to themselves and not 'man-made'. For example, the focus group participants described a range of habitats (including the sea) as characterised by the presence of many different species of plants, animals, birds, insects and fish.

Such cultural ideas of nature as 'other' are also associated with an aesthetic notion of the 'sublime' (awe and wonder) and an ethical belief in 'purity' (fresh air, clean air and water), derived from the considerations of nature by the Romantic movement of the early 19th Century. This sensibility grew as the need to believe that 'pure nature', untainted by industrialisation and the appalling conditions of life for the poor in Victorian cities, could still be found in the wild parts of the UK; it soon became an established ideological position (Williams 1980).

Nature is a word with a history as old as human thought itself (Williams 1976). 'Environment', on the other hand, is one of a family of new 'eco-words' which began to appear in the late 19th and 20th Centuries to express a scientific agenda. As Worster (1994), in his study of the interweaving of ecological and economic thought over the last two centuries, argues:

"Every generation ... writes its own description of the natural order, which generally reveals as much about human society and its changing concerns as it does about nature. And these descriptions linger on in bits and pieces, often creating incongruous or incompatible juxtapositions. ... The 'New Ecology' that had emerged by the middle of the twentieth century saw nature through a different set of spectacles: the forms, processes and values of the modern economic order as shaped by technology." (Worster 1994).

The phrase 'natural environment', together with 'natural resources', has also been used for many decades to explain relationships between human activities and the natural world. In the (Defra 2007a) study, the focus group

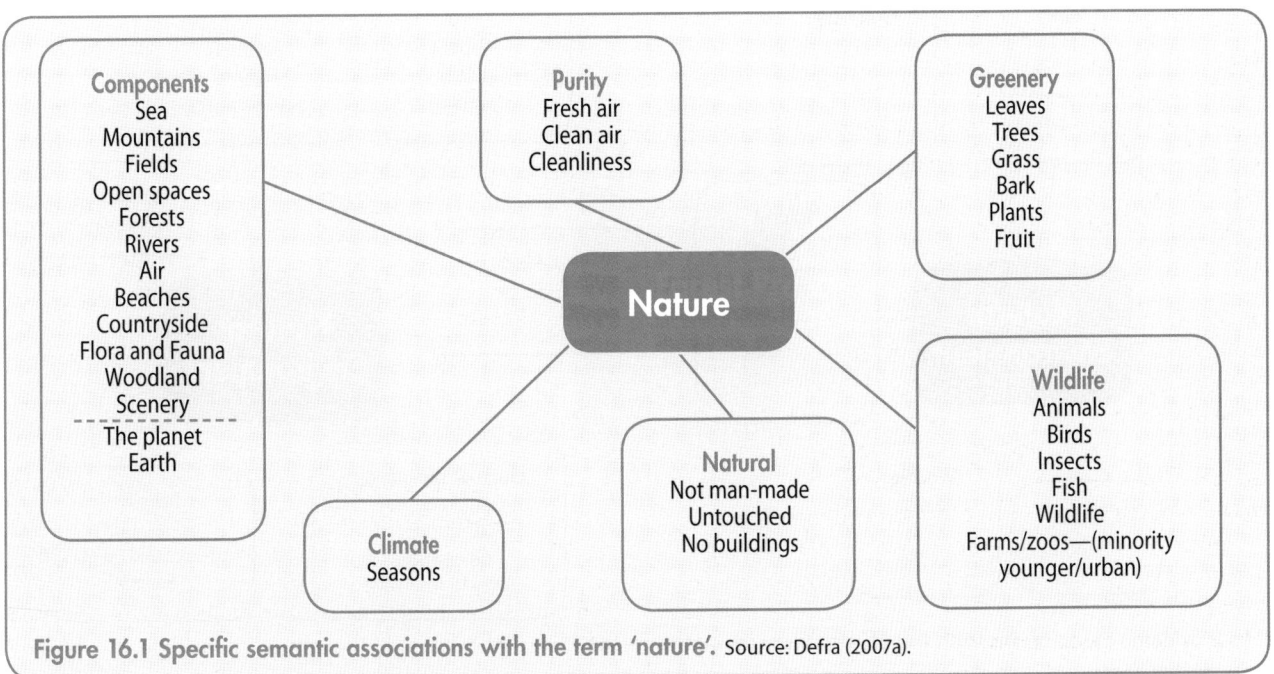

Figure 16.1 Specific semantic associations with the term 'nature'. Source: Defra (2007a).

participants iterated ideas of 'naturalness' but also showed understanding of human impacts on the natural environment (**Figure 16.2a, b**). **Figure 16.2b** shows a more use-orientated understanding through associations of the words 'natural environment' with farming and gardening, leisure experiences in parks and the countryside, awareness of some of the negative impacts of economic activity on the natural environment (such as climate change), and the need for nature conservation. These semantic diagrams provide interesting visual representations of the 'bits and pieces' which constitute common sense knowledge of 'nature' and 'natural environment' in contemporary UK culture as people draw on material learned at school. The teenagers in the focus groups, for example, remembered the 'ecosystem' concept from science lessons, mass media, and the many other forms of lay (as opposed to specialist) knowledge (Defra 2007a).

16.1.2.2 Ecosystems and ecolinguistics

Ecolinguistics emerged as a new discipline in the 1990s, bringing together research from a number of different academic disciplines which focused on the ways in which scientific, professional, amateur and popular knowledge about the natural world was constructed. It considers how different media shapes the environmental messages being communicated and how environmental issues have become politicised with the rise of non-governmental organisations (NGOs) and pressure groups from the late 1960s onwards (Fill 2001). One strand of research uses content analysis: a quantitative technique used in social psychology and mass communication research which measures the frequency of words and phrases in written and spoken texts. The massive expansion of computing power and accessibility to digitised resources is enabling a new generation of content-analytic

research and such a study commissioned for the UK NEA is described in **Box 16.1** below.

The CLAEVIPS project is a rich resource for further analysis. Relevant to this discussion, the study provides quantitative support for many of the observations based on qualitative analysis in the Defra 2007a report discussed above. The key findings in the CLAEVIPS study include:

- Ambiguity in terms of whether human beings are a part of nature or separate from it is apparent in the quantitative data.
- 'Nature' is often used to modify another noun when the sense meant is that of 'the physical world and living things'. The study shows that 'nature' appears twice as frequently in the government corpus than in the other two specialised collections of written material. In all

---

Box 16.1 CLAEVIPS—Corpus linguistics analysis of ecosystems vocabulary in the public sphere.

The UK NEA commissioned a quantitative study of how more than 100 words and phrases related to 'ecosystems' are currently being used in public discourse (Wild & McCarthy 2010). The study was carried out using UK Web as Corpus (UKWaC, Ferraresi *et al.* 2008), which is a body of over 1.5 billion words of UK English in the public domain. In addition, the researchers used 100 seed words as the basis of a computerised process that drew material from the world-wide-web to create three new collections of written material (known in linguistics as a 'language corpus') relating to ecosystems. Material was collected from: a) academic websites; b) government websites; and c) newspapers, non-governmental organisation (NGO) websites and blogs. Software known as Sketch Engine (Kilgarriff *et al.* 2004) provides an interface that gives measures of how frequently words are used and the way they co-occur with other words in particular grammatical relationships. Comparisons can be made between the three specialised collections of written material; but caution should be taken, since it is possible that a seed word was used in the automatic creation of one collection, but not in another.

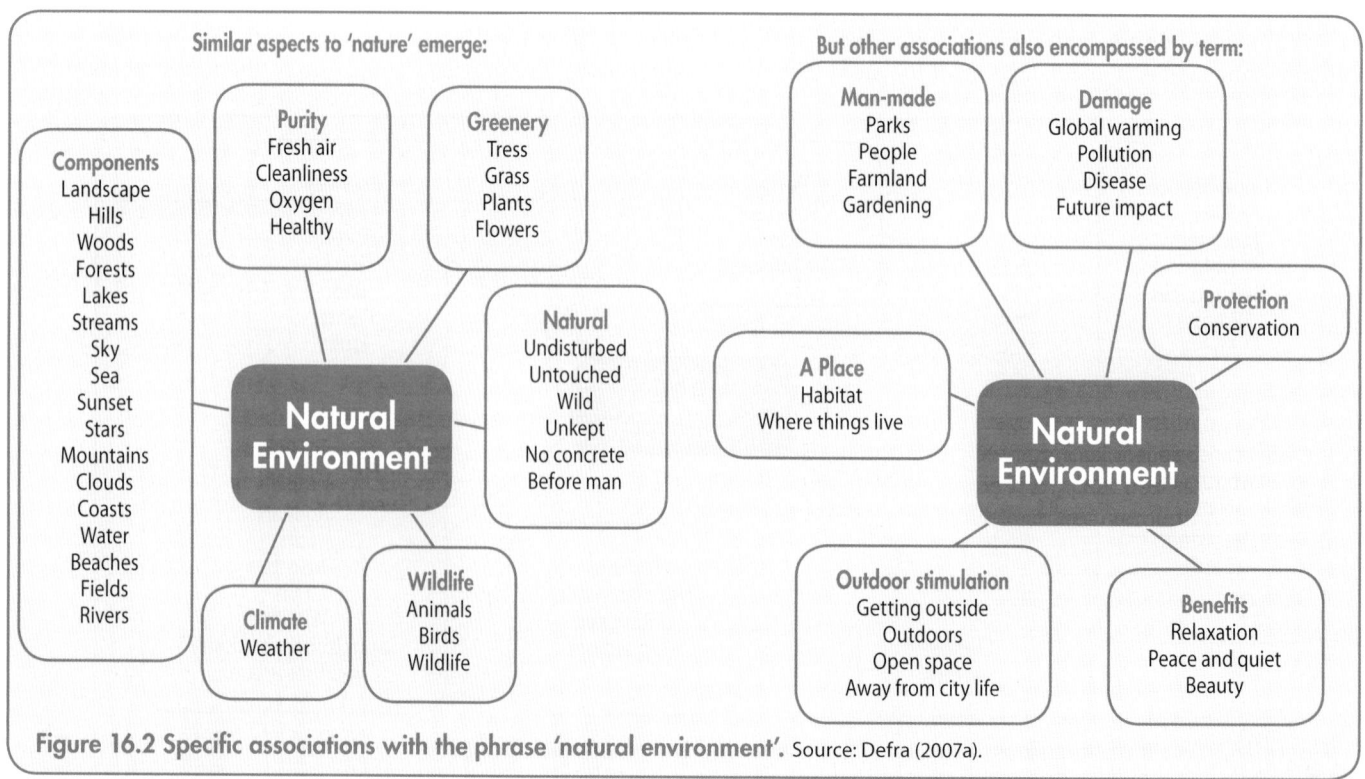

Figure 16.2 Specific associations with the phrase 'natural environment'. Source: Defra (2007a).

three corpus', key phrases are 'nature conservation', and 'nature reserve' while in the government corpus, 'nature interest' and 'nature value' are also salient.

- A number of positive verbs and adjectives co-occur with nature and landscape including 'experience', 'enjoy', 'solitude', 'peaceful' and 'beautiful'. Therefore, it is not surprising that there is a great deal of evidence in the UKWaC—as in the specialist public corpus—that the natural world continues to be used as a promotional device in advertising a very wide range of goods and services (Williamson 2000), which is an indication of its cultural value.

- 'Ecosystem' appears more than twice as frequently in the academic corpus as it does in the government and public ones, with government much more likely to use the phrase 'ecosystem goods and services'. The study finds key adjectives and nouns associated with 'ecosystem' are those indicating habitat type (such as 'marine', 'aquatic' and 'forest'). Adjectives which indicate vulnerability (such as 'fragile', 'threatened', 'endangered' and 'delicate') are most commonly used in conjunction with 'ecosystem'. Most frequently used verbs are those indicating harm done to ecosystems (such as 'degrade', 'disrupt', 'damage', 'harm', 'threaten', 'upset' and 'suffer'), as well as verbs referring to the protection and restoration of ecosystems ('conserve', 'preserve' and 'protect').

- The word which is used most similarly to ecosystem in the UKWaC is 'habitat'. While habitats and ecosystems are equally likely to be described as degraded, ecosystems are more likely to be described as delicate and habitats are more regularly described as 'valuable' and 'rare'; this reflects the characteristic framing of nature by conservationists since the Second World War (WWII) (Wild & McCarthy 2010; Evans 1997).

One distinctive grammatical feature of environmental discourse in these three collections of words is a process known as 'nominalisation', combined with the passive rather than active form of the verb. This results in a strong tendency not to identify *who* did *what* when discussing environmental change. This is achieved in a number of ways, such as using the passive rather than active voice, or omitting the grammatical subject and using the object instead; for example, 'the habitat was destroyed' rather than 'the developer destroyed the habitat'. This choice of syntax obscures agency, thereby concealing responsibility for negative changes in environmental conditions (Burgess *et al.* 2000; Goatly 2001; Kuha 2007; Wild & McCarthy 2010). Relevant to this discussion, in the CLAEVIPs analysis, the most salient verb collocate of ecosystem is 'degrade', but over 90% of occurrences use the passive form such as 'ecosystems are degraded' or 'degraded ecosystems'. One implication of this pattern of language use is that audiences are not being given full information about who (or what) is causing these disturbing environmental changes. In such circumstances, individuals may ignore the message altogether because it is uninteresting, or they may use pre-existing interpretive frameworks to create a meaning for themselves which may or may not be an accurate representation of the specific circumstances being

discussed (Burgess *et al.* 1988; Burgess *et al.* 2000; Myerson & Rydin 1996; Holliman 2004; Philo 2008).

16.1.3. An Approach for Understanding Cultural Ecosystem Services in the UK

The global scale of the MA (2005a, 2005c) required considerable experimentation with conceptual approaches, especially given the paucity of quantitative and/or experimental data. Subsequent commentaries suggest that, particularly in sub-global assessments, cultural services are seen by stakeholders as highly important, but that there is uncertainty over how they should be addressed (Raudsepp-Hearne & Capistroana 2010). In the following sections, we attempt to develop an interpretive framework for examining cultural services that reflects our understanding of culture as a dynamic and transformative process involving the enormous range of social communications and social practices that enfold nature, places and landscapes into everyday life.

How might this interpretive approach contribute to a science- and economics-based assessment of ecosystem services? From science comes the definition of an ecosystem as "a complex where interactions among the biotic (living) and abiotic (non-living) components of that unit determine its properties and set limits to the types of processes that take place there." (Chapter 2). As humans are simply one biological species among a multitude (albeit with particularly interesting technological and linguistic capabilities), places are fundamental to human life, too. From environmental and ecological economics comes an understanding of the many contributions or 'goods' ('good things') that ecosystems make to human welfare (Chapter 2). Agreed definitions of what constitutes 'good things' or, more generally, the 'good life' are a reflection of how ideas about individual and collective well-being are expressed, and these change over time. In other words, different cultural groups at different times and in different places share an interpretive framework of 'the good life'.

Philosophical discussion on the meaning of the good life may be traced back to Aristotle in Western thought (Coleman 2000). There is a body of work, ranging from psychology to philosophy, which suggests that underpinning cultural diversity is a relatively small number of fundamental human needs that require satisfaction if well-being is to be achieved (McGillivary 2006). What change through time are the specific means through which these needs are satisfied. In many areas of social science, there is also debate as to the nature of human needs and well-being, how these might be measured, and how they are affected by the natural environment and sustainable development (Alkire 2002; McGillivary 2006; Newton 2007). Chapter 2 outlines the general approach and definitions used in the UK NEA to address well-being and emphasises the importance of understanding how ecosystem services, and the goods that arise from them, contribute to economic, health and shared values. We extend these ideas by suggesting an approach for cultural services that explores in more depth the interactions between ecosystem services, goods and the satisfaction of human needs that contributes to well-being.

16.1.3.1 The Human-Scale Development Matrix (H-SDM) and its relevance for the UK NEA

The Human-Scale Development Matrix (H-SDM), conceived by the Chilean development economist Manfred Max-Neef (1989; 1992), is attracting attention from academics and policy makers working on global development issues (Alkire 2002; Gasper 2004), producing new indices to measure sustainable economic welfare (Bleys 2007) and quality-of-life (Costanza *et al.* 2007; Dodds 1997), and promoting more sustainable consumption and production practices (Jackson & Marks 1999; Jackson 2009). We believe the H-SDM also has potential to provide a conceptual approach for examining systematically the extent to which cultural ecosystem services and different kinds of cultural 'goods' (e.g. material objects, abstract ideas, emotional experiences, social practices, living things, etc.) are valued because they are able to satisfy a substantial number of fundamental human needs. No empirical research to test this proposition has yet been undertaken, but it would be possible, following Cruz *et al.* (2009) for example, to adapt the H-SDM for a deliberative process that could engage citizens, stakeholders and specialists in a participatory ecosystem assessment.

The basic argument for the H-SDM rests on the proposition that, beyond the need for subsistence to stay alive, there is no rigid hierarchy of human needs as was suggested by Maslow (1954). Rather, Max-Neef argues for a relatively small number of fundamental human needs which are equally important in contributing to a 'good life', but not all of which may be satisfied at any given time. Furthermore, individuals and groups make trade-offs between the satisfaction of different needs, often using different satisfiers to do so. Economic, social and cultural values arise from the extent to which different satisfiers are able to meet individual and societal needs.

The H-SDM is shown in **Table 16.1**; the matrix consists of four columns ('being', 'doing', 'having' and 'interacting') and nine rows, each expressing a different human need. The four columns represent four human qualities or contexts within which specific needs should, or could be, satisfied. Max-Neef calls these qualities 'existential' in the sense that each is absolutely necessary to the ways in which we human beings, as social animals, structure our existence (**Table 16.1** refers to these four as existence needs).

- **Being** addresses personal and/or collective attributes such as physical and mental health, adaptability, self-esteem, receptiveness, curiosity and rationality.
- **Having** refers to the institutions, norms and resources necessary for society to function effectively, with attributes such as health systems, education, work, family relations, language, religion and historical memory.
- **Doing** captures personal and/or collective action such as cooperating, cultivating, investigating, relaxing and developing awareness.
- **Interacting** recognises what is all too easily forgotten because it is self-evident. Human life is 'environed', lived within natural and technologically mediated settings which change over the lifespan and at different spatial and timescales. What characterises modern, Western societies, such as the UK, is the extent to which science and technology have mediated society-nature interactions at the level of living spaces and/or habitats. One outcome is a growing experiential disconnect between people and the natural environment, recognised as a challenge, for example, in discussions about future social resilience and adaptation to climate change.

The rows across the matrix represent human needs which require satisfaction in order to achieve 'a good life'. Max-Neef describes these as 'axiological values' in the sense that there is general acceptance of the proposition that each need is fundamental to our sense of our humanity. These are referred to in Table 16.1 as the value needs for: *'subsistence', 'protection', 'affection', 'understanding', 'participation', 'creativity', 'leisure', 'identity' and 'freedom'.* Subsistence is the category of need which must be satisfied for human survival, but all other value-based needs can, in some sense, be traded-off one against another, or in one existence mode against another. Cultural differences between countries in different parts of the world arise, in part, through the different kinds of trade-offs that might be possible or thought desirable. There is some discussion in the literature about the labels Max-Neef uses to describe these needs, for example: some replace 'idleness' with leisure because of the specific negative connotations 'idleness' has in many Protestant countries; protection may be termed 'security' in some studies; and other studies have added a separate category to cover 'reproduction' (Costanza *et al.* 2007). The nine axiological categories are comparable with other studies of well-being and assessments of happiness, although the terminology may vary slightly (Diener & Seligman 2004; Blanchflower & Oswald 2008; Thompson *et al.* 2008; Bacon *et al.* 2010). **Table 16.2** shows how, in the abstract, the 36-cell matrix can be populated, suggesting, for example, how it might be possible to integrate scientific, economic and interpretive information in a systematic framework.

Table 16.1 the Human-Scale Development Matrix.
Source: Max-Neef (1992).

Value needs	Existence needs			
	Being	**Having**	**Doing**	**Interacting**
SUBSISTENCE				
PROTECTION				
AFFECTION				
UNDERSTANDING				
PARTICIPATION				
LEISURE *				
CREATIVITY				
IDENTITY				
FREEDOM				

*Max-Neef's term translates as 'idleness'

Table 16.2 The Human-Scale Development Matrix. Source: adapted from Max-Neef (1992).

Needs according to existential (existence) characteristics	Needs according to axiological (value) characteristics			
	Being (personal or collective **attributes**)	*Having* (registers **institutions**, norms, rules and resources)	*Doing* (registers personal & collective **actions**)	*Interacting* (registers **times and spaces**)
SUBSISTENCE	1/ Physical health, mental health, sense of humour, adaptability	2/ Food, shelter, work	3/ Feed, procreate, rest, work, take exercise	4/ Living environments, social settings
PROTECTION	5/ Care, adaptability, autonomy, solidarity	6/ Insurance systems, savings, social security, health systems, work rights, family	7/ Co-operate, prevent, plan, take care of, cure, help	8/ Living space, dwelling, social environment
AFFECTION	9/ Self-esteem, respect, tolerance, passion, determination.	10/ Friendships, family, partnerships, relations with nature	11/ Caress, express emotions, take care of, cultivate, appreciate	12/ Private spaces, intimacy, home, spaces of togetherness
UNDERSTANDING	13/ Critical conscience, receptiveness, curiosity, discipline, intuition, rationality	14/ Literature, teachers, method, education policies, communication policies	15/ Investigate, study, experiment, educate, analyse, meditate	16/ Settings of formative interaction, schools, universities, groups, gardens, natural habitats
PARTICIPATION	17/ Adaptation, receptiveness, solidarity, willingness, determination, respect, etc	18/ Rights, responsibilities, duties, privileges, work	19/ Affiliate, co-operate, propose, share, dissent, obey, interact, express opinions	20/ Parties, churches, communities, neighbourhoods, parks, greenspaces, natural habitats
LEISURE	21/ Curiosity, receptiveness, imagination, recklessness, tranquillity	22/ Games, spectacles, clubs, holidays	23/ Daydream, remember, relax, connect, have fun, play	24/ Privacy, time, intimate spaces, surroundings, landscapes
CREATIVITY	25/ Passion, determination, imagination, boldness, rationality, inventiveness, curiosity	26/ Abilities, skills, method, work	27/ Work, invent, build, design, compose, interpret	28/ Productive and feedback settings, cultural groups, * spaces for expression, temporal freedom.
IDENTITY	29/ Self-esteem, sense of belonging, consistency, differentiation, assertiveness	30/ Symbols, language, religion, habits, customs, reference groups, values, norms, historical memory, work	31/ Commit oneself, integrate, confront, decide, recognise oneself, grow	32/ Social rhythms, natural rhythms, everyday settings, maturation stages
FREEDOM	33/ Autonomy, self-esteem, determination, passion, assertiveness, boldness, rebelliousness, tolerance	34/ Equal rights	35/ Dissent, chose, run risks, develop awareness, commit oneself, disobey	36/ Temporal and spatial plasticity—offering multiple opportunities and meanings

16.1.4 Environmental Settings as an Ecosystem Service

16.1.4.1 The H-SDM and environmental settings

As stated above, it has not been possible within the constraints of the UK NEA to undertake empirical research to evaluate the H-SDM in an assessment of ecosystem cultural services. Furthermore, the needs discussed in the matrix are not neatly separated, so it will often be hard to identify which need a particular satisfier is addressing. We have used the H-SDM as a conceptual device—a 'thought experiment' in scientific parlance—to challenge us to articulate more clearly what final cultural ecosystem services might be, and how cultural ecosystem 'goods' can be understood as 'benefits' because they satisfy one or more human need. We shall take this in two stages. The first is to use the H-SDM to help give clarity to the definition of final cultural ecosystem services in order to be able to incorporate new insights since the MA was published (Fisher *et al.* 2008). The second is to

discuss a number of cultural goods which could be said to have value because they are capable of satisfying a number of human needs.

The MA (2005a) recognised the challenges involved in identifying cultural services at a global scale and drew on a variety of mainly environmental and ecosystem studies to produce the following list of cultural services:

- **Cultural identity:** the current cultural linkage between humans and their environment.
- **Heritage values**: 'memories' in the landscape from past cultural ties.
- **Spiritual services**: sacred, religious, or other forms of spiritual inspiration derived from ecosystems.
- **Inspiration:** the use of natural motives or artefacts in arts, folklore, and so on.
- **Aesthetic appreciation:** of natural and cultivated landscapes.
- **Recreation and tourism:** the use of natural and cultivated landscapes for pleasure.

The MA chapter on cultural and amenity services (MA 2005a p.457) categorise cultural services as "ecosystem and amenity services provided by ecosystems and landscapes". The term amenity is used to acknowledge the challenge of separating out individual cultural services and that they will often need to be valued collectively as providing amenity (see section 16.3.1 below for a consideration of amenity value in the UK NEA). There is considerable overlap between the list of services above, which increases the difficulty of undertaking a defensible economic valuation. The NEA conceptual framework (Chapter 2) would define some elements of the list above as services and others as goods. The MA chapter recognises the importance of cultural landscapes but the list above refers to 'natural and cultivated landscapes'. Landscapes are a further complex component of cultural services as they are socio-cultural constructions. Landscapes are produced through the combination of human labour and the application of technology, *and* the interpretive frameworks which particular social groups use to create shared meanings for their assemblages of physical, biological and technological processes and products. Unlike a landform created by a specific set of geophysical processes, 'landscape' is not an objective category.

Fisher *et al.* (2008) draw a distinction between intermediate and final ecosystem services and benefits: "ecosystem services are the ecological phenomena, and the benefit is the thing that has direct impact on human welfare. Benefits are typically generated by ecosystem services in combination with other forms of capital like people, knowledge or equipment". More conceptual clarity into the definition of cultural services may assist in the development of more defensible measures of their value in future assessments.

The H-SDM offers a way forward. One of the four human 'existence needs' is for 'settings' in which people can be located together and with nature in place and in time, allowing interaction with others and with the living world (Pilgrim & Pretty 2010). According to the H-SDM the settings of everyday life are essential for human well-being and include 'environmental (natural/naturalistic) settings' where ecosystems are clearly present, such as gardens and parks. Our proposition is that environmental settings represent a final cultural ecosystem service. The intermediate services that underpin this cultural ecosystem service are geophysical, hydro-meteorological and biological products and processes. These intermediate services will be crucial in shaping environmental settings even though many people will be unaware of the influence of some of these processes. In the expert discourse of the UK NEA, these are regulating, supporting and provisioning services. In public discourse, as we have seen above, they are simply 'the natural environment' and 'nature'. Through the interactions between these other ecosystem services and human intellectual, material and social capital over very long periods of time, environmental settings emerge as a final cultural ecosystem service from which a number of time- and space-specific cultural goods arise—these were termed 'benefits' by Fisher *et al.* (2008). These environmental settings are discussed in more detail in Section 16.2; they are very diverse and include domestic gardens, local greenspaces, landscapes and the countryside.

Some of the cultural services identified by the MA, such as recreation and tourism, are better described as goods as, in keeping with the Conceptual Framework for the UK NEA (Chapter 2), they are 'good things' that arise at particular places and points in time through the interaction between environmental settings and human capital inputs. Section 16.3 provides an assessment of specific cultural goods, such as heritage and recreation, which are linked to environmental settings. These goods will, of course, be influenced by all other ecosystem services, but the aim of this chapter is to explore how they interact with the final cultural service of environmental settings.

A valuable characteristic of environmental settings is that they have spatial limits. These may vary depending on how individuals and groups interact with these settings to satisfy needs. For example, people will differ in their views as to where countryside starts and ends, but, in contemporary culture, virtually everyone will accept the idea of a space that can be termed 'the countryside'. Spatially defined environmental settings are better suited for the assessment of status and trends compared to certain MA cultural services (e.g. inspiration) as spatially disaggregated data can be compiled for many environmental settings and their associated goods and values. Data for environmental settings can then be integrated with spatially disaggregated data concerning other ecosystem services and will allow a consideration of cultural services to be included in various policy activities that guide and shape ecosystem management. In this way, cultural services and goods are not simply a discrete 'box' in ecosystem assessments, but they can be incorporated into the decision-making and trade-offs involved with managing and conserving ecosystems.

16.1.4.2 Environmental settings, habitats and landscapes

Conceptually, environmental settings overlap with spatially defined habitats or ecosystems (Chapter 2). Environmental settings are, however, distinct from these other conceptual entities as they are the places at certain points in time that are valued because they satisfy the fundamental human need for social interaction with others and with nature. Consequently, in any of the eight Broad Habitat types identified by the UK NEA a range of different environmental settings will be present. Equally, in any environmental setting several habitat types might be present which, in their assemblage, could satisfy needs for understanding, aesthetic pleasure and active recreation. A large country park may allow visitors to walk through Woodland, Enclosed Farmland and Semi-natural Grassland, for instance, providing a range of habitats that may satisfy various needs such as for identity and leisure. The habitat type may influence the nature of the interactions people can have with others and with nature, but there are also a range of other factors that collectively shape our interactions in environmental settings.

Environmental settings also combine with built environments, human activities and our imaginations to produce what we often term 'landscapes'. The European Landscape Convention (COE 2004) defines landscape as "an area, as perceived by people, whose character is the result of the action and interaction of natural and/or human factors".

Habitats turn into landscape through the intervention of culture and cognition: classifying visual experience by taking a perspective that encompasses and organises a view (Appleton 1975; Cosgrove & Daniels 1988; Pretty 2002). Ingold (2000) describes the engagement people have with the environment and landscape through practice as a process of 'dwelling'. The experience and appreciation of landscapes is acquired and reflects aesthetic sensibilities at particular points in time, and between different cultures (Tuan 1979; Harrison 1992; Barrell 1980; Palmer & Brady 2007; Tolia-Kelly 2007a). For the historian, Simon Schama, "landscape is the work of the mind. Its scenery is built up as much from strata of memory as from layers of rock" (1995, p.7). Some of the empirical data used in this chapter to examine environmental settings assesses landscape change which emphasises how the environmental settings that constitute final ecosystem services are the result of interactions between natural and social systems over long periods of time.

16.2 Cultural Services and Environmental Settings: Status, Trends and Drivers

16.2.1 The Nature of Environmental Settings

The final cultural ecosystem service is the series of environmental settings shown on one axis in **Figure 16.3**, ranging from domestic gardens to country territories. Over millennia, these have been co-produced by the constant interactions between people and nature. Environmental settings are inscribed with the legacies of past and current societies, technologies and cultures. In contemporary society, people tend to perceive these environmental settings as distinct from technologically produced ('man-made') settings such as the interior of the home, workplaces and shopping malls (although the air in such indoor spaces means nature is always present and it can also be manifested in plants, shrubs and visual representations). Therefore, the environmental settings in **Figure 16.3** are all outdoor places where there are opportunities for people to engage with nature and with each other.

Figure 16.3 represents an adaptation of the Max-Neef (1992) framework to address the specific spatial challenges of an ecosystem assessment. These environmental settings provide spaces for social interaction that our current culture sees as important as highlighted in a recent 2009/10 survey of the adult population of England. The survey found that:

- 88% agreed that spending time outdoors was an important part of their life;
- 93% agreed that having greenspaces near to where they lived was important to them (Natural England 2010).

The environmental settings in **Figure 16.3** are distinct from each other by virtue of their geography and proximity to our daily lives. More than 80% of households in the UK have access to a private/shared garden or yard—an environmental setting adjoined to their homes (Mintel 2010). The places where we spend much of our everyday lives provide informal, local, green and blue settings (such as footpaths, bridleways, canal and riversides, and hedgerows), and also contain formal local settings designed for certain activities, such as recreation in parks, angling at lakes, food-growing in allotments or retreat and contemplation in cemeteries. One advantage of basing the analysis of cultural services on environmental settings is that they have a number of readily measured features and characteristics that can be incorporated into empirical assessments of value.

For some people their locality will contain the countryside or seaside, but many people will have to travel to these environmental settings. In 2009–10, just under half the visits made to natural environment by adults in England were to the countryside (Natural England 2010). Wherever people live, however, there will be an environmental setting that is the more distant wider countryside or seaside that they will have to make a journey to visit.

Human interactions with nature are, in part, conditioned by an environmental setting defined by country boundaries.

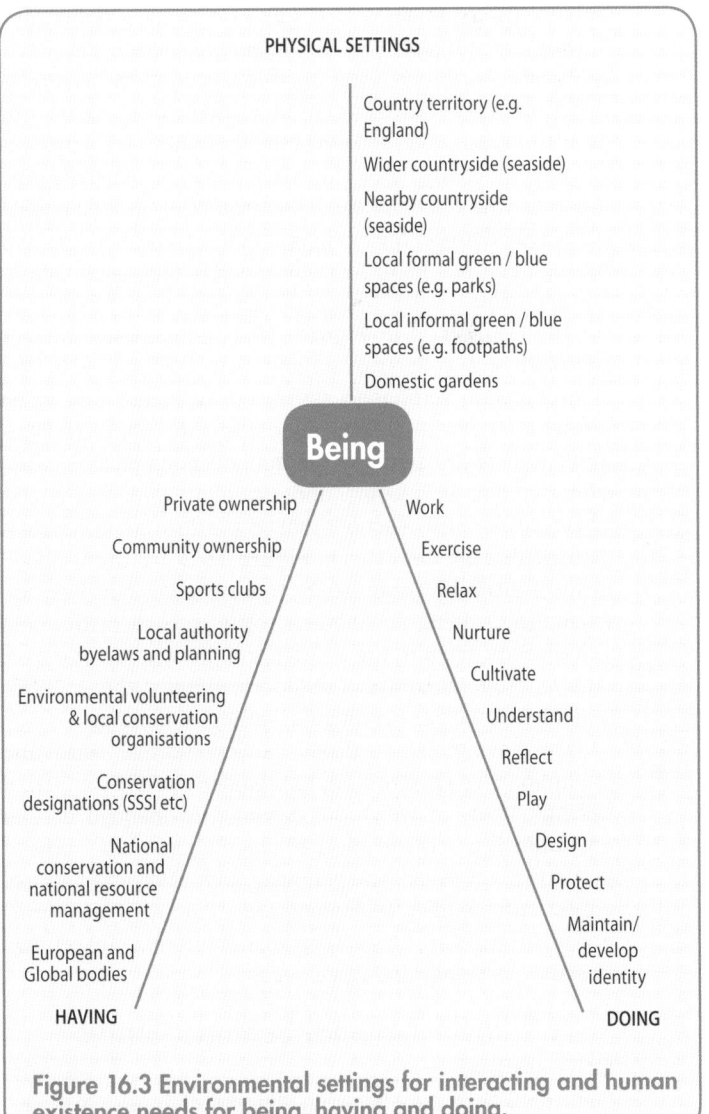

Figure 16.3 Environmental settings for interacting and human existence needs for being, having and doing.

As Chapters 17–20 show, the countryside of Scotland, Wales, England and Northern Ireland is perceived as having natural and cultural features that are distinct to that particular country, and so, shape human-nature relationships.

The environmental settings shown in **Figure 16.3** can satisfy a number or even all of our value needs at any point in time. A garden or allotment can provide food and subsistence, be a space for leisure, and promote our sense of affection and creativity. People walking in open access countryside in the Highlands of Scotland may feel a sense of freedom and connect to a Scottish sense of identity. Different settings can satisfy different value needs. As this chapter shows, however, due to cultural, economic and technological change how we satisfy our value needs has changed. The process of needs satisfaction has shaped, and been shaped by, the changes in environmental settings. A key aim of this chapter is to outline how our changing value needs interact with changing environmental settings and the ecosystem services that underpin these environmental settings.

16.2.2 Environmental Settings and Human Existence Needs

The adapted Max-Neef (1992) framework summarises how our need for 'environmental settings for interacting' must be considered alongside our need for 'being', 'doing' and 'having', which are also fundamental to our existence. In **Figure 16.3**, our being need is placed at the centre of the diagram to reflect that an individual's need to 'be'—by developing personal and collective attributes—is a process of endless change that involves constant tensions and relations with the other axes; these other axes outline what people are doing in the environmental settings and how our having need results in the ways society organises natural environments.

The doing axis in **Figure 16.3** summarises the key personal and collective actions that take place in the environmental settings to satisfy our existence and value needs; thus, these actions also shape the characteristics and status of the settings. The doing actions include work, exercise, and developing understanding and awareness. There are many other actions that people do in environmental settings that are not listed in **Figure 16.3**, but are included in the H-SDM in **Table 16.2**. Those shown, however, are examples of doing actions that relate to each of the nine value needs listed in the H-SDM and, in contemporary UK culture, often make use of outdoor settings. Other cultures will interact with environmental settings differently.

The having axis outlines the key norms, rules and institutions we need to have to organise the environmental settings, many of which are designed to manage natural environments. They include regulations for private property ownership, local planning authorities and national conservation bodies. In contemporary culture, these norms and institutions are how we organise environmental settings to satisfy existence and value needs.

16.2.3 Environmental Settings: Status and Trends

Since 1945, there have been fundamental changes in people's interactions with environmental settings. These can be understood both through analysis of changing patterns of mobility, work, social behaviour and consumption trends, and through analysis of the processes underpinning these patterns. Together, they chart changing relations between people and environmental settings.

In relation to changes in patterns, the growth of settlements defined as 'urban' means that more people have a set of local environmental settings with urban characteristics. However, at the same time, increased mobility has allowed people to travel longer distances to environmental settings for tourism and recreation purposes. From the late 1980s, with the introduction of cheap air travel, these destinations have expanded across the globe. Data limits the interpretations of changes in domestic gardens and local green/blue spaces. Marked changes did occur, however, in certain countryside settings of the UK during the second half of the 20th Century, especially those in and around large urban areas. The characteristics of other settings have remained more static.

Since 1945, these changes have been accompanied by a large number of protection schemes instigated by UK and European governments aiming to conserve what are seen culturally as highly valued environmental settings.

This section outlines key aspects of the status, trends and drivers of the different environmental settings shown in **Figure 16.3** and draws on the detailed evidence presented in some of the UK NEA habitat and country synthesis chapters. Evidence is uneven, so it is possible to provide a more detailed assessment of some environmental settings than it is for others. This section also discusses the key drivers reflecting our existence needs for being, doing and organising that have collectively interacted with and shaped these environmental settings.

Overall, there is a mixed picture of change in environmental settings, with maintenance and enhancement of character in some settings, and loss or neglect in others. In some, such as playing fields, a decline in quality or extent has recently been arrested.

16.2.3.1 Domestic gardens

In 2005, domestic gardens in England accounted for just over 4% (564,500 hectares (ha)) of total land cover (GLUD 2005). Yet, in 2010, 83% of adults had access to a private/shared garden or yard (Mintel 2010). In the urban areas of England, gardens may account for up to 13% of land (Bibby 2009), and in the 35 major cities of Scotland, the percentage of the land footprint occupied by gardens and allotments varies between 6–50% (Birnie *et al.* 2002; Greenspace Scotland 2009).

A detailed discussion of domestic gardens that considers biodiversity issues can be found in Chapter 10; it notes that a negative trend has been the increase in paving over front gardens which results in less percolation and increased runoff. This trend may not continue due to new legislation, but incomplete evidence suggests that, by 2006, 47% of front gardens were more than three quarters paved in North East England and 31% in Scotland (RHS 2006).

Domestic gardens also provide an important heterogeneous Urban subhabitat in which species variety is likely to be beneficial for pollination (Chapter 10), but they

Figure 16.4 The great tit (*Parus major*) is one of a wide range of bird species attracted to domestic gardens.
Photo by iJammin available under a Creative Commons Attribution license.

can also contain some invasive non-native species which may threaten ecosystem services (Reichard & White 2001). A number of studies in urban and rural areas have suggested domestic gardens can contain more species diversity than comparably sized areas of open country, partly due to changes in planting habits and the way gardeners construct habitat mosaics (Walters 1970; Phillips *et al.* 2008; Smith *et.al.* 2006; **Figure 16.4**).

16.2.3.2 Local, formal green and blue spaces

Evidence suggests that the decline in either the amount or the quality of formal green and blue spaces has been arrested in recent years. Parks and greenspaces have experienced a significant decline in their quality in the last few decades, especially in deprived areas, but as the social and health benefits of parks have been recognised, this has been reversed by a range of policy initiatives (Chapter 10). The decline in numbers of playing fields due to an estimated 10,000 being sold between in the 1980s and 90s (DCMS

2008) has also been arrested in recent years. Certain parks and greenspaces, however, are of exceptionally high quality and, in 2010, there were 1,606 parks on the Register of Parks and Gardens of Special Historic Interest for England—an increase of 115 since 2002. Most of the new parks on the register were added between 2002 and 2004, and, in 2010, 99 parks (6.2%) were identified as being at risk (English Heritage 2010).

Legislation over the last 50 years has also seen the growth of other formal greenspaces where public use and access is encouraged. The 1949 National Parks and Access to the Countryside Act initiated the designation of Local Nature Reserves (LNRs) and, in England, there are now over 1,100 reserves in very varying habitats, covering nearly 35,000 ha. Country Parks were established under the 1968 Countryside Act and there are now just over 400 identified Country Parks that have more than 70 million visitors per year (Natural England 2011a).

The number and extent of allotments have also declined over recent decades. The Second World War stimulated a marked increase in allotment plots, but decline since means there are now only approximately 160,000 plots in England, equating to 10% of the post-war acreage (Campbell & Campbell 2009), and 211 plots in Scotland (SAGS 2007). Nonetheless, many areas in the UK have witnessed an increase in allotment waiting lists, and new allotments have opened in many parts of the UK (Chapter 18).

The first city farm in the UK is generally acknowledged to be the one that opened in Kentish Town in 1972. There are now over 100 city farms that seek to promote improved understanding about agriculture and the environment. CABE (2010) identifies 197 city farms and community gardens, and the Federation of City Farms and Community Gardens (2010) identifies 48 city farms that are open for visits by the public.

There are approximately 18,000–20,000 Church of England burial grounds in England and Wales, which can act as sites encouraging biodiversity. However, Chapter 10 concludes that the lack of a centralised record of such spaces makes it difficult to assess trends in burial ground extent and quality.

16.2.3.3 Local, informal green and blue spaces

The diversity of species and habitats found in some informal spaces in urban areas was referred to by the naturalist Richard Mabey in the 1970s as 'The Unofficial Countryside'; this is in contrast to the 'official' countryside conserved in national parks and other designations (Mabey 2010). Chapter 10 concludes that greenspaces in cities are not systematically monitored and, for some informal spaces, such as green corridors and hedges, very little evidence of status or trends exists. Evidence does exist regarding changes in the quality of street trees and some bluespaces.

Surveys of Urban trees in 1992 and 2004–05 (DoE 1993; DCLG 2008) indicate a regional increase in street tree density in South East and South West England. On a national level, 70% of Urban street trees surveyed in 2004 were in good condition. Despite this, trends are not clear as there was an overall decline in the percentage of good condition trees, but a decrease in the percentage of trees considered poor, dead or dying.

There are many informal blue spaces such as rivers, lakes, canals and the coast (**Figure 16.5**). Chapter 9 indicates that there are 160,000 km of rivers in the UK, and almost 6,000 permanent lakes. In the urban areas of the UK, 0.8% of the land is classified as Urban Freshwater, but there are marked variations between some major cities (GLUD 2005). The chemical and biological quality trends for lakes are not clear, but for rivers the trends are generally positive since 1990, with local variations; for example, rivers in urban areas or locations with intensive agriculture have significantly lower sanitary quality and more elevated nutrients (e.g. nitrate >5 mg/L) than elsewhere (Chapter 9).

Figure 16.5 Canals, such as this one in Warwickshire, England, along with hedges can be classified as informal blue and greenspace. ©David Hughes, 2011 used under license of Shutterstock.com.

Table 16.3 The importance of greenspace in England in 2007. Source: Defra (2009) © Crown copyright 2009.

Importance of greenspace	Percentage of people (%)
Very important	74
Fairly important	21
Not very important	4
Not at all important	1

Table 16.4 The frequency of greenspace use in England in 2007. Source: Defra (2009) © Crown copyright 2009.

Frequency of greenspace use	Percentage of people (%)
6–7 days a week	10
3–5 days per week	12
1–2 days per week	27
Once a fortnight month	26
Several times a year	16
Less often	10

Table 16.3 and **Table 16.4** indicate that, in England, people regularly use local, formal and informal greenspace and place considerable importance on it as a local environmental setting: three quarters of the population consider it to be a very important part of the local environment, and 50% use it at least once a week.

16.2.3.4 The nearby and wider countryside and seaside

The UK is a predominantly urban society; in 2009, approximately 90% of people lived in areas defined as 'urban', an increase from 79% in 1951 (DCMS & ONS 2009; House of Commons 1999). Yet not much land is categorised as being urban. In England, 10.5% of land (1,378,800 ha) is classified as urban, compared to 4.2% of Wales (86,000 ha), 2.9% (50,600 ha) in Northern Ireland and only 1.9% (148,300 ha) in Scotland. In England, agriculture covers approximately 70% of the land area outside built up areas, with woodland cover and forestry making up 8% (CRC 2008). The Land Cover of Scotland Report f(1988) found that over 50% of the land area of Scotland was covered by semi-natural vegetation, mainly heather moorland and peatland, a further 15% was woodland, and less than 3% was urban or rural development (MLURI 1993). In Wales, 52% of land area was Enclosed Farmland in 2004 and 5% was urban, gardens and amenity (Chapter 20).

There are, therefore, large areas of what, in contemporary culture, is referred to as 'countryside'. For some people this will be located nearby, but for others, it is a more distant, wider countryside. Recent surveys suggest that, in 2009–10, 41.4 million adults resident in England made 2.86 billion visits to the natural environment, 48% (1.38 billion) of which were to places the adults defined as the countryside, 7%(0.21 billion) were to a greenspace in a seaside town or resort, and 4% (0.11 billion) were to other seaside coastlines.

The Countryside Quality Counts (CQC) project provides an indicator of change in the countryside quality of England and is the most comprehensive data on changes in countryside environmental settings, including coastal features. It involves integrating data mainly from 10 different national datasets and producing measurements of landscape change in 159 'landscape character areas' (geographical areas that have distinct landscapes).

The CQC analysis for 1990 to 1998 indicated that about 40% of English landscapes were stable, the changes occurring on a further 37% were not significant to overall landscape character, but 26% were experiencing change that was marked and inconsistent with landscape type. Yorkshire and Humberside, the East, the North West and the North East landscapes stood out as being the most stable. By contrast, marked and inconsistent changes in landscapes were concentrated in 'middle England', especially across central England and around the conurbations of Manchester, Bristol and Birmingham (Defra *et al.* 2008).

The CQC assessment for 1999 to 2003 showed a good level of consistency with the analysis for 1990 to 1998. Landscape character was maintained in 51% of landscapes and enhanced in a further 10%, but there was loss or neglect of character in 20% of landscapes, and new characteristics emerging in 19% (Defra *et al.* 2008).

In coastal locations, the sea will make a significant contribution to the environmental settings in both urban and rural areas. The contribution of the Marine environment to culturally valued environmental settings is only partially understood and is the subject of ongoing research. English Heritage has commissioned pilot and demonstration studies to develop a Historic Seascape Characterisation for England.

Chapter 12 concludes that the UK's seas are increasingly important to personal quality of life, but are currently less well protected than terrestrial environments. For example, under the Habitat's Directive in the UK, out of a total of 621 designated Special Areas of Conservation (SACs), only 81 are for marine locations. The Marine and Coastal Access Act 2009, however, will establish Marine Conservation Zones that are designed to enhance the protection of the Marine ecosystem and its biodiversity.

16.2.3.5 National country environmental settings

The country boundaries of England, Northern Ireland, Scotland and Wales mark out an area in which environmental settings can have distinct meanings to people, often linked to the history and identity of that country (**Figure 16.6**).

In Northern Ireland, a recent survey of tourist attitudes found that the vast majority of visitors agreed that the country had 'unique and distinctive landscapes and coastlines' and that the activities rated most important were sightseeing opportunities of the countryside and coast, along with cities, towns and villages that give Northern Ireland a distinctive sense of place (NITB 2009).

The interactions between history, scenery and landscape have, for a long time, been central to Scotland's distinct brand as a tourism destination, affecting how Scottish people perceive and experience the national landscape (McCrone *et al.* 1995). Species, as well as landscape, can be perceived as having national qualities as has been found in studies of heritage trees in Scotland (Rodger *et al.* 2006).

Chapter 20 highlights that perceptions of landscape for many Welsh people are intimately linked with culture and the Welsh language partly due to the existence of Welsh terms and words that define aspects of biodiversity and marine produce. The chapter also notes that distinctive features of landscapes in parts of Wales have been, and are, under threat from intrusive developments linked to energy, transport, tourism and the planting of conifer trees.

Figure 16.6 National country environmental settings: a) Dorset coast, England. *Photo ©David Hughes 2011 used under license of Shutterstock.com.* **b) The Giant's Causeway, Northern Ireland.** *Photo ©Josemaria Toscan 2011 used under license of Shutterstock.com.* **c) View from Snowdon, Wales.** *Photo by Andrew Michaels available under a Creative Commons Attribution-NonCommercial-NoDerivs license.* **d) Cairngorm National Park, Scotland.** *Photo by Peter Mulligan available under a Creative Commons Attribution license.*

The connections between the national land base as an environmental setting and the satisfaction of human needs are complex and no quantitative data currently exists that allows an accurate assessment of status or trends; however, in Section 16.3, the significance of national landscapes for identity and other value needs is discussed.

16.2.4 The Drivers of Change in Environmental Settings

The varied characteristics and geography of environmental settings means there is a wide range of cultural, social, technological and political drivers. The cultural significance of these settings arises from the role they play in meeting people's value and existence needs. This section, therefore, focuses on the key drivers that have shaped the way people meet their needs through interactions in environmental settings. As indicated in **Figure 16.3**, our being needs, as individuals and social groups, are inseparable from our interacting, having and doing needs. The discussion of key drivers is divided between drivers concerned with institutions, norms and legislation relating to our having needs, and those drivers based on personal and collective actions linked to our doing needs.

16.2.4.1 Drivers and having needs: institutions, rules and norms

A key strand of evidence concerning the drivers of environmental settings is the changing institutions and laws for protecting and conserving the countryside. This has altered the relations between humans and certain settings, often making places available where people can undertake recreation activities or appreciate flora and fauna. There are now 15 National Parks in the UK and they protect environmental settings and landscapes of particular cultural significance. The 10 National Parks in England (listed in **Table 16.5**) cover 9.3% of the country land area, the 3 in Wales (Snowdonia, Pembrokeshire Coast and Brecon Beacons) cover 19.9%, and the 2 in (Cairngorms, Loch Lomond and the Trossachs) cover 7.2% (Natural England 2011b).

National Nature Reserves (NNRs) are designated by Natural England and include a number of important sites

for wildlife and geology. There are currently 222 NNRs in England, covering more than 92,000 ha, which amounts to approximately 0.6% of England's land surface. Initially developed to protect sensitive features and to provide 'outdoor laboratories' for research, the focus of NNRs has now widened. Today, one of their main purposes is to provide an environment for the public, schools and specialist audiences to experience.

On the edge of larger cities in England, the environmental settings and landscapes are protected by designated green belt land which, as at 31 March 2009, is estimated to be 1,638,800 ha, 1.2% of the land area of England (DCLG 2009). The green belt covers 156,720 ha in Scotland and 2,540 ha in Wales. Northern Ireland has an extensive green belt which covers 29.9% of the land area (DCLG 2009).

The environmental settings of the countryside are also protected by conservation designations, most notably the national designation of Sites of Special Scientific Interest (SSSIs) and the European designation of SACs. Sites of Special Scientific Interest are those areas designated as containing some of the country's very best wildlife and geographical sites. There are over 4,000 SSSIs in England, covering around 7% of the country's land area. More than 70% of these sites (by area covered) are also designated as SACs, Special Protection Areas (SPAs) or Ramsar sites due to their international importance for wildlife. Many of SSSIs are also designated as either NNRs or LNRs.

Special Areas of Conservation are given protection through the EU's Habitats Directive. There are 231 SACs in England, with a total area of 846,200 ha (all terrestrial SACs in England are also SSSIs). In Scotland, there are 236 SACs totalling 921,230 ha; in Wales, there are 85 SACs with a total area of 590,800 ha; and, in Northern Ireland, there are 54 making up 66,600 ha. Further SACs are designated across the borders between England, Scotland and Wales, and there are 7 SACs in overseas territories and in UK offshore waters. This amounts to a total of 623 SACs covering an area of 2,906,600 ha across the UK.

Environmental settings have also been affected by the growth of the planning system and changes in urban settlement patterns since 1945. New transport technologies, planning regulations and the growth of job opportunities in rural areas and smaller towns mean that larger urban areas and conurbations have become less crowded, while smaller settlements and rural areas, especially in Southern England, have become more crowded. Rural Wales and Scotland, however, still contain relatively few people (Southall 2009). Since the New Towns Act of 1946, 30 New Towns have been built in the UK: 21 in England, 2 in Wales, 2 in Northern Ireland and 5 in Scotland. The local environmental settings in New Towns will be distinct as they were built with relatively high levels of greenspace compared to other urban areas (Ward 1993). In 2001, the New Towns had a combined population of nearly 3 million (just under 5% of the UK total) (Alexander 2009; Census of Population 2001).

The processes affecting the connections between humans and environmental settings are not just shaped by formal institutions and legislation. The groundswell of protests by local communities and specialist interest groups against planning decisions opened the way for massive changes in

Table 16.5 Cumulative National Park area in England.
Source: based on Natural England (2011b).

Year	Total area ('000 hectares)	National Park confirmed
1951 (April)	143.8	Peak District
1951 (May)	373	Lake District
1951 (October)	468.4	Dartmoor
1952 (November)	612	North York Moors
1954 (October)	788.9	Yorkshire Dales
1954 (October)	858.2	Exmoor
1956 (April)	963.1	Northumberland
1989 (April)	993.4	The Broads
2005 (March)	1,050	New Forest
2010 (March)	1,214	South Downs

urban and rural areas which began in the mid-1950s. Over the next 30 years or so, a substantial body of academic research and policy-practice concentrated on trying to better understand why particular environmental settings and landscapes seemed to be so highly valued that people would willingly engage in political protest to protect them. Debates raged about what constituted 'natural' and 'cultural' heritage; about whether it was possible to determine, in any scientifically robust way, a cause-effect relationship between assemblages of physical terrain, vegetation cover, human artefacts and expressions of landscape preferences (Moore-Colyer & Scott 2005); and about whose tastes and views were being favoured when certain landscapes were protected and others were allowed to be damaged or destroyed. Institutional recognition of the right of the public and stakeholders to participate in planning decisions was achieved in the 1968 Town and Country Planning Act; subsequently, this has developed in a variety of ways, but always with the intention of providing opportunities for participants to offer alternative perspectives on whether, and how, developments should take place.

16.2.4.2 Drivers and doing needs: work, mobility, leisure and consumption

The doing needs of people are summarised in **Figure 16.1** and have been shaped by a range of drivers resulting in changes in the way people interact with environmental settings. Workers in agriculture have a particular engagement with ecosystems and environmental settings that has changed markedly due new agricultural technology and the decline of the workforce. In 1951, the 1 million agricultural workers represented 5% of the British workforce, but the 470,000 agricultural workers in 2001 constituted fewer than 2% of the total workforce. In England and Wales, no local authority district has more than 2% of the workforce employed at the production end of the agricultural chain (University of Portsmouth 2009).

The changes in work have been accompanied by changes in personal mobility. **Table 16.6** shows that the number of journeys that people make by private car, bicycle or on foot have grown only slightly, although there has been a modal shift to cars from bicycles and walking. **Table 16.7** illustrates, however, that distance travelled has increased by about 25% for commuting/business travel and by over 30% for other journey types. People are increasingly living in, or close to, urban settlements, but they are also able to travel further to access environmental settings, services and

work in their local area. Some of the leisure miles travelled in **Table 16.7** will involve trips to access the natural environment and specific environmental settings.

Leisure and consumption habits have changed markedly in the last 60 years, but the depth and breadth of cultural engagement with nature and wildlife across the UK continues to flourish (Rackham 1986; Mabey 1996; Cocker & Mabey 2005; Macfarlane 2007; Pretty 2007; Marren & Mabey 2010). In the 21st Century, the cultural life of the UK is diverse and dynamic (Wood et al. 2006). Yet encounters with the natural world maintain their fascination for very substantial numbers of people, as reflected, for example, in the huge audiences for television wildlife documentaries, the membership of a very wide range of civil society organisations embracing landscape and nature interests, the numbers of people who use urban parks and greenspaces on a daily basis, and the massive popularity of gardening across the UK. Daily contact with nature is still part of being human. Even in the most extreme built environments, such as Canary Wharf in London Docklands, professional workers seek out patches of greenery in which to eat their lunch (Hitchings 2010). Several million people across the UK actively support a wide range of conservation organisations through paying membership fees and donations, and, to a lesser extent, volunteering their time (Lowe & Godyer 1983; Eden et al. 2006).

The interactions between people and environmental settings have been affected by the changing relationship between the public and the land—in a paradigmatic sense—since the 1970s. Until then, the relationship was an essentially consumptive one, informed by a rights agenda that invoked the 18th and 19th Century government-mandated enclosures as evidence of landowners assuming powers that were not theirs to assume (Shoard 1987; Harrison 1991; Ravenscroft 1995; 1998). For many people, their connection to the land is still enacted largely through consumption under conventional liberal market regimes (albeit shifting from, say, the supermarket to the farmers' market—what Hegarty (2007) terms 'green-shifting') and is, therefore, intimately tied to established social structures such as class (Ilbery & Maye 2006; London Food Link 2007; Sustain 2008).

The last two to three decades, however, have witnessed some people combining consumption-based connections to the land with increasingly ecologically productive forms of engagement with the land. Production, in this sense, is understood through two related concepts:

Table 16.6 Average number of trips per person per year in Great Britain*. Source: data from Department for Transport; Defra (2009) © Crown copyright 2009.

Period	Walk and Bicycle	Private motor vehicles	Public transport and taxis
1989–1991	349	629	113
2006	265	669	103

* Note: Figures for 1995 onwards are based on weighted data and are not directly comparable with earlier years. The effect of weighting is broadly to uplift the number of trips by approximately 4%. The sample size of the survey tripled in 2002.

Table 16.7 Distance travelled (miles) per person per year (miles) in Great Britain by broad trip purpose*. Source: data from Department for Transport; Defra (2009) © Crown copyright 2009.

Period	Leisure/ other	Commuting and business	Shopping and personal business	Education and children being escorted to education
1985–1986	2,224	1,631	1,256	206
2006	2,853	2,073	1,902	305

* Note: Figures for 1995 onwards are based on weighted data and are not directly comparable with earlier years. The effect of weighting is broadly to uplift the number of trips by approximately 4%. The sample size of the survey tripled in 2002.

- **Environmental and personal security:** managing ecosystems to provide a mix of services that increase environmental and personal security while reducing carbon and water dependence, increasing carbon sequestration, and mitigating and adapting to climate change.
- **Individual responsibility and self-determination:** the development of a deeper and more sustained relationship between people and ecosystems in which people increasingly produce their own lifestyles (through volunteering to undertake conservation work, or engaging in community farming and gardening, for example) as part of a shift towards more secure, ethical and environmentally aware practices. This latter construct is akin to Stebbins' (1992; 1997) concept of 'serious leisure' in which people pursue non-work interests—and take on non-work identities—in ways more conventionally associated with work. Although not referred to explicitly by Stebbins, these 'serious leisure' practices could include voluntary participation in community recycling schemes, local food cooperatives and community transport initiatives. Such lifestyle production could also include what Stebbins (2001) has referred to as 'busy leisure': voluntary activities undertaken primarily by the retired and unemployed to 'keep themselves busy'.

An example of these changes is the process of identity formation through attachment to specific landscapes and ways of living (Marsden *et al.* 2003; CCRCD 2007; Curry 2009). This has led to significant numbers of people relocating to rural areas (Halfacree 1995) and taking up lifestyle and consumption practices which they see as more sustainable. It has also led to a reappraisal of how to improve personal safety and feelings of belonging in different urban and rural environments (BEN 2006; Defra 2008). For increasing numbers of people, however, the commitment extends beyond the market to encompass new approaches to lifestyle based on a creative (re)connection with the land and environment in a positive, productive, way (Halfacree 2001). The ultimate form of engagement in this reconnection with the land is through farming and food security. Halfacree (2001) has found examples of people relocating to rural areas to run smallholdings, while Ravenscroft and Taylor (2009) have identified that increasing numbers of people are getting involved in farming through the membership of cooperatives and various forms of community supported agriculture (Hollins & Hollins 2007; The Countryside Agency 2005; Soil Association 2005; McFadden 2003a; 2003b).

The underlying impulse for this shift in connections to the land has been about establishing new forms of citizenship, often linked to earlier historical social movements (Parker 2002), that support individual responsibility and self-determination within a newly emerging understanding of environmental security. This reflects what Rojek (2001) has termed a new 'life politics' in which people seek 'civil labour' as a primary means of expressing their identity. Faced with the growing threat of environmental insecurity, increasing numbers of people are seeking new avenues to assert their identity and environmental awareness, and, in the process, are supporting new approaches to ecosystem management and governance. Ideas relating to ecosystem services are part of this new consciousness.

16.3 Cultural Goods

16.3.1. Cultural Goods, Needs Satisfaction, Economic Value and Well-being

16.3.1.1 Environmental settings and cultural goods

Cultural goods emerge through the interaction of human needs satisfaction with a range of environmental settings. Frameworks of interpretation and social practices associated with the production and uses of environmental settings are dynamic: meanings, values and behaviours change over time in response to economic, technological, social, political and cultural drivers. "Cultural change is, among other things, the consequence of dropping traditional satisfiers for the purpose of adopting new or different ones" (Max-Neef 1992). What this means for ecosystem cultural goods and benefits is that the capacity of environmental settings to satisfy human needs is contingent, fluid and mutable. Change can be rapid and far-reaching in its implications; for instance, the rise in cheap airline flights since the 1960s has encouraged millions of people to take holidays in distant locations rather than following earlier generations to UK coastal resorts, mountains and moorlands, and historic towns. In this example, existence needs are still being met by 'having' the necessary financial resources, technologies and institutions to support medium and long-haul travel; 'doing' all the things which help to create the 'exotic holiday experience'; and 'being' a particular kind of tourist (types and roles recognisable from social marketing surveys which range from sun-sea-sand hedonists to discerning travellers seeking 'authentic' encounters with their host communities). The environmental settings are no longer mundane, of course, and that is part of the attraction.

One purpose of the UK NEA's economic valuation has been to measure the utility of certain cultural goods and to infer, from analysis of patterns of expenditure, how individual welfare/well-being has been improved. Expressing a preference for a good could also be described as an individual wanting one or more value needs to be satisfied. But what kind of satisfaction does the individual achieve? The rapid development of happiness research in economics and policy-political initiatives to measure levels of happiness among populations reflects statistical evidence that, although people are far better off in material terms than they have ever been, rates of depression, mental illness, obesity and family breakdown are also increasing (Layard 2005). Evidence suggests that contemporary consumption practices are not satisfying our human needs adequately.

16.3.1.2 The nature of need satisfiers

Writing in the context of a highly charged political discussion about the nature of Latin American development, Max-Neef

(1992, p.205) suggested it might be possible to distinguish analytically between five categories of human needs 'satisfiers'. These were:

1. **violators or destroyers** which paradoxically appear to satisfy one need but systematically destroy opportunities for the satisfaction of others;
2. **pseudo-satisfiers** which appear to satisfy, but ultimately disappoint;
3. **inhibiting satisfiers** which satisfy one need (in an often over-determined way) and thereby inhibit the satisfaction of other needs;
4. **singular satisfiers** which satisfy one need only; and
5. **synergistic satisfiers** which, in satisfying one need, are also able to satisfy others.

It is clear that there is a strong ideological position underpinning these categories. When addressing ecosystem cultural goods and benefits, it is important not to slip into the trap of judging in advance what kinds of satisfiers might be life-enhancing or not. There is little empirical evidence upon which to base a judgement. Furthermore, identifying what kind of satisfier particular goods and services might be is difficult given the range of producer and consumer interests involved, although successive government policies to reduce smoking, promote healthy eating, and encourage more pro-environmental behaviours indicate some prioritisation. The goods that people derive from environmental settings act as satisfiers for existence and value needs leading to changes in well-being.

This process of needs satisfaction through cultural goods is immensely complex as ecosystem services and environmental settings provide multiple assemblages of living and non-living features, species, spaces and opportunities for people to satisfy needs by creating a range of activities, experiences, attachments, feelings, emotions and memories which are meaningful (Castree 2005; Natural England 2005).

In addition, taste and sensibilities towards environmental settings, as well as attitudes and values towards environmental issues, vary across demographic, socioeconomic and cultural groups, as demonstrated in recent large-scale quantitative research (Defra 2007b; Natural England 2010). Environment attitudes range from those who are defined as 'green' in outlook to those who are disinterested in the environment, or who face long-term restrictions on changing their environmental behaviors (Defra 2007b).

Max-Neef (1992) described the process of cultural change as the substitution of new for traditional satisfiers. In addressing the question of how, specifically, cultural ecosystem goods have changed, one way is to consider whether traditional satisfiers (objects, activities, ideas) have been replaced and, if so, by what and for what reasons. Take, for example, outdoor play in parks and informal greenspaces which is widely acknowledged to provide multiple benefits for children and youth (Burgess *et al.* 1988; Louv 2005; CABE 2006; Gleave 2009). Outdoor play could reasonably be classified as a 'synergistic satisfier'. However, over the last forty years, increased volumes of traffic, exaggerated fears about 'stranger-danger', loss of opportunities as local authorities have disinvested from parks, and development pressures on brown- and greenfield sites have meant that many children no longer have the freedom to play outdoors which their parents and grandparents enjoyed (Veitch *et al.* 2007; Gleave 2009). Computer games, journeys to school by car and organised activities could be considered as 'inhibiting satisfiers', replacing what has been lost, but could be equally beneficial in other ways.

A slightly different substitution process could be evident in cultural encounters with wildlife. The UK has a long tradition of amateur naturalists watching and recording wildlife, while many millions of people simply enjoy sharing their everyday lives with birds and animals (Macfarlane 2007; Pretty 2007). As the numbers of many species of birds, butterflies and mammals have declined, so have opportunities to satisfy a number of value needs. A cultural substitution is offered by wildlife documentaries on television, which attract audiences in the millions and do satisfy the value need for understanding. But there is a struggle between conservationists and documentary filmmakers about the impact of this substitution on the fate of actual wildlife; the virtual-zoo is an example, some would argue, of a pseudo-satisfier (Davies 1999; Scott 2003).

Individuals vary in terms of how they interact with different environmental settings to satisfy their value needs. Many people consider their garden to be an important environmental setting in which to engage with nature (Bhatti & Church 2001), as well as an important site for consumption (Hitchings 2003; see Robbins & Sharp 2003); others, meanwhile, feel the need to escape to remote 'wilderness' settings to achieve a fulfilling connection to nature (Pretty 2007; Natural England 2009a). Consumer surveys of adults with access to a domestic garden show that 25% consider themselves committed gardeners and knowledgeable about nature, whereas 15% are not interested in their garden and do little gardening (Mintel 2004). Max-Neef (1992) observes, however, that satisfiers can change quite quickly and unpredictably. The role of some environmental settings in meeting needs has changed rapidly in recent years. For example, few would have predicted the changing use of the domestic garden for food growing over the last 25 years. Only 20% of those with access to a garden grew vegetables in 1996, compared with 35% ten years earlier (Mintel 1999); nevertheless, there has been a recent resurgence in people using their gardens to grow food (Mintel 2010).

Given this range of meanings, values, attitudes and behaviours, along with the diverse environmental settings found in the UK, it is not possible to argue that some environmental settings will be somehow 'better satisfiers' than others in terms of the cultural goods they generate (Edensor 2000). Wild mountains in the wider countryside may provide the spaces mountaineers or wilderness-lovers need to pursue their cultural activities, but urban trees, gardens and local parks also play important roles in providing contact with nature and the living world for those who cannot, or do not wish to, travel to more remote locations (Harrison *et al.* 1987; Burgess *et al.* 1988; Dwyer *et al.* 1991; Crouch & Lubbren 2003).

16.3.1.3 Cultural goods, monetary and non-monetary values, and well-being

Given the complex ways cultural goods satisfy needs and how this can change over time, the rest of this chapter discusses cultural goods from a number of perspectives using a range of evidence. Some of the evidence is derived from existing studies on the characteristics of cultural goods. Other new evidence, especially on the economic value of cultural goods, has been generated especially for the UK NEA, the characteristics of which are discussed in Chapter 22.

A wide range of cultural goods emerge from the interactions between environmental settings and the processes of satisfying existence and value needs. Not all cultural goods are considered in this chapter, but the goods discussed are those for which there are quantitative and/or qualitative evidence to allow an assessment of their characteristics and to examine how the goods interact with environmental settings as the cultural ecosystem service. These goods have also been highlighted in previous studies and ecosystem assessments as being significant for human well-being and valued by different groups of people (MA 2005a; MA 2005c; Natural England 2009a). The following five main groups of goods are considered:

- Leisure, recreation and tourism goods
- Health goods
- Heritage goods
- Education and ecological knowledge goods
- Religious and spiritual goods

Each of these goods is the subject of a separate section which consider issues such as the nature of the good, how it satisfies need, changes in the good over time, how the good is shaped by the interactions between humans and environmental settings, and the monetary and non-monetary value of the good. Given the different characteristics of these goods, these issues are explored using economic/monetary, non-monetary and subjective well-being analysis involving both quantitative and qualitative evidence.

The economic valuation reported here, based on a standard welfare economics conceptual approach, aims to value, in monetary terms, the welfare benefits accruing from a selected number of cultural goods for which data are available. According to the total economic value framework, values can occur from use of a resource (either directly through personal contact or via books, film or other media), potential future use (i.e. option values), or be unrelated to any kind of use (i.e. non-use values, relating to altruistic, bequest or existence motivations). Most of the economic assessment reported here focuses on use values (or potential use), with non-use being considered by a study of environmental bequests.

Several monetary values are presented using new economic evidence generated specifically for the UK NEA; a far more detailed discussion of the approach used in the UK NEA for the economic valuation of ecosystem services can be found Chapter 22. The rest of this chapter summarises some of the key findings of that work. The existence of significant data gaps, however, means that monetary values have not been estimated for all the goods considered.

For example, there is currently insufficient quantitative information to make a reliable estimate of the monetary value of some of the spiritual and religious goods associated with environmental settings.

The non-monetary evidence presented is both qualitative and quantitative and is mostly drawn from previous studies. Some new quantitative measures relating to self-reported health benefits are presented, which were generated as part of the economic valuation conducted for the UK NEA (Chapter 22; Mourato et al. 2010). Further quantitative non-monetary evidence is also drawn from the subjective well-being (or life satisfaction) analysis undertaken by Mourato and other researchers specifically for the UK NEA, based on original data which measures the impact of environmental settings and related goods on well-being (Chapter 22; Mourato & MacKerron et al. 2010).

The distinction made in this chapter between monetary and non-monetary evidence is designed to avoid some of the conceptual difficulties raised by the discussion of cultural services in the MA (2005a) and other sub-global ecosystem assessments which identify so-called 'non-material benefits' arising from cultural services such as inspiration, aesthetic experiences, recreation and tourism. Difficulties arise, in part, because recreation and tourism linked to environmental settings can also be conceptualised as a material benefit with a market value. For example, recreational anglers who pay to catch fish clearly obtain a material benefit through a market mechanism, with an instrumental value to them as consumers. Furthermore, 'non-material' cultural goods must not be viewed as not having monetary value as they can be reflected in actual uses that can be measured in quantitative and monetary terms. For example, people may pay a premium to buy a house in a remote coastal location because of the sense of calm and escape, but those feelings can, in part, be captured in house price differentials. By discussing monetary and non-monetary values in a manner consistent with economic terminology, this chapter aims to avoid some of the difficulties that can arise with the general use of the term 'non-material benefit'.

This does not mean, however, that some of the more 'subjective' cultural goods that are usually described as 'non-material', such as inspiration and aesthetic experiences, are not considered in the discussion of cultural goods in this chapter. Previous research highlights their significance. Openness and remoteness in landscapes have been linked to feeling calm, relaxed and a sense of escape (Pretty 2007; Natural England 2009a). Research into an evolutionary, cross-cultural basis for our aesthetic preferences has shown the significance of particular kinds of natural landscapes for feelings of safety, and how natural beauty functions to produce emotions linked to inspiration, harmony, peace and security (Appleton 1975; Kellert 1993; Grinde &Patil 2009). These types of benefit involve very complex and not fully understood human cognitive and pre-cognitive processes linked to all the different cultural goods discussed in this chapter. Therefore, rather than discussing benefits such as inspiration or sense of security separately, they are considered in the discussions of the different cultural goods.

A related important point to note is that the benefits which arise from the various types of goods considered in this chapter are often bundled together, so it may not be possible to identify them separately (Chapter 22; Mourato *et al.* 2010). For example, a leisure visit may result in health, heritage and spiritual benefits. To address this issue, the economic valuation for the UK NEA calculated the overall 'amenity value' of environmental settings. Amenity value refers to the increase in welfare associated with living in, or within close proximity to, certain settings. This amenity value will be affected by a range of cultural goods that individuals experience from their interaction with particular settings and provides an aggregate measure of a number of benefits that are bundled together. Section 16.3.7 reports on measures of the aggregate contribution of cultural services and goods to human well-being by drawing on some of the key findings of new research undertaken for the UK NEA involving amenity value analysis, as well as the subjective well-being analysis relating to cultural goods and environmental settings in the UK NEA (Chapter 22).

A group of cultural goods that is not discussed fully in this chapter arise from the role played in ecosystems by wild species. The Conceptual Framework for the UK NEA (Chapter 2) notes that wild species as part of biodiversity occupy a complex position within ecosystem thinking. Wild species are both a service and a good (Bharucha & Pretty 2010). Wild species diversity is also identified in Chapter 2 as contributing to both provisioning and cultural services. The genetic diversity of wild species is involved in provisioning services and affects the characteristics of certain goods linked to provisioning services. For example, the diversity of wild crop relatives can contribute to food as a provisioning good by influencing strains of farm crops. Similarly, the characteristics of environmental settings that constitute cultural services can be affected by the absence or presence of wild species (Hinchcliffe *et al.* 2005). Consequently, human interactions with wild animals and plants can generate cultural goods partly because people value environmental settings where certain types of animals or plants are present. The complex nature of wild species and biodiversity in general means that they are considered in detail in other chapters of the UK NEA (Chapter 3 on biodiversity, Chapter 15 on provisioning services and the country synthesis chapters 17–20). As a result, the cultural goods directly linked to wild species are not examined in detail in this chapter, apart from a short discussion on the Royal Society for the Protection of Birds (RSPB)'s Big School Birdwatch in section 16.3.5 on education and ecological knowledge goods.

16.3.2 Leisure, Recreation and Tourism Goods

16.3.2.1 Definitions of leisure, recreation and tourism

There have been many attempts to identify what constitutes recreation and leisure. It is generally accepted that 'leisure' is a combination of time, activity and state of mind (Ravenscroft 1985), with recreation, tourism and sport comprising parts of its activity component. Broadhurst (2001, p.4) suggests that 'recreation' describes what we do with, or at, our 'leisure', while tourism encompasses the travel and accommodation required to gain access to some recreation and leisure activities. Following Mieczkowski (1981), we can

conceptualise the relationship between leisure, recreation, tourism and outdoor activities as shown in **Figure 16.7**.

This is consistent with Max-Neef (1992) in addressing the four existence human needs:

- **being** at leisure;
- **having** physical and legal access to a range of habitats (acknowledging that choices are often constrained (Green 1985; Curry & Ravenscroft 2001));
- **doing** recreation;
- and **interacting** with others through recreation and leisure in natural environments.

16.3.2.2 The role of environmental settings

Natural environments have been one of the most enduringly popular locations for recreation and leisure (Curry 1994), and all UK NEA Broad Habitats offer scope for addressing the existence needs of having and doing. Opportunities include:

- relatively generic opportunities to walk, run or cycle;
- specific opportunities only available in a few habitats (e.g. surfing on the sea);
- and unique settings that offer opportunities to achieve specific benefits related, for example, to seeing particular fauna and flora, or being able to climb particular crags (**Figure 16.8**).

Table 16.8 identifies the habitats and/or habitat features, the opportunities, and the potential benefits that can be derived from these services.

As **Table 16.8** indicates, those habitats that provide unique cultural services tend to be physically remote from urban populations and in places that are not suited to extensive development. This means that there are significant constraints in gaining access to them (Curry 1994). These constraints help limit human impacts, although it is recognised that additional management is often required to prevent degradation of the sites (Keirle 2002). Specific cultural services can be provided by a range of habitats,

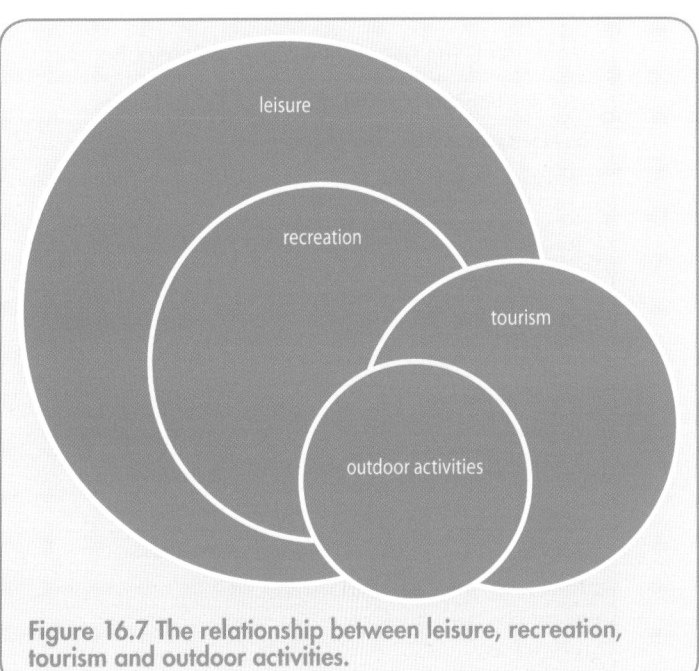

Figure 16.7 The relationship between leisure, recreation, tourism and outdoor activities.

Figure 16.8 Climbers on the Cow & Calf rocks near Ilkley, West Yorkshire, England. *Photo by Jim Moran available under a Creative Commons Attribution-NonCommercial-NoDerivs license.*

usually under particular atmospheric conditions such as snow, rain or wind. While some of these sites will be remote, others will be local and will provide a broad range of services that are meaningful to local people. Typical of this would be an urban park that might be used for snow sports at certain times of the year. Finally, many habitats, whether managed for recreation or not, offer opportunities for a broad range of cultural services. These environments include parks, tracks, paths, roads, verges and other elements of a 'green network' (Natural England 2009b).

16.3.2.3 Changing access to environmental settings

Access to ecosystem cultural services for recreation is highly differentiated throughout the UK (Curry 1994). A number of measures have been implemented to address this. These include Natural England's Accessible Natural Greenspace Standard (ANGSt), which provides a set of benchmarks for ensuring access to places near to where people live (Harrison *et al.* 1995; Handley *et al.* 2003). These standards recommend that people living in towns and cities should have:

- an accessible natural greenspace of at least 2 ha in size, no more than 300 m (5 minutes' walk) from home;
- at least one accessible 20 ha site within 2 kilometres of home;
- one accessible 100 ha site within 5 kilometres of home;
- one accessible 500 ha site within 10 kilometres of home;
- and statutory LNRs at a minimum level of 1 ha per thousand population.

It is recognised that, in some areas, this will be hard to achieve in the short-term (LUC2008), but Natural England argues that it should be a long-term aim for all local authorities within their Greenspace Strategies (Barker 1997; CABE 2006). Currently, in England, only 13% of homes in urban areas are within 300 m of a natural greenspace of at least 2 ha in size (CABE 2010), but this figure varies from 7% in Yorkshire and Humberside to 18% in the West Midlands.

Table 16.8 The opportunities and potential benefits of different habitats for recreation and tourism.

Habitat/habitat characteristic	Opportunities	Potential benefits
Unique opportunities—landscapes		
Mountains, crags and hills	Vertical and near vertical inclines	Climbing, mountaineering, rock scrambling, long range views and picnicking
Sea	Wind and waves	Surfing, kite surfing
Upland streams	Fast flowing shallow waters	Game angling, white water canoeing and rafting
Limestone rocks	Caves and fissures	Caving and potholing
Unique opportunities—landscapes/local places		
Alpine landscapes	Snow cover	Snow sports
Woodlands	Tree cover with tracks, rides and clearings	Walking, cycling, horse riding, many types of informal recreation
Estuarine environments	Sheltered waters	Moorings, marinas
Lakes	Wind	Sail sports
Beaches	Sand and sea	Outdoor swimming and beach activities
Generic opportunities—local places		
Parks and open spaces	Publicly accessible greenspaces	Walking, dog walking, cycling, running, picnicking and informal recreational activities

Recent legislative changes have contributed to improving access to some landscapes, with the Countryside and Rights of Way Act 2000 providing access to the uplands, downs and commons, and the Marine and Coastal Access Act 2009 promising to do the same for access to the coast. The 2008–09 audit of coastal access in England revealed that, of the 4,422 km (2,748 miles) of coast audited, 66% (2,940 km, 1,827 miles) had a legally secure and satisfactory path (Natural England 2009c). However, certain parts of England—in particular, some which are dominated by intensive lowland farming such as Lincolnshire—continue to offer limited accessibility to outdoor environments compared to other parts of the UK.

16.3.2.4 Environmental settings and trends in leisure, recreation and tourism

Research for Natural England (2009a) has identified that ecosystem services for recreation and leisure are often linked to settings where there is a lot to do, such as the local park or stretches of coastline. They are also associated with settings that have easy access, places that have rocks, crags, or things to climb, as well as lanes, roads and pathways. Woodlands are valued for the multiple benefits they provide including opportunities for walking and cycling.

In 2005, the last time that a national leisure visits survey was conducted for England, approximately two thirds of the English adult population visited natural habitats. Two thirds of their visits were to inland towns and/or cities, with the remaining one third, being to countryside, coast and woodlands (Natural England 2005). The duration of the visits was split equally between more than and less than three hours, with nearly 60% using a car and 25% walking to the site. This suggests a fairly even spread of visits between local 'doorstep' sites and those located further from home. The main activities undertaken during leisure visits were eating and drinking, walking, visiting friends and relatives, and shopping. Natural England (2010), the Department for Environment, Food and Rural Affairs and the Forestry Commission recently introduced a new survey, *Monitoring Engagement with the Natural Environment (MENE)*, to provide baseline and trend data on how people use the natural

environment in England. In the period March 2009 to February 2010, just over half the adult population normally visited the natural environment once a week, with a further 8% visiting on occasion. This equates to approximately 2.86 billion leisure visits for the 12-month period, which is in the order of 7% more than in 2005 (care has to be taken with this comparison since there are differences in scope and methodology between the 2005 and 2010 surveys). In common with previous surveys, the Monitoring Engagement with the Natural Environment survey found that visits to the natural environment are highest among people aged 45 to 64, people in employment, and people in the ABC1 socioeconomic categories. Interestingly, the proportion of visits to natural environments that take place in urban areas has fallen since 2005, with more visits to the countryside instead. This is consistent with Sport England's (2009) findings which revealed that there is substantial and growing participation in a number of outdoor sports that largely take place away from urban areas (**Table 16.9**).

Scottish Natural Heritage's Scottish Recreation Survey 2007 (TNS 2009) found that just under half of the adult population in Scotland had made at least one visit per week to the outdoors for leisure and recreation purposes in 2007—the same level as was recorded during 2006. Four fifths (80%) of the adult population claimed to have made at least one trip to the outdoors in the previous 12 months, which equates to around 340 million visits to the outdoors in Scotland during 2007 and a 3% increase on the estimate for 2006. One key trend observed in Scotland has been the year-on-year increase in the number of shorter duration visits made closer to home since 2004, with an average distance travelled of 18 km in 2007 (down from 26 km in 2004). Also, the proportion of visits taken on foot has increased from 50% in 2004 to 61% in 2007, while the proportion of visits taken by car has fallen from 43% to 31% over the same period of time.

In contrast, the 2008 Welsh Outdoor Recreation survey found that more than 90% of the Welsh population participate in some form of outdoor recreation, although less than 30% of these are classed as regular participants

Table 16.9 Sports participation: at least once a week for 30 minutes at moderate intensity. Note: The data is for moderate intensity activity resulting in participation levels for some activities (e.g. angling) appearing well below the overall participation level. Data is not included for walking due to the low intensity level of physical activity. Source: Sport England (2009).

Sport	Participation 2007–2008	Participation 2008–2009	Percentage (%) of adults
Angling	No data	56,700	0.14
Canoeing/Kayaking	43,500	62,900	0.15
Cycling	1,767,100	1,880,000	4.5
Equestrian	341,700	341,500	0.82
Golf	948,300	897,600	2.15
Mountaineering	86,100	83,900	0.2
Rowing	54,900	49,000	0.12
Sailing	89,900	83,000	0.2
Snow sports	120,600	106,800	0.26
Swimming (indoor and outdoor)	3,244,300	3,162,400	7.57

(at least five times per week) (Forestry Commission and Countryside Council for Wales 2008). Parks, woodlands and hilly areas are the most popular sites, with walking (often with dogs) being the most popular activity. The Welsh survey is due to be repeated in 2011. There are no comparable data for Northern Ireland, although the Forest Service reported that, in 2002–03, approximately 2 million visits were made to Forest Service woodlands, and over 400,000 visits were made to recreation areas in which a charge was made. Tourism data for Northern Ireland suggest that there has been a long-term increase in visits to natural environments, although there has been a recent (2008–09) downturn in visits. In contrast, visits to natural environments by local people are thought to be increasing.

16.3.2.5 The monetary value of environmental settings for leisure, recreation and tourism

Economic studies have highlighted the benefits and monetary value that arise from being able to access environmental settings. For example, Cheshire and Sheppard (2002) found that the economic benefits associated with accessible open space, such as parks, considerably exceeded those from more inaccessible open space such as green belt and farmland.

Hedonic pricing studies have shown that many people recognise the value of environmental settings by choosing to live near them, including those locations designated for leisure and recreational use such as National Parks. This means that the value of marginal changes in proximity to these environmental amenities is reflected in house and land prices. Of course, house prices will reflect a range of benefits linked to National Parks, such as health and aesthetic beauty, as well as leisure and tourism benefits. The economic valuation undertaken for the UK NEA (Chapter 22; Mourato et al. 2010) looked at more than 1 million housing transactions taking place between 1996 and 2008 and found that, proximity to National Parks sites was related to an increase in house prices: for each 1 km increase in distance from the nearest National Park house prices decreased by 0.24% or £460 at 2008 prices. In addition, location within a National Park can add 5% to house prices compared to the national average house prices. While being broadly transferable to the UK as a whole, the results exhibit significant regional variations, with people in the Midlands, for example, willing to pay more to live in a National Park than people living elsewhere (Chapter 22; Mourato et al. 2010).

In work commissioned for the UK NEA on the recreation value of UK habitats (Sen et al. 2010) using Site Prediction Models, Trip Generation Functions and Meta-Analysis, broadly similar relationships were revealed. They indicated that, for most habitats, visit numbers are highly influenced by travel time and associated costs, with the availability of substitute sites reducing people's value estimates of individual sites. This is less the case with highly prized landscapes (such as south-west England, the north Norfolk coast and the English Lake District), where visitors are prepared to pay high travel and associated costs to visit them. Using this methodology, Sen et al. (2010) estimated that, in 2000, 3.2 billion people per annum visited UK habitats,

generating a value of just over £10 billion (the estimates for England were 2.9 billion visits generating a value of £8.8 billion). This is somewhat lower than the recent estimate of £17 billion estimated for UK seaside tourism (Beaumont et al. 2010), although it is more consistent with other estimates (ONS 2005, 2006; Tinch et al. 2010). As Chapter 22 observes, given the size of expenditures involved and the likelihood of ecosystem services making a significant contribution to such values, there is a need for further investigation to determine more robust value estimates.

16.3.2.6 Changing satisfiers

The benefits of regular engagement with the natural environment are synergistic satisfiers. As the trend data suggests, more people have been enjoying these satisfiers in recent years, particularly as they visit the countryside and participate in informal recreation activities such as walking. These synergistic satisfiers are able to address all four existence human needs (being, having, doing and interacting). In addition, outdoor recreation and leisure are able to address a number of the axiological needs identified by Max-Neef (1992), including leisure, identity, participation, creation and freedom. Some aspects of outdoor recreation and leisure may also facilitate or promote understanding of the natural environment.

Alongside the growth in synergistic satisfiers has been a similar growth in pseudo-satisfiers such as wildlife and nature programmes on television and the rise of 'artificial' recreation experiences like indoor climbing walls and virtual reality simulators. Wildlife programmes have become popular across a broad spectrum of the viewing population and watching these programmes can appear to satisfy both existence and value needs, especially those related to leisure (being) and understanding. For some people they are synergistic to actual visits to the countryside (for example, the 'Springwatch effect' which has generated new tourism in Scotland; Scottish Government Social Research (2010)), but for others they may fail to deliver sustained satisfaction because the world they offer cannot be accessed by all. In the case of computer games and 'theme' parks, the experiences threaten to deny authentic engagement with the natural environment, rendering them inhibiting satisfiers. Equally, intense engagement in specific recreation activities, such as angling or canoeing, can become singular satisfiers, where just one need is satisfied (often the doing need) at the expense of all the others. Indeed, in the case of angling and canoeing, recent evidence from the National Assembly for Wales (NAW 2010) indicates that entrenched singular satisfiers can undermine being, having and interacting needs in the pursuit of a singular participatory goal.

In conclusion, the recent growth in engagement with natural environments is not necessarily an indication of the increasing value of ecosystem cultural services in economic or broader social or environmental terms. Indeed, increasing participation in individual sports activities could be associated with the increasing dominance of singular satisfiers, while growing reliance on television programmes, as well as actual experience, may promote pseudo- rather than synergistic satisfaction, or may become inhibiting satisfiers.

16.3.3 Health Goods

16.3.3.1 Environmental settings, physical activity and health

Environmental settings can contribute to a wide range of health goods, often by providing places where people can undertake physical activity and interact with nature. This physical activity can synergistically meet a range of our existence and value needs discussed in the conceptual approach in **Table 16.1**. It is particularly important for meeting our being and subsistence needs for good physical and mental health. By undertaking physical activity we can also meet our value needs to participate in activities, as well as meeting our having and doing existence needs by accessing open spaces designed for a range of formal and informal physical activity.

Within the last generation, physical activity levels have dropped to less than 40% of men and 28% of women in England (Craig & Mindell 2008) meeting UK Government guidelines to perform 30 minutes of exercise on most days. In the UK, energy expenditure per person declined by 800 kcal per day between 1945 and 1995 (Brownson et al. 2005; Davis et al. 2007).

Obesity has risen from 3–6% of adult populations to more than 25% in many industrialised countries (Foresight 2007); 23% of men and 26% of women lead sedentary lives (NICE 2009). Physical inactivity is known to track from childhood. It is associated with increased risk of obesity, is a key risk factor in many chronic diseases of later life, and leads to a reduced life expectancy (Dobbins et al. 2009). Physical inactivity results in 1.9 million deaths worldwide annually (WHO 2004)—roughly one in 25 of all deaths. The costs of inactivity in the UK are £8.3 billion per year, equating to £5 million for each Primary Care Trust (NICE 2009). It is estimated that a 1% reduction in inactivity would save 1,063 lives per year, reduce morbidity by 15,000 cases and save £1.4 billion. The monetary benefits (not including the mental health benefits) amount to £2,423 per additionally active person per year (NICE 2008).

Physical activity improves both physical and mental health (Laumann et al. 2003; DH 2004; Foresight 2007; Sandercock et al. 2010). Regular physical activity improves the survival of the elderly and their quality of life (Lim & Taylor 2004). It is now well-established that exposure to natural places, whether a view of nature from a window, being within natural places or exercising in these environments, can lead to positive mental health outcomes (Moore 1982; Ulrich 1984; Hartig et al. 2003; Pretty et al. 2005, 2007; Barton et al. 2009). Green space is important for mental well-being and levels of interaction/engagement with it have been linked with longevity and decreased risk of mental ill-health in Japan, Scandinavia and The Netherlands (Takano et al. 2002; de Vries et al. 2003; Grahn & Stigsdotter 2003). In addition, the importance of vitamin D—obtained from being outdoors in sunshine—has recently been identified as playing a role in long-term health (**Box 16.2**).

Urban noise, especially from transport, can affect well-being (Stansfield et al. 2000). Some environmental settings, particularly the countryside, offer less noisy, more tranquil locations. Traffic generated noise is one of the main sources of noise pollution, with excessive noise from traffic and railways in urban areas commonly resulting in stress (den Boer & Schroten 2007; Ozer et al. 2008). Ecosystems containing trees and shrub vegetation have been demonstrated to be particularly effective at providing barriers to noise in urban settings (Frumkin et al. 2004; Ozer et al. 2008; Fitter et al. 2010; Ernstson et al. 2010). Recent research suggests that certain countryside landscapes offer experiences that provide people with a sense of calm and tranquillity (Natural England 2009a). The Campaign to Protect Rural England have undertaken a series of studies to map changes in tranquillity and argue that the proportion of England defined as tranquil is declining (tranquillity mapping is explored further in Chapter 17).

'Green exercise', defined as physical activity taking place in the presence of nature, has been shown to lead to positive health outcomes (Ulrich et al. 1991; Hartig et al. 1991; van den Berg 2003; Morita et al. 2006; Hine et al. 2007; Mind 2007; Pretty et al. 2007; Barton & Pretty 2010), as well as promoting ecological knowledge (Burgess 1995; Pilgrim et al. 2007, 2008; Pretty 2007), fostering social bonds (Burgess et al. 1988; Kawachi et al. 1997; Takano et al. 2002; Pretty 2007) and influencing behavioural choices (Kuo et al. 1998; Maas et al. 2006; Mitchell & Popham 2008; Peacock et al. 2008).

There is still a need for further research into the benefits of green exercise (Barton & Pretty 2010). Increases in physical activity produce physical and mental health benefits and the outcomes vary among subgroups of the population. A systematic review of previous studies has shown that the extent to which outdoor environments produce a greater effect on physical and mental well-being than indoor environments is still uncertain (Thompson Coon 2011); however, recent research shows the additional benefits of outdoor over indoor activity for clinical populations suffering mental ill-health (Barton et al. 2011).

16.3.3.2 Health, nature and urban greening

A substantial body of research on the associations between nature and health has been produced from the UK, US,

---

> **Box 16.2 Sunlight and vitamin D.** Source: Holick (2004); Kampman et al. (2007).
>
> Humans depend on exposure to the sun for the synthesis of adequate amounts of vitamin D. Ultraviolet B light is absorbed by dehydrocholesterol in the skin; this is transformed and further converted to vitamin D3 which is metabolised by the liver to its biologically active form. Lack of vitamin D has long been recognised as causing rickets in children, as well as exacerbating osteoporosis and even osteomalacia in adults. More recently, it has been recognised that vitamin D deficiency is associated with increased risks of some cancers, cardiovascular disease, multiple sclerosis, rheumatoid arthritis and type I diabetes, with possible links to type II diabetes and schizophrenia (Holick 2004). Furthermore, the incidence of multiple sclerosis has been shown to be affected by latitude, with people at lower latitudes having an increased risk of developing it due to reduced sunlight exposure, although Norway appears to be an exception possibly as a result of increased summer outdoor activities in childhood and diet both of which have been shown to protect against MS. It is conceivable that concerns over skin cancers combined with less time spent in outdoor environmental settings is reducing exposure to sunlight and, therefore, contributing to the incidence of some of these chronic diseases. However, sensible exposure to the sun for five to ten minutes three times per week is likely to be highly beneficial.

Scandinavia and Japan. This research addresses a wide range of themes including:

1. **Levels of engagement with nature:** the view from the window (Moore 1982; Ulrich 1984; Kaplan 1995; Kaplan 2001; Parsons *et al.* 1998; Diette *et al.* 2003; Pretty *et al.* 2005); the role of nearby nature and urban greenspace (Harrison *et al.* 1987; Burgess *et al.* 1988; Takano *et al.* 2002; de Vries *et al.* 2003; Grahn & Stigsdotter 2003; Tabbush & O'Brien 2003); the outcomes from countryside activities (Butryn & Furst 2003; Hartig *et al.* 2003; Morita *et al.* 2006; Yamaguchi *et al.* 2006; Pretty *et al.* 2007); and the outcomes from wilderness programmes (Davis-Berman & Berman 1989; Cason & Gillis 1993; Russell 2003).

2. **Types of engagement with a wide range of activities** including walking, gardening, fishing, hunting (Samson & Pretty 2005; Pretty 2007), and different types of settings from the urban built environment to countryside and wilderness.

3. **Mental health outcomes** using a range of measures of self-esteem, mood and stress (Ulrich *et al.* 1991; Hartig *et al.* 1991, 2003; van den Berg 2003; Pretty *et al.* 2005, 2007; Peacock *et al.* 2007).

4. **Physical health outcomes** using heart rate, blood pressure, Body Mass Index, waist measures (waist circumference and waist to hip ratios) and physical activity level (Laumann *et al.* 2003; Hartig *et al.* 2003; Pretty *et al.* 2005; Wells *et al.* 2007; Sandercock *et al.* 2010).

5. **Epidemiological studies** showing associations between home proximity to greenspace and health (Maas *et al.* 2006; Mitchell & Popham 2008), and associations between the presence of nature on urban estates and reduced recorded crime (Kuo *et al.* 1998; Kuo & Sullivan 2001a, 2001b).

Large-scale quantitative studies have shown that the prevalence of psychiatric morbidity is greater in urban areas and less common in rural domains, after adjusting for confounding variables (Galea *et al.* 2005; Lewis & Booth 1994; White & Heerwagen 1998). Lewis & Booth (1994) found that the prevalence of psychiatric morbidity among urban residents (33.7%) was higher than their rural counterparts (24.8%), after controlling for socioeconomic and other extraneous variables. Income-related inequalities in health also depend on exposure to greenspace. People who live in greener areas reported lower levels of health inequality relating to income deprivation for both all-cause mortality and mortality from circulatory diseases (Mitchell & Popham 2008). The presence of urban nature is a well-documented example of a synergic satisfier, meeting a substantial number of human needs at the same time. Empirical evidence demonstrates that green urban environmental settings:

- improve human health and well-being (Kaplan & Kaplan 1989; Frumkin 2001; Irvine & Warber 2002; HCN 2004);
- facilitate the taking of exercise (Giles-Corti & Donovan 2002; Giles-Corti *et al.* 2005);
- improve behaviour and cognitive functioning (Wells 2000; Taylor *et al.* 2001);
- provide an outdoor classroom (Kaplan & Kaplan 1989; Kahn & Kellert 2002);

- facilitate social networking (Kuo *et al.* 1998; Ward-Thompson *et al.* 2006; Hitchings 2010);
- reduce levels of crime, aggression and violence (Kuo & Sullivan 2001a; 2001b);
- and improve the aesthetic value of urban environments (Sheets & Manzer 1991; Frumkin *et al.* 2004; Frumkin 2005).

[The terms 'health' and 'human well being' are often used interchangeably, but the term 'health' usually incorporates physical health, mental or emotional health, social health, spiritual health, lifestyle and functionality.]

A direct link between the amount of accessible local greenspace and health has also been evidenced, using large-scale epidemiological studies in other countries (de Vries *et al.* 2003; Grahn & Stigsdotter 2003; Takano *et al.* 2002). Tree-lined streets, parks and other environmental settings play a key role in longevity and decreased risk of mental ill-health (Takano *et al.* 2002). Self-reported health data from over 10,000 Dutch respondents reported that people living in greener neighbourhoods enjoyed better general health (de Vries *et al.* 2003). The type of environmental setting did not seem to alter effectiveness, however. The total amount of greenspace in the living environment seemed to be the most relevant predictor. This crude measure does not acknowledge that the exposure to greenspace may vary considerably between residents of the same neighbourhood and that durations of exposure may also differ (Harrison *et al.* 1995). Empirical research by Sugiyama *et al.* (2008) demonstrates that perceived neighbourhood greenness is also strongly associated with better mental and physical health. Respondents who perceive their neighbourhood as highly green are 1.37 and 1.60 times more likely to have better physical and mental health respectively, in comparison with those who perceived it as low in greenery. The degree of species richness in urban greenspaces has also been positively associated with the psychological well-being of visitors (Fuller *et al.* 2007), emphasising the importance of locally managed biodiversity for sense of place and reflection.

In terms of overall health, studies of local park users in the USA reported fewer visits to a physician for purposes other than routine check-ups in comparison with non-park users. This difference was apparent even when controlling for the effects of age, income, education level, health status and other potential confounding variables (Godbey *et al.* 1998). Frequently active park users also scored better on self-reported health indices and perceived their health states to be better than passive users and non-park users (Godbey *et al.* 1998). Thus, people engaging in recreation in local parks seem to be in disproportionately better health than non-users and are also less likely to be obese than the general population (Ho *et al.* 2003). Godbey and Blazey (1983) also investigated the leisure behaviour of adults participating in light to moderate aerobic activity in urban parks and found that over half reported better moods after visiting the park. In addition, More and Payne (1978) also in the USA found that participants' negative moods improved and that park users reported lower levels of anxiety and depression. Often visitors started their recreation experiences in a better mood and their positive moods remained on leaving, implying that outdoor recreation and park use might enhance positive moods, reduce negative ones and alleviate stress. Similar findings are reported from Sweden (Grahn & Stigsdotter 2003).

Research on associations between physical access to greenspace, frequency of use, physical activity and health (including obesity) which draws together Geographical Information System (GIS) data, including the Index of Multiple Deprivation, with quantitative social surveys is developing in the UK (Hillsdon et al. 2006; Jones et al. 2009; Coombes et al. 2010). The research, conducted in Bristol, provides robust statistical evidence that the frequency of reported greenspace use declines with increasing distance from the home, and that a statistically significant relationship exists between physical activity and accessible greenspace, even when adjustments for respondent characteristics, area deprivation and neighbourhood characteristics are made to the data.

A number of the studies discussed above in this section identify associations rather than causal relationships between greenspace and health. Casual relationships can be hard to identify, partly because—as is the case in many epidemiological studies—directionality is unclear. Existing health can affect an individual's use of greenspace or choice of residence near a particular environmental setting, and vice versa. Nevertheless, these findings suggest more attention should be given to developing the use of green exercise as a therapeutic intervention ('green care'), and planners and architects should be encouraged to improve access to greenspace ('green design'). Some of the substantial mental health challenges facing society (Foresight 2008) and physical challenges arising from modern diets and sedentary lifestyles (Wanless 2002; DH 2004; Sport England 2006; Wells et al. 2007; DCSF 2009; NICE 2009) could be addressed by increasing physical activity in natural places. If we encourage and enable children to undertake more green exercise, they are more likely to have active exposure to nature embedded in their lifestyle as adults and will reap the associated improvements in health.

16.3.3.3 Access to nature and the health and well-being of children

Open greenspace and access to nature is important for children (Ward 1978, 1988; Harrison et al. 1987; Kaplan & Kaplan 1989; Kahn & Kellert 2002; Bingley & Milligan 2004; Thomas & Thompson 2004; Louv 2005; Ward-Thompson et al., 2008; Gleave 2009; Pretty et al. 2009). The quality of their environmental exposure is inextricably linked to their well-being (Thomas & Thompson 2004). Children's relationship with nature is a fundamental part of their development, allowing opportunities for self-discovery and natural environmental experience (Nabhan & Trimble 1994; Bird 2007). The outdoor environment is perceived as a social space which influences their choice of informal play activities and promotes healthy personal development (Burgess et al. 1988; Thomas & Thompson 2004). Nature allows unstructured play, generating a sense of freedom, independence and inner strength which children can draw upon when experiencing future incidents of stress (Orr 2002; Wells & Lekies 2006).

Wells (2000) conducted a longitudinal study with children of low income urban families and assessed the effects of nature on their cognitive functioning. When the families were relocated to houses with more nearby nature they had higher levels of cognitive functioning and their enhanced ability to direct attention continued for several months after moving. Another quasi-experimental study explored the idea that nature could act as a buffer to stressful events among rural children. Wells and Evans (2003) reported that 8–10-year old children exposed to high levels of nearby nature, both indoors and outdoors, were less stressed and recovered from stressful events more successfully than those in homes or with backyards that lacked contact with nature. However, cause and effect can be difficult to disentangle and decipher. Does contact with nature aid the development of stress-coping mechanisms which are used in later life? Or does nearby nature provide the opportunity for stress recovery? Additionally, does nearby nature provide the opportunity to play with other children (social contact), or is the improved tolerance to stress due to a combination of many factors? Further research is needed to establish the health effects of nature on children.

Taylor et al. (1998) found that nearly twice as many children chose to play in open spaces with trees compared with barren spaces lacking nature. They engaged in much more creative play and were more likely to spend time with adults, which facilitated social development. This was particularly apparent in a study involving children with Attention Deficit Hyperactivity Disorder (ADHD) (Taylor et al. 2001). Children worked better and their concentration improved after participating in activities in green surroundings. Bingley and Milligan (2004) assessed how recalled childhood play experiences (from ages 7–11 years) in the form of memories and imaginings have an influence on the mental well-being of adults. For instance, childhood experiences of unstructured play with minimal adult supervision in woodland areas significantly influenced the perception of woodlands in adult life and the seeking out of outdoor spaces when stressed.

Infrequent woodland or greenspace experiences as a child correlates with a lower frequency of visits during adulthood (Ward-Thompson et al. 2008). Therefore, lack of outdoor experiences during childhood may hinder any desires to visit such places as adults, to engage in physical activity, or to benefit from its emotional restorative qualities. It is also known that children's social play, concentration and motor ability are all positively influenced by playing in nature. Yet the opportunities for children resident in both urban and rural neighbourhoods to join in safe play are rapidly diminishing, partly because of parental fear of crime and volume of road traffic (Holloway & Valentine 2000; 2003). Children spend less time outdoors today than they used to (Orr 2002; Louv 2005), and as children have become more disconnected from the natural environment, they understand it less (Bird 2007).

16.3.3.4 Environmental settings: the benefits for health and well-being

Measuring the value of the health and well-being benefits that arise from contact with environmental settings and undertaking outdoor exercise raises particular challenges.

For example, assessments of the environmental and mental health benefits of outdoor exercise need to estimate additional exercise that is directly attributable to particular settings and would not have occurred anyway either in an environmental setting or an indoor environment (CJC Consulting and Willis 2005).

The economic valuation for the UK NEA (Chapter 22) uses secondary data to examine the link between greenspace and created physical exercise within the sedentary portion of the UK population. The study suggests that there are potentially large-scale economic benefits from increasing physical activity among sedentary people.

However, the study surmises that there is "no conclusive evidence on the strength of the relationship between the amount of greenspace in the living environment and the level of physical activity. Hence, it is not possible to accurately value, at the present time, the health benefits of created exercise due to additional greenspace provision" (Chapter 22; Mourato *et al.* 2010).

As part of the economic valuation in Chapter 22, the UK NEA collected new primary data on the interactions between environmental settings and health (for full details see the supporting report by Mourato *et al.* 2010). A geographically referenced quota survey of 1,851 respondents was undertaken to examine the physical and mental health effects associated with various forms of contact and exposure to environmental settings, habitats and other natural amenities. Using this data, ordinary least squares (OLS) regression models were developed in which the explanatory variables included attributes relating to certain environmental settings and other environmental characteristics. Two dependent variables were based on validated measures of respondents' self-reported physical and mental health. The nature of the dependent variables is central to understanding the analysis undertaken, so they are summarised in **Table 16.10** and the regression results are presented in **Table 16.11**.

One of the key limitations of the OLS regression is that any association identified cannot be interpreted as a causal effect, but could be because of omitted variables that could affect dependent or independent variables (Chapter 22; Mourato *et al.* 2010). Also, when considering the results in **Table 16.11**, it is particularly important to bear in mind that causality between dependent and independent variables is likely to be bidirectional. For example, physical functioning could influence the use of an environmental setting, but not *vice versa*. This is a limitation of many epidemiological and survey-based studies examining health and environmental settings. More detailed controlled experiments are needed to establish causality.

Nevertheless, the OLS regression does show statistically significant relationships between both health measures and the use of the environmental settings of domestic gardens and local greenspaces. Respondents who visit non-countryside greenspaces, such as urban parks, at least once a month report significantly better health on both measures compared to those who do not. The same results are also shown for respondents who spend time in their garden at least once a week. Visits to the countryside at least once a month only have a positive relationship with physical functioning, but the association is likely to

Table 16.10 Health dependent variables. Source: Mourato *et al.* (2010).

Dependent variable	Description	Survey items
Physical functioning	SF-36 subscale: mean of 10 coded survey items	The following items are about activities you might do during a typical day. Does **your health now limit you** in these activities? If so, how much? • **Vigorous activities** such as running, lifting heavy objects, participating in strenuous sports • **Moderate activities** such as moving a table, pushing a vacuum cleaner, bowling, or playing golf • **Lifting** or carrying groceries • Climbing **several** flights of stairs • Climbing **one** flight of stairs • Bending, kneeling, or stooping • Walking **more than a mile** • Walking **several blocks** • Walking **one block** • Bathing or dressing yourself Yes, limited a lot = 0 Yes, limited a little = 50 No, not limited at all = 100
Emotional well-being	SF-36 subscale: mean of 5 coded survey items	How much of the time during the **past 4 weeks...** • Have you been a very nervous person? (–) • Have you felt so down in the dumps that nothing could cheer you up? (–) • Have you felt calm and peaceful? (+) • Have you felt downhearted and blue? (–) • Have you been a happy person? (+) All of the time = 100 (+) / 0 (–) Most of the time = 80 (+) / 20 (–) A good bit of the time = 60 (+) / 40 (–) Some of the time = 40 (+) / 60 (–) A little of the time = 20 (+) / 80 (–) None of the time = 0 (+) / 100 (–)

Table 16.11 Physical functioning and emotional well-being scores from UK NEA ordinary least squares **(OLS) regressions.**
Notes: The 'a' models include all respondents from England, Wales, Scotland and Northern Ireland, and have only a subset of spatial variables available. The 'b' models include all spatial variables, but are limited to England and Wales. The statistical significance relates to the precision of the estimate, and the degree of confidence that the association is not a feature of this particular sample rather than an underlying relationship in the population. Three stars indicates that the chance of observing this estimate if there is no underlying relationship is less than 0.1%, two stars indicates 1%, one star 5%, and the cross indicates a weak level of statistical significance at 10%. No stars indicates that there is a high chance of observing this coefficient even if there is no underlying relationship, i.e. the coefficient is statistically insignificantly different from zero at the 10% level. †Income is logged to account for diminishing marginal returns. The income measure used is household income divided by weighted household size. ‡Summed self-reported housing problems, out of: infestations, damp, mould, serious draughts, inadequate heating, low daylight. §Number of rooms divided by number of residents. Source: Mourato et al. (2010).

Demographics	SF-36 physical functioning (0–100)		SF-36 emotional well-being (0–100)	
	(1a)	(1b)	(2a)	(2b)
Male (0/1)	1.48	0.98	1.89*	2.17*
Age	-0.61**	-0.48*	-0.56**	-0.42*
Age‡	0.00012	-0.0012	0.0083***	0.0068***
Log (income) †	3.74***	3.88***	3.33***	3.39***
Living alone (0/1)	1.54	1.68	-2.23+	-1.76
Unemployed (0/1)	8.66***	7.65**	1.59	0.19
Religious (0/1)	-3.59**	-3.15*	-1.03	-0.68
Exercise (IPAQ total MET-hours/week)	0.012**	0.015**	0.011**	0.011**
Housing				
Homeowner without mortgage (0/1)	3.40*	2.84+	1.98	2.40+
Social tenant (0/1)	-9.06***	-9.07***	0.64	0.58
Housing problems (count) ‡	-4.67***	-5.24***	-4.79***	-5.09***
House crowding §	-3.16+	-2.86	0.48	0.65
Green space use and views				
Home views of grass (0/1)	2.08	1.98	5.03***	5.20***
Home views of water (0/1)	0.94	0.34	2.28	3.21
Weekly+ use of garden (0/1)	3.30*	3.54*	3.25**	3.70**
Monthly+ countryside visits (0/1)	3.08*	2.83+	1.31	0.91
Monthly+ other greenspace visits (0/1)	4.15**	3.44*	2.62*	2.58*
National Park visits per year (count)	-0.26	-0.26	0.18	0.26
Marine and Coastal Margins	-0.0063	-0.012	0.027	0.037
Freshwaters—Openwaters, Wetlands and Floodplains	0.039	0.056	0.0095	0.0093
Mountains, Moorlands and Heaths	-0.094	0.079	-0.034	0.0025
Semi-natural Grasslands	0.0018	0.021	-0.019	-0.018
Enclosed Farmland	-0.0043	0.016	-0.0019	0.018
Coniferous Woodland	0.035	-0.031	0.033	-0.020
Broadleaved/Mixed Woodland	0.023	0.058	0.00028	0.046
Inland bare ground	0.075	0.13	-0.10	-0.032
Distance to nearest...and other variables				
National Park boundary (km, 0 if inside)		-0.0079		0.022
National Trust site (km)		-0.086		0.026
Coastline (km)		0.0072		0.022
Motorway (km)		0.020		-0.014
A-road (km)		0.19		-0.067
Railway station (km)		-0.19		-0.18
Population density (1,000/km2)		0.66+		0.67*
Standardised house price index		0.011		-0.019
Countries (base category is England)				
Wales (0/1)	-4.37	-4.18	-2.50	-2.31
Scotland (0/1)	-3.47		-2.30	
Northern Ireland (0/1)	3.44		-2.69	
Constant	65.6***	57.9***	29.2***	19.4*
Observations	1851	1647	1851	1647
Adjusted R-squared	0.181	0.181	0.135	0.141

be bidirectional (Chapter 22; Mourato *et al.* 2010). A view of grass from the home was seen to have a significantly positive impact on emotional well-being.

16.3.4 Heritage Goods

16.3.4.1 Heritage and environmental settings

'Heritage' is the term often used to refer to what the past bequeaths the present; like many other cultural goods, it is a contested concept since the elements of the past valued by one social group may not be valued by another. There is often disagreement between experts and lay publics about, for example, the appropriateness of restoring historic buildings, parks and landscapes (Rackham 1986; Laurier 1998; Harvey 2001). The role of ecosystem services in the emergence of heritage goods in the UK is complex, and the experience of heritage will vary markedly between different groups of people in different parts of the country (English Heritage 2000). In the UK, ecosystems, habitats and environmental settings are all heavily infused with the cultural values and histories of human use, with each adaptation imprinting the values and assumptions of the cultures of that time and place on the different environmental settings.

At a larger geographical scale, certain types of cultural landscapes based on a range of environmental settings and built environments act as synergistic satisfiers for human needs. In particular, these wider landscapes, such as the Highlands of Scotland or the Welsh borders, can contribute to the human value need for 'identity' (both individual and collective) and for a range of democratic 'freedoms' including the rights and responsibilities associated with ideas of citizenship (Lowenthal 1985; Cosgrove & Daniels 1988; Tilley 2006; Graham & Howard 2008). The artistic and creative endeavour that is often involved in the emergence of cultural landscapes indicates that heritage goods can play a role in the meeting of value needs for creativity (Cosgrove & Daniels 1988).

Through their differing heritages, however, every environmental setting is capable of being interpreted as possessing a distinctive sense of place (English Heritage 2000). Thus, they can contribute to a range of human needs, such as the need for 'protection' by creating a sense of local solidarity, or the need for 'affection' by nurturing passion for places, as well as contributing to the need for identity, leisure and understanding. Equally, some notions of heritage attached to particular environmental settings can be exclusive and ignore the heritage others feel is present. The intricacies and personal nature of the relationship between needs, environmental settings and the past creates analytical challenges, but is fundamental to understanding heritage goods. As Lowenthal (1985) observes, every society "inherit(s) a legacy no less precious for being often indecipherable or inconvenient. To be is to have been, and to project our messy, malleable past into our unknown future"; furthermore, "what people treasure about it (the past) arises out of needs and desires seldom analysed" (p.63).

The complex emotional and personalised characteristics of heritage goods mean that there are noticeable social differences in how heritage is perceived. In 2000, one of the most detailed quantitative studies of public attitudes towards heritage and the historic environment in England was carried out by Ipsos MORI for English Heritage (2000). With a sample of 3,000 people and, for the first time, a specific quota sample of individuals drawn from Black and Asian communities, the research provides statistically significant evidence of the continuing importance of heritage and access to historic environmental settings across the country. The Ipsos MORI survey embraced a range of environmental settings including parks, gardens, countryside, inner city streets, market towns and rural villages, as well as sites of historical interest such as castles, ecclesiastical buildings, stately homes and archaeological sites.

The Ipsos MORI study showed that almost every feature in an environmental setting will have a form of value for someone through personal memories and attachments. The survey confirmed that people's ideas and values relating to heritage are both idiosyncratic in terms of their everyday lives and environmental settings, as well as consensual when considering what constitutes national heritage. Accordingly, 98% of adults thought that heritage is important to educate children about the past and that all school children should be given the opportunity to find out about England's heritage. In addition, 88% of adults agreed that it is right that there should be public funding to preserve the country's heritage (English Heritage 2000). Such surveys often produce high levels of agreement, especially if respondents are not presented with trade-offs over which to make judgements of relative importance. Nevertheless, these findings suggest a consensus around the importance of heritage in general. However, nearly half of the respondents from Black and Asian communities did not consider English country houses and ancient monuments to be relevant to their experiences and interests. These feelings, often expressed as a sense of exclusion, have also been conveyed by members of ethnic minorities in the context of outdoor recreation and use of the countryside (The Countryside Agency 2003).

Consequently, there is a very diverse range of heritage goods that are linked to ecosystem services ranging in scale and ease of identification from perceived national landscapes, through territorially demarcated National Trust land, to the subtle and personal historical meanings people may attach to some urban commons. This section cannot provide a detailed overview of all these heritage goods; instead, it aims to provide a framework for interpretation by drawing on existing evidence, case studies and new evidence of monetary value estimated for the UK NEA to highlight certain key heritage goods at the national and local level.

16.3.4.2 Landscape, heritage goods and national identity

The interactions between cultures, environmental settings and habitats have led, over long periods of time, to the emergence of a series of landscapes that constitute heritage goods based on material objects, imaginations and memoires. The cultural appreciation of high hills, mountains and moorlands in England, Wales and Scotland as landscapes of wilderness in an urbanised world has lasted for over two centuries, but has also been used culturally to promote ideas of national identity and difference. The landscape heritage of the UK has been used as visual evidence for a variety of (often contradictory) national narratives, some working with a myth of a deep Albion, others with Celtic identity, Anglo-Saxon heritages and more (Smiles 2003; Bender 2004). It is no coincidence that the movement for founding the National Trust arose from efforts to preserve ancient monuments, nor that the first generation of National Parks followed the Romantic landscape vision in focusing on upland Britain (Squire 1988; Shoard 1982; Stephenson 1989). Additionally, the cultural heritage of the land is not easy to distinguish from the geophysical heritage when, for instance, archaeologists and geomorphologists clash over the 'naturalness' of clearings in block fields (Tilley *et al.* 2000).

The connection of natural areas with cultural heritage has a long and distinctive history in the UK, linked to the notable tradition of art and literature in transforming the landscape from an environmental setting to a "scenery with amenity value" (Andrews 1999, p.56). Of particular interest, the interpretive frameworks brought to bear on the scenery of mountains and moorlands address abstract values of national 'identity' and democratic 'freedom'. For example, early 18th Century appreciation of the sublimity of mountainous landscapes undoubtedly played a major role in transforming relationships to environmental settings, but the connection to ideas of national identity is complex (Darby 2000). Wordsworth's *Guide to the Lakes* (1810) refers to the Lake District as being "a sort of national property" while, at the same time, using North American archetypes to describe a primordial wildwood and Alpine archetypes for the mountains (Whyte 2000). Alpine ecosystems could be said to have played a significant role in British cultural heritage (Zaring 1977) and British culture, especially through the activities of its 19th Century mountaineers (Hansen 1995) who changed how alpine lands were seen.

The era of European nation-building coincided with the Romantic era, and romantic nationalism has accordingly been characterised by an intense relationship to nature. Nation-states needed to build collective memories at a scale larger than the locality—a sense of 'imagined community' (Anderson 1991)—in order to generate loyalty to the new space of the nation. Zimmer (1998) argues that, not only was there a process of 'nationalising of nature', drawing territorial boundaries around habitats and landscapes considered 'native' or 'authentic' to a country, but also of 'naturalsizing the nation', with social identities being authenticated or regenerated through contact with nature (Tolia-Kelly 2007b). An identification with certain sites and environments provided a means through which national citizenship could be built; a great variety of cultural products, including painting, literature, music, sculpture, television and film, have been deployed in such representational work (Higson 1987; Daniels 1993; Cant & Morris 2006).

While certain versions of national identity have gathered around urban areas and spectacular architectural sites and monuments across the UK, the defining senses of place appear to be built around typically rural landscapes (Weiner 2004); although Turner's many seascape paintings also have strong resonances with national identity, in part, due to their connections to a specific 19th Century period in naval history. English identities, in particular, have coalesced around the notion of 'deep England' (Matless 1998), with agricultural lowland landscapes as symbols of continuity, social stability and a productive nature (Lowenthal 1991). Shoard (1982) and Matless (1993; 1998) show how, in the 20th Century, debates about landscape, place-based conservation and citizens' engagement with nature collectively constructed a 'moral geography' of English identity in landscape. Askins (2009) argues that this invocation creates an urban-rural dichotomy which works to exclude ethnic groups from claims to 'English' landscapes and places. The rural in the sense of not-urban has provided a resource for a variety of English nationalisms. Inevitably, this has involved repressing a variety of entangled histories that show the countryside of the pastoral idyll has never been separate from histories of social class, colonialism (Perry 1994; Fraiman 1995; Winter 1996; Howkins 2003; Woods 2003; Tolia-Kelly 2010) and black presences in places and landscapes (Bressey 2009).

In Scotland, the national sense of place is divided between the lowlands and the highlands, with the latter providing the nation with its globally powerful, externally projected identity of 'Tartanry' and 'Balmorality' (McCrone *et al.* 1995). Lorimer (1997; 2000) shows how, for example, educational opportunities offered to children from urban Scotland to engage with wild landscape in the Highlands promoted a particular form of national citizenship. Rennie (2006) notes how the easy passage of the National Parks (Scotland) Act 2000 signified a desire that the Highland landscapes be enshrined in legislation as a symbol of devolved Scottish identity; but she also argues that debates around the Bill revealed a far more fluid sense of place-based identity. Thus, the landscape and habitats of the Scottish Highlands, largely artefacts of sporting interests and the eradication of marginal agriculture (Lorimer 2000), have become to be seen as crucibles of a popular national identity. The appeal to 'Scottishness' works despite a history that has excluded substantial sectors of the population, especially visible minorities (Askins 2006).

In Wales, a strong sense of place-based identity developed during the 20th Century with the emergence of an urban, industrial and largely English-speaking identity in the south, and a rural, agricultural and Welsh-speaking one in the north-west in particular. For many politicians and other commentators, the rural has been viewed as a more 'authentic' identity, based on the Romantic era notion of the *gwerin* ('folk') living sustainable lives free from the corruption of capitalism (Gruffudd 1994). The defence of these rural landscapes and their populations from perceived threats have provided instances of mass political and civic engagement (Gruffudd 1995). The emergent sense of a deeply layered cultural relationship to place has recently been embodied in the Countryside Council for Wales' (CCW 2008) LANDMAP methodology for assessing the cultural landscape. Not only is the visual and material record of importance, "but the relationship also manifests itself in immaterial ways, in the way we think of landscape and respond to it, how we describe it, and how we acquire our 'sense of place'" (CCW 2008, p.1). The connections between history, culture and environment were further emphasised in

The Welsh Assembly Government's (WAG 2006) first position statement on the Historic Environment which identified listed buildings and ancient monuments, as well as 58 'historic landscapes'—a designation that has no equivalent in the UK or Europe. The interrelationship between cultural identity and sense of place has also been acknowledged in the recent call by the Institute of Welsh Affairs (IWA) for National Park Authorities in Wales to be given legislative responsibility for social and cultural affairs in addition to environmental concerns (IWA 2009).

16.3.4.3 Environmental settings, heritage goods and local identity: some examples

Environmental settings also function as a generator of a vast range of local identities based around a more local and everyday sense of heritage. Heritage goods, therefore, can be a source of community empowerment, as well as potential conflict between different interests (Cloke *et al.* 1996; Clifford & King 2006; Common Ground 2009a; Schofield & Szymanski 2011), and this section provides some examples of the interconnections between heritage goods and local identities.

The environmental education charity Common Ground provides a case study of an organisation that has campaigned to protect what it calls 'local distinctiveness', not only because of the value of ecological diversity, but also because of the enriching social and spiritual value of sense of place:

"...many of us have strong allegiances to places, complex and compound appreciation of them, and we recognise that nature, identity and place have strong bonds. We sometimes forget that ours is a cultural landscape. It is our great creation: underpinned by nature, it is a physical thing and an invisible web... Places are process and story as well as artefact, layer upon layer of our continuing history and nature's history intertwined. Places offer an exposition of their evolution, given sensitive development and barefoot education, everyplace is its own living museum, dynamic and filled with sensibilities to its own small richnesses. These are places we know when we are in them. Meaning is entrapped in the experience of change, symbolisms and significance cling to seemingly ordinary buildings, trees, artefacts" (Common Ground 2009a).

One of Common Ground's most creative methods for generating community spirit around a place has been the Parish Maps project. The significance of the parish is explained thus:

"We are trying to focus on locality, the smallest arena in which life is played out. The territory to which you feel loyalty, which has meaning to you, about which you share some knowledge, for which protectiveness is easily roused, the neighbourhood of which you have the measure, which in some way helps to shape you. This is the local, the actual place, where the reference is reality, indifference is unusual, detachment is difficult. Here we are somehow entangled, although we may behave thoughtlessly, responsibility tries to

surface. It is here that values and facts act upon each other and are passed on by us to create wisdom about nature, about living, dying and remembering. And more prosaically, it is where 'strategy' and 'policy' are tested to breaking point" (Common Ground 2009b).

The acts of survey, data gathering (including defining what constitutes data), and representation all potentially generate a sense of individual and collective connection to place and are empowering. 'Knowing your place' leads to a willingness to take an active part in its upkeep and defence (Crouch & Matless 1996; Thompson 2007).

Since 2002, English Heritage, on behalf of the Historic Environment Forum, has produced an annual report called *Heritage Counts* that considers the economic and social role of heritage and historic environments. The 2009 *Heritage Counts* report examined the role of historic environments in influencing how people felt about where they lived, their sense of place and their social capital, as indicated through community involvement. A regression analysis was undertaken using the results of a national survey of 500 adults and 700 children. This highlighted the importance of historic buildings because a high proportion of such buildings had a statistically significant influence on sense of place and people who had recently visited a historic building had higher levels of social capital.

Land and seascapes provide a rich source of inspiration for many artists seeking to represent local distinctiveness and identities. Qualitative research investigating how people connect to nature invites participants to compose poems or keep nature diaries in order to express how local places are meaningful to them (Natural England 2009a). Artists are inspired to design site-specific artworks which draw upon the distinctive aesthetic qualities of particular places; **Box 16.3** provides an example from Cumbria.

While it is clear that iconic landscapes and places, and those that conform to notions of environmental and aesthetic 'value', have benefits for individual and local community identity, it is important to note that marginal landscapes can also function in this way and bring significant meaning to people's lives. One of the best examples is the urban allotment garden discussed in **Box 16.4**.

16.3.4.4 The monetary value of heritage goods

The large numbers of people that are members of certain environmental charities suggests many people will make a monetary contribution to conserve the mix of landscapes,

> **Box 16.3 Art, landscape, place and inspiration: Andy Goldworthy, Sheepfolds (1996 to 2003).**
> Source: Cumbria County Council (2007).
>
> *Sheepfolds* is a sculpture project combines artistic creativity with the cultural heritage of a rural area:
> "Rather than making new *Sheepfolds*, Goldsworthy committed himself to working with existing folds in various states of disrepair or, in some cases, folds which had disappeared altogether but were clearly indicated on old maps. This enabled him to connect directly with the farming tradition and history of Cumbria, but, at the same time, as each sheepfold was rebuilt, so he invigorated them with a new energy by incorporating his sculptural response".

Originally created in response to rural depopulation and migration to urban areas, the 'classic' allotment was carved out of remnant railway-owned land, so was found in semi-industrial parts of cities (**Figure 1**). Allotments—mainly managed by elderly, working-class men—sustained many families for decades during the 20th Century (Crouch & Ward 1988), but fell into decline after WWII. In recent years, however, they have enjoyed resurgence and, although there are uncertainties with the evidence, waiting lists have increased in the last decade especially (Campbell & Campbell 2009). There is also evidence that they have attracted a greater diversity of users, with growing numbers of women, minority ethnic groups and young people managing plots. Buckingham's (2005) survey of allotment users in West London showed that in some boroughs up to a third of plot-holders were women. She also noted that "other advantages claimed by, particularly Asian, low income women, who are more likely to be gardening collectively, are the social benefits which appear to be reducing the isolation they feel living in blocks of flats" (Buckingham 2005). Milligan et al. (2004) studied the therapeutic benefits of gardening for older people in the north of England using a mixed methodology incorporating focus groups, interviews, participants' diaries and longitudinal data about health and well-being. They argue that communal gardening on allotment sites combats social isolation and creates support networks (for a comparative study from the USA see Teig et al. 2009). Fieldhouse (2003) examined the effects of being part of an allotment group on people who had experienced mental ill health and found that gardening on an allotment was de-stigmatising, developed skills, and promoted social cohesion and mutual support. Given this kind of evidence, it is not surprising that the UK Government recognised the role that allotment gardening might play in generating social capital and in its sustainable development agenda (Milligan et al. 2004).

Figure 1 An allotment garden filled with flowers and vegetables.
Photo by © joingate, 2011. Used under license of Shutterstock.com.

places and habitats that represent heritage goods. The first amenity society, the Open Spaces Society, was set up in 1865 to defend common land and rights of way. It was followed by The National Trust which was founded in 1895 to protect threatened countryside, coast and buildings. The National Trust started out with just 100 members, rising to 12,000 by 1946. Recent growth in membership has been rapid and there are now 3.6 million members—more than 5% of the total UK population (National Trust 2010). In 2006–07, just over 49,000 people volunteered for the National Trust, an increase from 38,000 in 2001/02, although many of these volunteers would have been associated with activities in buildings (English Heritage 2009).

During the mid-19th Century, there was also a shift in sensibilities and an increase in repulsion at the mass slaughter of birds, ensuring the establishment of early nature conservation legislation and movements such as the Sea Birds Preservation Act (1869) and the Wild Birds Protection Act (1880). In 1889, The Royal Society for the Protection of Birds (RSPB) was founded by a group of influential women protesting against the destruction of birds solely for the trade in plumage. The RSPB now has over one million members and, like the National Trust, is becoming a substantial landowner, committed to the management and restoration of habitats across the UK. The RSPB oversees nature reserves covering 142,044 ha in the UK; the National Trust owns 254,000 ha of countryside, moorland, beaches and coastline in England, Wales and Northern Ireland, and a further 76,000 ha of countryside is owned by the National Trust for Scotland which has 310,000 members.

An analysis of the income and legacies donated to these environmental charities was conducted as part of the economic valuation undertaken for the UK NEA (Chapter 22; Mourato et al. 2010). Legacies could potentially be interpreted as a (market) proxy for non-use values reflecting altruistic, bequest or existence motivations. This analysis found that in terms of the total income raised by the top 500 UK charities in 2008/09, charities in the environmental area were ranked 7th (cancer, social welfare and animal charities ranked highest). Environmental charities, however, were ranked 4th in terms of income from legacies. In 2008/09, the National Trust raised a total of £97.8 million (44% from legacies), making it the 12th largest charity in the UK. The RSPB was ranked 16th having raised £64.9 million (41% from legacies).

The analysis of income and legacies conducted for the UK NEA in Chapter 22 also found that the total value of annual legacies to the National Trust, the RSPB and the National Trust for Scotland has doubled over the last two decades despite falling death rates in the UK. For the National Trust and the RSPB, this is partly a result of an increase in mean legacy values and the number of legacies. However, while mean legacy value may have risen, GDP per capita has risen faster, so the mean legacy value as a proportion of GDP per capita has, in fact, fallen (Chapter 22; Mourato et al. 2010).

The monetary value of National Trust sites were also considered in the hedonic pricing study undertaken for the UK NEA (Chapter 22; Mourato et al. 2010) based on an analysis of over 1 million housing transactions between 1996 and 2008 (see Section 16.3.7.1, **Table 16.13**). This considered the effect on house prices of marginal changes in proximity to National Trust sites and showed that proximity to these heritage sites had a statistically significant influence on house prices. Each 1 km increase in distance from the nearest National Trust owned site was associated with a

0.7%, or £1,350, fall in 2008 house prices. Certain types of heritage, therefore, clearly have an economic value which is reflected in house prices.

The 2010 Heritage Counts report produced by English Heritage focused on economic impact issues and mainly considered historic built environments through an analysis of existing research and new studies of 17 areas that had received investment in the regeneration of an historic environment. The survey concluded that, over a 10-year period, £1 of investment in an historic environment generates £1.60 of additional economic activity and approximately half of the jobs generated by historic environment attractions are based in local businesses (English Heritage 2010).

The economic and social significance of heritage goods in people's lives is now subject to ongoing monitoring. The Taking Part survey commissioned by the Department for Culture, Media and Sport (DCMS & ONS 2010) collects data at the national level for England about participation in the historic environment. Between 2005 and 2009, nearly 97,000 people responded to the survey. In 2005/06, 57.2% of adults had visited at least two historic environment sites in the previous 12 months; this figure rose to 61.9% in 2007/08, but fell back to 58.0% in 2008/09. These historic environment sites will often contain historic buildings, but the environmental settings of many sites will also contribute to their heritage and the reasons for visiting.

This ongoing monitoring, and other future studies, should provide further insights to the complex and often highly personalised ways environmental settings influence peoples' sense of heritage and how this affects the satisfaction of various needs such as for identity and understanding. What is less well understood is how heritage goods that represent the environment, but are not physically based in environmental settings, such as books and TV programmes concerned with the countryside, satisfy our value and existence needs or are a form of pseudo-satisfiers. However, Section 16.3.5 indicates that environmental representations produced by the media can have an influence on the nature of ecological knowledge and environmental education.

16.3.5 Education and Ecological Knowledge Goods

16.3.5.1 Environmental settings and green education

Environmental settings provide surroundings for outdoor learning where engaging with nature can lead to enhanced connectedness to nature and increased ecological knowledge (**Figure 16.9**). Ecological knowledge has been defined as 'accumulated knowledge about nature' and can be acquired through contact with local environments (Pilgrim *et al.* 2008). A study comparing the UK with India and Indonesia suggested that ecological knowledge declines in association with economic growth (Pilgrim *et al.* 2008), partly due to a lack of transfer to younger people. Other studies have noted the value of ecological knowledge among lay people can contribute to conservation and environmental management (Davis & Wagner 2003).

One way to increase children's contact with nature, and potentially their future ecological knowledge, is within the formal education system, both in terms of: i) the amount of

exposure to nature in the learning environments outside the classroom; and ii) actually learning about nature, sometimes known as 'green education'. The Office for Standards in Education (Ofsted 2008) has recently published guidance on learning outside the classroom. Outdoor learning is more than just fieldwork for natural history or geography; it is the notion that learning for all disciplines can take place in outdoor settings (Rickinson *et al.* 2004). There is evidence that this leads to improved cognitive outcomes, better behaviour in the classroom and at home, and improved working conditions for teachers (Sibley & Etinier 2003). Furthermore, outdoor learning provided by third sector organisations, such as care farms, is often funded by a range of public sector education, social care and offender management organisations as it has provided beneficial educational opportunities for young people not in formal education, training or employment (Hine *et al.* 2008). **Box 16.5** presents two case studies on the range of benefits of green education outside the classroom.

Some evidence suggests, however, that the provision of education outside the classroom and the acquisition of ecological knowledge through green education could be improved. A government assessment of education outside the classroom in 2006 (DfES 2006) found that teachers involved with these activities, especially in primary schools, saw the objectives as being linked to personal development rather than the acquisition of knowledge. They also discovered that there was inequality of provision in terms of education outside the classroom: pupils from schools with low levels of achievement and in areas of high deprivation had fewer opportunities for visits to local sites away from school. In addition, there were regional inequalities, with teachers in schools in the North and the Midlands less likely to have undertaken such visits with pupils than teachers in the South of England. Similar regional differences were found in surveys by English Heritage and the National Trust of school visits to historic environments (English Heritage 2009).

More positively, the National Trust (Peacock 2006) undertook an in-depth survey of young people who had formerly been involved in primary school visits to eight of their sites where many of the learning opportunities were concerned with the natural environment. This survey found evidence that the trips had influenced school behaviour and skills and had also impacted on local environmental knowledge, although this was often not linked to more general environmental issues.

Ecological knowledge can also be acquired outside the classroom, but still within school grounds. Learning through Landscapes, founded in 1990, is a UK national charity running programmes in England, Scotland and Wales. Working in partnership with private, public and other third sector organisations, it helps schools to make physical improvements to their school grounds including creating nature or 'wilderness' areas, digging ponds, growing food, and enhancing many other outdoor activities through imaginative design and introduction of new equipment.

Learning through Landscapes funds independent research to evaluate the success of its interventions and demonstrate the value of outdoor learning. In 2003, Ipsos MORI carried out a national survey of 351 schools who had

Figure 16.9 Environmental education session at Conkers Discovery Centre, Derbyshire, England. *Photo courtesy of Christopher Beech/National Forest Company.*

Box 16.5 Case studies on green education.

Eastfeast

Eastfeast is a team of professional gardeners, artists and teachers that helps schools deliver more effective learning based on working a school allotment through the seasons, culminating in a community feast. Eastfeast started in 2005 with a year-long pilot programme at Aldeburgh Primary School in Suffolk; the project continues to evolve in partnership with a growing number of schools in East Anglia and through a series of linked, but independent, creative learning programmes. Pupils involved in Eastfeast schools spend more time outdoors as children and become involved in activities focused around working an allotment. This creates connections between nature and learning that can result in memories which impact on choices young people make later in life—helping them to choose to spend more time outdoors. The Eastfeast initiative has been shown to be successful in developing links between creative learning activities and local resources such as allotments, growers, food producers and cultural centres. By helping to get the local community involved, a 'shared learning ethos' is developed both inside and outside the formal school boundaries which helps pupils to gain the confidence to make their own decisions about learning and is likely to have an effect on life courses (Eastfeast 2009).

Forest schools

Based on an educational initiative established in Scandinavia in the 1950s, Forest Schools have been educating children regularly in UK woodlands since the mid-1990s. Normally working with a particular group over a period of several months, they provide learning activities linked to the national curriculum. An evaluation by O'Brien and Murray (2007) of Forest Schools and their pupils in England and Wales found that such children had improved: physical and motor skills; language and communications skills; social skills, including team working; knowledge and understanding of the environment; self-confidence and self-belief; and motivation and concentration.

improved their outdoor spaces within the previous four years (Learning through Landscapes 2003). The survey assessed their motivations for the improvements, which are shown in **Figure 16.10**. The results suggest that behaviour and citizenship are slightly more important motivations than knowledge linked to the curriculum, but that an ecological motivation was important for about 75% of the sample. The survey did not include a question on any ecological improvements or knowledge enhancement that may have taken place over the period, but **Table 16.12** shows that the results reinforce the case for environmental improvements having synergistic outcomes in meeting a number of school and pupil needs, especially for play and social interaction.

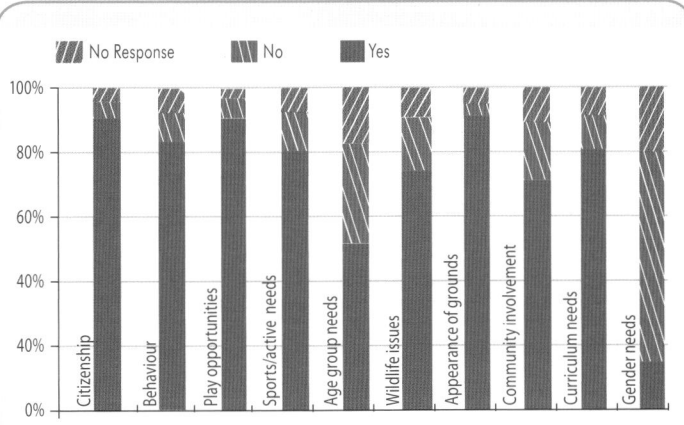

Figure 16.10 Reasons for participation in Learning through Landscapes school grounds improvement programmes. *Source: Learning through Landscapes (2003).*

Far less evidence exists regarding the acquisition of ecological knowledge among young people and adults outside the formal education system. A recent study by the Sustainable Development Commission (SDC 2010), however, indicates that the skills and knowledge gained from volunteering in outdoor environments can improve the resilience, responsibility and employment chances of marginalised young people. The study also found that environmental volunteering opportunities are often not part of social inclusion policies targeted at young people.

16.3.5.2 The monetary value of green education and ecological knowledge

The economic valuation of cultural goods conducted for the UK NEA examined two components of ecological knowledge using differing methods (Chapter 22). Firstly, an accounting framework was used to examine a portion of the ecological component of school education. Secondly, two case studies were used to estimate the monetary value of ecological knowledge acquired through outdoor learning by examining the 'cost of investment' associated with these activities.

The accounting framework is designed to measure the 'investment value' of enhanced earnings and leisure benefits linked to educational attainment in GCSE and A2 geography, science and biology, which all contain significant proportions of ecological knowledge as part of their curricula. The authors conclude that the accounting framework is very approximate as it has to estimate the proportion of ecological knowledge in each curriculum and does not estimate the net benefit of ecological knowledge relative to other education. But the "findings are instructive, not least in indicating, in explicit terms, the value of ecological knowledge is possibly substantial" (Chapter 22; Mourato *et al.* 2010). The tentative findings produce an estimate of £2.1 billion for the value of the ecological knowledge contained in the education attainment of pupils in 2010 completing GCSE and A2 geography, science and biology.

The monetary value of outdoor learning was explored through a case study of the 'cost of investment' in 1,968 organised school trips to 51 RSPB nature reserves during 2009/10. The analysis notes that, while ecological knowledge is acquired in school, it is difficult to ascribe a gain in knowledge to a specific trip or location. The approach, therefore, involves examining travel costs and resource costs in order to estimate investment costs over and above those involved in gaining knowledge in a classroom situation. The analysis estimates that trips to the RSPB reserves by schools were based on total investment costs of between £850,000 and just over £1.3 million (Chapter 22).

A second case study was made of the RSPB Big School Birdwatch initiative which involves pupils and teachers counting species of birds visiting school grounds for an hour on any day in a two-week period. In 2010, 69,100 pupils and nearly 6,300 adults took part, compared to a total of 14,675 people in 2004. As with the first case study, the 'cost of investment ' approach does not reveal the level or benefit of ecological knowledge acquired, but gives an indication of the financial outlay for an activity which can contribute to the acquisition of ecological knowledge. By using government estimates of the cost to government of students aged 3–19 in education, the analysis suggests the value of pupil and teacher time contributing to the RSPB Big School Birdwatch is £374,000 or an average of £188 per school (Chapter 22).

16.3.6 Religious and Spiritual Goods

16.3.6.1 Ecosystems and the nature of religious and spiritual goods

The MA (2005a) identified spirituality as a type of cultural service, and spirituality is mentioned frequently in discussions of cultural services with, according to Cooper (2009), the word having distinct meanings. On the one hand, spirituality connotes the religious values held by indigenous people, and on the other, the values of those in developed countries who find spiritual inspiration from nature. Such inspiration may be variously characterised as 'enrichment', 'experience', 'solace', 'enlightenment', 'fulfilment', 'renewal' or 'reflection'. These different types of inspiration will be forged by such a wide range of social, cultural and psychological factors. In this section, we focus on the role environmental settings play in the emergence of religious and spiritual goods arising from human engagement with the environment of the UK.

It must also be acknowledged that people without religious faith may have spiritual experiences and, for such people, spiritual inspiration may contribute to the emergence of other goods already discussed, such as leisure or health. Religious and spiritual goods are clearly linked to our existence need for being, but the extent to which religious encounters with specific environmental settings are synergistic satisfiers for value needs, such as participation and identity, resides in the character and qualities of belief.

Table 16.12 Learning through Landscapes' National School Grounds Survey 2003. Source: Learning through Landscapes (2003).

Has your school grounds improvement...	Yes (%)	No (%)	No response (%)
... increased the number of children who 'enjoy' and 'have fun' being in their grounds?	90	2	8
... stimulated increased active play and games?	85	6	9
.... increased the perceived quality of the environment by pupils, teachers, parents, etc.?	87	1	12
.... improved pupil behaviour?	73	9	18
.... Improved quality of other play?	83	6	11
....increased the number of lessons taught outside?	65	17	18
.... improved pupil attitudes towards learning?	65	8	27
... increased the number of activities and opportunities provided for pupils at break and lunchtimes?	85	4	11
...changed levels of self-esteem?	64	8	28
......improved social interaction between pupils, and pupils and staff?	84	2	14
....increased community/parental involvement?	66	18	11

16.3.6.2 Ecosystems, nature and changing religious and spiritual goods

The importance of ecosystems in religious terms has almost certainly increased in the post-war period in the UK, notwithstanding secularisation and the decline of conventional religious observance. There has, apparently, been an increase in the incidence of both pilgrimage and of religious retreats, although it is extremely difficult to identify any quantitative measures of this trend. Writing from anecdotal evidence, Inge (2003) sees this increase as representing grassroots protest against the loss of place imposed on Christians by Modernism and reformed Christianity. Similarly, Wynn (2007) talks of the 'localisation of divine presence' that is implied in pilgrimage.

Alongside changes in conventional protestant Christianity, religious pluralism has characterised the last 60 years—what Heelas and Woodhead (2005) call a 'spiritual revolution'—and marks a shift from church religiosity to holistic spirituality. Based on a detailed empirical case study of Kendal in the Lake District, Heelas and Woodhead (2005) identify two cultural practices. On the one hand, 'religions of difference' exist—conventional Christian denominations which distinguish sharply between God, the human, and the natural world ; on the other hand, 'spiritualities of life' adopt a holistic perspective and stress the fundamental identity between the divine, the human and the natural world. Many of the latter have fused with more orthodox Christian theology; some Christians are linked to 'New Age' thinking with origins in the 1960s. The best-known example is the Findhorn community in the north-east of Scotland (Sutcliffe 2000). New Age spirituality places particular emphasis on holism and 'connectedness' to nature, believing humans should not attempt to control and dominate nature, but should live in an ecologically friendly way in 'green communities' (Heelas 2006; Hatton 2008). Specific geographical places are associated with the holistic milieu, either because of historic links with spirituality, such as Glastonbury (Wylie 2002), or because of more recent socio-demographic trends, such as Totnes, whose reputation is derived from the practices of innovative local landowners—the Elmhirsts at Dartington and Maurice Ash at Sharpham—which have a particular connection with Buddhism (Snelling 1992).

While not undermining conventional religious space, the new spirituality has undermined any monopoly religious places might have held in terms of providing spiritual solace and/or meaning, as well as promoting new leisure and recreational uses. Sacralisation of new places may come about through new rituals of grief, such as temporary wayside shrines marking fatal traffic accidents, green burial places, and places where ashes may be scattered. The place-based rituals of death are no longer confined to the traditional graveyard as people strive to find new ways to "encounter the significance of the historical person" (Hunt 1995). Clearly, there is a temporary nature to some of these new sacred sites.

Notwithstanding the depth and breadth of this tradition of valuing nature spiritually, we face serious problems in seeking to assess the precise contribution of UK ecosystems to spiritual and religious experiences and the related activities and products. Much of the academic endeavour related to this topic is normative: theological and ethical writings abound (Bauckham 2009; Carruthers 2009). Empirical social scientific evidence of the extent and nature of religious and spiritual beliefs, or experiences related to nature, are much harder to find, especially in the UK context, the reasons for which are rooted in the historical and contemporary sociology of religion.

Historically, Protestant Christianity has not been sympathetic to a theology of sacred places as efficacious, in and of themselves, to religious well-being. Thus, it stands in contrast to the importance attached to religious sites and places in pre-Reformation Britain (Duffy 1992), to the sites and landscape features sacred to Hinduism (Smith 2002), or to the specific territories with national and religious identities most associated with Judaism (Smith 2003). However, the 20th Century has witnessed a modest reassessment within mainstream protestant denominations (including the Anglican Church) and pilgrimage, retreats and ideas of sacred space have become much more acceptable.

In the 1990s, this movement gathered pace and became more explicitly a multi-faith phenomenon with examples emerging from other faith traditions. For example, in Manchester at the Cheetham Al Hilal Community Project, the Muslim community has participated in an innovative project to improve the built and natural environment including the creation of a garden with an Islamic theme. The Sacred Land Project, supported by WWF and launched by the Archbishop of Canterbury in April 1997, set out to revive and create sacred sites in the UK and overseas. In the UK the project has involved Buddhist, Christian, Hindu, Jewish, Muslim and secular communities in: creating and reviving inner city and community gardens; conserving and celebrating holy wells; rediscovering and renewing pilgrimage trails; protecting trees and woodlands; regenerating community meeting places and their ecosystems; and celebrating sacred places with works of art and poems (The Sacred Land Project 2001 see also www.arcworld.org/projects.asp?projectID=9). Two case studies from the Sacred Land Project are provided in **Box 16.6**.

Hay and Hunt (2002) report on people's religious or spiritual experiences in Britain. Based on national survey data, the proportion of the population claiming to have had such experiences increased from 48% to 76% between 1987 and 2000, with the awareness of a sacred presence in nature increasing from 16% to 29%. Relatively few studies have focused empirically on the motivations and experiences of those for whom religious experiences are linked in some way to particular places and ecosystems. Research often focuses on elements of the built environment, such as churches and cathedrals, as pilgrimage destinations (Winter & Gasson 1996).

A few academics are focusing on the practice of pilgrimage rather than the destination (Frey 1998; Coleman & Eade 2004; Bremborg 2008). For example, Frey (1998) studied those walking on the pilgrimage route to Santiago de Compostela and found the sacred goal to be less important to many than the journey through wild and beautiful terrain. Linked to this, 'get out in nature' headed a list of 12 motivations for the journey.

Our Lady of the Crag

In Knaresborough in North Yorkshire, the ancient shrine of Our Lady of the Crag can be found in a cave cut into the rocky crags overlooking the river Nidd, which cuts a gorge through the centre of the town (**Figure 1**). According to local legend, the shrine was dedicated to Our Lady in the 12th Century by John the Builder in thanks for a miracle that saved the life of his son from a rock-fall; but some say it is very much older. Nearly 500 years ago, the shrine was suppressed during the Reformation, and became neglected and forgotten. In the early 1990s, a local group formed to renovate the shrine and to create a sacred garden around it, supported by the Sacred Land Project. Now a stunning new Madonna and Child—commissioned by Arts and Sacred Places to be carved from Yorkshire granite by local sculptor, Ian Judd—has been installed in the cave.

Vrindavan Garden

In Leicester, in a predominantly Hindu neighbourhood, a sacred garden was inaugurated in October 2000 beside Rushey Brook, in the grounds of Rushey Mead School, as a quiet space and an environment in which pupils could produce works of art. The idea for the garden was inspired by Friends of Vrindavan, a Hindu community group, whose inspiration comes from the sacred forests of Krishna in Vrindavan, India. The garden, designed by landscape architect Rebecca Cotton, is based upon the theme of Krishna's struggle with the serpent Kaliya, who poisoned the sacred River Yamuna in Vrindavan. This theme was chosen to symbolise the struggle to clean our rivers and environment. Pupils of Rushey Mead School have created their own works of art to be placed in the garden.

Figure 1 Chapel of Our Lady of the Crag. *Photo by R/DV/RS available under a Creative Commons Attribution license.*

The importance of 'natures' and the countryside to national identity can be seen in many political, social and literary writings of the 20th Century in the UK, some of which are explicitly linked to religious discourses. Matless (1998) shows how advocates of organic farming and ruralism both drew from and further developed Christian thinking: "the model is of a universal parochial church, attentive to often semi-pagan seasonal ritual, with place itself becoming a church to belong to and revere". Moore-Colyer (2001) has examined one of these thinkers, Rolf Gardiner, in more detail, investigating his attempts to enlist Church leaders and people in a greater understanding of the spirituality of nature and of rural living.

Alongside the growth of pilgrimage as 'moving though nature', there has also been a recent marked growth in religious retreats to particular places in nature. There are currently 132 places of Christian retreat in the UK listed by the Retreat Association, located in both urban and rural locations. Conradson is researching four retreat centres in southern England, using participant observation and interviews with monks and guests on retreat. Two Benedectine places of retreat in southern England, Alton Abbey and Elmore Abbey, are explored in particular. His work demonstrates clearly the spatiality of these religious places, not just the abbey buildings themselves, but also the surrounding gardens and countryside. So for those on retreat, the 'stillness' they seek may be found in both the Benedictine monastic liturgy and in the abbey grounds and gardens.

16.3.6.3 Environmental settings and religious and spiritual goods

It is extremely hard to pinpoint evidence of particular landscapes or ecosystems being conducive to religious experiences. The configuration of Marine and Coastal habitats which appear to contribute to spiritual/religious experiences on the holy islands of Iona, Lindisfarne and Bardsley have to be seen in the context of other highly popular sites of pilgrimage that are inland and

not characterised by dramatic landscape or ecological characteristics, such as Walsingham in North Norfolk. There is relatively little evidence on the specific role of nature and religious pilgrimage in human well-being. Conradson (2008) couches his research in terms of the therapeutic role of stillness, and so, by implication, religious places are important to human well-being in their provision of 'therapeutic stillness'. Clearly, diminution of the qualities (peace, beauty) that characterise pilgrimage journeys and places of retreat would have a potentially marked impact on the well-being of participants.

Wynn (2009) seeks to explain how "our encounter with particular places, each characterised by its own phenomenology and distinctive possibilities for bodily appropriation, may prove to be religiously significant" (p44). He outlines three ways in which this might be the case: firstly, particular places may come to hold a religious significance because they carry some microcosmic significance, epitomising in some way the nature of things more generally; secondly, God is taken to be presupposed in some particular material context which may be a place or landscape or habitat; and thirdly, specific places represent the meaning of past religious events that occurred there. In all three contexts, the religious experiences can have positive implications for faith, relationships and action. In the first and second of these possibilities, outdoor and open places may be more important than the traditional built or enclosed sites of religious devotion, but further research is needed to explore these complex issues.

16.3.7 Cultural Services and Goods: the Contribution to Human Well-being

16.3.7.1 Environmental settings and amenity value

The preceding discussion of the various cultural goods has already highlighted some of the specific contributions that environmental settings make to satisfying human needs and, consequently, human well-being. As noted in Section

16.3.1, however, the benefits that individuals experience from environmental settings can be multiple and bundled together. A trip to a local park can generate health, leisure and spiritual benefits. The economic valuation for the UK NEA addresses this by calculating the amenity value of environmental settings as an aggregate measure of the benefits gained from cultural services and goods (Chapter 22). The amenity value is based on a measure of well-being associated with living in, or within close proximity to, certain settings.

A hedonic pricing study of over 1 million housing transactions between 1996 and 2008 was used to assess the effect of environmental settings on amenity value and concluded "that the house market in England reveals substantial amenity value attached to a number of habitats, protected and managed areas, private gardens and local environmental amenities" (Mourato *et al.* 2010; Chapter 22). **Table 16.13** is taken directly from Mourato *et al.* (2010) and summarises the key findings of the hedonic regression analysis according to their statistical significance.

The hedonic regression found that, for census wards in England, a 1 percentage point increase in the land use share made up of the environmental setting of greenspace added 1.04% to house prices (£2,020 at 2008 prices) compared to national average house prices. The comparable figure for domestic gardens was 1.01% (£1,970 at 2008 prices), and 0.97% for water (£1,886 at 2008 prices). Environmental settings with designations also affected amenity value: a location within a green belt surrounding a major metropolitan area can add 3% to house prices (£5,880 at 2008 prices) compared to national average house prices.

Table 16.13 also shows that certain broad and component habitat types have a high amenity value. A 1 percentage point increase in the share of Broadleaved Woodland, Coniferous Woodland, Enclosed Farmland, or Freshwater—Open Waters, Wetlands and Floodplains within the one km² containing a house has a statistically significant effect on house prices compared to national average house prices.

There are certain limitations in the hedonic regression that generated the findings in **Table 16.13** (Mourato *et al.* 2010; Chapter 22). For example, due to data that is currently available, it is a cross sectional study only for England. The analysis only examines land cover in the vicinity of a property and the distance to the nearest environmental setting or amenity. The diversity of land cover, or the benefits of accessibility to multiple instances of a particular

Table 16.13 Implicit prices for environmental settings and related environmental amenities in England (£ capitalised values). Note: The stars indicate statistical significance levels: *** p<0.01, ** p<0.05, * p<0.10. Source: Mourato *et al.* (2010).

Environmental setting/ Environmental amenity	% change in house value with:	Implicit price in relation to average 2008 house price	
	1 percentage point increase in share of land cover of habitat type:		
Marine and Coastal Margins	0.04% increase in house prices	£70	
Freshwater—Open Waters, Wetlands and Floodplains	0.40% increase in house prices	£768	***
Mountains, Moorlands and Heath	0.09% increase in house prices	£166	
Semi-natural Grassland	0.01% decrease in house prices	-£27	
Enclosed Farmland	0.06% increase in house prices	£113	***
Broadleaved Woodland	0.19% increase in house prices	£377	***
Coniferous woodland	0.12% increase in house prices	£227	*
Inland bare ground	0.38% decrease in house prices	-£738	***
	1 percentage point increase in land use share of environmental setting:		
Domestic gardens	1.01% increase in house prices	£1,970	***
Greenspace	1.04% increase in house prices	£2,020	***
Water	0.97% increase in house prices	£1,886	***
	1 percentage point increase in land use share of designation:		
Being in the green belt (in major metropolitan areas)	3.00% increase in house prices	£5,800	**
Being in a National Park	5.00% increase in house prices	£9,400	
	1 km increase in distance:		
Distance to coastline	0.14% fall in house prices	-£275	
Distance to rivers	0.91% fall in house prices	-£1,751	*
Distance to National Parks	0.24% fall in house prices	-£461	***
Distance to nature reserves	0.07% fall in house prices	-£143	
Distance to National Trust land	0.70 % fall in house prices	-£1,347	***

environmental setting, are not considered, nor are the visibility of settings and environmental amenities. Nevertheless, a variety of different regressions confirm that the findings are robust and that environmental settings and habitats do influence house prices. Individual well-being is influenced by a wide range of social, economic, cultural and genetic factors (Defra 2007c), but the increased monetary value of an individual's home may contribute to enhanced well-being.

16.3.7.2 Environmental settings and subjective well-being

Further aggregate measures of the benefits gained from environmental settings are provided in the analysis of subjective well-being and the environment undertaken for the UK NEA economic valuation (Mourato & MacKerron 2010; Chapter 22). The measures of subjective well-being are based on data obtained from a geo-located web survey completed by 1,851 panel respondents in August 2010. The respondents were asked to self-assess life satisfaction using the European Social Survey 0–10 life satisfaction scale. The measures of life satisfaction acted as the dependent variable in an OLS regression model. The survey also obtained data on time spent by respondents in different environmental settings. The UK Land Cover 2000 map was used to generate measures of the proximity of respondents' homes to particular habitats.

The results from the OLS regression model are shown in **Table 16.14** (Mourato & MacKerron 2010; Chapter 22); the caveats associated with the model are discussed in Mourato & MacKerron (2010) and Chapter 22. Two models were estimated: model (a) for the UK as a whole, which had fewer variables; and model (b) for just England and Wales. The statistically significant associations between life satisfaction and the demographic and housing variables are to be expected given the findings of previous research.

Table 16.14 reveals that people who visit non-countryside greenspaces, such as urban parks, at least once a month, and those who spend time in their own gardens at least once a week, have statistically significant higher life satisfaction measures than those who do not. This appears to confirm the significance of local greenspace and private gardens to increases in well-being, as indicated by the hedonic regression reported in the previous section above.

Certain broad and component habitats were also found to have statistically significant associations with life satisfaction. Proximity of respondents' home to Broadleaved or Mixed Woodland was associated with higher life satisfaction. By contrast, proximity of Mountain, Moorlands and Heath were associated with slightly lower life satisfaction.

16.4 Knowledge Gaps

An ecosystem services approach to understanding culture-nature interactions is a relatively new perspective; consequently, many key sources of social, economic and environmental data are not designed to examine key aspects of cultural services and goods. There are knowledge gaps related to data collection and the uneven monitoring of change of different environmental settings. The Countryside Quality Counts analysis (Defra *et al.* 2008) is providing a consistent approach to examining the changing nature of landscapes in countryside environmental settings. Chapter 10, however, notes that for urban landscape morphology and character there is no single data inventory and a lack of harmonisation between sources. Data on the nature and quality of local formal and informal greenspace has been improving, but is still limited. Since 2006, Natural England has been seeking to collate the different digital data sets of urban and rural accessible greenspace to provide a single inventory, but, to date, only 70% of 32 possible datasets have been collated (Chapter 10). National planning guidance also instructs local authorities to audit the use and access to open spaces, but the approaches adopted are not consistent (CABE 2010).

The Ordnance Survey, through its product Master Map, has developed increasingly reliable digital inventories of the coastline and 'inland water', including enclosed water bodies, rivers, canals and smaller streams, which are refreshed every six weeks at scales of 1:1250, 1:2500 and 1:10,000 in urban, rural and mountain areas, respectively. The requirements of the Water Framework Directive now mean that the quality of data on the biological and chemical characteristics of many inland water bodies, especially rivers, has improved. A number of organisations, such as the Environment Agency and British Waterways, hold information on the uses of certain inland waterways, but there is no consistent dataset on public use or access to inland blue spaces (University of Brighton 2008); the situation on the coast, however, has improved, partly due to the audit of coastal access undertaken by Natural England in preparation for the Marine and Coastal Access Bill.

The development of consistent terminology and data collection approaches for digital data on environmental settings and their use by the public will be central to developing an ecosystem approach that takes account of cultural services and goods. For future economic valuation exercises, the availability of consistent digital data on changes over time to environmental settings will also be required.

Knowledge, data and evidence is also uneven for the different cultural goods discussed in this chapter. For health goods, there is well-established evidence of the potential of environmental settings to play a role in facilitating exercise and other activities that enhance mental and physical health (Pretty *et al.* 2005; Mitchell & Popham 2008; Barton & Pretty 2010). Nevertheless, further research is required—particularly longitudinal studies—to understand the social and physiological processes involved in adults and children acquiring mental and physical health benefits from engagement with environmental settings and nature, in order to ensure that the management of environmental settings for long-term behaviour change can be more effective (Thompson Coon 2011).

The economic valuation for the UK NEA (Chapter 22) also recommends undertaking further studies to examine

Table 16.14 Life satisfaction ordinary least squares regressions (web survey). Notes: [†] Income is logged to account for diminishing marginal returns. The income measure used is household income divided by weighted household size; [‡] Summed self-reported housing problems, out of: infestations, damp, mould, serious draughts, inadequate heating, low daylight; [§] Number of rooms divided by number of residents; models (a) and (b) are based on UK and England and Wales samples, respectively; significance levels: *** $p<0.001$, ** $p<0.01$, * $p<0.05$, + $p<0.1$. Source: Mourato & MacKerron (2010).

Variables	Life satisfaction (0–10)	
	(a)	(b)
Demographics		
Male (0/1)	-0.19*	-0.16+
Age	-0.054***	-0.054**
Age squared	0.00069***	0.00070***
Log(income) [†]	0.24***	0.25***
Living alone (0/1)	-0.35**	-0.37**
Unemployed (0/1)	-1.09***	-1.13***
Religious (0/1)	0.30**	0.32**
Exercise (IPAQ total MET-hours/week)	0.00048	0.00044
Self-rated health (1–5)	0.82***	0.82***
Housing		
Homeowner without mortgage (0/1)	0.58***	0.62***
Social tenant (0/1)	0.49***	0.43**
Housing problems (count) [‡]	-0.14+	-0.18*
House crowding [§]	0.028	0.16
Greenspace use and views		
Home views of grass (0/1)	0.037	0.036
Home views of water (0/1)	0.069	0.14
Weekly+ use of garden (0/1)	0.28*	0.20+
Monthly+ countryside visits (0/1)	0.11	0.098
Monthly+ other green space visits (0/1)	0.19+	0.18+
National Park visits per year (count)	0.014	0.010
Land cover (ha within 1 km radius of postcode centroid—base category is urban)		
Marine and Coastal Margins	0.0018	-0.00074
Freshwater—Open Waters, Wetlands and Floodplains	0.0079	0.0068
Mountains, Moorlands and Heath	-0.0078	-0.020+
Semi-natural Grasslands	0.0023	0.0019
Enclosed Farmland	-0.0010	-0.00063
Coniferous Woodland	-0.0041	-0.0035
Broadleaved/Mixed Woodland	0.0042+	0.0067*
Inland bare ground	-0.0047	-0.0036
Distance to nearest…		
National Park boundary (km, 0 if inside)		0.0020
National Trust site (km)		-0.0071
Coastline (km)		-0.0019
Motorway (km)		0.00059
A-road (km)		0.060
Railway station (km)		-0.0043
Countries (base category is England)		
Wales (0/1)	0.15	0.16
Scotland (0/1)	0.22	
Northern Ireland (0/1)	-0.14	
Population density (1,000/km2)		0.048+
Standardised house price index		-0.0028*
Constant	1.72*	1.42+
Observations	1851	1647
Adjusted R-squared	0.290	0.292

people's exercise habits and understand what proportion of exercise is a direct consequence of the provision of greenspaces. This could involve revealed and stated preference techniques, or possibly experimental methods where behavioral change can be monitored before and after the provision of new green- and/or bluespaces.

One of the ongoing challenges facing the evaluation of leisure, recreation and tourism goods has been a lack of consistent data over time regarding the use of environmental settings. The potential of certain previous datasets, such as the English Leisure Visits Survey, was limited by changes in measurement and also one-off events such as the outbreak of Foot and Mouth Disease. Recently, the situation has improved as new surveys have sought to establish reliable time-series data to monitor the impacts of a range of policy measures. These include Sport England's (2009) Active People survey of physical activity and the DCMS & ONS (2010) survey, Taking Part, which examines participation in culture, leisure and sport. The Monitoring Engagement with the Natural Environment (MENE) survey was introduced in 2009 by Natural England (2010), the Department for Environment Food and Rural Affairs and the Forestry Commission to provide baseline and trend data on how people use the natural environment in England, but the introduction of more precise measures of destination and origin in this survey would enhance future economic valuation using travel cost methods.

A number of organisations, such as English Heritage and the National Trust, provide regular monitoring reports on the quality and use of heritage and historic environment sites. These usually focus on built features and less on the natural environment, but the annual report *Heritage Counts*, produced by English Heritage, does consider changes to certain open spaces such as registered parks and gardens, ancient woodland and battlefields. English Heritage (2009) is also undertaking a historic characterisation mapping exercise for England that, by 2009, had been finished for 81% of the country and, if completed, will provide valuable insights into the connections between heritage goods and landscape. The UK NEA was not able to obtain accurate data on the nature or value of heritage goods produced by different forms of the media that rely on representations of nature and environmental settings, such as wildlife documentaries and TV programmes about the countryside. A future analysis of the economic value of this type of heritage good would need to be accompanied by quantitative and qualitative research to understand how such goods link to other forms of environmental behaviour and whether they satisfy our needs as synergistic satisfiers or are pseudo/inhibitor satisfiers.

Many people experience heritage goods through their role as volunteers. English Heritage and the National Trust monitor volunteering in historic environments, but far less reliable data is available on environmental volunteering despite the valuable social role of such activity recently identified by the Sustainable Development Commission (SDC 2010). Similarly, the economic valuation of cultural goods for the UK NEA (Chapter 22) concluded that little is known about charitable bequests and giving in the UK, and that there is only limited available data on donation patterns, the demographic characteristics of donors and how these change over time. The current UK government's desire to encourage volunteering, charitable giving and localism may make collecting data on environmental volunteering and charitable giving a priority if the costs and benefits of such activities are to be fully understood and incorporated within an ecosystem approach to the environment.

A key knowledge gap regarding education and ecological knowledge goods concerns the processes by which adults acquire ecological knowledge, their participation in nature-based educational activities, and how knowledge acquisition is influenced by engagement with environmental settings as a form of cultural service. A number of studies have highlighted the importance of lay, as well as expert, knowledge in shaping the public understanding of key environmental issues (Dickens 2004). Furthermore, research has revealed how engagement with environmental settings, especially in childhood, can shape ecological attitudes and future environmental behaviour (Ward-Thompson *et al.* 2008). The UK NEA economic valuation considered the value of nature-based school visits and noted that a comprehensive database of school visits would be required to allow a national assessment of their worth (Chapter 22). Such a database would also be useful for assessing the extent of inequalities in school visit opportunities identified in 2006 (DfES 2006).

For religious and spiritual goods the knowledge gaps are particularly notable. There is a marked lack of evidence on the numbers of people for whom religious/spiritual experience and well-being is related to experiences of nature. We do not know how many people in the UK go on pilgrimages or spiritual retreats, or for whom contact with nature is an intrinsic part of their religious/spiritual lives. There is a need to take the sophisticated approach to spirituality and space (Wynn 2009) and relate it to different types of ecosystems. It is necessary to do more research to see if pilgrimages and retreats are growing in the UK, and the degree to which moving through nature is important.

This chapter has highlighted some of the important contributions environmental settings make to a range of goods that influence well–being, but there is already evidence to show that there are marked inequalities in access to environmental settings linked to residential location, social background and income (CABE 2010). Initiatives to tackle any of the knowledge gaps linked to cultural services and goods must, therefore, seek to take account of related inequalities that could be addressed in future ecosystem management.

Addressing these knowledge gaps will require the regular and consistent collection of quantitative data at the national scale. Many of the gaps, however, require an understanding of the complex ways in which individuals and groups of people engage with environmental settings, and the social and cultural benefits that may arise (Burgess 2000; Burgess *et al.* 2007) Recent guidance published by the Department for Environment, Food and Rural Affairs (Fish *et al.* 2011) emphasises that the cultural goods linked to ecosystem services cannot just be understood in monetary terms; in future, their collective and non-monetary value will need to be understood using a range of participatory and deliberative techniques, such as multi-criteria analysis, that require both quantitative and qualitative methods.

16.5 Conclusions

Over the last decade, the concept of 'cultural services and goods' linked to ecosystems has been adopted by many academics and environmental policy makers to describe what are experienced as meaningful interactions between people and nature. As such, cultural goods and services represent the newest way of interpreting human-environment relations: a 21st Century framing in a sequence covering millennia through which societies have expressed the centrality of the natural environment in supporting human life and well-being. However, evidence presented in the early section of this chapter shows that 'ecosystem' and 'ecosystem services' were not words to be found in popular discourse. The implication is that the expert knowledge captured in such terms is unlikely to be shared among the wider public. It follows that using these terms is unlikely to be the most effective means of communicating knowledge about how human life and well-being is dependent upon the earth's geophysical, hydro-meteorological and biological systems. The linguistic analysis shows that the cloud of words people associate with the idea of 'nature' and the 'natural environment' are much more meaningful.

Moreover, there are clearly articulated individual and social values which arise from human interaction with nature. Cultural analysis explores the production, circulation and reception of shared meanings and practices, including those with the natural world. Communicating the cultural significance of nature in everyday life—especially in ways which emphasise its positive benefits rather than resorting to the clichés of destruction and despair which have marked environmental discourse over the last four decades—is very important for the mobilisation of wider public support for sustainable environmental management.

In this chapter, the argument is made for a more theoretically informed approach to the definition of cultural services and goods. The MA (2005)'s approach to cultural services and the 'non-material' benefits of ecosystems, had to be flexible enough to embrace countries at very different stages of economic development and with divergent systems of knowledge. For the UK NEA, and acknowledging the insight from Fisher *et al.* (2008) that final ecosystem services include the application of human as well as natural capital, leads us to argue for a final cultural ecosystem service, defined as 'environmental settings which provide the sites for human interactions with nature and others'. Environmental settings range in geographical scale from domestic gardens to regional landscapes, but are distinct from habitats or ecosystems as they are, culturally, the locations within which people interact with one another and with nature. Environmental settings are also spatially delimited, which is useful since they are units for which spatially disaggregated data exists or can be collected. This can then be integrated with other data on ecosystem services to ensure cultural services are readily incorporated into assessments and studies seeking to enhance the management of ecosystems.

In the UK NEA conceptual framework (Chapter 2) wild species diversity is identified as contributing to both provisioning and cultural services. As discussed earlier in this chapter in Section 16.3.1, human interactions with wild animals and plants, usually as components of environmental settings, can generate a range of cultural goods which would benefit from further research. Wild species and ecosystem services are considered in detail in Chapters 3 and 15 concerned with biodiversity and provisioning services.

The argument has been made for environmental settings to be identified as a final ecosystem cultural service. A mixed picture of changes in the character and quality of environmental settings since 1945 has emerged from the evidence presented in the chapter. The growth of cities and towns means that for many people their local environmental settings are urban, dominated by buildings and transport infrastructure. However, increased mobility afforded by the massive expansion of car ownership among the UK's population and the introduction of cheaper air travel has dramatically increased accessibility to a huge variety of environmental settings both in the UK and elsewhere. Quite marked changes have occurred in environmental settings in some peri-urban locations, but elsewhere, the nature of these settings has changed far less. Urbanisation since 1945 has also been accompanied by the emergence of a series of protected environmental settings ranging from Local Nature Reserves to National Parks.

The cultural goods linked to environmental settings are many, so this chapter has concentrated on a limited number that could be readily identifiable and for which some quantitative or qualitative data could be used to assess their characteristics. The chapter has focused on health, tourism/leisure/recreation, heritage, education/ecological knowledge and religious goods.

New evidence gathered as part of the economic valuation for the UK NEA (Chapter 22) measured the economic value of environmental settings and cultural goods, and their contribution to well-being. Specifically, a new hedonic price analysis showed that the house market in England reveals substantial amenity value attached to a number of habitats, designations, private gardens and local environmental settings. In particular, protected areas (National Parks, National Trust land and metropolitan green belt), local environmental settings (domestic gardens, local greenspaces, rivers) and several habitats (such as woodland, farmland and freshwater) are a statistically significant factor in explaining higher house prices (Chapter 22). In parallel, a new well-being survey also revealed that respondents who visit non-countryside greenspaces, such as urban parks, at least once a month, and those who spend time in their own gardens at least once a week, have higher life satisfaction than those who do not. Survey respondents who used domestic gardens at least once a week and local greenspaces at least once a month also showed better self-reported health, measured by physical functioning and emotional well-being, compared to those who do not; in addition, having a view over greenspace from one's house was seen to have a significantly positive impact on emotional well-being (Chapter 22).

The contribution of environmental settings to human well-being stems from their ability to satisfy human needs in context-specific ways. Given the scale of attempting a global assessment, the MA was not able to drill down into specificities of how cultural meanings and values might be satisfied through interactions with nature. In this chapter, we have argued that working with the H-SDM, conceived by Max-Neef (1989; 1992), could provide a useful framework for more detailed exploration of cultural ecosystem goods and benefits. The H-SDM identifies four human existence needs (to be, to have, to do and to interact) and nine human value needs, (e.g. subsistence, understanding, freedom and leisure). Some cultural goods arising from interactions with environmental settings may well be what the H-SDM terms 'synergistic satisfiers', i.e. satisfying a number of different needs at the same time. Other goods may act more as 'singular satisfiers', meeting just one need is satisfied at a time. Other possibilities were also discussed, such as the ways in which modern consumption practices have been able to substitute technology for nature as in, for example, artificial settings for natural settings. We have drawn on the H-SDM to help create a rational framework for the discussion. The next step would be to undertake empirical research to test its robustness.

More generally, there are major problems with the lack of evidence to underpin any assessment of cultural ecosystem services and goods. Drawing on what data are available, we have begun to open up discussion about how environmental settings and related cultural goods meet human needs, often in a contingent manner, with needs satisfaction varying markedly between individuals and in different settings. This is only a part of the process of developing an ecosystem service approach to the natural environment that is based on evidence concerning the cultural aspects of human-nature relations.

A key research agenda is to deepen knowledge and understanding of the interactions between human needs and ecosystem services. This will require more theoretical development combined with substantial methodological innovation in the collection and analysis of data, both quantitative and qualitative. These innovations will also need to be designed to understand the inequalities that currently exist in terms of how people experience the goods and benefits of cultural services.

Improvements in the collection of quantitative data at the national level are required to facilitate further economic valuation studies, especially of health goods, heritage goods and ecological knowledge. Existing guidance from the Department for Environment, Food and Rural Affairs (Fish *et al.* 2011) indicates, however, that understanding the complex economic, social, cultural and psychological dimensions of the individual and collective interactions between humans and ecosystems also requires qualitative studies using multi-criteria analysis and participatory deliberative techniques. Such techniques must be underpinned by high quality information and clear conceptual frameworks to guide the deliberations of organisations and people taking part (Fish *et al.* 2011). The UK NEA's economic valuation (Chapter 22) has provided new quantitative knowledge that can reliably inform these qualitative techniques, and the H-SDM provides one conceptual approach to ensure future studies are rigorous in covering all aspects of human needs that will be affected by ecosystem services.

References

Alexander, A. (2009) Britain's New Towns. Garden cities to sustainable communities. Routledge, Abingdon and New York.

Alkire, S. (2002) Dimensions of human development. *World Development*, **30**, 181–205.

Anderson, B. (1991) Imagined Communities: Reflections on the Origin and Spread of Nationalism. Verso, London.

Andrews, M. (1999) Landscape and western art. Oxford University Press, Oxford.

Appleton, J. (1975) The Experience of Landscape. Wiley, London.

Askins, K. (2006) New Countryside, New Country: visible communities. In the English National parks. The new countryside? Ethnicity, Nation and Exclusion in Contemporary Rural Britain (eds J. Agyeman & S. Neal), pp. 149–172. Policy Press, London.

Askins, K. (2009) Crossing divides: Ethnicity and rurality. *Journal of Rural Studies*, **25**, 365–35

Bacon, N., Brophy, M., Mguni, N., Mulgan, G. & Shandor, A. (2010) The state of happiness: can public policy shape people's wellbeing and resilience? The Young Foundation, London.

Barker, G. (1997) A framework for the future: green networks with multiple uses in and around towns and cities. English Nature Research Reports 256. English Nature, Peterborough.

Barrell, J. (1980) The dark side of the landscape: the rural poor in English painting 1730–1840. Cambridge University Press, Cambridge.

Barton, J., Hine, R. & Pretty, J. (2009) The health benefits of walking in green space of high natural and heritage value. *Journal of Integrated Environmental Sciences*, **6**, 1–18.

Barton, J. & Pretty, J. (2010) What is the Best Dose of Nature and Green Exercise for Improving Mental Health? A Multi-Study Analysis. *Environmental Science & Technology*, **44**, 3947–3955.

Barton, J., Griffin, M. & Pretty, J. (2011) Exercise, nature and socially interactive-based initiatives improve mood and self-esteem in the clinical population. *Perspectives in Public Health* (in press).

Bauckham, R. (2009) Reading the Sermon on the Mount in an age of ecological catastrophe, *Studies in Christian Ethics*, **22**, 76–88.

Beaumont, N., Hattam, C., Mangi, S., Moran, D. van Soest, D., Jones, L. & Tobermann, M. (2010) Economic analysis of ecosystem services provided by UK Coastal Margin and Marine Habitats, Final Report. The Economics Team of the UK National Ecosytem Assessment, Plymouth Marine Laboratory.

BEN (Black Environment Network) (2006) The BEN Rainbow Countryside Scheme. BEN, Llanberis.

Bender, B. (2004) Contested Landscapes: medieval to present day. Material Culture: critical concepts in the social sciences, Volume 3 (ed V. Buchli), pp. 27–51. Routledge, London.

Bharucha, Z. & Pretty, J. (2010) The role and importance of wild foods in agricultural systems. *Philosophical Transactions of the Royal Society of London B*, **365**, 2913–2926.

Bhatti, M. & Church, A. (2001) Cultivating Natures: Homes and Gardens in Late Modernity. *Sociology*, **35**, 365–383.

Bibby, P. (2009) Land use change in Britain. *Land Use Policy*, **26**, 2–13.

Bingley, A. & Milligan, C. (2004) Climbing Trees and Building Dens: Mental health and well-being in young adults and the long-term effects of childhood play experience. Institute for Health Research, Lancaster University, Lancaster.

Bird, W. (2007) Natural Fit. Can green space and biodiversity increase levels of physical activity? Royal Society for the Protection of Birds, UK.

Birnie, R.V.J., Curran, J.A., Macdonald, E.C., Mackey, C.D., Campbell, G., McGowan, S.F.C., Palmer, E., Paterson, E., Shaw, P. & Schewry, M.C. (2002) The land resources of Scotland: trend and prospects for the environment and natural heritage. The State of Scotland's Environment and Natural Heritage *(*eds M.B. Usher, E.C. Mackey & J.A. Curran), pp. 41–81. The Stationery Office, Edinburgh.

Blancheflower, D.G. & Oswald, A.J. (2008) Is well-being U-shaped over the life cycle? *Social Science and Medicine,* **66**, 1733–1749.

Bleys, B. (2007) Proposed changes to the Index of Sustainable Economic welfare: an application to Belgium. *Ecological Economics,* **64**, 741–751.

Bremborg, A.D. (2008) Spirituality in silence and nature: motivations, experiences and impressions among Swedish pilgrims. *Journal of Empirical Theology,* **21**, 149–165.

Bressey, C. (2009) Cultural archaeology and historical geographies of the black presence in rural England. *Journal of Rural Studies,* **25**, 386–395.

Broadhurst, R. (2001) Managing environments for leisure and recreation. Routledge, London.

Brown, M. P. (2007) The Holkham Bible Picture Book: a facsimile. British Library, London.

Brownson, R.C., Boehmer, T.K. & Luke, D.A. (2005) Declining rates of physical activity in the US: what are the contributors? *Annual Review of Public Health,* **26**, 421–43.

Buckingham, S. (2005) Women (re)construct the plot: the regen(d)eration of urban food growing. *Area,* **37**, 171–179.

Burgess, J. (1995) Growing in Confidence: a research project into public perceptions of risk in woodlands in the urban fringe. Countryside Commission, Cheltenham.

Burgess, J., Harrison, C.M. & Limb, M. (1988) People, Parks and the Urban Green: A Study of Popular Meanings and Values for Open Spaces in the City. *Urban Studies,* **25**, 455–473.

Burgess, J. Clark, J. & Harrison, C.M. (2000) Culture, communication and the information problem in contingent valuation surveys: a case study of a wildlife enhancement scheme. *Environment and Planning,* **18**, 505–524.

Burgess, J., Clark, J., Davies, G., Eames, M., Mayer, S., Staley, K., Stirling, A. & Williamson, S. (2007) Deliberative Mapping: exploring a new analytic-deliberative methodology. *Public Understanding of Science,* **16**, 299–322.

Butryn, T.M. & Furst, D.M. (2003) The effects of park and urban settings on the moods and cognitive strategies of female runners. *Journal of Sport Behaviour,* **26**, 335–355.

CABE (Commission for Architecture and the Built Environment) (2006) Green space strategies: a good practice guide. CABE, London.

CABE (Commission for Architecture and the Built Environment) (2010) Urban green nation: Building the evidence basis. CABE, London.

Campbell, M. & Campbell, I. (2009) A survey of allotment waiting lists in England. Transition Town West Kirby in conjunction with the National Society of Allotment and Leisure Gardeners Ltd, Corby.

Cant, S. & Morris, N. (2006). Engaging with place: artists, site-specificity and the Hebden Bridge Nature Trail. *Social and Cultural Geography,* **7**, 863–887.

Carruthers, P. (2009) The land debate – 'doing the right thing': ethical approaches to land-use decision-making. What is Land for? The Food, Fuel and Climate Change Debate (eds M. Winter & M. Lobley), pp. 293–318. Earthscan, London.

Cason, D.R. & Gillis, H.L. (1993) A meta-analysis of adventure programming with adolescents. *Journal of Experiential Education,* **4**, 25–27.

Castree, N. (2005) Nature. Routledge, London.

CCRCD (Carnegie Commission for Rural Community Development) (2007) A Charter for Rural Communities. Carnegie UK Trust, Dunfermline.

CCW (Countryside Council for Wales) (2008) LANDMAP Methodology: Guidance for Wales. [online] Available at: <http://www.ccw.gov.uk/landscape--wildlife/protecting-our-landscape/landmap/landmap-methodology.aspx> [Accessed 30.11.09].

Census of Population (2001) Office of National Statistics Census 2001 [online] Available at: <http://www.statistics.gov.uk/census2001/census2001.asp> [Accessed 23.11.10].

Cheshire, P.C. & Sheppard, S. (2002) Welfare Economics of Land Use Regulation. *Journal of Urban Economics,* **52**, 242–269.

CJC Consulting and Willis, K. (2005) Economic Benefits of Accessible Green Spaces for Physical and Mental Health: Scoping study. Final Report for the Forestry Commission. [online] Available at: <http://www.forestry.gov.uk/pdf/FChealth10-2final.pdf/$FILE/FChealth10-2final.pdf> [Accessed 26.10.11].

Clifford, S. & King, A. (2006) England in Particular: a Celebration of the Commonplace, the Local, the Vernacular and the Distinctive. Hodder & Stoughton, London.

Cloke, P., Milbourne, P. & Thomas, C. (1996) The English National Forest: Local Reactions to Plans for Renegotiated Nature-Society Relations in the Countryside. *Transactions Institute of British Geographers,* **21**, 552–571.

Cocker, M. & Mabey, R. (2005) Birds Britannica. Random House, London.

COE (Council of Europe) (2004) The European Landscape Convention Treaty Series no. 176. [online] Available at: <http://www.coe.int/t/dg4/cultureheritage/heritage/landscape/default_en.asp> [Accessed 02.02.11].

Coleman, J. (2000) A history of political thought: from ancient Greece to early Christianity. Blackwell, Oxford.

Coleman, S. & Eade, J. (2004) Reframing Pilgrimage: Cultures in Motion. Routledge, London.

Common Ground (2009a) Local Distinctiveness – Losing your Place: essay by Sue Clifford and Angela King. [online] Available at: <http://www.england-in-particular.info/cg/distinctiveness/d-place.html> [Accessed 02.12.09].

Common Ground (2009b) Places, People and Parish Maps: essay by Sue Clifford [online] Available at: <http://www.england-in-particular.info/cg/parishmaps/m-ppp.html> [Accessed 02.12.09].

Conradson, D. (2008) The experiential economy of stillness: places of retreat in contemporary Britain. Therapeutic Landscapes (ed A. Williams), pp.33–48. Ashgate, Farnham, UK.

Coombes, E., Jones, A.P. & Hillsdon, M. (2010) The relationship of physical activity and overweight to objectively measured greenspace accessibility and use. *Social Science and Medicine*, **70**, 816–822.

Cooper, N. (2009) The spiritual value of ecosystem services: an initial Christian exploration. Unpublished paper. Anglia Ruskin University and the Diocese of Ely.

Cosgrove, D. & Daniels, S. (1988) The iconography of landscape. Cambridge University Press, Cambridge.

Costanza, R., Fisher, B., Ali, S., Beer, C., Bond, L., Boumans, R., Danigelis, N.L., Dickinson, J., Elliott, C., Farley, J., Gayer, D.E., Macdonald Glenn, L., Hudspeth, T., Mahoney, D., McCahill, L., McIntosh, B., Reed, B., Rizvi, A.S.T., Rizzo D.M., Simpatico, T. & Snapp, T. (2007) Quality of life: an approach integrating opportunities, human needs, and subjective well-being. *Ecological Economics,* **61**, 267–276.

The Countryside Agency (2003) Capturing Richness: Countryside visits by black and ethnic minority communities. The Countryside Agency, Cheltenham.

The Countryside Agency (2005) The State of the Countryside 2005: Characteristics of Rural England. The Countryside Agency, Cheltenham.

Craig, R. & Mindell, J. (eds) (2008) Health Survey for England 2006: CVD and risk factors adults, obesity and risk factors children. National Statistics and NHS Information Centre, London. [online] Available at: <http://www.ic.nhs.uk/webfiles/publications/HSE06/HSE06_Summary.pdf> [Accessed 27.03.11].

CRC (Commission for Rural Communities) (2008) State of the Countryside 2008. [online] Available at: <http://webarchive.nationalarchives.gov.uk/20110215111010/http://ruralcommunities.gov.uk/state-of-the-countryside/state-of-the-countryside-2008/> [Accessed 01.04.11].

Crouch, D. & Ward, C. (1988) The Allotment: its Landscape and Culture. Faber, London.

Crouch, D. & Matless, D. (1996) Refiguring Geography: Parish Maps of Common Ground. *Transactions of the Institute of British Geographers*, **21**, 236–255.

Crouch, D. & Lubbren, N. (2003) Visual culture and tourism. Berg, London.

Cruz, I., Stahel, A. & Max-Neef, M. (2009) Towards a systematic development approach: building on the Human-Scale Development paradigm. *Ecological Economics*, **68**, 2021–2030.

Cumbria County Council (2007) Sheepfolds Cumbria. [online] Available at: <http://www.sheepfoldscumbria.co.uk/> [Accessed 01.12.09].

Curry, N. (1994) Countryside recreation, access and land use planning. E & FN Spon, London.

Curry, N. (2009) Leisure in the landscape: rural incomes and public benefits. Drivers of environmental change in the uplands (eds A. Bonn, T.E. Allott, K. Hubacek & J. Stuart), pp.277–290. Routledge, London.

Curry, N. & Ravenscroft, N. (2001) Countryside recreation provision in England: exploring a demand-led approach. *Land Use Policy*, **18**, 281–291.

Daniels, S. (1993) Fields of Vision: Landscape Imagery and National Identity in England and the United States. Polity Press, Cambridge.

Darby, W.J. (2000) Landscape and identity. Berg, Oxford.

Davies, G. (1999). Exploiting the archive: and the animals came in two by two. *Area,* **31**, 49–58.

Davis, A., Valsecchi, C. & Fergusson, M. (2007) Unfit for Purpose: How car Use Fuels Climate Change and Obesity. IEEP, London.

Davis, A. & Wagner, J.R. (2003) Who knows? On the importance of identifying "experts" when researching local ecological knowledge. *Human Ecology,* **31**, 463–489.

Davis-Berman J. & Berman, D.S. (1989) The wilderness therapy programme. *Journal of Contemporary Psychotherapy,* **19**, 271–281.

DCLG (Department of Communities and Local Government) (2008) Trees in Towns II. Department of Communities and Local Government, London, UK.

DCLG (Department of Communities and Local Government) (2009) Local Planning Authority Green Belt Statistics 2008/09. Department of Communities and Local Government, London, UK.

DCMS (Department for Culture Media and Sport) (2008) The Number of School Playing Fields – Freedom of Information Request Case 101795. Department for Culture Media and Sport, London. [online] Available at: <http://www.culture.gov.uk/about_us/freedom_of_information/foi_requests/5523.aspx> [Accessed 24.03.11].

DCSF (Department for Children, Schools and Families) (2009) Healthy Lives, Brighter Futures: The Strategy for Children and Young People's Health. Department for Children, Schools and Families & Department of Health, London.

DCMS & ONS (Department for Culture Media and Sport & Office for National Statistics) (2009) Taking Part: The National Survey of Culture, Leisure and Sport. PSA21: Indicator 6 – Rolling annual estimates from the Taking Part survey. DCMS, London.

DCMS & ONS (Department for Culture Media and Sport &Office for National Statistics) (2010) Taking Part: The National Survey of Culture, Leisure and Sport Adult and Child Report 2009/2010. DCMS, London. [online] Available at: <http://www.culture.gov.uk/publications/7386.aspx> [Accessed 24.03.11].

Defra (Department for Environment, Food and Rural Affairs) (2007a) Public Understanding of the concepts and language around ecosystem services and the natural environment. Defra, London.

Defra (Department for Environment, Food and Rural Affairs) (2007b) Survey of Public Attitudes and Behaviours Toward the Environment. Defra, London.

Defra (Department for Environment, Food and Rural Affairs) (2007c) Well-being: International policy interventions. Defra, London.

Defra (Department for Environment, Food and Rural Affairs) (2008) Outdoors for all? The action plan. Defra, London.

Defra (Department for Environment, Food and Rural Affairs), English Heritage & Natural England (2008) Countryside Quality Counts Tracking Changes in the Character of the English Landscape, 1999–2003. Department for Environment, Food and Rural Affairs, London.

Defra (Department for Environment, Food and Rural Affairs) (2009) Sustainable development Indicators in your pocket. Department for Environment, Food and Rural Affairs, London.

den Boer, L.C. & Schroten, A. (2007) Traffic noise reduction in Europe: Health effects, social costs and technology and policy options to reduce road and rail traffic noise. CE DELFT: solutions for environment, the Netherlands.

de Vries, S., Verheij, R.A., Groenewegen, P.P. & Spreeuwenberg, P. (2003) Natural environments – healthy environments? An exploratory analysis of the relationship between greenspace and health. *Environment and Planning,* **35**, 1717–1731.

DfES (Department for Education and Skills) (2006) Education outside the classroom: an assessment of activity and practice in schools and local authorities. DfES, London.

Dickens, P. (2004) Society and Nature: Changing Our Environment, Changing Ourselves. Polity, London.

Diener, E. & Seligman, M. (2004) Beyond money: towards an economy of wellbeing. *American Psychological Society,* **5**, 1–13.

Diette, G.B., Lechtzin, N., Haponik, E., Devrotes, A. & Rubin, H.R. (2003) Distraction therapy with nature sights and sounds reduces pain during flexible bronchoscopy. A complementary approach to routine analgesia. *Chest Journal,* **123**, 941–48.

Dobbins, M., De Corby, K., Robeson, P., Husson, H. & Tirlis, D. (2009) School-based physical activity programs for promoting physical activity and fitness in children and adolescents aged 6–18. *Cochrane Database Systematic Reviews,* **21**, CD007651.

Dodds, S. (1997) Towards a 'science of sustainability': improving the way ecological economics understands human well-being. *Ecological Economics,* **23**, 95–111.

DoE (Department of the Environment) (1993) Trees in Towns. Department of the Environment, London.

DH (Department of Health) (2004) At least five a week: Evidence on the impact of physical activity and its relationship to health. DoH, London.

Dryzek, J. S. (2002) Deliberative democracy and beyond: liberals, critics, contestations. Oxford University Press, Oxford.

Duffy, E. (1992) The Stripping of the Altars: Traditional Religion in England 1400–1580. Yale University Press, New Haven and London.

Dwyer, J.F., Schroeder, H.W. & Gobster, P.H. (1991) The significance of urban trees and forests: toward a deeper understanding of values. *Journal of Arboriculture,* **17**, 276–284.

Eastfeast (2009) Eastfeast: to know our world through a plot of land. [online] Available at: <http://www.eastfeast.co.uk> [Accessed 20.03.11].

Eden, S., Donaldson, A. & Walker, G. (2006) Green groups and grey areas: scientific boundary-work, nongovernmental organisations, and environmental knowledge. *Environment & Planning,* **38**, 1061–1076.

Edensor, T. (2000) Walking in the British Countryside: Reflexivity, Embodied Practices and Ways to Escape. *Body & Society,* **6,** 81–106.

English Heritage (2000) Attitudes toward the Heritage. English Heritage, London.

English Heritage (2009) Heritage Counts England. A Sense of Place. [online] Available at: <http://hc.english-heritage.org.uk/content/pub/HC09_England_Acc.pdf> [Accessed 23.03.11].

English Heritage (2010) Heritage Counts England. [online] Available at: <http://hc.english-heritage.org.uk/content/pub/HC-Eng-2010> [Accessed 23.03.11].

Ernstson, H., Barthel, S., Andersson, E. & Borgstrom, S.T. (2010) Scale-crossing brakers and network governance of urban ecosystem services: the case of Stockholm. *Ecology and Society,* **15,** 28.

Evans, D. (1997) A history of nature conservation. Routledge, London.

FCFGG (Federation of City Farms and Community Gardens) (2010) City Farms Visitor List [online]. Available at: <http://www.farmgarden.org.uk/farms-gardens/city-farms-list> [Accessed 20.03.11].

Ferraresi, A., Zanchetta, E., Baroni, M. & Bernadini, S. (2008) Introducing and evaluating UKWaC, a very large web-derived corpus of English. Proceedings of the Sixth International Conference on Language Resources and Evaluation, Marrakech, Morocco.

Fieldhouse, J. (2003) The impact of an allotment group on mental health client's health, well-being and social networking. *British Journal of Occupational Therapy,* **66**, 286–296.

Fish, R., Burgess, J., Chilvers, J., Footitt, A., Haines-Young, R., Russel, D., Turner, K. & Winter, D.M. (2011) Participatory and Deliberative Techniques for Embedding an Ecosystems Approach into Decision Making. Full Technical Report. (NR0124). Department for Environment, Food and Rural Affairs, London.

Fisher, B. & Turner, R.K. (2008) Integrating ecosystem services and economic theory. *Ecological Applications,* **18**, 2050–2067.

Fisher, B., Turner, K., Zylstra, M., Brouwer, R., de Groot, R., Farber, S., Ferraro, P., Green, R., Hadley, D., Harlow, J., Jerreriss,P., Kirkby, C., Morling, P., Mowatt, S., Naidoo, R., Paavola, J., Strassburg, B., Doug, Y. & Balmford, A. (2008) Ecosystem Services and economic theory: integration for policy-relevant research. *Ecological applications,* **18**, 2050–2067.

Fill, A. (2001) Ecolinguistics: State of the Art 1998. The Ecolinguistics Reader: Language, Ecology and Environment (eds F. Alwin & P. Mühlhäusler), pp. 43–53. Continuum, London.

Fitter, A., Elmquist, T., Haines-Young, R., Potscin, M., Rinaldo, A., Setala, H., Stoll-Kleemann, S., Zobel, M. & Murlis, J. (2010) An assessment of ecosystem services and biodiversity in europe. Ecosystem Services (eds R.M. Harrison & R.E. Hester), pp. 1–28. Royal Society of Chemistry, London.

Foresight (2007) Tackling obesities: Future choices. Government Office of Science, London.

Foresight (2008) Mental health: Future challenges. Government Office of Science, London.

Forestry Commission and Countryside Council for Wales (2008) Welsh Outdoor Recreation Survey. [online] Available at <http://www.forestry.gov.uk/forestry/INFD-7VQEPA> [Accessed 16.02.11].

Fraiman, S. (1995) Jane Austen and Edward Said: Gender, Culture, and Imperialism. *Critical Inquiry,* **21,** 805–821.

Frey, N.L. (1998) Pilgrim Stories: on and off the Road to Santiago. University of California Press, Berkeley.

Frumkin, H. (2001) Beyond Toxicity – Human Health and the Natural Environment. *American Journal of Preventive Medicine,* **20**, 234–241.

Frumkin, H., Frank, L. & Jackson, R. (2004) Urban Sprawl and Public Health. MIT Press, Cambridge, Massachusetts.

Frumkin, H. (2005) Environmental health: From global to local. Jossey Bass, San Fransisco.

Fuller, R., Irvine, K., Devine-Wright, P., Warren, P. & Gaston, K. (2007) Psychological benefits of greenspace increase with biodiversity. *Biology Letters,* **3**, 390–394.

Galea, S., Ahern, J., Rudenstine, S., Wallace, Z., & Vlahov, D. (2005) Urban built environment and depression: a multilevel analysis. *Journal of Epidemiology and Community Health*, **59**, 822–827.

Gasper, D. (2004) Human well-being: concepts and conceptualisations. Discussion Paper No. 2004/06. United Nations University – World Institute for Development Economics Research, Helsinki.

Giles-Corti, B. & Donovan, R. (2002) The relative influence of individual, social and physical environmental determinants of physical activity, *Social Science and Medicine*, **54**, 1793–1812.

Giles-Corti, B., Broomhall, M.H., Knuiman M., Collins, C., Douglas, K., Ng, K., Lange, A. & Donovan, R.J. (2005) Increasing walking: How important is distance to, attractiveness, and size of public open space? *American Journal of Preventive Medicine*, **28**, 169–176.

Gleave, J. (2009) Children's time to play: A literature review. Playday and NCB, London.

GLUD (Generalised Land Use Database) (2005) Physical Environments, Generalised Land Use Database Statistics for England 2005. [online] Available at: <http://www.communities.gov.uk/publications/planningandbuilding/generalisedlanduse> [Accessed 18.02.11].

Goatly, A. (2001) Green Grammar and Grammatical Metaphor, or Language and Myth of Power, or Metaphors We Die By. The Ecolinguistics Reader: Language, Ecology and Environment (eds F. Alwin & P. Mühlhäusler), pp. 203–225. Continuum, London.

Godbey, G. & Blazey, M. (1983) Old People in Urban Parks: An Exploratory Investigation. *Journal of Leisure Research*, **15**, 229–244.

Godbey, G., Roy, M., Payne, L., & Orsega-Smith, E. (1998) The Relation between Health and Use of Local Parks. National Recreation Foundation, Bloomington.

Graham, G. & Howard, P. (2008) Introduction: Heritage and Identity. Ashgate Research Companion to Heritage and Identity (eds G. Graham & P. Howard), pp. 1–18. Aldershot, Ashgate.

Grahn, P. & Stigsdotter, U.A. (2003) Landscape planning and stress. *Urban Forestry & Urban Greening*, **2**, 1–18

Green, B. (1985) Countryside conservation. Allen and Unwin, London.

Greenspace Scotland (2009) State of Scotland's Greenspace 2009. Greenspace Scotland, Stirling.

Gregory, R., Fischoff, B. & McDaniels, T. (2005) Acceptable input: using decision analysis to guide public policy deliberations. *Decision Analysis*, **2**, 4–16.

Grinde, B. & Patil, G.G. (2009) Biophilia: does visual contact with nature impact on health and well-being? *International Journal of Environmental Research and Public Health*, **6**, 2332–2343.

Gruffudd, P. (1994) Back to the land: historiography, rurality and the nation in inter-war Wales. *Transactions of the Institute of British Geographers*, **19**, 61–77.

Gruffudd, P. (1995) Remaking Wales: nation-building and the geographical imagination 1925–50. *Political Geography*, **14**, 219–40.

Halfacree, K. (1995) Talking about rurality: social representations of the rural as expressed by residents of six English parishes. *Journal of Rural Studies*, **11**, 1–20.

Halfacree, K. (2001) Going 'back-to-the-land' again: extending the scope of counterurbanisation. *Espace, Populations, Sociétés*, **1–2**, 161–170.

Hall, S. (1997). Introduction. Representation: cultural representations and signifying practices (ed S. Hall), pp. 1–12. Sage, London.

Handley, J., Pauleit, S., Slinn, P., Barber, A., Baker, M., Jones, C. & Lindley, S. (2003) Accessible Natural Green Space Standards in Towns and Cities: A Review and Toolkit for their Implementation. English Nature Research Reports 526. English Nature, Peterborough.

Hansen P.H. (1995) Albert Smith, the Alpine Club, and the Invention of Mountaineering in Mid-Victorian Britain. *The Journal of British Studies*, **34,** 300–324.

Harrison, C.M., Burgess, J. & Limb, M. (1987) Nature in the city: popular values for a living world. *Journal of Environmental Management*, **25**, 347–362.

Harrison, C. (1991) Countryside recreation in a changing society. The TMS Partnership, London.

Harrison, C., Burgess, J., Millward, A. & Dawe, G. (1995) Accessible natural greenspace in towns and cities: A review of appropriate size and distance criteria. Guidance for the preparation of strategies for local sustainability. English Nature Research Reports 153. English Nature, Peterborough.

Harrison, C.M. & Burgess, J. (2003) Social science concepts and frameworks for understanding urban ecosystems. Understanding urban ecosystems: a new frontier for science and education (eds A.R. Bekowitz, C.H. Nilon & K.S. Hollweg), pp. 137–149. Springer, New York.

Harrison, R.P. (1992) Forests: the shadow of civilisation. University of Chicago Press, Chicago.

Hartig, T., Mang, M. & Evans, G.W. (1991) Restorative effects of natural environment experiences. *Environment and Behaviour*, **23**, 3–26.

Hartig, T., Evans, G., Jamner, L.D., Davis, D.S. & Garling, T. (2003) Tracking restoration in natural and urban field settings. *Journal of Environmental Psychology*, **23**, 109–123.

Harvey, D.C. (2001), Heritage Pasts and Heritage Presents: Temporality, Meaning and the Scope of Heritage Studies. *International Journal of Heritage Studies*, **7**, 319–38.

Hatton, F. (2008) *Redefining the good life: an ethnography of Brithdir Mawr Community*. Unpublished PhD, School of Environmental Sciences, University of East Anglia.

Hay, D. & Hunt, K. (2000) Understanding the Spirituality of People who don't go to Church, Final report. Adult Spirituality Project, Nottingham University, Nottingham, UK.

HCN (Health Council of the Netherlands) (2004) The influence of nature on social, psychological and physical well-being. Nature and Health report. Health Council of the Netherlands, Gezondheidsraad.

Heelas, P. & Woodhead, L. (2005) The Spiritual Revolution: Why Religion is Giving Way to Spirituality. Blackwell, Oxford.

Heelas, P. (2006) The Infirmity Debate: On the Visibility of New Age Spiritualities of Life. *Journal of Contemporary Religion*, **21**, 223–240.

Hegarty, J.R. (2007) How to be a care-farmer for €73: a shareholder survey of the Fordhall Community Land Initiative. Paper presented at the COST Conference "*Green care: health effects, economics and policies*", a part of COST Action 866 – Green Care in Agriculture, hosted by Austrian Horticultural Society, Vienna, Austria, 20–22 June 2007.

Higson, A. (1987) Landscapes of television. *Landscape Research*, **12**, 8–13.

Hillsdon, M., Panter, J., Foster, C. & Jones, A. (2006). The relationship between access and quality of urban green space with population physical activity. *Public Health*, **120**, 1127–1132.

Hinchliffe, S., Kearnes, M., Degen, M. & Whatmore, S. (2005) Urban Wild Things: a cosmopolitical experiment. *Society & Space,* **23,** 643–658.

Hine, R., Peacock, J. & Pretty, J. (2007) Green Lungs for the East of England. Report for the National Trust. University of Essex, Colchester.

Hine, R., Peacock, J. & Pretty, J. (2008) Care farming in the UK: Contexts, benefits and links with therapeutic communities. *International Journal of Therapeutic Communities*, **29**, 245–260.

Hitchings, R. (2003) People, plants and performance: on actor network theory and the material pleasures of the private garden. *Society of Cultural Geography,* **4,** 99–114.

Hitchings, R. (2010) Seasonal climate change and the indoor city worker. *Transactions of the Institute of British Geographers,* **35**, 282–298.

Ho, C.H., Payne, L., & Orsega, E. (2003) Parks, recreation and public health. *Parks and recreation,* **21**, 18–27.

Holick, M.F. (2004) Sunlight and vitamin D for bone health and prevention of autoimmune diseases, cancers and cardiovascular disease. *American Journal of Clinical Nutrition,* **80**, 1678S–1688S.

Holland, A. (2002) Are choices trade-offs. Economics, Ethics and Environmental Policy (eds D.W. Bromley & J. Paavola), pp. 17–34. Blackwells, Oxford.

Hollaway, S.L. & Valentine, G. (2000) Children's geographies: playing, living, learning. Routledge, London.

Hollaway, S.L. & Valentine, G. (2003) Cyberkids: children in the information age. Routledge, London.

Holliman, R. (2004) Media coverage of cloning: a study of media content, production and reception. *Public Understanding of Science,* **13**, 107–130.

Hollins, B. & Hollins, C. (2007) The fight for Fordhall Farm. Hodder and Stoughton, London.

House of Commons (1999) A Century of Change: Trends in UK Statistics since 1900. Research Paper 99/111. [online] Available at: <http://www.parliament.uk/documents/commons/lib/research/rp99/rp99-111.pdf> [Accessed 01.04.11].

Howkins, A. (2003) The Death of Rural England: A Social History of the Countryside since 1900. Alun Howkins, London.

Hunt, D. (1995) Space and time transcended: the beginnings of Christian pilgrimage. The Sense of the Sacramental: Movement and Measure in Art and Music, Place and Time (eds D. Brown & A. Loads). pp. 59–78. SPCK, London.

Ilbery, B. & Maye, D. (2006) Regional economies of local food production: tracing food chain links between 'specialist' producers and intermediaries in the Scottish-English borders. *European Urban and Regional Studies,* **13**, 337–354.

Inge, J. (2003) A Christian Theology of Place. Ashgate, Farnham, UK.

Ingold, T. (2000) The perception of the environment: essays on livelihood, dwelling and skill. Routledge, London.

Irvine K.N. & Warber, S.L. (2002) Greening in healthcare: practicing as if the natural environment really mattered. *Alternative therapies in health and medicine,* **8**, 76–83.

IWA (Institute of Welsh Affairs) (2009) Living with our Landscape. IWA, Cardiff.

Jackson, T. & Marks, N. (1999) Consumption, sustainable wlefare and human needs – with reference to UK expenditure patterns between 1954 and 1994. *Ecological Economics ,* **28**, 421–441.

Jackson, T. (2009) Prosperity without growth? The transition to a sustainable economy. Sustainable Development Commission, London.

Jones, A., Hillsdon, M. & Coombes, E. (2009) Greenspace access, use and physical activity: understanding the effects of area deprivation. *Preventive Medicine,* **49**, 500–505.

Kahn, P.H. & Kellert, S.R. (2002) Children and Nature: Psychological, sociocultural and evolutionary investigations. MIT Press, Cambridge, Massachusetts.

Kampman, M.T., Wilsgaard, T. & Mellgren, S.I. (2007) Outdoor activities and diet in childhood and adolescence relate to MS risk above the Arctic Circle. *Journal of Neurology,* **254**, 471–7.

Kaplan, R. (2001) The Nature of the View from Home. *Journal of Environment and Behaviour,* **33**, 507–542.

Kaplan, S. & Kaplan, P. (1989) The visual environment: Public participation in design and planning. *Journal of Social Issues,* **45**, 59–86.

Kaplan, S. (1995) The restorative benefits of nature: towards an integrative framework. *Journal of Environmental Psychology,* **15**, 169–182.

Kawachi, I., Kennedy, B.P., Lochner, K. & Prothrow-Smith, D. (1997) Social capital, income inequality and mortality. *American Journal of Public Health,* **87**, 1491–8.

Keirle, I. (2002) Countryside recreation site management: a marketing approach. Routledge, London.

Kellert, S, R. (1993) The biological basis for human values of nature. The Biophillia Hypothesis (eds S.R. Kellert & E.O. Wilson), pp. 42–72. Island Press, Washington.

Kilgarriff, A., Rychly, P., Smrz, P. & Tugwell, D. (2004) 'The Sketch Engine' Proceedings of Euralex. Lorient, France, pp.105–116. [reprinted in Hanks, P. (ed) (2007) Lexicology: Critical concepts in Linguistics. Routledge, London].

Kuha, M. (2007) Acceptance and avoidance of responsibility in world leaders' statements about climate change. *Language and Ecology,* **2**(3). [online] Available at: <http://www.ecoling.net/journal.html> [Accessed 30.03.11].

Kuo, F.E., Sullivan, W.C., Coley, R.L. & Brunson, L. (1998) Fertile Ground for Community: Inner-City Neighbourhood Common Spaces. *American Journal of Community Psychology,* **26**, 823–51.

Kuo, F.E. & Sullivan, W.C. (2001a) Aggression and Violence in the Inner City: Effects of Environment via Mental Fatigue. *Environment and Behaviour,* **33**, 543–571.

Kuo, F.E. & Sullivan, W.C. (2001b) Environment and Crime in the Inner City – Does Vegetation Reduce Crime? *Journal of Environment and Behaviour,* **33**, 343–367.

Laumann, K., Gärling, T. & Stormark, K.M. (2003) Selective attention and heart rate responses to natural and urban environments. *Journal of Environmental Psychology,* **23**, 125–134.

Laurier, E. (1998) Replication and restoration – Ways of making maritime heritage. *Journal of Material Culture,* **3**, 21–50.

Layard, R. (2005) Happiness. Allen Lane, London.

Learning through Landscapes (2003) National School Grounds Survey 2003. [online] Available at: <http://www.ltl.org.uk/pdf/LTL-Survey-20031288585139.pdf> [Accessed 29.03.11].

Lewis, G. & Booth, M. (1994) Are cities bad for your mental health? *Psychological Medicine,* **24**, 913–915.

Lim, K. & Taylor, L. (2004) Factors associated with physical activity among older people – a population-based study. *Preventive Medicine*, **40**, 33–40.

London Food Link (2007) One planet dining. Sustain, London.

Lorimer, H. (1997) Happy hostelling in the Highlands: nationhood, citizenship and the Scottish inter-war youth movement. *Scottish Geographical Magazine*, **113**, 42–51.

Lorimer, H. (2000) Guns, game and the grandee: the cultural politics of deer-stalking in the Scottish Highlands. *Ecumene*, **7**, 431–459.

Lorimer, H. & Lund, K. (2003) Peak Performance: practising walking on Scotland's mountains. Nature Performed: environment, culture and performance (eds B.H. Szerszynski & C. Waterton), pp.130–44. Blackwells, London.

Louv, R. (2005) Last Child in the Woods. Algonquin Press, Chapel Hill, USA.

Lowe, P. & Goyder, J. (1983) Environmental Groups in Politics. George Allen & Unwin, London.

Lowenthal, D. (1985) The past is a foreign country. Cambridge University Press, Cambridge.

Lowenthal, D. (1991) British national identity and the English landscape. *Rural History*, **2**, 205–230.

LUC (Land Use Consultants) (2008) Understanding the relevance and application of the Access to Natural Greenspace Standard. Report prepared for Natural England. Land Use Consultants, London.

MA (Millennium Ecosystem Assessment) (2005a) Millennium Ecosystem Assessment. Current State and Trends Assessment. Island Press, Washington D.C.

MA (Millennium Ecosystem Assessment) (2005b) Millennium Ecosystem Assessment. Scenarios Assessment: Drivers of Change in Ecosystem Condition and Services. Island Press, Washington D.C.

MA (Millennium Ecosystem Assessment) (2005c) Millennium Ecosystem Assessment. Ecosystems and human well-being: synthesis. Island Press, Washington D.C.

Maas, J., Verheij, R.A., Groenewegen, P.P., De Vries, S. & Spreeuwenberg, P. (2006) Green space, urbanity, and health: how strong is the relation? *Journal of Epidemiology and Community Health*, **60**, 587–92.

Mabey, R. (1996). Flora Britannica. Sinclair-Stevensons, London.

Mabey, R. (2010) The Unofficial Countryside. Little Toller Books, Dorset.

Macfarlane, R. (2007) The Wild Places. Granta, London.

Marren, P. & Mabey, R. (2010) Bugs Britannica. Random House, London.

Marsden, T., Milbourne, P., Kitchen, L. & Bishop, K. (2003) Communities in nature: the construction and understanding of forest natures. *Sociologia Ruralis*, **43**, 238–256.

Maslow, A. (1954) Motivation and personality. Harper & Row, New York.

Matless, D. (1993) One Man's England: W.G. Hoskins and the English Culture of Landscape. *Rural History*, **4**, 187–207.

Matless, D. (1998) Landscape and Englishness. Reaktion, London.

Max-Neef, M. (1989) Human scale development: an option for the future. *Development Dialogue*, **1**, 5–81.

Max-Neef, M. (1992) Development and human needs.

Real life Economics (eds P. Ekins & M. Max-Neef), pp. 197–214. Routledge, London.

McCrone, D., Morris, A., & Kiely, R. (1995) Scotland – the Brand: the Making of Scottish Heritage. Edinburgh University Press, Edinburgh.

McEwan, I. (2010) Solar. Jonathan Cape, London.

McFadden, S. (2003a) The history of community supported agriculture, part 1: community farms in the 21st Century: poised for another wave of growth? [online] Available at: <http://newfarm.rodaleinstitute.org/features/0104/csa-history/part1.shtml> [Accessed 01.04.11].

McFadden, S. (2003b) The history of community supported agriculture, part 2: CSA's world of possibilities. [online] Available at: <http://newfarm.rodaleinstitute.org/features/0204/csa2/part2.shtml> [Accessed 01.04.11].

McGillivray, M. (2006) Human Wellbeing: Concept and Measurement. Palgrave Macmillan, New York.

Mieczkowski, Z. (1981) Some notes on the geography of tourism: a comment. *Canadian Geographer,* **215**, 189.

Milbourne, P. (2003) Hunting ruralities: nature, society and culture in 'hunt countries' of England and Wales. *Journal of Rural Studies,* **19**, 157–171.

Milligan, C., Gatrell, A. & Bingley, A. (2004) Cultivating health: therapeutic landscapes and older people in northern England. *Social Science and Medicine*, **58**, 1781–1793.

Mind (2007) Ecotherapy: The green agenda for mental health. Mind week report May 2007. Mind, London.

Mintel (1999) Gardening Review. Mintel Leisure Intelligence, London.

Mintel (2004) Gardening – The Consumer – UK – October 2004. Mintel Leisure Intelligence, London.

Mintel (2010) Garden products retailing – UK – July 2010. [online] Available at: <http://www.oxygen.mintel.com/> [Accessed 30.03.11].

Mitchell, R. & Popham, F. (2008) Effect of exposure to natural environment on health inequalities: an observational population study. *The Lancet*, **372**, 1655–1660.

MLURI (Macaulay Land Use Research Institute) (1993) The Land Cover of Scotland 1988. MLURI, Aberdeen.

Moore, E.O. (1982) A prison environment's effect on health care service demands. *Journal of Environmental Systems,* **11**, 17–34.

Moore-Colyer, R. (2001) Rolf Gardiner, English patriot and the council for the church and countryside. *Agricultural History Review*, **49**, 187–209.

Moore-Colyer, R. & Scott, A. (2005) What kind of landscape do we want? Past, present and future perspectives. *Landscape Research*, **30**, 501–523.

More, T.A. & Payne, B.R. (1978) Affective responses to natural areas near cities. *Journal of leisure research*, **10**, 7–12.

Morita, E., Fukuda, S., Nagano, J., Hamajima, N., Yamamoto, H., Iwai, Y., Nakashima, Y., Ohira, H. & Shirakawa, T. (2006) Psychological effects of forest environments on healthy adults: Shinrin-yoku (forest-air bathing, walking) as a possible method of stress reduction. *Public Health*, **121**, 54–63.

Mourato, S., Atkinson, G., Collins, M., Gibbons, S., MacKerron, G. & Resende, G. (2010) Economic assessment of ecosystem related UK cultural services. The Economics Team of the UK National Ecosystem Assessment, London School of Economics, London.

Mourato, S. & MacKerron, G. (2010) Cultural Services and Subjective Wellbeing. London School of Economics, London.

Myerson, G. & Rydin, Y. (1996) The language of environment: a new rhetoric. Routledge, London.

Nabhan, G.P. & Trimble, S. (1994) The geography of childhood: Why children need wild places? Beacon Press, Boston, Massachusetts.

National Trust (2010) Facts about the Trust. [online] Available at: <http://www.nationaltrust.org.uk/main/w-trust/w-thecharity/w-thecharity_our-present/w-what_we_do/w-factsabouttrust.htm> [Accessed 29.03.11].

Natural England (2005) English Leisure Visits Survey. Natural England, Cheltenham.

Natural England (2009a) Experiencing Landscapes: capturing the cultural services and experiential qualities of landscape. Natural England Commissioned Report NECR024. Natural England, Sheffield.

Natural England (2009b) Green growth for green communities. A selection of regional case studies. Proceedings of the Park City Conference 2009. Natural England, Cheltenham. [online] Available at: <http://www.naturalengland.org.uk/Images/GI%20case%20studies_tcm6-10331.pdf> [Accessed 04.04.11].

Natural England (2009c) Coastal access: an audit of coastal paths in England 2008–09. [online] Available at: <http://www.naturalengland.org.uk/Images/coastalaccessauditreport_tcm6-22716.pdf> [Accessed 22.03.11].

Natural England (2010) Monitor of Engagement with the Natural Environment: The national survey on people and the natural environment Technical Report NECR 50. Natural England, Sheffield.

Natural England (2011a) Country Parks. [online] Available at: <http://www.naturalengland.org.uk/ourwork/enjoying/places/countryparks/default.aspx> [Accessed 20.03.11].

Natural England (2011b) National Parks Facts and Figures. [online] Available at: <http://www.naturalengland.org.uk/ourwork/conservation/designatedareas/nationalparks/factsfigures.aspx> [Accessed 01.04.11].

NAW (National Assembly for Wales) (2010) Sustainability Committee Inquiry into access to inland waters in Wales. National Assembly for Wales Sustainability Committee, Cardiff.

Newton, J. (2007) Wellbeing and the Natural Environment: A brief overview of the evidence. Department for Environment, Food and Rural Affairs, London.

NICE (National Institute for Health and Clinical Excellence) (2008) Physical activity and the environment. National Institute for Health and Clinical Excellence, London.

NICE (National Institute for Health and Clinical Excellence) (2009) Promoting physical activity for children and young people. National Institute for Health and Clinical Excellence, London.

NITB (Northern Ireland Tourism Board) (2009) Northern Ireland – Destination NI: how well do we deliver? Northern Ireland Tourism Board, Belfast.

O'Brien, L. & Murray, R. (2007) Forest School and its impact on young children: case studies in Britain. *Urban Forestry and Urban Greening*, **6**, 249–265.

Ofsted (2008) Learning Outside the Classroom. Ofsted, London.

O'Neill, J. (1993) Ecology, Policy and Politics: human well-being and the natural world. Routledge, London.

O'Neill, J. (1997) Value pluralism, incommensurability and institutions. Valuing Nature? Economics, ethics and environment (ed J. Forster), pp. 75–88. Routledge, London.

ONS (Office for National Statistics) (2005) Regional trends 37: tourism, 1991 and 2001. Office for National Statistics, London.

ONS (Office for National Statistics) (2006) Regional trends 39: 2006 edition. Office for National Statistics, London.

ONS (Office for National Statistics) (2009) Office of National Statistics Geography Glossary. [online] Available at: <http://www.statistics.gov.uk/geography/glossary/u.asp> [Accessed 24.11.10].

Orr, D.W. (2002) Political economy and the ecology of childhood. Children and nature: psychological, sociocultural, and evolutionary investigations (eds P.H. Kahn & S.R. Kellert), pp. 279–304. Massachusetts Institute of Technology Press, Cambridge, Massachusetts.

Ozer, S., Irmak, A. & Yilmaz, H. (2008) Determination of roadside noise reduction effectiveness of *Pinus Sylvestris L.* and *Populus Nigra L* in Erzurum, Turkey. *Noise and Water Inception,* **144,** 191–197.

Palmer, C. & Brady, E. (2007) Landscape and value in the work of Alfred Wainwright (1907–1991). *Landscape Research,* **32**, 397–421.

Parker, G. (2002) Citizenships, contingency and the countryside. Routledge, London.

Parsons, R., Tassinary, L.G., Ulrich, R.S., Hebl, M.R. & Grossman-Alexander, M. (1998) The view from the road: Implications for stress recovery and immunization. *Journal of Environmental Psychology,* **18**, 113–139.

Peacock, A. (2006) Changing Minds: the lasting impact of school trips. Swindon: National Trust. [online] Available at: <http://www.nationaltrust.org.uk/main/w-schools-guardianships-changing_minds.pdf> [Accessed 30.03.11].

Peacock, J., Hine, R. & Pretty, J. (2007). Got the Blues, then find some Greenspace: The Mental Health Benefits of Green Exercise Activities and Green Care. Report for Mind. University of Essex, Colchester.

Peacock, J., Hine, R. & Pretty, J. (2008) The Turn Around 2007 Project. Report for the Wilderness Foundation. University of Essex, Colchester.

Perry, R. (1994) Austen and Empire: a thinking woman's guide to British Imperialism Persuasions. *Journal of the Austen Society of North America,* **16,** 95-106.

Phillips, M., Page, S., Saratsi, E., Tansey, K. & Moore, K. (2008) Diversity, scale and green landscapes in the gentrification process: Traversing ecological and social science perspectives. *Applied Geography*, **28,** 54–76.

Philo, G. (2008) Active audiences and the construction of public knowledge. *Journalism Studies*, **9**, 535–544.

Pilgrim, S., Smith, D.J. & Pretty, J. (2007) A cross–regional assessment of the factors affecting ecoliteracy: Implications for policy and practice. *Ecological Applications,* **17**, 1742–1751.

Pilgrim, S., Cullen, L., Smith, D.J. & Pretty J. (2008) Ecological knowledge is lost in wealthier communities and countries. *Environmental Science and Technology,* **42**, 1004–1009.

Pilgrim, S. & Pretty, J. (eds) (2010) Nature and Culture. Earthscan, London.

Pretty, J. (2002) Agri-Culture. Earthscan, London.

Pretty, J. (2007) The Earth Only Endures. Earthscan, London.

Pretty, J. (2011) This Luminous Coast. Full Circle Editions, Saxmundham, Suffolk.

Pretty, J., Peacock, J., Sellens, M. & Griffin, M. (2005) The Mental and Physical Health Outcomes of Green Exercise. *International Journal of Environmental Health Research*, **15**, 319–337.

Pretty, J., Peacock, J., Hine, R., Sellens, M., South, N. & Griffin, M. (2007) Green exercise in the UK countryside: effects on health and psychological well-being. *Journal of Environmental Planning and Management,* **50**, 211–231.

Pretty, J., Angus, C., Bain, M., Barton, J., Gladwell, V., Hine, R., Pilgrim, S., Sandercock, G. & Sellens, M. (2009) Nature, Childhood, Health and Life Pathways. iCES Occasional Paper 2009–2. University of Essex, Colchester.

Rackham, O. (1986) The History of the Countryside: The full fascinating story of Britain's landscape. J.M. Dent & Sons, London.

Raudsepp-Hearne, C. & Capistrano, D. (2010) The Millennium Ecosystem Assessment: amulti-scale assessment for global stakeholders. Taking Stock of Nature: Participatory Biodiversity Assessment for Policy, Planning and Practice (ed A. Lawrence), pp. 49–68. Cambridge University Press, Cambridge.

Ravenscroft, N. (1985) Recreation planning and development. Macmillan, Basingstoke.

Ravenscroft, N. (1995) Recreational access to the countryside of England and Wales: popular leisure and the legitimation of private property. *Journal of Property Research,* **12**, 63–74.

Ravenscroft, N. (1998) Rights, citizenship and access to the countryside. *Space & Polity,* **2**, 33–48

Ravenscroft, N. & Taylor, B. (2009) Public engagement in new productivism. What is land for? The food, fuel and climate change debate *(eds M. Winter & M. Lobley), pp. 213–232. Earthscan, London.

Reichard, S.H. & White, P. (2001) Horticulture as a pathway of invasive plant introductions in the United States. *Bioscience,* **51**, 103–113.

Renn, O. (2006) Participatory processes for designing environmental policies. *Land Use Policy,* **23**, 34–43.

Rennie, A. (2006) The importance of National Parks to nation-building: support for the National Parks Act (2000) in the Scottish Parliament. *Scottish Geographical Journal,* **122**, 223–232.

RHS (Royal Horticultural Society) (2006) Gardening Matters. Front Gardens: Are we parking on our gardens? Do driveways cause flooding? Royal Horticultural Society, London.

Rickinson, M., Dillon, J., Teamey, K., Morris, M., Choi, M., Sanders, D. & Benefield, P. (2004) A review of research on outdoor learning. Field Studies Council, Shrewsbury.

Robbins, P. & Sharp, J.T. (2003) Producing and Consuming Chemicals: The Moral Economy of the American Lawn. *Economic Geography,* **79,** 425–451.

Rodger, D., Stokes, J., & Ogilvie, J. (2006) Heritage Trees of Scotland. Forestry Commission for Scotland and the Tree Council, Edinburgh.

Rojek, C. *(2001) Leisure and life politics. Leisure Sciences,* **23**, 115–125.

Russell, K.C. (2003) A nation-wide survey of outdoor behavioural healthcare programs for adolescents with problem behaviours. *Journal Experiential Education,* **25**, 322–331.

Sagoff, M. (2004) Price, Principle, and the Environment. Cambridge University Press, Cambridge.

SAGS (Scottish Allotments and Garden Society) (2007) Finding Scotland's Allotments. Scottish Allotments and Gardens Society, Scotland.

Samson, C. & Pretty, J. (2006) Environmental and health benefits of hunting lifestyles and diets for the Innu of Labrador. *Food Policy,* **31**, 528–553.

Sandercock, G., Voss, C., McConnell, D. & Rayner, P. (2010) Ten year secular declines in physical capacity of affluent English children are largely independent of changes in body mass index. *Archives of Disease in Childhood,* **95**, 46–47.

Schama, S. (1995) Landscape and memory. HarperCollins, London.

Schofield, J. & Szymanski, R. (eds) (2011) Local heritage, global context: cultural perspectives on sense of place. Ashgate, Farnham, UK.

Scott, K.D. (2003) Popularising science and nature programming: the role of "spectacle" in contemporary wildlife documentary. *Journal of Popular Film and Television,* **31**, 29–35.

Scottish Government Social Research (2010) The economic impact of wildlife tourism in Scotland. [online] Available at: <http://www.scotland.gov.uk/Resource/Doc/311951/0098489.pdf> [Accessed 30.03.11].

SDC (Sustainable Development Commission) (2010) Improving Young People's Lives. The role of the environment in building resilience, responsibility and employment chances. Sustainable Development Commission, London.

Sen, A., Darnell, A., Bateman, I.J., Crowe, A., Munday, P., Foden, J., & Coombes, E. (2010) Economic assessment of the recreational value of ecosystems in Great Britain. The Economics Team of the UK National Ecosystem Assessment, CSERGE, School of Environmental Sciences, University of East Anglia.

Sheets, V.L. & Manzer, C.D. (1991) Affect, cognition and urban vegetation. *Environment and Behaviour,* **23**, 285–304.

Shoard, M. (1982) The lure of the moors. Valued Environment (eds J. Gold & J. Burgess), pp. 55–73. George Allen and Unwin, London.

Shoard, M. (1987) This land is our land. Paladin Grafton Books, London.

Shove, E. & Pantzar, M. (2005) Consumers, Producers and Practices: Understanding the invention and reinvention of Nordic walking. *Journal of Consumer Culture,* **5,** 43–64.

Sibley, B, A. & Etinier, J. (2003) Physical activity and cognition – meta-analysis. *Paediatric Exercise Science,* **15**, 243–56.

Smiles, S. (2003) Equivalents for Megaliths: Prehistory and English Culture, 1920–50. The geographies of Englishness: Landscape and the National Past 1880–1940 (eds D. Corbett, Y. Holt & F. Russell), pp. 199–223. Yale University Press, New Haven.

Smith, A.D. (2002) Hinduism. Religions in the Modern World (ed L. Woodhead), pp.18–46. Routledge, London.

Smith, A.D. (2003) Chosen Peoples: Sacred Sources of National Identity. Oxford University Press, Oxford.

Smith, R.M., Thompson, K., Hodgson, J., Warren, P. & Gaston, K. (2006) Urban domestic gardens (IX): Composition and richness of the vascular plant flora, and implications for native biodiversity. *Biological Conservation,* **129,** 312–322.

Snelling, J. (ed) (1992) Sharpham Miscellany: Essays in Spirituality and Ecology. The Sharpham Trust, Totnes, UK.

Soil Association (2005) Cultivating communities: farming at your fingertips. Soil Association, Bristol.

Southall, H. (2009) A vision of Britain through time. Agriculture in 2001. [online] Available at: <http://www.visionofbritain.org.uk> [Accessed 12.03.11].

Sport England (2006) Active people survey. Sport England, London.

Sport England (2009) Active people survey 2008/9. Summary findings. Sport England, London.

Squire, S. (1988) Wordsworth and Lake District Tourism: Romantic Reshaping of Landscape. *Canadian Geographer,* **32,** 237–247.

Stansfield, S., Haines, M. & Brown, B. (2000) Noise and health in the urban environment, *Review of Environmental Health*, **15**, 43–82.

Stebbins, R.A. (1992) Amateurs, professionals and serious leisure. McGill University Press, Montreal.

Stebbins, R.A. (1997) Serious leisure and well-being. Work, leisure and well-being (ed. Haworth, J.T.), pp. 117–130. Routledge, London.

Stebbins, R.A. (2001) Volunteering – mainstream and marginal: preserving the leisure experience. Volunteering in leisure: marginal or inclusive? (eds M. Graham & M. Foley), pp.1–10. LSA Publication No. 75. Leisure Studies Association, Eastbourne, UK.

Stephenson, T. (1989) Forbidden land. The struggle for access to mountain and moorland. Manchester University Press, Manchester.

Sugiyama, T., Leslie, E., Giles-Corti, B. & Owen, N. (2008) Associations of neighbourhood greenness with physical and mental health: do walking, social coherence and local social interaction explain the relationships? *Journal of Epidemiology and Community Health,* **62**, e9.

Sustain (2008) Ethical hijack: why the terms "local", "seasonal" and "farmers' market" should be defended from abuse by the food industry. Sustain, London.

Sutcliffe, S. (2000) A colony of seekers: Findhorn in the 1990s. *Journal of Contemporary Religion*, **15**, 215–231.

Tabbush, P. & O'Brien, L. (2003) Health and Well-Being: Trees, Woodlands and Natural Spaces. Forestry Commission, Edinburgh.

Takano, T., Nakamura, K. & Watanabe, M. (2002) Urban residential environments and senior citizens' longevity in megacity areas: the importance of walkable green spaces. *Journal of Epidemiology and Community Health*, **56**, 913–918.

Taylor, A.F., Wiley, A., Kuo, F.E. & Sullivan, W.C. (1998) Growing up in the inner city: green spaces as places to grow. *Environment and Behaviour, ***30**, 3–27.

Taylor, A.F., Kuo, F.E. & Sullivan, W.C. (2001) Coping with ADD: the surprising connection to green play settings. *Environment and Behaviour, ***33**, 54–77.

Teig, E., Amulya, J., Bardwell, L., Buchenau, M., Marshall, J.A. & Litt, J.S. (2009) Collective efficacy in Denver, Colorado: Strengthening neighbourhoods and health through community gardens. *Health & Place*, **15**, 1115–1122.

The Sacred Land Project (2001) Living with sacred space. A report by The Sacred Land Project to Community Action for Sacred Lands (CASL). [online] Available at: < http://www.arcworld.org/downloads/Sacred-Land-Report.pdf [Accessed 29.04.11].

Thomas, G. & Thompson, G. (2004) A Child's Place: Why Environment Matters to Children. Green Alliance / Demos Report, London.

Thompson, D. (2007) Norfolk allotments: the plot so far. Norfolk Recorders, Norwich.

Thompson, S., Marks, N., Aked, J. & Cordon, C. (2008) Five ways to wellbeing: the evidence. New Economics Foundation, London.

Thompson Coon, J., Boddy, K. Stein, K., Whear, R., Barton, J. & Depledge, M.H. (2011) Does Participating in Physical Activity in Outdoor Natural Environments Have a Greater Effect on Physical and Mental Wellbeing than physical activity indoors. *Environmental Science and Technology,* **45,** 1761–1772.

Tilley, C., Hamilton, S., Harrison, S., & Anderson, E. (2000) Nature, Culture, Clitter: Distinguishing Between Cultural and Geomorphological Landscapes; The Case of Hilltop Tors in South-West England. *Journal of Material Culture,* **5**, 197–224.

Tilley, C. (2006) Introduction: identity, place, landscape and heritage. *Journal of Material Culture*, **11**, 7–32.

Tinch,D., Hanley, N. & Beharry-Borg, N (2010) Economic assessment of ecosystem services provided by UK Mountains, moorlands and Heaths (MMH). The Economics Team of the UK National Ecosytem Assessment, University of Stirling.

TNS (Taylor Nelson Sofres) (2009) Scottish Recreation Survey: annual summary report 2007. Scottish Natural Heritage Commissioned Report No.321, Edinburgh.

Tolia-Kelly, D. (2007a) Fear in paradise: the affective registers of the English Lake District landscape revisited. *Senses and Society*, **2**, 329–351.

Tolia-Kelly, D. (2007b) Organic cosmopolitanism: challenging cultures of the non-native at the Burnley Millenium Arboretum. *Garden History*, **35,** 172–184.

Tolia-Kelly, D. (2010) Landscape, Race and Memory: Material Ecologies of Citizenship. Ashgate, Farnham, UK.

Tuan, Y.F. (1979) Landscapes of fear. Pantheon Books, New York.

Ulrich, R.S. (1984) View through a window may influence recovery from surgery. *Science,* **224**, 420–421.

Ulrich, R.S., Simons, R.F., Losito, B.D., Fiorito, E., Miles, M.A. & Zelson, M. (1991) Stress Recovery During Exposure to Natural and Urban Environments. *Journal of Environmental Psychology,* **11**, 201–230.

University of Brighton (2008) Water Framework Directive: Valuation of recreational benefits of improvements in water quality – potential benefits and data requirements. Collaborative Research Programme On River Basin Management Planning Economics   Project 4f – Use and Access. Department for Environment, Food and Rural Affairs, London. [online] Available at: <http://www.wfdcrp.co.uk/> [Accessed 21.03.11].

University of Portsmouth (2009) A vision of Britain through time. [online] Available at: <http://www.visionofbritain.org.uk/atlas/> [Accessed 29.03.10].

van den Berg, A.E., Koole, S.L. & van der Wulp, N.Y. (2003) Environmental preference and restoration: (How) are they related? *Journal of Environmental Psychology*, **23**, 135–46.

Vatn, A. & Bromley, D. (1994) Choices without prices without apologies. *Journal of Environmental Economics and Management*, **26**, 129–148.

Vatn, A. (2009) An institutional analysis of methods for environmental appraisal. *Ecological Economics,* **68**, 2207–2215.

Veitch, J., Salmon, J. & Ball, K. (2007) Children's perceptions of the use of public open spaces for active free play. *Children's*

Geographies: Advancing interdisciplinary understanding of young people's lives, **5**, 409–22.

WAG (Welsh Assembly Government) (2006) The Welsh Historic Environment: Position Statement 2006. Welsh Assembly Government, Cardiff.

Walters, S.M. (1970) The next twenty-five years. The flora of a changing Britain (ed F. Perring), pp. 136–141. Classey, Hampton.

Wanless, D. (2002) Securing Our Future Health: Taking a Long-Term View. HM Treasury, London.

Ward, C. (1978) The Child in the City. Architectural Press, London.

Ward, C. (1988) The Child in the Country. Hale, London.

Ward, C. (1993) New Town, Home Town. The Lessons of Experience. Calouste Gulbenkian Foundation, London.

Ward-Thompson, C., Travlõu, P. & Roe, J. (2006) Free-range Teenagers: the role of wild adventure space in children's lives. OPENSpace, Edinburgh.

Ward-Thompson, C., Aspinall, P. & Montarzino, A. (2008) The childhood factor. Adult visits to green places and the significance of childhood experience. *Environment and Behaviour* **40**, 111–143.

Weiner, M.J. (2004) English Culture and the decline of the industrial spirit 1850–1980. Cambridge University Press, Cambridge.

Wells, N.M. (2000) At home with nature: effects of "greenness" on children's cognitive functioning. *Environment and Behaviour,* **32**, 775–795.

Wells, N.M. & Evans, G.W. (2003) Nearby nature: a buffer of life stress among rural children. *Environment and Behaviour,* **35**, 311–330.

Wells, N.M. & Lekies, K.S. (2006) Nature and the life course: pathways from childhood nature experiences to adult environmentalism. *Children, Youth and Environments,* **16**, 1–24.

Wells, N.M., Ashdown, S.P., Davies, E.H.S., Cowett, F.D. & Yang, Y. (2007) Environment, design and obesity. *Environmental Behaviour,* **39**, 6–33.

White, G. (1977). The natural history and antiquities of Selborne. First published 1789. Penguin, Harmondsworth, London.

White, R. & Heerwagen, J. (1998) Nature and Mental health: Biophillia and Biophobia. In: The environment and mental health: a guide for clinicians (ed A. Lundburg), pp.175–192. Routledge: London

WHO (World Health Organization) (2004) World Health Report. World Health Organization, Geneva.

Whyte, I. (2000) William Wordsworth's "Guide to the Lakes" and the Geographical Tradition. *Area,* **32**, 101–106.

Wild, K. & McCarthy, D. (2010) *A corpus linguistics analysis of ecosystems vocabulary in the public sphere (claevips).* Report Commissioned by the National Ecosystem Assessment. Available from Lexical Computing Ltd. 80 Lyndhurst Road, Brighton & Hove, BN3 6FD.

Williams, R. (1976) Keywords: a vocabulary of culture and society. Penguin, Harmondsworth, London.

Williams, R. (1980) Ideas of Nature. Problems in materialism and culture: selected essays. (Williams, R.). Verso, London.

Williamson, J. (2000) Decoding advertisements: ideology and meaning in advertisements. Marion Boyars, London.

Wilson, M.A. & Howarth, R.B. (2002) Discourse-based valuation of ecosystems services: establishing fair outcomes through group deliberation. *Ecological Economics,* **41**, 431–443.

Winter, M. (1996) Rural Politics. Routledge, London and New York.

Winter, M. & Gasson, R. (1996) Pilgrimage and tourism: cathedral visiting in contemporary England. *International Journal of Heritage Studies,* **2**, 172–182.

Wood, P., Landry, C. & Bloomfield, J. (2006) Cultural diversity in Britain: A toolkit for cross-cultural co-operation. Joseph Rowntree Foundation, York.

Woods, M. (2003) Deconstructing rural protest: the emergence of a new social movement, *Journal of Rural Studies,* **19**, 309–325.

Worster, D. (1994) Nature's economy: a history of ecological ideas. Cambridge University Press, Cambridge.

Wylie, J. (2002) An essay on ascending Glastonbury Tor. *Geoforum,* **33**, 441–454.

Wynn, M. (2007) God, pilgrimage, and acknowledgement of place. *Religious Studies,* **43**, 145–163.

Wynn, M. (2009) Faith and Place: An Essay in Embodied Religious Epistemology. Oxford University Press, Oxford.

Yamaguchi, M., Deguchi, M. & Miyazaki, Y. (2006) The effects of exercise in forest and urban environments on sympathetic nervous activity of normal young adults. *The Journal of International Medical Research,* **34,** 152–159.

Zaring, J. (1977) The Romantic Face of Wales. *Annals of the Association of American Geographers,* **67**, 397–418.

Zimmer, O. (1998) In search of natural identity: Alpine landscape and the reconstruction of the Swiss nation. *Comparative Studies in Society and History,* **40**, 637–65.

Appendix 16.1 Approach Used to Assign Certainty Terms to Chapter Key Findings

This chapter began with a set of Key Findings. Adopting the approach and terminology used by the Intergovernmental Panel on Climate Change (IPCC) and the Millennium Assessment (MA), these Key Findings also include an indication of the level of scientific certainty. The 'uncertainty approach' of the UK NEA consists of a set of qualitative uncertainty terms derived from a 4-box model and complemented, where possible, with a likelihood scale (see below). Estimates of certainty are derived from the collective judgement of authors, observational evidence, modelling results and/or theory examined for this assessment.

Throughout the Key Findings presented at the start of this chapter, superscript numbers and letters indicate the estimated level of certainty for a particular key finding:

1. *Well established:*   high agreement based on significant evidence
2. *Established but incomplete evidence:* high agreement based on limited evidence
3. *Competing explanations:*   low agreement, albeit with significant evidence
4. *Speculative:*   low agreement based on limited evidence

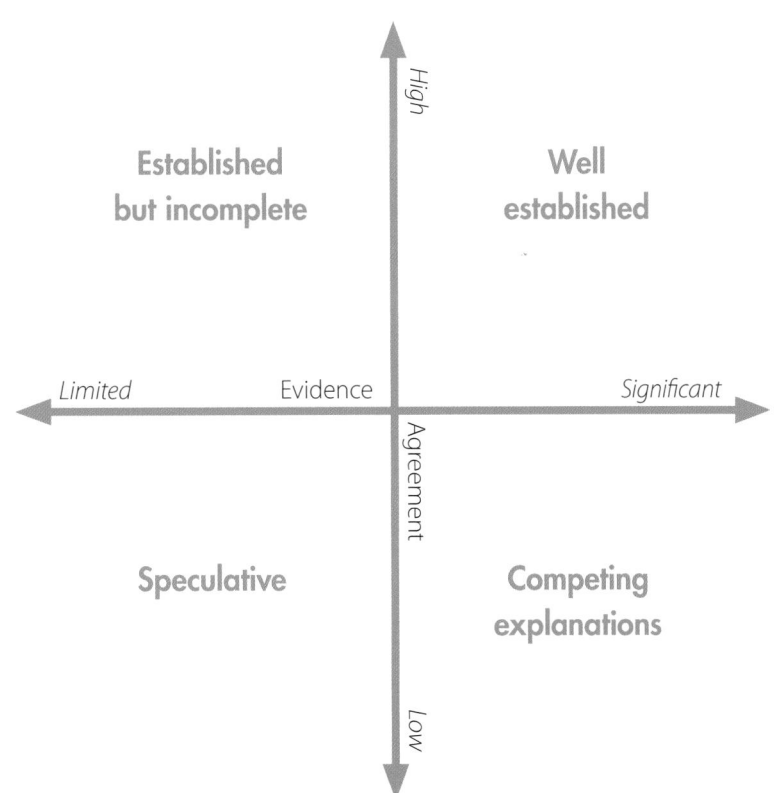

a. *Virtually certain:*   >99% probability of occurrence
b. *Very likely:*   >90% probability
c. *Likely:*   >66% probability
d. *About as likely as not:*   >33–66% probability
e. *Unlikely:*   <33% probability
f. *Very unlikely:*   <10% probability
g. *Exceptionally unlikely:*   <1% probability

Certainty terms 1 to 4 constitute the 4-box model, while *a* to *g* constitute the likelihood scale.

Chapter 17:
Status and Changes in the UK Ecosystems and their Services to Society: England

Coordinating Lead Authors: Pam Berry and John Hopkins
Contributing Authors: Todd Sajwaj, Melanie C. Austen, Laurence Jones and Emma Burnett

Key Findings*

About 70% of England is farmed. England has a population of over 52 million people, making it one of the world's most densely populated countries, with over 80% of the population living in towns and cities[1]. These urban areas are virtually certain to make the highest demands on, and be the greatest recipients of, ecosystem services[2].

[1] *well established*
[2] *established but incomplete evidence*

There have been significant changes to England's biodiversity, with declines in many well-recorded species over the last 50 years[1]. Recently (2003–2006) the overall trends in selected indicator species were positive[1], although 26% of England's species are still depleted or on the UK Biodiversity Action Plan (BAP) list[2]. Sites of Special Scientific Interest cover 8% of England and while many are not in favourable conservation status, it is likely that their condition is improving[2].

[1] *well established*
[2] *established but incomplete evidence*

England contains the majority of the UK's Enclosed Farmland[1]. The condition of the Broad Habitat has been declining over the last 50 years, very likely because of land use change and management, but with some recovery in the last 10 years[2].

[1] *well established*
[2] *established but incomplete evidence*

The area covered by Mountains, Moorlands and Heaths has significantly decreased over the last 60 years, very likely due to afforestation and conversion to rough and improved grassland in the uplands[1]. Loss of lowland heathland is likely to have been due to the development of towns and roads, afforestation and agricultural improvement[1]. There were some increases between 1998 and 2007, due to restoration and re-creation[1].

[1] *well established*

Most Semi-natural Grasslands have been lost, very likely due to conversion to arable or intensification, but many are now protected, with 68% lying within Sites of Special Scientific Interest (SSSIs) and 40% designated as Special Areas of Conservation (SACs)[1]. It is likely that Calcareous and Acid Grassland have experienced the greatest average loss of plant species of all Semi-natural Grasslands over the last 40 years[2].

[1] *well established*
[2] *established but incomplete evidence*

Arable Enclosed Farmland increased after the Second World War (WWII), but between 1998 and 2007 it decreased by 8.8%, while Improved Grassland increased by 5.2%[1]. This is very likely to be due to alterations in economic and technological drivers and policy (e.g. Common Agricultural Policy (CAP) reform)[1]. Some arable flowering plants have decreased dramatically in the last 50 years and are now likely to be amongst the most threatened elements of the flora[1]. Since 1982, about 90% of all yield increases in wheat and barley can probably attributed to new crop varieties[2].

[1] *well established*
[2] *established but incomplete evidence*

England is comparatively poorly wooded (9%), despite cover increasing by 45% since WWII[1]. Initially, mostly conifers were planted, but since the 1980s more broadleaves have been used[1]. Many woodland species have declined in numbers due to lack of management, deer grazing, fragmentation and, increasingly, climate change[2]. Woodland delivers the greatest number of identified ecosystem services[2].

[1] *well established*
[2] *established but incomplete evidence*

Wetlands only cover about 4% of England, but they have a disproportionally high biodiversity, including a significant number of internationally important species[2]. Consequently, 47% of England's wetlands are under SSSI protection[1]. England also has the greatest extent of chalk rivers in Europe[1]. Forty-four per cent of SSSI open waters and 21% of wetland are classified as favourable and 11% and 48% as recovering, respectively. Eutrophication is likely to be the main cause of unfavourable condition in open waters, and overgrazing, burning, pollution and drainage in wetlands[2].

[1] *well established*
[2] *established but incomplete evidence*

---

* Each Key Finding has been assigned a level of scientific certainty, based on a 4-box model and complemented, where possible, with a likelihood scale. Superscript numbers indicate the uncertainty term assigned to each finding. Full details of each term and how they were assigned are presented in Appendix 17.1.

England is more urbanised than the rest of the UK and Urban areas cover about 10% of the country[1]. Urban areas require more ecosystem services than they can provide; estimates suggest that London alone requires 293 times more land than its geographical area to support itself[1]. Urban habitats provide greenspace, which is of importance to Urban residents[1].

[1] *well established*

England holds 73% of the UK's Saltmarsh and 86% of its Shingle[1]. Saltmarsh, Shingle and Sand Dunes have suffered losses due to reclamation, development and erosion[1]. Coastal Margin habitats support a wide range of highly specialised species, and it is very likely that many of these are of international importance for conservation[2].

[1] *well established*
[2] *established but incomplete evidence*

England's Marine habitats support a high diversity of species[2]. Coastal erosion particularly affects England's coast, with 30% subject to erosion and 46% protected by engineering structures[2]. It is very likely that harvesting has adversely affected marine species[2]. Energy provision by the physical component of Marine habitats, and through biomass harvesting, is likely in the near future[4].

[2] *established but incomplete evidence*
[4] *speculative*

Supporting services in England function at rates similar to those of other countries in the UK, but are faced with significant pressures from human activities[2]. Nutrient cycling in England is influenced by anthropogenic nitrogen and phosphorus deposition from domestic, agricultural and industrial sources[1]. Tillage practices in arable regions are very likely to have a significant negative influence on soil erosion rates[2]. Annual losses of carbon due to peatland management are likely to exceed the rate of carbon sequestration by English peatlands that are in good condition[2]. It is likely that primary production is increasing in agricultural and Woodland habitats[2].

[1] *well established*
[2] *established but incomplete evidence*

The quality of many regulating services is improving; however, various forms of pollution continue to impact deleteriously on England's ecosystems[2]. England is a net source of greenhouse gases, but this trend is diminishing[1]. England's pollinating insects are declining, with significant consequences for agricultural production and several habitats[1]. Significant improvements in England's air quality have occurred over recent decades, but current concentrations and deposition rates often exceed recommended environmental thresholds[1]. Although the number of English rivers of good chemical quality is increasing, concentrations of phosphates and nitrates remain problematic[2].

[1] *well established*
[2] *established but incomplete evidence*

England's provisioning services contribute strongly to local and national economies and while environmental management is improving, significant impacts on interdependent regulatory, cultural and supporting services must be addressed[1]. It is likely that England's farmlands will continue to show steadily increasing agricultural yields with declining environmental impacts[1]. Landscape management, particularly agricultural management, plays a critical role for the continued delivery of other ecosystem services[2]. Landings of marine fish have declined since 1970[2]. Throughout the 20th and 21st Centuries, demand for water in England has steadily increased due to population growth and will continue to grow[2].

[1] *well established*
[2] *established but incomplete evidence*

England's landscape provides highly important cultural ecosystem services to local populations, individual residents and external visitors, the value of which is often difficult to quantify[2]. Urban and rural greenspaces provide important opportunities for recreation, aesthetic inspiration, community interaction and psychological well-being[1]. The habitats and landscapes of England provide important sources of tourist revenues that support rural communities[2].

[2] *established but incomplete evidence*

The main direct drivers of change primarily affect agriculture, woodland and urban land uses, while indirect ones concern economic forces and increasing population[2]. Agricultural expansion and intensification to meet the food demands of a growing urban population have led to habitat loss and degradation[1]. It is very likely that changes in woodland management have altered woodland species composition, as have pressures, such as deer grazing[2].

[1] *well established*
[2] *established but incomplete evidence*

The consequences of the change in Broad Habitats and their service delivery are only broadly understood². Enclosed Farmland, Semi-natural Grasslands and Woodlands are of high importance for provisioning services, but the increase of Enclosed Farmland and Woodlands has led to the loss of other habitats[1]. Enclosed Farmland management to increase the provision of food has affected biodiversity and decreased provision of some regulating and cultural services[2]. All habitats contribute to regulating services; the condition of many of these is recovering as a result of policy intervention[2]. All Broad Habitats are important for cultural services[2].

[1] *well established*
[2] *established but incomplete evidence*

Sustainable management of habitats and their services is critical to their long-term future and to providing an appropriate balance of services[1]. It is likely that a holistic ecosystems approach would help achieve this[2]. Further funding streams, as through Payments for Ecosystem Services schemes, are needed to support sustainable management[2].

[1] *well established*
[2] *established but incomplete evidence*

Synergies and trade-offs that occur between and within ecosystems and their services need to be managed sustainably[2]. Research and case studies are useful to demonstrate how synergies and trade-offs can be handled to achieve sustainable management[2].

[2] *established but incomplete evidence*

Our knowledge of the relationship between Broad Habitats and ecosystem services is lacking, especially in the case of multifunctional delivery. This is especially important for the dominant form of land use: agriculture[2]. There is also a lack of knowledge about the integrated impacts of the drivers of change. This significant knowledge gap will need to be filled so that future service delivery can be planned effectively[2].

[2] *established but incomplete evidence*

17.1 Introduction

England's distinctive landscape is characterised by a high percentage of farmland and large urban areas. This chapter concentrates particularly on England's Broad Habitats, their condition, status and trends (in space and time) and the ecosystem services that they deliver. It also provides a synopsis of the direct and indirect drivers of changes in status and trends of ecosystems and their services, before exploring possible future changes. Where possible, a valuation of ecosystem services is given, but as the different sources have used various methodologies, figures given do not represent a comprehensive and systematic picture. Valuation is difficult in the case of some cultural services, and often country-specific information is lacking. The chapter complements the UK National Ecosystem Assessment (NEA) Economics Chapter (Chapter 22), which undertook a rigorous analysis for each of the UK NEA Broad Habitats and for selected services, but is not always disaggregated to England.

Now and in the future there are possible synergies and trade-offs in many ecosystem services, especially between some agricultural activities, such as vital food supply, carbon sequestration and regulation of air and water quality. These are explored, along with sustainable management options, in order to see how ecosystem service provision can be sustained or enhanced. There is still much that is unknown about the relationship of biodiversity to ecosystem service provision, both in general and in particular. These knowledge gaps need be addressed, so as to improve future environmental management.

17.2 England—Key Environmental Features

With a land surface of 130,395 ha, England is the largest country of the United Kingdom (53.5% of the UK land area of 243,610 ha). It is also home to more than 52 million people, making it one of the world's most densely populated countries (Foresight 2010). The majority of England is lowland and underlain by recent rocks, such as the Cretaceous chalk that is extensive in parts of south and east England. The uplands cover approximately 17% of the country and occur mainly in the north and west, in areas with older, harder rocks resistant to erosion, such as the granite uplands of Devon and Cornwall and the more geologically varied Lake District. In large areas of the lowlands, the solid geology is overlain by alluvium, glacial and other drift, and peat. Additional soil diversity has been introduced by glaciation whose influence is most pronounced in the north and west of England. The resulting variation of soil attributes is one of the drivers behind the complexity of land use patterns in England.

The climate of England is typically warmer and drier than that of the other countries in the UK, with mean minimum and maximum temperatures of 5.6°C and 13.1°C respectively (all climate figures are for 1971–2000 from: Met Office 2010). Within England there is considerable variation in temperature due to increasing latitude, local elevational gradients and maritime influence. Between 1960 and 2006, most of England experienced a 1.0–1.4°C rise in mean annual temperature, although in parts of northern England it was less than 1.0°C (Jenkins *et al.* 2009; **Figure 17.1**).

The majority of England experiences higher amounts of total sunshine (1461.8 hours) than the rest of the UK and generally has a lower annual rainfall (838.7 mm). However, the South West and North West regions receive greater mean amounts of rainfall than the rest of England (**Figure 17.2**). Between 1960 and 2006, changes in mean annual precipitation varied across England from +/– 10% to increases of 10–25% (Jenkins *et al.* 2009). This masks seasonal variations, with some areas experiencing decreases of 10–25% in spring and 25–50% in summer, with increases in the other two seasons. The decreases in spring are almost entirely confined to England, whilst the increases in winter are much higher in North West England and in much of Scotland.

A few large river catchments, such as the Thames, Severn and Trent, drain most of England, although the many smaller rivers which drain the landscape beyond these major catchments form an important part of the hydrology of the country. The few large, natural lakes and waters in England are predominantly relics of glaciation and are found in the Lake District, with most other large open waters (i.e. larger ponds, reservoirs and the wetlands of the Broads in eastern England) constructed or restored by human activities.

Despite its population density, most of the land area of England remains rural. With approximately 70% of the land being farmed, the majority of England falls into the Arable and Horticultural and Improved Grassland habitat classes (**Table 17.1**). Arable farming predominates in South East England, as well as other regions where soil quality is high. The north and west of England and their associated uplands are characterised by poorer quality soils and consequently, livestock farming predominates.

The regional variation in land use stemming from the variations in soil and climatic conditions has considerable impacts on the distribution and condition of England's habitats, which are important in underpinning the various ecosystem services (Section 17.5).

Whilst the proportion of woodland in England is one of the lowest in the world (just over 9%), the extent of English woodlands has been steadily increasing throughout the 20th Century (barring the two World Wars), due in part to the planting of coniferous woodland in the uplands and other marginal lands. In England (unlike Scotland), there is a majority of broadleaved woodland habitat.

The 8,000 km of coast is ecologically and scenically diverse. The low-lying coasts of the East and North West are predominantly composed of mudflats, beaches and shingle, which contrast sharply with sea cliffs and rocky foreshores occurring along the English Channel and the South West region. Many areas of the English coastline have seen significant domestic, commercial and industrial development. Also, areas of coastal and intertidal habitats have been reclaimed and converted to agricultural land uses, particularly in the south and east.

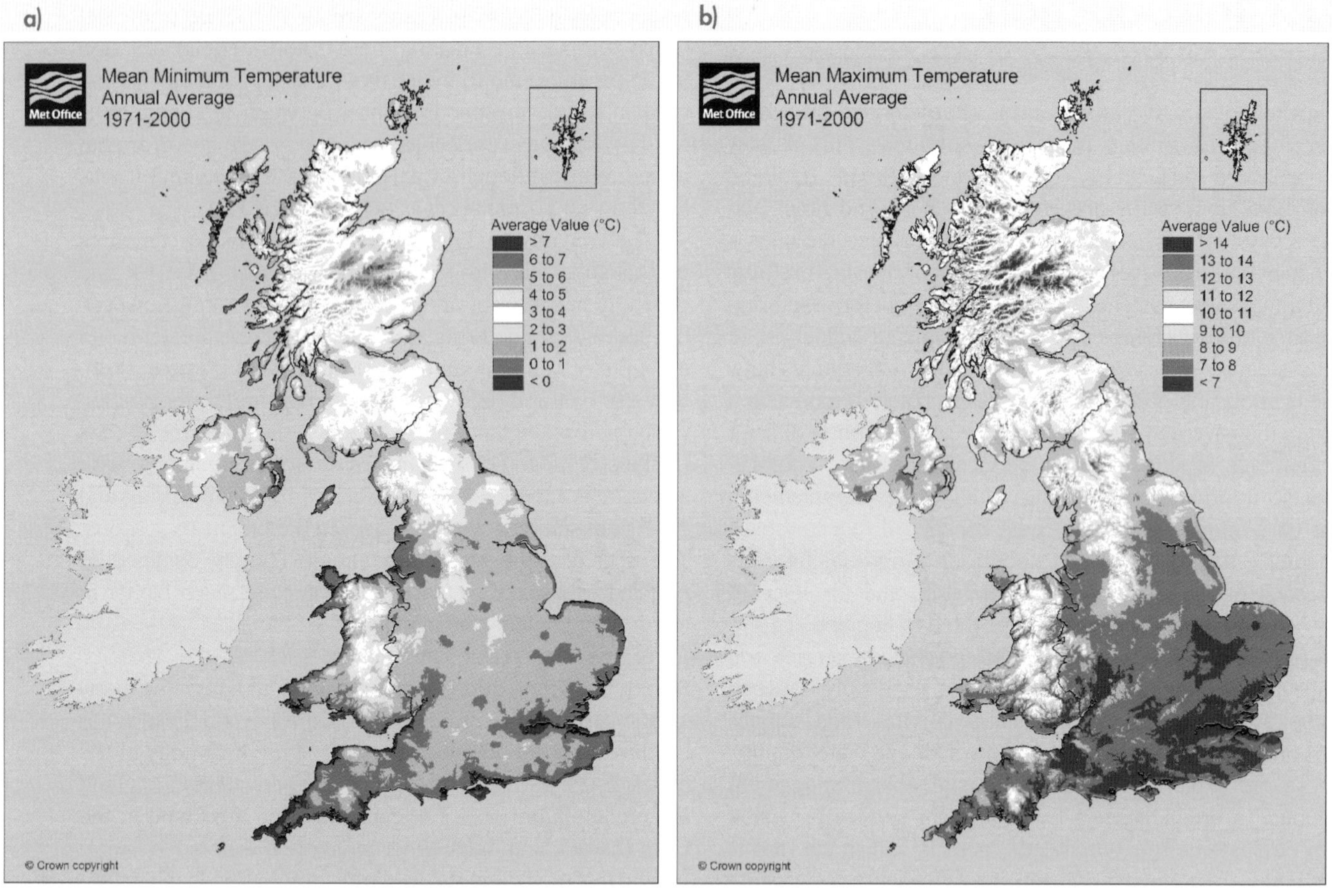

Figure 17.1 Mean annual minimum (a) and maximum (b) temperatures. Source: © Crown Copyright 2000, the Met Office.

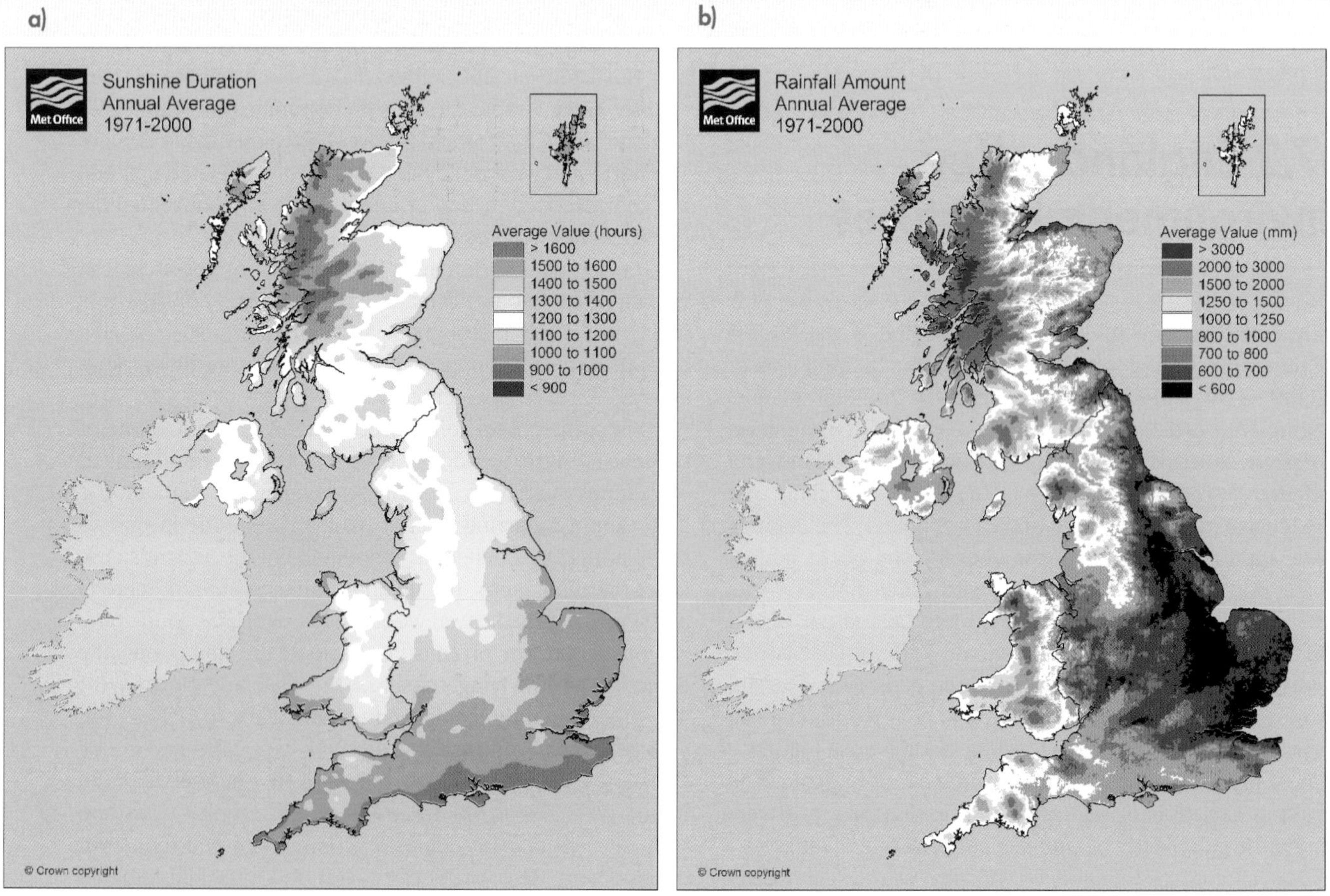

Figure 17.2 Mean annual hours of sunshine (a) and rainfall (b) in the UK. Source: © Crown Copyright 2000, the Met Office.

Table 17.1 Amounts and percentages of broad habitat classes in England from 1990 to 2007. Source: Countryside Survey (2009). Countryside Survey data owned by NERC – Centre for Ecology & Hydrology.

Broad habitats	1990		1998		2007	
	('000 ha)	% area of England	('000 ha)	% area of England	('000 ha)	% area of England
Broadleaved, Mixed and Yew Woodland	887	6.7	927	7.0	981	7.4
Coniferous Woodland	241	1.8	260	2.0	257	1.9
Boundary and Linear Features	380	2.9	354	2.7	353	2.7
Arable and Horticulture	4,380	33.2	4,389	33.3	4,002	30.4
Improved Grassland	3,075	23.3	2,714	20.6	2,856	21.7
Neutral Grassland	994	7.5	1,290	9.8	1,453	11.0
Calcareous Grassland	42	0.3	33	0.2	30	0.2
Acid Grassland	475	3.6	400	3.0	396	3.0
Bracken	93	0.7	109	0.8	91	0.7
Dwarf Shrub Heath	309	2.3	288	2.2	331	2.5
Fen, Marsh and Swamp	78	0.6	124	0.9	117	0.9
Bog	98	0.7	138	1.0	140	1.1
Standing Open Water and Canals*	105	0.8	88	0.7	97	0.7
Rivers and Streams*	33	0.2	32	0.2	29	0.2
Built-up Areas and Gardens	999	7.6	1,009	7.7	1,038	7.9
Other Land†	564	4.3	596	4.5	580	4.4
Unsurveyed Urban Land	428	3.5	428	3.5	428	3.5
Total	**13,180**	**100**	**13,180**	**100**	**13,180**	**100**

* Standing Open Water and Canals and Rivers and Streams broad habitat estimates were calculated using a different statistical model to the other broad habitats. It is not appropriate to use the consistent statistical model for these two habitats because of the distribution of the data. Change in these broad habitats is calculated independently from the differences between stock estimates.
† Other land is made up of the remaining small broad habitats and the difference between the sum of the broad habitat areas and area of England used to calculate percentage areas.

Urban areas cover between 10 and 14% of England (LCM 2000; GLUD 2005), and there has been continued growth, with 152,400 ha of new development between 1991 and 2006. Of this, an estimated 75% of new dwellings were built on brownfield (up from 57% in 1996; DCLG 2008), with only 0.4% of new dwellings built on undeveloped green belt land (Natural England 2010a). Approximately 80% of the English populace live in towns and cities, which puts increased strain on the surrounding ecosystems to deliver services, as cities are limited in the services they can produce (Gill *et al.* 2007). Urban ecosystems and the services they demand exhibit a disproportionately large importance relative to their areal extent.

17.3 Biodiversity

Biodiversity refers to the diversity of life on Earth (Chapter 4). It is, therefore, a complex concept including not only the diversity of species, but also the diversity of ecosystems and habitats. Due to its high climatic, geological and land use diversity, as well as the marked variations in depth, exposure and substrates of its seas, England's habitats exhibit wide variation by comparison with many other parts of the world of similar size. This variation of habitats and the way it has recently changed is summarised in terms of the eight UK

NEA Broad Habitats in Section 17.4; along with summaries of the ecosystem services each delivers.

Whilst the species diversity of England is not high in comparison with some areas of the world, nevertheless it has approximately 55,500 species of animals, plants and fungi. This includes five groups of species considered to be of outstanding significance in an international context: Atlantic ferns, mosses and lichens; breeding seabirds; wintering and passage waterbirds and gulls; grassland and woodland fungi; and heathland invertebrates (Natural England 2010b). England also has at least 40 endemic species and 54 species designated as internationally threatened. In addition, 492 species are known to have been lost from England, mostly since 1800. The better-known groups show losses of 22% of amphibians, 15% of dolphins and whales, 14% of stoneworts, 12% of terrestrial mammals and 12% of stoneflies (Natural England 2010b). Butterfly species are also well recorded, and in England between 1976 and 2009 there has been a moderate (19%) decline in 50 indicator butterfly species, with specialist species decreasing by 45% and generalists by 12% respectively (Brereton *et al.* 2010). Between 1990 and 2009, there have been significant declines in the abundance of farmland and woodland butterflies (42% and 65% respectively), although some improvements on land entered into agri-environment schemes are evident. An assessment of loss from 23 English counties since 1900 concluded that the highest rates of loss have generally been in southern and eastern counties, and this is partly mirrored by the figures for invertebrates (**Figure 17.3**). Local and regional losses have

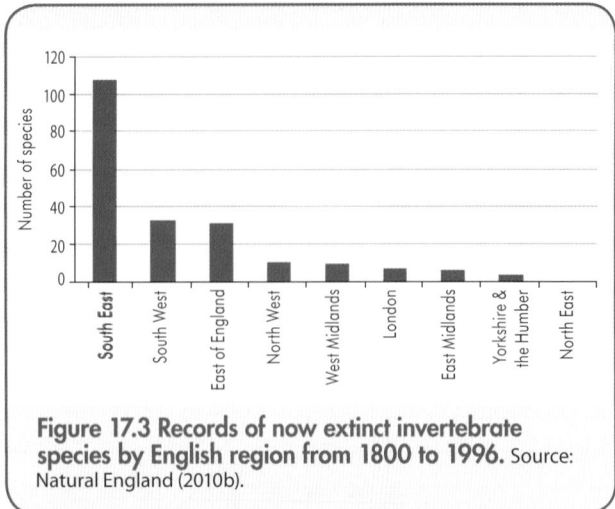

Figure 17.3 Records of now extinct invertebrate species by English region from 1800 to 1996. Source: Natural England (2010b).

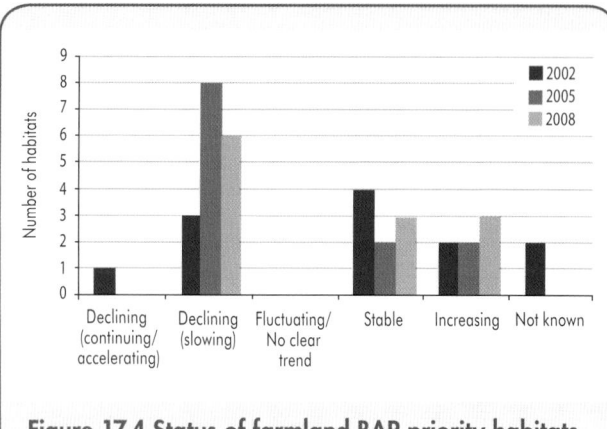

Figure 17.4 Status of farmland BAP priority habitats in England. Source: data from Natural England and JNCC; Defra (2010c) © Crown copyright 2010.

also been important, for example, the high brown fritillary butterfly (*Argynnis adippe*) has become extinct in the East Midlands, East Anglia, and South East regions in the last 50 years.

In 1993 the UK Biodiversity Action Plan (BAP) was published in response to the Convention on Biological Diversity, and between 1995 and 1999 Natural England published Action Plans for 391 priority species and 45 priority habitats. In 2002, the England Biodiversity Strategy (EBS) was published, setting out the strategy for achieving the 2010 target to halt biodiversity loss and its contribution to delivering the UK's BAP (Defra 2002). The EBS aimed to ensure a halt and, if possible, a reverse in declines of priority species and habitats. It recognised wild species and habitats as being part of healthy functioning ecosystems, and stressed that biodiversity's essential role in enhancing the quality of life should be generally accepted and that conservation should be considered in all decisions and policy making. A series of indicators were developed to help monitor the implementation of the EBS and to provide a measure of its progress. The review of EBS implementation 2003–2006 showed that, albeit over a short time span, the overall trends were positive (**Table 17.2** and **Figure**

17.4). Trends for farmland birds are discussed in Chapter 4 (Section A.4.1.9). An assessment of better-studied groups (Natural England 2010b), however, showed that there are still groups and species of conservation concern, as shown in their BAP status (**Table 17.3**). In 2008, 943 species were identified as being of conservation concern under the EBS and UK BAP, with only a few of the previous 391 being removed from the list. On average, 26% of England's species are depleted or on the BAP list. The figures for the better-known groups are shown in **Table 17.3**.

In England, the principal agents of species loss and decline have been habitat loss and fragmentation, management practices that adversely affect habitat quality, environmental pollution and, in the past, the persecution of wildlife (EBG 2008; Natural England 2010b). Other pressures include invasive non-native species and, increasingly, climate change, which also interacts with many of the above (EBG 2008).

Protected areas have been the focus of much of England's conservation strategy, including National Parks, National Nature Reserves (NNRs) and Sites of Special Scientific Interest (SSSIs). Like species, a number of these are not in favourable conservation status, but their condition is

Table 17.2 Progress of headline indicators from 2000 to 2009. Source: Defra (2008d). © Crown copyright 2011.

Indicator		Type	Year	Assessment	
				Long term	Since 2000
	Headline				
H1(a)	Populations of wild birds in England	State	2009	⊗	⊗
H1(b)	Populations of butterflies in England	State	2009	⊗	≈
H2	Condition of Sites of Special Scientific Interest (SSSIs) in England	State	2009	⋯	✓
H3	Status of Biodiversity Action Plan priority species and habitats in England	State	2009	⋯	✓
H4	Area of land under agri-environment scheme agreement in England	Response	2009	✓	✓
H5	Biological quality of rivers in England	State	2009	✓	≈
H6	UK fish stocks fished within safe limits	Pressure	2009	✓	✓
H7	Delivery of local biodiversity targets in England	Response	2008	⋯	✓
H8	Public attitudes to biodiversity	Response	2008	⋯	✓

✓ Improving
≈ Little or no change
⊗ Deteriorating
⋯ Insufficient or no comparable data/ no assessment made

Table 17.3 The degree of loss, depletion and decline in better-studied groups. Source: reproduced from Natural England (2010b).

Species group	Number of native species lost	Number of extant native species	Number of extant species on the UK BAP list	Number not on UK BAP list but with historically depleted populations	Proportion (%) of extant species with historically depleted populations or appearing on UK BAP list
Reptiles	0	7	7	0	100
Mammals—regularly occurring whales and dolphins	2	11	11	0	100
Amphibians	2	7	4	0	57
Freshwater fish	2	35	13	2	43
Mammals—terrestrial and seals	6	43	15	1	37
Bumblebees	4	20	5	2	35
Butterflies	18	57	23	2	33
Breeding birds	10	175	40	8	27
Vascular plants	20	1,297	121	194	24

improving. Agriculture-related causes of decline are shown in **Figure 17.5**. Other causes of decline include atmospheric and water pollution and lack of management. A gap analysis of England's terrestrial protected areas (based on 2001 data) showed that there were 206 NNRs and 4,091 SSSIs covering 8% of the country, with most being found in northern or coastal areas (Oldfield *et al.* 2004). Also, only 3.5% of English lowlands (less than 200 m above sea level) had protected area status, whereas 65.8% of land above 600 m above sea level was protected. Some of the protected areas are now Special Areas of Conservation (SACs) or Special Protection Areas designated under the EC Habitats Directive. In England, there are now 249 SACs, Sites of Community Importance or candidate SACs. These cover marine and terrestrial areas and management is aimed at conserving their important or threatened habitats and species.

The focus on integrating habitat and species conservation was increased in 2008 as a key aim of England's Biodiversity Framework which seeks (amongst other objectives), "to encourage the adoption of an ecosystem approach and embed climate change adaptation principles in conservation action, achieve biodiversity enhancements across whole landscapes and seascapes ..." (EBG 2008, p5), and whilst it does explicitly address ecosystem services, it recognises that they are underpinned by biodiversity. The relationship of different groups to ecosystem services is assessed in Table 4.2, Section 4.4, and whilst these relationships are likely to remain the same in England, as many of them are based on processes and the functioning of ecosystems and species, their relative importance may change in other parts of the UK, as do the drivers and pressures (Chapter 3, Table 3.3).

17.4 UK NEA Broad Habitat Types

Eight Broad Habitats form the basis of the UK NEA: Mountains, Moorlands and Heaths, Semi-natural Grasslands, Enclosed Farmland, Woodlands, Freshwaters—

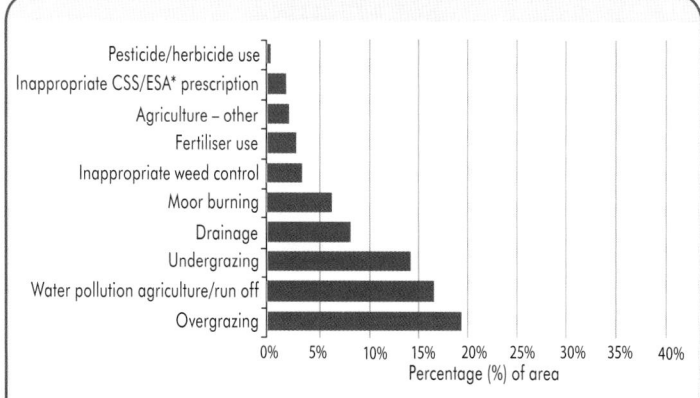

Figure 17.5 Overview of the main agricultural reasons for unfavourable conditions on SSSIs in England. Source: data from Natural England; Defra (2010c) © Crown copyright 2010. * CSS = Countryside Stewardship Scheme; ESA = Environmentally Sensitive Areas Scheme.

Openwaters, Wetlands and Floodplains, Urban, Coastal Margins and Marine. The Countryside Survey provides the most complete record of changes in land cover, although the types of habitat overlap with, but are different from, the UK NEA Broad Habitat types. This survey showed that arable and horticultural, improved grassland and neutral grassland (part of semi-natural grasslands) broad habitats covered 63.1% of the land area of England in 2007, woodlands (9.4%), with built-up areas and gardens (7.9%) being the next most important by area (Countryside Survey 2009); statistics which emphasise the largely agricultural character of England. Due to differences in physical setting, history and land use, the UK NEA

Broad Habitats are not evenly distributed across the UK (**Figure 17.6**), with England containing the majority of Enclosed Farmland and less Mountains, Moorlands and upland heaths, but more lowland heaths than other parts of the UK. Nevertheless, the more local Broad Habitats are important in giving character to landscapes in different areas. For example, lowland heaths in parts of Cornwall, Dorset, Hampshire and Surrey, wetlands in The Broads, East Anglia, and meres and mosses in the West Midlands are still significant features, while moorland characterises much of the uplands, with blanket bogs in the wetter parts (Natural England 2009a).

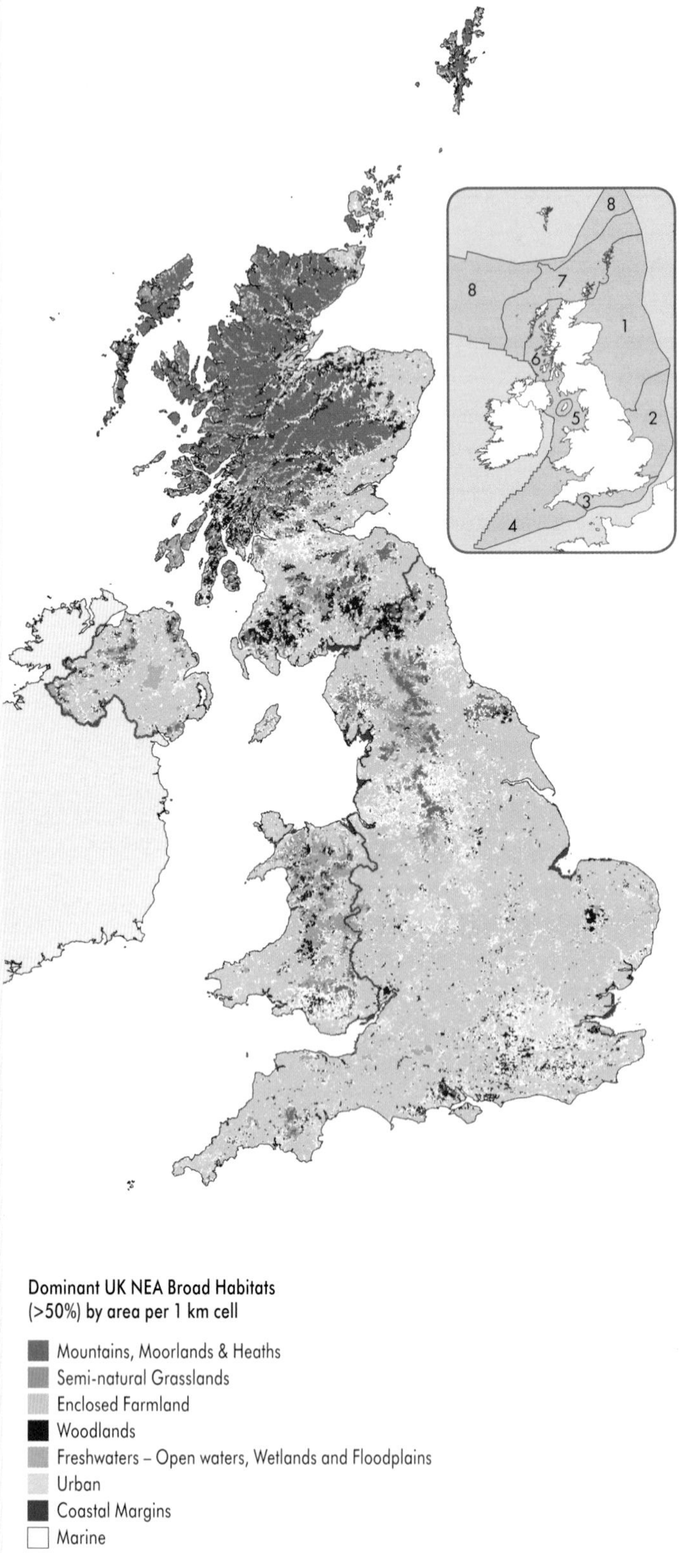

The Coastal Margins and Marine habitats vary primarily as a function of geology, with low-lying coasts, such as those in East Anglia and Lancashire, containing intertidal flats and saltmarshes, which provide habitats for England's internationally important wintering waders and wildfowl. More resistant geology, e.g. chalk in South East England and igneous rocks in the South West, has led to the development of cliffs. Offshore there is also a variety of substrata and habitats, such as mobile sandbanks off East Anglia, granite reefs off Cornwall and more underwater chalk reefs than anywhere in Europe. The area and condition of Coastal Margins and Marine habitats has been changing as a consequence of pressures, such as land and sea use change, management, pollution and invasive and alien species. These trends are reflected in **Figure 17.7**, which are very similar to those for the UK. The status, condition, trends and ecosystem services of each of the UK NEA Broad Habitats are discussed in the following sections.

17.4.1 Mountains, Moorlands and Heaths

17.4.1.1 Status, trends and condition

Mountains, Moorlands and Heaths include six component habitats: Bracken; Dwarf Shrub Heath; Bog; Upland Fen, Marsh and Swamp; Montane; and Inland Rock (Table 5.1, Section 5.1.1). Prior to human activity (about 5,000–6,000 years ago) woodland covered much of what is now Mountains, Moorlands and Heaths, except for the most exposed locations. Then, due to a combination of woodland clearance, managed burning, livestock grazing, the removal of turf and vegetation and climate, the extent of moorland and heath increased and regeneration was curtailed by browsing (Averis et al. 2004). Currently, Mountains, Moorlands and Heaths cover 679,000 ha, representing about 5% of England's area, which is very small compared with 43% of Scotland and 12% of both Wales and Northern Ireland. Montane habitats are the dominant cover only in the higher areas of the Lake District, Pennines, North York Moors and

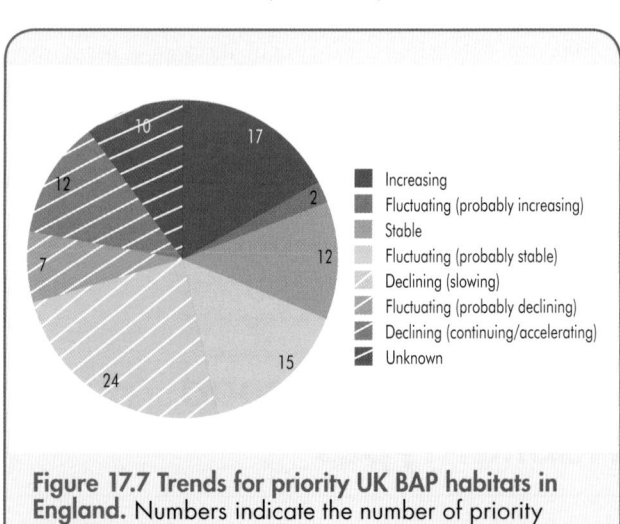

Figure 17.7 Trends for priority UK BAP habitats in England. Numbers indicate the number of priority habitats. Source: data from Biodiversity Action Reporting System (BARS 2011).

Dominant UK NEA Broad Habitats
(>50%) by area per 1 km cell

- Mountains, Moorlands & Heaths
- Semi-natural Grasslands
- Enclosed Farmland
- Woodlands
- Freshwaters – Open waters, Wetlands and Floodplains
- Urban
- Coastal Margins
- Marine

Figure 17.6 Distribution (%) of the UK NEA Broad Habitats types by area at 1x1 km resolution. Inset: Charting Progress 2, UK Regional Sea boundaries: 1) Northern North Sea; 2) Southern North Sea; 3) Eastern Channel; 4) Western Channel and Celtic Sea; 5) Irish Sea; 6) Minches and Western Scotland; 7) Scottish Continental Shelf; 8) Atlantic North-West Approaches, Rockall Trough and Faeroe/Shetland Channel. Source: Broad Habitat distribution – Land Cover Map 2000 (Fuller et al. 2002); Regional seas – based on UKMMAS (2010). Coastline: World Vector Shoreline@National – Geospatial Intelligence Agency. Source: NOASS, NGDC.

Dartmoor, whilst Inland Rock is not dominant in any grid cell. It does, however, cover about 1% of England, based on the Land Cover Map (LCM 2000), and England has about 80% of the UK's limestone pavements (Natural England 2008). These Inland Rock habitats form important refuges from grazing for several plant species.

There has been a significant decrease in Mountains, Moorlands and Heaths habitat over the last 60 years. In the uplands this has been primarily due to afforestation and conversion to rough grassland by drainage, liming, burning and grazing. A study of increased sheep numbers and loss of heather moor in the northern Peak District found that the former had trebled between 1930 and 1976, leading to a 36% decrease in moorland (Anderson & Yalden 1981), with an unknown effect on wildlife, although red grouse (*Lagopus lagopus scoticus*) declined by about two-thirds over a similar period. Monitoring following a reduction of grazing pressure on the Kinder Estate in the Peak District showed recolonisation by moorland vegetation (Anderson & Radford 1994). Airborne pollution, particularly nitrogen and sulphur, has also had a detrimental effect on the condition of Mountains, Moorlands and Heaths (Chapter 5.6.2.2). It has had the greatest impact on upland areas, in particular in the South Pennines (Lee 1998), but it was also a possible factor in the decline of Dorset heathland between 1987 and 1996 (Rose *et al.* 2000).

Inland Rock has been affected by mineral extraction and quarry landfill, but 57% is in unfavourable condition due to overgrazing, whilst lack of management, recreational pressure and air pollution have also contributed (BRIG 2006; Natural England 2008). For limestone pavements, the mechanised removal of stone meant that by 1975, only 75% of the area was intact and 3% remained undamaged (Braithwaite *et al.* 2006).

Lowland heathland has mostly been lost due to development of towns and roads, afforestation and agricultural improvement, as well as succession leading to woodland encroachment following abandonment. This loss has been particularly well documented for the Dorset heathlands and those in East Anglia (Webb & Haskins 1980; Webb 1990; Table 5.2, Section 5.2.1.1).

The most noticeable changes in areas of Mountains, Moorlands and Heath habitats in England between 1998 and 2007 is a strong increase (15%) in dwarf shrub heath (Countryside Survey 2009). This has been attributed to efforts to restore and recreate lowland and upland heathland (to meet BAP targets) through programmes such as Tomorrow's Heathland Heritage, Countryside Stewardship, and more recently the Higher Level Scheme in Environmental Stewardship. In the uplands, it has probably been helped by grazing pressure controls, possibly aided by livestock reductions, for example in Cumbria, following the 2001 outbreak of Foot and Mouth Disease. In the lowlands, the schemes have led to reductions in the extent of scrub and secondary woodland, the creation of new heathland sites (e.g. over 4,000 ha recreated or restored in the china clay area of Cornwall), the control of bracken and the reintroduction of grazing.

There are four main drivers of the contemporary changes in Mountains, Moorlands and Heaths habitats and their

ecosystem services: land use changes, airborne pollution, climate change and recreational pressures. These in turn depend on a number of underlying factors, including agricultural prices, Common Agricultural Policy (CAP) and agri-environmental schemes. These direct and underlying factors are moderated by a number of policy mechanisms (e.g. EC Birds, Habitats, Water Framework and National Emissions Ceilings Directives) and cultural pressures, such as those which led to the setting up of seven National Parks in the uplands and, more recently, the New Forest, which has important areas of lowland heath.

The status and condition of the Mountains, Moorlands and Heaths habitat have declined over the last 60 years and this is reflected in the Mountains, Moorlands and Heaths-related BAP habitats (UKBAP 2007). Their status and condition varies and, based on this, they have different conservation targets. Lowland heath is the only one that is increasing in area, as a consequence of restoration and recreation objectives; all the habitats have regionally differentiated targets aimed at increasing status and improving its condition (**Table 17.4**).

Many of these habitats are important for species of conservation importance. There are 133 BAP species associated with lowland heath, of which 53% require bare ground and early successional stages (Webb *et al.* 2009), and so are highly dependent upon management. Grazing, when combined with other management options, is important in providing such conditions (Lake *et al.* 2001), so livestock are now being reintroduced to many lowland heaths, often supported by agri-environment scheme funding. Important birds include Dartford warbler (*Sylvia undata*), which is in the northern part of its range in southern England. It is found almost exclusively on dry lowland heath, feeding on invertebrates, and its main threat is habitat loss (Cantos & Isenmann 1994; van den Berg *et al.* 2001). Given the increase in heathland, along with possible shifts in habitat and more

Table 17.4 Regional targets (ha) for upland heathland, blanket bog, upland calcareous grassland and limestone pavement.
Source: data from Measures (2008). *Area of existing BAP habitat to be in favourable or unfavourable recovering condition. †To ensure there is no further deterioration in the geodiversity/biodiversity interest.

Regions	Regional targets (ha)			
	Achieve condition* within SSSIs by 2015			Achieve condition† by 2015
	Upland heathland	Blanket bog	Upland calcareous grassland	Limestone pavement
North East	31,632	50,645	257	-
North West	31,805	48,866	2,619	1,276
Yorkshire & Humber	78,531	46,956	5,602	1,359
East Midlands	9,571	12,319	-	-
West Midlands	4,934	1,613	30	-
East of England	-	-	-	-
South East	-	-	-	-
London	-	-	-	-
South West	23,455	15,743	-	-
England Total	**179,928**	**176,142**	**8,507**	**2,635**

sympathetic management of plantation forests and farmland, this and several other birds have increased in population numbers—the Dartford warbler by 70% since 1994, nightjar (*Caprimulgus europaeus*) by 35% since the 1990s and woodlark (*Lullula arborea*) by 89% since 1997, whilst black grouse (*Tetrao tetrix*) numbers have stabilised (Baines 2005; RSPB 2005, 2006, 2007; Warren & Baines 2008).

17.4.1.2 Ecosystem services

In many cases the total service provision from Mountains, Moorlands and Heaths is low because they are concentrated in particular areas, although the provision per unit area may be high, e.g. water purification and provisioning functions. There is higher service provision from moorland, not because of profound ecological differences compared with other habitats, but because of its extent.

Regulating services. Peatlands are an important terrestrial carbon store and a potential sink, thus they contribute significantly to climate regulation. The largest stocks in England are in the north and it has been estimated that in their current state, English peatlands store 584 million tonnes of carbon, but are responsible for about 3 million tonnes of carbon dioxide equivalent (CO_2 e) emissions per year (Natural England 2010c). Changes in topsoil carbon stocks in England (1998–2007) were estimated as -9.3 teragrams carbon (Tg C) from bracken, -2.5 Tg C from fens, marsh and swamp, 11.6 Tg C from shrub heath and 10.4 Tg C from bogs (Chamberlain *et al.* 2010). Careful management and restoration of these habitats, and in particular peat, can ensure that they continue to deliver this service, as well as contributing to conservation objectives, thus achieving a synergy in services (Worrall *et al.* 2009). Restoration of key types of degraded peatlands could deliver emissions reductions of up to 2.4 million tonnes of CO_2 e each year, with 1.1 million tonnes of this reduction delivered by rewetting cultivated deep peatlands (Natural England 2010c). Restoration of degraded habitats may also contribute to small-scale flood risk mitigation. For example, grip blocking may be an effective measure, and in Upper Wharfedale has been shown to decrease flow velocities and discharge from drains (Holden 2005; Holden *et al.* 2008).

Blanket bogs and dwarf dry heaths are not good at sustaining flow in dry periods (Holden & Burt 2003b) and this, together with rapid runoff, means that reservoirs are needed for water regulation for human supply, although some lowland bogs and marshes trap water and prevent flooding (Natural England 2009a). The uplands receive disproportionate amounts of airborne pollutants including pesticide residues, nitrogen and sulphur compounds (Caporn & Emmett 2009), but they retain a proportion of these pollutants, including anthropogenic sulphur and nitrogen and heavy metals, that otherwise would contaminate drainage waters. This water quality service also helps to reduce downstream treatment costs. The provision of (relatively) clean water is a consequence of limited human impacts, relatively low weathering rates, extensive peat cover and widespread overland flow. The continued provision of the service is dependent on maintaining the stability of the peatlands (and other habitats) to avoid the release of these contaminants (Rothwell *et al.* 2007, 2008).

Maintaining intact ecosystems is also important for avoiding erosion with associated landscape degradation, contaminant activation, sediment affecting water quality and reservoir capacity. The extent of areas affected by erosion within upland England and Wales has been estimated at 24,566 ha, which represents 2.46% of the total upland area surveyed in 1999, with sheep being a major driver (McHugh *et al.* 2002). A reduction of sheep grazing pressure in a catchment in the Peak District showed that recolonisation of vegetation can be a relatively rapid process (5–10 years), but it may take decades on high slopes (Evans 2005).

Provisioning services. Livestock grazing on Mountains, Moorlands and Heaths has long contributed to a variety of ecosystem services, including landscape appearance, habitat management (especially of undesirable vegetation) and rural economies (in the production of grazing beef and lamb/mutton). There has been a fall in grazing livestock numbers since 2004 in Less Favoured Areas (LFAs) in England (more so than on lowland agricultural habitats), with the number of breeding ewes falling by 12%, beef cows by 13%, dairy cows and the number of other cattle and calves by 11% (Defra 2010a). This relates to LFAs in general, not Mountains, Moorlands and Heaths habitats specifically, although the impacts have been most felt in areas such as the North York Moors, the South West's moors and parts of the South Pennines. Many rare breeds are grazed on Mountains, Moorlands and Heaths and thus they provide a service in maintaining genetic diversity (Tisdell 2003). Wool fibre from sheep used to be an important commodity, from medieval times through to the 19th Century. Wool as a commodity is also covered under Enclosed Farmland (Section 17.4.3).

Historically, peat has been used as a fuel due to its calorific value of around 20 megajoules per kg, which is similar to wood and lignite and, more recently, for horticulture, with gardeners now responsible for 69% of total peat usage. Extraction for these uses is still significant, but more localised and declining (ADAS & Enviros 2008). The decline is partly a consequence of the UK government's target for 2010 that 90% of total market requirements for soil improvers and growing media should be supplied by non-peat materials. Coal is also extracted from sites with Mountains, Moorlands and Heaths, including extensive open cast mines, but no figures were found for England. Both these activities could be considered antagonistic to service delivery in that they result in habitat destruction, although in both cases some restoration is often undertaken (Natural England 2010c).

The uplands are important for water supply, due to their higher rainfall (Malby *et al.* 2007) and rapid runoff (Holden and Burt 2003a). Contributions to water regulation are addressed in the previous section. A number of minor products are gathered from heaths and moorland (Sanderson & Prendergast 2002), including:

- heather for animal bedding, thatch, use in air and water filters, fencing and screening;
- bracken for soap making, animal bedding, as a soil improver, and recently bracken has been trialled as a horticultural medium, suitable for ericaceous/calcifuge plants;
- whinberries (*Vaccinium myrtillus*), which are gathered in Shropshire; and

- honey: heath and moorland are important to beekeepers as heather honey commands a price premium.

Shooting is a major driver of land management in parts of the Pennines, North York Moors and Cheviots, where upland heath may be managed by rotational burning to promote new grass or heather growth for red grouse. Shooting makes only a minor contribution to food supply, being primarily for sport, and thus is also a cultural service. In England, grouse shooting has risen from 1,560 potential shooting days per year, with 196 game keepers employed in 2000, to 1,898 potential shooting days per year, with 253 game keepers employed in 2009 (Natural England 2009a).

Cultural services. The majority of National Parks contain Mountains, Moorlands and Heaths. Areas of moorland and lowland heathland are valued for their perceived wildness, openness and 'bleakness', although they are not universally thought to be beautiful places (Natural England 2009a). Moorland, like many other Broad Habitats, is often important for those living within it (e.g. Exmoor) by contributing to a sense of local identity. Bogs and marshes are seen as not delivering many cultural services, other than for birdwatchers (Natural England 2009a), but may also be important as biological and historical archives.

Mountains, Moorlands and Heaths are also important for tourism and recreation, although moorland is less accessible than some other landscape types due to its location away from population centres. Focus group research showed that areas of lowland heathland (e.g. in and around the New Forest) were seen as more accessible than other habitat types (Natural England 2009a). However, in England, National Parks, the great majority of which are in the uplands, have 69.4 million visitor days per year, with the Lake District and Peak District being the most visited (Natural England 2005b). Mountains, Moorlands and Heaths can also be of spiritual and religious value through experience of the wild and beautiful terrain (Natural England 2009a). There are also many monuments related to religious practices, such as ancient burial mounds and stone circles, on Mountains, Moorlands and Heaths, whilst some pilgrimages involve passing through these habitats (e.g. St. Cuthbert's Way in Northumbria, a 100 km trail from Melrose to Lindisfarne). Mountains, Moorlands and Heaths have inspired writers like Thomas Hardy and William Wordsworth and artists such as Turner.

17.4.1.3 Valuation

There is no complete valuation of Mountains, Moorlands and Heaths services across England, although six case studies which were undertaken as part of an economic valuation of uplands ecosystem services provide illustrative figures (Natural England 2009b). Case studies relating to particular services include Thirgood and Redpath (1997), who estimated the cost of losing the hunting service for a commercial shoot in the UK to be about £100,000 per year. A choice experiment to assess non-market landscape benefits of Mountains, Moorlands and Heaths (Hanley *et al.* 2007; Hanley & Colombo 2009) is reported in Chapter 5, Box 5.9.

Given the importance of peat as a carbon store, the restoration of cultivated or agriculturally improved deep peat has been calculated to produce net economic benefits of up to £19,000/ha after 40 years, even at the lowest shadow carbon value, whilst the restoration and management costs associated with blocking moorland drainage ditches can be repaid by the value of emissions reductions over this period (Natural England 2010c). If the mid-range shadow carbon values are used, all the peatland restoration techniques considered deliver net economic benefits after 40 years, which makes most peatland restoration options a cost-effective means of reducing greenhouse gas emissions.

17.4.2 Semi-natural Grasslands

17.4.2.1 Status, trends and condition

There are an estimated 4.8 million ha of grassland (all types) in England, based on Land Cover Map (LCM 2000) data. This is primarily agriculturally improved grassland, with Semi-natural Grasslands making up only about 3% (Natural England 2008), although semi-improved grasslands can be important for biodiversity, especially where the Semi-natural Grasslands resource is low (e.g. parts of Lincolnshire and Cambridgeshire). There are various types of Semi-natural Grasslands, including Acid, Neutral and Calcareous Grassland habitats, along with purple moor-grass and rush pastures, which are part of the Fen, Marsh and Swamp habitat. Within these, a number of specific Semi-natural Grasslands types are UK BAP priority habitats: lowland and upland hay meadows, lowland dry acid grassland, purple moor-grass and rush pastures, and lowland and upland calcareous grasslands. In terms of area, upland Acid Grassland is an important component of both UK and England's Semi-natural Grasslands, but it is not considered a priority habitat, as it is often the result of overgrazing of moorland, and is relatively extensive.

The distribution of these habitat types varies across England, with the South West region containing 44% of England's Semi-natural Grasslands, including 61% of Calcareous Grassland and 57% of purple moor-grass and rush pastures, whilst upland hay meadows and upland calcareous grasslands are largely confined to North Lancashire, Cumbria and the North Pennines. The New Forest and Breckland are important for lowland dry acid grasslands, which often occur in association with lowland heathland (Natural England 2008). A history of the impacts of agricultural intensification on grasslands in Great Britain is provided by Green (1990), but in England and Wales, a 97% loss of semi-natural enclosed grasslands between 1930 and 1984 has been reported (Fuller 1987). This was primarily due to conversion of grassland to arable or intensification by ploughing, drainage and reseeding and improvement with fertilisers and herbicides, driven by Government incentives and grant aid. Atmospheric deposition of nitrogen is also thought to have impacted upon grassland diversity in a similar way to agricultural improvement (Stevens *et al.* 2004). A sample survey of about 500 non-SSSI Semi-natural Grasslands sites in England showed that 24% of sites more closely resembled agriculturally-improved grassland types, indicating a significant loss of Semi-natural Grasslands between 1980 and 2003 (Hewins *et al.* 2005). This is reflected in the Countryside Survey 2007 findings (Carey *et al.* 2008) that in England there was a significant increase (12.6%) in the area of Neutral Grassland between 1990 and 2007, but a significant decrease in plant-species richness in botanically-rich Neutral and Acid Grasslands between 1998 and 2007. Also, in the Neutral Grasslands there was a significant reduction in the number of food plants for butterfly larvae and farmland birds and a significant increase in more competitive, nutrient-demanding plant species. There was a significant decrease in the area of Calcareous and Acid Grassland between 1990 and 1998, however, there was no significant change in their extent between 1998 and 2007. These two component habitats have experienced the greatest average loss of plants in Semi-natural Grasslands over the last 40 years (Preston *et al.* 2002).

Semi-natural Grasslands support a rich flora and fauna and many types are typically plant-species rich and provide habitat for important and rare species. Of the 1,150 species of conservation concern named in the UK BAP, lowland Semi-natural Grasslands are home to 206 of them, whilst upland grassland priority habitats are home to 41. Declines in individual species have been linked to certain aspects of agricultural improvement (Green 1990), for example, bird losses have been attributed to the intensification of agriculture, which has substantially reduced the suitability of grassland as a feeding and breeding habitat for grassland birds (Vickery *et al.* 2001). The switch from hay making to silage has had a strong impact on some bird species, with earlier cutting dates resulting in nest destruction before the chicks have fledged (e.g. yellow wagtail *Motacilla flava*; Nelson *et al.* 2003) or the loss of important feeding sites during the breeding season (e.g. twite *Carduelis flavirostris*; Raine *et al.* 2009). Also, specialist butterflies (Section 6.2.4.1) strongly associated with agriculturally managed Semi-natural Grasslands declined in England by 26% between 1990 and 2007.

Sixty-eight per cent of Semi-natural Grasslands lie within SSSIs and 40% are designated as SACs, of which Salisbury Plain SSSI and SAC make up just under half (Natural England 2008). About 6% of upland Acid Grasslands are in SSSIs,

because of their importance for breeding birds. The status and condition of the Semi-natural Grasslands habitat types varies (**Table 17.5**), but the trend for all of the BAP habitats is declining, apart from upland calcareous grasslands, which are stable. The main issues for the lowlands are undergrazing and scrub encroachment, whilst overgrazing is the main cause of unfavourable condition in the uplands, with atmospheric nitrogen deposition as another pressure. In England, the Environmental Stewardship Higher Level Scheme (HLS) is the principal mechanism for maintaining, restoring and creating Semi-natural Grasslands, and 60,733 ha of grassland is entered into the maintenance and restoration of grassland options of either the 'Classic schemes', i.e. Countryside Stewardship, Environmentally Sensitive Areas (ESA), or the HLS. In the HLS, 2,373 ha have been entered into the creation of the species-rich grassland option (Natural England 2009c). There are also various forms of specific funding for the uplands, including LFAs established by the EU in 1975 as a means for providing aid specifically to socially and economically disadvantaged areas in the uplands. In England, some 2.2 million ha of land is classified as LFA and of this, 1.8 million ha are in agricultural production (approximately 17% of the total agricultural land in England). The LFAs are predominantly found in the northern and south-western areas of England and in areas of the Welsh Borders. There is also the new (2010) Upland Entry Level Stewardship, which rewards farmers for the provision and maintenance of landscape and environmental benefits, thus ecosystem services.

There are regionally differentiated targets for the restoration and expansion of various grassland habitats (**Table 17.6**), with the South East and East of England being particularly important in this regard for lowland dry acid and calcareous grassland.

17.4.2.2 Ecosystem services

There are many services provided by Semi-natural Grasslands. Some, like biomass energy, water regulation and carbon sequestration, are complementary whilst others,

Table 17.5 Status and trends of Semi-natural Grassland habitats. Sources: *UK BAP Target Review (2006), [†]Countryside Survey (2009), [‡]Natural England SSSI information system (ENSIS), [¶]Hewins *et al.* (2005). **Percentage of SSSI area in favourable or unfavourable recovering condition. [††]Percentage of stands considered to be in favourable condition based on mandatory non-statutory condition assessment targets.

UK BAP priority habitat*	Area (ha)	Condition (%) SSSI (2009)[‡]**	Condition (%) Non-SSSI (2005)[¶][††]	Factors affecting condition
Lowland calcareous grassland	38,687	92.4/47.4	28	Agricultural intensification, undergrazing and lack of scrub control
Lowland dry acid grassland	20,142	84.5/26.1	21	Agricultural intensification, undergrazing and lack of scrub control
Lowland meadows	7,282	76.2/44.1	16	Agricultural improvement, abandonment and supplementary feeding
Upland hay meadows	870	91.3/65.3	7	Over-intensive management, particularly grazing levels and excessive input of nutrients from both organic manures and artificial fertilisers
Purple moor-grass & rush pasture	21,544	78.1/34.7	35	Agricultural improvement, abandonment and inappropriate management
Upland calcareous grassland	16,000	92.4/27.2	no data	Overgrazing, too heavy and too light grazing, quarrying
Other Semi-natural Grassland				
Upland acid grassland[†]	376,000	85.2	no data	Overgrazing and poorly timed grazing, particularly by sheep, burning and inappropriate stock feeding

such as productivity and diversity, may be antagonistic (Section 17.8.1), although with appropriate management they can be complementary.

Regulating services. Semi-natural Grasslands contribute to climate regulation, but the amount of carbon storage reported varies according to methods of recording and calculation. Bellamy *et al.* (2005) estimated that between 1978 and 2007 there was no consistent change in soil carbon in Neutral and Acid Grasslands in England and Wales, whilst Chamberlain *et al.* (2010) estimated that there had been net gains in England between 1998 and 2007 in topsoil carbon stocks of 5.6 Tg C and 10.5 Tg C respectively. This means that they account for 21% of soil carbon in Countryside Survey 2007 broad habitats in England.

Semi-natural Grasslands potentially deliver pollination and pest control services to agriculture, as they provide habitat for the relevant species. For example, Ricketts *et al.* (2008) showed that proximity to semi-natural habitat increased pollination by native bees of field beans (*Vicia faba*), whilst Goulson *et al.* (2004) attributed bumblebee declines and associated loss of pollination directly to the loss of Semi-natural Grasslands during the 20th Century. The effects of Semi-natural Grasslands on harbouring the natural enemies of pests have been less studied, although declines in carabid beetles (not all of which are predatory) may also be related to losses of Semi-natural Grasslands or related habitats (Kotze & O'Hara 2003).

Semi-natural Grasslands can provide valuable water purification services. Within the Peak District, Calcareous Grassland accumulated up to 89% of deposited nitrogen, while Acid Grassland stored up to 38% (Phoenix *et al.* 2008). The soil is able to store significant amounts of this deposited nitrogen and perennial grasses appear to play a dominant role in maintaining low inorganic nitrogen leaching rates, and are likely to be most important in providing the service of clean groundwater. Information about the impact of Semi-natural Grasslands on water quantity and quality, however, is generally in relation to its conversion to alternative land uses, such as intensive grazing, where compaction causes

decreased infiltration and increased runoff, which both lead to localised increased flood risk and reduced aquifer recharge (Weatherhead & Howden 2009). Measures of streamwater quality across gradients from low-intensity grassland to arable and between intensive livestock pastures in upland and lowland Britain showed how intensive grassland use by livestock can increase nitrogen and phosphorus inputs into streams (Jarvie *et al.* 2008, 2010).

Provisioning services. An analysis of sheep numbers (not differentiated by habitat) has shown that between 1950 and 1990 they have more than doubled in Wales and England (181% and 142% increase respectively), whilst in Scotland (32%) they have been relatively stable (see figures from Fuller & Gough 1999). The increase has been primarily since the mid-1970s, with a modest decrease in England and Scotland since 1990. There are regional differences, with the most marked recent decreases in the lowland regions of south and east England. The pattern of change in East Anglia and the south of England has been especially volatile, with sharp recent declines following very high rates of increase between 1980 and 1990. Stocking densities have been highest in Wales and the Welsh borders, followed by South West England, northern England, the southern Midlands, and Kent. Major ecological impacts of increased grazing pressure from sheep are expected to be focused on Wales and the Welsh borders, but also include parts of upland northern England's semi-natural grasslands, moorland and heaths.

The level of production from unfertilised Semi-natural Grasslands has been shown to range from less than 20% to about 80% of the production that might be expected from agriculturally improved and intensively managed grasslands and the metabolisable energy values of herbage cut for hay from 10 to 40% less (Tallowin & Jefferson 1999). Also, the levels of nitrogen, phosphorus and magnesium are either below the metabolic requirement of livestock or inadequate to sustain high individual animal performance.

Stocking levels, therefore, are much lower on Semi-natural Grasslands (Tallowin *et al.* 2005). Nevertheless, the quality in terms of flavour, protein and low fat content of lamb raised on

	Lowland meadows		Lowland dry acid grassland		Lowland calcareous grassland		Purple moor-grass and rush pasture	
	Restoration by 2015	Expansion by 2015	Restoration by 2015	Expansion by 2015	Restoration by 2015	Expansion by 2015	Restoration by 2015	Expansion by 2015
North East	25	25	17	10	25	285	10	10
North West	45	25	23	20	10	100	15	25
Yorkshire & Humber	40	35	23	15	50	450	15	15
East Midlands	50	35	34	30	50	430	10	10
West Midlands	100	35	28	35	15	60	10	10
East of England	40	25	57	60	100	1,200	20	20
South East	70	30	52	55	190	2,575	10	10
London	5	15	10	10	5	25	-	-
South West	110	35	46	40	280	3,300	40	50
England Total	**485**	**260**	**285**	**275**	**725**	**8,425**	**130**	**150**

Table 17.6 Regional targets (ha) for grassland restoration and expansion. Source: data from Measures (2008).

species-diverse pastures is better (Whittington *et al.* 2006). It was suggested that rare or traditional breeds were better for grazing Semi-natural Grasslands, but Isselstein *et al.* (2007) showed that the traditional breeds had a lower performance at sites in North Devon and France, but not in Germany. Fraser *et al.* (2009) also found that liveweight gains were consistently higher on improved permanent pasture. A comparison of Semi-natural Grasslands and improved permanent pasture showed that cattle grazed on Semi-natural Grasslands had more Vitamin E in the meat and lower concentrations of most fatty acids. It is probable that rare breeds on Semi-natural Grasslands can provide dual benefits for the conservation of the breed and the habitat, but one is not essential to the other. Rare breeds are valuable, therefore, in providing aesthetic, cultural and historical benefits, as well as genetic resources for future breeding programmes (Anon 2006).

Many traditional garden plants used to be sourced from Semi-natural Grasslands, e.g. bugle (*Ajuga reptans*), clustered bellflower (*Campanula glomerata*), but nowadays they are sourced from abroad (Dehnen-Schmutz *et al.* 2007). However, a significant amount of seed from Semi-natural Grasslands is used in creating species-rich grasslands under agri-environment schemes and other conservation initiatives. The Natural England's GENESIS database indicates that of the 2,486 (April 2010) Higher Level Stewardship agreements which involve maintenance, restoration or creation of species-rich grassland, 421 receive a supplement for using native seed sourced from Semi-natural Grasslands.

It has been suggested that hay from Semi-natural Grasslands could be used as biomass for fuel, but there are no UK studies, and those from elsewhere provide conflicting results on its effectiveness (e.g. Tilman *et al.* 2006; Richter *et al.* 2010). A field experiment on the biomass potential of Semi-natural Grasslands at six sites in Germany showed that its fuel composition was less suitable for combustion than that of perennial energy grasses, but comparable to that of cereal straw. Whilst currently not suitable for use in small boilers, it could provide synergies between bioenergy production and conservation (Tonn *et al.* 2010).

Cultural services. A survey of the cultural services derived by people from landscapes showed that positive attitudes to certain of England's National Character Areas (NCAs) were related to grassland or pastoral farming, e.g. the Devon Redlands; the North Downs; the Cotswolds; the Eden Valley and the Yorkshire Wolds (Anon 2009). Although grassland is often regarded as uninteresting in landscape terms, it can contribute to open views from high ground (Natural England 2005a). National Parks, which are valued for recreation, greenspaces, education, etc., all contain significant areas of Semi-natural Grasslands, which contribute to their wildlife, historical and landscape value (e.g. the Yorkshire Dales and South Downs National Parks).

A European overview of the implications of environmental schemes and subsidies for conservation and restoration of Semi-natural Grasslands in terms of their value for biodiversity, cultural heritage, a vital countryside, and effects on the economy, concludes that a broader landscape perspective is required in order to improve the long-term preservation of values associated with Semi-natural Grasslands (Lindborg *et al.* 2008).

Many archaeological sites and monuments are better preserved on Semi-natural Grasslands, as they have been subject to less intensive management. English Heritage's Monuments at Risk Initiative showed that of the 19,709 scheduled monuments in England, only 23% are in optimal condition, and that 35% are in grassland (Semi-natural Grasslands and improved). A number of distinctive regional features have disappeared following post-World War II agricultural intensification, including Iron Age 'banjo enclosures'—a form of prehistoric stock corral, which were characteristic of the Wessex chalklands. In the East Midlands, a survey up to 1996 confirmed that of the 2,000 (township) settlements identified, only 104 retained more than 18% of their original coverage of ridge and furrow and of these, only 43 townships retained significant areas of ridge and furrow (Hall 2001).

Salisbury Plain Defence Training Estate is the largest (38,000 ha) and most important military training area in the UK, and about 56% of it consists of Semi-natural Grasslands. The Defence Estates undertake widespread conservation activities and Salisbury Plain was chosen for the re-introduction of the great bustard (*Otis tarda*; Osborne 2005).

17.4.2.3 Valuation

The Culm grasslands in Devon and Cornwall are species rich and host rare species, such as the marsh fritillary butterfly (*Eurodryas aurinia*). An investigation of willingness to pay found that the total benefits of conserving and expanding the Culm grasslands by 10% were in excess of £136 million, with costs ranging from £5 million to £35 million, depending on how conservation and expansion are achieved (Natural England, 2008).

A 2003 study of the South Downs showed that they received about 39 million visitor days per annum, that visitors spent about £333 million and that about 8,000 jobs were supported (Chapter 6).

17.4.3 Enclosed Farmland

17.4.3.1 Status, trends and condition

The two main components of Enclosed Farmland: Arable and Horticultural, and Improved Grassland, cover 60% of England and are divided up into a patchwork by field boundaries of hedgerows, walls and fences. In 2007, Arable and Horticultural land (**Figure 17.8**) accounted for 30.4% of England's land cover (Countryside Survey 2009), compared with 3.4% of Wales, 3.5% Northern Ireland and 6.5% in Scotland (Carey *et al.* 2008). It is more prevalent in the drier south and in East Anglia, with between 80 and 100% of annually tilled land, as a percentage of total farmed area, in many eastern counties (Figure 7.2, Section 7.2.1.1). Improved Grassland covers 21.7% of England, 34.4% of Wales, 40.5% of Northern Ireland and 11.2% of Scotland, and in England is predominantly found in the north and the South West. England also has the majority of the UK's other farmland habitats, including about 97% of traditional orchards and about 69% of hedgerows (Natural England 2009a).

Various changes in farming practices, such as increases in winter-sown instead of spring-sown cereals since the 1970s, a switch from haymaking to silage production

(Chamberlain *et al.* 2000) and the removal of subsidies for the 274,000 ha of set-aside land in 2007, have had important consequences for biodiversity. In response to the latter, the voluntary Campaign for the Farmed Environment has been set up, with the aim of retaining and exceeding the environmental benefits that used to be provided by set-aside.

The area of Arable and Horticultural habitat decreased significantly by 8.8% between 1998 and 2007, whilst the area of Improved Grassland has increased by 5.2%, with a significant 14% increase in the easterly lowlands (Countryside Survey 2009). These changes are likely to be a consequence of alterations in economic and technological drivers and policy (e.g. CAP reform). The distribution of some arable flowering plants has decreased dramatically during the last 50 years and they are now amongst the most threatened elements of England's flora (Rich & Woodruff 1996; Preston *et al.* 2002); 18 of the 30 vascular plants that have shown the greatest relative declines across Britain and Ireland are characteristic of arable and other cultivated ground (Preston *et al.* 2002). Declines in farmland birds, particularly specialists, were also associated with changes in agricultural practices, including increased specialisation and mechanisation, switching to autumn sowing of cereals, intensification of grassland management, increased use of agrochemicals and loss of field margins and hedges, but recent declines in some species are more complex and not solely due to agriculture. The smoothed farmland bird index for 19 species in 2009 was 53% below the 1966 starting level (Defra 2010b), but farmland specialist species, such as the goldfinch (*Carduelis carduelis*) and whitethroat (*Sylvia communis*), have increased by 39% and 31% respectively since 1994. One or two farmland specialist species, such as the wood pigeon (*Columba palumbus*), may have benefited from changes, such as an increased area of oilseed rape production (Defra 2008a). The loss of semi-natural landscape elements in farmland, however, has also been identified as a key driver of pollinator declines (Tscharntke *et al.* 2005).

The Enclosed Farmland Broad Habitat contains two BAP habitats with the number of BAP priority species shown in brackets: arable field margins (65) and ancient and/or species-rich hedgerows (83). Both habitats are estimated to be increasing in extent, although there are targets to increase them further (**Table 17.7**).

England possesses 69% of the UK's length of ancient and/or species-rich hedgerows and the focus is on maintaining their extent and species richness and improving their condition, along with halting the decline of herbaceous hedgerow flora. There are also UK targets to achieve an average of 800 km per year net increase in the length of hedgerows between 2010 and 2015, with the percentage increase equally spread across England, Scotland and Wales.

Various regulations, guidelines and agri-environment schemes have been used with some success to enhance biodiversity and ecosystem services. Under the CAP, England has given high priority to the agri-environment measures, allocating 82% of total Axis 2 support payments to them (Farmer *et al.* 2008). There are now over 58,000 agri-environment scheme agreements covering 66% of agricultural land in England, which have improved biodiversity, but not enough time has elapsed to assess their effect on halting its

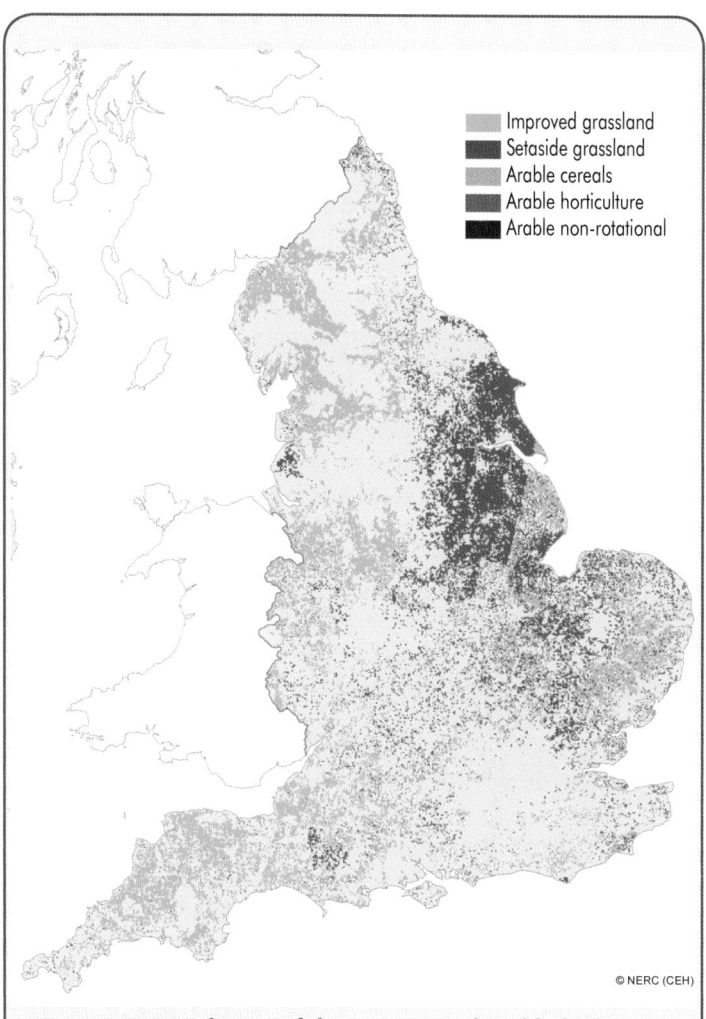

Figure 17.8 Distribution of the main agricultural habitats (>51% area per 1 km cell).

Legend:
- Improved grassland
- Setaside grassland
- Arable cereals
- Arable horticulture
- Arable non-rotational

© NERC (CEH)

Table 17.7 BAP targets for UK and England for cereal field margins. Source: data from BARS (2008).

Target for expansion	UK		England		
	2005 base (ha)	Change by 2010 (%)	2005 base (ha)	2010 target (ha)	Change by 2010 (%)
Cultivated, low-input field margins	8,859	85	5,381	10,000	92
Margins providing wild bird seed	5,367	289	3,570	18,000	404
Flower-rich field margins	1,858	546	1,858	12,000	546
Permanent grass margins	26,582	1.7	25,178	25,178	0

loss on Enclosed Farmland (Davey *et al.* 2010; McCracken & Midgley 2010a). There is, however, some evidence that farmland birds can recover with appropriate management practices and low(er) inputs (Vickery *et al.* 2004; Henderson *et al.* 2009), as can bumblebees (Carvell *et al.* 2007). A study of the effectiveness of Entry Level Stewardship agreements (introduced in 2005) showed only limited evidence for short-term effects on lowland farmland bird populations, with only the corn bunting (*Emberiza calandra*) and starling (*Sturnus vulgaris*) showing some landscape-specific positive associations with areas under Entry Level Stewardship management (Davey *et al.* 2010). In 2010, Uplands Entry Level Stewardship replaced the Hill Farm Allowance. It is designed to ensure support for farmers in maintaining historic uplands landscapes, such as the Cumbrian Fells, Dartmoor and the Peak District. Agri-environment schemes also have enhanced the protection of more than 6,000 archaeological features on farmland, including more than half of all scheduled monuments and registered battlefields, and in 2008 enabled more than 170,000 people to make educational visits to farms (Natural England 2009a).

17.4.3.2 Ecosystem services

Most Enclosed Farmland is managed for the production of food, fibre, feed for animals and energy, although it contributes to a number of other services, both positively and negatively (Pretty *et al.* 2000). An overview is provided in Table 7.3 in Section 7.3, and Tscharntke *et al.* (2005) provide a review of positive and negative effects of agriculture on biodiversity conservation, the potential mechanisms of biodiversity-ecosystem service relationships, the role of biodiversity in multifunctional agriculture, and analyses the importance of biodiversity for ecosystem services.

Regulating services. Insects are important in Enclosed Farmland, as pollination is critical for maintaining production in some crops (Section 17.5.2.4). Certain insects are also useful for biological pest control (17.5.2.3), although others can become pests in high numbers.

In the Arable and Horticultural component habitat there have been significant decreases in carbon density between 1978 and 2007 and particularly between 1998 and 2007, whilst in Improved Grassland carbon density has increased, possibly as a result of increased fertiliser usage (Smith *et al.* 2008). Agriculture is a net producer of greenhouse gases, but there are some opportunities to reduce these through improved crop, soil, fertiliser and agrochemical management (Smith *et al.* 2008; Macleod *et al.* 2010), anaerobic digestion and bioenergy crops, and also for carbon sequestration (Smith *et al.* 2008). The industry has recently committed to reducing greenhouse gas emissions through its Greenhouse Gas Action Plan.

Most farmland is well drained and thus it has a low water storage capacity (Foster 2006), although floodplain meadows (or wetlands) can be important for attenuating flood peaks, and their restoration can be a part of adaptation to climate change-induced impacts of flooding (Morris *et al.* 2004a), with benefits for biodiversity (Berry 2009). The flooding of grassland, for example, could potentially reverse the decline of grassland waders (Wilson *et al.* 2004) and thus also contribute to cultural services. Agriculture is more significant in its impact on soil and water quality, with excess application of fertilisers leading to soil acidification and eutrophication (Jarvie 2010), as well as atmospheric emissions.

Provisioning services. England is the main contributor to UK crop production (**Table 17.8**) and cereals are the

Table 17.8 Percentage of particular farm types in each country in the UK in 2008*. Source: data from June Surveys/Census of Agriculture; Defra (2009a).

Farm type	England (%)	Northern Ireland (%)	Scotland (%)	Wales (%)
Dairy	59.1	19.9	8.2	12.9
Grazing Livestock (Less Favoured Areas)	23.9	26.9	25.6	23.6
Grazing Livestock (Lowland)	78.8	10.6	4.3	6.3
Cereals	83.4	2.1	13.1	1.4
Mixed	68.6	6.6	16.8	8.0

* Farm type is classified by the predominant farming activity taking place on the holding based on an economic measure of profitability (Standard Gross Margin, SGM). The farm type is defined as the activity which contributes more than two-thirds of the total SGM for the holding.

dominant crop, with wheat (1.79 million ha) and barley (584,000 ha) accounting for almost 95% of the UK total cereal area (Table 15.1, Section 15.2.2; Figure 7.8, Section 7.3.1.1). An analysis of increases in UK cereal yields (which will be reflected in England) has shown that winter wheat yields have more than trebled over the last 60 years from about 2.5 tonnes per ha in the mid-1940s to 8 tonnes per ha today. Since 1982, around 90% of all yield increases in wheat and barley have been due to the introduction of new crop varieties, whilst fertilisers, pesticides and machinery have played a minor part, although remaining an important part of crop production (BSPB 2010).

Other crops, such as sugar beet, brassicas, field beans, peas and maize may be grown primarily for food or animal fodder. Potatoes are grown particularly on the silt and peat soils of eastern England, Shropshire and Cheshire, whilst orchards are concentrated in Kent, Herefordshire and Worcestershire; vegetable growing is mainly between Humberside and Essex and flowers are grown in Lincolnshire and Cornwall (including the Isles of Scilly).

Livestock numbers generally rose during the 20th Century until the 1990s, then decreased, although stocking densities have shown a consistent increase (Figure 7.22; Figure 7.4, Section 7.2.1.1). Totals for cattle, sheep and pigs are given in Figure 17.22 (Table 15.2, Section 15.2.3). Production from Improved Grassland is difficult to assess, as some bullocks are raised in intensive indoor rearing units, whilst others graze Semi-natural Grasslands, and many sheep are raised on unimproved upland pastures. Dairy cattle usually graze Improved Grassland and in 2009 the population was 1.8 million, with a yield of about 7,000 litres of milk per cow per year. Sheep numbers increased after joining the EU in 1973, with the increase occurring particularly in Wales. The greatest increases in England were in the north, Peak District, Exmoor and Dartmoor (Fuller & Gough 1999), and were much lower on lowland enclosed farmlands (for more detail see Chapter 7). There are no reported figures for wool production from England alone, but in 2009 the UK was the seventh largest producer of wool in the world, responsible for about 2% of global production (BWMB 2010), and the amount is roughly in proportion to sheep numbers.

In the UK, government incentives have been introduced, e.g. the Energy Crops Scheme (Natural England 2010a), to encourage the establishment of bioenergy crops, and the area of agricultural land under such crops is increasing. In England, approximately 7,500 ha were established under this scheme between 2001 and 2007 (Lovett *et al.* 2009). Kilpatrick (2008) indicated that cereals and oilseed rape straw represent a significant (and the largest) potential biomass resource, although not all would agree with this and a range of other sources are possible, including root crops and short rotation coppice, using, for example, willow. Biomass could also be sourced from straw or energy crops from set-aside land brought into production, the conversion of temporary grassland to energy crops and conversion of permanent grassland and rough grazing to short rotation forestry. De Wit & Faaij (2010) calculated that whilst maintaining food self-sufficiency, CAP reform by 2030 could free up 0–6.5% of land in eastern England and up to 31% in the South West, which potentially could be used for energy crops. Planting on surplus arable land has been calculated as being the best climate change mitigation option (Smith *et al.* 2000), but this would have biodiversity, landscape and cultural service implications.

The likely impacts of biomass crops on ecosystem services and biodiversity are given in Table 7.5, Section 7.3.1.3. A combined GIS-based yield and suitability mapping has been used to identify the areas for Miscanthus (*Miscanthus* x *giganteus*) as a biomass crop and possible locations for expansion under different scenarios (Lovett *et al.* 2009). This showed that the East Midlands and East of England could be particularly suitable, whilst the west was less so. The areas with the highest biomass yields co-locate with food producing areas on high-grade land and thus the potential conflicts that could occur are identified. If such high-grade land and unsuitable areas are excluded, the policy-related scenario for increased planting on 350,000 ha utilised between 4 and 28% of the lower grade land (depending on the region) and would not necessarily greatly impact on UK food security, but would contribute to the climate regulation service.

Wild species diversity, as has been seen earlier, is mainly associated with specific habitats within the Enclosed Farmland landscape, such as cereal field margins and hedgerows. Some are also important for wild foods, e.g. field mushroom, blackberry, sloes and watercress (Mabey 1972). In addition, game birds and mammals are shot as part of crop protection activities (deer, rabbits, pigeons) and recreational shooting of grey partridge (*Perdix perdix*), red-legged partridge (*Alectoris rufa*) and pheasant (*Phasianus colchicus*), although recreational shooting could be considered more part of cultural services. Although technically wild, many game species are subject to some form of management, including release into the wild after captive breeding (Section 15.5) and will be used for food.

Cultural services. Arable and Horticulture, Improved, Neutral (and Acid) Grassland are seen as contributing to the quality of the landscape and giving distinctive character to certain NCAs, such as the Hampshire Downs (arable), Severn and Avon Vales (horticulture), and the Shropshire Hills (improved, neutral and acid grasslands; Natural England 2009a). As seen above, agri-environment schemes include the maintenance of agricultural landscapes considered to be of cultural value, as well as archaeological features, and encourage public access. In the lowlands, Enclosed Farmland can be important for recreation due to the number of footpaths, their proximity to centres of population and accessibility to people with a wide range of fitness levels. Also, there is increasing interest in green gyms and care farming: the use of commercial farms and agricultural landscapes as a base for promoting mental and physical health (Hine *et al.* 2008).

17.4.3.3 Valuation

The valuation of agricultural habitats is difficult, as there are both costs and benefits involved. A report on the annual environmental costs of agriculture showed that in England the benefits included: broad habitat types (SSSIs): £260 million and linear features: £1.67 million. Annual costs included: river water quality: £45 million, bathing water: £7.95 million, water quality in estuaries: £2.51 million, greenhouse gas emissions: £839 million and air quality pollutant emissions: £434 million (Jacobs 2008). Conversely, the costs of agri-environment schemes to achieve different policy objectives have been estimated at £1,258 million, with nearly half of this being represented by biodiversity (Cao *et al.* 2010). The full breakdown is given in Table 7.6, Section 7.5.3. In England and Wales, the benefits from broad habitat types (non-SSSIs) have been costed as £165 million and linear features as £1.67 million, whilst the landscape value of semi-natural habitats and linear features in agricultural landscapes have been estimated as £143.5 million, and the biodiversity value of habitats (SSSIs) and species as £628.8 million in 2007 (Countryside Survey 2009).

Valuation of individual services suggests that the economic value of traditional orchards in Herefordshire, Worcestershire and Gloucestershire could be in excess of £1.5 million a year (in Natural England 2009a), whilst the annual value of insect pollination in the England in 2007 was estimated to be £367 million (BHS 2008).

17.4.4 Woodlands

17.4.4.1 Status, trends and condition

Compared to the rest of Great Britain, and much of the EU, England is poorly wooded, with woodland of all types, including both broadleaved and conifer, covering just over 9% of the country. This is substantially lower than the woodland cover in Scotland (17%) and the 37% average in EU member states. In contrast to other countries of the UK, where conifer woodlands predominate, about 66% of England's woodland is broadleaved, most of which is found in the lowlands.

Broadleaved woodlands are found on a wide range of soils, from alkaline to acid and in all climate zones. As a consequence, they show a very wide range of ecological variation, from base-rich ash-dominated types, to the acid sessile oak woodlands, which particularly characterise the north and west (**Figure 17.9**). The majority of broadleaved woodland is semi-natural and England accounts for 64% of the semi-natural woodland in the UK. England's woodland comprises 206,000 ha of ancient and semi-natural woodland

and 210,000 ha of other semi-natural woodland (Forestry Commission 2009a). In addition to the ancient and semi-natural woodland there are 135,000 ha of plantations on ancient woodland sites and these two make up the category of ancient woodland (i.e. woodland that has been in continuous existence since 1600). The semi-natural woodland is composed largely of native species, with oak (*Quercus* species), ash (*Fraxinus excelsior*), birch (*Betula* species) and beech (*Fagus sylvatica*) making up 24.5, 16.2, 10.8 and 9.9% of the area respectively (Forestry Commission 2003). There is little regeneration of young trees due to the impacts of grazing animals; outside woodlands, grazing and burning mean there is little natural spread of trees (EFTEC 2009). A range of woodland birds, such as nightingale (*Luscinia megarhynchos*), lesser spotted woodpecker (*Picoides minor*), and willow warbler (*Phylloscopus trochilus*) have declined, at least partially, as a result of pressures, notably from climate change, deer browsing and reductions in active management, but also from other activities (e.g. recreation, woodfuel). If grazing pressure from deer, for example, continues, there could be large shifts in woodland bird community composition in lowland England (Fuller 2001), with species such as nightingale being adversely affected (Fuller *et al.* 1999).

Traditional broadleaved woodland management in England tended to rely on vegetative regrowth from coppice stools and pollards. These systems declined during the 20th Century due to the focus on production and plantation forestry using fast-growing, non-native conifer species, leading to the replacement of semi-natural broadleaved woodland. About 40% of the ancient woodland that existed in the 1930s was converted to plantations, mostly between 1950 and 1980 (Harmer & Kiewett 2006). This practice ceased in 1985 and these plantations on ancient woodland sites have been a focus of restoration.

The decrease in coppice and coppice with standards has led to a change in the structural characteristics of woodlands, with an increase in the amount of high forest, with closed canopies, denser shading and a loss of floristic diversity (Kirby *et al.* 2005; Hopkins & Kirby 2007). For example, woodland specialist butterflies declined significantly (74%) from 1990 to 2007 and wider countryside (generalist) butterflies by 65% (Brereton *et al.* 2010). The decline in woodland butterflies is considered to be chiefly due to a corresponding loss of open habitats within woodlands, the decline in traditional woodland management (e.g. coppicing), the reduction in felling areas and the shading of rides and glades. The decline may also

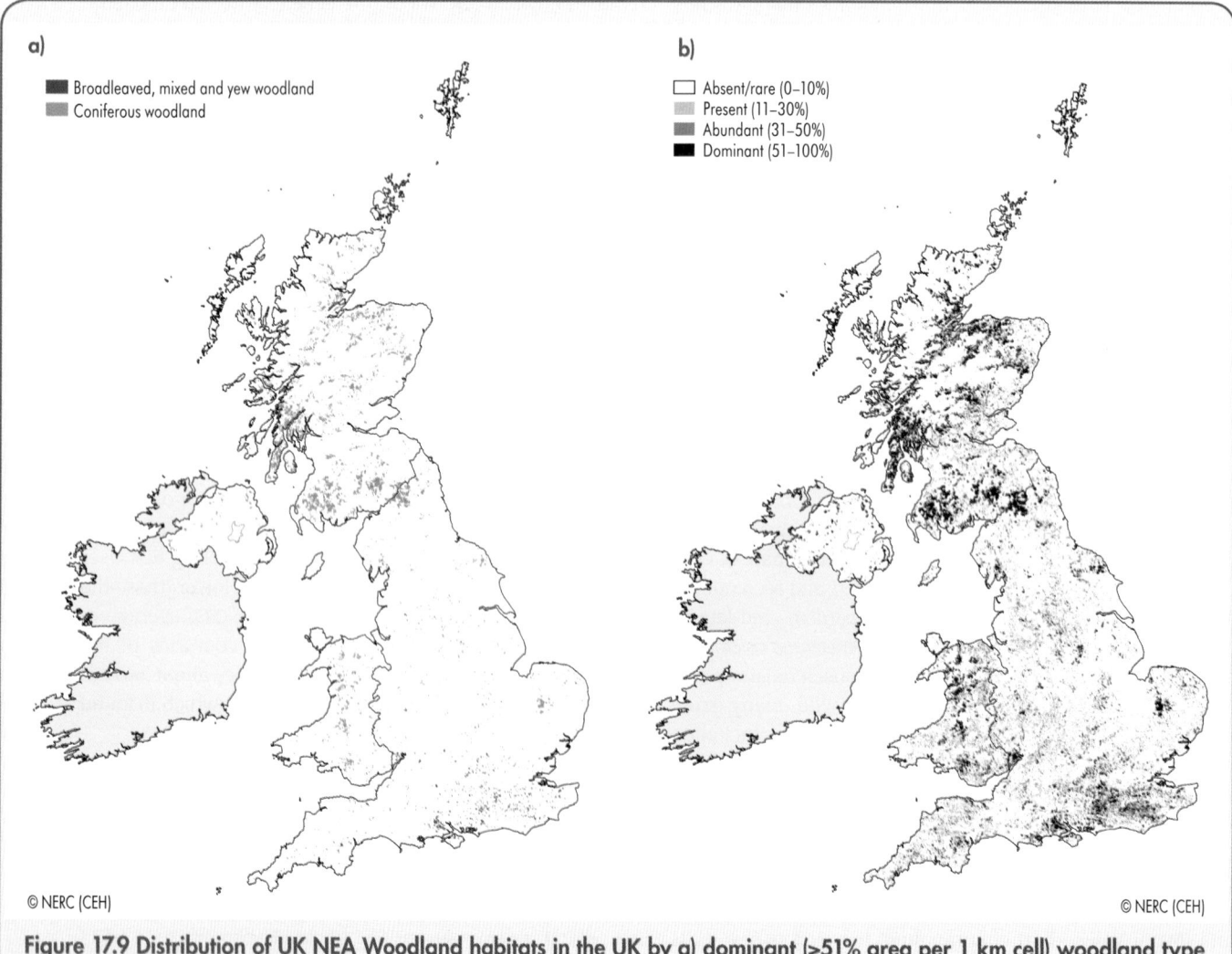

Figure 17.9 Distribution of UK NEA Woodland habitats in the UK by a) dominant (>51% area per 1 km cell) woodland type and b) percent cover per 1 km cell.

be linked to increasing deer numbers (locally), habitat fragmentation and climate change (Fox *et al.* 2006).

There has been increased interest in the natural regeneration of woodland and more traditional management practices (Evans 1988; Harmer *et al.* 2010). The small area of coppicing in the UK (0.9% by area) is undertaken almost exclusively in England and a further 1% of the woodland is coppice with standards (Forestry Commission 2009a), although maintaining or restoring coppice, as well as natural regeneration, is now severely limited due to deer numbers (Fuller & Gill 2001).

Apart from relatively small stands of yew and juniper scrub, all other conifer woodlands in England are primarily planted, initially for commercial production of timber and other wood products. One-fifth of England's forestry is found in the uplands, most notably in Kielder Forest, Northumberland and on poorer acid soils in the lowlands, often on areas of former heathland, mostly in parts of Dorset, Hampshire, Thetford Forest, Norfolk and the Thames Basin. Scots pine (*Pinus sylvestris*) and Sitka spruce (*Picea sitchensis*) are the dominant species planted, making up 24.1 and 23.5% of the conifer area respectively.

The UK BAP recognises two broad woodland habitats: Broadleaved Mixed and Yew Woodland and Coniferous Woodland, but only the former occurs in England. The Broadleaved Mixed and Yew Woodland broad habitat is split into eight priority habitat types, of which lowland mixed deciduous woodland, lowland beech and yew woodland, wood-pasture and parkland, wet woodland, upland mixed ash woodland and upland oak woodland are found in England. Despite its limited extent, semi-natural woodland remains one of the richest habitats, with about one-quarter (256) of BAP priority species in England associated with woodlands (Webb *et al.* 2009). Coniferous Woodland in the North East have been highlighted as of key strategic importance in sustaining England's red squirrel population (Forestry Commission 2007) and are also developing their own distinctive mixtures of habitats and assemblages.

Since the extensive felling during the Second World War, there has been a 45% increase of woodland area. Whilst between the 1940s and 1960s much of this expansion was due to conifer planting, since about 1980 the increase has been very largely due to the expansion of broadleaved woodland (Hopkins and Kirby 2007). There is, however, some evidence of increased planting of conifers in recent years (**Figure 17.10**), possibly signalling a greater interest in commercial forestry, but also the recent developments in climate change adaptation/mitigation programmes (Read *et al.* 2009). This may shift the balance more towards conifers and highly productive broadleaved species. One significant woodland development is The National Forest, covering 50,000 ha of the Midlands (Derbyshire, Leicestershire and Staffordshire). It seeks to increase woodland cover to about one-third of the area and already cover has increased from 6% in 1991 to around 19% in 2011, whilst ensuring it delivers multiple services, including commercial forestry with ecological, landscape and public benefit, as well as helping in climate change mitigation (The National Forest 2011). Economic regeneration in the area is through the restoration of mining sites, as well as opportunities for rural diversification.

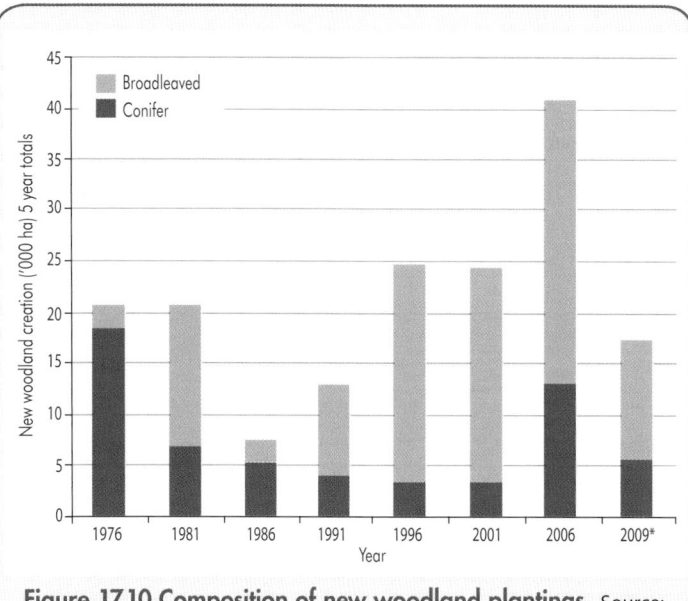

Figure 17.10 Composition of new woodland plantings. Source: reproduced from Forestry Commission (2009a). * 2009 value is 3 Year Total 2006–2009.

Woodlands are seen as being subject to a large number of pressures, and the cumulative effects of these pressures may be significant. Broadleaved woodland is sensitive to changes in land management and support through grants, and coniferous woodland to changes in forest and conservation policy and market conditions.

The BAP targets (UKBAP 2007) for the future of native woodland include:

- the maintenance of the current extent and distribution of native ancient semi-natural woodland;
- the restoration of existing plantations on ancient woodland sites such that, by 2020, 85% of them will already be broadleaved, fully restored, under restoration or being actively conserved, and a further 14,000 ha of the coniferous or mixed plantations on ancient woodland sites will be managed so as to conserve and enhance biodiversity;
- increasing the area of broadleaved woodland by 5,300 ha (1%) per annum;
- achieving favourable or recovering condition of 5,300 ha per annum of native woodland by 2015.

This woodland expansion needs to be undertaken in locations where it will enhance existing native woodland, particularly ancient woods, and other priority habitats. It is expected to be achieved by: buffering the margins of woodland or other habitats; expanding small woods; complementing and diversifying the age structure of even-aged woods; contributing to habitat networks and 'ecological connections' across landscapes; developing clusters of interconnected woodland and creating some large new woods. The regional targets for this restoration and expansion are shown in **Table 17.9**.

17.4.4.2 Ecosystem services

Woodlands provide amongst the highest identified number of ecosystem services, including regulating climate, air

Table 17.9 Regional targets for restoration and expansion of woodland. Source: reproduced from Measures (2008).

Native woodland	Restoration (ha by 2015)	Expansion (ha by 2015)
North East	2,700	12,508
North West	3,130	7,426
Yorkshire & Humber	3,780	7,154
East Midlands	3,440	6,923
West Midlands	4,750	5,261
East of England	3,220	6,444
South East	7,840	3,342
London *	-	20
South West	7,140	3,942
England Total	**36,000**	**53,000**

*London: priority is on achieving favourable condition of existing BAP woodland resource. A nominal expansion target is suggested based on London Biodiversity Partnership's targets (2006).

quality and water flows, providing timber and other wood products, as well as a range of cultural benefits.

Regulating services. Until recently the regulating services provided by woodland have been little recognised. Woodlands have considerable potential in indirect climate regulation through carbon sequestration. For example, oak forests in England have been measured as removing around 15 tonnes of carbon dioxide per hectare per year, compared with 24 tonnes carbon dioxide per hectare per year for coniferous forest in southern Scotland. The largest vegetation store of carbon in the UK is the woodland of southern England (Milne & Brown 1997), but this is minute in comparison with soil storage, particularly in heathlands and blanket bogs. There have been various estimates of topsoil carbon concentrations, and a study of changes in woodlands in Great Britain between 1971 and 2000–2003 found no significant change from 88 g C/kg (Kirby et al. 2005), although Chamberlain et al. (2010) estimate that there has been a 0.5 Tg C increase in broadleaved woodland and a 9.2 Tg C decrease in the total topsoil carbon stocks between 1998 and 2007. Woodland planted since 1990, with a woodland creation programme of 23,000 ha per year could, by 2050, sequester 10% of UK carbon emissions.

In addition, trees and woodlands regulate climate through shading and the cooling of evapotranspiration can reduce local temperatures by 3–4°C (Morecroft et al. 1998). Shading of rivers streams and other water bodies by trees can deliver similar cooling, with beneficial effects for fisheries and wildlife, and street trees can have a similar effect in urban areas (Handley & Gill 2009).

Provided care is taken during harvesting and other operations, woodland can play a valuable role in preventing soil erosion, maintaining carbon content, free drainage and other aspects of soil quality regulation, as set out in the UK Forestry Standard (Forestry Commission 2009b). They can also be important for flood protection through increased flood storage, decreased flood flow velocity and peak discharge (Thomas & Nisbet 2007; Nisbet et al. 2009)

and water quality regulation, although this can be positive or negative, depending on the context.

Trees, especially evergreen species, are effective at scavenging air pollutants such as sulphur dioxide, ammonia and particulates. In urban areas, trees can provide a more valuable role in air quality regulation than other types of vegetation, especially beside roads and near intensive livestock units in the countryside (Pitcairn et al. 1998; Bignal et al. 2004; Woodland Trust 2010). Whilst nitrogen may increase growth for some trees, a study of beech woodlands showed that local sources of nitrogen can impact ground flora composition (Kennedy & Pitman 2004). Trees and other tall vegetation can play a valuable role in noise regulation due to the absorption of lateral sound waves and damping of sound reflection.

Provisioning services. The historical survival, and most planting, of woodlands in the past have been due to the provisioning services they provide. Since the Second World War, the expansion of woodland was driven by the need for timber production, and currently about 80% of UK wood and timber products are imported. This proportion is likely to be higher in England, as more of the demand is for conifer wood, which accounts for only a small part of the woodland area.

The use of wood as a fuel has declined during the past 60 years, although in recent years the market for woodfuel has been more buoyant due to increases in costs of other fuel types, interest in decreasing carbon footprint and improved domestic and industrial burners. The Woodfuel Strategy for England aims to bring 2 million extra tonnes of woodfuel into the market by 2020, approximately 50% of the annual increment (Forestry Commission 2009c). There is a small but stable production of charcoal, nearly all for domestic use (Sanderson & Prendergast 2002). Elderflowers, sloes, damsons and bullaces, nettles, hazel fences and spars for thatching, fungi, moss and foliage are other locally important products from woodlands, but the quantities used are small (Sanderson & Prendergast 2002).

In the lowlands, woodlands are a critical part of most game shoots, for example, for the location of release pens (Sage et al. 2005), and this activity has grown in the past 50 years. Of the 1.9 million shooting days in the UK, 40% is in woodland, accounting for about 28,000 jobs, and a high proportion of this is likely to be in England. In the past 50 years the wild deer population in England has grown dramatically, causing widespread woodland damage. In England, most deer stalking occurs in woodlands and some of the meat enters the venison market, but the income barely covers the costs (Section 8.3.2.2).

Cultural services. Since the mid-1980s, forestry policy has increasingly sought to promote a mix of services (including biodiversity, cultural and regulating), resulting in a widening of the Forestry Commission's remit (Forestry Commission 2007), increased planting of broadleaved tree species and a diversification of plantation structures.

Woodlands contribute to the structural diversity of landscape and many are important in forming the key characteristics of Natural England's NCAs, e.g. the Chilterns, New Forest and Border Moors and Forests. A survey showed that broadleaved woodlands generally were the preferred type and that externally, deciduous woodlands were key to the aesthetics/colours of a 'whole view' (especially the colours in autumn), whilst coniferous woodlands were valued, but more for recreation, including horse riding, biking and long walks. In some of the NCAs they were also valued as a 'productive' landscape component, associated with the local identity of the place and people's livelihoods (Natural England 2009a, b). Woodlands were seen as delivering many of the cultural services, being most important for calmness/tranquillity/peace/spiritualism (mainly broadleaved) and the leisure side of recreation (mixed and coniferous). In South East England, woodlands provide more than half of the accessible green space (McKernan & Grose 2007), although this excludes much that is in private ownership. A Forestry Commission survey (Carter *et al.* 2009) showed that the public thought that the two main future benefits should be to provide places for wildlife to live (over 45%) and places to walk (just under 45%).

In England, over half the area of woodland has public access, and currently, 55% of the population have access to woods greater than 20 ha within 4 km of where they live, and 10% have access to woods greater than 2 ha within 500 m of their home, but if inaccessible woods were opened up, then about an extra 26% of the population would have access to each category (Woodland Trust 2004). The England Leisure Visits Survey (Natural England 2006) showed that in 2005, 5% of all leisure visits included a trip to a woodland or forest, where walking was the main activity (62% of respondents). Overall, 62% of people who went to a wood did so to walk and only 9% to cycle (Natural England 2006).

Ancient woodland is also increasingly appreciated for its archaeological content, which may not only reflect its management history, but also retain traces of earlier land uses, as the soil has been relatively undisturbed (Rotherham *et al.* 2008).

17.4.4.3 Valuation

It has been estimated that English-grown timber and woodland management is associated with businesses which contribute £2.1 billion to GDP and employ 64,000 people. Around 16% of these are woodland-based businesses, such as recreation and tourism (Defra 2008b). Given that woodlands can provide multiple services, there would be considerable opportunity for revenue generation from any future payments for ecosystem services schemes, although consideration will need to be given to trade-offs between conflicting services. There is a lack of figures for many of the services, but Sanderson and Prendergast (2002) include various estimated figures for forest products, including hazel spars at £2 million and UK production of charcoal at approximately £1.3 million per year. The annual turnover of Bottle Green, who use wild elderflower for their drinks, was about £5 million.

Woodland creation is a highly cost-effective and achievable form of emission abatement at less than £100 per tonne CO_2e. Whilst conifer plantations and energy crops may be the most cost-effective options for carbon sequestration, mixed and broadleaved woodlands deliver a wider range of other benefits were only valued at about £41 per tonne CO_2e. (Matthews & Broadmeadow 2009).

A survey of the contribution of forests to tourism showed that forest-related tourism expenditure for day visits in England is just over £2 billion, compared with £2.3 billion for Great Britain (Willis *et al.* 2003), whilst the Natural England study (2009) valued trips to woods/forests at £1.8 billion. Biodiversity is also an important value of forests and the marginal benefits per household per year for an increase of 12,000 ha was estimated at 84p for lowland new broadleaved native forest and £1.13 for ancient and semi-natural woodland (Willis *et al.* 2003).

17.4.5 Freshwaters – Openwaters, Wetlands and Floodplains

17.4.5.1 Status, trends and condition

England has approximately 136,000 km of rivers and streams, 2,624 km of canals, 54,330 km of roadside ditches and over 97,000 ha of standing waters. Within standing waters, there are approximately 234,000 ponds and around 5,710 permanent lakes and reservoirs greater than 1 ha in size (Hughes *et al.* 2004; Countryside Survey 2009; **Figure 17.11**). In addition, there are an estimated 528,884 ha of wetland habitat in England. The wetland area is roughly 4% of England's land area, and of this, 47% (247,298 ha) is under SSSI protection.

The character of freshwaters varies, depending on the underlying geology. Eutrophic waters, draining soft rock or glacial drift catchments with higher levels of nutrients, make up approximately 60% of England's waters. The remaining 40% are split almost evenly between oligotrophic waters, draining from areas of hard rock geology and low in dissolved nutrients, and mesotrophic waters, often draining from sedimentary rocks. Of these, oligotrophic-mesotrophic base-rich waters and lowland oligotrophic waters on acid sand deposits are internationally significant and are poorly represented in Europe outside of the UK. Similarly, England's 3,900 km of chalk rivers are the longest in European extent and a key habitat for water crowfoot (*Ranunculus*) species. In addition, there are six standing water types in England that are found in Annex I of the EC Habitats Directive (92/43/EEC). Although canals are not recognised as a habitat under this Directive, they have been shown to offer temporary refuge for species driven from their natural habitats by declines in water and habitat quality. The Rochdale Canal in northern England, for example, supports several EC Annex II species. Recently changes in pressures, such as land use and management, have led to hydromorphological modification, flow alteration and quality changes in open waters (Chapter 9).

Wetlands, which include UK BAP priority habitats blanket bogs, coastal and floodplain grazing marsh, lowland fens, lowland raised bogs, reed beds and upland fens, flushes and swamps, comprise the largest proportion of designated SSSIs and are represented in numerous SACs. Wetlands cover just under half the total area of England's SSSI series and include 90% of the available fenland and raised bog, whilst only 16% of grazing marsh is SSSI designated (Natural England 2008). Blanket bog and grazing marsh comprise 93% of the total wetland area, and are especially prevalent along the Pennines, and in the North West and South West (**Figure 17.12**). The other three habitats (fens, reedbeds and

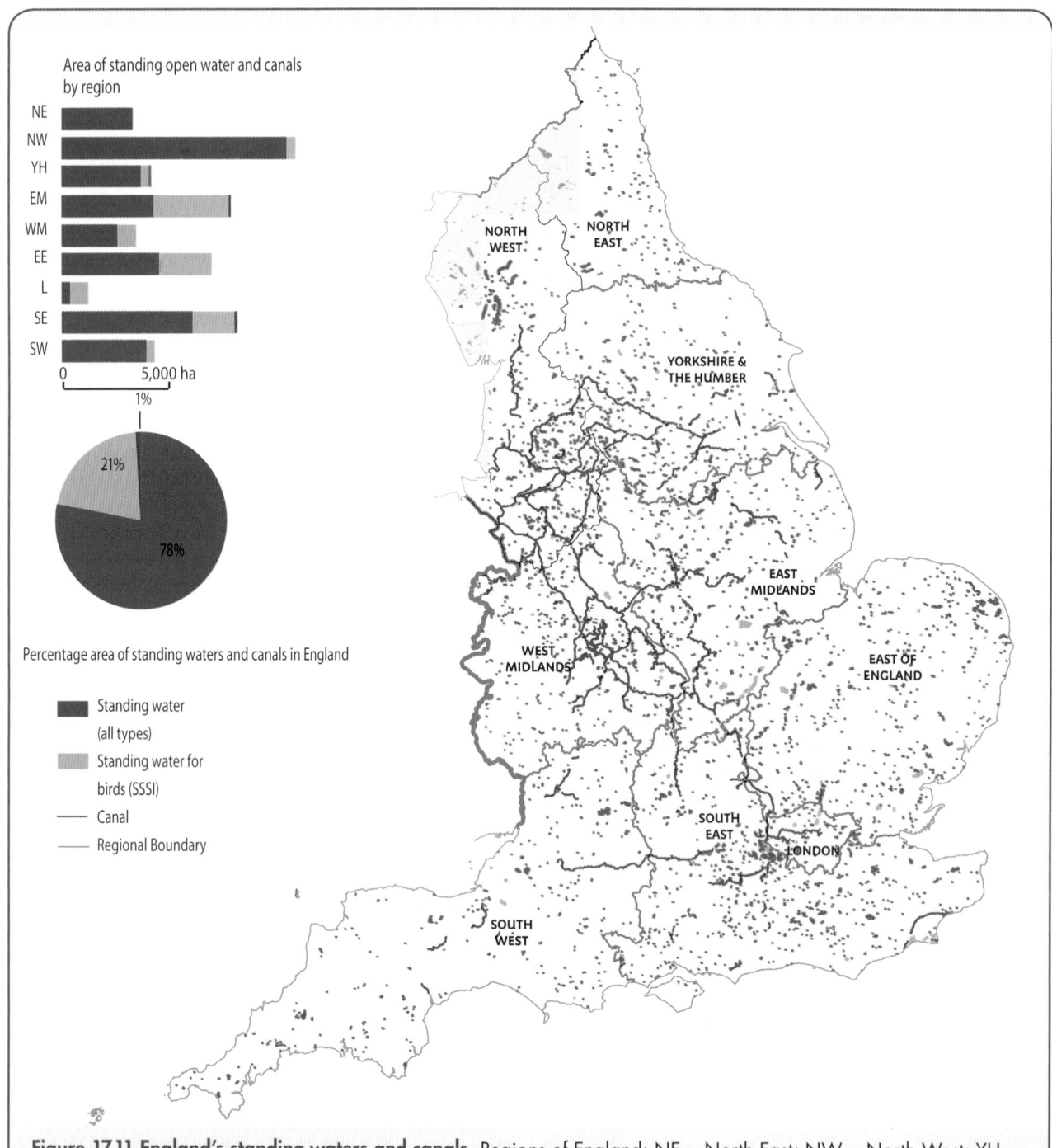

Figure 17.11 England's standing waters and canals. Regions of England: NE = North East; NW = North West; YH = Yorkshire and the Humber; EM = East Midlands;WM = West Midlands; EE = East of England; L = London; SE = South East; SW = South West. Source: Natural England (2008). Data from Great Britain Lakes Inventory, Ordance Survey Strategi data, Natural England (2008). © Crown copyright. All rights reserved. Natural England 100046223 2008.

lowland raised bogs) combined contribute 7% of the total area. Both the type and extent of wetlands vary between regions, with those with extensive upland/coastal areas or major fluvial floodplains supporting the greatest area of wetland. The South West holds the largest proportion of lowland wetlands, of which the majority is coastal and floodplain grazing marsh on the Somerset Levels. Other important wetland areas are concentrated in the South East and East of England.

The status of SSSI freshwaters provides an indication of water conditions: 44% of SSSI open waters are classified as favourable and 11% as recovering. Eutrophication is the cause for the majority of freshwaters classified as unfavourable,

due to inputs from point source pollution in 70% of the cases (e.g. sewage outfall) and diffuse pollution sources in 40% (e.g. agricultural fertilisers) with overlap in some locations (Countryside Survey 2009). This is an issue particularly in standing water, with a sample of 100 SSSI lakes showing that 80% were affected by eutrophication (Carvalho & Moss 1998; **Figure 17.13**). In addition, phosphate pollution was identified as a risk for 41% of water bodies in England and Wales in terms of the Water Framework Directive (UKTAG 2005) and there is growing concern that airborne pollution (acidification and atmospheric nitrogen) and climate change pose significant risks to vulnerable ecosystems, such as shallow ponds (Mountford & Strachan 2007).

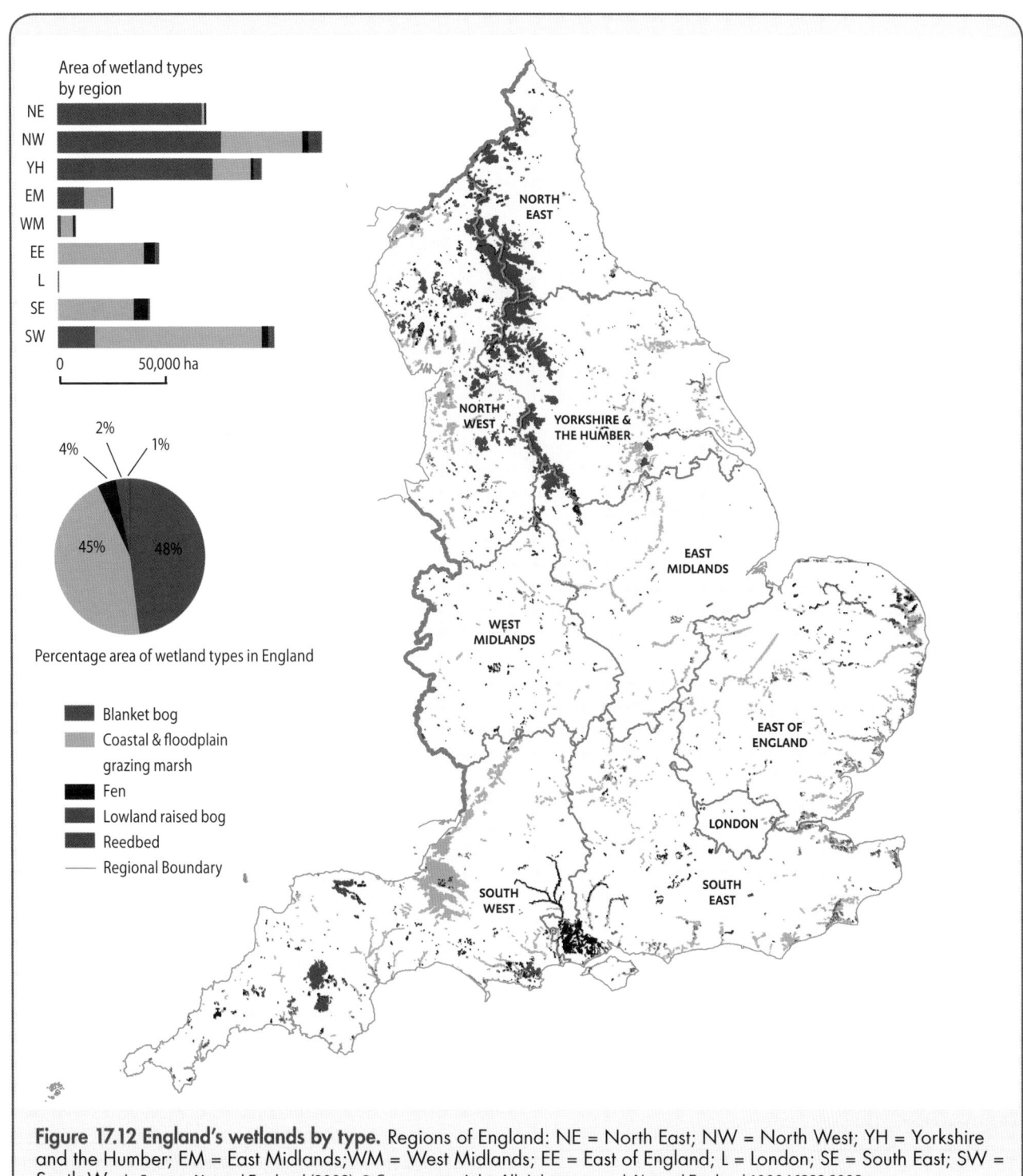

Figure 17.12 England's wetlands by type. Regions of England: NE = North East; NW = North West; YH = Yorkshire and the Humber; EM = East Midlands; WM = West Midlands; EE = East of England; L = London; SE = South East; SW = South West. Source: Natural England (2008). © Crown copyright. All rights reserved. Natural England 100046223 2008.

In terms of the Water Framework Directive 75% of rivers and a similar proportion of lakes in England are not in good condition and 80% of ponds are in poor condition. For SSSI wetlands 21% are classified as being in favourable condition and 48% as recovering (Natural England 2008). Unfavourable conditions in recorded SSSI sites are caused by overgrazing (58%), burning (36%) and drainage (23%) in the uplands, and by water pollution (29%), drainage (21%) and inappropriate water levels (17%) in the lowlands (Natural England 2008). Information is scarce about England's wetlands' condition outside of SSSIs. Dutt (2004) suggests that two-thirds of grazing marsh are in good condition for breeding waders, whilst the Norfolk Wildlife Trust (2006) found that only 31%

of non-SSSI fens in Norfolk were in favourable or recovering condition, compared to 51% in SSSI fens. However, it is expected that 1,500 ha of fens in England (19% of the 8,000 ha) will undergo restoration of former habitat by 2015, especially in the East (400 ha) and North West (360 ha; Measures 2008). One thousand hectares of lowland raised bogs are expected to be restored in England by 2015, especially in the North West (760 ha), and there is a planned expansion of 1,900 ha of reedbeds, especially in the East (740 ha; Measures 2008).

Semi-natural freshwaters provide valuable habitats for diverse plant, fish and invertebrate communities, whilst man-made pits and reservoirs are important for birds and can also support uncommon plants and invertebrates.

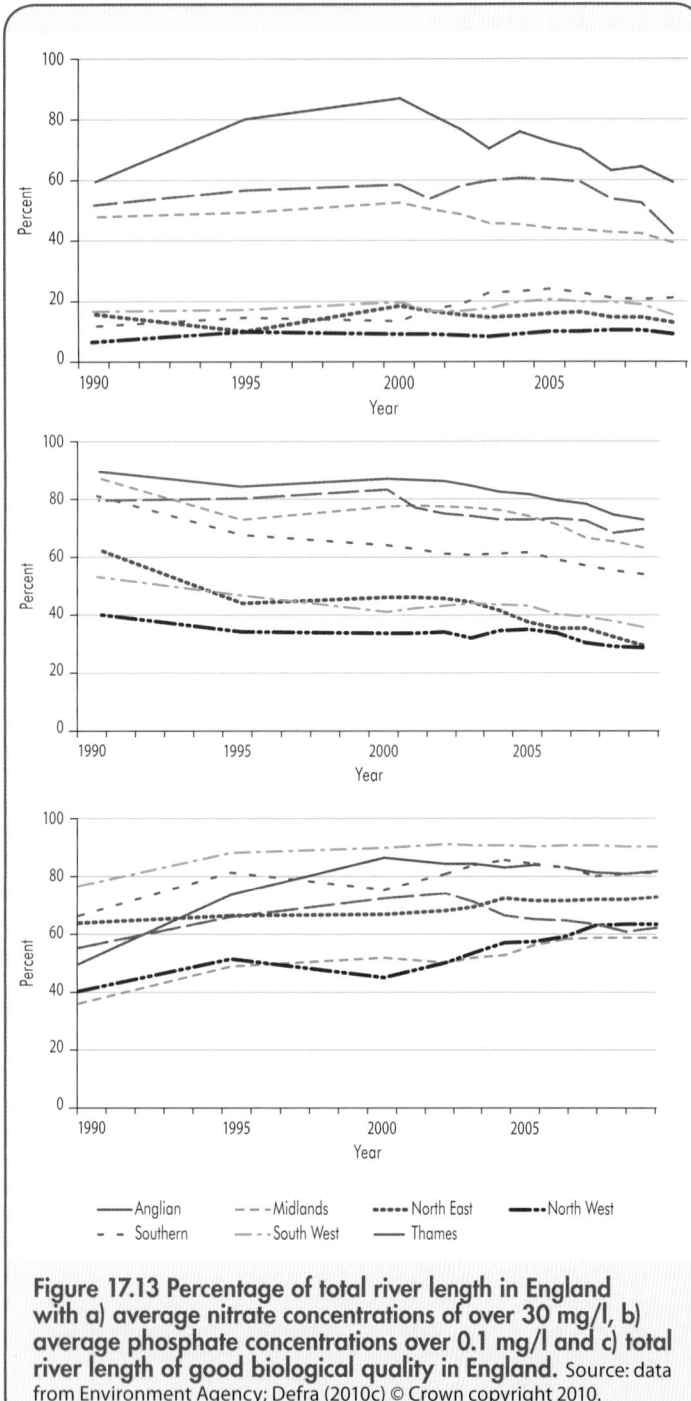

Figure 17.13 Percentage of total river length in England with a) average nitrate concentrations of over 30 mg/l, b) average phosphate concentrations over 0.1 mg/l and c) total river length of good biological quality in England. Source: data from Environment Agency; Defra (2010c) © Crown copyright 2010.

crayfish (*Austropotamobius pallipes*), freshwater pearl mussel (*Margaritifera margaritifera*), great crested newt (*Triturus cristatus*), natterjack toad (*Epidalea calamita*), salmon (*Salmo salar*) and vendace (*Coregonus albula*), all of which are recognised as internationally significant and, in some cases, are protected under the Habitats Directive. Furthermore, approximately 25% of all beetles are dependent on wetlands, and bogs and fens provide habitat for a variety of other invertebrates, including the fen raft spider (*Dolomedes plantarius*), the swallowtail butterfly (*Papilio machaon*), and dragonflies.

Relatively few mammals are directly associated with freshwaters with the exception of the water vole (*Arvicola amphibius*), water shrew (*Neomys fodiens*), some bats, otter (*Lutra lutra*) and American mink (*Mustela vison*). Water voles were England's most rapidly declining mammal due to predation by American mink and habitat deterioration (Strachan & Moorhouse 2006), but they are now slowly expanding their range. Otters were lost from many catchments across England in the 1950s to 1970s, but have been recovering and have now spread into northern rivers as water quality improves (Crawford 2003). Water voles may benefit from otters recolonising much of their former range and displacing mink (Bonesi & Macdonald 2004).

All amphibian species in England have declined, especially severely in the case of species with specific habitat requirements. These include the natterjack toad, which has lost over three-quarters of its former English range since 1900 (Beebee 1976; Banks *et al.* 1994); the great crested newt, which was lost from around half of its former English breeding sites (Beebee 1975), but now may be locally numerous in parts of lowland England, though it is absent or rare in Cornwall and Devon (Langton *et al.* 2001); the common toad (*Bufo bufo*), which declined by up to 50% in parts of southern and eastern England between 1985 and 2000 (Carrier & Beebee 2003); and the pool frog (*Pelophylax lessonae*), which became extinct in England during the 1990s and was reintroduced during 2005–2008.

Freshwater fish populations have also declined due to overfishing, eutrophic waters, habitat loss, etc. Salmon have declined since the 1970s and have remained at low levels since the 1990s. Elver (*Anguilla anguilla*) recruitment is down 95% and the current population is 5% of 1970s levels. Vendace populations have also declined, with low populations noted in Bassenthwaite Lake, but a stable population with some recruitment in Derwent Water (Winfield *et al.* 2004).

General environmental quality trends for rivers are positive, with long-term monitoring data showing a major improvement in the 40,000 km of English rivers. The patterns in recovery vary significantly within the UK, with biological recovery in English (and some Scottish) rivers, and continued biological decline in Wales (Chapter 9). The Thames, for example, where stretches were 'biologically dead', now supports over 125 species of fish, including the internationally important smelt and shad, and record numbers of salmon and sea trout have been found in the Thames, Mersey and Tyne. Concentrations of nitrate, however, have increased in 4,000 km of English rivers (Section 9.3.8) and phosphorus levels remain elevated in many areas, contributing to prolonged eutrophication (Mainstone *et al.* 2008). On

England's wetland areas have disproportionally large biological diversity per unit volume and support over 3,500 species of invertebrates, 150 species of aquatic plant, 22 species of duck and 33 species of wader (Merrit 1994). There are several restricted birds species, such as the marsh harrier (*Circus aeruginosus*), bittern (*Botaurus stellaris*) and bearded tit (*Panurus biarmicus*), particularly associated with reedbed/marsh habitats. Birds such as the common sandpiper (*Actitis hypoleucos*) and dipper (*Cinclus cinclus*) may be good indicators of habitat quality in rivers. Conversely, the spread of cormorants (*Phalacrocorax* species) to inland freshwaters has been perceived as a problem for freshwater fish populations.

Of particular interest are English populations of floating water plantain (*Luronium natans*), stoneworts, white clawed

the other hand, chemical evidence shows recovery from acidification to be underway, although there is less evidence for recovery in biological systems (Davies *et al.* 2005). Lakes show similar trends to rivers with respect to acidification, with some showing evidence for biological recovery of macrophytes and invertebrates (Monteith *et al.* 2005).

Problems with pesticides have declined over recent decades and increases in sensitive species, such as the otter, illustrate how threats from organochlorines, such as dieldrin, have now been effectively eliminated. Sediment-related problems have increased in the most intensively used catchments, with increased sediment fluxes over the last 40–100 years, particularly in areas where no active management has taken place to reduce them. Increasing evidence shows that even surprisingly low levels of input can impact sensitive organisms, particularly in upland regions where loads exceed natural exposure rates. Dissolved organic carbon shows a widespread increase with average trends exceeding +90% in some upland locations (Evans *et al.* 2005; Worral & Burt 2007a). Positive trends in fish populations have been seen in the re-establishment of native Atlantic salmon populations in the formerly polluted Tyne and Tees. Some concern remains over shifts in the demographic structure of Atlantic salmon populations in rivers from many sea-winter fish to 1-year grilse, commensurate with the impacts of overexploitation on lifecycles. Furthermore, in some catchments, juvenile populations of brown trout (*Salmo trutta*) and Atlantic salmon have declined by 50–60%, and there are major declines amongst other species (e.g. eels). Invasive species of fish and other organisms are also a growing concern; examples include the North American signal crayfish (*Pacifastacus leniusculus*), which has spread along many English rivers.

Various estimates suggest that as much as 90% of the national resource of English wetlands has been lost since Roman times, with as much as 13% of the floodplain resource degraded or completely disconnected from river channels. In the Thames Estuary, for example, two-thirds of the coastal and floodplain grazing marsh was lost between the 1930s and 1980s, and of 44,000 ha of grazing marsh within the North Kent, East Essex, Foulness and Inner Thames area, 28,000 ha were converted to other land uses (Ekins 1990; Thornton & Kite 1990). Originally covering 38,000 ha in England, peat bog now covers less than one-tenth of that area, mainly due to losses in the lowlands (English Nature 2002). In the case of lowland raised bog, the area retaining a largely undisturbed surface has declined by 94%. Data from The Countryside Survey in 2007 showed that there had been a small decrease in reedbeds since 1990, but also showed a significant increase in the extent of bogs, from 78,000 ha to 117,000 ha from 1990 to 2007 (Countryside Survey 2009).

17.4.5.2 Ecosystem services

Regulating services. Regulating services for freshwater often impact upon provisioning services. These include aquifer recharge (important, especially when water is continually extracted for irrigation), water quality (the dispersal and dilution of pollutants and purification of water) and vegetation growth (which may act as both as a purifier and hazard regulator).

In addition, freshwater plays significant roles in regulating flooding, erosion, sedimentation, local climates and water quality (Chapter 9). In England, there are a number of examples of freshwater systems, both man-made and natural, providing a range of ecosystem services, especially regulation. Examples include the town of Upton in the East Midlands, where a series of ponds and wetlands is used to capture runoff, regulate flooding and purify water. They also provide habitat for biodiversity and greenspace for local residents (Natural England 2009d). Another example is peat bogs, where waterlogged conditions and a lack of oxygen prevent biomass from fully decaying, thus they act as stores for carbon. The extraction of peat for fuel and fertiliser releases the stored carbon and decreases the habitat available for specialist species. Due to action taken by the government, however, locations such as Humberhead Peatlands and Wedholme Flow have been secured against continued peat extraction by large companies (English Nature 2002).

Provisioning services. Floodplains are the most important freshwater habitat for food and fibre production, with 57% of Grade 1 agricultural land in England being on the indicative floodplain (Section 9.2.1.3). Freshwaters provide for both consumptive and non-consumptive uses of water, including all forms of wetland-related crops, plants, livestock, fish (wild and domesticated), and energy, whilst crops dependent on irrigation rely on freshwater supplies. For example, parts of East Anglia are considered semi-arid, and require irrigation through dry months (Weatherhead & Knox 2000). This will continue, and may increase, as climate change affects rainfall totals and variability during growing months. Floodplains also play an important role in provisioning, due to their high soil fertility (Box 9.1, Section 9.2.1.3).

Wild fisheries provide species, such as salmon, brown trout and eel, which depend on freshwater as habitat and for breeding and nurseries. Aquaculture supplies fish and invertebrate species for a number of uses, including nursery-reared fish and invertebrate species such as freshwater white clawed crayfish, freshwater pearl mussels, brown trout and Arctic char (*Salvelinus alpinus*) for conservation restocking. Overall, England produces annually approximately 11,373 tonnes of farmed fish and invertebrates (James & Slaski 2009).

In addition, trees, standing vegetation and peat are important energy sources created or fed by freshwater systems. Other provisioning services include potable, domestic and industrial water and hydropower.

Cultural services. Rivers, lakes and wetlands have significant cultural value, especially in terms of recreation, tourism and education. Furthermore, they play a key cultural role as an inspiration for the arts and religion.

Tourism continues to focus on water-based holidays, advertising leisure activities such as sailing, swimming and fishing. Recreational fishing is of importance as a free-time activity, with over 1.3 million fishing licences being sold in 2009 (Environment Agency 2010a). Birdwatching can be especially gratifying around freshwater environments, as wetland habitats are particularly important for a number of species, especially ducks and waders.

Regions featuring freshwater have played an important role in English history and culture. For example, the Romantic poets William Wordsworth and Samuel Taylor Coleridge based themselves in the Lake District in the early 1800s. Much of their writings were influenced by the surrounding landscape, which featured lakes, waters and mountains (Icons 2006). Writers, such as Ted Hughes, have used rivers as a source for their work.

Housing along or on rivers and canals is in high demand, and often priced at a premium. Currently, construction along the Thames in London is set to provide increased housing (both competitively priced and at affordable prices), as well as increasing access to the riverside for leisure (Environment Agency 2009).

17.4.5.3 Valuation

An accurate valuation of all the benefits provided by the freshwater resource is difficult, but it has been estimated that the mean average benefits of inland lowland wetlands in England are between £3,400 and £5,240/ha/yr and between £1,700 and £2,630/ha/yr for all inland lowland and upland wetlands in England (Chapter 22). A 2005 survey reviewing England's Leisure Visits demonstrated that leisure visits to water locations result in expenditure of £1,060 million annually in locations with boats and £793 million in locations without boats. Fishing is the most widespread participatory sport in the UK, with in excess of 4 million anglers across all social strata. Coarse fisheries alone contribute £1,030 million to the economy out of a total spend exceeding £3 billion by rod fishermen in England and Wales (Environment Agency 2004). For migratory salmonids, the capital value of fishing rights alone is estimated at £165 million (Aprahamian *et al*. 2010). In addition, reservoirs like Rutland Water in the East Midlands also provide monetary value, with 64% (£79–138 million) of its total annual value of £123–215 million attributable to functions other than its primary purpose as a reservoir.

A study undertaken by NERA provides an indication of the value placed by case study households in England and Wales on their freshwater environment. Participants were asked how much they would be willing to pay to improve water quality to a situation where 95% of water bodies reached good ecological status and an average of between £45–167 per household per year was stated (NERA 2007). The money raised by the Great Fen Partnership in East Anglia also demonstrates the value local partners placed on the environment, with £17 million being raised in six years, 80% of which came from private sources or charitable grants, such as the Heritage Lottery Fund. This money enabled the partnership to secure 1,700 ha of farmland adjacent to NNRs in the area to create an enveloping 'waterland' around them, stimulating socioeconomic benefits for people, including much increased local community involvement and opportunities for access and recreation. An £18 million government grant was used to buy out the peat producers at Thorne and Hatfield Moors (which together cover over 3,300 ha) in Yorkshire and the Humber Region, thus preventing further habitat deterioration and loss of carbon regulation.

17.4.6 Urban

17.4.6.1 Status, trends and condition

There is no consensus regarding how urban environments are identified. The Land Cover Map 2000 (LCM 2000) identifies 10.6% of the land area in England as 'built up areas', whilst 14.2% is similarly described by the Office of National Statistics Output Area (GLUD 2005), which defines 'urban' as contiguous physical settlement areas containing 10,000 or more people. This is far greater than the 'built up' or 'urban' areas in Scotland (1.9% and 3% respectively), Wales (4.1% and 7.9%) or Northern Ireland (3.6% and 3%). Understanding the habitats within Urban boundaries becomes complex, especially when the dominant features within Urban boundaries tend to be the built environment and the people it houses.

Within Urban boundaries, however, many habitats and services may be identified. These range in size and complexity and include public parks and gardens, private gardens, semi-natural green spaces, such as woodland, scrub and grassland, urban trees and outdoor sports facilities. Allotments, urban farms and community gardens also play large roles in people's interaction with land. Previously developed land (PDL or brownfield), cemeteries, churchyards, and burial grounds further contribute habitat for native species within Urban boundaries. Increasingly, interest in biodiversity conservation has led to wildlife gardening, including pond creation, hedgehog, bird and bat houses, and specially chosen plants for invertebrates. Many of England's residents provide feed for birds, which may help winter survival.

It has long been understood that cities have a larger impact on the surrounding ecosystems than rural communities (Folke *et al*. 1997). Though limited in extent, whatever greenspaces exist within city boundaries do contribute to ecosystem services. Therefore, it is important to inventory and protect the greenspaces and the benefits they provide, as well as their accessibility to residents, to ensure that increasing demand for housing and other development in cities does not lead to a loss of greenspace. The outward sprawl of cities in England has been limited by the Green Belt Policy, which covers 13% of England's land area, and green belts surround some of the most densely populated urban areas (Natural England/CPRE 2010e). Whilst this policy provides people with limited access to open greenspace outside cities, much of it is private farmland. Green belts can also be important habitats for biodiversity, though the promotion of biodiversity conservation and recreation are not explicitly stated purposes of this land. Recent policy has encouraged the re-use of PDL or brownfield within cities, as opposed to continuing the outward sprawl. However, city densities are projected to increase, which may force cities to expand their borders as well as increasing construction within existing boundaries, impacting both green belts and inner-city greenspaces. For instance, in London, population projections estimate an increase from 7.5 million in 2006 to 8.5 million by 2026 (Natural England 2009d), which will require the provision of additional housing, infrastructure and jobs, as well as greenspace. Domestic gardens and brownfield have proven to be good habitat for invertebrates and local plant species, and losing these habitats to accommodate an increase in population would negatively impact species' populations which depend on already limited space (Angold *et al*. 2006; Natural England 2008). In an effort to protect gardens from 'garden grabbing' and development, Planning Policy Statement 3 was passed in 2010, increasing their status to above brownfield equivalent (Clark 2010).

In England, local authorities were required to develop Green Space Strategies in order to decide how they intended to plan use of greenspace and the resources, time and methods required. A study of four English cities (Newcastle, Northampton, Coventry and Liverpool) showed that the total mapped public greenspace covers between 17 and 24% of the Urban area (Box 10.1, Section 10.1.3). Often the distribution of greenspace is not even across the individual cities and not all of it is freely accessible to the public. For instance, golf courses and school playing fields are often privately owned and not publicly accessible (CABE 2010).

Table 17.10 inventories greenspace in urban authorities in England based on a variety of sources; however, it does not include private gardens, which contribute to a wide range of provisioning, regulating and cultural benefits.

17.4.6.2 Ecosystem services

There is no doubt that cities require more services than they can provide. Current estimates for London suggest that it requires 293 times more land than its geographical area in order to sustain itself, equivalent to twice the productive land in Britain (Best Foot Forward 2002). The services provided by most habitats in Urban environments are limited, primarily providing cultural and regulating services, although increasingly allotment and community farm space is contributing to local food production (Garnett 2000).

Regulating services. Greenspace in urban environments helps to regulate climate, decrease runoff from paved surfaces and improve air quality. Temperatures are often much higher within cities than in surrounding areas—it is estimated that the temperature difference between London and its surrounding suburbs may be as high as 9°C (GLA 2006a). These urban heat islands can be mitigated by increased greenspace—urban trees, green roofs, woodland, community farms and allotments and brownfield can all help in the regulation of heat due to direct shading and cooling by evapotranspiration,

whilst reducing wind speeds helps to prevent heat loss from buildings in winter (Woodland Trust 2010). Green roofs can also dramatically reduce energy demand from buildings and decrease maximum surface temperature (Gill et al. 2007), as well as providing high-density buildings with localised greenspace. It has been projected that by 2050 the temperature in Manchester will have risen by 3°C due to climate change. This could be avoided by increasing greenspace by 10% (Handley & Carter 2006).

Trees have the added benefit of effectively filtering pollutants, including gaseous components, such as oxides of nitrogen and sulphur, as well as particulate matter, especially Particulate Matter up to 10 Microns in Diameter (PM_{10}) (Tiwary et al. 2009). In addition, trees and other woody vegetation mitigate noise by absorbing both reflected and laterally transmitted noise, especially at high frequencies.

Runoff is another problem that can be mitigated by urban greenspace. Green roofs, parks and gardens, urban woodlands, allotments and farms and even stand-alone trees can all reduce runoff from paved surfaces (Gill et al. 2007) and many Urban areas now promote sustainable urban drainage systems (Section 17.4.5).

Provisioning services. Allotments and community farms comprise 1,829.6 ha of urban land in England (CABE 2010). These sites provide crops and sometimes livestock to local communities, and require a minimum of transport to deliver products to consumers. In 1975 the Royal Horticultural Society estimated food production on allotments and community gardens at 'best practice' to be around 21.4 t/ha. Garnett (2000) halves this estimate to 10.7 t/ha, a more conservative estimate which allows that not all farmers or gardeners can grow at optimal conditions. Using a conservative estimate, the potential urban food production in England is about 19,576 tonnes of fruit and vegetables. Crop production from these sites could theoretically feed over 100,000 people their recommended daily intake of 0.4–0.5 kg of fruit and vegetables (WHO & FAO 2004).

Private gardens in England are estimated to cover over 400,000 ha of land (Gilbert 1989) and also contribute to crop

Table 17.10 Public Urban greenspace in England (does not include private gardens). Source: reproduced from Commission for Architecture and the Built Environment (CABE 2010).

Greenspace type	Number	Area (ha)	Data
Allotments	997	1356.8	Allotment sites 2004–2005
Cemeteries	1,643	3,679.1	Burial grounds 2006
Community farms	197	472.8	Community gardens and city farms 2004–2005
Country parks	72	5,765.9	Country parks
Doorstep greens	82	140.3	Doorstep greens
Golf courses	361	5,720.6	Golf courses
Grass pitches	10,243	8,170.4	Sport England/Fields in Trust
Millennium greens	91	164.5	Millennium greens
Nature reserves	663	14,308.0	National nature reserves; local nature reserves
Parks	1,770	52,243.2	Registered parks and gardens 2008; Public parks assessment; Green Flag parks 2006–2007
National Trust	128	14,537.0	National Trust
All types	**16,247**	**106,549.6**	

growth and genetic resources. Although 70% of the plants used in domestic gardens are non-native, of the 20 most commonly used species 55% are native (Natural England 2008). Gardens, allotments and community farms also contribute to cultural and regulating services, by providing local greenspace for residents and making unfriendly habitats permeable for local species.

Cultural services. About 80% of the population of England lives in Urban areas (CABE 2010) and although access to greenspace increases the health and happiness of residents (Fuller *et al.* 2007), it is inevitably limited in cities, because of restricted space and high land prices. Proximity to accessible greenspaces, especially those encompassing a variety of plant and animal species, has physical and psychological benefits and increases social cohesion (Fuller & Gaston 2009). Green patches in the urban environments may act as valuable corridors into and through cities, especially if the pathways are targeted toward and designed for a specific species or group of species (Angold *et al.* 2006). In this way urban greenspaces may be able to fill a number of niches, supplying habitat to species within cities and increasing the value of that space to urban residents. In England, some species, including the common frog (*Rana temporaria*), song thrush (*Turdus philomelos*) and hedgehog (*Erinaceous europaeus*), that have declined in the wider countryside have found urban greenspaces, especially domestic gardens, suit them well. Brownfield sites have also contributed to urban wildlife conservation, along with providing open space and accessible educational opportunities for urban residents. For example, Canvey Wick, Essex was an oil refinery and is now a post-industrial SSSI site. It has become a habitat for a number of Red Data Book and UK BAP priority species, including herb-rich grassland, early successional habitat and scrub edge and brackish habitats, and provides habitat for the nationally important shrill carder bee (*Bombus sylvarum*), as well as a wide array of plants (English Nature 2005; Natural England 2008).

Access to open greenspace, however, is varied. In the North East, for instance, only 8% of homes are within 300 m of a greenspace larger than 2 ha (**Figure 17.14**). And although the overall amount of greenspace for urban residents in England is on average 1.79 ha per 1,000 people (CABE 2010), the quantity of greenspace available in areas with high concentrations of minority groups is significantly lower, negatively impacting access to such facilities as outdoor sports fields (CABE 2010). This can have severe harmful impacts on community cohesion and residents' health, whilst greenspaces that are accessible and connected are valuable both to wildlife and human users. Utilising space along waterways and disused railway lines can offer a range of benefits, including interconnectedness, accessibility and, in the case of derelict land, affordability.

17.4.6.3 Valuation

The benefits of urban greenspaces have been touched upon in the previous sections, and are explored in Section 10.1.3. Health, social cohesion, opportunities for engagement in outdoor activities and accessible educational opportunities are all provided for residents by urban greenspace. Additionally, the quality and economic value of the local

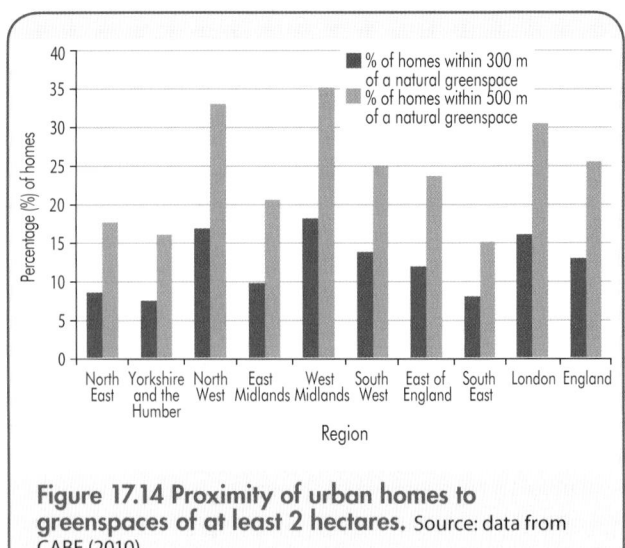

Figure 17.14 Proximity of urban homes to greenspaces of at least 2 hectares. Source: data from CABE (2010).

environment (including air, water, noise and climate) are improved by proximity to greenspace (CABE 2005). Proximity to, and views of, high quality greenspaces can increase house prices by 6 to 15%, whilst views of apartment blocks can reduce value by up to 7% (CABE 2005).

CABE (2010) measured how urban residents assign value to greenspace, asking whether 'access to nature' and 'parks and open spaces' are important to them. Responses varied across the country, with parks and open spaces considered more important in highly urbanised regions (for instance, London and the North West), and less so in more rural regions (for instance, the East Midlands and the South West). Interestingly, London residents had amongst the lowest concern for 'access to nature', whilst residents of the South West considered it comparably more important.

17.4.7 Coastal Margins

17.4.7.1 Status, trends and condition

In England, the Coastal Margins comprise five UK NEA component habitats (Sand Dunes, Saltmarsh, Shingle, Sea Cliffs and Coastal Lagoons); the sixth, Machair, is found only in Scotland and Ireland. Sand Dunes and Saltmarsh are the most extensive, although at a UK scale Shingle is also important, with England holding 73% and 86% of the national resource for Saltmarsh and Shingle respectively (**Table 17.11**; Section 11.2.7.2). **Figure 17.15** shows the distribution of the principal soft coast habitats around England. Sand Dunes and Saltmarsh are particularly important in the North West from Merseyside up to Cumbria, and on the east coast around the Wash and Essex coast. As with the rest of the UK, considerable loss of sand dune area has occurred due to agricultural land claim, golf courses and development for housing and tourism, and at some sites, afforestation. Development along the Sefton coast, illustrated in **Figure 17.16**, is typical, with losses probably comparable to the UK figure of 30% loss since 1900 (Jones *et al.* 1993; Delbaere 1998). Habitat quality has also declined, with most dunes becoming overstabilised since 1945 (Radley 1994).

Saltmarsh incurred major losses prior to the 1980s due to widespread, large-scale reclamation for agriculture or development (Morris *et al.* 2004b). In the Wash, 3,000 ha of marsh were reclaimed in the 20th Century alone (Doody 2008). The current major losses in Saltmarsh extent are in the South East of England. Between 1973 and 1998, over 1,000 ha were lost (Cooper *et al.* 2001). However, in larger estuaries, such as Morecambe Bay, Saltmarsh has extended seaward due to vegetative colonisation of mudflats, often by *Spartina anglica*, and the net change in area since 1945 is uncertain.

Shingle borders approximately 30% of the coastline of England, with well-known examples such as Chesil Beach, Dorset and Dungeness, Kent. The extent of vegetated shingle has declined since 1945 due primarily to infrastructure development, for example, as recently as the 1980s at 'The Crumbles', East Sussex, and aggregate extraction.

Hard cliffs are widely distributed along exposed coasts, occurring principally in South West and South East England (the latter area having the bulk of the 'hard' chalk cliffs), whilst soft cliffs are more restricted, occurring mainly on the eastern and central south coasts of England. It is assumed that the length of cliff is largely unchanged. However, cliff habitat quality has declined since 1945, not so much due to armouring, but due to agricultural encroachment at the cliff-top and reductions in grazing and traditional forms of management, leading to excess scrub development.

There are 177 saline lagoons in England, comprising approximately 25% of the UK total lagoon area. It is assumed there has been no net change in lagoon area as losses are largely balanced by creation of new, artificial lagoons.

The coastal margin habitats contain a very wide diversity of ecological niches (e.g. Howe 2002; Whitehouse 2007; Howe *et al.* 2008; 2010; Everard *et al.* 2010). The dynamic nature of these habitats means that they provide amongst the best examples of early successional environments in England. Due also to the harsh environmental gradients associated with proximity to the sea, they support a wide range of highly specialised species. Lundy cabbage (*Coincya wrightii*), for example, is only found on cliffs on Lundy Island and is host to the endemic Lundy cabbage flea beetle (*Psylliodes luridipennis*) and the Lundy cabbage weevil (*Ceutorhynchus contractus pallipes*), whilst the fiery clearwing (*Pyropteron chrysidiformis*) is restricted to the chalk cliffs of Kent and Sussex, and a water beetle, *Ochthebius poweri*, occurs predominantly in small seepages on red sandstone cliff faces in South West England (Natural England 2008).

England's Sea Cliffs are important breeding grounds for internationally important numbers of birds, including gannets (*Morus bassanus*), guillemots (*Uria aalge*), and kittiwakes (*Rissa tridactyla*), with the cliffs at Flamborough supporting the largest known kittiwake colony in the North Atlantic, as well as England's only, and Britain's largest, mainland gannet colony (Natural England 2008). Sand Dunes, Saltmarshes and Shingle beaches hold important breeding colonies of gulls and terns. England hosts about 36% of the global population of the *graellsii* race of lesser black-backed gull (*Larus fuscus*), and is also important for a number of other species, including Sandwich tern (*Sterna sandvicensis*) and shag (*Phalacrocorax aristotelis*), little tern (*Sternula albifrons*) and puffin (*Fratercula arctica;* Brown & Grice 2005). England supports some 4.3–4.7 million non-breeding waders in winter (approximately 70 to 80% of the GB total), with The Wash alone supporting a peak of 400,000 birds in winter (Brown & Grice 2005). England's coastal habitats also provide vital stopover sites for large numbers of waders on migration between their breeding grounds in the high Arctic and wintering areas in southern Europe and West Africa.

The general unsuitability of coastal habitats for agricultural development means that they form important refugium habitats for species lost from other lowland habitats. This diversity supports a number of services: directly via provisioning of wild food and commercially harvestable resources, and through the ecosystem level processes underlying the regulating services including, to a greater or lesser extent, sea defence and pest control and pollination. A large proportion of the area of Coastal Margin habitats is designated as SAC under the Habitats Directive, is SSSI, or comes under other designations such as AONB. Therefore, protection and maintenance of the biodiversity, geomorphological interest and unspoilt character remain primary objectives. This biological diversity and the underlying geomorphological processes are part of the reason for the high proportion of total land area under statutory protection. They also form a major part of the cultural value attached to these systems, and underpin the basic processes upon which the supporting services depend.

The major drivers of change in the English coastal margin habitats, as discussed above, include changing tourism patterns and interests and land use demands, as well as nitrogen deposition and sea-level rise. Nitrogen deposition ranges from approximately 10 kg nitrogen per hectare per year on the west coast reaching up to about 20 kg nitrogen per hectare per year on the east coast (Jones *et al.* 2004), reflecting prevailing wind directions and accumulated pollution from industrial, vehicular and agricultural sources. Deposition loads have increased considerably since 1945 (Fowler *et al.* 2004) and this increase is likely to have caused reductions in plant species diversity and altered soil processes in coastal habitats (e.g. Jones *et al.* 2004; 2008). Isostatic adjustment is negative along the south and east English coasts, but positive in the North West. Nonetheless, sea level rise will have impacts on all English coastal margin habitats, with a sea level rise of 26.3 cm predicted for London under a medium emissions scenario by 2060 (Lowe *et al.* 2009). There are regional targets to restore various coastal habitats, including 200 ha of sand dunes by 2015, with 37.5% of this being in the North West region (Measures 2008). There is also a target of a 200 ha expansion by 2015 of maritime

Table 17.11 Area of Coastal Margin habitats in England, and as a proportion of UK total. *Cliffs are measured as length (km). Trends: ↓ weak decline, ↓↓ strong decline, ? trend unknown, = stable. Source: data from JNCC (2007).

	Area (ha)	% of UK total	Trend
Sand dunes	11,897	16.6	↓
Saltmarsh	32,462	72.9	↓↓
Vegetated shingle	5,023	85.8	↓
Maritime cliffs*	1,082	23.8	?
Saline lagoons	1,205	23.2	=

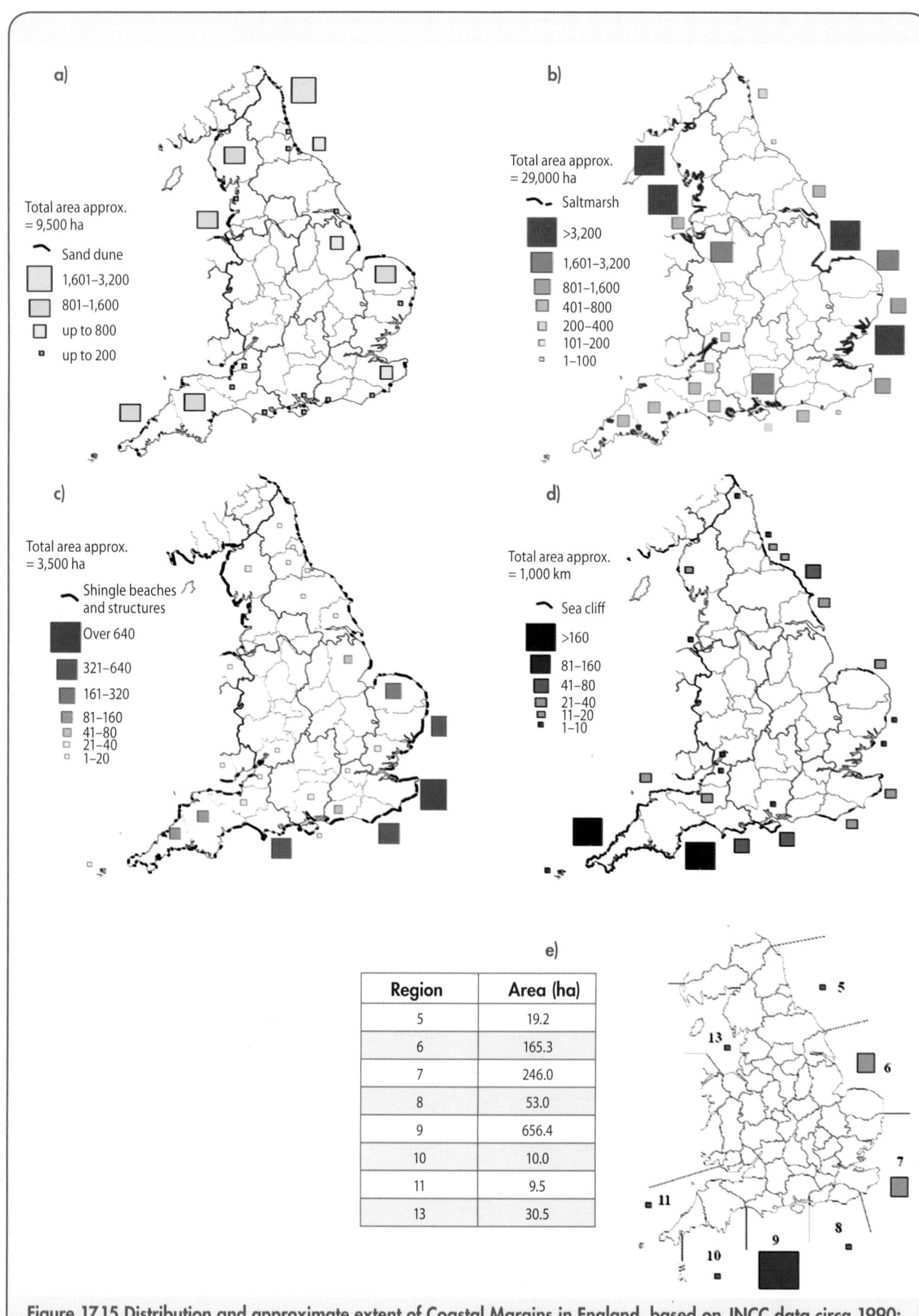

Region	Area (ha)
5	19.2
6	165.3
7	246.0
8	53.0
9	656.4
10	10.0
11	9.5
13	30.5

Figure 17.15 Distribution and approximate extent of Coastal Margins in England, based on JNCC data circa 1990: a) Sand Dunes, b) Saltmarsh, c) Shingle, d) Sea Cliffs (more than 20 m high), e) Coastal Lagoons. Note: figures (ha and km) are based on 1:50000 maps and are meant to facilitate comparisons. Field survey since they were drawn up have greatly increased our knowledge of the resource which is bigger than indicated by the figures. Source: all maps provided by JP Doody; Coastal Lagoons map includes data from Barne *et al.* (1995–1998).

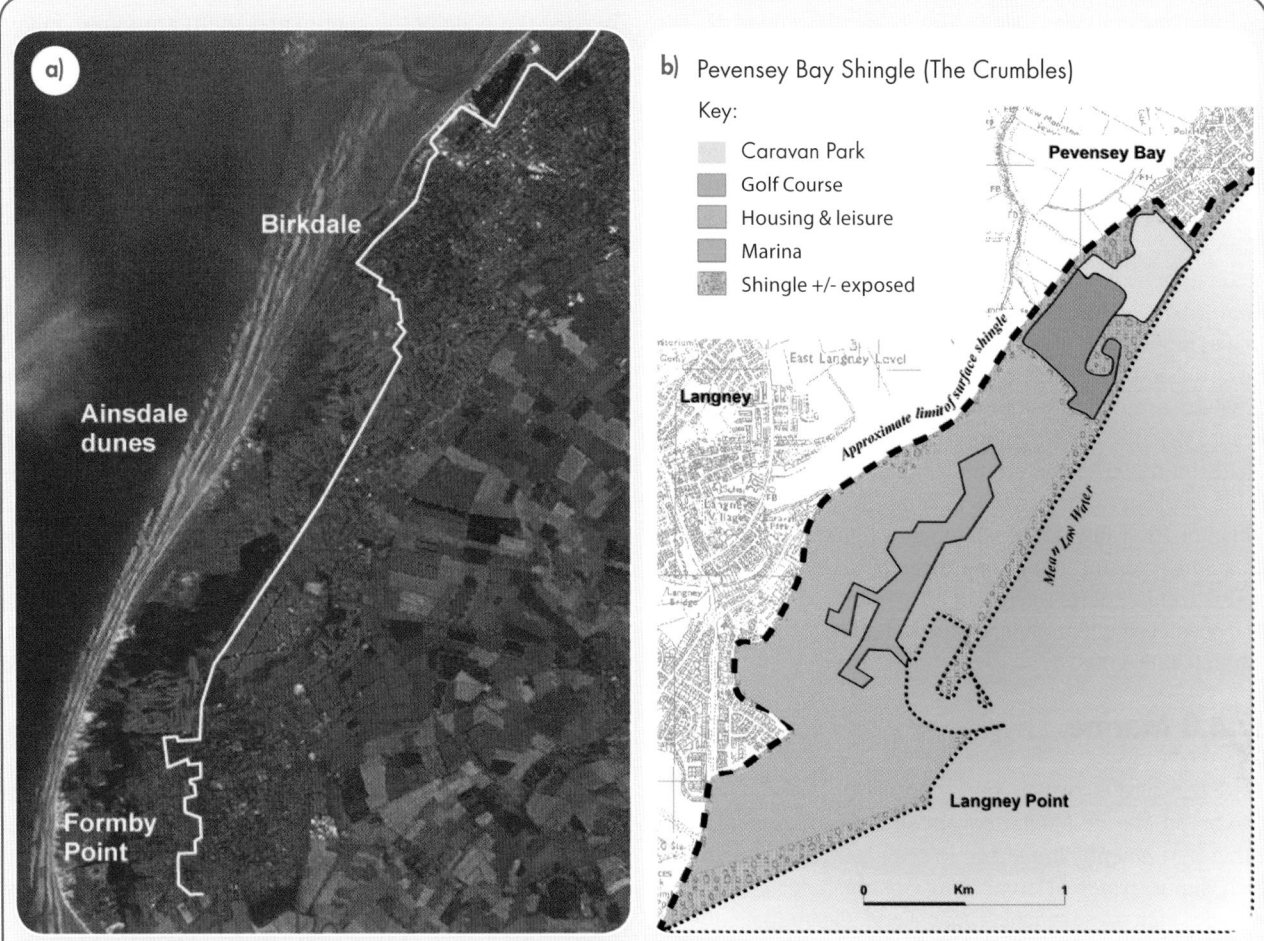

Figure 17.16 Examples of habitat loss: a) Sand Dunes on the Sefton coast, north-west England, lost to urbanisation, forestry and golf courses; and b) almost complete loss of Shingle due to development pressures at The Crumbles, East Sussex. The white line shows seaward limit of urban extent in 1945. Note the subsequent development at Ainsdale and Formby. Golf courses and afforestation of dunes pre-date 1945. Source: a) ArcGIS World Imagery Map: ESRI, i-cubed, USDA FSA, USGS, AEX, GeoEye, Getmapping, Aerogrid, IGP; urban extent courtesy of Sefton Borough Council. b) Map courtesy of JP Doody.

cliffs and slopes, with just over 40% of this in the South West region, and a 100 ha expansion of saline lagoons.

17.4.7.2 Ecosystem services

Regulating services. The principal regulating service is sea defence, which is of high importance, as 30% of the English coastline is eroding and 46% has some form of sea defence works (Masselink & Russell 2008). Saltmarshes dissipate energy, reducing the size of landward defences needed: up to 50% of wave energy is dissipated in the first 10–20m of vegetated saltmarsh (Moller 2006), and 370 km of the 440 km (84%) of Essex seawalls rely upon fronting saltmarsh to maintain defence integrity. Dunes protect residential areas and high quality farmland, particularly in north-west England and along the Norfolk Broads (Everard et al. 2010). Shingle provides important natural defence structures on the south and south-east coasts, such as Chesil Beach, Hurst Spit and Pevensey. Many of these features are now maintained by artificial nourishment, re-shaping or reuse to retain shingle in front of human assets. Estimates vary, but together the soft coasts provide £3.1–33.2 billion worth of sea-defence service in England alone (Chapter 11, Key Findings; Section 11.3.2).

Carbon sequestration rates are high in Saltmarsh and Sand Dunes due to rapid soil development or sediment accumulation. West coast UK sand dunes store 0.58–0.73 t C/ha/yr (Jones et al. 2008), whilst saltmarsh stores 0.64–2.19 t C/ha/yr (Cannell et al. 1999). However, the net benefit in England is small due to the low total area of these habitats.

Provisioning services. Goods relating to provisioning services in the English coastal margins are relatively minor. The most important are meat and wool on Saltmarsh. There is some commercial stock grazing on dunes in the North West (e.g. Walney Island); grazing on cliffs is minimal, and occurs primarily for conservation purposes on land owned by the National Trust. The harvesting of samphire (*Salicornia* species) is a traditional, but small-scale industry predominantly in Norfolk. There is some timber provision from the larger extents of afforested dunes at Ainsdale, but both wood quality and economic returns are low, so amenity uses linked with biodiversity enhancement tend to be more important. Other non-food provisioning services include use of land for power stations requiring cooling water, e.g. Dungeness, and military uses of dunes in Devon.

Cultural services. As an island nation, the coast has an important place in our national psyche. Negative associations include the threats of invasion, flooding and sea-level rise, whilst positive connotations include an empire based on naval strength, livelihoods such as fishing, and seaside holidays. The coast is highly valued by the public for a variety of reasons (Section 11.3.3), but social and cultural services are the most important ecosystem services provided by coastal margin habitats in England. The seaside accounted for 24% of all overnight domestic tourism spend in England in 2009, having a value of £4.1 billion (UKTS 2010), and generates more spend than overnight trips to the countryside and villages combined. The pattern of tourism has changed over time and there has been a general decline in overnight leisure visits to the coast since the peak in the 1960s, replaced to some extent by day visits. In 2002 there were around 200 million day visits to the English coast, of which around one-third are to natural habitats such as beaches, sand dunes, shingle and cliffs (UKLDVS 2004; VisitBritain 2007). The annual estimated total recreational value of visits to the coast is between £121 and 149 million (Chapter 22, Table 22.21). Demand for specialist activities, including coastal hiking, birdwatching, whale-watching and extreme sports such as cliff climbing, sand yachting and coasteering that require specific habitats, has increased (Mintel 2005, 2008).

17.4.8 Marine

17.4.8.1 Status, trends and condition

The broad Marine habitat covers all English areas that are either permanently immersed in seawater or are inundated with saline water at some stage in the tidal cycle. This includes estuaries, beaches, coasts and all subtidal habitats out to the limit of England's marine area (Figure 12.2, Section 12.1). England and its larger islands have over 10,077 km of coastline (Frost 2010) and a wide range of Marine habitats (Hiscock 1996). These habitats support a high diversity of animals and plants, ranked as one of the highest in Europe (Defra 2005).

Information collated for the Charting Progress reports (Defra 2005, UKMMAS 2010) form the basis of our understanding of the status and trends of England's Marine habitats and species.

Intertidal Rock habitats are widespread except in south-eastern and north-western coasts, where the intertidal zone is dominated by sandy beaches or intertidal mudflats. Large stretches of coastline in England (and Wales) are composed of Intertidal Sediments. Within estuaries, intertidal muddy sediments are particularly prevalent, with saltmarshes typically occurring landward of intertidal muds.

In the subtidal zone, sedimentary habitats such as sand, gravel, muds and mixed sediments cover almost all the continental shelf. Shallow Subtidal Sediment, which can be regularly disturbed by surface waves, is widespread in the Irish Sea, the Eastern Channel and the Southern North Sea; they also occur in Coastal Lagoons, particularly in southern England. Shelf Subtidal Sediment is only rarely disturbed by surface waves because of its greater water depth, and therefore supports more stable communities. Shelf Subtidal Sediment occurs throughout offshore areas of most regional seas, but also much closer to coasts where the water deepens rapidly, such as around Cornwall. Subtidal Rock habitats, including biogenic reefs, occur extensively in South West England. Deep-sea Habitats (below 200 m,

beyond the edge of the continental shelf) are found only in the extreme south-west Celtic Sea and are under pressure from deep-sea trawling (Benn *et al.* 2010).

England's Marine habitats have been subject to the same pressures over the last 10 years as those for the rest of the UK, although 30% of the English coast is subject to erosion compared with 17% for the UK. This has led to 46% of the coast being protected by engineering structures, compared with only 12% in Scotland (MCCIP 2010). Other pressures include adverse effects on some local Intertidal Rock communities from the harvesting of edible shellfish, and the occurrence of non-native species, as well as changes in species composition in the Channel and Celtic Seas likely to have been induced by warmer waters (Benjamins 2010). Intertidal sediment, such as mudflats and saltmarshes, is impacted by historical land claim from the sea and the construction of coastal defences and other structures which cause widespread habitat loss. These actions have particularly affected England. In the southern North Sea and Eastern Channel, the spread of non-native species, such as common cord-grass (*Spartina anglica*), has led to changes to Saltmarshes and mudflats. Although water quality levels have improved overall, there are still some small inshore areas (particularly within the North Sea and Irish Sea) where pollution and nutrient enrichment are a problem. Beach litter levels remain high and have been increasing in almost all areas except the eastern English Channel. The pressure on this habitat has increased over the last 10 years.

Large areas of subtidal sediments in most areas have been adversely affected by mobile fishing gear, such as bottom trawls and dredges, with less severe impacts in the Eastern Channel. Locally, extraction of aggregates has altered small areas of the seabed in the Eastern Channel, southern North Sea, Bristol Channel and Irish Sea. There is also pressure from wind farm developments, particularly on shallow sandbanks, and this is likely to increase in the future. Some estuaries and subtidal coastal habitats along the south coast and in the Irish Sea continue to experience nutrient enrichment and hazardous substances pollution.

Over the past two decades there has been a large increase in phytoplankton biomass in offshore waters, large changes (a 'regime shift') in the plankton community, particularly in the North Sea, and in the seasonal occurrence of phytoplankton taxa; and since the mid-1980s there has been an increase in the abundance of planktonic larvae of benthic animals in the North Sea (Reid & Edwards 2010). It is likely that warming sea temperatures, as well as fishing pressure, have driven these changes.

There have been improvements in diversity and overall abundance of demersal (bottom-dwelling) fish populations in the last five years (Pinnegar *et al.* 2010). However, demersal fish populations are severely depleted compared with 50 or 100 years ago, especially in the southern North Sea, the Western Channel and Celtic Sea, and there has been a long-term trend of overexploitation impacting fish communities as a whole. The situation for most estuarine and marine fish communities seems to have improved recently, but certain vulnerable fish have continued to decline, including sharks, rays and skates, and transitional/diadromous species that move between fresh and salt water, such as the European eel and sturgeon.

Commercial fisheries continue to exert a significant pressure on target and non-target fish populations, but there are improvements in the proportion of stocks being harvested sustainably. In the North Sea and eastern Channel the total fishing effort (kW days) of the international fishing fleets has declined by around 27% since 2002. In contrast, fishing effort in the western Channel appears to have increased since 2000 (UKMMAS 2010) although there has been a steady decline in the number of UK vessels operating out of ports in the South West. Climate change is also beginning to have a detectable impact on fish populations, with marked changes in distribution, the timing of migration, overall reproductive output (recruitment) and growth rates.

Populations of charismatic species are often highly valued (e.g. to the local tourist industry). Although harbour seal (*Phoca vitulina*) populations in England are very small, pressure on these individuals is considered significant (Duck *et al.* 2010). Abundances of cetacean populations are more difficult to assess, and although it appears that the five most abundant species have a favourable conservation status assessment, the status of others is largely unknown (Pinn *et al.* 2010).

Seabird and waterbird populations have increased in size over the last century as a direct result of increased protection from hunting and persecution (Mitchell 2010). Generally seabird populations are stable, except in the eastern English Channel where there has been a decline in numbers of breeding common tern (*Sterna hirundo*) due to natural causes (i.e. predation and storm events). The status of waterbirds has been improving since the mid-1970s, except in the Irish Sea where populations are moving east, away from traditional sites. The reasons for this change are unknown, but may be due to climate change.

17.4.8.2 Ecosystem services

Marine habitats and their diversity of organisms provide a wide range of ecosystem goods, services and benefits of significant value, which are described in more detail in Section 12.3.

Regulating services. Humans use rivers, estuaries and coastal water for direct and indirect disposal of various types of waste materials. Marine ecosystems that receive human waste materials are therefore providing a waste breakdown and detoxification service. The deleterious effects of recently introduced and less well-studied environmental contaminants and chemicals such as nanoparticles and pharmaceuticals which pass through sewage treatment plants is of concern, and the capacity of ecosystems to break down and detoxify these products is largely unknown (Celiz *et al.* 2009; Readman 2006). Localised problems of eutrophication occur in some estuaries and coastal waters in the east, south and North West, where nutrient enrichment derives from urban wastewater and agricultural runoff, such as fertilisers, manures and slurries.

The chemical composition of the atmosphere and ocean is maintained through a series of biogeochemical processes regulated by marine living organisms. The maintenance of a healthy, habitable planet is dependent on processes such as the regulation of the volatile organic halides, ozone, oxygen and dimethyl sulphide, and the exchange and regulation of carbon by marine organisms. For example, marine organisms play a significant role in climate control through their regulation of carbon fluxes, by acting as a reserve or sink for carbon dioxide in living tissue and by facilitating burial of carbon in seabed sediments. Of all the carbon dioxide captured in the world by photosynthesis and stored as living or dead material of biological origin, over half (55%) is captured by marine living organisms (Nellemann *et al.* 2009). However, there is no readily available data for England that quantifies total living biomass in marine and estuarine sediments and the water column, or the total amount of non-living sequestered carbon in marine ecosystems, or the role of coastal and shelf marine organisms in sequestering carbon further offshore into deeper water and sediments. Fowler *et al.* (2008) have estimated that in England energy related activity overall contributes to about 80% of greenhouse gas emissions, with agriculture and land use change contributing about two thirds of the remainder.

Living marine flora and fauna can play a valuable role in the defence of coastal regions by dampening environmental disturbances (Beaumont *et al.* 2007, 2008). A diverse range of species in England bind and stabilise sediments and create natural sea defences, for example biogenic reefs, seagrass beds, mudflats and salt marshes.

Provisioning services. Provisioning services include finfish and shellfish stocks for consumption both from wild capture and aquaculture; fishmeal and fish oil as inputs for aquaculture and food supplements; algae and seaweed as inputs into pharmaceuticals and biofuels, and bait used during sea angling. Fisheries are an important socioeconomic activity in South West England, providing employment for fishermen in aquaculture farms and in fish processing and associated industries.

Landings of fish for England and Wales are divided into three separate fisheries statistics categories: 1) demersal fish species which live on or near the sea bed including cod (*Gadus callarias*), haddock (*Melanogrammus aeglefinus*), plaice (*Pleuronectes platessa*), whiting (*Merlangius merlangus*), pollack (*Pollachius pollachius*), and sole (*Solea solea*); 2) pelagic fish species, such as herring (*Clupea harengus*) and mackerel (*Scomber scombrus*), which are typically found in mid and upper waters; and 3) shellfish including scallops (*Pecten* species), oysters (*Ostrea* species), mussels (*Mytilus edulis*), cockles (*Cerastoderma edule*), octopus (*Octopus vulgaris*), squid (*Loligo subulata*), cuttlefish (*Sepia officinalis*), prawns, crabs, and lobsters. Since 1956 there has been a decline in landings of demersal finfish, pelagic landings have shown instability, whilst shellfish landings have increased and the value of demersal fish and shellfish landings has increased (**Figure 17.17**).

The trends in demersal and pelagic finfish landings can be attributed to a number of factors including declining fish stocks due to fishing and environmental change; catch quotas; restrictions on the number of days allowed at sea; a shift to shellfish harvesting; and latterly decommissioning schemes that have seen reductions in the size of the overall fishing fleet. The increase in scallop fishing is partly due to stringent quotas being placed on demersal and pelagic fish

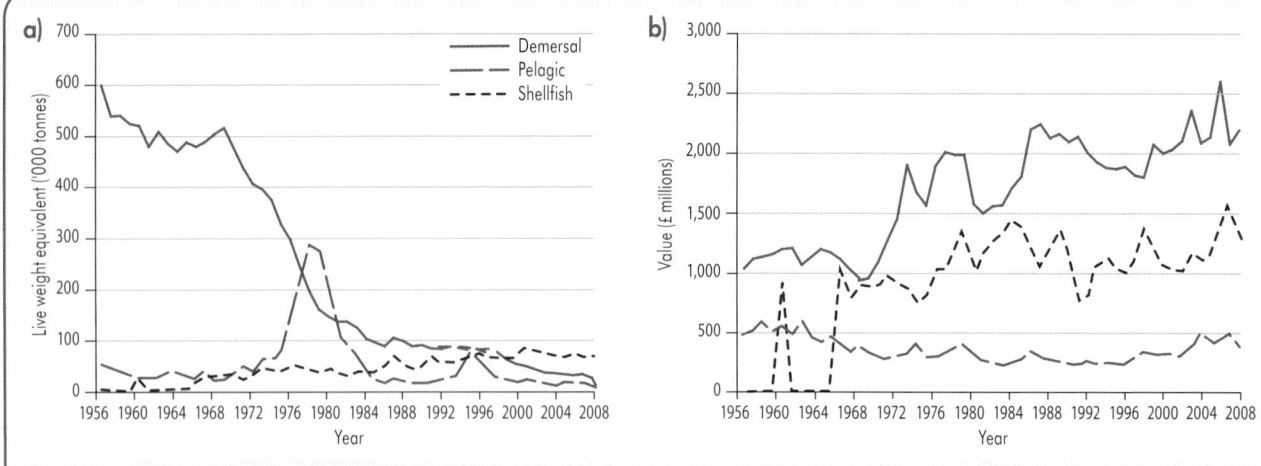

Figure 17.17 Landings into England and Wales by UK and foreign vessels from 1956 to 2008 by a) live weight equivalent and b) value of three categories of landings: demersal, pelagic and shellfish. Values were adjusted to 2008 prices using the Retail Price Index. Source: extracted from Marine Management Organisation (MMO 2010).

species, but also the ease by which boats fitted for demersal trawling can be converted to activities such as scallop dredging. In addition, most shellfish species are not under quota restrictions.

Wild fish capture for food generates employment both for fishermen and in secondary services associated with fishing (MMO 2010). In 1960 there were 12,712 regular fishermen; by 2009 this number had fallen to 4,768 (**Figure 17.18**). In 2009 the English fishing fleet consisted of 3,169 vessels with the number of small vessels greatly exceeding that of larger vessels, although the catching power of the latter fleet (indicated by engine power) is considerably greater (**Table 17.12**).

Much aquaculture data is reported for England and Wales and cannot be disaggregated: in 2008 there were 518 registered fish and shellfish farms, of which 197 were trout and other finfish farms (marine and freshwater fish are not separated) and 128 shellfish farms; the remainder were coarse fish farms (Shellfish News reports, CEFAS 2008, 2009). Shellfish farm production has been gradually

rising (Figure 12.11, Section 12.3.1.1). A total of 3,905 tonnes of shellfish worth £4.5 million were produced by English aquaculture in 2007, comprising mainly mussels with small quantities of Pacific oyster (*Crassostrea gigas*) and native oyster (*Ostrea edulis*), and very small quantities of clam and cockle (Saunders 2010).

Shellfish aquaculture is often considered relatively sustainable, especially where spat collection results as a consequence of natural settlement (as is the case of many mussel farms) and where harvesting is based on hand collection or raking. Where bottom cultivation is used and harvesting (including spat collection) is undertaken by dredging (e.g. for mussels and oysters) there are concerns regarding the physical damage and environmental impact harvesting could cause. Other concerns over shellfish aquaculture include localised depletion of phytoplankton where overstocking has occurred and the introduction of non-indigenous species.

Large amounts of bait worms are dug from intertidal sediments each year, both commercially and for personal use, to support recreational sea angling, but little of this activity is recorded or declared.

Cultural services. As an island nation, the English population has a strong affinity for the sea, and much of our heritage is linked to maritime activities. Reminders of this maritime heritage are still in existence today (e.g. fishing villages, fish and chips, the navy, lighthouses, and museums and literature on smuggling and sea adventures). In a UK-wide poll undertaken by The Wildlife Trusts in 2007, 78% of respondents stated that the UK's seas are important to their personal quality of life (The Wildlife Trusts 2007).

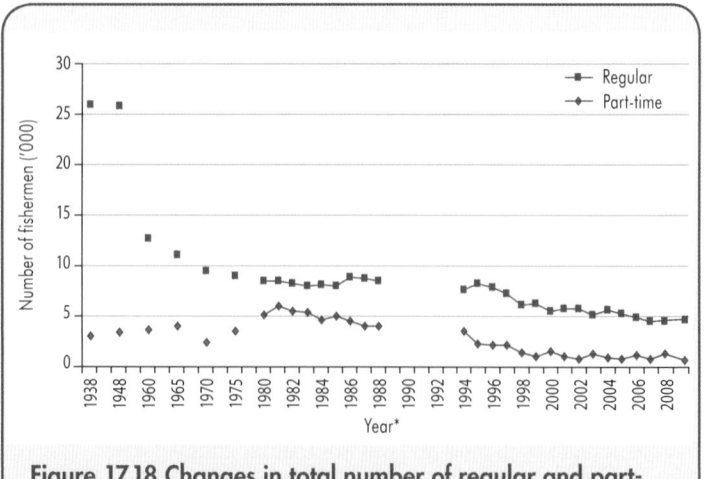

Figure 17.18 Changes in total number of regular and part-time fishermen in England. Data not collected from 1989 to 1993. From 1966 these figures exclude 'hobby' fishermen, i.e. fishermen who do not fish commercially. Source: data extracted from MMO (2010) *1987 includes 1986 figures for Newlyn and Plymouth.

Table 17.12 Fleet capacity in England in 2009. Source: data extracted from MMO (2010).

Length of vessel	Number of vessels	Capacity (gross tonnage)	Engine power (kW)
Greater than 10 m	570	53,253	169,952
Less than 10 m	2,599	9,142	141,759

Even though much of the marine environment is hidden from view, it has been a source of artistic inspiration over the centuries, leading to a wealth of literature, works of art and schools of artists (e.g. The Newlyn and St. Ives Schools), as well as underwater film documentaries and children's cartoons (e.g. Popeye, Captain Pugwash, Spongebob Square Pants).

The marine environment presents a number of educational opportunities; school trips to the beach and/or aquaria are common, particularly in coastal communities, but people living some distance away from the coast are also able to learn about marine life through visits to aquaria and sea-life centres throughout England (e.g. Birmingham and Alton Towers). There is significant investment in marine research in both the public and private sectors, but the proportion of research that is focused entirely on UK seas, let alone the English component, is unknown.

Advancements in understanding the marine environment have led to a corresponding increase in interest amongst the public for underwater heritage resources (Kaoru & Hoagland 1994) and wider marine issues. To date, no assessment of the heritage value of the marine environment in UK or English waters has been undertaken, but a growing number of marine sites are receiving protected status because of their historical importance.

Currently protection of the marine environment falls short of that on land. For example, only two Special Protection Areas designated under the Birds Directive (1979) are entirely marine (the Outer Thames Estuary and Liverpool Bay). Although there are a small number of ASSIs/SSSIs below the low water mark, for example The Wash and Morecombe Bay, many coastal ASSIs/SSSIs do not offer protection to subtidal marine life (JNCC 2010a). The sea around Lundy Island was designated as England's first, and currently only, Marine Conservation Zone in January 2010, which includes a no-take zone of 3.3 km² in which all fishing is prohibited.

Not all protected areas are protected by statutory designations. The Royal Society for the Protection of Birds (RSPB), for example, owns a number of reserves around the coast which provide protection for important seabird colonies (e.g. Hayle estuary, Arne, Bempton Cliffs); the Wildlife Trusts also own a number of coastal nature reserves. Neither of these organisations has dedicated marine reserves, however, largely because of the inability to purchase the seabed and designate it as a reserve. Protection within the marine environment around the UK will see dramatic change in the near future, as the Marine and Coastal Access Act (2009) requires the designation by 2012 of an ecologically coherent network of Marine Conservation Zones. More details of the legislative changes affecting the UK are given in Section 12.5.1.

The most obvious cultural benefit that society receives from the marine environment is the opportunity for leisure and recreational activities. The England Leisure Visits 2005 Survey (Natural England 2005b) reports 0.07 billion leisure visits (trips occurring within one day including, for example, dog walking but also including tourism visits of more than 3 hours) to the coast during that year: approximately 2% of all England leisure visits. In 2005, 37% of the adult population

had visited the seaside coast and 62% had visited a seaside city or town. Expenditure at the coast was £1.4 billion and in seaside cities and towns was £4.7 billion, which comprised approximately 2% and 5% respectively of total spend on leisure trips. The most popular activities were walking and visiting the beach (**Table 17.13**). Natural England, Defra and the Forestry Commission are undertaking a new survey called Monitor of Engagement with the Natural Environment (MENE) to provide baseline and trend data on how people use the natural environment in England.

It is difficult to account for the contribution of the marine environment to these figures as there is little quantitative documentation, but anecdotal evidence suggests that wildlife-watching, including rockpooling, is an increasingly popular activity at the coast (Crabtree et al. 2005).

Recreational sea angling, however, is a popular activity and is comparatively well quantified in terms of number of participants, their expenditure and the jobs associated with this leisure industry. In 2003, 1.1 million households in England and Wales contained one or more members who partook in sea angling and the mean number of sea angling days per year was 11.3 (Defra figures in Crabtree et al. 2005). The industry was estimated to have a value of £538 million per year and to support 18,889 jobs (FTE). Estimates from the South West alone (Invest in Fish South West 2005) suggest that 240,000 residents participate in sea angling, plus an additional 750,000 angling days by visitors. The value of the industry is estimated at £165 million and supports more than 3,000 jobs. All of these studies found that the majority of anglers fished within 80 km of their homes. Visiting anglers make a considerable contribution to the total angling

Table 17.13 Main leisure activities. Source: reproduced from Natural England (2006).

Leisure activities	Seaside coast (%)	Seaside town/city (%)
Walk, ramble	33	19
Visit beach, sunbathe, paddle in the sea	23	12
Visit friends, relatives at their home	8	9
To eat or drink out	7	17
Hobby or special interest	4	10
Take part in sports or active pursuits – indoor, outdoor field, water	4	7
Drive, sightsee, picnic, pleasure boating	4	4
To go shopping (not food and not regular)	3	8
Visit leisure attraction, place of interest, special event/exhibition	3	2
For entertainment (e.g. cinema, theatre, club)	2	5
To take part in informal sports, games, relaxation and well-being	2	3
Swimming	2	2
Cycling, mountain biking	2	-
Visit park or garden	1	1
Watching live sport or attending a live event (not on TV)	1	1

expenditure. Crabtree *et al.* (2005) estimated this as £192 million per year or 35% of the total for 2002, which equates to 1% of all tourism spend in 2002 for England and Wales (UKTS 2002).

Supporting services. The essential supporting services, such as nutrient cycling and provision of biologically mediated habitats, are not well quantified for UK or English waters and are, therefore, described in more detail in Section 12.3.4. Marine microbial organisms in the water column and seabed habitats play a key role in cycling storage and supply of nutrients, such as carbon, nitrogen, phosphorus, silicon and iron, which are essential for the maintenance, growth and production of marine organisms. This supporting service underpins all of the other marine ecosystem services and benefits they provide. Microbial processing of nutrients in the sediment is mediated by the activity of invertebrates that disturb and irrigate the sediment.

Many marine organisms provide structured space or living habitat for other organisms through their normal growth; for example, reef-forming invertebrates, meadow-forming seagrass beds, marine algae forests and networks of burrows and holes in the sediment (Beaumont *et al.* 2007). These biogenic marine habitats can provide essential feeding, breeding and nursery space for other plants and animals, which can be particularly important for the continued recruitment of commercial and/or subsistence fish and shellfish species. Such habitat can provide a refuge for plants and animals, including surfaces for feeding and hiding places from predators. Living habitat plays a critical role in species interactions and regulation of population dynamics, and is a prerequisite for the provision of many goods and services. Specific examples of living habitat include kelp and seagrass beds, maerl grounds (calcified red seaweed), mussel patches and coldwater coral reefs. These living habitats, especially reefs, are vulnerable to damage from seabed fishing with trawl nets and dredging fishing gears. Shallow water and intertidal living habitats are vulnerable to invasive macroalgae species (Milneur *et al.* 2008) as well as smothering by opportunistic algae such as *Ulva* species, particularly in nutrient-enriched areas (Fletcher 1996). At a more local level they can be damaged by boat anchoring, propeller scarring and channel dredging.

Wild species. Marine flagship species occurring in English waters are mainly the large megafauna, such as turtles, seals and cetaceans (whales, dolphins and porpoises), as well as smaller species such as seabirds and seahorses. Flagship habitats include saltmarsh, seagrass beds and maerl beds (Hiscock *et al.* 2005). Some smaller invertebrate species can also be flagship species. For example, closure to benthic trawls and scallop dredging in an area of 60 km² of Lyme Bay in south-west England in 2008 was prompted by the need to protect marine biodiversity, including the fragile reefs of the pink sea fan (*Eunicella verrucosa*; Rees *et al.* 2010).

The significance of flagship species is that their importance goes beyond their ecological function, being related primarily to their appeal to the wider public. For example, relatively small populations (in some cases fewer than 10 individuals) of the harbour seal on the south and west coasts of England may not have a huge ecological impact, yet the populations are well known to locals and

popular with tourists, thus providing a significant boost to the local economy.

On a larger scale, the economic benefits of well-established populations of flagship species are derived from a wide range of activities linked to their presence, including diving and snorkelling, rockpooling, boat trips (i.e. whale- and dolphin-watching, shark-spotting and visits to seal colonies) and aquarium visits. Seabirds are also hugely popular and a major factor in encouraging wildlife tourism. Spectacular seabird 'cities' and particular species such as the Atlantic puffin (*Fratercula arctica*) draw many visitors, providing an important source of income for local economies (RSPB 2010a, b; Mitchell 2010).

17.5 Ecosystem Services

17.5.1 Supporting Services

Supporting services provide the underpinnings of all other ecosystem services through the functions of soil formation, primary production, decomposition and nutrient and water cycling (EASAC 2009). The provision of supporting services is dependent on a myriad of complex biological, chemical and physical processes and is further influenced by anthropogenic environmental pressures.

The timescales at which supporting services operate range from short-term (days to months in the case of decomposition) to long-term (decades to millennia in the case of soil formation). Therefore, the repercussions of anthropogenic environmental pressures might not be immediately observed in the supporting system of interest. Since supporting services provide the foundational processes that underpin other ecosystem services, human-induced pressures might not be readily apparent in the supporting services themselves; rather, they might manifest themselves in changes to linked provisioning or regulating services.

Despite the above, our understanding of the mechanisms by which ecological interactions influence ecosystem processes and the delivery of supporting services is limited, as is our knowledge of their contribution relative to abiotic factors as drivers of supporting services at the landscape scale (Bardgett & Wardle 2010).

17.5.1.1 Soil formation

Measured and modelled rates of soil formation vary widely, but typically are in the range of 0.04–0.08 mm/yr or less than 1 cm per century (EASAC 2009). However, considerable uncertainty exists around the details of soil formation processes. Soil erosion is a natural process that is commonly exacerbated by land use. Wilkinson and McElroy (2007) estimated the global mean natural erosion rate over the past 542 million years to be 0.4 t/ha/yr, with a peak of 1.4 t/ha/yr in the Tertiary period. Rates of soil loss can be much higher than soil formation rates. Estimates of erosion rates in England are scant, however, Verheijen *et al.* (2009) cite erosion rates of 0.02 to 1.27 t/ha/yr for non-peaty soils. Agricultural practices have the potential to significantly increase erosion rates; for example, soil loss due to tillage erosion can be as high as 10 t/ha/yr (Verheijen *et al.* 2009).

A wide range of soil-forming factors interacting over various spatial and temporal scales has resulted in the diversity of soil types in England (Figure 13.2, Section 13.2.1). Luvisols, cambisols and gleysols dominate much of England due to its lowland topography. These mineral soils with lower organic carbon content support most of England's agricultural production. The less extensive upland soils of England have surface horizons rich in organic matter and thus harbour a disproportionately large part of the country's carbon.

Data on the status and trends of England's soils have received little attention, however, three issues are particularly relevant: 1) the loss of soil to urbanisation, 2) the impact of agricultural activity on soil and 3) loss of peat soils (histosols), due to their importance as a carbon sink. The net rate of conversion of agricultural land to built development is estimated at 5,000 ha/yr (DCLG no date), a practice which destroys or seals the soil, effectively halting most soil formation. A range of agricultural activities influence soil formation, including ploughing, fertilising, draining and grazing, which can cumulatively change the properties of soil over decadal timescales. This is particularly the case where it results in nutrient enrichment and related reductions of soil carbon. Peatland carbon stocks in England have only been estimated to 1 m depth, giving 296 Mt C (Bradley *et al.* 2005), which places England below Scotland and Wales in terms of total carbon stocks. The current rate of carbon fixation for English peatland is difficult to determine, but is likely between 0.27 Mt C/yr and 0.7 Mt C/yr for peatlands in good condition (Cannell *et al.* 1999). Losses due to land management practices (draining, agriculture and peat cutting) have been estimated at 1 Mt C/yr and fluvial losses at 1 Mt C/yr (Cannell *et al.* 1999).

17.5.1.2 Nutrient cycling

The severity of changes in nutrient cycling varies, but the predominant problems associated with semi-natural terrestrial, freshwater and marine habitats relate to nutrient enrichment. Increased nutrient levels can influence the composition and diversity of plant communities and soil biota, with consequences for a range of ecosystem services via mechanisms that are poorly understood. Whilst nutrient cycling data for the various UK habitats are sparse, the Countryside Survey (2009), the UK Environmental Change Network (ECN) and RoTAP (2011) have provided information on key trends. Nitrogen and phosphorus are generally the most significant nutrients limiting ecosystem productivity. However, high levels of anthropogenic enhancement of these two elements can result in significant disruption of ecosystem processes, with consequent effects on a range of ecosystem services.

Nitrogen: Nitrogen mineralisation occurs as soil microbes break down organic nitrogen and convert it into inorganic forms. It is a critical process in many habitats as it determines the availability of nitrogen for primary production. Significant differences in nitrogen amounts and rates of mineralisation in topsoils (0–15 cm) of England's terrestrial habitats relate generally to the total amount of organic matter present and the intensity of agricultural improvement (Emmett *et al.* 2010; Figure 13.6, Section 13.3.1.1).

Atmospheric nitrogen deposition has significantly enriched England's habitats since 1960 and declines in nitrogen deposition have not been observed during the period 1984–2005, despite declines in oxidised (50%) and reduced (24%) nitrogen emissions (RoTAP 2011). United Kingdom NEA Broad Habitats are, therefore, still subject to nitrogen deposition and remain at risk of damage. Most of England's habitats are nitrogen limited and it is possible that a moderate proportion of anthropogenic nitrogen will be sequestered in soil organic matter (Phoenix *et al.* 2004), thereby moderating the negative impacts of nitrogen deposition (Aber *et al.* 1989). Data from the Environmental Change Network between 1993 and 2007 (Morecroft *et al.* 2009) suggest that nitrogen is being retained within the terrestrial system or lost as nitrogen gas. Findings of the Countryside Survey support the idea that nitrogen enrichment has increased plant production leading to carbon fixation and its transfer to soil (Emmett *et al.* 2010).

Of importance to aquatic nitrogen cycling is the trend of declining nitrate concentrations in rivers over the last 10 years. In 2000, most river segments in the Midlands and the East of England exceeded 30 mg nitrate per litre (this limit roughly corresponds with a 95 percentile limit of 50 mg/l used in the EC Nitrates Directive and the EC Drinking Water Directive). The proportion of river segments exceeding this threshold has declined since 2000 from 90% to 60% and from 50% to 40% in the Anglian and Midlands regions respectively (Figure 13.7 (a), Section 13.3.1.1). The proportion of rivers in the West of England exceeding 30 mg nitrate per litre is relatively low (10–20%) and has remained constant (Environment Agency 2008). The Irish Sea has been found to contain raised levels of anthropogenic nitrogen (Gowen *et al.* 2008) with a trend of increasing nitrate concentrations from 1960 to 1980, followed by a decline in the 1990s (Evans *et al.* 2003).

Phosphorus: Phosphorus has been reported to be accumulating globally at rates between three and 10 times higher than during the industrial era due largely to agricultural activity (Lavelle *et al.* 2005). However, the UK Countryside Survey (Emmett *et al.* 2010) reported that the amount of soil phosphorus available to plants has decreased from 1998 to 2007. The average decline across all English habitats is about 16%, with some habitats exhibiting more pronounced declines (e.g. heathland and Acid Grassland) than others (e.g. agricultural habitats). The cause of this general decline has been linked to increasing prices of phosphorus fertiliser and so decreased usage (Cordell *et al.* 2009) and the steady decline in livestock numbers (Defra 2009a). Despite reductions in fertiliser use and livestock numbers, the Countryside Survey (2009) was cautious about attributing the decline in soil phosphorus to agriculture.

Environment Agency (2008) data suggest a similar trend between 1990 and 2008 of decreasing phosphate concentrations in rivers in arable regions of England and Wales (Figure 13.7 (b), Section 13.3.1.1). The observed declines are consistent with reductions in soils, yet it is unclear whether the two are causally linked. Other sources of phosphorus are significant, for example the water industry (White & Hammond 2009). Data from the Countryside Survey have identified a clear link between changes in riparian vegetation, lower phosphorus concentrations, and an improvement in headwater quality (Dunbar *et al.* 2010). In the Irish Sea there is evidence of increased phosphate concentrations during the period 1960–1980, also followed by a decline in the 1990s that paralleled observed trends in rivers that feed into the Irish Sea (Evans *et al.* 2003).

Soil acidity and trace elements: The Countryside Survey revealed that the mean pH of surface soils increased in habitats across England from 1979 to 2007 (Countryside Survey 2009; Emmett *et al.* 2010). Similar results have been observed by various soil monitoring programmes (Morecroft *et al.* 2009; Kirk *et al.* 2010; RoTAP 2011). Significant declines in soil solution sulphate concentrations have also been detected in surface soils (i.e. in the surface A horizon) of some ECN upland sites, although no trends were apparent for most sites. Despite the lack of evidence for declining soil sulphate concentrations within the ECN data, widespread increases in soil pH have been associated with reductions in habitats exceeding critical loads of acidity, which fell from 71% to 58% from 1996 to 2006, a trend that is projected to continue (RoTAP 2011). These trends seem likely to be related to the increased rainfall pH as a result of emission controls in the mid-1970s (Morecroft *et al.* 2009).

Soil concentrations of trace elements are related to parent material and also to soil pH. Most trace elements become more available to plants and microbes in neutral or slightly acid soils, although others (e.g. molybdenum) become more available in alkaline soils. In England, boron, copper and zinc can be deficient within particular soil types. With acid sulphate deposition, sulphur nutrition in UK crops was adequate. However, the recent decline in sulphur deposition, and the development of high yielding crop varieties, has meant that it is now necessary to add sulphur fertiliser to UK soils (Zhao *et al.* 2002). Evidence from the British Survey of Fertiliser Practice reports (Defra 2009b) indicate that use of sulphur fertiliser has increased in England from 1998 to 2009 for cereal crops and oilseed rape, but has remained largely static for grassland management.

17.5.1.3 The water cycle

The water cycle is most appropriately considered with respect to major water fluxes (rainfall, evapotranspiration,

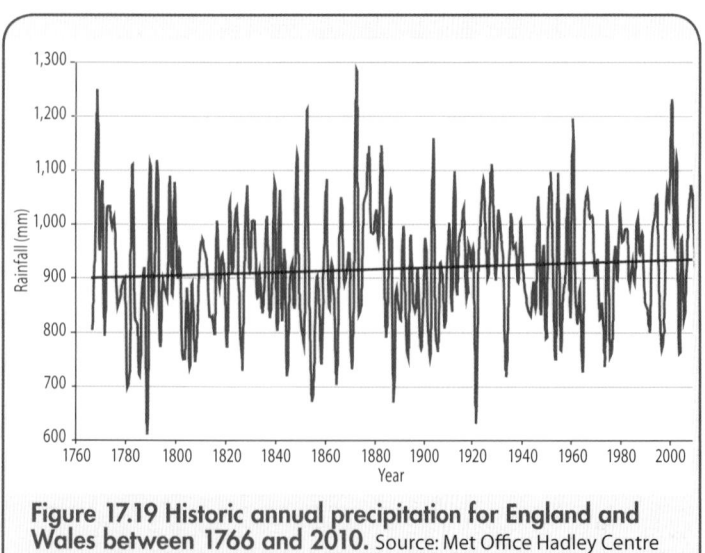

Figure 17.19 Historic annual precipitation for England and Wales between 1766 and 2010. Source: Met Office Hadley Centre Observation Data (2011).

river-flow) and major water storages (soil, groundwater, lakes) that combine to determine the availability of water in time and space. Pathways that move water between the major storages are also important, as is water quality, because poor chemical and/or microbiological quality can render the water effectively unavailable for supporting some services.

Spatial variation in average rainfall across England is high: annual totals can exceed 3,000 mm in parts of the North West and South West, whilst totals in the driest parts of lowland England can be an order of magnitude less (Section 17.2.2).

National rainfall assessments for England and Wales are available back to 1766; however, no significant trend is apparent (Alexander & Jones 2001; **Figure 17.19**).

The UK Met Office Rainfall and Evaporation Calculation System (MORECS) provides assessments of potential and actual evaporative losses for 40 km squares throughout Great Britain and indicates that over 40% of rainfall is lost to evaporation and in the driest parts of the English Lowlands this rises to nearly 80% (Hough & Jones 1997).

River flows integrate precipitation and evaporation processes. Measured runoff represents the most appropriate variable upon which to assess overall water resources; however, it must be noted that river flows in England are profoundly affected by abstractions and river regulation. Trend analysis of annual runoff over the period 1973–2002 at the UK Benchmark Catchments indicates predominantly non-significant increases in runoff (Hannaford & Marsh 2008) for most monitored catchments in England, with a few exceptions in the South West and North West, although the recent past has been characterised by notable year-on-year variability (Hannaford & Marsh 2006). Low flows (30-day minima) at the Benchmark Catchments over the period 1973–2002 indicate little evidence of decrease in low flows across the UK (Hannaford & Marsh 2006).

Groundwater storage provides a significant component of water resources used in England and aquifers are generally replenished by winter rainfall. The longest continuous record of groundwater level in the England dates back to 1838 at Chilgrove in West Sussex. A drought index, representing cumulative departures from mean monthly levels, shows no consistent trends over this period, but reveals distinct patterns of change or quiescence at decadal scales. Trends at decadal timescales most often result from changes in historical abstraction.

Water quality is considered in detail under regulating services (Chapter 14, Section 9); however, a few key trends are mentioned here. One important aspect of water quality with respect to the supporting services (i.e. water cycle and nutrient cycling) involves the trophic status and biodiversity of waters. As noted above, two key chemical elements affecting the trophic status are nitrogen and phosphorus. Evidence of long-term trends in river and lake phosphorus concentrations from Dorset generally indicate a decline in recent years, mainly as a result of policy initiatives to reduce phosphorus fluxes from sewage outfalls in response to the EU Urban Wastewater Directive (Bowes *et al.* 2009). There is also widespread evidence of ongoing recovery of UK freshwaters from the effects of acidification, with reductions in acidity and labile aluminium (RoTAP 2009). For example, trends in rainfall acidity across the UK show significant declines over the monitoring period and for most of the country, with more polluted regions such as eastern England improving dramatically.

17.5.1.4 Primary production

Primary production typically refers to the fixation of atmospheric and/or aquatic carbon dioxide. Only a proportion of fixed carbon dioxide is retained, whilst the rest is lost through respiration. The overall amount of organic carbon fixed is described as gross primary production (GPP), whilst the amount retained after respiration is defined as net primary production (NPP). Net primary production provides the foundation of food and timber harvesting in managed systems, food webs in semi-natural and natural ecosystems, and underpins climate regulation by removing carbon dioxide from the atmosphere.

Primary production data in England are limited as direct measurements are only possible at local scales. Currently there are significant limitations to estimates of fixed carbon below-ground in terrestrial systems, the magnitude of organic and inorganic carbon fluxes to surface waters and the response functions to different climate, soil, ecological and management variables. These issues limit our ability to upscale primary production estimates in both time and space.

Various approaches have been employed to bypass these issues and provide estimates of primary production at a range of scales from plot to catchment, to regional and national levels. These include the use of net ecosystem exchange of carbon dioxide (NEE), net ecosystem productivity (NEP), plant standing biomass or biomass increments, crop, herbage and timber yields (e.g. Jenkinson *et al.* 1994), carbon accumulation rates and remotely sensed absorption by plants and algae. Each approach involves many assumptions and various limitations (Lovett *et al.* 2006). Modelling approaches that incorporate field and remotely collected data provide a valuable tool to upscale

and integrate measurements, and can also be used to forecast changes under different climate, pollution and management scenarios. For example, the JULES model (The Joint UK Land Environment Simulator) is a community tool that can produce a range of outputs of which one is primary production (**Figure 17.20**). However, a great deal of testing and development of the JULES model is required before its outputs can be used with any confidence.

In forests, annual stem increment data plus litter fall, and assumptions for below-ground root production, are often used in combination with remotely sensed plant biomass data to derive net primary production values. Current forestry production rates in the UK have recently been estimated to be responsible for removing 15 Mt carbon dioxide from the atmosphere every year with a total stock of carbon of 790 Mt C in trees and forest soils (Read *et al.* 2009; Chapter 8; Chapter 17.4.4; Chapter 12.4.1).

Plymouth Marine Laboratory (PML) produce estimates of net primary production for the seas around the UK. These models do not account for the effects of suspended particulate matter (notably in the Thames estuary, southern North Sea and Bristol Channel) nor for coloured dissolved organic matter (i.e. the optically measurable component of the dissolved organic matter in water) from riverine sources (such as in Liverpool Bay). In these areas, primary production is likely to be overestimated. Work at PML is aiming to improve these coastal estimates.

In freshwaters, primary production is estimated from the surrogate phytoplankton chlorophyll *a* concentration. Primary productivity in most freshwaters systems was thought to be largely phosphorus limited, but there is now strong evidence that nitrogen limitation and nitrogen and phosphorus co-limitation is widespread, especially in UK upland environments (Maberly *et al.* 2002). Long-term historical trends of 36 years are available for four lakes in the Lake District and there is some evidence of suppression of chlorophyll *a* concentration with higher rainfall in small lakes with shorter residence times, but on the whole there

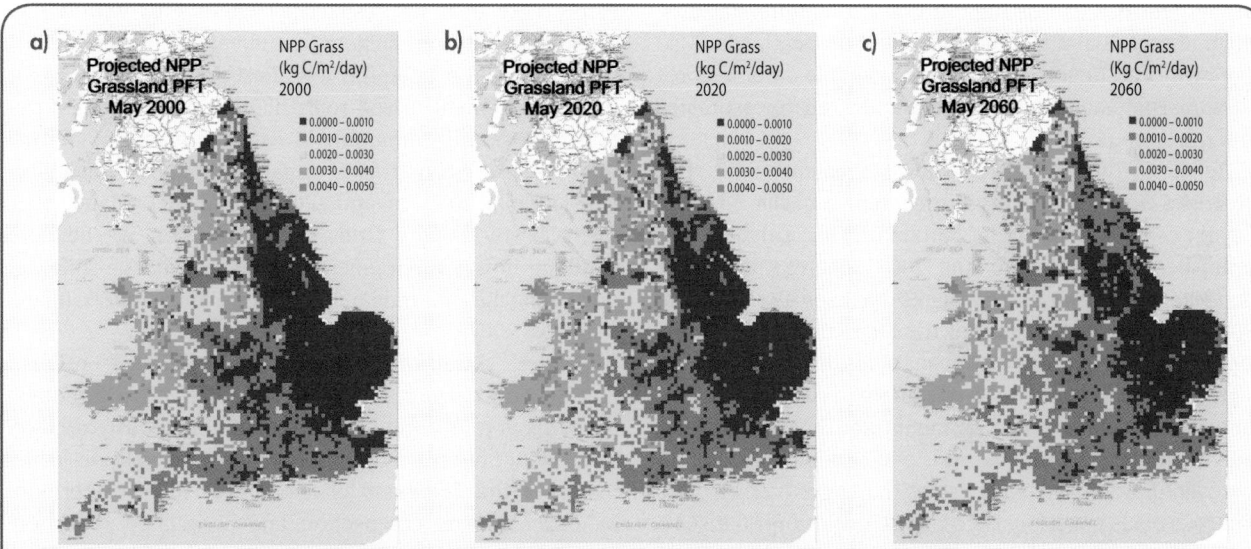

Figure 17.20 Forecast of primary production for 2020 (b) and 2060 (c), compared to 2000 (a), for grassland using the JULES Land-atmosphere model. Note: these are modelled results and subject to a range of associated uncertainties. NPP = net primary production; PFT = Plant Functional Type. Source: D Cooper, pers. comm. (2010); data © NERC (CEH).

was no overall trend in chlorophyll *a* concentrations (George *et al.* 2004).

17.5.2 Regulating Services

Regulating services provide benefits obtained from ecosystems' regulation of ecological processes and are the largest group within the UK NEA typology. They can act as final ecosystem services or contribute significantly to final ecosystem services, whilst others are primary/intermediate ecosystem services. The regulating services include those ecological processes that influence water quality and quantity, pollination, climate, hazard severity and frequency, soil quality, noise, air quality and diseases and pests. Apart from climate regulation, direct markets for most regulating services do not exist, however methods are available to estimate their economic value to human societies.

17.5.2.1 Climate regulation

Ecosystems and their interactions with the biosphere regulate climate by controlling the fluxes of greenhouse gases (i.e. carbon dioxide, methane and nitrous oxide), aerosols, heat/energy, moisture and momentum (e.g. Bonan 2008). Ecosystems also regulate microclimate more directly by moderating temperature through the provision of shade and shelter. Photosynthesis and evapotranspiration are essential ecosystem processes that regulate carbon dioxide and water vapour, respectively, with evapotranspiration also having local cooling effects. Ecosystems also influence land surface albedo values (the proportion of incoming solar radiation that is reflected from the Earth's surface); a change in albedo can have a cooling or heating effect on the surface climate and may further affect precipitation.

Whilst it is estimated that almost 10 billion tonnes of carbon is stored in UK soils, particularly organic soils (Smith *et al.* 2007), the majority lies outside of England (Figure 14.1, Section 14.2.1). Soil carbon densities are greatest under semi-natural habitats, especially peatlands, and woodlands. Soil carbon densities are relatively low under agricultural land and Urban habitats that dominate much of England. Soil carbon densities can be high in Coastal Margins habitats, which are more abundant in England than peatlands. Also of relevance to England are the considerable carbon stores in the marine habitats, but there are few reliable estimates from the literature.

Because the cropland and settlement land use categories are net sources of greenhouse gases, England is a net ecological source of carbon dioxide although this diminished between 1990 and 2007, whereas the other countries in the UK are net sinks (Jackson *et al.* 2009a, 2009b). Nitrous oxide emissions from agricultural soils arise from nitrogen application, leaching of fertiliser and manure to ground and surface water, ploughing in of crop residues, atmospheric deposition of ammonia and nitrogen oxides, cultivation of highly organic soils and biological fixation in improved grass. These sources are the largest contributors to nitrous oxide emissions across the UK and contribute 64% of nitrous oxide emissions in England. Enclosed Farmland has the greatest nitrous oxide emissions whilst Woodlands and Mountains, Moorlands and Heaths contribute less than 5% to the total soil emissions (Sozanska *et al.* 2002).

The status and trends in climate regulation by habitat are summarised in Table 14.3, Section 14.2.1.

17.5.2.2 Hazard regulating services

Maintenance of the integrity of land surfaces. Rates of geomorphic change in England are modest and the integrity of land surfaces is rarely threatened; however, there are two significant exceptions. First, the beaches, dunes and saltmarshes of the coast are wasting assets whose capacity to protect hinterlands is declining, particularly in the south and east (Pye & French 1993). It is estimated that 17% of the UK coast is experiencing erosion. Thirty per cent of the eroding coastline occurs in England (Masselink & Russell 2008) and represents a significant loss of important habitat, including estuarine saltmarsh and dune systems, particularly in the south. The second threat occurs largely in uplands, and comprises landslides, debris flows and peat-slides, although much of England is not characterised by the steep slopes required for major landslides (Chapter 14).

Maintenance of soil cover. In the absence of human activity, most of the land surface would be covered by vegetation, resulting in minimal erosional threats to soil cover and therefore low suspended sediment inputs to rivers. Unfortunately, this is not the case in England. English uplands are commonly assessed as being in poor condition, with large areas of bare organic soils (McHugh *et al.* 2002), gullying in peatlands (Evans & Warburton 2006) and high sediment export (Holden *et al.* 2007). Whilst measures have been undertaken to improve upland condition (e.g. reseeding, blocking artificial drains, reduced grazing) their effectiveness is uncertain and their full effects may take years to be realised (Holden *et al.* 2007; Orr *et al.* 2008). In uplands, semi-natural grassland and coastal sand dunes there has been evidence of an increased exposure of subsoil due to footpath erosion and high grazing density.

On arable land, water, wind and tillage erosion have accelerated over the last half-century. However, quantification of these processes at regional or national scale remains a challenge. Wind erosion has been observed to be more common, especially where soils with a high organic content are subject to cultivation in areas with a high desiccation potential (e.g. East Anglia). Advances in the measurement of soil redistribution have revealed that tillage erosion is commonly of equal or higher magnitude than water erosion. This is of particular significance since considerable areas of agricultural land in England occur on modestly sloping lands. Tillage erosion is, therefore, resulting in the development of a heterogeneous soilscape on sloping agricultural land (Quine & Zhang 2002; Quine & Van Oost 2007).

Water retention, storage and delayed release. Landscape changes that promote water erosion, notably the reduction of vegetation cover, simultaneously promote lower water retention and more rapid water release, which increases the likelihood of flooding events. Furthermore, increases in soil compaction and associated reductions in soil infiltration on grasslands have been linked to high grazing intensity. In the uplands, changes in flood frequency have been attributed to the creation of rapid flow pathways such as grips to drain moorland (Longfield & Macklin 1999) in Yorkshire. Changes in flood frequency and magnitude have been analysed with respect to climate change, but a clear link has not been identified (Wilby *et al.* 2008). However, land management measures which reduce flood risk seem prudent against such a future scenario given current scientific uncertainties, yet these measures are often expensive and their effectiveness is uncertain.

Climate change trends. Climate change might lead to an intensification of the hydrological cycle and an increase in floods in many parts of the world. In England, increased winter precipitation could increase the risks of flooding events (Hulme & Dessai 2008). Considerable uncertainties still exist in projections of extreme events. Therefore, a greater emphasis must be placed on the climate models to be fit-for-purposes with particular regard to changes in the frequency and severity of extreme events.

17.5.2.3 Disease/pest regulation

The role of biodiversity in regulating diseases and pests. England has relatively few agricultural insect pests, the main group being aphids. Approximately 250 aphid species feed on agricultural and horticultural crops, causing significant damage and transmitting viruses including Barley Yellow Dwarf Virus (BYDV). Natural enemies, such as predators, parasitoids and pathogens, are key regulators of aphids and their exclusion can result in reduced crop yields. Other research indicates that natural enemy species diversity and abundance, habitat diversity and maintenance of arable field margins are all commonly associated with reduced pest and disease incidence. Whilst the evidence base from England is sparse, agri-environment schemes may have improved species and habitat diversity in some regions and thereby increased the regulation of pests and diseases.

Specific components of biodiversity may be responsible for the regulation of disease. For example, Lyme borreliosis (Lyme Disease) is caused by the bacterium *Borrelia burgdorferia*. The principal vector in the UK is the sheep tick (*Ixodes ricinus*), which also feeds on a range of wild vertebrates. The incidence of Lyme Disease has increased dramatically over the last decade. Deer numbers have been positively associated with the abundance of the tick vector, as deer are key reproductive hosts for ticks (Scharlemann *et al.* 2008).

Specific components of biodiversity may also act as a reservoir of disease, so providing 'an ecosystem disservice'. Bovine Tuberculosis (bTB) is caused by *Mycobacterium bovis* and has considerable economic and human health consequences. Infection rates have risen since the mid-1980s (Krebs *et al.* 1997) with human-to-human transmission being reported relatively recently (Evans *et al.* 2007). It is rare or absent in many cattle-raising areas where there are no major wildlife reservoirs of disease (Krebs *et al.* 1997), however, the European badger (*Meles meles*) has been implicated as an important wildlife reservoir (Woodroffe *et al.* 2006), notably in the west of England where badger numbers have been increasing (Bourne *et al.* 2005). The distribution of the incidence in cattle now encompasses most of the south-west and mid-west of England.

The role of anthropogenic intervention in suppressing or regulating pests and diseases. The primary forms of anthropogenic intervention that influence and regulate pests and diseases include the increased application of herbicides and changes in agricultural land use. The composition of arable weed flora in recent decades has been increasingly dominated by grass species, probably as a result of the increasing prevalence of cereal crops that leave fewer opportunities in the cropping cycle for the control of grasses. In addition, the evolution of resistance to certain chemical herbicides has tended to increase the predominance of certain grass weeds. Moreover, during the last quarter century, the number of herbicide applications has increased, and the active ingredients applied act upon a broader range of target species (Marshall *et al.* 2001, 2003). Consequently most of the innocuous weed species, including those supporting the arable food web, have declined (Hawes *et al.* 2009).

Some pathogens have been successfully suppressed through anthropogenic intervention. Bluetongue Virus (BTV) is a midge-borne virus of livestock that has emerged into southern Europe in the last century. Transmission by European midge vectors has subsequently facilitated the establishment of the disease in cooler and wetter areas in Europe. After first being detected in September 2007 in Suffolk, BTV went on to affect 137 premises that year (OIE 2009), but was successfully controlled by the use of inactivated vaccines.

Possible regulatory breakdown when novel pathogens invade the UK. As with many invasive species, newly introduced pathogens can spread rapidly, which implies that the usual regulatory mechanisms have broken down, a risk which may be increased where components of biodiversity which provide regulation have been lost. The prime examples include 'Dutch Elm Disease' (*Ophiostoma novo-ulmi*) that has been responsible for killing some 30–50 million elms in the UK, and *Phytophthora ramorum* that infects a broad range of plant species, including oaks, causing 'sudden oak death'. The *Phytophthora* pathogen was first detected in the UK in 2002; since then it has increased in north and south-west England. Whilst phytosanitary measures may have contained its spread between nurseries, its spread to adjacent semi-natural habitats remains a significant concern (Xu *et al.* 2009). *Phytophthera kernoviae* has more recently been detected on whinberry/bilberry (*Vaccinium myrtillus*), and other heathland species are known to be susceptible, leading to the suggestion that this is a potential threat for UK heathland (Beales *et al.* 2009). Since the 1990s a stream of such invasive fungal plant pathogens have been entering the UK, which are potentially damaging to trees, natural ecosystems and horticulture (Brasier 2008).

17.5.2.4 Pollination

Pollination services are provided by domestic honeybees and a wide range of wild insects including bumblebees and other bees (approximately 250 species), hoverflies (approximately 250 species) and butterflies (56 species). Pollinator-dependent crops (e.g. oilseed rape, apples, pears and strawberries), which are restricted to enclosed agricultural land, comprised 20% of the cropped area in England during 2007. This represents a 41% increase since the late 1980s (BHS 1999, 2008; Defra 2009a). The production function value of biotic pollination in England as a contribution to crop market value in 2007 was £367 million (Gallai *et al.* 2009), or approximately 8% of the total value of the market.

The value of pollinators and pollination services to wild flowers is unknown, but in the UK, since 1980, animal-pollinated plants have declined more than either self- or wind-pollinated species (Biesmeijer *et al.* 2006), and 76% of bumblebee forage plants have decreased in frequency (Carvell *et al.* 2007). Pollinators also contribute to the provision of cultural services. For example, several studies indicate that assemblages of wildflowers make important contributions to the aesthetic qualities of landscapes and roadside verges within the UK (Willis & Garrod 1993; Akbar 2003; Natural England 2009a).

Honeybees (*Apis mellifera*) are most often managed by hobby beekeepers, who are primarily interested in honey production rather than providing pollination services. The number of managed honeybee colonies declined by 54% between 1985 and 2005, with the trend expected to continue in the short-term (Potts *et al.* 2010). Declines in honeybee colonies are associated with introduced pests and diseases of honeybees (e.g. Varroa mite) which may become problematic for wild species.

Honeybees are not as effective at pollinating some crops (e.g. field beans, apples, raspberry) as wild pollinators; consequently, Biodiversity Action Plans (BAPs) have been developed to conserve these species and the valuable services they provide. To date 20 bee species, 24 butterfly species and seven hoverfly species have BAPs. Wild bee diversity has declined in most landscapes since 1980 with greater losses of habitat- and diet-specialist species than generalist species (Biesmeijer *et al.* 2006); hoverflies showed mixed shifts in diversity for the same time period, but again specialists fared poorly. Increased atmospheric nitrogen deposition has been implicated in the reduced species richness of grassland habitats in England (Phoenix *et al.* 2003, 2004) which has direct consequences on food availability for wild pollinators. Butterflies, though rarely significant pollinators in the UK, have also undergone major range and population shifts (Asher *et al.* 2001). Moths also are important pollinators and have declined by 33% since 1970 (Conrad *et al.* 2006). The loss of natural and semi-natural habitats, the widespread application of both pesticides and herbicides and climate change have all been implicated in the loss of pollinators in England, although agri-environment schemes and initiatives such as the Campaign for the Farmed Environment have a significant contribution to make to help pollinator services.

17.5.2.5 Noise regulation

Major surveys of noise levels in England have been restricted to Urban areas. A survey of 24-hour urban noise levels outside 1,000 dwellings in England and Wales was conducted in 1990 and 2000 (Skinner & Grimwood 2002). In both studies, daytime levels of noise were typically 8–9 dB higher than during the night. In a comparison of sites measured in both 1990 and 2000, there was a small but significant decrease in daytime noise levels from 57.1 to 56.5 dB, and the level of night-time noise was stable.

Vegetation reduces noise both by reducing its lateral transfer through mainly woody vegetation, and by reducing its reflection from rough, vegetated surfaces including lawns and other grasslands, effects which are likely to be most relevant in urban areas and close to major sources of noise such as roads.

In rural areas, noise studies have been integrated with visual impact. The proportion of England that suffers from some degree of noise or visual disturbance has been estimated to have increased from 25% in the early 1960s to 50% in 2007. The effect has not been related to specific habitats.

17.5.2.6 Soil quality

Soil quality has a pivotal role in regulating services, along with air and water quality. We are reliant upon our soils to capture and release carbon, nutrients and water, detoxify pollutants, purify water and suppress soil-dwelling pests and pathogens.

Unlike air and water quality, there is no legislation to specifically protect soil quality to maintain regulating services. However, there are national headline indicators on soil organic matter through the Sustainable Food and Farming Strategy in England and Wales in recognition of its importance to a range of ecosystem services. Indicators of soil quality relevant to regulating services have been extensively reviewed for the purposes of UK monitoring and to aid policy decisions (e.g. Environment Agency 2006). Also, the Soil Strategy for England (Defra 2009a) had the vision that: "By 2030, all England's soils will be managed sustainably and degradation threats tackled successfully. This will improve the quality of England's soils and safeguard their ability to provide essential services for future generations" p4. It seeks to protect agricultural soils and, on development sites, to protect and enhance stores of soil carbon, prevent soil pollution and build resilience to climate change. Thus it will address various aspects of the loss of soil services. However, the Soil Strategy for England currently has uncertain policy standing as it was published under the last government.

Retention, detoxification and degradation of pollutants, nutrients and carbon. Soil carbon acts as a surrogate measure for soil organic matter content, which is vital for regulation. As well as binding and buffering release of chemicals, soil organic matter affects water retention and infiltration. Since the 1970s, topsoil soil carbon content has shown no significant change in soils under most semi-natural habitats, but small declines in arable soils (Bellamy *et al.* 2005; Carey *et al.* 2008). Of particular importance in England, where arable crops dominate significant portions of the landscape, is increasing evidence that a significant proportion of arable soils are close to or below the critical threshold for soil organic matter (Emmett *et al.* 2010). It must be noted that the quantitative evidence base for critical thresholds for soil organic matter is sparse (Loveland & Webb 2003). However, there is evidence of a desirable range of soil organic carbon covering a wide spectrum of soils, but the quantitative evidence needs considerable development.

Concentrations of heavy metal pollutants in soils reflect historical and current pressures alongside natural conditions. The recent UK Soil and Herbage Survey (Environment Agency 2007) indicates that concentrations of copper, lead, mercury, nickel, zinc and tin are higher in urban and industrial soils than rural soils. In the main, these reflect inputs from industry and transport. Recent trends in GB-wide topsoil metal concentrations from the Countryside Survey suggest there have been relatively small changes in metal concentrations between 1998 and 2007.

The UK Soil and Herbage Survey results (Environment Agency 2007) indicate that soil dioxin levels increased between 1850 and 1980, predominantly in urban and industrial areas due to industrial processes, but that levels have since dropped by about 70%. Results, therefore, indicate that UK soils are maintaining a capacity to detoxify and degrade organic pollutants.

Many UK NEA Broad Habitats in England are displaying nutrient enrichment through agricultural inputs and from atmospheric deposition, as evidenced by the extensive exceedance of critical loads for several habitats for nitrogen (RoTAP 2011), changes in plant community composition (Smart *et al.* 2003) and changes to soil microbial communities (Smith *et al.* 2003).

Regulating the release of water. Regional changes to soil moisture deficits over the last 30 years reflect changing rainfall patterns (Defra 2003). Broadly speaking, information concerning trends in water release amongst habitats is lacking; however, circumstantial evidence suggests that soil water retention capacity may be at risk. Results on soil bulk density from the Countryside Survey indicate that many arable and horticultural soils (of importance in England) are showing signs of reduced aeration which may influence water flow (Carey *et al.* 2008).

17.5.2.7 Air quality regulation

The main air pollutants of concern to national and international policy makers are particles, ozone, nitrogen oxides, ammonia and the deposition of nitrogen and sulphur. The significant improvements in England's air quality over recent decades have largely been driven by reductions in anthropogenic emissions (Defra 2007a; RoTAP 2011). However, current concentrations and deposition rates still exceed thresholds for effects on human health and ecosystem services over significant areas of England. Substantial areas of exceedance of critical loads and critical levels are predicted to remain in 2020, despite planned policy measures (RoTAP 2011).

Ecosystem regulation can influence concentrations and deposition of air pollutants in three major ways:

Ecosystems remove pollutants from the atmosphere, reducing local and regional air pollutant concentrations. Evidence indicates that trees are effective at capturing pollutant particles and gases through direct deposition in calmed air within the canopy and uptake through leaf stomata (Fowler *et al.* 1989; Beckett *et al.* 1998). McDonald *et al.* (2007) estimate that the current 7% tree cover in the West Midlands region reduces mean air concentrations of PM10 (particles above 10 µm) by 4%, and that increasing this to a theoretical maximum of 54% would reduce mean PM10 concentrations by 26%. Tiwary *et al.* (2009) used a similar modelling approach in East London and concluded that two deaths and two hospital admissions would be averted each year as a result.

Ecosystems contribute directly to emissions to the atmosphere. The major contributor is emissions of ammonia, for which over 90% of UK emissions are from the agricultural sector (**Figure 17.21**). Intensive pig and poultry production facilities produce a significant proportion of ammonia emissions, with additional large contributions from grazing animals (primarily cattle), manure spreading and fertiliser use. These national ammonia emissions rose to a peak around 1990, but have subsequently declined, which corresponds to declining trends in livestock populations in England (RoTAP 2011).

Emissions from ecosystems contribute indirectly to air pollution levels via chemical processing in the atmosphere. The most important of these effects is the emission of reactive volatile organic compounds which contribute significantly to the formation of ozone, especially during the summer (AQEG 2009). National inventories of biogenic emissions exist (e.g. the National Atmospheric Emissions Inventory, AEA, 2010), but past and future trends are uncertain (AQEG 2009).

Measures to reduce emissions to, or deposition from, the atmosphere can increase the potential for air quality regulation by ecosystems. This is primarily because any pollutant deposited or absorbed from the atmosphere by ecosystems is more likely to have adverse effects when concentrations or deposition rates are high. An important trend in recent decades is the effect of reduced anthropogenic emissions, leading to decreased urban concentrations of smoke and sulphur dioxide . Emissions of sulphur dioxide in the UK declined from 6,365,000 tonnes to 512,000 tonnes between 1970 and 2008 (NAEI 2009). This reduction has allowed increased planting of conifer species, particularly

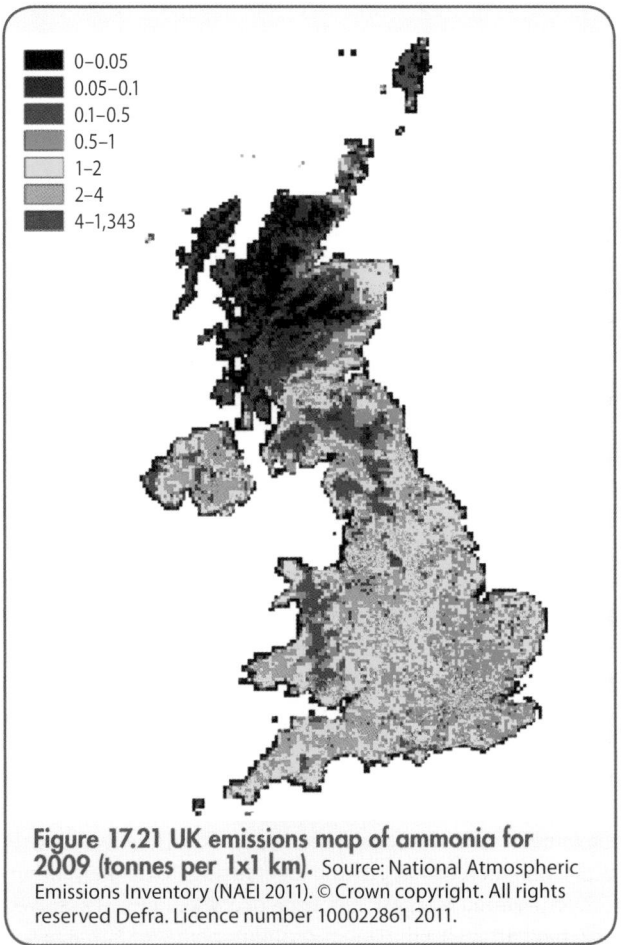

■	0–0.05
■	0.05–0.1
■	0.1–0.5
▨	0.5–1
▢	1–2
▨	2–4
■	4–1,343

Figure 17.21 UK emissions map of ammonia for 2009 (tonnes per 1x1 km). Source: National Atmospheric Emissions Inventory (NAEI 2011). © Crown copyright. All rights reserved Defra. Licence number 100022861 2011.

in urban areas, which increases interception and deposition of air pollution near its source, hence further improving air quality. At a national scale, there is evidence that the UK landscape has become a more efficient absorber of sulphur dioxide as concentrations have fallen, further decreasing air concentrations (RoTAP 2011).

17.5.2.8 Water quality regulation

Water quality is determined primarily by catchment processes including plant and microbial nutrient uptake, pollutant accumulation in soil organic matter and adsorption onto mineral surfaces, acidity buffering, organic pollutant breakdown and denitrification. Water quality can be further influenced by drainage systems which can dilute, assimilate or transport pollutants. This particular ecosystem service is often confused with the provisioning service for drinking water, which stems from the overlap of definitions of these services.

Unfortunately, there is little monitoring of the ecosystem processes which regulate water quality and only inferences can be made from existing data, which point to ecosystems contributing to a general improvement, which is also influenced by decreased inputs and improved treatment in sewerage works and elsewhere. General Quality Assessments showed that the number of English rivers of good chemical quality increased from 55% to 79% from 1990 to 2008 (Defra 2009c). Concentrations of phosphates were high (>0.1 mg P/l40) in 52% of English rivers, whilst 32% of English rivers exhibited high concentrations (>30 mg NO_3/l) of nitrates (Chapter 9; Section 17.4.5, Figure 17.4.5a and b).

Data from the Harmonised Monitoring Scheme (HMS) indicates that organic pollution (measured in terms of biological oxygen demand and ammoniacal nitrogen) have declined in England since the 1980s, leading to increased dissolved oxygen concentrations. Phosphate concentrations have fallen substantially in most areas since the mid-1990s, whilst nitrate has shown little change.

Data from HMS monitoring in England further indicates that heavy metal concentrations have declined, whilst the large majority of pesticides are below detection limits (Figure 14.6, Section 14.9.1). Faecal indicator organisms (FIOs) are measured routinely at (predominantly coastal) bathing waters. English coastal waters complying with mandatory standards set by the EC Bathing Water Directive increased from 65% in 1988 to 98% in 2007, whilst the stricter Guideline standards, which indicate excellent bathing water quality, were met in 29% of English waters in 1992, but rose to 71% in 2007.

Upland water quality is more strongly coupled to ecosystem processes; however, far fewer data sets are available to infer with the magnitude of water quality regulation by upland ecosystems. As it is relatively unpolluted, water draining the uplands performs a key regulatory service by diluting pollution that enters river systems further downstream. Whilst England-specific data is lacking, general trends from UK-wide data sources show that upland waters experienced elevated acidification during the 1960s–80s. However reports of recent increasing pH and decreasing toxic aluminium concentrations suggest recovery (AWMN 2009). Dissolved organic carbon from waters draining peaty soils has risen

across the UK in the last 20–30 years (Evans et al. 2005; Worrall & Burt 2007b), whilst suspended sediment levels are elevated in areas of active soil erosion, notably downstream of eroding peatlands, such as those of the South Pennines, indicating that ecosystem damage is a significant cause of this adverse change (Evans et al. 2006).

17.5.3 Provisioning Services

Provisioning services provide the material goods directly (or in the case of genetic resources, indirectly) consumed by humans. Many of these are produced as private goods, for which there are established markets. Consequently, production and trading in recognised provisioning services (e.g. wheat, beef, fresh water, etc.) has often been a major influence on other ecosystem services for which markets do not exist, and which have been substantially overlooked in land management decisions. Perhaps the greatest challenge faced by land managers and policy makers is balancing the high demand for essential provisioning services required by human populations, most notably food and water, and the impacts of this elevated emphasis on provisioning services on the interdependent regulatory, cultural and supporting ecosystem services.

17.5.3.1 Food from agriculture

Approximately 70% of England is managed as farmland and thus agriculture has a major influence on nearly all other ecosystem services. In the past 50 years, there have been major increases in domestic food production. Despite an increase in population, self-sufficiency in food production increased in the UK from 40 to 50% in the 1950s to 60% in the 2000s (Defra 2006a). Most of this increase was due to higher levels of farm production in England. There has been a trend towards farm specialisation, with a loss of mixed farming and its associated matrix of habitats and within-farm nutrient recycling between crops and livestock. This trend has had pronounced impacts on the landscape and the supply of other ecosystem services.

Crops. Between 1940 and 2009, the areal extent of land growing crops in England rose from roughly 3 million ha to 4.2 million ha, or a 41% increase. The extent and types of crops grown has also changed. For example, the area of wheat has risen whilst that of oats has fallen. Yields also increased in all major crops as a result of intensification, most dramatically for wheat, which rose from 2.5 tonnes/ha in 1940 to 8 tonnes/ha in 2008, or a 3.2-fold increase. This has had significant consequences stemming largely from increased inputs of fertilisers, pesticides, energy and tillage, all of which typically exert negative pressures on biodiversity. The area of vegetables increased between 1940 and 2009 (Section 15.2.2), but orchards declined from 102,000 ha to 25,000 ha. Fallow land fell from 2.3% to 0.36% (25,000 ha) of cropped area.

Livestock. English livestock populations of sheep and pigs rose from 1940 to 1980 and then declined, while cattle followed the same trend, but continued to rise until the 1990s (**Figure 17.22**). Whilst the total livestock population has fallen during the period of interest, local densities of livestock have risen significantly due to the development of industrial livestock rearing methods. These concentrated animal populations, coupled with certain recent husbandry practices, have contributed to periodic outbreaks of infectious diseases, such as Bovine Spongiform Encephalopathy (BSE) or contagious diseases, such as Foot-and-Mouth. Bovine Spongiform Encephalopathy can be spread through the feeding of animal by-products to bovine herds and also can be spread to humans who consume brains or spinal cord materials. Elevated livestock densities are also associated with increased ammonia emissions and its significant impacts on air quality and ecosystem processes. In 2008, cattle farming accounted for nearly 47% of ammonia emissions in the UK (AEA 2010).

Dairy. Dairy production is associated with intensive grassland management. In England, the yield has increased from 3,500 litres per cow per year in 1960 to 7,000 litres per cow per year in 2009 (Capper *et al.* 2009). Genetic selection of higher yielding cows, technological innovation and incentives from agricultural subsidies accounts for increases. Production was capped by CAP reform of 1984 and market forces have driven down farm gate prices in the 2000s. Declines in market prices had the follow-on effect of simultaneously reducing the number of farms and increasing the density of herds. Modern dairy production levels are still above 1940 outputs, though achieved with fewer cows held in fewer, larger farm businesses.

Beef. Rearing systems vary from outdoor suckler cow production on semi-natural habitats (including nature reserves and special wildlife sites) with low input requirements, to intensive indoor rearing and finishing, with environmental impacts at an industrial scale. The UK beef herd saw a modest increase between 1940 and 1970 and there was also a more significant increase in the English beef herd from 1981 to 1995, which grew by 45%. The increases in herd size were accompanied by increases in carcass weights from 267 kg in 1980 to 316 kg in 2003. Since then, the English beef herd has experienced a significant decline due to a reduced numbers of animals entering the beef-rearing sector from dairy herds. The elevated levels of cattle production produced by modern husbandry techniques are not without consequences: diseases such as BSE and Foot-and-Mouth have had significant financial repercussions due to the costs of disease control and the closure of foreign markets, which depressed farm gate prices for beef. Agri-environment payments for grazing on semi-natural habitats locally support low-intensity beef rearing to meet environmental goals, notably biodiversity.

Sheep. The growth in the sheep population in England between 1940 and 1990 was significantly influenced by increased subsidies to hill farmers. The major growth, therefore, took place in upland habitats, prompting concern about the impacts of overgrazing. Declines in the English sheep flock were exacerbated by outbreaks of Foot and Mouth in 2001.

Pigs and poultry. From 1940 to 2009 pig farming evolved from extensive (even household-scale) husbandry towards intensively-reared indoor industrial-scale units. However, issues related to animal welfare and the environmental impacts of high-density pig lots have prompted an opposing trend towards outdoor pig-rearing, on well-drained land that is part of an arable rotation scheme. Whilst environmental

impacts from outdoor pig-rearing are not well understood, there is potential for increased diffuse pollution of surface and groundwater, substantially increased soil erosion and an issue of waste disposal. Most of the 3.8 million pigs in the United Kingdom (2009) are reared in England, especially in the east and in Wiltshire, which is famed for its ham and pork products.

There were about 166 million hens in England in 2008, including 30 million laying hens producing 868 million eggs (Section 15.2.3.4).

Fibre from agriculture. Historically, flax has been produced at low levels since the 1940s, when 11,000 ha of land was used for the production of flax for textiles and rope production. There was a brief surge of flax production in the early 2000s due to increases of the CAP subsidy, but production levels have since declined with its withdrawal.

The UK is the seventh largest wool producer in the world, with some regions of England (e.g. the Cotswolds) noted for their historic wool trade. Other than for specialist suppliers (e.g. fine wool goats), the value of wool to farmers is typically low. The amount of wool produced is proportionate to the numbers of sheep. The trend for wool production has been increasing; 25 million kg of wool was produced in 1950, rising to 49 million kg in 1998.

Biomass and bioenergy. At the end of the 20th Century almost no biomass crops were grown commercially in England. In 2005, 436 ha of short rotation coppice willow was recorded in the UK (NNFCC 2009), and by 2007 this had increased fivefold (Table 15.4, Section 15.2.5). Similar increases were noted in Miscanthus (*Miscanthus* x *giganteus*) and reed canary grass (*Phalaris arundinacea*) over the same timescale, both of which are grown for biomass. Monoculture plantings of Miscanthus offer very little by way of habitat and as such, careful consideration must be given to ensure that impacts on local floral and faunal populations are minimised. Plantings for biomass and bioenergy have largely been driven by a combination of market opportunity

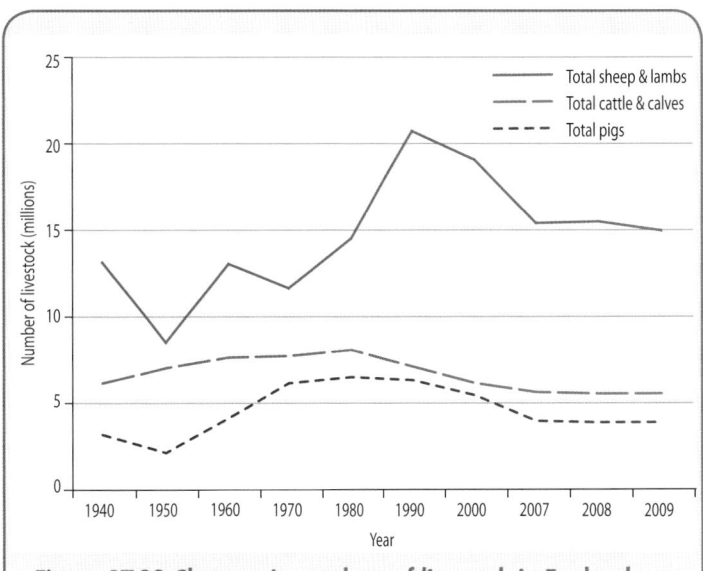

Figure 17.22 Changes in numbers of livestock in England between 1940 and 2009. Source: June census records from Defra; data available at: http://www.defra.gov.uk/statistics/foodfarm/landuselivestock/junesurvey/.

and policy. Relevant policies are not necessarily agricultural, but include incentives for energy generators to include a certain proportion of renewable materials in their feedstock, and for some large establishments to have biomass boilers. Oilseed rape is used to produce biodiesel and its increasing popularity stems from EU policies set in 2005 to increase the proportion of renewable fuels used to power Europe's growing fleet of automobiles and lorries.

Fish from marine ecosystems. Interpreting the statistics of marine fisheries is problematic for the purposes of this review, since UK registered fishing vessels do not land all of their catch in UK (or English) ports. Similarly, non-UK registered fishing vessels will land some of their catch in UK ports depending on market conditions. A further problem comes from the methods used to collate fishing statistics, recorded by ICES (International Council for the Exploration of the Sea) rectangles, which are several thousand square kilometres in extent and commonly transcend national boundaries. Finally, landing statistics do not contain landings from small inshore vessels.

Landings into British ports were 883,000 tonnes per annum in 1950 and at a relatively constant level until 1970, when they increased significantly to 1 million tonnes. Since the peak in the early 1970s, fish landings declined to 409,000 tonnes per annum in 2008, its lowest modern peacetime level (outside of the two World Wars), with the total landings into England by UK vessels being 89,313 tonnes. These trends differ amongst demersal, pelagic and shellfish species. Landings of demersal fish (e.g. cod, plaice and haddock) living on the seabed exhibited the sharpest decline, with landings decreasing from 456,000 tonnes to 190,000 tonnes per annum during the period from 1994 to 2008. Pelagic fish (e.g. herring and mackerel) landings declined more modestly, decreasing from 388,900 tonnes to 247,900 tonnes per annum from 1994 to 2008. Landings of shellfish increased slightly between 1994 and 2008, from 114,400 tonnes to 150,500 tonnes per annum (MFA 2009). The trends in fish landings do not necessarily indicate declines in species' populations, as they are also significantly influenced by conservation measures (e.g. the EU Common Fisheries Policy), fishing effort, EU policies concerning the fishing fleet and reductions of fisheries subsidies provided to domestic fleets. Between 1996 and 2008 the number and fleet tonnage of the English fleet had fallen, suggesting the overall level of fishing capacity had declined, despite increases in the power and efficiency of the fleet. These developments can explain a portion of the decline in landings.

Aquaculture. Nearly 80% of marine aquaculture (predominantly salmon) in the UK occurs in Scotland and is, therefore, of minor significance in England, with the notable exceptions of the rainbow trout (an introduced species which has naturalised in some British rivers) farms in southern England and the Pennines that produced 7,294 tonnes in 2006. Shellfish farms produced 14,553 tonnes of mussels and 880 tonnes of oysters in 2006 (Defra 2009a). Aquaculture operations increase the input of nitrogen and phosphorus into aquatic environments, enhancing the local growth of marine plants and algae, and also reducing the diversity of benthic organisms underneath aquacultural facilities (Mayor *et al.* 2010).

Capture of migratory salmon and trout. Catches by rod and fixed engine boats and nets rose between 1956 and 1969 to more than 140,000 fish. Since this period, these totals have fallen sharply to fewer than 40,000 fish (Figure 15.5, Section 15.5.3). Since 2004, more fish have been caught by rod than by net for the first time since records began in 1956. This trend has been influenced by legislative controls and formal agreements limiting 'mixed stock' (from different rivers) fishing on the high seas and ceding control to the catchment scale where licensing of commercial activities can be controlled in relation to escapement of spawning fish. Angling interests, supported by numerous River Trusts, have also been active in buying out estuarine netting and also promoting 'catch and release' recreational angling.

Game species (birds and mammals). Game species are those hunted for food and/or sport including reared and released pheasant and red-legged partridge, wild red grouse and several species of deer. Additional species are culled due to their role as pests (e.g. deer, rabbits and pigeons). Regardless of why they are hunted or culled, the majority end up in the human food chain. Whilst the amount of wild game represents only a very small component of food consumed in England, these species exert a disproportionately large influence on land use, as habitats are specifically managed to improve game bird abundance. Prominent examples of these activities include the management of heather moorland in northern England for red grouse and the management of small woods, hedges and field margins in lowland farmland of southern England for pheasant and partridge.

Trends in the number of birds shot per unit area depend on the species and their management activities. Within the moorlands, there have been wide variations in the number of grouse shot from the mid-1970s to 2007 due to population fluctuations; however, the overall trend has been a decline from 100 birds per 100 ha in 1975 to 30 birds per 100 ha in 2007 (GWCT 2009).

In the lowlands, the amount and extent of habitats supporting game birds breeding in the wild declined throughout the 20th Century, due to intensification of arable farming. The number of grey partridge shot similarly declined from 14 birds per 100 ha in 1960 to one bird per 100 ha in 2005 (GWCT 2009). Pheasant and red-legged partridge are introduced species whose populations are artificially maintained by regular releases of reared birds. It has been estimated that 35 million pheasants were released in 2004, of which 15 million were shot, and 6.5 million red-legged partridge were released, of which 2.6 million were shot.

During the 1960s, bags of roe deer (*Capreolus capreolus*) were restricted to Scotland, north-east England and some southern counties of England. Over the next few decades the deer spread across much of England, and in much of southern England (particularly East Anglia), bag densities exceeded one deer per 100 ha in the 1990s. Few roe deer were shot in the English Midlands during the period 1960–2000, though overall numbers can be seen to have increased (GWCT 2009; **Figure 17.23**).

During the 1960s fallow deer (*Dama dama*) were shot in only a few localities in the UK. By the 1990s, bags of fallow deer had increased significantly across southern England, particularly in Gloucestershire where bag densities exceeded one bag per 100 ha (**Figure 17.24**) (GWCT 2009).

During the period 1960–2000 shooting of red deer (*Cervus elaphus*) gradually increased in North West England, East Anglia and South West England. **Figure 17.25** shows that no red deer were shot in the Midlands or South East England between 1960 and 2000 (GWCT 2009).

Wild foods. No precise figures for honey production are available for England; however, Jones (2004) has provided initial estimates of honey production based on the number of colonies kept and a mean honey production value per colony (Figure 15.8, Section 15.6). The most desirable plants for honeybees have nectar with a high sugar content and are found in quantities substantial enough to sustain colonies. Crops such as oilseed rape and white clover are particularly important. The one wild, nectar-rich species growing *en masse* is heather, which is the main summer food supply for honeybees in the North York Moors and Devon. Some hives are permanently stationed on moorlands. In other cases, hives are deliberately moved to heather to encourage foraging exclusively from wild flowers. Heather honey has twice the value of other types of British honey, £4.40–£5.50/kg bulkweight compared with £2.20–£2.30/kg (Prendergast & Sanderson 2002).

A number of other wild foods are gathered from English habitats such as edible mushrooms, wild basil, wild marjoram, marsh samphire, watercress, bog myrtle, burdock, common sorrel, garlic mustard, nettle, (non-native) sweet cicely, wild thyme, wood sorrel, the fruits of cowberry, crab apple, hawthorn, hazel, wild blackberry, wild raspberry, rose, rowan, sloe, wild strawberry, whinberry, the flowers of elder, the roots of (non-native) horseradish and tuber-roots of pignut, and the buds of broom (Prendergast & Sanderson 2002). Unfortunately, little information is available on quantities harvested.

17.5.3.2 Resources

Timber. The harvest of hardwood timber in England accounts for 88% of the UK total, but has been in long-term decline since 1975, unlike in Wales and Scotland, where harvests have remained at low levels (Figure 15.10, Section 15.7.1). In 1975, more than 1,000 green tonnes of hardwood was harvested in England, but by 2008, less than 400 green tonnes were harvested (Forestry Commission 2009d). However, harvested softwood amounts exceed hardwood totals in England (approximately 2,000 tonnes of softwood versus 400 tonnes of hardwoods in 2008), with the softwood total being about one-third that of Scotland's (Figure 15.12, Section 15.7.1). England is not self-sufficient in timber production and relies on imported timber, particularly from Scotland and other timber exporting nations.

The most significant threat to the future supply of provisioning services from woodlands lies in the possibility of disease, particularly sudden oak death, which causes the sudden death of both native oak species (*Quercus robur and Q. petraea*), acute oak decline, and red band needle blight (caused by the fungus *Dothistroma septosporum*).

Biochemicals. A number of biochemicals are produced in England, largely from the bark and needles of woodland tree species. These include shikimic acid, which is derived

from spruce needles and is the primary precursor of Tamiflu; taxol, which is derived from the bark and needles of yew and is used to treat a variety of cancers; and Pycnogenol™, a herbal nutritional supplement based upon polyphenolics found in pine needles and bark and reputed to be an effective

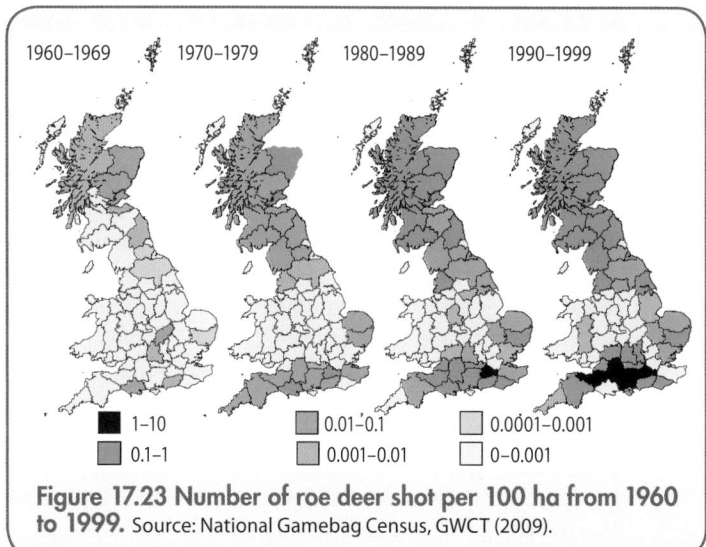

Figure 17.23 Number of roe deer shot per 100 ha from 1960 to 1999. Source: National Gamebag Census, GWCT (2009).

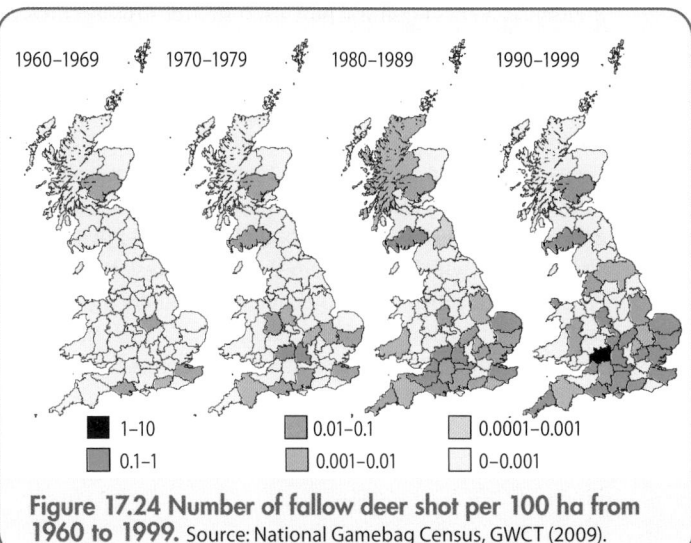

Figure 17.24 Number of fallow deer shot per 100 ha from 1960 to 1999. Source: National Gamebag Census, GWCT (2009).

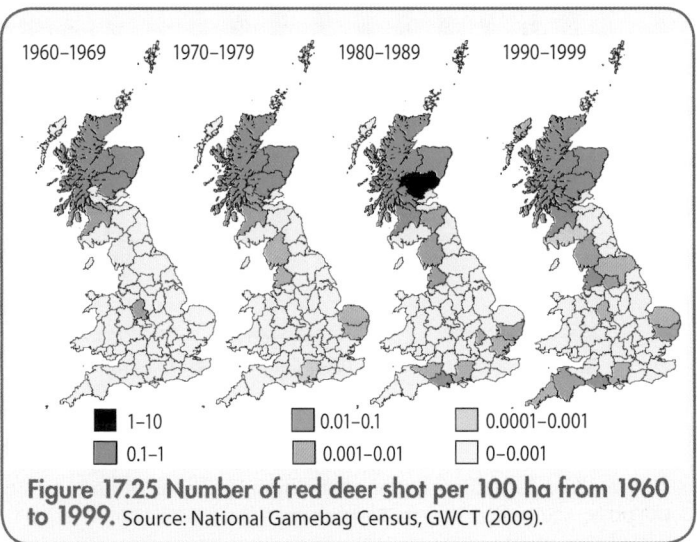

Figure 17.25 Number of red deer shot per 100 ha from 1960 to 1999. Source: National Gamebag Census, GWCT (2009).

antioxidant. Non-woodland species providing biochemicals include *Eryngium* species, whose roots produce potent inflammation modulators.

Roof thatching. Roughly 60,000 thatched properties occur in Britain, mainly in southern and central England, and their popularity appears to be increasing (Hawke & José 1996). For example, about one new property in 50 built by one developer in southern England is thatched, whilst council planners in Dorset are advocating that one in six new houses in that county should be thatched (Maclaren 2000). Roof thatching is most often with common reed (*Phragmites australis*), but saw sedge (*Cladium mariscus*), heather (*Calluna* species) and other traditional species can also be used (Sanderson & Prendergast 2002). Some 365 ha of reedbed are harvested in England, predominantly from Norfolk and Suffolk (Rayment 1995). English reed production has been estimated to be at least 226,975 bundles per year (Bateman *et al.* 1991) with a total value greater than £400,000 per annum. The other main source of thatching is from long straw wheat which is grown over a small acreage in southern England and plays an important role in the conservation of genetically important landrace wheat varieties (Hopkins & Maxted 2011).

Peat extraction. Today, almost all peat extraction in England is for horticultural purposes. Nearly all commercially extracted peat comes from lowland raised bog sites, which are a rare wetland type. Upland peats are extensive, but not suitable for horticultural purposes. Most commercial peat production in Great Britain is located in England and has been declining in recent years. In 1999, 1,224,000 m³ were sold in England, predominantly from sites in the North East and North West. By 2008, 496,000 m³ were sold in England, almost all of which came from the North West (ONS 2000). Production declines can be attributed to industry agreements with Natural England (and its predecessor, English Nature) on extraction from SSSIs, as well as reduced commercial use.

Ornamental resources. During 2006, 4,578 ha of open fields in England were used to produce flowers for commercial markets, predominantly in Scilly, Cornwall and Lincolnshire. This included 3,871 ha of daffodils and smaller amounts for gladioli and pinks. The amount of land used for commercially produced flowers has declined steadily due to cheaper products coming from Europe and Africa. The total area of outdoor flowers and hardy nursery stock (e.g. shrubs, roses and ornamental trees) in England has grown steadily from 6,900 ha in 1940 to nearly 12,800 ha in 2000 due to increased home ownership, greater amounts of personal income and wider interest in gardening (Section 15.9).

17.5.3.3 Water supply

Throughout the 20th and 21st Centuries, demand for water in England has steadily increased due to population growth. Despite this growth, the amount of water put into the public water supply in England and Wales declined modestly between 1990 and 2009, which roughly coincides with the privatisation of the water industry in 1989. The drivers behind the decline are unclear, but enhanced infrastructure and management under private water companies will have had an influence.

It will be noted from **Figure 17.26** that considerable variation exists in the amount of water annually entering the public water supply (Defra 2010h). Another potential driver of this variation is annual change in weather, but looking at the number of drought orders and rainfall totals from the Environment Agency, there is no obvious relationship. Presumably there are complex interactions between climate, regional weather patterns, and economic forces that drive water use and supply patterns.

Another important aspect of water abstraction is that most of this service is consumed downstream away from its source. Therefore whole-catchment management of this and related services is essential for sustainability. Catchment-

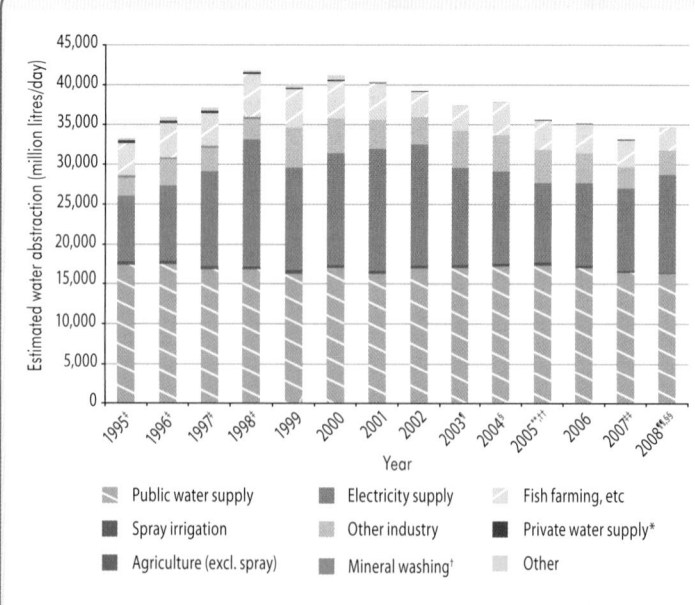

*Private abstractions for domestic use by individual households.
[†] In 1999, mineral washing was not reported as a separate category. Licences for mineral washing are contained in "Other industry".
[‡] Under-estimate of actual abstraction during the period 1995 to 1998 due to licences being assigned as industrial cooling rather than electricity supply (North East Region). [¶] Three licences re-assigned in 2003 to other industry from electricity supply (Midlands Region). [§] Reduced abstraction in 2004 at Dinorwig and Ffestiniog Power Stations (hydropower) (Wales Region). ** Reduced hydropower abstraction in 2005 (North East & Midlands Region). [††] Reduction in agricultural abstraction due to deregulation of licences as of 1 April 2005. [‡‡] Spray irrigation is very sensitive to prevailing weather conditions. This is reflected in a decrease in actuals for spray irrigation due to wet summers in 2007 and 2008. [¶¶] Return requirements were changed from 01/04/2008 whereby licences that abstract under 100m³/day no longer had to send returns back this has mainly affected agricultural, private water supply/other and small industrial licences. [§§] Return requirements were standardised across all regions from 01/04/2008 and requested by financial years. Prior to April 2008 returns were requested by calendar year for the majority of regions. To collect data for all of 2008 two requests were made, at the end of the period January 2008 to March 2008 and end of period April 2008 to March 2009. This may have had the effect of underestimating actual abstraction where returns may have been received for only part of the calendar year.

Figure 17.26 Estimated water abstractions (millions of litres per day) for England and Wales from all sources (except tidal) by purpose. Source: data from the Environment Agency; Defra (2010h).

level management required for the continued provision of clean water might also positively influence flood regulation and reduce soil erosion.

17.5.4 Cultural Services

Since 1945, people's perceptions of and interactions with their local environments have expanded considerably. A wider range of benefits are being recognised and sought after within natural and semi-natural environments including their roles in local and national identity, education, spirituality, art, physical and psychological health and recreation. Changes in mobility, work patterns, social behaviours and consumption have contributed to these altered relations between people and their local natural environment. Generally, more people have a local environment with urban characteristics, but increased mobility allows people to travel longer distances within their local area, increasing the potential opportunities to engage with local places. Satisfaction with local environments, however, has fallen slightly in recent years (Defra 2010e).

Urban settlement patterns have changed considerably since 1950 due, in part, to new transport technologies and the growth of job opportunities in rural areas. Eighty-one per cent of the UK population now live in urban areas (CABE 2010), compared to approximately 70% in 1951. This change has been uneven: larger urban areas and conurbations have become less crowded, whilst smaller settlements and rural areas, especially in southern England, have become more crowded (FLUFP 2010). Rural communities have also undergone changes that will influence the interactions between people and ecosystem services. For example, agricultural workers, who are especially engaged with rural environments, accounted for 5% of the British workforce in 1951, but now constitute fewer than 2% of the total workforce.

These changes in work and settlement patterns have been accompanied by changes in mobility. Defra (2008c) data indicate a modal shift to cars from bicycles and walking. **Figure 17.27** illustrates that the distance travelled has increased by about 25% for commuting/business travel and by over 30% for other journey types. People are increasingly living in or close to urban settlements, but they are also able to travel further regularly to access opportunities, services and work in their local area.

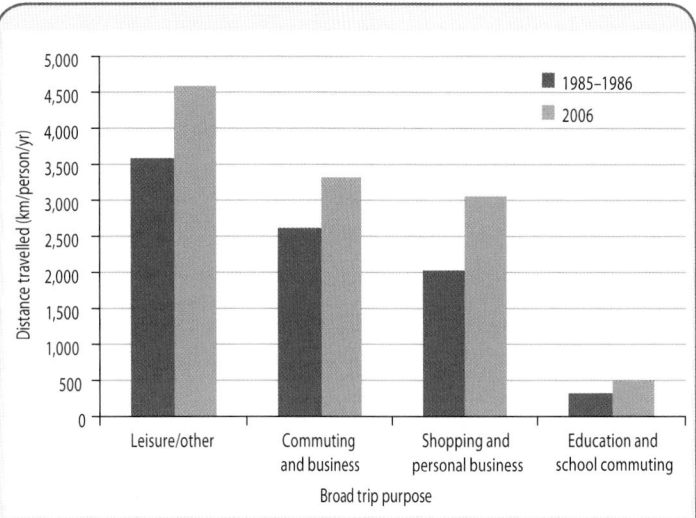

Figure 17.27 Distance travelled (km per person per year) in Great Britain by broad trip purpose*. Source: data from Department for Transport; Defra (2009) © Crown copyright 2009. * Note: Figures for 1995 onwards are based on weighted data and are not directly comparable with earlier years. The effect of weighting is broadly to uplift the number of trips by approximately 4%. The sample size of the survey tripled in 2002.

Figure 17.28 indicates that in England people also place considerable importance on the natural environment in the form of greenspace in their local area, with three-quarters of the population considering it to be an important part of the local environment and almost 50% using it at least once a week. Recently national surveys have started systematically to measure people's satisfaction with their local area (Defra 2010e).

17.5.4.1 Environmental settings

The last century has witnessed marked changes in certain landscapes of the United Kingdom, especially those in and around large Urban areas. The State of the Countryside 2008 report for England (CRC 2008) indicates that 8.6% of land cover in England is of built up areas (although a large portion of this land is gardens or greenspace), whilst the Countryside Survey (2009) estimates a higher urban cover at 10.6%. Major conurbations and cities (defined as populations over 100,000) occupy about 5.3% of the land, other urban areas (populations 10,000 to 100,000) cover 2.2%, rural towns 0.8% and villages

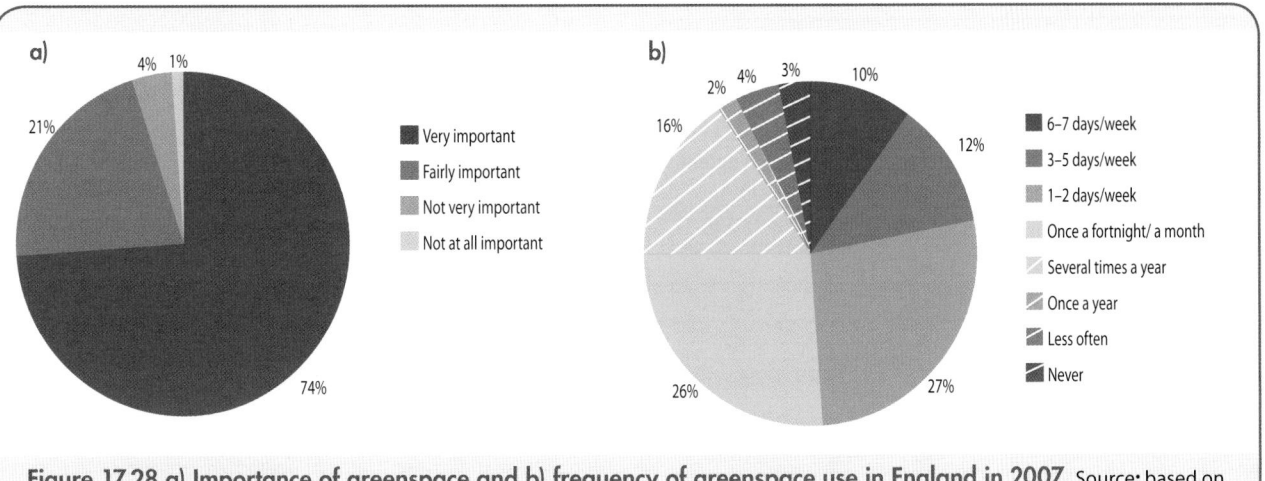

Figure 17.28 a) Importance of greenspace and b) frequency of greenspace use in England in 2007. Source: based on data from Alex Thornton (2009). © Queen's Printer and Controller of HMSO 2007.

and hamlets 1%. Agriculture covers approximately 70% of the land area outside built up areas, with woodland cover and forestry making up about 9% (CRC 2008).

There are 10 National Parks in England and they protect landscapes of particular social value. Other parts of the countryside are protected by conservation designations, most notably Sites of Special Scientific Interest (SSSIs), Special Areas of Conservation (SACs), Special Protection Areas (SPAs), Ramsar sites, National Nature Reserves (NNRs) and Local Nature Reserves (LNRs). On the edge of larger cities in England, considerable portions of the landscape are protected by green belt land, which in 2010 was estimated to be 1,619,835 ha (Natural England 2010d). **Table 17.14** indicates the type, number and spatial extent of several protected landscape designations in England.

The Countryside Quality Counts (CQC) project was designed to provide an indicator of change in countryside quality of England and gives the most comprehensive data on landscape change. Its analysis for 1990–1998 indicated that about 40% of English landscapes were stable, 37% of landscapes experienced changes that did not significantly alter overall landscape character, and 10% of landscapes are being enhanced. Yorkshire and Humberside, the East of England, the North West and the North East landscapes stood out as being the most stable. By contrast, marked and inconsistent change in landscapes was concentrated in the Manchester, Bristol and Birmingham conurbations.

Some measures of landscape change are, however, pessimistic. The Campaign for the Protection of Rural England (CPRE 2003) highlights several changes in land use that it believes will have negative consequences for English landscapes. These include the following points:

- Every year in the 1990s an area the size of Hull was developed (DETR 2001).
- Between 1984 and 1993 there was a 17% net loss of hedgerows (Barr *et al.* 1993).
- Meadows covering an area the size of the country of Bedfordshire were lost between 1992 and 1998.
- Between 1990 and 1998, plant diversity in some meadows fell by 8% (Haines-Young 2000).
- Once extensive ancient woodland cover in the UK is now reduced to only 2% of land use (Haines-Young 2000).

English Heritage has commissioned pilot and demonstration studies to develop a Historic Seascape Characterisation for England. The Defra report Charting progress: An integrated assessment of the state of the UK seas (Defra 2005) identified the following key issues:

- Levels of contaminants in the UK seas have decreased significantly.
- Significant contaminated areas are associated with industrial estuaries and are due to a legacy from the past.
- Widespread commercial fishing continues to threaten many fish stocks.
- Whilst the impacts of climate change on marine ecosystems are the subject of considerable ongoing research, our understanding is very limited.

This mixed picture of landscape and seascape change results from the maintenance and enhancement of character in some landscapes and loss or neglect in others. Some of these changes can be attributed to improved legal protection of landscapes (e.g. the implementation of the European Landscape Convention, designation of SSSIs, etc.) whilst others result from greater public awareness of the uniqueness of English landscapes.

17.5.4.2 Leisure, recreation and tourism

Outdoor environments have been one of the most enduringly popular locations for recreation and tourism (Curry 1994), with a variety of ecosystem features and habitats offering a wide range of goods and services. Research for Natural England (2009a) has identified that ecosystem services for recreation are often linked to places where there is a lot to do, such as the local park or stretches of coastline. They are typified by easy access, opportunities for specific physical activity (e.g. scrambling or climbing on rocks and crags), or scenic rights of way (e.g. lanes, roads and pathways). Woodlands are also valued for the multiple benefits they provide, including opportunities for walking and cycling. The recreation and tourism benefits derived from ecosystem services are synergistic with other benefits, particularly education, spirituality and physical health.

Natural England's (2005b) English Leisure Visits Survey (ELVS) provides information on the characteristics of the leisure visit, based on a survey of 23,542 respondents. The findings indicate that in 2005 approximately two-thirds of visits were to inland towns/cities, whilst the remaining one-third were to the countryside, coast and woodlands. Interestingly, the proportion of the adult population undertaking countryside, seaside or urban visits was fairly constant, at just under two-thirds of the adult population. The duration of the visits was split equally between more than and less than three hours, with nearly 60% using a car and 25% walking, suggesting that there is likely to be a fairly even division between visits to meaningful local places and visits to more distant socially valued landscapes.

Many people utilise natural landscapes for active recreation and more passive forms of enjoyment. **Figure 17.29** illustrates data assembled by the Foresight Land Use Futures Project (2010), drawing on surveys carried out since

Table 17.14 Number of designated sites in England and their spatial extent. Source: data compiled by T Sajwaj (2010).

Protected Land Designation	Number of sites	Areal extent (ha)
National Parks	10	1,216,000
National Nature Reserves	222	92,000
Greenbelt	n/a	1,638,000
Ramsar sites	31	356,000
SSSIs	4117	1,000,000+
SACs	231	846,000
Special Protection Areas	79	1,051,000
Local Nature Reserves	1280	Circa 40,000

2000 on the percentages of the adult population in England who visit the countryside and parks and greenspaces, and the frequency with which they visit.

Tourism, recreation, ecosystem services, habitats: Destinations of foreign visitors to England are strongly divided between rural and urban destinations, with rural destinations accounting for roughly 55% of all international visitors (Foresight Land Use Futures Project 2010). Domestic tourism is more problematic to assess as preferences shift considerably for urban, rural and coastal destinations. Recent estimates suggest that rural tourism in the English countryside is worth nearly £14 billion a year and supports 380,000 jobs (GFA-Race & GHK 2004). The importance of these revenues to rural and coastal populations is considerable as they contribute disproportionately large amounts of income to rural economies and quality of life (Deloitte MCS Ltd 2008).

Table 17.15 identifies the habitats/habitat features, opportunities and potential benefits that can be derived from various ecosystems. Whilst not necessarily physically remote from urban populations, these habitats tend to be found in places that are not suited to extensive development, meaning that there are significant constraints in gaining access to them (Curry 1994). These constraints help to limit human impacts, although it is recognised that additional management is often required to prevent degradation of the sites (Keirle 2002). Many habitats offer opportunities for a broad range of recreational activities and include parks, tracks, paths, roads, verges and other elements of the 'green network' (Natural England 2009d).

Informal access to the countryside for recreation is both extensive and diverse. In England:

- Country parks created under the Countryside Act 1968 cover nearly 39,000 hectares of land (Urban Parks Forum, undated report).

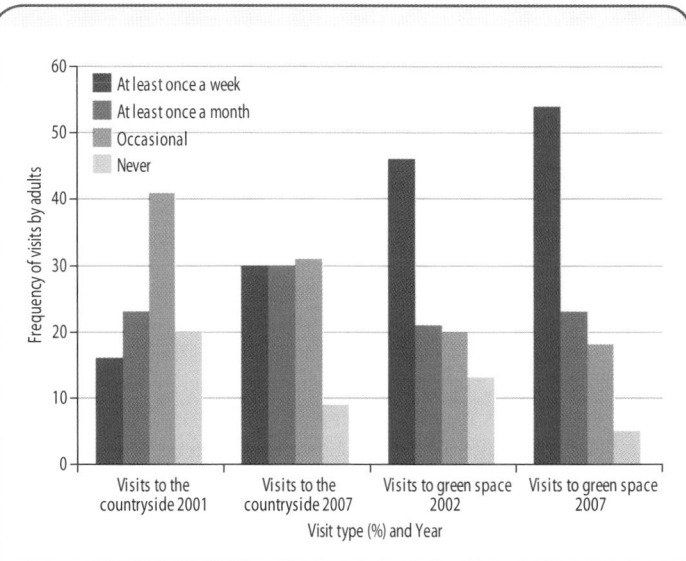

Figure 17.29 Frequency of visits to the countryside and greenspaces in England. Source: data from Foresight Land Use Futures Project (FLUFP 2010).

- There are 188,500 km of public rights of way, of which 78% are footpaths (Natural England 2008); 13 National Trails in England total 3,787 km.
- England has a considerable area of openwaters (Section 17.4.5.1). Whilst some of these waterside features are often accessible by paths or roads, many are not readily accessible.
- About 865,000 ha of land are open country (as in the Countryside and Rights of Way Act 2000) or registered common land. Other locally protected landscapes such as country parks and local nature reserves also offer important nature experiences but do not have well-documented estimates of their extent.

Table 17.15 The opportunities and potential benefits of different habitats for recreation and tourism. Source: reproduced from Chapter 16.

Habitat/habitat characteristic	Opportunities	Potential benefits
Unique opportunities—landscapes		
Mountains, crags and hills	Vertical and near vertical inclines	Climbing, mountaineering, rock scrambling, long range views and picnicking
Sea	Wind and waves	Surfing, kite surfing
Upland streams	Fast flowing shallow waters	Game angling, white water canoeing and rafting
Limestone rocks	Caves and fissures	Caving and potholing
Unique opportunities—landscapes/local places		
Alpine landscapes	Snow cover	Snow sports
Woodlands	Tree cover with tracks, rides and clearings	Walking, cycling, horse riding, many types of informal recreation
Estuarine environments	Sheltered waters	Moorings, marinas
Lakes	Wind	Sail sports
Beaches	Sand and sea	Outdoor swimming and beach activities
Generic opportunities—local places		
Parks and open spaces	Publicly accessible greenspaces	Walking, dog walking, cycling, running, picnicking and informal recreational activities

- There are 490,000 ha of publicly accessible woodland in England.
- Some form of access exists to some 70% of the coastline of England.

Access to ecosystems for recreation is highly variable throughout England (Curry 1994). Measures to address this issue include Natural England's Accessible Natural Greenspace Standard (ANGSt) and the Forestry Commission's Accessibility of Woodlands and Natural Spaces (O'Brien & Tabbush 2005) amongst others. These documents provide benchmarks for ensuring access to greenspaces near local populations (see Harrison *et al.* 1995; Handley *et al.* 2003). For example, the ANGSt recommendation is that local populations should have:

- an accessible natural greenspace of at least 2 ha in size, no more than 300 m (5 minutes' walk) from home;
- at least one accessible 20 ha site within 2 km of home;
- one accessible 100 ha site within 5 km of home;
- one accessible 500 ha site within 10 km of home;
- statutory Local Nature Reserves at a minimum level of 1 ha per thousand people.

It is recognised that this will be hard to achieve in the short term (LUC 2008), but Natural England advocates that all local authorities improve access through Green Space Strategies (Barker 1997; CABE Space 2006). The interest in green infrastructure may help increase the accessibility of greenspace. In East London, for example, deficiencies in access to various types of parks have been identified, with about 30% of people in the Urban area having no access to a local park of more than 2 ha within 400 m of home (GLA 2006b).

Recent legislative changes have contributed to improving access to some landscapes, with the Countryside and Rights of Way Act 2000 providing access to the uplands, downs and commons and the Marine and Coastal Access Act 2009 promising to do the same for access to the coast. However, those parts of England that are dominated by intensive lowland farming (e.g. East Anglia, Lincolnshire fenland and the Lancashire Plain) continue to offer relatively limited accessibility to outdoor environments.

17.5.4.3 Health

Within the last generation, the number of men and women in England performing 30 minutes of exercise on most days declined to fewer than 40% of men and 28% of women (Craig & Mindell 2008). The proportion of people leading sedentary lives and the prevalence of adult obesity has risen over the past 50 years (Foresight 2007; NICE 2009). Physical inactivity is associated with increased risk of obesity, chronic diseases of later life, and reduced life expectancy. The costs of inactivity in the UK are £8.3 billion per year, equating to £5 million for each Primary Care Trust (NICE 2009). Research by Foresight (2007) estimates that medical conditions associated with obesity have direct costs of £4.2 billion to the National Health Service and £16 billion a year to wider society. This latter figure could rise to £50 billion if current trends continue. Greenspaces and other open spaces can mitigate both the health and economic consequences of

obesity. Urban greenspaces provide important opportunities for, and also play a significant role in encouraging, physical activity (NICE 2009).

Physical activity improves both physical and mental health (Department of Health 2004; Foresight 2007). It is also now well-established that exposure to natural places, whether a view of nature from a window, being within natural places or exercising in these environments, can lead to positive mental health outcomes (Moore 1982; Ulrich 1984; Hartig *et al.* 2003; Pretty *et al.* 2005, 2007; Barton *et al.* 2009). Research on green exercise (i.e. physical activity in the presence of nature) in England has been linked to a range of benefits to human well-being including positive health outcomes (Hine *et al.* 2007; Pretty *et al.* 2007), promoting ecological knowledge (Burgess 1995; Pilgrim *et al.* 2007, 2008; Pretty 2007), fostering social bonds (Burgess *et al.* 1988; Pretty 2007) and influencing behavioural choices (Michell & Popham 2008; Peacock *et al.* 2008). Other research has considered:

- Levels of engagement with nature—the view from the window (Moore 1982; Ulrich 1984; Pretty *et al.* 2005); the role of nearby nature and urban greenspace (Harrison *et al.* 1987; Burgess *et al.* 1988) and the outcomes from countryside activities (Pretty *et al.* 2007).
- Types of engagement with a wide range of activities including walking, gardening, fishing and hunting (Pretty 2007), in different types of environment from the urban built environment to countryside and wilderness.
- Mental health outcomes using a range of measures of self-esteem, mood and stress (Pretty *et al.* 2005, 2007).
- Physical health outcomes using heart rate, blood pressure, body mass index, waist measures (waist circumference and waist to hip ratios) and physical activity level (Pretty *et al.* 2005; Sandercock *et al.* 2009).
- Associations between home proximity to greenspace and health (Mitchell & Popham 2008).

The health benefits of urban greening: Large-scale quantitative studies have shown that the prevalence of psychiatric morbidity is greater in urban than rural areas (Lewis & Booth 1994). Income-related inequalities in health also depend on exposure to greenspace. People who live in greener areas reported lower levels of health inequality relating to income deprivation for both all-cause mortality and mortality from circulatory diseases (Mitchell & Popham 2008). Empirical evidence demonstrates that urban greenspace provides unique outdoor educational opportunities (Kahn & Kellert 2002) and facilitates social networking (Hitchings 2010). It should be noted that considerable controversy surrounds what constitutes robust and reliable evidence for these types of research. Much of the well-being-related research is placed in the context of physical and mental health and has been criticised for not meeting the medical professions' exacting requirements for robust quantitative evidence (Newton 2007). These criticisms should not be used to discount the wealth of qualitative research into greenspace and human well-being, but should alternatively be used to improve the quality of research and the conclusions they produce.

Ongoing research in England on associations between physical access to greenspace, frequency of use, physical activity and health draws together diverse spatial and social data (see Hillsdon *et al.* 2006; Jones *et al.* 2009; Coombes *et al.* 2010). Research conducted in Bristol indicates that frequency of greenspace use declines with increasing distance from the home, thus suggesting a significant relationship between physical activity and accessible greenspace.

Children's access to nature and its impacts on their health and well-being: Open greenspace and access to nature are important for children (Kahn 1999; Kahn & Kellert 2002; Bingley & Milligan 2004; Michell & Popham 2008) and this consideration has been included in recent education policy. The outdoor environment is perceived as a social space which influences their choice of informal play activities and promotes healthy personal development (Burgess *et al.* 1988). Bingley and Milligan (2004) assessed how recalled childhood play experiences (from ages 7 to 11 years) in the form of memories and imaginings have an influence on the mental well-being of adults. The authors concluded that childhood experience of unstructured play with minimal adult supervision, in woodland areas, significantly influenced the perception of woodlands in adult life and the seeking out of outdoor spaces when stressed.

It is also known that children's social play, concentration and motor ability are all positively influenced by playing in nature. Yet the opportunities for children resident in both urban and rural neighbourhoods to join in safe play are rapidly diminishing, in part because of parental fear of crime and volume of road traffic (Holloway & Valentine 2000, 2003). Children spend less time outdoors today than they used to, a situation whose likely consequence is that children have become more disconnected from the natural environment (Bird 2007).

17.5.4.4 Aesthetics—places and landscapes

As a cultural service, aesthetic experiences of places and landscapes provide enjoyment, inspiration and contribute to human well-being. This 'good' is produced through people interacting with aesthetic qualities in local places and landscapes. For example, openness and remoteness in landscapes have been linked to feeling calm and relaxed (Natural England 2009a). Aesthetics and inspiration overlap with and potentially support other cultural benefits, by contributing to a distinctive sense of place, to the cultural value of a particular site, to places which have spiritual value, and to the enjoyment afforded by tourism and recreation. Qualitative research investigating how people connect to nature invites participants to compose poems or keep nature diaries in order to express how places are meaningful to them (Natural England 2009a).

Aesthetics and well-being: Research into the basis of aesthetic preferences has shown the importance of natural landscapes for feelings of safety, inspiration, harmony, peace and security (Appleton 1975). Links have been made between aesthetics and environmental ethics, where people potentially show greater care and concern for places that they find aesthetically valuable. For example, motivations of individuals engaged in community gardening and forms of environmental volunteering in various locations in England have been shown to be associated with aesthetic values (Brady 2006). Another example of aesthetic values interacting

with emotions is the feeling of tranquillity and calm that can be engendered by a landscape (Natural England 2009a). The Campaign to Protect Rural England mapped tranquillity in England using a variety of datasets and undertook a nationwide survey to ascertain the experiences people associated with tranquillity (**Figure 17.30**).

In the post-war period, various factors indicated decreasing opportunities for aesthetic and inspirational experiences of local places and socially valued landscapes. Changing patterns in population and work, as well as the expansion of urban settlements, suggest that there are fewer opportunities to interact with rural landscapes. However, the creation of National Parks, Areas of Outstanding Natural Beauty and Landscape Character Assessments, as well as recent efforts to protect marine and coastal areas, have provided protection of landscapes of high aesthetic value and enabled their enjoyment by both visitors and residents. Ecological restoration and re-wilding projects have also provided new opportunities for aesthetic interaction, especially where places have been managed for optimum biodiversity and the restoration of qualities associated with high aesthetic value, such as wildness.

There has also been a rise in local initiatives to protect and manage places (e.g. Wildlife Trusts, community orchards), which have raised awareness and provided more everyday opportunities for aesthetic enjoyment and inspiration within and at the fringes of towns and cities (Clifford & King 2006). Establishing local nature reserves and other local greenspaces will enable more people to be stimulated by natural spaces.

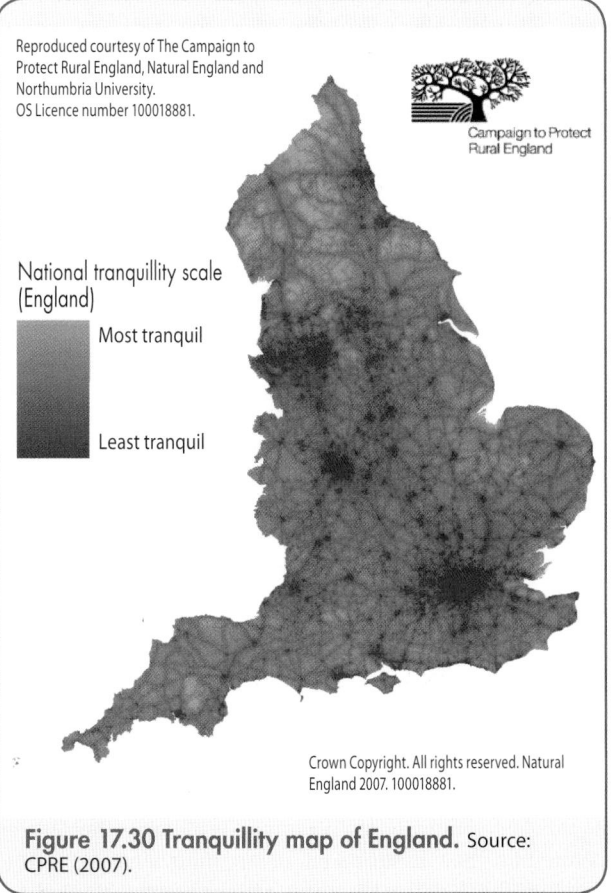

Campaign to Protect Rural England

National tranquillity scale (England)

Most tranquil

Least tranquil

Figure 17.30 Tranquillity map of England. Source: CPRE (2007).

17.5.4.5 Education

One way to increase children's contact with nature is within the formalised educational system, both in terms of the amount of exposure to nature in the learning environment and learning about nature (green education). The Office for Standards in Education (OFSTED 2008) has recently published guidance on learning outside the classroom. Outdoor learning is more than just fieldwork for natural history or geography: it is the notion that outdoor settings facilitate learning in all disciplines (Rickinson *et al.* 2004). Learning through Landscapes (LTL) is a UK national charity running programmes in England that funds independent research to evaluate the success of its interventions and demonstrates the value of outdoor learning. A national survey of 351 schools by LTL (2003) indicated that 75% of school improvements were driven in part by ecological motivations.

17.5.4.6 Religion and spirituality

Evidence, ecosystems, religion and spirituality: We face serious problems when assessing the extent, condition or configuration of English ecosystems as they contribute to spiritual and religious experiences. Cooper (2009), for example, devotes most of his paper to biblical exposition, seeking to explore 'the implications of a Christian worldview for the practice of valuing ecosystem services'. Empirical social scientific evidence of the extent and nature of religious and spiritual beliefs or experiences related to nature are much harder to find. At the risk of gross simplification we can identify two key issues, both legacies of the Reformation. The first is the uncertain status of sacred spaces and species in Protestant theology and ecclesiology. Sacred spaces and their spiritual value have been discussed at great length in contemporary writings (e.g. Brown 2004; Inge 2003; Sheehy 2007; Wynn 2007, 2009). Sacred species have received less attention in England; however, a flavour of their value can be found in the Flora Britannica (Mabey 1996) which assembles folklore, ecology, poetry and anecdotes from varied contributors. The second key issue is the rise of new forms of religiosity and religious pluralism. It is important to note that other religions such as Islam, Hinduism and pantheistic traditions also find spiritual inspiration through natural environments, with some placing particular importance on special species or places.

People, places, landscapes and religious/spiritual goods and benefits: In a religious/spiritual context, ecosystem goods and benefits refer to instances where ecosystems play a positive and formative role in religious practice and faith as well as providing a framework within which human accomplishments and aspirations can be considered. Historically, the Anglican Church has not had a strong tradition of sacred places. However, the 20th Century has witnessed a modest reassessment within the Anglican Church concerning ideas of pilgrimage, retreats and sacred spaces. In the 1990s this movement became a multi-faith phenomenon, with examples emerging from other faith traditions in England. For example, in Manchester at the Cheetham Al Hilal Community Project, the Muslim community has participated in an innovative project to improve the built and natural environment including the creation of a garden with an Islamic theme. The Sacred Land Project, supported by the World Wildlife Fund and launched by the Archbishop of Canterbury in April 1997, set out to revive and create sacred sites in Britain and overseas and involved Buddhist, Christian, Hindu, Jewish, Muslim and secular communities. Two examples of Sacred Lands Projects from the website are given in **Boxes 17.1** and **17.2**.

Whilst little explicit evidence from England exists, Hay and Hunt (2000) report on people's religious or spiritual experiences in Britain. Based on national survey data, the proportion of the population claiming to have had such

---

Box 17.1 Cultural services: sacred cave in North Yorkshire.

In Knaresborough in North Yorkshire is the ancient shrine of Our Lady of the Crag, in a cave cut into the rocky crags overlooking the river Nidd (**Figure 1**). According to local legend the shrine was dedicated to Our Lady in the 12th Century by John the Builder in thanks for a miracle that saved the life of his son from a rockfall. Nearly 500 years ago the shrine was suppressed during the Reformation, and became neglected and forgotten. In the early 1990s, a local group formed to renovate the shrine and to create a sacred garden around it, supported by the Sacred Land project. Now a new Madonna and Child, the work of Yorkshire sculptor, Ian Judd and commissioned by Arts and Sacred Places, has been installed in the cave.

Figure 1 Chapel of Our Lady of the Crag. *Photo by R/DV/RS available under a Creative Commons Attribution license.*

Box 17.2 Cultural services: sacred gardens in Leicester.

In Leicester, in a predominantly Hindu neighbourhood, a sacred garden was inaugurated in October 2000 beside Rushey Brook in the grounds of Rushey Mead School. The idea for the garden was inspired by Friends of Vrindavan, a Hindu community group whose inspiration comes from the sacred forests of Krishna in Vrindavan, India. The garden is based upon the theme of Krishna's struggle with the serpent Kaliya, who poisoned the sacred River Yamuna in Vrindavan. This theme was chosen to symbolise the struggle to clean our rivers and environment. Pupils of Rushey Mead School have created their own works of art to be placed in the garden.

experiences increased between 1987 and 2000 from 48% to 76%, with awareness of a sacred presence in nature increasing from 16% to 29%. Perhaps the most common natural environments that foster spiritual experiences are churchyards and burial grounds, as evidenced by the Church of England's average weekly attendances of over 1 million (Church of England 2007). Whist relatively few studies have focused empirically on religious experiences that are linked to particular places and ecosystems, the popularity of nature hymns at family services such as weddings and funerals (e.g. All Things Bright and Beautiful, Morning Has Broken) suggest its underlying importance to spiritual inspiration.

Whilst most research focuses on the built environment, a few academics are focusing on the practice of pilgrimage rather than the destination (Coleman & Eade 2004). The importance of nature and the countryside to English national identity occurs in political, social and literary writings, some of which are explicitly linked to religious discourses. Matless (1998) shows how advocates of organic farming and ruralism both drew from and developed Christian thinking. Moore-Colyer (2001) has examined one of these thinkers, Rolf Gardiner, and his attempts to enlist Church leaders and congregation members in a greater understanding of the spirituality of nature and of rural living. These strands of thought suggest that for some individuals, important spiritual experiences take place whilst interacting with nature via farming, gardening and a rural lifestyle.

Alongside the growth of pilgrimage as 'moving through nature', there has also been a growth during the 20th Century in the popularity of religious retreats to particular places in natural surroundings. There are currently 132 places of Christian retreat in Britain listed by the Retreat Association. David Conradson at Southampton University is researching retreat centres in southern England, using participant observation and interviews with monks and guests. Two Benedictine places of retreat in southern England, Alton Abbey and Elmore Abbey, are explored in Conradson (2008). His work demonstrates clearly the spatiality of these religious places, not just the abbey buildings themselves, but also the surrounding gardens and countryside. So for those on retreat, the 'stillness' they seek may be found in both the Benedictine monastic liturgy and in the abbey grounds and gardens.

It is extremely hard to pinpoint evidence of particular landscapes or ecosystems being conducive to spiritual and religious experiences. The configuration of marine and coastal habitats which appear to contribute to spiritual/religious experiences for some visitors at the holy island of Lindisfarne have to be seen in the context of other highly popular sites of pilgrimage that are inland and not characterised by dramatic landscape/ecological characteristics, such as Walsingham in North Norfolk with its woodlands and understorey of dense snowdrops. There is relatively little evidence on the specific role of nature and religious pilgrimage in human well-being. Conradson (2008) couches his research in terms of the therapeutic role of stillness and so, by implication, religious places are important to human well-being in their provision of 'therapeutic stillness'. Clearly diminution of the qualities (peace, beauty) that characterise journeys of pilgrimage and places of retreat would, potentially, have a marked impact on the well-being of participants.

Wynn (2009) seeks to explain how "our encounter with particular places, each characterised by its own phenomenology and distinctive possibilities for bodily appropriation, may prove to be religiously significant" (p44). He outlines three ways in which this might be the case. First, particular places may come to hold a religious significance because they carry some microcosmic significance, epitomising in some way the nature of things more generally. Second, God is taken to be presupposed in some particular, material context which may be a place or landscape or habitat. Third, specific places represent the meaning of past religious events that occurred there. In all three contexts, the religious experiences can have positive implications for faith, relationships and action. In the first and second of these possibilities, outdoor and open places may be more important than the traditional built or enclosed sites of religious devotion.

17.6 Drivers of Change

The environment is constantly changing as a result of a number of natural and anthropogenic drivers of change. These drivers put pressure on the environment, which affects ecosystems and the services they provide. The drivers may be direct, such as land use, and modify the physical, chemical and biological processes in, and nature of, ecosystems. Indirect drivers are of more anthropogenic origin and affect human impacts on ecosystems through such things as subsidies or policy development. These may then feed back into the direct drivers, for example, by causing changes in land use. Both types of drivers have varied across England and through time in their importance and impacts, which may be represented as threats or opportunities. **Tables 17.16** and **17.17** outline the key post-Second World War drivers and some of their effects, whilst more detailed information can be found in the be found in Section 17.4 (Broad Habitats).

Given that agriculture and forestry affect about 80% of England (Natural England 2008), then changes in farming practices and agricultural policy will have an important effect on the sustainability of ecosystem services through their direct effect on production, and indirectly through the regulating and cultural services. Since the 1950s, there has been increased specialisation and intensification of agricultural land, which has resulted in habitat loss and degradation. This has led to consequent changes in species composition and the loss or reduction in species populations, such as farmland birds, and has damaged soils, depleted aquifers, drained wetland sites and impacted surrounding habitats through agrochemical runoff. There is some evidence that some of these adverse effects are now mitigated by agri-environment schemes (Natural England 2009c), but also by other mechanisms and initiatives, such as the Voluntary, Catchment Sensitive Farming Delivery and Tried & Tested nutrient management plan initiatives. Also, in recent decades more environmentally favourable management practices have been advocated in forestry. An assessment of the environmental and economic

Table 17.16 Direct drivers of ecosystem change in England (continued over).

Main driver	Specific driver	Description
Habitat change	Productive area: expansion, conversion, abandonment	Arable cultivation has expanded significantly in post War years, although the latest Countryside Survey indicates an 8.8% decrease in area in the first decade of the 21st Century (Carey *et al.* 2008). Coniferous plantations have expanded to accommodate production forestry. In the lowlands, semi-natural habitats, including heathlands, fens and Woodlands are commonly managed less intensively or abandoned. Semi-natural Grassland declined by 97% in England and Wales due to fertiliser application.
	Mineral and aggregate extraction	There has been a long-term decline in coal mining with extensive restoration of despoiled areas. Open cast coal mining has expanded dramatically in the last 50 years most extensively in the North East. English coalfields now account for approximately 50% of production. More complex trends in the mining and quarrying of other minerals have been observed. The amount of marine aggregate extraction has more than doubled in the past 50 years. Although current extraction is concentrated in previously worked areas, a large part of this reserve is a finite resource.
	Urbanisation and sealed surfaces	In recent years there has been a significant switch from building on agricultural land to building on previously developed sites (brownfield), but this can lead to loss of valuable space for invertebrates and plants (Angold *et al.* 2006; Natural England 2008). Urban sprawl is limited by green belts and their area is stable. Increased paved surfaces lead to loss of services through increased urban heat islands and rapid storm runoff. Cities in England have taken action to increase urban trees and other greenspaces in order to combat some of these effects (Woodland Trust 2010).
	Infrastructure	Increasingly, space in England has been designated support infrastructure for society. The 2010 National Infrastructure Plan describes examples of infrastructure in need of improvement, including the approximately 299,300 km of public sewers in England and Wales. There has also been a rapid growth in demand for goods and travel, which have increased road use by 85% since 1980. If unchecked, congestion could cost England £22 billion in wasted time yearly, and could increase costs to businesses by £10 billion.
	Conservation management	There have been major increases since 1986 in the number of farmed areas in agri-environment schemes. In 2009, there were 42,500 agreement holders enrolled in the Entry Level Scheme and 4,300 agreement holders in the Higher Level Scheme, an increase from 28,500 and 1,200 in 2006 respectively. SSSIs comprise 7% of English land area and as of 2009, 95% were judged to be in favourable condition. There have also been significant increases in the land area managed by conservation NGOs in England (e.g. the National Trust, RSPB and Wildlife Trusts).
Pollution and nutrient enrichment	Pollution emissions and deposition	There have been major reductions of black smoke and sulphur dioxide emissions indicated by increasing extent of lichens and rising soil pH. There has been an improved biological and chemical quality of many of England's rivers since 1990, but increasing anthropogenic nitrogen emissions have led to widespread eutrophication of habitats. Approximately 60% of England's waters are considered eutrophic.
	Nutrient and chemical inputs (fertilisers; pesticides)	Dramatic increases in fertiliser application led to rising nitrogen and phosphorus concentrations, which have been associated with reductions of grassland biodiversity. For nitrogen, the major inputs to soil are from fertilisers and manures. In recent years agrochemical use has declined modestly. While pesticide use increases, as does their toxicity and persistence, usage increases do not directly equate to increased environmental impacts. Pesticides and herbicides are strongly linked with declines of farmland biodiversity.
Main driver	**Specific driver**	**Description**
Overexploitation of resources	Livestock stocking rates	Livestock populations have risen and declined over the past 50 years resulting in overgrazed uplands and the intensification of lowland farming. The increases in pigs and poultry have mainly been in housed rearing systems, but mostly have indirect impacts e.g. through the release of ammonia and disposal of slurry.
	Fisheries harvesting	In 2008, the total landings into England by UK vessels was 89,313 tonnes. Aquaculture is playing an increasingly important role in supplying the high demand for fish in the UK, with England contributing 6% of the output, mostly rainbow trout and mussels (James & Slaski 2009).
	Water abstraction	Overall trends in water abstraction amounts do not indicate a clear trend. Water abstraction by agriculture is a small part of abstraction, but has declined in recent years, although it may increase under climate change.
	Timber harvesting	From 1976 to 2009, softwood timber harvests have increased by 54%, while hardwood timber harvests have fallen by 46% (Forestry Commission 2010). Changes in woodland management have impacted forest structure, increasing the density of high forest with closed canopies, denser shading and less floristic diversity. However, a recent revival in traditional woodland practices, including the production of traditional coppice products, may help increase woodland biodiversity.
	Agricultural harvests	Seventy percent of England is designated as agriculture, focused in the lowlands, though pressure for stock grazing has increased expansion into the uplands. Cereals (mainly wheat and barley), oilseeds and other arable crops, such as sugar beets, comprise 71% of the crop area, with potatoes making up a further 2%. Land designated to agriculture in England has fallen by 2.8% from 1990 to 2007 (Countryside Survey 2009; Defra 2009c).

Table 17.16 continued. Direct drivers of ecosystem change in England.

Climate variability and change	Temperature and precipitation trends	Mean annual temperatures have increased across England particularly in East Anglia and the south east. The growing season has increased notably in northern England. Air frost incidence has reduced and there has been a 0.7°C increase in sea surface temperature since 1980. Annual mean precipitation has not changed, but there has been a decrease in summer precipitation.
	Carbon dioxide and ocean acidification	Though other parts of the UK are net sinks, England is a net source of carbon dioxide because agriculture and urban areas are sources of greenhouse gas emissions, although this has declined recently (DECC 2010). The highest emissions come from Greater London, followed by the north west. Carbon dioxide emissions have resulted in increased ocean acidification, with an average pH decrease from 8.2 to 8.1.
	Sea level change	Sea levels have risen 10 cm around the UK since 1900 (Jenkins *et al.* 2009). This poses threats of coastal flooding and erosion, especially in the south and east of England. It will also increase the salinity of rivers and ground water, impacting fish stocks, recreation, and access to fresh water.
	Extreme weather events	The observed (1960–2006) climate changes are projected to continue, with decreased summer precipitation and increased summer temperatures which may lead to drought, with increased winter precipitation and summer downpours leading to flash floods (Jenkins *et al.* 2009).
Introductions of invasive species and domestic species	Crop, livestock and forest species introductions	New crop strains have been developed from imported germplasm (e.g. short-straw varieties of wheat), and have helped increase yields for some crops more than threefold. Changes in crop types have also occurred, notably the introduction in the 1970s of oil seed rape as a crop which is now extensively grown, and, more recently, the production of bioenergy from Miscanthus grass and short rotation coppice. Significant genetic changes to livestock breeds used in commercial production have occurred (e.g. use of Holstein-type cattle for genetic improvement of dairy herds) and a range of imported beef, cattle and sheep breeds are now widely reared (e.g. Simmental and Charolais beef cattle; Texel sheep). Intensive livestock and crop husbandry practices have also contributed to high yielding farming systems. Introduced conifer species, such as Sitka spruce, were used increasingly in forestry in the first decades after World War Two, but this use has not intensified in recent decades.
	Alien and non-native invasive species	More than 100 non-native plant and animal species have been identified as invasive species. Non-native plants are not common components of English rural vegetation as most occur in urban areas, but may become so with climate change. The majority of introduced species appear to cause no adverse impacts, while some cause widespread damage (e.g. Dutch Elm Disease). Many ornamental/exotic plant species have increasingly established wild populations and whilst many remain very local, others have spread to become abundant and problematic e.g. Australian swamp stone crop (*Crassula helmsii*).
	Outbreaks of native species	Some opportunist native species have persisted through changes to habitats and climate, and have capitalised on vacant niches. These include foxes and some bird, bat and invertebrate species in urban environments. Deer populations, especially roe deer (*Capreolus capreolus*), have increased dramatically since the removal of predators. Plants such as ragwort (*Senecio species*) have spread, especially along railway tracks.
	Extinctions and declines	Four hundred and twenty nine species have disappeared from England, mostly in the past 200 years (Natural England 2010b). The UK Biodiversity Action Plan and the England Biodiversity Strategy identified 943 species as being of conservation concern.

sustainability of agricultural production systems in the UK showed that land use and greenhouse gas emissions are the most significant factors determining sustainability (Glendining *et al.* 2009). It also suggested that agricultural systems are sustainable at rates close to current production levels and that extensification would result in the loss of non-food ecosystem services, so intensification would be preferable, although recent changes in the price of oil and the value of arable crops and livestock may affect this balance.

Indirectly, changes in policies have impacted agricultural land. For instance, the introduction, and later the cutback, of EU mandated set-aside land on farms affected farmland species. Removal of this requirement left each country to encourage policy uptake, as with Natural England's Environmental Stewardship programmes. Similarly, the EU CAP reform in 2013 could have a significant effect, not only on the English landscape, but also on biodiversity and ecosystem service delivery.

Atmospheric pollution has had a major effect on habitat condition and composition and decreased species richness. Critical loads are being exceeded for a number of chemicals, leading to acid deposition, eutrophication, ground level ozone and heavy metal pollution, although in some cases the situation is improving (RoTAP 2011).

Development, another major driver, is limited in part by legislation such as the Green Belt Policy, which regulates expansion of cities in order to control urban sprawl. However, development continues to happen, especially on greenfield sites, and will continue to do so due to increasing demand for housing. Between 2000 and 2003, 34% of all development happened outside of existing urban areas, on agricultural or other non-urban land (Natural England 2008). This profoundly affects the landscape, species dependent on the lost habitat, and the quality of services that can be expected from a built area (Natural England 2008). Positively, assessment of past mistakes, some developing

Table 17.17 Indirect drivers of ecosystem change in England.

Main driver	Specific driver	Description
Socio-political	Legislation, regulation	Key areas of legislation/regulation have been: town and country planning, pollution control, emissions regulation, protection of biodiversity, amenity and natural beauty.
	Financial support mechanisms	The 1947 Agriculture Act and 1973 EU Common Agriculture Policy (CAP) shaped agricultural production subsidies resulting in the transformation of most semi-natural systems into farmland. Recent CAP reform has decoupled production and financial support. Increasing farm payment has come through agri-environment schemes, which supported 65% of English farms in 2009. Thus financial support solely encouraging production is replaced by financial support that enhances biodiversity and promotes multi-functional forestry. A growing NGO movement has supplemented public investment in environmental management for conservation and other purposes.
Economic	Market forces	Markets for agricultural and horticultural produce have impacted most ecosystems, given the extent of agricultural land in England. Arable cultivation and dairy farming are currently the most profitable, while livestock and mixed farming are the least profitable. Niche markets include organic produce and natural products (e.g. reeds for roof thatching), which play a role in sustaining management of some ecosystems. The market collapse of charcoal and traditional forest products has resulted in the large-scale abandonment of broadleaved woodland management, however, the growth of biomass fuel markets may reverse this trend. Fish consumption has contributed to declining fish stock and the disturbance of marine habitats.
	Business size and globalisation	Primary products are supplied by a large number of small producers, while other parts of the supply chain are increasingly dominated by a small number of multi-national agricultural corporations that impose price and quality contrasts upon production.
Science and technology	Innovation / technological change	Mechanisation has enabled the intensification of farm production (greater efficiencies of ploughing, harvesting, etc.). The expansion in fertiliser and pesticide use further increases agricultural intensification. Precision farming has been introduced recently to improve resource use and moderate environmental impacts. Similar transformations of commercial forestry and commercial fishing have occurred.
	Biotechnology	Genetically Modified crops have been heavily regulated and their impact upon farming practices negligible. However, there have been major innovations in plant and animal breeding e.g. development of rape as an oil seed, short-straw wheat, and Holstein genetics in dairy cattle.
	Energy production	Fossil fuels and nuclear have been the dominant energy sources of the 20th Century. Policy changes to support renewable energy have led to increased wind power generation and the expansion of biofuel crops and short rotation coppice. Modest increases in woodfuel consumption has occurred, with some biodiversity benefits in neglected woodlands.
	Transport	Major increases in transport mechanisation have resulted in major road expansion, while increased global air and shipping freight may have increased rates of alien species introduction.
Cultural and behavioural	Consumption choices	Consumer choice of foodstuffs has increased sharply and currently represents a lower proportion of income. There has been more recent consumer interest in organic, local and other more sustainable consumption.
	Attitudes and the media	There has been a significant increase in media coverage of environmental issues in the past 50 years, increased membership of environmental NGOs (e.g. RSPB, Wildlife Trusts) and greater environmental awareness amongst the English populace.
	Knowledge individual & societal	The understanding of key issues, such as the health impacts of air pollution, biodiversity loss and environmental impacts of acid rain have driven significant changes of policy.
Demographic	Population and demographic change	England's population grew by 10.1 million from 1951 to 2008 giving rise to population densities that can reach 3.95 people per hectare. This is the highest in the UK and one of the highest in the world. There is, however, significant variation in population density which reaches 131 people per hectare in Kensington and Chelsea, but is only 0.2 people per hectare in Eden, Cumbria.
	Migration and ethnicity	Net migration from abroad has become a main contributor to population growth in England (Jefferies 2005). There has also been a significant internal migration of UK population towards southern England and movement of people out of metropolitan areas (Champion 2005). Ethnic diversity in England has increased significantly in the past 50 years (Jefferies 2005).

technologies and careful planning can offer opportunities to lessen our environmental impact. For example, the maintenance, or sometimes restoration, of brownfield sites can increase habitats for certain species. This can be especially important in invertebrate conservation, as at least 40 invertebrate species are confined to brownfield sites (Natural England 2008). Sustainable housing and transport will play a pivotal role in how we impact the environment, whilst changing agricultural practices to low-input (and possibly smaller-scale) operations will affect large areas of land and habitats.

17.7 Consequences of Change

The accounts of the Broad Habitats (Sections 17.4.1 to 17.4.8) have shown that each delivers a range of ecosystem services, but they vary in their importance for delivering specific services. They also vary in the recent trends in their ability to deliver ecosystem services (**Figure 17.31**). This figure provides an overall picture of the relative importance of each Broad Habitat for ecosystem service provision, but it was derived from available literature and

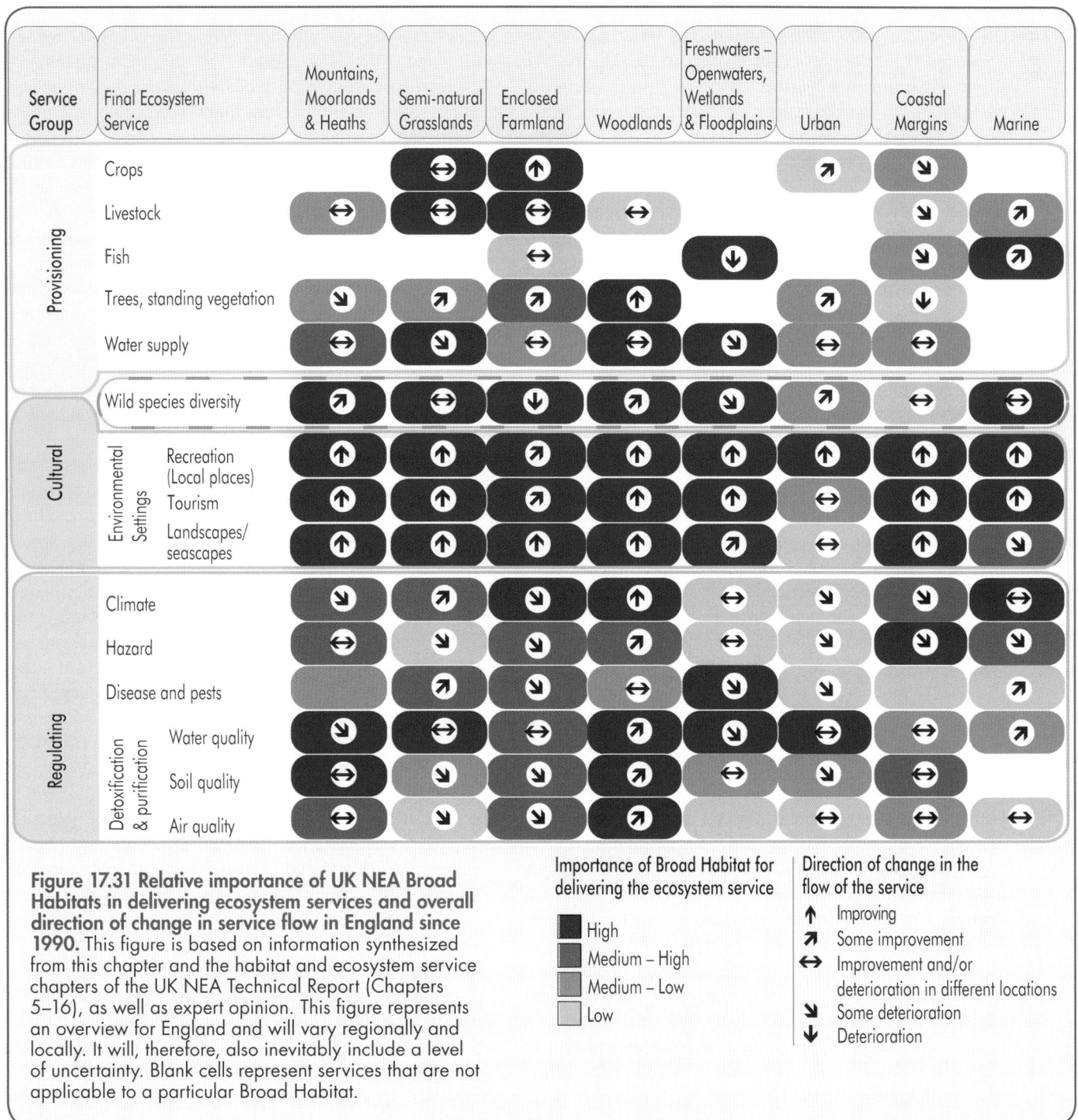

Figure 17.31 Relative importance of UK NEA Broad Habitats in delivering ecosystem services and overall direction of change in service flow in England since 1990. This figure is based on information synthesized from this chapter and the habitat and ecosystem service chapters of the UK NEA Technical Report (Chapters 5–16), as well as expert opinion. This figure represents an overview for England and will vary regionally and locally. It will, therefore, also inevitably include a level of uncertainty. Blank cells represent services that are not applicable to a particular Broad Habitat.

Importance of Broad Habitat for delivering the ecosystem service
- High
- Medium – High
- Medium – Low
- Low

Direction of change in the flow of the service
- ↑ Improving
- ↗ Some improvement
- ↔ Improvement and/or deterioration in different locations
- ↘ Some deterioration
- ↓ Deterioration

expert opinion and can conceal high intra-habitat and regional variations. It thus should be taken as indicative rather than definitive.

Amongst the provisioning services, Enclosed Farmland and Semi-natural Grasslands are of highest importance for crops and livestock and Woodlands for timber, whilst many of the semi-natural habitats are important for water supply. For the regulating services, Enclosed Farmland, Woodlands and Mountains, Moorlands and Heaths are of high or high-medium importance. This serves to underline the significance of these habitats, which is partly a consequence of their large areal extent, but also of their structure and functioning. The high importance of all Broad Habitats for cultural services reflects their value to human health and well-being through people's direct experience.

Our more limited knowledge of the ecological trends of Urban habitats makes assessment of change in their ecosystem service delivery difficult to assess. Similarly, our more limited knowledge of Marine habitats over time limits our ability to assess the change occurring in the ecosystem services they deliver.

Changes among ecosystem service delivery in the eight Broad Habitats over the last 20 years have shown that a significant proportion of service provision has declined (**Figure 17.31**). These adverse trends are likely to be even more noticeable over the longer timescale of the last 50 years, especially amongst regulating services. However the period since 1998 has been one in which England's countryside has remained relatively stable in ecological character by comparison with the last decades of the 20th

Century (Carey *et al.* 2008); although, as noted above, we know much less about recent change in the Marine and Urban environments. Further, there is now a range of mechanisms in place to variously restore biodiversity, Broad Habitat function and/or ecosystem services. Although this list is far from complete, these include improvements in the management of the protected area series, including approximately 7% of England which is notified as SSSI (95% of which is currently in favourable or unfavourable recovering condition); implementation of the EBS, which has ambitious objectives to increase the area of priority habitats (Defra 2006a); a major expansion of agri-environment schemes delivering a range of ecosystem services (Natural England 2009c); coastal realignment at 23 sites on the English coast, providing natural flood protection and a range of other services (Morris *et al.* 2008).

Despite these changes in service delivery, England's ecosystems provide considerable benefits to humans, both in terms of well-being as well as economically. In recent years, the economic value of ecosystem services has been demonstrated in a wide range of studies relevant to policy and other decisions (e.g. Shepherd *et al.* 2007; Willis *et al.* 2003; Harlow *et al.*; Chapter 22).

However, given the multiple drivers which affect the Broad Habitats, it is important that they are protected and managed sustainably in order to continue future service delivery (Section 17.8). This is particularly challenging, as some of the main drivers, notably air pollution and climate change, cannot be addressed by local ecosystem management alone and require action across all of society. The drivers will affect ecosystems and service delivery in two main ways in the future, firstly, through competition for space and, secondly, through changes in habitat and species condition. The projected population expansion and the associated demands for housing and infrastructure (particularly in southern England) and food provision are likely to lead to additional habitat loss, although there could be opportunities to minimise these losses through the development of brownfield sites and further use of biotechnology. Whilst regulation has reduced the emissions of many major pollutants and improved habitat condition, population pressure and climate change will continue to affect future pollution risks to the natural environment (Natural England 2008). Climate change will directly affect the distribution, condition and functioning of habitats, which will pose challenges for their conservation. It will also lead to sea level rise affecting marine and coastal habitats, the spread of pests and diseases and opportunities for cultural pursuits.

17.8 Sustainable Management

The drivers of change (Section 17.6) and the consequences of changes observed since the Second World War (Section 17.7) have shown the need for sustainable management if ecosystems are to continue meeting the needs for human well-being. This was captured by the UK's Sustainable Development Commission, which had as one of its principles 'Living within environmental limits—respecting the limits of our planet's environment, resources and biodiversity—to improve our environment and ensure that the natural resources needed for life are unimpaired and remain so for future generations' (Defra 2005). In England, the Natural Environment White Paper, due in 2011, will outline the government's vision for the natural environment.

The Convention on Biological Diversity endorsed the application of the ecosystems approach at its fifth Conference of the Parties, as a strategy for the integrated management of land, water and living resources, and at the seventh Conference of Parties it gave priority to facilitating the implementation of this approach. The ecosystem approach is being promoted by Defra through its Ecosystems Approach Action Plan (Defra 2007a, 2010g) and is seen as involving a more holistic and integrated approach based on a consideration of whole ecosystems; it requires that the value of ecosystems and their services is reflected in policy and decision making across Government departments. In England, the Action Plan is also being taken forward by non-departmental public bodies such as Natural England, the Forestry Commission and the Environment Agency and they are undertaking case studies demonstrating the benefits of the approach (Everard 2009; Harlow *et al.* 2010). An evidence base is also being developed through such projects as Making Space for Water and Valuing Ecosystem Services in the East of England (Glaves *et al.* 2009), and several projects funded under the Asset Management Programme (AMP; Anderson 2010; Water UK 2009), which test and demonstrate the application of the ecosystems approach. In addition, tools for valuing ecosystem services have been developed and applied to support environmental management decisions. These have shown the importance of a healthy natural environment for current and future economic prosperity, as well as a range of societal benefits (e.g. Defra 2007c; Natural England 2009e; Chapter 22).

As discussed below, there are many potential trade-offs between ecosystem services. Arguably the most significant change in ecosystem services in the past 50 years has been the dramatic increase in the provisioning service of food production, which has resulted in a prolonged period of food security in England. For example there has been a 320% per hectare increase in wheat production (Section 17.5.3.1) that has had an adverse effect on regulatory services (e.g. climate regulation and hazard regulation) and cultural services (e.g. aesthetics) (Braat *et al.* 2008; de Groot *et al.* 2010).

Understanding the underlying economic process is critical to interpreting these changes and identifying solutions. Most provisioning services create goods (e.g. food and timber) that can be sold, which then enables producers to increase their supply by intensifying production systems, or overexploiting wild stocks. In contrast, most regulatory and cultural services are public benefits for which beneficiaries do not pay, so those who manage or exploit ecosystems are unrewarded. There is currently much interest in payment for ecosystem services (PES) schemes, which pay ecosystem owners and managers for the supply of non-market goods and benefits from ecosystem services, as a mechanism for supporting a more balanced supply of ecosystem services (Defra 2010e). It is important to note that such approaches are difficult to apply to marine ecosystems where the property rights needed to operate such schemes do not apply, other than in some intertidal situations. Regulatory and voluntary regimes will continue to play a significant role in management of marine ecosystems.

The largest PES scheme in England is the government's agri-environment schemes under the Rural Development Programme for England that explicitly promotes conservation of genetic diversity of livestock, flood regulation and the protection of soil and water. It also plays a significant role in the protection of biodiversity, landscape and historic heritage. Other services such as pollination and climate regulation are incidental benefits of the schemes. In 2009, agri-environment scheme agreements covered over 6 million ha (66% of England's agricultural land) and provided payments of approximately £400 million a year to farmers (Natural England 2009c). Private investment in PES is also occurring, for example, water companies are investing in bog restoration and other forms of habitat management in several upland catchments that supply potable water, such as in the Forest of Bowland and the Peak District. The objective is to improve raw water quality and thereby reduce water treatment costs in the future, but the scheme may simultaneously improve water storage, carbon storage and biodiversity (Anderson 2010; Water UK 2009). Further water industry-funded catchment management schemes in the lowlands have focused upon reducing inputs of nutrients and pesticides from farming (Water UK 2009).

The current state of land use, as well as the needs of the future, were assessed by the Foresight Land Use Futures Project (FLUFP 2010). Among its objectives was an assessment of strategies for sustainable land use and methods to increase its value for people and the economy. It recognised the importance of public goods and services provided by the land and the amount of England's landscape that is held in private ownership. It also highlighted potential pressures on land in the South East, as well as water use in the South East and the East of England. To ensure the continued delivery of these services it suggested promoting the multi-functionality of land as an appropriate and potentially sustainable response, through an area or catchment-based approach to land use policy. An additional future consideration for landscape planners and policy makers is the range of potential impacts of climate change that will require a land use planning approach that integrates strategies for mitigation and adaptation to climate change.

17.8.1 Synergies and Trade-offs

The development of such a multifunctional approach to land use would require the recognition that any ecosystem delivers a variety goods and services and the setting of multiple objectives for its management. This requires an integrated understanding and management of ecosystems, including synergies and trade-offs between ecosystem services under different land uses and management regimes.

There are concerns about a perceived trade-off between the conservation of natural resources and economic growth (Natural England 2009e), with the former often regarded

as a luxury and the latter as a necessity (Dasgupta 2007). However, the evidence currently suggests that the two need not conflict and that natural, ecosystem-based solutions can be cost effective in addressing environmental issues, such as climate change adaptation, with potentially profound economic consequences (EFTEC 2009; TEEB 2009). For example, there are several documented cases of floodplain restoration providing benefits for both water regulation and biodiversity. Morris *et al.* (2004a) provide five case studies that demonstrate both the compatibility and conflict between flood defence, biodiversity and other ecosystem services, these studies include the Beckingham Marshes, River Trent, Long Eau Washlands and Lincolnshire and Harbertonford Flood Alleviation Scheme.

Similarly, the 23 English managed coastal re-alignment schemes (Morris *et al.* 2008), which relocated sea walls and restored intertidal habitats, provided synergies between increased natural flood protection and a range of other ecosystem services. One such example is the Wallasea Island Wild Coast, Europe's largest intertidal habitat creation project at over 700 ha (Morris *et al.* 2008, RSPB 2008). Its multiple objectives include creating new intertidal habitats to compensate for habitats and species losses elsewhere, reducing coastal flood damage risks, carbon storage, protection of potential nursery habitats for commercial fish stocks and an extensive area of accessible coastal land for recreation and the enjoyment of nature. A further interesting synergy is the use of material from Crossrail, the new rail route under London, for habitat creation. Negative effects on habitats and ecosystem services by the scheme were assessed as negligible or minor, since the project used materials excavated during construction for mitigation of negative impacts through habitat creation.

There are particular concerns about the synergies and trade-offs between ecosystem services when transformation occurs between habitats, particularly when changes in service provision is marked. For example, the conversion of floodplains to agricultural land or urban development would enhance the provision of food or space for housing and infrastructure respectively; but many of the water, soil and carbon regulating services provided by the floodplain would be severely diminished or lost. Such floodplain transformation has occurred in many parts of England (e.g. London, York and Oxford) and has created developed areas with increased flood risk. Nevertheless, there are plans, such as in the Thames Gateway, to restore some floodplain functioning as a means of sustainable development (Lavery & Donovan 2005). Flood risk management through changing land use practices also forms part of some agri-environment schemes, for example in the Belford catchment, Northumberland, where ecosystem management is thought to have played a role in mitigation of floods in September 2008 (Wilkinson *et al.* 2010).

Increasingly, research projects are examining cases where complex balances of synergies and trade-offs between services must be considered alongside scenarios to meet health and well-being requirements. In a project investigating peatlands on the Somerset Moors and Levels and on Thorne and Hatfield Moors, it was found that stakeholders saw the key synergies as being between cultural heritage and carbon storage, and between carbon storage, biodiversity and recreation (Bonn *et al.* 2009). The key conflicts were identified as peat extraction versus carbon storage, and greenhouse gas emissions and cultural heritage versus peat extraction (Box 5.10, Section 5.4), although these may be context dependent. Other examples include the potential synergies between biodiversity and pollination services (Tscharntke *et al.* 2005). An assessment of trade-offs and synergies and the role for sustainable management for coastal margins habitats is given in **Box 17.3**.

There is an increasing awareness in government and land management organisations of the need for sustainable and integrated management of ecosystems and their services. This will require further refinement of our understanding of trade-offs and synergies between ecosystem services, some of which are likely to emerge from operationalising an ecosystem approach.

17.9 Knowledge Gaps

There is already a large amount known about ecosystems in England. However, significant gaps in our knowledge base remain, as described below. Addressing these gaps may help to provide guidelines for future research and information for policy making and management.

17.9.1 Status, Condition and Trends
Basic information on the extent of most Broad Habitats has been recorded since 1990 through the Countryside Survey (2009), although this only covers a number of sample sites in detail and is undertaken periodically. Fewer data sets are available prior to 1990, which makes the assessment of long-term trends more challenging. Whilst coastal margins and woodlands have been reasonably well recorded, other habitats are lacking in full information about extent or trends.

These include: Urban habitats, where currently there is no agreed definition of 'urban', nor are there comprehensive data on the extent of greenspace and Mountains, Moorlands and Heaths, which require better inventories and integrated monitoring of the extent and condition, especially the impacts of grazing on biodiversity. Information on condition is generally less well established.

Species monitoring, especially if carried out for a range of taxa, can be an important guide to habitat condition, particularly as most recording is done annually and covers a wide range of habitats (e.g. the BTO/JNCC/RSPB Breeding Bird Survey). Lower plants and organisms, however, are less well-recorded and may be particularly important in supporting ecosystem services.

17.9.2 Ecosystem Services
Quantifying the role of biodiversity, including uncharismatic and speciose groups of organisms such as invertebrates, lower plants and fungi, in ecosystem function and service provision, was one of 12 research priorities identified by Anton *et al.* (2010). The authors recognised that it is often species, or groups of species within habitats, that actually deliver the services. This aspect has not been considered in the UK NEA, partly due to our lack of knowledge on species as opposed to habitat delivery. Basic quantification of many of the ecosystem services is difficult, as it often requires extensive and long-term monitoring. For example, on arable land, water, wind and tillage erosion have accelerated over the 50 years; however, quantification of these processes at regional or national scale remains a challenge.

Given the multifunctional nature of ecosystems, greater understanding of the interactions between the habitats (and their component species) and ecosystem service delivery is necessary. This is particularly the case for some supporting services which underpin the delivery of the other services. If human needs are to be met, then assessing the current status of ecosystems in terms of their capacity to deliver services and identifying the most imperilled services will

---

Box 17.3 Evaluation of the likely synergies and trade-offs for Coastal Margin habitats.

There is a potential for clear synergies between different services, allowing the identification of 'win-win' combinations. Examples include environmentally friendly 'soft' engineering approaches to sea defence such as beach nourishment of shingle beaches. These have less impact and may help create conditions for shingle beach vegetation to develop. Potential conflicts include forestry on dunes which locally draws down the water table by around 50 cm (Clarke & Sanitwong 2010), with possible implications for the local hydrological regime and the associated dune slack flora and fauna.

In general, sustainable management should enhance or maintain the specific characteristics of coastal margin habitats in England, rather than replicating services provided better elsewhere. It should also take into account the uniqueness and non-replaceability of services. 'Win-win' combinations of services can be achieved by identifying complementary services within the context of sustainable management of these largely natural systems. Two main issues are relevant to the sustainable management of coastal margin habitats in England: sediment supply and managed realignment of coastal flood defences. Sediment supply is often interrupted by coastal protection works, and coastal sediment cells need to be considered to avoid causing sea defence issues downdrift, or possible negative consequences on protected areas. In the south and southeast, the trend is for nourishment schemes such as shingle bypassing (e.g. Shoreham harbour) and recycling (e.g. Dungeness). The Dungeness nuclear power stations require the transport of 67,000 cubic metres/134,000 tonnes of shingle annually 6.5 km from the east to the west to maintain the beach protecting them from the sea (Doody 2001; Chapter 11). Managed realignment, or roll-back, has primarily been applied to saltmarshes in England, but is increasingly being considered for other habitats such as dunes and shingle (e.g. Pye *et al.* 2007). With relatively minimal pre-treatment and/or management of the area, allowing tidal ingress through a simple, relatively small breach of the existing sea wall onto low-lying agricultural land will quickly produce inter-tidal mudflats which are colonised by salt marsh plants (French *et al.* 2000). There is growing evidence that restored salt marsh can perform many of the ecosystem services provided by natural systems including coastal defence and storage of pollutants. Where saltmarsh regenerates on former agricultural land, and where grazing is not introduced, there may be a transfer in services from provisioning services (e.g. farmed food and fibre) towards regulatory services (e.g. flood risk), supporting services (e.g. biodiversity) and cultural services (e.g. amenity). It can form one of the management options to maintain the extent of coastal margin habitats threatened by sea level rise and the services they provide. Artificial re-mobilisation of overstabilised or reclaimed habitats may rejuvenate natural processes, with the aim of restoring the dynamic processes which allow coastal margin habitats to self-adjust to changing environmental conditions, with long-term benefits for biodiversity (e.g. Garbutt *et al.* 2006).

provide guidance for management and policy making. This will involve determining the extent and condition of the particular habitat needed to maintain adequate levels of service provision as well as identifying limitations to the delivery of that service.

There is also a need to improve our understanding of how various drivers, such as climate change, are affecting ecosystem services (Haines-Young & Potschin 2008; Haines-Young & Potschin 2010) and to develop predictive tools to assess how the provision of ecosystem services might change in the future. These tools could be further used to explore the sensitivity of various ecosystem service provision drivers and to identify non-linear responses and thresholds in service delivery (Anton et al. 2010). The extent to which ecosystems exhibit distinct thresholds is uncertain, particularly in the context of England's natural environment, and so a gradual degradation of ecosystems and ecosystem services might be more probable than a sudden collapse.

17.9.3 Measurement and Monitoring
Much of the data used to establish and measure ecosystem services have been collected for entirely different purposes and further consideration should be given to data that are fit-for-purpose. Consistent, standarised data are needed for many services, as highlighted by terrestrial primary production where data collection is limited to local scales, and for freshwater and marine productivity where surrogates and models are used (17.5.1.4). Repeated consistent and thorough survey methodologies for each habitat would allow more accurate estimates of change in extent and condition over time and should, if possible, be designed to incorporate previous research data. Indicator taxa whose presence, abundance or density reveal different levels of service provision (or the lack of it) could be identified and used as assays for the state of systems as appropriate, either via bespoke field protocols or by making use of existing data sets or data collection. Additional research would be required to establish connections between species and services to ensure appropriate monitoring protocols.

Additional monitoring could be prioritised for those habitats or services which are under particular threat, so as to enhance our knowledge of changes under pressure and the existence of possible limits on their service delivery. It can also be useful in providing information on the effectiveness of new, sustainable management practices. If it is not possible to undertake such monitoring then consideration could be given to the use of indicators of habitat condition or service delivery as used for UK biodiversity, including three indicators on ecosystem integrity and ecosystem goods and services, relating to marine, terrestrial and freshwater ecosystems (Defra 2010f).

17.9.4 Valuation
Ecosystem services have often been regarded as 'free goods', particularly those for which there is no market. This includes some of the supporting and cultural services, such as decomposition and aspects of traditional conservation of biodiversity (Haslett et al. 2010). Defra and Natural England are currently assessing the value of the non-market benefits of environmental stewardship, but there is still a need to refine methods to quantify the value of non-monetary services and broad habitats to improve decision making (Defra 2007b).

Whilst there are techniques to value some environmental impacts, a systematic and comprehensive method integrating both positive and negative impacts on the natural environment is lacking within the decision-making process (Defra 2007b). Often this has led to overexploitation of ecosystem services. Improved accounting of the value of natural capital and ecosystem services is needed, as well as ways of making ecosystem services more part of the formal economy (Natural England 2009e).

There is also a need to account for multiple services and resolving trade-offs between them. For example, resolving tensions between different cultural services, such as solitude and wildness experience versus increasing recreational use of the coast, and between societal and environmental services, particularly the role of biodiversity.

17.9.5 Management
A range of services are delivered by ecosystems that are poorly understood, despite their importance. These gaps in understanding impact upon management decisions and can affect policy making over the longer term. Amongst these knowledge gaps is the limited understanding of moor and heathland responses to various management options and grazing regimes in relation to greenhouse gas emissions. There are also concerns about eutrophication in land and water systems from agricultural sources and their influence on the composition and diversity of plant communities and soil biota, impacting ecosystem services via poorly understood mechanisms. Some of these concerns may be addressed by assessing past management decisions in the context of indicator data to improve future management. For instance, decreased fertiliser use and its relationship with improved local water quality might be examined using trends in native water-based flora and fauna. In coastal habitats, the management options required to respond to sea-level rise need more attention: in particular, how to apply rollback or managed realignment to Coastal Margin habitats, including Saltmarsh, and what habitat restoration measures are needed to make this feasible.

It should be acknowledged, however, that at no point will a complete picture be available. There will always be gaps in our knowledge, and the discussion above highlights some of the main gaps identified in previous sections. Nevertheless, progress is ongoing to address these gaps and to develop a robust evidence base demonstrating the effectiveness of integrating ecosystem management with ecosystem service delivery.

17.10 Conclusions

Whilst England's landscape is dominated by agricultural habitats, it is the mix of UK NEA Broad Habitats combined with the local climate, geology, soils and relief that provides the character of the landscapes, and the delivery of the services is a function of both the nature of these habitats and human management practices. In terms of area, agricultural habitats, especially Enclosed Farmland, are important both for the delivery of production services and for the indirect effects which agricultural practices have on other habitats and their service delivery. The pressure on the agricultural habitats is driven by the increasing population of England and the demands made on the various provisioning services. These demands cannot be, or are not being, met by service provision within England and thus we are dependent on services from other countries and vice versa. England, for example, is the main contributor to UK crop production (17.4.3) and through increasing yields, has contributed more to greater self-sufficiency in food production in the UK. Nevertheless, England, like the rest of the UK, is dependent on non-UK ecosystem services (Chapter 21). In England, this is to meet the demand of its largely urban and growing population.

Some services, e.g. regulating and cultural, are provided locally or regionally, for example, through woodlands regulating water and air quality, whilst also providing greenspace for recreation and human well-being. Others can be local, such as recreation and tourism, but the demand may also be met from other parts of the UK as people seek particular activities or experiences and vice versa. For example, coasts are a popular holiday destination, as are certain other areas, such as the Lake District. This supply can also come from outside England, e.g. Snowdonia, the Cairngorms or the Fermanagh Lakelands. Similarly, carbon sequestration is local, but the benefits in contributing to emission targets for climate mitigation are at regional to national, if not global, scales. Thus it can be seen that service demand and supply cannot be considered entirely in the context of England alone, and whilst this chapter has assessed England's UK NEA Broad Habitats and their services, they need to be seen in this broader perspective.

The assessment of the status and trends of England's Broad Habitats has shown that Enclosed Farmland and Urban areas have increased significantly over the last 70 years, at the expense of the other Broad Habitats. The latter have not only decreased in area (excluding Marine), but also, all have declined in condition as they have been affected by changes to soil, air and water quality arising from farming practices and urban pollution. There has been recent improvement in their condition in many areas as a consequence of various agri-environment schemes, legislation and guidance (e.g. on air, water and soil) and policy shifts. Their condition is important for the delivery of a range of ecosystem services and this improvement in condition is reflected in **Figure 17.31**, although the situation in several of the habitats with regards to many of the regulating services still requires attention.

The recognition of the importance of ecosystem services, and the role of habitats and their condition on delivery, has led to research into more sustainable management, as well as a more holistic ecosystem approach. Both should help to ensure that ecosystems continue to deliver the service needs of humans and their well-being, and that the concerns about the synergies and trade-offs that may occur between ecosystems and their services are addressed. In addition, investigation into the economics of ecosystem services has served to show the value of ecosystem services at national, as well as regional and local levels.

Whilst there is still much that we do not know about the exact nature of the relationship between the Broad Habitats and each of the ecosystem services, there is enough evidence to show that each habitat contributes, to varying degrees, to the delivery of a variety of services. This multifunctional delivery is dependent on the status and condition of the habitat and thus it is important that the habitats are maintained or enhanced through sustainable management. This is particularly the case for agricultural habitats, which dominate England's land cover and impact on the delivery of a number of services. With agriculture likely to become more important in the future, there will be a need for food production to be achieved with a lower environmental impact. In addition to this ecological appreciation of habitats, economic valuation has shown how many of the services they provide make a substantial contribution to national gross domestic product, as well as to local and regional economies. As drivers and pressures change, for example with forthcoming changes to EU agricultural policy and with climate change, it is important that England's habitats and services are regularly monitored, so that their capability to meet the demands of future generations can be assessed.

References

Aber, J.D., Nadelhoffer, K.J., Steudler P. & Melillo, J.M. (1989) Nitrogen saturation in northern forest ecosystems. *BioScience*, **39**, 378–386.

ADAS & Enviros (2008) Monitoring of peat and alternative products for growing media and soil improvers in the UK 2007. Second biennial report by ADAS UK Ltd and Enviros Consulting Ltd. Report to Defra.

AEA (2010) Air quality pollutant inventories for England, Scotland, Wales and Northern Ireland: 1990–2008. National Atmospheric Emissions Inventory report.

Akbar, K.F., Hale, W.H.G. & Headley, A.D. (2003) Assessment of scenic beauty of the roadside vegetation in northern England. *Landscape and Urban Planning*, **63**, 139–144.

Alexander, L.V. & Jones, P.D. (2001) Updated precipitation series for the U.K. and discussion of recent extremes. *Atmospheric Science Letters*, **1**(2), 142–150.

Alex Thornton (2009) Public attitudes and behaviours towards the environment – tracker survey: A report to the Department for Environment, Food and Rural Affairs. TNS. Defra, London.

Anderson, P. & Yalden, D.W. (1981) Increased sheep numbers and the loss of heather moorland in the Peak District, England. *Biological Conservation*, **20**, 195–213.

Anderson, P. & Radford, E. (1994) Changes in vegetation following reduction in grazing pressure on the National Trust's Kinder Estate, Peak District, Derbyshire, England. *Biological Conservation*, **69**, 55–63.

Anderson, P. (2010) Sustainable catchment management programme: monitoring progress report year 4. United Utilities, Warrington. [online] Available at: <http://www.unitedutilities.com/Documents/scamp1.pdf> [Accessed 21.02.11].

Angold, P.G., Sadler, J.P., Hill, M.O., Pullin, A., Rushton, S., Austin, K., Small, E., Wood, B., Wadsworth, R., Sanderson, R. & Thompson, K. (2006) Biodiversity in Urban Habitat Patches. *Science of the Total Environment*, **360**(1–3), 196–204.

Anon (2009) Experiencing landscapes: capturing the cultural services and experiential qualities of landscape. Natural England Report NECR0124. Natural England, Sheffield.

Anon (2006) UK National Action Plan on Farm Animal Genetic Resources. Defra, London. [online] Available at: <http://www.defra.gov.uk/fangr/> [Accessed 21.02.11].

Anton, C., Young, J., Harrison, P.A., Musche, M., Bela, G., Feld, C.K., Harrington, R., Haslett, J.R., Patai, G., Rounsevell, M.D.A., Skourtos, M., Sousa, J.P., Sykes, M.T., Tinch, R., Vandewalle, M., Watt, A. & Settele, J. (2010) Research needs for incorporating the ecosystem service approach into EU biodiversity conservation policy. *Biodiversity and Conservation*, **19**(10), 2979–2994.

Appleton, J. (1975) The Experience of Landscape. Wiley, London.

Aprahamian, M.W., Hickley, P., Shields, B.A. & Mawle, G.W. (2010) Examining changes in participation in recreational fisheries in England and Wales. *Fisheries Management and Ecology*, **17**(2), 93–105.

AQEG (Air Quality Expert Group) (2009) Ozone in the United Kingdom. Report of the Air Quality Expert Group. Defra, London.

Asher, J., Warren, M., Fox, R., Harding, P., Jeffcoate, G. & Jeffcoate, S. (2001) The Millennium Atlas of Butterflies in Britain and Ireland. Oxford University Press, Oxford.

Averis, A., Averis, B., Birks, J., Horsfield, D., Thompson, D. & Yeo, M. (2004) An illustrated guide to British Upland vegetation. JNCC.

AWMN (Acid Waters Monitoring Network) (2009) Acid Waters Monitoring Network 20 year review. Defra, London.

Baines, D. (2005) Black Grouse and Capercaillie. The Game Conservancy Trust Review of 2005, 78–79. Game Conservancy Trust, Hampshire.

Banks, B., Beebee, T.J.C. & Cooke, A.S. (1994) Conservation of the natterjack toad in. Britain over the period 1970–1990 in relation to site protection and other factors. *Biological Conservation*, **67**, 111–118.

Bardgett, R.D. & Wardle, D.A. (2010) Aboveground-Belowground Linkages: Biotic Interactions, Ecosystem Processes, and Global change. Oxford Series in Ecology and Evolution. Oxford University Press, Oxford.

Barker, G. (1997) A framework for the future: green networks with multiple uses in and around towns and cities. English Nature, Peterborough.

Barr, C.J., Bunce, R.G.H., Clarke, R.T., Fuller, R.M., Furse, M.T., Gillespie, M.K., Groom, G.B., Hallam, C.J., Hornung, M., Howard, D.C. & Ness, M.J. (1993) Countryside Survey 1990: main report. (Countryside 1990 vol.2). Department of the Environment, London.

BARS (Biodiversity Action Reporting System) (2011) UK & Country trend overviews. [online] Available at: <http://ukbars.defra.gov.uk/status/uk.asp> [Accessed 05.04.11].

Barton, J., Hine, R. & Pretty, J. (2009) The health benefits of walking in greenspaces of high natural and heritage value. *Journal of Integrative Environmental Sciences*, **6**(4), 1–18.

BHS (Basic Horticultural Statistics) (1999) Basic Horticultural Statistics for the United Kingdom, 1999. [online] Available at: <http://archive.defra.gov.uk/evidence/statistics/foodfarm/landuselivestock/bhs/index.htm> [Accessed 15.05.11].

BHS (Basic Horticultural Statistics) (2008) Basic Horticultural Statistics for the United Kingdom, 2008. [online] Available at: <http://archive.defra.gov.uk/evidence/statistics/foodfarm/landuselivestock/bhs/index.htm> [Accessed 15.05.11].

Bateman, S., Turner, R.K. & Bateman, I.J. (1991) Socio-economic impact of changes in the quality of thatching reed on the future of the reed-growing and thatching industries and on the wider rural economy. Rural Development Commission, Salisbury.

Beales, P.A., Giltrap, P.G., Payne, A. & Ingram, N. (2009) A new threat to UK heathland from *Phytophthora kernoviae* on *Vaccinium myrtillus* in the wild. *Plant Pathology*, **58**, 393–393.

Beaumont, N.J., Austen, M.C., Mangi, S.C. & Townsend, M. (2008) Economic Valuation for the Conservation of Marine Biodiversity. *Marine Pollution Bulletin*, **56**, 386–396.

Beaumont, N.J., Austen, M.C., Atkins, J., Burdon, D., Degraer, S., Dentinho, T.P., Derous, S., Holm, P., Horton, T., van Ierland, E., Marboe, A.H., Starkey, D.J., Townsend, M. & Zarzycki, T. (2007) Identification, definition and quantification of goods and services provided by marine biodiversity: Implications for the Ecosystem Approach. *Marine Pollution Bulletin*, **54**, 253–265.

Beckett, K.P., Freer-Smith, P.H. & Taylor, G. (1998) Urban woodlands: their role in reducing the effects of particulate pollution. *Environmental Pollution*, **99**, 347–360.

Beebee, T.J.C. (1975) Changes in status of the great crested newt *Triturus cristatus* in the British Isles. *British Journal of Herpetology*, **B**, 481–490.

Beebee, T.J.C. (1976) The natterjack toad (*Bufo calamita*) in the British Isles: a study of past and present status. *British Journal of Herpetology*, **5**, 515–521.

Bellamy, P., Loveland, P.J., Bradley, R.I., Lark, R.M. & Kirk, G.J.D. (2005) Carbon losses from all soils across England and Wales. *Nature*, **437**, 245–248.

Benjamins, S. (2010) Benthic Habitats. Charting Progress 2: Healthy and Biologically Diverse Seas Evidence Group Feeder Report. UKMMAS (2010) (ed. M. Frost) Defra. [online] Available at: http://chartingprogress.defra.gov.uk/chapter-3-healthy-and-biologicaly-diverse-seas [Accessed 15.05.11].

Benn, A., Hughes, J.A. & FitzGeorge-Balfour, T. (2010) Evaluation and gap analysis of current and potential indicators for Deep Sea Habitats. In: Charting Progress 2: Healthy and Biologically Diverse Seas Evidence Group Feeder Report.

Berry, P.M. (ed.) (2009) Biodiversity in the Balance – Mitigation and Adaptation Conflicts and Synergies. Pensoft Publishing, Sofia, Bulgaria.

Best Foot Forward Ltd (2002) City Limits: A resource flow and ecological footprint analysis of Greater London. Oxford.

Biesmeijer, J.C., Roberts, W.P.M, Reemer, M., Ohlemüller, R., Edwards, M., Peeters, T., Shaffers, A.P., Potts, S.G., Kleukers, R., Thomas, C.D., Settele, J. & Kunin, W.E. (2006) Parallel declines in pollinators and insect-pollinated plants in Britain and the Netherlands. *Science*, **313**, 351–354.

Bignal, K., Ashmore, M. & Power, S. (2004) Ecological effects of diffuse air pollution from road transport. English Nature, Peterborough.

Bingley, A. F. & Milligan, C. (2004) Climbing trees and building dens: mental health and well-being in young adults and the long-term effects of childhood play experience. Research report, Institute for Health Research, Lancaster University.

Bird, W. (2007) Natural Fit. Can green space and biodiversity increase levels of physical activity? Royal Society for the Protection of Birds, Sandy.

Bonan, G. (2008) Ecological climatology: Concepts and applications. 2nd Edition. Cambridge University Press, Cambridge.

Bonn, A., Holden, J., Parnell, M., Worrall, F., Chapman, P.J., Evans, C.D., Termansen, M., Beharry-Borg, N., Acreman, M.C., Rowe, E., Emmett, B. & Tsuchiya, A. (2009) Ecosystem Services of Peat. Project SP0572 report to Defra.

Bourne, J. (2005) Bovine Tuberculosis – towards a science based control strategy. *Science in Parliament*, **62**, 25–28.

Bowes, M.J., Smith, J.T., Jarvie, H.P., Neal C. & Barden, R. (2009) Changes in point and diffuse source phosphorus inputs to the River Frome (Dorset, UK) from 1966 to 2006. *Science of the Total Environment*, **407**, 1954–1966.

Braat, L., ten Brink, P., Bakkes, J., Bolt, K., Braeuer, I., ten Brink, B., Chiabai, A., Ding,H., Jeuken, M., Kettunen, M., Kirchholtes, U., Klok, C., Markandya, A., Nunes, M., van Oorschot, M., Rayment, M., Travisi, C. & Walpole, M. (2008) The Cost of Policy Inaction: the Case of Not Meeting the 2010 Biodiversity Target, European Commission, Brussels.

Bradley, R.I., Milne, R., Bell, J., Lilly, A., Jordan, C. & Higgins, A. (2005) A soil carbon and land use database for the United Kingdom. *Soil Use and Management*, **21**, 363–369.

Brady, E. (2006) Aesthetics in practice: valuing the natural world. *Environmental Values*, **15**, 277–291.

Braithwaite, M.E., Ellis, R.W. & Preston, C.D. (2006) *Change in the British Flora 1987–2004* (A report on the BSBI Local Change survey). Botanical Society of the British Isles, London.

Brasier, C.M. (2008) The biosecurity threat to the UK and global environment from international trade in plants. *Plant Pathology*, **57**, 792–808.

Brereton, T., Roy, D.B., Middlebrook, I., Botham, M. & Warren, M. (2010) The development of butterfly indicators in the United Kingdom and assessments in 2010. *Journal of Insect Conservation*, **15**(1–2), 139–151. DOI 10.1007/s10841-010-9333-z.

Brown, D. (2004) God and Enchantment of Place: Reclaiming Human Experience. Oxford University Press, Oxford.

Brown, A. & Grice, P. (2005) Birds in England. T. & A.D. Poyser, London.

Burgess, J., Harrison, C. M. & Limb, M. (1988) People, Parks and the Urban Green: A Study of Popular Meanings and Values for Open Spaces in the City. *Urban Studies*, **25**, 455–473.

Burgess, J. (1995) Growing in Confidence: a research project into public perceptions of risk in woodlands in the urban fringe. Countryside Commission, Cheltenham.

BWMB (British Wool Marketing Board) (2010) Wool Statistics. [online] Available at: <http://www.britishwool.org.uk/pdf/Factsheet4.pdf> [Accessed 21.02.11].

CABE (Commission for Architecture and the Built Environment) (2005) The Value of Public Space: How high quality parks and public spaces create economic, social and environmental value. CABE, London.

CABE (Commission for Architecture and the Built Environment) (2006) Green space strategies: a good practice guide. CABE, London.

CABE (Commission for Architecture and the Built Environment) (2010) Urban green nation: Building the evidence basis. CABE, London.

CPRE (Campaign for the Protection of Rural England) (2003) Lie of the land: Championing landscape character. CPRE, London.

CPRE (Campaign to Protect Rural England) (2007) Developing an intrusion map of England. CPRE, London.

Cannell, M.G., Milne, R., Hargreaves, K.J., Brown, T.A., Cruickshank, M.M., Bradley, R.I., Spencer, T., Hope, D., Billett, M.F., Adger, W.N. & Subak S. (1999) National Inventories of Terrestrial Carbon Sources and Sinks: The UK Experience. *Climate Change*, **42**(3), 505–530.

Cantos, F.J. & Isenmann, P. (1994) Dartford warbler (*Sylvia undata*). The EBCC Atlas of European Breeding Birds (eds W.J.M. Hagemeijer & M.J. Blair), pp. 585–586. Poyser, London.

Capper, J.L., Cady, R.A. & Bauman, D.E. (2009) The environmental impact of dairy production: 1944 compared with 2007. *Journal of Animal Science*, **87**, 2160–2167.

Carey, P.D., Wallis, S., Emmett, B.A., Maskell, L.C., Murphy, J., Norton, L.R., Simpson, I.C. & Smart, S.M. (2008) Countryside Survey: UK Headline Messages from 2007. NERC/Centre for Ecology & Hydrology (CEH Project Number: C03259).

Carrier, J.A. & Beebee, T.J.C. (2003) Recent, substantial, and unexplained declines of the common toad *Bufo bufo* in lowland England. *Biological Conservation*, **111**, 395–399.

Carter, C., Lawrence, A., Lovell, R. & O'Brien, L. (2009) The Forestry Commission Public Forest Estate in England: social use, value and expectations. Final report, October 2009. Forest Research, Farnham.

Carvalho, L. & Moss, B. (1998) Lake SSSIs subject to eutrophication – an environmental audit. English Nature Freshwater Series No 3. English Nature, Peterborough.

Carvell, C., Meek, W.R., Pywell, R.F., Goulson, D. & Nowakowski, M. (2007) Comparing the efficacy of agri-environment schemes to enhance bumble bee abundance and diversity on arable field margins. *Journal of Applied Ecology*, **44**, 29–40.

CEFAS (Centre for Environment, Fisheries and Aquaculture Science) (2008) Shellfish News 26, Autumn/Winter 2008. Centre for Environment, Fisheries and Aquaculture Science. [online] Available at: <http://www.cefas.co.uk/news-and-events/shellfish-news.aspx> [Accessed 21.02.11].

CEFAS (Centre for Environment, Fisheries and Aquaculture Science) (2009) Shellfish News 27, Spring/Summer 2009. Centre for Environment, Fisheries and Aquaculture Science. [online] Available at: <http://www.cefas.co.uk/news-and-events/shellfish-news.aspx> [Accessed 21.02.11].

Celiz, M.D., Tso, J. & Aga, D.S. (2009) Pharmaceutical metabolites in the environment: analytical challenges and ecological risks. *Environmental Toxicology and Chemistry*, **28**, 2473–2484.

Chamberlain, D.E., Fuller, R.J., Bunce, R.G.H., Duckworth, J.C. & Shrubb, M. (2000) Changes in the abundance of farmland birds in relation to the timing of agricultural intensification in England and Wales. *Journal of Applied Ecology*, **37**, 771–788.

Chamberlain, P.M., Emmett, B.A., Scott, W.A., Black, H.I.J., Hornung, M. & Frogbrook, Z.L. (2010) No change in topsoil carbon levels of Great Britain, 1978–2007. *Biogeosciences Discuss*, **7**, 2267–2311.

Champion, T. (2005) Popluation movement within the UK. Focus on People and Migration. (eds R. Chappell). Palgrave Macmillan, Hampshire. pp. 92–113.

Clark, G. (2010) Previously Developed Land and Density. [online] Available at: <http://www.communities.gov.uk/statements/corporate/pps3statement> [Accessed 21.02.11].

Clarke, D. & Sanitwong na Ayutthaya, S. (2010) Predicted effects of climate change, vegetation and tree cover on dune slack habitats at Ainsdale on the Sefton Coast, UK. *Journal of Coastal Conservation*, **14**(2), 115–125.

Clifford, S. & King, A. (2006) England in Particular: a Celebration of the Commonplace, the Local, the Vernacular and the Distinctive. Hodder & Stoughton, London.

Coleman, S. & Eade, J. (2004) Reframing Pilgrimage: Cultures in Motion. Routledge, London.

Conrad, K.F., Warren, M.S., Fox, R., Parsons, M.S. & Woiwod, I.P. (2006) Rapid declines in common moths underscore a biodiversity crisis. *Biological Conservation*, **132**, 279–291.

Conradson, D. (2008) The experiential economy of stillness: places of retreat in contemporary Britain. Therapeutic Landscapes (ed A. Williams), Ashgate, Aldershot.

Coombes, E., Jones, A.P. & Hillsdon, M. (2010) The relationship of physical activity and overweight to objectively measured greenspace accessibility and use. *Social Science and Medicine*, **70**, 816–822.

Cooper, J.A.G. (2009) Coastal economies and people review in Marine Climate Change Ecosystem Linkages Report Card 2009 (eds J.M. Baxter, P.J. Buckley, & M.T. Frost), Online science reviews, [online] Available at: <www.mccip.org.uk/elr/coasts> [Accessed 21.02.11].

Cooper, N. (2009) The spiritual value of ecosystem services: an initial Christian exploration. Unpublished paper.

Cooper, N.J., Cooper, T & Burd, F. (2001) 25 years of salt marsh erosion in Essex: Implications for coastal defence and nature conservation. *Journal of Coastal Conservation*, **7**(1), 31–40.

Cordell, D., Drangert, J.O. & White, S. (2009) The story of phosphorus: Global food security and food for thought. *Global Environmental Change*, **19**, 292–305.

Countryside Survey (2009) England Results from 2007. NERC/Centre for Ecology & Hydrology, Department for Environment, Food and Rural Affairs, Natural England.

Crabtree, B., Willis, K., Powe, N., Carman, P., Rowe, D., Macdonald, D. & Usher-Curtin, S. & Wilkes, K. (2005) British wildlife tourism operators: current issues and typology. *Current Issues in Tourism*, **8**(6), 455–478.

Craig, R. & Mindell, J. (2008) Health survey for England 2006. Information Centre, London. [online] Available at: <http://www.ic.nhs.uk/webfiles/publications/HSE06/HSE06_Summary.pdf> [Accessed 21.02.11].

Crawford, A. (2003) Fourth otter survey of England 2000 – 2002. Environment Agency, Bristol.

CPRE (Campaign to Protect Rural England) (2007) Tranquillity map: England. National tranquillity mapping data 2007 developed for CPRE and Natural England by Northumbria University.

CRC (Commission for Rural Communities) (2008) State of the Countryside 2008. [online] Available at: <http://www.ruralcommunities.gov.uk/files/The%20State%20of%20the%20Countryside1.pdf> [Accessed 21.02.11].

Curry, N. (1994) Countryside recreation, access and land use planning. Spon, London.

Dasgupta, P. (2007) Nature and the Economy. *Journal of Applied Ecology*, **44**, 475–487.

Davey, C.M., Vickery, J.A., Boatman, N.D., Chamberlain, D.E., Parry, H.R. & Siriwardena, G.M. (2010) Assessing the impact of Entry Level Stewardship on lowland farmland birds in England. *Ibis*, **152**, 459–474.

DCLG (Department for Communities and Local Government) *Soil loss to development in England, 1994 to 2006.* DCLG, UK.

DCLG (Department for Communities and Local Government) (2008) Land Use Change in England: Residential Development to 2006. [online] Available at: <http://www.communities.gov.uk/publications/planningandbuilding/landusestats> [Accessed 04.04.11].

DECC (Department of Energy and Climate Change) 2010 Greenhouse Gas Inventory National System. Available at: http://ghgi.decc.gov.uk/ [Accessed 06.05.11].

Defra (Department for Environment, Food and Rural Affairs) (2002) Working with the grain of nature: A biodiversity strategy for England. [online] Available at: <http://www.defra.gov.uk/publications/2011/03/29/pb7718-biodiversity/> [Accessed 21.02.11].

Defra (Department for Environment, Food and Rural Affairs) (2003) Re-assessing drought risks for UK crops using UKCIP02 climate change scenarios – CC0368. Report to Defra.

Defra (Department for Environment, Food and Rural Affairs) (2005) 3: Marine Habitats and Species. Charting Progress – an Integrated Assessment of the State of UK Seas. Defra, London [online] Available at: <http://chartingprogress.defra.gov.uk/charting-progress-2005/3.%20Marine%20Habitats%20and%20Species.pdf> [Accessed 08.04.11].

Defra (Department for Environment, Food and Rural Affairs) (2006a) Food Security and the UK: An Evidence and Analysis Paper. Food Chain Analysis Group, Defra. [online] Available at: <http://archive.defra.gov.uk/evidence/economics/foodfarm/reports/documents/foodsecurity.pdf> [Accessed 08.04.11].

Defra (Department for Environment, Food and Rural Affairs) (2006b) Working with the grain of nature- taking it forward: Volume 1- Full report on progress under the England Biodiversity Strategy 2002–2006. Defra, London.

Defra (Department for Environment, Food and Rural Affairs) (2007a) The Air Quality Strategy for England, Scotland, Wales and Northern Ireland. TSO (The Stationery Office), London.

Defra (Department for Environment, Food and Rural Affairs) (2007b) Securing a healthy natural environment: An action plan for embedding an ecosystems approach. Defra, London.

Defra (Department for Environment, Food and Rural Affairs) (2007c) An introductory guide to valuing ecosystem services. Defra, London.

Defra (Department for Environment, Food and Rural Affairs) (2008a) A biodiversity strategy for England: measuring progress. [online]. Defra, London.

Defra (Department for Environment, Food and Rural Affairs) (2008b) A Strategy for England's Trees, Woods and Forests. [online] Available at: <http://www.defra.gov.uk/rural/documents/forestry/20070620-forestry.pdf> [Accessed 21.02.11].

Defra (Department for Environment, Food and Rural Affairs) (2008c) Outdoors for all? The action plan. Defra, London.

Defra (Department for Environment, Food and Rural Affairs) (2008d) England biodiversity strategy indicators: assessment of indicators published since April 2008. [online] Available from: <http://archive.defra.gov.uk/environment/biodiversity/documents/indicator/ind-assess.pdf> [Accessed 08.04.11].

Defra (Department for Environment, Food and Rural Affairs) (2009a) Agriculture in the UK 2009. [online] Available at: <http://www.defra.gov.uk/statistics/2010/03/18/auk-2009/>[Accessed 08.04.11].

Defra (Department for Environment, Food and Rural Affairs) (2009b) Safeguarding our soils. A strategy for England. [online] Available at: <http://archive.defra.gov.uk/environment/quality/land/soil/documents/soil-strategy.pdf> [Accessed 08.04.11].

Defra (Department for Environment, Food and Rural Affairs) (2009c) River Water Quality Indicator for Sustainable Development – 2008 results. Statistical Release Ref. 203/09. [online] Available at: <http://www.defra.gov.uk/statistics/environment/inland-water/> [Accessed 21.02.11].

Defra (Department for Environment, Food and Rural Affairs) (2009d) Sustainable development indicators in your pocket. [online] Available at: <http://archive.defra.gov.uk/sustainable/government/progress/data-resources/sdiyp.htm> [Accessed 15.05.11].

Defra (Department for Environment, Food and Rural Affairs) (2010a) Farming in the English Uplands. Defra Agricultural Change and Environment Observatory Report No. 20. [online] Available at: <http://archive.defra.gov.uk/evidence/statistics/foodfarm/enviro/observatory/research/documents/uplands2010short.pdf> [Accessed 21.02.11].

Defra (Department for Environment, Food and Rural Affairs) (2010b) Wild Bird Populations: Farmland Birds in England 2009. [online] Available at:
<http://www.defra.gov.uk/news/2010/07/29/birds-stats/> [Accessed 21.02.11].

Defra (Department for Environment, Food and Rural Affairs) (2010c) Observatory Programme Indicators. Natural England/JNCC. [online] Available at: <http://www.defra.gov.uk/statistics/foodfarm/enviro/observatory/programme-indicators/> [Accessed 08.04.11].

Defra (Department for Environment, Food and Rural Affairs) (2010e) Measuring progress: sustainability development indicators 2010. [online] Available at: <http://sd.defra.gov.uk/2010/07/measuring-progress-sustainable-development-indicators-2010/> [Accessed 21.02.11].

Defra (Department for Environment, Food and Rural Affairs) (2010f) Delivering a healthy natural Environment. An update to "Securing a healthy natural environment: An action plan for embedding an ecosystems approach". Defra, London. [online] Available at: <http://archive.defra.gov.uk/environment/policy/natural-environ/documents/healthy-nat-environ.pdf> [Accessed 15.05.11].

Defra (Department for Environment, Food and Rural Affairs) (2010g) UK Biodiversity Indicators in your Pocket. [online] Available at: <http://jncc.defra.gov.uk/biyp/> [Accessed 21.02.11].

Defra (Department for Environment, Food and Rural Affairs) (2010h) e-Digest of Environmental Statistics. Inland water quality and use. Table 23.e: Estimated abstractions from all sources except tidal by purpose and Environment Agency region: 1995– 2008. [online] Available at: <http://archive.defra.gov.uk/evidence/statistics/environment/inlwater/iwabstraction.htm> [Accessed 15.05.11].

De Groot, R.S., Alkemade, R., Braat, L., Hein, L. & Willemen, L. (2010) Challenges in integrating the concept of ecosystem services and values in landscape planning, management and decision making. Ecological Complexity, 7, 260–272.

Dehnen-Schmutz, K., Touza, J., Perrings, C. & Williamson, M. (2007) The horticultural trade and ornamental plant invasions in Britain. Conservation Biology, 21, 224–231.

Delbaere, B.C.W. (1998) Facts and figures on European biodiversity; state and trends 1998–1999. European Centre for Nature Conservation, Tilburg, The Netherlands.

Deloitte MCS (2008) The Economic Case for the Visitor Economy. Final Report for Visit Britain. Deloitte MCS, London.

DETR (Department for Environment, Transport and the Regions) (2001) Land Use Change in England, No 16, DTLR Statistical Bulletin. Department for Transport, Local Government and the Regions, London.

Department of Health (2004) At least five a week: Evidence on the impact of physical activity and its relationship to health. Department of Health, London.

DETR (Department for Environment, Transport and the Regions) (2001) Land Use Change in England, No 16, DTLR Statistical Bulletin. DTLR, London.

De Wit, M. & Faaij, A. (2010) European biomass resource potential and costs. Biomass and Energy 34, 188–202.

Doody, J.P. (2001) Coastal Conservation and Management: an Ecological Perspective. Conservation Biology Series, 13, Kluwer, Academic Publishers, Boston, USA.

Doody, J.P. (2008) Saltmarsh conservation, management and restoration. Coastal Systems and Continental Margins Series. Springer, USA.

Duck, C. (2010) Seals. In: Charting Progress 2 Feeder Report: Healthy and Biologically Diverse Seas. UK Marine Monitoring and Assessment Strategy (UKMMAS), Defra. [online] Available at: <http://chartingprogress.defra.gov.uk/chapter-3-healthy-and-biologicaly-diverse-seas> [Accessed 21.02.11].

Environment Agency (2004) Our Nations Fisheries. [online] Available at: <http://www.environment-agency.gov.uk/research/library/publications/38069.aspx> [Accessed 21.02.11]

Environment Agency (2006) The development and use of soil quality indicators for assessing the role of soil in environmental interactions. Environment Agency, Bristol.

Environment Agency (2007) UK Soil and Herbage Survey. . Environment Agency, Bristol.

Environment Agency (2008) Indicators: Rivers with high levels of nutrients", based on data from the General Quality Assessments. [online] Available at: http://www.environment-agency.gov.uk/research/library/data/58820.aspx [Accessed 15.05.11].

Environment Agency (2009) Creating a better Thames. Environment Agency, Bristol.

Environment Agency (2010a) Buy your rod licence online. [online] Available at: <http://www.environment-agency.gov.uk/homeandleisure/recreation/fishing/31497.aspx> [Accessed 21.02.11].

EFTEC (Economics for the Environment Consultancy) (2009) Economic Values for a Healthy Natural Environment. A report to Natural England. [online] Available at: <http://naturalengland.etraderstores.com/NaturalEnglandShop/NE220> [Accessed 21.02.11].

Ekins, R. (1990) Changes in the extent of grazing marshes in the Greater Thames Estuary. RSPB Report

Emmett, B.A., Reynolds, B., Chamberlain, P.M., Rowe, E., Spurgeon, D., Brittain, S.A., Frogbrook, Z., Hughes, S., Lawlor, A.J., Poskitt, J., Potter, E., Robinson, D.A., Scott, A., Wood, C. & Woods, C. (2010) Countryside Survey: Soils Report from 2007. NERC/Centre for Ecology and Hydrology.

EBG (England Biodiversity Group) (2008) Securing biodiversity: A new framework for delivering priority habitats and species in England. Natural England, Sheffield.

English Nature (2002) Peat bog conservation: the importance of lowland raised bogs. [online] Available at: <http://naturalengland.etraderstores.com/NaturalEnglandShop/IN77> [Accessed 21.02.11].

English Nature (2005) Canvey Wick SSSI, Essex. [online] Available at: <http://www.english-nature.org.uk/special/sssi/images/uploaded_files/2000497.pdf> [Accessed 21.02.11].

EASAC (European Academies Science Advisory Council) (2009) Ecosystem Services and Biodiversity in Europe. The Royal Society, Clyvedon Press, Cardiff.

Evans, J. (1988) Natural regeneration of broadleaves. Forestry Commission Bulletin 78. HMSO, London.

Evans, G.L., Williams, P.J. le B. & Mitchelson-Jacob, E.G. (2003) Physical and anthropogenic effects on observed long-term nutrient changes in the Irish Sea. *Estuarine, Coastal and Shelf Science,* **57**, 1159–1168.

Evans, R. (2005) Curtailing grazing-induced erosion in a small catchment and its environs, the Peak District, central England. *Applied Geography,* **25**, 81–95.

Evans, J. T.,E., Smith, G., Banerjee, A., Smith, R.M.M., Dale, ., Innes,J.A., Hunt,D., Tweddell, A., Wood, A., Anderson, C., Hewinson, R.G., Smith, N.H., Hawkey, P.M. & Sonnenberg, P. (2007) Cluster of human tuberculosis caused by Mycobacterium bovis: Evidence for person-to-person transmission in the UK. *The Lancet,* **369**, 1270–1276.

Evans, C.D., Monteith, D.T. & Cooper, D.M. (2005) Long-term increases in surface water dissolved organic carbon: Observations, possible causes and environmental impacts. *Environmental Pollution,* **137**, 55–71.

Evans, M.G., Warburton J. & Yang, J. (2006) Eroding blanket peat catchments: global and local implications of upland organic sediment budgets. *Geomorphology,* **79**, 45–57.

Everard, M. (2009) Ecosystem services case studies. Environment Agency, Bristol.

Everard, M., Jones, M.L.M. & Watts, B. (2010) Have we neglected the societal importance of sand dunes? An ecosystem services perspective. *Aquatic Conservation: Marine and Freshwater Ecosystems.* **20**, 476–487.

Farmer, M., Cooper, T., Swales, V. & Silcock, P. (2008) Funding for farmland biodiversity in the EU: gaining evidence for the EU budget review. A report for the RSPB by Institute for European Environmental Policy and Cumulus Consultants.

Fletcher, R.L. (1996) The occurrence of "green tides" – a review. Marine Benthic Vegetation: Recent Changes and the Effects of Eutrophication (eds W. Schramm & P.H. Nienhuis), pp. 7–42. Springer, Berlin.

Folke, C., Jansson, Å., Larsson, J. & Costanza, R. (1997) Ecosystem Appropriation by Cities. *Ambio,* **26**(3), 167–172.

Foresight (2007) Tackling Obesities: Future Choices. Government Office of Science, London.

Foresight Land Use Futures Project (2010) Final Project Report. The Government Office for Science, London.

Forestry Commission (2003) National Inventory of Woodlands and Trees. Forestry Commission, Edinburgh.

Forestry Commission (2007) Strategy for England's Woods Trees and Forests. Forestry Commission England, Cambridge.

Forestry Commission (2009a) Forestry Statistics. [online] Available at: <http://www.forestry.gov.uk/pdf/ForestryStatistics2009.pdf/$FILE/ForestryStatistics2009.pdf> [Accessed 21.02.11].

Forestry Commission (2009b) The UK Forestry Standard. Forestry Commission, Edinburgh.

Forestry Commission (2009c) A Woodfuel Strategy for England. Forestry Commission, Edinburgh. [online] Available at: <http://www.forestry.gov.uk/pdf/fce-woodfuel-strategy.pdf/$FILE/fce-woodfuel-strategy.pdf> [Accessed 15.05.11].

Forestry Commission (2009d) Forestry Statistics 2009. [online] Available at: <http://www.forestry.gov.uk/website/forstats2009.nsf/LUContentsTop?openview&RestrictToCategory=1> [Accessed 12.04.11].

Forestry Commission (2010) Wood production: England 1976–2009. [online] Available at: www.forestry.gov.uk/.../Woodproduction1976-2009final.../Woodproduction1976-2009final.pdf [Accessed 27.04.11].

Foster, I.D.L. (2006) Lakes in the Sediment Delivery System. Soil Erosion and Sediment Redistribution in River Catchments (eds P.N. Owens & A.J. Collins), pp. 128–142. CAB International, Wallingford.

Fowler D., Cape, J.N & Unsworth, M.H. (1989) Deposition of atmospheric pollutants on forests. *Philosophical Transactions of the Royal Society London B.* **324**, 247–265.

Fowler, D., O'Donoghue, M., Muller, J.B.A., Smith, R.I., Dragosits, U., Skiba, U., Sutton, M.A. & Brimblecombe, P. (2004) A chronology of nitrogen deposition in the UK between 1900 and 2000. *Water, Air, & Soil Pollution: Focus,* **4**(6), 9–23.

Fowler, D., Skiba, U., Moncrieff, J. B. & Polson, D. (2008) Greenhouse gas emissions, inventories and validation. Land Management in a Changing Environment. (eds. Crichton, K. and Audsley, R.). *SAC and SEPA Biennial Conference,* **SAC**, 134–151.

Fox, R., Asher, J., Brereton, T., Roy, D. & Warren, M. (2006) The state of butterflies in Britain and Ireland. Pisces Publishing, Oxford.

Fraser, M.D., Davies, D.A., Vale, J.E., Nute, G.R., Hallett, K.G., Richardson, R.I. & Wright, I.A. (2009) Performance and meat quality of native and continental cross steers grazing improved upland pasture or semi-natural rough grazing. *Livestock Science,* **123**, 70–82.

French, C.E., French, J.R., Clifford, N.J., & Watson, C.J. (2000) Sedimentation-erosion dynamics of abandoned reclamations:

the role of waves and tides. *Continental Shelf Research*, **20**, 1711–1733.

Frost, M. (2010) Charting Progress 2 Feeder Report: Healthy and Biologically Diverse Seas. UK Marine Monitoring and Assessment Strategy (UKMMAS), Defra. [online] Available at: <http://chartingprogress.defra.gov.uk/chapter-3-healthy-and-biologicaly-diverse-seas> [Accessed 21.02.11].

Fuller, R.M. (1987) The changing extent and conservation interest of lowland grasslands in England and Wales – a review of grassland surveys 1930–84. *Biological Conservation*, **40**, 281–300.

Fuller, R.J., Henderson, A.J.B. & Williams, A.M. (1999) The nightingale in England: problems and prospects. *British Wildlife*, **10**, 221–230.

Fuller, R.J. & Gough, S. (1999) Changing patterns of sheep stocking in Britain and implications for bird populations. *Biological Conservation*, **91**, 73–89.

Fuller, R.J. (2001) Response of woodland birds to increasing numbers of deer: a review of evidence and mechanisms. *Forestry*, **74**(3), 289–298.

Fuller, R.J. & Gill, R.M.A. (2001) Ecological impacts of deer in British woodland. *Forestry*, **74**, 193–299.

Fuller, R.M., Smith, G.M., Sanderson, J.M., Hill, R.A. & Thomson, A.G. (2002) The UK Land Cover Map 2000: construction of a parcel-based vector map from satellite images. *Cartographic Journal*, **39,** 15–25.

Fuller, R.A., Irvine, K.A., Devine-Wright, P., Warren, P.H. & Gaston, K.J. (2007) Psychological benefits of greenspace increase with biodiversity. *Biology Letters*, **3**, 390–394.

Fuller, R.A. & Gaston, K.J. (2009) The scaling of green space coverage in European cities. *Biology Letters*, **5**, 352–355.

Gallai, N., Salles, J.M., Settele, J. & Vaissiere, B.E. (2009) Economic valuation of the vulnerability of world agriculture confronted with pollinator decline. *Ecological Economics*, **68**, 810–821.

GWCT (Game & Wildlife Conservation Trust) (2009) National Game Bag Census. [online]. Available at: <http://www.gwct.org.uk/research__surveys/wildlife_surveys/national_gamebag_census/trends_in_game_bags/default.asp> [Accessed 08.04.11] .

Garbutt, R.A., Reading, C.J., Wolters, M., Gray, A.J. & Rothery, P. (2006) Monitoring the development of intertidal habitats on former agricultural land after the managed realignment of coastal defences at Tollesbury, Essex, UK. *Marine Pollution Bulletin*, **53**, 155–164.

Garnett, T. (2000) Urban agriculture in London: rethinking our food economy. Deutsche Stiftung fur Internationale Entwicklung. Available at <www.pdf-finder.com/URBAN-AGRICULTURE-IN-LONDON:-RETHINKING-OUR-FOOD-ECONOMY.html> [Accessed 06.05.11].

George, D.G., Maberly, S.C. & Hewitt, D.P. (2004) The influence of the North Atlantic Oscillation on the physical, chemical and biological characteristics of four lakes in the English Lake District. *Freshwater Biology*, **49**, 760–774.

GFA-Race & GHK (2004) Revealing the value of the natural environment in England. Report for Defra. [online] Available at: <http://www.hm-treasury.gov.uk/d/2%281%29.pdf> [Accessed 12.04.11]

Gilbert, O.L. (1989) The Ecology of Urban Habitats. Chapman & Hall, London.

Gill, S., Handley, J., Ennos, A. & Pauleit, S. (2007) Adapting cities for climate change: the role of the greenspace. *Built environment*, **33**(1), 115–133.

Glendining, M.J., Dailey, A.G., Williams, A.G., van Evert, F.K., Goulding K.W.T. & Whitmore, A.P. (2009) Is it possible to increase the sustainability of arable and ruminant agriculture by reducing inputs? *Agricultural Systems*, **99**, 117–125.

GLUD (Generalised Land Use Database) (2005) Generalised Land Use Database: Neighbourhood statistics, period 2005. Produced by the Office of National Statistics for the Department of Communities and Local Government. [online] Available at: <http://www.neighbourhood.statistics.gov.uk/dissemination/LeadTableView.do?a=7&b=276743&c=london&d=13&e=8&g=325264&i=1001x1003x1004&m=0&r=1&s=1283092428171&enc=1&dsFamilyId=1201> [Accessed 21.02.11].

Goulson, D., Hanley, M.E., Darvill, B., Ellis, J.S. & Knight, M.E. (2004) Causes of rarity in bumblebees. *Biological Conservation*, **122**, 1–8.

Gowen, R.J., Tett, P., Kennington, K., Mills, D.K., Shammon, T.M. Stewart, B.M., Greenwood, N., Flanagan, C., Devli, M. & Wither, A. (2008) The Irish Sea: Is it eutrophic? *Estuarine, Coastal and Shelf Science*, **76**, 239–254.

GLA (Greater London Authority) (2006a) London's Urban Heat Island: A Summary for Decision Makers. London.

GLA (Greater London Authority) (2006b) East London Green Grid Primer. London. [online] Available at: <http://static.london.gov.uk/mayor/auu/docs/elgg-primer.pdf> [Accessed 12.04.11].

Green, B.H. (1990) Agricultural intensification and the loss of habitat, species and amenity in British grasslands: a review of historical change and assessment of future prospects. *Grass and Forage Science*, **45**, 365–372.

Haines-Young, R.H., Barr, C.J., Black, H.I.J., Briggs, D.J., Bunce, R.G.H., Clarke, R.T., Cooper, A., Dawson, F.H., Firbank, L.G., Fuller, R.M., Furse, M.T., Gillespie, M.K., Hill, R., Hornung, M., Howard, D.C., McCann, T., Morecroft, M.D., Peti, S., Sier, A.R.J., Smart, S.M., Smith, G.M., Stott, A.P., Stuart, R.C. & Watkins, J.W. (2000) Accounting for nature: assessing habitats in the UK countryside. Defra, London.

Haines-Young, R. & Potschin, M. (2008) England's Terrestrial Ecosystem Services and the Rationale for the Ecosystem Approach. Full Technical Report, Defra Project Code NR0107.

Haines-Young R. & Potschin M. (2010) The links between biodiversity, ecosystem services and human wellbeing. Ecosystem ecology: a new synthesis. (eds Raffaelli D., Frid C.). BES ecological reviews series. CUP, Cambridge.

Hall, D. (2001) Turning the Plough. Midland open fields: landscape character and proposals for management. English Heritage and Northamptonshire County Council. [online] Available at: <http://www.english-heritage.org.uk/publications/turning-the-plough-loss-of-a-landscape-legacy/turningplough.pdf> [Accessed 15.05.11].

Handley, J., Pauleit, S., Slinn, P., Barber, A., Baker, M., Jones, C. & Lindley, S. (2003) Accessible Natural Green Space Standards in Towns and Cities: A Review and Toolkit for their Implementation. English Nature, Peterborough.

Handley, J. & Carter, J. (2006) Adaptation Strategies for Climate Change in the Urban Environment. Draft final report to the National Steering Group, Centre for Urban and Regional Ecology, University of Manchester.

Handley, J. & Gill (2009) Combating climate change – a role for UK forests. An assessment of the potential of UK's trees and woodlands to mitigate and adapt to climate change. In: Read, D.J., Freer-Smith, P.H., Morison, J.I.L., Hanley, N., West, C.C. & Snowdon, P. (eds) (2009) Combating climate change – a role for UK forests. An assessment of the potential of the UK's trees and woodlands to mitigate and adapt to climate change. The synthesis report. The Stationery Office, Edinburgh.

Hanley, N., Colombo, S., Mason, P. & Johns, H. (2007) The Reform of Support Mechanisms for Upland Farming: Paying for Public Goods in the Severely Disadvantaged Areas of England. *Journal of Agricultural Economics*, **58**(3), 433–453.

Hanley, N. & Colombo, S. (2009) The economic value of landscapes in the uplands of England. Drivers of environmental change in uplands (eds Bonn, A., Allott, T., Hubacek, K.& Stewart, J.), pp. 323–338. Abingdon, Oxon.

Hannaford, J. & Marsh, T.M. (2006) An assessment of trends in UK runoff and low flows using a network of undisturbed catchments. *International Journal of Climatology*, **26**, 1237–1253.

Hannaford, J. & Marsh, T.M. (2008) High-flow and flood trends in a network of undisturbed catchments in the UK. *International Journal of Climatology*, **28**, 1325–1338.

Harlow, J., Hopkins, J., Stone, D., Waters, R., Lovett, J. & Dorling, A. (2010) No Charge? Valuing the natural environment: Technical report. Natural England Research Report NERR032. Natural England, Sheffield.

Harmer, R. & Kiewitt, A. (2006) Restoration of lowland conifer PAWS. Forest Research Annual Report 2005–2006. [online] Available at: <http://www.forestresearch.gov.uk/pdf/FR_report_2005–6_paws.pdf/$FILE/FR_report_2005-6_paws.pdf> [Accessed 21.02.11].

Harmer, R., Kerr, G. & Thompson, R. (2010) Managing Native Broadleaved Woodland. Forestry Commission. Stationery Office Books.

Harrison, C.M., Burgess, J. & Limb, M. (1987) Nature in the city: popular values for a living world. *Journal of Environmental Management*, **25**, 347–362.

Harrison, C., Burgess, J., Millward, A. & Dawe, G. (1995) Accessible natural greenspace in towns and cities: A review of appropriate size and distance criteria. Guidance for the preparation of strategies for local sustainability. English Nature, Peterborough.

Hartig, T., Evans, G.W., Jamner, L.D., Davis, D.S., & Gärling, T. (2003) Tracking restoration in natural and urban field settings. *Journal of Environmental Psychology*, **23**, 109–123.

Haslett, J.R., Berry, P.M., Bela, G., Jongman, R.H.J., Pataki, G., Samways M.J. & Zobel, M. (2010) Changing conservation strategies in Europe: a framework integrating ecosystem services and dynamics. *Biodiversity and Conservation*, **19**, 2963–2977.

Hawes, C., Haughton, A.J., Bohan, D.A., & Squire, G.R. (2009) Functional approaches for assessing plant and invertebrate abundance patterns in arable systems. *Basic and Applied Ecology*, **10**, 34–42.

Hawke, C. & José, P. (1996) Reedbed management for commercial and wildlife interests. RSPB, Sandy.

Hay, D. & Hunt, K. (2000) Understanding the Spirituality of People Who Don't Go to Church: A Report on the Findings of the Adults' Spirituality Project. University of Nottingham.

Henderson, I.G., Ravenscroft, N., Smith, G. & Holloway, S. (2009) Effects of crop diversification and low pesticide inputs on bird populations on arable land. *Agriculture, Ecosystems and Environment*, **129**, 149–156.

Hewins, E.J., Pinches, C., Arnold, J., Lush, M., Robertson, H. & Escott, S. (2005) The condition of lowland BAP priority grasslands: results from a sample survey of non-statutory stands in England. English Nature Research Reports, No 636. English Nature, Peterborough.

Hillsdon, M., Panter, J., Foster, C. & Jones, A. (2006) The relationship between access and quality of urban green space with population physical activity. *Public Health*, **120**, 1127–1132.

Hine, R., Peacock, J. & Pretty, J. (2007) Green Lungs for the East of England. Report for the National Trust. [online] Available at: <http://www.essex.ac.uk/ces/occasionalpapers/Kerry/Green%20Lungs%20for%20the%20East%20of%20England%208.0%20final.pdf> [Accessed 12.04.11].

Hine, R., Peacock, J. & Pretty, J. (2008) Care Farming in the UK – Evidence and opportunities. Report for the National Care Farming Initiative (UK). University of Essex.

Hiscock, K. (1996) Marine Nature Conservation review: Rationale and Methods. Joint Nature Conservation Committee, Peterborough.

Hiscock, K., Sewell, J. & Oakley, J. (2005) Marine Health Check 2005. A report to gauge the health of the UK's sea-life. WWF-UK, Godalming.

Hitchings, R. (2010) Seasonal climate change and the indoor city worker. *Transactions of the Institute of British Geographers*, **35**(2), 282–298.

Holden, J. & Burt, T.P. (2003a) Runoff production in blanket peat covered catchments. *Water Resources Research,* **39**(7), art. no. 1191.

Holden, J. & Burt, T.P. (2003b) Hydraulic conductivity in upland blanket peat: measurement and variability. *Hydrological Processes,* **17**, 1227–1237.

Holden, J. (2005) Peatland hydrology and carbon release: why small-scale process matters. *Philosophical Transactions of the Royal Society A*, **363**, 2891–2913.

Holden, J., Gascoign, M. & Bosanko, N.R. (2007) Erosion and natural revegetation associated with surface land drains in upland peatlands. *Earth Surface Processes and Landforms*, **32**, 1547–1557.

Holden, J., Kirkby, M.J., Lane, S.N., Milledge, D.J., Brookes, C.J., Holden, V. & McDonald, A.T. (2008) Factors affecting overland flow velocity in peatlands. *Water Resources Research*, **44**, W06415.

Hollaway, S.L. & Valentine, G. (2000) Children's geographies: playing, living, learning. Routledge, London.

Hollaway, S.L. & Valentine, G. (2003) Cyberkids: children in the information age. RoutledgeFarmer, London.

Hopkins, J. & Kirby, K.J. (2007) Ecological change in British broadleaved woodland since 1947. *Ibis*, **149**, 29–40.

Hopkins, J.J. & Maxted, N. (2011) Crop Wild Relatives: Plant conservation for food security. Natural England Research Report 037. Natural England, Sheffield.

Hough, M.N. & Jones, R.J.A. (1997) The United Kingdom Meteorological Office rainfall and evaporation calculation system: MORECS version 2.0 and overview. *Hydrology and Earth Systems Science*, **1**, 227–239.

Howe, M.A. (2002) A review of the coastal cliff resource in Wales, with particular reference to its importance for invertebrates. CCW Natural Science Report. 02/5/1. Countryside Council for Wales, Bangor.

Howe, M.A., Whitehouse, A.T. & Knight, G.T. (2008) Life on the edge – key coastal soft cliffs for invertebrates in England and Wales. *British Wildlife*, **19**(3), 172–181.

Howe, M.A., Knight, G.T., Clee, C. (2010) The importance of coastal sand dunes for terrestrial invertebrates in Wales and the UK, with particular reference to aculeate Hymenoptera (bees, wasps & ants). *Journal of Coastal Conservation*, **14**(2), 91–102.

Hughes, M., Hornby, D.D., Bennion, H., Kernan, M., Hilton, J., Phillips, G. & Thomas, R. (2004) The development of a GIS-based inventory of standing waters in Great Britain together with a risk-based prioritisation protocol. *Water, Air and Soil Pollution: Focus*, **4**, 73–84.

Icons (2006) Icons: A portrait of England. The Lake District. [online] Available at: <http://www.icons.org.uk/theicons/collection/the-lake-district/features/the-lake-poets> [Accessed 21.02.11].

Inge, J. (2003) *A Christian Theology of Place*. Ashgate, Farnham.

Isselstein, J., Griffith, B.A., Pradel, P. & Venerus, S. (2007) Effects of livestock breed and grazing intensity on biodiversity and production in grazing systems. Nutritive value of herbage and livestock performance. *Grass and Forage Science*, **62**, 145–158.

Jacobs (2008) Environmental Accounts for Agriculture. Report to Defra. [online] Available at: <http://www.dardni.gov.uk/environmental-accounts.pdf> [Accessed 12.04.11].

Jackson, J., Choudrie, S., Thistlethwaite, G., Passant, N., Murrells, T., Watterson, J., Mobbs, D., Cardenas, L., Thomson, A. & Leech, A. (2009a) UK Greenhouse Gas Inventory, 1990 to 2007: Annual Report for submission under the Framework Convention on Climate Change. Didcot, AEA Technology plc, pp. 250 (AEAT/ENV/R/2764).

Jackson, J., Li,Y., Murrells, T., Passant,N., Sneddon, S., Thomas,J., Thistlethwaite, G., Dyson,K. & Cardenas, L. (2009b) Greenhouse Gas Inventories for England, Scotland, Wales and Northern Ireland: 1990 – 2007. Report to the Department for Energy and Climate Change, The Scottish Government, The Welsh Assembly Government and The Northern Ireland Department of Environment. (AEAT/ENV/R/2873).

James, M.A. & Slaski, R.J. (2009) A strategic review of the potential for aquaculture to contribute to the future security of food and non-food products and services in the UK and specifically England. Report commissioned by the Department of the Environment and Rural Affairs, pp.121.

Jarvie, H.P., Withers, P.J.A., Bowes, M.J., Palmer-Felgate, E.J., Harper, D., Wasiak, K., Wasiak, P., Hodgkinson, R.A., Bates, A., Stoate, C., Neal, M., Wickham, H.D., Harman, S.A. & Armstrong, L.K. (2010) Streamwater phosphorus and nitrogen across a gradient in rural-agricultural land use intensity. *Agriculture, Ecosystems and Environment*, **135**, 238–252.

Jarvie, H.P., Haygarth, P.M., Neal, C., Butler, P., Smith, B., Naden, P.S., Joynes, A., Neal, M., Wickham, H., Armstrong, L., Harman, S. & Palmer-Felgate, E.J. (2008) Stream water chemistry and quality along an upland-lowland rural land-use continuum, south west England. *Journal of Hydrology*, **350**, 215–231.

Jefferies, J. (2005) The UK population: past, present and future. Focus on People and Migration. (eds R. Chappell). Palgrave Macmillan, Hampshire. pp. 1–18.

Jenkins, G., Perry, M. & Prior, J. (2009) The Climate of the UK and recent trends. Met Office Hadley Centre.

Jenkinson, D.S., Potts, J.M., Perry, J.N., Barnett, V., Coleman, K. & Johnston, A.E. (1994) Trends in herbage yields over the last century on the Rothamsted Long-term Continuous Hay Experiment. *Journal of Agricultural Science (Cambridge)*, **122**, 365–374.

JNCC (Joint Nature Conservation Committee) (2010) Different Types of Marine Protected Areas. [online] Available at: <http://www.jncc.gov.uk/PDF/MPAsInfoDoc_v2_1.pdf> [Accessed 22.03.11].

Jones, A., Hillsdon, M. & Coombes, E. (2009) Greenspace access, use and physical activity: understanding the effects of area deprivation. *Preventive Medicine*, **49**, 500–505.

Jones, C.R., Houston, J.A. & Bateman, D. (1993) A history of human influence on the coastal landscape. The Sand Dunes of the Sefton Coast (eds D. Atkinson & J.A. Houston), pp 3–20. Liverpool Museum, Liverpool.

Jones, R. (2004) European beekeeping in the 21st century: strengths, weaknesses, opportunities, threats. *Bee World*, **85**, 77–80.

Jones, M.L.M., Wallace, H.L., Norris, D., Brittain, S.A., Haria, S., Jones, R.E., Rhind, P.M., Reynolds, B.R. & Emmett, B.A. (2004) Changes in vegetation and soil characteristics in coastal sand dunes along a gradient of atmospheric nitrogen deposition. *Plant Biology,* **6**(5), 598–605.

Jones, M.L.M., Sowerby, A., Williams, D.L., Jones, R.E. (2008) Factors controlling soil development in sand dunes: evidence from a coastal dune soil chronosequence. *Plant and Soil,* **307**(1–2), 219–234.

Kahn, P.H. Jr. (1999) The human relationship with nature: Development and culture. MIT Press, Cambridge, MA.

Kahn, P.H. & Kellert, S.R. (2002) Children and Nature: Psychological, sociocultural and evolutionary investigations. MIT Press, Cambridge, MA.

Kaoru, Y. & Hoagland, P. (1994) The value of historic shipwrecks: Conflicts and management. *Coastal Management*, **22**(2), 195–213.

Kennedy, F. & Pitman, R. (2004) Factors affecting the nitrogen status of soils and ground flora in Beech woodlands. *Forest Ecology and Management*, **198**, 1–14.

Keirle, I. (2002) Countryside recreation site management: a marketing approach. Routledge, London.

Kilpatrick, J. (2008) Addressing the land uses issues for non-food crops, in response to increasing fuel and energy generation opportunities. ADAS Rosemaund Ltd, Hereford.

Kirby, K.J., Smart, S.M., Black, H.I.J., Bunce, R.G.H., Corney, P.M., & Smithers, R.J. (2005) Long term ecological change in British woodlands (1971–2001), English Nature, Peterborough.

Kirk, G.J.D., Bellamy, P.H. & Lark, R.M. (2010) Changes in soil pH across England and Wales in response to decreased acid deposition. *Global Change Biology*, **16**(11), 3111–3119.

Kotze, D.J. & O'Hara, R.B. (2003) Species decline – but why? Explanations of carabid beetle (*Coleoptera, Carabidae*) declines in Europe. *Oecologia*, **135**, 138–148.

Krebs, J.R., Anderson, R., CluttonBrock, T., Morrison, W.I., Young, D.B., Donnelly, C.A., Frost, S., & Woodroffe, R. (1997) Bovine tuberculosis in cattle and badgers – An independent scientific review. MAFF, London.

LUC (Land Use Consultants) (2008) Understanding the relevance and application of the Access to Natural Greenspace Standard. Report prepared for Natural England. Land Use Consultants, London.

Lake, S., Bullock, J.M. & Hartley, S. (2001) Impacts of livestock grazing on lowland heathland in the UK. ENRR 422, English Nature, Peterborough.

Langton, T.E.S., Beckett, C.L. & Foster, J.P. (2001) Great Crested Newt Conservation Handbook. Froglife, Halesworth.

Lavelle, P., Dugdale, R., Scholes, R., Berhe, A.A., Carpenter, E. Codispoti, L., Izac, A.-M. & Lemoalle, J., Luizao, F., Scholes, M., Tréguer, P. & Ward, B. (2005) Nutrient Cycling. Ecosystems and Human Well-being: Synthesis Report, The Millenium Ecosystem Assessment, pp. 353. Island Press, Washington, DC.

Lavery, S. & Donovan, B. (2005) Flood risk management in the Thames Estuary looking ahead 100 years. *Philosophical Transactions of the Royal Society A: Mathematical, Physical and Engineering Sciences*, **363**(1831), 1455–74.

LCM (Land Cover Map) (2000) Land Cover Map, Biodiversity Action Plan classification. [online] Available at: <http://www.countrysidesurvey.org.uk/archiveCS2000/mod7_info.htm> [Accessed 21.02.11].

Lee, J.A. (1998) Unintentional experiments with terrestrial ecosystems: ecological effects of sulphur and nitrogen pollutants. *Journal of Ecology*, **86**, 1–12.

Lewis, G. & M. Booth (1994) Are cities bad for your mental health? *Psychological Medicine*, **24**, 913–915.

Lindborg, R., Bengtsson, J., Berg, A., Cousins, S.A.O., Eriksson, O., Gustafsson, T., Hasund, K.P., Lenoir L., Pihlgren, A., Sjödin, E. & Stenseke, M. (2008) A landscape perspective on conservation of semi-natural grasslands. *Agriculture, Ecosystems and Envrionent*, **125**, 213–222.

Longfield, S.A. & Macklin, M.G. (1999) The influence of recent environmental change on flooding and sediment fluxes in the Yorkshire Ouse Basin. *Hydrological Processes*, **13**, 1051–66.

Loveland, P. & Webb, J. (2003) Is there a critical level of organic matter in the agricultural soils of temperate regions: a review. *Soil and Tillage Research*, **70**, 1–18.

Lovett, G.M., Cole, J.J. & Pace, M.L. (2006) Is net ecosystem production equal to ecosystem carbon accumulation. *Ecosystems*, **9**, 1–4.

Lovett, A.A., Sünnenberg, G.M., Richter, G.M., Dailey, A.G., Riche, A.B. & Karp, A. (2009) Land use implications of increased biomass production identified by GIS-Based suitability and yield mapping for Miscanthus in England. *Bioenergy Research*, **2**, 17–28.

Lowe, J.A., Howard, T.P., Pardaens, A., Tinker, J., Holt, J., Wakelin, S., Milne, G., Leake, J., Wolf, J., Horsbaugh, K., Reeder, T., Jenkins, G., Ridley, J, Dye, S. & Bradley, S. (2009) UK Climate Projections Science report: Marine and Coastal Projections. Met Office Hadley Centre, Exeter.

LTL (Learning through Landscapes) (2003) National School Grounds Survey. [online] Available at: <www.ltl.org.uk> [Accessed 21.02.11].

Mabey, R. (1972) Food for Free. Collins, London.

Mabey, R. (1996) *Flora Britannica*. Sinclair-Stevenson, London.

Maberly, S.C., King, L., Dent, M.M., Jones, R.I. & Gibson, C.E. (2002) Nutrient limitation of phytoplankton and periphyton growth in upland lakes. *Freshwater Biology*, **47**, 2136–2152.

Maclaren, D. (2000) Under the thatch. London and Country Properties Issue 38, Autumn–Winter.

Mainstone, C.P., Dills, R.M., & Withers, P.J.A. (2008) Controlling sediment and phosphorus transfer to receiving waters: a strategic management perspective for England and Wales. *Journal of Hydrology*, **350**, 131–143.

Malby, A.R., Whyatt, J.D., Timmis, R.J., Wilby, R.L. & Orr, H.G. (2007) Long Term Variations in Orographic Rainfall: Analysis and Implications for Upland Catchments. Hydrological Sciences – *Journal des Sciences Hydrologiques*, **52**(2), 276–291.

Marshall, E.J.P., Brown, V.K., Boatman, N.D., Lutman, P.J.W. & Squire, G.R. (2001) The impact of herbicides on weed abundance and biodiversity. UK Pesticides Safety Directorate. Report PN0940 2001 MAFF.

Marshall, E.J.P., Brown, V.K., Boatman, N.D., Lutman, P.J.W., Squire, G.R. & Ward, L.K. (2003) The role of weeds in supporting biological diversity within crop fields. *Weed Research*, **43**, 77–89.

Masselink, G. & Russell, P. (2008) MCCIP Annual Report Card 2007–2008 Scientific Review – Coastal Erosion and Coastal Geomorphology. [online] Available at: <http://www.mccip.org.uk/annual-report-card/2007-2008/marine-environment/coastal-erosion.aspx> [Accessed 21.02.11].

Matless, D. (1998) Landscape and Englishness. Reaktion, London.

Matthews, R.W. & Broadmeadow, M.S.J. (2009) The potential of UK forestry to contribute to Government's emissions reduction commitments. Combating climate change – a role for UK forests. An assessment of the potential of UK's trees and woodlands to mitigate and adapt to climate change. (eds D.J. Read, P.H. Freer-Smith, J.I.L. Morison, N. Hanley, C.C. West, and P. Snowdon), pp. 139–161. TSO, London.

Mayor, D.J., Zuur, A.F., Solan, M., Paton, G.I. & Killham, K. (2010) Factors affecting benthic impacts at Scottish fish farms. *Environmental Science and Technology*, **44,** 2079–2084.

McDonald, A.G., Bealey, W.J., Fowler, D., Dragosits, U., Skiba, U., Smith, R.I., Donovan, R.G., Brett, H.E., Hewitt, C.N. & Nemitz, E. (2007) Quantifying the effect of urban tree planting on concentrations and deposition of PM10 in two UK conurbations. *Atmospheric Environment*, **41**, 8455–8467.

McHugh, M., Harrod, T. & Morgan, R. (2002) The extent of soil erosion in upland England and Wales. *Earth Surface Processes and Landforms*, **27**, 99–107.

McKernan, P. & Grose, M. (2007) An analysis of accessible natural greenspace provision in the South East. South East AONBs Woodlands Programme, the Forestry Commission and Natural England. [online] Available at: <http://www.forestry.gov.uk/pdf/accnatgreenrep-report.pdf/$FILE/accnatgreenrep-report.pdf> [Accessed 21.02.11].

Measures, G. (2008) Biodiversity Targets by Government Region. Paper prepared for the England Biodiversity Group. [online] Available at: <http://ukbap-reporting.org.uk/news/details.asp?X=60> [Accessed 21.02.11].

Met Office (2010) England 1971–2000 averages. [online] Available at: <http://www.metoffice.gov.uk/climate/uk/averages/19712000/areal/england.html> [Accessed 21.03.11].

Met Office Hadley Centre Observation Data (2011) Monthly England and Wales precipitation data [online] Available at: <http://www.metoffice.gov.uk/hadobs/hadukp/data/monthly/HadEWP_monthly_qc.txt> [Accessed 05.05.11].

MFA (Marine and Fisheries Agency) (2009) UK Sea Fisheries Statistics 2009. [online] Available at: <http://marinemanagement.org.uk/fisheries/statistics/documents/ukseafish/2009/final.pdf> [Accessed 12.04.11].

Michell, R. & Popham, F. (2008) Effect of exposure to natural environment on heatlh inequalities: an observational population study. *The Lancet*, **372**, 1655–1660.

Milne, R. & Brown, T.A. (1997) Carbon in the vegetation and soils of Great Britain. *Journal of Environmental Management*, **49**, 413–433.

Milneur, F., Johnson, M.P. & Maggs, C.A. (2008) Non-indigenous marine macroalgae in native communities: a case study in the British Isles. *Journal of the Marine Biological Association of the UK*, **88**, 693–698.

Mintel (2005) Extreme Sports – UK. Mintel International Group.

Mintel (2008) Wildlife Tourism – International. Mintel International Group.

Mitchell, P.I. (2010) Marine Birds. *In:* Charting Progress 2 Feeder Report: Healthy and Biologically Diverse Seas. UK Marine Monitoring and Assessment Strategy (UKMMAS), Defra. [online] Available at: <http://chartingprogress.defra.gov.uk/chapter-3-healthy-and-biologicaly-diverse-seas> [Accessed 24.01.11].

MMO (Marine Management Organisation) (2010) United Kingdom Sea Fisheries Statistics 2009. Marine Management Organisation. [online] Available at: <www.mmo.gov.uk> [Accessed 21.02.11].

Moller, I. (2006) Quantifying saltmarsh vegetation and its effect on wave height dissipation: Results from a UK east coast saltmarsh. *Estuarine and Coastal Shelf Science*, **69**, 337–351.

Monteith, D., Hildrew, A.G., Flower, R.J., Raven, P.J., Beaumont, W.R.B, Collen, P., Kreiser, A., Shilland, E.M. & Winterbottom, J.H. (2005) Is the decline in acidity prompting improvements in freshwater flora and fauna? (ed D. Monteith) UK Acid Water Monitoring Network: 15 Year Report, Analysis and interpretation of results: April 1988 – March 2003. ENSIS, London.

Moore, E.O. (1982) A prison environment's effect on health care service demands. *Journal of Environmental Systems*, **11**, 17–34.

Moore-Colyer, R. (2001) Rolf Gardiner, English patriot and the council for the church and countryside. *Agricultural History Review*, **49**, 187–209.

Morecroft, M.D., Taylor, M.E. & Oliver, H.R. (1998) Air and soil microclimates of deciduous woodland compared to an open site. *Agricultural and Forest Meteorology*, **90**, 141–156.

Morecroft, M.D., Bealey, C.E., Beaumont, D.A., Benham, S., Brooks, D.R., Burt, T.P., Critchley, C.N.R., Dick, J., Littlewood, N.A., Monteith, D.T., Scott, W.A., Smith, R.I., Walmsley, C. & Watson, H. (2009) The UK Environmental Change Network: Emerging trends in the composition of plant and animal communities and the physical environment. *Biological Conservation*, **142**, 2814–2832.

Morris, J., Hess, T.M., Gowing, D.J., Leeds-Harrison, P.B., Bannister, N., Wade, M. & Vivash, R.M. (2004a) *Integrated Washland Management for Flood Defence and Biodiversity*. English Nature Research Reports. Peterborough: English Nature.

Morris, R.K.A., Reach, I.S., Duffy, M.J., Collins, T.S., & Leafe, R.N. (2004b) On the loss of salt marshes in south-east England and the relationship with Nereis diversicolor. *Journal of Applied Ecology*. **41**, 787–791.

Morris, R.K.A. (2008) English Nature's Estuaries Initiative: A review of its contribution to ICZM. *Ocean & Coastal Management*, **51**, 25–42.

Mountford, E. & Strachan, I. (2007) *Annex 5 2005–7 UK BAP Priority Habitats review. Detailed proposals and explanation of decisions for terrestrial and freshwater habitats.* Joint Nature Conservation Committee, Peterborough.

NAEI (National Atmospheric Emissions Inventory) (2011) Emission for ammonia in 2009. [online] Available at: <http://naei.defra.gov.uk/mapping/mapping_2009.php> [Accessed 05.05.11].

Natural England (2005a) The condition of lowland BAP priority grasslands: results from a sample survey of non-statutory stands in England. English Nature Research Report Number 636.

Natural England (2005b) English Leisure Visits Survey. Natural England, Cheltenham.

Natural England (2006) England Leisure Visits: report of the 2005 survey. Natural England Report, NE 13. [online] Available at: <http://naturalengland.etraderstores.com/naturalenglandshop/product.aspx?ProductID=e21aa150-6e4c-4928-9e4b-f67c516f2d73> [Accessed 21.02.11].

Natural England (2008) The State of the Natural Environment. Natural England Commissioned Report NE85, Peterborough.

Natural England (2009a) Experiencing landscapes: capturing the cultural services and experiential qualities of landscape. Natural England Commissioned Report NECR024, Peterborough.

Natural England (2009b) Economic Valuation of Uplands Ecosystem Services. Report by EFTEC NECR029. [online] Available at: <http://naturalengland.etraderstores.com/NaturalEnglandShop/NECR029> [Accessed 12.04.11].

Natural England (2009c) Agri-environment schemes in England 2009. A review of results and effectiveness. [online] Available at: <http://www.naturalengland.org.uk/Images/AE-schemes09_tcm6-14969.pdf> [Accessed 21.02.11].

Natural England (2009d) Green Growth for Green Communities: A selection of regional case studies. Park City Conference 2009. [online] Available at: <www.naturalengland.org.uk/Images/GI%20case%20studies_tcm6-10331.pdf> [Accessed 21.02.11].

Natural England (2009e) No charge? Valuing the natural environment. Natural England Report NE220. [online] Available at: <www.naturalengland.org.uk/Images/nochargev2_tcm6-14259.pdf> [Accessed 12.04.11].

Natural England (2010a) Green Belts: a greener future, Natural England and the Campaign to Protect Rural England NE196. [online] Available at: <http://naturalengland.etraderstores.com/NaturalEnglandShop/ne196> [Accessed 12.04.11].

Natural England (2010b) Lost Life: England's lost and threatened species. Natural England Report NE 233. [online] Available at: <http://naturalengland.etraderstores.com/NaturalEnglandShop/NE233> [Accessed 21.02.11].

Natural England (2010c) England's peatlands – carbon storage and greenhouse gases. Natural England Report NE257. [online] Available at: <http://naturalengland.etraderstores.com/NaturalEnglandShop/NE257> [Accessed 21.02.11].

Natural England (2010d) Energy Crops Scheme. [online] Available at: <http://www.naturalengland.org.uk/planning/grants-funding/energy-crops/default.htm> [Accessed 21.02.11].

Nellemann, C., Corcoran, E., Duarte, C.M., Valdés, L., De Young, C., Fonseca, L. & Grimsditch, G. (eds) (2009) Blue Carbon. A Rapid Response Assessment. United Nations Environment Programme, GRID-Arendal.

Nelson, S.H, Court, I., Vickery, J.A., Watts, P.N. & Bradbury,

R.B. (2003) The status and ecology of the yellow wagtail in Britain. *British Wildlife*, **14**, 270–274.

NERA (2007) The Benefits of Water Framework Directive Programmes of Measures in England and Wales. A final report to DEFRA. [online] Available at: <http://www.wfdcrp.co.uk/pdf%5CCRPSG%204bcd%20Final.pdf> [Accessed 12.04.11].

Newton, J. (2007) Wellbeing and the Natural Environment: A brief overview of the evidence. Report to Defra. [online] Available at: <http://www3.surrey.ac.uk/resolve/seminars/Julie%20Newton%20Paper.pdf> [Accessed 12.04.11].

NICE (National Institute for Health and Clinical Excellence) (2009) Promoting physical activity for children and young people. London.

Nisbet, T.R., Silgram, M., Shah, N., Morrow, K. & Broadmeadow, S. (2009) Woodland and the Water Framework Directive. Environment Agency, Bristol.

NNFCC (National Non-Food Crops Centre) (2009) Area Statistics for Non-food crops. [online] Available at: <http://www.nnfcc.co.uk/metadot/index.pl?id=2179;isa=Category;op=show> [Accessed 21.02.11].

OFSTED (Office for Standards in Education, Children's Services and Skills) (2008) Learning Outside the Classroom. Ofsted, London.

O'Brien, E. & Tabbush, P. (2005) Accessibility of woodlands and natural spaces: addressing crime and safety issues. Forestry Commission report. 48pp.

Oldfield, T.E.E., Smith, R.J., Harrop, S.R. & Leader-Williams, N. (2004) A gap analysis of terrestrial protected areas in England and its implications for conservation policy. *Biological Conservation*, **120**, 307–313.

ONS (Office of National Statistics) (2000) Mineral Extraction in Great Britain [online]. Available at: <http://www.statistics.gov.uk/downloads/theme_commerce/PA1007_1999.pdf> [Accessed 21.02.11].

Orr, H.G., Wilby R.L., McKenzie-Hedger, M., & Brown, I. (2008) Climate change in the uplands: a UK perspective on safeguarding regulatory ecosystem services. *Climate Research*, **37**, 77–98.

Osborne, P. (2005) Key issues in assessing the feasibility of reintroducing the great bustard *Otis tarda* to Britain. *Oryx*, **39**, 22–29.

Peacock, J., Hine, R. & Pretty, J. (2008) The TurnAround 2007 Project. Report for the Wilderness Foundation, University of Essex.

Phoenix, G.K., Booth, R.E., Leake, J.R., Read, D.J., Grime, J.P. & Lee, J.A. (2003) Effects of enhanced nitrogen deposition and phosphorus limitation on nitrogen budgets of semi-natural grasslands. *Global Change Biology*, **9**, 1309–1321.

Phoenix, G.K., Booth, R.E., Leake, J.R., Read, D.J., Grime, J.P. & Lee, .J.A. (2004) Simulated pollutant nitrogen deposition increases P stress and enhances root-surface phosphatase activities of three plant functional types in a calcareous grassland. *New Phytologist* **161**, 279–289.

Phoenix, G.K., Johnson, D., Grime, J.P. & Booth, R.E. (2008) Sustaining ecosystem services in ancient limestone grassland: importance of major component plants and community composition. *Journal of Ecology*, **96**, 894–902.

Pilgrim S., Smith, D.J. & Pretty, J. (2007) A cross-regional assessment of the factors affecting ecoliteracy: Implications for policy and practice. *Ecological Applications*, **17**(6), 1742–1751.

Pilgrim S., Cullen L., Smith D.J. & Pretty J. (2008) Ecological knowledge is lost in wealthier communities and countries. *Environmental Science Technology*, **42**(4), 1004–1009.

Pinn, E. (2010) Cetaceans. *In:* Charting Progress 2 Feeder Report: Healthy and Biologically Diverse Seas. UK Marine Monitoring and Assessment Strategy (UKMMAS), Defra. [online] Available at: <http://chartingprogress.defra.gov.uk/chapter-3-healthy-and-biologicaly-diverse-seas> [Accessed 26.01.11].

Pinnegar, J., Greenstreet, S., Fraser, H. & Greathead, C. (2010). Fish. *In:* Charting Progress 2 Feeder Report: Healthy and Biologically Diverse Seas. UK Marine Monitoring and Assessment Strategy (UKMMAS), Defra. [online] Available at: <http://chartingprogress.defra.gov.uk/chapter-3-healthy-and-biologicaly-diverse-seas> [Accessed 26.01.11].

Pitcairn, C.E.R., Leith, I.D., Sheppard, L.J., Sutton, M.A., Fowler, D., Munro, R.C., Tang, S. & Wilson, D. (1998) The relationship between nitrogen deposition, species composition and foliar nitrogen concentrations in woodland flora in the vicinity of livestock farms. *Environmental Pollution*, **102**, 41–48.

Potts, S.G., Roberts, S.P.M., Dean, R., Marris, G., Brown, M., Jones, R. & Settele, J. (2010) Declines of managed honeybees and beekeepers in Europe. *Journal of Apicultural Research*, **49**, 15–22.

Prendergast, H.D.V. & Sanderson, H. (2002) Britain's Wild Harvest: The commercial uses of wild plants and fungi. Royal Botanic Gardens, Kew, London.

Preston, C.D., Telfer, M.G., Arnold, H.R., Carey, P.D., Cooper, J.M., Dines, T.D., Pearman, D.A., Roy, D.B. & Smart S.M. (2002) The changing flora of the UK. Defra, London.

Pretty, J.N., Brett, C., Gee, D., Hine, R.E., Mason, C.F., Morison, J.I.L., Raven, H., Rayment, M.D. & van der Bilg, G. (2000) An assessment of the total external costs of UK agriculture. *Agricultural Systems*, **65**, 113–136.

Pretty, J.N., Peacock, J., Sellens, M. & Griffin, M. (2005) The Mental and Physical Health Outcomes of Green Exercise. *International Journal of Environmental Health Research*, **15**(5), 319–337.

Pretty J.N. (2007) *The Earth Only Endures*. Earthscan, London.

Pretty, J.N., Peacock J., Hine R., Sellens M., South N. & Griffin, M. (2007) Green Exercise in the UK Countryside: Effects on Health and Psychological Well-Being, and Implications for Policy and Planning. *J. Environ. Planning and Manage*, **50**(2) 211–231.

Pye, K. & French, P.W. (1993) Targets for coastal habitat recreation. Research and Survey in Nature Conservation no. 13. English Nature, Peterborough.

Pye, K., Saye, S. & Blott, S. (2007) Sand dune processes and management for flood and coastal defence. R&D Technical Report FD1302/TR to Defra and Environment Agency.

Quine, T.A. & Zhang, Y. (2002) An investigation of spatial variation in soil erosion, soil properties, and crop production within an agricultural field in Devon, United Kingdom. *Journal of Soil and Water Conservation*, **57**, 55–65.

Quine, T.A. & Van Oost, K. (2007) Quantifying carbon sequestration as a result of soil erosion and deposition: retrospective assessment using caesium-137 and carbon inventories. *Global Change Biology*, **13**, 2610–2625.

Radley, G.P. (1994) Sand dune vegetation survey of Great Britain: England Pt. 1: A National Inventory. Joint Nature Conservation Committee.

Raine, A.F., Brown, A.F. Amano, T. & Sutherland, W.J. (2009) Assessing population changes from disparate data sources: the decline of the Twite *Carduelis flavirostris* in England. *Bird Conservation International*, **19**, 1–16.

Rayment, M. (1995) Nature Conservation, employment and local economies: a literature review. RSPB, Sandy.

Read, D.J., Freer-Smith, P.H., Morison, J.I.L., Hanley, N., West, C.C. & Snowdon, P.R. (2009) Combating climate change – a role for UK forests. TSO, Edinburgh.

Readman, J.W. (2006) The world's waters: a chemical contaminant perspective. In: An Introduction to Pollution Science (ed R.M. Harrison). Royal Society of Chemistry publications. 77–121.

Rees, S.E., Attrill, M.J., Austen, M.C., Mangi, S.C., Richards, J. & Rodwell, L.D. (2010) Is there a win-win scenario for marine nature conservation? A case study of Lyme Bay, England. *Ocean and Coastal Management*, **53**, 135–145.

Reid, P.C. & Edwards, M. (2010) Plankton. In: Charting Progress 2 Feeder Report: Healthy and Biologically Diverse Seas. UK Marine Monitoring and Assessment Strategy (UKMMAS), Defra. [online] Available at: <http://chartingprogress.defra.gov.uk/chapter-3-healthy-and-biologicaly-diverse-seas> [Accessed 26.01.11].

Rich, T.C.G. & Woodruff, E.R. (1996) Changes in the vascular plant floras of England and Scotland between 1930–1960 and 1987–1988: The BSBI monitoring scheme. *Biological Conservation*, **75**, 217–229.

Richter, F., Fricke, T. & Wachendorf, M. (2010) Utilization of semi-natural grassland through integrated generation of solid fuel and biogas from biomass. III. Effects of hydrothermal conditioning and mechanical dehydration on solid fuel properties and on energy and greenhouse gas balances. *Grass and Forage Science*, **65**, 185–199.

Ricketts, T.H., Regetz, J., Steffan-Dewenter, I., Cunningham, S.A., Kremen, C., Greenleaf, S.S., Klein, A.M., Mayfield, M.M., Morandin, L.A., Ochieng, A., Potts, S.G., & Viana, B.F. (2008) Landscape effects on crop pollination services: are there general patterns? *Ecology Letters*, **11**, 499–515.

Rickinson, M., Dillon, J., Teamey, K., Morris, M., Choi, M., Sanders, D., & Benefield, P. (2004) *A review of research on outdoor learning.* Field Studies Council, Shrewsbury.

Rose, R.J., Webb, N.R., Clarke, R.T., & Traynor, C.H. (2000) Changes on the heathlands in Dorset, England, between 1987 and 1996. *Biological Conservation*, **93**, 117.

RoTAP (Review of Transboundary Air Pollution) (2011) Review of Transboundary Air Pollution: Acidification, Eutrophication, Ground Level Ozone and Heavy Metals in the UK. Contract Report to the Department for Environment, Food and Rural Affairs. Centre for Ecology & Hydrology.

Rotherham, I.D., Jones, M, Smith, L. and Handley, C. (2008) The Woodland Heritage Manual. Wildtrack Publishing, Sheffield.

Rothwell, J.J., Evans, M.G., Liddaman, L. & Allott, T.E.H. (2007) The role of wildfire and gully erosion in particulate Pb export from contaminated peatland catchments in the Southern Pennines, UK. *Geomorphology*, **88**(3–4), 276–284.

Rothwell, J.J., Evans, M.G., Daniels, S.M. & Allott, T.E.H. (2008) Peat soils as a source of lead contamination to upland fluvial systems. *Environmental Pollution*, **153**(3), 582–589.

RSPB (Royal Society for the Protection of Birds) eds. (2005) The state of the UK's birds 2004. Sandy: RSPB.

RSPB (Royal Society for the Protection of Birds) eds. (2006) The state of the UK's birds 2005. Sandy: RSPB.

RSPB (Royal Society for the Protection of Birds) eds. (2007) The state of the UK's birds 2006. Sandy: RSPB.

RSPB (Royal Society for the Protection of Birds) (2008) Wallasea Island Wild Coast Project – creating a new coastal nature reserve. Environmental Statement. Report from Marine Environmental Research.

RSPB (Royal Society for the Protection of Birds) (2010a) Challenge 2010: politicians must cut waste – and invest in nature. [online] Available at: <http://www.rspb.org.uk/Images/challenge_tcm9-238034.pdf> [Accessed 12.04.11].

RSPB (Royal Society for the Protection of Birds) (2010b) The Local Value of Seabirds: Estimating spending by visitors to RSPB coastal reserves and associated local economic impact attributable to seabirds. RSPB, Sandy, UK.

Sage, R.B., Ludorf, C. & Robertson, P.A. (2005) The ground flora of ancient semi-natural woodlands in pheasant release pens in England. *Biological Conservation*, **122**, 243–252.

Sandercock, G., Voss, C., McConnell, D. & Rayner, P. (2009) Declines in aerobic fitness are largely independent of body mass index in affluent English schoolchildren. *Arch Dis Child* (in press).

Sanderson, H. & Prendergast, H. (2002) Commercial uses of wild and traditionally managed plants in England and Scotland. Unpublished Research Report, RBG, CA, English Nature, SNH.

Saunders, J. (2010) Charting Progress 2 Feeder Report: Productive Seas. UK Marine Monitoring and Assessment Strategy (2010), Defra. [online] Available at: <http://chartingprogress.defra.gov.uk/productive-seas-feeder-report-download> [Accessed 26.01.11].

Scharlemann, J.P.W., Johnson, P.J., Smith, A.A., MacDonald, D.W., & Randolph, S.E. (2008) Trends in ixodid tick abundance and distribution in Great Britain. *Medical and Veterinary Entomology*, **22**, 238–247.

Sheehy, J. (2007) Sacred space and the incarnation. In Sacred Space: House of God, Gate of Heaven. North, P. & North, J. (eds), Continuum, London.

Shepherd, D., Burgess, D., Jickells, T., Andrews, J., Cave, R., Turner, R.K., Aldridge, J., Parker, E.R., & Young, E. (2007) Modelling the effects and economics of managed realignment on the cycling and storage of nutrients, carbon and sediments in the Blackwater estuary UK. *Estuarine, Coastal and Shelf Science*, **73**, 355–367.

Skinner, C.J. & Grimwood, C.J. (2002) The UK National Noise Incidence Study 2000/2001. Noise Forum Conference 20 May 2002. London.

Smith, P., Milne, R., Powlson, D.S., Smith, J.U., Falloon, P.D. & Coleman, K. (2000) Revised estimates of the carbon mitigation potential of UK agricultural land. *Soil Use and Management*, **16**, 293–295.

Smith, P., Martino, D., Cai, Z., Gwary, D., Janzen, H.H., Kumar, P., McCarl, B., Ogle, S., O'Mara, F., Rice, C., Scholes, R.J., Sirotenko, O., Howden, M., McAllister, T., Pan, G., Romanenkov, V., Schneider, U., Towprayoon, S., Wattenbach, M. & Smith, J.U. (2008) Greenhouse gas mitigation in agriculture. *Philosophical Transactions of the Royal Society*, **363**(1492), 789–813.

Smith, R.S., Shiel, R.S., Bardgett, R.D., Millward, D., Corkhill, P., Rolph, G., Hobbs, P.J. & Peacock, S. (2003) Soil microbial community, fertility, vegetation and diversity as targets in the restoration management of a meadow grassland. *Journal of Applied Ecology*, **40**(1), 51–64.

Smith, P., Smith, J.U., Flynn, H., Killham, K., Rangel-Castro, I., Foereid, B., Aitkenhead, M., Chapman, S., Towers, W., Bell, J., Lumsdon, D., Milne, R., Thomson, A., Simmons, I., Skiba, U., Reynolds, B., Evans, C., Frogbrook, Z., Bradley, I., Whitmore, A. & Falloon, P. (2007) *ECOSSE: Estimating Carbon in Organic Soils – Sequestration and Emissions: Final Report*. Scottish Executive Environmental and Rural Affairs Department, Edinburgh, 166pp.

Sneddon, S., Brophy, N., Li, Y., MacCarthy, J., Martinez, C., Murrells, T., Passant, N., Thomas, J., Thistlethwaite, G., Tsagatakis, I., Walker, H., Thomson, A. & Cardenas, L. (2010) Greenhouse Gas Inventories for England, Scotland, Wales and Northern Ireland: 1990 – 2008. Report to the Department for Energy and Climate Change, The Scottish Government, The Welsh Assembly Government and The Northern Ireland Department of Environment. ISBN 978-0-9565155-1-3 and AEAT/ENV/R/3067 Issue 1. September 2010. [online] Available at <http://uk-air.defra.gov.uk/reports/cat07/1009070945_DA_GHGI_report_2008_maintext_Issue_1.pdf> [Accessed 06.04.11].

Sozanska, M., Skiba, U. & Metcalfe, S. (2002) Developing an inventory of N$_2$O emissions from British soils. *Atmospheric Environment*, **36**(6), 987–998.

Strachan, R. & Moorhouse, T. (2006) Water vole conservation handbook. 2nd Edition, Wildlife Conservation Research Unit, Oxford, England.

Stevens, C.J., Dise, N.B., Mountford, J.O. & Gowing, D.J. (2004) Impact of nitrogen enrichment on species richness of grasslands. *Science*, **303**, 1876–1879.

Tallowin, J.R.B. & Jefferson, R.G. (1999) Hay production from lowland semi semi-natural grasslands: a review of implications for ruminant livestock systems. *Grass and Forage Science*, **54**, 99–115.

Tallowin, J.R.B., Smith, R.E.N., Goodyear, J. & Vickery, J.A. (2005) Spatial and structural uniformity of lowland agricultural grassland in England: a context for low biodiversity. *Grass and Forage Science*, **60**(3), 225–236.

TEEB (The Economics of Ecosystems & Biodiversity) (2009) TEEB Climate Issues Update, September 2009.

The National Forest (2011) What is the National Forest? [online] Available at: <http://www.nationalforest.org/forest/whatis/> [Accessed 22.03.11].

The Wildlife Trusts (2007) Marine Opinion Poll. [online]. Available at: <http://www.wildlifetrusts.org/index.php?section=marinebill:opinionpoll> [Accessed 12.04.11]

Thirgood, S. & Redpath, S. (1997) Red grouse and their predators. *Nature*, 390, 547.

Thomas, H. & Nisbet, T. R. (2007) An assessment of the impact of floodplain woodland on flood flows. *Water and Environment Journal,* 21, 114–126.

Thornton, D. & Kite D.J. (1990) Changes in the extent of Thames Estuary grazing marsh. NCC Report.

Tilman, D., Hill, J. & Lehman, C. (2006) Carbon-negative biofuels from low-input high-diversity grassland biomass. *Science*, **314**, 1598–1600.

Tisdell, C. (2003) Socioeconomic causes of loss of animal genetic diversity: analysis and assessment. *Ecological Economics*, **45**, 365–376.

Tiwary, A., Sinnett, D., Peachey, C., Chalabi, Z., Vardoulakis, S., Fletcher, T., Leonardi, G., Grundy, C., Azapagic, A. &

Hutchings, T.R. (2009) An integrated tool to assess the role of new planting in PM10 capture and the human health benefits: A case study in London. *Environmental Pollution,* **157**(10), 2645–2653.

Tonn, B., Thumm, U. & Claupein, W. (2010) Semi-natural grassland biomass for combustion: influence of botanical composition, harvest date and site conditions on fuel composition. *Grass and Forage Science*, **65**(4), 383–397.

Tscharntke, T., Klein, A.M., Kruess, A., Steffan-Dewenter, I. & Thies, C. (2005) Landscape perspectives on agricultural intensification and biodiversity – ecosystem service management. *Ecology Letters*, **8**, 857–874.

UKBAP (UK Biodiversity Action Plan) (2007) UK Priority Habitats. [online] Available at: <http://www.ukbap.org.uk/UKPriorityHabitats.aspx> [Accessed 12.04.11].

UKLDVS (UK Leisure Day Visits Survey) (2004) Report of the 2002–03 GB Day Visits Survey. [online] Available at: <http://www.naturalengland.org.uk/ourwork/enjoying/research/monitor/leisuredayvisits/default.aspx> [Accessed 04.02.11].

UKMMAS (UK Marine Monitoring and Assessment Strategy) (2010) Charting Progress 2: The State of UK Seas. Published by the Department for Environment Food and Rural Affairs on behalf of UKMMAS**.** TSO, London. 166pp. ISBN 9780112432937. Available at: <http://chartingprogress.defra.gov.uk/resources> [Accessed 06.06.10].

UKTAG (2005) UK Technical Advisory Group on the Water Framework Directive. Outline of Groundwater Classification for the purposes of the Water Framework Directive (public working draft). [online] Available at: <www.wfduk.org/tag_guidance/Article_08/TAG_11b/view> [Accessed 12.04.11].

UKTS (UK Tourism Survey) (2002) Activities Undertaken by Domestic Tourists 2000–03. [online] Available at: <http://www.enjoyengland.com/Images/Activities%20undertaken%20by%20domestic%20tourists%2C%202000-3_tcm21-171031.pdf> [Accessed 08.04.11].

UKTS (UK Tourism Statistics) (2010) The UK Tourist: Statistics 2009. Tourism volumes and values in 2009. [online] Available at: <http://www.visitbritain.org/Images/UK%20Tourist%202009_tcm29-14574.pdf> [Accessed 12.04.11].

Ulrich, R.S. (1984) View through a window may influence recovery from surgery. *Science*, **224**, 420–421.

Urban Parks Forum and the Garden History Society (Undated) Towards a Country Park Renaissance. Report for the Countryside Agency.

van den Berg, L.J.L., Bullock, J.M., Clarke, R.T., Langston, R.H.W. & Available at: Rose, R.J. (2001) Territory selection by the Dartford warbler (*Sylvia undata*) in Dorset, England: the role of vegetation type, habitat fragmentation and population size. *Biological Conservation*, **101**(2), 217–228.

Verheijen, F.G.A., Jones, R.J.A., Rickson, R.J. & Smith, C.J. (2009) Tolerable versus actual soil erosion rates in Europe. *Earth-Science Reviews*, **94**, 23–38.

Vickery, J.A., Tallowin, J.R., Feber, R.E., Asteraki, E.J., Atkinson, P.W., Fuller, R.J. & Brown, V.K. (2001) The management of lowland neutral grasslands in Britain: effects of agricultural practices on birds and their food resources. *Journal of Applied Ecology*, **38**, 647–664.

Vickery, J.A., Bradbury, R.B., Henderson, I.G., Eaton, M.A. & Grice, P.V. (2004) The role of agri-environment schemes and farm management practices in reversing the decline of farmland birds in England. *Biological Conservation,* **119**, 19–39.

VisitBritain (2007) England Tourism Day Visits 2005. VisitBritain, London.

Warren, P. & Baines, D. (2008) Current status and recent trends in numbers and distribution of black grouse *Tetrao tetrix* in northern England. *Bird Study,* **55**, 94–99.

Water UK (2009) Water Company Proposed PR09 Catchment Management schemes. Water UK, London. [online] Available at: <http://www.water.org.uk/home/events/water-uk-catchment-management-forum/summary-of-information.pdf> [Accessed 01.02.11].

Weatherhead, E.K. & Knox, J.W. (2000) Predicting and mapping the future demand for irrigation water in England and Wales. *Agricultural Water Management,* **43**, 203–218.

Weatherhead, E.K. & Howden, N.J.K. (2009) The relationship between land use and surface water resources in the UK. *Land Use Policy,* **26**, S243–S250.

Webb, N.R. & Haskins, L.E. (1980) An ecological survey of heathlands in the Poole Basin, Dorset, England, in 1978. *Biological Conservation,* **17**, 281–96.

Webb, N.R. (1990) Changes on the heathlands of Dorset, England, between 1978 and 1987. *Biological Conservation,* **51**, 273.

Webb, J.R., Drewitt, A.L. & Measures, G.N. (2009) *Managing for species: integrating the needs of priority species into habitat management.* Natural England Research Report NERR 024, Sheffield.

Whitehouse, A.T. (2007) Managing coastal soft cliffs for invertebrates. Buglife – The Invertebrate Conservation Trust, Peterborough.

WHO & FAO (World Health Organization & Food and Agriculture Organization) (2004) Fruit and Vegetables for Health. Kobe, Japan.

Wilby, R.L., Beven, K.J. & Reynard, N.S. (2008) Climate change and fluvial flood risk in the UK: more of the same? *Hydrological Processes,* **22**, 2511–2523.

Wilkinson, B.H. & McElroy, B.J. (2007) The impact of humans on continental erosion and sedimentation. *Geological Society of America Bulletin,* **119**, 140–156.

Wilkinson, M.E., Quinn, P.F. & Welton, P. (2010) Runoff management during the September 2008 floods in the Belford catchment, Northumberland. *Journal of Flood Risk Management,* **3**, 285–295.

Willis, K.G. & Garrod, G.D. (1993) Valuing landscape – a contingent valuation approach. *Journal of Environmental Management,* **37**, 1–22.

Willis, K.G., Garrod, G., Scarpa, R., Powe, N., Lovett, A., Bateman, I.J., Hanley, N. & Macmillan, D.C. (2003) The social

and environmental benefits of forests in Great Britain. Forestry Commission, Edinburgh.

Wilson, M., Ausden, M. & Milsom, T.M.P. (2004) Changes in breeding wader populations on lowland wet grasslands in England and Wales: causes and potential solutions. *Ibis,* **146**(2), 32–40.

Winfield, I.J., Fletcher, J.M. & James, J.B. (2004) Conservation ecology of the vendace (*Coregonus albula*) in Bassenthwaite Lake and Derwent Water, UK. *Ann. Zool. Fennici,* **41**, 155–164.

White, P.J. & Hammond J.P. (2009) The sources of phosphorus in the waters of Great Britain. *Journal of Environmental Quality,* **38**, 13–26.

Woodland Trust (2004) Space for People. Targeting action for woodland access. Woodland Trust, Grantham. [online] Available at: <http://www.woodlandtrust.org.uk/SiteCollectionDocuments/pdf/spaceforpeople.pdf> [Accessed 08.01.11].

Woodland Trust (2010) Greening the Concrete Jungle. Woodland Trust. [online] Available at: <http://www.woodlandtrust.org.uk/en/more-trees-more-good/Documents/mtmg-urban-trees-report.pdf> [Accessed 08.01.11].

Woodroffe, R., Donnelly, C.A., Jenkins, H.E., Johnston, W.T., Cox, D.R., Bourne, F.J., Cheeseman, C.L., Delahay, R.J., Clifton-Hadley, R.S., Gettinby, G., Gilks, P., Hewinson, R.G., McInerney, J.P. & Morrison, W.I. (2006) Culling and cattle controls influence tuberculosis risk for badgers. *Proceedings of the National Academy of Sciences,* **103**, 14713–14717.

Worrall, F. & Burt, T.P (2007a) Flux of dissolved organic carbon from UK rivers. *Global Biochemical Cycle,* **21**(1) GB1013.

Worrall, F. & Burt T. (2007b) Trends in DOC concentration in Great Britain. *Journal of Hydrology,* **346**, 81–92.

Worrall, F., Evans, M.G., Bonn, A., Reed, M.S., Chapman, D. & Holden, J. (2009) Can carbon offsetting pay for upland ecological restoration? *Science of the Total Environment,* **408**, 26–36.

Wynn, M. (2007) God, pilgrimage, and acknowledgement of place. *Religious Studies,* **43**, 145–163.

Wynn, M. (2009) Faith and Place: An Essay in Embodied Religious Epistemology, p 44. Oxford University Press, Oxford.

Xu, X.M., Harwood, T.D., Pautasso, M., & Jeger, M.J. (2009) Spatio-temporal analysis of an invasive plant pathogen (*Phytophthora ramorum*) in England and Wales. *Ecography,* **32**(3), 504–516.

Zhao, F.J., McGrath, S.P., Blake-Kalff, M.A.A., Link, A. & Tucker, M. (2002) Crop responses to sulphur fertilisation in Europe. Proceedings No. 504. International Fertiliser Society, York.

Appendix 17.1 Approach Used to Assign Certainty Terms to Chapter Key Findings

This chapter began with a set of Key Findings. Adopting the approach and terminology used by the Intergovernmental Panel on Climate Change (IPCC) and the Millennium Assessment (MA), these Key Findings also include an indication of the level of scientific certainty. The 'uncertainty approach' of the UK NEA consists of a set of qualitative uncertainty terms derived from a 4-box model and complemented, where possible, with a likelihood scale (see below). Estimates of certainty are derived from the collective judgement of authors, observational evidence, modelling results and/or theory examined for this assessment.

Throughout the Key Findings presented at the start of this chapter, superscript numbers and letters indicate the estimated level of certainty for a particular key finding:

1. *Well established:* high agreement based on significant evidence
2. *Established but incomplete evidence:* high agreement based on limited evidence
3. *Competing explanations:* low agreement, albeit with significant evidence
4. *Speculative:* low agreement based on limited evidence

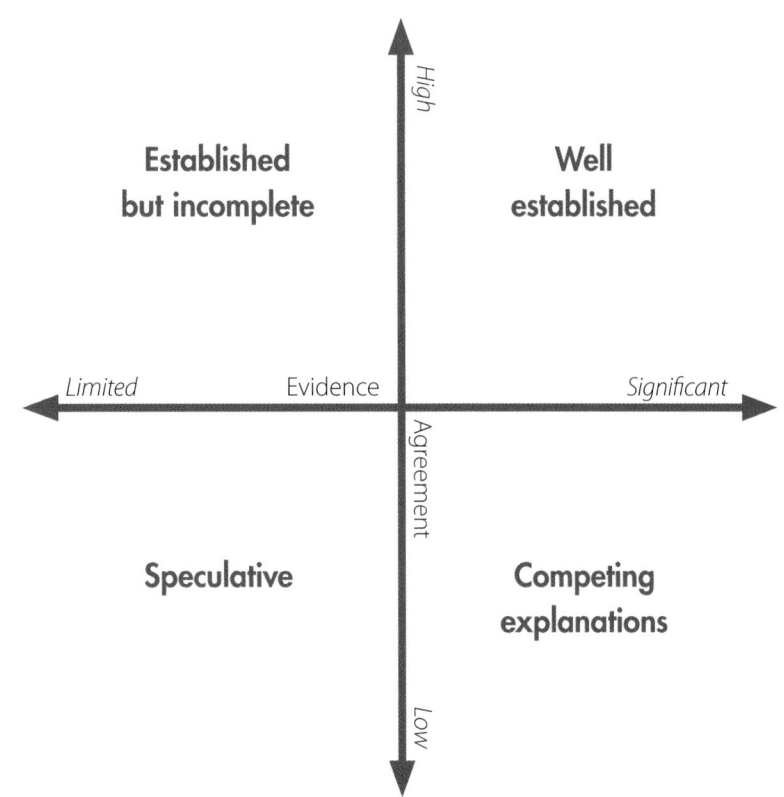

a. *Virtually certain:* >99% probability of occurrence
b. *Very likely:* >90% probability
c. *Likely:* >66% probability
d. *About as likely as not:* >33–66% probability
e. *Unlikely:* <33% probability
f. *Very unlikely:* <10% probability
g. *Exceptionally unlikely:* <1% probability

Certainty terms 1 to 4 constitute the 4-box model, while *a* to *g* constitute the likelihood scale.

Chapter 18:
Status and Changes in the UK Ecosystems and their Services to Society: Northern Ireland

Coordinating Lead Author: Susan Christie
Lead Authors: David McCann (Coordinator and Lead Researcher), Judith Annett, Judith Bankhead, Diane Burgess, Patrick Casement, Peter Christie, Alan Cooper, John Griffin, Neil Halliday, Hilary Kirkpatrick, Cathy Maguire, Jim McAdam, Ronan McColgan, Melina McMullan, Julian Orford, Dave Schoeman, Robert Scott, Roy Tomlinson and Mark Wright
Contributing Authors: Peter Archdale, Caroline Barry, Tony Bazley, Martin Bradley, Joe Breen, Lee Bruce, Christine Butler, Martin Carey, Patrick Cregg, Peter Cush, Iain Davies, Colum Delaney, Philip Downey, John Early, Lindsay Easson, Clifford Henry, Dermot Hughes, Crawford Jordan, Eimear Kearney, Jonathan Kingham, Lisa Kirkwood, Declan Lawlor, Aileen Lawson, Chris Maggs, Orla Maguire, John Martin, Marcus McAuley, Thomas McCann, Neil McCulloch, Damian McFerran, Philip McMurray, Jonathan McNee, Arthur Mitchell, Alan Moore, Stuart Morwood, Joan Moss, Archie Murchie, Ken Neill, Geoff Nuttall, Julia Nunn, John O'Neill, Brian Poots, David Porter, Neil Reid, Robert Rosell, Diane Ruddock, Richard Schaible, Matthew Service, Maxime Sizaret, Emily Smyth, Jude Stephens, Andrew Upton, Claire Vincent and Michael Young

Key Findings*

There are many different factors that affect the environment, how it is used and what ecosystem services can be delivered[1]. Northern Ireland's history has meant that the environment has been given a low political priority relative to social and economic factors. This has been changing since the advent of the Northern Ireland Assembly in 2007. A large proportion of local environmental legislation is directly related to EU and UK legislation. The Common Agricultural Policy (CAP) has had significant impacts on land use, including through agri-environment schemes. Targets for the designation, protection and management of sites and species have repeatedly been delayed. The Programme for Government is a major driver for political action, supported by major strategies including the Sustainable Development Strategy, Regional Development Strategy and Biodiversity Strategy. Climate change, invasive alien species and plant and animal pathogens are having impacts on habitats and ecosystem services. Consumer preferences, international trade, the costs and availability of commodities and energy may also have impacts on the demands made on land and sea resources. There is a need for greater recognition of the ability of land to deliver many functions simultaneously under integrated management regimes.

[1] well established

Northern Ireland has a unique and important biodiversity[1]. Mechanisms to protect biodiversity are having beneficial outcomes[2]. The principal pressures on Northern Ireland's species diversity come from human activities such as agriculture, forestry, fisheries and building development which have led to significant habitat loss. Climate change has had little impact up to 2010, but seasonal changes have been noted for both plants and animals. Non-native invasive species have considerable localised impacts and are becoming a problem in many habitats. There has been some loss of species and others are declining. Further information is required on trends in the conservation status of priority species and habitats.

[1] well established
[2] established but incomplete evidence

The area, composition and ecosystem services delivered by Northern Ireland's habitats have changed over time and contribute to the delivery of a range of ecosystem services[2]. The Northern Ireland Countryside Survey provides the major source of information on habitat change since 1989. Key changes noted between 1989 and 2007 include increases in Improved Grassland, built-up land and Broadleaved Woodland and decreases in arable land, Neutral Grassland and peatland. Between 1998 and 2007, Improved Grassland increased at the expense of both Neutral Grassland and arable farmland, but there was considerable loss of both Improved and Neutral Grassland to building development. Smaller amounts of Neutral Grassland, Bog, fen, Coniferous Woodland and Improved Grassland were converted to Broadleaved Woodland.

[2] established but incomplete evidence

Mountains, Moorlands and Heaths contain the largest tracts of semi-natural habitats and cover an estimated 13% of Northern Ireland, with the vast majority being upland blanket bog (10% of Northern Ireland)[1]. The overall area has been relatively stable over the past 20 years, although changes between some of the constituent habitats have occurred due to changes in landuse. Although most of the blanket bog has been physically modified, the majority is still capable of forming peat, and Northern Ireland has a large proportion of the UK and EU blanket peat resource. Peat has a high carbon content, and bogland vegetation sequesters carbon and represents a substantial carbon store, especially where the hydrology of pristine sites is maintained and that of degraded sites restored. Uplands are used for low-intensity livestock grazing and are of high scenic and recreational value. Water storage in intact peatlands can contribute to flood alleviation.

[1] well established

Semi-natural Grasslands cover an estimated 18% of Northern Ireland and are composed predominantly of Neutral Grassland (16%)[1]. This habitat has undergone a major decline in the past 60 years due to fragmentation and agricultural intensification. There is some change in management between intensive and Semi-natural Grassland, with a high proportion of Neutral Grassland being highly productive agriculturally and species poor. Maintenance of these habitats requires very specific management regimes, with grazing intensity particularly important, both to avoid soil and plant damage and to halt scrub encroachment. Some of the associated flora and fauna are very important in both a UK and an EU context. Semi-natural Grassland is used primarily for low intensity livestock grazing. Perennial grassland is a valuable carbon store.

[1] well established

---

* Each Key Finding has been assigned a level of scientific certainty, based on a 4-box model and complemented, where possible, with a likelihood scale. Superscript numbers indicate the uncertainty term assigned to each finding. Full details of each term and how they were assigned are presented in Appendix 18.1.

Enclosed Farmland is the largest of the UK NEA Broad Habitats and covers an estimated 44% of Northern Ireland, with the majority consisting of Improved Grassland (40% of Northern Ireland)[1]. Agricultural systems have changed markedly over the last century due to intensification, which has led to some loss of habitat and species diversity. Field boundaries, with their associated open wet drains, are important for biodiversity. Since the 1950s many field boundaries have been removed, but this trend is declining. Enclosed Farmland gives the countryside its characteristic appearance and provides most of Northern Ireland's agricultural output, largely from livestock and associated products. It is also a significant source of greenhouse gas emissions and pollutants in soil and water. Perennial grassland is a potential carbon sink and increasing amounts of land are used for energy production.

Northern Ireland is one of the least wooded countries in the EU, with coniferous plantations (predominantly Sitka spruce) covering about 4% of the land area and Broadleaved Woodland, including a small amount of ancient woodland, transitional scrub and recent plantings, covering another 6%[1]. There has been a large increase in total woodland cover since the 1950s, with the last 10 years responsible for a major increase in Broadleaved Woodland. Woodlands dating to 1830 or earlier cover less than 1% of Northern Ireland's land area and are highly fragmented (most <2 hectares; ha). Woodlands provide many ecosystem services, often simultaneously, and these include timber production, carbon sequestration, biodiversity and recreational opportunities.

Northern Ireland is notable within the UK for its large area of freshwater habitats, their flow dynamics, their nutrient characteristics and their biodiversity, including internationally important bird populations[1]. Openwaters and Wetlands cover an estimated 7% of Northern Ireland (75,000 ha) and there has been little change in this area over the past 50 years. There are three large lakes of particular importance for recreation and tourism, but they are eutrophic. Lowland raised bogs cover 1.5% of Northern Ireland and are important in a UK context. These and many other minor wetland habitats have decreased over the past 10 years. Arterial drainage works carried out until the 1990s resulted in Northern Ireland having the highest percentage of modified rivers in the UK, with accompanying impacts on biodiversity. More recently, priority has been given to restoring riverine habitats and recognising their role in flood prevention. Openwaters and Wetlands provide the benefits of water, food, recreation and biodiversity as well as detoxifying pollutants and contributing significantly to flood control.

The Urban habitat (settlements, roads and rural buildings) covers 7.5% of Northern Ireland; there was a 30% increase between 1998 and 2007[1]. Much of this is on the edges of existing built-up areas, but there is significant development in the countryside, principally of single dwellings with attendant issues concerning the provision of infrastructure. Urban areas generally rely on the countryside to provide ecosystem services including food, water, waste disposal and recreation. However, they provide greenspace and some sites of high conservation value. Greenspace in cities provides major health and well-being benefits to residents and helps to detoxify pollutants generated by the city.

Although Coastal Margin habitats (Sea Cliffs, Shingle, Sand Dunes, Saltmarsh, Coastal Lagoons) cover only 0.25% of Northern Ireland, they have high biodiversity value, with seabird populations and levels of insect diversity that are important from a UK and Irish perspective[1]. The overall area has remained relatively stable over the past 20 years. However, the quality of individual sites and the amount of scientific knowledge available are highly variable. About 75% of the coast is protected, much of it by multiple designations. Coastal Margins provide major benefits in terms of recreation, culture and tourism and help to alleviate flooding, as well as being major sites for biodiversity.

Northern Ireland waters to 12 nautical miles include 450,000 ha of the Irish Sea and Atlantic Ocean, of which about 11,000 ha are the intertidal zone[1]. The Marine habitat contains around half of its overall biodiversity, with Strangford Lough and Rathlin Island together containing 90% of the marine biodiversity. However, catches of many finfish have decreased and there is evidence of damage to habitats and deterioration of water quality, especially in coastal areas. Northern Ireland's fisheries are important locally and the development of marine renewable energy projects has begun. The Marine environment is valued for its cultural heritage, recreational value and tourism, and is a vital component of energy, nutrient and water cycles, with major roles in regulating carbon.

Northern Ireland's ecosystems contribute to provisioning, regulating, cultural and supporting services[2]. There is limited information available to enable assigning these outputs to specific habitats.

[2] *established but incomplete evidence*

Provisioning services:

- Northern Ireland's primary agricultural outputs are livestock and dairy products. Large amounts of grain are produced, but most of this is for livestock feed rather than human consumption. Over the past 150 years there has been a shift away from producing grain and potatoes to raising livestock; the total area of land in production (crops and pasture) in 2009 was slightly above that of 1959, but much less than in 1859 and 1909. More livestock were produced in 2009 than in 1959 or earlier. In the past 30 years cattle have slightly and steadily increased in number, the number of pigs has decreased and sheep numbers have decreased after a peak in the 1990s. Livestock (cattle, sheep and pigs) accounted for £407 million, the dairy industry an additional £514 million, and poultry and eggs £218 million of output in 2008.

- Arable production has declined since 1981, with considerable change in the types of crops produced over the past 28 years. Potatoes, apples and mushrooms are the main crops for human use, with wheat, arable crop silage and other crops increasing in recent years. Crops and horticultural products accounted for £126 million of agricultural output in 2008.

- The agriculture and food processing industries are major employers and significant contributors to the local economy. However, farm numbers and incomes have been declining for the past 28 years, while the value of farmland has been increasing rapidly since the mid-1990s to nearly £20,000/ha.

- Marine fisheries from Northern Ireland waters accounted for some £25 million in 2008 (4% of the UK catch) and have shown a shift from finfish to shellfish (primarily *Nephrops*) since about 2004. In 2008 the value of shellfish was nearly three times the value of finfish. There has been a decline in fish stocks over the past decade.

- Freshwater fisheries for salmon and eels have decreased significantly since 2000. The eel fishery in Lough Neagh accounted for some £2 million in 2008, down from £5 million, and has been declining since 1983. Salmon has declined by some 85% since a peak in 1995 in terms of numbers caught, but the value per kg has increased.

- Aquaculture (both marine and freshwater) was valued at nearly £11 million in 2009, including mussels, oysters, salmonids and living trout ova.

- Most forestry consists of exotic conifers, yielding relatively low-quality timber; this was valued at over £7 million in 2009. Production gradually increased to around 400,000 m^3/yr from 50,000 m^3/yr in the 1970s. There has been a recent shift to small-scale planting of broadleaved trees in lowlands, with emphasis on the many benefits of mixed woodlands.

- Around 98% of drinking water is abstracted from rivers, lakes and reservoirs in Northern Ireland, unlike England and Wales where 35% is extracted from groundwater. Annual water costs were over £186 million in 2007–2008, an increase of one-third since 2004. The water quality of Northern Ireland's rivers and lakes has a direct relationship to the cost of water treatment which, along with high overall annual water costs, is high in comparison to Great Britain. Historic underinvestment in the infrastructure is being addressed, with capital investment over five years to upgrade the system for piping, sewage treatment and drinking water treatment exceeding £1 billion. Low flow levels, particularly resulting from possible climate change impacts, are a concern.

- Peat is a traditional energy source, but levels of extraction and usage are now low following significant extraction in the 1980s and 1990s. However, the area of peat extraction for horticulture has increased since 1990. Peat extraction leads to major carbon losses from peatland. Extraction of major lignite deposits has been suggested.

- Upland areas are the main location for windfarms, an increasingly important source of electricity. Marine renewables (wind, tidal or wave power) have significant potential for development to meet renewable targets. Hydropower is mostly on a small scale, and there is increasing research into, and commercial interest in, short rotation coppice and anaerobic digestion. Renewable development has increased over the past 10 years and is likely to continue to expand to meet government targets.

Regulating services[2]:

[2] established but incomplete evidence

- An estimated 386 million tonnes of carbon is held in Northern Ireland's soils. Peat soils occupy 15% of the land area, but contain 42% of the carbon stock. The highest soil carbon densities (>5,000 t carbon/ha) are in deep peat, and peaty soils account for a further 10% of the carbon stock. Northern Ireland's soils have much higher carbon content on average (5%) than those in the rest of the UK (2–3%). Total vegetation stores of carbon are relatively higher in agricultural soils in Northern Ireland than in Great Britain (36% versus 10%) and lower in woodland (55% versus 80%), due to differences in land cover percentages. Land use changes have affected these values over time.

- Agriculture accounted for 23% of greenhouse gas emissions in Northern Ireland in 2007, up slightly from 22% in 1990 and compared to 7% in the UK as a whole.

- Northern Ireland's territorial waters may contribute to cycling of nitrogen- and sulphur-based greenhouse gases indirectly through ocean temperatures and the activities of marine algae. The marine environment receives and processes nutrient pollution from the land, some sewage, much litter and all of the wastes from marine aquaculture.

- Although overall soil degradation is low in comparison to the situation in Great Britain, many agricultural soils have elevated nitrogen and phosphorus levels and are a source of these nutrients to surface waters. The Nitrates Directive and the Water Framework Directive have encouraged tighter control of nitrogen and phosphorus inputs from agriculture, resulting in decreased fertiliser use, and there have been improvements in soil phosphate levels in recent years. There is still a major surplus in most soils, especially those under intensive grassland.

- Water quality problems in Northern Ireland are mostly due to diffuse nutrient pollution from agriculture; fewer than 6% of rivers show no nutrient enrichment. There have, however, been improvements in nitrate and phosphate pollution levels in rivers since 1994. Despite this, there is no evidence yet of any improvement in the biological aspects of water quality. River pollution incidents decreased in both number and average severity between 2001 and 2008. Water courses were affected by major drainage schemes and canalisation between the 1950s and 1980s.

- Air quality has improved in recent years and is good in general. Domestic heating and transport are the main sources, as there is relatively little industry. High levels of ammonia can occur in rural areas near intensive animal production facilities.

- Apples are the main crop pollinated by insects, 80% by honeybees; the market value of apple pollination is over £7 million/yr. Vegetables and soft fruit are also partially dependent on insect pollination, worth an additional £100,000/yr. There are several agricultural pests and diseases with variable economic impacts of up to many millions of pounds a year (bovine TB, New Zealand flatworm, *Phytophthora ramorum*), but there are few data on their control by natural systems.

- Flooding occurs sporadically in some parts of Northern Ireland and the human and financial cost can be high. In urban areas it is usually pluvial rather than from rivers. Investment in water and sewage infrastructure aims to address this, but increasing levels of hardstanding contribute to flooding. On floodplains building development control is provided through the planning system. Flood maps have been prepared to help identify areas at risk (including under changing climatic conditions). There are some coastal defences, most of which were developed in the mid-20th Century; increasingly, emphasis is on managed retreat with recognition of the value of 'natural' flood defences for both the coast and rivers.

Cultural services[2]:

[2] established but incomplete evidence

- There is no public 'right to roam' in Northern Ireland and there are no National Parks. Public access is largely restricted to lands in public or charitable ownership, and both membership of, and volunteering for, organisations that provide access to their properties are popular. Parks, play areas, allotments and community gardens are important and facilities are provided for cycling and walking, which are encouraged as part of a healthy lifestyle.

- There is a strong appreciation of the social value of farming in relation to the agricultural landscape.

- Tourism is becoming increasingly important and is responsible for about 5% of Northern Ireland's economy: some £1.5 billion and 40,000 jobs. Northern Ireland has a rich cultural and archaeological heritage and some unique landscapes, but the history of violent conflict has restricted the willingness of tourists to visit over the past 30 years. In 2009 there were 3.3 million visitors; this is low compared to the other countries of the UK. There is scope for expansion, especially in relation to unique and distinctive landscapes which are a major attraction for visitors. The Giant's Causeway, a World Heritage Site, is an especially important tourist destination.

- Coarse, game and sea/shore angling are popular among residents and visitors, with the former contributing about £40 million and the latter £3.5 million/annum to the local economy.

- Northern Ireland has a long history of literature, poetry, music and the visual arts and the landscapes have inspired many local artists. Religious traditions form an important part of local culture.

Supporting services[2]:

- There is a wide variety of geological substrata and hence of soils. Soil degradation is generally lower in Northern Ireland than in other parts of the UK, partly due to the cool and wet climate, which slows down decomposition and results in soils that are high in organic matter and generally of good quality. Climatic conditions ensure a good supply of fresh water; however, levels of pollutants and changing patterns of temperature and rainfall are affecting water bodies. Basic nutrient and water cycles are functioning, but are affected by human activities in some areas.

[2] established but incomplete evidence

Ecosystem services contribute significantly to the economy of Northern Ireland, but valuation of the direct and indirect benefits is still at its beginnings, with many conclusions speculative[2]. Little work has been done on the economic values of the final goods produced by ecosystem services in Northern Ireland, especially those that have no market price. The ecosystem services for which economic values exist tend to be those provisioning services for which there are markets, for example agriculture, fishing and timber. However, these may not reflect the full benefits or costs, as only the direct, private good aspects have been captured. The agricultural industry had a net output of £1.3 billion in 2008, with a gross margin of £615 million. Data presentation makes comparisons difficult, but fisheries, aquaculture and marine tourism together are valued at £135 million/yr.

[2] established but incomplete evidence

The net cost of agriculture to the environment in Northern Ireland has been calculated to be £34.2 million/yr. The market price of agricultural goods does not include external benefits and costs.

A valuation of water quality in 2006 found a benefit of at least £8 million/yr which, if quality were improved, could rise to at least £13 million.

A 2006 study estimated that the natural environment contributed £573 million to the economy. In 1996 the 'non-market benefits' of the Environmentally Sensitive Area scheme were estimated at £13 million/yr. Direct costs of controlling invasive alien species amount to well over £100,000/year.

Northern Ireland depends on external ecosystem services for basic food and other commodities[2]. Northern Ireland's ecological, carbon and greenhouse gas footprints are slightly lower than the UK *per capita* average. The ecological footprint of Northern Ireland's food consumption in 2006 was 1.2 global ha/capita, the largest contribution of any sector. The value of food imports and exports is very similar (around £5 billion) but the make-up differs markedly. Exports consist largely of milk and meat products, whereas most fruit and vegetables and many processed food products are imported.

[2] established but incomplete evidence

There are limited data on the consequences of change to habitats and ecosystem services, so conclusions are speculative[2]. Natural ecosystems provide considerable value to the people of Northern Ireland through a wide range of ecosystem services, although the specific services change over time. Some benefits such as carbon sequestration and hazard resilience are not currently recognised as having financial value, but this may change. Data have been collected at differing scales, using different methodologies and for varying purposes. Changes to habitats, their current and past management, and the extent of knowledge concerning past trends all vary. In many cases, trends differ markedly between different sub-habitats and the direction of changes has shifted over the 20-year time frame. Qualitative and quantitative changes may complement or contradict each other.

[2] established but incomplete evidence

Sustainable management mechanisms have enhanced the delivery of ecosystem services from Northern Ireland's habitats[2].

[2] established but incomplete evidence

- The sustainable management of ecosystems is supported primarily through designations, the planning system and financial incentives for agricultural land management.
- The Northern Ireland government, Crown Estate and charities own considerable areas of land, much of it managed for conservation purposes. Most land, however, is owned by private landowners, primarily farmers. Land management is strongly influenced by government and EU policies and financial measures to support these objectives (specifically CAP measures).
- Land is subject to a complex of 'rights' including turbary (peat-digging), fishing, shooting, mineral and water rights, which may or may not correspond to land ownership.
- The network of Areas of Special Scientific Interest (ASSIs) is still some years from completion; 305 sites (amounting to about 7% of Northern Ireland) had been declared by the start of 2010. Area of Special Scientific Interest designation forms the basis of terrestrial Natura 2000 sites, Special Areas of Conservation (SACs) and Special Protection Areas (SPAs). There is one Marine Nature Reserve in Strangford Lough, and 10 of the 15 SPAs have a marine component.
- Designation alone does not ensure protection. In 2008, 916 features had been assessed on 195 ASSIs. The general results, focused on Natura 2000 sites, show that condition varied across the UK NEA

Broad Habitats but that overall, fewer than half of the sites were in favourable condition, but a number were 'recovering'.

- 'Wider countryside' and 'landscape-scale' conservation are largely through Areas of Outstanding Natural Beauty (AONBs), which cover over 22% of Northern Ireland, but powers are limited. Sites of Local Nature Conservation Importance (SLNCI), country parks, regional parks and forest parks also allow for sustainable management options.
- Planning is centralised but is scheduled to transfer to local authorities before 2015. A Regional Development Strategy, supported by a suite of Planning Policy Statements (PPSs) is delivered locally through Area Plans. Environmental Impact Assessments and Strategic Environmental Assessments are legal requirements for many major developments, plans and programmes.
- River Basin Districts (RBDs) serve as the administrative areas for coordinated water management. River Basin Management Plans use an integrated approach to the protection, improvement and sustainable use of the water environment.
- The Northern Ireland Countryside Management Scheme (NICMS) was introduced in 2008 to deliver on a wide range of targets and includes previous agri-environment schemes. By the end of 2010 the total area under agri-environment schemes reached 468,000 ha, or 42% of the agricultural land area.
- The Woodland Grant Scheme encourages the creation of new Woodland to increase wood production, improvement of the landscape and woodland biodiversity, and the sustainable management of forests and Woodlands. Since 1988, it has supported the planting of almost 12,000 ha.
- Almost 70% of farms in Northern Ireland are located on land designated as Less Favoured Areas (LFA).

Considerable information is available on the state of Northern Ireland's habitats, but there is little work linking specific habitats to the delivery of ecosystem services, and understanding of the functioning of ecosystems as a whole is still incomplete[2]. Data and research issues centre on whether data exist, their accessibility and their comparability and compatibility. Baseline information on ecosystem services and their valuation is required. Integration across scientific disciplines and political boundaries is needed to fully understand and optimise management of ecosystems. Further study is required to develop practical management mechanisms to optimise delivery of multiple ecosystem services.

[2] *established but incomplete evidence*

18.1 Introduction

18.1.1 Scope and Purpose

The Northern Ireland Ecosystem Synthesis provides an introduction to the habitats and ecosystems of Northern Ireland and how the various services provided by those ecosystems impact on Northern Ireland's people. Within the context of the UK National Ecosystem Assessment (UK NEA) it identifies unique aspects, issues and opportunities of particular relevance to Northern Ireland.

The document provides an assessment of the extent and condition of Northern Ireland's habitats. It looks at what ecosystem services they provide and at what information is available on the value of those services in economic, social and health terms. It goes on to identify existing and potential future drivers for change and to identify where additional work is required if the ecosystem approach is to realise its full potential. It provides a baseline of existing information in 2010, but it is not exhaustive due to timescale and resource limitations. Additional information on a variety of topics is included in a Technical Supplement. The Northern Ireland Synthesis document should be seen as a first step, an introduction to how the ecosystem approach can be used to inform policy development and management decisions to help Northern Ireland's environment continue to function efficiently and deliver a range of benefits to its residents and visitors.

Placing a financial value on ecosystem services is difficult and controversial. Recent work has attempted to address this issue (Rockström *et al.* 2009a; TEEB 2009; Comhar SDC 2010b; TEEB 2010a,b,c) and it is a major aspect of the UK NEA. In the past the tendency has been to assign a 'zero' or minimal value to functioning ecosystems, landscape and biodiversity when conducting economic valuations and assessments of alternative land use proposals. The ability to provide even general financial values for functioning natural environments is fundamental to ensuring that retention of ecosystem services is considered when land use decisions, or policy decisions to encourage shifts in land use, are being made. The assignment of values to ecosystems in Northern Ireland is still developing, but the value of regulating and cultural services in particular is increasingly recognised in government policy (Section 18.5.6).

The ecosystems approach provides a mechanism for the integrated management of land, air, water and living resources that promotes conservation and sustainable use, recognising that people and their culture are an integral part of ecosystems (Defra 2007b). It is a holistic, system-oriented approach looking at the interdependence and interactions of natural resources (physical, chemical and biological) and human (socio-economic) systems. A healthy ecosystem demonstrates resilience, a capacity to respond to disturbances without loss of functional capability (Bennett & Balvanera 2007; Petchey & Gaston 2009), which allows it to recover from and adapt to change. Resilience and functional capacity are the criteria for monitoring ecosystem health and assessing the sustainability of human uses of ecosystems (Defra 2007c; Comhar SDC 2010a).

The Economics of Ecosystems and Biodiversity (TEEB), a 2-year study sponsored by the United Nations Environment Programme (UNEP), was launched at the Convention on Biological Diversity (CBD) meeting in Nagoya in October 2010. It highlights the economic value of ecosystem services around the world and uses these figures to develop policy and business recommendations aimed at improving the global situation with regard to loss of biodiversity and consequent loss of ecosystem services (TEEB 2009; TEEB 2010a,b,c). Although many of the values are context-specific, the concepts can be applied to inform planning and policy decisions locally (Section 18.5.6).

A concept closely related to ecosystem services is green infrastructure, which seeks to address biodiversity loss by highlighting the value of biodiversity and ecosystem services to the economy and society and allowing the integration of that value into business decisions. A functioning green infrastructure enhances human well-being while improving resilience and adaptation to climate change and other perturbations. It can be defined as 'an interconnected network of green space that conserves natural ecosystem values and functions and provides associated benefits to human populations the ecological framework needed for environmental, social and economic sustainability—in short it is a nation's natural life sustaining system' (Benedict & McMahon 2002). Striving to maintain effective green infrastructure should be incorporated into policy to get the best outcomes from ecosystems for human well-being. Comhar Sustainable Development Council has produced a Green Infrastructure report for the Republic of Ireland (Comhar SDC 2010b) highlighting the importance of the approach and its many benefits. The National Parks and Wildlife Service estimate that the current marginal value of biodiversity and certain ecosystems in the Republic of Ireland in terms of their contribution to productive output and human utility is over €2.6 billion per annum (DEHLG 2008). This is considered a conservative estimate because it does not include services such as food production and waste assimilation, so the true figure will be much higher (Comhar SDC 2010b). The recent Lawton report makes a strong case for the need for a coherent network of well-managed, planned and high quality wildlife sites underpinning wider countryside sustainable management in England (Lawton *et al.* 2010).

This chapter was compiled and collated by the authors between May and November 2010, with final editing and incorporation of reviewers' comments in December 2010 and January 2011. The process involved four major meetings, from which the Lead Authors compiled drafts which were circulated for comments to all contributors using an iterative process to develop the final document. It has had to be shortened and edited, and much important detail is provided in a Technical Supplement for those interested. The resulting document is variable in the degree of detail in different sections, depending on the information provided by the contributors.

Time constrained the depth of the literature search, so the chapter relies primarily on the information provided by the authors supplemented by available government data. It rapidly became clear that much of the information available for Northern Ireland is 'grey literature', primarily government publications, which has not been published in the scientific literature but nonetheless provides a significant body of information on the state of Northern Ireland's environment. The chapter is based on the information available at the time of compilation and provides pointers as to what data need to be collected to enable a comprehensive assessment. The document as a whole is intended as a reference document, providing a baseline of available information and an indication of the usefulness of the ecosystems approach. There are also numerous references to data which have been provided by scientists actively working as 'pers. comm.' or 'unpublished data'; this allows inclusion of the most up-to-date information.

18.1.2 Pen Picture of Northern Ireland

Northern Ireland shares many of its ecological and cultural features with the wider Atlantic region of Europe which stretches from Norway to Spain (Aalen 1997). However, traditional patterns of land ownership and management differ from other areas of the UK and the Republic of Ireland, with implications for land use and ecosystem services.

Northern Ireland is warmer than Scotland in winter and cooler than most of England and Wales in summer (Ratcliffe 1968; Section 18.3). It is in close proximity to the tracks of Atlantic depressions and generally experiences stronger winds than more southerly parts of the UK and Ireland (Betts 1982). Heavy falls of snow are relatively rare. Days with snow lying are fewest on the east coast of County Down and the lowlands of Lough Foyle and the valleys of the rivers Roe and Lower Bann, while the uplands have a snowfall frequency of over 30 days per annum (Betts 1982).

Northern Ireland also differs from other parts of the United Kingdom by virtue of its separation from Great Britain by the Irish Sea and the land border that it shares with another EU member state, the Republic of Ireland. The rise in sea level after the last Ice Age occurred before many species had colonised Ireland, although they had reached Britain. Northern Ireland is diverse in its natural habitats, although the island effect means that there is, overall, a lower level of species diversity than in Great Britain (Webb 1982). Intentional and accidental introductions are now significant components of the biodiversity in many taxa (Ian Montgomery pers. comm.). While biodiversity of species and habitats is independent of the political boundary, the border has profound impacts on ecosystems (EPA 2008). Legislation, policy, economic drivers and management practice differ between the two countries. The differences between the island's ecosystems and those of the other countries within the UK require consideration when legislation and policy are developed on a UK basis and applied to Northern Ireland (Section 18.3).

The human population of Northern Ireland was 1.79 million in 2009 and is expected to reach 1.92 million by 2020 (NISRA 2005b). There are two major cities and 41 large towns which are home to about 65% of the population, with half of these living in the Belfast Metropolitan area (NISRA 2005b). The remaining people live in smaller settlements, many with fewer than 4,500 people, or in the open countryside (NISRA 2005b). Settlement patterns differ across Northern Ireland depending on local history and topography, but in the lowlands generally there is little truly 'open' country and even the marginal hill-lands retain evidence of fields and farms from the 19th and 20th Centuries. Settlements and farms are linked by a high density, well-maintained network of roads, many of them very narrow. There is high dependence on personal transport, which is seen as essential for rural areas due to the dispersed nature of the population. There are few places in Northern Ireland more than 2 hours by car from Belfast. The attachment to land and family and the dense road network mean that considerable numbers of people commute to work by car, often from large, new houses built on former farmland or semi-natural habitats in the open countryside (NIEL 2009b; Section 18.4.7).

Tertiary basalt lavas cover almost one-third of the landscape of Northern Ireland, representing the largest continuous unit of basic igneous rock in Britain and Ireland (Hamilton 1982). Northern Ireland has a wide variety of soil types, which helps to create a diversity of habitats and land uses. In spite of its small size, Northern Ireland exhibits at least 308 different soils on 97 parent materials (Cruickshank 1997). There has been little serious degradation of these soils through industrial processes, as industry has been focused mainly on a small number of towns and cities. Although there are many soil types, 60% of the land area has gleyed (poorly draining) soils (Cruickshank 1997). Many of the soils have been modified by farming and drainage operations; even grassland farming is only possible on the most gleyed soils because of field drainage. In addition, upland areas have predominantly peat or peaty soils, some of which have been drained for farming or forestry. Only a limited amount of the land is of sufficiently high quality to support profitable arable agriculture, primarily on the better drained soils of the Foyle valley, the Lower Bann and north Down (Cruickshank 1997). As recently as the late 1940s a larger area of Northern Ireland was under arable crops as part of general mixed farming. The present dominance of grass is a feature of agriculture since the Second World War (WWII) in response to national and later European agricultural policies. 'Lazy beds' and abandoned farmsteads provide evidence of potato and subsistence farming high into the upland margins in previous centuries. There is evidence of some alien species (tropical nematodes, New Zealand flatworms) having negative impacts on grassland (Murchie et al. 2003; Fleming et al. 2008; Sections 18.3, 18.5.2 & 18.5.5).

Around three-quarters of the 1,351,000 hectares (ha) land area of Northern Ireland is used for agriculture, primarily rough and improved grazing for cattle and sheep and for silage production. In 2008 agriculture supported roughly 24,000 full-time equivalent (FTE) jobs and provided £348 million gross value added (GVA), or 1.2%, of income to the regional economy (DARD 2009d). This rises to about £878 million GVA (3.1%) and 42,400 employees (5.5%) if the food and drinks processing sector is included (DARD 2009d). Key features include small farms, part-time farmers and conacre (Section 18.5.2.1), with a variety of farming practices and differing impacts on the environment. Most land is in private ownership with an average farm size of 40 ha, which is smaller than the UK average of 54 ha (DARD 2010o). There is a strong attachment to the land (Alexander 1964). However, only about half of farms are entirely owner occupied, with around one-third of the land in conacre (DARD 2010o; Sections 18.4.3, 18.4.4 & 18.5.2.1).

Uplands include the Mournes in the south east, Cuilcagh and Slieve Beagh in the south west, the Sperrins in the North West and the Antrim Plateau in the North East. Slieve Donard in the Mournes is the highest peak in Northern Ireland at 852 m (Met Office 2007). Upland moorland remains extensive despite some plantation of conifers, draining for farmland and extraction of peat, and most is used for rough grazing, primarily by sheep. Much of the peatland is degraded through agriculture, forestry and especially past peat cutting, with 47% cut-over at some time in the past, but some large tracts of intact bog remain in the uplands, as well as some significant areas of lowland raised bog. Peat is a major carbon store, with over 50% of soil carbon stocks in peat and peaty soils (Sections 18.4.2, 18.4.6.3, 18.5.2 & 18.5.3).

Northern Ireland is the least wooded country in the EU, with only 6% cover as opposed to 12% in the rest of the UK, 44% being the EU average (McEvoy & McAdam 2004; Forestry Commission 2009a). Only 0.75% of the land area is covered with woodland that dates back to at least 1830. Around 0.04% of Northern Ireland is woodland that can be classified as ancient (continuously present since at least 1600) with a high degree of certainty, compared with 2% in Britain (Woodland Trust 2010a). While there have been significant increases in both broadleaved and coniferous woodland since 1986, and especially since 1998, some of this woodland is successional from a range of semi-natural habitats which had biodiversity value in their own right, including cutover bog margins (Section 18.4.5).

In Northern Ireland there are three major lakes within two lakeland areas and three key river basins. A total of 4.4% of Northern Ireland's surface area is water, four times more than that of Great Britain (Smith *et al.* 1991). Lough Neagh, in the centre, is the largest lake in the British Isles at 38,300 ha, but is shallow (mean depth of 8.9 m with a maximum of 30 m; LNAC 2002). The Lough Neagh system is of international conservation importance, particularly for its populations of wetland and migrant birds. The Erne lakelands in the south west are similarly important for wetland birds and for the wet grasslands that surround the lakes. They are also a major focus for tourism, with links through to the Shannon river system that help encourage boating and angling holidays (Sections 18.4.6, 18.5.4.2 & 18.5.4.3).

Northern Ireland has an extremely rich coastal and marine biodiversity due to its location at the transition between cold northern waters from the north-east Atlantic and warmer southern waters from the Irish Sea. It is responsible for managing an estimated 450,000 ha of Marine environment, containing around half of Northern Ireland's total biodiversity (NIEA 2010h; AFBI & NIEA 2011). The coastline is an estimated 650 km in length (DOE & NISRA 2010) and is punctuated by five major sea loughs. Strangford Lough is the largest (150,000 ha; EHS *et al.* 2001) and is Northern Ireland's only Marine Nature Reserve, containing almost three-quarters of the marine biodiversity of Northern Ireland and including many internationally important bird populations (Brown 1990). The Giant's Causeway World Heritage Site is Northern Ireland's major tourism attraction (Section 18.5.4.2). The largest offshore island is Rathlin Island,

off the north coast, which rises steeply and is surrounded by waters exhibiting a high level of marine biodiversity. It is also the only permanently populated offshore island. There is a substantial fishing industry (mainly Dublin Bay prawn, *Nephrops*) concentrated on the County Down coast, responsible for roughly 5% of total UK landings and worth £34 million annually (2008 figures; MFA 2009; Sections 18.4.8, 18.4.9 & 18.5.2.2).

Approximately 430,000 ha of Northern Ireland have been designated for conservation purposes (NIEA unpublished data; see **Table 18.20** for details). Designations include: Area of Special Scientific Interest (ASSI), Special Area of Conservation (SAC), Special Protection Area (SPA), Area of Outstanding Natural Beauty (AONB), although AONB is not primarily a conservation designation, Ramsar site (wetlands of international importance), and Marine Nature Reserve (there is one MNR: Strangford Lough). This area includes some very large sites which have multiple designations. In addition to the designated areas, the Environmentally Sensitive Areas (ESA) Scheme and Countryside Management Scheme (CMS) have provided a significant incentive to undertake sensitive land management on farms. Agri-environment schemes cover 42% of the agricultural land area (DARD 2008a; Sections 18.8.1 & 18.8.5).

There is more limited public access than elsewhere in the UK, with no 'right to roam' (EHS 2004c). In Northern Ireland the townland has been the basic system of land division since at least the medieval period (Proudfoot 1990; Aalen 1997). Turbary (bog turf or peat-cutting), water, mineral, shooting and other 'rights' are complex, rooted in history, and often do not correspond with land ownership. This can lead to time-consuming site designation practices (ASSIs, National Nature Reserves (NNRs), etc.) and complex land management arrangements. Tourism is a valuable local industry accounting for about 5% of the Northern Ireland economy. However, this is lower than in the rest of the UK (9.7%) and the Republic of Ireland (6.3%; Sections 18.5.4 & 18.5.4.2).

There has been a low level of mining and industry and consequently relatively little industrial pollution. Northern Ireland is geologically rich, with a wide diversity of construction aggregates providing an industry with a 2009 turnover of approximately £450 million, which has declined from £730 million (Bell 2008) since the economic downturn. Hard rock is quarried in all counties, and sand and gravel from glacial deposits are also dredged from Lough Neagh. At present no marine sand is extracted from Northern Ireland waters. Damage to ecosystems is localised, and many abandoned quarries have been used for waste disposal while others are providing valuable natural habitat (Section 18.5.2.13).

Pollution is primarily agricultural or urban in origin, including diffuse pollution from agricultural runoff. The impacts on aquatic ecosystems continue to be severe. Air pollution was traditionally primarily from solid fuel heating, but since the 1950s is now primarily from motor vehicle traffic (POST 2002; Section 18.5.3.10).

Northern Ireland had a 3.5% share of UK total net greenhouse gas emissions in 2008, with a decline of 11.2% since 1990. However, due to the significance of agriculture, it accounts for 13.5% of UK emissions for agricultural methane (AEA 2010; DOE 2010c). While carbon dioxide emissions decreased by only 6.7% between 1990 and 2008, the decrease in methane was by 23.8% and of nitrous oxides was 26.8%. However, hydro fluorocarbon emissions increased by 650% and sulphur hexafluoride by 261% (DOE 2010c). The energy sector as a whole (electricity, transport, domestic) is responsible for 73.2% of emissions of greenhouse gas (lower than the UK average of 85.1%) and agriculture is responsible for 20.8%, much higher than the UK average of 7%, but not as high as the Republic of Ireland at 27.7% (in 2006; EPA 2008). Northern Ireland is a small net sink of carbon dioxide from land use, land use change and forestry, with cropland a net source and grassland a net sink (DOE 2010c). While detailed targets have not yet been set for Northern Ireland, the Executive has committed to delivering on UK targets and, given the different profile for Northern Ireland's emissions, there are likely impacts on land use (Sections 18.5.3.1, 18.5.3.2, 18.5.3.3, 18.5.3.4 & 18.5.3.5).

18.2 Drivers of Change

This section reviews some of the major drivers affecting land use and ecosystem services in Northern Ireland at the beginning of the second decade of the 21st Century. Many factors impact on the way the land, sea, ecosystems and landscape are managed. Recognising the different outputs that can be obtained from ecosystems adds to the value of the land economically and socially, as well as environmentally. Increasing demands on land will add to the need for delivery of multiple benefits but it will also result in conflicts between different uses (Coates & Hadden 2010; Foresight 2010; Lawton *et al.* 2010; Section 18.1).

The high profile and political emphasis given to social and economic factors as a result of Northern Ireland's past has meant that the environment has generally not had a high political priority (Macrory 2004; Bell *et al.* 2007). Environmental action has increased in recent years, with AONBs declared in the 1960s and 1970s and the Convention on Biological Diversity (CBD), EU Directives and the Northern Ireland Biodiversity Strategy in the 1990s. An important driver has been EU legislation and the possible financial consequences of not meeting targets for water quality, waste management and site and species protection (Macrory 2004). However, Northern Ireland still lags behind other UK countries in designation, protection and management of sites and species (Macrory 2004; Bell *et al.* 2007). For example:

■ Northern Ireland adopted the target of halting biodiversity loss by 2016 (NIBG 2009), in comparison with the international target of halting biodiversity loss by 2010 (although this target has since been revised to 2020);

■ the target for ensuring features on designated sites are in or approaching favourable condition is 2016, compared to 2010 in the rest of the UK (NIBG 2009);

■ the revised Sustainable Development Strategy, including biodiversity targets, only came into force in mid-2010;

■ data on many aspects of biodiversity are still lacking and full designation of the ASSI network is not planned to be complete until 2016 (EHS 2003a); and,

■ there are no National Parks.

Human health and well-being are dependent on ecosystem services, so land use must be actively planned and a long-term view of investment in environmental protection adopted (MA 2005a; TEEB 2009, 2010a,b,c). However, in Northern Ireland, as with the UK as a whole, the economic impacts of the 2009 recession may result in the environment receiving less attention, as limited available funding is targeted at health, education and social care. It is important to identify the factors which influence environmental attitudes, management and priorities if ecosystem services are to be understood, a prerequisite for their protection. The need for a healthy environment to underpin human health has direct impacts on spending in the health service, but such links are seldom made when funding decisions are taken (Comhar SDC 2010b).

Drivers of change can be either direct, with a clear causal relationship between the driver and the resulting environmental changes, or indirect, where change factors have a more general influence on the environment. In the UK NEA, drivers of change are considered under six major headings (Birnie *et al.* 2002; Miller *et al.* 2009) and the same general factors are identified in the Land Use Futures project (Foresight 2010). **Table 18.1** presents some of these drivers, the relevant manifestations and potential impacts in Northern Ireland and some relevant changes of the past 20 years.

These drivers interact and overlap and the overall impacts are often highly complex. The differences between private and public goods in terms of management costs and beneficiaries of investment in land management need to be considered. Another important consideration in future policies is the need to develop multifunctional use of land and sea to enable resilience. The potential for different policies to complement and/or conflict with each other (at all levels: local, Northern Ireland, UK and EU) requires forward planning in advance of implementation. Work such as the Foresight studies and the scenario work of the UK NEA provide mechanisms to identify such potential issues and devise ways to address them (Foresight 2010; Chapter 25). A schematic representation of the factors impacting on land use and ecosystem services is presented in **Figure 18.1**. Specific knowledge, skills and training of landowners or managers is essential for the delivery of integrated ecosystem services.

In Northern Ireland the Programme for Government is the main driver for national action, supported by a number of other key strategies (including the Sustainable Development Strategy, Regional Development Strategy, Regional Transport Strategy, Waste Management Strategy, Biodiversity Strategy) and implemented through a programme of national legislation. A significant proportion of local environmental legislation and policy, delivered through regulation and funding schemes, is directly related to EU and UK legislation (Bell *et al.* 2007; Commission of the European Communities 2008). Major environmental matters are dealt with by a

Table 18.1 Examples of major drivers of change and their impacts on human well-being, habitats and services in Northern Ireland. Trends observed over the past 20 years are also shown.

Drivers of change	Examples of changes with possible impacts on habitats and services	Observed changes since 1990
Demographic		
Demographic change	Increasing/ageing population; Changing motivation and behaviours of farmers and consumers.	Gradually increasing population (births and immigration with some emigration, especially by young people); Decreasing numbers of farmers; Increasing average age of farmers.
Migration	Vulnerability of farming and rural communities through emigration of young people; Immigration/increased multiculturalism; Second homes.	Development in both urban and rural areas; Increasing housing development and supporting infrastructure, especially single homes in the countryside; Rapid rise followed by an even more rapid decrease in house prices; Continued increase in land prices; Loss of young rural population; Changing use of marginal land.
Land manager characteristics	Lack of new entrants to rural economies; Increase in non-traditional land owners; Increasing/decreasing environmental awareness among land managers.	Decreasing numbers of farms Increasing price for land, especially with planning permission; Viability of many farms dependent upon diversification or off-farm income for the farm family; Increasing rural to urban commuter-based lifestyle; Loss of skilled land management, funding and succession planning especially in marginal areas and on small farms.
Land use changes	Urbanisation/suburbanisation/peri-urban; Changes in crops; Energy/climate change land uses; Farm diversification; Farm amalgamation; Policy changes (national and European); Competing pressures for the allocation of scarce land resources.	Decreasing numbers of livestock; Decreasing amount of arable crops; Increasing silage production rather than hay Increasing broadleaved woodland; Development of renewable energy projects; Decline in peat harvesting for fuel; Decreasing farm viability; Changing use of marginal agricultural land.
Policy and Institutional		
Governance	Devolved/undevolved matters; Review of Public Administration (RPA) Lack of independent Environmental Protection Agency; Low political priority for environmental matters.	Variation between devolved and undevolved government until Northern Ireland Assembly in 2007 established local rule; Local governance responding to economic and other pressures; RPA and uncertainty around it potentially leading to fragmentation of policy and practice.
Legislation	Multi-layered legislation (regional, UK, EU, international).	Major environmental legislation driven by EU policy and requirements through UK commitments; EIAs and SEAs increasing in quality and quantity; Increasing emphasis on climate change mitigation and adaptation and biodiversity in line with EU and UK policies; Local legislative programme delivering significant local legislation.
Policy and strategy frameworks	Multiple Departments and Strategies with impacts on land management; Lack of full integration amongst policies, strategies and funding.	Improved understanding of interactions and impacts; Management changes recognising different priorities and social goods; Regional Development Strategy 2001, revision 2011; Waste Management Strategy 2005; Sustainable Development Strategy 2010; Implementation Plans 2011; Rural White Paper 2011; Sustainable Duty 2007; Biodiversity Duty 2011.
Guidance and subordinate regulations	Agri-environment schemes; Planning Policy Statements; Pollution control regulations; Possible changes in delivery of public goods and services to promote multi-functionality and incentivising private land owners to deliver public benefits.	Planning Policy Statements; River Basin Management Plans 2010; Countryside Management Schemes; Environmentally Sensitive Areas (ESAs).
Designations	Local, national or international conservation designations.	Programme for designation of Areas of Special Scientific Interest (ASSIs); Special Areas of Conservation (SACs); Special Protection Area (SPAs) and Areas of Outstanding Natural Beauty (AONBs); expected completion of ASSI network in 2016; National Parks (NPs) legislation planned for 2011; Multiple designations of single sites; Lack of monitoring and enforcement; Lack of funds for management of designated sites.

Table 18.1 continued

Drivers of change	Examples of changes with possible impacts on habitats and services	Observed changes since 1990
Collaboration and delivery arrangements	Greater integration of management and objectives.	Northern Ireland Biodiversity Group; Coastal Zone Forum; NGO/government collaborative projects; Catchment Management Groups; local Partnerships; NGO/government partnership mechanisms; local government partnerships.
Economics		
International impacts	Globalisation, trade, global market, consumption patterns; Exchange rates; Possible drive for more local self-sufficiency regarding food and energy.	Increased globalization for provision of all commodities; Increasing awareness of 'local food' and problem of external sources of energy supply.
Grants and payments	Altered economic incentives leading to possible land use changes and degrees of environmental protection – impacts could be positive or negative.	Reliance on CAP and CFP requirements shaping how land is used and fishing arrangements; Common Fisheries Policy (CFP); Common Agricultural Policy (CAP) (Less Favoured Area (LFA), Single Farm Payment (SFP)), Countryside Management Scheme (CMS), Environmentally Sensitive Area (ESA); Management of Special Sites (MOSS); Northern Ireland Rural Development Programme (NIRDP).
Prices and exchange rates	Market prices; Proximity to the Republic of Ireland; Possible price and support differentials across border.	Role of supermarkets in driving supply; International border driving behaviour for shopping, fuel, farming.
Infrastructure provision (housing and transport)	Demands for rural infrastructure; Land price changes; Urbanisation of the countryside; Septic tanks and pollution.	Increase in rural housing due to demographic changes; PPS21 (DOE 2010e); Rural transport (spatially diverse population); Depopulation due to farm viability.
Resource consumption	Demand for water coupled with reduced availability; Energy cost and security.	Increasing costs/decreasing availability of resources; energy, chemicals, water; Evolving consumption patterns; Recent increase in awareness.
Social and Cultural		
Public attitudes and behaviours	Reconciling conflicting public attitudes; influencing land use through incentives, market, regulation, decision-making; traditional/historical attitudes; changing consumer preferences.	Shift in priorities for land use; greater responsiveness to market and policy drivers; Greater environmental and sustainable development awareness; Changes in action slowly increasing Environment increasingly on people's agendas.
Motivation of decision makers	Fiscal and policy drivers to address multiple issues through integrated incentive programs.	Profile of environmental issues in Assembly; Concentration on RPA priority away from environmental issues towards economic drivers; Green New Deal, fuel poverty, climate impacts on infrastructure, energy security, Carbon Reduction Commitments may drive greater Funding for Green New Deal in 2011–2014 budget.
Heritage marketing and promotion	Scheduled monuments; Listed Buildings; Registered historic parks, gardens and demesnes.	Promotion of tourism and cultural heritage as factors strongly influencing land use; 'Sustainable tourism' accepted as policy goal; Planning legislation and regulation protects heritage sites.
Cultural and religious	Recognition of cultural value and 'sense of place'; Spiritual value of nature; Ecological learning.	Northern Ireland still 'in transition' to peaceful society; 'Troubles' decreasing in public priority/profile; Shifting political priorities; Changes/increase in designated areas.
Technological		
New products	New developments in crops and manufacturing techniques leading to economies of scale; New roles for land (energy); Landscape impacts.	Government support for research and development (R&D) and employment of low carbon technology and renewable energy; Development of renewable energy products and businesses; Trial of Marine Current Turbine.
Improved husbandry	New management techniques or breeding improvements.	Improved efficiency; Decreased greenhouse gas production; Recent research at the Agri-food and Biosciences Institute (AFBI) into husbandry mechanisms to reduce greenhouse gas.

number of Government Departments and Agencies in Northern Ireland (**Table 18.2**). The Mid Term Evaluation of the Northern Ireland Rural Development Programme 2007–2013 has stated that 'there is a strong belief that future Rural Development programmes will focus on greenhouse gases and climate change, with a clear focus on emissions' (NISRA 2010b) with clear implications for future land use. The recent recognition of the importance of food security, food traceability and food carbon costs should also be recognised as an important driver.

Underpinning, but often independent of, the policy, legislative and financial drivers, are environmental changes which can have major impacts. Climate change (Section 18.3.4), invasive alien species (Section 18.3.3) and pests and diseases (Section 18.5.3.12) are areas where impacts on habitats and ecosystem service delivery could be severe, unexpected and expensive to address. Ensuring that ecosystems have sufficient resilience to deal with these perturbations is an important role of policy and other drivers under direct government control. Consumer preferences,

Table 18.1 continued

Drivers of change	Examples of changes with possible impacts on habitats and services	Observed changes since 1990
Renewable energy	Wind; marine; biomass; anaerobic digestion; waste management.	Continuing conflicts between renewable exploitation and landscape conservation interests Research and development of short rotation coppice and anaerobic digestion; Landscape impacts; Integrated waste and renewable; Farm wastes; Seascape.
Environmental		
Climate change	Mitigation; Adaptation; Move to low carbon economy; Weather impacts; Unpredictability; Droughts and floods; Changes in crops; Energy crops; Waste management; Changes in habitats/species; Need for 'wildlife corridors' and designated sites; Water availability/conflicting demands on river flows; Sea level rise.	Targets for renewable energy; Use of land for sequestration; Promotion of land uses with lower carbon outputs; Slow political acceptance of climate change action relevance to Northern Ireland; No local Act – Targets as 'part of' UK targets.
Habitat loss (change)	Degradation of habitats or loss of area; Loss of species; Degradation of ecosystem service delivery.	Land abandonment, changes in management regime (overgrazing and burning); Nitrogen deposition (in the uplands), runoff, estuaries, chemical use (pesticides, herbicides, molluscicides, fungicides, fertilisers); Undergrazing in some areas (often following decades of overgrazing); Agri-environment schemes popular, 20% of land in ESA; Designation of ASSIs but target for completion repeatedly changed; General land management and pollution levels improving (Water and Waste Framework Directives).
Species introduction or removal	Invasive species; Extinctions of native species; Changes in pollinators; Changing geographical distributions of pests and diseases; Cost of prevention, Eradication or control measures; Major habitat loss or degradation.	Awareness of invasive species recognised by Invasive Species Ireland project; Not high on public agenda; Problems increasing as new species become established.
Eutrophication	Algal mats; Anoxic zones; Species diversity variation.	Decreasing water quality; increase in the cost of water treatment; habitat degradation; Species loss; Following major efforts at addressing point source pollution inputs in the 1980s levels improved, but still high primarily from diffuse agricultural pollutants; Major reduction in phosphate inputs through fertiliser use reduction; Major fish kills still annual occurrences.
Wild harvesting	Marine fish stocks and economics of coastal and fishing communities; River fishing; Game hunting.	Sustainable management; Loss of stocks; Decreasing profitability of industry; Most fish species over-exploited, catches decreasing; Eels in crisis; Dredging of Strangford Lough for scallops has damaged horse mussel beds severely.
Soil degradation	Land degradation; erosion; poaching	Decreasing productivity; Pollution of waterways; Soil quality generally reasonable; Problems of compaction and loss of earthworms.
Carbon sequestration/loss	Carbon storage in soils and vegetation.	Opportunities for sequestration especially in uplands; Value beginning to be realised; Major peat extraction has decreased but could increase depending on oil prices.
Air quality	Primarily an urban issue; Disease, decrease in human well-being.	Major improvements due to fuel switch from coal to oil/gas; Traffic main contributor.
External inputs	Fertilisers, pesticides; Water; Habitat degradation.	Decreasing use of fertilisers; Still very little irrigation needed; Better treatment of waste materials.

international trade, costs and availability of commodities and energy sources also have impacts which could lead to major changes in the demands on land and sea.

There is research evidence that land is increasingly recognised as a valuable public resource and that it needs to be managed in ways which benefit the community at large. Research which attempts to quantify the environmental, economic and social benefits provided by ecosystem services is also increasing (Heal 2000; eftec 2005; Kremen 2005; Barbier 2007; Brauman *et al.* 2007; TEEB 2009; Comhar SDC 2010b; TEEB 2010a,b,c).

Some of the many functions which land can provide are water resource management, nature conservation, agriculture, woodland and forestry, flood defence, energy, residential and commercial development, transport, recreation, waste management and education. Not every piece of land is suitable for delivery of all ecosystem services but in total, the land of Northern Ireland delivers all of these benefits. In some areas there is significant delivery of many ecosystem services from single areas. By using a systems view of the environment, its functions and the drivers that affect it, the stakeholders are better able to understand

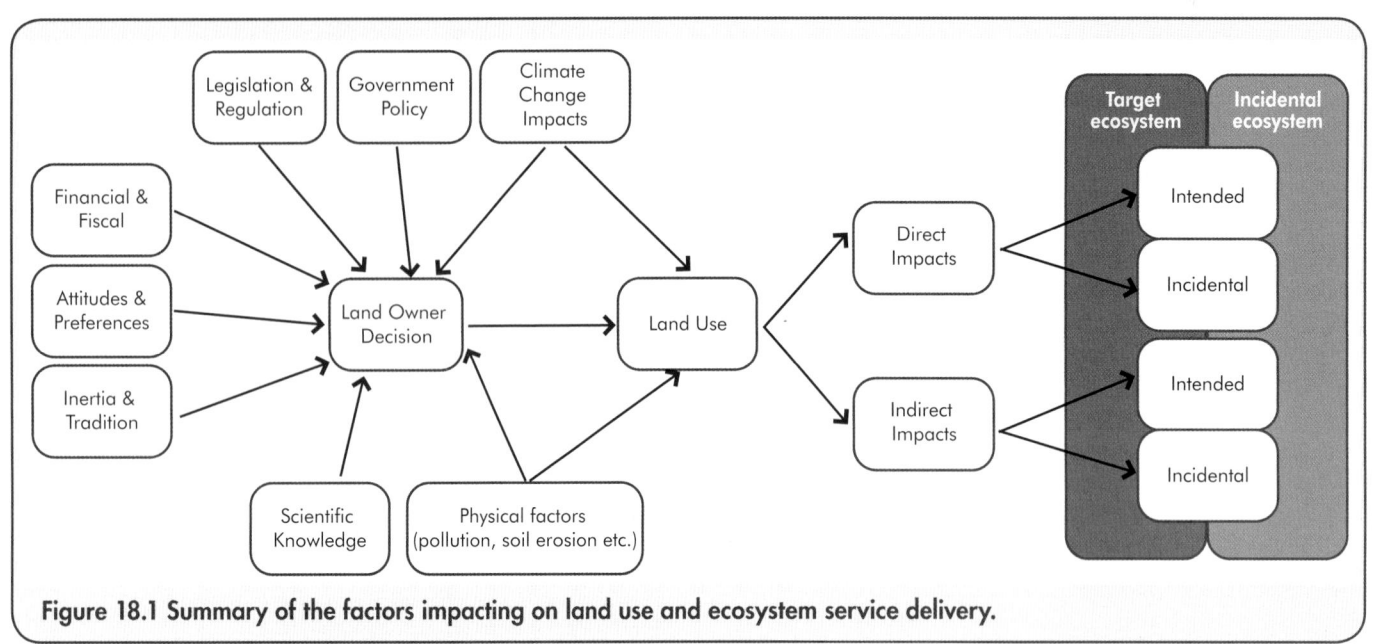

Figure 18.1 Summary of the factors impacting on land use and ecosystem service delivery.

Table 18.2 Examples of major legislative, policy, strategy and funding measures affecting the environment of Northern Ireland.

Key areas	Responsibility	Examples of key legislation	Examples of key plans and strategies
Overarching	Inter/multi-departmental	Northern Ireland Act 1998; Northern Ireland Act 2009	Sustainable Development Strategy for Northern Ireland; Programme for Government (PfG); Northern Ireland Budget
Planning	DOE (Planning Service, NIEA etc.); DRD (Roads Service)	The Planning (NI) Order 1991; The Planning Reform (NI) Order 2006; EIA Regulations (NI) 1999; The Planning Fees Regulations (NI) 2005 Planning Bill 2011; Local Government Reform (2011)	Regional Development Strategy for Northern Ireland 2025; Northern Ireland Rural Development Programme 2007–2013; Review of Public Administration (RPA); Regional Transport Strategy for Northern Ireland 2002–2012; Planning Policy Statements; Planning Strategy for Rural Northern Ireland
Land use/ Agriculture	DARD; AFBI; DETI; DOE	Groundwater Regulations (NI) 2009; Environmental Liability (Prevention and Remediation) Regulations (NI) 2009; Control of Pollution (Silage, Slurry and Agricultural Fuel Oil) Regulations (NI) 2003; Wildlife Order (NI) 1985; Wildlife and Environment Bill (2010)	Code of Good Agricultural Practice (COGAP); NI Countryside Management Scheme; Rural White Paper (2011); River Basin Management Plans
Food	DARD; AFBI; DETI (Invest NI, SIB)	Food and Environment Protection Act 1985	Investment Strategy for Northern Ireland 2005/15; Focus on Food' partnership Strategy for the NI Food Industry 2010
Environmental protection	DOE	Wildlife Order (NI) 1985; Conservation Regulations (NI) 1995; Environment (NI) Order 2002; Nature Conservation and Amenity Lands (NI) Order 1985; EIA Regulations (NI) 1999; Wildlife and Natural Environment Bill 2009; Water (NI) Order 1999; Radioactive Substances Act 1993; Pollution Prevention and Control (NI) Order 2002; EU Marine Strategic Framework Directive.	Integrated Coastal Zone Management Strategy; Northern Ireland Biodiversity Strategy; Waste Management Strategy 2006–2020; River Basin Management Plans
Climate change	DETI; DOE; Rivers Agency	UK Climate Change Act 2008; EU Emissions Trading Scheme; Floods Directive	Regional Development Strategy for Northern Ireland 2025; Flood Risk Maps and Management Plans; Planning Policy Statement 15 – Planning and Flood Risk (DOE 2006b)
Forestry	DARD; DOE (Planning Service)	Forestry Act (NI) 2010	NI Forestry – A Strategy for Sustainability and Growth 2006
Waste	DOE	Landfill Directive (1999/31/EC); Waste Emissions Trading Act 2003; Waste and Contaminated Land (NI) Order 1997; EU Waste Framework Directive and Revised WFD 2011	NI Waste Management Strategy 2006; NI Landfill Allowance Scheme

and determine how best to manage it for future benefits to themselves and society at large (Sections 18.4.2, 18.4.3, 18.4.4 & 18.4.5).

Most land is in private ownership so influencing its management must be through legislation, fiscal drivers and education. The Common Agricultural Policy (CAP) has demonstrated that financial incentives do impact on land management (sometimes having negative impacts on ecosystem service delivery) and therefore can be used to encourage landowners to manage land in ways which deliver public goods in exchange for payment. The Single Farm Payment's environmental conditions (Cross-Compliance; Good Agricultural and Environmental Conditions) do this to a limited extent. Future EU programmes should include ecosystem service delivery as a goal while addressing other issues including food and energy security and climate change adaptation and mitigation (NIBG 2009; SEL 2009; Comhar SDC 2010b; Godfray *et al.* 2010; Lawton *et al.* 2010).

18.3 Biodiversity in Northern Ireland

Biodiversity is the diversity and abundance of living things, including the visible plants, animals and fungi but also the bacteria and microscopic life which are particularly important to decomposition and nutrient cycles. Organisms are fundamental to the service delivery by an ecosystem and awareness of their health and vigour is essential to determining the overall health and resilience of any ecosystem (NIBG 2009; SCBD 2010). It is becoming clear from research on a range of taxa from algae to mammals that many Irish species have a unique genetic composition. Further, comparison of plant communities with their counterparts in Great Britain indicates differences that are important and should be maintained (QUB unpublished data).

Managing land in ways which maintain or increase natural biodiversity improves the delivery of all classes of ecosystem services, as well as improving the resilience of the area if it is subjected to stress (Foresight 2010). Natural flood control, pollination, erosion control and pollution abatement are all areas where the natural biodiversity of an area can greatly improve its ability to deliver benefits to people.

There are many examples where the decline of a key species or the introduction of a non-native, invasive species has led to severe declines of natural habitats and degradation of many ecosystem services (EHS 2008a; NIBG 2009). For example, the accidental introduction of zebra mussels in Lough Erne has altered nutrient cycling, increased water clarity and reduced the abundance of phytoplankton. This has led to significant changes in native fauna and flora, including loss of species and excessive weed growth (Minchin *et al.* 2002; Maguire & Sykes 2004). Furthermore, the phytoplankton species composition has recently shifted

towards increasing prevalence of cyanobacteria (notably the potentially toxic *Microcystis*), causing surface blooms (Mooney *et al.* in press). Removing a species, or adding one which significantly changes the balance between organisms, can restrict the ability of any habitat to deliver the services which people require, be that cleaning up wastes, mitigating flooding, providing food or conserving carbon (Goldschmidt 1997; Foresight 2010; Section 18.3).

Biodiversity is of value to people. It provides protection from climate change and maintains soil fertility, clean water and fresh air; it is the source of commodities such as timber, paper and fibres for clothing and it provides the raw resources for developing new pharmaceuticals and many other potential products. Currently, many of these services are considered to be provided for 'free' because no financial value is put on them; their loss is seen as having no financial cost. Building the economic value of the natural world into accounting systems is essential to ensure that its value is recognised by governments, financial institutions and business, and is fully factored into management decisions. This is the principle behind The Economics of Ecosystems and Biodiversity approach (TEEB 2009, 2010a,b,c).

Northern Ireland has about 11,500 freshwater and terrestrial (CEDaR 2010c) and around 2,400 currently identified marine species (CEDaR 2010a,b), but this is likely to be a substantial underestimate, especially when fungi and microorganisms are considered. While Northern Ireland has fewer taxa than Great Britain, due partly to its smaller size and offshore position, it does host some species and subspecies that are endemic to the island of Ireland (**Table 18.3**).

The principal pressures on Northern Ireland's species diversity are human activities leading to habitat loss through agriculture, forestry, fisheries and building development. To date climate change has had relatively little impact, but phenological changes have been noted for both plants and animals (times of flowering, migration dates) which may result in wider ecosystem impacts (Woodland Trust 2010c). The impacts of non-native invasive species are second only to habitat destruction as a cause of global biodiversity loss (Pejchar & Mooney 2009). In Northern Ireland invasive species are becoming a problem in many habitats (Stokes *et al.* 2006; Arkell *et al.* 2007; Invasive Species Ireland 2008). For example, the grey squirrel (*Sciurus carolinensis*) has had significant impact upon the red squirrel (*Sciurus vulgaris*; O'Neill & Montgomery 2003), the New Zealand flatworm (*Arthurdendyus triangulatus*; Murchie *et al.* 2003; Fleming *et al.* 2008) and zebra mussel (*Dreissena polymorpha*; Minchin *et al.* 2002) have had major effects and numerous plants, especially aquatic ones, have become costly problems (ISI 2010).

Examples of species lost in Northern Ireland include the corn bunting (*Miliaria calandra*), small blue butterfly (*Cupido minimus*) and elegant feather-moss (*Eurhynchiastrum pulchellum*), and threatened species include the Irish damselfly (*Coenagrion lunulatum*), white-clawed crayfish (*Austropotamobius pallipes*), freshwater pearl mussel (*Margaritifera margaritifera*), chough (*Pyrrhocorax pyrrhocorax*) and Irish hare (*Lepus timidus hibernicus*) (Habitas 2002; EHS 2005m; NIEA 2011).

Table 18.3 Numbers of species in selected taxonomic groups present in Northern Ireland compared to overall figures for the UK. Source: data from Northern Ireland Fungi Group (2007); Fungus Conservation Forum (2009); Northern Ireland Biodiversity Group (2009); CEDaR (2010b); AFBI & NIEA (2011) Roy Anderson, Neil McCullough, NIEA (pers. comm.).

| Group | Number of species | |
	UK	Northern Ireland
Marine	e.g. 28 species of cetaceans, 2 seal species (Chapter 12)	2,400 including 2 seal (common (*Phoca vitulina*) and grey (*Halichoerus grypus*)) and 13 cetacean species; some may be endemic e.g. 29 new species of marine sponge off Rathlin Island in 2005; several internationally important waders and wildfowl—Strangford Lough contains 72% of marine biodiversity in Northern Ireland waters; 'over half' of all biodiversity in NI (AFBI & NIEA 2011).
Freshwater fauna	Circa 50 species (Britain; PAA 2003)	Includes native fish such as pollan (*Coregonus pollan*; not found anywhere else in Europe), dollaghan (*Salmo trutta*) and ferox trout; Ireland is the last European stronghold of the white-clawed crayfish (*Austropotamobius pallipes*).
Mammals	62 including 17 bats	26 including 8 bats and the native Irish hare (*Lepus timidus*).
Birds	258 regular breeders or migrants	170 regular breeders and non-breeding seasonal migrants; not including rare or vagrant species.
Invertebrates	13,500 including approximately 2,500 British Lepidoptera and 347 British carabids	Includes approximately 1,015 Lepidoptera; 207 carabids; 21 Odonata; several species found in Ireland do not occur in Britain.
Reptiles	6	Common lizard (*Zootoca vivipara*); leatherback turtle (*Dermochelys coriacea*) occasionally.
Amphibians	7	2—common frog (*Rana temporaria*) and smooth newt (*Lissotriton vulgaris*).
Plants	1,760 higher plants including 1,142 native land plants and 1,000 lower plants and liverworts	Estimated 850 vascular plants (Mark Wright, NIEA, pers. comm.); 665 mosses and liverworts.
Fungi	12,000–15,000	2,347 described so far; plus 969 lichens.

18.3.1 Priority Habitats and Species

The western oceanic climate of Ireland, its island biogeography (isolated from Britain and Europe) and the varied geology, soil topography, long coastline and varied landscapes, contribute to the unique species composition and structure of the ecosystems of Northern Ireland.

In 2002 the Northern Ireland Biodiversity Strategy noted that Northern Ireland has a target to halt biodiversity loss by 2016 (NIBG 2009; NI Executive 2008) which compares with the international target of 2010. Priority habitats and species have been identified on a UK basis as part of compliance with the EU Habitats and Species Directive. All those that exist in Northern Ireland are priorities for Northern Ireland. However, some habitats and species require particular attention because of their status in Northern Ireland, or jointly with the Republic of Ireland.

At the start of 2011 there were 51 Northern Ireland priority habitats and 481 priority species following the UK and Northern Ireland priority habitats and species reviews (lists available from Northern Ireland Environment Agency, www.doeni.gov.uk/niea/). Prior to the reviews there were 40 Northern Ireland priority habitats, including three unique to Northern Ireland (crowfoot rivers, marl lakes and montane heath), and 271 priority species. The Northern Ireland Environment Agency has published 35 Northern Ireland Habitat Action Plans (HAPs) and 33 Northern Ireland Species Action Plans (SAPs), as well as seven all-Ireland SAPs. Habitat or Species Action Plans contain information on the habitat or species, its management and status. Reviews of the status of priority habitats and species have been undertaken in 2002, 2005 and 2010 (NIBG 2009; NIEA 2011; **Figures 18.2**; **Figure 18.3**). It is envisaged that SAPs will not be required for most of the new priority species.

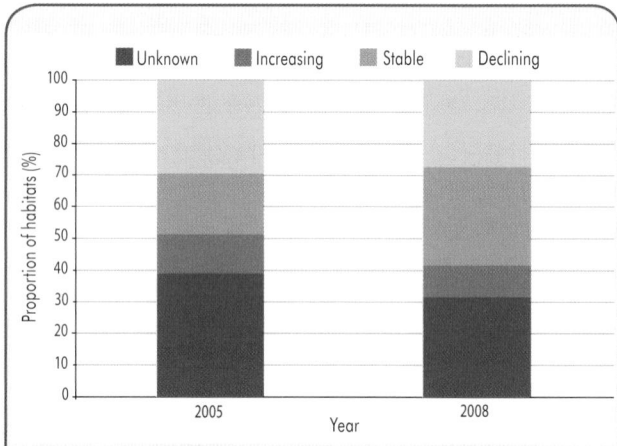

Figure 18.2 Status of Northern Ireland priority habitats in 2005 and 2008. Source: reproduced from NIEA (2011).

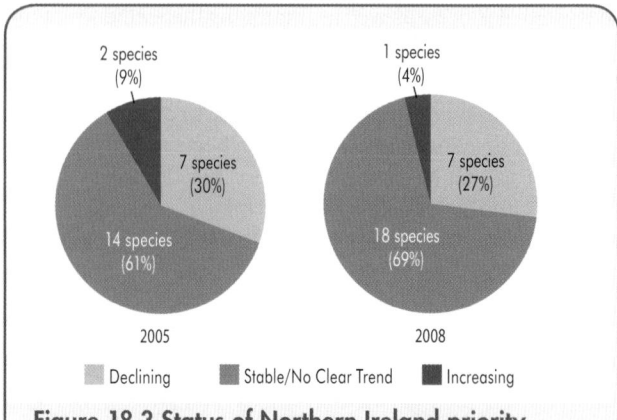

Figure 18.3 Status of Northern Ireland priority species in 2005 and 2008 which were reported on. Source: reproduced from DOE & NISRA (2010).

However, it is intended that Species Statements will indicate the conservation action required for each. Information on over two-thirds of the new priority species is available on the Habitas website and progress is being made in providing the full set of Species Statements.

Progress towards the achievement of the objectives of the Northern Ireland Biodiversity Strategy was reviewed in 2005 (NIBG 2005) and 2009 (NIBG 2009). Progress has been made, for example the introduction of 21 SAPs, 35 HAPs, local biodiversity officers within 11 out of 26 local authorities in 2009, the development of local Biodiversity Action Plans (BAPs) at both administrative and natural resource area levels, and the introduction of Biodiversity Implementation Plans (BIPs) in most government departments (NIBG 2009). However, overall the data indicate that fewer than half of the priority species or habitats reported on are stable or increasing, with data lacking or unavailable in many areas. The Northern Ireland Biodiversity Group Report (2009) made a series of recommendations covering the ecosystem approach, policy and legislation, planning and implementation, implementation tools, communication, awareness and engagement, local authorities, industry and commerce, monitoring, measurement and evaluation, all-Ireland measures for biodiversity, biodiversity indicators, habitats, species, rare breeds and cultivars, and climate change drivers for biodiversity action.

Biodiversity Delivery Groups (BDGs) were set up by the Northern Ireland Environment Agency and the Department of Agriculture and Rural Development to co-ordinate delivery of HAPs and arrangements for monitoring and reporting on priority habitats through partnerships between government and other relevant groups. Current trends in the area of priority habitats in Northern Ireland are available in The Second Report of the Northern Ireland Biodiversity Group 2005–2009 (NIBG 2009). The assessment, with only 17 habitats increasing or stable, caused the Northern Ireland Biodiversity Group concern (NIBG 2009; see **Figure 18.2**). To date, only priority habitats with ASSIs are monitored for their condition (see **Figure 18.60**). The condition of some priority habitats in the wider countryside will be able to be determined through further analysis of the Northern Ireland Countryside Survey data (NIEA pers. comm.).

Exemplar priority species were selected by the Northern Ireland Biodiversity Group in agreement with the Northern Ireland Environment Agency to cover the range of habitats represented by the BDGs (NIBG 2009). While the exemplar species represent a limited sub-set of priority species, the trends observed caused the Northern Ireland Biodiversity Group concern as, based on available data, over half of the exemplar species are declining, are at an extremely low level or, in the case of the small blue butterfly, feared extinct in Northern Ireland (NIBG 2009; **Figure 18.4**). Of the 18 Biodiversity Exemplar Species reported on to the Northern Ireland Biodiversity Group, five have a Species Action Plan, five were included within a HAP, three were subject to an All-Ireland Action Plan and five had no Action Plan (NIBG 2009).

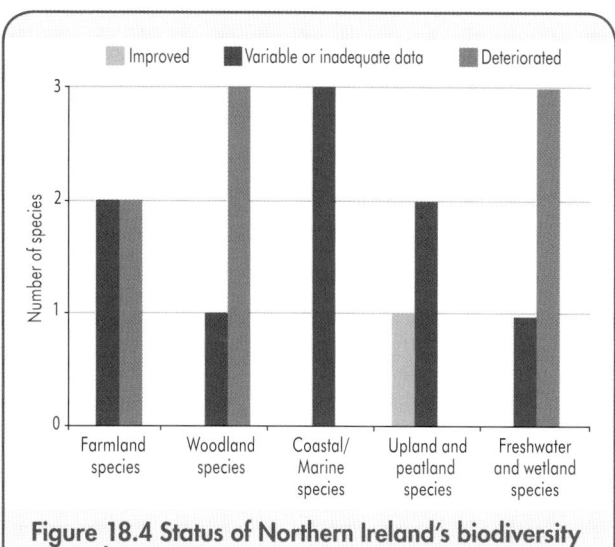

Figure 18.4 Status of Northern Ireland's biodiversity exemplar species. Source: reproduced from NIBG (2009).

biodiversity as they move between a wide range of habitats. However, in Northern Ireland there is a lack of data, especially for the west, compared to that available in Great Britain, which reduces the effectiveness of this indicator. Data are also available for wetland birds (DOE & NISRA 2010).

Indicators need to cover as wide a range of taxa as is feasible. Birds are relatively large and easy to identify, and so have practical benefits as indicators. However, there is no evidence that they are a reliable indicator of fungal and invertebrate biodiversity. Since fungi and invertebrates are the most species-rich groups they should be considered in monitoring programmes. Veteran trees can feature in most terrestrial habitats, such as farmland, urban and woodland. They support their own distinctive assemblages of epiphytes, fungi and invertebrates but also provide structural diversity which enhances the habitats of many other species, including people.

Monitoring of the Irish hare, the only mammal endemic to Ireland, has shown that there has been a large decline in the 50 years up to the 1960s, although there has been a slight increase in recent years (Reid *et al.* 2007; Reid *et al.* 2008; Reid *et al.* 2009). Caution is necessary when looking at trends on a yearly basis, as the Irish hare has exhibited cyclic population changes in the past. A main cause of decline has been changing habitat management, i.e. earlier cutting of silage. A delayed cutting option was introduced into the Northern Ireland Countryside Management Scheme (NICMS; Section 18.8.5) to help tackle this.

Grey squirrels were introduced into County Longford in Ireland in 1911 and have subsequently colonised most of Northern Ireland. A study by Queen's University Belfast in 2003 found that grey squirrels were absent in parts of north-east Antrim and that although red squirrels are still found throughout Fermanagh, Tyrone and Londonderry, the last remaining stronghold is within north-east Antrim (O'Neill & Montgomery 2003). However, grey squirrels are now colonising this area (Andrew Upton, UWT, pers. comm.)

18.3.2 Other Biodiversity Indicators

A number of biodiversity indicators are available. Populations of wild birds may be a good indicator of the broad state of

18.3.3 Invasive Alien Species

Non-native invasive species have been receiving increasing attention as a driver of biodiversity loss and the evidence base on their distribution is increasing (Stokes *et al.* 2006; Early *et al.* 2009). The cost of control can be high; the CABI (2010) report estimated the direct market costs of non-native invasive species to the British economy at £1.7 billion per year (Williams *et al.* 2010). By far the greatest impact is on the agriculture and horticulture sector, and invasive plants overall have the highest costs (£483 million), with plant pathogens (£403 million) and mammals (£402 million) also costing large sums (Williams *et al.* 2010). This study did not include Northern Ireland, where the major invasive species work has been done on a cross-border basis with the Republic of Ireland through the Invasive Species Ireland project (Maguire & Sykes 2004; Stokes *et al.* 2006; Habitas 2008; ISI 2010).

Non-native species must be addressed on a biogeographical basis, and this has been the approach in Northern Ireland. Data collection, analysis and risk assessment have mainly been carried out on an all-island basis so it is not possible to provide an analysis for Northern Ireland alone, nor is it meaningful to do so. Negative impacts on biodiversity can occur through a range of mechanisms such as competition, herbivory, predation, alteration of habitats and food webs, introduction of parasites and pathogens and through the dilution of native gene pools. Specific habitat types currently under specific threat include freshwater rivers and lakes; coastal floodplains, saltmarsh and sand dunes; maritime cliff and slopes; woodland; lowland heath and semi-natural grassland. A variety of native species including the Irish hare, red squirrel, white-clawed crayfish, freshwater pearl mussel, red deer (*Cervus elaphus*) and earthworms are threatened by non-native species (Stokes *et al.* 2006; ISI 2010).

Estimates of the number of non-native species in Ireland do not always distinguish between non-native species and invasive species; not all non-native species are invasive or have an impact on biodiversity. The total number of alien species has been estimated at 596 (DAISIE 2009); estimates for particular biodiversity groups include 99 non-native animal species (Stokes *et al.* 2006); 716 non-native terrestrial plants (Reynolds 2002); 112 aquatic and 63 cryptogenic aquatic invasive alien species (Minchin 2007). A pan-European analysis of the presence of the 163 'worst' terrestrial and freshwater invasive alien species threatening biodiversity in Europe showed that, in 2006, Ireland had 34 of these species (EEA 2010b) and since then a further seven have been recorded (ISI unpublished data). The introduction of non-indigenous individuals to replenish depleted local populations should be undertaken with extreme care as there may be damage to locally distinct gene pools; there is increasing evidence of such genetic distinctiveness across several taxa in Northern Ireland (Ian Montgomery, QUB, pers. comm.).

Invasive alien species impacts often occur in the context of other drivers of ecological change such as land use, climate change and pollution and it can be difficult to determine the specific degree of the impacts on biodiversity and therefore ecosystem services. There are limited studies of impact for each factor and variation in assessing the impacts amongst those studies. Data on invasive alien species status, trends and impacts are not currently linked to ecosystem services and therefore any assessment would be qualitative. However,

there is increasing interest in this area as invasive species, and freshwater plant species in particular, are a growing problem and their establishment in lakes has directly impacted on cultural services such as recreation, tourism and amenity value (Cathy Maguire, ISI, pers. comm.).

Intercontinental ocean-based transport routes (via ballast water) and aquaculture (via the escape of farmed species) mean that Northern Ireland has a number of marine invasive species. Of these, perhaps the most significant to date has been the Japanese wireweed (*Sargassum muticum*). This brown alga was initially reported from Strangford Lough in 1995, but has spread rapidly from there. Although its main impacts seem to be related to fouling of man-made structures, it can also have ecological consequences for the benthos (Roberts *et al.* 2004; Strong *et al.* 2006). A recent addition to the list of confirmed invasive species is the slipper limpet (*Crepidula fornicata*), which has established populations in Belfast Lough (McNeill *et al.* 2010). The Asian tunicate (*Styela clava*), has also established in Northern Ireland's waters (Nunn & Minchin 2009). Although the Northern Ireland Environment Agency Invasive Alien Species website (Habitas 2008) lists several other species that are likely to invade Northern Ireland's Marine ecosystems, none are currently known to have established viable populations in the wild. An increasing reliance on aquaculture to produce seafood, together with climate change, means that the threat posed by marine invasive species is likely to increase.

There has been widespread control of invasive species across Northern Ireland as a result of training provided by the Northern Ireland Environment Agency (NIEA) and through the Invasive Species in Ireland Project. There are numerous examples including Roads Service Northern Ireland widely spraying Japanese knotweed (*Fallopia japonica*), Ballinderry river giant hogweed (*Heracleum mantegazzianum*) control, Belfast Hills Partnership project and work by a number of councils. In Northern Ireland the Rivers Agency spent £200,000 on a 19 km stretch of the River Roe clearing Japanese knotweed, the Killyhelvin waste water treatment works required a £120,000 refit due to zebra mussels, and a number of projects to address floating pennywort (*Hydrocotyle ranunculoides*) have together cost £85,000, mostly in staff time. The Northern Ireland Environment Agency has spent an estimated £415,000 on clearing invasives from its country parks and over £32,000 at its nature reserves since 2005 (NIEA unpublished data).

18.3.4 Climate Change

The climate of Northern Ireland is already changing in line with predictions (UKCP09 2009). Air temperature is rising and the number of hot days is increasing; the proportion of rainfall falling in summer is decreasing, while winters are slightly wetter, and in 2009 and 2010 record low winter temperatures were recorded. Record breaking cold winter temperatures sustained for relatively long periods may become more frequent, with possibly severe impacts on native biodiversity; while some of these impacts may be positive (e.g. killing of pest species such as aphids) there are likely to be negative impacts as well as native species encounter more severe conditions. In Europe, annual air temperature has increased between 0.3°C and 0.6°C since 1900. Temperature change at local levels may be more variable (Albanito *et al.* 2008; Sweeney *et al.* 2008). These changes are expected to accelerate over the coming century. Average temperature may rise by 3°C or more; summer rainfall may fall by up to 50% while winters may be 25% wetter (SNIFFER 2008). Furthermore, relative sea levels may begin to rise. Although there are ongoing efforts to mitigate climate change, principally by reducing emissions, some climate change is now inevitable. Adaptation to climate change—reducing risks and realising opportunities—is therefore required (Arkell *et al.* 2007; Coll *et al.* 2008).

Threats from climate change to the conservation, biodiversity and habitats of Northern Ireland include (SNIFFER 2002; Arkell *et al.* 2007; NIEL 2009a; IACCF 2010):

- distribution and species composition of habitats changing in response to warmer winters;
- increases in the range of invasive non-native species, which may threaten ecosystems in response to warmer temperatures;
- intertidal habitats, salt marshes and mudflats threatened through flooding and erosion;
- loss of coastal grazing marsh;
- estuarine and river ecology threatened by tidal flooding; and
- warmer sea temperatures affecting phytoplankton communities—the resulting decline in sand eel populations would adversely affect a wide range of seabirds (e.g. breeding seabird productivity at Isle of Muck has declined significantly in the past decade; Andrew Upton, UWT, pers. comm.).

The opportunities that a changing climate could bring to the conservation, biodiversity and habitats of Northern Ireland include expansion of some species (for example the spread of little egrets; Andrew Upton, UWT, pers. comm.) but this tends to be accompanied by equivalent threats (loss of other species and drier summers). Phenological changes for individual species have already been noted (Woodland Trust 2010c) with resultant ecological impacts including mismatching of species' life cycle events and food sources, decoupled predator-prey relationships, new invasions and the likely spread of already established invasive alien species (EEA 2010a). Distribution and range changes due to direct impacts or habitat loss are also possible, especially for species at the extremes of their ranges.

18.4 Northern Ireland's Habitats

18.4.1 Data Available for Northern Ireland's Habitats

The assessment of ecosystem services requires reliable data on the types, structure, species composition and extent of habitats, as well as information on how the habitats are used and how they change with time. Terrestrial, freshwater and marine habitat classifications give useful categories within which ecosystems and their services can be assessed (Smart *et al.* 2010).

This section summarises some of what is known about the habitats of Northern Ireland, how they are being managed and how they have changed over recent decades. A wide variety of data have been used to carry out the assessment, and in some instances comparisons between different data can be difficult. However, using all relevant data is still possible as long as it is made clear on what basis data were collected and care is taken in comparing across different methods.

Statistics are based on inventory data and sample-based surveys. In most cases data have not been collected using the habitat categories used in the Northern Ireland Synthesis exercise. For example, the Department of Agriculture and Rural Development definition of 'farmland' is a land-use term that includes parts or all of at least five of the habitat categories used in the Northern Ireland Synthesis. In addition, percentage area calculations vary slightly, depending on whether the land area used as the base for Northern Ireland includes or excludes lakes and/or islands.

For data compiled over many years, for example by the Department of Agriculture and Rural Development, the mechanisms and categories have often changed through time. Data presented in tables show values which have been corrected by the originating organisation to the extent possible.

18.4.1.1 Northern Ireland Countryside Survey

The Northern Ireland Countryside Survey (NICS) is one of the main data sources for the Northern Ireland Synthesis. It is a field-based research programme structured on statistical sampling principles and standard survey protocols with the aim of understanding how land use and environmental change influence Primary Habitat diversity. It provides information on how the habitats have changed in a time-series; 1986/1991 (baseline), 1998 and 2007 (Cooper & Murray 1987; Murray *et al.* 1992; Cooper *et al.* 2002; Cooper *et al.* 2009). It gives estimates of primary habitats with descriptive statistics from the sample. Field survey and analytical protocols are given by McCann *et al.* (2009).

The NICS uses a system of primary habitat mapping, derived from the UK Joint Nature Conservation Committee (JNCC) standard classification Phase I (McCann *et al.* 2009; JNCC 2010). Agreed combinations of primary habitats have been used to obtain broad habitat estimates. The broad habitat classification was constructed to communicate policy on habitats at a UK level (UK Biodiversity Steering Group1995a,b; Jackson 2000; Cooper *et al.* 2009; McCann *et al.* 2009).

18.4.1.2 Habitat classifications and National Ecosystem Assessment habitat categories

For the purposes of the Northern Ireland Synthesis, NICS primary habitat and broad habitat data have been combined to provide area and percentage cover estimates for each of the UK NEA categories (Cooper & McCann 2010; **Table 18.4**; **Figure 18.5**; **Figure 18.6**). As NICS is a survey of terrestrial

Table 18.4 UK NEA Broad Habitats and estimated Net change between 1998 and 2007. Source: figures derived from NICS data, calculated to HWMMT (High Water Mark of Medium Tides), as a percentage of Northern Ireland (1,416,047 ha; Cooper & McCann 2010).

UK NEA Broad Habitats	UK NEA component habitats	Estimate from Northern Ireland Countryside Survey	1998		2007		Net change	
			ha	% NI	ha	% NI	ha	%
Mountains, Moorlands & Heaths	Bracken	BH09 Dense bracken	3,084	0.22	2,645	0.19	-439	-14.2
	Dwarf Shrub Heath	BH10 Dwarf shrub heath	13,909	0.98	16,751	1.18	2,842	20.4
	Upland Fen, Marsh & Swamp	S16 Poor fen	24,784	1.75	21,005	1.48	-3,779	-15.2
	Bog	BH12 Bog (Above 150 m)*	140,814	9.94	139,796	9.87	-1,018	-0.7
	Montane	BH15 Montane vegetation	735	0.05	735	0.05	0	0.0
	Inland Rock	BH16 Inland rock	7,969	0.56	5,450	0.39	-2,519	-31.6
	Mountains, Moorlands & Heaths Total		**191,295**	**13.45**	**186,382**	**13.11**	**-4,913**	**-2.6**
Semi-natural Grasslands	Acid Grassland	BH08 Acid grassland	13,324	0.94	10,369	0.73	-2,955	-22.2
	Neutral Grassland	BH06 Neutral grassland	263,902	18.64	231,116	16.32	-32,786	-12.4
	Calcareous Grassland	BH07 Calcareous grassland	1,765	0.13	1,802	0.13	37	2.1
	Purple Moor-grass & Rush Pasture	S02 Species-rich wet grassland	13,396	0.95	13,186	0.93	-210	-1.6
		S65 Fen meadow	6,533	0.46	5,290	0.37	-1,243	-19.0
	Semi-natural Grasslands Total		**298,920**	**21.12**	**261,763**	**18.48**	**-37,157**	**-12.4**
Enclosed Farmland	Arable & Horticulture (including orchards & short rotation coppice)	BH04 Arable and horticulture	57,213	4.04	48,917	3.46	-8,296	-14.5
		W12 Orchard	1,623	0.12	1,165	0.08	-458	-28.2
	Improved Grassland	BH05 Improved grassland	554,982	39.19	573,010	40.47	18,028	3.2
	Boundary and linear features†	BH03a Field Boundaries (km)	226,296	n/a	225,917	n/a	-379	-0.2
	Enclosed Farmland Total‡		**613,818**	**43.35**	**623,092**	**44.01**	**9,274**	**1.5**
Woodlands	Broadleaved, Mixed & Yew Woodland	BH01 Broadleaved, mixed and yew woodland (Not including W12 Orchard)‡	61,884	4.37	80,534	5.69	18,650	30.1
	Coniferous Woodland	BH02 Coniferous woodland	62,135	4.39	60,617	4.28	-1,518	-2.4
	Woodlands Total		**124,019**	**8.76**	**141,151**	**9.97**	**17,132**	**13.8**

habitats, spatial analysis (NIEA 2010h) was used to calculate a figure for the Marine category (see **Table 18.4**; **Figure 18.5**; **Figure 18.6**).

18.4.1.3 UK NEA Broad Habitat categories

Mountains, Moorlands and Heaths cover 13.1% of Northern Ireland (Cooper *et al.* 2009). Blanket bog is extensive, with smaller areas of heath in the uplands and rush-dominated poor fen in the marginal uplands, with some dense bracken and Inland Rock. Much of the Bog has been cut-over for peat fuel in the past, but the rate of habitat decrease between 1998 and 2007 slowed to 3.4% (Cooper *et al.* 2002, 2009).

Semi-natural Grasslands consist largely of Neutral Grassland, with smaller areas of species-rich wet grassland, acidic hill grassland, Calcareous Grassland and fen meadow. Collectively, Semi-natural Grasslands cover 18.5% of Northern Ireland and a large proportion has field boundaries (Cooper *et al.* 2009). Since the development of agricultural technology in the 1950s (Hunter 1987), there has been a large decrease in the area of Semi-natural Grasslands. The rate of decrease, mainly by conversion to more productive agricultural grassland, has slowed to 12.4% in the past decade (Cooper *et al.* 2002; Cooper *et al.* 2009).

Enclosed Farmland includes lowland and marginal upland habitats, largely used for grass production, and a smaller area of cereal crops and other arable production. Small family farms predominate (Hunter 1987). Enclosed Farmland covers 44% of Northern Ireland (Cooper *et al.* 2009). Their area increased by 1.5% between 1998 and 2007, mainly as a result of agricultural conversion from Semi-natural Grasslands. There is an extensive system of hedge and earthbank field boundaries. Since the 1950s many field boundaries have been removed, largely as a result of increased farm field sizes, but recent data (1992–1998) show a lower rate of decrease (Cooper *et al.* 2002; Cooper *et al.* 2009).

Woodlands are distributed across the uplands, marginal uplands and lowlands, covering 10.0% of Northern Ireland (Cooper *et al.* 2009). Just over half of this is broadleaved woodland (including scrub) and the rest is conifer plantation (largely Sitka spruce). The area of conifer plantation has changed little in the last 10 years. However, since 1986 there has been an increase in broadleaved woodland and scrub cover, mainly due to planting and ecological succession in other habitats (Cooper *et al.* 2002; Cooper *et al.* 2009). The figure quoted by the Forest Service for the total area of woodland cover in Northern Ireland is 87,903 ha (Forestry Commission 2009a), representing 6.2% of Northern Ireland.

Table 18.4 continued.

UK NEA Broad Habitats	UK NEA component habitats	Estimate from Northern Ireland Countryside Survey	1998		2007		Net change	
			ha	% NI	ha	% NI	ha	%
Freshwaters – Openwaters, Wetlands & Floodplains	Standing open water (lakes, ponds & canals)	BH13 Standing open water	61,785	4.36	61,332	4.33	-453	-0.7
	Rivers and streams	BH14 Rivers and streams	5,390	0.38	5,495	0.39	105	1.9
	Lowland raised bog*	BH12 Bog (Below 150 m)	23,402	1.65	21,106	1.49	-2,296	-9.8
	Fens, grazing marsh & swamp	S17 Reedbeds	2,958	0.21	2,563	0.18	-395	-13.4
		S18 Fen	2,723	0.19	2,499	0.18	-224	-8.2
		S66 Swamp	2,280	0.16	2,524	0.18	244	10.7
		S68 Water inundation vegetation	260	0.02	187	0.01	-73	-28.1
	Freshwater Total		**98,798**	**6.98**	**95,706**	**6.76**	**-3,092**	**-3.1**
Urban	Built-up Areas & Gardens	BH17 Built up areas	56,847	4.01	74,098	5.23	17,251	30.3
		BH03b Roads, tracks and hard verges	29,449	2.08	30,951	2.19	1,502	5.1
	Urban Total		**86,296**	**6.09**	**105,049**	**7.42**	**18,753**	**21.7**
Coastal Margins	Sea Cliffs	BH18 Supralittoral rock	1,717	0.12	1,581	0.11	-136	-7.9
	Shingle							
	Coastal Lagoons							
	Saltmarsh	BH19 Supralittoral sediment	1,859	0.13	1,995	0.14	136	7.3
	Sand Dunes							
	Coastal Margins Total		**3,576**	**0.25**	**3,576**	**0.25**	**0**	**0.0**
Marine	Intertidal Rock	BH20 Littoral rock	Not recorded	n/a	1,212	n/a	**n/a**	**n/a**
	Intertidal Sediment	BH21 Littoral sediment	Not recorded	n/a	9,518	n/a	**n/a**	**n/a**
	Subtidal Rock	12 NM Territorial Waters¶	~450,000	n/a	~450,000	n/a	0	0
	Subtidal Sediment—shallow & shelf							
	Deep-sea Habitat							

* Lowland raised bog is included in the NICS broad habitat BH12 Bog, but is a constituent of the UK NEA Broad Habitat Freshwaters – Openwaters, Wetlands and Floodplains.

† A large proportion of these features are associated with the UK NEA Broad Habitat Semi-Natural Grasslands.

‡ Short rotation coppice is included in the NICS broad habitat BH01 Broadleaved, mixed and yew woodland, but is a constituent of the UK NEA Broad Habitat Enclosed Farmland.

¶ The 12 NM Territorial Waters area is an estimate calculated using GIS (ArcGIS; NIEA 2010h) by drawing a mid-line through trans-boundary waters out to the 12 NM limit (or midway between Northern Ireland and Scotland).

The reasons for the difference between the two figures are further explored in Section 18.4.5 and are largely due to differing definitions of woodland.

Freshwaters – Openwaters, Wetlands and Floodplains, mostly rivers, loughs (Lough Neagh and Lough Erne being the largest) and bog, but also streams, fen, swamp, reedbeds and water-inundated vegetation, collectively cover 6.8% of Northern Ireland (Cooper *et al.* 2009). The small area of Fen, Marsh and Swamp vegetation occurs largely in drumlin hollows and around lough margins. Land drainage and flood defence engineering schemes after the 1950s resulted in large decreases in the area of wetland vegetation, but there has been little change from 1998 to 2007 (Cooper *et al.* 2002; Cooper *et al.* 2009). Lowland raised bogs are included in this UK NEA habitat category.

Urban settlements (including rural buildings and roads) cover 7.4% of Northern Ireland (Cooper *et al.* 2009). A large increase in area, particularly between 1998 and 2007 (21.7%), occurred mainly over Enclosed Farmland and Semi-natural Grasslands (Cooper *et al.* 2002; Cooper *et al.* 2009).

Coastal Margins in Northern Ireland consist of Sea Cliffs, Sand Dunes, Saltmarsh, Shingle and Coastal Lagoons. They covered 3,576 ha of Northern Ireland (0.3%) in 2007 and there has been no change in the overall area since 1998 (Cooper *et al.* 2002; Cooper *et al.* 2009).

Marine habitats, as defined by the UK NEA, are either permanently immersed in saline water or are inundated by seawater over part of the tidal cycle. The area includes both the intertidal zone (HWMMT High Water Mark of Medium Tides) to LWMMT (Low Water Mark of Medium Tides) covering an estimated 10,730 ha (Cooper *et al.* 2009), and the subtidal zone (LWMMT to 12 nautical miles (NM)) covering an estimated 450,000 ha (NIEA 2010h). The 12NM territorial waters area is an estimate calculated using GIS (ArcGIS) by

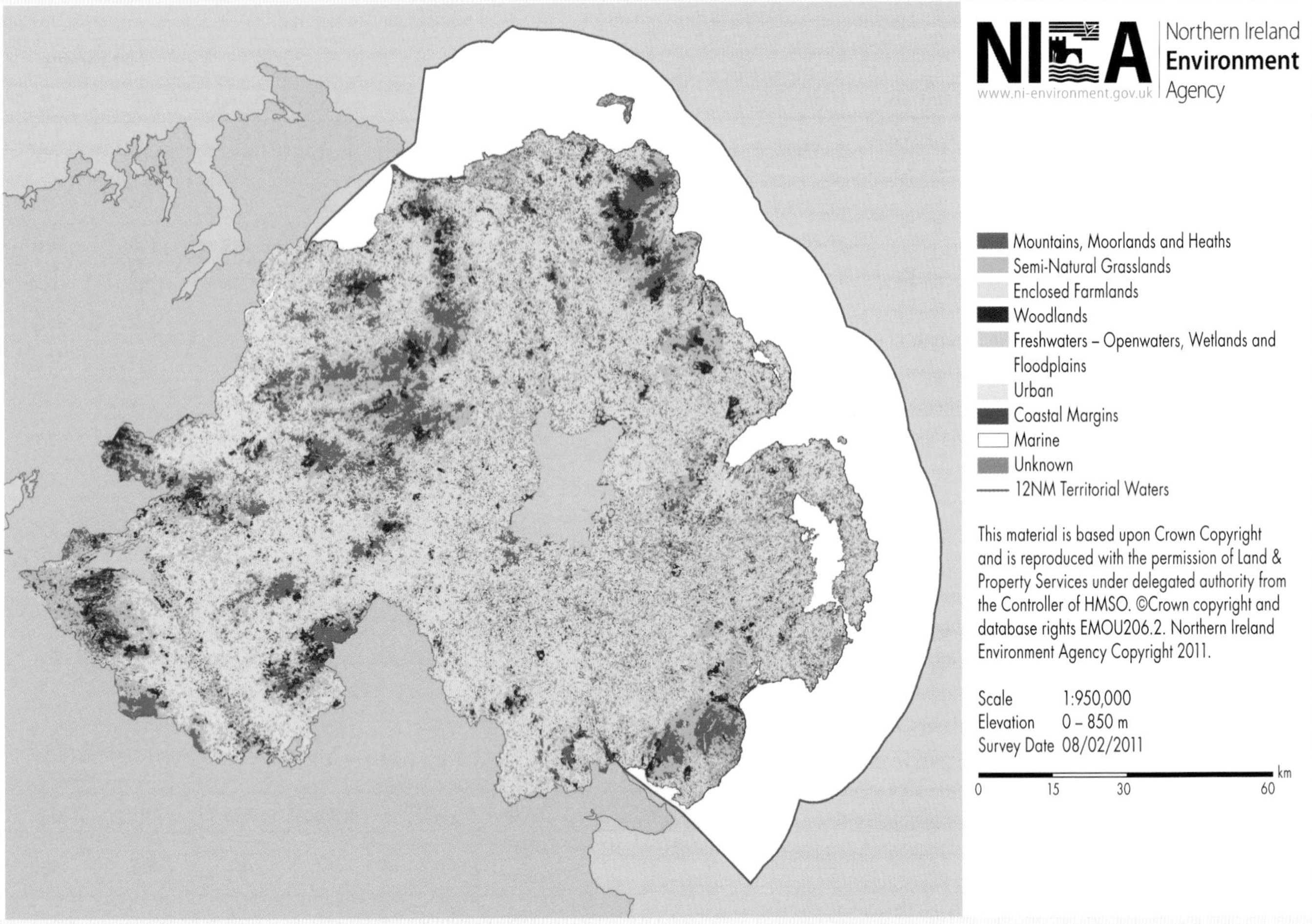

Mountains, Moorlands and Heaths
Semi-Natural Grasslands
Enclosed Farmlands
Woodlands
Freshwaters – Openwaters, Wetlands and Floodplains
Urban
Coastal Margins
Marine
Unknown
12NM Territorial Waters

Scale   1:950,000
Elevation   0 – 850 m
Survey Date 08/02/2011

0   15   30   60 km

Figure 18.5 Land Cover Map of Northern Ireland showing distribution of UK NEA Broad Habitats. Source: NIEA (unpublished data).

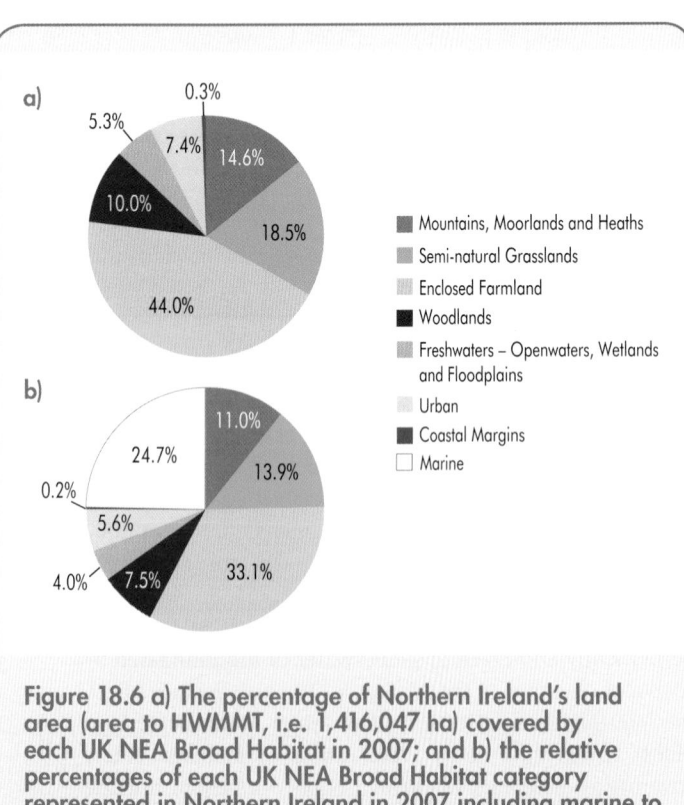

Figure 18.6 a) The percentage of Northern Ireland's land area (area to HWMMT, i.e. 1,416,047 ha) covered by each UK NEA Broad Habitat in 2007; and b) the relative percentages of each UK NEA Broad Habitat category represented in Northern Ireland in 2007 including marine to 12 nautical miles. Source: data from a) Cooper & McCann (2010); NIEA (2010h) and b) Cooper & McCann (2010) (NIEA 2010h).

drawing a mid-line through trans-boundary waters out to the 12NM limit (or midway between Northern Ireland and Scotland).

18.4.1.4 Changes in Broad Habitat area

Key changes in Broad Habitats identified between 1986/1991 and 1998 (see **Figure 18.7**) were an increase in the area of Improved Grassland (BH05); a decrease in the area of arable crops (BH04) and Neutral Grassland (BH06) due to conversion to Improved Grassland (BH05); a decrease in the area of Fen, Marsh and Swamp (BH11), which includes fens, reedbeds, swamps and water inundation vegetation (Section 18.4.6.4), species-rich wet grassland and fen meadow (Section 18.4.3.3) and poor fen (Section 18.4.2.3); damage to Bog (BH12), which includes lowland raised bog (Section 18.4.6.3) and blanket bog (Section 18.4.2.2) by peat cutting; and reduced ecological condition of Bog (BH12) and Dwarf Shrub Heath (BH10) due to grazing pressure. Also identified as important processes were ecological succession to broadleaf woodland (BH01) on a wide range of habitats including Bog (BH12), Fen, Marsh and Swamp (BH11) and Neutral Grassland (BH06), and an increased area of building (BH17) on Improved Grassland (BH05) and Neutral Grassland (BH06; Cooper *et al.* 2002).

Between 1998 and 2007 (**Figure 18.7**) there were smaller decreases in the areas of arable crops (BH04), Neutral Grassland (BH06) and Fen, Marsh and Swamp (BH11). Damage to Bog (BH12) from peat cutting was minimal and there was evidence of Dwarf Shrub Heath (BH10) restoration. Conversion of Acid Grassland (BH08) to more productive agricultural grassland, a process recorded between 1987–1992 and 1998, increased in the marginal uplands between 1998 and 2007. Ecological succession to broadleaved woodland (BH01) over species-rich habitats was greater between 1998 and 2007 and there was increased broadleaved tree planting on Improved Grassland (BH05) and Neutral Grassland (BH06). The large increase in area of building (BH17) over a wide range of habitats found from 1998 to 2007 was almost twice that reported from 1987–1992 to 1998 (**Figure 18.8**).

18.4.2 Mountains, Moorlands and Heaths

Northern Ireland, on the extreme north west of Europe, has a marked oceanic climate that is much warmer than expected for its latitude (Kirkpatrick & Rushton 1990). This is due to the proximity of the North Atlantic Drift and because it receives predominantly moist, westerly air masses from the Atlantic. By forcing westerly air to rise, the uplands receive more precipitation, mostly in the form of rain, than the lowlands.

The extreme oceanicity of Northern Ireland makes its peatland habitats important in a UK, Ireland and European context (Kirkpatrick & Rushton 1990). They provide significant carbon storage, biodiversity, landscape and recreation ecosystem services and constitute a major opportunity for integrated management to deliver multiple benefits. A high proportion of the total area is designated for biodiversity, landscape or agricultural purposes and a significant area carries multiple designations (see **Figure**

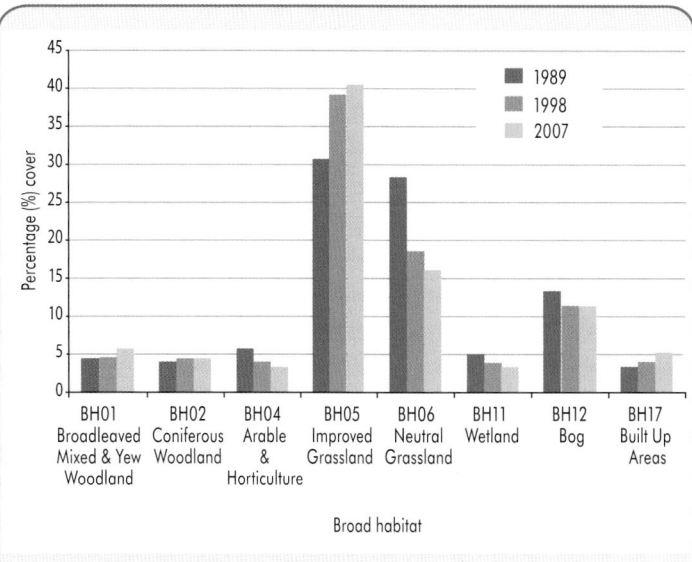

Figure 18.7 Change in the percentage cover of the main Northern Ireland Countryside Survey broad habitats between the baseline survey (1986–1991) and the resurveys in 1998 and 2007. Source: data from Cooper *et al.* 2002 and Cooper *et al.* 2009.

18.61; **Figure 18.63**; **Figure 18.65**; Sections 18.8.2, 18.8.3 & 18.8.7).

With acidic parent rocks and glacial till, soils are generally acidic. The wet conditions promoted blanket peat development when the woodland cover was removed, particularly between 2000–1700 BP and around 700 BP. Peat became the major source of fuel in Ireland during the 17th and 18th Centuries (Aalen 1997). Cultivation expanded in the late 18th and early

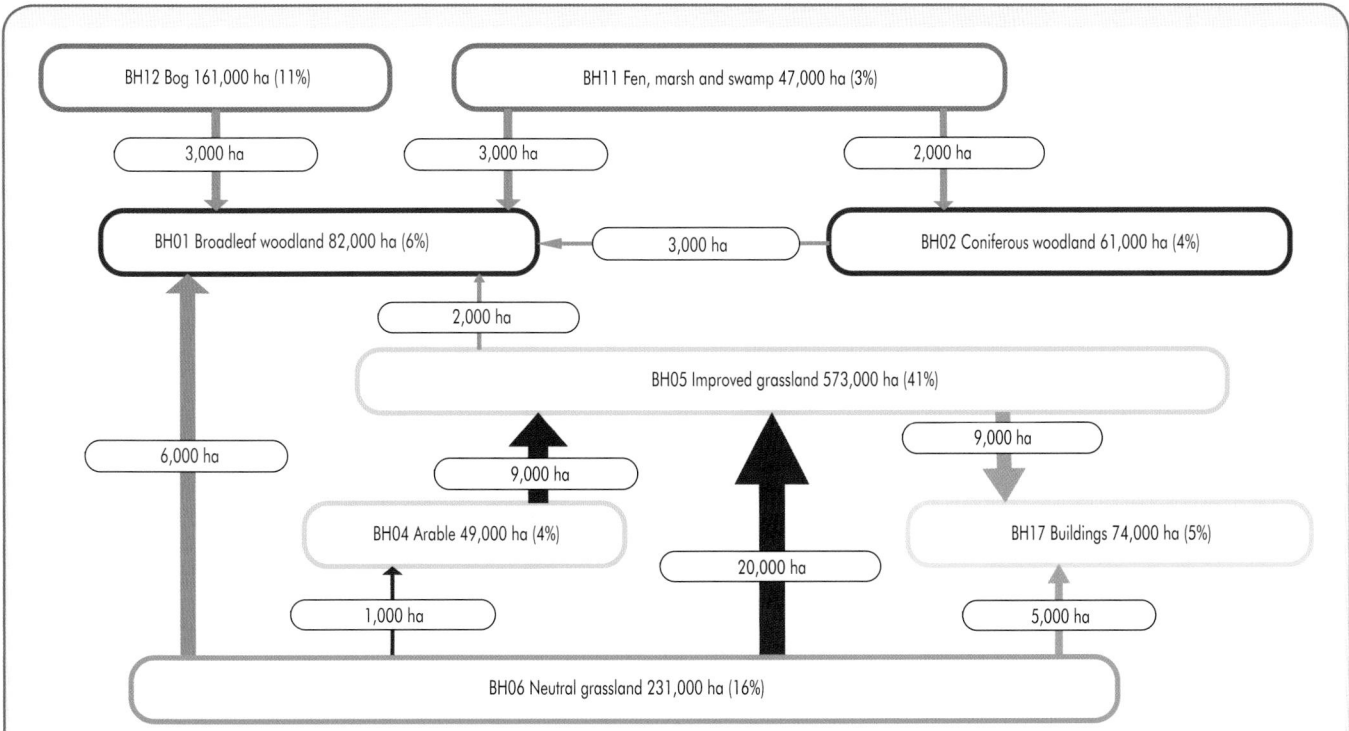

Figure 18.8 Net transitions (of >1,000 ha) between Countryside Survey broad habitats from 1998–2007. The area of each broad habitat is for 2007. Arrows: brown = mainly agricultural conversion; green = mainly ecological succession or conversion to woodland; grey = building. Colour of box border denotes the predominant UK NEA Broad Habitats: light green = Semi-natural Grasslands; yellow = Enclosed Farmland; light pink = Urban, dark green = Woodlands; pink = Mountains, Moorlands and Heaths. Source: data from Cooper *et al.* (2009).

19th Centuries. However, the limits of cultivation contracted after the Great Famine of the 1840s (Proudfoot 1990).

Mountains, Moorlands and Heaths in Northern Ireland can be generalised as a sequence from rare montane heath on a few summits to eroded peat on high mountain ridges and their steep slopes; extensive deep peat; extensive cutover peat; and smaller areas of poor fen (rush-dominated) and Acid Grassland (Section 18.4.3) on marginal agricultural land on lower slopes (with bent-fescue grasses on mineral soils and mat-grass on better-drained peaty soils) (Cooper *et al.* 2002; EHS 2003d; Omagh District Council & UWT 2008; Newry & Mourne DC & UWT 2009; Cooper *et al.* 2009).

Mountains, Moorlands and Heaths contain the largest tracts of semi-natural habitats and cover roughly 13.1% of Northern Ireland (Cooper *et al.* 2002; Cooper *et al.* 2009; see **Figure 18.36**) compared with 43% in Scotland, 12% in Wales, 5% in England and a UK average of approximately 18%. The overall area of Mountains, Moorlands and Heaths has been relatively stable over the past 20 years, although changes have occurred between some of the constituent habitats (Cooper *et al.* 2002; Cooper *et al.* 2009). Over a longer period use has shifted between low-level grazing and subsistence agriculture. Potential major future impacts could occur as a result of climate change, agricultural land use change and locally significant damage due to recreational use.

Bog, characterised by bog-moss (*Sphagnum*), covers much of the Mountains, Moorlands and Heaths area. The lower margin of blanket peat is generally correlated with the 1,250 mm mean annual rainfall isohyet (Hamilton 1982). It consists of a wide range of peatland types (usually deeper than about 50 cm), ranging from high quality wet bog to cutover and degraded bog. There was a small decrease in area between 1998 and 2007. However, much of this was bog in lowland landscapes (Cooper *et al.* 2009; Section 18.4.6). This follows an 8% decrease in Bog recorded between 1986 and 1998 (Cooper *et al.* 2002). The main change was succession to scrub at the edge of lowland bog complexes (Cooper *et al.* 2009). Mountains, Moorlands and Heaths also include small areas of other habitats, mainly poor fen and dwarf shrub heath (Cooper *et al.* 2002; Cooper *et al.* 2009).

18.4.2.1 Bog

The bogs in Ireland have been classified as either upland blanket (Section 18.4.2.2) or lowland raised (Cruickshank & Tomlinson 1988, 1990; see **Figure 18.36**; Section 18.4.6.3). Blanket bog has built up over soil and rock, but lowland bogs are often filled-in basins and have a 'dome' structure. All bog types in Northern Ireland have been harvested for fuel peat (Section 18.5.2.7) and some lowland and a few upland bogs have been harvested for 'milled' peat most commonly used for horticulture (Section 18.5.2.14). The Northern Ireland Peatland Survey (Cruickshank & Tomlinson 1988) looked at a total peatland resource (excluding fen) of 167,580 ha, of which 15% was lowland and 85% upland. It found that only 8% of lowland and 15% of upland bog was intact. The NICS (Cooper *et al.* 2002) recorded a loss of 8% of vegetation in lowland raised bogs (EHS 2003e), 25% in upland bog (EHS 2003b,c) and 18% in fens between 1992 and 1998 (EHS 2005g) with damage due to drainage, overgrazing and peat cutting (EHS 2003c). Much of the 25% decrease in upland bog was

bare peat created by machine peat cutting. Although most of this now has vegetation cover, the full biodiversity of pristine peat will take much longer to re-establish. More recent NICS data (Cooper *et al.* 2009) show that between 1998 and 2007 the area of lowland bog decreased by a further 10% and that upland bog decreased by just under 1% (1,018 ha). There are distinct HAPs for Upland and Lowland Bogs (EHS 2003e,g).

Although there was a significant amount of machine peat cutting (Cooper & McCann 1995) between 1986 and 1998 which caused bog degradation, the area that was cut-over is recovering (Tomlinson 2010). Damage was also caused by drainage for forestry and agriculture and by heavy grazing. A recent reduction in peat cutting (1998 to 2007; Cooper *et al.* 2009) is linked to habitat conservation measures and to the largely favourable economics of oil fuel prices compared with peat cutting costs between 1998 and 2007. However, there is anecdotal evidence that hand cutting of peat has started in parts of Counties Tyrone and Fermanagh in the past few years (Andrew Upton, UWT, pers. comm.). There is an obvious need to consider the implications of significant oil price increases, but up to 2010 price rises did not appear to lead to renewed activity on a large scale (Roy Tomlinson, QUB, unpublished data).

Peatlands are home to many iconic and unique species such as the carnivorous plants sundew (*Drosera* species) and butterwort (*Pinguicula* species). The Antrim Hills are designated as a Special Protection Area (SPA) for the hen harrier (*Circus cyaneus*) and merlin (*Falco columbarius*) while the Garron Plateau, the largest area of intact blanket bog in Northern Ireland and one of the best examples in the UK, is designated as a Ramsar site. Hen harrier populations have increased in recent years, probably due to the expansion of young forest plantations, from 38 pairs in 1998 to 50–60 pairs in 2004 (Habitas 2010). Unusually, in Northern Ireland the hen harrier also nests in mature forest plantation (Scott 2000; EHS 2005h). Peatlands are also a habitat for migratory and wetland birds, including the curlew (*Numenius arquata*), dunlin (*Calidris alpina*) and golden plover (*Pluvialis apricaria*), and are increasingly important since alternative habitats such as damp lowlands have been drained. They are also a habitat for the Irish hare (*Lepus timidus hibernicus*), another priority species.

18.4.2.2 Blanket peat

Approximately 85% of Bog in Northern Ireland is blanket peat, which occurs predominantly in the uplands. Most blanket peat (73%) is in the west (Cruickshank & Tomlinson 1990) where uplands are more extensive, rainfall is higher, cloud cover is greater and temperatures are more equable. These conditions enable blanket peat to extend to low altitudes. For example, Bog on the Pettigoe Plateau is unique in Northern Ireland, as it has lowland Atlantic blanket peat vegetation similar to that found in western coastal regions of Ireland (Cruickshank & Tomlinson 1990). Within the upland Bog habitats there are areas with deep basin and raised bogs, complete with well-developed pool and hummock complexes.

Cruickshank & Tomlinson (1988) estimated that Northern Ireland has approximately 140,000 ha of blanket bog vegetation. About 15% of this area (22,000 ha) remains intact, with 10% (14,000 ha) having been drained and 46%

(64,400 ha) hand-cut for fuel. The remaining 29% (40,600 ha) of blanket bog vegetation is a mix of vegetation types including large areas of eroded peatland (Roy Tomlinson, QUB, pers. comm.). In addition, significant proportions of peat soil, probably in excess of 10%, no longer support semi-natural vegetation. These soils have not been included in the blanket bog inventory. Loss of blanket bog has also been attributed to afforestation which occupies approximately 20% of peat soils (Cruickshank 1997), accounting for up to 40% (around 30,000 ha) of the Forest Service estate (EHS 2003c).

The most extensive tracts of blanket bog tend to occur at altitudes above 200 m and are concentrated on the Antrim Plateau, the Sperrin Mountains and in County Fermanagh. In the north and west, where annual rainfall is much higher than in central and eastern regions of Northern Ireland, a number of blanket bogs occur in the altitude range 150–200 m. In the extreme west, blanket bogs have developed as low as 90 m. Peat depth is also variable, with 0.5 to 3 m being fairly typical. However, where peat has accumulated in depressions, depths in excess of 5 m are not unusual (EHS 2003c).

Although much of the blanket bog in Northern Ireland has been physically modified over centuries, most is still 'active', i.e. capable of forming peat. This active bog generally has a high proportion of peat-forming species such as bog-mosses, hare's-tail cottongrass (*Eriophorum vaginatum*) and deer sedge (*Scirpus caespitosus*). The NICS estimate of upland blanket bog from the 2007 survey is 139,796 ha, of which just over one-quarter has a *Sphagnum* cover of less than 10%. Between 1998 and 2007, the proportion of wet bog and wet heath (the main habitats of blanket bog) with a *Sphagnum* cover of more than 25% decreased by almost 10% (Cooper & McCann 2010). This high proportion of active bog contrasts with Great Britain, where significant areas have been subject to more intensive grazing and more frequent burning in recent decades. However, the decrease in the past 10 years of high *Sphagnum* cover areas indicates continued degradation.

Peat erosion is widespread on the higher hills, with networks of erosion channels on flatter parts and erosion gullies on higher slopes. Approximately 46% of the blanket peat has been cut-over at some time in the past (Cruickshank & Tomlinson 1990). In some areas this has left thin peat with poor fen heath or acidic grassland, whilst in others the intricate patchwork of cutting and remnant deeper peat provides a diversity of habitats that characterise the upland landscapes of Northern Ireland.

In the Sperrins almost all the lower levels are affected by past cutting; this forms a belt around the High Sperrins and completely covers peripheral lower ridges. The highest areas of the Sperrins have intensive peat erosion and the steepest slopes have thin or no peat. Blanket peat is widespread on the more modest uplands of mid-Tyrone, where a high proportion of the 15% of intact blanket peatland is found (Cruickshank & Tomlinson 1990). Cuilcagh Mountain and Slieve Beagh also have extensive intact blanket peat. However, in the 1980s and 1990s small-scale machine extraction was common in these three areas and some of this extended on to intact bog. Cooper *et al.* (2001) showed good plant community regeneration on blanket bog after mechanised cutting.

In the east there is little intact blanket peat, with large areas affected by past cutting and erosion. Of high conservation interest, however, are the Garron Plateau (Co. Antrim) for its extensive, diverse blanket bog and the Mourne Mountains (Co. Down) for their heathlands.

18.4.2.3 Poor fens

Poor fens (1.5% of Northern Ireland) arise where water originates over base-poor rock such as sandstones and granites and occur mainly in the upland margins. Some are associated with lowland heaths or raised bogs. Poor fens are likely to have a moss layer including, or dominated by, bog-mosses, purple moor-grass (*Molinia caerulea*), bottle sedge (*Carex rostrata*) and the smaller sedges, such as star sedge (*C. echinata*). Common sedge (*C. nigra*), may dominate amongst the vascular plants.

18.4.2.4 Heathland

Heath (1.2% of Northern Ireland) occurs on some upland slopes where past cutting of peat has left shallow peat (<0.5 m), or on turf banks (>0.5 m) on which common heather (*Calluna vulgaris*) is dominant. Wet heath also occurs as a mosaic of habitats with remnants of deeper bog. In other parts, cutover areas are dominated by Acid Grassland and Purple Moor-grass and Rush Pasture. Such habitat mosaics give a diverse flora and fauna and are characteristic of the upland landscapes of Northern Ireland. The Mournes and Slieve Gullion regions have the largest area of dry heath in Northern Ireland (Cooper *et al.* 2002), characterised by bell heather (*Erica cinerea*) and western gorse (*Ulex gallii*) in areas where mountain slopes are too steep for the formation of deep peat. This vegetation reflects the milder oceanic climate and shows affinities with the heaths of south-west Britain and the Wicklow Mountains in the Republic of Ireland. There is considerable diversity of heath habitats in the Mournes, depending on physical conditions, grazing intensity and land use history. Juniper, a Northern Ireland priority species, is subject to a restoration project in the Mournes (Mourne Heritage Trust 2010). Rhododendron (*Rhododendron ponticum*) has invaded localised parts of heaths, for example in the Mournes, and also bog elsewhere across Northern Ireland.

18.4.3 Semi-natural Grasslands

Like many other habitats in Northern Ireland, Semi-natural Grasslands are unique because Northern Ireland's biogeography, climate and cultural use have resulted in variations from the equivalent vegetation communities found elsewhere in the UK (Rodwell 1992; Jeffrey *et al.* 1995). While this can mean a smaller flora, there is one notable exception, the fen meadow habitat. This sedge-rich community may contain more than 40 plant species, including blue-eyed grass (*Sisyrinchium bermudiana*) and Irish lady's tresses orchid (*Spiranthes romanzoffiana*), found virtually nowhere else in the UK. Its associated fauna includes significant populations of the marsh fritillary butterfly (*Euphydryas aurinia*), increasingly rare elsewhere in the UK. The existence and survival of fen meadows depend on continued extensive cattle grazing (Upton & Bain 2006).

Semi-natural Grasslands cover about 18.5% of Northern Ireland and support a range of grassland fungi, notably waxcap (genus *Hygrocybe*), which are restricted in range throughout Europe. Found predominantly on drier grassland types, e.g. Acid Grassland and Calcareous Grassland, these species can also be found in high numbers and diversity on relatively small areas such as old churchyards or lawns (Neutral Grassland). Often botanically species-poor sites can be of high mycological interest and have been ignored by traditional nature conservation activities (McHugh *et al.* 2001; Genney *et al.* 2009).

Changes in agricultural practices in Northern Ireland since the 1950s have led to the replacement of much of its Semi-natural Grasslands with intensively managed grasslands dominated by ryegrass and clover (*Lolium-Trifolium* mix), a trend similar to that exhibited in the rest of the UK (Cooper & McCann 1994; Jeffrey *et al.* 1995). This trend has continued over the past 20 years with significant losses of species-rich grasslands. A high proportion of the Neutral Grassland is agriculturally productive and not species rich. Remaining species-rich Semi-natural Grasslands occur as small areas in the marginal uplands and farms. Much of this habitat has been, and continues to be, converted to other types of agricultural grassland, while areas which are not accessible to farm machinery, or where there are other physical constraints on management, tend to be invaded by scrub (Murray *et al.* 1992; Cooper *et al.* 2002; Cooper *et al.* 2009).

Neutral Grassland covers an estimated 230,000 ha (in 2007), about 16% of Northern Ireland, which is by far the largest Broad Habitat in the Semi-natural Grasslands category. It has decreased by 30,000 ha over the last 10 years. The total area of the other habitat categories of Semi-natural Grasslands amounted to around 30,000 ha in 2007 (Cooper *et al.* 2009). There has also been a loss in Acid Grassland of nearly 3,000 ha and over 1,000 ha of fen meadows over that period, while areas of Calcareous Grassland and species-rich wet grassland have been relatively stable. Semi-natural Grasslands often occur in a mosaic with other habitats and need specific management (EHS 2005b,i). The losses in the last 20 years, coupled with changing agricultural practices and subsidies, could lead to a further decline in these habitats.

Agricultural use of Semi-natural Grasslands is largely for livestock grazing or winter feed, overwhelmingly by sheep at relatively low stocking densities in the uplands and cattle in species-rich wet grassland and fen meadows. Recent agri-environment policies (e.g. NICMS) have encouraged low stocking densities through requiring NICMS participants to remove livestock for specified periods during the year with the aim of increasing biodiversity. This approach will require monitoring as understocking could lead to degradation of some areas, including scrub encroachment and loss of habitat condition. The proportion of purple moor-grass and rush pasture priority habitat with shrub cover is 44% (Cooper & McCann 2010), highlighting the potential threat to these habitats from succession to scrub (Upton & Bain 2006). The influence of evolving agricultural policies and their delivery is likely to have significant impacts on these grasslands, for example Single Farm Payment eligibility (NIEA unpublished data).

The plant community composition and structure of habitats in Semi-natural Grasslands and Enclosed Farmland can change with management (in particular, grazing pressure). This is typified by shifts from one primary habitat type to another, or even from Semi-natural Grasslands to Enclosed Farmland habitat (Brennan 2005). Large decreases in species richness resulting from changed management are generally not reversible, but smaller decreases can be addressed (Brennan 2005). A Northern Ireland Environment Agency survey of farmland priority habitats found that lowland meadow, purple moor-grass and rush pasture, and fen meadow have declined in area over the past 10–20 years, but that upland calcareous grassland was stable, possibly because much of it is designated as ASSIs, following a steep decline in the 1990s. Lowland acid grassland showed no clear trend (NIEA 2008a).

Protection of Semi-natural Grasslands in Northern Ireland is mainly through designation as ASSIs, although the condition, even within ASSIs, is variable. For example, of 12 lowland meadow ASSIs, three are in favourable condition and nine are in unfavourable condition; of 23 purple moor-grass and rush pasture ASSIs, eight are favourable and 14 unfavourable; and of five Calcareous Grassland ASSIs, three are favourable and two are unfavourable (NIBG 2009; Section 18.8).

18.4.3.1 Neutral Grassland

Neutral Grassland (16% of Northern Ireland) consists largely of agricultural grasslands managed less intensively than ryegrass and with a more diverse floristic composition. The net change between Neutral Grassland and Improved Grassland conceals a much larger shift between these two habitats; while there was a loss of 90,268 ha of Neutral Grassland to Improved Grassland, 70,649 ha of Improved Grassland became Neutral Grassland between 1998 and 2007, indicating a high degree of change in management between these two habitats (Cooper *et al.* 2009). These changes are likely to have been caused by different agricultural policies, new technology, fiscal drivers including fuel costs, and lack of active management. Scrub invasion and succession onto species-rich grassland is an important issue (Cooper *et al.* 2009).

18.4.3.2 Calcareous Grassland and Acid Grassland

Calcareous Grassland is a scarce habitat covering only 0.1% of Northern Ireland and occurring largely in the Fermanagh uplands. There was no change in the 1,802 ha of Calcareous Grassland in the past 20 years. Acid Grassland is also uncommon, covering only 0.7% of Northern Ireland. There was a significant loss in this habitat (3,000 ha), largely to Dwarf Shrub Heath in the Mourne Mountains (Murray *et al.* 1992; Cooper *et al.* 2002; Cooper *et al.* 2009).

18.4.3.3 Species-rich wet grassland and fen meadows

Species-rich wet grassland and fen meadows are rare, covering 0.9% and 0.4% of Northern Ireland respectively. Transitions between other agricultural grassland and species-rich wet grassland have mainly been at the borders between the two habitats (Brennan 2005). The loss of the latter to species-rich wet grassland has been significant (due to natural species compositional changes), but there has been a gain to the habitat by succession from other agricultural grassland over the past 10 years. Losses are mainly due to agricultural conversion and some conifer afforestation. Gains are of poor quality species-rich wet grassland from Enclosed Farmland habitats (Cooper *et al.* 2009).

18.4.4 Enclosed Farmland

Enclosed Farmland covers 44% of Northern Ireland (Cooper *et al.* 2009). Overall, about three-quarters of Northern Ireland is used for agricultural purposes (76% in 2005; EHS 2008a), including areas of peatland (Mountains, Moorlands and Heaths), Semi-natural Grasslands, Woodlands and Freshwater (Openwaters, Wetlands and Floodplains). This compares to 61% in the Republic of Ireland, 77% in the UK and 47% in the EU15 (DARD 2010o).

Agricultural systems have changed markedly over the past century, and with intensification (particularly since the 1950s) there has been a marked loss of habitat and species diversity. Historically, a higher proportion of Northern Ireland was cultivated for arable crop production (Cruickshank 1997; see **Figure 18.23**; Section 18.5.2). In the mid-19th Century, over 400,000 ha of land were in cropland (the area in 2010 is less than 50,000 ha); of that area some 150,000 ha were in potatoes and flax, while figures for potatoes now are around 5,000 ha and almost no flax is grown. There has always been a high proportion of land used for hay or silage and pasture to produce animals, with that proportion increasing since 1859 (see **Figure 18.24**; Section 18.5.2).

There is variation in the agricultural potential of land (**Figure 18.9**), with most arable farming in the south east and parts of the north west. Seventy per cent of all farms in Northern Ireland are designated as Less Favoured Area (LFA), with beef production the main farming activity in most of these areas (DARD 2009f, 2010o).

There has been a slight net increase in Enclosed Farmland in recent years to just over 620,000 ha in 2007 (Section 18.4.1; see **Table 18.4**), with a net decrease of 8,000 ha (15%) in Arable and Horticulture to 49,000 ha, on top of a 25% decrease between 1989 and 1998, largely from conversion to Improved Grassland (Cooper *et al.* 2009). This includes around 3,000 ha of horticulture in 2009 (DARD 2010c). Improved Grassland increased by 33% between 1989 and 1998 with a further increase from 1998 to 2007 of some 18,000 ha (3%), largely by conversion from Neutral Grassland (Section 18.4.3). In Northern Ireland the overwhelming majority of Improved Grassland is ryegrass, used for grazing of animals, production of silage and for hay (**Figures 18.10**; **Figure 18.12**). There was a small recorded loss (379 km; 0.2%) in field boundaries recorded between 1998 and 2007 (Cooper *et al.* 2009).

Figure 18.10 presents a breakdown of how the land has been used since 1981. Much of this change has been in response to support structures and policies which encouraged different stocking densities, and price structures which have encouraged changes in crops, in particular through the CAP, which has been the main force determining production since the UK joined the European Union in 1973. Stocking densities have varied over time in response to market forces, subsidies and cross-compliance conditions (Section 18.5.2).

Enclosed Farmland, in particular mixed farmland, is very important for biodiversity, especially in relation to farmland

birds such as the yellowhammer (*Emberiza citrinella*), which is now largely restricted to east Down (EHS 2005m), and the corncrake (*Crex crex;* EHS & NPWS 2005). Arable farmland is particularly important for overwintering birds (RSPB & DARD 2004a–l). There are targets for halting declines of individual farmland bird species within Northern Ireland Species Action Plans (RSPB & DARD 2004a–l). Data collected in the previous

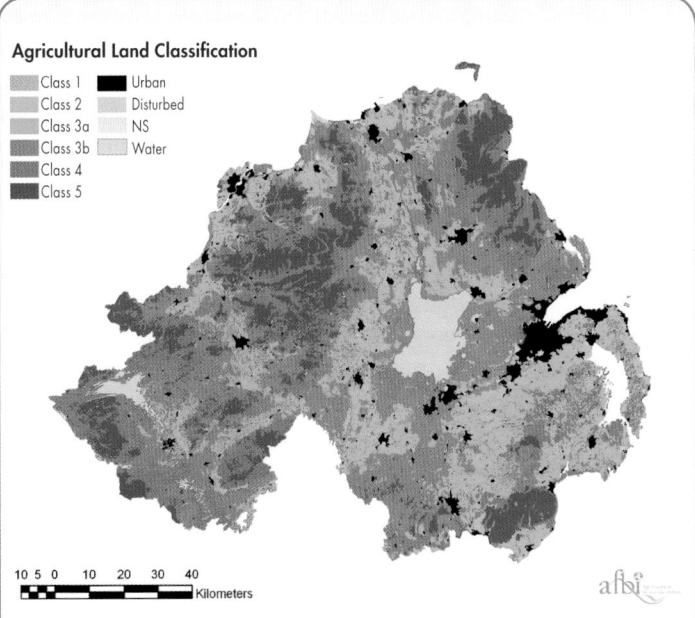

Figure 18.9 AFBI Agricultural Land Classification of Northern Ireland. Land classes graded as: Class 1 = Excellent quality; Class 2 = Very good quality; Class 3a = Good quality; Class 3b = Moderate quality; Class 4 = Poor quality; Class 5 = Very poor quality. Source: based on Cruickshank (1997).

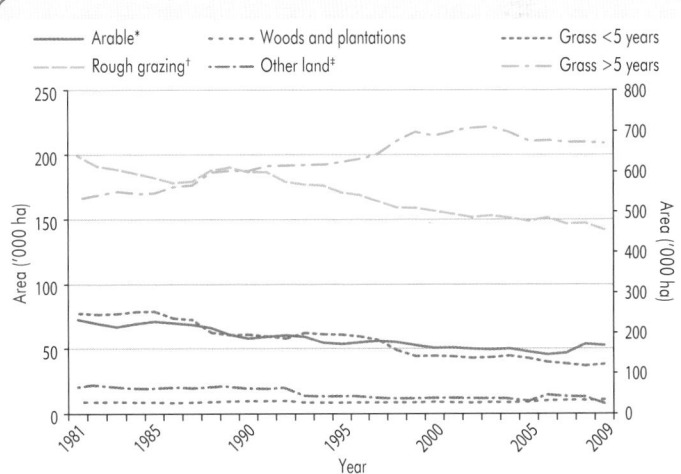

Figure 18.10 Agricultural land use from 1981 to 2009. Values based on numbers corrected for variations in data collection techniques of the June Farm Census. 'Arable, Rough grazing, Woods and plantations' are plotted against the axis on the left; Grass <5 years and Grass >5 years are plotted against the axis on the right. Grass is by far the largest land use. *Arable = arable silage and arable forage crops as well as oats, wheat, barley, mixed corn, potatoes, oilseed rape and some other crops. Data for forage crops only included in total from 1997 onwards. †Excludes common rough grazing; ‡Includes set aside. Source: data from DARD (2010c).

decades suggest that populations of many specialist farmland birds have been declining rapidly (RSPB 2009).

18.4.4.1 Improved Grassland

There has been an increase in permanent grassland over 5 years old during the past 28 years, with a decline in the amount of Improved Grassland under 5 years old of approximately 32% between 1997 and 2007 (see **Figure 18.10**). Estimated yields of grass silage have remained relatively constant between 1981 (31.4 t/ha) and 2008 (30.76 t/ha), despite a decline in nitrogen fertiliser usage over the period, from 125 kg nitrogen/ha to 90 kg nitrogen/ha. This maintenance of yield despite a decrease in fertiliser usage (**Figure 18.11**) is probably a consequence of grass breeding for improved yield and improvements in crop technology (Section 18.5.3) and there may also have been an increase in the efficiency of use of manures and slurries over this period (DOE 2009a). However, there has also been an increase in the amount of imported feed used, which provides indirect nutrient input, so much more information would be required to draw meaningful conclusions. The amount of grassland being reseeded (based on grass seed sales), has shown a steady decline (Gilliland *et al.* 2007), some of which may be due to a reduction in reclamation. In terms of utilising grassland as a resource in production, the Ulster Grassland Society (UGS 2010) has calculated that although the average dry matter (DM) production for grassland is about 7 tonnes DM/ha, utilised DM in grazed grassland is about 5 tonnes DM/ha, well short of the potential average production of about 12 tonnes DM/ha.

There is a trend towards a reduction in numbers of sheep and cattle in Northern Ireland, probably due to a lack of profitability in these sectors and a move away from headage-based subsidies to area-based payments (Aileen Lawson, UFU, pers. comm.; Section 18.5.2). However, the situation may be more complex than this implies, as the Single Farm Payment (SFP) has led to a reduction in livestock numbers on many farms but others have intensified to remain competitive. Munton (2009) suggests this as a common trend across the UK, although there do not appear to be any empirical data specific to Northern Ireland on this matter.

There are now issues with undergrazing in many areas, particularly in the hills, due to the decrease in sheep numbers (DARD 2010m; Section 18.5.2). This has resulted in scrub encroachment which has implications for biodiversity. Factors involved in the degradation of grassland ASSIs in Northern Ireland between 2002 and 2008 include intensification (16 sites), undergrazing/scrub encroachment (11 sites) and overgrazing (three sites; NIEA unpublished data). A development plan has been prepared for grazing management that promotes biodiversity (Upton & Bain 2006).

Management of grassland for silage production rather than for hay (**Figure 18.12**) has had impacts on the land and biodiversity. Northern Ireland has seen a dramatic switch from hay to silage production since 1950, with most of the decline in the last two decades. Most hay production has been replaced with 'big bale' silage, which can maintain species-rich grassland, but only when there are no other management changes which lead to increased intensification (McGurn 2008). Instead of the traditional single annual cut of grass for hay, usually at least two cuts are taken for silage. The gap between successive cuts is often too short to allow full development of the grasses and they go to seed for only a short period of time, if at all (EHS 2006b). Birds and all other animals have had to adapt to this change, with significant impacts on some species; the shift to silage production is responsible for the decline of the corncrake (EHS & NPWS 2005; Hynes & Hanley 2008). Other animals including the Irish hare and skylark (*Alauda arvensis*) use silage fields, but cutting of silage can cause problems for young birds and leverets which cannot escape the machines (BBC News 2010). The longer growing seasons resulting from climate change are also impacting on silage cutting times and hence on these species.

18.4.4.2 Field boundaries

Since the 1950s many field boundaries have been removed, largely to increase field sizes, but recent data (1992–1998) show a slowing of this trend (Cooper *et al.* 2002; Cooper *et al.* 2009). The length of field boundaries, a characteristic feature of small, family farms in Northern Ireland, was almost a quarter of a million kilometres in 1998. Hedges are a major source of biodiversity on Enclosed Farmland and in 1997 the length of hedges in Northern Ireland was 118,619 km. The width, height, management and species composition of hedgerows are also highly variable and impact on their value to biodiversity. Most hedges in Northern Ireland are composed of hawthorn, ash and gorse, although Fermanagh has some hedges dominated by willow species (Robinson 1977). Hedgebanks (of different ages and forms) are common and have been a feature of the landscape since the early 19th Century (Aalen & Whelan 1997). Most of Northern Ireland's hedges, unlike those in Great Britain, date from the last 200 years (Robinson 1977). Information on trees and hedgerows is provided in Woodlands (Section 18.4.5). There were also 41,284 km of earth banks, 8,830 km of dry stone walls and 55,130 km of wire fences (Cooper *et al.* 2002). Although there was little overall change in boundaries (-1.5%), dry stone walls decreased by an estimated 13%, while fences increased by an estimated 12% (McCann *et al.* 2010).

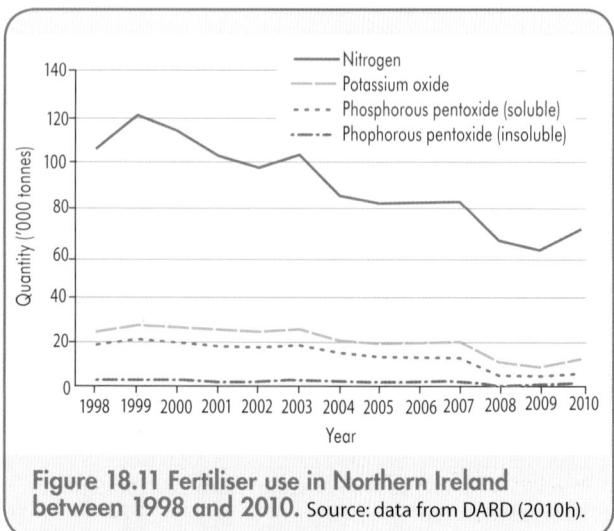

Figure 18.11 Fertiliser use in Northern Ireland between 1998 and 2010. Source: data from DARD (2010h).

The main threats to hedges and earthbanks are removal and lack of management. Between the mid-1970s and 1987 in the Glens of Antrim ESA, 6% of field boundaries were removed (Cooper & Murray 1987) and in the Mourne ESA, removal over a similar timescale was much higher (Cooper *et al.* 1993). In Northern Ireland as a whole there was a continued decrease in the length of hedges, earthbanks and dry stone walls and a corresponding increase in wire fences between 1989 and 1998 (Cooper *et al.* 2002). Maintaining a functional network of hedges, earthbanks and dry stone walls with their associated open wet drains (often modified streams) is a key biodiversity issue, as these features offer habitat for a wide range of wildlife, including plants, invertebrates, mammals and birds.

Within Northern Ireland, species-rich hedgerows are important for a number of UK priority species, identified as part of the UK BAP programme, including red squirrel, common pipistrelle (*Pipistrellus pipistrellus*), soprano pipistrelle (*P. pygmaeus*), linnet (*Carduelis cannabina*), reed bunting (*Emberiza schoeniclus*), spotted flycatcher (*Muscicapa striata*), tree sparrow (*Passer montanus*), bullfinch (*Pyrrhula pyrrhula*), song thrush (*Turdus philomelos*) and purple ramping fumitory (*Fumaria purpurea*). In addition a number of Northern Ireland priority species utilise hedgerows, such as whitethroat (*Sylvia communis*) and barn owl (*Tyto alba*; DARD 2006). Seed-eating birds that live in farmland habitats include yellowhammers, while wetland birds such as lapwings (*Vanellus vanellus*) are also important (Bradbury *et al.* 2000; EHS 2005m). Under the Rural Development Programme there are two schemes operating, the NICMS and the Organic Farming Scheme (OFS; Section 18.8). The Management of Special Sites (MOSS) scheme is also in place to address particular issues which fall outside the remit of the NICMS (Section 18.8).

18.4.4.3 Arable crops

The proportion of Northern Ireland's agricultural land devoted to arable crops is lower than in the past, and over time there have been considerable changes in which crops have been grown (see **Figure 18.10**; Section 18.5.2). Agri-environment schemes promote retention of natural vegetation in field boundaries and winter stubble, valuable habitat for overwintering birds (Section 18.8).

Cereal yields per hectare have increased in line with trends in the UK as a whole. For example, in Northern Ireland mean barley yield increased from 3.34 tonnes per hectare (t/ha) in 1981 to 5.22 t/ha in 2009 and wheat yield increased from 5.00 t/ha to 7.23 t/ha over the same period (DARD 2010i). Fertiliser usage over that period was fairly constant but has fallen substantially since the introduction of the Nitrates Action Programme in 2008 (DOE 2009a; see **Figure 18.11**). The total weight of pesticides applied has decreased since 1998 (Withers *et al.* 2008). For example, in 2006, 203 tonnes of pesticides were applied to arable crops in Northern Ireland and this amount had decreased to 169 tonnes (down 20%) by 2008. The increase in yield of arable crops may be attributable mainly to crop breeding and improved husbandry, but to some extent, reductions in the amounts of pesticides applied may be due to improvements in pesticides themselves (newer, narrow spectrum active ingredients) and

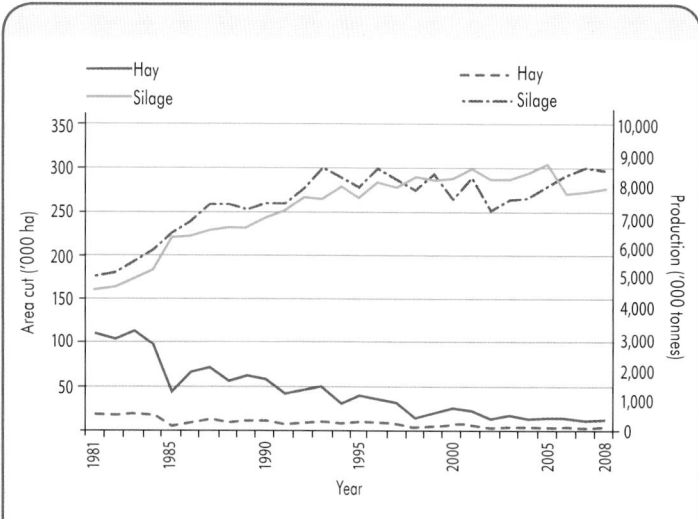

Figure 18.12 Hay and silage area cut (solid lines) and production (dashed lines) from 1981 to 2009. Source: data from DARD (2010i).

in the training of farmers in pesticide application techniques. Overall, although there have been significant changes in the areas of crops grown, the biodiversity value of arable areas and quality of water runoff from cereals has probably increased because of reduced fertiliser and agrochemical application (Jim McAdam, AFBI, pers. comm.).

Almost all grain grown in Northern Ireland is used for animal feeds, with some oats for human use and a very small amount of wheat used for milling (NIGTA unpublished data). While oil seed rape has experienced an increase in the 2000s, it still falls short of the levels seen in the early 1990s. Other forage crops (including forage maize, cabbage, turnips, swedes, root crops, kale, fodder beet and other forage and stock feed crops) have seen a major increase (although the overall area is still small), as has wheat production, especially since the mid-1990s. Significant decreases have been seen in potatoes and fruit, which appear to be on a steady downward trend (**Figure 18.13**; and see **Figure 18.25**).

18.4.4.4 Horticulture and orchards

Cooper *et al.* (2009) estimated the area of orchards in 2007 at 1,165 ha (0.08% of Northern Ireland), a decrease of 28% on the total in 1998 of 1,623 ha (Cooper *et al.* 2009). The Agri-food and Biosciences Institute states that 99% of orchards are Bramley apples with dessert apples and plums making up the remainder (Withers *et al.* 2008). Mushroom production involves little land but is financially significant (Section 18.5.2.1). It is also a significant user of peat (Tomlinson 2010).

18.4.4.5 Short rotation coppice

Research into the possible production of willow to use as biomass fuel has been supported by the Department of Agriculture and Rural Development and Agri-food and Biosciences Institute for many years. Forest Service (2010a) reports that 64 ha of short rotation coppice were planted in 2000–2009 and 36 ha in 2009–2010 (Forest Service 2009a, 2010a), adding to more than 500 ha of planting between 2004 and 2006. In the past, short rotation coppice was occasionally planted on land containing semi-natural habitat

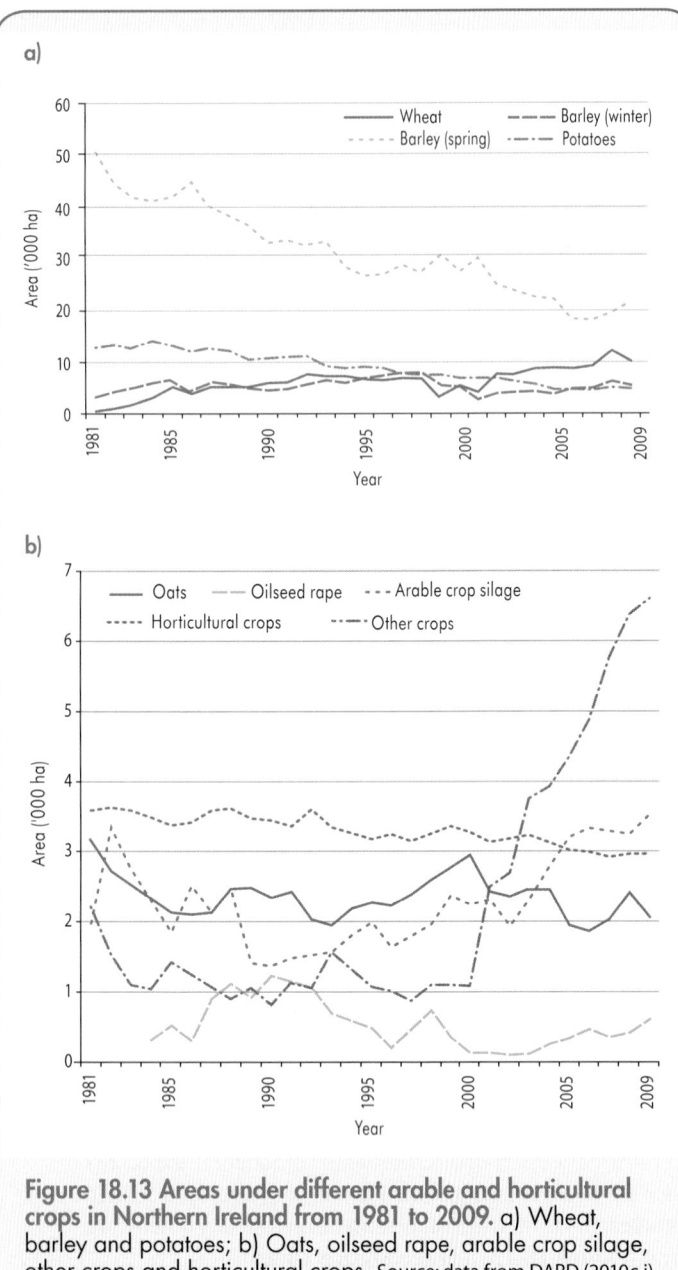

a)

b)

Figure 18.13 Areas under different arable and horticultural crops in Northern Ireland from 1981 to 2009. a) Wheat, barley and potatoes; b) Oats, oilseed rape, arable crop silage, other crops and horticultural crops. Source: data from DARD (2010c,j).

of importance for biodiversity, e.g. planting of willow on wet grassland leads to a loss of breeding waders. However, development of improved guidance on implementation of the EIA (Forestry) Regulations has prevented a reoccurrence. Dawson (2007) provides a detailed evaluation of short rotation coppice, including a summary of its environmental impacts, which include providing nesting habitat for farmland birds, overwintering birds and numerous invertebrates. The history of short rotation coppice willow in Northern Ireland from 1973 to the late 1990s has been analysed by McCracken & Dawson (1998). The Northern Ireland Executive has introduced the Short Rotation Coppice Scheme (DARD 2007b) to help with the economics of the practice (Dawson 2007; Section 18.5.2.11).

18.4.5 Woodlands

Beginning in Neolithic times, the woodland that covered Ireland was cleared, primarily for agriculture but with added

economic (timber, charcoal, tanning), political and military benefits (Hall 1992). By 1600 Ireland was only one-third as wooded as England, with a woodland cover of 2–3%. Further woodland clearance resulted from the Plantation of Ulster in the 17th Century for iron-making and coopering (McCracken 1971). In the early 18th Century woodland in the Glens of Antrim was used for burning chalk to make fertiliser (McCracken 1971). As landowners developed their demesne estates, woodland and parkland designed landscapes were established, some of which are still significant features of the landscape. From the middle of the 19th Century, in the wake of the famine and mass emigration, semi-natural woodland developed on abandoned land. The 20th Century saw a large area of commercial afforestation, the majority of it coniferous woodland. In 1968 almost 37,000 ha had been acquired for forestry in Northern Ireland and conifers formed 94% of all plantings (McCracken 1971).

Northern Ireland has less woodland cover than other European countries (6.2%; Forestry Commission 2009a). The Forest Service estimates the total woodland cover in Northern Ireland as of March 2010 to be 87,903 ha, which includes 61,200 ha of woodland managed by Forest Service (mainly coniferous woodland; **Table 18.5**; **Figure 18.14**) and 26,703 ha of non-Forest Service woodland (based on a 1970s inventory of private woodland (Graham 1981), plus subsequent planting supported by the Woodland Grant Schemes (John Griffin, Forest Service, pers. comm.; NIEA 2011). This represents an increase from an estimated 13,000 ha in 1924 (Forestry Commission 2009b) and is lower than the woodland estimate of 10.0% provided by the NICS (Cooper *et al.* 2009; see **Table 18.4**). This is due in part to limitations in the current woodland inventory, but is mostly because of variations in woodland definition. For example, the Forest Service estimate excludes scrub areas dominated by non-tree species such as European gorse and areas of grassland recently colonised by semi-natural broadleaves where a change of land use by the landowner has not been declared.

The NICS 2007 revealed changes in the area of woodland over the preceding 20 years. There was a 9% increase in the area of broadleaved woodland between 1989 and 1998 and an additional 29% (18,193 ha) increase between 1998 and 2007. There was an increase of 2% in coniferous woodland from 1989 to 1998 and no significant change in area from 1998 to 2007 (Cooper *et al.* 2009). The main increases from 1998 to 2007 were in broadleaved transitional woodland (<5 m high), Broadleaf woodland (>5 m) and scrub, with the increases mainly through successional processes on a wide range of unmanaged habitats, including birch woods developing on cutover bogland and scrub on abandoned farmland. The characteristic biodiversity of these open habitats (for example, species-rich grasslands, fen and fragmented heath/ bog edge vegetation) is at risk from this change, and this is a key biodiversity issue; however much of the new woodland is also valuable for biodiversity (Cooper *et al.* 2009).

A new Forestry Act was passed in July 2010, replacing the 1953 Forestry Act. The new Act specifically states that the Department of Agriculture and Rural Development has the general duty of promoting afforestation and sustainable forestry (Forestry Act, enacted 25 May 2010). The Act also

Table 18.5 Area of woodland under Forest Service management by main tree species in 2010. Source: Forest Service (unpublished data).

Species	Area (ha)	%
Sitka spruce	39,769	68.4
Lodgepole pine	5,074	8.7
Larch (Japanese, European and hybrid)	3,136	5.4
Norway spruce	2,562	4.4
Oak	1,081	1.9
Scots pine	965	1.7
Douglas fir	500	0.9
Noble fir	426	0.7
Others	4,639	7.9
Total	**58,152**	**100**

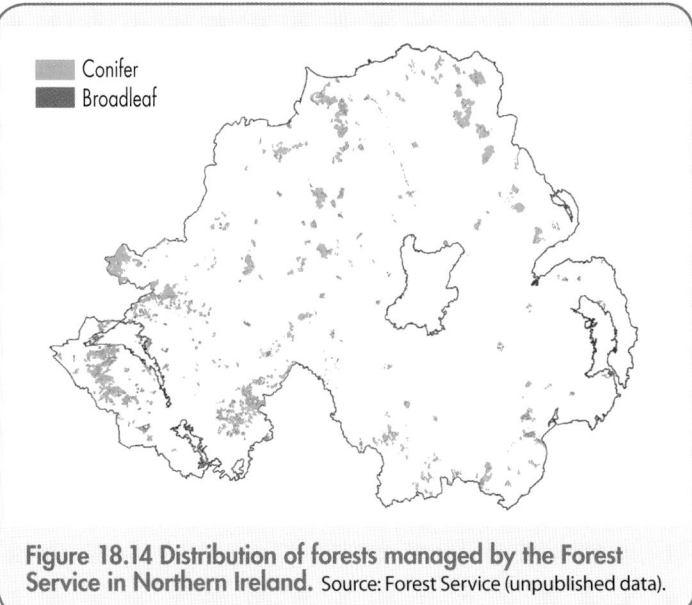

Conifer
Broadleaf

Figure 18.14 Distribution of forests managed by the Forest Service in Northern Ireland. Source: Forest Service (unpublished data).

includes a new requirement for felling licences, which will come into effect following the completion of subordinate legislation.

Tree Preservation Orders (TPOs) are designed primarily to protect individual trees which add to the character and appearance of an area, to keep and protect the structure and variety of woodland, especially where they offer protection to natural wildlife habitats, and to ensure that new developments take into account the landscape setting. Healthy trees of significance may be designated by the Department of the Environment's Planning Service and can only be cut down with permission; ignoring this is an offence which can elicit a fine of up to £30,000 (NIPS 2005).

Woodlands provide many ecosystem services, often simultaneously, including timber production, carbon sequestration, increased biodiversity and recreational opportunities. From 1955 to 1983 the Forest Service designated a number of areas of forest in key locations as Forest Parks, which are managed primarily for recreational use. Currently, the public have permissive access to 68,137 ha of woodland and associated open land owned by the Department of Agriculture and Rural Development and managed by the Forest Service (Forest Service unpublished data). In Forest Parks and Forest Recreation Areas specific provision is made for public access; however, all forest land is available for public access subject to environmental regulation, forest bylaws and Forest Service operations or permitted activities (Forest Service 2004).

A public opinion survey of forestry, conducted on behalf of the Forest Service in 2010, found that almost nine out of 10 people felt that 'a lot more trees should be planted' to help reduce the impacts of climate change. The majority of respondents would also welcome additional woodland in their own localities, especially near towns or villages, and there was almost universal support for the use of public money for forestry, particularly in relation to the provision of wildlife habitats and outdoor recreation (Forestry Commission 2010b; Forest Service 2010a).

18.4.5.1 Broadleaved woodland

Broadleaved woodland is widely dispersed throughout Northern Ireland. It is highly variable in character depending on soils and topography. Mixed ashwood is the main priority habitat found on base-rich soils, particularly the Tertiary basalts of County Antrim and the Carboniferous limestones of County Fermanagh. Oakwood priority habitat occurs on less base-rich soils, and is particularly common in the Sperrins and Co. Fermanagh. Although most of the oak woodlands are small, they are important in a national and European context as examples of Atlantic oakwoods; the mild, humid conditions encourage the growth of epiphytic mosses, lichens and ferns. In the larger woodlands, variation in ground conditions, including acidity and nutrient richness of the soils, leads to diverse ground flora. Wet woodland occurs on floodplains, in river valleys and as a successional habitat associated with fens, mires and bogs. Parkland priority habitat is characterised by veteran scattered trees or small groups of trees over grassland, mainly associated with demesne estates, for example Crom in Fermanagh and Glenarm in Antrim (Corbett 2007).

Ancient woods are generally recognised as being of very high ecological value by virtue of their long continuity, and therefore act as reservoirs of biodiversity. However, in Northern Ireland most ancient woodlands are very small and the total resource is highly fragmented, as shown by the ancient woodland inventory (AWI; Woodland Trust 2010a). Only 0.75% of the land area is covered with woodland that dates back to at least 1830. Around 0.04% (10,000 ha) of Northern Ireland is woodland that can be classified as ancient (continuously present since at least 1600) compared with 2% in Britain (Woodland Trust 2010a). Typically, the woodland recorded on the inventory consists of isolated fragments, with the majority less than 2 ha in area. About one-tenth of the area is parkland priority habitat.

Nearly two-thirds of woodland on the ancient woodland inventory is plantation, with ownership evenly divided between public bodies (mainly Forest Service) and private landowners (almost half of which is managed under agri-environment schemes administered directly by the Department of Agriculture and Rural Development). Restoration of some Forest Service planted ancient woodland sites to native woodland is underway. The current emphasis is to protect remnant ancient woodland features on all ancient woodland inventory sites (Richard Schaible, Forest Service, pers. comm.).

The value of forestry for nature is explicitly acknowledged in the concept of High Nature Value Forestry which is being considered by Europe for potential inclusion in the next CAP round (Caroline Barry, NIEA, pers. comm.; IEEP 2007). There are 73 ASSIs in Northern Ireland, including 26 SACs, covering nearly 3,000 ha (**Table 18.6**) designated for their woodland features. In addition, two large areas including Forest Service upland coniferous woodland plantations are designated as SPA for 'hen harrier' and 'hen harrier and merlin' respectively. Overall more than 18,000 ha (24%) of the land managed by the Forest Service is protected by conservation designations. In 2010 roughly 74% of the area of woodland managed for timber in Northern Ireland, including all Forest Service land, is certified as managed sustainably in accordance with the requirements of the UK Woodland Assurance Standard (UKWAS; Forest Service unpublished data).

18.4.5.2 Coniferous woodland

Coniferous woodland currently covers 4.3% of Northern Ireland. The Forest Service has not planted significant areas of conifer woodland since 2004 (**Figure 18.15**). The loss of habitat diversity through conifer afforestation in the habitat-rich marginal uplands has been a biodiversity issue for many years. The Forest Service publication Afforestation—The DANI Statement on Environmental Policy (1993) marked a change in direction which stated a presumption against planting on species-rich marginal grassland sites which were later to become priority habitats under the Northern Ireland Biodiversity Strategy.

The year 2010 marked the centenary of state forestry in Ireland. State planting and grant aid in Northern Ireland have contributed to an increase in overall woodland cover (both broadleaved and coniferous) from an estimated 1.1% in 1905 to 6.5% in 2009 (Forestry Commission 2009b). The Department of Agriculture and Rural Development Forest Service owns and manages over 70% of the woodlands with the remainder in private ownership (DOE & NISRA 2010). When the Ministry of Agriculture assumed responsibility for forestry in 1923 there were fewer than 2,000 ha of all forestry

(Tomlinson 1997a). In 1985 the total area of planted forest belonging to the Department of Agriculture was 55,767 ha (Kula & McKillop 1988) and 61,147 ha were managed by the Forest Service in 2010 (Forest Service 2010a). The rate of state forest expansion increased markedly from the 1950s, largely due to the introduction of mechanisation, and reached a peak in the 1970s with the relatively large-scale conifer afforestation of upland blanket bog. As a result, most of the forest land managed by the Forest Service is in upland areas in the north and west of Northern Ireland.

Upland coniferous woodland consists predominantly of Sitka spruce plantations (see **Table 18.5**) ranging in area from around 1,000 ha to 10,000 ha, in areas of open bog and heathland (Richard Schaible, Forest Service, pers. comm.). In contrast, forests in lowland areas are less extensive and often include the surviving remnants of former estates. Lowland forests generally include Sitka spruce and other conifers such as European and Japanese larch, Norway spruce and Scots pine, with some broadleaved species, particularly oak and ash (both native to Northern Ireland) and beech (non-native; see **Table 18.5**). They are less extensive compared with forests in the uplands and are often associated with former demesne woodland and historic estates (John Griffin, Forest Service, pers. comm.).

18.4.5.3 New woodland planting

The area of new planting of coniferous woodland has decreased over the past decade, with a dramatic drop after 2003–2004 (**Figure 18.16**). Most of Northern Ireland's coniferous woodlands are located in the uplands on blanket peat where land was easier to acquire than in the lowlands with their better soils. However, since 1993 the Forest Service has not planted new areas of oligotrophic or dystrophic peat because of their high biodiversity value and the economic and environmental implications of dependency on repeated fertiliser applications required for timber production (Forest Service 1993).

An estimated 2,324 ha of broadleaved woodland were planted by private landowners, largely over Enclosed Farmland and Semi-natural Grassland, between 1998 and 2007 (Cooper et al. 2009), probably related to policy and financial initiatives promoting farm woodland. Long-term increases in characteristic broadleaved woodland ground flora species in planted woodland is possible if management includes biodiversity objectives, but unlikely if management is for agro-forestry (i.e. integrated sheep and timber production; Cooper et al. 2009) or willow biomass production (recorded in the sample for the first time in 2007).

In 2008–2009, 225 ha and in 2009–2010, 177 ha were planted with grant aid from the Forest Service (DOE & NISRA 2010), short of its target of 550 ha per annum (Forest Service 2009a, 2010a; this does not include planting of short rotation coppice). Of this, 82% in 2008–2009 and 98% in 2009–2010 was classified as broadleaved woodland, approximately one-quarter of which in 2009–2010 was classified as new native woodland (Forest Service 2009a, 2010a). During 2009–2010 the Forest Service instituted a number of initiatives to encourage woodland creation by landowners, including increasing grant rates under both Woodland Grant Scheme and Farm Woodland Premium Scheme. In its Strategy the

Table 18.6 Designated woodland habitats. Source: NIEA (unpublished data).

Priority habitats	Number of ASSIs	Extent of feature (ha)	Number of SACs	Total extent of priority habitat (ha)
Mixed ashwoods	19	517	2	3,430
Wet woodlands	13	687	9	2,600
Designated for both Wet and Ash Woodlands features	2	123	-	
Oakwoods	37	1,146	15	2,350
Parkland	2	353	-	1,100
Total	**73**	**2,826**	**26**	**9,480**

Forest Service places a strong emphasis on sustainability issues, focusing on forest creation and the sustainable management of existing forests. The Strategy also commits government to maintain the supply of timber from forests as well as providing environmental benefits and public access and contributing to the reduction of greenhouse gas emissions (Forest Service 2006, 2009b). These commitments were carried forward into primary legislation in 2010 (Forestry Act 2010). There are now targets to double the area of woodland in Northern Ireland by 2050, largely by encouraging the use of agricultural land for forestry. The Forest Service notes that the current rate of afforestation (500 ha per annum) will not be sufficient to meet this target (Forest Service 2006). There is also a short-term target to plant 1,650 ha of woodland between 2008 and 2011 (NI Executive 2008).

18.4.5.4 Hedgerows and hedgerow trees

Although Northern Ireland has a low level of woodland compared to the other parts of the UK, the Republic of Ireland and the EU, it has the highest density of field boundaries in the UK at 226,021 km and an average of 16.7 km (compared to 118,619 km and an average of 8.8 km in the UK; Section 18.4.4.2). The NICS 2000 estimated that 4% of hedgerows had been lost between 1986 and 1998 (Cooper *et al.* 2002) and decreased by a further 4% between 1998 and 2007. Work carried out by the Woodland Trust in England has found that the total area covered by hedgerow trees, in-field trees, small copses and shelter belts can be as great as, or even greater than, the area covered by woodland, and that their contribution to biodiversity, and to other ecosystem services, can be high, especially in areas of low woodland cover. Most of the species in hedges are woodland edge species (Woodland Trust 2010b).

18.4.5.5 Woodland condition

Woodland surveys in the late 1980s (Tomlinson 1986a,b, 1988a,b, 1989) showed that most woodlands were in a poor condition. Many were open to grazing by farm livestock and few saplings were found; where saplings occurred they were often of ash, the seeds coming from adjacent hedgerow trees, and rarely of oak. There is little evidence of past organised coppice systems (i.e. wood management with panels and rides) as is found in lowland England and its introduction as a management tool was not recommended as many of the rich epiphytic communities could be lost. However, the surveys revealed that piecemeal coppice was common, with cutting of poles and branches to meet an immediate need for fence mending and filling gaps in field boundaries. Estate and demesne woodlands, in general, were also found to be in poor condition, with few showing replacement planting. In contrast, some estates included excellent examples of woodland, e.g. the beech woodlands in Mourne Park, Kilkeel, the ancient trees of Crom, Co. Fermanagh, and the woodlands of Finnebrogue/Quoile Pondage, Co. Down (Section 18.8.1).

Ramorum disease of Japanese larch (*Phytophthora ramorum*) has been confirmed in seven woodlands on the southern half of the Antrim plateau and one in mid Co. Down (December 2010). The best method to prevent the spread of the disease is to fell infected larch and apply the necessary bio-security measures. Around 268 ha of public forest estate

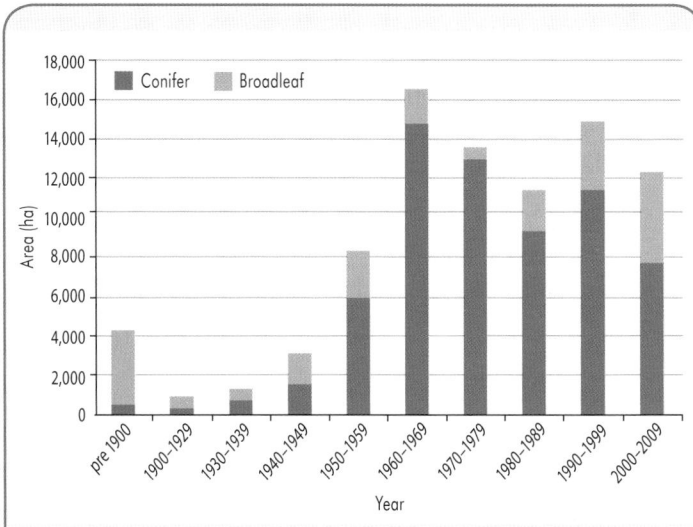

Figure 18.15 Age structure of woodland in Northern Ireland comparing broadleaved and coniferous planting. Source: Forest Service (unpublished data).

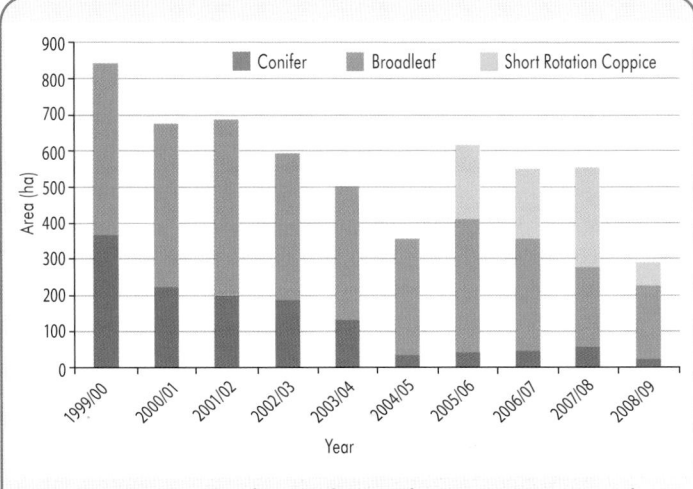

Figure 18.16 Areas of new planting by Forest Service and private planting. Source: reproduced from DOE & NISRA (2010).

and a further 6 ha of private woodland will need to be felled by spring 2011. A system is in operation to permit logs to be taken from affected forests, under licence, to authorised wood processing facilities. Both movement and processing of logs are subject to bio-security precautions to prevent accidental spread of the disease. The disease has also been confirmed in Japanese larch woodland in the south of Ireland, England and Wales (Forest Service 2010d).

18.4.5.6 Woodland biodiversity

State forestry has established monocultures of exotic tree species, often on areas of upland peat that have been drained. This has resulted in lower biodiversity, often poor tree growth on unsuitable sites, and soil erosion, especially of peaty soils. There is some interest in restoring unsuitable low-yielding areas after timber harvesting by not replanting and by impeding drainage to restore the local hydrology so that peat formation can resume. Clearfelling and restocking provide opportunities to enhance the biodiversity and landscape value of upland forests by diversifying their structure and composition.

Broadleaf and coniferous woodland provide refuges for the red squirrel, which is in decline due principally to the expanding distribution of the grey squirrel. Other protected native mammal species found in woodlands include the pine marten (*Martes martes*) and eight bat species. Red deer (*Cervus elaphus*), Sika deer (*Cervus nippon*) and fallow deer (*Dama dama*) are widespread in Northern Ireland and there are indications that the muntjac deer (*Muntiacus reevesi*) has naturalised, with confirmation of a roadkill in Co. Down during 2009. Deer may pose a major threat to woodland biodiversity.

Broadleaf woodland in Northern Ireland is particularly important for lower plants, including mosses, liverworts and lichens. Oceanic species are dependent on mild winters, cool summers, plentiful rain and high humidity, particularly in counties Fermanagh, Londonderry and Antrim. At Correl Glen, Fermanagh, for example, 131 species of lichen have been recorded (NIEA 2010c). The ground flora of woodland is of biodiversity importance and takes many years to develop in new planting.

18.4.5.7 Scrub

The main species in scrub habitats are blackthorn (*Prunus spinosa*), European gorse (*Ulex europaeus*), hawthorn (*Crataegus monogyna*), and willow (*Salix* species) and there are often small, regenerating ash (*Fraxinus excelsior*), birch (*Betula* species) or rowan (*Sorbus aucuparia*). Bramble (*Rubus fruticosus*) is often dominant. The 2007 scrub area was estimated at 12,408 ha, representing an increase of 33% since 1998. Transition to scrub was primarily from a wide range of semi-natural habitats and secondarily from agricultural grassland.

18.4.6 Freshwaters – Openwaters, Wetlands and Floodplains

Openwaters and wetlands provide an environment for specialised organisms that are not found in any other habitat. They also provide services such as resting and feeding points for birds; regulating and providing water for domestic, agricultural and industrial use; a variety of sporting, recreational and tourism uses; and are important sources of fish and valuable materials such as sand and peat. Of the 55 plants protected under the Wildlife (NI) Order 1985, 29 are found in wetlands (NIEA 2009e). Northern Ireland has 21 Ramsar sites, encompassing 88,170 ha (NIEA unpublished data) including the two eutrophic standing water sites of Lough Neagh/Lough Beg and Upper Lough Erne (see **Table 18.20**, Section 18.8.1; EHS 2005f). Wetlands are prime examples of ecosystems capable of multiple uses and the delivery of numerous ecosystem services. However, as with all systems, they are highly vulnerable to disruption, especially from pollution. The increasing use of the river basin catchment as a unit of management has been recognised in development of River Basin Management Plans (Section 18.8.4).

Northern Ireland is notable within the UK for the large area of freshwater habitats, their flow dynamics, nutrient characteristics and their resident species. Of the four river basin districts in Northern Ireland, only one, the North Eastern (NIEA 2009g), is situated entirely within Northern Ireland. The others cross the international border with the Republic of Ireland: Neagh Bann (NIEA 2009f); North Western (NIEA 2009h); and Shannon (DEHLG 2010) (**Figure 18.17**). There is therefore a strong need for cross-border cooperation in water management as both the Water Framework Directive (introduced in 2000) and the Floods Directive (2007) require catchment level approaches. This approach was adopted in work done on the Foyle and Erne catchment strategies of the early 1990s The primary government bodies involved in managing catchments include the Department of Agriculture and Rural Development (especially Rivers Agency), Department of the Environment (DOE) (especially Water Management Unit), Department of Culture, Arts and Leisure (DCAL) (Inland Waterways and Fisheries), Waterways Ireland and the Environmental Protection Agency in the Republic of Ireland. Also of significance are the Loughs Agency which is a cross border body, the Office of Public Works (OPW) which carries out river maintenance in the Republic of Ireland and Inland Fisheries Ireland (formerly the Irish Central and Regional Fisheries Boards) whose remit includes guidance to OPW on environmental river management. In Northern Ireland there is a range of legislation for controlling or regulating activities which can cause morphological changes to waters. There is no streamlined comprehensive system to control physical modifications at present. Following an initial review of the legislation, Environmental Policy Division (DOE) did not identify any gaps in existing legislation (EPD unpublished data). However, further work is anticipated to examine cross-departmental guidance and to further review existing legislation to establish if it needs to be consolidated.

Rivers, lakes and wetlands cover nearly 75,000 ha of Northern Ireland. Standing open water comprises the bulk of this, occupying 4% of Northern Ireland. Fen, swamp, reedbeds and water inundation vegetation occupy 0.55% of Northern Ireland and can be found on the fringes of freshwater bodies such as loughs. These habitats are a major source of biodiversity. There was a decrease in fen, reedbeds and water inundation vegetation but an increase in swamp between 1998 and 2007.

Around 15% of Northern Ireland's bogs were classified as raised bog in 1988 (Cruickshank & Tomlinson 1988) with a total area of 25,196 ha, and they are a priority habitat, with 8% uncut or not drained in 2003 (EHS 2003e). Tomlinson found that peat extraction had expanded from 576 ha in 1990–1991 to 689 ha in 2007–2008 (Tomlinson 2010).

Changes to precipitation patterns resulting from climate change, particularly decreased flow, will compound the problems of planning for and managing changing patterns of supply and demand (Paddy Brow, NI Water, pers. comm.). Northern Ireland has particular problems and pressures with regard to fresh water, primarily arising from historic modifications to drainage patterns (NIEA 2009f), diffuse and point source pollution. All of these have led to habitat damage at various scales in water bodies of all types. A Regulatory Impact Assessment, commissioned by the Northern Ireland Environment Agency, stated that 71% of all water bodies in Northern Ireland were failing to reach the water quality standards set by the European Commission Water Framework Directive (NIEA 2009l; Section 18.5.3).

18.4.6.1 Standing open water

Standing open waters comprise one of Northern Ireland's most extensive natural habitats. There are more than 1,600 lakes, ranging in size from small ponds up to Lough Neagh (NIEA 2010f). There are two major lakeland areas: Lough Neagh and Fermanagh (containing Upper and Lower Lough Erne), which together make up 90% of the total hectarage of lakes >50 ha in Northern Ireland (DOE & NISRA 2010). All of the main monitored lakes are classed as eutrophic (including Lough Neagh and Upper and Lower Loughs Erne), with total phosphorus over double OECD levels and increasing between 2003 and 2005 (EHS 2008a). From 2004 to 2007 the numbers of eutrophic and hypertrophic lakes increased from 11 to 15 (DOE & NISRA 2009; Section 18.5.3). The situation with regard to dissolved oxygen and chlorophyll is better, with more than half of the monitored lakes showing high or good quality by those criteria (DOE & NISRA 2010).

Lough Neagh is the largest lake in the British Isles at 38,300 ha, but is shallow with a mean depth of around 9 m and a maximum depth of 30 m. The total Lough Neagh and Lower Bann catchment is 574,000 ha, of which 536,000 ha is in Northern Ireland, representing about 40% of Northern Ireland's land area (LNAC 2002; NIEA 2009f). Six major rivers flow into Lough Neagh (Blackwater, Ballinderry, Moyola, Six Mile Water, Main and Upper Bann) and it discharges to the sea via the Lower Bann River. Lough Neagh is a major source of drinking water. The Lough Neagh system is of international importance to conservation, particularly for its populations of wetland and migrant birds, and is designated as a Ramsar site, an SPA and an ASSI (EHS 2005m). There is a very important eel fishery based in the Lough, but output of grown eels has halved and natural recruitment of juvenile eels has fallen by over 90% since 1990 (Robert Rosell, AFBI, unpublished data; Section 18.5.2).

The Fermanagh lakelands (Upper and Lower Lough Erne) in the south west have a catchment of 435,000 ha (Rivers Agency 2010). They are important for wetland birds and the wet grassland habitats that surround them, and are a major focus for tourism, with international links through to the Shannon river system encouraging boating holidays and angling (EHS 2005f).

Water levels in Lough Neagh are controlled under legislation (Lough Neagh Levels Scheme 1955; as amended). Water levels in Lough Erne are controlled under the Erne Drainage and Development Act (NI) 1950 and are undertaken in conjunction with the Electricity Supply Board in the Republic of Ireland under the terms of an agreement made in 1950 when the River Erne was harnessed for hydroelectric power generation (DARD 2010l). Both Lough Erne and Lough Neagh have had their levels lowered during the 20th Century reducing the areas of land flooded occasionally, including those areas most useful for wetland birds (LNLBAC 2006).

The Silent and Annalong Valley reservoirs in the Mourne Mountains provide roughly 400,000 people with up to 130 million litres of water per day. The Mourne Conduit carries the water to Belfast (56 km). Other important reservoirs include Dungonnell and Altnahinch on the edge of the Antrim plateau, and Altnaheglish and Banagher Glen in the Sperrins. These reservoirs have their feeder streams in blanket peat and peaty slopes (NI Water 2007).

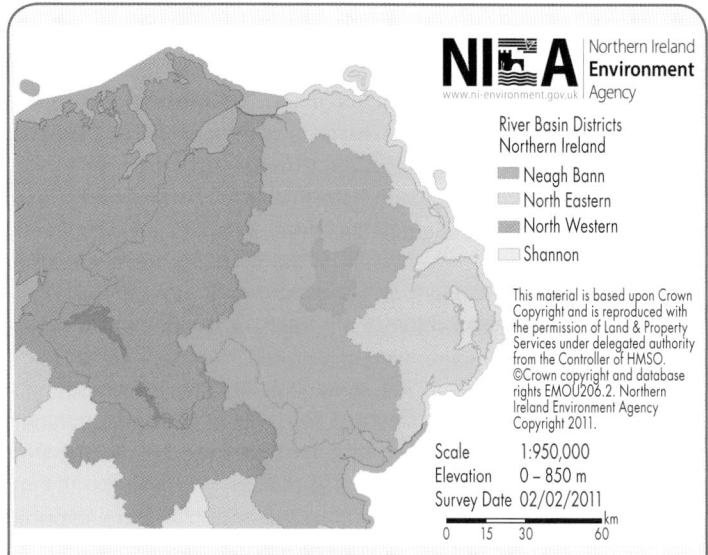

Figure 18.17 River Basin catchment areas in Northern Ireland including major lakes and rivers. Source: NIEA (unpublished data).

There are seven canals in Northern Ireland: Broharris (Co. Londonderry), Coalisland (Co. Tyrone), Dukart's (Co. Tyrone), Newry (Co. Down), Shannon-Erne Waterway (Co. Fermanagh), Strabane (Co. Tyrone) and Ulster (Co. Armagh, Tyrone, Fermanagh). Coalisland and Newry still function for land drainage, the Ulster has been partly lost and subsumed into farming land, and Dukart's is largely lost, with only the dry inclines over which barges were hauled up remaining. The Lagan is present except for the section between Lisburn and Moira where it has been buried under the M1 motorway. There is public access for walking and cycling along most of the Lagan towpath and all of the Newry and Coalisland canals (Judith Bankhead, Rivers Agency, pers. comm.). The Shannon-Erne is open for navigation and there are plans to reopen portions of the Newry canal for canoe trails. However, reopening canals linking catchments can permit the spread of invasive species and impacts must therefore be properly assessed in advance.

18.4.6.2 Rivers and streams

There are 15,445 km of rivers (defined in the NICS as >2.5 m in width) in Northern Ireland which support habitats and species of national and international importance, including otter (*Lutra lutra*), salmon (*Salmo salar*) and freshwater pearl mussel (EHS 2008a). Threats to rivers include nutrient enrichment, habitat destruction, littering, illegal dumping, runoff, siltation, flood damage, bank erosion, eutrophication, invasive species, poor planning decisions, *ad hoc* bank protection works, obstacles to fish passage and damage to spawning beds.

Approximately one-third of rivers are monitored annually against national water quality standards for the Water Framework Directive. It is important that both biological and chemical classifications are monitored, as the chemical quality can recover after damage more quickly than the biological status. Both chemical and biological river quality standards (DOE & NISRA 2010) specify that all water bodies should be 'at least good—A or B with no downward movement between classes'. Until 2007, monitoring was done by river length, and in 2005–2007, 58% were of at least a good chemical standard and 41% were of at least a good biological standard (Class B or above; **Figure 18.18**; **Figure 18.19**). Trends for the preceding 10 years were generally improving for chemical but more static for biological quality. Since 2007 monitoring is by water body, with broader environmental objectives, so figures are not directly comparable. In 2008 only 57.9% of rivers were classified as chemically 'high' or 'good', and only 41% of river water bodies classed as biologically 'high' or 'good' (DOE & NISRA 2010). When plants were monitored, only 5.6% of Northern Ireland's rivers did not show signs of nutrient enrichment (EHS 2008a). About 28% (4,280 km) of Northern Ireland's rivers were designated in 2004 under the Freshwater Fish Directive as either salmonid (4,154 km) or cyprinid (126 km). In 2008 6% of the salmonid length and 22% of the cyprinid

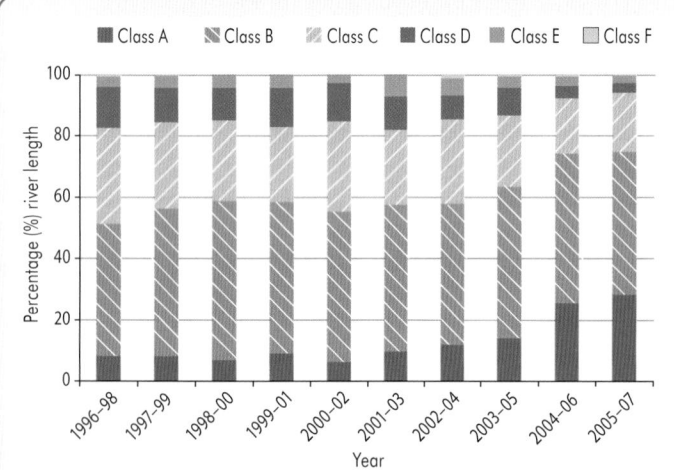

Figure 18.18 Chemical classification between 1996/98 and 2005/07. General Quality Assessment (GQA) chemical classification: Class A (Very good) to Class F (Bad), on a three year rolling sampling period. Methodology details changed between 2001 and 2002. Source: reproduced from DOE & NISRA (2009).

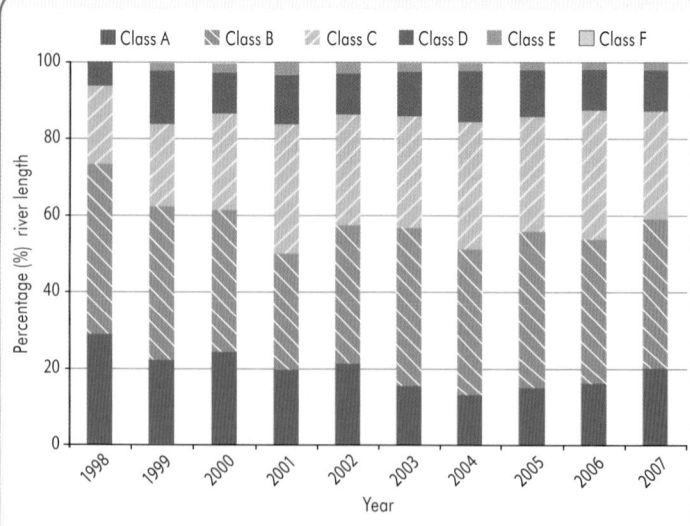

Figure 18.19 Biological classification between 1998 and 2007. GQA biological classification: Class A (Very good) to Class F (Bad). Methodology details changed between 1998 and 1999. Source: reproduced from DOE & NISRA (2009).

designated length failed to reach Directive standards (DOE & NISRA 2010).

The Rivers Agency manages a network of 130 hydrometric stations across Northern Ireland, of which 102 monitor and record level and flow and 28 monitor and record level only. Changes in water quantity can also be affected by development, particularly as Sustainable Urban Drainage has not yet been taken up as standard practice for new development. Channel works may be carried out on urban watercourses in order to facilitate increased urban runoff from development sites. Currently there is no single overarching legislation to licence river works. Consequently, a number of government bodies need to be contacted for permissions, but small-scale or piecemeal works which do not affect hydraulic capacity or fishery habitat are not controlled. In Scotland, physical modifications are controlled under the CAR Regulations to ensure achievement of the Water Framework Directive objectives (Judith Bankhead, Rivers Agency, pers. comm.).

Shallow, fast-flowing reaches of rivers and streams are the spawning and nursery beds for salmonids and can be adversely affected by forestry and drainage (DCAL 2009b; Sections 18.4.2 & 18.4.5). Application of fertilisers, runoff of pesticides, harvesting, drainage and planting activities can be harmful to upland streams, although much has been done to develop management policies to prevent harm. Yearly Catchment Status Reports for the Foyle and Carlingford areas provide information on river habitat monitoring, conservation limits, water quality and examples of habitat improvement works (Loughs Agency 2009).

Most water abstracted for human use comes from surface waters in Northern Ireland, so the quality of the rivers and lakes has a direct relationship to the cost of water treatment (Section 18.5.2.6). While it is often thought that flooding is the major problem with water-flow for abstraction, there is a considerable threat from low water volumes in rivers, perhaps exacerbated by the predicted effects of climate change. Low flows concentrate pollutants, increase costs of purification and have direct impacts on the plants and animals living in and adjacent to flowing water (Paddy Brow, Northern Ireland Water, pers. comm.).

A comprehensive programme of arterial drainage works in Northern Ireland commenced following WWII. The need for the work was identified due to food shortages suffered during the war years, and flooding in areas which had potential for agricultural productivity. The government undertook a Northern Ireland-wide programme of straightening, deepening and widening of rivers, focused on the main rivers of each catchment. Riparian woodlands and other vegetation were lost during the canalisation work. This can be restored to some extent and would considerably improve water quality, fisheries and riparian biodiversity. This has resulted in Northern Ireland having the highest percentage of severely modified rivers in the UK (5% compared to 3.5% UK average) and the lowest percentage of pristine rivers in the UK (10.1% compared to 15.1% UK average; Raven et al. 1998). A total of 6,800 km of watercourses including rivers, streams and canals have been designated under the terms of the Drainage Order (Northern Ireland) 1973. Designation means that the maintenance of the land drainage and flood defence function of these key watercourses is deemed to be beyond the scope of riparian landowners. Significant drainage programmes continued up until the 1990s, with drainage activities along the River Blackwater being one of the final schemes completed. These schemes and their subsequent maintenance have had significant impacts on the salmonid fishery resource (Evans et al.2006). There is a current focus, resources permitting, on restoring habitats for salmonids within formerly drained river channels. Physical restoration usually involves the replacement of the physical structure of habitat diversity, such as channel sinuosity, pool-riffle sequences, spawning gravel replacement and juvenile salmonid nursery areas. Restoration works to date have been contained within the formerly drained and straightened channels (DCAL 2009b). The Lagan Valley Regional Park shows what can be done to improve its value to recreation and potentially to health. A hydromorphology group has been set up in the Northern Ireland Environment Agency and will report on the quality of Water Framework Directive monitored river habitats in line with Water Framework Directive guidance, using methods currently under development (Robert Rossell, AFBI, pers. comm.).

18.4.6.3 Lowland raised bogs

Raised bogs are found in lowland areas, generally below 150 m, in river valleys, lake-basins and between drumlins, having developed when peat accumulating in fens became isolated from groundwater. The surface of a raised bog is a mixture of pools, raised mossy hummocks and flatter lawns, and is colonised by plants and animals adapted to the acidic conditions and low levels of nutrients found there. This favours the growth of plants such as heather, cottongrasses and *Sphagnum* mosses. These plants die to form peat that is markedly different from fen peat, and often up to 12 m deep. The largest areas of raised bog are in the eastern lowland corridor extending north along the Bann Valley from the Lough Neagh basin. There are also small raised bogs in counties Down, Armagh and Fermanagh (EHS 2004a). Cruickshank and Tomlinson (1988) estimated that the Northern Ireland lowland raised bog resource was 25,196 ha of which 2,270 ha, about 9%, was still intact in 1988; in 2003 this figure was estimated at 8% (EHS 2003e). The NICS estimate for lowland bog in 2007 was 21,106 ha (Cooper et al. 2009), which includes regenerating cutover bog. The difference in the estimated area is derived from different methodologies rather than by a major loss of peatland between the two survey dates. Bogs were drained for agriculture and peat, with some major excavations of lowland bogs to provide horticultural peat still taking place in 2010 (Section 18.5.2).

Northern Ireland has a large proportion of the UK raised bog resource and Ireland as a whole is internationally important for peatlands. Lowland raised bog habitats, including both intact surfaces and regenerating cutover bog, are important for a number of UK priority species identified as part of the UK BAP programme. These include skylark which breeds on lowland raised bog (EHS 2003e).

Cutover edges of some bogs and the whole of some former raised bogs have developed into fens. Where peat cutting lowered the land surface such that mineral water gained access to the former bog site, plants colonised which are more nutrient-demanding than those associated with bogs. This has happened extensively in the drumlin country of Counties Down and Armagh; fen now occupies many inter-drumlin sites where bog has been removed completely or where only small patches remain. Many cutover edges of raised bogs have been colonised by woodland of birch or, if ground conditions are wet, of alder and willow. Brackagh Moss, near Portadown, is a good example; it has remnant bog, species-rich fen, poor fen and dense alder and willow carr. These woodlands are a valued habitat in Northern Ireland; not only is woodland generally scarce, but along with other oceanic woodland types, they provide habitats for mosses and lichens that depend on the mild, humid conditions (Tomlinson 2010).

Although most of Northern Ireland's raised bogs have been affected by past peat cutting, some are large and still have their unique central dome of peat and intact edges. Many smaller remnant bogs have an intact central dome, often including unique pool and hummock complexes, but the laggs (areas between the raised bog and upland terrain) and rands have been removed by cutting for fuel. Wishart (1978) examined three bogs in north Antrim looking at the then current (1970s) levels of use and spatial changes over the last two centuries and found decreases of between 43 and 62%. Lowland bog reclamation in the mid- to late 20th Century was often grant aided under the Farm Capital Grant Scheme. The bog was levelled by a bulldozer and lime rotavated onto the peat, followed by reseeding and later use of plastic pipe drainage where necessary. This reclaimed land could be used for light cattle and sheep but not heavy cattle (Wishart 1978). Of the lowland raised bogs that remained in the 1980s, some are the uniquely northern representatives of the Irish Midland type, whereas others have a more oceanic flora and fauna and yet others are transitional to blanket bog (Leach & Corbett 1987; Cruickshank & Tomlinson 1990).

18.4.6.4 Fen, grazing marsh and swamp

Freshwater wetlands are areas of land, usually fringing standing open water, that are inundated by surface or groundwater and support vegetation typically adapted for life in saturated soils. Most of Northern Ireland's lakes are fringed by fen, marsh and swamp where this has not been drained for agricultural use. Upper Lough Erne is especially important for these types of habitats with the shoreline at Crom supporting particularly rich and diverse examples (Phil Davidson, National Trust, pers. comm.). However, these types of wetlands can also occur in low-lying wet ground or poorly drained marginal grassland (Section 18.4.3). These wetlands help prevent flooding by slowing down flows and absorbing water, which they gradually release to rivers and streams to maintain the flow throughout the summer, and to recharge groundwater aquifers (NIEA 2010f).

18.4.6.5 Reedbeds

Reedbeds in Northern Ireland are especially associated with lowland wetlands around the large lakes and inter-drumlin wetlands. Inter-drumlin fens have declined substantially as open water has been filled in by marginal plants which have grown prolifically due to increasingly eutrophic conditions. These marshy areas are then invaded by willow scrub, resulting in the loss of a unique asset to our biodiversity. Several large stands (> 10 ha) occur around Lough Neagh (e.g. at Portmore Lough and Blackers Rock) and in the Lough Erne catchment. There are also a significant number of stands greater than 2 ha, including an estimated 40 sites in Counties Down and Armagh (Shaw *et al.* 1996). This is similar to the situation elsewhere in the UK where, out of 900 or so reedbed sites, only about 50 are larger than 20 ha, and these make a large contribution to the total area. Historically there has been significant loss of reedbeds in the UK which may be as high as 40% between 1945 and 1990 (Hawke & José 1996). It is likely that similar losses also occurred in Northern Ireland during this period. NICS 2000 indicates that there was little overall change in the area of swamp and reedbeds in Northern Ireland between 1988 and 1998 (Cooper *et al.* 2002). Between 1998 and 2007 there was an increase in swamp but a decrease in reedbeds of nearly 400 ha (Cooper *et al.* 2009).

Reedbeds in Northern Ireland are generally unmanaged. Their extent is governed by water levels, nutrient enrichment, ecological succession and grazing. Historically, relatively few reedbeds were harvested for thatching material (e.g. around the shores of Lough Neagh) and there is virtually no reed harvesting occurring at present. This contrasts with Great Britain, where many of the most important reedbeds have been traditionally managed as natural resources, usually by cutting for thatch, which maintained them as reed-dominated sites, effectively limiting the process of succession. In the Republic of Ireland small scale reed harvesting occurs, notably along the Shannon estuary (EHS 2005j).

Northern Ireland's reedbeds are an important habitat for several UK priority species identified in the UK BAP programme, particularly reed bunting, the reed beetle (*Donacia aquatica*) and greater water parsnip *(Sium latifolium)* (EHS 2005j).

There is limited use of artificial reedbeds in sewage treatment (e.g. Castle Espie Wildfowl and Wetlands Centre). Planning Services can require reedbed installation after septic tank treatment for new housing in areas of permeable soils. However, so far this is on a very limited scale and overall, there remains a problem of pollution from poorly functioning septic tanks for rural dwellings.

18.4.6.6 Groundwater

Groundwater in Northern Ireland may typically be only tens of years old. There is some older slow-moving water, for example at depth beneath the basalts of County Antrim, so that a pollution event occurring at the surface today may not manifest itself in the groundwater body for several years or even decades. A diffuse or dispersed pollutant accumulating over a long period of time would be difficult and costly to deal with, even after the source of the pollution is removed. Therefore, surface-water catchments upstream of 'losing' sections of rivers should be considered as part of the groundwater system. The protection of groundwater can be critical to both the quantity and quality of baseflow to surface waters and hence drinking water resources (EHS 2001, 2008a).

Northern Ireland Water abstracts 98% of its water from surface sources (49% from impounding reservoirs, 49% from rivers and loughs) with groundwater sources (boreholes) making up the other 2%. This is in contrast to Great Britain, where most water is abstracted from groundwater (NIEA 2009b). Private supplies in Northern Ireland are used by less than 1% of the population. About 8% of the all of the water used in Northern Ireland is drawn directly from private boreholes and springs for industrial, agricultural or domestic use. Groundwater storage contributes baseflow to surface waters such as streams and rivers that in turn provide water for public supply (EHS 2001). Overall, abstraction from groundwater bodies is generally only a very small proportion of recharge; therefore confidence can be high in assigning good status under this overall water balance test (NIEA 2009j).

Wetlands can also be fed from groundwater, with the ecology particularly sensitive to changes in the level of the water table. Groundwater therefore is an important and valuable resource which requires protection in both quality and quantity and requires land management for its maintenance. Northern Ireland's groundwater in 2008 was of high quality, with less than 2% of monitoring sites having an annual mean concentration of >40 mg nitrate/l (DOE & NISRA 2010).

There are two major risks to groundwater. Firstly, over-abstraction from an aquifer may reduce the level of the water table, causing depletion of baseflow to surface waterways or a decrease in yields for some groundwater users and an adverse effect on groundwater quality by encouraging deeper saline water to come into circulation. Secondly, human activities such as waste disposal, industry and agriculture can pollute groundwater.

18.4.6.7 Floodplains

Floodplains are defined as flat areas adjacent to watercourses (including standing open water) or the sea where water flows in time of flood or would flow but for the presence of flood defences (DOE 2010d). In addition, there is a considerable area of floodplain adjacent to lakes. For planning purposes, and taking into account present scientific evidence, the limits of floodplains are defined as:

- Rivers—the extent of a flood event with a 1% annual probability of exceeding the peak floodwater level.
- The coast—the extent of a flood event with a 0.5% annual probability of exceeding the peak floodwater level.

There is no assessment of the area of floodplain in the NICS as all land is categorised under its more common purpose, usually Enclosed Farmland, Semi-natural Grassland or Urban Settlements. However, the floodplains are shown on the Strategic Flood Map (Rivers Agency 2010), which identifies areas at risk from flooding from rivers and the sea, including the predicted potential impacts of climate change up to 2030. The number of properties within the indicative floodplain in Northern Ireland is estimated at 46,000 with about 15,500 of those benefiting from flood defences or the culvert network (Rivers Agency 2008a).

The Department of Agriculture and Rural Development, through the Rivers Agency, is the competent authority for the Floods Directive (Directive 2007/60/EC). The Directive requires the production of a Preliminary Flood Risk Assessment (PFRA) for all river basin districts and coastal areas which considers the impact on human health, the environment, cultural heritage and economic activity. Areas deemed to have a significant potential flood risk are then required to have flood risk and hazard maps produced, along with flood risk management plans. The PFRA is to be completed by the end of December 2011, with flood risk management plans to be completed by December 2015.

The importance of floodplains has become much more apparent in recent years. The production of Planning Policy Statement 15 (PPS15 Planning and Flood Risk) in June 2006 recognised the impact of development in floodplains, and the consequent effect on flooding: "within floodplains the Department will not permit development unless it falls within one of the following exceptions or it is demonstrated that the proposal is of overriding regional importance" (DOE 2006b). Floodplain usage for flood alleviation is seen as part of sustainable flood management; other aspects include land usage, floodplain forestry and peat bog management. There is a role for all such techniques, but none provide complete flood alleviation, rather a mosaic of different techniques needs to be considered together. Land use management has a role to play in flood alleviation, but is not the only solution. Studies (Parrott *et al.* 2009; Hess *et al.* 2010) suggest that the impact is greatest in high frequency events, i.e. smaller floods, but that a range of factors including slope and soil type, have a role to play.

18.4.7 Urban

The UK NEA includes all built-up areas within this section, including buildings and hard standing in rural and peri-urban areas as well as towns and cities. The NICS 2007 found a 30% increase in built-up area between 1998 and 2007 (including both urban expansion and development in rural areas), almost twice that reported between 1989 and 1998. There has been a subsequent loss of habitats, largely Enclosed Farmland, Semi-natural Grassland and Woodlands (Cooper *et al.* 2002; Cooper *et al.* 2009). This has had profound implications on the countryside, particularly given the additional infrastructure required to support such developments, including transport access, septic tanks and connection to the electricity grid. The Regional Development Strategy for Northern Ireland 2025 has stated the need for future development to be concentrated in urban centres to reduce such impacts and build a more economical 'critical mass' to provide services and infrastructure (DRD 2008a).

Historically, Northern Ireland has had a dispersed population, with most of the countryside settled and farmed for centuries (Whelan 1997a,b; EHS 2008a). In contrast to Great Britain, Northern Ireland's urban areas have not had extensive links to heavy industry such as coal mining (West Midlands, Scottish west central lowlands), potteries (Stoke-on-Trent) or steel works (Teesside/Sheffield). Towns and cities tend to be small, with many situated in coastal or riverside locations. Priority habitats, designated sites and small areas of other broad habitats (e.g. woodland, lowland meadows) often occur within urban areas, parks and gardens and are a substantial form of land use in most larger towns and cities.

Given the size and distribution of the population, most of Northern Ireland can actually be considered as 'peri-urban' with only a small minority of people living more than 10 km from a sizeable town. Similarly, even most Belfast residents live less than 5 km from the open countryside. Residential trends of the past 50 years have led to significant development in the countryside in the greater Belfast area, with the population of Belfast city declining steadily since 1981. There has, however, been no decline in the Belfast conurbation or the 'Belfast travel to work area,' which is now considered to include over half of Northern Ireland's population and a high proportion of the area east of Lough Neagh (Belfast City Council 2005a).

The population density of Northern Ireland has increased from 105 people/km² in 1960 to 133/km² in 2010; this is projected to continue with a density of 153/km² predicted for 2050. Current density is much higher than Scotland (67/km²), about the same as Wales (145/km²) and considerably lower than England (401/km²), but all countries are expected to increase significantly over the next 40 years (ONS 2010a).

18.4.7.1 Demography and population distribution

Northern Ireland was home to 1.79 million people in 2009, a figure which has been slowly increasing for about 35 years and is expected to reach 1.92 million by 2020 (NISRA 2005a). There are two major cities and 41 large towns which are home to about 65% of the population (half of these in the Belfast metropolitan area; NISRA 2003, 2005b; **Figure 18.20**). The remaining people live in smaller settlements, many of fewer than 4,500 people, or in the open countryside (NISRA 2005b; **Table 18.7**). While the population of Northern Ireland as a whole has increased by some 19% since 1960, the population of Belfast has increased by 40% (NISRA 2002, 2009).

18.4.7.2 Urban land use

Prior to 2007, applications for residential development in Northern Ireland reached historical highs (see **Figure 18.21**), driven by, among other things, increasing ease of credit, high levels of growth in the Republic of Ireland ('the Celtic Tiger') and a general knowledge that tougher planning legislation was being considered for rural areas in particular as a result of the Regional Development Strategy for Northern Ireland 2025. Planning approval, even without subsequent development, automatically helped to increase land and property value in a booming marketplace. Since 2002 the number of applications has fallen by around 19% (see **Figure 18.21**). There were 19,557 planning applications across Northern Ireland from 2009 to 2010, a 4.5% fall from the previous year (NIPS 2010a). Belfast showed the greatest decrease in applications over that period, a fall of 20.6% from 2008. Overall, 92.2% of applications were approved. In relation to residential development, 91.4% and 96.6% of applications were approved for rural areas and urban areas respectively. There has been a much lower level of development in all areas in 2009 and 2010 (**Table 18.8**) in response to economic pressures, but there is still substantial pressure for housing in rural areas, including many extant planning permissions.

The increase in urban development includes both green- and brownfield sites. The Northern Ireland Planning Service

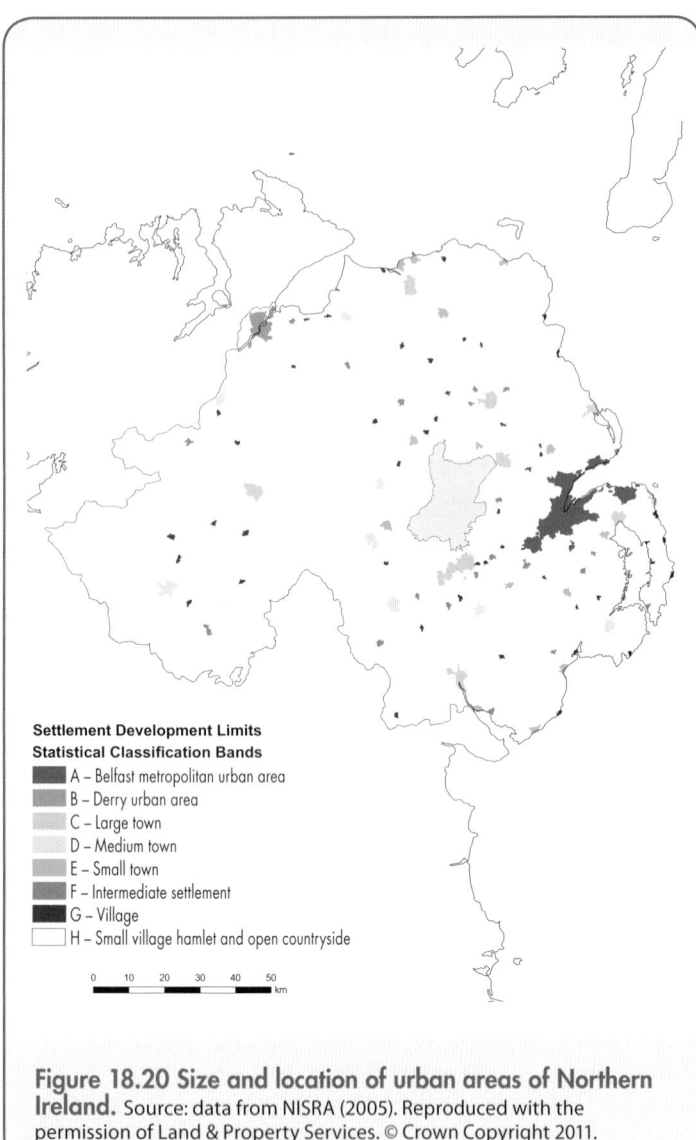

Figure 18.20 Size and location of urban areas of Northern Ireland. Source: data from NISRA (2005). Reproduced with the permission of Land & Property Services. © Crown Copyright 2011.

Settlement Development Limits
Statistical Classification Bands
A – Belfast metropolitan urban area
B – Derry urban area
C – Large town
D – Medium town
E – Small town
F – Intermediate settlement
G – Village
H – Small village hamlet and open countryside

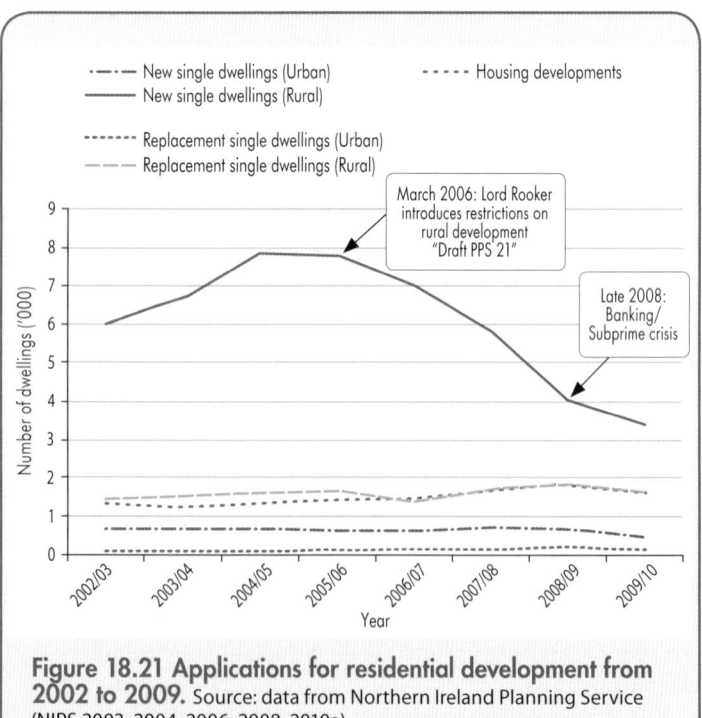

Figure 18.21 Applications for residential development from 2002 to 2009. Source: data from Northern Ireland Planning Service (NIPS 2003, 2004, 2006, 2008, 2010a).

(NIPS) defines brownfield as any land in the urban area, including gardens, playing fields and parks, with greenfield sites being those outside the 'urban footprint' (DRD 2008a,b); this differs from the definition commonly used in Great Britain. The target in the Regional Development Strategy is for 60% of new development to be provided within urban footprints over the period of the strategy up to its review in 2010 (DRD 2008a). On average, 6,200 residential units have been built per annum on urban sites and 5,000 per annum on greenfield or other sites (NISRA 2010a) with the proportion within the urban footprint varying between 65% and 85% from 2001 to 2007 (DRD 2009b). Mean household size was 2.48 in 2008–2009, with the mean number of persons per room amounting to 0.45 (DSD 2009). Northern Ireland Housing Executive has not built new housing since 2002, but there has been development in the social rented sector through housing associations amounting to 4,976 residential units between 2004 and 2010 (DSD 2006, 2007, 2008, 2009, 2010). The majority of these were in urban areas, notably Belfast, Craigavon, Fermanagh and Lisburn.

In recent years there has been some movement back to the city and central Belfast is now home to people who largely live in new developments centred around the River Lagan. There are, however, still relatively fewer high rise flats than in other major UK cities and the majority of new build homes are suburban, either as grouped developments of houses or single homes in the countryside. Planning policy has been reformed in 2010 to encourage grouping of houses around existing infrastructure and to discourage single dwellings (DOE 2010e), but there are still many extant planning permissions in the open countryside and in 2005 there were more applications approved for single dwellings in the countryside in Northern Ireland than in England, Wales and Scotland combined. While this has obvious implications for the appearance and attractiveness of the countryside, the most significant environmental issues are associated with the infrastructure required to support scattered single dwellings, including water provision, septic tanks, electricity and phone lines and the amount of transport required by the residents. Although housing developments over the past 20 years have tended to lack greenspace, Planning Policy Statement 8 (PPS8: Open Space, Sport & Outdoor Recreation; DOE 2004) only permits proposals for new residential developments of 25 units or more where public open space is provided as an integral part of the development.

Redevelopment of existing mature sites within urban areas has often resulted in one large dwelling with a sizeable garden being replaced by an apartment block or several houses or flats, with hard surfaced car parking replacing the original garden. There is also a trend of replacing hedges with wooden fencing and paving front gardens. This has negative impacts on biodiversity and aesthetics, but perhaps more importantly has led to rapid water runoff which has contributed to flooding in the Belfast urban area during heavy rainstorms. The Rivers Agency publishes an interactive strategic flood map which identifies all areas subject to flooding across Northern Ireland (Rivers Agency 2010) and Belfast City Council commissioned a report in 2009 outlining flooding hotspots in its area (BRC 2010) which states that 10,000 properties in the Belfast area are at risk from coastal or river flooding.

Table 18.7 Distribution of Northern Ireland's population based on settlement size according to the 2001 census. Source: data from NISRA (2005b).

	Classification (Population Range)								
	Belfast Urban Area	Derry Urban Area	Large Towns (18,000–75,000)	Medium Towns (10,000–18,000)	Small Towns (4,500–10,000)	Intermediate Settlement (2,250–4,500)	Village (1,000–2,250)	Small Village, Hamlet and Open Countryside (<1,000)	Northern Ireland
Total (number) in 2001	579,276	90,663	223,524	100,149	101,535	64,722	67,647	461,784	1,689,300

Table 18.8 Planning application approval from 2003 to 2009. Source: data from NIPS (2003, 2004, 2006, 2008, 2010a).

Application Category	2003/4		2004/5		2005/6		2006/7		2007/8		2008/9		2009/10	
	No.	%	No.	%	No.	%	No.	%	No.	%	No.	%	No.	%
Agricultural	83	-	106	91.0	219	92.0	209	86.4	178	86.8	335	94.1	213	91.0
Commercial	1,382	96	1,329	95.0	1,359	92.0	1,252	89.9	1,273	89.8	1,184	92.1	1,221	92.9
Government and Civic	1,761	98	1,923	98.0	1,836	97.0	1,880	97.0	1,774	97.5	1,889	97.1	1,629	96.0
Industrial	366	96	357	94.0	371	95.0	335	88.6	341	88.6	388	93.0	306	89.2
Mixed Use	193	93	179	96.0	189	94.0	182	94.8	244	90.4	334	90.5	209	89.3
Residential	17,652	92	19,985	89.0	20,001	81.0	19,020	80.5	19,273	91.5	17,783	94.6	14,246	94.6
Others	951	94	930	92.0	1,120	91.0	1,131	86.3	1,270	89.4	1,298	87.9	1,192	88.9
Environmental Installations*	-	-	32	97	31	97	35	100	88	99	87	94	210	96
All Applications	22,388	94.8	24,841	94.0	25,126	92.4	24,044	90.4	24,441	91.6	23,298	92.9	19,226	92.2

*Environmental installations include wind turbines, solar water heating panels, wood pelletising plants and solar panels.

Planning policies and development control decisions have a major impact on both urban and rural ecosystems. There has been recent loss of urban wildlife habitats due to planning decisions, but Planning Policy Statement 7 (PPS7: Quality Residential Environments; DOE 2001) and PPS7 Addendum (Residential Extensions & Alterations; DOE 2008) both seek as a policy objective to promote biodiversity. McKenzie et al. (2011) found significant impact of development in rural areas and stressed the importance of a consistent rural development strategy across government in protecting habitats and ensuring effective delivery of ecosystem services. Planning in Northern Ireland is centralised but in 2010 a major review was undertaken (part of the ongoing Review of Public Administration and Planning Reform processes) which may lead to transfer of some planning powers to local authorities in 2011, prior to a further transfer, perhaps in 2015.

Recent development and promotion of health and exercise trails encourage recognition of the benefits of the natural environment on health. Visits to parks continue to be popular and are promoted through numerous events and activities based in parks. Belfast City Council offers grants for park-based community events (Belfast City Council 2010). The Health Protection Agency has published a Children's Environment and Health Strategy for the UK (2009) which makes explicit the link between the health of the natural environment and the health of children (HPA 2009). They

also published a document in 2008 regarding the health impacts of climate change (HPA 2008).

18.4.7.3 Urban greenspace

There are some important nationally designated sites in urban areas, including Lough Foyle in Derry/Londonderry (an ASSI, SPA and Ramsar site) and the Belfast Lough Shore (Ramsar, SPA and ASSI sites). There is a new UK priority habitat, 'open mosaic habitats on previously developed land', the criteria and survey methodology for which have yet to be finalised, but it seems likely that areas within Belfast Harbour Estate, for example, will be included.

Nevertheless, the majority of urban greenspace is of more local significance. Both Belfast and Derry/Londonderry have major policies and action programmes promoting sites and action in their areas (Belfast City Council 2007; Derry City Council 2008), and many local councils have equally important plans in place (e.g. Banbridge District Council 2007; Coleraine District Council 2008; Larne Borough Council 2008; Omagh District Council 2008). A variety of types of extensive parkland designations are in force in and near major urban centres; Regional Parks, Country Parks and non-governmental organisation (NGO)-managed properties (e.g. National Trust) provide significant areas of urban and near-urban recreational, educational and high biodiversity land. These areas have great potential for management for a wide variety of uses. At least 10 Local Nature Reserves

(LNRs) have been established or are proposed in urban areas, including in Belfast, Bangor, Derry/Londonderry and Craigavon. These areas are a considerable resource for their local areas in financial (**Table 18.9**) as well as recreational, cultural and aesthetic terms.

As of May 2010, Belfast City Council maintained a total of 114 open spaces for various uses including parks, playing fields, allotments, playgrounds, graveyards and memorial sites (see **Table 18.9**). This amounts to a total area of over 1,000 ha. In Derry/Londonderry a figure of 305 ha was reported for various classifications of open spaces including watercourses, shrub and flower beds, playing fields, graveyards and amenity grass. Lisburn City Council also maintains 26 open spaces covering almost 160 ha (NIPS 2007).

Some councils are managing open space for biodiversity, in particular with woodland planting and wildflower meadow creation in parkland formerly managed as mown grass (e.g. Barnett's Park in Belfast). However, there is a demand on public parks for a variety of uses, including golf courses, sports facilities, allotments and burial grounds (Robert Scott, Belfast City Council, pers. comm.).

To the end of 2010, 12 of the 26 councils have Local BAPs which attempt to address priority habitats and species while involving local people in promoting biodiversity in their area. A duty to promote biodiversity on government and public authorities is part of the Wildlife and Environment Bill 2010.

Street trees have many benefits—biodiversity, shade, pollution abatement, aesthetics, and greenhouse gas abatement—and they contribute significantly to property values (Morales 1980; Anderson & Cordell 1988; CABE Space 2005; Landry & Chakraborty 2009). Belfast City Council cites the number of street trees in its area as 11,000 (Belfast City Council 2005b).

Tree Preservation Orders (TPOs) can be applied to protect trees under threat of destruction, and the Planning Service declared 531 TPOs between 2003 and 2008 (NISRA 2010a). In addition, all trees within the boundaries of a Conservation Area (designated by the Planning Service under the Planning (NI) Order 1991) are protected as if a TPO were in place.

Many councils are developing new allotment sites and community gardens, and allotments are being provided by the private sector. An Allotments Forum has been active since 2008, involving council officers and others in promoting the uptake and development of sites. Schools have also become involved and there are excellent examples of school grounds being used for growing vegetables as part of their curriculum to promote healthy eating (O'Hagan 2010).

School grounds are also increasingly used to promote environmental lessons and many grounds have wildlife areas. Eco-Schools is an international programme run locally by TIDY Northern Ireland, which encourages students to address numerous topics to improve the sustainability of their schools and over half of all schools in Northern Ireland participate (TIDY NI 2008). Organisations including Northern Ireland Water, the RSPB, the Ulster Wildlife Trust, the Woodland Trust and the Wildfowl and Wetlands Trust participate with schools in a certified scheme called Facilitating Primary Schools in Key Stage 1 & 2 Education Programmes 'The World Around Us', which incorporates sustainability and biodiversity (NI Curriculum 2010). Some funding is provided for education work through the Natural Heritage Grants Programme of the Northern Ireland Environment Agency.

18.4.7.4 Urban-rural interactions

The complex Urban ecosystem can have a significant impact on other habitats; not only are most of the materials required by cities sourced from rural areas, but urban areas rely on many services provided by rural ecosystems for disposal and detoxification of wastes. Many of Northern Ireland's large urban areas border coasts or estuaries and therefore urban pollution, reclamation, disturbance and waste disposal impact on coastal and marine environments.

Compared to the rest of the UK, limited information exists on how residents of Northern Ireland visit and use the countryside (CAAN 2008). However, it is clear that many people regularly visit rural areas for some form of recreation (Forestry Commission 2005, 2010b; Section 18.5.4).

Some progress seems to have been made with regard to raising public awareness of and interest in environmental issues. According to the Northern Ireland Statistics and Research Agency's (NISRA) Continuous Household Survey, people who were very or fairly concerned about the environment rose from 76% in 2004 to 82% in 2009 (NISRA 2010a). Most types of environmental concern have increased during this period, with climate change, household waste disposal, traffic fumes and urban smog, and traffic congestion being areas of highest concern in 2007–2008. Climate change concern has risen from 13% in 2003–2004 to 39%, the highest level of concern of any of the issues tested, in 2007–2008 (NISRA 2009) but decreased slightly to 37% in 2010(DOE & NISRA 2010).

The Regional Development Strategy (DRD 2008b) and a revised draft currently in development aim to facilitate movement of goods and people around Northern Ireland and improve links with both Great Britain and the Republic of Ireland (DRD 2011). One of the biggest impacts on ecosystems is transport, at all levels, from carbon emissions to pollution

Table 18.9 Estimated resource value of the open space areas of Belfast City Council. Source: Belfast City Council (2005b and unpublished data).

Type of site	Number	Estimated resource value	Area (ha)
City Parks	2	£4,480,000	15.1
District Parks	9	£8,265,000	153.9
Local Parks	36	£14,109,000	168.6
Country Parks	5	£1,884,000	444.3
Playing Field Sites	8	£2,942,000	87.1
Cemeteries	9	£3,512,000	118.0
Playgrounds	41	£3,210,000	Unavailable
Allotments	4	£40,000	Unavailable
Other	-	£240,000	Unavailable
Total	**114**	**£38,682,000**	

to habitat destruction for road construction. Within Belfast there is increasing emphasis on providing public and active transport (DRD 2002a). However, investment remains heavily concentrated on roads, and the relatively large travel to work area of Belfast's population means that some public transport options are not currently financially viable (e.g. trams), so there is a continued emphasis on roads-based transport. Some initiatives ('cycle city', electric vehicles, park and ride) seek to address the issue, but for the foreseeable future Northern Ireland will continue to rely on an extensive road network with significant implications for the natural environment.

18.4.8 Coastal Margins

Northern Ireland has over 650 km of coastline (DOE & NISRA 2010), with a wide range of topography and habitat types from sandy beaches to massive igneous cliffs. Sea loughs are a key feature and have particularly high biodiversity value (Section 18.4.9). The social and cultural identity of Northern Ireland is positively associated with its coast. Dramatic cliff lines on the north coast and sweeping landscapes from mountain to coastal zones (especially along the east coast) are iconic images of Northern Ireland and significant attractions to tourists. Consequently, coastal ecosystems are particularly valuable for their cultural and recreational aspects. The coastal zone is narrow, but of high scenic, ecosystem and resource value, and is under pressure for many different uses and types of development. Even relatively minor perturbations due to development, weather and erosion can have major impacts.

The UK NEA defines habitats of the Coastal Margins as Sea Cliffs, Shingle, Sand Dunes, Saltmarsh, Coastal Lagoons and Machair (absent in Northern Ireland). These habitats are discussed within this section with all other coastal and marine habitats discussed in Marine Habitats (Section 18.4.9). The NICS divides the coast between supralittoral rock and supralittoral sediment. There was no overall change in the area of coast between 1998 and 2007, at just over 3,500 ha, or 0.25% of Northern Ireland (Cooper *et al.* 2009).

Coastal Margins habitats support a wide range of unique and rare species. Much of this diversity is dependent on natural dynamics creating early successional habitats. This is reflected in the number of sites designated for their biological importance, with sites such as Strangford Lough holding many designations (Section 18.8). However, there are also problems with invasive species impacting on high value sites. About 75% of the coast is protected, much of it by multiple designations (NIEA 2010g). It includes 52 SACs, 10 SPAs, 17 Ramsar sites and Northern Ireland's only World Heritage Site, the Giant's Causeway and Causeway Coast. Around one-quarter of Northern Ireland's 47 NNRs are on the coast and Strangford Lough was designated as Northern Ireland's first MNR in the mid-1990s. Recently there has been work promoting an integrated approach to coastal zone management (DOE 2006; McCusker 2009).

The sea level around Northern Ireland's coast is determined by two opposing forces, increasing sea depth due to climate change and land lift which has been proceeding since the end of the last ice age (Kelly *et al.* 2006; Orford *et al.* 2006; Orford *et al.* 2007a). Tidal range varies from 5 m (south east) to 1–2 m (north). The entire coastline is characterised as storm dominated, with both the north and east coasts subjected to extreme storm severity (Orford *et al.* 2007b). Coastal habitats occupy a relatively narrow zone characterised by complex environmental gradients and spatial mosaics which support large numbers of plant and animal species.

The National Trust owns and cares for 123 km of the Northern Ireland coastline (National Trust Regional Office). Indeed, nearly 90% of the National Trust's total UK coastline is in Northern Ireland. The remainder of Northern Ireland's coastline is mainly in private ownership, although district councils have significant land holdings, especially popular beaches. The Crown Estate owns and manages most of the foreshore. With the exception of industrial uses around Belfast Lough, military ranges at Magilligan and Ballykinlar, and coastal recreation and tourism developments (e.g. links golf courses, marinas, hotels), most coastal lands are either nature reserves or in agricultural use. Coastal defences are managed by three authorities; DRD Roads Service are responsible for defences which protect roads, the Harbour Commissioners manage most (but not all) harbour installations, and the Rivers Agency manages just over 26 km of designated sea defence, mainly at Lough Foyle and Strangford Lough (UKMMAS 2010).

18.4.8.1 Sea Cliffs

About half of Northern Ireland's coast is defined as Sea Cliffs (JNCC 1997). The dramatic cliffs along the north and north-east coasts rise, often quite precipitously, from the sea to 100 m or more, creating some of the iconic landscapes of the Giant's Causeway and Glens of Antrim. Coastal villages lie between cliffs and shore, with building development both within villages and in the countryside often encroaching on narrow beaches. Rathlin Island, the largest island off the Northern Ireland coast, has precipitous basalt and some limestone cliffs which are very important for nesting seabirds and continue into the sea to provide diverse underwater habitats of high biodiversity.

18.4.8.2 Seabird nesting islands

Rathlin Island has by far the largest cliff-nesting colonies of seabirds in Northern Ireland, followed by Gobbins and the Isle of Muck near Larne Lough. Rathlin has 6% and 10% of the British and Irish populations of guillemots (*Uria aalge*) and razorbills (*Alca torda*), respectively. Rathlin also has 5% and 22% of the Irish populations of nesting fulmars (*Fulmaris glacialis*) and kittiwakes (*Rissatridactyla*), respectively (Mitchell *et al.* 2004). However, there has been an estimated 50% decline in puffin (*Fratercula arctica*), razorbill and fulmar populations on Rathlin Island between 1999 and 2007, possibly as a result of reduced food availability (AFBI & NIEA 2011). Islands in Larne Lough (including Swan Island, an SPA and NNR for tern populations), Strangford Lough and Carlingford Lough are also important for bird populations, particularly for breeding gulls and terns (BTO 2010).

The Copeland Islands have 1.4% of the British and Irish populations of Manx shearwater (*Puffinus puffinus*). Northern Ireland has 5.7% of the British and Irish breeding populations of cormorants (*Phalacrocorax carbo*; Swan Island SPA), 5% of breeding black-headed gulls, 14% of sandwich terns (*Sterna sandvicensis*) and 12% of common terns (*Sterna hirundo*). Recent seabird colonists in Northern Ireland include breeding great skua (*Stercorarius skua*, at Rathlin) and Mediterranean gull (*Larus melanocephalus*). There has been a dramatic decline of about 97% in nesting herring gulls (*Larus argentatus*) since the mid-1980s in Northern Ireland, largely attributable to birds feeding on rubbish dumps and becoming infected with botulism (Ian Humphreys, Copeland Bird Observatory, pers. comm.). However, improved management of landfill sites may be addressing this problem. The rare roseate tern (*Sterna dougallii*) continues to nest (Mitchell *et al.* 2004), but only one pair nested in 2010 (D. Allen & K. Leonard, pers. comm.; BTO 2010).

18.4.8.3 Shingle

Shingle coasts form in wave-dominated locations where suitably sized material is available (2–200 mm). An estimated 50 ha of vegetated Shingle occurs in Northern Ireland (Paul Corbett, NIEA, pers. comm.). Of this, approximately 30 ha are considered stable. The most extensive areas have been surveyed for their biodiversity, for example Ballyquintin Point National Nature Reserve (NNR) and Gransha Point on Strangford Lough. These areas support a range of plant communities, including scrub and grassland, often rich in lichens. It is these areas of stable Shingle that are the main focus of the Coastal Vegetated Shingle Habitat Action Plan (EHS 2005e).

18.4.8.4 Sand Dunes

Most of the Sand Dunes in Northern Ireland have formed due to the falling sea level over the last 5,000 years. While there are estimated to be approximately 3,000 ha of dunes in Northern Ireland, Sand Dune vegetation is estimated to be between 1,300 and 1,500 ha (EHS 2005d).

Marram grass (*Ammophila arenaria*) plays an essential role in the formation of dunes by acting as a stabilising agent as sand accumulates (NIEA 2009d). The largest dune systems are at Magilligan (around 900 ha) and Portstewart Strand on the north coast and at Murlough on the County Down coast. Some of the dunes at the Bann Estuary (Grangemore) are considerably older than others in Northern Ireland and have particular floristic significance. Murlough also contains examples of communities which generally occur further south in the British Isles, and all of the systems contain a range of plant species that are scarce in Northern Ireland (EHS 2005d). The Umbra at Magilligan has priority species including small eggar (*Eriogaster lanestris*) and scarce crimson and gold (*Pyrausta sanguinalis*) moths, and northern mining bee (*Colletes florialis*) (EHS 2005a). Well-managed grazing (including by rare breeds such as Dexter cattle) is essential to maintain high levels of biodiversity and to fend off scrub growth which would otherwise colonise areas of bare ground necessary for dune mobility (EHS 2005d).

Murlough is managed by the National Trust and the dunes are estimated to be 6,000 years old, providing a habitat for 22 species of butterfly and up to 5,000 wildfowl and waders. The dunes also support 55 species of bee, ant and wasp (which equates to 33% of the Irish total), 213 species of

moth (48% of moths in Northern Ireland) and 21 species of butterfly (roughly 71% of butterflies in Northern Ireland; EHS 2005d). Murlough SAC, Magilligan SAC, Bann Estuary SAC and White Park Bay (North Antrim SAC) are all designated for their sand dune qualities featuring rare species. The main threats to dunes are a lack of management leading to scrub encroachment and invasive non-native species such as sea–buckthorn (*Elaeagnus rhamnoides*) and other nitrogen fixers (EHS 2005d).

Dune systems have been converted to agricultural use for centuries and a number of areas have been turned into golf courses, including Royal Portrush (1888) and Royal County Down (1889), which is set amid the Murlough dune complex (STRI 2010). While these have financial and tourism benefits, the dune systems were essentially destroyed in the process with concomitant loss of natural habitats and species. Also, dunes tend to be important as low grade coastal defences and their loss can impact on natural dune–beach sediment interactions, especially where artificial features are erected. At Portballintrae most of the sand from the Bay has disappeared over the last century, probably due to a jetty set up at the entrance of the bay (Carter 1991). Similarly, the harbour at Magilligan Point has affected coastal dynamics and therefore dunes.

Local landowners have traditional rights to remove sand and cobbles from beaches for use in agriculture as animal bedding and gateway maintenance, primarily on the north-east coast, and this has become a significant problem in some areas (Carter 1991).

18.4.8.5 Saltmarsh

Saltmarshes develop where fine sediments accumulate in relatively low-energy environments and salt-tolerant vegetation establishes where there is an accumulation of mud in estuaries. The composition of Saltmarsh flora and fauna is determined by complex interactions between flooding frequency, salinity, sediment water content, particle size, slope, and herbivory. While saltmarshes in England are dominated by lateral spreads of vegetation dependent on tidal inundation, the narrow and restricted spatial zones of marsh in Northern Ireland are often flooded by fresh water, preventing this lateral spread.

There are roughly 250 ha of Saltmarsh in Northern Ireland (Boorman in press) representing about 0.5% of the total UK Saltmarsh resource. The extent of loss of Saltmarsh in Northern Ireland is unknown (EHS 2005c). However, saltmarshes are under pressure from coastal development and are prone to damage from agricultural or golf course management.

There are two main types of Saltmarsh in Northern Ireland. The first, and more extensive, is the estuarine type with conspicuous natural transitions from low to upper marsh communities. Saltmarsh plays a major role in estuarine processes, both through the cycling of nutrients within the estuary and through its ability to dissipate wave energy and thus act as a natural coastal defence. The largest of the estuarine saltmarshes are found in the Roe Estuary in Lough Foyle, around Strangford Lough (where it is important for winter grazing by light-bellied brent geese, *Branta bernicla hrota*), at Ballycarry in Larne Lough, in the

Bann Estuary and at Mill Bay in Carlingford Lough. These five sites account for 90% of the Saltmarsh area of Northern Ireland. The second main type is the smaller beach-head type, which tends to occur as small pockets on rocky shores (Barne *et al.* 1997). Other saltmarshes occur as a narrow coastal marginal fringe or as very small parcels (Baxter & Boaden 1990).

Saltmarshes are important habitats for a range of organisms, in particular specialist plant communities and associated animals, especially breeding and wintering birds which both feed and roost there, and often have a high conservation interest (EHS 2005c).

18.4.8.6 Coastal/Saline Lagoons

The key characteristics of saline lagoons are that they are shallow, quiet water bodies, adjacent to the sea, but sheltered from its direct effects and with a restricted connection to it. This leads to salinity from brackish to hypersaline, which can be highly variable spatially or temporally, depending on the hydrodynamics (EHS 2003f).

In Northern Ireland saline lagoons are not common. Of the 19 saline lagoons investigated by Carroll (1994), Donnan (1994) and Gorman (1994), only three were considered to be natural; a brackish wetland at Rathgorman (County Down), a series of pools on Grannagh Island and a series of salt pans and creeks at The Dorn (both in Strangford Lough). The remainder were considered to be artificial (EHS 2003f), but some of these are of high ecological value. A total of 16 saline lagoons occur in designated sites including ASSIs, SPAs and Ramsar sites. Lough Foyle ASSI and SPA include some saline lagoon habitat. Strand Lough is an SPA and is included in Killough Bay and Strand Lough ASSI (EHS 2005l).

18.4.9 Marine

Northern Ireland's territorial waters are defined as extending from the high water mark of medium tides (HWMMT) out to 12NM. The waters of Loughs Foyle and Carlingford are shared with the Republic of Ireland. The total surface area of the intertidal zone (HWMMT to LWMMT) is estimated to be 10,730 ha (Cooper *et al.* 2009) of which 1,212 ha is composed of rock and 9,518 ha is sediment. The total surface area of the subtidal zone under Northern Ireland jurisdiction (LWMMT to 12NM) is estimated to be 450,000 ha (NIEA 2010h; calculated using a geographic information system (ArcGIS) by drawing a mid-line through trans-boundary waters out to the 12NM limit (or midway between Northern Ireland and Scotland)).

Most of Northern Ireland's territorial waters are over the continental shelf. The deepest waters (approximately 270 m) are north of Rathlin Island, but most are shallower than 100 m (Barne *et al.* 1997). At these depths water movements are dominated by tides and wind-driven surface currents, the latter following the predominant westerly airflow and occasionally reversing the direction of flow through the North Channel (Davies *et al.* 2002; Lynch *et al.* 2004). Tide ranges vary from microtidal (<2 m) on the Londonderry and Antrim coasts, to mesotidal (2–4 m) from Larne to just south of Dundrum Bay and macrotidal (>4 m range) south of this. Wave exposure mirrors this pattern, decreasing from the

west to the south east of Northern Ireland (Jackson & Cooper 2010). The combination of wind- and tide-driven processes means that the waters of the north coast of Northern Ireland (Lough Foyle to Larne) are well mixed (Lynch *et al.* 2004). Sea surface temperatures range from roughly 6°C in winter to 17°C in summer, with means of 7°C and 13.5°C, respectively (Barne *et al.* 1997). Recent data demonstrate an increase in ocean temperature of between 0.5 to 0.75°C in Northern Ireland waters over the past 20 years (Lynam *et al.* 2010). Offshore salinity is fairly stable in space and time at about 34 practical salinity units (PSU) (Barne *et al.* 1997).

Habitats on the seafloor (sublittoral benthic habitats) are diverse. Some of these habitats are defined primarily on the basis of the physical substratum (e.g. circalittoral muds and sublittoral chalk), while in other instances the biota themselves generate the three-dimensional structures that define the habitat (e.g. seagrass beds and biogenic reefs). While there are no classically-defined habitats that are unique to Northern Ireland waters, there are several priority habitats that are significant not only to the UK, but also more broadly to the EU (**Table 18.10**).

Northern Ireland's marine biodiversity is typical of that of the broader UK. However, given its small size, its contributions to overall biodiversity inventories are relatively large, for example 30% of cetaceans resident in the UK are regularly seen in Northern Ireland waters. Of particular importance are biodiversity hotspots. Chief amongst these is Rathlin Island, with its rich assemblages of rare sponges (Picton & Goodwin 2007) as well as large nesting seabird colonies. In fact, 50–60% of all of Northern Ireland's sublittoral benthic species are found off Rathlin Island (Barne *et al.* 1997; Goodwin *et al.* 2008). By adding the species present in the next most important biodiversity hotspot, Strangford Lough, roughly 90% of Northern Ireland's known sublittoral benthos is represented (Erwin *et al.* 1990). However, care must be taken to ensure that observed 'hotspots' of diversity are not an artefact of increased study effort, and more information is still required to determine if this is the case for Northern Ireland, as it appears to vary with the group studied (Blight *et al.* 2009). Positioned at the interface between Boreal (cold, northern) and Lusitanian (warmer, southern) marine biogeographical provinces (Dinter 2001; Hiscock *et al.* 2004), Northern Ireland's marine waters provide important opportunities to study the ecological consequences of climate change.

18.4.9.1 Intertidal zone

The low eastern coasts provide mixed sand and gravel beaches, sometimes partitioned to show an upper gravel beach and a lower sand terrace; most beaches show sand and gravel systems graded by varying proportions of the two substrates. Apart from the major sediment sink of Dundrum Bay (Orford *et al.* 2003), most of these beaches are backed by small, depleted dune stores.

Intertidal invertebrate communities are a major ecological community, helping to purify water, stabilise sediments and providing important feeding areas for water birds and waders. Harvesting of lugworms, winkles, cockles and other shellfish has proceeded on a small scale for decades. However, harvesting on a larger scale is having

Table 18.10 Priority habitats in Northern Ireland's marine environment. Source: Dave Schoeman, University of Ulster (unpublished d

Type	Habitat	Brief description	Location	Frequency of occurrence
PHYSICALLY DEFINED	Tidal rapids (EHS 2003i)	Strong, turbulent tidal streams often in natural constrictions and generally shallower than 5 m.	Shallow subtidal.	Frequent.
	Sheltered muddy gravels (EHS 2003h)	Shallow, poorly sorted soft sediment with gravel fraction.	Sheltered areas, particularly loughs and estuaries, lower intertidal to shallow subtidal.	Rare in Northern Ireland and the rest of the UK.
	Circalittoral muds (EHS 2005j)	Mud banks (fine soft sediments) often in sheltered areas.	Generally at 20–30 m depth.	Common, especially in the Irish Sea.
	Sublittoral sands and gravels (EHS 2005n)	Banks of soft sediments that are coarser than mud; come in a range of types, from coarse, stable gravels to mobile sand banks.	From the shallow subtidal to deeper than 50 m.	Most common habitat around UK, including Northern Ireland.
	Littoral and sublittoral chalk (EHS 2005e)	Soft sedimentary rock (calcium carbonate).	From the intertidal to depths of 50 m.	Rare in Europe, including most of UK. Possibly more common in waters around Northern Ireland than elsewhere, but poorly mapped.
	Saline lagoons (EHS 2003f)	Marine waters with restricted access to the sea; frequently brackish due to freshwater input.	Coastal, blocked from the open sea by some form of barrier.	Rare. Out of approximately 30 in Northern Ireland, only 3 are thought to be natural. However, the distinction is often difficult because of historical modifications of existing seascape features.
BIOLOGICALLY DEFINED	Seagrass beds (EHS 2003g)	Beds of sea grasses (the only marine flowering plants); three species of *Zostera* and two of *Ruppia*.	Sheltered, shallow water, mainly in loughs.	Frequent in Lough Foyle and Strangford Lough, but poorly mapped elsewhere.
	Maerl beds (EHS 2003e)	Beds of living or dead calcified (coraline) marine algae; complex biogenic reef.	Mainly shallow, sheltered water to about 40 m depth.	Unknown, not well mapped.
	Modiolus modiolus beds (EHS 2005i)	Beds of horse mussels, which are long-lived, slow-growing bivalve molluscs; form complex low-profile biogenic reefs.	5 m to more than 50 m depth.	Species is common in the northern hemisphere, but biogenic reefs are rare, only 4 are known in Northern Ireland.
	Sabellaria alveolata reefs (EHS 2005l)	Honeycomb worms form reefs of closely-packed sandy tubes.	Areas with a degree of wave action and necessary sediment available.	Unknown, not well mapped.
	Sabellaria spinulosa reefs (EHS 2005m)	Generally solitary, these polychaete tubeworms can in places form reefs of densely-packed sandy tubes; complex biogenic reef.	Areas with a degree of wave action and necessary sediment available; depth up to 40 m.	Unknown, probably rare, not well mapped (only 3 or 4 known reefs).

an impact on wildlife around Strangford Lough, not only having potential impacts on the food chain but also causing disturbance to seal haul-outs and roosting and breeding birds (Kelso & Service 2000; Johnson *et al.* 2008). On the North Foreshore of Belfast Lough a large area of mudflat was used as the major waste landfill site for greater Belfast from 1958 until 2007. For the past 20 years or so this area has been lined and 'capped' and much of the site is now being managed as a nature reserve (Belfast City Council 2008).

18.4.9.2 Sea loughs

Northern Ireland has five major sea loughs (Belfast, Carlingford, Foyle, Larne, and Strangford), all of which are high in biodiversity and of great scenic and recreational value. Both Belfast and Derry/Londonderry are sited on major loughs. Strangford Lough is Northern Ireland's only Marine Nature Reserve, as well as being a European Natura 2000 site; the other loughs have SAC or SPA status. Strangford Lough is of particularly high value biologically

Management value	Threats/Vulnerabilities	Listed in EC Habitats Directive?	Level of protection
Diverse algal and epifaunal communities.	Possibly sea-level rise and renewable energy installations (tidal power).	Not listed, but could be a component of Annex 1 listed habitat (Reefs).	Some protection in Strangford Lough MNR and SAC.
Characteristic specialist biodiversity; occasional high abundance of resident species; generally poorly studied due to nature of substrate.	Vulnerable to changes in hydrodynamics; sensitive to physical disturbance, including by fishing gear.	Not listed.	Some protection in Strangford Lough MNR and SAC.
Large communities of burrowing megafauna; important for shellfisheries, especially *Nephrops*.	Vulnerable to disturbance from fishing, particularly beam trawls; prone to accumulating pollutants, transported and aggregated by the same oceanographic processes that transport muds.	Not listed, but could be a component of some Annex 1 listed habitats.	Well represented in SACs.
Wide range of biotic communities and biodiversity; very rich communities when found in sheltered habitats; can support fisheries for bivalves; likely important nursery areas for juvenile fish.	Vulnerable to fisheries.	Not listed, but could be a component of Annex 1 listed habitat (Sandbanks which are slightly covered by sea water all of the time).	Some of the most diverse examples in Northern Ireland are represented in SACs.
Prone to formation of caves, which support specialised, rich biotic communities, including rare species of algae and sponges; rich in fossils.	Flat chalk reefs can be vulnerable to fishing gear and ocean acidification.	Not listed, but could be a component of Annex 1 listed habitat (Submerged or partially submerged sea caves).	Reasonable protection within ASSIs and SACs.
Specialised brackish-water biota; can be important to wildfowl and migrating birds.	Prone to eutrophication; vulnerable to coastal squeeze caused by the combination of sea level rise and infrastructural development.	Listed under Annex 1.	Well represented in ASSIs, SPAs and Ramsar sites.
Highly productive; support a wide range of biota; act as important nursery habitats for fish; provide food for overwintering wildfowl.	Sensitive to physical disturbance and turbidity; prone to invasion by *Sargassum muticum*; particularly vulnerable to climate change, especially sea-level rise.	Not listed, but could be a component of some Annex 1 listed habitats.	Well represented in ASSIs, SACs, SPAs and NNRs.
High biodiversity.	Sensitive to disturbance, e.g. scallop dredging and boat anchoring; vulnerable to sea-level rise.	Not listed, but could be a component of some Annex 1 listed habitats; listed under Appendix Vb.	Some representation in Strangford Lough MNR and SAC.
High biodiversity.	Extremely vulnerable to benthic fishing gear and slow to recover; may also be sensitive to other forms of physical disturbance.	Not listed, but could be a component of Annex 1 listed habitat (Reefs).	Large patch of reef protected in SACs and Strangford Lough MNR.
Tend to be low biodiversity habitats; at the northern edge of their distribution in Northern Ireland.	Vulnerable to changing sediment loads and hydrodynamic conditions.	Not listed, but could be a component of Annex 1 listed habitat (Reefs).	May be protected in some ASSIs.
High biodiversity.	Sensitive to physical disturbance, e.g. by fishing gear; vulnerable to changing sediment load and hydrodynamic conditions.	Not listed, but could be a component of Annex 1 listed habitat (Reefs).	Not known to be protected.

and recreationally, with major populations of overwintering birds, extensive sand/mudflats and numerous small islands, which make it extremely scenic as well as of high value for nesting birds, breeding seals and shellfish cultivation. The eel grass (*Zostera marina*) community in Strangford Lough provides overwintering grounds for up to 75% of the world population of light-bellied brent geese as well as shelter for young fish and invertebrates (National Trust 2010). Many large rivers drain into the sea loughs (e.g. the Roe into Lough

Foyle and the Lagan into Belfast Lough), which themselves are estuarine in nature, or smaller bays (e.g. Killough Harbour and Dundrum Inner Bay). Numerous smaller estuaries are also scattered along the coast.

Northern Ireland's sea loughs regularly host more than 120,000 birds each winter, including internationally important populations of mute swan (*Cygnus olor*), whooper swan (*Cygnus cygnus*), light-bellied brent geese, shelduck (*Tadorna tadorna*), knot (*Calidris calidris*), bar-tailed godwit (*Limosa lapponica*) and redshank (*Tringa totanus*; AFBI & NIEA 2011). Between 2004 and 2009 Strangford Lough was the twelfth most important site for wintering wetland birds in the UK. An average of 80,931 wetland birds used the site during the winters. Lough Foyle, Belfast Lough, Outer Ards shoreline, Carlingford Lough, and Larne Lough are also important sites for wading birds and waterfowl (Calbrade *et al.* 2010). Shorelines of all loughs are highly desirable for development, either for individual houses or expansion of development near existing settlements. Agriculture goes close to or even onto the shore in some areas, particularly on islands.

Alien species are becoming established in some of Northern Ireland's coastal waters and loughs, including *Spartina* in Strangford Lough. *Spartina anglica* was deliberately established in Ardmillan Bay during the 1940s in an attempt to stabilise a causeway which was silting up and for erosion protection of the National Trust property at Mount Stewart (Roberts *et al.* 2004). A major effort was launched in 1978 to eradicate *Spartina* from the Lough and the plant was virtually cleared by application of a selective herbicide. However, fears that this operation might be having an adverse effect on farmed shellfish and the introduction of tighter environmental controls on the use of chemicals in the marine environment led to the suspension of the spraying operation. As a result, the grass has recolonised much of the former range and has spread to many new locations. In 1997, *Spartina* covered over 30 ha in Strangford Lough. After much research on the impact of different herbicides in the marine environment, spraying was re-initiated in 1997–1998 with Dalapon. However, these control measures have been unsuccessful and *Spartina* continues to spread within the Lough (Hammond *et al.* 2002; Roberts *et al.* 2004).

18.4.9.3 Open ocean

The Marine environment of Northern Ireland includes portions of two distinct bodies of water, the north-east Atlantic and the north-western Irish Sea, which are linked through the North Channel. The predominant oceanic process is the north-eastward flow of the North Atlantic Current, which brings cool-temperate water to the shelf-break (Davies *et al.* 2002; Lynch *et al.* 2004). Northern Ireland's location, at a transition between cold northern and warm southern waters, gives an extremely rich marine biodiversity (see **Table 18.10**; AFBI & NIEA 2011).

There is a strong relationship between habitat complexity and the diversity of resident biotic communities (e.g. Kiessling *et al.* 2010). Habitat complexity can be the result of the resident organisms, which amplify biodiversity by creating niches within which other organisms can thrive. Examples of such biogenic habitats in Northern Ireland's territorial waters include extensive kelp beds in the shallow waters off rocky shorelines, seagrass beds in the shallow waters of some loughs, as well as maerl, horse mussel and honeycomb worm reefs. Among the residents of such habitats are juveniles of many commercially important and rare species. Biogenic reefs are vulnerable to the effects of climate change and are particularly heavily impacted by mobile fishing gear, which is a particular problem because the gear destroys the habitat upon which the commercial species, and many others, depend. Besides supporting

general marine biodiversity, Northern Ireland's territorial waters also house several charismatic species that capture the public attention (often referred to as flagship or indicator species; Heink & Kowarik 2010), thereby providing an impetus for conservation initiatives. In the local context these include basking sharks (Berrow & Heardman 1994; Southall *et al.* 2006), puffins, marine mammals (Berrow 2001) and sea turtles, which frequently travel along the coast of Northern Ireland (King & Berrow 2009). The utility of these species in representing the general health of the coastal waters of Northern Ireland has not been examined but the concept of focal species in marine conservation has a long and reasonably successful history (Zacharias & Roff 2001), although its utility has been disputed (e.g. Andelman & Fagan 2000). The emergent communities of The Dorn in Strangford Lough are of particular value (NIEA 2010i).

18.4.9.4 Water quality

Coastal water quality is monitored and new legislation and policies have been introduced over the years to address nutrient enrichment of coastal and marine waters (including the Water Framework Directive, Bathing Waters Directive, Urban Waste Water Treatment Directive, Nitrates Directive and the Ship-Source Pollution Directive). The Northern Ireland Environment Agency has called eutrophication "the most widespread threat to water quality in Northern Ireland" (EHS 2008a; **Figure 18.22**). Their data show that between 1994 and 2002 agriculture contributed over 70% of nitrogen loading to water in sea loughs, but that urban sources were the main contributors to ammonia and dissolved reactive phosphorus. Coastal waters were assessed as to the percentage which were 'at risk' under the Water Framework Directive in 2004. The factors driving classification in coastal waters tend to be nutrient concentrations and plant life. Nutrients and dissolved oxygen concentrations are the most important elements in determining status in transitional waters. Alien species, diffuse and point source pollution and morphological alterations were identified as the major threats (EHS 2008a). It was found that 66% of transitional and coastal water bodies in Northern Ireland are at moderate status, with approximately 27.5% at good status and 6.5% at high status by area/km^2 (DOE & NISRA 2010).

18.5 Northern Ireland's Ecosystem Services

18.5.1 Introduction to Ecosystem Services

An ecosystem is an interdependent system of living things (animals, including humans, plants and microorganisms) and their physical environment. A change in any one of these components can impact on the entire ecosystem. Ecosystems can be terrestrial or marine, inland or coastal, rural or urban and can vary in size and over time. In many cases, ecosystems overlap and interact. A healthy ecosystem is one that is resilient; able to adapt to changes in the external

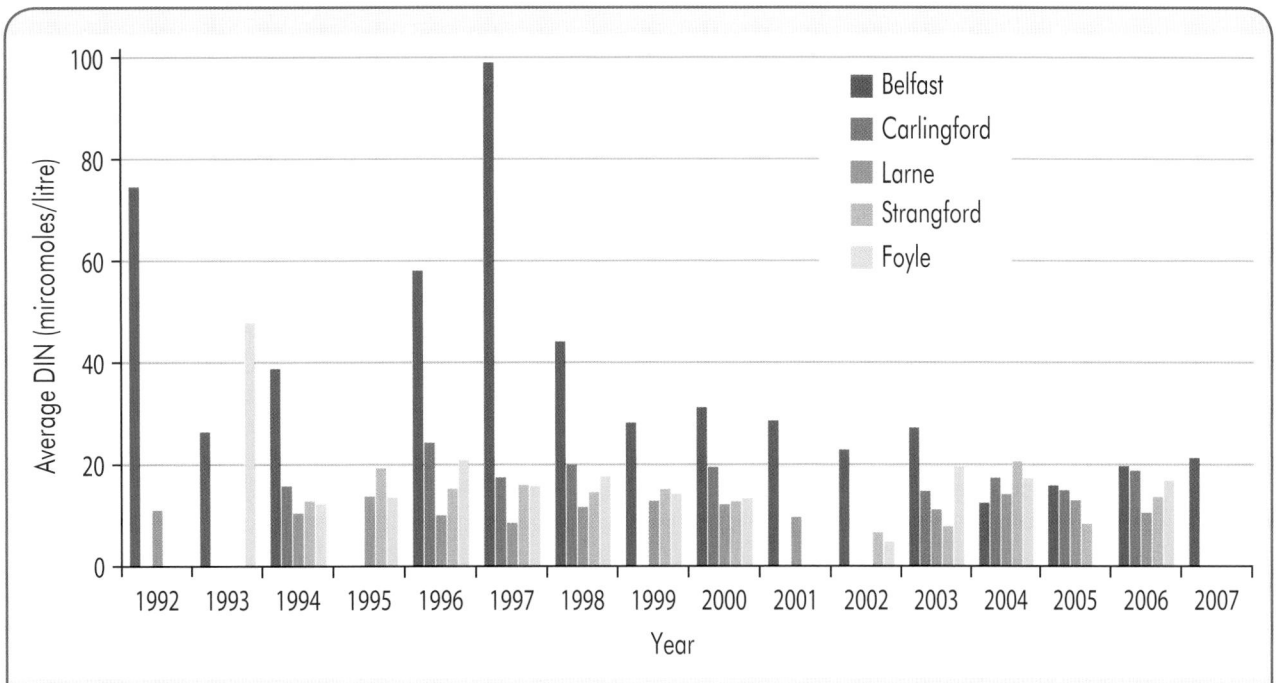

Figure 18.22 Winter dissolved inorganic nitrogen (DIN) for five sea loughs from 1992 to 2005. For all sea loughs (excluding Lough Foyle) the winter DIN values represented are averages from salinities of between 32–34.5 practical salinity units (PSU). Lough Foyle is the only sea lough which exhibits the characteristic range of salinities and associated DINs typical of a transitional water and for this reason, the annual DIN value is not an average but is the DIN normalised to 32 PSU for that year. Source: reproduced from EHS (2008a).

environment such as fires, flooding, insect population explosions, human activities and the introduction of exotic plant or animal species (Defra 2007c).

Ecosystem services are defined by the Millennium Ecosystem Assessment (MA) as the benefits provided by ecosystems that contribute to making human life both possible and worth living (MA 2005b). For the UK NEA (and the MA) Ecosystem Services are grouped into four categories:

- Provisioning ecosystem services: the products obtained from ecosystems such as food, fibre and fresh water;
- Regulating ecosystem services: the benefits obtained from the regulation of ecosystem processes such as regulation of pollination, the climate, noise and water;
- Cultural ecosystem services: the non-material benefits obtained from ecosystems, for example through spiritual or religious enrichment, cultural heritage, recreation and tourism or aesthetic experience; and,
- Supporting ecosystem services: ecosystem functions that are necessary for the production of all other ecosystem services, such as soil formation and the cycling of nutrients and water.

These ecosystem services can potentially be provided by all ecosystems, including both those relatively undisturbed and those heavily modified, such as agricultural land and urban settlements. However, it is important to recognise that some of these services are mutually exclusive, i.e. the provision of one particular service may occur at the expense of another. This is particularly the case when people have modified an ecosystem to concentrate on the production of a single service. For example, when a wetland is drained to increase agricultural output or for residential/industrial

development, it can no longer provide effective flood protection, improve water quality, maintain biodiversity or sequester carbon.

The resilience of many ecosystems around the world has been weakened by their past and current use by societies. Loss of resilience means than an ecosystem is unable to adapt to an external change and retain its structure and functions. This can have negative impacts on the ecosystem services it provides. When ecosystem resilience is damaged beyond a certain level the consequences of a small, additional change can be extreme or catastrophic (Goldschmidt 1997; Diamond 2005). However, a high level of uncertainty surrounds the scientific understanding of how these complex systems work and what these threshold limits or tipping points are (Rockström 2009b). There are also uncertainties around many elements of the structure and function of ecosystems, including the many types of bacteria, fungi and other small organisms, many of which are not yet identified, and whose roles are still poorly understood.

Degradation of ecosystem services has occurred at local, regional and global scales. The Millennium Ecosystem Assessment (MA 2005a,b) reported that approximately 60% of global ecosystem services are degraded or overexploited, often resulting in significant harm to human well-being. Species extinction, habitat loss, and decreased soil fertility and water holding capacity are examples which continue to have major impacts on human populations. All of these impacts have been noted in Northern Ireland to a greater or lesser extent.

Environmental management has shifted towards adopting the ecosystem approach (Defra 2007b,c), defined by the Convention on Biological Diversity (CBD) as 'a strategy for the integrated management of land, water and living resources that promotes conservation and sustainable use in an equitable way'. It involves management at the ecosystem scale as opposed to management at the administrative level (land ownership, political boundaries). A good example of such management is the River Basin Management Plans (RBMP) proposed under the Water Framework Directive (WFD) which include actions for both Northern Ireland and the Republic of Ireland (NIEA 2009f,g,h).

The Department for Environment, Food and Rural Affairs action plan for ecosystem management (Defra 2007c) is based on a number of core principles:

- taking a more holistic approach to policy-making and delivery, with the focus on maintaining healthy ecosystems and ecosystem services;
- ensuring that the value of ecosystem services is fully reflected in decision-making;
- ensuring that environmental limits are respected in the context of sustainable development, taking into account ecosystem functioning;
- taking decisions at the appropriate spatial scale while recognising the cumulative impacts of decisions; and
- promoting adaptive management of the natural environment to respond to changing pressures, including climate change.

The benefits of this approach include:

- more effective delivery of environmental outcomes;
- better-informed decisions that take full account of environmental impacts, helping us to achieve sustainable development;
- better prioritisation and more efficient use of our resources; and
- more effective communication and greater awareness of the value of the natural environment and ecosystem services.

Ecosystem assessment recognises the complex interactive nature of organisms and their physical environment and the provision by ecosystems of benefits to people. The interactions amongst animals and plants mean that disturbance of one component can have major impacts on the others. One example of this is reduced crop yields caused by poor pollination due to reduced bee population numbers. Ecosystem scale management provides a mechanism for identifying interrelationships within and between complex ecosystems, explicitly recognising the multiple benefits they provide. Understanding the trade-offs and synergies between different ecosystem services is crucial for informed, effective decision making which optimises all benefits to society in the short and longer terms.

18.5.2 Provisioning Services

Provisioning services are those goods provided by ecosystems for direct use by people including food, fibre, fuel, fresh water and minerals. In comparison to regulatory and cultural services, they are more easily quantified and it is easier to assign a financial value to them; however, the different ways in which products are valued makes comparison and the determination of total contributions difficult. Land is

consciously and actively managed by people for products; it is used to produce crops or animals which are then used directly by people or cycled back through systems to produce other outputs (for example, cereal may be eaten directly or fed to animals which produce milk or meat). Provisioning services are widely recognised as being essential for human well-being. However, the degree to which provisioning services are dependent on other ecosystems and ecosystem services is less clearly understood. Resources from the marine environment are generally not owned or managed to the same degree as those on land, with resulting issues of overexploitation.

18.5.2.1 Food from agriculture and horticulture

Northern Ireland's climate and soils are highly suitable for growing grass. Currently most of Northern Ireland's land is used for producing meat and dairy products, including the production of silage and cereals to feed the animals. The production-based subsidies of the CAP have also contributed to the major expansion of the dairy, beef and sheep sectors (Cruickshank 1997). However, this policy driver has reduced since the introduction of the Single Farm Payment in 2005, with clear results.

Some land, mostly in the east, is used for arable production of cereals, potatoes and, increasingly, additional crops such as oil seed rape and fodder maize (DARD 2010i). Around three-quarters of the 1,351,000 ha land area of Northern Ireland is agricultural. This is primarily rough and improved grazing for cattle and sheep with some arable farming, predominantly in the east; 93% grass and rough grazing; 5% agricultural crops; 0.3% horticultural crops; 1% woods and plantations (state forestry is in addition to this); and 0.7% other (DARD 2010o). Farms are traditionally small and managed by the farmers and their families, with occasional additional help. In recent years some larger farms, especially in the east, have increased in size and become more intensive livestock or dairy enterprises, while smaller farms have become less viable. Farmland is sometimes sold as building plots to provide (often essential) farm income. The impacts of the current recession on farmland sales for building are not yet known, but planning applications have decreased in recent years (see **Table 18.8**). This may in part be due to changing policies, which themselves may have an impact on the selling of building plots as the new PPS21 requires new dwellings to be integrated with existing farm buildings. The increasing capital value of land far outstrips any other investment which can lead to 'land rich, cash poor' farmers and unviable farms not being abandoned or sold. There is a widespread system of conacre, a system of letting land for the short term in which it is the use of the land for a specific purpose, rather than the land itself, which is rented (Alexander 1963).

There have been significant changes over the past 150 years in terms of the production of crops and animals (**Figure 18.23**; **Figure 18.24**; **Figure 18.25**). Trends over the past 50 years have continued those begun 150 years ago except for pig production, which dropped in recent years following a major rise in the first half of the 20th Century. Over this period there has been a significant shift in production from cereals and potatoes (and flax up until 50 years ago) to hay/silage

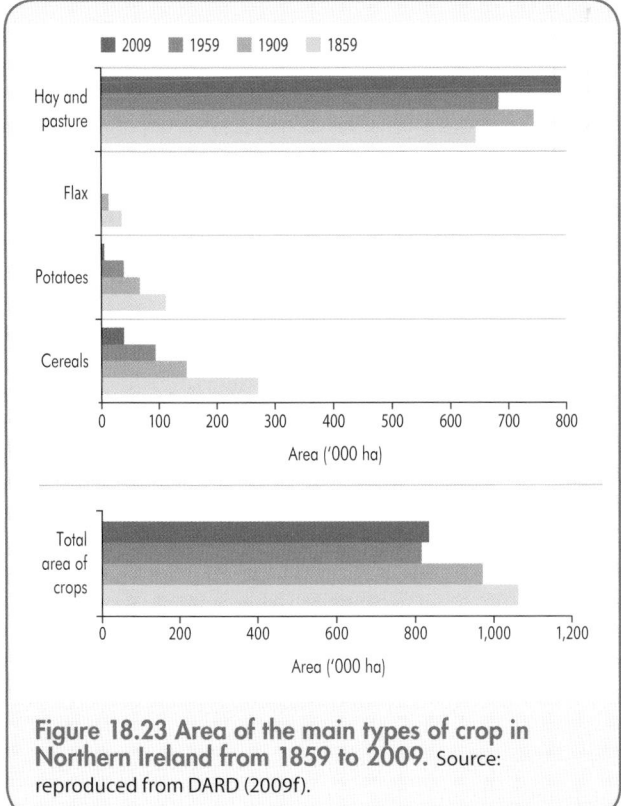

Figure 18.23 Area of the main types of crop in Northern Ireland from 1859 to 2009. Source: reproduced from DARD (2009f).

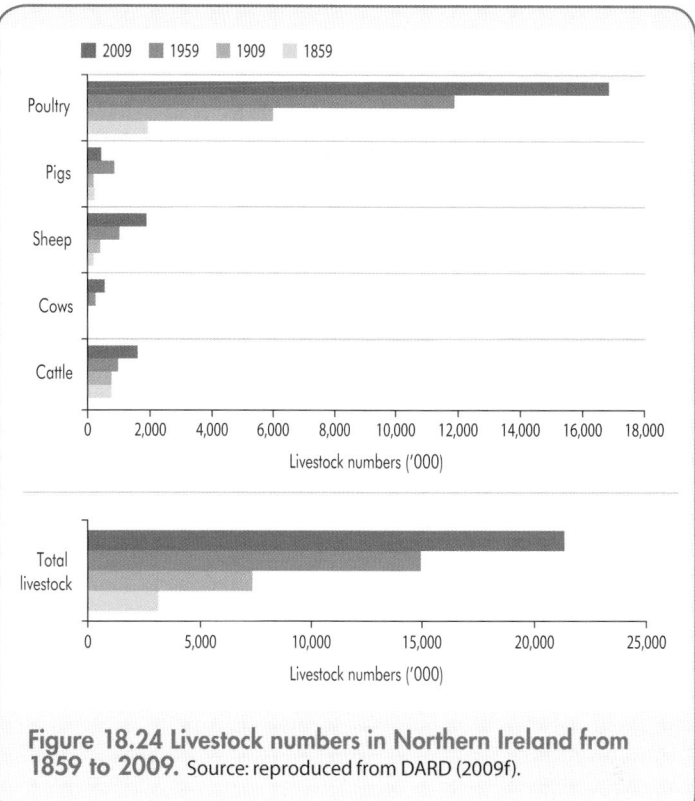

Figure 18.24 Livestock numbers in Northern Ireland from 1859 to 2009. Source: reproduced from DARD (2009f).

and pastureland. The overall amount of land in production decreased from 1850 to 1950, but has remained relatively constant since then. However, this does not take into account the intensity of land use (e.g. low level grazing on uplands is not differentiated from intense livestock farming).

Most of Northern Ireland's arable farmland is currently used for producing grain for animals rather than crops for direct human consumption (NIGTA unpublished data). The types of crops raised have varied over the years, and there have been changes in land use between arable crops and grassland as well (DARD 2010c). Such changes have been driven by markets, policies, subsidies and farmer preferences and indicate a fair degree of flexibility of the land to provide different outputs. The ability to respond to economic drivers is constrained by the soil and climate, and thus the impact of climate change must be considered highly significant for future agricultural production and land use patterns. **Figure 18.13** (area) and **Figure 18.25** (tonnage) present data on what crops have been grown over the past 28 years. Crop yield per hectare has shown an increasing trend over the period, except for grass silage for which it has remained relatively constant (DARD 2010i). The vast majority of arable land is used to produce cereals, mostly spring barley, and potatoes. There has been a significant increase in the area under wheat in recent years and a drop in potato and spring barley production.

Although the area of land used to produce fruit has decreased substantially since 1981, the tonnage of fruit produced has risen during that period (**Figure 18.26**; **Figure 18.27**). Most fruit production is apples, 1,165 ha in 2007 (Cooper *et al.* 2009), and 99% of orchards grow Bramley apples with the remaining produce consisting of plums and dessert apples (Withers *et al.* 2008). Productivity is relatively volatile, but the area of land under orchards has shown a

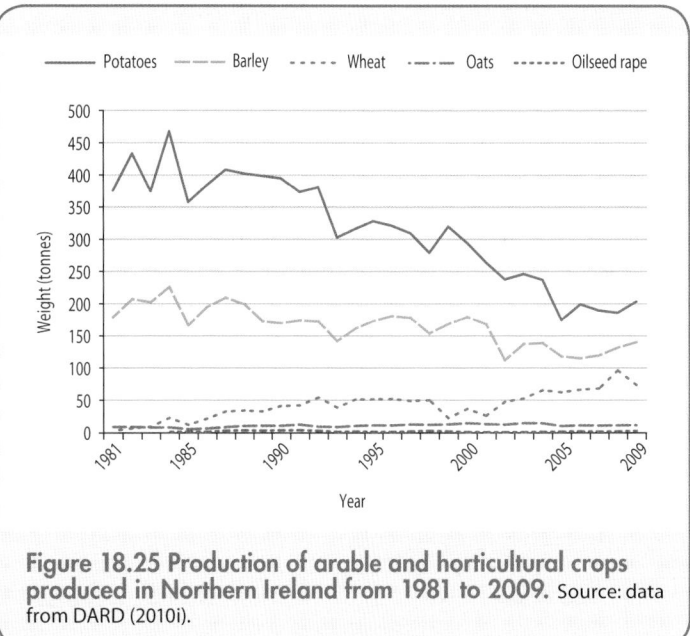

Figure 18.25 Production of arable and horticultural crops produced in Northern Ireland from 1981 to 2009. Source: data from DARD (2010i).

steady decrease since 1981. There has been a slight increase in land devoted to vegetable growing.

Mushroom production increased in value from £5.1 million in 1981 to £19.9 million in 2009. However, there has been a decline in output and value from its peak value of £32 million in 1996 (DARD 2010j; Section 18.5.2).

Most of Northern Ireland's land is used to rear livestock (DARD 2010o; **Figure 18.28**). There was a considerable drop in the number of pigs in the mid-1990s, following an increase in the cost at abattoirs (Defra 2004) and market forces against which the pig market is less protected via subsidy than cattle and sheep (Thankappan & Flynn 2006). Sheep numbers show fluctuation but have decreased from

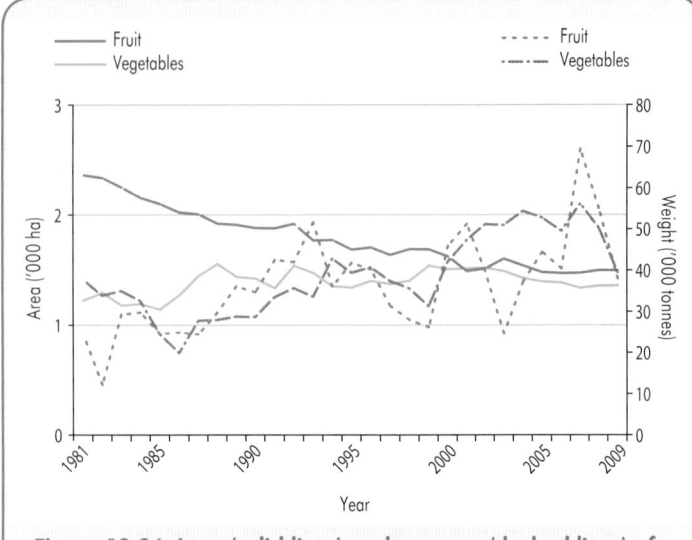

Figure 18.26 Area (solid lines) and tonnage (dashed lines) of fruit (including apples) and vegetables raised in Northern Ireland between 1981 and 2009. Source: data from DARD (2010c,k).

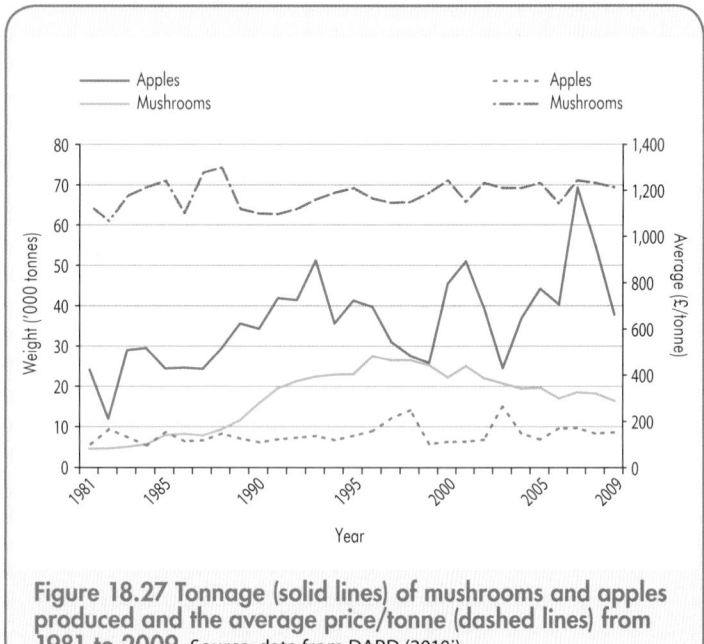

Figure 18.27 Tonnage (solid lines) of mushrooms and apples produced and the average price/tonne (dashed lines) from 1981 to 2009. Source: data from DARD (2010j).

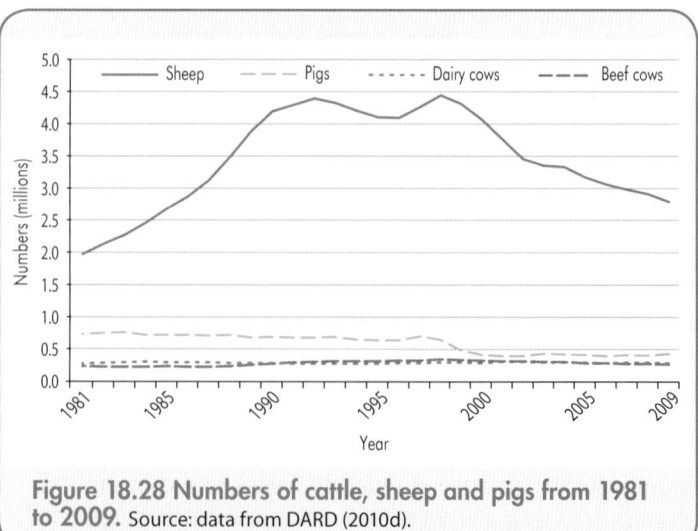

Figure 18.28 Numbers of cattle, sheep and pigs from 1981 to 2009. Source: data from DARD (2010d).

very high levels in the late 1980s to the early 2000s, the rise being related to CAP payment calculated on headage. This trend was also seen in beef cattle but not to the same degree. Dairy cows have remained relatively constant over this period, following a drop in numbers in 1998. Adverse effects of the preceding BSE crisis and the outbreak of foot-and-mouth disease in 2001, in addition to the relative strength of the pound making exports less competitive, have been important drivers in this regard (Mead 2003).

Given global instability in the food supply chain and price, increasing human population, costs of transport, drives for greater food security (at UK and Northern Ireland levels) and the impacts of climate change, it is likely that food supply will rise up the political agenda in Northern Ireland in parallel with the emphasis in the UK as a whole. However, there are many interacting factors with implications for land use, including the value of unploughed pastureland as a carbon store, future CAP reform, increasing emphasis on food security, rising global food prices, animal welfare, reducing food miles, drives for renewable energy production, increasing costs of fuel and chemicals, consumer preferences, food traceability and an increasing demand for meat globally. All these factors make predicting future trends difficult. There is a strong attachment to the small family farm in Northern Ireland due to the history of land ownership. This often goes against rational options for farm management and is a factor limiting structural reform (Moss & Chilton 1997a,b).

In 2009 there were 48,031 farm workers (full-time, part-time, casual and spouses) equating to 28,000 Annual Work Units (approximately equivalent to Full Time Equivalent), a 26% decline since 1988 (when the figure was 66,312) and a 30% decline since 1981 (DARD 2010f; **Figure 18.29**). Most of these are farm owners. This is around 4% of total civil employment in Northern Ireland compared to 1.6% in the UK, 5% in the Republic of Ireland and 3.7% in the EU15 (DARD 2010o). Off-farm sources of income are vitally important for many farmers.

There has been a shift from full-time towards part-time and casual working patterns. Fewer farms in Northern Ireland are now economically sustainable, and over half of all farmers were over 55 years of age in 2005 (DARD 2007a; Spedding 2009). Diversification is an important source of farm income for some farmers, with 13% of farms involved in diversification activities such as organic beef production or providing bed and breakfast accommodation in 2001 (DARD 2002). In 2007 1,604 farms (6%) were involved in diversification projects, excluding contracting/haulage (2,339, or 9%, if this is included), with such projects encouraged and supported through EU structural funds (DARD 2008d).

Northern Ireland's average farm size of approximately 40 ha compares to the UK average of 54 ha, the Republic of Ireland average of 32 ha and the EU15 average of 27 ha (DARD 2010o). Between 2004 and 2009 average farm size increased from 38.5 to 39.9 ha, with a corresponding decrease in numbers of farms from 27,614 to 25,264, representing a drop of 9% (DARD 2010o). In 2009 almost a quarter of all farms had less than 10 ha of crops and grass while over 1,300 farms (5%) had 100 ha or more; these latter occupied 24% of the total area of crops and grass. Roughly half of all farmers had

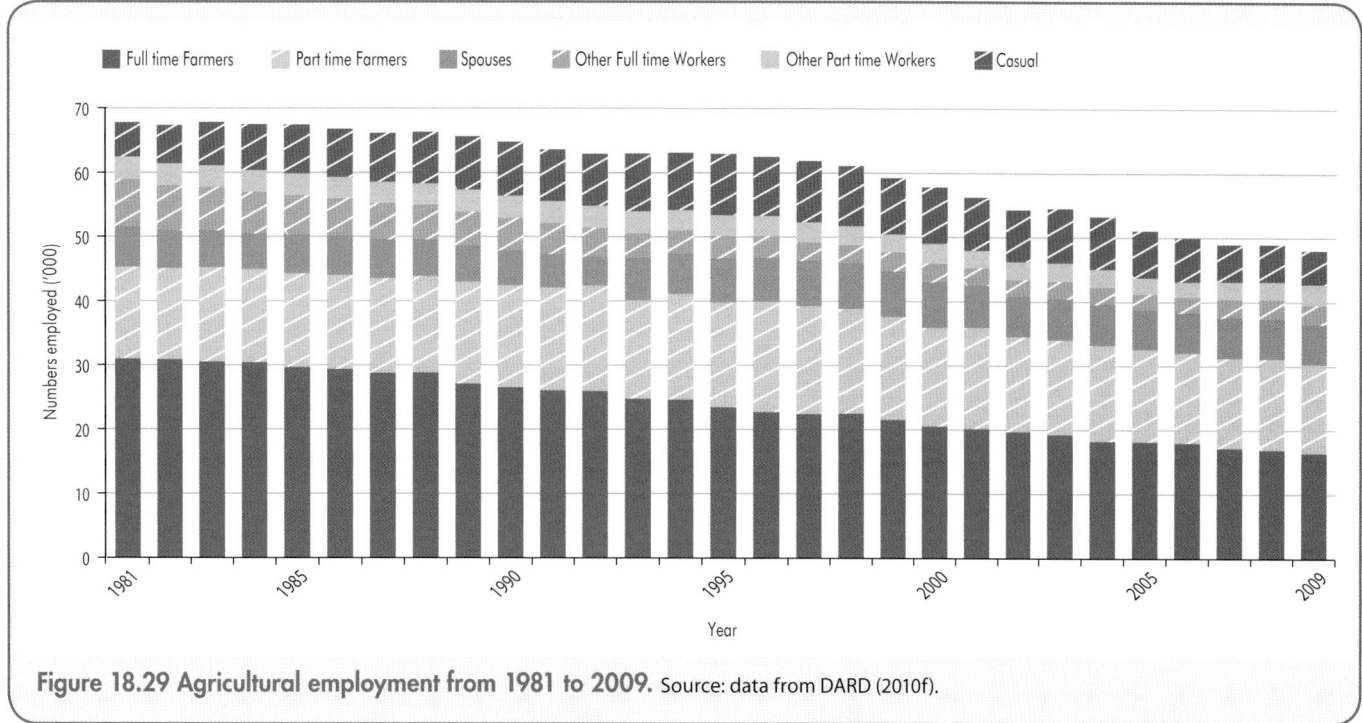

Figure 18.29 Agricultural employment from 1981 to 2009. Source: data from DARD (2010f).

off-farm income, including both earned income and social security benefits (DARD 2010e). The downward trend in the number of farms is approximately 2% per year over the past 10 years (DARD 2010b; **Figure 18.30**). In 1963 there were 68,000 agricultural holdings but only 46,000 separate farm businesses, emphasising the importance of inheritance and conacre in farm viability. In Northern Ireland 48.9% of farms are entirely owner occupied, 28.5% are 50–100% owner occupied, 16.3% are 0–50% owner occupied, and 6.3% are not owner occupied (probably most of these involving conacre (DARD 2010o)) which, combined with inheritance tax, allows for some transfer of land management without impacting on land ownership. Turbary, water, mineral, shooting and other 'rights' are complex, rooted in history, and often do not follow land ownership (Cruickshank & Tomlinson 1995). About one-third of land farmed in Northern Ireland was let out through conacre in 2005 (DARD 2010o). Conacre price varies by purpose, from £41/ha for rough grazing up to £686/ha for potatoes in 2008 (DARD 2010o).

Land prices had remained relatively static at around £6,000/ha from 1981 to 1992 before rising to £10,000/ha in 2001. Following a steep rise since 2001 they are now some of highest in Europe at £19,837/ha in 2005 (DARD 2009a, 2010o).

Northern Ireland is a net exporter of food, primarily animal products produced on large areas of rough and improved grazing land (Section 18.6). Livestock and livestock products accounted for an estimated £1.14 billion of agricultural output in 2008 compared to £66 million for crops and £59.6 million for horticultural products (DARD 2010o; **Table 18.11**). Milk (1.9 million litres; £514 million), beef (£280 million), pork (£77 million) and sheepmeat and wool (£51 million) are important products (output values), with exports to Great Britain contributing around half of that total. There is also a thriving chicken industry annually producing around 247,400 tonnes live weight of poultry meat

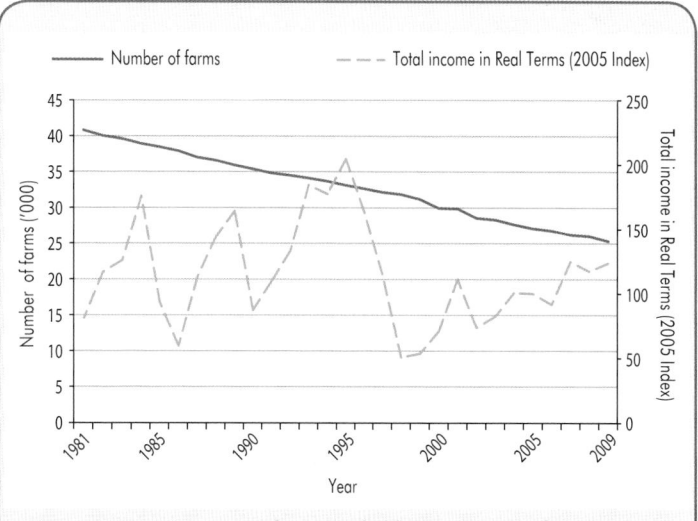

Figure 18.30 Farm numbers and relative income from 1981 to 2009. The 2005 index value was set at 100. Source: data from DARD (2010g,q).

(including broilers) and 738 million eggs (DARD 2010o,n; **Table 18.11**). Comparison of values is difficult due to different recording methodology, definitions and times.

There are 3,457 dairy farms in Northern Ireland, with a cumulative total of 290,000 dairy cows, producing 1.9 billion litres of milk. Businesses which pasteurise milk and those which manufacture milk products such as butter, cheese, ice cream and yoghurt employed 2,352 full-time workers in 2008 and represent around 12% of the agri-food industry in total. The largest single sector in terms of numbers employed is involved in beef- and sheep meat-related activities, i.e. all the businesses involved in the slaughtering of cattle and sheep and the processing of their meat. This employed 3,316 full-time workers in 2008, equal to 17% of the total (DARD 2010n).

Table 18.11 Agricultural products for Northern Ireland in 2009. # signifies data not available. Source: data from DARD (2010o).

Sector		Numbers or Area (ha)	Quantities of the main product	Output (£ million)	Input (£ million)	Gross Margin (£ million)
Livestock and livestock products	Dairy cows & followers	1.62 million (including 290,000 dairy cattle & 266,000 beef cattle)	Milk: 1,906 million litres	514.5	164.6	349.9
	Beef cattle, rearing & fattening		Cattle & calves: 140,749 t dressed carcass weight (dcw)	279.7	198.8	80.9
	Sheep and wool	1.97 million (including 935,000 breeding ewes)	Sheep & lambs: 18,818 t dcw	50.6	31.5	19.1
	Pigs	402,000 (including 37,000 breeding pigs)	Pigs: 70,155 t dcw	76.9	57.4	19.5
	Poultry	17.13 million (11.54 million broilers & 2.40 million laying birds)	Poultry: 247,000 t liveweight (lwt); Eggs: 61.5 million dozen	217.6	188.3	29.3
	Total	**Grass: 789,600 ha; Rough Grazing: 147,100 ha**	n/a	**1,139.3**	**640.6**	**498.7**
Agricultural crops	Cereals	40,600 ha	239,400 t	45.5	13.2	32.3
	Potatoes	5,100 ha	160,700 t	20.5	6.1	14.4
	Other	9,800 ha				
	Total	**55,500 ha**	**400,100 t**	**66.0**	**19.3**	**46.7**
Horticulture	Fruit	1,500 ha	54,800 t	8.9	#	#
	Vegetables	1,400 ha	50,300 t	#	#	#
	Mushrooms	100 ha	18,200 t	22.4	#	#
	Ornamentals			11.7		
	Total	**3,000 ha**	**123,300 t**	**59.6**	**17.4**	**42.2**
Other	**Total**	**22,300 ha**		**37.1**	**9.2**	**27.8**
Agriculture Total		**1,017,500 ha**	**n/a**	**1,302.0**	**686.5**	**615.5**

The food and drink processing sector provided a gross turnover of £2,724 million in 2007, with a value added of £530 million (DARD 2009d). Beef and sheep meat were the primary sources of this revenue, making up 25% of gross turnover in the sector (DARD 2009d). The sector employed over 18,000 people in 2007 with export sales (outside the UK) of £645 million (DARD 2009d). **Figure 18.31** shows the destinations of Northern Ireland's produce, with sizeable exports of meat and milk products (Section 18.7 shows a comparison with imports). Not all of this value is directly related to the provisioning service (including human input and additional processing), but all relies on it for its existence.

Northern Ireland is a net importer of animal feed (2,296,000 tonnes at a cost of £518.1 million (gross) in 2009 (DARD 2010o), which accounts for 37% of the total expenses of Northern Ireland agriculture, compared to 19% in the UK (DARD 2010o).

Linking production outputs to UK NEA habitats is difficult, as categories do not coincide and data are not collected on a habitat basis, but the vast majority of arable land is categorised as Enclosed Farmland, which also includes most of the silage production and considerable grazing, particularly for milk production. Farm census criteria have been altered repeatedly, including when the UK became a member of the EU (McAdam 1988), so there are difficulties comparing livestock numbers from the post-war period to the present day.

Semi-natural Grasslands are largely used for low intensity grazing, and are particularly suited to native Irish cattle breeds which respond well to the wet conditions. The output from the smaller areas of specialised habitats is relatively small, but Neutral Grassland covers a significant proportion of the farmland of Northern Ireland. It is not possible to disaggregate the output from these habitat types from that of other agricultural production, but the Semi-natural Grassland habitat is largely in the Less Favoured Area (LFA) designated parts of Northern Ireland and LFAs are used largely for beef cattle and sheep. Less Favoured Areas account for 70% of agricultural land involving 57% of all farms (DARD 2009d, 2010n). Agricultural use of uplands is largely for livestock grazing, overwhelmingly for sheep at relatively low stocking densities. In addition, animals may move between Enclosed Farmland and open moorland over the year. However, a number of sources point to increased pressure on moorland grazing in the 1970s and 1980s. McAdam (1988) found that the number of sheep on Northern Ireland hill farms increased from 150,000 in 1960 to 290,000 in 1975, Edwards (1987) reported an increase of nearly 70% in the Northern Ireland hill sheep flock from 1974 to 1985, and the Ballycastle District saw an increase of 30% in its sheep flock from 1983 to 1988 (Kirkpatrick et al. 1999; see **Figure 18.28**). A subsidy regime which rewarded those who increased their sheep numbers led to a peak of just under 4.5 million sheep in 1998, but by 2009 numbers were down

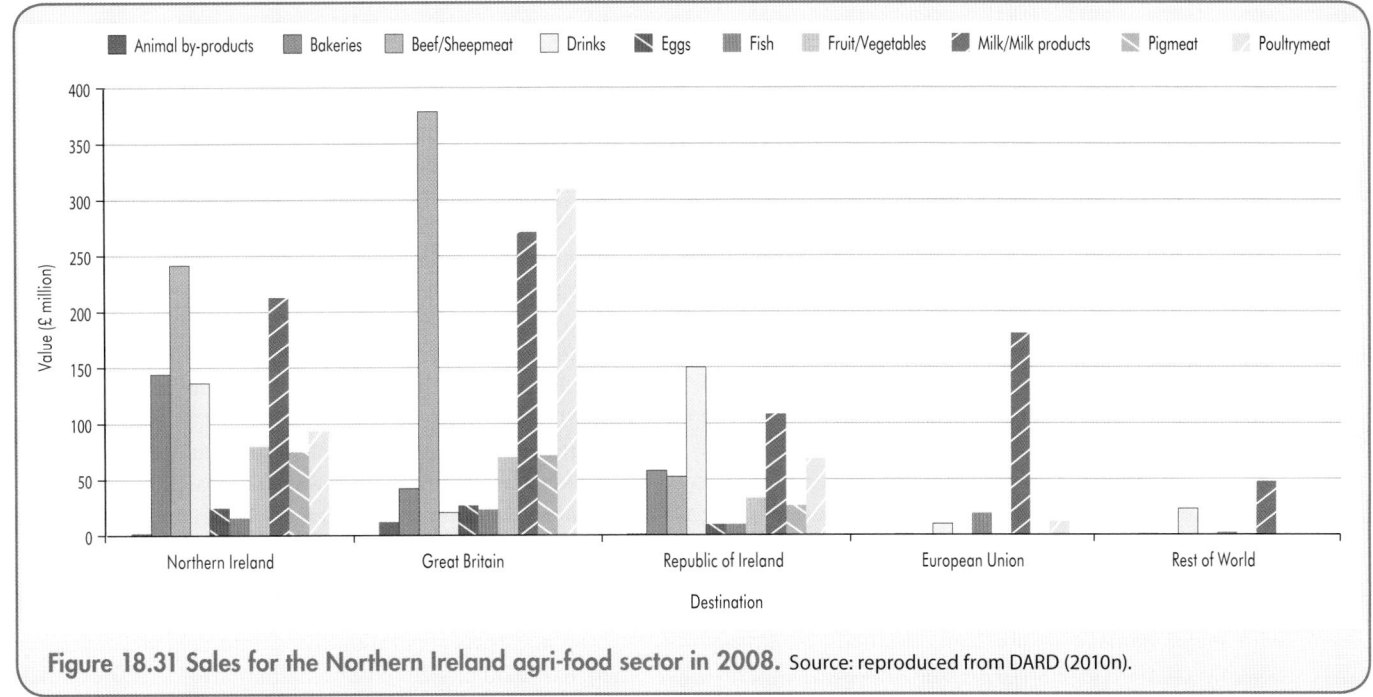

Figure 18.31 Sales for the Northern Ireland agri-food sector in 2008. Source: reproduced from DARD (2010n).

to 2.7 million (DARD 2010d; see **Figure 18.28**) as a result of agri-environment policies, for example through requiring Northern Ireland Countryside Management Scheme members to remove sheep for specified periods in the year and thereby encourage plant growth and biodiversity. However, under-grazing can also have negative biodiversity impacts (Upton & Bain 2006). There is still some limited grazing of cattle and sometimes sheep on coastal dunes, but this was higher in the past. Reclamation of tidal lands has occurred in most of Northern Ireland's sea loughs for agriculture (e.g. south side of the Foyle at Eglinton, Ballykelly).

18.5.2.2 Marine fisheries

Northern Ireland's seas (shore to 12 NM) support a substantial amount of the UK's marine biodiversity with some 4,000 species (NIEA 2010g). The total value of fish landed by Northern Irish vessels was £23.2 million in 2008 (DOE 2010a; AFBI & NIEA 2011). There were around 625 fishermen, some of whom were part-time (DARD 2009d; DOE 2010a), and Northern Ireland accounted for approximately 4–5% of UK landings (Cracknall 2009; DOE 2010a; MFA 2009). In 2008 this amounted to 14,900 tonnes of shellfish, 12,100 tonnes of pelagic and 2,900 tonnes of demersal finfish for a total of 29,900 tonnes (Cracknall 2009; DOE 2010a; MFA 2009). There has been a significant shift from 1993 to 2007 from finfish to shellfish (DCAL 2008; **Figure 18.32**). An additional 615 full-time and nearly 200 part-time employees were involved in the industry in processing, marketing and other work (DARD 2009d).

At the end of 2008 the Northern Ireland fishing fleet comprised some 147 fishing vessels over 10 m in length and 204 vessels 10 m and under in length. However, this does not include full data on the commercial operations of the 10 m and under inshore fleet, for which data submission is voluntary for species other than crabs and lobsters (DOE 2010a).

In addition to the capture of wild fish stocks, Northern Ireland also produces a significant amount of seafood via aquaculture. In marine aquaculture Northern Ireland's

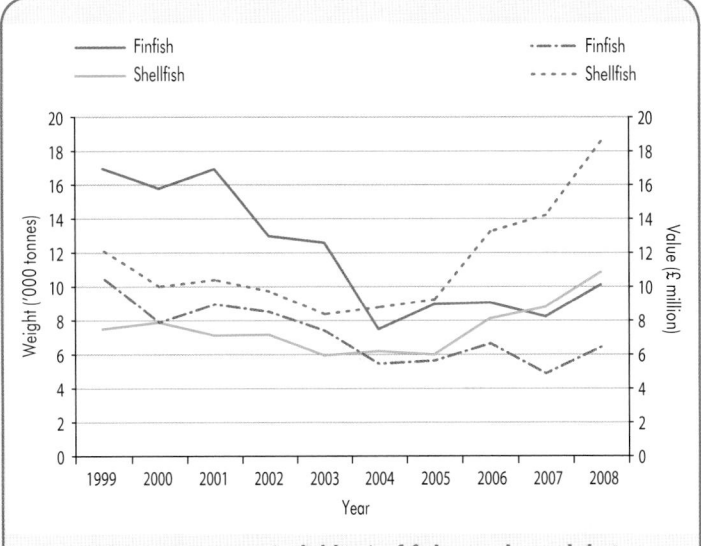

Figure 18.32 Tonnage (solid line) of fish caught and their value (dashed line) from 1999 to 2008. Source: data from DARD (2005; 2009d).

production focuses on shellfish, primarily bottom-grown mussels, and here it outperforms other regions in relative terms, producing 25% of the UK's cultured shellfish harvest (UKMMAS 2010). Fisheries, aquaculture and marine tourism together generated £135 million and supported about 1,400 full-time jobs in 2008 (DOE 2010a).

In addition to the direct depletion of the target stock by capture fisheries there is unintended damage to the physical environment and other species through bycatch, disturbance and destruction of seabed communities. Although Northern Ireland specific data are not available, in general, fishing focuses first on predators (such as cod, which are near the top of the food web) and then moves down to lower trophic levels as predator populations decrease, with resulting significant impacts on the marine food web (Pauly et al. 1998), often resulting in population explosions of bottom-feeding invertebrates, such as shrimp (*Pandalus* species;

Worm & Myers 2003; Frank *et al.* 2005). Impacts of fishing are more severe in sheltered habitats, such as sea loughs, that characterise the Irish Sea.

Overall, EU fisheries have declined by about 30% in 10–15 years (Lynam *et al.* 2010). In 1994 roughly 45% of the Northern Ireland catch comprised bottom-dwelling species (Cracknell 2009), mainly cod, hake, whiting, monkfish, flatfish and dogfish, which were caught by trawl (Barne *et al.* 1997). The remaining catch was roughly evenly split between pelagic species, such as herring, and shellfish including *Nephrops* (caught by otter trawl) and mussels. By 2008 bottom-dwelling fish made up only 10% of the catch, with shellfish increasing to 50% and pelagic species to 40% (Cracknell 2009).

This suggests that the threat of habitat destruction as a result of fishing is declining, although mobile bottom gear, including scallop dredges, is still in operation, some in sensitive areas such as the waters off Rathlin Island, and these activities are particularly significant (Foden *et al.* 2010), with major damage to horse mussel beds in Strangford Lough (Roberts *et al.* 2004). However, this also suggests that the marine food web in Northern Ireland has been fished to close to its base (Le Loc'h & Hily 2005). Further disruption of the marine food web could result in negative consequences, such as outbreaks of jellyfish, seaweeds or slimes (Pauly 2009; Richardson *et al.* 2009), which are among the few macroscopic organisms with a lower trophic level than the shellfish. The overall impact of fishing is to deplete higher trophic levels, allowing opportunistic species characteristic of unstable, regularly disrupted communities, to establish. Many notable commercial species, such as scallops, depend on stable habitats and communities.

Although there is some evidence of recent stabilisation or recovery of fish stocks (UKMMAS 2010), stocks are lower than they were a decade ago (Thurstan *et al.* 2010). Nevertheless, the importance of Northern Ireland fisheries from a socio-economic perspective suggests that fishing effort will decline only slowly, and that heavily exploited stocks and habitats will continue to be impacted into the future, albeit at slightly lower levels than have been experienced over the past three decades. The Common Fisheries Policy (CFP) Review, currently being undertaken by the EU Fisheries Council, is likely to have implications for Northern Ireland in its attempt to combat such trends while maintaining the economic viability of the industry (NI Executive 2010a).

18.5.2.3 Freshwater fisheries

There are two major freshwater fisheries in Northern Ireland: eels and salmon. The production of eels from Lough Neagh is around 400 t/yr. With a value at £5/kg this would be worth £2 million and the industry employs an estimated 300 people part-time (April–September; Rosell *et al.* 2005). At its peak, this industry had a value of £5 million. There is a demand for eels, but not in Northern Ireland; most of the catch from the Lough Neagh fisheries is exported, mainly to Holland (Hansard 2010).

The stock of European eels has been in rapid decline since around 1980, so that by 2005 numbers had declined by as much as 95–99% (ICES 2006). The European Commission adopted regulations (Eel Regulation (EC) 1100/2007) in 2007 to establish measures to help facilitate its recovery, which require the establishment of eel management plans for the three Northern Ireland river basins (DCAL 2007; 2009a). Lough Neagh is home to Europe's largest eel fishery, but numbers of eels have been declining since 1983. Lough Neagh fishermen now have to source elvers from catchments in Southern Europe in order to sustain numbers. Eel numbers in Lough Erne have fallen so low that commercial eel fishing has now been banned there (NI Assembly 2010).

The Neagh Bann River Basin in Northern Ireland is now the only region in the United Kingdom where eel fishing is permitted. The European Eel Regulations demand that it be demonstrated that at least 40% of the adult eels from each river basin are escaping to spawn, compared with the best estimate of the potential escapement in the absence of human activity. Lough Erne is transnational and therefore a cross-border management plan must be devised by the relevant Departments in Northern Ireland and the Republic of Ireland. A 'trap and truck' operation to capture eels and transport them to the other side of Ballyshannon hydroelectric dam is used to prevent death of eels in hydroelectric machinery. The objective of this is to transport 22.5 tonnes of eels during 2009, and four fishermen have been employed to do this conservation work (Hansard 2009).

Northern Ireland has a total of 27 salmon rivers over the two fisheries jurisdictions (Loughs Agency and the Fisheries Conservancy Board; NASCO 2009). Salmon fishing has decreased in recent years to just over 5,000 kg in 2007 (**Figure 18.33**) but has stabilised since then. In 2009 the Department of Agriculture and Rural Development issued 34 commercial fishing licences (20 drift net, 12 draft net, two bag net; John McCartney, Loughs Agency, pers. comm.) and DCAL issued six licences (two drift net, two tidal draft net, two bag net; Fiona Lavery, DCAL Inland Fisheries, pers. comm.). The catch in 2009 of 16.7 tonnes represented a significant decline on the previous 5-year average of 22.5 tonnes, with nearly two-thirds of the catch now caught by line rather than net (Kennedy *et al.* 2010). The number and proportion of salmon caught at sea and in estuaries has decreased markedly since 2002 (**Figure 18.34**).

18.5.2.4 Aquaculture

The global tendency for wild fisheries to be replaced by aquaculture production is apparent in the UK in general, and specifically in Northern Ireland (Lynam *et al.* 2010). While most wild capture fisheries are in decline, aquaculture output is increasing. These trends represent opportunities both for new economic activity and for initiatives that seek more sustainable approaches to seafood production, and to environmental threats.

The aquaculture industry, particularly the shellfish sector, has developed significantly in recent years in Northern Ireland. There are currently 81 licensed fish farms (covering 100 sites) of which 48 are shellfish farms and 33 are finfish farms. The main species cultured are common/blue mussels (*Mytilus edulis*) and Pacific oysters (*Crassostrea gigas*; **Table 18.12**), although there are also small quantities of native oysters (*Ostrea edulis*), clams (*Venerupis semidecussata*), scallops (*Aequipecten opercularis*), rainbow trout (*Onchorhynchus* *mykiss*) and Atlantic salmon (*Salmo salar*; DARD 2010b). The estimated production of the aquaculture sector in 2009 was valued at £10.9 million, with over 8,000 tonnes of mussels (£6,743,700), 282 tonnes of oysters (£902,400), 1,102 tonnes of salmonids (£3,141,750) and more than 35 million trout ova (£188,000). In total the aquaculture sector in Northern Ireland directly employs around 150 people within some 25 businesses (Lantra 2009).

The Pacific oyster is listed among the species with a potential to invade Northern Ireland's waters (Habitas 2008), and is reported to have established in Strangford Lough (Guy & Roberts 2009), but the remaining species are indigenous. Threats in addition to the escape of cultured species include eutrophication and pollution of enclosed or sheltered waters (where aquaculture installations tend to be located), the capture of wild-caught fish to feed finfish and possibly the increased abundance of parasites due to artificially high concentrations of cultured species.

18.5.2.5 Timber

Northern Ireland's sawn timber is used primarily for fencing (47%), pallets and packaging (25%) and construction (26%) and is traded into Northern Ireland, UK and European markets (Forestry Commission 2010a, 2010c). Timber production increased from just under 50,000 m³ in 1974–1975 to a peak of almost 440,000 m³ in 2004–2005 after which it fell to roughly 400,000 m³ and has remained at that level since. For 2008 and 2009 the Forest Service has slightly exceeded its target to sell at least 400,000 m³ of timber (2008–2009: 404,000; 2009–2010: 402,000; Forest Service 2010b), bringing in receipts of over £7.5 million and £7.2 million of timber sales for the 2 years respectively. Of all woodland in Northern Ireland, 73% is certified to UK Woodland Assurance Standard (Forestry Commission 2010c) and 95% of this certified woodland is under the management of the Northern Ireland Forest Service. All Forest Service-managed woodland is certified (Forest Service 2010a). Sales of broadleaved timber are negligible (Forest Service 2010a).

Most of Northern Ireland's coniferous forests are in the uplands where land was easier to acquire than in the lowlands with their better soils. Much of the forest is on blanket peatland. However, since 1993 the Forest Service has not planted new areas on oligotrophic or dystrophic peat because of the realisation of the uniqueness of the habitat and the need to sustain species and habitat diversity (Forest Service 1993). As forests mature and are harvested, most will be replanted to trees (Forest Service 2007a).

18.5.2.6 Water

Northern Ireland Water is the only public water supplier in Northern Ireland and is government owned. It supplies over 600 million litres (l) of high quality drinking water each day to approximately 795,000 properties, both domestic and non-domestic. Households account for most of this, with agriculture, industry and commerce each using substantial amounts (**Figure 18.35**). Northern Ireland Water utilises approximately 34 water sources, which include upland impounding reservoirs (49%), rivers and loughs (49%) and boreholes (NI Water 2010b). This contrasts with England and Wales where overall 35% is extracted from groundwater,

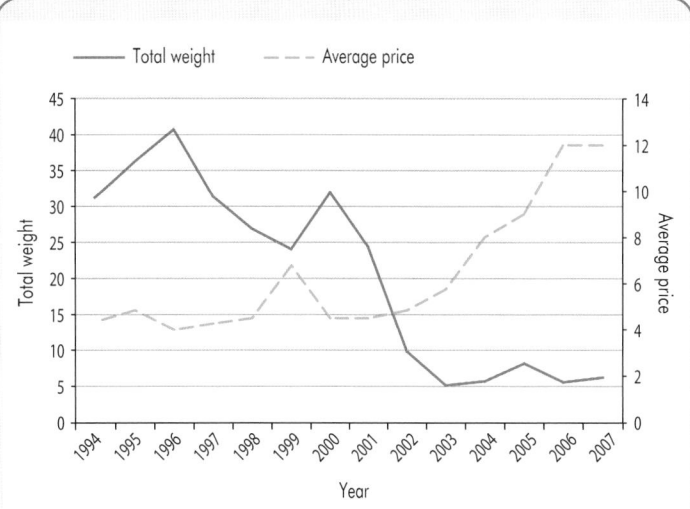

Figure 18.33 Commercial salmon catch in Northern Ireland by weight (solid line) and value (dashed line) from 1994 to 2007. Figures do not include the Foyle Catchment, which lands fish primarily in the Republic of Ireland. Source: data from DCAL (2008).

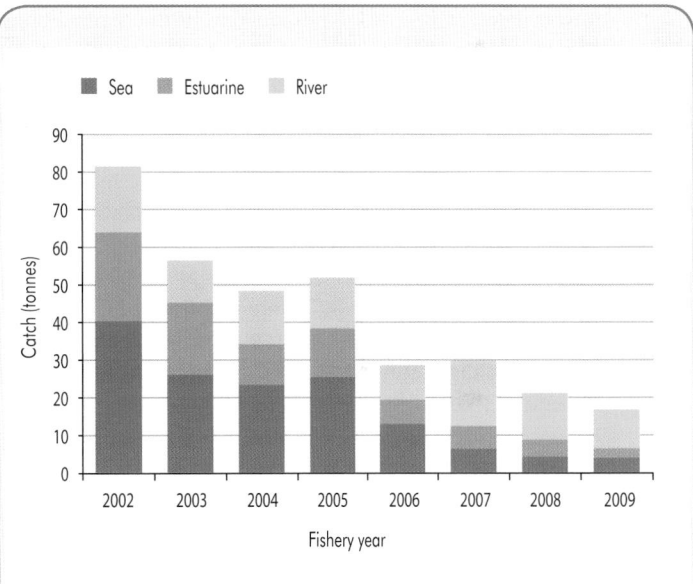

Figure 18.34 Northern Ireland salmon catch from 2002 to 2009 from freshwater, transitional and coastal waters. Source: reproduced from Kennedy *et al.* (2010).

Table 18.12 Active aquaculture areas in five Northern Ireland sea loughs. Source: data from Ferreira *et al.* (2007).

Lough	Lough area (ha)	Common/blue mussel		Pacific oyster	
		Area (ha)	Type	Area (ha)	Type
Carlingford (NI area)	4,900	168	Bottom Culture & Rafts	83	Trestles
Strangford	14,900	6	Rafts	24	Trestles
Belfast	13,000	953	Bottom Culture	0	n/a
Larne	800	10	Bottom Culture	60	Trestles
Foyle	18,600	1,603	Bottom culture	0.1	Trestles

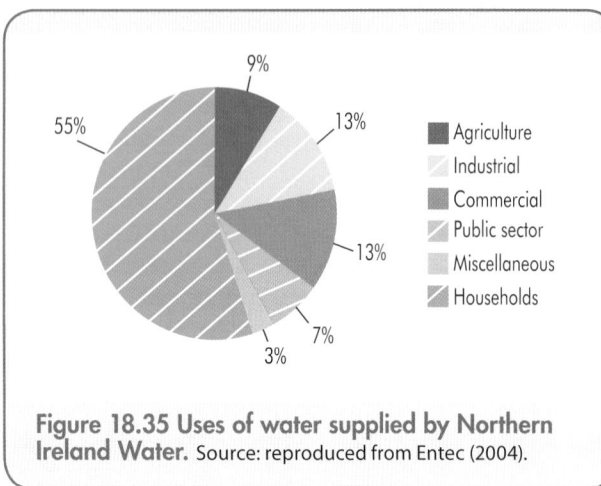

Figure 18.35 Uses of water supplied by Northern Ireland Water. Source: reproduced from Entec (2004).

Pie chart segments: 9%, 13%, 13%, 7%, 3%, 55%. Legend: Agriculture, Industrial, Commercial, Public sector, Miscellaneous, Households.

exceeding 70% in the south east (Shand *et al.* 2007). The majority of water is supplied for domestic use, with non-domestic users supplied with approximately 153,000 m³ per day. Over 99% of households in Northern Ireland are connected to the mains for their supply of clean water. The best estimate of *per capita* household consumption in Northern Ireland is 145 l/person/day. With a population of 1,742,000 in 2006–2007, this suggests a total household consumption of 250 million l/day. Growth in households (due to a small rise in population coupled with a fall in average household size) is expected to increase domestic demand for water (Entec 2004; NIEA 2009k). Agricultural water consumption is approximately 39.2 million l/day (DRD 2002b). Furthermore, it was estimated that agriculture water use from boreholes could be as high as 11 million l/day (Robins 1996). Industrial water consumption is 31.79 million l/day (DRD 2002b). Industry is required to adhere to trade effluent discharge consents, although compliance varies for different activities. Severe disruption in water supplies in December 2010 to January 2011 following extreme cold has further exposed the problems of the infrastructure, but has raised water up the political agenda.

Less than 1% of water comes from private water supplies (NIEA 2009b). The Northern Ireland Environment Agency monitors drinking water for compliance with international standards (NIEA 2010e). There are 1,276 private water supplies (approximately 3,000 people) currently registered with the Northern Ireland Environment Agency. It is estimated that there are a further 4,000 private supplies to individual private domestic dwellings which do not need to be registered under the 1994 Regulations. The majority (98%) of private supplies in Northern Ireland are from groundwater sources. 91% (1,162) of the private water supplies registered with the Northern Ireland Environment Agency are dairy farms; the remaining 9% (114) are commercial and domestic supplies. There are 114 private water supplies monitored: 82% are commercial/public supplies; and 18% are domestic premises (groupings of two or more houses; Caroline Barry, NIEA, pers. comm.).

Northern Ireland Water also treats around 127 million m³ of wastewater daily from the 663,000 properties connected to the wastewater system. According to the Utility Regulator's 2007–2008 Cost and Performance Report, wastewater treatment compliance in Northern Ireland remained the lowest in the UK (NIAUR 2008). Decreasing water quality

not only has implications for the habitats and species it supports, it also results in the loss of valuable ecosystem services including food and recreation, natural means of flood prevention, drought mitigation, soil fertilisation and water purification. This has implications for government finances in addition to the cost of treating drinking water often extracted from the same water bodies that treated water is discharged into. Northern Ireland Water's annual operating costs were £186.1 million for 2007–2008, an increase of 35.2% since 2004–2005 and high compared with those of Great Britain's water companies (NIAUR 2008). There has been extensive recent investment in the provision of wastewater collection and treatment systems in Northern Ireland; over the five years up to 2008 £1.1 billion was spent on infrastructure and upgrading, protecting both public health and the environment. Operating costs for Northern Ireland Water in 2008–2009 were £262.2 million (NI Water 2010a) and they estimate the cost of phosphate removal at wastewater treatment works (WWTWs) is now in the order of £600,000 annually (NIEA 2009l).

Upland habitats are important to the water supply. For example, much of the water supply for south Belfast and Co. Down is from the reservoirs in the Mournes (e.g. Silent Valley, Spelga). Other important reservoirs include Dungonnell and Altnahinch on the edge of the Antrim Plateau and Altnaheglish and Banagher Glen in the Sperrins. These reservoirs have their feeder streams in blanket peat and peaty slopes. Management of these lands to ensure high quality water has favourable outcomes for habitat conservation, such as reduced sheep grazing in the Mournes and retention of high quality peat bog in the Garron Plateau (RSPB unpublished data). In the west and north of Northern Ireland a significant proportion of the water supply is abstracted from local rivers whose headwaters lie in the blanket peat upland slopes.

18.5.2.7 Fuel peat

Blanket peat has for generations provided fuel for rural homes. Coal has a calorific value of around 6,000 cal/g while hand-cut turf, with a water content of around 35%, produces around 2,600 cal/g (Hamilton 1982). Ignition occurs between 150 and 210°C, a temperature at which much of the carbon is lost (Hamilton 1982), making it a convenient but not a carbon-efficient fuel. Hand cutting of peat turves was once widespread (47% of remaining blanket peatland has been cut-over at some time in the past and a large area has been totally removed), but by the mid-20th Century it was much reduced; electricity had reached most rural homes, oil heating was available and many family members had moved to the towns and cities and were no longer available for the intense work required to dig, dry and harvest the turf. However, in the late 1970s and early 1980s high global oil prices and the introduction of a compact harvester, attached to a farm tractor, which could cut a plot of peat sufficient for a year's fuel in a few hours, resulted in widespread cutting across the blanket bog, predominantly near to roads and tracks and on blanket peat that had previously been hand cut. Although widespread, it occupied a total area of 3.6% of the blanket peat (**Figure 18.36**). Whilst this cutting was of value to rural households, reducing expenditure on fuel,

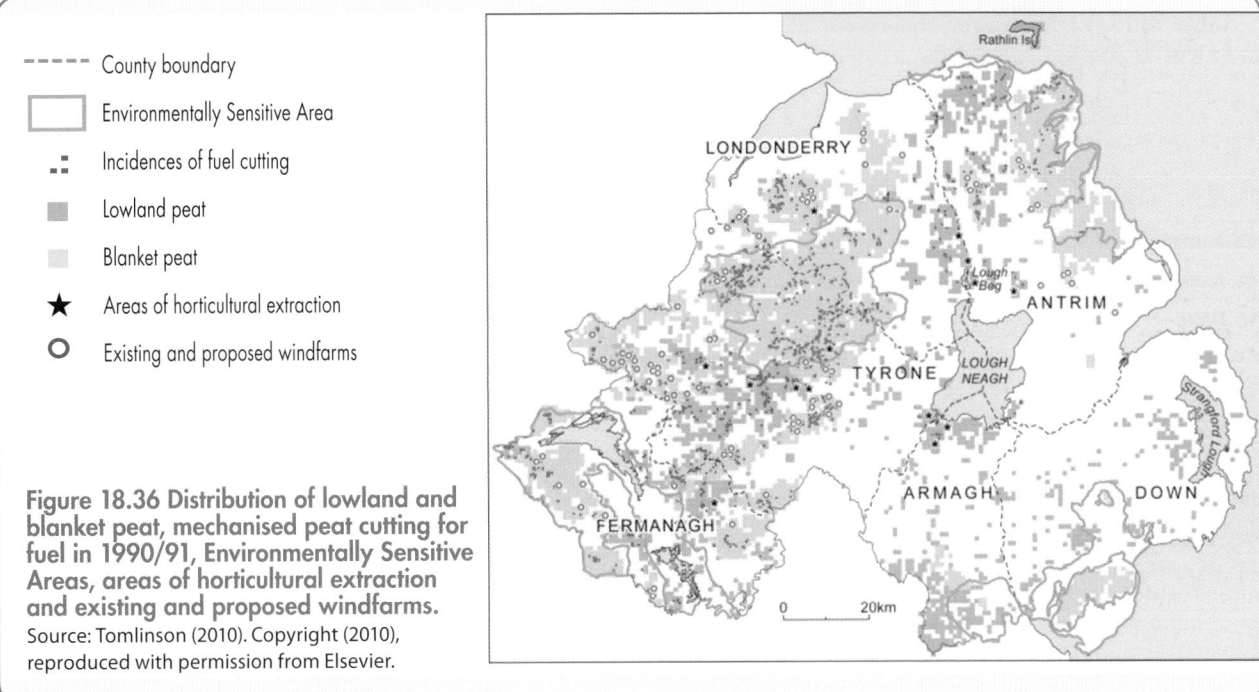

- - - - - County boundary
☐ Environmentally Sensitive Area
.: Incidences of fuel cutting
■ Lowland peat
▨ Blanket peat
★ Areas of horticultural extraction
○ Existing and proposed windfarms

Figure 18.36 Distribution of lowland and blanket peat, mechanised peat cutting for fuel in 1990/91, Environmentally Sensitive Areas, areas of horticultural extraction and existing and proposed windfarms.
Source: Tomlinson (2010). Copyright (2010), reproduced with permission from Elsevier.

it had adverse effects on the environment, including loss of plant species, disturbance of migratory and wetland birds, and damage to spawning and nursery beds of salmonids through settlement of peat particles. Since the early 1990s this peat cutting has declined to an estimated 330 ha, less than 10% of the area cut in 1990–1991 (Tomlinson 2010). The estimates of carbon loss from peat extraction in 2008 range from 42,751 to 47,452 tonnes of carbon per year (tC/yr), or approximately 30% and 40% respectively of estimated losses in 1990–1991. Whereas in 1990–1991, peat extraction for fuel (hand and mechanical) accounted for 76–81% of carbon loss from peat extraction, in 2008 it accounted for only 16–24%, with extraction for horticultural peat now dominant (Tomlinson 2010).

Unlike the Republic of Ireland, Northern Ireland does not use peat to fuel electricity power stations. Peat-burning power stations in the Republic of Ireland have been in operation since the 1940s. Peat has a high methane content which is released when burned, although the power stations at Lough Ree and Shannonbridge have to meet strict emissions regulations. Some have labelled peat 'new coal', due to its effect on the atmosphere. The Irish Government sees peat as a key feature of the country's energy mix. A report published in 2006 states that intended projects involving lignite and peat power stations in the Republic equate to 600,000 kW (VGB Secretariat 2006).

The reduction in peat harvesting has a number of explanations. In 2005 new criteria were introduced into the ESA scheme and CMS, limiting the area of peat cutting to 0.1 ha maximum for domestic use, and mechanised cutting was not permitted. However, even before this, peat extraction for fuel had declined due to falling demand for fuel peat, largely due to rising standards of living and reduced availability of labour. Other possible causes of the decline in cutting for fuel include windfarm construction, peatland conservation and forestry. The majority of windfarms built and proposed over recent years occur on upland blanket

peat and several coincide with areas that were machine cut in 1990/1991, for example in the Slievemore-Cappagh hills, in the west Sperrins and on Long Mountain. Peat cutting has ceased or its extent has been reduced at existing windfarms. Designation of additional peat conservation areas since 1991 has also led to restrictions on cutting. In the early 1990s Forest Service extended planting onto some areas formerly subject to peat extraction, but after 1995 planting of new areas declined steeply to zero in 2007. New state forest areas have not had a significant role in the decline of peat cutting, and while private forests have extended, this has not been over areas of former peat extraction (Tomlinson 2010).

18.5.2.8 Terrestrial renewable energy

Invest Northern Ireland states that the existing generation capacity of Northern Ireland's onshore wind power resources is 164.6 MWe (Mega Watts electrical). As the report was being published in 2008, another 392.7 MWe of wind power had been approved or was already under construction (Invest NI 2008). About 94% of identified renewable energy production would come from onshore and offshore wind (Action Renewables 2004, **Table 18.13**). The equivalent for biomass-generated electricity and heat (which includes anaerobic digestion, gasification, cogeneration, and boilers using chips, pellets and logs) was 3.05 MWe and 0.73 MWe respectively. Landfill gas capture was included in the report as an emerging technology, and since then the technology has been employed at the North Foreshore landfill site in Belfast and at other locations in Northern Ireland, in compliance with European waste management directives. **Table 18.13** presents information on the anticipated scale of various renewable energy technologies as of 2004; these figures are considered still valid (Action Renewables pers. comm.).

Many windfarms are located on blanket peat uplands, with possible impacts on wild birds, bats and scenery. Although construction of wind turbines and related

Table 18.13 Potential renewable resources in Northern Ireland (megawatts electrical). Source: data from Action Renewables (2004).

	Onshore wind	Offshore wind	Hydro	Short Rotation Coppice (SRC) willow	Poultry waste	Sawmill residue	Municipal solid waste	Landfill gas	Agricultural wastes	Total
Co. Antrim	94.0	100.0	4.7	1.5	2.2	0.1	13	10.2	1.0	**226.7**
Co. Armagh	12.5	-	3.0	0.8	0.5	-	-	3.0	0.6	**20.4**
Co. Down	92.5	200.0	0.4	1.3	0.7	-	-	5.1	0.9	**300.9**
Co. Fermanagh	89.3	-	0.2	0.9	-	3.3	-	0.9	0.5	**95.1**
Co. Londonderry	70.5	200.0	1.7	1.0	0.3	1.8	-	2.9	0.7	**278.9**
Co. Tyrone	205.8	-	0.6	1.7	1.9	0.1	-	1.6	1.2	**212.9**
Northern Ireland	**564.6 (49.75%)**	**500.0 (44.06%)**	**10.6 (0.93%)**	**7.2 (0.63%)**	**5.6 (0.49%)**	**5.3 (0.47%)**	**13.0 (1.15%)**	**23.7 (2.09%)**	**4.9 (0.43%)**	**1,134.9 (100%)**

infrastructure can lead to significant peat loss and erosion, these impacts can be offset by accompanying cessation of peat cutting and reduced grazing impacts, which can have beneficial impacts on recovery of the vegetation. A recent Northern Ireland Environment Agency scoping report into wind energy demonstrated in detail the inevitable trade-off between the positive impact in terms of increased use of indigenous renewable energy resources and consequent greenhouse gas reduction and the negative environmental and scenic impacts of such energy developments (NIEA 2010k). A Planning Policy Statement on Renewable Energy (PPS18; DOE2009b) and guidance on siting of wind farms (EHS 2008b) have been produced to ensure proper consideration of all issues before developments proceed.

18.5.2.9 Marine renewable energy

There are significant opportunities for the generation of renewable energy through wind and tidal generators in the marine environment (DETI 2010b). While there are currently no offshore wind farms in Northern Ireland waters, the region is host to the first commercial scale tidal generator in the world operated at Strangford Lough (capacity of 1.2 MW) which has been operating since 2008. The extensive and external environmental monitoring of this unique project has identified that there have been no apparent impacts on the environment from its operation over the last two years and has provided a significant amount of evidence on the interaction of marine devices with the environment.

The Department of Enterprise, Trade and Investment (DETI)' s Strategic Energy Framework published in 2010 set a target of 40% of Northern Ireland's electricity consumption from renewable resources by 2020 and its Offshore Renewable Energy Strategic Action Plan (ORESAP) identifies how offshore resources can contribute to that challenging target. The Plan, which was the subject of a Strategic Environmental Assessment (SEA) has proposed targets of at least 600 MW of offshore wind and 300 MW of tidal energy by 2020 (see **Figure 18.37**) the main commercial scale sites are off the North and East Coasts for offshore wind and off the North Coast for tidal. As owners of the seabed, The Crown Estate announced the process for the Northern Ireland Leasing Round in March 2011 and would plan to seek

Expressions of Interest from developers in Autumn 2011 with potential development rights offered by Spring 2012.

The regional economic development body, Invest Northern Ireland, is promoting the business and supply chain opportunities for Northern Ireland companies in the growing international offshore renewable energy market (Invest NI 2008). DETI has identified that potential levels of marine renewables could give rise to possible investment of £330 million to £880 million by 2020. The ORESAP estimated the potential employment figure to be in the order of 4,500 by 2020, although it is acknowledged that the number of regional jobs could be fewer than this estimate given the current relative immaturity of the sector (DETI 2010c).

The comprehensive SEA carried out by DETI on offshore renewable development in Northern Ireland waters identified that the proposed levels of generation could be developed without significant impact on the environment or other marine users with appropriate mitigation measures at both strategic and project level. Potential impacts on and mitigation measures to address key issues such as coastal processes, changes to habitats, collision risk, noise, barriers to movements, landscape and seascape, fishing and shipping sectors have been identified. Work is underway to consider how strategic data gaps within the marine environment could be addressed and how the necessary mitigation measures can be taken forward to the development of projects in due course through a Project Level Mitigation Strategy. As recommended by the SEA, DETI has established the Offshore Renewable Energy Forum with representation from the key marine stakeholders to advise on the implementation of its offshore plans and it has published Regional Locational Guidance to assist possible siting of projects to minimise/avoid possible impacts on the environment and other marine users.

18.5.2.10 Hydropower

Hydroelectric technology has a long history in Northern Ireland, with many old mill sites coming back into use. Local government schemes over the years, for example under the First and Second Order of the Non-Fossil Fuel Obligations (NI-NFFO) in the 1990s and the more recent £8 million Reconnect scheme undertaken by the Department of

Enterprise, Trade and Investment, have helped promote new interest in the technology. It also continues to be a source of interest for local engineering firms looking to develop supply chain opportunities in the marketplace.

There is a potentially significant renewable energy resource from flowing or stored water, but to date installations have been generally small scale, from 250 to 500 kW. A 1999 assessment of renewable energy potential in Northern Ireland indicated that the maximum estimated contributions from small-scale hydro by 2010 would be 25 GW h/y (DETI 2001). There has been little development of small-scale hydropower since then; however, there are currently 80 such applications in the planning process and Invest Northern Ireland believes a reasonable-sized industry of around 1,100 new installations will emerge over the coming decade (Sam Knox, Invest NI, pers. comm.).

There is concern about the potential impacts of hydroelectric installations on fish and water quality, especially during periods of low water flow. The Northern Ireland Environment Agency is the environmental regulator of hydro schemes. It has recently proposed a restoration scheme on the River Roe at its Roe Valley Country Park site. The proposal, intended as an industry benchmark, recognises the primacy of environmental protection with specifications ensuring the project will not have a significant negative impact on fish or the river ecology (NIEA pers. comm.).

18.5.2.11 Biomass

Research on short rotation coppice willow as a biomass crop started in Northern Ireland in the early 1970s in response to increasing oil prices, with experimental stands in Loughgall in County Armagh and in County Fermanagh. Short rotation coppice willow also has significant potential for the bioremediation/biofiltration of effluents and sludges; it takes up large volumes of water and can utilise the nitrogen and to some extent the phosphorous in high nutrient wastes. Current Agri-food and Biosciences Institute research includes the use of short rotation coppice willow for the treatment of primary sewage effluent, and initial results indicate that irrigation of willow with sewage effluent is a sustainable approach to waste management. Future research will be conducted at sites at the Agri-food and Biosciences Institute Hillsborough (farm wastewater) and Greyabbey (sewage effluent). One commercial farmer has been growing willows for a combined heat and power plant and is interested in the use of sewage sludge and slurry as nutrient sources for the crop. Future potential will depend partly on government support for renewable energy. The biomass can be used by domestic consumers in the form of 'chips' for solid fuel heating systems or by industry for heat and electricity generation (Alistair McCracken, AFBI, pers. comm.). Between 2004 and 2006 around 500 ha of short rotation coppice willow was planted (Dawson 2007) and the

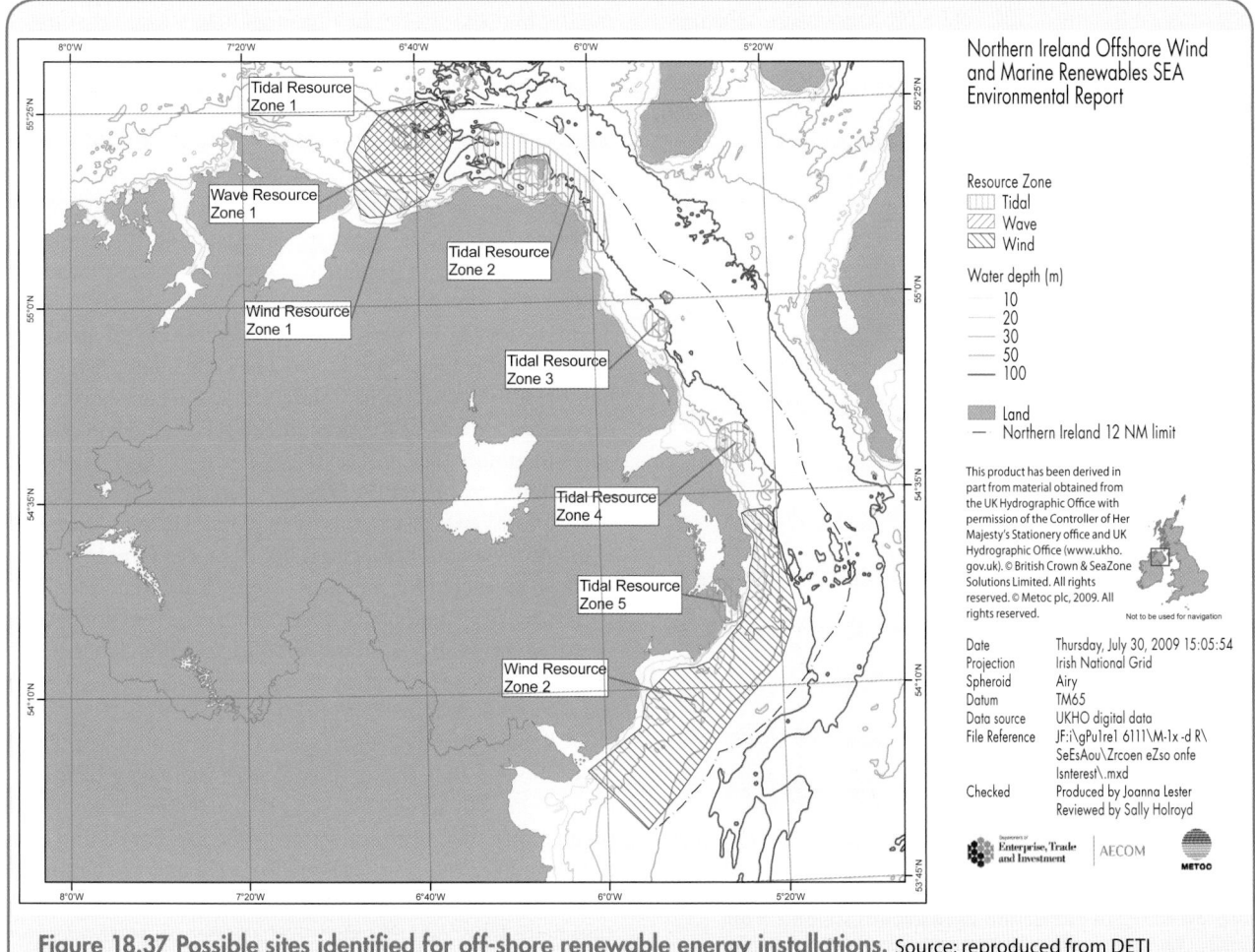

Figure 18.37 Possible sites identified for off-shore renewable energy installations. Source: reproduced from DETI Offshore Renewable Energy Strategic Action Plan (2009b); www.offshorenergyni.co.uk

best estimate of the total figure in 2009 is around 1,000 ha (Easson 2009).

Miscanthus×gigantea (elephant grass, sterile hybrid) is a biomass crop native to the Far East. The Agri-food and Biosciences Institute has been conducting research on the establishment and growth of the grass for about 6 years, with experimental stations at Loughgall and Hillsborough. *Miscanthus* is already grown extensively in some parts of England, where it has been the subject of research for a longer period. The major advantages of *Miscanthus* are its ability to produce large biomass yields for perhaps up to 15 years on some sites without any fertiliser input. The potential market in Northern Ireland is difficult to predict at present. The scale of operation currently envisioned would be groups of farmers supplying biomass to small companies for combined heat and power units (Lindsay Easson, AFBI, pers. comm.).

18.5.2.12 Geothermal energy

Geothermal energy is an important emerging field which needs to be supported by government if it is to meet its future targets. A Renewable Heat Route Map has been promised as a strategy for delivering the 10% renewable heat by 2020 target in Northern Ireland (DETI 2010d).

18.5.2.13 Stone and aggregate

There is a significant quarry industry in Northern Ireland with a turnover of approximately £600 million in 2010, 3% of Northern Ireland's GDP, and 3,750 employees, which is a 25% reduction from 2008 (DETI unpublished data). In 2009 about 23 million tonnes of minerals at a value of £90 million were extracted, down from almost 30 million tonnes in 2007 (**Figure 18.38**). There are around 180 quarries and sand pits in Northern Ireland extracting material primarily for local markets, although some 25% is exported to Great Britain and the Republic of Ireland. The construction industry, which contributes around 10% of GDP, relies on quarrying

and the annual demand for aggregates in Northern Ireland is approximately 25 million tonnes (14.7 t/head of population). Northern Ireland is an important source of high quality aggregate for use in road surfaces across the UK and Europe. The quarry products industry in Northern Ireland also produces a wide range of stone products such as kerbstones, concrete floors and beams, paving slabs and concrete pipes of a wide range of diameters used to upgrade the roads, water and sewage facilities and buildings. The Quarry Products Association Northern Ireland has a biodiversity action plan (Bell 2008).

The presence of rich, land-based sources of aggregate means that there are currently no licences for marine aggregate extraction (EHS 2005k) and the current economic climate suggests that such activity is not likely to escalate in the near future. Nevertheless, because of its multiple impacts in other UK waters (Foden *et al.* 2010), any future escalation in marine aggregate extraction should be carefully monitored. While the health of the marine ecosystem will not impact on the delivery of this service, the extraction of marine aggregates can have significant impacts on the resident benthic and pelagic communities (Cooper *et al.* 2008; Foden *et al.* 2010).

In recent years Northern Ireland has had an Aggregates Levy Credit Scheme whereby producers of aggregate received an 80% rebate of the Aggregates Levy in exchange for carrying out environmental improvements. This scheme was cancelled from 1st December 2010 following an EU ruling, but the Minister for the Environment has stated his support for reintroducing the scheme if possible (NI Executive 2010c; Parliament 2010).

18.5.2.14 Peat for horticulture

Extraction of peat for horticulture is largely from lowland raised bogs and, unlike fuel cutting, has not declined. Whereas extraction provides a fuel and horticultural resource, it affects regulating services such as carbon storage and emissions.

In a survey of sites used for extraction of peat for horticulture in 1990–1991, most sites were small (<5 ha) and had been in operation for many years. Vacuum harvesting accounted for 57% of the area of extraction and sod cutting accounted for 18%. An extensive site of extraction for horticulture in 1990–1991 was at Altahullion; unusually for horticultural extraction this was a blanket peat site and extraction was not by vacuum but of blocks of peat similar to those extracted for fuel peat. The site accounted for 22% of the area of extraction for horticulture. The remaining sites of extraction for horticulture listed in planning applications and consents produced peat for the mushroom-growing industry (Cruickshank *et al.* 1996).

A resurvey of extraction sites for horticulture in 2007–2008 showed that the total area had increased from 576 ha in 1990–1991 to 689 ha. Sod extraction sites had ceased production or had been converted to vacuum harvesting, and the Altahullion site had declined from 178 ha to 39 ha (much of the area is now a windfarm). Some vacuum harvesting sites had expanded and new sites had opened, and areas can vary from year to year, depending on weather and markets (Tomlinson 2010).

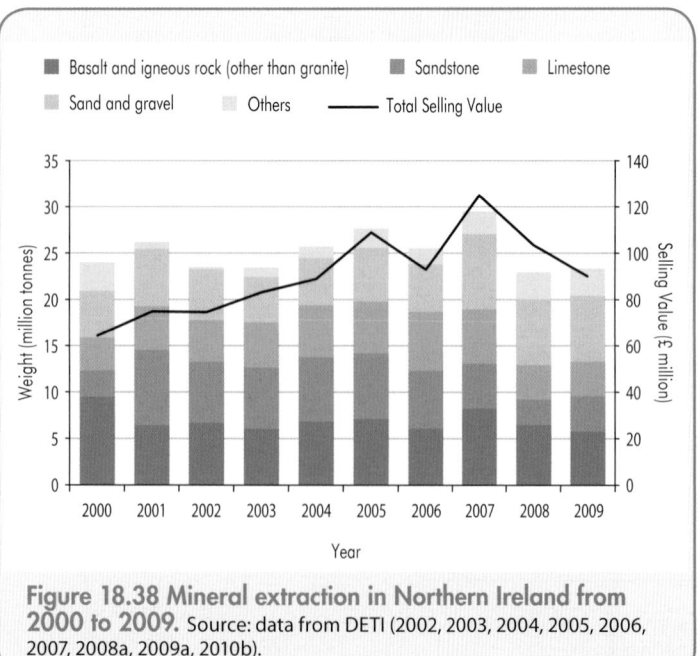

Figure 18.38 Mineral extraction in Northern Ireland from 2000 to 2009. Source: data from DETI (2002, 2003, 2004, 2005, 2006, 2007, 2008a, 2009a, 2010b).

18.5.2.15 Lignite

Lignite is similar to peat and coal in terms of emissions. Northern Ireland has seen attempts in recent years to open up tracts of land around Belfast and near Ballymena for open cast lignite mining (Belfast Telegraph 2006). The plan was eventually rejected, but pressure to tap these resources remains (Belfast Telegraph 2008).

18.5.3 Regulating Services

Regulating services buffer the effects of climate change; detoxify wastes and pollutants in air, water and soil; support species diversity and the services they provide (pollination, pest control); and play a major role in addressing hazards of all types (droughts, floods, fires, earthquakes) by providing the basis for resilience and supporting the ability to deliver all other ecosystem goods and services. They include the services which ameliorate and repair the damage to natural systems caused by human use.

Climate change may place additional strain on many regulating services. Climate regulation is discussed in this section, but its impacts are apparent throughout all ecosystem services; direct and indirect, mitigation and adaptation. Soils, in particular, are large stores of carbon, and dealing with carbon loss from these stores needs at least as much attention as reducing current emissions (Section 18.5.3.1.). Pure water is vital to all life and globally, water shortage is a major problem. The marine environment is also a major store of carbon, as well as providing crucial functions in all nutrient and hydrological processes. Changes in global marine temperature and acidity would have major impacts on all ecosystems.

The quality of soil and air in Northern Ireland is relatively good, and there are encouraging signs in terms of some aspects of water quality (Section 18.4.6). However, most lakes are eutrophic (many increasingly so), pollution of rivers (point source and particularly diffuse) causes biological damage and is costly, while the provision of fresh drinking water and treatment of waste water are increasingly expensive, due to heavy reliance on electricity and consequently carbon. The first effects of climate change will most likely be felt in our aquatic systems—floods and droughts—and these impacts will exacerbate current problems, escalating variability and unpredictability of flows in rivers and increasing their vulnerability to pollutants (Section 18.4.6).

Ecosystems may detoxify pollutants, but only if regulating functions are intact and the amount of toxin relative to the water, soil or air into which it is being discharged is within the capacity of the receiving ecosystem. While it is hard to estimate the direct economic benefits of fully functioning regulating services, it is often possible to estimate the costs of undertaking remediation if those natural systems are not functioning (Section 18.5.6). However, comprehensive figures are not available for Northern Ireland and it is important that this is addressed at both UK and Northern Ireland levels.

18.5.3.1 Carbon storage in peatland

Northern Ireland is committed to playing its part in addressing climate change as part of UK, EU and global action. Although only responsible for 3.5% of UK emissions (Committee for the Environment 2009), it has potentially much greater relative significance as a carbon sink. Northern Ireland, along with Scotland and Wales, is a net sink of carbon, but England is a net source; this is due to Northern Ireland's peatlands, forests and long-term grasslands (Sections 18.4.2 & 18.5.2). The proportion of greenhouse gas emissions from agriculture is very large in Northern Ireland; over 20% of total greenhouse gas compared to 7% in the UK as a whole (AEA 2010), and there are major possibilities for agriculture to contribute significantly to greenhouse gas reduction targets if this were to be assigned a high priority (Mayne 2010). Specific targets for reducing carbon emissions for Northern Ireland have not been established, nor will sectoral targets be set until baseline data are compiled (Committee for the Environment 2009). There are also possibilities in Northern Ireland for carbon capture and storage in underground strata (Lewis *et al.* 2009).

Cruickshank *et al.* (1998) estimated the stock of carbon held in the soils of Northern Ireland at 386 million tonnes. Although occupying 15% of the land area, peat soils contain 42% of the carbon stock and peaty soils account for a further 10% of the carbon stock, with the highest soil carbon densities (>5,000 tC/ha) in deep peat. Peatland vegetation stores some 6% of the vegetation carbon, but soil carbon stock is around 80 times that of the vegetation carbon stock. The role of forests in sequestering and storing carbon is often emphasised, but conserving the biodiversity and uniqueness of Northern Ireland's peatlands has a vital role in conserving carbon. Eroding peat bogs lose carbon from the peat and stop sequestering carbon (Cruickshank *et al.* 1993; Cruickshank *et al.* 2000). Organic carbon stored within peat has accumulated over thousands of years but can be lost in days (Flitcroft 2006).

Peat carbon stocks have been reduced by peat extraction. In 1990–1991 the loss of carbon as a result of mechanical extraction for fuel (by compact harvester) was between 75,936 and 126,623 tC/yr. For 2008, the estimate was between 6,481 and 10, 807 tC/yr. At both dates the majority of extraction for fuel was from blanket peat (Section 18.4.2). Carbon lost through hand cutting for fuel has also declined (Tomlinson 2010). Carbon is also lost through extraction of peat for horticulture, almost entirely from lowland raised bogs. Carbon loss due to peat extraction increased from an estimated 30,000 tC/yr in 1990–1991 to 36,000 tC/yr in 2007–2008 (Tomlinson 2010).

18.5.3.2 Carbon storage in soil

Peaty soils hold 42% of the soil carbon stock on 15% of the land area. Stagnogleys and stagnohumic gleys, which occupy around 53% of the land area, have 36% of the soil carbon stock. Brown earths, brown sands, brown calcareous soils and brown alluvial soils, which account for around 15% of the land, hold around 12% of the soil carbon stock (Cruickshank *et al.* 1998). The carbon density of a soil is affected by the vegetation or cover type as well as its management regime (e.g. ploughing frequency, depth, timing; fertilising). For example, a soil under semi-natural vegetation has a higher carbon density than that soil under improved grass, which in turn has a higher carbon density than that soil under arable crops. In Northern Ireland in 1990, soils with an arable cover had 2% of the soil carbon stock, soils under improved grass held 43% of the soil carbon stock, soils under semi-natural cover (mainly peat and peaty soils and vegetation) held another 43% of the soil carbon stock, soils under coniferous woodland had 9% and soils under broadleaved woods, 2% of the soil carbon stock (Cruickshank *et al.* 1998).

The distribution of soil carbon (**Figure 18.39**) shows the highest carbon densities in the blanket peatlands and deep-peat lowland bogs. Thinner peats and peaty soils have intermediate levels of carbon stocks, forming a fringe to the uplands. Elsewhere, carbon densities for mineral soils are generally low on the Enclosed Farmland of the lowlands. This broad pattern mirrors that of the vegetation or biomass carbon stocks; the peatland vegetation is mostly in the uplands and the highest vegetation carbon densities are evident in the larger forests. The lowest vegetation carbon densities dominate over much of the lowlands and correspond with the 'improved land' of Enclosed Farmland (Cruickshank *et al.* 1998).

The overall soil carbon stock in Northern Ireland was estimated by Bradley *et al.* (2005) to be 296 million tonnes in the top 100 cm. Carbon stocks to 1 m depth under semi-natural vegetation were estimated to be 86 million tonnes at a carbon density of 39 kg/m^2.

Undisturbed habitats are significant contributors to carbon sequestration through vegetation, some of which is stored in the soils. The impacts of climate change on these habitats could be significant due to habitat dependence on water levels. The general lack of fertilisation on Semi-natural Grasslands means that emissions of nitrogen dioxide are low and lower stocking densities decrease methane emissions relative to improved grassland used for animal production (Cruickshank *et al.* 1998; Sections 18.4.3 & 18.4.5).

18.5.3.3 Carbon sequestration in vegetation

Cruickshank *et al.* (1998) estimated that 55% of the vegetation (biomass) carbon in Northern Ireland in 1990 was held by forests and woodland (compared with 80% in Great Britain), which accounted for only 5% of the land area. By contrast, improved grassland accounted for 17% of the biomass carbon stock but covered 56% of the land area. Nevertheless, in Northern Ireland the percentage of carbon stored in agricultural vegetation was more than three times the proportion in Great Britain (36% compared with 10%). Forests and woodlands are clearly important carbon stores and of continuing importance as they grow and increase in biomass (provided that felled forests are replaced).

18.5.3.4 Greenhouse gases in agriculture

Agriculture accounted for 23% of greenhouse gas emissions in Northern Ireland in 2007, up slightly from 22% in 1990 (DOE & NISRA 2010) and compared to 7% in the UK as a whole (AEA 2010). Some statistics are encouraging; for example the amount of methane produced per litre of milk from grass-based production has decreased from over 32 l/kg in 1980 to just over 26 l/kg in 2008 (T. Yan unpublished data). Research at Agri-food and Biosciences Institute Hillsborough is showing significant decreases in greenhouse gas emissions from changing diets of cattle and improved slurry management (Yan 2009), as well as potential for capture of gasses to produce energy (Frost & Gilkinson 2010).

Land use change can be either a net contributor or sink for greenhouse gases. Over the period, 1939 to 2000 there was little change in the soil carbon stock, even though in 1939 there was more arable agriculture than at present. The Northern Ireland Environmental Statistics Report (DOE & NISRA 2010) estimates the total greenhouse gas absorption contribution from land use change of just over 1% of total emissions (DOE & NISRA 2010).

There are significant opportunities for reducing greenhouse gas emissions from agriculture and, given the significance of emissions of methane (at 23 times carbon dioxide value) and nitrous oxide (at 310 times carbon dioxide), this is an extremely important area. However, it is not an easy area to tackle, and the Republic of Ireland has cited its large agriculture base as a reason why it is having difficulty meeting its Kyoto commitments (Styles *et al.* 2008).

18.5.3.5 Climate regulation by oceans

Several aspects of the ocean's biogeochemical cycles contribute to climate regulation, most importantly the absorption and sequestration of atmospheric carbon through the processes of dissolution and photosynthesis. Northern Ireland's territorial waters are relatively small and shallow, therefore direct contributions in this regard are limited. However, even on such small scales, marine systems

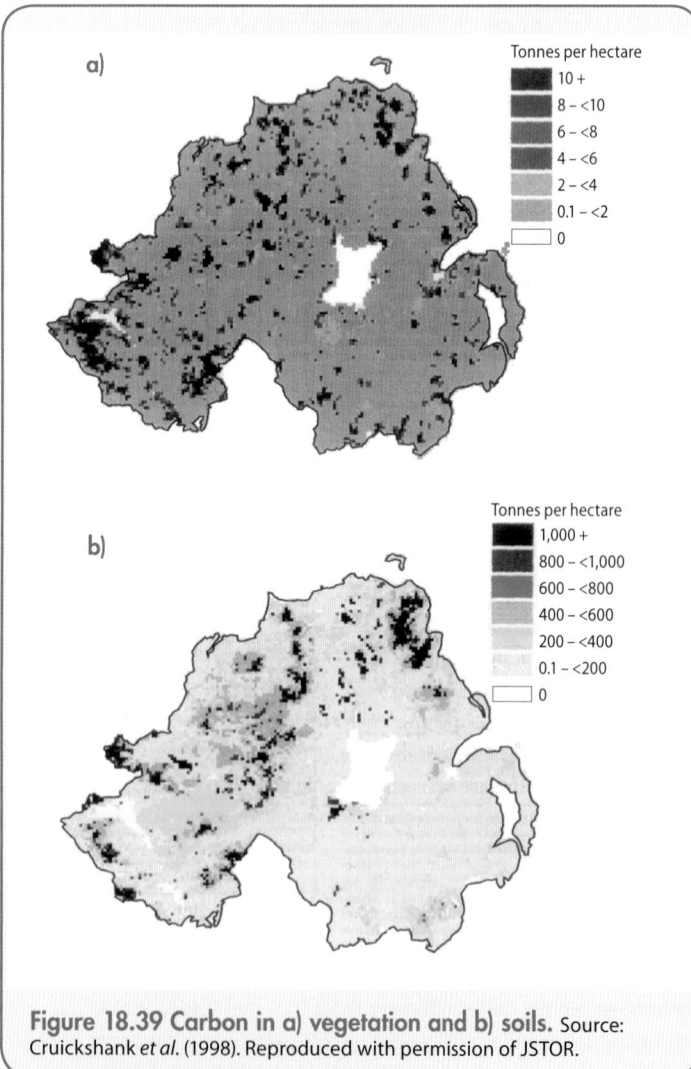

Figure 18.39 Carbon in a) vegetation and b) soils. Source: Cruickshank *et al.* (1998). Reproduced with permission of JSTOR.

can play an important role in cycling nitrogen- and sulphur-based greenhouse gases. For example, chemicals produced by marine algae can enhance cloud formation (Seymour *et al.* 2010). On a local scale, these clouds can produce precipitation, and on a global scale, they can contribute to increasing the Earth's albedo, reflecting more solar radiation back into space (Woodhouse *et al.* 2010).

By the end of this century, UK waters are predicted to be 1.5–4.0°C warmer, 0.2 practical salinity units (PSU) fresher (although there is greater uncertainty about this), and 0.3 pH units more acidic (UKMMAS 2010). Northern Ireland has so far largely been spared the effects of sea-level rise because isostatic uplift (the slow bounce-back of the land since the weight of the last glaciation was removed) has slightly exceeded sea-level rise (Orford *et al.* 2006). However, the escalating rate of sea-level rise globally (Rahmstorf *et al.* 2007; Nicholls & Cazenave 2010) means that this is likely to become an increasing threat in the near future, especially for shallow-water and light-limited marine habitats.

Northern Ireland's territorial waters have warmed by about 0.5–0.74°C since the 1990s, with accompanying shifts in fish species (including both commercial and non-commercial species, so this is not due to overfishing; Beaugrand *et al.* 2009; Lynam *et al.* 2010). These changing biotic assemblages may include new species that could have unforeseen consequences for marine habitats, possibly altering marine food webs or allowing establishment of invasive species (Sorte *et al.* 2010). This could cause challenges for management and the integrity of the marine ecosystem as a whole, including carbon sequestration, waste processing and nutrient cycling (Hoegh-Guldberg & Bruno 2010).

18.5.3.6 Waste production and disposal

Around 16 million tonnes of waste are generated each year in Northern Ireland. Of this about 10 million tonnes are agricultural wastes, 4 million tonnes are construction, demolition and excavation (CD&E) waste, 1 million tonnes are municipal waste and another 1 million tonnes are commercial and industrial (C&I) waste. Municipal waste increased by an average of 1% per annum between 2002–2003 and 2006–2007 with decreases in 2007–2008 and 2008–2009, so that 6,000 tonnes less were produced in the latter year than in 2002–2003. These changes are thought to relate closely to the economic climate (DOE unpublished data). Municipal recycling rates have increased by 68% in the 5 years from 2004 (DOE & NISRA 2010). The total amount of municipal waste arising in 2009–2010 was 1,004,020 tonnes, a decrease of 1.3% on the amount in 2008–2009. Of this waste, 33.1% was sent for recycling (including composting), an increase from 31.6% in 2008–2009 and just 8.9% in 2002. Banbridge District Council had the highest municipal recycling rate of 51.6%, while Belfast City Council had the lowest rate, 22.3%. The majority of the remaining municipal waste was sent to landfill (66.1%), with a very small amount reused. The percentage of municipal waste landfilled has decreased over the years, falling from 91.1% in 2002 to 66.1% in 2009–2010 (NISRA & NIEA 2010).

Efforts are underway to increase the percentages reused and recycled in all waste streams, but recent figures still indicate a substantial amount going to landfill (EHS2007;

NIEA 2009i). Most of this waste is disposed of in managed sites, including landfill gas capture at some sites. However, there is a substantial problem with illegal waste disposal, some of it involving cross-border transfer following the implementation of waste charging in the Republic of Ireland. There are also older landfill sites which are not built to modern standards, with resultant potential pollution problems and release of landfill gas (NIEA 2009j).

In 2003 it was projected that there would be 53,000 tonnes of sewage sludge produced, some of which was to be spread on agricultural land and some incinerated (EHS 2003b). In the past much of this was disposed of to sea, but since this was banned in December 1998 in line with the EC Urban Wastewater Treatment Directive (91/271/EEC), most has been incinerated with energy recovery.

Agricultural wastes are considered in a draft Biodegradable Waste Strategy produced by the Environment and Heritage Service (EHS 2003b) and are the responsibility of the Department for Agriculture and Rural Development. In 2003 there were 15,438,000 tonnes of biodegradable agricultural waste produced per annum (the vast majority of which was slurries and manures, but also small amounts of straw, vegetable processing and packaging waste). The majority of this was disposed of 'on farm' at the point of origin. Much research has taken place since then on uses for biodegradable waste, including for energy production through anaerobic digestion. Because most of these wastes are managed primarily by land-spreading and are not deemed controlled waste (where spread on land in accordance with the Nitrates Directive) detailed information on amounts and disposition is not available. Excessive or uncontrolled application of these wastes can lead to pollution of air and water (EHS 2008a).

There is potential to use biodegradable waste to produce energy, especially from farm or food processing wastes. The Agri-Food and Biosciences Institute is currently conducting research on a variety of possible mechanisms for utilisation of animal and food wastes, both to provide energy and to reduce pollution problems, for example through anaerobic digestion, irrigation of short rotation coppice willow with organic wastes, and low-trajectory methods of landspreading of slurry (AFBI 2007).

18.5.3.7 Detoxification in the marine environment

In Northern Ireland nutrients entering the marine environment are predominantly from agricultural sources and human sewage, as there has been a reduction in industrial sources with a rapid late 20th Century decline in secondary industrial capacity. There is a persistent problem of bathing beaches and sewage, as shown by Good Beach Guide changes (2009–2010). These show two failed beaches, two beaches with downward trends, 12 beaches staying the same and six beaches with an upward trend (MCS 2010). Water quality at over 80% of coastal sites tested was deemed to be 'at risk' under the Water Framework Directive from morphological alterations, about 85% at risk from point source pollution and around 50% each at risk from diffuse pollution and alien species (EHS 2008a).

Northern Ireland's marine ecosystem receives most of the wastes passed into rivers and estuaries, much of

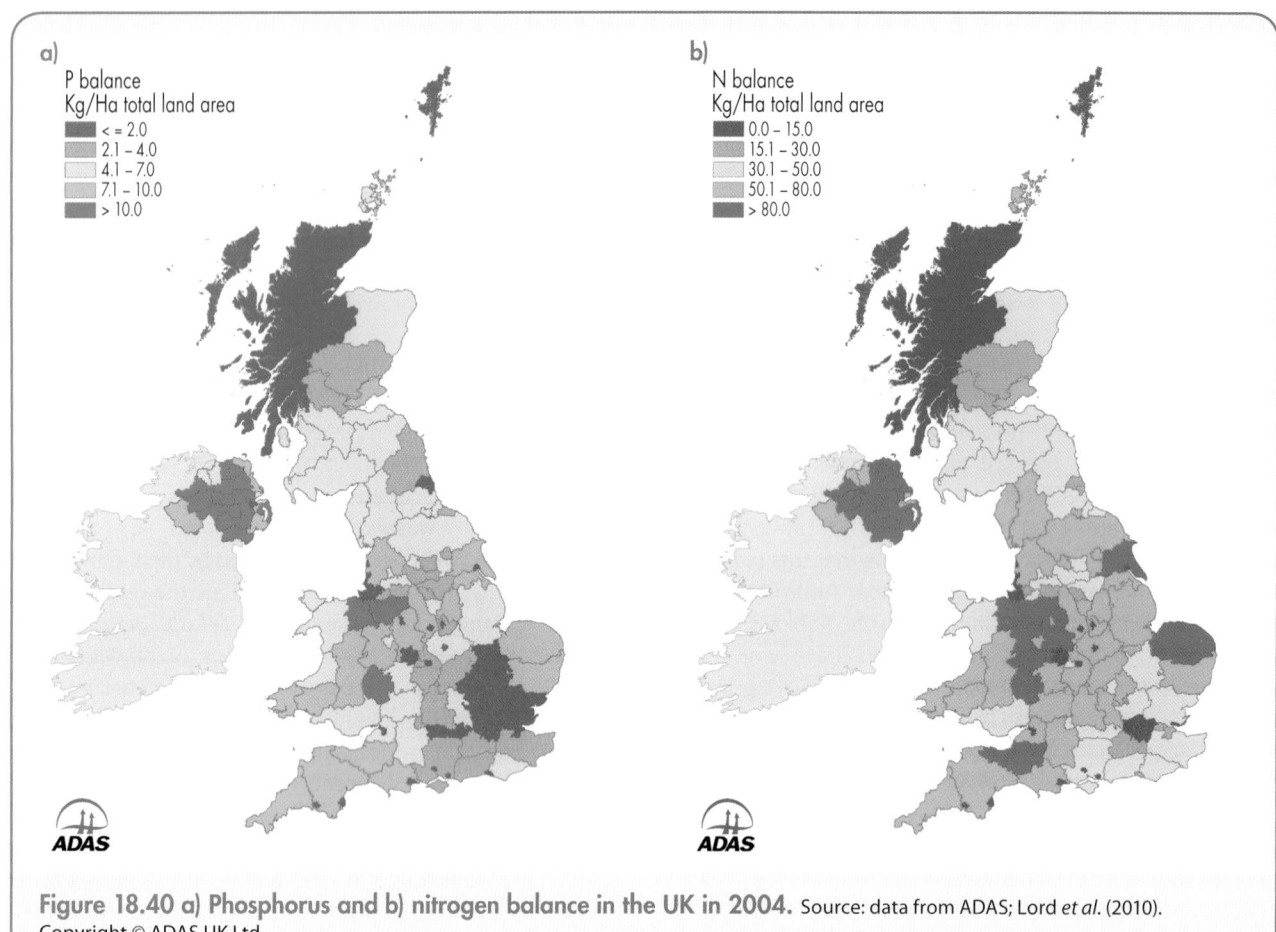

Figure 18.40 a) Phosphorus and b) nitrogen balance in the UK in 2004. Source: data from ADAS; Lord *et al.* (2010). Copyright © ADAS UK Ltd.

the nutrient load of nitrogen- and phosphorus-enriched groundwater (originating from intensive agriculture on land), some of the sewage, significant amounts of litter and all of the wastes produced by marine aquaculture. They also absorb a large amount of the carbon dioxide, which originates from the many activities that require the burning of fossil fuels. With the exception of recalcitrant flotsam, such as plastics, many of these organic waste products are processed and detoxified by healthy marine systems using natural pathways that convert much of the waste into useful production. However, all marine systems have their limits, and these limits are lowest for sheltered (or enclosed) waters, like those off Northern Ireland's Irish Sea coast, and particularly in the sea loughs. Unfortunately, this is where most of the waste loads enter coastal waters.

18.5.3.8 Soil quality

The main greenhouse gases from agricultural soils are nitrous oxide from nitrogenous fertiliser applications, methane from waterlogged soils and carbon dioxide from soil respiration. Atmospheric deposition of ammonia and nitrogen oxides from intensive livestock systems occurs. Northern Ireland has high levels of soil phosphorus and nitrogen compared to other parts of the UK, due to the importance of livestock farming (Foy & Jordan 2011; **Figure 18.40**). Agriculture contributed 81% of nitrous oxide emissions in Northern Ireland in 2007 (Chapter 14).

Soils capture and release carbon, nutrients and water and through these processes they detoxify pollutants, purify water, and provide the physical and chemical support systems for land plants and animals. The ability to deliver these outputs effectively is determined by the chemical, physical and biological properties of soils and their interactions (EHS 2008a). Soil quality is fundamental to the productivity and condition of habitats and hence the delivery of all ecosystem services.

Most of the soil carbon resides in the soil organic matter, and this is an aspect of soil quality that influences the degree of compaction, water storage, capacity for resisting erosion and other properties which, in combination with the plant nutrients in the soil, determine its productivity. The role of soils in sequestering carbon is discussed in Section 18.5.3.1. Undisturbed soils sequester large amounts of carbon, which is lost through oxidation when soils are cultivated. The value of soil as a carbon store will become increasingly important and could become a major determinant of land use in the future (Azeez 2009).

In the 1940s most soils (73%) were low or deficient in phosphorus and hence agriculture benefited from phosphorus fertiliser inputs. By the 1990s excess phosphorus levels occurred in 48% of soils in Northern Ireland and in 52% by 2005. Agricultural production on these soils will not benefit from the addition of more phosphorus (Foy & Jordan 2011; **Figure 18.41**; **Figure 18.42**; Section 18.4.6). Measures to decrease nutrient losses from agriculture are enforced through the Nitrates Directive. However, passive losses from soils can still occur, especially losses of phosphorus. Calculation of farm nutrient balances shows that Northern

Ireland has high phosphorus surpluses, reflecting the large area of intensive grassland and correspondingly small arable sector. Northern Ireland also has high nitrogen balances compared with most parts of the UK (see **Figure 18.40**).

Farm nutrient balances can be calculated by comparing inputs such as fertilisers and animal feeds with outputs such as milk, meat or other agricultural products exported from the system (Foy & Jordan 2011). Large imbalances with surpluses of major nutrients such as nitrogen and phosphorus lead to environmental degradation by eutrophication of rivers and lakes. It was established that an action programme would be applied to the total territory of Northern Ireland under the Protection of Water Against Agricultural Nitrate Pollution Regulations (Northern Ireland) 2004 (DOE 2009a). The Nitrates Action Programme Regulations (Northern Ireland) 2006 set out an action programme applying to all farms across Northern Ireland from 1st January 2007. In addition, other controls such as the Phosphorus (Use In Agriculture) Regulations (Northern Ireland) 2006 were introduced across Northern Ireland and these measures collectively are designed to reduce nutrient inputs from agriculture that contribute to eutrophication. Controls on the storage and application of nitrate and phosphorus fertilisers, at farm level, are an important contribution to tackling Northern Ireland's eutrophication problem. Many soils have accumulated excessive phosphorus from fertiliser application since WWII and phosphorus in animal feedstuffs is also a major input (see **Figure 18.41**). To comply with the Water Framework Directive, controls have been introduced on application rates of phosphorus fertilisers and new phosphorus regulation links the use of phosphorus fertilisers to a definable need. In 2004–2006 about half of all grassland had levels of phosphorus above the normal range, but for intensive grassland soils this was 75% (see **Figure 18.42**). Since 2003 there has been a decrease of over 70% in phosphorus-based fertiliser sales. Regulatory controls of phosphorus fertiliser use and voluntary agreements to lower phosphorus in animal diets have reduced the phosphorus surplus from 16.8 kilograms of phosphorous per hectare (kg P/ha) in 2003 to 8.6 kg P/ha in 2008. Phosphorus balance has been reduced to historically low levels, with beef and sheep farms now close to balance (or with a negative balance; Foy & Jordan 2011). However, 50% of dairy and almost all poultry and pig farms are above 10 kg P/ha. In theory, these farms are also stocked above the 170 kg N/ha limit and so will be exporting surplus phosphorus and, after exporting, these farms should mostly be below 10 kg P/ha. As a result, monitoring by the Northern Ireland Environment Agency of long-term trends in soluble reactive phosphorus in rivers has shown a decline which was significant between 1999 and 2007 at 74% (182) of sampling sites (DOE 2009a). Further research is required into exerting further controls over nutrient cycling in agricultural systems (Foy & Jordan 2011).

Sulphur deficiency in Northern Ireland was highlighted 24 years ago by Stevens & Watson (1986) and may be more widespread now. Crops use nitrogen less efficiently when sulphur is deficient. It is therefore necessary to encourage farmers to test their soils or forages for sulphur status in the

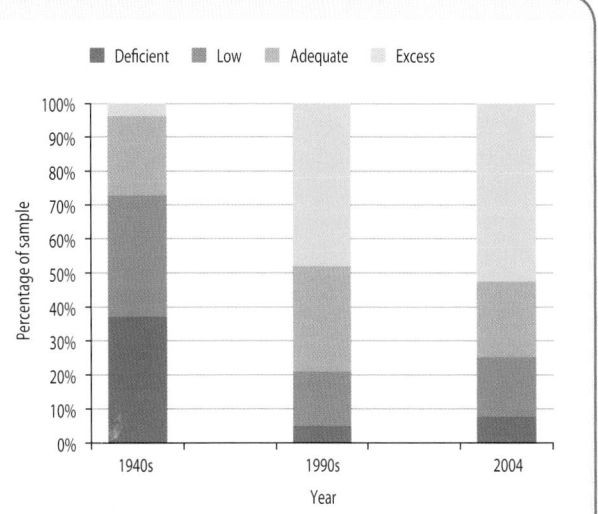

Figure 18.41 Soil phosphorus status for grass production in Northern Ireland in the 1940s, 1990s and 2004. In the 1940s most soils were deficient in phosphorus; by the 1990s 48% had excess phosphorus due to cumulative impacts of phosphorus fertiliser applications above plant requirements. Source: reproduced from Foy & Jordan (2011).

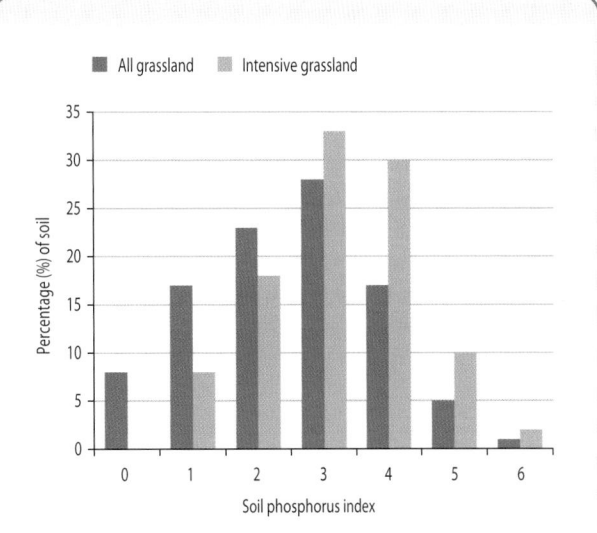

Figure 18.42 Soil phosphorus index of grassland soils (ADAS indices for extractable (Olsen) phosphorus 0=deficient, 2=normal (target), 6=excessive) in Northern Ireland in 2004/6. Agri-Environment Branch, Soil Survey based on 5 km grid sampling showing that 51% of all soils had phosphorus above the normal range, but for intensive grassland soils this figure was 75%. Intensive data based on random sampling of 100 fields on farms stocked at >170 kg organic nitrogen/ha. Source: reproduced from Foy & Jordan (2011).

future. They will need to apply sulphur fertilisers in order to correct any deficiency, which will allow the efficient use of all major nutrients to control diffuse pollution (Balsom 2010).

Soil microorganisms and fauna are as important to ecosystem functioning as the above-ground biota, but are more difficult to study and therefore less well understood. Soil microbes, nematodes and earthworms are important detritivores that are critical for delivering services such as the cycling of nutrients in soils and the detoxification of pollutants. Alien flatworms which prey on earthworms (Boag & Yeates 2001) are an issue in Northern Ireland. Although there are no particular differences from the rest of the UK, livestock density in agricultural land is greater and invasive flatworms are more prevalent than in most parts of Great Britain and Ireland (Murchie *et al.* 2003).

18.5.3.9 Water quality

There is a substantial history of both direct and diffuse pollution in Northern Ireland's water bodies, but major concern in recent years has been with diffuse pollution from agriculture (Foy & Girvan 2004). This has led to significant acidification and eutrophication of areas of sensitive habitats (roughly 70% and 80% respectively exceeded critical loads during the past 10 years; NIEA 2011) and large lakes (39% eutrophic, 32% mesotrophic, 25% hypertrophic and 4% oligotrophic; Lough Neagh is hypertrophic; Lough Erne is eutrophic; Foy & Jordan 2011).

In 2009 less than 30% (ranging from 15 to 30% for the different River Basin Districts, or RBDs) of Northern Ireland's surface waters met the EU water quality standard of 'good ecological status' which they are required to meet by 2015 under the Water Framework Directive (NIEA 2009f,g,h; **Table 18.14**; **Figure 18.43**). Many ecosystem services depend on water quality, and compliance with Water Framework Directive targets and delivery of River Basin Management Plans are prime drivers for environmental action (EHS 2008a).

Agriculture contributes 70% to nitrogen loading, while urban sources are the largest contributors to both ammonium (67%) and phosphorus (54%), with only 5.6% of monitored rivers not showing nutrient enrichment (EHS 2008a). Agricultural wastes, including silage effluent, slurry and dirty yard water, have a very high pollution potential;

Table 18.14 The percentage (%) of each River Basin District at different levels of Ecological Status. Source: data from NIEA (2009f,g,h).

River basin district	Ecological status of waterbodies			
	Heavily modified and artificial waterbodies		Natural or moderately modified waterbodies	
	Moderate ecological potential or worse (%)	Good ecological potential or better (%)	Less than good status (%)	Good or better (%)
North Eastern	17.0	2.0	65.0	16.0
North Western	7.0	0.0	63.0	30.0
Neagh Bann	12.6	0.4	72.6	14.4

silage effluent has approximately 200 times the pollution potential of raw domestic sewage. Water quality is showing signs of general improvement, with recent legislation leading to decreases in inputs of artificial fertilisers and restrictions on timing and conditions of slurry spreading.

Nutrient cycling studies in which nitrate has been monitored at river sites has shown that nitrate levels tend to peak in winter, corresponding to high rates of nitrogen use in agriculture. Long-term trend analysis of nitrate in surface waters from 1994 to 2009 shows a significant decrease in nitrate at 35% of sites and increases at 5%. Northern Ireland remains a low nitrate area with 99% of surface water sites and 82% of groundwater sites having annual average concentrations of less than 25 mg nitrate/l (DOE 2009a; **Figure 18.44**; **Figure 18.45**).

Northern Ireland has over 1,000 lakes and reversing eutrophication in these lakes is a key water quality objective. Agriculture is the largest source of nutrients to these lakes and they remain enriched despite phosphate stripping at all large waste water treatment works (Foy & Jordan 2011; see **Figure 18.40**; **Figure 18.41**; **Figure 18.42**; Section 18.4.6). Phosphorus is an important plant nutrient, but at excessive levels in water it is a major cause of eutrophication. In 2007, 16% of rivers in Northern Ireland exceeded the EU standard for soluble reactive phosphorus, but that is a major decrease since 2000, when 27% exceeded the threshold (DOE & NISRA 2009). This period coincides with a major decrease in the amount of fertiliser applied, with a decrease from 470 to 314 thousand tonnes purchased from 1999 to 2006 (EHS 2008a).

In 2008, 2,244 water pollution incidents were reported to the Northern Ireland Environment Agency, of which 1,237 were substantiated as having an impact on the water quality of the receiving water course. This is 21% fewer than the number substantiated in 2001, and in 2008 only 20% of pollution incidents were considered to be of high or medium severity (DOE & NISRA 2010). There are localised and cumulative environmental problems in rural areas caused by sewage from scattered houses and industry, which are typically treated by privately operated septic tanks or small treatment works. In 2009 more than 110,000 properties (approximately 20% of the total) in Northern Ireland were

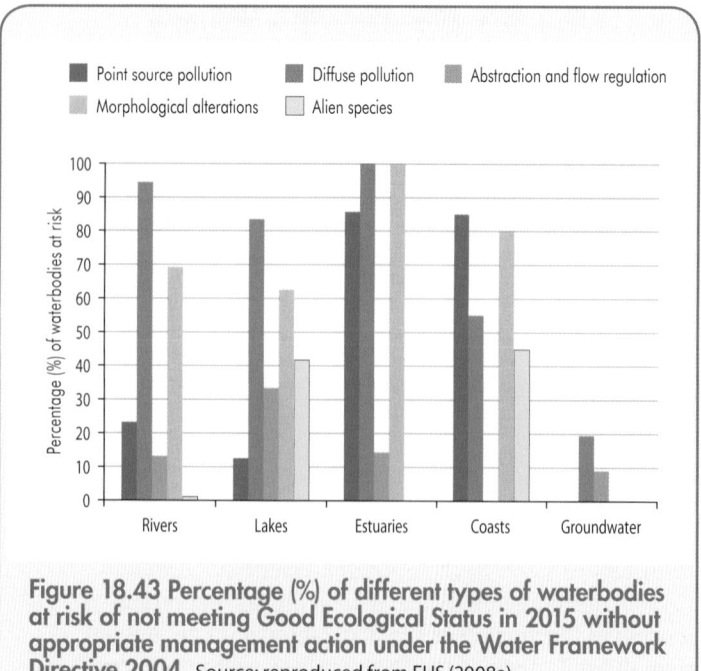

Figure 18.43 Percentage (%) of different types of waterbodies at risk of not meeting Good Ecological Status in 2015 without appropriate management action under the Water Framework Directive 2004. Source: reproduced from EHS (2008a).

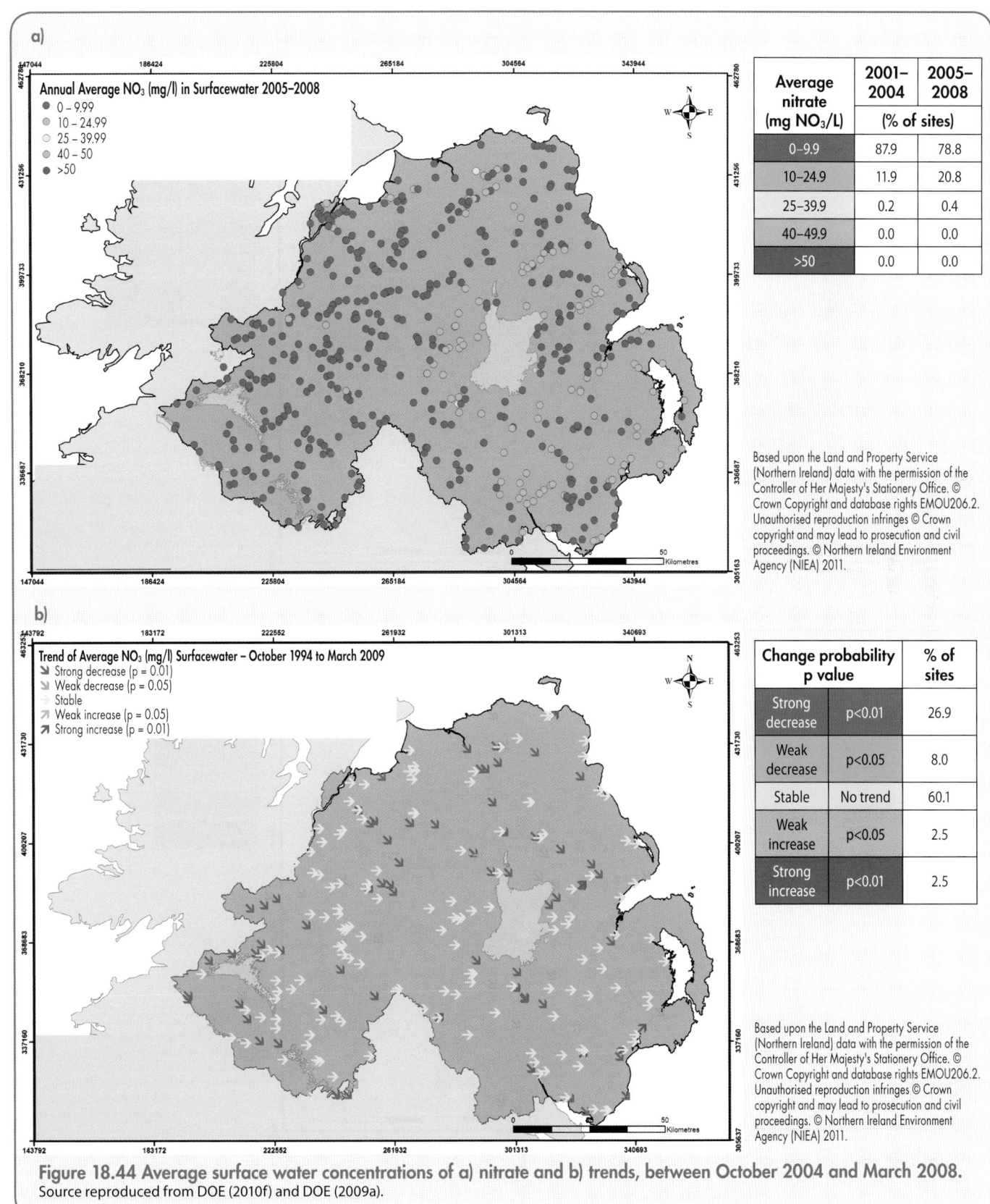

Average nitrate (mg NO$_3$/L)	2001–2004	2005–2008
	(% of sites)	
0–9.9	87.9	78.8
10–24.9	11.9	20.8
25–39.9	0.2	0.4
40–49.9	0.0	0.0
>50	0.0	0.0

Annual Average NO$_3$ (mg/l) in Surfacewater 2005–2008
- 0 – 9.99
- 10 – 24.99
- 25 – 39.99
- 40 – 50
- >50

Based upon the Land and Property Service (Northern Ireland) data with the permission of the Controller of Her Majesty's Stationery Office. © Crown Copyright and database rights EMOU206.2. Unauthorised reproduction infringes © Crown copyright and may lead to prosecution and civil proceedings. © Northern Ireland Environment Agency (NIEA) 2011.

Trend of Average NO$_3$ (mg/l) Surfacewater – October 1994 to March 2009
- Strong decrease (p = 0.01)
- Weak decrease (p = 0.05)
- Stable
- Weak increase (p = 0.05)
- Strong increase (p = 0.01)

Change probability p value		% of sites
Strong decrease	p<0.01	26.9
Weak decrease	p<0.05	8.0
Stable	No trend	60.1
Weak increase	p<0.05	2.5
Strong increase	p<0.01	2.5

Based upon the Land and Property Service (Northern Ireland) data with the permission of the Controller of Her Majesty's Stationery Office. © Crown Copyright and database rights EMOU206.2. Unauthorised reproduction infringes © Crown copyright and may lead to prosecution and civil proceedings. © Northern Ireland Environment Agency (NIEA) 2011.

Figure 18.44 Average surface water concentrations of a) nitrate and b) trends, between October 2004 and March 2008. Source reproduced from DOE (2010f) and DOE (2009a).

without public sewerage provision, representing around 0.3 million people (one-fifth of Northern Ireland's population), and generating around 65 million litres of wastewater a day (NIEA 2009g).

Water discharge is regulated through Water Order consents for private sewage and trade effluent. Both have registered a slight improvement in percentage compliance since 2000, with reported figures in 2008 of 86% and 87%, respectively (DOE & NISRA 2010).

Sustainable Urban Drainage Schemes (SuDS) are now incorporated into PPS15 and River Basin Management Plans, but have not been used as much to date in Northern Ireland as in Great Britain (NIEA 2009c). The lack of regulation on conversion of soil to hard surfacing in gardens or new

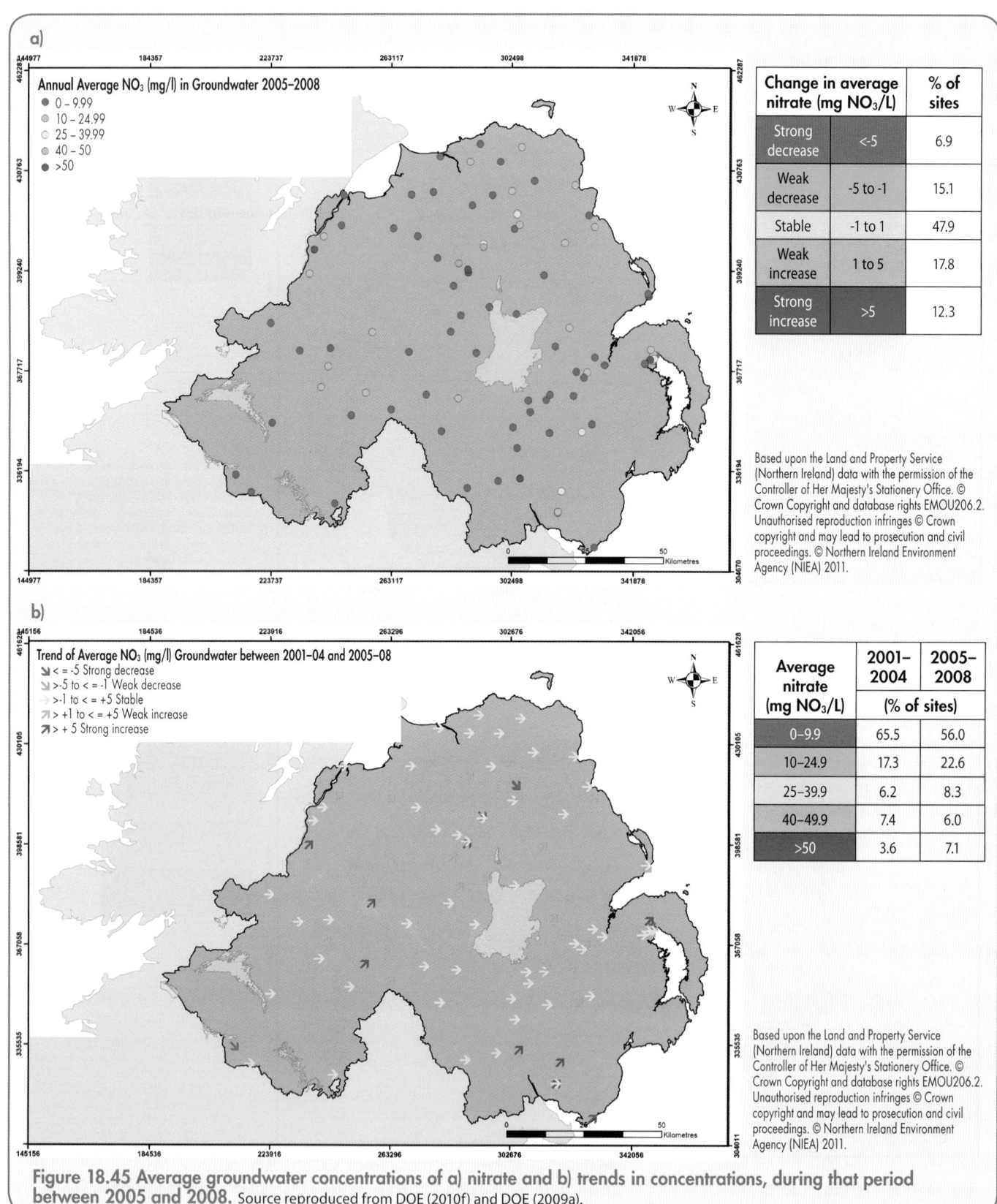

Figure 18.45 Average groundwater concentrations of a) nitrate and b) trends in concentrations, during that period between 2005 and 2008. Source reproduced from DOE (2010f) and DOE (2009a).

development can contribute to flood danger and resulting damage. Culverting of watercourses is also an issue in terms of water quality and the difficulty of tracing pollution incidents as well as the loss of habitat value.

18.5.3.10 Air quality

Northern Ireland's air quality has improved in recent years, with most pollutants below target values (**Table 18.15**).

This is primarily due to the use of catalytic converters in cars and a move away from domestic coal burning to gas central heating. Air quality for the majority of Northern Ireland's population is affected by urban ecosystems; street trees and urban green spaces can improve air and water quality, remove some pollution and help with noise reduction (Broadmeadow & Freer-Smith 1996; Stewart *et al.* 2003). Green roofs can also contribute to pollution

UK National Ecosystem Assessment: Technical Report

Table 18.15 Air pollutants, their impacts and their status in Northern Ireland. Sources: data from EHS (2008a); DOE & NISRA (2009, 2010); Chapter 10.

Air pollutant	Major effects	Ecosystem regulation impacts	Northern Ireland status
Particulate matter (PM)	Human health	Pollen, fire, deposition on plants	Urban areas are higher than rural areas but both are well below the UK Air Quality Objective (DOE & NISRA 2010).
Ozone (O_3)	Human health, reduced crop yield, changes in species composition	Deposition and absorption by plants; emissions of volatile organic compounds (VOCs) contribute.	Highly variable with target levels exceeded especially in Londonderry (DOE & NISRA 2010).
Nitrogen oxides (NO_x) Ammonia (NH_3) Nitrogen deposition	Human health, eutrophication, acidification	Deposition reduces impacts on health and ecosystem services. Heavy levels of deposition impact on habitats. Emissions from livestock and farming.	NO_x levels stable, higher at roadsides, within target limits. Ammonia has decreased slightly, with 94% from livestock and 6% from fertiliser applications (DOE & NISRA 2010).
Sulphur deposition	Acidification	Deposition impacts on health and other ecosystem services. Heavy levels of deposition can impact on habitats.	Significant decrease since 1992 (EHS 2008).

abatement, temperature regulation and carbon balance (Rowe 2010).

Ecosystems influence concentrations and deposition of air pollutants in four major ways:

1. They remove pollutants from the atmosphere; e.g. trees, green spaces and vegetation in urban areas reducing local air pollution.
2. They contribute directly to the emissions to the atmosphere; e.g. ammonia from intensive agriculture.
3. They contribute indirectly to air pollution levels via chemical processing in the atmosphere, e.g. volatile organic compounds (VOCs) that contribute to ozone.
4. Measures to reduce emissions to, or deposition from, the atmosphere can increase the potential for air quality regulation by ecosystems, e.g. reducing high levels improves functioning.

Northern Ireland does not have a history of extensive concentrations of heavy industry as in northern England. However, levels of atmospheric nitrogen increase towards the east of Northern Ireland. High levels of ammonia have been recorded in the Mournes and the Antrim Plateau and may encourage grasses at the expense of heather (EHS 2004b). Studies in the UK have shown that drift of fertiliser during application to adjacent fields and enriched runoff can also affect lowland peat bogs (Tang *et al.* 2004). There has been no attempt to value air pollution effects on grassland/heathland ecosystems in Northern Ireland. As in the case of forestry, the absence of reliable scientific research to underpin valuation is a limiting factor. Although some effects of air pollution on these vegetation types are documented, the problem of identifying the role of air pollution from other influences such as grazing management and erosion remains (MacMillan *et al.* 2001).

18.5.3.11 Pollination
The relationship between natural ecosystems and crops with regard to pollination and pest control is complex; the natural systems provide many services to the crops, but also benefit from the crops which provide food and shelter.

Honeybees pollinate both crops and natural plants; natural habitats provide pollen and nectar for the bees when crops are not flowering. Most honey production is small scale, with around 1,000 beekeepers and 4,000 hives. Honey production is estimated at 30 tonnes worth some £220,000 per annum (DARD 2010p).

In Northern Ireland the main crops pollinated by insects are apples, with over £7 million as the estimated market value of insect pollination; an estimated 80% of this is by honeybees. Strawberries, beans, oilseed rape, raspberries, currents and other soft fruit are also partially dependent on insect pollination, with an additional £100,000 estimated value of insect pollination (Archie Murchie, AFBI, pers. comm.).

18.5.3.12 Pest control
Natural ecosystems can contribute significantly to the control of pests in crops, providing nesting sites and food for animals which prey on plant pests. However, they are also potential reservoirs of diseases and can provide habitats or hiding places for crop pests. The dangers of plant and animal pests and diseases have been dramatically demonstrated in recent years (BSE, Foot-and-Mouth, Dutch elm) and continue to cause serious concern and significant costs (e.g. New Zealand flatworm (Section 18.5.3.4), nematodes, bovine TB, *Phytophora ramorum*; Forest Service 2010c). Appropriate management of both natural and cropped land can address some of these issues and the benefits of using natural pest control have been established in a range of habitats (greater biodiversity seems to improve natural pest control and disease resistance, see Chapter 14).

The impacts of pest species are highly variable and dependent on many factors, principally weather, but also the fluctuating value of the crop and the cost of control measures. Crops can be impacted upon by both decreased yield and loss of quality. The latter is particularly important with crops that are marketed directly to consumers (e.g. eating apples), where cosmetic damage can be very important and may even lead to rejection of a consignment by traders or supermarkets.

Aphids are a major worldwide pest of most crops. Their impact is by two mechanisms: direct feeding on the host plant's phloem and the transmission of viral diseases. A general estimate of damage in cereals assumes a 10% loss of yield (Tatchell 1989). However, clearly this is dependent on the level of infestation and whether or not viral diseases are vectored. Nevertheless, taking this as a basis and given that the average farm income from cereal crops in Northern Ireland is approximately £40,000 (DARD 2009d) then the economic impact of aphid pests could be around £3,000–£4,000 on average each year per cereal farm (Archie Murchie, AFBI, pers. comm.).

The major crop in Northern Ireland is grass, making up 80% of agricultural land and supporting the dairy and beef industries. The total value of the grass crop is difficult to ascertain because it is used on farm for grazing and silage. However, estimates would be between £300 and £700 million per annum. The New Zealand flatworm (*Arthurdendyus triangulatus*) has reduced earthworm biomass by 20% in experimental plots (Archie Murchie, AFBI, pers. comm.). If it is assumed that earthworms contribute to grass yield between 10 and 30% (Stockdill 1982), then the presence of *A. triangulatus* could be reducing grassland productivity by 2 to 6%. The flatworm is present in 70% of grassland in Northern Ireland (Murchie *et al.* 2003). Acknowledging that these are very rough estimates and that there are many caveats, the economic impact of *A. triangulatus* could then be calculated as between £4.2 and £29.4 million per annum (Archie Murchie, AFBI, pers. comm.).

The Agri-food and Biosciences Institute is also investigating midges (*Culicoides* species) as vectors of Bluetongue. The impact of an outbreak of that insect-vectored disease would be very costly. In Scotland there was an estimate of £100 million per annum (30% of direct losses and 70% of indirect costs). It is likely that the impact on Northern Ireland would be slightly less but in that region (Archie Murchie, AFBI, pers. comm.). Bovine tuberculosis is regarded as a major problem for Northern Ireland agriculture, with the cost of its control estimated at £200 million over the past 10 years (NI Assembly 2009).

18.5.3.13 Flood control

Flooding occurs sporadically within Northern Ireland, although most urban flooding occurs from pluvial flooding rather than from rivers. The Rivers Agency is the government agency with the flood defence and land drainage remits. After WWII there was an emphasis on land drainage, but in more recent years this has swung towards flood defence and, more latterly, flood risk management. This is shown through the Agency's role as the competent authority for the Floods Directive (a sister directive to the Water Framework Directive), the subsequent production of flooded area maps, and the production of PPS15 (with the Planning Service) dealing with floodplain development. Urban flood defence aims to protect housing and infrastructure to a 1:100 level, whilst agricultural land is protected to a 1.3/5 level on average. Studies on more catchment-based sustainable flood management are currently underway. Sustainable urban drainage systems (SuDS) have not yet been adopted as standard methodology for development sites (Judith Bankhead, Rivers Agency, pers. comm.).

The value of natural habitats (especially those adjoining rivers, streams and lakes) in providing floodplains which help to regulate flood risk has been increasingly recognised in recent years, with a shift away from drainage, culverting and canalisation of rivers to more natural treatments which work with natural habitats to help reduce flood damage locally or further downstream (Jackson *et al.* 2008). The value of wetlands in general, both natural and artificial, is increasingly recognised for both flood control and pollution abatement. Planning Policy Statement 15 assists in limiting development in floodplain areas, but catchment-wide management for flooding is also required in the long term (SNIFFER 2009). Flood maps which identify areas at risk from flooding, including future climate change scenarios have been prepared by the Rivers Agency (Rivers Agency 2008b). Further need for flood defence is likely under climate change conditions (Sayers & Calvert 2007), and the possibility of multiple use of natural habitats to include flood defence could be encouraged. In 2009 significant flooding occurred in both Belfast (BRC 2010) and County Fermanagh (OFMDFM 2010b), causing severe and widespread damage, not only in economic terms (both business and residents suffered significantly), but also to residents' well-being, causing a general feeling of being under threat from similar events in the future.

Much of the damage caused by storm surges is a result of wave action, and the nearshore marine ecosystem can play a large role in regulating these waves. For example, sand bars, rocky reefs and biogenic reefs can cause ocean swell to shoal and break, thereby dissipating energy that would otherwise be expended on the coast. The greater the amount of energy dissipation, the lower the degree of coastal erosion (e.g. Uda 2009; Harris *et al.*). The degree to which any nearshore marine habitat can contribute to this service is dependent on the efficacy of the management of coastal sediment budgets, the amount of aggregate extraction and the degree and frequency of disturbance by mobile fishing gear deployed at the seabed.

Coastal defences have been developed as a result of government support for coastal agricultural activity (e.g. low cost revetments and clay-based flood embankments), urban protection (sea walls as flood defence) and infrastructure defence (roads, ports and airports). The total percentage of open coastline defended is limited (around <15%), though defence of lough shores is high (e.g. Belfast Lough at around 90%). Most defences are of mid-20th Century origin, though the recent trend of revitalising old defences on a hold-the-line basis without regard for modern approaches is disconcerting (Julian Orford, QUB, pers. comm.). The cost of defences is high, but there are some incidences of private landowners infilling with hardcore rubble on both loughside tidal marshes and open coast cliff foots. The natural shifting boundary of dune and beach is also being fixed by the introduction of static defences on coastal golf courses. In coastal areas managed retreat, as with inland floodplains, could be used to avoid damage which could increase with climate change, but knowledge is needed on how the sediments are moving to ensure that land is managed to avoid further damage. The first trial of managed retreat was begun in 2009 at Anne's Point, Strangford Lough, with the Rivers Agency and National Trust working together to lower sections of sea defence to allow controlled inundation and increase brackish habitat (Judith Bankhead, Rivers Agency, pers. comm.).

18.5.4 Cultural Services

Cultural Services are defined in the Millennium Ecosystem Assessment (MA) as "the non-material benefits people obtain from ecosystems through spiritual enrichment, cognitive development, reflection, recreation and aesthetic experiences" (MA 2005b). The MA highlighted that human use of ecosystems for non-material benefits had increased over the past 50 years and pointed out that "the impact of the loss of cultural services is particularly difficult to measure, but it is especially important for many people" (MA 2005b).

Cultural ecosystem services address the need to interact (socially and with our surrounding environment), in time and space ranging from homes, streets, neighbourhoods, towns/cities and landscapes and back gardens, public parks, and natural habitats. The UK NEA identifies the spaces in which people interact with nature as environmental settings which is split into two overlapping categories: small-scale meaningful local places and large-scale socially valued landscapes, both of which have biotic (living) and abiotic (non-living) factors (Chapter 16).

It is becoming increasingly recognised that interactions, both socially and with the environment, lead to better physical and mental health, resulting in longer and healthier lives and more productive and secure societies (Chapter 16). This has obvious benefits directly in terms of reduced health care costs, increased tourism and recreation infrastructure and more generally in terms of providing cultural and emotional benefits for all citizens. People use the natural environment for a wide range of cultural benefits, directly for recreation, leisure or tourism or indirectly for providing them with a sense of their heritage and a source of inspiration. It is important to have a variety of habitats available for a wide range of purposes; some people wish to actively participate in countryside activities, others like to visit more passively, and still others may simply wish to know that the natural environment exists in a healthy and diverse state. Natural settings receive a large number of visitors because they provide a wide range of opportunities: activities, experiences, attachments, feelings, emotions and memories, engagement with history and culture, photography, relaxation, gardening, pleasant settings (Castree 2005; Natural England 2005). They hold different values for different people and usage and the value assigned to it varies markedly across demographic, socioeconomic and cultural groups and different environmental attitudes (Pretty 2007). While some people enjoy gardens as their prime contact with nature, others feel the need to escape to remote wilderness locations to feel a connection with nature (Natural England 2009).

Because of this range of meanings, values, attitudes and behaviours by people to nature, and the diversity of the natural environment itself, it is not possible to argue that some natural environment spaces, features or habitats will be somehow more 'useful' in cultural terms than others. Wild mountains may provide the spaces mountaineers or wilderness lovers need to pursue their cultural activities but local parks also play important roles in providing contact with nature and the living world for those who cannot or do not wish to travel to more remote locations (Harrison et al. 1987; Burgess et al. 1988; Crouch & Lubbren 2003). Investing in heritage both makes people feel better and makes sound economic sense through tourism and local jobs associated with the heritage (English Heritage 2010).

Many people in Northern Ireland enjoy membership of or volunteer for organisations that provide access to their properties (e.g. National Trust, Wildfowl and Wetlands Trust, Colin Glen Forest Park, Ulster Wildlife Trust) with a wide range of functions and outputs, and which provide a range of benefits to members. Total membership of environmental organisations is over 100,000, but some individuals may be members of more than one organisation (Envision Management Consultants 2010).

There is a strong appreciation of the social value of farming in relation to the agricultural landscape. Research indicated that 89% of Northern Ireland's people agreed that farmers 'keep the countryside alive' and 83% claimed that farming adds to the beauty of the landscape. There is a strong attachment 'to the land' in Northern Ireland, with many people only one or two generations removed from living in the countryside themselves, and many wishing to live outside of cities for the benefits of a rural lifestyle (Sluka 1999). There is a general pride in the natural beauty of Northern Ireland amongst its citizens, but the fragility of that environment is not always recognised as changes to it are slow relative to a human lifespan (Shortall 2006).

Northern Ireland has a rich cultural and archaeological heritage extending over 9,000 years (Gormley et al. 2009). Many sites are popular visitor attractions, and the 'existence value' of the cultural heritage is particularly strong; even if they do not wish to visit sites personally, people place a value on having them preserved (Claire Foley, NIEA, pers. comm.).

There is no public 'right to roam' in Northern Ireland and there are relatively few public rights of way or public pathways (EHS 2006a). Councils have a duty under the Access to the Countryside (NI) Order 1983 to assert and protect rights of way. However, public access is largely restricted to lands in public or charitable ownership such as the Forest Service, Northern Ireland Environment Agency Country Parks, local authorities, the National Trust or Northern Ireland Water (Annett et al. 2006). Accordingly, access to open countryside is more restricted than in other parts of the UK. Northern Ireland does not have any National Parks, although there have been campaigns for and studies commissioned on the issue for many years (Annett et al. 2006). While many benefits have been identified and there is a substantial argument in favour of establishing parks, there is local opposition from landowners, largely based around worry that control of their land would be taken from them. Background work on the legislation necessary to introduce parks has begun, but is not scheduled for the Assembly term leading up to elections in May 2011.

18.5.4.1 Health, leisure and recreation

The physical, mental and emotional benefits of access to natural environments are well established. Positive physical health outcomes using heart rate, blood pressure, body mass index (BMI), waist measurements and physical activity level have all been noted. Epidemiological studies show associations between home proximity to green space and health and associations between the presence of nature on urban estates and reduced recorded crime (Chapter 16). However, these are not always fully recognised or quantified when people start to put an economic value on the natural environment (NI Green NGOs & EHS2007; Section 18.5.6). Some of the economic value of leisure, recreation and tourism can be captured through expenditure to undertake these activities, and certainly these activities have a direct relationship with human health and well-being. Northern Ireland has a rich variety of outdoor recreation and leisure activities, with a strong recognition that the natural environment is one of its prime attractions to tourists (Forest Service 2009b; **Table 18.16**).

Green spaces have a crucial role to play in mental and physical health within towns and cities. There is evidence that contact with nature can aid recovery from physical and mental illness (Bell *et al.* 2008). A UK study of 336,000 patient records showed a trend of significantly less health inequality between the wealthy and the poor in areas with higher levels of green space than between similar groups in areas with less green space. In areas with high concentrations of green space there was a 25% lower all-cause mortality rate (FPH 2010).

Parks, play areas, allotments and community gardens can help maintain physical fitness, alleviate social isolation and encourage social interaction between all age groups. This supports the development of social networks, understanding and cross-community relationships which are essential to Northern Ireland's healing process. In Northern Ireland, 25% of the population is obese and half is overweight (Belfast Healthy Cities 2010). This trend is increasing and will inevitably impact on the health service and economy. Parks and walks such as Belfast's Lagan Walkways provide a safe and attractive route in and around the city and there has been an increase in 'green exercise' through voluntary work with organisations such as the Conservation Volunteers and Groundwork. Improved road safety on active travel routes will encourage walking and cycling, helping to reduce obesity and maintain fitness. In 2010 70% of all journeys in

Table 18.16 Some examples of recreational, tourism and leisure uses of Northern Ireland's natural environment.

	Assets and uses	Some issues
Mountains	Recreational use of upland habitats is of increasing importance (CAAN 2007). Around 370 ha of upland heathland/moorland are managed for public access and conservation in the Belfast Hills; walking, camping and nature based tourism (bird watching, angling).	Erosion of footpaths, particularly of peaty soils and thin mineral soils on steeper slopes, especially where marked 'Ways' cross blanket peatland (CAAN 2007).
Forests	Two million visits annually to Forest Service properties involving 473,368 paying visitors (Forest Service 2010a). Partnerships with a wide range of environmental NGOs, local authorities and others to carry out a variety of projects and events (Forest Service 2010a). Forests are also an important part of upland recreation (Tomlinson & Fennessy 2009).	Only 7.2% of people have access to a wood of at least 2 ha within 500 m of their homes and only 40.2% have access to a wood of at least 20 ha within 4 km of their home. The UK average figures are 15.6% and 64.8% respectively (Woodland Trust 2010b).
Urban areas	Opportunities for healthy activity from cycle networks, city/village parks, rivers, lakes, canals, cemeteries, allotments and various Highway to Health routes.	Conflicts due to other pressures on land use.
Coast and sea	Eight Blue Flag Beaches, one Blue Flag Marina and eight beaches with the Seaside Award (Tidy NI unpublished data). Scuba diving, boat tours, Cruise ships: 39 ships brought more than 64,000 visitors to Belfast in 2008 (Belfast City Council 2008). Sailing; many marinas, yachting clubs—approx. 12,000 participants in 2008 (CAAN 2009).	Litter, lack of facilities, car access to dunes.
Hiking and walking	Lagan Towpath (most popular public pathway in Northern Ireland); Ulster Way.	No 'right to roam'; few Public Rights of Way; damage from overuse (e.g. Mournes).
Horse riding	Popular, some trekking, but few bridleways.	Not included in access legislation.
Fishing	Salmon and sea trout angling, especially Lough Erne; world class sea angling on the Antrim Causeway Coast; DCAL estimated 25,000 freshwater anglers in Northern Ireland and 4,500 visitors in 2007 (DCAL *et al.* 2007).	Upland rivers and streams can be adversely affected by forestry and farming (UK NEA Freshwaters – Open waters, Wetlands & Floodplains; UK NEA Woodlands).
Shooting	Organised game shooting in upland habitats of Northern Ireland is limited and restricted largely to pheasant and partridge.	The red grouse is a red list species of conservation concern, showing a 60% decline in the last 30 years (Gibbons *et al.* 1993; Newton *et al.* 1999).
Archaeology and historic buildings	European Heritage Open Days which attracted a record 56,000 visitors (an increase of 8% from 2008 figures (NIEA 2010a). National Trust properties—the National Trust in Northern Ireland estimates that over 1.5 million people visit its coast, countryside and gardens annually.	Destruction or damage to monuments and buildings due to neglect and/or vandalism. There is a lack of adequate funding for their upkeep.

Northern Ireland were made by car and these account for 81% of the total distance travelled (NISRA 2010c).

Recreational use of farmland is limited as access is often restricted. There is no 'right to roam', and many farmers are highly resistant to extending access, and particularly to the designation of National Parks. A major reason for reluctance to provide access is the issue of a landowner's legal responsibility for users of his/her land (CAAN 2007). The relevant legislation, the Occupiers' Liability Act (NI) 1957 and the Occupiers' Liability (NI) Order 1987, place a duty of care on the occupier to take reasonable steps to ensure the safety of visitors. The duty of care also applies to trespassers (i.e. where no permission or consent has been granted). However, case law indicates that it would be extremely rare for landowners to be deemed liable in these circumstances (Maia Taylor, NIEA, pers. comm.). Landowners also express concern about the cost of repairing any damage to property, e.g. walls knocked down or gates left open.

It is generally agreed that sport can improve physical, social and psychological well-being. Most of Northern Ireland's population lives within easy access of the countryside, hence it is a valuable recreational asset for both land and water sports. A report by the Countryside Access and Activities Network (CAAN 2009) identified key trends in outdoor activities between 1995 and 2008. It noted an increase in participation in the activities under study and a growth in the number of private estates offering their land for recreational use. There is, however, a shortage of suitable facilities and qualified instructors and certain social groups (disadvantaged, ethnic and disabled) were reported to be under-represented in sporting activities. Barriers to their participation included low awareness, the lack of a suitable public transport system, physical inaccessibility, and patchy information and marketing (CAAN 2008).

18.5.4.2 Tourism

Tourism is a significant industry in Northern Ireland. In 2009 there were 3.3 million visitors, 1.9 million from out of state (26% for holiday, leisure and recreation); 1.4 million domestic, generating a total revenue of £529 million (£337 million out of state visitors, £192 million domestic). Tourism is responsible for 4.9% or £1.5 billion of the Northern Ireland economy and over 40,000 jobs (5.6% of the workforce), with one in 18 jobs directly supported by the visitor economy and an additional 25.5 jobs for every £1 million generated. This is low in comparison with the other countries on these islands (9.7% for the UK and 6.3% for the Republic of Ireland in 2010; WTTC 2010a,b,c). The history of violent conflict in Northern Ireland has often restricted the willingness of tourists to visit (Jafari 2003), however, sites associated with the 'Troubles' are now of particular interest to many international visitors (NITB 2010a). This is sometimes referred to as 'dark tourism' (The Guardian 2006).

The Giant's Causeway is a World Heritage Site and hosted some 714,612 visitors in 2009, a reduction of 5% from 2008 figures (NITB 2010d). Of the 1.9 million out of state tourists in 2009 (down from 2 million in 2008); 53% of them came from Great Britain, 25% from the Republic of Ireland, 11% from Europe, 7.5% from North America and 3.5% from rest of the world (NITB 2010b). While visitors from overseas were

increasing to 2008, there has been an overall drop since then with a decrease of 14.2% between 2008 and 2009. From 1967 to 1997 tourism grew very slowly, with visits doubling from 1 million to 2 million over that 30-year period. The political situation restricted the potential of tourism when most western economies were seeing their tourism sector flourish. In contrast, the 10 years from 1997 to 2007 saw rapid growth, with the number of visits increasing by 65%. The global financial crisis (late 2007 onwards) has had an impact on all business activity and has led to a decline in tourism globally (DETI 2010a; **Figure 18.46**).

A Northern Ireland Tourist Board survey in 2010 (NITB 2010c) found that the most highly rated and important motivating activities were sightseeing opportunities of the country and coast, with slightly lower ratings for:

- cities, towns and villages that give Northern Ireland a distinctive sense of place;
- unique things to do that reflect local culture;
- information at visitor attractions which tells the story of the place you are visiting; and
- information provided about places you can visit.

The vast majority of visitors surveyed stated that the "unique and distinctive landscapes and coastlines" and the "warm and welcoming people" appealed to them. Most visitors to Northern Ireland undertook a wide range of leisure activities. The most commonly undertaken pursuits were visiting a pub; visiting castles, historic houses or other historic monuments; hiking or walking; visiting a park or garden and going to a visitor or interpretation centre. Activities make a significant contribution to the overall quality of Northern Ireland visitor experiences, more so than any other part of the 'visitor journey' (NITB 2010c).

Figure 18.46 Tourism in Northern Ireland from 1959 to 2009. Note: A change in methodology occurred in 2005 when NITB adopted figures produced by the Central Statistics Office (CSO) for Republic of Ireland residents visiting.1959 to 2004 domestic visits and revenue relate to holiday visits only. 2005 to2009 figures relate to total domestic trips (i.e. holiday, visiting friends/relatives, business and other) and therefore 2005 to 2009 data are not directly comparable with data pre-2005. Source: data from NITB (2010e).

Northern Ireland Tourist Board Research (NITB 2010d) shows that the total number of trips and short breaks taken within Northern Ireland by local residents increased by over one-third between January and December 2009 compared with the same period in 2008. Approximately 9.9 million visits were made to participating visitor attractions during 2009. Most of the top visitor attractions in Northern Ireland have an important ecosystem component (**Figure 18.47**). By 2020 a focused effort could increase employment supported by tourism to 50,000 jobs, increase the number of visitors to 4.5 million, generate £1 billion total revenue and be a source of civic pride (DETI 2010a).

The most visited site was Crawfordsburn Country Park with 950,000 visitors, closely followed by the Giant's Causeway Visitor Centre with over 714,000. Most of the latter are probably 'unique visitors', while it is likely that some people will visit country parks many times each year. An overwhelming majority of the top attractions rely to a large extent on the natural environment (NITB 2010d; see **Figure 18.47**).

Events which decrease access to the natural environment have a dramatic impact on tourism. For example, the restrictions to movement following the Foot-and-Mouth Disease outbreak in 2001 resulted in losses to the tourism sector in the UK in the region of £3.2 billion (Curry 2009). A small drop was recorded in Northern Ireland during that year also (see **Figure 18.46**).

18.5.4.3 Angling

It is estimated that in 2005 there were 24,890 resident and 4,463 tourist or visiting coarse and game anglers in Northern Ireland. This represents an increase, of 10% and 2% respectively, on the number of resident and visiting anglers in 2003. Taking into account the game, coarse and sea/shore angling areas, the aggregate gross expenditure contribution of domestic game anglers in Northern Ireland is estimated to be around £39.3 million while visitor/tourist anglers contribute around £3.5 million. Analysis of the number of visiting anglers, the number of trips and days/nights per trip and average expenditure, shows that the gross expenditure contribution arising from visitor/tourist anglers totalled approximately £3.5 million during 2005. Compared to other studies, as noted above, the contribution of tourist anglers to the overall angler expenditure in Northern Ireland (8%) is significantly lower

than the proportion of expenditure provided by foreign tourist anglers in Ireland (44%) and Scotland (52%).

By monitoring the waterways, contributing funding through the sale of licences and investing in nursery areas, anglers have made a positive impact on the environment in Northern Ireland. Anglers regularly highlight areas of pollution to watchdog organisations such as the Fisheries Conservancy Board, and private fisheries and angling clubs have also been proactively involved in developing nursery areas that nurture fish and other wildlife (DCAL *et al.* 2007).

18.5.4.4 Cultural heritage, landscape and sense of place

Northern Ireland is traditionally a rural society; many people see themselves as having 'rural roots' and therefore feel a strong sense of connection to the rural land and landscape. This is in part what has fuelled the 'suburbanisation' of the countryside, with few places now truly rural, to the detriment of landscape, scenery, and tourist potential. Recent changes to planning policy seek to address this, but it is yet to be seen whether this will be effective; the recession is also having a significant impact on the building sector in general (Section 18.4.7). A recent report, building on a Landscape Character Assessment carried out in 2000, looked at the roles of different government and non-government bodies in addressing landscape-scale issues and how the European Landscape Convention is being implemented in Northern Ireland (Coates & Hadden 2010).

There are also strong cultural links to the marine environment (McCaughan & Appleby 1989). By virtue of its central role in connections between Northern Ireland, Scotland and the Republic of Ireland, the sea has long underpinned the formation of the social and cultural identities of its surrounding communities. The sea facilitated a sense of interconnectedness and a broader concept of place and belonging. Stories, music and songs connected to the sea are recurrent features of folk traditions, while the aesthetic value of the marine landscape has inspired generations of artists and architects to capture its character and essence. Coastal communities have been involved in the systematic exploitation of its resources, with fishing concentrated on the eastern seaboard and the smaller northern settlements involved in kelp harvesting for agricultural and industrial purposes (Forsythe 2006).

While English is now spoken by almost all people in Northern Ireland, both Irish (Gaeilge) and Ulster Scots play an important role in its culture and heritage in mythology, folklore, literature, place names, music and song. Many place names have their origins in Irish, Ulster Scots, Norse, Anglo-Norman or Latin and many are linked with plants, animals and physical habitat features, e.g. Derry from Gaelic *doire* meaning oak grove, Whappstown from Ulster Scots *whaup* meaning curlew, Strangford from Norse *Strangfjörthr* meaning sea inlet (Culture Northern Ireland 2010).

The uplands provide outstanding scenery and wilderness, with views from upland, especially peatlands, being spectacular and appreciated as 'typical' scenery of Northern Ireland and having strong cultural associations. Peat cutting is an ancient cultural tradition and ancient Irish

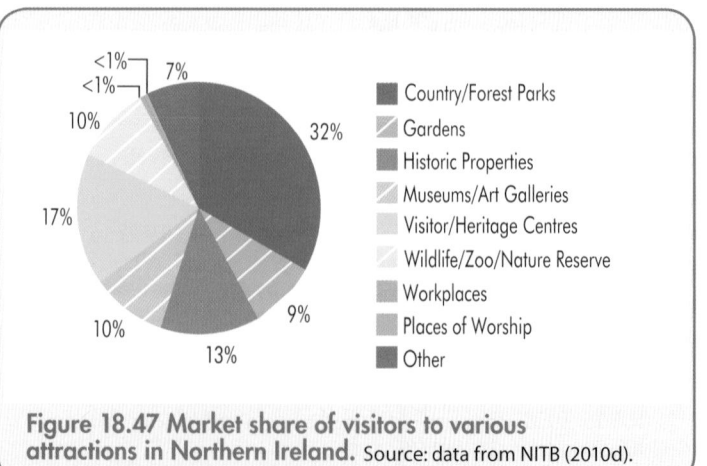

Figure 18.47 Market share of visitors to various attractions in Northern Ireland. Source: data from NITB (2010d).

laws contain references to turf cutting. In the Irish language there are 130 words specific to bogland (Aalen 1997).

18.5.4.5 Archaeology and built heritage

Northern Ireland is rich in archaeological remains and the landscape itself is dotted with raths, long-abandoned hill forts and monuments from the past 9,000 years (Hall 1994). There are over 16,000 monuments and archaeological sites located throughout the countryside in all habitats, many of which are in state care or open for visits (**Figure 18.48**). Northern Ireland has 1,864 scheduled monuments (NIEA 2010j); around 8,500 listed buildings (NIEA 2010d); around 157 registered historic parks, gardens and demesnes. These cover an area 17,921 ha, equivalent to around 1.3% of Northern Ireland (NIEA unpublished data).

The 2009 Condition and Management Survey of the Archaeological Resource in Northern Ireland (CAMSAR) report assessed the survival and condition of sites and monuments in Northern Ireland, focusing on sites earlier than 1700AD (Gormley *et al.* 2009). The report found that only 4% of sampled sites were in good or excellent condition, and 44% had no upstanding visible remains. It found that the worst survival rates for archaeological sites and monuments were on areas of arable land, improved grassland and areas of built development. Of the sample sites that were protected under the Historic Monuments and Archaeological Objects (NI) Order 1995, 93% were found to be in fair, good or excellent condition. The CAMSAR report identified a close connection between the management of archaeological sites and monuments and agricultural practice. This is significant, given that around 75% of Northern Ireland's land is in agricultural use. European agricultural policies in the 1970s and 1980s led to changes in marginal land use, damaging or destroying many archaeological sites in the process, leading to the introduction of the ESA Scheme in 1986. The Countryside Management Scheme was introduced in 2000 and ensures that historic features are protected by improved agricultural management. Light grazing is usually the best management for archaeological sites as it keeps scrub growth at bay and enables all the features to be seen and appreciated. Maintaining a good grass sward also helps to protect buried remains (Gormley *et al.* 2009; **Figure 18.49**).

Blanket and lowland raised bogs are of particular archaeological significance as their anaerobic conditions sustain evidence of past lifestyles and landscapes through the pollen record. In some areas blanket peat covers old soil systems that attest to past, possibly Neolithic, agriculture and settlements. There are 222 sites and monuments within the Northern Ireland Sites and Monuments Record (NISMR) on peatlands (NIEA unpublished data). Excavation of sites and increasing access to them can damage peatland and pose conflicts over different management regimes.

While many vernacular buildings have been lost to development, some remain and there are numerous stately homes, historic demesnes and parks and gardens interspersed in the farmed landscape, many owned by the National Trust and allowing public visits. Some of these properties are extensive, and the Trust manages its land following sustainability principles, providing working examples of management demonstrating new and traditional techniques.

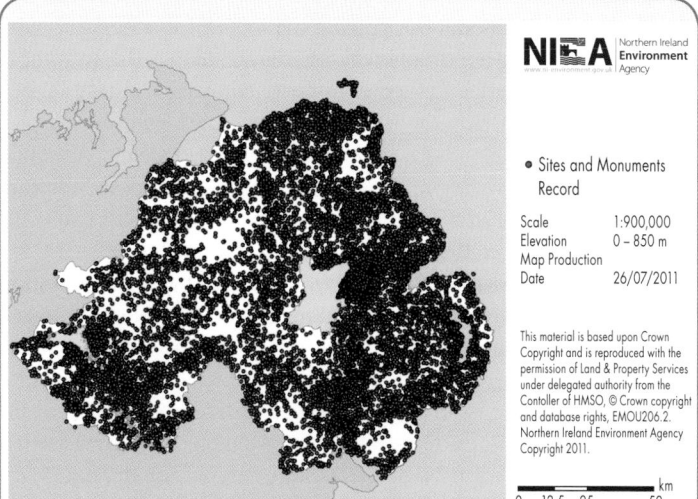

Figure 18.48 Archaeological sites in the Northern Ireland Sites and Monuments Record demonstrating their distribution across the country. Source: reproduced from NIEA (2010j).

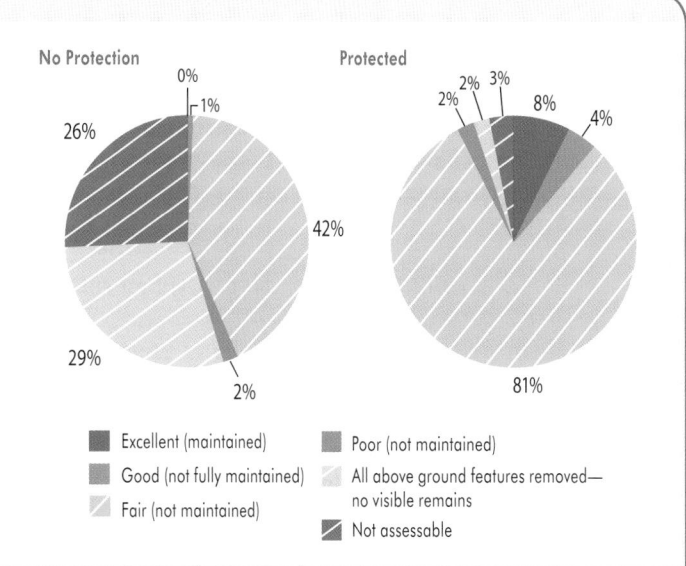

Figure 18.49 A comparison of the condition of monuments in the CAMSAR sample between protected and unprotected sites. Source: data from Gormley *et al.* (2009).

There are a number of historical and archaeological sites, scheduled monuments and state care sites in forests. Forests and woodland also form a significant part of the historic environment in respect of historic parks, gardens and demesnes. Around one-tenth of the woodland recorded on the Ancient Woodland Inventory was parkland. Many of these sites contain some of Northern Ireland's oldest trees, many of which are of high ecological value, particularly for lichens and insects (Woodland Trust 2007).

18.5.4.6 Land ownership and use

The farmed landscape of Northern Ireland is relatively recent; the pattern of small, family-owned farms date from the late 19th Century when tenants were given the right and assistance to purchase land through the Purchase of Land (Ireland) Act introduced in 1885 (enclosed fields are an older feature; Steele 1968; Cameron 2005). However, enclosure of the land generally stopped at the foot of the mountain, with hill grazing apportioned by 'soums'. A soum is the amount of pasture needed to support a cow or equivalent (e.g. five sheep equated to one cow (Symons 1963). Each joint-owner of a stretch of upland was entitled to a number of soums. Although common grazing and joint ownership have declined through inheritance and purchase of shares, they are still extensive and influence the use of uplands (DARD 2010o).

Land ownership is a very important part of the culture of rural Northern Ireland; many farmers are reluctant to sell land that came into the family only a little over 100 years ago or to accept 'direction' from government as to how to use and manage the land. For example, acquisition of large areas for forest planting is more difficult with multiple landowners than where land is in single ownership, part of the explanation for the disjointed pattern of forests. Jointly owned land can be entered into the Northern Ireland Countryside Management Scheme (NICMS; DARD 2008b), but all the common graziers must participate in NICMS, CMS or the ESA Scheme, and this requirement can limit uptake of the scheme and thereby the success of environmental policies. However, other factors (such as the funding available for the scheme) may be more important. The complex of small farms situated along the upland margins, where owners may have different attitudes to farming, has produced high biodiversity. The drivers creating this biodiversity need further research, especially in the light of government policies to expand forestry (Forest Service 2006).

18.5.4.7 Aesthetic, inspirational, spiritual and religious aspects

Northern Ireland has a long history of literature, poetry, music and the visual arts. Artists have been inspired by diverse landscapes such as the Antrim Coast, the Sperrin and Mourne Mountains, and the Fermanagh lakelands. These have provided the raw material for a rich tradition in the arts. Nobel Laureate Seamus Heaney was born on a farm near Bellaghy in County Londonderry and his work clearly demonstrates an important connection with the landscape and environment. C. S. Lewis reportedly received inspiration from the Mournes for the Chronicles of Narnia (Gormley 1998). A classical writer once described the Celts as being so wretched that "their drink is the drink of swine, and they burn their very earth for warmth" (i.e. they drank beer and burned turf; Feehan & O'Donovan 1996). Bogs have also been the inspiration of countless artists, including T. P. Flanagan and Basil Blackshaw. Nor has Northern Ireland's troubled past escaped attention. Contemporary painters continue to be inspired by its landscapes and many have integrated the rural idyll depicted by Sir John Lavery, William Conor, Paul Henry, and John Luke with darker elements of violence. The resulting combination of rural tranquillity with terror has produced a unique genre of Northern Irish art, most notably in the work of Dermot Seymour and Jack Pakenham.

Monastic sites and medieval castles, abbeys, celtic crosses, round towers, churches and holy wells are to be found in every county; for example St. Aidan's 13th Century church, in County Derry/Londonderry, has an ancient holy well said to have healing properties. St. Patrick is patron saint and spiritual symbol of Ireland and consequently Northern Ireland's links with him are very important, with Armagh City and Downpatrick having particularly strong associations. Slemish Mountain is an important place of pilgrimage on St. Patrick's Day. The mountain, where St. Patrick is reputed to have spent his early days as a slave, is significant both for its Christian connections and as evidence of a volcanic past.

18.5.4.8 Education and ecological knowledge

The use of outdoor settings for educational purposes is now a compulsory element of primary and secondary education. "When planned and implemented well, learning outside the classroom contributed significantly to raising standards and improving pupils' personal, social and emotional development" (Ofsted 2008). "...children engaged in Learning Outside the Classroom achieve higher scores in class tests, have greater levels of physical fitness and motor skills development, increased confidence and self-esteem, show leadership qualities and are socially competent and more environmentally responsible" (Malone 2008).

While Northern Ireland Environment Agency government sites have information signs, they have not been supported by full-time education officers since 2009 (NIEA pers. comm.). However, there are a number of outdoor education centres run by both Education and Library Boards and charities such as the Field Studies Council, and several NGOs run educational programmes either based at their own sites or in partnership (e.g. National Trust, Ulster Wildlife Trust, Wildfowl and Wetlands Trust, Colin Glen Trust, RSPB). In addition, the Eco-Schools programme is very popular in Northern Ireland and currently more than half of all schools in Northern Ireland are registered (Tidy NI unpublished data). Universities conduct research in the natural environment, with student projects having provided considerable data over the years; however, this is often not publicly available.

18.5.5 Supporting Services

Supporting ecosystem services are those that are fundamental to the delivery of all of the others, including soil formation, primary production and nutrient cycling. They are even more difficult to value and quantify than the others, as they often operate on much longer time periods and at greater spatial scales than individual political jurisdictions.

Soil formation in temperate regions is so slow that soil erosion is more important in practical terms and soil must therefore be regarded operationally as a non-renewable resource. In general, soil quality is closely related to organic matter content (and therefore carbon content). Soil degradation tends to be lower in Northern Ireland than in most other parts of the UK (**Figure 18.50**) and this is aided by the relatively wet and cool climate which slows down the rate of decomposition and thus promotes the retention of carbon in the soil, including the formation and maintenance of peat.

Primary production in pristine natural and semi-natural terrestrial ecosystems is limited by the supply of nitrogen and phosphorus and these limits help to maintain species diversity, which in turn maintains the character of these areas. Protecting natural habitats from excessive nutrients from intensive agricultural areas avoids eutrophication, which would tend to increase primary production, reduce biodiversity and change the character of natural areas, which in turn can reduce their value for recreation, well-being and supplying clean air and water (Sections 18.5.3.3 & 18.5.3.4). Atmospheric pollution by ammonia is higher in Northern Ireland than in other parts of the UK because of gaseous emissions from intensive animal agriculture, and research has shown that atmospheric nitrogen inputs are high enough to threaten the ecology of all natural habitats, including protected areas, especially peatland and grassland (Tang *et al.* 2004), although field data are not yet available on whether there have been floristic changes in Northern Ireland in response to these levels.

Primary production in intensive animal farming has provided food and economic benefits. However, in addition to gaseous losses of nitrogen, excessive inputs of nitrogen and phosphorus in fertilisers and animal feeds have led to serious eutrophication of groundwater, rivers and lakes. Phosphorus has accumulated in most soils in Northern Ireland and some is transferred to surface waters by drainage and surface runoff. Because of intensive livestock systems, agricultural nutrient budgets show greater surpluses of nitrogen and phosphorus than the nutrient balances for most other parts of the UK (Sections 18.5.3.3 & 18.5.3.4). Legal controls over the application of phosphorus fertilisers may have recently started to reverse the eutrophication of rivers and lakes by phosphorus from sheep and beef cattle, and these controls, together with new controls over the quantities of phosphorus incorporated into animal feeds plus mitigation of nitrogen and phosphorus from dairy farming, can continue that trend (Section 18.5.3.3).

Although poorly managed intensive agriculture has led to eutrophication of air and water, the predominance of perennial grassland ecosystems helps to maintain (and even slowly build up) soil organic matter and may help to optimise soil storage of carbon and maintain good soil structure (Simpson 1983).

18.5.5.1 Soils and nutrient cycling

Moderately high altitude, oceanic position, acidic parent geological materials, and post-Neolithic woodland clearance have led to the formation of peat and peaty soils in the uplands of Northern Ireland. Northern Ireland's peatlands have been used traditionally for fuel, but during the 20th Century large-scale drainage of peatland and harvesting to produce fuel and horticultural peat have led to a serious decline in this important resource. Protecting and restoring peatlands is an important way to keep carbon from the atmosphere to help mitigate climate change (Section 18.5.3). In Great Britain, peat erosion is of much concern and there is considerable emphasis on restoration; however, it can take a very long time to re-establish the full range of biodiversity. In Northern Ireland it appears that many eroded areas are recovering naturally (Tomlinson 2010) and some restoration work has been undertaken at Cuilcagh and the Peatlands Park, with growth of bog mosses in channels. Further research is needed to determine long-term results. Some marginal hill-lands were drained up to the 1970s to encourage vegetative growth for grazing, whereas other slopes were more completely reclaimed (drained, deep ploughed, limed, fertilised and reseeded). The present state

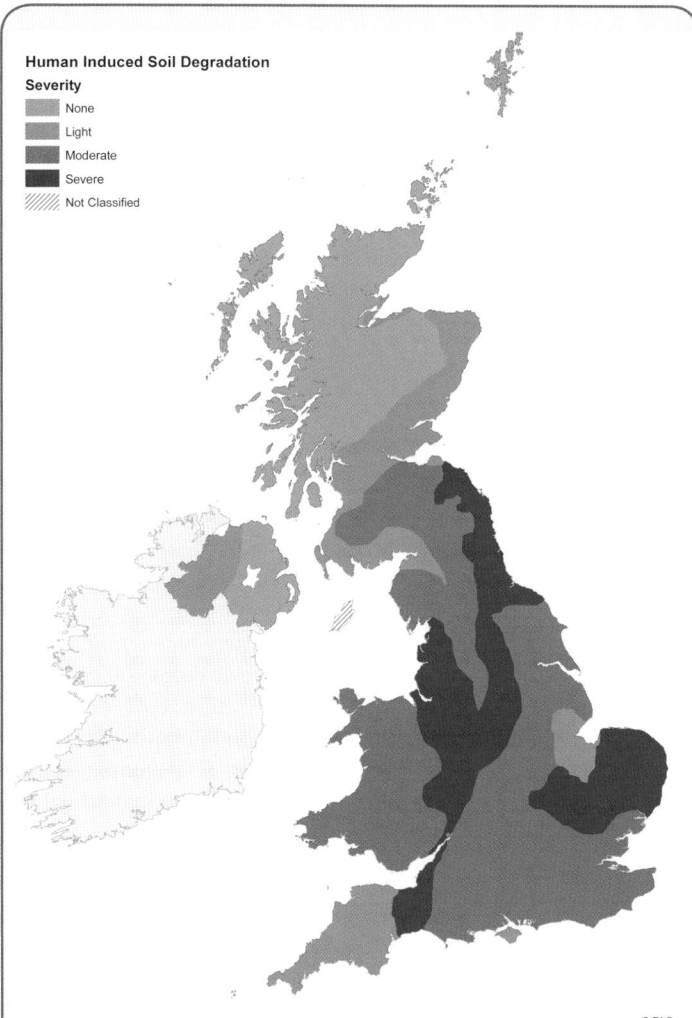

Figure 18.50 Severity of human induced soil degradation in the UK. Note, this map was published in 1990 and therefore does not represent the current status of soil degradation. The average scale of the map was 1:10,000,000 and was intended to create global awareness on the issue of soil degradation and may not be an accurate indication at the national level. Source: data from the GLASOD project reproduced with permission from FAO (2005). Copyright © FAO AGL (2005).

of these areas, and the location, extent, factors encouraging and effects of current reclamation all need to be investigated. There is little current research on the primary production of upland ecosystems and hence on the rate of peat accumulation. Indeed, little or no local evidence is available from the International Biological Programme studies started in the 1960s; carbon studies in Northern Ireland have relied on research from the Republic of Ireland and Great Britain (Cruickshank *et al.* 1998; Tomlinson & Milne 2006). Upland ecosystems have a supporting role in water cycling, in the interdependence of farming (use of upland, combined with marginal and lowland, grazing), and in supporting the urban population by providing landscapes for aesthetic and recreational fulfilment.

Soil formation is a slow process in Northern Ireland as in other parts of the UK, but the soils are distinct in that they tend to have relatively high organic matter content, especially in the west and in the uplands, due to the wet and cool climate. Northern Ireland has a wide range of soil types that have developed from the solid geography. They have been studied extensively, with a major soil map and supporting document produced in 1997 (Cruickshank 1997) and the ongoing TELLUS project which is carrying out geophysical and geochemical mapping of the entire country (Young 2007; Beamish & Young 2009; **Figure 18.51**; **Figure 18.52**). Every major rock type except one is represented. Northern Ireland has a preponderance of gleys (56%) with a consequent requirement for artificial drainage for productive agriculture (Cruickshank 1997; Section 18.5.3).

Soil organic matter provides a service by sequestering carbon and keeping it out of the atmosphere. Although intensive agricultural practices will have lowered the organic matter content and biodiversity of some soils, in general soil quality is good, with little or no degradation (see **Figure 18.50**; Section 18.5.3.3). Indeed, Northern Ireland is the only country in the UK in which there has been no moderate or severe human-induced soil degradation. Soils in the east of Northern Ireland are not degraded and some soils in the west are only lightly degraded. Drivers of change are climate and land use. There was a much larger agricultural land area devoted to arable crops 100 years ago (Section 18.5.2.1). Grassland agriculture now dominates and continuing grassland systems will help to maintain or enhance soil quality by maintaining soil organic carbon (Simpson 1983). As 76% of the agricultural area in Northern Ireland is grass (Tomlinson 1997b), carbon sequestration could have a significant impact on Northern Ireland's

greenhouse gas inventory and also on the calculation of the carbon footprint of ruminant products. The trade-off is the problem of diffuse nitrogen and phosphorus pollution from intensive dairy farming systems.

Soils provide a service both as a substrate and through providing nutrients for plant growth, with high primary production achieved in intensive grassland agriculture. However, the trade-offs are reduced biodiversity and excessive nitrogen and phosphorus in soils, which act as a diffuse source of pollution of surface waters. Many of the soils in Northern Ireland are vulnerable to compaction by grazing animals and heavy agricultural machinery, especially in the wetter climate of the west. Compacted soils do not support good plant yields and are subject to severe nutrient runoff. They are thus a major source of the phosphorus eutrophication of waterways (Sharpley 1985).

18.5.5.2 Marine ecosystems and nutrient cycling

The sustainability of life is fundamentally dependent on the ability of biophysical systems to recycle limiting compounds in biogeochemical cycles (Falkowski *et al.* 2008; Doney 2010). Since much of the earth is covered by ocean systems, many of the most important biogeochemical cycles are dependent on marine processes, and many of these, in turn, are dependent on marine biota. Some of these cycles are important in removing material from circulation, including the biological carbon pump, which is vital in removing

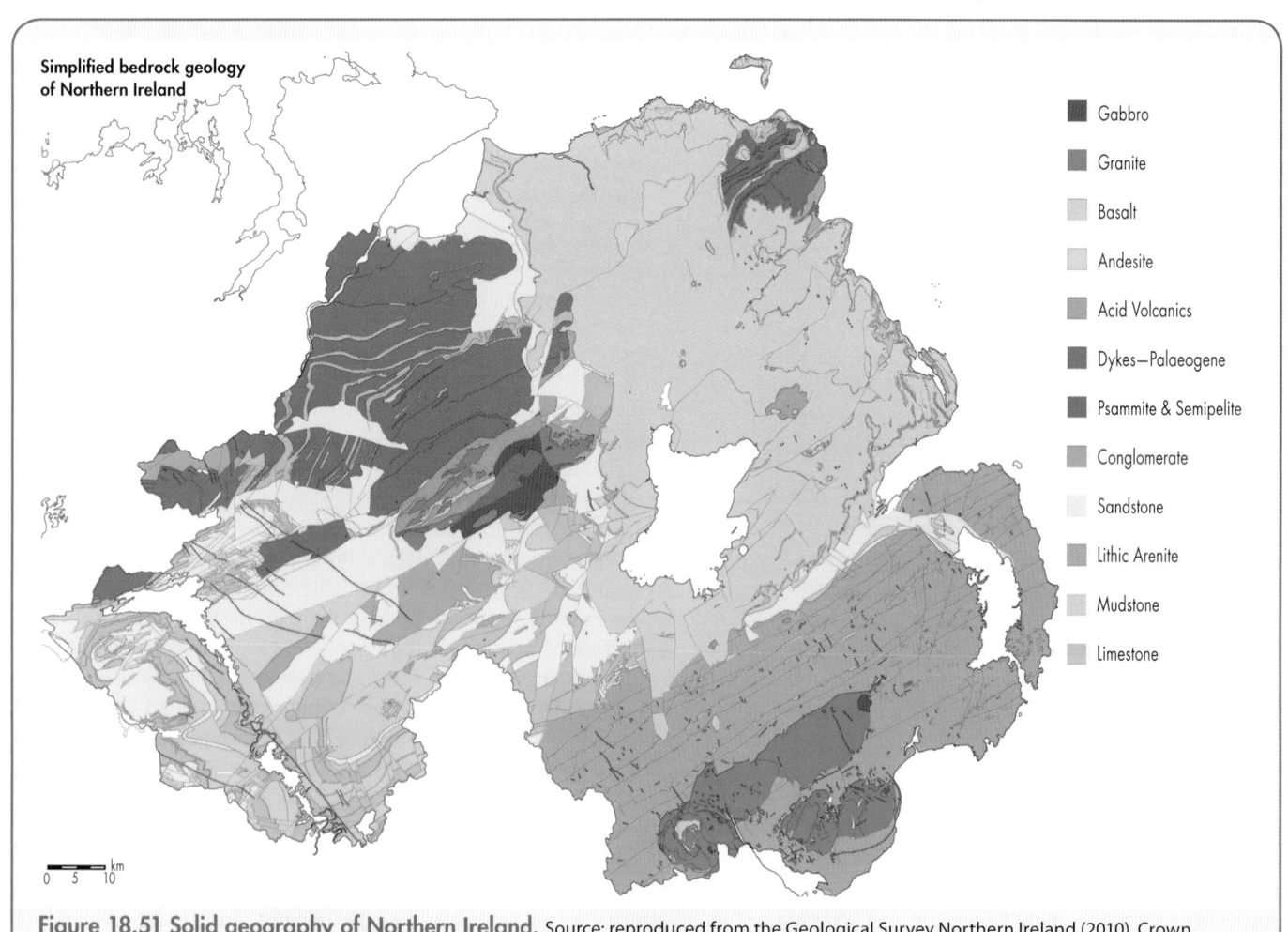

Simplified bedrock geology of Northern Ireland

■	Gabbro
■	Granite
□	Basalt
□	Andesite
▨	Acid Volcanics
■	Dykes—Palaeogene
■	Psammite & Semipelite
▨	Conglomerate
□	Sandstone
▥	Lithic Arenite
▨	Mudstone
▨	Limestone

0 5 10 km

Figure 18.51 Solid geography of Northern Ireland. Source: reproduced from the Geological Survey Northern Ireland (2010). Crown Copyright and derived from the Solid Geology (Second Edition, 1997) 1:250,000.

UK National Ecosystem Assessment: Technical Report

carbon dioxide from the atmosphere (via photosynthesis) and transporting it to the deep ocean floor (via various links and processes in the marine food web), where it can be sequestered in the long term (Riebesell *et al.* 2009). This process has both laid down many of the marine fossil fuel reserves and has ensured that the earth has not yet entered a phase of runaway warming.

Other biogeochemical cycles are important in transforming compounds from harmful to beneficial forms and keeping them in circulation. Photosynthesis (which transforms carbon dioxide to oxygen) and nutrient cycles, including nitrogen (Gruber & Galloway 2008), are most important. Not only are products of these cycles important ecosystem services in their own right, but they also support the ongoing existence of biotic assemblages in the sea and on land. The sea is also fundamental in driving the water cycle, receiving waters from land and returning it to the air for ultimate recycling onto the land.

Coasts are active in sediment storage and exchange between habitats, providing physical substrates or protection which allows other habitats to develop and biochemical exchange between the water column and shoreline habitats.

18.5.5.3 The water cycle

The cool and moist climate of Northern Ireland ensures a good supply of fresh water, especially in the west. However, freshwater services have been affected by major drainage

schemes and canalisation of major rivers from the 1950s to the 1980s (Section 18.4.6.2) which have speeded up the hydrological cycle, reduced biodiversity and increased the risk of flooding. The biological quality of surface waters can decline despite decreasing trends in river nitrate and phosphorus concentrations (EHS 2000). The Water Framework Directive requires water to be of good quality by 2015, and this includes biological quality (Sections 18.4.6 & 18.5.3.4).

18.5.5.4 Primary production

Ecological interactions depend on biotic and abiotic factors and drivers of change include biodiversity, nutrient inputs and climate change. Historical change has mainly been a reduction in biodiversity and changes in species composition resulting from anthropogenic nutrient inputs and physical disruption. Primary production via photosynthesis drives all ecosystems on land and in coastal seas (Sections 18.3 & 18.8).

18.5.5.5 Decomposition

Decomposition is fundamental to cycling of all nutrients; without the biota which decompose all organic matter to release nutrients, no habitat could function effectively. Threats to decomposition include chemicals used to treat parasites in domestic animals, which then lead to degradation of the natural soil organisms (Strong 1993), compaction of soils, which inhibits drainage and alien flatworms, which prey on earthworms (Boag & Yeates 2001).

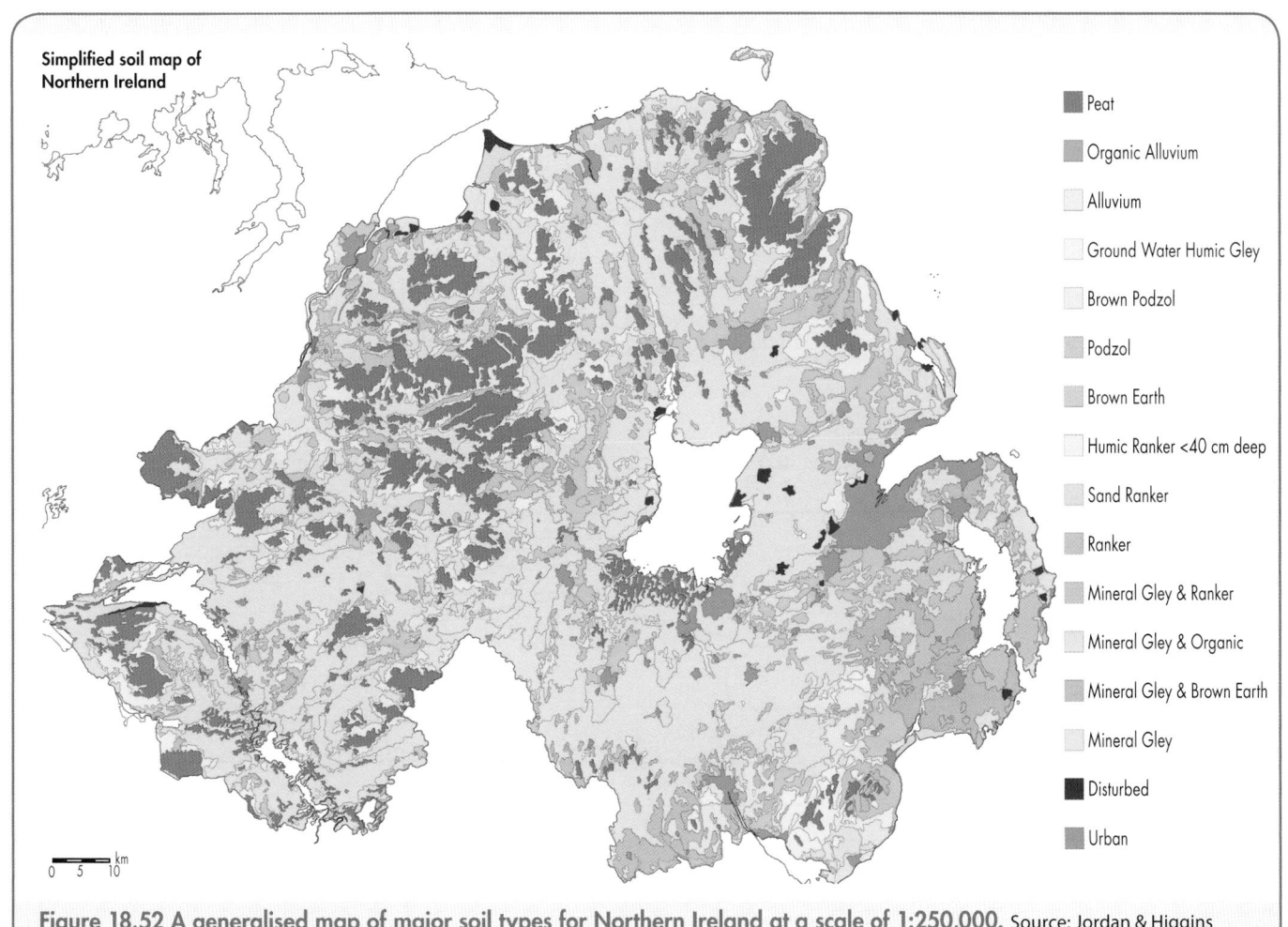

Simplified soil map of Northern Ireland

Peat
Organic Alluvium
Alluvium
Ground Water Humic Gley
Brown Podzol
Podzol
Brown Earth
Humic Ranker <40 cm deep
Sand Ranker
Ranker
Mineral Gley & Ranker
Mineral Gley & Organic
Mineral Gley & Brown Earth
Mineral Gley
Disturbed
Urban

Figure 18.52 A generalised map of major soil types for Northern Ireland at a scale of 1:250,000. Source: Jordan & Higgins (2007), Agri-Food and Biosciences Institute.

While many of these issues are shared across other regions of the UK, local conditions can vary the specific impacts.

18.5.6 Valuation of Ecosystem Services

A key objective of the UK NEA is a systematic and comprehensive valuation of ecosystem services which links ecosystems to human welfare by assessing the benefits accruing to society and economic prosperity from the UK's natural environment. The Economics of Ecosystems and Biodiversity (TEEB) work supports this goal. Assigning economic values to particular areas, ecosystems or habitats is difficult. Much of the TEEB work, as well as the information specifically available for Northern Ireland, concentrates on products, the costs of providing services if nature did not do so (pollination, water purification), the costs of ameliorating environmental damage (flooding, pollution, invasive species) and the economic benefits provided through tourism or recreation expenditure and income (TEEB 2009, 2010a,b,c).

Ecosystem services can potentially provide a wide range of benefits to society, such as:

- Market values—employment and income from direct use of the ecosystem services e.g. food and timber production.
- Shadow values—employment and income from the indirect use of ecosystem services by businesses which are highly dependent on the services, e.g. tourism and recreation activities; and household location decisions (i.e. increase in house values in the vicinity of the ecosystem service).
- Non-market values—the benefits derived from ecosystem services for which no market exists (direct and indirect), e.g. biodiversity, landscape, water and air quality; informal recreational use (bird-watching, hiking, cycling, boating) and values attributed to the continued existence of these features based on non-use motivations, such as for the sake of future generations.
- Social values—ecosystem services that contribute to the social well-being of local communities by providing a sense of identity and belonging, social capital building and social entrepreneurship.

It is clear that the value of ecosystem services goes far beyond the value of the products derived and that in many cases the additional values can be much greater than those of the products.

A further differentiation is made to the MA classification of provisioning, regulating, cultural and supporting services to separate ecosystem services into 'intermediate processes and services' and 'final services' that directly deliver goods and benefits to people (MA 2005a,b). Additionally, the UK NEA recognises capital inputs (including manufacturing, transport, processing and engineering) into the production of the goods/benefits derived from ecosystems (**Figure 18.53**).

There has been much recent work on valuing ecosystems and biodiversity. The TEEB project, which received a very high profile at the Nagoya COP Biodiversity summit in November 2010, is a major study providing a large amount of international information and expertise (TEEB 2009, 2010a,b,c). Another major group working in this field is the Natural Capital Project, a joint venture between Stanford University's Woods Institute for the Environment, the University of Minnesota's Institute on the Environment, the Nature Conservancy, WWF and a number of other institutions in the public, private and non-profit sectors. The Natural Capital Project has the goal of engaging leaders in key institutions, linking world-class research and development with influential, practical conservation programs and developing tools that facilitate the incorporation of natural capital into decisions (Natural Capital Project 2006). These and other organisations are developing techniques, progressing the concept and providing tools to help make these calculations and help ensure that the full value of biodiversity and ecosystem services is available to influence decisions.

Some rough estimates arising from this type of analysis are becoming available. The TEEB project (TEEB 2009, 2010a,b,c) estimates that $2–$4.5 trillion is lost every year due to global deforestation and that the total economic value of insect pollination is €153 billion. Expansion by non-native species is currently one of the biggest threats to the ecology and economy of the planet, costing an estimated £914 billion annually worldwide and causing 50% of all known extinctions (TEEB 2009, 2010a,b,c).

The National Parks and Wildlife Service of the Republic of Ireland estimate that the current marginal value of

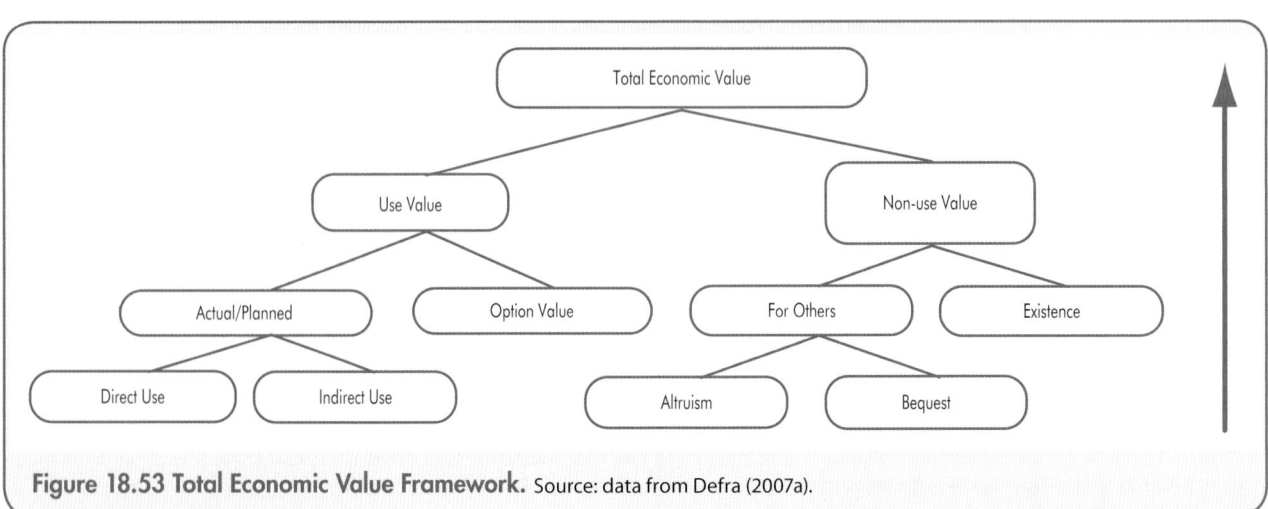

Figure 18.53 Total Economic Value Framework. Source: data from Defra (2007a).

biodiversity and certain ecosystems in the Republic of Ireland in terms of their contribution to productive output and human utility is over €2.6 billion per annum (DEHLG 2008). This is considered a conservative estimate because it does not include services such as food production and waste assimilation, so the true figure will be much higher (Comhar SDC 2010b).

When looking at the valuation of services it is important to recognise the concept of thresholds and tipping points, also called 'planetary boundaries'. These are boundaries that, if breached, could lead to major environmental consequences and therefore need to be identified and quantified (Rockström et al. 2009a). This approach aims to prevent human activities from producing unacceptable environmental change and defines preconditions for human development. The costs of breaching these boundaries are extremely high and the closer the boundaries are approached, the higher the marginal costs (if there are 500,000 ha of wilderness providing multiple services, the value of each hectare is much less than if there are only 10 ha remaining). This has profound implications for valuing ecosystem services in financial terms, both globally and locally. While this concept is generally applied on a global scale, it has local ramifications as local limits are approached.

Little valuation work has been undertaken on the economic values of the final goods provided by the ecosystem services in Northern Ireland, especially those which have no market price. The absence of data or values does not indicate that there is no impact on human welfare, rather that no quantification of the value for Northern Ireland has been undertaken. While attempts have been made to value some of the ecosystem services (i.e. Jacobs et al. 2008), these have used economic values derived in non-Northern Ireland based studies. Therefore these findings have not been included within this review. Information about economic valuation is covered in detail in the UK NEA Conceptual Framework (Chapter 2).

The ecosystem services for which economic values exist tend to be the provisioning services for which there are markets (e.g. agriculture, fishing and timber). However, even these values may not reflect the full benefits (or costs) of these ecosystem services as only the direct, private good aspects have been captured. For example, the value of forestry recreation reported below reflects only a proportion of the recreational benefits as charges are made at only nine of the 124 publicly owned forests of Northern Ireland.

Furthermore, if the provision of a good which is valued in the market depends on a number of ecosystem services for which no markets exist, the market price may not reflect the full economic value. For example, agricultural production, in addition to producing food, affects the goods provided by other ecosystem services which are not captured by the market, including landscapes (cultural), climate and flood regulation (regulating), water availability (provisioning), soil formation and nutrient cycling (supporting). The calculation indicated that the net negative impact of agriculture on the environment of Northern Ireland was £34.2 million per annum (excluding air pollution which has a cost to society of £189.71 million (net present value)). However, there is a lack of data on the level of provision. The market price of

agricultural output does not take these external benefits and costs into account (Jacobs et al. 2008).

Even the inclusion of those ecosystem services which have market values can be problematic because the scale at which they were derived does not correspond to UK NEA habitat classifications. For example, while the economic value of agriculture is widely reported (e.g. DARD 2009f, 2010a), these data are reported at either the Northern Ireland level or at scales appropriate to agricultural/rural policy (e.g. the Less Favoured Areas) which do not relate to the UK NEA Habitats. In this case, rather than splitting the figure between the relevant UK NEA Habitat categories, the Northern Ireland figure is reported under the Enclosed Farmland habitat. As a consequence, it would appear that a gap exists for the value of the provisioning ecosystem services of Mountains, Moorlands and Heaths and Semi-natural Grasslands whereas, in fact, these ecosystems contribute a considerable (but unquantifiable at present) portion of the agricultural output. **Table 18.17** provides examples of the values of some ecosystem services in Northern Ireland.

While it can be difficult to assign an economic value to benefits, costs may be more easily established. The cost of controlling invasive species has begun to be recorded and calculated (Section 18.3). For example, the Rivers Agency spent £200,000 on a 12-mile stretch of the River Roe clearing knotweed, the Killyhelvin waste water treatment works required a £120,000 refit due to zebra mussels, and a number of projects to address floating pennywort have together cost £85,000, mostly in staff time. The Northern Ireland Environment Agency has spent an estimated £415,000 on clearing invasives from its country parks and over £32,000 at nature reserves since 2005 (John Early, NIEA, pers. comm.).

A study of the ESA scheme conducted in 1997 assessed the socio-economic benefits of the scheme through a household survey and found that the 'non-market benefits' were estimated at £13.1 million per year for the preceding 5 years. This was a benefit-to-cost ratio of 32:1. A contingent valuation aspect found that people were willing to pay £15–£31 per person for landscape value in the Mourne ESA which, when summed across households, yielded a value of £19 million (Moss & Chilton 1997a,b). A study of the Rural Environment Protection (REP) Scheme's contribution to rural landscapes in the Republic of Ireland in 2006 estimated the value put on landscape benefits alone amount to almost the entire cost of the scheme (Campbell et al. 2006).

In 2006 it was estimated that the natural environment contributed 32,750 full-time jobs and over £573 million to the economy through protection and management of the environment, sustainable use of natural resources, environment-dependent tourism and recreation and environmental management in industry and government (NI Green NGOs & EHS 2007; **Table 18.18**). In 2010, a survey of environmental NGOs (eNGO) was conducted which found that 38 eNGOs surveyed had a turnover of nearly £32 million, over half of which came from non-governmental sources. In addition, the value of volunteer input for the 38 bodies was estimated at £3.7 million (Envision Management Consultants 2010), comparing well to the estimate of £3.4 million in 2006 (NI Green NGOs & EHS 2007). Overall, for every £1 invested

Table 18.17 Examples of studies which have valued ecosystem services in Northern Ireland.

UK NEA Broad Habitats	Ecosystem service	Final good	Valuation
Mountains, Moorland and Heaths (MMH)	Cultural	Landscape	In 1996, annual benefits of £13.09 million derived from the ESA scheme to protect rough land, rebuilding and maintaining stone walls, replanting and maintaining hedges, repairing traditional farm build buildings and painting buildings in approved colours (Moss & Chilton 1997a,b).
		Recreation	A 2008 Travel Cost study found that visitors to the Mourne Mountain gained annual benefits of £25.06 per person. A choice experiment was also carried out examining a number of potential management options identified benefits of £3–£12 per trip per person (Rowan & Longo 2009).
Enclosed Farmland incl. MMH and Semi-natural Grassland	Provisioning	Food and fibre	Gross output of Northern Ireland agriculture estimated at £1.3 billion for 2009 while GVA (taking into account capital & other inputs) was estimated as £304 million in 2009 (DARD 2010a).
Woodlands	Provisioning	Fibre	Timber: 403,000 m³ of timber produced in 2008/9, with a gross output value of £7.5 million (Forest Service 2009).
	Cultural	Recreation	Two million recreational visits in 2008/9, more than 500 permits for organised events within forests. £0.7 million received through charges. However, only 9 of the 124 state owned forests charge (Forest Service 2009). A contingent valuation study in 1992, undertaken as part of a EU project funded under the CAMAR programme, valued the recreation benefits in Northern Ireland's forests at £2.6 million annually (Ni Dhubhain et al. 1994).
Open waters, Wetlands and Floodplains	Regulating	Pollution control	A contingent valuation study in 2003/4 valued water quality of all the rivers and lakes in Northern Ireland. Benefits of £8–£12 million/annum if current water quality is maintained and £13–£18million/annum if quality is improved (Hutchinson et al. 2005).
	Cultural	Existence of fish	A choice experiment to estimate benefits of conserving rare and endangered fish species in the Lough Melvin Catchment in Northern Ireland and the Republic of Ireland. Benefits (in Euros/year) ranged from €9.63 to €20.50 per person for the individual fish species and €25.57 per person to conserve all the species (Campbell 2008).
		Recreational fishing	A study using Travel Cost and Contingent Valuation methods valued gross domestic user benefits in 1988 at £8–£10 million. Visiting anglers generated expenditures of a further £1.5 million (Davis & O'Neill 1992). The average Northern Ireland resident angler (all types) spent £1,313 during the 2005 season on angling-related spend; each visiting angler typically spent £707. Aggregate gross expenditure for game and course fishing is approximately £31.9 million for Northern Ireland residents and £3.2 million for visiting anglers (DCAL et al. 2007).
Urban	Cultural	Good health	A choice experiment in 2001 aimed to elicit people's preferences for potential regeneration of St. Anne's Square in Belfast. Although it was unable to calculate figures for St. Anne's Square, it found that increasing open space within a hypothetical square by 50% would produce benefits of £3 per person and an increase in building height would induce a cost of £7.20 per person. The study did find that respondents preferred regeneration alternatives for St. Anne's Square that entailed more open space (Alberini et al. 2003).
Coastal Margins and Marine	Provisioning	Food	In 2008, 20,300 tonnes of fish with a gross output value of £23.2 million were landed in Northern Ireland by UK registered vessels (shellfish—10,900 tonnes worth £17.4 million, demersal—1,900 tonnes worth £3.2 million, pelagic—7,500 tonnes worth £2.5 m; MFA 2009). No data exist for the GVA of the fishing sector within Northern Ireland. At the UK level, GVA is approximately 50% of gross output of fishing (SeaFish 2007). From 2000 to 2009, an average £17.69 million of fish landed annually (Outcrop/rocky reef—£0.16 million, shelf trough —£0.33million, coarse sediment—£2.38 million, mixed sediment –£0.62million, sand—£3.23 million, mud –£9.55 million, sea loughs—£1.42 million; Strong 2010). In 2007, the aquaculture sector produced 8,400 tonnes of shellfish valued at £5.8 million and over 999 tonnes of finfish valued at £1.85 million. This sector directly employs 113 full time and 48 part time employees (DARD 2010b). Some of this value may be attributable to inland water, not the coast or Marine ecosystems.
	Cultural	Recreation and good health	Trips to the Causeway Coast and Glens were worth £134.2 million in 2007 (26% of all tourist spend; NITB 2007). The aggregate gross expenditure contribution by sea/shore anglers was approx. £7.4 million for Northern Ireland residents and approx £0.3 million from visiting anglers (DCAL et al. 2007).

Table 18.18 Contribution of the environment to the Northern Ireland economy in 2006. Source: data from NI Green NGOs & EHS (2007).

	Full time equivalent jobs	Gross Value Added (£million)
Protection and management of the environment	9,413	226
Sustainable use of natural resources	17,071	211
Environment dependent tourism and recreation	6,125	130
Environment management in industry	140	6
Total	**32,749**	**573**

by government annually in the eNGO sector an additional £3.37 was invested through volunteers or other funding (Envision Management Consultants 2010).

18.6 Northern Ireland's Dependence on External Ecosystem Services

Northern Ireland is at the end of the supply chain for many of the commodities used by its citizens, with a high dependence on external provisioning services. This, plus the restricted range of local produce, has a strong impact on prices and security of supply and therefore has implications for how land is used. This also illustrates why Northern Ireland's dependence on other parts of the UK, as well as other parts of the world, is high. The importation of biological products and financial dependence on overseas economies are two of the more apparent examples. Dependence on external cultural services is primarily through tourism, and there is also strong support for local cultural services from tourists coming to Northern Ireland. Northern Ireland also relies on other countries for some less quantifiable services such as climate regulation.

Northern Ireland imports almost all of the energy it uses (DETI 2010d), making it highly vulnerable to both supply and price fluctuations. Significant amounts of food and building materials are also imported. Northern Ireland's ecological, carbon and greenhouse gas footprints are slightly lower than the UK *per capita* average (Curry *et al.* 2004; Maguire *et al.* 2008; **Table 18.19**). The ecological footprint of Northern Ireland's food consumption in 2006 was 1.2 global hectares/capita, making up some 28% of its residents' total footprint, and was the largest contribution of any sector (**Figure 18.54**). Other categories closely related to ecosystem service delivery include housing and transport, animal and vegetable oils, mineral fuels and crude materials. It is clear from **Figure 18.54**, **Figure 18.55** and **Figure 18.56** and

Table 18.19 that Northern Ireland relies heavily on other regions for delivering the goods which its citizens require.

Food and live animals grown and raised in Northern Ireland provided around 14% of total exports in 2009 (see **Figure 18.55**). The value of these food imports and exports are very similar (around £5 billion), but the make-up varies significantly. Exports consist largely of milk and meat products, while most fruit and vegetables and many processed food products are imported. Northern Ireland is a net exporter of meat and dairy products but overall exports of food and live animals only slightly exceed imports (see **Figure 18.55**; **Figure 18.56**). Most exports are to other parts of the UK and the Republic of Ireland, with only milk/milk products and fish having significant markets further afield. A detailed breakdown of imported products is not possible within the scope of this exercise. However, it is clear that Northern Ireland does not produce the food and other products which its citizens require on a daily basis, with 65% of exports being meat or animal products and only 8% vegetables and fruit. A number of factors, from policy changes to oil price to consumer preferences to transport disruption, could increase the pressure to address this situation, with potentially large impacts on land use (Chapter 21).

While these figures include some of the value of provisioning ecosystem services, it is not possible to conclude that the entirety of the value is directly attributable to ecosystems, due to the input of capital and human labour during manufacturing and processing. It does, however, show which products were exported and their destinations. Obviously much more work is required on the

Table 18.19 Comparison of Northern Ireland's ecological, carbon and greenhouse gas footprints with those of the UK in 2004. Source: data from Stockholm Environment Institute (2009).

	Ecological footprint (global ha/capita)	Carbon footprint (tonnes of carbon dioxide/capita)	Greenhouse gas footprint (carbon dioxide equivalent/capita)
Northern Ireland	4.85	11.18	15.09
UK	5.30	12.08	16.34

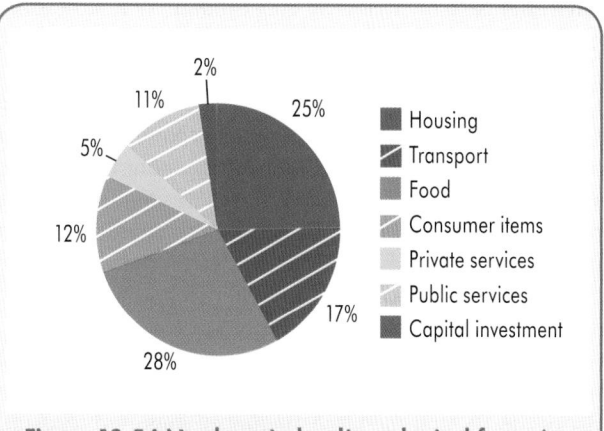

Figure 18.54 Northern Ireland's ecological footprint by sector in 2006. Source: reproduced from Stockholm Environment Institute (2009).

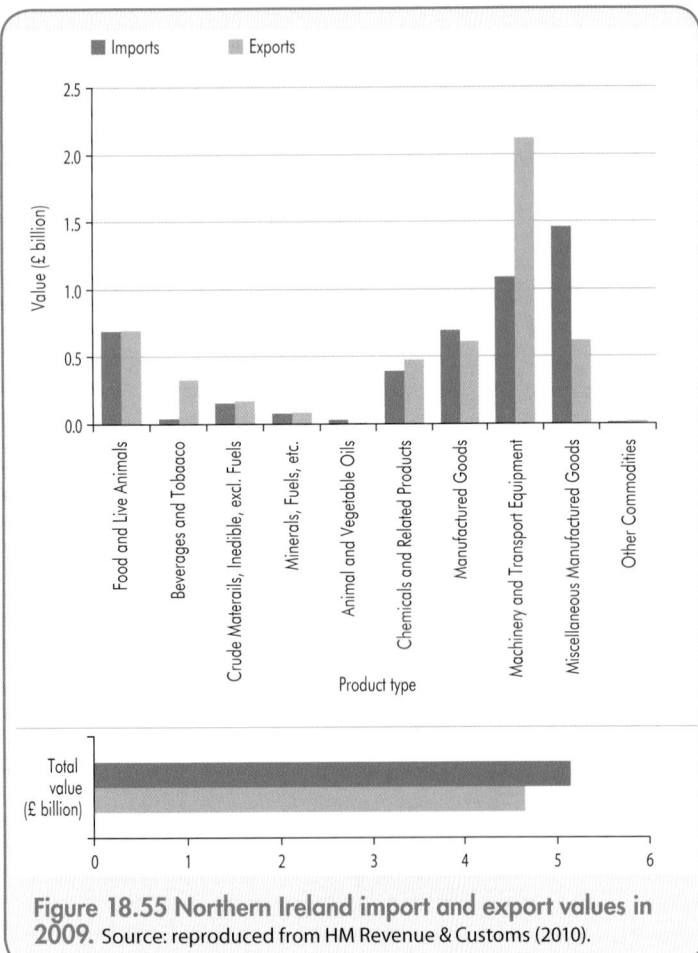

Figure 18.55 Northern Ireland import and export values in 2009. Source: reproduced from HM Revenue & Customs (2010).

production levels and the subsequent need to import large amounts of animal feedstuffs, mainly from Latin America. In general, Northern Ireland imports more biomass commodities *per capita* than other parts of the UK across the categories identified, almost double that in England and over six times more than in Wales. The dependance of Northern Ireland on overseas ecosystems, in particular those of the EU15 and Latin America, for sustaining its socioeconomic activity is apparent. With the predicted 7% rise in population in Northern Ireland by 2020 (NISRA 2005a) and the likely increase in general demand for bioenergy and food in coming years, dependence on flows from overseas ecosystems are set to increase, given Northern Ireland's relatively limited capacity to increase domestic production on the same scale (DETI 2008b). Subsequently, given the potential of consumption of biomass from international sources to drive ecosystem change, the need to monitor the scale, nature and impact of these flows more accurately should be a key objective of regional administrations in the UK, as stated in the recently published Sustainable Development Strategy for Northern Ireland (OFMDFM 2010a).

18.7 Consequences of Change

This document shows that the natural ecosystems and their biodiversity, coupled with sensitive management, have provided and will continue to provide considerable value to the people of Northern Ireland through a wide range of ecosystem services. The specific products have changed over time, and changes will continue. Some outputs, such as carbon sequestration and hazard resilience, are not currently recognised as having financial value but may become highly important in the future.

Figure 18.59 provides a very general assessment of two factors, namely the relative importance of a particular ecosystem for the delivery of specific ecosystem services and the direction of change over the past 20 years. Population of the table has been carried out by local experts working together. There are serious issues in combining a large range of habitats, sites, aspects of benefits (e.g. types of crops) and trends into a single 'directionality' arrow, and the confidence with which colours and arrows have been assigned varies with regard to the spatial variability of the habitats, their current and past management and the degree of knowledge of past trends. It is also difficult to determine directionality of change over time; in several areas the trend has been generally downward, but over the past 1 or 2 years improvements have occurred.

It is clear that the habitats in general contribute greatly to the various services, and which services are delivered by these various habitats. Perhaps the most useful aspect of the table is to highlight areas of synergy or of particular concern. Those habitats which are very important for a particular service and where the trend is downward indicate areas for possible future concern.

material flow analysis of the UK regions to establish the precise dependence of Northern Ireland's production and consumption patterns on domestic, UK and international ecosystems, although these figures give an indication of directions and relative magnitude of flows. They suggest the need not only to maintain the regional ecosystems on which Northern Ireland depends, but also to maintain the ecosystems further afield on which it relies.

Imports of cereals, animal feeds and wood are noticeably high and obviously related to local needs. More surprising is the relatively high level of meat and dairy/eggs imports, given the high level of exports in both categories, but this may relate partially to UK-wide distribution of and demand for goods by large retailers. In general, the higher codes, particularly code 6 (see **Figure 18.57**), represent more highly processed commodities. It is important to recognise that customs data fail to identify those commodities which may have passed through more than one other UK country. Beyond very general conclusions, far more detailed analysis is required of what exactly is happening regarding import and export data. What is clear is that Northern Ireland relies significantly on imports for subsistence products and on external markets for its domestic produce.

The data indicate the larger size (relative to population) of the Northern Ireland agricultural sector compared to the rest of the UK and the large amount of imported feedstuff required to sustain it (**Figure 18.57**). These imports come primarily from the EU15 and Eastern Europe (**Figure 18.58**). In addition, the figures for cereals indicate small domestic

UK National Ecosystem Assessment: Technical Report

It is important to note that most of the available habitat data are quantitative only, with little information available on the habitat's quality or its ability to deliver various services. Quality and quantity may, or may not, move in similar directions. If they do not, there are difficulties in determining which aspect is of greater importance, a factor not addressed in this table.

18.8 Sustainable Management

Some land in Northern Ireland is owned by charities. The National Trust owns 11,090 ha (National Trust Regional Office), the RSPB manages 2,794 ha of land as nature reserves (537 ha owned, 2,257 ha leased; RSPB NI Office) and the Woodland Trust manages 321 ha (125 ha owned, 195 ha leased). The Crown Estate owns property in Northern Ireland worth £10.9 million, including a marine estate which comprises the foreshore and seabed out to 12 NM (The Crown Estate 2010). The Government of Northern Ireland is a significant landowner. Much of its land is designated for environmental or heritage purposes, including 68,000 ha owned by Forest Service (Forest Service, pers. comm.), 10,795 ha owned by the Northern Ireland Environment Agency and 8,647 ha by Northern Ireland Water (NI Water unpublished data). Most of the land is owned by private citizens, primarily

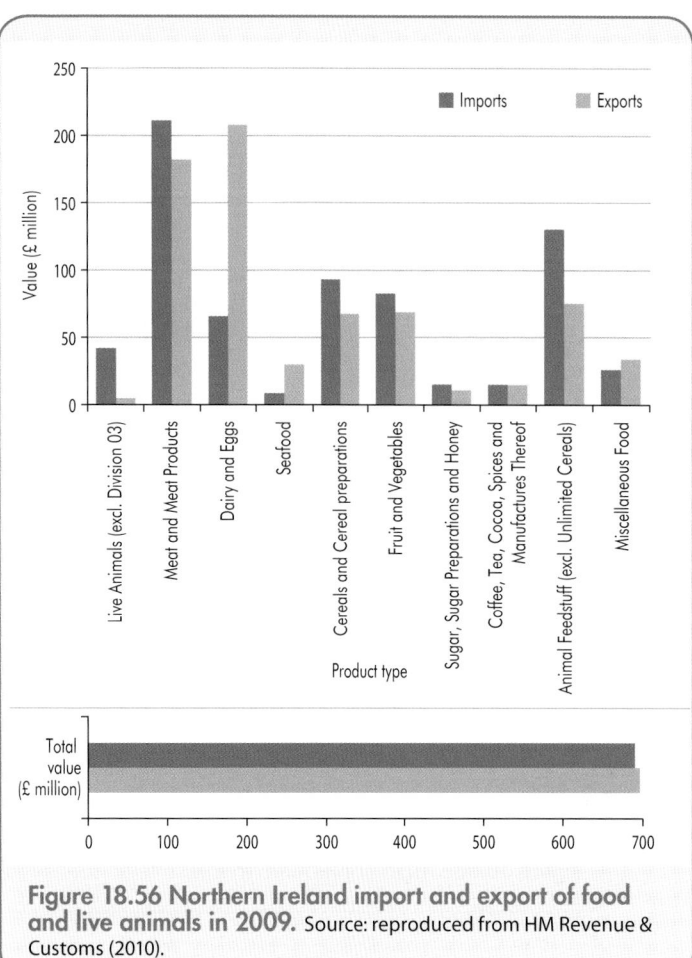

Figure 18.56 Northern Ireland import and export of food and live animals in 2009. Source: reproduced from HM Revenue & Customs (2010).

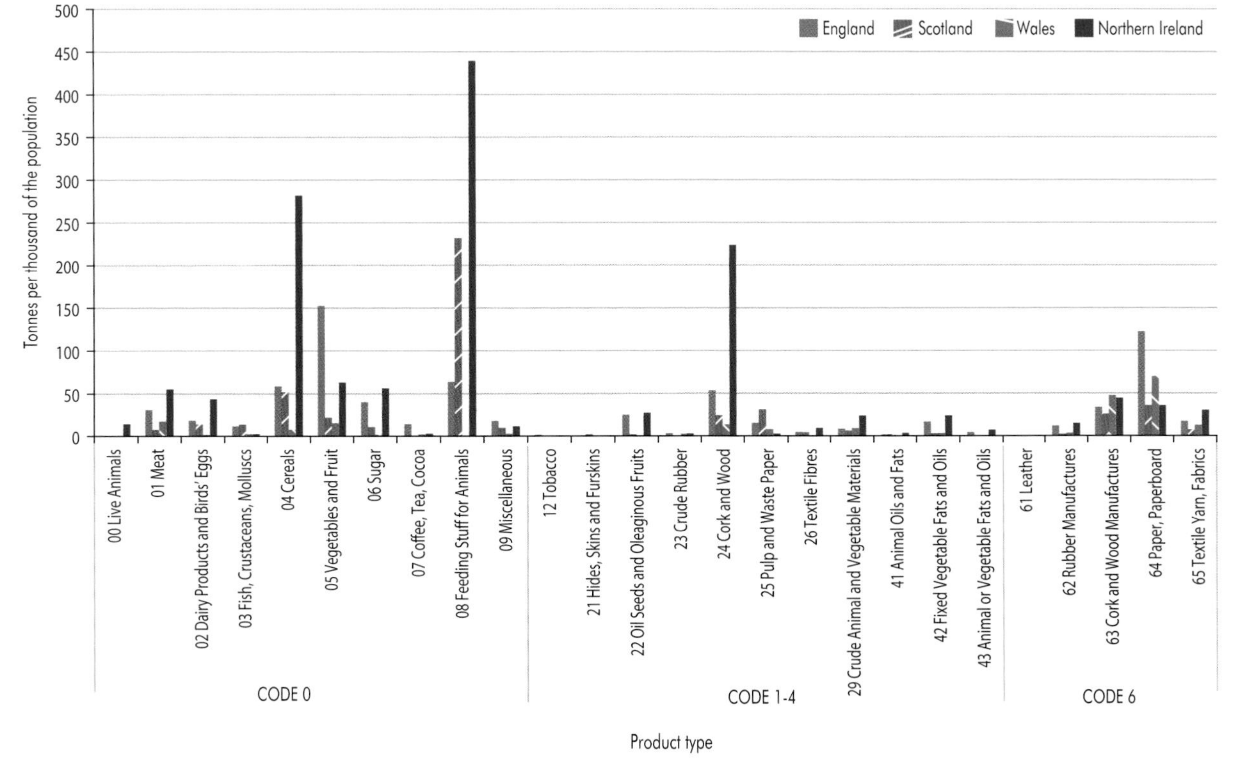

Figure 18.57 Profile of UK regional biomass imports, *per capita*, in 2009. Sources: data from HM Revenue & Customs (2010) and ONS (2010a,b).

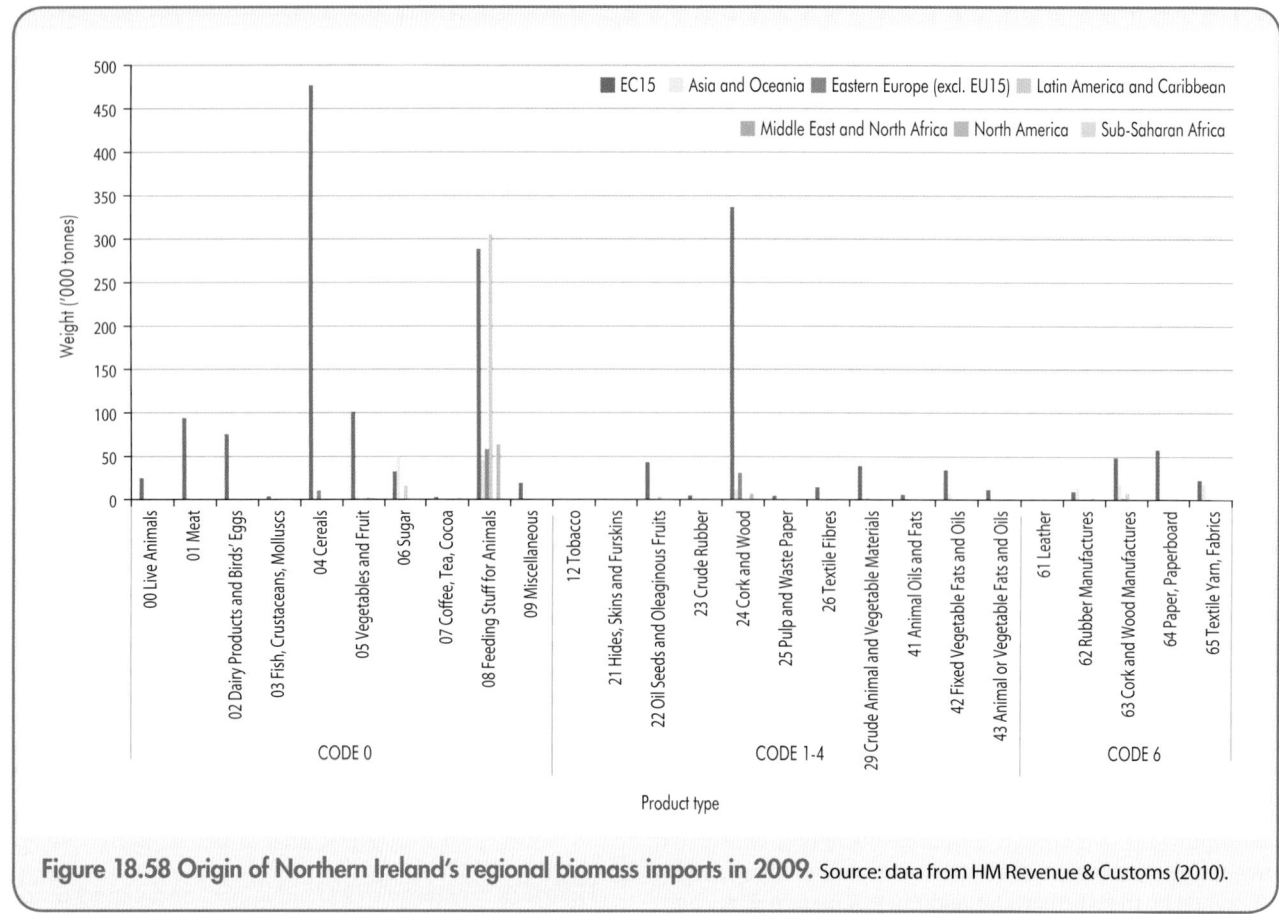

Figure 18.58 Origin of Northern Ireland's regional biomass imports in 2009. Source: data from HM Revenue & Customs (2010).

farmers (Section 18.6.2). In addition, much land is subject to a complex system of 'rights', including turbary, fishing, shooting, minerals and water (Cruickshank & Tomlinson 1995).

Sustainable management needs to deal with a variety of issues, including environmental (climate change, invasive alien species, pollution, habitat loss and fragmentation), social (farming practices, new land uses including renewable energy and flood control, public involvement) and economic (consumer preferences, viability of farms, subsidies). This requires a full suite of tools including legislation, planning policies, designations, restrictions on activities, fiscal drivers, education and awareness (NIBG 2009). Management of ecosystems has primarily been through designations, the planning system and financial incentives for agricultural management, primarily directed by the Department of Agriculture and Rural Development under various agri-environment schemes.

The ecosystem assessment process has identified a variety of issues and threats, and sustainable management of both special sites and the wider countryside is needed to protect and enhance ecosystem services, biodiversity and human well-being.

18.8.1 Designated Sites

One of the main mechanisms for protecting biodiversity and habitats is through designation, although designation alone does not automatically ensure protection. Northern Ireland has been delivering a programme of designating sites at the local level to underpin international designations and obligations since the 1965 Act (ASIs then), but the network

of Areas of Special Scientific Interest (ASSIs, comparable to SSSIs in the rest of the UK) is still some years from completion. The Northern Ireland Environment Agency intends to have a total of 440 ASSIs declared by 2016, with an undetermined number to be declared after that date (NIEA 2009a). By the beginning of 2010 a total of 305 sites had been declared as ASSIs (NIEA 2010a). Around 7.1% of Northern Ireland is designated as ASSIs (NIEA pers. comm. May 2011). The ASSI network forms the basis of international designations including terrestrial Natura 2000 sites, Special Areas of Conservation (SACs) and Special Protection Areas (SPAs). Northern Ireland has one Marine Nature Reserve in Strangford Lough covering a total area of 150 km^2 and 10 of the 15 SPA-designated sites have a marine component. There has been a gradual increase in the total area of designated sites between 1990 and 2009 (**Table 18.20**).

In terms of the state of biodiversity and ecosystems within these sites the Northern Ireland Environment Agency started a programme of condition assessment in 2002 using Common Standards Monitoring guidelines developed by the JNCC. Under this protocol the habitat and species features of a site are assessed every 6 years (DOE 2010b). In March 2008 the Northern Ireland Environment Agency had assessed 916 features on 195 ASSIs, with the first report published in autumn 2008 (NIEA 2008b) and an update proposed for 2010 (NIEA 2011). The general results focus on Natura 2000 sites (**Table 18.21; Figure 18.60**). The majority of designated geological sites are in favourable condition, while the majority of some habitats are in unfavourable condition.

Of course, much important biodiversity also lies outside the nationally designated sites. In order to try to protect this,

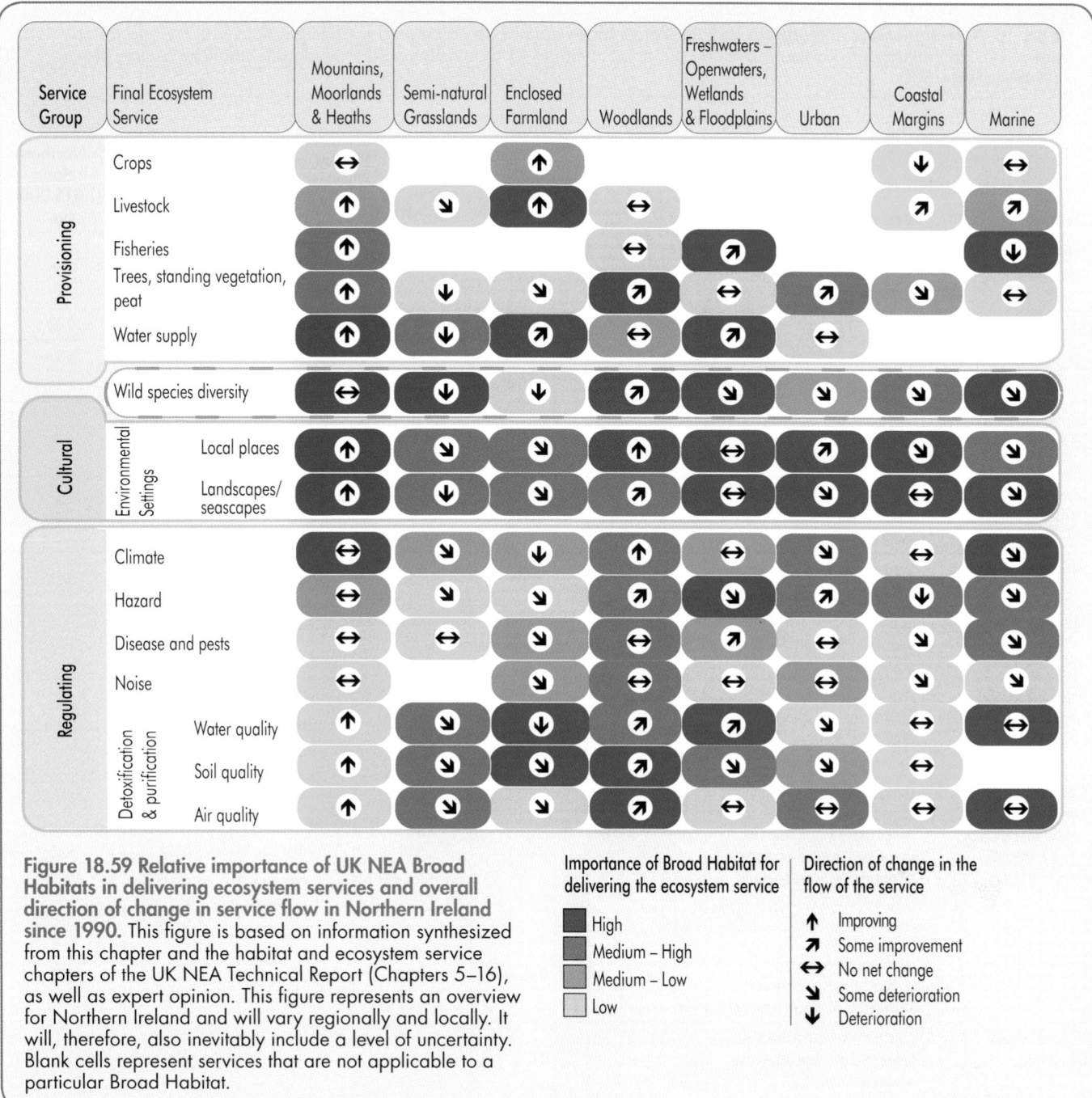

Figure 18.59 Relative importance of UK NEA Broad Habitats in delivering ecosystem services and overall direction of change in service flow in Northern Ireland since 1990. This figure is based on information synthesized from this chapter and the habitat and ecosystem service chapters of the UK NEA Technical Report (Chapters 5–16), as well as expert opinion. This figure represents an overview for Northern Ireland and will vary regionally and locally. It will, therefore, also inevitably include a level of uncertainty. Blank cells represent services that are not applicable to a particular Broad Habitat.

Importance of Broad Habitat for delivering the ecosystem service
- High
- Medium – High
- Medium – Low
- Low

Direction of change in the flow of the service
- ↑ Improving
- ↗ Some improvement
- ↔ No net change
- ↘ Some deterioration
- ↓ Deterioration

Sites of Local Nature Conservation Importance (SLNCI) have been introduced in a number of statutory development plans. In 2000 there were 81 SLNCIs and in 2009 there were 889, but only 137 have been formally adopted within the local development plans to the end of 2010. It is to be hoped that the revised Planning Policy Statement 2 on Nature Conservation (due to be published in 2011) will review and safeguard SLNCIs, but this is not guaranteed as it will be subject to consultation. It should be noted that the National Trust and other charities also have a significant role in conserving sites, including Strangford Lough and the Murlough sand dunes.

The Management of Special Sites (MOSS) scheme helps deliver appropriate management of designated sites in Northern Ireland by providing landowners with a grant payment for undertaking general conservation activity in agreement with the Northern Ireland Environment Agency. The scheme was reviewed in 2009 and now addresses the protection and management of habitats not covered by other schemes, primarily the NICMS, such as elements of biodiversity or habitats that require specific attention. It aims to have 95% of the relevant areas being in favourable or unfavourable recovering condition by 2016 (DARD 2009c).

18.8.2 Wider Countryside and Landscape-scale Conservation

There is recognition that 'wider countryside' and 'landscape-scale' conservation measures are required (NIBG 2009) but to date movement in this direction has been limited. The problems of changes in quality and extent of priority habitats and species within and outside of the designated sites related to climate change impacts, the need for buffer zones around designated sites and the importance of establishing wildlife corridors have been raised at conferences (e.g. Biodiversity and Climate Change in Ireland,

Table 18.20 Designations in Northern Ireland. Percentages cannot be calculated for designations that include marine areas. The percentage of Northern Ireland cannot be summed as many sites hold multiple designations. Source: NIEA unpublished data (2011).

Designation	Description	Area (ha) 1999 (31/3/99)	Area (ha) 2008 (31/3/08)	Increase in area 1998/99–2007/08 (%)	No. of sites 2010 (1/4/2010)	Area (ha) 2010 (1/4/2010)	% Northern Ireland (1,415,000 ha)
Area of Special Scientific Interest (ASSI)	Land identified by scientific survey as being of the highest conservation value.	83,535	95,555	14	304	100,474	7.10
ASSI Features	Earth Science	27,801	33,452	20	107	36,846	2.60
	Habitats	80,775	92,412	14	219	98,037	6.93
	Species	79,623	89,738	13	138	91,236	6.45
Special Protection Area (SPA)	Safeguard the habitats of migratory birds and certain particularly threatened birds.	71,035	108,607	53	17	114,402	N/A
Special Area of Conservation (SAC)	Protect the 220 habitats and approximately 1,000 species of European interest.	44,950	66,321	48	55	67,579	N/A
Ramsar Site	Conservation and wise use of wetlands.	84,330	86,214	2	20	88,170	6.23
Marine Nature Reserve	Conserve marine flora and fauna and geological features of special interest.	16,500	16,500	0	1	16,500	N/A
Area of Outstanding Natural Beauty (AONB)	Protect and enhance the qualities of landscapes of distinctive character and special scenic value.	284,948	288,592	1	9	312,610	22.09
Site of Local Nature Conservation Importance (SLNCI)	Designated for their habitats, species and/or earth science, which make a contribution to the local natural heritage & contribute to National and European biodiversity.	N/A	N/A	N/A	911	36,092	2.55
Country Parks	Promote access to the countryside, encouraging a greater understanding and knowledge of the environment.	2,424	2,424	0	8	2,424	0.17
National Nature Reserves	Conserve terrestrial flora and fauna and geological features of special interest.	1,249	1,675	34	12	1,808	0.13
Local Nature Reserves	Areas set aside for biodiversity and where people can enjoy wildlife.	69	541	684	23	865	0.06

Table 18.21 Current status of designated sites. Source: data from NIBG (2009).

Status of features (basis of designation)	Favourable condition (%)	Unfavourable –recovering (%)	Unfavourable (%)
ASSI	62	3	35
SPA	83	-	17
SAC	39	10	51
Ramsar sites	84	-	16

NIBG and Comhar SDC conference, November 2008) and have recently received major attention throughout the UK following the publication of the Lawton Report (Lawton *et al.* 2010). Protection for some features lies within planning guidelines and this comes into effect when planning permission is sought for development. Although there was provision in the 1965 Amenity Lands Act, Northern Ireland does not have National Parks. There are no facilities for buffer zones or stricter management conditions near designated sites, so management outside of a designated site can have impacts within it (pollution, erosion, disturbance, drainage operations, intensive farming). Also many animals range far beyond a designated site during

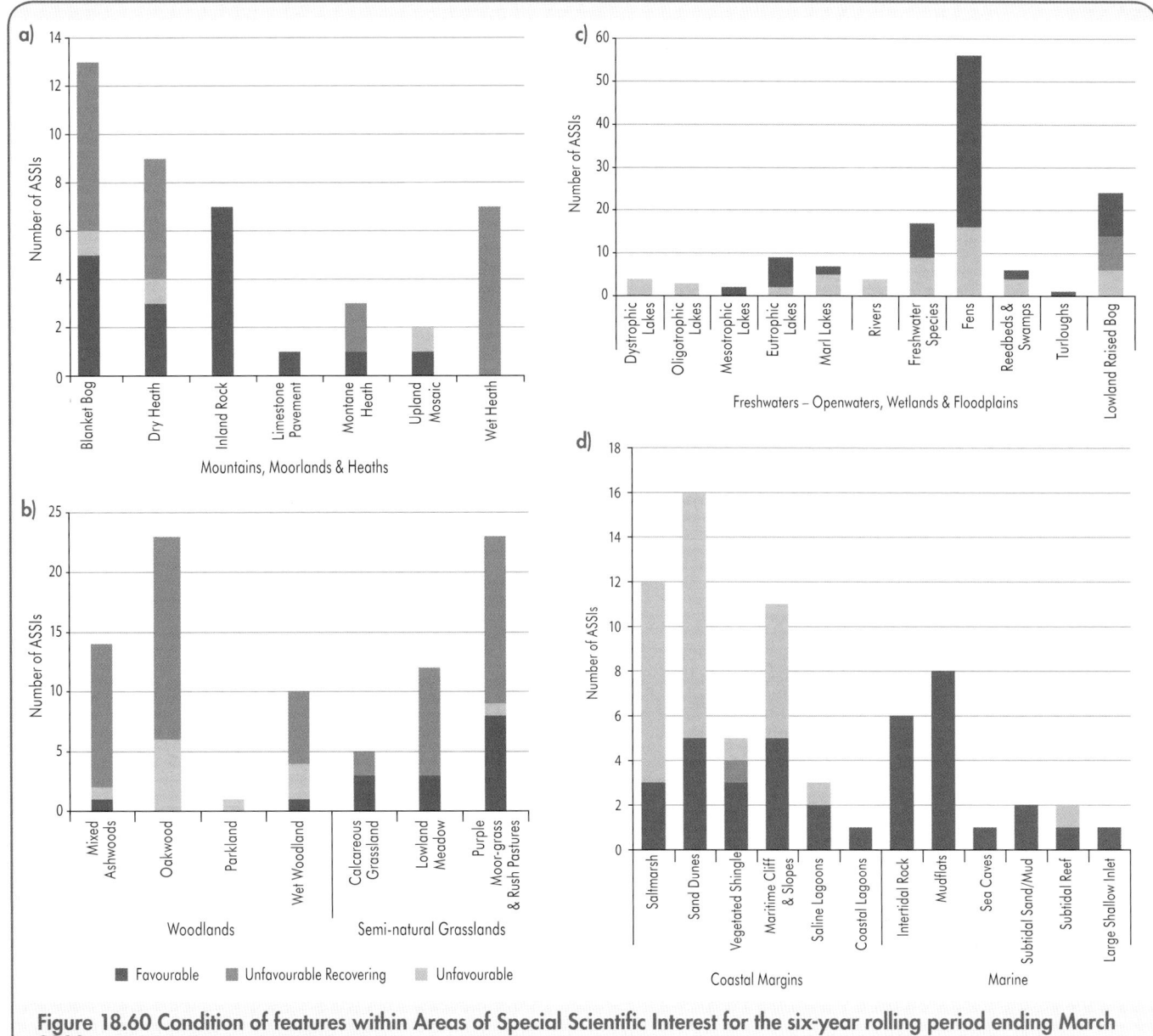

Figure 18.60 Condition of features within Areas of Special Scientific Interest for the six-year rolling period ending March 2008. Source: reproduced from NIEA (2008c).

their lifespan. Identifying issues and developing ways to address them in a wider countryside context is particularly important as the impacts of climate change become more significant in determining where animals and plants are able to live (Defra 2006).

Identifying areas of particular conservation value and then using this to target their protection and proactive management is a technique which has been pioneered internationally ('hotspots' of biodiversity; Conservation International 2007). One way to begin this process is to look at sites which are subject to multiple designations. There are numerous areas in Northern Ireland which fulfil this criterion, including Strangford Lough, Lough Neagh and parts of the Mourne Mountains (**Figure 18.61**).

Work on biodiversity conservation in the wider countryside is encouraged primarily through agri-environment schemes (Section 18.8.5). These schemes are also dependent on individual farmers joining them, which can result in a patchwork effect, especially as the entire farm has to be in the CMS in Northern Ireland (unlike England and Wales). Consequently, if a farm has Semi-natural Grasslands, which are very important habitats for biodiversity and landscape, the fact that other areas within the farm are under intensive agriculture may prevent it from being part of the scheme.

As with other parts of the UK, Northern Ireland does have Areas of Outstanding Natural Beauty (AONBs). This is a designation managed by the Northern Ireland Environment Agency under the Nature Conservation & Amenity Lands (NI) Order 1985. There is a very low level of financial support available for management of these areas, which cover upwards of 20% of Northern Ireland's land area (EHS 2008a; see **Figure 18.60**). The Mourne Mountain Landscape Partnership has been awarded a Development Grant by the Heritage Lottery to work towards a £2 million Landscape Partnership Scheme which will preserve and celebrate aspects of the rich natural and cultural heritage of the Mournes, including heather heathland, Mourne juniper, water supply, Mourne granite and traditional farming (MHT pers. comm.). There is a proposal to introduce legislation to

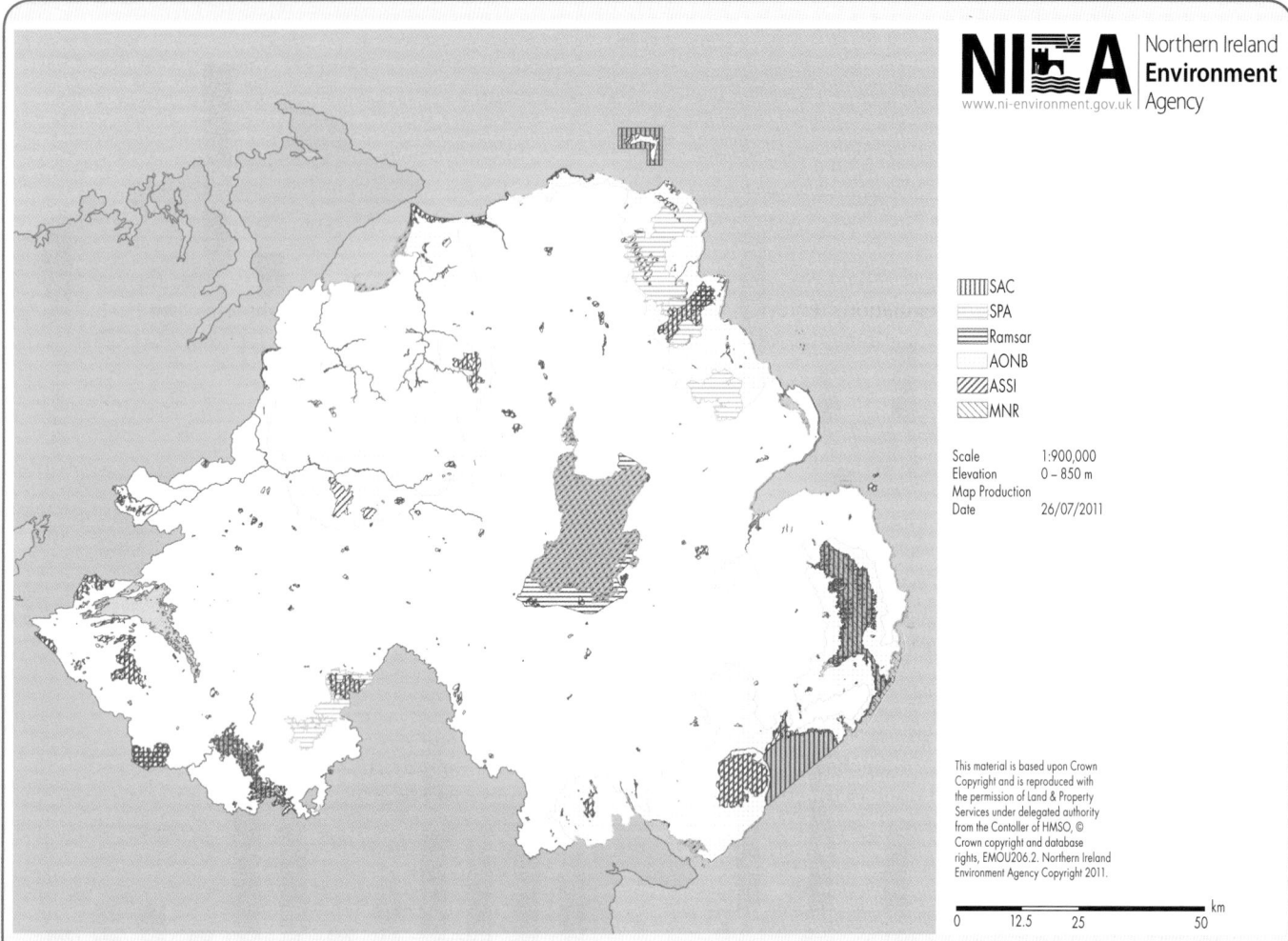

||||||SAC
═══SPA
━━━Ramsar
☐AONB
▨ASSI
▧MNR

Scale 1:900,000
Elevation 0 – 850 m
Map Production
Date 26/07/2011

This material is based upon Crown
Copyright and is reproduced with
the permission of Land & Property
Services under delegated authority
from the Contoller of HMSO, ©
Crown copyright and database
rights, EMOU206.2. Northern Ireland
Environment Agency Copyright 2011.

km
0   12.5   25   50

Figure 18.61 Areas designated for conservation purposes in Northern Ireland. Source: NIEA (unpublished data). Reproduced with the permission of Land & Property Services. © Crown Copyright 2011.

allow the formation of National Parks to the Assembly, but this will differ from the legislation in Great Britain in that there are unlikely to be any planning responsibilities for a National Parks authority in Northern Ireland. The timing is still unclear and designation of specific areas may be some years after the legislative process, which itself will take at least 2 years.

Country parks were first established in Northern Ireland following the introduction of the Amenity Lands Act (Northern Ireland) 1965. This set up the Ulster Countryside Committee which advised government on the purchase and management of land for recreational use, primarily by urban dwellers. Seven country parks were established between then and 2004 (Castle Archdale, Crawfordsburn, Ness & Ervey Woods, Peatlands, Redburn, Roe Valley and Scrabo) and they are important for educational purposes and conservation of the natural heritage (EHS 2004c). Additional country parks are managed by local authorities, and include Creggan, Carnfunnock, Delamont, Cave Hill, Ballyarnett, Maghery and Loughgall. In addition, there is the large and well-used Lagan Valley Regional Park running from Belfast to Lisburn along the old Lagan Canal. These sites, plus Forest Parks and sites managed by charities such as the National Trust, are vital areas for public access to the countryside where there is a limited system of public rights of way and no 'right to roam'.

18.8.3 Land Use Planning

Planning in Northern Ireland is based on the Regional Development Strategy, supported by a suite of Planning Policy Statements (PPSs) and delivered locally through Area Plans. Planning policy and practice have been undergoing many changes since the resumption of Assembly in 2007. A new Regional Development Strategy is expected to be released for public consultation in early 2011 after several years of development, PPSs are being revised and republished, while Area Plans, which should form the main basis for determining planning, remain at various stages, and the planning system is being significantly reformed through the Planning Bill progressing through the Assembly in early 2011. There is still uncertainty around the timing and extent of the Review of Public Administration, which has been under development since 2000 and aims to reduce the number of Councils while increasing their remit (substantially so in the case of planning powers and corresponding developmental control). A review of development control and other practical aspects of planning came into effect in 2010, and coupled with the revised PPSs on Sustainable Development in the Countryside (DOE 2010e), the Planning Bill and the reform of local government, may have significant impacts on land use and management.

Environmental Impact Assessments and Strategic Environmental Assessments (SEA) are legal requirements for many major developments, plans and programmes. Major SEAs have recently been carried out in Northern Ireland for the Regional Development Strategy (DRD 2009a) and for marine renewable resources (DETI 2009b). These assessments offer the opportunity for identification and mitigation of environmental issues before development proceeds. They rely on the quality and thoroughness of the assessment to identify potential issues and options.

Environmental Impact Assessment Regulations (e.g. Environmental Impact Assessment Regulations (Forestry) NI 2006) apply to specific projects above a minimum threshold (which can be nil as in the case of deforestation within a designated area). Assessments of plans or projects may also be required in respect of the Conservation (Natural Habitats, etc.) Regulations 1995 and 2004. A considerable body of work is undertaken by statutory bodies including the Forest Service and the Northern Ireland Environment Agency each year in respect of both sets of regulations.

18.8.4 River Basin Management
River catchments have been assigned to River Basin Districts, which serve as the administrative areas for coordinated water management. Of the four RBDs, one is entirely contained within Northern Ireland (North Eastern), while three cross the border into the Republic of Ireland (Neagh Bann, North Western and Shannon) and are therefore designated as International RBDs (**Table 18.22**). A small

portion of County Fermanagh contributes to groundwater flow in the headwaters of the Shannon catchment, therefore the Shannon RBD is classified as an International RBD.

River basin plans take an integrated approach to the protection, improvement and sustainable use of the water environment. The objective is to improve the ecological health of waters, support more sustainable use of water, create better habitats for wildlife in and around water, reduce the pollution of groundwater, and contribute to mitigating the effects of floods and drought. The river basin management plans are renewed every 6 years. For example, chemical classification varies among the three RBDs, with the North Eastern RBD having the highest percentage of 'poor' and 'bad' quality in 2008–2009 (**Figure 18.62**).

18.8.5 Agri-Environment Schemes
Agri-environment Schemes include the Countryside Management Scheme, Environmentally Sensitive Areas scheme, Northern Ireland Countryside Management Scheme and Organic Farming Scheme. These schemes have been developed by the Department of Agriculture and Rural Development to encourage farmers and landowners to adopt environmentally friendly management practices. The schemes are co-funded by the European Union.

The ESA Scheme was introduced in 1988 and was the first 'on farm' programme designed to promote the integration of production of wholesome food with responsible management

Table 18.22 Summary information on the three main River Basin Management Districts of Northern Ireland. Source: data from NIEA (2009f,g,h).

	Neagh Bann	North Eastern	North Western
Area	574,000 ha including Lough Neagh at 39,200 ha	300,000 ha including 100,000 ha of marine waters	490,000 ha including Foyle and Erne basins
Sites of importance	10 loughs over 50 ha, 36 drinking water protected areas, wetlands around Lough Neagh. 16 Water Dependent SACs, 4 Water Dependent SPAs.	0.7 million people live in the district including the population of Belfast and surrounding commuter areas. 18 rivers, 2 lakes, 2 coastal waters and 2 transitional waters. 16 Water Dependent SACs, 9 Water Dependent SPAs.	24 Water Dependent SACs, 4 Water Dependent SPAs, 3 Bathing Waters, 2 Shellfish Waters, 1,681 km Freshwater Fish Directive rivers, 14,900 ha Freshwater Fish Directive lakes, 4 Urban Waste Water Directive sites.
Status			
Surface water bodies below good status	73%	65%	63%
Groundwater bodies below good status	7%	data not provided	data not provided
Benefits £3 million–£15 million investment (all figures relate to values discounted over 15 years)	Quantifiable benefit of £23 million–£25 million.		
	Non-monetary benefits include improvements to tourism and recreation, enhanced soil quality and biodiversity, greater flood resilience, and moderate savings to water consumers.		
Targets by 2015			
Surface water bodies at good status or better	43% (117 of 270)	46% (61 of 133)	67%
Good ecological potential or better in heavily modified water bodies	3% (9)	3%	2%
Groundwater bodies maintained at good status	93%	88% (7 of 8)	100%

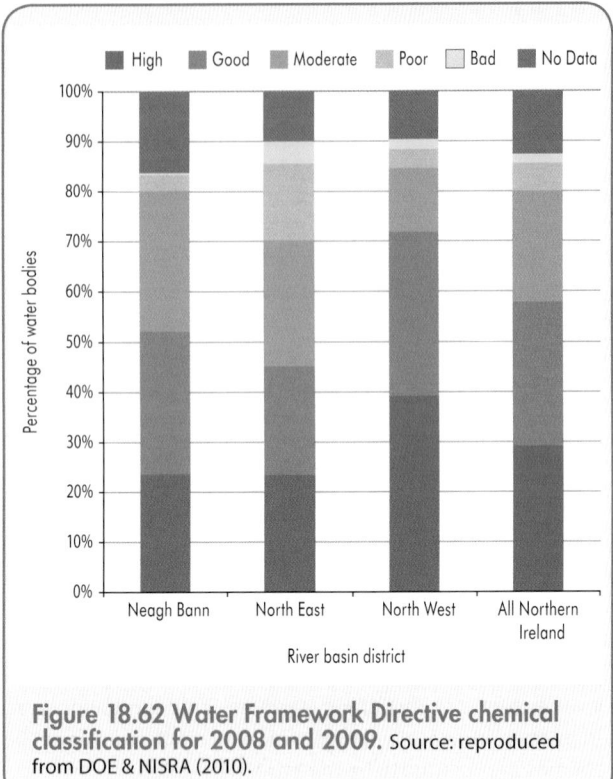

Figure 18.62 Water Framework Directive chemical classification for 2008 and 2009. Source: reproduced from DOE & NISRA (2010).

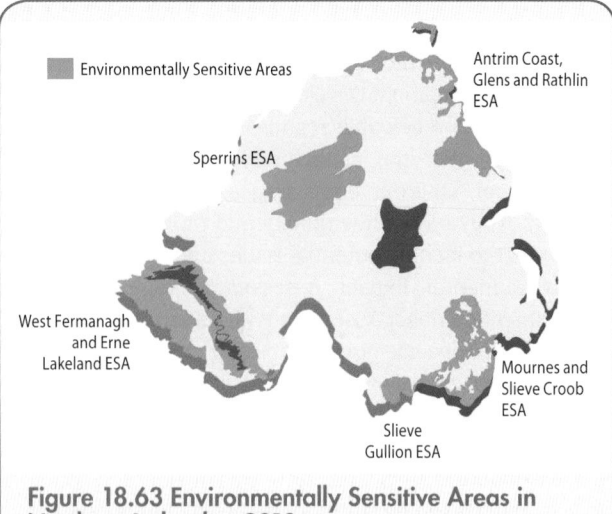

Figure 18.63 Environmentally Sensitive Areas in Northern Ireland at 2010. Source: image used courtesy of the Department of Agriculture and Rural Development.

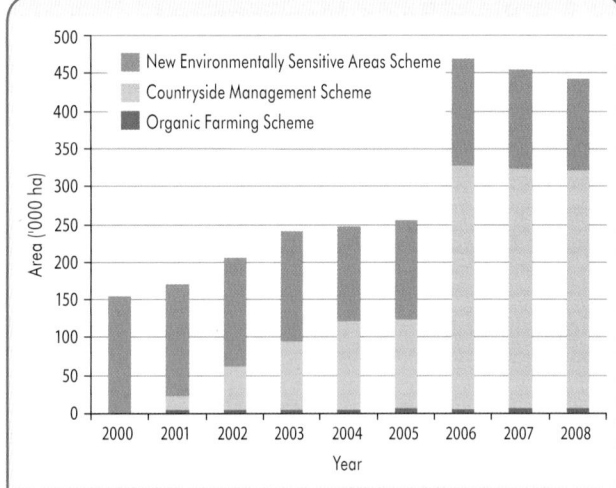

Figure 18.64 Areas under agri-environment scheme agreements from 2000 to 2008. Source: reproduced from DOE & NISRA (2010).

of the countryside. By 1994 some 20% of the land area had been designated as environmentally sensitive in five distinct areas (Mournes and Slieve Croob, Antrim Coast, Glens and Rathlin, West Fermanagh and Erne Lakeland, Sperrins and Slieve Gullion; **Figure 18.63**) and by 1995 the Organic Aid Scheme (OAS) had also been launched.

In 1999 the new Countryside Management Scheme was introduced for those farms outside ESA scheme areas. Coupled with this was the Organic Farming Scheme, which came into operation in 1999. Agri-environment scheme participation, which is voluntary, expanded rapidly in 2005 with increased funding and the introduction of the Single Farm Payment which removed the link between production and subsidies (Cooper *et al.* 2009). The most recent agri-environment scheme, the Northern Ireland Countryside Management Scheme, was launched in 2008 along with the New Organic Farming Scheme (NOFS). It is an integral part of the Northern Ireland Rural Development Programme 2007–2013. The likely future emphasis on climate change and emissions reduction was highlighted in the mid-term evaluation of the Northern Ireland Rural Development Programme (NISRA 2010b).

The NICMS covers all of Northern Ireland. It is a single unified countryside management scheme to maintain and enhance biodiversity in line with the Northern Ireland Biodiversity Strategy and the Northern Ireland Programme for Government 2008–2011 through the positive management of wildlife habitats to enhance ASSI/Natura 2000 sites. It also aims to assist in the implementation of the Water Framework Directive. It is claimed through the IACS Single Application Form (SAF) and in exchange for an enhanced payment, farmers actively manage their farms to achieve a number of benefits (**Table 18.23**; **Table 18.24**). Any farmer or land manager with a Business Identification Number and

with at least 3 ha of eligible land can apply on submission of appropriate documents (DARD 2008a).

The total area under agri-environment schemes in Northern Ireland is approximately 468,000 ha, 42% of the agricultural land area under agreement (**Figure 18.64**). The priority target in the Northern Ireland (NI) Programme for Government 2008–2011 is to have 50% under environmental enhancement agreement by 2013 (DARD 2008b). In late 2010 there were about 13,000 agri-environment scheme agreement holders, with a further 4,500 applicants awaiting announcements on funding (Aileen Lawson, UFU, pers. comm.).

The estimated percentage of HAP habitats within the schemes as of 31 December 2009 is presented in **Table 18.25**. While variable, it is clear that a significant proportion of all of these habitats lies within these schemes. Less clear is the extent to which the schemes have been successful in protecting the habitats from damage (habitat quality is not recorded, only area) and monitoring of results for both general and specific outcomes is needed to assess overall effectiveness. Many additional benefits have been identified

Table 18.23 The Northern Ireland Countryside Management Scheme aims, targets and potential outcomes. Source: data from DARD (2008a).

Aims	Maintain and enhance biodiversity in line with the Northern Ireland Biodiversity Strategy (NIBS) and the Programme for Government (PfG) 2008–2011 by maintaining species diversity through the positive management of wildlife habitats and to protect and enhance ASSI/ Natura 2000 sites.
	Assist implementation of the Water Framework Directive.
	Enhance landscape and heritage features by integrating their management into the everyday workings of the farm.
Target	• The target in the Programme for Government is to increase to 50% the area of agricultural land in Northern Ireland covered by environmental enhancement agreements by 2013, allowing 18,000 farmers to participate in agri-environment schemes. • Reversing the decline in farmland biodiversity. • Enhancing the landscape. • Managing natural resources to improve the quality of water, air and soil.
Payments and Options	• Payment rates are typically 25% higher than legacy schemes to reflect the increased costs associated with the new scheme. • Minimum Entry Environmental Benefit (MEEB), where landowners undertake habitat enhancement to manage specific habitats on their farms, resulting in greater environmental and financial benefit. • Special Environmental Project (SEP) option, enabling farmers to propose projects individually and jointly with other agreement holders which are capable of delivering environmental benefits.
Water protection	Water Environment (Water Framework Directive/WFD) Regulations (NI) 2003, aim to establish overall framework for protection of surface and ground waters. Compliance with Nitrates Directive and agri-environment schemes deliver water quality benefits that will help with WFD compliance. The new option—Farm Waterway and riparian zone management aims to enhance farm waterways and their associated riparian zones in terms of water quality improvement through practical management measures.
Biodiversity	NICMS aims to make a major contribution to the conservation action required for many priority Northern Ireland habitats and species. Specific habitat management requirements specify how participants can contribute to the conservation of these habitats and species. Several new options deliver on biodiversity – Pollen and Nectar Mixture (benefits insects) and Delayed cutting/grazing of grassland (positively managing land for Irish hare).
Natura 2000	Special Protection Areas (SPAs) and Special Areas of Conservation (SACs) along with Areas of Special Scientific Interest (ASSI) are a priority for the new Scheme.
Climate Change	Climate change objectives have been identifies in NICMS.

Table 18.24 Summary of agri-environment schemes. Source: data from DARD (2008c).

Environmentally Sensitive Areas Scheme	Designed to integrate the production of wholesome food with responsible management of the countryside.	Highly successful, covering 20% of Northern Ireland. It applied only to land inside one of the five designated ESA areas.
Countryside Management Scheme	First introduced in 1999, encouraging farmers to positively manage habitats, improve water quality and protect heritage.	The CMS applied to land outside the ESAs.
Northern Ireland Countryside Management Scheme (NICMS)	To enhance landscape and heritage features; to assist implementation of the WFD and to maintain and enhance biodiversity.	All of Northern Ireland but selection criteria may be applied to prioritise entry which achieves the greatest environmental benefit
Organic Farming Scheme	Provides payments to help farmers with the additional costs and loss of income that occurs during the conversion period to organic production.	Participants must adhere to the organic standards specified by their chosen certification body and maintained for the duration of a five year agreement. Eligible land in an ASSI or Natura 2000 site may be entered into the OFS.

(DARD 2008a), and as of 31 December 2010 (DARD pers. comm.):

■ 14,156 ha of species rich grassland are under agreement by 3,764 participants;
■ 496 ha of grass margins are managed by 1,199 participants;
■ 627 ha of native trees have been planted by 2,431 participants;
■ 1,857 ha of wild bird cover have been grown by 699 participants;
■ 578 ha of ancient monuments are protected by 888 participants;

■ Farmers have agreed to restore almost 600 km of field boundaries; and
■ 7,148 ha of farmland are managed for breeding lapwing, curlew, redshank and snipe by 1,339 participants.

18.8.6 Woodland Grants and Certifications

The Woodland Grant Scheme aims to expand the amount of tree cover in Northern Ireland by encouraging the creation of new woodland, subsequently increasing the production of wood, improving the landscape and woodland biodiversity,

Table 18.25 Priority Habitats and agri-environment schemes in 2010. Note: these data must be viewed with care as the definitions used by NIEA and DARD do not always correspond. * wet heath and dry heath; † due to differences in DARD and NIEA classification of parkland. Sources: data from NIBG (2009); updated by DARD (2010 unpublished data).

Priority Habitat	HAP estimated total area (ha)	Area under agri-environment scheme (AES) agreement (ha)	% HAP area in AES
Upland Heathland	10,972	33,743*	100
Blanket Bog	140,000	14,066	10
Lowland Raised Bog	21,106	5,140	24
Mixed Ashwoods	3,430	3,520	100
Oakwood	2,350	914	39
Wet Woodland	2,600	1,613	70
Parkland	1,100	2,772	100†
Calcareous Grassland	1,156	1,162	100

Table 18.26 Agri-environment scheme woodland plantings in 2010. Source: Forest Service (unpublished data).

Habitat type	Area (ha)
Ungrazed oak woodland	894
Grazed oak woodland	20
Ungrazed wet woodland	1,508
Grazed wet woodland	105
Wet carr (ungrazed)	200
Ungrazed ash woodland	3,266
Grazed ash woodland	234
Farm woodland (ungrazed)	1,175
Parkland and lowland wood pasture	2,772

and encouraging the sustainable management of forests and woodlands. The amount of funding depends on the tree species being planted; conifers covering over 0.2 ha will earn £1,250/ha, broadleaves earn £1,850/ha. Grants are paid in two instalments; 70% after planting and the remaining 30% after 5 years. The scheme came into effect in 1988 and has been periodically updated since then, supporting the planting of almost 12,000 ha (Forest Service 2007b).

Under agri-environment the minimum width of the planted area must be 2 m and each area planted must be 0.2 ha or less within a field. The minimum area is 0.01 ha in any one field and the maximum area that can be planted on each farm is 1 ha. Five hundred and ninety-five hectares have been planted with native trees in margins/field corners and 31 ha in riparian zones (Forest Service unpublished data).

Agri-environment schemes give financial encouragement to farmers for adopting farming practices that maintain and enhance the conservation value of farm woodland habitat by encouraging natural regeneration of native species and increasing the diversity of woodland ground flora. Since 2005 farm woodlands have been classified into three types: mixed ash, oak and wet woodland. There are two grazing options for managing these three woodland types: no grazing and light grazing. There are 7,043 ha of farm woodland managed as ungrazed woodland and 359 ha managed as grazed woodland. Prior to 2005 all woodland entering into agri-environment schemes was classified as 'farm woodland' or 'carr'. These woodlands may include examples of oak, ash or wet woodland types. Parkland and lowland wood pasture are areas of open grassland with mature trees spaced at various densities within a historic designed landscape. Parkland and lowland wood pasture are often associated with other habitats such as woodlands, lakes, ponds, rivers and streams. The trees, which will have been planted to enhance the landscape, are present as specimens, clumps, avenues, lines and copses and the open parkland will have a history of being grazed (**Table 18.26**).

In Northern Ireland there are two protocols for Sustainable Forest Management, the UK Forestry Standard

(2nd edition 2004, 3rd edition due to be published in 2011; Forest Service pers. comm.) and the UK Woodland Assurance Standard. The latter is a certification standard endorsed by the Forest Stewardship Council and provides consumers with assurance that the wood product is produced from a sustainable source. The Forest Service estimate that in 2010 there are 64,000 ha of certified woodland in Northern Ireland, most of which is managed by the Forest Service. Applications for Woodland Grant Schemes are assessed in relation to criteria in the UK Forestry Standard and in respect of the Environmental Impact Assessment Regulations (Forestry) NI 2006.

18.8.7 Less Favoured Areas

The UK designates Less Favoured Areas (LFAs) as land areas of limited agricultural potential; areas where the economic results of farming is below 75% of the national average, population is less that 36 inhabitants/km², more than 19% of the working population are engaged in farming, or mountain regions above 600 m or with steep slopes greater than 20% incline. Poor farming conditions were defined as producing crop yields of less than 80% of the national average and below the community average, and with stocking densities of less than one Livestock Unit (LU) per hectare and by land values below the national average. Almost 70% of all farmland in Northern Ireland is located in LFA designated areas (DARD 2009b; **Figure 18.65**). This compares to 75% in the Republic of Ireland, 47% in the UK and 61% in the EU15 (DARD 2010o). Payment rates for 2011 will be £23.81/ha for Disadvantaged Areas and £47.62/ha for Severely Disadvantaged Areas (NI Executive 2010b). The scheme is open to farmers whose land is used to breed cattle, sheep, deer and goats (DARD 2010j).

18.9 Knowledge Gaps

A coherent baseline is required on the state of and impacts on Northern Ireland's ecosystems and services, including economic valuation, and how they relate to both

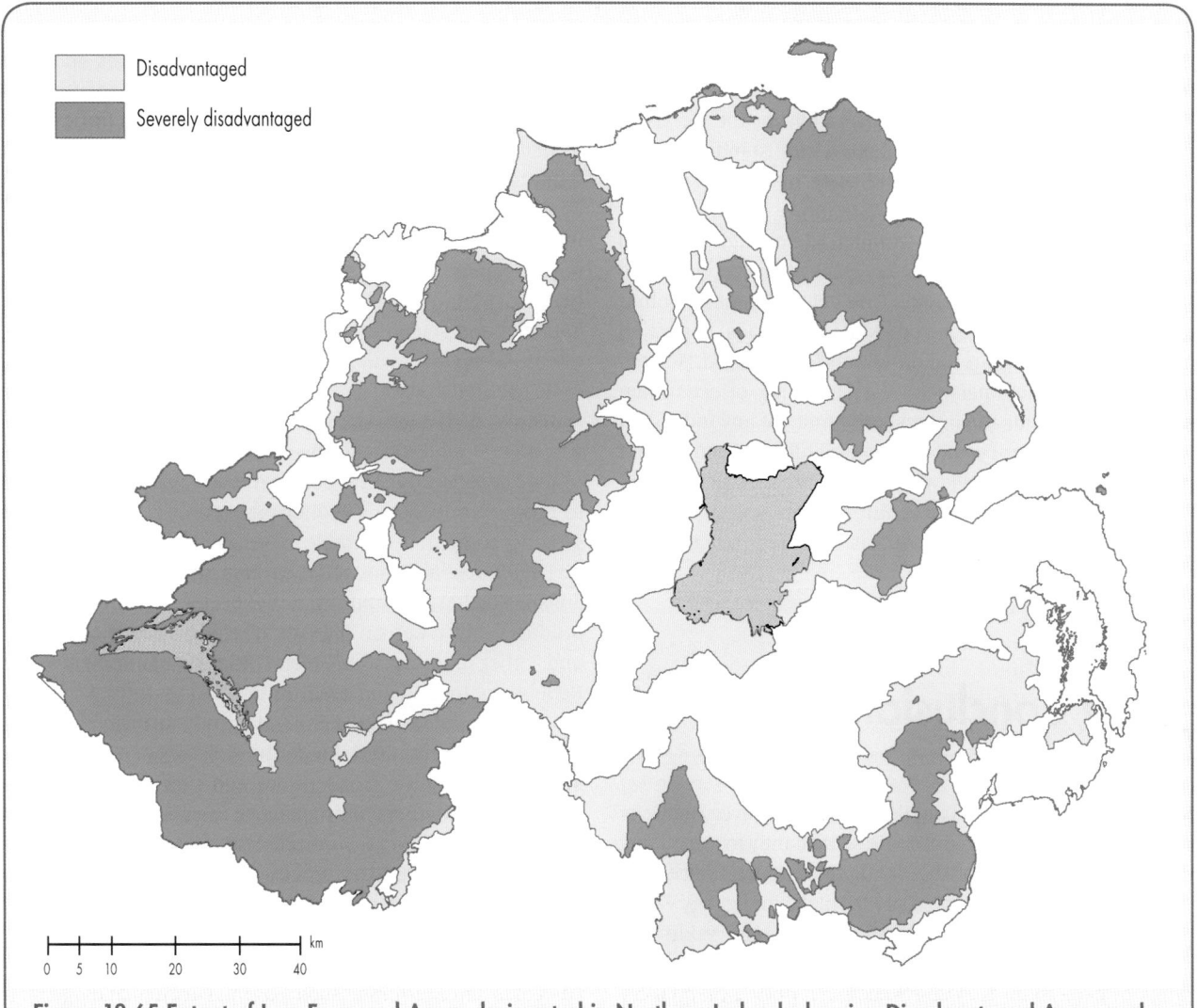

Figure 18.65 Extent of Less Favoured Areas designated in Northern Ireland, showing Disadvantaged Areas and Severely Disadvantaged Areas. Source: reproduced from DARD (2009e). Reproduced with the permission of Land & Property Services and Department of Agriculture and Rural Development © Crown Copyright 2011.

the remainder of the UK and the Republic of Ireland. The Northern Ireland Synthesis is a valuable starting point, but much more work is required. This should not be seen as justifying any delay in progressing the issues identified, but rather as a statement that in the time available this is an incomplete picture. Further data exist and are anticipated to be made available in the coming months. An ongoing mechanism to add data to this work should be developed to ensure that it is progressed in a coherent fashion.

Research is needed on how to maintain and enhance ecosystems and identify threats, values and roles. In particular, there is a lack of knowledge in terms of the ecosystem services provided by the marine environment and a need for better understanding of system boundaries and interactions. Lack of information on an ecosystem service or lack of economic value does not imply an absence of value, but this is sometimes not taken into account when decisions on resource use are made.

Data and research issues centre around whether data exist, their accessibility and their comparability and compatibility. There is an increasing problem of data being seen as 'intellectual property' and therefore not being publicly accessible. Also, many sources of data exist

as unpublished reports or in formats that are not easily accessed. There are a number of positive developments, including Inspire and Freedom of Information. Government departments and agencies should be encouraged to continue to improve accessibility, particularly in these times of financial restraint.

Understanding of functioning of ecosystems as a whole is still incomplete. Some ecosystems and some aspects are well understood, but other areas and the complex interactions are under-studied or under-represented. In particular, lack of understanding of underlying biodiversity/physical interactions (especially of soil and marine) makes understanding of ecosystem function difficult. These are complicated areas to study but their importance is increasingly recognised.

Integration across scientific and social disciplines is needed to improve communication and promote understanding of ecosystems and ecosystem services. This requires a 'common language'. Work is also needed to determine how people engage with, are affected by, and use the environment and from that, to understand how to promote the need for environmental protection. This will lead to improved ability to value the environment and make decisions concerning its use.

An agreed set of standardised indicators and definitions is needed across the UK and Ireland. This will allow progress to be easily monitored and compared across regions. Examination of the available information for the Northern Ireland Synthesis has identified a lack of standardisation of methodology, terminology and scale of reporting which makes comparison difficult.

A strategic plan for environmental management and resource use which identifies key ecosystem services and the most appropriate sites for future development and other changes in usage is required. Many decisions impacting on the environment are taken within focused and isolated policy and practical perspectives. The value of ecosystem services transcends the interests or remits of any individual Department or Agency and can only be fully recognised and properly valued when viewed from a broader perspective which looks at all impacts in an integrated fashion. Integration across government is required for effective ecosystem service delivery.

18.10 Conclusions

Northern Ireland's habitats and biodiversity deliver a suite of ecosystem services and contribute significantly to the quality of life and well-being of the population. Maintenance of a cohesive network of protected sites of high biodiversity value, within an appropriately managed wider countryside and marine environment, is key to ensuring delivery of a wide range of ecosystem services. Recognising the potential for multiple ecosystem outputs and establishing the importance of a resilient natural system to mitigate against unexpected natural and man-made impacts can deliver a highly valuable service to all the people of Northern Ireland. Some systems and habitats are currently robust, but others are partially degraded and require positive management to maximise their potential. Delivery of the major 'public goods' for the benefit of the wider community will need to be through landowners and managers, but to do so they require knowledge, skills and financial support. There is a need for a framework within which landowners and managers can operate a vision for the wider environment and improved understanding of its potential for improving human well-being.

The complexities of ecosystem services and their interactions are becoming better understood by ecologists. However, this knowledge and understanding needs wider dissemination and promotion to facilitate its incorporation in government decision-making processes. Many scientific data are not accessible in Northern Ireland as they have been gathered by government departments and agencies but have not been published. Much of the data which do exist are descriptive; valuation data based on ecosystem services are scarce and these are required to make the case for the integrated ecosystem approach to land and sea management. Recent work on River Basin Management Plans offers the potential to deliver more integrated valuation and quantification of benefits and threats.

Northern Ireland has a range of policies and legislation that impact directly and indirectly on ecosystems and their service delivery, including the responsibility to ensure local compliance with UK and EU legislation. The funding needed to deliver positively on these policies is limited and is not likely to increase during the coming years as fiscal strictures increase. This competition for scarce government funding means environmental protection, aimed at enabling long-term delivery of ecosystem services, may not receive the necessary financial support. The ability to place a value, both financial and social, on the maintenance and enhancement of natural systems will be crucial if the necessary funding is to be secured.

Direct ecosystem outputs include the provision of food, wood, fuel and water. The outputs have changed over time. There is now less peat harvesting, a shift from hay to silage production, a higher proportion of land used for grazing compared to arable crops and increasing reliance on *Nephrops* and aquaculture compared to wild-caught finfish. Northern Ireland is a net exporter of meat and dairy products, but relies on imports of energy, many foodstuffs and other commodities. Major export markets are the Republic of Ireland and Great Britain.

The true value of the countryside and marine ecosystems are not fully recognised due to the difficulty of externalising and quantifying the many values and services ecosystems provide. Landowners are managing their areas in response to a range of drivers, primarily for provisioning services for which they receive monetary benefits, but are also often required to deliver 'public goods' (such as scenery, biodiversity, flood regulation, avoidance of pollution) without being paid directly for such delivery (although subsidies can encourage such action). Farmers manage land primarily for provisioning services and to a lesser extent for cultural services (tourism, recreation). This impacts on other ecosystem services including regulating (purification and detoxification) and supporting services. Beneficiaries of these services include Northern Ireland residents, visiting tourists, people elsewhere consuming exported goods, and in the case of carbon sequestration/storage, the global population. Development in Northern Ireland has resulted in a 'peri-urban' countryside with a dispersed population of commuters, many of whom also have limited awareness of the value of rural ecosystems. As a result, many urban dwellers are not fully aware of the benefits they derive from rural areas and the associated ecosystem services and hence may not value rural areas highly. Equally, ecosystem services currently, and potentially, provided in urban areas are also not widely recognised.

In the future there may be opportunities for multiple use management of habitats and possible changes in what food is produced and how this is done. These changes will impact on individuals whose livelihoods directly depend on ecosystems and on all citizens through the use of the products and the wealth they create. Farming practices and products have changed over time in response to market forces, policy and fiscal drivers, for example the decline in arable farming since World War II and the increase in improved grassland. Dealing with competing land and sea use for food and renewable energy production, recreation and tourism, carbon sequestration and flood control is likely to become a more important issue.

Identification and delivery of multiple outputs from single ecosystems is still in its early stages in Northern Ireland. Traditionally land was viewed as having a single purpose: farmland to produce food, forests to produce timber, or peatland to provide fuel. In recent decades this view has been changing, in particular with the tourism, recreation and leisure aspects of ecosystems such as uplands, coasts and forests being identified and developed. Some multiple service delivery models are being developed, for example woodland to deliver biodiversity and recreation services in addition to timber provision, and the potential of short rotation willow coppice to produce fuel and detoxify sewage. Opportunities for multiple service delivery exist for almost all habitats and encouragement of decision-makers to think more broadly in terms of multiple delivery is beginning to be seen in government policy and funding packages. There is considerable opportunity to increase this multiple delivery model by taking an ecosystem service perspective when looking at policies and fiscal incentives for land and sea management.

Valuation of ecosystem services is still at an early stage. Taking an ecosystem service view of land and sea offers the potential to identify and put a value on delivery of 'services' which are currently undervalued or even assigned no value at all in standard economic assessments. Valuation of ecosystem services could lead to a radically different approach to ecosystems and their use. The concept of 'public goods' and of supporting people to manage land to deliver these, in addition to or in some cases instead of traditional outputs of livestock, crops and fisheries, may become more acceptable. The value of ecosystem services must be included in the overall assessment of policies and practice.

18.11 Key Recommendations

Resilient, biodiverse ecosystems underpin economic and social prosperity by providing a wide range of valuable services. Mechanisms that fully reflect this value in economic and policy decisions are required. An ecosystems approach can demonstrate the synergies between services and lead to integrated management, to the benefit of habitats and citizens. Future challenges (weather, pests and diseases, changing consumer demands, changing political priorities, economic impacts, etc.) could place unanticipated demands on both natural and man-modified ecosystems. Resilience is key to dealing with these challenges.

- An ecosystems approach will conserve the biodiversity and countryside for people to enjoy, but also assist water management, flood control and carbon sequestration and storage, and provide the economic goods derived from these provisioning, regulating and cultural services. In particular, Northern Ireland has abundant peatlands, some unique in their biodiversity, which are valuable as carbon stores in a UK and an EU context.

- Marine and coastal ecosystems are highly diverse and productive, with areas such as Strangford Lough of international importance for biodiversity and important for tourism and recreation. Indeed, Strangford Lough could exemplify the need for a holistic ecosystems approach so that its unique habitats and species can be protected whilst providing living space, employment, recreation opportunities and tourism.

- The abundant freshwater ecosystems, many internationally important for wildfowl, migrant wetland birds and fish, also provide most of Northern Ireland's drinking water and are of value for recreation and tourism. However, many large lakes are eutrophic or hypertrophic as a result of human activity, and this has environmental impacts and imposes a direct financial cost for water treatment.

- Farming in Northern Ireland currently is centred around improved grassland to produce meat and dairy products for both local use and export. With appropriate management, farmland also has potential for contributing to greenhouse gas reduction targets through sequestering carbon and storing carbon in the soil, enhancing biodiversity, ameliorating flooding and addressing waste management and pollution issues.

Ecosystems and their services are complex and interdependent and must be managed in ways that reflect this. The Northern Ireland NEA should inform policy and decision-making to ensure long-term sustainable management of ecosystems and delivery of their services. This requires legislation, guidelines, planning policies, designations, restrictions, fiscal drivers, education and awareness. A fully integrated cross-departmental and inter-sectoral approach to managing ecosystems is needed. Aspects of all Government Departments and numerous agencies impinge on the delivery of ecosystem services, and all sectors both benefit from and impact upon ecosystems and their ability to deliver services. Although there has been a lack of integration of policies and their delivery in Northern Ireland, it is increasingly recognised that the principles of sustainable development are key to ensuring that ecosystem services are maintained and optimised in the long term, both on land and at sea.

Greater understanding is required of the value and benefits that accrue from ecosystem services and the degree to which people rely on the natural environment. There are currently limited data demonstrating and valuing ecosystem services in the UK, especially in a Northern Ireland context. Much greater understanding is required at public and political levels of what ecosystem services are, what benefits society and individuals gain from them, why natural habitats are crucial for providing the resilience necessary for meeting global and local challenges including climate change and food security, and how to manage ecosystems to deliver multiple services. Particularly important to promote are the physical and mental health benefits provided by ecosystems and their role in supporting human infrastructure. Education programmes are beginning to address these issues, but a full programme to inform and involve people during the progression of this agenda is required.

The role of ecosystem services in mitigating the effects of all human impacts, including climate change and biodiversity loss, should be considered in all decisions about the use of land and sea. Conserving ecosystem functionality can avoid or minimise the high costs associated with environmental degradation. Increasing ecosystem resilience will reduce costs by retaining restoration ability in changing circumstances, including unanticipated events. While direct impacts of climate change may be lower in Northern Ireland than in many other parts of the world, impacts of unanticipated events (including severe weather) and changing weather patterns are already apparent. The multiple roles of habitats (for example, of wetlands and peatlands in water management, of Woodlands and peatlands in carbon storage, of coasts and Marine habitats in flood control, of Enclosed Farmland and Semi-natural Grasslands in providing food, and the potential for all habitats to provide renewable energy) need to be fully recognised as underpinning the ability of people to live safely and sustainably. The ability of ecosystems to buffer changes and biodiversity to deliver ecosystem services need to be given full value in policy decisions affecting the environment.

The unique and internationally important biodiversity of Northern Ireland requires specific management and protection measures in an overall context of land and sea management. United Kingdom policies need to be integrated and coherent, but cognisant of and flexible in their response to the unique conditions in Northern Ireland. A network of ecologically coherent sites should form a core for integrated management within the wider environment, delivering ecosystem services and minimising negative environmental impacts, including adapting to climate change. Designation of high conservation value, multiple use sites, including completion of the ASSI network on which EU designations are based, is an important first step. Sites also require effective management to retain or regain favourable condition. Landowners and managers need to be rewarded to deliver 'public goods'. Given the various challenges to special sites (including invasive aliens, climate change, pollution, development), a protection policy is required which ensures that sites are linked and that potentially damaging activities are avoided in their vicinity (buffer zones with some restrictions on permitted activities within them). Invasive species are a major threat and need to be prevented from establishing whenever possible and controlled if they do become established, in order to avoid ecological damage and higher financial costs.

There is an overall trend of a decline in semi-natural ecosystems of high biodiversity with an increase in less biodiverse areas more heavily influenced by human activities. The last 50 years have seen changes in agricultural practices such as a shift from hay to silage production and a decrease in mixed and arable farming; a loss of peatlands, Semi-natural Grasslands and some wetland habitats due to a range of factors including conversion to intensive grassland; development; drainage; peat cutting; and planting of coniferous trees. Some of these trends have halted or even reversed in recent years in response to changing policies, funding and priorities (e.g. uplands previously often suffered from overgrazing, but undergrazing is now a threat to some semi-natural habitats). However, the continuation of these positive changes will require supportive policy and financial encouragement. Urbanisation of the countryside is continuing, both on natural/semi-natural habitat and on valuable agricultural land.

Carbon storage and sequestration are vital ecosystem services and are cost-effective ways to mitigate and adapt to climate change. Carbon management needs to be seen as an important part of management for multiple service delivery. Key aspects include soils, peatlands, permanent pasture and Woodlands. The full value of sequestration in existing habitats must be factored into carbon/greenhouse gas budgets and targets and given weight when making decisions on changing management regimes. There is a significant opportunity due to the scale of the resource in Northern Ireland, including potential financial benefits through carbon credits and targeting new markets for low carbon livestock production.

Planning and management policies need to be aligned with natural processes which maintain the capacity to deliver multiple services. Decisions on land and sea management need to be at a strategic level and sustainable in the long term, regarding trade-offs between outputs, opportunities for multiple service delivery and addressing competing demands. Implementing these strategic decisions locally requires a mixture of incentives and regulations for landowners which put an economic value on the 'public goods' delivered by functioning ecosystems.

An Ecosystem Assessment which incorporates the wider British Isles, the Republic of Ireland and the surrounding marine areas would be worthwhile. The island of Ireland should be considered as a whole for ecosystem management. Northern Ireland is unique since its legislation is decided by the Northern Ireland Assembly or UK Government, but it shares a land and sea border with another EU member state, the Republic of Ireland. The international border raises issues of differential management, protection, legislation and funding within single ecosystems. Work on River Basin Management and invasive alien species is proceeding on a cross-border basis and these are positive examples of how management of natural ecosystems benefit from international cooperation. Fiscal drivers can be particularly important in determining how people move, shop and spend their leisure time with regard to the border and the ecosystems which traverse it.

Issues of different data collection methods, metrics and scales make comparisons and long-term monitoring and reporting difficult. Limited data exist in Northern Ireland on local habitats and ecosystem services. Further research, especially around establishing financial values for service delivery, is required. However, there are also issues around what data exist, their accessibility and their comparability/compatibility with other data sets. There is a need for comparable and repeatable methods across the EU, establishing ecosystem indicators and minimum baseline standards to which Northern Ireland data contribute. A variety of methods increases the information available, but mechanisms to compare data sets are crucial.

References

Aalen, F.H.A. (1997) The making of the Irish landscape. Atlas of the Irish Rural Landscape (eds F.H.A. Aalen, K. Whelan & M. Stout), pp. 4–30. Cork University press, Ireland.

Aalen, F.H.A. & Whelan, K. (1997) Fields. Atlas of the Irish Rural Landscape (eds F.H.A. Aalen, K. Whelan & M. Stout), pp. 134-144. Cork University press, Ireland.

Action Renewables (2004) A Study into the Renewable Energy Resource in the Six Counties of Northern Ireland. Generic Resource Opportunities. Action Renewables, Belfast.

AEA (2010) Greenhouse Gas Inventories for England, Scotland, Wales and Northern Ireland: 1990-2008. Report to the Department for Energy and Climate Change, the Scottish Government, the Welsh Assembly Government and the Northern Ireland Department of the Environment. AEA, Oxfordshire. ISBN 978-0-9565155-1-3.

AFBI – see **Agri-Food & Biosciences Institute**

Agri-Food & Biosciences Institute(AFBI) (2007) Annual Report and Statement of Accounts 2006-07. [online] Available at: <http://www.afbini.gov.uk/afbi-annual-report06_07.pdf> [Accessed 07.03.11].

Agri-Food & Biosciences Institute & Northern Ireland Environment Agency(AFBI & NIEA) (2011) State of the Seas Report [online] Available at: <http://www.afbini.gov.uk/index/research/hp-work-area-fisheries-aquatics/stateoftheseas.htm> [Accessed 10.05.11].

Albanito, F., Brereton, A., Caffarra, A., Charlton, R., Donnelly, A., Fealy, R., Fitzgerald, J., Holden, N., Jones, M. & Murphy, C. (2008) Climate Change: Refining the Impacts for Ireland. Prepared for the Environmental Protection Agency. [online] Available at: <http://www.epa.ie/downloads/pubs/research/climate/sweeney-report-strive-12-for-web-low-res.pdf> [Accessed 07.03.11].

Alexander, D.J. (1963) A note on the conacre system in Northern Ireland. *Journal of Agricultural Economics*, **15**(3), 471-475.

Alexander, D.J. (1964) Farm land mobility and adjustments in farming in Northern Ireland**.** *Journal of the Statistical and Social Inquiry of Ireland*, **XXI**(III), 1-14.

Andelman, S.J. & Fagan, W.F. (2000) Umbrellas and flagships: Efficient conservation surrogates or expensive mistakes? *Proceedings of the National Academy of Sciences of the United States of America*, **97**, 5954-5959.

Anderson, L.M. & Cordell, H.K. (1988) Influence of Trees on Residential Property Values in Athens, Georgia (U.S.A.): A Survey Based on Actual Sales Prices. *Landscape and Urban Planning*, **15**(1-2), 153-164.

Annett, J.A., Joyce, J. & Scott, P. (2006) National Parks – Potential Impacts of National Park Designation in Northern Ireland. Countryside Consultancy, Kilkeel County Down, Northern Ireland.

Arkell, B., Darch, G. & McEntee, P. (2007) Preparing for a Changing Climate in Northern Ireland. SNIFFER UKCC13, Edinburgh.

Azeez, G. (2009) Soil Carbon and Organic Farming. Soil Association, Bristol.

Balsom, A. (2010) Address sulphur and improve nitrogen use efficiency. [online] Available at: <http://www.fwi.co.uk/Articles/2010/02/18/120004/Address-sulphur-and-improve-nitrogen-use-efficiency.htm> [Accessed 07.03.11].

Banbridge District Council (2007) Local Biodiversity Action Plan. [online] Available at: <http://www.banbridge.com/uploads/docs/BanbridgeDistrictBiodiversityActionPlan.pdf> [Accessed 10.05.11].

Barbier, E.B. (2007) Valuing Ecosystem Services as Productive Inputs. *Economic Policy*, **22**, 177-229.

Barne, J., Robson, C., Kaznowska, S., Davidson, N. & Doody, J. (1997) Coasts and Seas of the United Kingdom, Region 17: Northern Ireland. Joint Nature Conservation Committee, Peterborough.

BBC News (2010) Irish Hares Fall Foul of Eco Trap. [online] Available at: <http://www.bbc.co.uk/news/10432753> [Accessed 07.03.11].

Beamish, D. & Young, M. (2009) The Geophysics of Northern Ireland: the Tellus Effect. *First Break*, **27**, 43-49.

Beaugrand, G., Luczak, C. & Edwards, M. (2009) Rapid biogeographical plankton shifts in the North Atlantic Ocean. *Global Change Biology*, **15**, 1790-1803.

Belfast City Council (2005a) Belfast: City Region. Development Department.

Belfast City Council (2005b) Strategy for Open Spaces: Your City, Your Space.

Belfast City Council (2007) Local Biodiversity Action Plan for Belfast.

Belfast City Council (2008) Development Committee, Agenda Item 4, Presentation by Belfast Visitor and Convention Bureau of Draft Marketing and Visitor Servicing Plan 2009 to 2012.

Belfast City Council (2010) Park Events Small Grants Scheme. [online] Available at: <http://www.belfastcity.gov.uk/parksandopenspaces/grantscheme.asp> [Accessed 07.03.11].

Belfast Healthy Cities (2010) Healthy Places = Strong Foundations.

Belfast Telegraph (2006) Lignite mine controversy fuels passion. Conor Scullion. 2006.

Belfast Telegraph (2008) Why rejection of Antrim mine has hit us very hard in the pocket. Eric Waugh. Tuesday 9th September 2008.

Bell, G., Burke, T. & Turner, S. (2007) Foundations for the Future: The Review of Environmental Governance.

Bell, L. (2008) Our Nature with Aggregates: A Strategy to Conserve and Enhance Biodiversity and Geodiversity for the Aggregates and Quarry Products Industry in Northern Ireland. QPANI, Belfast.

Bell, S., Hamilton, V., Montarzino, A, Rothnie, H., Travlou, P. & Alves, S. (2008) Greenspace and quality of life: a critical literature review. Greenspace Scotland research report.

Benedict, M.A. & McMahon, E.T. (2002) Green Infrastructure: Smart conservation for the 21st Century. *Renewable Resources Journal*, **20**(3), 12-17.

Bennett, E.M. & Balvanera, P. (2007) The future of production systems in a globalised world. *Frontiers in Ecology and the Environment,* **5**(4),191-198.

Berrow, S. (2001) Biological diversity of cetaceans (whales, dolphins and porpoises) in Irish waters. Marine Biodiversity in Ireland and Adjacent Waters. Proceedings of the Estuarine and Coastal Sciences Association conference (ed J.D. Nunn), pp. 115-120. MAGNI Publications, Belfast.

Berrow, S.D. & Heardman, C. (1994) The basking shark *Cetorhinus maximus* (Gunnerus) in Irish waters – patterns of distribution and abundance. *Proceedings of the Royal Irish Academy – Biology and the Environment*, **94B**, 101-107.

Betts, N.L. (1982) Synoptic climatology of Northern Ireland. Northern Ireland: environment and natural resources (eds J.G. Cruickshank & D.N. Wilcox) pp. 9-42. Queen's University of Belfast and New University of Ulster.

Birnie, R., Curran, J., MacDonald, J.A., Mackey, E.C., Campbell, C.D., McGowan, G., Palmer, S.C.F., Paterson, E., Shaw, P. & Shewry, M.C. (2002) The land resources of Scotland: trends and prospects for the environment and natural heritage. The State of Scotland's Environment and Natural Heritage (eds M.B. Usher, E.C. Mackey & J.C. Curran). HMSO, Edinburgh.

Blight, J.A., Allcock, A.L., Maggs, C.A., Johnson, M.P. (2009) Intertidal molluscan and algal species richness around the UK coast. *Marine Ecology Progress Series*, **396**, 235-243.

Boag, B. & Yeates, G.W. (2001) The potential impact of the New Zealand flatworm, a predator of earthworms, in Western Europe. *Ecological Applications*, **11**, 1276-1286.

Bradbury, R.B., Kyrkos, A., Morris, A.J., Clark, S.C., Perkins, A.J. & Wilson, J.D. (2000) Habitat associations and breeding success of yellowhammers on lowland farmland. *Journal of Applied Ecology*, **37**(5), 789-805.

Bradley, R.I., Milne, R., Bell, J., Lilly, A., Jordan, C. & Higgins, A. (2005) A soil carbon and land use database for the United Kingdon. *Soil Use and Management*, **21**(4), 363-369.

Brauman, K.A., Daily, G.C., Duarte, T.K. & Mooney, H.A. (2007) The Nature and Value of Ecosystem Services: An overview highlighting hydrologic services. *Annual Review of Environment and Resources*, **32**, 67-98.

BRC – see **British Red Cross**

Brennan, C. (2005) Wetland vegetation dynamics and management in the Irish agricultural landscape of the Lough Erne region of Co. Fermanagh. University of Ulster. PhD thesis.

British Red Cross (BRC) (2010) Living in Fear of the Rain: The Impact of Recent Flooding in Greater Belfast. [online] Available at: <http://www.redcross.org.uk/About-us/News/2010/May/New-study-shows-way-ahead-for-Belfast-flooding-victims> [Accessed 07.03.11].

British Trust for Ornithology (BTO) (2010) Breeding Bird Survey: Population changes for species in Northern Ireland. [online] Available at: <http://www.bto.org/volunteer-surveys/bbs/latest-results/population-trends/northern-ireland-trends [Accessed 10/05/11].

Broadmeadow, M.S.J. & Freer-Smith, P.H. (1996) Urban Woodland and the Benefits for Local Air Quality. Research for Amenity Trees No. 5. HMSO, London.

Brown, R. (1990) Strangford Lough: The Wildlife of an Irish Sea Lough. The Institute of Irish Studies, Queen's University Belfast, Belfast. ISBN 0 85389 356 X.

BTO – see **British Trust for Ornithology**

Burgess, J., Harrison, C. M. & Limb, M. (1988) People, Parks and the Urban Green: A Study of Popular Meanings and Values for Open Spaces in the City. *Urban Studies* **25**, 455-473.

CAAN – see **Countryside Access and Activities Network**

Countryside Access and Activities Network (CAAN) (2007) Mourne Area of Outstanding Natural Beauty Access Study. Study commissioned by Environment & Heritage Service.

Countryside Access & Activities Network (CAAN) (2008) Barriers to Participation: A review of why specific communities in Northern Ireland do not use the countryside for recreation. Study commissioned by Environment & Heritage Service.

Countryside Access & Activities Network (CAAN) (2009) Trends in Outdoor Recreation: 1995-2008. Commissioned by Sport NI and the Northern Ireland Tourist Board.

CABE Space (2005) *Does Money Grow on Trees?* Commission for Architecture and the Built Environment.

Calbrade, N., Holt, C., Austin, G., Mellan, H., Hearn, R., Stroud, D., Wotton, S. & Musgrove, A. (2010) Waterbirds in the UK 2008/9: The Wetland Bird Survey (WeBS). BTO/RSPB/JNCC in association with WWT, Thetford.

Cameron, E.A. (2005) Communication or Separation? Reactions to Irish Land Agitation and Legislation in the Highlands of Scotland, c. 1870-1910. *English Historical Review*, **120**(487), 633-666.

Campbell, D., Hutchinson, W.G., Scarpa, R., O'Leary, T., McCormack, A. & Riordan, B. (2006) *Quantifying the landscape benefits arising from the Rural Environment Protection Scheme: results from a public survey.* The Rural Economy Research Centre, Working Paper Series 06-WP-RE-08.

Carroll, S. (1994) Brackish water lagoons in Northern Ireland: a floral analysis. Unpublished MSc thesis. Queen's University Belfast.

Carter, R.W.G. (1991) Shifting Sands: a study of the coast from Magilligan to Larne. Countryside and Wildlife Research Series No2, HMSO, Belfast.

Castree, N. (2005) Nature: The Adventures of a Concept. Routledge, London.

CEDaR – see **Centre for Environmental Data and Recording**

Centre for Environmental Data and Recording (CEDaR) (2010a) Marine database (Ulster Museum). National Museums Northern Ireland.

Centre for Environmental Data and Recording (CEDaR) (2010b) Marine Recorder database. National Museums Northern Ireland.

Centre for Environmental Data and Recording (CEDaR) (2010c) Recorder database. National Museums Northern Ireland.

Coates, S. & Hadden, E. (2010) For the Achievement of Valued Places for People Through Design. University of Ulster, Coleraine.

Coleraine Borough Council (2008) Local Biodiversity Action Plan. [Online] Available at: <http://www.colerainebc.gov.uk/docs/environment/Biodiversity-ActionPlan.pdf> [Accessed 07.03.11].

Coll, J., Maguire, C. & Sweeney, J. (2008) Biodiversity and Climate Change in Ireland. Irish Climate Analysis and Research Units & Envirocentre.

Comhar SDC (Sustainable Development Commission) (2010a) *Biodiversity and Ecosystem Indicators Issues Paper.* Comhar Sustainable Development Council.

Comhar SDC (Sustainable Development Commission) (2010b) *Creating Green Infrastructure for Ireland: Enhancing Natural Capital for Human Wellbeing.* Comhar Sustainable Development Council.

Commission of the European Communities (2008) Commission Staff Working Document on the Report of the

Northern Ireland Task Force. Commission of the European Communities, Brussels.

Committee for the Environment (2009) Inquiry in Climate Change, Volume Three. NI Assembly. Hansard.

Conservation International (2007) Hotspots in Context. [online] Available at: <http://www.biodiversityhotspots.org/xp/Hotspots/hotspotsScience/pages/hotspots_in_context.aspx> [Accessed 07.03.11].

Cooper, A. & McCann, T. (1994) The Botanical Composition of Grassland Land Cover Types in Northern Ireland: Contract Report to Environment Service, DOE (NI).

Cooper, A. & McCann, T. (1995) Machine peat cutting and land use change on blanket bog in Northern Ireland. *Journal of Environmental Management*, **43**, 153-170.

Cooper, A. & McCann, T. (2010) Northern Ireland Countryside Survey and National Ecosystem Assessment. Draft report to the Northern Ireland Environment Agency. In press.

Cooper, A., McCann, T. & Smith, D. (1993) Land cover monitoring in the Mourne Environmentally Sensitive Area. University of Ulster, Coleraine.

Cooper, A., McCann, T. & Hamill, B. (2001) Vegetation regeneration on blanket mire after mechanised cutting. *Global Ecology and Biogeography*, **10**, 275-289.

Cooper, A., McCann, T. & Meharg, M. (2002) Habitat change in the Northern Ireland countryside: summary report of the Northern Ireland Countryside Survey 2000. Environment and Heritage Service. Belfast.

Cooper, A., McCann, T. & Rogers, D. (2009) Northern Ireland Countryside Survey 2007: Broad Habitat Change 1998-2007. Northern Ireland Environment Agency. Research and Development Series No. 09/06.

Cooper, A. & Murray, R. (1987) A landscape ecological study of the Antrim Coast and Glens and Causeway Coast Areas of Outstanding Natural Beauty. University of Ulster, Coleraine.

Cooper, K., Barriofrojan, C., Defew, E., Curtis, M., Fleddum, A., Brooks, L. & Paterson, D. (2008) Assessment of ecosystem function following marine aggregate dredging. *Journal of Experimental Marine Biology and Ecology*, **366**, 82-91.

Corbett, P. (2007) A review of woodland ASSIs in Northern Ireland. A report for the Northern Ireland Environment Agency.

Cracknell, R. (2009) Sea fisheries statistics. House of Commons Library. Standard Note: SN/SG/2788.

Crouch, D. & Lubbren, N. (2003) Visual culture and tourism. Berg, London.

Cruickshank, J.G. (1997) Soil and Environment: Northern Ireland. Agricultural and Environmental Science Division, DANI and The Agricultural and Environmental Science Department, Queen's University Belfast. ISBN 0 85389 699 2.

Cruickshank, M.M. & Tomlinson, R.W. (1988) Northern Ireland Peatland Survey. Department of the Environment for Northern Ireland (Countryside and Wildlife Branch). Belfast.

Cruickshank, M.M. & Tomlinson, R.W. (1990) Peatland in Northern Ireland: Inventory and Prospect. *Irish Geography*, **23**, 17-30.

Cruikshank, M.M. & Tomlinson, R.W. (1995) Peat Extraction, Conservation and the Rural Economy in Northern Ireland. *Applied Geography*, **15**(4), 365-383.

Cruickshank, M.M., Tomlinson, R.W. & Trew, S. (2000) Application of CORINE land-cover mapping to estimate carbon stored in the vegetation of Ireland. *Journal of Environmental Management*, **58**, 269-287.

Cruickshank, M.M., Tomlinson R.W., Devine, P.M., & Milne, R. (1996) Carbon pools and fluxes in Northern Ireland. *Carbon sequestration in vegetation and soils*, **4**, 1-36.

Cruickshank, M.M., Tomlinson, R.W., Devine, P.M. & Milne, R. (1998) Carbon in the vegetation and soils of Northern Ireland. *Biology and Environment: Proceedings of the Royal Irish Academy*, **98B**, 9-21.

Cruickshank, M.M., Tomlinson, R.W., Dunwoody, C., Bond, D. & Devine, P.M. (1993) A peatland database for Northern Ireland: methodology and potential resource. *Biology and Environment: Proceedings of the Royal Irish Academy*, **93B**, 13-24.

Culture Northern Ireland (2010) Maps and Mayhem. Lee Henry. [online] Available at: <http://www.culturenorthernireland.org/article.aspx?art_id=1962> [Accessed 03.10.10].

Curry, N. (2009) Leisure in the landscape: rural incomes and public benefits. Drivers of environmental change in the uplands (eds A. Bonn, K. Hubacek, T.E. Allott & J. Stuart). Routledge, London.

Curry, R., Simmons, C. & McDaid, C. (2004) Northern Limits: a resource flow analysis and ecological footprint for Northern Ireland. [Online] Available at: <http://www.northern-limits.com/reports/footprint_report_final.pdf> [Accessed 07.03.11].

DAISIE European Invasive Alien Species Gateway (2009) European Summary: Aliens by Country. [Online] Available at: <http://www.europe-aliens.org/europeanSummary.do#> [Accessed 07.03.11].

Davies, A.M., Hall, P., Howarth, M.J. & Knight, P. (2002) Modelling and measuring the wind forced inflow to the Irish Sea through the North Channel. *Continental Shelf Research*, **22**, 749-777.

Davis, J. & O'Neill C.E. (1992) Discrete Choice Valuation of Recreational Angling in Northern Ireland. *Journal of Agricultural Economics*, **43**(1), 452-458.

Dawson, M. (2007) Short rotation coppice willow best practice guidelines.

DARD – see **Department of Agriculture & Rural Development**

DCAL – see **Department of Culture, Arts & Leisure**

DEFRA – see **Department for Environment, Food & Rural Affairs**

DEHLG – see **Department of the Environment, Heritage & Local Government**

Department for Environment, Food & Rural Affairs (Defra) (2004) Animal Health and Welfare Strategy for Great Britain. Defra Publications. [online] Available at <http://archive.defra.gov.uk/foodfarm/policy/animalhealth/strategy/ahws.pdf> [Accessed 11.05.11].

Department for Environment, Food & Rural Affairs (Defra) (2006) Climate Change: the UK programme 2006. Defra, CM6764.

Department for Environment, Food & Rural Affairs (Defra) (2007a) An introductory guide to valuing ecosystem services.

Department for Environment, Food & Rural Affairs (Defra) (2007b) Conserving Biodiversity: the UK Approach.

Department for Environment, Food & Rural Affairs (Defra) (2007c) Securing a Healthy Natural Environment: An action plan for embedding an ecosystems approach. [online] Available at <http://archive.defra.gov.uk/environment/policy/natural-environ/documents/eco-actionplan.pdf> [Accessed 11.05.11].

Department for Regional Development (DRD) (2002a) Shaping Our Future: Regional Transportation Strategy for Northern Ireland 2002-2012. [online] Available at: <http://www.drdni.gov.uk/index/transport_planning/tp-rts_2002.htm> [Accessed 11.05.11].

Department for Regional Development (DRD) (2002b) Water Resource Strategy for Northern Ireland 2002-2030.

Department for Regional Development (DRD) (2008a) Shaping Our Future: Adjustments to the Regional Development Strategy (RDS) – 2025. [online] Available at: <http://www.drdni.gov.uk/index/regional_planning/rp-focused_assessment.htm> [Accessed 11.05.11].

Department for Regional Development (DRD) (2008b) Shaping Our Future: Regional Development Strategy for Northern Ireland. [online] Available at: <http://www.drdni.gov.uk/sof.pdf> [Accessed 11.05.11].

Department for Regional Development (DRD) (2009a) SEA of the Regional Development Strategy for Northern Ireland: Scoping Report. [online] Available at: <http://www.drdni.gov.uk/23260rr011i2.pdf> [Accessed 11.05.11].

Department for Regional Development (DRD) (2009b) Shaping Our Future Together. Monitoring Report April 2007 - March 2008: Regional Development Strategy for Northern Ireland 2025. [online] Available at: <http://www.drdni.gov.uk/annual_monitoring_report_2007-2008_final_~_review_of_performance_indicators_for_the_regional_development_strategy.pdf> [Accessed 11.05.11].

Department for Regional Development (DRD) (2011) Draft Revised Regional Development Strategy: Shaping Our Future. Consultation. 10 Year Review. [Online] Available at: <http://www.drdni.gov.uk/shapingourfuture/> [Accessed 11.05.11].

Department for Social Development (DSD) (2006) Northern Ireland Housing Statistics 2005-06. [online] Available at: <http://www.dsdni.gov.uk/index/publications/housing_stats.htm> [Accessed 07.03.11].

Department for Social Development (DSD) (2007) Northern Ireland Housing Statistics 2006-07. [online] Available at: <http://www.dsdni.gov.uk/index/publications/housing_stats.htm> [Accessed 07.03.11].

Department for Social Development (DSD) (2008) Northern Ireland Housing Statistics 2007-08. [online] Available at: <http://www.dsdni.gov.uk/index/publications/housing_stats.htm> [Accessed 07.03.11].

Department for Social Development (DSD) (2009) Northern Ireland Housing Statistics 2008-09. [online] Available at: <http://www.dsdni.gov.uk/index/publications/housing_stats.htm> [Accessed 07.03.11].

Department for Social Development (DSD) (2010) Northern Ireland Housing Statistics 2009-10. [online] Available at: <http://www.dsdni.gov.uk/index/publications/housing_stats.htm> [Accessed 07.03.11].

Department of Agriculture & Rural Development (DARD) (2002) Farmers and Farm Families in Northern Ireland.

Department of Agriculture & Rural Development (**DARD**) (2005) Northern Ireland Agri-food Key Statistics for 2005. [online] Available at: <http://www.dardni.gov.uk/index/

dard-statistics/statistical-reports/agricultural-statistics-ni-agri-food-sector-key-statistics.htm> [Accessed 07.03.11].

Department of Agriculture and Rural Development (DARD) (2006) Environmentally Sensitive Areas Scheme: Countryside Management Scheme – Agri-environment Scheme Explanatory Booklet.

Department of Agriculture and Rural Development (DARD) (2007a) Northern Ireland Rural Development Programme 2007-13.

Department of Agriculture and Rural Development (DARD) (2007b) Short Rotation Coppice Scheme.

Department of Agriculture & Rural Development (DARD) (2008a) Agri-environment Schemes 1988-2008: Making a difference. [online] Available at: <http://www.dardni.gov.uk/ruralni/sucesses_master_v1_cmb.pdf> [Accessed 10.05.11].

Department of Agriculture & Rural Development (DARD) (2008b) Northern Ireland Countryside Management Scheme 2007-2013: Information Booklet.

Department of Agriculture & Rural Development (DARD) (2008c) Organic Farming Scheme 2007-2013: Information Booklet.

Department of Agriculture & Rural Development (DARD) (2008d) The EU Farm Structure Survey 2007. [online] Available at: <http://www.dardni.gov.uk/euss2007.08.213_european_union_structure_survey_publication_2007.pdf.pdf> [Accessed 10.05.11].

Department of Agriculture & Rural Development (DARD) (2009a) Agricultural Land Prices for Northern Ireland. [online] Available at: <http://www.dardni.gov.uk/index/publications/pubs-dard-statistics/pubs-dard-agricultural-statistics-agri-land-prices.htm> [Accessed 07.03.11].

Department of Agriculture & Rural Development (DARD) (2009b) Less Favoured Areas Compensatory Allowances Scheme (Accessed 06/12/10). [online] Available at: <http://www.dardni.gov.uk/index/rural-development/rdp-campaign/rdp-campaign-development-funding-schemes-and-programmes/rdp-campaign-development-environment/rdp-development-less-favoured-areas-scheme.htm> [Accessed 07.03.11].

Department of Agriculture & Rural Development (DARD) (2009c) Management of Sensitive Sites (MOSS) - A New Approach. [online] Available at: <http://www.ni-environment.gov.uk/other-index/news.htm?act=d&id=25516> [Accessed 07.03.11].

Department of Agriculture & Rural Development (DARD) (2009d) Northern Ireland Agri-food Sector: Key Statistics.

Department of Agriculture and Rural Development (DARD) (2009e) Review of Support Arrangements for Less Favoured Areas in Northern Ireland.

Department of Agriculture & Rural Development (DARD) (2009f) The Agricultural Census in Northern Ireland: Results for June 2009.

Department of Agriculture & Rural Development (DARD) (2010a) Aggregate Agricultural Account 1981-2009. [online] Available at: <http://www.dardni.gov.uk/index/publications/pubs-dard-statistics/pubs-dard-statistics-agricultural-aggregate-account.htm> [Accessed 07.03.11].

Department of Agriculture & Rural Development (DARD) (2010b) Aquaculture Background Information. [online]

Available at: <www.dardni.gov.uk/index/fisheries-farming-and-food/fisheries/aquaculture/aqua-info.htm> [Accessed 07.03.11].

Department of Agriculture & Rural Development (DARD) (2010c) Crops and Grass Areas since 1981-2009. [online] Available at: <http://www.dardni.gov.uk/index/publications/pubs-dard-statistics/pubs-dard-statistics-cropareas.htm> [Accessed 07.03.11].

Department of Agriculture & Rural Development (DARD) (2010d) Enterprises: Numbers and Average Size, Northern Ireland 1981-2009. [online] Available at: <http://www.dardni.gov.uk/enterprise_size_2009.pdf> [Accessed 07.03.11].

Department of Agriculture & Rural Development (DARD) (2010e) Farm Incomes in Northern Ireland 2008/09. [online] Available at: <http://www.dardni.gov.uk/farm_incomes_in_northern_ireland_2008-2009.pdf> [Accessed 12.05.11].

Department of Agriculture & Rural Development (DARD) (2010f) Farm Labour Statistics in Northern Ireland 1981-2009. [online] Available at: <http://www.dardni.gov.uk/index/publications/pubs-dard-statistics/pubs-dard-statistics-labour-figures.htm> [Accessed 07.03.11].

Department of Agriculture & Rural Development (DARD) (2010g) Farm Number Northern Ireland, 1981-2009. [online] Available at: <http://www.dardni.gov.uk/farms_2009.pdf> [Accessed 07.03.11].

Department of Agriculture & Rural Development (DARD) (2010h) Fertiliser Statistics 1998-2010. [online] Available at: <http://www.dardni.gov.uk/index/dard-statistics/agricultural-statistics/agricultural-statistics-ferts.htm> [Accessed 07.03.11].

Department of Agriculture & Rural Development (DARD) (2010i) Northern Ireland Crop Production 1981-2009. [online] Available at: <www.dardni.gov.uk/crop-prod-table.25.xls> [Accessed 07.03.11].

Department of Agriculture & Rural Development (DARD) (2010j) Output of Apples and Mushrooms, 1981-2009. [online] Available at: <http://www.dardni.gov.uk/index/publications/pubs-dard-statistics/pubs-dard-statistics-apples.htm> [Accessed 07.03.11].

Department of Agriculture & Rural Development (DARD) (2010k) Quantities of the Main Products in Output 1981-2009. [online] Available at: <http://www.dardni.gov.uk/index/publications/pubs-dard-statistics/pubs-dard-statistics-outputs-quantities.htm> [Accessed 07.03.11].

Department of Agriculture & Rural Development (DARD) (2010l) Rivers Agency explores the Lough Erne system. DARD Press release: 18th March 2010. [online] Available at: <www.riversagencyni.gov.uk/rivers_agency_news_lough_erne.pdf> [Accessed 07.03.11].

Department of Agriculture & Rural Development (DARD) (2010m) Sheep Numbers in Northern Ireland, 1981-2009. [online] Available at: <www.dardni.gov.uk/sheep_2009.pdf> [Accessed 07.03.11].

Department of Agriculture & Rural Development (DARD) (2010n) Size and Performance of Food and Drinks Processing Sector: Subsector Statistics 2008 with Provisional Estimates for 2009.

Department of Agriculture & Rural Development (DARD) (2010o) Statistical Review of Northern Ireland Agriculture 2009. [online] Available at: <http://www.dardni.gov.uk/statistical_review_of_northern_ireland_agriculture_-_2009.pdf> [Accessed 12.05.11].

Department of Agriculture & Rural Development (DARD) (2010p) Strategy for the Sustainability of the Honey Bee. Consultation Document.

Department of Agriculture & Rural Development (DARD) (2010q) Summary Income Indicators, 1981-2009. [online] Available at: <http://www.dardni.gov.uk/pubs-dard-statistics-income-indicators> [Accessed 07.03.11].

Department of Culture, Arts & Leisure (DCAL) (2007) Eel Conservation. [online] Available at: <http://www.dcalni.gov.uk/index/inland_waterways-fisheries-r08/angling-conservation-and-protection/eel_conservation.htm> [Accessed 07.03.11].

Department of Culture, Arts & Leisure (DCAL), The Loughs Agency of the Foyle, Carlingford and Irish Lights Commission & the Northern Ireland Tourist Board (2007) The Social and Economic Impact to Northern Ireland, and areas within the Loughs Agency, of Recreational Fisheries, Angling and Angling Resources. Report prepared by Price Waterhouse Coopers, July 2007.

Department of Culture, Arts & Leisure (DCAL) (2008) Salmon and Inland Fisheries: Annual Report 2007.

Department of Culture, Arts & Leisure (DCAL) (2009a) Eel Management Plan: Neagh/Bann River Basin District. The scientific basis for the viability of current management of eel in the Lough Neagh and Lower Bann River Basin.

Department of Culture, Arts & Leisure (DCAL) (2009b) NASCO – Focus Area Report on Protection, Restoration and Enhancement of Salmon Habitat. [online] Available at: <http://www.nasco.int/pdf/far_habitat/HabitatFAR_NIreland.pdf> [Accessed 07.03.11].

Department of the Environment (DOE) (2001)PPS 7: Quality Residential Environments [online] Available at: <http://www.planningni.gov.uk/index/policy/policy_publications/planning_statements/pps07.htm> [Accessed 05.05.11].

Department of the Environment (DOE) (2004) PPS 8: Open Space, Sport and Outdoor Recreation. [online] Available at: <http://www.planningni.gov.uk/index/policy/policy_publications/planning_statements/pps08.htm> [Accessed 05.05.11].

Department of the Environment (DOE) (2006) An Integrated Coastal Zone Management Strategy for Northern Ireland 2006-2026. DOENI.

Department of Environment (DOE) (2006b) PPS 15: Planning and Flood Risk. [online] Available at: <http://www.planningni.gov.uk/index/policy/policy_publications/planning_statements/pps15.htm> [Accessed 07.03.11].

Department of the Environment (DOE) (2008) PPS 7 (Addendum): Residential Extensions and Alterations [online] Available at: <http://www.planningni.gov.uk/index/policy/policy_publications/planning_statements/pps07_addendum.htm> [Accessed 05.05.11].

Department of the Environment (DOE) (2009a) Review of 2007-2010 Action Programme for the Nitrates Directive Northern Ireland: Recommendations from the Scientific Working Group 21 December 2009. [online] Available at: <http://www.doeni.gov.uk/nap_review_final.pdf> [Accessed 07.03.11].

Department of the Environment (DOE) (2009b) PPS18: Renewable Energy. [online] Available at: <http://www.

planningni.gov.uk/index/policy/policy_publications/planning_statements/planning_policy_statement_18__renewable_energy.pdf> [Accessed 07.03.11].

Department of the Environment (DOE) (2010a) A Northern Ireland Marine Bill – Policy Proposals. Consultation Document. Planning and Natural Resources Division.

Department of the Environment (DOE) (2010b) A Strategy for Surveillance and Monitoring for European Protected Habitats and Species in Northern Ireland. Implementing Regulations 3 and 6 of the Conservation (Natural Habitats, etc.) (Amendment) Regulations (Northern Ireland) 2009 for the protection of habitats and species of community interest in Northern Ireland.

Department of the Environment (DOE) (2010c) Northern Ireland Greenhouse Gas Inventory, 1990-2008. Department of the Environment, Belfast.

Department of the Environment (DOE) (2010d) PPS15 Planning and Flood Risk: FLD1 Definition of a Floodplain. [online] Available at: <http://www.planningni.gov.uk/index/policy/policy_publications/planning_statements/pps15/pps15_planning_policies/pps15_policy_fld1/pps15_definition_flood_plain.htm> [Accessed 07.03.11].

Department of the Environment (DOE) (2010e) PPS21 Sustainable Development in the Countryside. [online] Available at: http://www.planningni.gov.uk/index/policy/policy_publications/planning_statements/common-policypps21.htm_ [Accessed 12.05.11].

Department of the Environment (DOE) (2010f) Average NO_3 in Surfacewaters 2005-08 and Groundwaters 2005-08 maps. From a Powerpoint Presentation made by a delegation from Northern Ireland to the European Commission Nitrates Committee on 15 January 2010.

Department of the Environment & Northern Ireland Statistics and Research Agency (DOE & NISRA) (2009) Northern Ireland Environmental Statistics Report. [online] Available at: <http://www.doeni.gov.uk/niea/northern_ireland_enviornmental_statistics_report_-_january_2009.pdf> [Accessed 12.05.11].

Department of the Environment & Northern Ireland Statistics and Research Agency (DOE & NISRA) (2010) Northern Ireland Environmental Statistics Report. [online] Available at: <http://www.doeni.gov.uk/northern_ireland_environmental_statistics_report_2010-2.pdf> [Accessed 12.05.11].

Department of the Environment, Heritage & Local Government (DEHLG) (2008) The Economic and Social Aspects of Biodiversity: Benefits and Costs of Biodiversity in Ireland. [online] Available at: <http://www.environ.ie/en/Heritage/PublicationsDocuments/FileDownLoad,17321,en.pdf> [Accessed 12.05.11].

Department of Environment, Heritage & Local Government (DEHLG) (2010) Water Matters: Our Plan! Shannon River Basin Management Plan (2009-2015). [online] Available at: <http://www.shannonrbd.com/Final%20RBMP/Final_ShIRBD_RBMP_18Mar2010.pdf> [Accessed 12.05.11].

Department of Enterprise, Trade & Investment (DETI) (2001) Renewable Energy in Northern Ireland: Realising the Potential. Consultation document.

Department of Enterprise, Trade & Investment (DETI) (2002) Annual Mineral Statement 2001.[online]

Available at: <http://www.qpani.org/documents/AnnualMineralsStatement2001.pdf> [Accessed 12.05.11].

Department of Enterprise, Trade & Investment (DETI) (2003) Annual Mineral Statement 2002.[online] Available at: <http://www.qpani.org/documents/AnnualMineralsStatement2002.pdf> [Accessed 12.05.11].

Department of Enterprise, Trade & Investment (DETI) (2004) Annual Mineral Statement 2003.[online] Available at: <http://www.qpani.org/documents/AnnualMineralsStatement2003.pdf> [Accessed 12.05.11].

Department of Enterprise, Trade & Investment (DETI) (2005) Annual Mineral Statement 2004.[online] Available at: <http://www.qpani.org/documents/AnnualMineralsStatement2004.pdf> [Accessed 12.05.11].

Department of Enterprise, Trade & Investment (DETI) (2006) Annual Mineral Statement 2005.[online] Available at: <http://www.qpani.org/documents/AnnualMineralsStatement2005.pdf> [Accessed 12.05.11].

Department of Enterprise, Trade & Investment (DETI) (2007) Annual Mineral Statement 2006.[online] Available at: <http://www.qpani.org/documents/AnnualMineralsStatement2006.pdf> [Accessed 12.05.11].

Department of Enterprise, Trade & Investment (DETI) (2008a) Annual Mineral Statement 2007.[online] Available at: <http://www.detini.gov.uk/annual_mineral_report_2007.pdf> [Accessed 12.05.11].

Department of Enterprise, Trade & Investment (DETI) (2008b) Executive Summary of a Report on the Assessment of the Potential of Bioenergy Development in Northern Ireland. AEA.

Department of Enterprise, Trade & Investment (DETI) (2009a) Annual Mineral Statement 2008.[online] Available at: <http://www.detini.gov.uk/annual_mineral_report_2008.pdf> [Accessed 12.05.11].

Department of Enterprise, Trade & Investment (DETI) (2009b) Strategic Environmental Assessment (SEA) of Offshore Wind and Marine Renewable Energy in Northern Ireland.

Department of Enterprise, Trade & Investment (DETI) (2010a) A Draft Tourism Strategy for Northern Ireland to 2020. Consultation for the draft Tourism Strategy for Northern Ireland 2020.

Department of Enterprise, Trade & Investment (DETI) (2010b) Annual Mineral Statement 2009.

Department of Enterprise, Trade & Investment (DETI) (2010c) Energy: A Consultation on an Offshore Renewable Energy Strategic Action Plan 2009-2020.

Department of Enterprise, Trade & Investment (DETI) (2010d) Energy: A Strategic Energy Framework for Northern Ireland.

Derry City Council (2008) Wildlife in Action: Derry/Londonderry's Biodiversity Action Plan.

DETI – see **Department of Enterprise, Trade & Investment**

Diamond, J. (2005) Collapse: How Societies Choose to Fail or Survive. Penguin Books, London.

Dinter, W.P. (2001) Biogeography of the OSPAR Maritime area. A synopsis and synthesis of biogeographical distribution patterns described for the North-East Atlantic. Bundesamt für Naturschutz (BfN). 167 pp.

DOE – see **Department of Environment**

Doney, S.C. (2010) The Growing Human Footprint on

Coastal and Open-Ocean Biogeochemistry. *Science*, **328**, 1512-1516.

Donnan, H.E. (1994) An investigation into the fauna of brackish water ponds and saline lagoons in Northern Ireland. Unpublished MSc thesis. Queen's University Belfast.

DRD – see **Department for Regional Development**

DSD – see **Department for Social Development**

Early, J., McDowell, S., Caffrey, J., O'Callaghan, D., Meenan, K., Toomath, C., Fitzsimons, B. & Kelly, J. (2009) Field Guide to Invasive Species in Ireland. 2nd edition. NIEA.

Easson, L. (2009) Developing biomass sources in Northern Ireland and their use for renewable energy. NI Energy & Environment Conference 2009. Agri-Food & Biosciences Institute & Invest NI.

EC 1100/2007 (2007) Council Regulation (EC) Establishing Measures for the Recovery of the Stock of European Eel. Official Journal of the European Union.

Edwards, C.J.W. (1987) The changing role of sheep production in Northern Ireland agriculture. *Irish Geography*, **20**, 98-100.

EEA – see **European Environment Agency**

Eftec – see **Economics for the Environment Consultancy**

EHS – see **Environment & Heritage Service**

EPA – see **Environmental Protection Agency**

European Environment Agency (EEA) (2010a) 10 messages for 2010: Climate change and biodiversity.[online] Available at: <http://www.eea.europa.eu/publications/10-messages-for-2010-climate-change> [Accessed 12.05.11].

European Environment Agency (EEA) (2010b) Number of the listed 'worst' terrestrial and freshwater invasive alien species threatening biodiversity in Europe. [online] Available at: <http://www.eea.europa.eu/data-and-maps/figures/number-of-the-listed-worst-terrestrial-and-freshwater-invasive-alien-species-threatening-biodiversity-in-europe> [Accessed 07.03.11].

Economics for the Environment Consultancy (eftec) (2005) The Economic, Social and Ecological Value of Ecosystem Services: A literature review. On behalf of Defra.

Entec (2004) Valuing Water Use in Scotland and Northern Ireland for WFD Implementation Purposes. Scotland and Northern Ireland Forum for Environmental Research.

Environmental Protection Agency (EPA) (2008) Ireland's Environment 2008. Environmental Protection Agency, County Wexford, Ireland.

Environment & Heritage Service (EHS) (2000) Managing the Water Environment of Northern Ireland 2000, pp.1. EHS Water Management Unit, Belfast.

Environment & Heritage Service (EHS) (2001) Policy and Practice for the Protection of Groundwater in Northern Ireland.

Environment & Heritage Service (EHS),Department of Agriculture & Rural Development, Ards Borough Council & Down District Council (2001) Strangford Lough SAC/SPA Management Scheme. [online] Available at: <www.ukmpas.org.uk/pdf/Sitebasedreports%5CStrangfordMgmtScheme.pdf> [Accessed 07.03.11].

Environment & Heritage Service (EHS) (2003a) A Forward Programme for the Declaration of Areas of Special Scientific Interest in Northern Ireland.

Environment & Heritage Service (EHS) (2003b) Biodegradable Waste Strategy for Northern Ireland Draft.

[online] Available at: <http://www.ni-environment.gov.uk/draftbiodegradablewastestrategy.pdf> [Accessed 07.03.11].

Environment & Heritage Service (EHS) (2003c) Northern Ireland Habitat Action Plan: Blanket Bog.

Environment & Heritage Service (EHS) (2003d) Northern Ireland Habitat Action Plan: Lowland Heathland.

Environment & Heritage Service (EHS) (2003e) Northern Ireland Habitat Action Plan: Lowland Raised Bog.

Environment & Heritage Service (EHS) (2003f) Northern Ireland Habitat Action Plan: Saline Lagoons.

Environment & Heritage Service (EHS) (2003g) Northern Ireland Habitat Action Plan: Upland Heathland.

Environment & Heritage Service (EHS) (2004a) Peatlands Formation. [online] Available at: <http://www.peatlandsni.gov.uk/formation/nipeatlnds.htm> [Accessed 07.03.11].

Environment & Heritage Service (EHS) (2004b) Peatlands: Pollution.[online]Available at: <http://www.peatlandsni.gov.uk/issues/pollution.htm> [Accessed 07.03.11].

Environment & Heritage Service (EHS) (2004c) The Management of Country Parks: A Statement of Policy.

Environment & Heritage Service (EHS) (2005a) A Survey of the Scarce Crimson and Gold (*Pyrausta sanguinalis*) in Northern Ireland. [online] Available at: <http://www.doeni.gov.uk/niea/print/biodiversity/nh-research/area_of_research/habitat_and_species_survey.htm> [Accessed 07.03.11].

Environment & Heritage Service (EHS) (2005b) Northern Ireland Habitat Action Plan: Calcareous grassland.

Environment & Heritage Service (EHS) (2005c) Northern Ireland Habitat Action Plan: Coastal Saltmarsh.

Environment & Heritage Service (EHS) (2005d) Northern Ireland Habitat Action Plan: Coastal Sand Dunes.

Environment & Heritage Service (EHS) (2005e) Northern Ireland Habitat Action Plan: Coastal Vegetated Shingle.

Environment & Heritage Service (EHS) (2005f) Northern Ireland Habitat Action Plan: Eutrophic Standing Water.

Environment & Heritage Service (EHS) (2005g) Northern Ireland Habitat Action Plan: Fens.

Environment & Heritage Service (EHS) (2005h) Northern Ireland Habitat Action Plan: Hen harrier, *Circus cyaneus*.

Environment & Heritage Service (EHS) (2005i) Northern Ireland Habitat Action Plan: Lowland Dry Acid Grassland.

Environment & Heritage Service (EHS) (2005j) Northern Ireland Habitat Action Plan: Reedbeds. [online] Available at: <http://www.ni-environment.gov.uk/reedbeds_pdf-2.pdf> [Accessed 07.03.11].

Environment & Heritage Service (EHS) (2005k) Northern Ireland Habitat Action Plan: Sublittoral Sands and Gravels.

Environment & Heritage Service (EHS) (2005l) Small Water Bodies Short Method Statement: Water Framework Directive Article 5 Characterisation Technical Report.

Environment & Heritage Service (EHS) (2005m) Northern Ireland Species Action Plan: Yellowhammer.

Environment & Heritage Service (EHS) (2006a) A Guide to Public Rights of Way and Access to the Countryside – Guidance Notes on Law, Practices and Procedures in Northern Ireland.

Environment & Heritage Service (EHS) (2006b) Northern Ireland Species Action Plan: Twite, *Carduelis flavirostris*.

Environment & Heritage Service (EHS) (2007) Commercial & Industrial Waste Arisings Survey 2004/05.

Environment & Heritage Service (EHS) (2008a) Our Environment, Our Heritage, Our Future: State of the Environment Report for Northern Ireland.

Environment & Heritage Service (EHS) (2008b) Wind Energy Development in Northern Ireland's Landscapes: Draft Supplementary Planning Guidance to Accompany Planning Policy Statement 18 'Renewable Energy'.

Environment & Heritage Service & National Parks & Wildlife Service (EHS & NPWS) (2005) All Ireland Species Action Plan: Corncrake, *Crex crex*.

English Heritage (2010) Heritage Counts England 2010 [online] Available at: <http://hc.english-heritage.org.uk/content/pub/HC-Eng-2010> [Accessed 10.05.11].

Envision Management Consultants (2010) *The Environmental NGO Sector in Northern Ireland*.

Erwin, D.G., Picton, B.E., Connor, D.W., Howson, C.M., Gilleece, P. & Bogues, M.J. (1990) Inshore Marine Life of Northern Ireland. HMSO, Belfast.

Evans, D.J., Gibson. C.E. & Rosell, R.S. (2006) Sediment loads in heavily modified Irish catchments: A move towards informed management strategies. *Geomorphology*, **79**, 93-113.

Falkowski, P.G., Fenchel, T. & Delong, E.F. (2008) The microbial engines that drive Earth's biogeochemical cycles. *Science*, **320**, 1034-1039.

FAO – see **Food & Agricultural Organization**

Food & Agriculture Organization (FAO) (2005) National Soil Degradation Maps. Land and Water Development Division of the FAO. [online] Available at: <http://www.fao.org/landandwater/agll/glasod/glasodmaps.jsp?country=GBR&search=Display+map+!> [Accessed 07.03.11].

Feehan, J. & O'Donovan, G. (1996) The bogs of Ireland: an introduction to the natural, cultural and industrial heritage of Irish peatlands. The Environmental institute, University College, Dublin.

Ferreira, J.G., Hawkins, A.J.S., Monteiro, P., Service, M., Moore, H., Edwards, A., Gowen, R., Lourenco, P., Mellor, A., Nunes, J.P., Pascoe, P.L., Ramos, L., Sequeira, A., Simas, T. & Strong, J. (2007) SMILE – Sustainable Mariculture in Northern Irish Sea Lough Ecosystems – Assessment of Carrying Capacity for Environmentally Sustainable Shellfish Culture in Carlingford Lough, Strangford Lough, Belfast Lough, Larne Lough and Lough Foyle. IMAR – Institute of Marine Research.

Fleming, C.C., Craig, S.D., McDowell, M. & Entwistle, K. (2008) Plant Parasitic Nematodes: A New Turf War. *Biologist*, **55**(2), 76-82.

Flitcroft, C. (2006) Carbon Report January 2006. Moors for the Future.

Foden, J., Rogers, S.I. & Jones, A.P. (2010) Recovery of UK seabed habitats from benthic fishing and aggregate extraction-towards a cumulative impact assessment. *Marine Ecology Progress Series*, **411**, 259-270.

Foresight (2010) Land Use Futures: Making the most of land in the 21st century. Final Project Report. The Government Office for Science, London.

Forestry Commission (2005) GB Public Opinion of Forestry 2005.

Forestry Commission (2009a) Forestry Facts & Figures 2009: A summary of statistics about woodland and forestry.

Forestry Commission (2009b) Forestry Statistics 2009. Woodland Areas and Planting. Area of Woodland: Changes Over Time. [online] Available at: <http://www.forestry.gov.uk/website/forstats2009.nsf/0/4E46614169475C868025735D00353CC8> [Accessed 07.03.11].

Forestry Commission (2010a) Forestry Statistics 2010: UK Grown Timber. [online] Available at: <http://www.forestry.gov.uk/website/forstats2010.nsf/0/606D7E35D65B9717802573210052 1AC9?open&RestrictToCategory=1> [Accessed 07.03.11].

Forestry Commission (2010b) Public Opinion of Forestry 2010, Northern Ireland. Economics & Statistics, Forestry Commission, Edinburgh.

Forestry Commission (2010c) Statistical Release: Woodland Area, Planting and Restocking. 10 June 2010.

Faculty of Public Health (FPH) (2010) Great Outdoors: How our natural health service uses green space to improve wellbeing – an action report.

Forest Service (1993) Afforestation: the DANI statement on environmental policy. Department of Agriculture Northern Ireland.

Forest Service (2004) Options for Forestry: Consultation Paper. Department of Agriculture and Rural Development.

Forest Service (2006) Northern Ireland Forestry: A Strategy for Sustainability and Growth. Department of Agriculture and Rural Development.

Forest Service (2007a) Harvesting Our Timber. Department of Agriculture and Rural Development. [online] Available at: <http://www.forestserviceni.gov.uk/index/about-us/what-we-do/harvesting-our-timber.htm> [Accessed 07.03.11].

Forest Service (2007b) Woodland Grant Scheme Farm Woodland Premium Scheme Information Booklet. Department of Agriculture and Rural Development.

Forest Service (2009a) Annual Report 2008-2009. Department of Agriculture and Rural Development.

Forest Service (2009b) Strategy to Develop the Recreational and Social use of Our Forests. Department of Agriculture and Rural Development.

Forest Service (2010a) Annual Report 2009-2010. Department of Agriculture and Rural Development.

Forest Service (2010b) Annual timber production from Northern Ireland's state forests 1974-2008. Department of Agriculture and Rural Development [online] Available at: <http://www.forestserviceni.gov.uk/index/about-us/what-we-do/harvesting-our-timber/how-much-is-harvested-from-our-state-forests.htm> [Accessed 07.03.11].

Forest Service (2010c) DARD combats Japanese Larch tree disease. Department of Agriculture and Rural Development [online] Available at: <http://www.forestserviceni.gov.uk/index/forest-service-press-releases/press_releases-2010/press_releases-phytophthora-ramorum.htm> [Accessed 07.03.11].

Forest Service (2010d) Outbreak of *P. ramorum* in Japanese larch woodland. Department of Agriculture and Rural Development [online] Available at: <http://www.forestserviceni.gov.uk/index/forestry-grant-schemes-and-plant-health/private_woodlands_and_plant_health_p_ramorum_update.htm> [Accessed 07.03.11].

Forsythe, W. (2006) The archaeology of the Kelp industry in the northern islands of Ireland. *International Journal of Nautical Archaeology*, **32**, 218-229.

Foy, R.H. & Girvin, J. (2004) An evaluation of nitrogen sources and inputs to tidal waters in Northern Ireland.

Foy, R. & Jordan, C. (2011) Progress to lowering the phosphorus surplus in Northern Ireland agriculture. Agri-Food and Biosciences Institute, Belfast.

FPH – see **Faculty of Public Health**

Frank, K.T., Petrie, B., Choi, J.S. & Leggett, W.C. (2005) Trophic cascades in a formerly cod-dominated ecosystem. *Science*, **308**, 1621-1623.

Frost, P. & Gilkinson, S. (2010) Interim Technical Report: First 18 Month Performance Summary for Anaerobic Digestion of Dairy Cow Slurry at AFBI Hillsborough.

Genney, D.R., Hale, A.D., Woods, R.G. & Wright, M. (2009) Guidelines for selection of biological SSSIs Rationale Operational approach and criteria: Detailed guidelines for habitats and species groups. [online] Available at: <http://www.jncc.gov.uk/pdf/sssi_ptC20_newjune2009.pdf> [Accessed 07.03.11].

Gilliland, T.J., Johnston, J. & Connolly, C. (2007) A review of forage grass and clover seed use in Northern Ireland between 1980 and 2004. *Grass and Forage Science*, **62**, 239-254.

Godfray, H.C.J., Beddington, J.R., Crute, I.R., Haddad, L., Lawrence, D., Muir, J.F., Pretty, J., Robinson, S., Thomas, S.M. & Toulmin, C. (2010) Food Security: The Challenge of Feeding 9 Billion People. *Science*, **327**, 812-818.

Goldschmidt, T. (1997) Darwin's Dreampond. MIT Press, Cambridge, Massachusetts.

Goodwin, C.E., Picton, B.E., Breen, J. & Edwards, H. (2008) Sublittoral Survey Northern Ireland. A review of the status of Northern Ireland Priority Species of marine invertebrates. Project Report from the Sublittoral Survey Northern Ireland Survey project May 2006-2008. National Museums Northern Ireland and Northern Ireland Environment Agency, Belfast. 143pp.

Gorman, C. (1994) A study of the benthic fauna of brackish lagoons in Northern Ireland. Unpublished MSc thesis. Queen's University Belfast.

Gormley, B. (1998) C.S. Lewis: The Man Behind Narnia. Eerdmans Books for Young Readers.

Gormley, S., Donnelly, C., Hartwell, B. & Bell, J. (2009) Condition and Management Survey of the Archaeological Resource in Northern Ireland. A report commissioned by the Northern Ireland Environment Agency.

Graham, T. (1981) Private Woodland Inventory of Northern Ireland 1975-79. Commissioned by Forest Service.

Gruber, N. & Galloway, J.N. (2008) An Earth-system perspective of the global nitrogen cycle. *Nature*, **451**, 293-6.

Guy, C. & Roberts, D. (2009) Pacific Oysters (*Crassostrea gigas*) in Strangford Lough, Northern Ireland. Proceedings from the Third Annual Invasive Species Ireland Forum, April 2009. [online] Available at: <http://invasivespeciesireland.com/wp-content/uploads/2010/11/C_Guy_Apr_09.pps> [Accessed 07.03.11].

Habitas (2002) Small Blue. [online] Available at: <http://www.habitas.org.uk/moths/species.asp?item=5537> [Accessed 07.03.11].

Habitas (2008) Invasive Alien Species in Northern Ireland. [online] Available at: <http://www.habitas.org.uk/invasive/splist.asp> [Accessed 07.03.11].

Habitas (2010) Northern Ireland Priority Species: Circus cyaneus – Hen Harrier. [online] Available at: <http://www.habitas.org.uk/priority/species.asp?item=286> [Accessed 07.03.11].

Hall, V.A. (1992) The woodlands of the lower Bann Valley in the seventeenth century: the documentary evidence. *Ulster Folklife*, **38**, 1-11.

Hall, V.A. (1994) Landscape development in northeast Ireland over the last half millennium. *Review of Palaeobotany and Palynology* **82,** 75-82.

Hamilton, A.C. (1982) Peatland. Northern Ireland: Environment and Natural Resources (eds J.G. Cruickshank & D.N. Wilcox), pp. 185-206. The Queen's University of Belfast and the New University of Ulster.

Hammond, M.E.R., Mlavarez, G.C. & Cooper, A. (2002) The distribution of *Spartina anglica* on esturine mudflats in relation to wave-related hydrodynamic parameters. *Journal of Coastal Research*, **36**, 352-355.

Hansard (2009) Official Report: Friday 27th November 2009. Volume 46. No. WA 1. [online] Available at: <http://www.niassembly.gov.uk/qanda/2007mandate/writtenans/2009/pdf/091127.pdf> [Accessed 07.03.11].

Hansard (2010) Official Report: 22nd April 2010. Committee for Culture, Arts and Leisure: Eel Fishing Regulations 2010. [online] Available at: <http://www.niassembly.gov.uk/record/committees2009/CAL/100422_Eelfishingregulations.htm> [Accessed 07.03.11].

Harris, L., Nel, R., Smale, M. & Schoeman, D.S. (*In Press*) Swashed away? Storm impacts to sandy beach macrofaunal communities at Sardinia Bay, South Africa. *Estuarine, Coastal and Shelf Science.*

Harrison C.M., Burgess J. & Limb M. (1987) Nature in the city: popular values for a living world. *Journal of Environmental Management*, **25**, 347-362.

Hawke, C.J. & José, P.V. (1996) Reedbed management for commercial and wildlife interests. RSPB, Sandy.

Heal, G. (2000) Nature and the Marketplace: Capturing the Value of Ecosystem Services. Island Press, Washington D.C.

Heink, U. & Kowarik, I. (2010) What are indicators? On the definition of indicators in ecology and environmental planning. *Ecological Indicators*, **10**, 584-593.

Hess, T.M., Holman, I.P., Rose, S.C., Rosolova, Z. & Parrott, A. (2010) Estimating the impact of rural land management changes on catchment runoff generation in England and Wales. *Hydrological Processes*, **24**(10), 1357-1368.

Hiscock, K., Southward, A., Tittley, I. & Hawkins, S. (2004) Effects of changing temperature on benthic marine life in Britain and Ireland. *Aquatic Conservation: Marine and Freshwater Ecosystems*, **14**, 333-362.

HM Revenue & Customs (2010) UK Regional Trade in Goods Statistics: Quarter 2, 2010 Press Release. [online] Available at: <https://www.uktradeinfo.com/index.cfm> [Accessed 07.03.11].

Hoegh-Guldberg, O. & Bruno, J.F. (2010) The impact of climate change on the world's marine ecosystems. *Science*, **328**, 1523-1528.

Health Protection Agency (HPA) (2008) Health Effects of Climate Change in the UK 2008: An Update of the Department of Health Report 2001/02. Department of Health.

Health Protection Agency (HPA) (2009) A Children's Environment and Health Strategy for the UK. Department of Health.

HPA – see **Health Protection Agency**

Hughes, S.L., Holliday, P.N., Kennedy, J., Berry, D.I., Kent, E.C., Sherwin, T., Dye, S., Inall, M., Shammon, T. & Smyth, T. (2010) Temperature (Air and Sea). Marine Climate Change Impacts Partnership (MCCIP) Annual Report Card 2010-11.

MCCP Science Review, pp. 16. [online] Available at: <http://www.mccip.org.uk/media/6784/mccip201011_temperature.pdf> [Accessed 07.03.11].

Hunter, W.I. (1987) Agriculture, forestry and fishing. Province, city and people (eds R.H. Buchanan & B.M. Walker). British Association, Belfast.

Hynes, S. & Hanley, N. (2008) The *Crex crex* Lament: Estimating Landowners Willingness to Pay for Corncrake Conservation on Irish Farmland. Stirling Economics Discussion Paper 2008-14. University of Stirling.

IACCF – see **Inter-Agency Climate Change Forum**

IEEP – see **Institute for European Environmental Policy**

ICES – see **International Council for the Exploration of the Sea**

Inter-Agency Climate Change Forum (IACCF) (2010) Biodiversity and Climate Change – A Summary of Impacts in the UK.

International Council for the Exploration of the Sea (ICES) (2006) Report of the ICES/EIFAC Working Group on Eels. ICES C.M. 2006/ACFM: 16.

Institute for European Environmental Policy (IEEP) (2007) Guidance Document to the Member States on the Application of the High Nature Value Indicator. Report for DG Agriculture.

Invasive Species Ireland (2008) Invasive Species Ireland Risk Assessment.

Invasive Species Ireland (2010) Most Unwanted. [online] Available at: <http://invasivespeciesireland.com/most-unwanted-species/> [Accessed 14.03.11].

Invest Northern Ireland (2008) Sustainable Energy: Maximising Business Opportunities from Sustainable Energy.

Jackson, B.M., Wheater, H.S., McIntyre, N.R., Chell, J., Francis, O.J., Frogbrook, Z., Marshall, M., Reynolds, B. & Solloway, I. (2008) The Impact of Upland Management on Flooding: Insights from a Multiscale Experimental and Modelling Programme. *Journal of Flood Risk Management*, **1**(2), 71-80.

Jackson, D.L. (2000) Guidance on the interpretation of the Biodiversity Broad Habitat Classification (terrestrial and freshwater types): definitions and the relationship with other classifications. JNCC Report No. 307. ISSN 0963 8091.

Jackson, D.W.T. & Cooper, J.A.G. (2010) Application of the equilibrium planform concept to natural beaches in Northern Ireland. *Coastal Engineering*, **57**, 112-123.

Jacobs, Scottish Agricultural College & Cranfield University (2008) Environmental Accounts for Agriculture. Report prepared for the Department for Environment, Food and Rural Affairs; Welsh Assembly Government; Scottish Government; Department of Agriculture & Rural Development (Northern Ireland) [online] Available at: <www.dardni.gov.uk/environmental-accounts.pdf> [Accessed 07.03.11].

Jafari, J. (2003) The Encyclopaedia of Tourism. Routledge, London.

Jeffrey, D.W., Jones, M.B. & McAdam, J.H. (1995) Irish Grassland: Their Biology and Management. Royal Irish Academy, Dublin. ISBN 1874045216.

Johnson, M.P., Portig, A., Smyth, D. & Roberts, D. (2008) Unregulated harvesting of intertidal shellfish in Strangford Lough. NIEA Research and Development Series No. 09/05.

JNCC – see **Joint Nature Conservation Committee**

Joint Nature Conservation Committee (JNCC) (1997) Coasts and seas of the United Kingdom, Region 17 Northern Ireland. Coastal Directories Series.

Joint Nature Conservation Committee (JNCC) (2010) Handbook for Phase 1 habitat survey: A technique for environmental audit. JNCC, Peterborough. ISBN 0 86139 636 7.

Jordan, C. & Higgins, A. (2007) A generalised map of major soil types for Northern Ireland at a scale of 1:250,000. Agri-Food and Biosciences Institute, Belfast. Based on information from Cruickshank, J.G. (ed) 1997, Soil and Environment : Northern Ireland. Agricultural and Environmental Science Department, Queen's University, Belfast.

Kelly, J.T., Cooper, J.A.G., Jackson, D.W.T., Belknap, D.F. & Quinn, R. (2006) Sea-level change and inner shelf stratigraphy off Northern Ireland. *Marine Geology*, **232**, 1-15.

Kelso, B. & Service, M. (2000) Environmental Effects of Shellfish Cultivation and Harvesting. The Queen's University of Belfast and Department of Agriculture and Rural Development, Belfast.

Kennedy, R., Crozier, W.W. & Boylan, P. (2010) Summary of Salmon Fisheries and Status of Stocks in Northern Ireland for 2009. Working Group on North Atlantic Salmon, Copenhagen 2010, Working Paper 07.

Kiessling, W., Simpson, C. & Foote, M. (2010) Reefs as cradles of evolution and sources of biodiversity in the phanerozoic. *Science*, **327**, 196-198.

King, G.L. & Berrow, S.D. (2009) Marine turtles in Irish waters. Special Supplement to the Irish Naturalist's Journal.

Kirkpatrick, A.H. & Rushton, B.S. (1990) The oceanicity/continentality of the climate of the north of Ireland Weather 45, 322-326. The oceanicity/continentailty of the climate of the north of Ireland. *Weather*, **45**, 322-326.

Kirkpatrick, A.H., Sydes, C.S. & Rushton, B.S. (1999) Agricultural intensification and the loss of heather moorland: a case study from Fair Head, Northern Ireland. *Journal of Practical Ecology and Conservation*, **3**(1), 33-47.

Kremen, C. (2005) Managing Ecosystem Services: What Do We Need To Know About Their Ecology? *Ecology Letters*, **8**(5), 468-479.

Kula, E. & McKillop, D.G. (1988) A planting function for private afforestation in Northern Ireland. *Journal of Agricultural Economics*, **39**, 133-141.

Landry, S.M. & Chakraborty, J. (2009) Street Trees and Equity: Evaluating the Spatial Distribution of an Urban Amenity. *Environment and Planning A*, **41**(11), 2651-2670.

Lantra (2009) Research Factsheet for Aquaculture: Labour Market Information.

Larne Borough Council (2008) Local Biodiversity Action Plan: The Future in Our Hands.

Lawton, J.H., Brotherton, P.N.M., Brown, V.K., Elphick, C., Fitter, A.H., Forshaw, J., Haddow, R.W., Hilborne, S., Leafe, R.N., Mace, G.M., Southgate, M.P., Sutherland, W.J., Tew, T.E., Varley, J. & Wynne, G.R. (2010) Making Space for Nature: a review of England's wildlife sites and ecological network. Report to Defra.

Leach, S.J. & Corbett, P.M. (1987) A preliminary survey of raised bogs in Northern Ireland. *Glasra*, **10**, 57-73.

Le Loc'h, F. & Hily, C. (2005) Stable carbon and nitrogen isotope analysis of *Nephrops norvegicus/Merluccius merluccius* fishing grounds in the Bay of Biscay (Northeast Atlantic). *Canadian Journal of Fisheries and Aquatic Sciences*, **132**, 123-132.

Lewis, D., Bentham, M., Cleary, T., Vernon, R., O'Neill, N., Kirk, K., Chadwick, A., Hildritch, D., Karsten, M., Allinson, G., Neal, P. & Ho, M. (2009) Assessment of the Potential for Geological Storage of Carbon Dioxide in Ireland and Northern Ireland. *Energy Procedia*, **1**(1), 2655-2662.

Lord, E., Cottrill, B., Newell-Price, P. & Smith, K. (2010) Soil Nutrient Balances Draft Report. FERA contract T4QT UK Nutrient Balances methodology review. ADAS report for FERA/Defra. ADAS, Wolverhampton.

Lough Neagh Advisory Committee (LNAC) (2002) Lough Neagh Management Strategy: Recommendations from the Lough Neagh Advisory Committee 2002-2007. [online] Available at: <http://www.ni-environment.gov.uk/lnms_june_02.pdf> [Accessed 07.03.11].

Lough Neagh & Lower Bann Advisory Committee (LNLBAC) (2006) Lough Neagh: Facts & Figures. [online] Available at: <http://www.loughneagh.com/facts%20and%20 figs.html> [Accessed 07.03.11].

Loughs Agency (2009) Carlingford Tributaries Catchment Status Report 2009. [online] Available at: <http://www. loughs-agency.org/archive/StatusReports/Carlingford%20 Tributaries%20Catchment%20Status%20Report%202009.pdf> [Accessed 07.03.11].

Lynam, C.P., Cusack, C. & Stokes, D. (2010) A methodology for community-level hypothesis testing applied to detect trends in phytoplankton and fish communities in Irish waters. *Estuarine, Coastal and Shelf Science*, **87**, 451–462.

Lynch, D., Smith, K. & Cahill, B. (2004) Seasonal mean circulation on the Irish shelf – a model-generated climatology. *Continental Shelf Research*, **24**, 2215–2244.

MA (Millennium Ecosystem Assessment) (2005b) Ecosystems and Human Well-being: Synthesis. Island Press, Washington D.C.

MacMillan, D., Ferrier, B. & Hanley, N. (2001) Valuation of Air Pollution Effects on Ecosystems: A Scoping Study. A Report to the Department for Environment, Food & Rural Affairs.

Macrory, R. (2004) Transparency and Trust: Reshaping Environmental Governancein Northern Ireland. Centre for Law and the Environment, Faculty of Laws, University College, London.

Maguire, C.M. & Sykes, L.M. (2004) Zebra Mussel Management Strategy 2004–10. Queens University Belfast & Environment & Heritage Service.

Maguire, C., Curry, R. & McClenaghan, A. (2008) Northern Visions: Identifying priority areas for action and a programme for sustainable resource use in Northern Ireland.

Malone, K. (2008) Every Experience Matters: An evidence based research report on the role of learning outside the classroom for children's whole development from birth to eighteen years. Report commissioned by Farming and Countryside Education for UK Department Children, School and Families, Wollongong, Australia.

Marine and Fisheries Agency (MFA) (2009) UK Sea Fisheries Statistics 2008. Published by the Department for Environment, Food and Rural Affairs.

Marine Conservation Society (MCS) (2010) Good Beach Guide. [online] Available at: <www.goodbeachguide. co.uk/search-results?region=N+Ireland&wq_ grade=recommended&form_build_id=form-bf9d7b9fa14b99 ed2944cd34f110e05f&form_id=stbeach_search_short_form> [Accessed 07.03.11].

Mayne, S. (2010) A review of greenhouse gas emissions from the agri-food sector in Northern Ireland, potential mitigation options and current evidence gaps. Unpublished DARD research report.

McAdam, J.H. (1988) The impact of sheep and cattle grazing on upland pasture. The High Country: land use and land use change in the Northern Irish uplands (eds W.I. Mongomery, J.H. McAdam & B.J. Smith) pp. 14–23. Institute of Biology and the Geographical Society of Ireland.

McCann, T., Rogers, D. & Cooper, A. (2009) Northern Ireland Countryside Survey 2007: Field methods and technical manual. *Northern Ireland Environment Agency, Research and Development Series*, No. 09/07. Belfast.

McCann, T., Rogers, D. & Cooper, A. (2010) Northern Ireland Countryside Survey 2007: Field Boundaries. Draft contract report to Northern Ireland Environment Agency.

McCaughan, M. & Appleby, J. (1989) The Irish Sea: Aspects of Maritime History. Institute of Irish Studies, Belfast.

McCracken, A.R. & Dawson, W.M. (1998) Short rotation coppice willow in Northern Ireland since 1973: development of the use of mixtures in the control of foliar rust (*Melampsora* spp.). *European Journal of Forest Pathology*, **28**(4), 241–250.

McCracken, E. (1971) The Irish Woods Since Tudor Times: distribution and exploitation. David and Charles for the Institute of Irish Studies, Queen's University of Belfast.

McCusker, T. (2009) Report into the economic implications of a Marine Management Organisation in Northern Ireland. Report commissioned by the Northern Ireland Marine Task Force.

McEvoy, P.M. & McAdam, J.H. (2004) Woodland grazing in Northern Ireland: Effects on botanical diversity, tree regeneration and tree damage. Silvopastoralism and Sustainable Management, International Congress, Lugo, Spain, pp91, April 2004.

McGurn, P. (2008) Hay Meadow management Systems in Fermanagh. A thesis submitted for the degree of Doctor of Philosphy. UU, Coleraine.

McHugh, R., Mitchel, D., Wright, M. & Anderson, R. (2001) The fungi of Irish grasslands and their value for nature conservation. *Proceedings of the Royal Irish Academy*, **101B**(3), 225–242.

McKenzie, P., Cooper, A., McCann, T. & Rogers, D. (2011) The ecological impact of rural building on habitats in an agricultural landscape. *Landscape and Urban Planning*, **101**, 262–268.

McNeill, G., Nunn, J. & Minchin, D. (2010) The slipper limpet *Crepidula fornicata* Linnaeus, 1758 becomes established in Ireland. *Aquatic Invasions*, **5**(S1), S21–S25.

MCS – see **Marine Conservation Society**

Mead, S. J.H. (2003) An analysis of trends in the UK beef industry and the key dynamics of change for 2015. *Journal of the Royal Agricultural Society of England*, **164**, 1–12.

Met Office (2007) National Meteorological Library and Archive: Fact Sheet No. 9 – Weather Extremes.

MFA – see **Marine and Fisheries Agency**

Miller, D., Schwarz, G., Sutherland, L-A., Morrice, J., Aspinall, R., Barnes, A., Blackstock, K., Buchan, K., Donnelly, D., Hawes, C., McCrum, G., McKenzie, B., Matthews, K., Miller, D., Renwick, A., Smith, M., Squire, G. & Toma L. (2009) Changing land use in rural Scotland – drivers and decision-making. Scottish Government Social Research.

Minchin, D. (2007) A checklist of alien and cryptogenic aquatic species in Ireland. *Aquatic Invasions*, **2**(4), 341-366.

Minchin, D., Lucy, F. & Sullivan, M. (2002) Zebra mussel: impacts and spread. Invasive Aquatic Species of Europe (eds Leppäkoski, E., Gollasch, S. & Olenin, S.), pp 135-146. Kluwer Academic Publishers, Dordreicht.

Mitchell, P.I., Newton, S.F., Ratcliffe, N. & Dunn, T.E. (2004) Seabird populations of Britain and Ireland: results of the Seabird 2000 census. Poyser, London.

Mooney, K.M., Hamilton, J.T., Floyd, S.D., Foy, R.H. & Elliott, C.T. (In press) Initial studies on the occurrence of cyanobacteria and microcystins in Irish lakes. *Environmental Toxicology.*

Morales, D.J. (1980) The Contribution of Trees to Residential Property Values. *Journal of Aboriculture*, **6**(11), 305-308.

Moss, J.E. & Chilton, S.M. (1997a) A Socio-Economic Evaluation of the Mourne Mountains and Slieve Croob Environmentally Sensitive Areas Scheme. Centre for Rural Studies, QUB, Belfast, 128 pp, ISBN 0-85389-683-6.

Moss, J.E. & Chilton, S.M. (1997b) A Socio-Economic Evaluation of the Mourne Mountains and Slieve Croob Environmentally Sensitive Areas Scheme - Technical Supplement. Centre for Rural Studies, QUB, Belfast, 116 pp.

Mourne Heritage Trust (2010) Juniper Conservation Handbook. Mourne Heritage Trust.

Munton, R. (2009) Rural land ownership in the United Kingdom: Changing patterns and future possibilities for land use. *Land Use Policy,***26**(S1), S54-S61.

Murchie, A.K., Moore, J.P., Walters, K.F.A. & Blackshaw, R.P. (2003) Invasion of agricultural land by the earthworm predator, *Arthurdendyus triangulatus* (Dendy). *Pedobiologia*, **47**, 920-923.

Murray, R., McCann, T. & Cooper, A. (1992) A land classification and landscape ecological study of Northern Ireland. University of Ulster Contract report to DOENI.

National Trust (2010) Strangford Lough. [online] Available at: <www.nationaltrust.org.uk/main/w-vh/w-visits/w-great_days_out/w-nature-places_to_visit/w-nature-places_to_visit-strangford_lough.htm> [Accessed 07.03.11].

Natural Capital Project (2006) About the Natural Capital Project. [online] Available at: <http://www.naturalcapitalproject.org/about.html> [Accessed 07.03.11].

Natural England (2005) English Leisure Visits Survey. Natural England, Cheltenham.

Natural England (2009) Experiencing Landscapes: capturing the cultural services and experiential qualities of landscape. Natural England Commissioned Report NECR024.

Newry & Mourne District Council & Ulster Wildlife Trust (2009) Newry & Mourne District Local Biodiversity Action Plan.

NIA – see **Northern Ireland Assembly**

NIAUR – see **Northern Ireland Authority for Utility Regulation**

NIBG – see **Northern Ireland Biodiversity Group**

Nicholls, R.J. & Cazenave, A. (2010) Sea-level rise and its impact on coastal zones. *Science*, **328**, 1517-20.

NIE – see **Northern Ireland Executive**

NIEA – see **Northern Ireland Environment Agency**

NIPS - **Northern Ireland Planning Service**

NISRA – see **Northern Ireland Statistics and Research Agency**

NITB – see **Northern Ireland Tourist Board**

North Atlantic Salmon Conservation Organisation (2009) Focus Area Report on Protection, Restoration and Enhancement of Salmon Habitat: UK-Northern Ireland.

Northern Ireland Assembly (NIA) (2009) Bovine TB Cost Taxpayer £200 Million. Press Release. [online] Available at: <http://www.niassembly.gov.uk/public/2007mandate/press/pac120809.htm> [Accessed 07.03.11].

Northern Ireland Assembly (NIA) (2010) Eel Fishing Regulations 2010. Research and Library Service Briefing Note. Paper 136/0.

Northern Ireland Authority for Utility Regulation (NIAUR) (2008) Cost and Performance Report: An assessment of Northern Ireland Water's costs and performance in 2007/8.

Northern Ireland Biodiversity Group (NIBG) (2005) Delivery of the Northern Ireland Biodiversity Strategy 2002-2005: First Report of the Northern Ireland Biodiversity Group.

Northern Ireland Biodiversity Group (NIBG) (2009) Delivery of the Northern Ireland Biodiversity Strategy: The second report of the Northern Ireland Biodiversity Group 2005-2009.

Northern Ireland Curriculum (2010) The World Around Us: Implementation Report.

Northern Ireland Environment Agency (NIEA) (2008a) Reporting on Priority Farmland Habitats.

Northern Ireland Environment Agency (NIEA) (2008b) The condition of Northern Ireland's Areas of Special Scientific Interest: the results of the first condition assessment monitoring cycle 2002-2008. Research and Development Series No. 08/10.

Northern Ireland Environment Link (NIEL) (2009a) Climate Change: Dealing with the Reality. Conference Proceedings. Northern Ireland Environment Link, Belfast.

Northern Ireland Environment Link (NIEL) (2009b) Sustainable Transport Report. Northern Ireland Environment Link, Belfast.

Northern Ireland Environment Agency (NIEA) (2009a) Areas of Special Scientific Interest. [online] Available at: <http://www.ni-environment.gov.uk/print/areas_of_special_scientific_interest-_worthy_of_protection-2.pdf> [Accessed 07.03.11].

Northern Ireland Environment Agency (NIEA) (2009b) Drinking Water Quality in Northern Ireland 2009 Report. [online] Available at: <http://www.ni-environment.gov.uk/drinking_water_quality_in_northern_ireland_2009.pdf> [Accessed 07.03.11].

Northern Ireland Environment Agency (NIEA) (2009c) Managing Stormwater: A Strategy for Promoting the Use of Sustainable Urban Drainage Systems within Northern Ireland. Consultation document.

Northern Ireland Environment Agency (NIEA) (2009d) Natural Heritage: Sand Dunes. NH009.

Northern Ireland Environment Agency (NIEA) (2009e) Natural Heritage: Wetlands. NH005.

Northern Ireland Environment Agency (NIEA) (2009f) Neagh Bann: River Basin Management Plan Summary.

Northern Ireland Environment Agency (NIEA) (2009g) North Eastern: River Basin Management Plan Summary.

Northern Ireland Environment Agency (NIEA) (2009h) North Western: River Basin Management Plan Summary.

Northern Ireland Environment Agency (NIEA) (2009i) Northern Ireland 2008 C&I Report: Comparing 2008 estimates with those from 2005/06.

Northern Ireland Environment Agency (NIEA) (2009j) River Basin Management Plans: Groundwater Classification. Water Balance. [online] Available at: <http://www.ni-environment.gov.uk/waterbalance_gw.pdf> [Accessed 12.05.11].

Northern Ireland Environment Agency (NIEA) (2009k) River Basin Management Plans: Report of the economic analysis required by Article 5. [online] Available at: <http://www.ni-environment.gov.uk/wfd_article5_dec09.pdf> [Accessed 07.03.11].

Northern Ireland Environment Agency (NIEA) (2009l) Strategic Regulatory Impact Assessment of River Basin Management Plans Summary. [online] Available at: <http://www.ni-environment.gov.uk/strategic_regulatory_impact_assessment_of_river_basin_management_plans_-_summary.pdf> [Accessed 07.03.11].

Northern Ireland Environment Agency (NIEA) (2010a) Annual Report and Accounts: For the year ended 31 March 2010.

Northern Ireland Environment Agency (NIEA) (2010b) Areas of Outstanding Natural Beauty <http://www.ni-environment.gov.uk/places_to_visit_home/aonb.htm> (Accessed 10/12/2010).

Northern Ireland Environment Agency (NIEA) (2010c) Correll Glen Nature Reserve. [online] Available at: <http://www.ni-environment.gov.uk/nature_reserves/nature_reserves_correlglen.shtml> [Accessed 07.03.11].

Northern Ireland Environment Agency (NIEA) (2010d) Criteria for Listing: A consultation on proposed revisions to Annex C of Planning Policy Statement 6.

Northern Ireland Environment Agency (NIEA) (2010e) *Drinking Water Quality in Northern Ireland 2009*. A report by the Drinking Water Inspectorate for Northern Ireland.

Northern Ireland Environment Agency (NIEA) (2010f) Freshwater and wetlands. [online] Available at: <http://www.ni-environment.gov.uk/biodiversity/habitats-2/freshwater_and_wetlands.htm> [Accessed 07.03.11].

Northern Ireland Environment Agency (NIEA) (2010g) NIEA Coast Magazine. Issue 6: 2010. [online] Available at: <http://www.ni-environment.gov.uk/coast_-_6th_edition.pdf> [Accessed 07.03.11].

Northern Ireland Environment Agency (NIEA) (2010h) *Northern Ireland Offshore Waters*. Unpublished raw data. Conservation Science Unit.

Northern Ireland Environment Agency (NIEA) (2010i) Strangford Lough Part III ASSI. [online] Available at: <http://www.doeni.gov.uk/niea/protected_areas_home/new_assi_landing_page/county_down-2/strangford_lough_part_iii_assi.htm> [Accessed 07.03.11].

Northern Ireland Environment Agency (NIEA) (2010j) The Schedule of Historic Monuments.

Northern Ireland Environment Agency (NIEA) (2010k) Wind Energy Development in Northern Ireland's Landscapes: Supplementary Planning Guidance to Accompany Planning Policy Statement 18 'Renewable Energy'.

Northern Ireland Environment Agency (NIEA) (2011) State of Northern Ireland Biodiversity. In prep.

Northern Ireland Executive (NIE) (2008) Programme for Government 2008-2011.

Northern Ireland Executive (NIE) (2010a) June 2010 Press Release: Gildernew Briefs New EU Fisheries Commissioner on Local Fishing Industry. [online] Available at: <http://www.northernireland.gov.uk/index/media-centre/news-departments/news-dard/news-dard-june-2010-news-releases/news-dard-240610-gildernew-briefs-new.htm> [Accessed 07.03.11].

Northern Ireland Executive (NIE) (2010b) November 2010 Press Release: Gildernew Announces Payment Rates for LFA Scheme. [online] Available at: <http://www.northernireland.gov.uk/news-dard-111110-gildernew-announces-payment> [Accessed 07.03.11].

Northern Ireland Executive (NIE) (2010c) Poots disappointed at suspension of Aggregates Levy Credit Scheme. [online] Available at: <http://www.northernireland.gov.uk/news/news-doe-261010-poots-disappointed-at> [Accessed 07.03.11].

Northern Ireland Green NGOs (NI Green NGOs)& the Environment & Heritage Service (2007) Valuing our Environment: The Economic Impact of the Environment in Northern Ireland. Summary Report.

Northern Ireland Planning Service (NIPS) (2003) Development Management Statistics Northern Ireland: 2002/3 Annual Statistical Bulletin (April 2002 to March 2003).

Northern Ireland Planning Service (NIPS) (2004) Development Management Statistics Northern Ireland: 2003/4 Annual Statistical Bulletin (April 2003 to March 2004).

Northern Ireland Planning Service (NIPS) (2005) A Guide to Planning Enforcement in Northern Ireland.

Northern Ireland Planning Service (NIPS) (2006) Development Management Statistics Northern Ireland: 2005/6 Annual Statistical Bulletin (April 2005 to March 2006).

Northern Ireland Planning Service (NIPS) (2007) Belfast Metropolitan Area Plan 2015 District Proposals: Lisburn City Open Space, Sport & Outdoor Recreation. [online] Available at: <http://www.planningni.gov.uk/index/policy/dev_plans/devplans_az/bmap_2015/bmap_district_proposals/bmap_lisburn/bmap_lisburn_city/bmap_lisburn_city_open.htm> [Accessed 07.03.11].

Northern Ireland Planning Service (NIPS) (2008) Development Management Statistics Northern Ireland: 2007/8 Annual Statistical Bulletin (April 2007 to March 2008).

Northern Ireland Planning Service (NIPS) (2010a) Development Management Statistics Northern Ireland: 2009/10 Annual Statistical Bulletin (April 2009 to March 2010).

NISRA (Northern Ireland Statistics and Research Agency) (2002) Northern Ireland Census Population Report and Mid Year Estimates.

Northern Ireland Statistics and Research Agency (NISRA) (2003) Small Area Population Estimates (Rounded) 2003. NISRA Data Catalogue. [online] Available at: <http://www.ninis.nisra.gov.uk/mapxtreme/DataCatalogue.asp?button=Population> [Accessed 07.03.11].

Northern Ireland Statistics and Research Agency (NISRA) (2005) Settlement Development Limits Statistical Classification Bands. [online] Available at: <http://www.nisra.gov.uk/geography/default.asp9.htm> [Accessed 20 July 2011].

Northern Ireland Statistics and Research Agency (NISRA) (2005a) Population Projections 2006-2021. NISRA Data Catalogue. [online] Available at: <http://www.ninis.nisra.gov.uk/mapxtreme/DataCatalogue.asp?button=Population> [Accessed 07.03.11].

Northern Ireland Statistics and Research Agency (NISRA) (2005b) Report of the Inter-Departmental Urban-Rural

Definition Group: Statistical classification and delineation of settlements.

Northern Ireland Statistics and Research Agency (NISRA) (2009) Population Statistics: Northern Ireland Population 1901-2009. [online] Available at: <http://www.nisra.gov.uk/demography/default.asp3.htm> [Accessed 07.03.11].

Northern Ireland Statistics & Research Agency (NISRA) (2010a) Continuous Household Survey: 2009/10 Bulletin.

Northern Ireland Statistics & Research Agency (NISRA) (2010b) Mid-term evaluation of the Northern Ireland Rural Development Programme (NIRDP) 2007-2013.

Northern Ireland Statistics & Research Agency (NISRA) (2010c) *Travel Survey for Northern Ireland Headline Report 2007-2009*. A report commissioned by Roads Service, an Agency within the Department for Regional Development.

Northern Ireland Statistics and Research Agency (NISRA (& Northern Ireland Environment Agency (2010) Waste Management Statistics: Annual Report 2009/10.

Northern Ireland Tourist Board (NITB) (2010a) Knowing the Visitor: Tourism facts 2009.

Northern Ireland Tourist Board (NITB) (2010b) Out of State Visitors to Northern Ireland January-December 2009.

Northern Ireland Tourist Board (NITB) (2010c) The Mournes Experience. The Signature Project Experience: How well do they deliver?

Northern Ireland Tourist Board (NITB) (2010d) Visitor Attractions Survey Northern Ireland: Performance during 2009.

Northern Ireland Tourist Board (NITB) (2010e) Visits to NI and Revenue Generated (1959-2009). Available at: <http://www.nitb.com/FileHandler.ashx?id=1122> [Accessed 03/12/2010].

Northern Ireland Water (2007) Discover Silent Valley.

Northern Ireland Water (2010a) Annual Report 2009/2010.

Northern Ireland Water (2010b) Drinking Water Quality: Annual Report 2009.

Nunn, J.D. & Minchin, D. (2009) Further expansions of the Asian tunicate *Styela clava* Herdman 1882 in Ireland. *Aquatic Invasives*, **4**, 591-596.

Office of First Minister and Deputy First Minister (OFMDFM) (2010a) Everyone's Involved: Sustainable Development Strategy.

Office of First Minister and Deputy First Minister (OFMDFM) (2010b) Report of the Flooding Taskforce on the Fermanagh Flooding of November 2009.

OFMDFM – see **Office of First Minister and Deputy First Minister**

Office of National Statistics (ONS) (2010a) Population Density for the Constituent Countries of the United Kingdom for Selected Years. [online] Available at: <http://www.theyworkforyou.com/wrans/?id=2010-03-01d.319821.h> [Accessed 07.03.11].

Office of National Statistics (ONS) (2010b) Population Estimates for UK, England and Wales, Scotland and Northern Ireland. Mid Year Population Estimates 2009: 24/06/10

Ofsted (2008) Learning Outside the Classroom: How far should you go? Ofsted, London.

O'Hagan, B. (2010) *Food in Northern Ireland: Current Issues, Programmes, Concepts and Initiatives*. Northern Ireland Environment Link.

Omagh District Council (2008) Local Biodiversity Action Plan.

Omagh District Council & Ulster Wildlife Trust (2008) Omagh District Local Biodiversity Action Plan.

ONS – see **Office of National Statistics**

O'Neill, K. & Montgomery, I. (2003) *Recent changes in the distribution of red squirrels in Northern Ireland.* Environment and Heritage ServiceReport.

Orford, J.D., Smith, D. E., Harman, M. & Murdy, J. (2007a) *Recent sea-level changes in Northern Ireland.* Unpublished Report for the Environment & Heritage Service.

Orford, J.D., Betts, N., Cooper, J.A.G. & Smith, B.J. (2007b) Future Coastal Scenarios for Northern Ireland. Unpublished Report for National Trust (NI), 158pp.

Orford, J.D., Murdy, J. & Freel, R. (2006) Developing constraints on the relative sea-level curve for the north-east of Ireland from the mid-Holocene to the present day. *Philosophical Transactions of the Royal Society A*, **364**, 857-866.

Orford, J.D., Murdy, J. & Wintle, A. (2003) Prograded Holocene beach-ridges with superimposed dunes in north-east Ireland: mechanisms and timescales of fine and coarse beach sediment decoupling and deposition. *Marine Geology*, **194**, 47-64.

PAP – see **Professional Anglers Association**

Parliament (2010) Written Answers to Questions: 18th November 2010. Treasury: Aggregates Levy Northern Ireland. [online] Available at: <http://www.publications.parliament.uk/pa/cm201011/cmhansrd/cm101118/text/101118w0001.htm#10111865001819> [Accessed 07.03.11].

Parliamentary Office of Science and Technology(POST) (2002) Number 188: Air Quality in the UK.

Parrott, A., Brooks, W., Harmar, O. & Pygott, K. (2009) Role of rural land use management in flood and coastal risk management. *Journal of Flood Risk Management*, **2**(4), 272-284.

Pauly, D. (2009) Beyond duplicity and ignorance in global fisheries. *Scientia Marina*, **73**, 215-224.

Pauly, D., Christensen, V., Dalsgaard, J., Froese, R. & Torres, F. (1998) Fishing down marine food webs. *Science*, **279**, 860-863.

Pejchar, L. & Mooney, H.A. (2009) Invasive species, ecosystem services and human well-being. *Trends in Ecology and Evolution*, **24**(9), 497-504.

Petchey, O.L. & Gaston, K.J. (2009) Effects on ecosystem resilience of biodiversity, extinctions, and the structure of regional species pools. *Theoretical Ecology*, **2**(3), 177-187.

Picton, B. & Goodwin, C. (2007) Sponge biodiversity of Rathlin Island, Northern Ireland. *Journal of the Marine Biological Association of the UK*, **87**, 1441-1458.

POST – see **Parliamentary Office of Science and Technology**

Pretty J. (2007) The Earth Only Endures. Earthscan, London.

Professional Anglers Association (PAP) (2003) British Freshwater Fish. [online] Available at: <http://www.paauk.com/Fish/freshwater.php> [Accessed 22/10/2010].

Proudfoot, V.B. (1990) Farms and Fields in Northern Ireland *Proceedings of the Royal Irish Academy*, **35**, 24-33.

RA – see **Rivers Agency**

Rahmstorf, S., Cazenave, A., Church, J.A., Hansen, J.E., Keeling, R.F., Parker, D.E. & Somerville, R.C. (2007) Recent climate observations compared to projections. *Science*, **316**, 709.

Ratcliffe, D.A. (1968) An ecological account of Atlantic bryophytes in the British Isles. *New Phytologist*, **67**, 365-439.

Raven, P.J., Holmes, N.T.H., Dawson, F.H., Fox, P.J.A., Everard, M., Fozzard, I.R. & Rouen, K.J. (1998) River Habitat Quality: the physical character of rivers and streams in the UK and Isle of Man. River Habitat Survey Report No. 2, Environment Agency, Bristol.

Reid, N., Harrison, A.T. & Robb, G.N. (2009) *Northern Ireland Irish Hare Survey 2009.* Report prepared by Quercus for the Northern Ireland Environment Agency (DOE).

Reid, N., Ruddock, M., Barratt, I., Robb, G.N. & Montgomery, W.I. (2008) *Northern Ireland Irish Hare Survey 2008.* Report prepared by Quercus for the Environment and Heritage Service (DOE).

Reid, N., Sweeney, O., Wilson, C., Preston, S.J. & Montgomery, W.I. (2007) *Northern Ireland Irish hare survey 2007.* Report prepared by Quercus for the Environment and Heritage Service (DOE).

Reynolds, S.C.P. (2002) *A Catalogue of Alien Plants in Ireland.* Occasional Papers No. 14: pp 414. Office of Public Works, Ireland.

Richardson, A.J., Bakun, A., Hays, G.C. & Gibbons, M.J. (2009) The jellyfish joyride: causes, consequences and management responses to a more gelatinous future. *Trends in Ecology & Evolution,* **24,** 312-22.

Riebesell, U., Körtzinger, A. & Oschlies, A. (2009) Sensitivities of marine carbon fluxes to ocean change. *Proceedings of the National Academy of Sciences,* **106,** 20602-20609.

Rivers Agency (RA) (2008a) 2nd Generation Analysis of 'Properties At Risk' and 'Defended Properties' within Northern Ireland (internal document).

Rivers Agency (RA) (2008b) Strategic Flood Map (NI) – Rivers and Sea. Information Leaflet.

Rivers Agency (RA) (2010) Strategic Flood Map (NI) – Rivers & Sea. [online] Available at: <http://www.riversagencyni.gov.uk/index/stategic-flood-maps.htm?Submit=View+the+Strategic+Flood+Map+%28NI%29+-+Rivers+%26+Sea> [Accessed 07.03.11].

Roberts, D., Davies, C., Mitchell, A., Moore, H., Picton, B., Portig, A., Preston, J., Service, M., Smyth, D., Strong, D. & Vize, S. (2004) Strangford Lough Ecological Change Investigation (SLECI). Report to Environment & Heritage Service by the Queen's University, Belfast.

Robins, N.S. (1996) Hydrogeology of Northern Ireland. HMSO for the British Geological Survey, London.

Robinson, P. (1977) The spread of hedged enclosure in Ulster. *Ulster Folklife,* **23,** 57-69.

Rockström, J., Steffen, W., Noone, K., Persson, Å., Chapin, F.S. III, Lambin, E., Lenton, T.M., Scheffer, M., Folke, C., Schellnhuber, H., Nykvist, B., De Wit, C.A., Hughes, T., van der Leeuw, S., Rodhe, H., Sörlin, S., Snyder, P.K., Costanza, R., Svedin, U., Falkenmark, M., Karlberg, L., Corell, R.W., Fabry, V.J., Hansen, J., Walker, B.H., Liverman, D., Richardson, K., Crutzen, C. & Foley. J. (2009a) A safe operating space for humanity. *Nature,* **461,** 472-475.

Rockström, J., Steffen, W., Noone, K., Persson, Å., Chapin, F.S. III, Lambin, E., Lenton, T.M., Scheffer, M., Folke, C., Schellnhuber, H., Nykvist, B., De Wit, C.A., Hughes, T., van der Leeuw, S., Rodhe, H., Sörlin, S., Snyder, P.K., Costanza, R., Svedin, U., Falkenmark, M., Karlberg, L., Corell, R.W., Fabry, V.J., Hansen, J., Walker, B., Liverman, D., Richardson, K., Crutzen, P. & Foley, J. (2009b) Planetary Boundaries: Exploring the Safe Operating Space for Humanity. *Ecology and Society,* **14**(2), 32.

Rodwell, J.S. (1992) British Plant Communities Volume 3. Grasslands and Montane Communities. Cambridge University Press, Cambridge.

Rosell, R., Evans, D. & Allen M. (2005) The eel fishery in Lough Neagh, Northern Ireland – an example of sustainable management? *Fisheries Management and Ecology,* **12,** 377–385.

Rowe, D.B. (2010) Green Roofs as a Means of Pollution Abatement. *Environmental Pollution.*

Royal Society for the Protection of Birds (2009) Sustainable Development: Farmland Birds.

Royal Society for the Protection of Birds (RSPB) & Department of Agriculture & Rural Development (2004a) Farm Management to Benefit Wildlife in Northern Ireland: Barn Owl.

Royal Society for the Protection of Birds (RSPB) & Department of Agriculture & Rural Development (2004b) Farm Management to Benefit Wildlife in Northern Ireland: Curlew.

Royal Society for the Protection of Birds (RSPB) & Department of Agriculture & Rural Development (2004c) Farm Management to Benefit Wildlife in Northern Ireland: Lapwing (peewit, peesweep).

Royal Society for the Protection of Birds (RSPB) & Department of Agriculture & Rural Development (2004d) Farm Management to Benefit Wildlife in Northern Ireland: Linnet.

Royal Society for the Protection of Birds (RSPB) & Department of Agriculture & Rural Development (2004e) Farm Management to Benefit Wildlife in Northern Ireland: Red grouse.

Royal Society for the Protection of Birds (RSPB) & Department of Agriculture & Rural Development (2004f) Farm Management to Benefit Wildlife in Northern Ireland: Redshank.

Royal Society for the Protection of Birds (RSPB) & Department of Agriculture & Rural Development (2004g) Farm Management to Benefit Wildlife in Northern Ireland: Reed bunting.

Royal Society for the Protection of Birds (RSPB) & Department of Agriculture & Rural Development (2004h) Farm Management to Benefit Wildlife in Northern Ireland: Skylark.

Royal Society for the Protection of Birds (RSPB) & Department of Agriculture & Rural Development (2004i) Farm Management to Benefit Wildlife in Northern Ireland: Snipe (heather bleat).

Royal Society for the Protection of Birds (RSPB) & Department of Agriculture & Rural Development (2004j) Farm Management to Benefit Wildlife in Northern Ireland: Swallow.

Royal Society for the Protection of Birds (RSPB) & Department of Agriculture & Rural Development (2004k) Farm Management to Benefit Wildlife in Northern Ireland: Tree sparrow.

Royal Society for the Protection of Birds (RSPB) & Department of Agriculture & Rural Development (2004l) Farm Management to Benefit Wildlife in Northern Ireland: Yellowhammer.

RSPB – see **Royal Society for the Protection of Birds**

Sayers, P. & Calvert, M. (2007) National Flood Risk Assessment for Northern Ireland: Flood Mapping Strategy (Interim). Report EX 5299. HR Wallingford.

SCBD – see **Secretariat Convention on Biological Diversity**

Scotland & Northern Ireland Forum For Environmental Research (SNIFFER) (2002) Implications of Climate Change for Northern Ireland: Informing Strategy Development.

Scotland & Northern Ireland Forum For Environmental Research (SNIFFER) (2008) A Changing Climate in Northern Ireland.

Scotland & Northern Ireland Forum For Environmental Research (SNIFFER) (2009) Assessing the Benefits of Flood Warning: Phase 3.

Scott, D. (2000) Marking a decade of tree nesting by Hen Harriers, *Circus cyaneus*, in Northern Ireland, 1991-2000. *Irish Birds*, **6**, 586-589.

Scottish Environment Link (2009) Living With the Land: Proposals for Scotland's first sustainable land use strategy.

Secretariat Convention on Biological Diversity (SCBD) (2010) *Global Biodiversity Outlook 3.*

Seymour, J.R., Simo, R., Ahmed, T. & Stocker, R. (2010) Chemoattraction to Dimethylsulfoniopropionate throughout the marine microbial food web. *Science*, **329**, 342-345.

Shand, P., Edmunds, W.M., Lawrence, A.R., Smedley, P.L. & Burke, S. (2007) The natural (baseline) quality of groundwater in England and Wales. British Geological Survey Research Report No. RR/07/06.

Sharpley, A.N. (1985) Depth of surface soil-runoff interactions as affected by rainfall, soil slope and management. *Soil Science Society of America Journal*, **49**, 1010-1015.

Shaw, S.C., Wheeler, B.D., Frith, J., Bailey, M., Dixon. M. & Boffey, C. (1996) Survey of Fens in Down and Armagh. Final Report to Environment and Heritage Service, DOE NI, Belfast. Environmental Consultancy University of Sheffield.

Shortall, S. (2006) A 'green and pleasant land'? Public attitudes to the countryside in Northern Ireland. Northern Ireland Life and Times Survey, 2004.

Simpson, K. (1983) Soil. Longman Scientific and Technical, London.

Sluka, J. (1999) Culture and Policy in Northern Ireland: Anthropology in the Public Arena. *American Anthropologist*, **101**, 449–451.

Smart, S., Dunbar, M.J., Emmett, B.A., Marks, S., Maskell, L.C., Norton, L.R., Rose, P. & Simpson, I.C. (2010) An Integrated Assessment of Countryside Survey Data to Investigate Ecosystem Services in Great Britain. Centre for Ecology & Hydrology, Oxfordshire.

Smith, S.J., Wolfe-Murphy, S.A., Enlander, I. & Gibson, C.E. (1991) The Lakes of Northern Ireland: an annotated inventory. Countryside and Wildlife Research Series Belfast: HMSO.

SNIFFER – see Scotland & Northern Ireland Forum For Environmental Research

Sorte, C.J., Williams, S.L. & Zerebecki, R.A. (2010) Ocean warming increases threat of invasive species in a marine fouling community. *Ecology*, **91**, 2198-2204.

Southall, E., Sims, D., Witt, M. & Metcalfe, J. (2006) Seasonal space-use estimates of basking sharks in relation to protection and political–economic zones in the North-east Atlantic. *Biological Conservation*, **132**, 33-39.

Spedding, A. (2009) New Blood: Attracting the Best Young People to Agriculture. Royal Agricultural Society of England.

Sports Turf Research Institute(STRI) (2010) Guide to the Wildlife and Habitat Conservation: Conservation status of Royal County Down Golf Club. [online] Available at: <www. royalcountydown.org/files/download/guide-to-wildlife-and-habitat-conservation.pdf> [Accessed 07.03.11].

Steele, E.D. (1968) Ireland and the Empire in the 1860s. Imperial Precedents for Gladstone's First Irish Land Act. *The Historical Journal*, **11**, 64-83.

Stevens, R.J. & Watson C.J. (1986) The response of grass for silage to sulphur application at 20 sites in Northern Ireland. *Journal of Agricultural Science*, **107**, 565-571.

Stewart, H., Owen, S., Donovan, R., Mackenzie, R., Hewitt, N., Skiba, U. & Fowler, D. (2003) Trees and Sustainable Urban Air Quality: Using Trees to Improve Air Quality in Cities. Lancaster University.

SEI (Stockholm Environment Institute) (2009) Footprint Results from BRIO Model, October 2009. Biology Department, University of York.

Stockdill, S.M.J. (1982) Effects of introduced earthworms on the productivity of New Zealand pastures. *Pedobiologia*, **24**, 29-35.

Stokes, K., O'Neill, K. & McDonald, R.A. (2006) Invasive species in Ireland. Report to Environment & Heritage Service and National Parks & Wildlife Service by Quercus, Queens University. Environment & Heritage Service, Belfast and National Parks & Wildlife Service, Dublin.

STRI – see **Sports Turf Research Institute**

Strong, J.A., Dring, M.J. & Maggs, C.A. (2006) Colonisation and modification of soft substratum habitats by the invasive macroalga *Sargassum muticum*. *Marine Ecology Progress Series*, **321**, 89-97.

Strong, L. (1993) Overview: the impact of avermectins on pastureland ecology. *Veterinary Parasitology*, **48**, 3-17.

Styles, D., Thorne, F. & Jones, M.B. (2008) Energy Crops in Ireland: An Economic Comparison of Willow and Miscanthus Production with Conventional Framing Systems. *Biomass and Bioenergy*, **32**(5), 407-421.

Sweeney, K., Fealy, R., McElwain, L., Siggins, L., Sweeney, J. & Trinies, V. (2008) Changing Shades of Green: The environmental and cultural impacts of climate change in Ireland. The Irish American Climate Project and Rockefeller Family Trust.

Symons, L. (1963) Land Use In Northern Ireland. University of London Press.

Tang, Y.S., van Dijk, N., Love, L., Dragosits, U., Vieno, M., Smith, R.I., Rippey, B. & Sutton, M.A. (2004) Ammonia monitoring in Northern Ireland. Project UKPIR04 Final Report. Scottish and Northern Ireland Forum for Environmental Research, Edinburgh.

Tatchell, G.M. (1989) An estimate of the potential economic losses to some crops due to aphids in Britain. *Crop Protection*, **8**, 25-29.

TEEB – see **The Economics of Ecosystems and Biodiversity**

Thankappan, S. & Flynn, A. (2006) Exploring the UK Red Meat Supply Chain. Working Series Paper No. 32. The Centre for Business Relationships Accountability, Sustainability and Resources.

The Crown Estate (2010) Northern Ireland: Financial highlights for the year ended 31 March 2010.

The Economics of Ecosystems and Biodiversity (TEEB) (2009) The Economics of Ecosystems and Biodiversity for National and International Policy Makers.

The Economics of Ecosystems and Biodiversity (TEEB) (2010a) A quick guide to TEEB for Local and Regional Policy Makers.

The Economics of Ecosystems and Biodiversity (TEEB) (2010b) Mainstreaming the Economics of Nature: A synthesis of the approach, conclusions and recommendations of TEEB.

The Economics of Ecosystems and Biodiversity (TEEB) (2010c) The Economics of Ecosystems and Biodiversity Report for Business.

The Guardian (2006) Belfast and Beirut tipped as 'must see' cities. Liane Katz, Wednesday 15th November 2006.

Thurstan, R.H., Brockington, S. & Roberts, C.M. (2010) The effects of 118 years of industrial fishing on UK bottom trawl fisheries. *Nature Communications*, **1**, 1-6.

Tidy Northern Ireland (2008) The Joint Green-Schools and Eco-Schools Handbook: For Schools in Both the Republic of Ireland and Northern Ireland.

Tomlinson, R.W. (1997a) Forests and Woodlands. Atlas of the Irish Rural Landscape (eds F.H.A. Aalen, K. Whelan & M. Stout), pp. 122-133. Cork University press, Ireland.

Tomlinson, R.W. (1997b) Land cover - based on Corinne land cover programme. Soil and Environment: Northern Ireland (ed J.G. Cruickshank), p. 101. Department of Agriculture and Rural Development/Queen's University Belfast.

Tomlinson, R.W. (1986a) Antrim AONB tree survey. Report to Wildlife and Countryside Branch, DOE (NI).

Tomlinson, R.W. (1986b) Tree survey of the Mournes and Slieve Croob AONB.

Tomlinson, R.W. (1988a) Armagh AONB tree survey. Report to Countryside & Wildlife Branch, DOE (NI).

Tomlinson, R.W. (1988b) Lagan Valley Regional Park tree survey. Report to Countryside & Wildlife Branch, DOE(NI).

Tomlinson, R.W. (1989) Tree Survey of the Sperrins and North Derry AONB.

Tomlinson, R.W. (2010) Changes in the extent of peat extraction in Northern Ireland 1990-2008 and associated changes in carbon loss. *Applied Geography*, **3**, 294–301.

Tomlinson, R.W. & Milne, R.M. (2006) Soil carbon stocks and land cover in Northern Ireland from 1939 to 2000. *Applied Geography*, **26**, 18-39.

Uda, T. (2009) Beach erosion arising from anthropogenic factors. *Proceedings of Coastal Dynamics*, **1**, 3–19.

UKBSG – see **UK Biodiversity Steering Group**

UK Biodiversity Steering Group (UKBSG) (1995a) Biodiversity: The UK Steering Group Report. Volume 1: Meetingthe Rio Challenge. HMSO, London.

UK Biodiversity Steering Group (UKBSG) (1995b) Biodiversity: The UK Steering Group Report. Volume 2: ActionPlans. HMSO, London.

UKCP09 (2009) Adapting to Climate Change: UK Climate Projections 2009.

UKMMAS – see **UK Marine Monitoring and Assessment Strategy**

UK Marine Monitoring and Assessment Strategy (UKMMAS) (2010) Charting Progress 2: The State of UK Seas. Published by the Department for Environment Food and Rural Affairs on behalf of UKMMAS. TSO, London. 166pp. ISBN 9780112432937. Available at: <http://chartingprogress.defra.gov.uk/resources> [Accessed 14.03.11].

Ulster Grassland Society (2010) Grazing Management.

Upton, A. & Bain, R. (2006) Development Plan for Grazing Animal Project in Northern Ireland.

VGB Secretariat (2006) Facts and Figures: Electricity Generation 2006.

Webb, D.A. (1982) The Flora of Ireland in its European Context. *Journal of Life Sciences, Royal Dublin Society*, **1983**, 143-160.

Whelan, K. (1997a) The modern landscape: from plantation to present. Atlas of the Irish Rural Landscape (eds F.H.A. Aalen, K. Whelan & M. Stout) pp. 67-103. Cork University Press, Ireland.

Whelan, K. (1997b) Towns and Villages. Atlas of the Irish Rural Landscape (ed F.H.A. Aalen, K. Whelan & M. Stout), pp. 80-1996. Cork University Press, Ireland.

WHO – see **World Health Organization**

World Health Organization (WHO) (2005) Ecosystems and Human Well-Being: Health Synthesis. Island press, Washington D.C.

Williams, F., Eschen, R., Harris, A., Djeddour, D., Pratt, C., Shaw, R.S., Varia, S., Lamontagne-Goodwin, J., Thomas, S.E. & Murphy, S.T. (2010) The Economic Costs of Invasive Non-Native Species on Great Britain. Centre for Agricultural Bioscience International, Wallingford, UK.

Wishart, J.H. (1978) Changing peatlands in North Antrim. Unpublished MSc thesis, School of Biological and Environmental Studies of the New University of Ulster, Coleraine (held in UU library at Coleraine).

Withers, J.A., Jess, S., Kirbas, J.M., Matthews, D. & Kelly, T. (2008) Northern Ireland Arable Crops 2008: Pesticide Usage in Northern Ireland. Survey Report 230. Agri-Food & Biosciences Institute, an Agency. Department of Agriculture & Rural Development for Northern Ireland. ISBN 1-84807-135-3.

Woodhouse, M.T., Carslaw, K.S., Mann, G.W., Vallina, S.M., Vogt, M., Halloran, P.R. & Boucher, O. (2010) Low sensitivity of cloud condensation nuclei to changes in the sea-air flux of dimethyl-sulphide. *Atmospheric Chemistry and Physics*, **10**, 7545-7559.

Woodland Trust (WT) (2007) Back On the Map: an inventory of ancient and long-established woodland for Northern Ireland.

Woodland Trust (WT) (2010a) An inventory of ancient and long-established woodland for Northern Ireland.

Woodland Trust (WT) (2010b) *Hedges and hedgerow trees*. Position Statement.

Woodland Trust (WT) (2010c) Will earlier springs throw nature out of step? [online] Available at: <http://www.woodlandtrust.org.uk/en/news-media/releases/Pages/early-spring.aspx> [Accessed 07.03.11].

World Travel & Tourism Council (WTTC) (2010a) Travel & Tourism Economic Impact: Executive Summary.

World Travel & Tourism Council (WTTC) (2010b) Travel & Tourism Economic Impact: Ireland.

World Travel & Tourism Council (WTTC) (2010c) Travel & Tourism Economic Impact: United Kingdom.

Worm, B. & Myers, R.A. (2003) Meta-Analysis of Cod–Shrimp Interactions Reveals Top-Down Control in Oceanic Food Webs. *Ecology*, **84**, 162-173.

WT – see **Woodland Trust**

Yan, T. (2009) Development of dietary and animal approaches to reduce methane emission from dairy cattle. Proceedings of the XV International Silage Conference, College of Agricultural Life Sciences, University of Wisconsin, Madison, pp. 29–30.

Young, M. (2007) The Tellus Project: Geochemical and geophysical surveys in Northern Ireland. [Lecture] Contaminated Land: Opportunities and Challenges in Northern Ireland, Belfast, UK, 16 Jan 2007.

Zacharias, M.A. & Roff, J.C. (2001) Use of focal species in marine conservation and management: a review and critique. *Aquatic Conservation – Marine and Freshwater Ecosystems*, **11**, 59-76.

Appendix 18.1 Approach Used to Assign Certainty Terms to Chapter Key Findings

This chapter began with a set of Key Findings. Adopting the approach and terminology used by the Intergovernmental Panel on Climate Change (IPCC) and the Millennium Assessment (MA), these Key Findings also include an indication of the level of scientific certainty. The 'uncertainty approach' of the UK NEA consists of a set of qualitative uncertainty terms derived from a 4-box model and complemented, where possible, with a likelihood scale (see below). Estimates of certainty are derived from the collective judgement of authors, observational evidence, modelling results and/or theory examined for this assessment.

Throughout the Key Findings presented at the start of this chapter, superscript numbers and letters indicate the estimated level of certainty for a particular key finding:

1. *Well established:* high agreement based on significant evidence
2. *Established but incomplete evidence:* high agreement based on limited evidence
3. *Competing explanations:* low agreement, albeit with significant evidence
4. *Speculative:* low agreement based on limited evidence

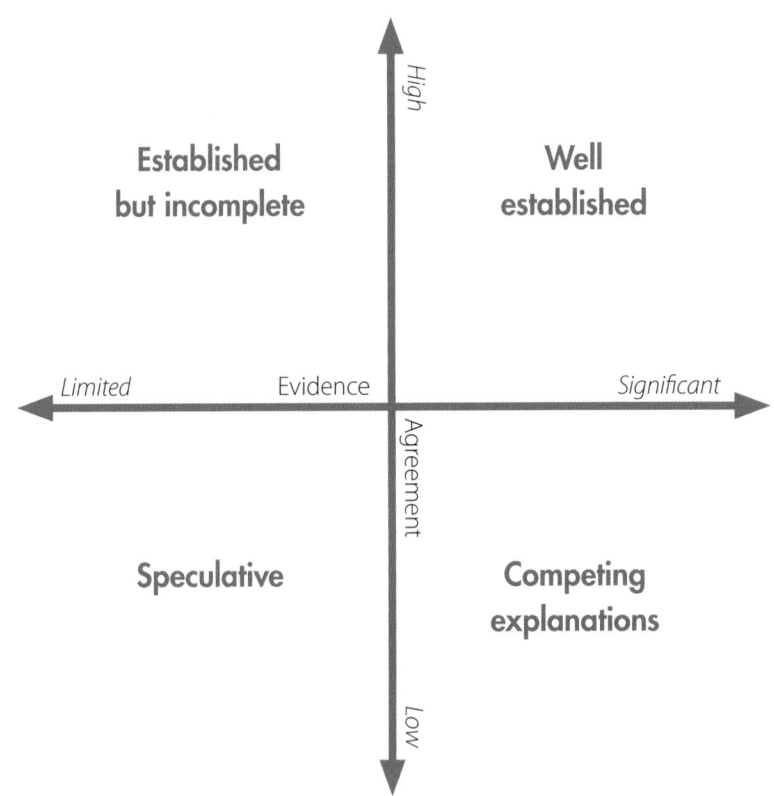

a. *Virtually certain:* >99% probability of occurrence
b. *Very likely:* >90% probability
c. *Likely:* >66% probability
d. *About as likely as not:* >33–66% probability
e. *Unlikely:* <33% probability
f. *Very unlikely:* <10% probability
g. *Exceptionally unlikely:* <1% probability

Certainty terms 1 to 4 constitute the 4-box model, while *a* to *g* constitute the likelihood scale.

Chapter 19:
Status and Changes in the UK Ecosystems and their Services to Society: Scotland

Coordinating Lead Author: Richard Aspinall
Lead Authors: David Green, Chris Spray, Tracy Shimmield and Jeremy Wilson

Key Findings*

Scotland has a distinctive biodiversity with about 90,000 species: about 50,400 on land and 39,200 in the seas around Scotland[1]. Scotland's biodiversity has unique assemblages of species found in many habitats, including Atlantic and montane floras, and fungal communities reflecting combinations of boreal, Arctic-alpine, oceanic and Lusitanian elements. Similar distinctive patterns are found in bryophytes, lichens and birds[1]. There have been significant changes to Scotland's biodiversity and ecosystems over the last 70 years, with examples of species with ranges that are expanding into Scotland as well as others that are contracting in range[1]. The delivery of provisioning services has increased considerably, especially from agricultural systems. This development has had significant impacts and consequences for biodiversity in Scotland, with declining capacities of all ecosystems to support sustained use. Habitats and ecosystems have declined in both area and condition[2]. Biodiversity has shown both declines and increases, although the general trend has been one of decline[2].

[1] well established
[2] established but incomplete evidence

The ecosystems and landscapes of Scotland provide significant ecosystem goods and services and considerable economic benefit to the nation[1]. Provisioning services have a particularly high economic value[2]. Values for other services have not always been assessed and in many cases are unknown[2]. The role of agriculture and forestry in shaping landscapes and ecosystems in Scotland is important because they affect a large proportion (92%) of Scotland's land area. Continued loss of habitat, changes in nutrient storage and cycling, climate change and the impacts of climate change on biological function within habitats have significant consequences for human well-being. Supporting, regulating and provisioning services depend on the continued physical, chemical and biological operation of Scotland's land and marine ecosystems. One of the dominant drivers of change in these ecosystems is resource management.

[1] well established
[2] established but incomplete evidence

The areal extent of many of Scotland's habitats has declined since the 1940s[1]. Mountain, Moorland and Heathland habitats currently occupy about 46% of Scotland; the area of mire and Bog habitats has declined from about 2.3 million hectares (ha) in the 1940s to about 1.8 million ha in the 1980s. Grasslands occupy about 25%, but Semi-natural Grasslands, of highest biodiversity and conservation value and of international significance, are less than 1% of the total area of grassland in Scotland. Enclosed Farmland occupies about 11% of Scotland. The area has declined from over 1.3 million ha in the 1940s–1960s to 950,000 ha in the 2000s. Yields per unit area have increased for barley, wheat, oats and potatoes; the total production of barley increased by a factor 10 and wheat by a factor of 7 between the 1940s and 2000s[1]. The area of permanent grassland increased from about 450,000 ha in the 1940s to over 900,000 by the 2000s[1]. Woodlands currently occupy about 17% of Scotland. Planting rates for new woodlands are currently less than 5000 ha per year[1]. Freshwater systems occupy about 2.5% of Scotland by area and Scotland has about 70% of the UK's freshwater by area and 90% by volume[1]. There are changes in the hydrological regimes of Scottish rivers, reflecting changes in rainfall patterns since the 1960s. River flow is becoming much more seasonal, with increasing discharge in winter months[1]. Urban areas occupy about 2.5% of the land area and are home to over 80% of the population. The extent of Urban areas is increasing in Scotland[1]. The length of Scotland's coastline is over 11,800 km, and about 13% of the total land area of Scotland consists of islands. Coastal Margin habitats are under threat from habitat destruction and rising sea levels[1]. The seas around Scotland are potentially among the most biologically productive seas on the planet, but many Marine habitats are of bad and deteriorating status, damage being caused by climate change, human activities including fishing practices, pollution and infrastructure development[1].

[1] well established

---

* Each Key Finding has been assigned a level of scientific certainty, based on a 4-box model and complemented, where possible, with a likelihood scale. Superscript numbers indicate the uncertainty term assigned to each finding. Full details of each term and how they were assigned are presented in Appendix 19.1.

Supporting services function effectively in Scotland's ecosystems[2]. Scotland has abundant peat and organic-rich soils; Scotland's peatland soils are estimated to store 1,620 megatonnes (Mt) of carbon. Nutrient cycling in Scotland's ecosystems has been altered by pollution, including nitrogen deposition, and by fertilisation in arable systems. The extensive uplands of Scotland receive considerable rainfall and large loads of pollutants through atmospheric deposition. Nutrient inputs are damaging for many native species of high conservation importance and also damage soils[1]. Scotland has abundant water, lochs storing almost 35 billion cubic metres (m^3), and soils storing up to 42 billion m^3 [1]. The quality of the water environment is generally good[1]. Primary production in land and marine ecosystems displays strong seasonal patterns and supports a very broad range of land- and marine-based activities[1].

[1] *well established*
[2] *established but with incomplete evidence*

Regulating services contribute significantly to Scotland's economy[2]. Climate regulation occurs through carbon sequestration in peat soils, woodlands and grasslands on land, and in marine systems[1]. The marine ecosystem also exerts a significant climate regulating effect on Scotland's land areas[1]. Flood and other hazard regulation contributes to social and economic well-being in Scotland[2]; changes in the flow regimes of rivers associated with changing climate patterns are of concern for flood regulation and control. Disease and pest regulation is effective in Scotland[1], although much of this is based on pesticide use rather than ecosystem-based regulation. New diseases and pests are increasingly likely to become established in Scotland, possibly as a result of climate change or movement of infected plants or animals[1]. These diseases may pose significant threats to Scotland's ecosystems, species and habitats. Pollination contributes significantly to biodiversity conservation and through contributions to Scottish agriculture, adds significant economic value to provisioning services[1]. Scotland's ecosystems have a significant capacity for noise, soil, air and water quality regulation[1].

[1] *well established*
[2] *established but with incomplete evidence*

Provisioning services from Scotland's ecosystems contribute significant quantities and varieties of raw materials, as well as economic value to Scotland[2]. Food production from agriculture is highly developed in Scotland and has an impact over about 75% of the land area[2]. Livestock represents the dominant agricultural product in Scotland at over 47% of the value of agricultural production, with livestock products contributing a further 16%. Milk and milk products contribute 14%, beef production contributes about 28%, lamb meat about 10%, pork about 3.5% and poultry almost 5% of the value of agricultural output. Fish production from marine systems is important and has historically supported the economy of coastal and island communities in Scotland. The catch of wet fish has, however, declined, mainly through long-term overfishing. Demersal fish currently constitute about 60% by weight and 40% by value of fish caught and landed by Scottish boats in Scotland. Pelagic fish constitute about 20% of the value of marine fish caught. The shellfish fishery has grown since the 1960s and currently contributes 39% of the total value of fish caught. Aquaculture is growing rapidly, mainly for salmon, trout and shellfish. Salmon and migratory trout in estuary and freshwater areas are important, although numbers caught have declined since the 1950s; catch and release schemes are used to conserve declining stocks. Game from the hunting of birds and mammals is important, especially in upland ecosystems, and field sports provide significant income to sporting estates. The size of game bags for both birds and mammals has declined since the mid-1970s. Timber and a wider variety of timber products are obtained from Scotland's forest ecosystems. Softwood makes up more than 99% of the wood harvest; about 44% of Great Britain's (GB) softwood production is managed by sawmills in Scotland. Softwood is also sold to bioenergy plants. Non-timber forest products are particularly important in Scotland with about 300 species used. Peat is used as fuel for heating, for horticultural compost and in the whisky industry. The area of peat extraction has fallen recently. Ornamental resources are a high value product produced from a relatively small area of land. Scotland has remarkable capacity for generation of renewable energy from land- and marine-based wind power, and from wave and tidal sources.

[2] *established but with incomplete evidence*

Scotland benefits from diverse and extensive cultural services from ecosystems[1]. Local places and landscapes and seascapes are valued highly by Scotland's population and visitors. The landscapes and seascapes of Scotland are distinctive and contribute to Scotland's brand, nationally and internationally. Habitats and landscapes provide opportunities for recreation and tourism and are well used by the Scottish population and by visitors. Nature-based tourism in Scotland is estimated to provide about £1.4 billion in income, with about 39,000 full-time equivalent jobs. Scotland's landscapes are also of high aesthetic and inspirational value.

[1] well established

The Scottish government is actively developing Acts and policies that encourage the enhancement of Scotland's environment while using the many ecosystem services to promote the health and well-being of Scotland's population. Many Acts and policies require the development of an integrated approach to the many pressures and demands placed on Scotland's ecosystems from environmental change and human activity.

19.1 Introduction

19.1.1 Scope and Purpose

The geographical diversity of environmental conditions and history of human impacts in Scotland have produced a rich and varied suite of ecosystems, providing landscapes with distinctive regional character and offering a wide range of ecosystem services that support economic and social development and well-being. The purpose of this chapter is to give an overview and analysis of the status, condition and trends of ecosystems, ecosystem services and drivers of change in Scotland. The chapter identifies Scotland's characteristic ecosystems through a series of broad habitat types, and recognises some of their differences from other parts of the UK (and in some cases, possibly also Europe). The chapter also briefly examines consequences of change, sustainable management to enhance biodiversity, ecosystem services, human well-being, and also knowledge gaps. Although not a policy analysis the chapter aims to give clear messages that can help policy makers to identify where priorities might lie. This is especially important where the UK narrative elsewhere in the UK National Ecosystem Assessment (UK NEA) may not address important aspects of the environment and its services to society in Scotland.

Ecosystem assessment invites a *whole systems* view of the interdependence of natural (physical, chemical and biological) and socio-economic (human) resources. The holistic character of this systems view is important. First, it allows interactions between people and the environment to be structured and understood in ways that mirror the rich complexity of human relations with the 'natural' environment. Second, it recognises the complexity and interdependencies that are encapsulated in biodiversity, geodiversity and ecosystem functioning (Woodward 2009), these being important aspects of the way in which environments support human uses. Third, a whole systems understanding is also important for developing an evidence base to inform policy and management (Aspinall *et al.* 2010)

The concept of ecosystem health is closely aligned with that of ecosystems and ecosystem services and relates to biodiversity and ecosystem function. Healthy ecosystems:

- are able to deliver the ecosystem services that support all forms of life including human, and
- do not suffer loss of productivity or carrying capacity to sustain society and biodiversity.

For an ecosystem to be considered in good health it must demonstrate resilience (Rapport 2007). Resilience is the capacity of an ecosystem to respond to disturbances without loss of structure and functional capability (Bennett & Balvanera 2007; Petchey & Gaston 2009). A healthy ecosystem can, therefore, recover from and adapt to change. Resilience and functional capacities provide benchmark criteria for monitoring ecosystem health and for assessing the sustainability of human uses of ecosystems; biodiversity is an indicator of ecosystem health.

19.1.2 Ecosystems in Scotland

The ecosystems of Scotland, with their rich environmental and biological features, structures and variability, reflect the geography of environmental conditions (climate, geology, soils, vegetation) and processes in Scotland, as well as long environmental and land use histories.

Scotland is located on the north-west coast of Europe at latitudes between 54.6°N and 60.9°N at the interface of polar, continental and Atlantic airstreams (Manley 1952), with sub-polar and sub-tropical influences, and with exceptionally high geological variety (Gordon *et al.* 2004; Gordon 2008). This allows Scotland to support a diversity of ecosystems and habitats rarely equalled in areas of similar size elsewhere in the world (Watling 1997; Baxter *et al.* 2008). Strong topographic and latitudinal variation, and island and coastal effects, add to the variability of regional and local climates and the diversity of ecosystems within Scotland's land and sea area and in turn influence the distribution and abundance of flora and fauna (McVean & Lockie 1969). These underlying patterns of environmental variability produce clear ecological and land use distinctions between different parts of Scotland. Variability in the natural environment also provides a template on which environmental and human histories have shaped the detailed and particular nature of the different ecosystems found, as well as the contemporary uses of ecosystems to support human needs. The majority of the ecosystems in Scotland are profoundly influenced by centuries of management and use, and by the demands placed on them by people. Knowledge of the history of human impacts on ecosystems is therefore important for understanding their current state as well as their functional capacity, health and resilience.

Although environmental variation in geographic space is often gradual (Mather & Gunson 1995), it can be codified in biogeographic zonations (Carey *et al.* 1994; Carey *et al.* 1995; Matthews *et al.* 1997; Kiemer *et al.* 1998), and in mapping of ecosystems and land cover as exemplified by the Land Cover of Scotland, 1988 (MLURI 1993), the Great Britain (GB) Countryside Survey (Norton *et al.* 2009) and national assessments of Land Capability for Agriculture (Bibby *et al.* 1982) and Forestry (Bibby *et al.* 1988; Pyatt *et al.* 2001). The patterns of environmental variability are also mirrored in the Scottish Government's classification of rural accessibility[1].

The UK NEA documents ecosystems and ecosystem services using definitions of Broad Habitat types from the EU Habitats Directive, UK BAP and GB Countryside Survey. These Broad Habitats are used both to identify and characterise the ecosystems of interest. However, ecosystems reflect more than the dominant habitat, vegetation or land cover type, and where possible, reference is made to other qualities that are relevant to the function and health of ecosystems associated with each of the Broad Habitat types.

---

1 The Scottish Government uses a 6-fold and an 8-fold classification of Scotland that recognises urban and rural areas. Urban areas include different categories based on population size of towns. Rural areas are separated into accessible rural (within 30 minutes' drive time of the centre of a town with a population of 10,000 or more) and remote rural. Unless otherwise stated, this chapter includes both accessible rural and remote rural within 'rural'.

19.2 Scotland's Land, Seas and People

Scotland's land area is about 7.9 million hectares (ha). About 13% of this is islands, including almost 200 of at least 40 ha (Haswell-Smith 1996). A highly varied geology within a limited area produces a diverse topography, ranging from significant mountain areas to fertile lowlands. With over 30,000 natural lochs, lochans and pools, and more than 100,000 km of rivers, Scotland's freshwaters represent over 90% of the volume and 70% of the surface area of freshwater in the UK, and include 14 of its 15 largest standing waters. Scotland has 88,600 square kilometres (km^2) of seabed within the 12 nautical mile (nm) limit, and a total surrounding sea area of about 470,000 km^2 to the 200 nm international limit. Around Scotland's coast the same varied geology supports spectacular marine diversity, from voes, sea lochs, lagoons, large estuaries and firths, and thousands of kilometres of rocky coasts, sandy beaches and island shores. Sea lochs such as Loch Alsh and Kyle Rhea have strong tidal streams and contain soft corals, sea firs, sea mats, sponges, anemones, and beds of mussels and brittlestars (Scottish Biodiversity Forum 2003). There are 139 saline coastal lagoons in Scotland, internationally important priority habitats due to their rarity and species (Scottish Biodiversity Forum 2003). The vast majority of the deep seabed in UK waters is found off the north and west coasts of Scotland.

Land throughout rural Scotland is used to produce food, energy and timber, to supply and store water, and to provide for recreation, sport, tourism, and conservation of biodiversity, among other uses. Renewable energy production is emerging as an important land use and ecosystem service, especially in the hills and uplands where there is already well-developed hydropower and also considerable wind energy potential that has long been recognised (Golding 1961), and in coastal areas where there is potential for wind, wave and tidal energy (Brown & Hunter 1961). Coastal systems and floodplains provide coastal defences and flood mitigation using natural environmental system processes. The soils of Scotland, most particularly but not exclusively the organic peat soils in the uplands, are recognised as important stores of carbon and, where active peat-forming vegetation is present, for their capacity to sequester carbon. More generally, the role and central importance of soils in support of ecosystem services is now acknowledged, with attention being paid to soil conservation and management (Sutherland *et al.* 2006; Ritz *et al.* 2009) to ensure healthy soil functions (Puri & Gordon 1998) as a basis for maintenance of supporting, regulating and provisioning ecosystem services. It is important to recognise soil health as an essential element of ecosystem health (Janvier *et al.* 2007; Kibblewhite *et al.* 2008; van Eekeren *et al.* 2009), providing major ecosystem functions including carbon transformations, nutrient cycles, maintenance of soil structure, regulation of pests and diseases, and regulation of water flows and quality. These functions are supported by the combined actions of biological and environmental processes, including by interaction of soil organisms in the abiotic soil environment.

Establishing connections between soil health and broader aspects of biodiversity, including that of microorganisms, is critical for sustainable use of natural resources as soils are a major determinant of the capacity of land to support agriculture and other uses, and hence of many cultural landscapes across Scotland. International and UK work on the function and importance of soil biodiversity has been led by projects taking place in the UK's Natural Environment Research Council (NERC) funded Soil Biodiversity Research Programme (Fitter *et al.* 2005; Usher *et al.* 2006). The field location for this programme was a grassland site at Sourhope in the Cheviot Hills in southern Scotland, already the most studied site in the 10-year MICRONET programme funded by the Scottish Executive (Ritz *et al.* 2004). The Soil Biodiversity Programme investigated the diversity and function of soil microbes (Griffiths *et al.* 2006), soil mycorrhizal fungi (Krsek & Welllington 2006), soil protozoa (Esteban *et al.* 2006) and meso- and macro-fauna (Cole *et al.* 2006), as well as dynamics of carbon cycling (Leake *et al.* 2006), the importance of soil biodiversity to soil structure (Davidson & Grieve 2006) and impacts of management with fertilisers (Murray *et al.* 2006). The work clearly demonstrates the importance of soil microbial populations to ecosystem function (Irvine *et al.* 2006).

There is a strong agricultural influence on landscapes and ecosystems throughout Scotland. Agricultural uses extend to about 75% of the land area (Rural and Environment Research and Analysis Directorate 2009c), arable production taking place on about 11.2% of the land (predominantly in the east) with additional non-enclosed systems, especially improved and upland grasslands, and heaths and moors being used as rangeland pastures for grazing. The interdependence of arable (cereal) production and livestock grazing is marked. About 50% of cereals grown in Scotland are used for animal feed (DTZ 2007). Livestock in some areas are moved from grazing land and into arable areas during winter when the upland grazing areas cannot support large numbers of animals and the weather is cold. The static picture provided by snapshot surveys of land cover and habitat data, and by the June Agricultural Census, hides this well recognised and long-standing interdependence and dynamic of Scotland's agricultural systems.

Grazing animals are not only important for agriculture, but are also an important tool in the management of upland systems for biodiversity conservation, landscape character and sport shooting. Recent declines in sheep and cattle numbers have been identified, after reaching their highest recorded levels (cattle: 1974; sheep: 1990/1) in the late 20th Century (RSE 2008; SAC 2008). Relationships between grazing intensities and biodiversity are well studied (SNH 2000; Albon *et al.* 2007; Pearce-Higgins *et al.* 2008) and it is increasingly recognised that low intensity agricultural systems, especially those based on cattle grazing and limited arable production to provide feedstocks, are of high importance for biodiversity conservation (Bignal & McCracken 1996; Dennis *et al.* 1997; Evans *et al.* 2006). This is recognised in the emerging conceptualisation, identification and mapping of High Nature Value farming systems across Europe (European Environment Agency 2004), and their strong representation in Scotland.

Land tenure continues to be important for ecosystem change and use. The Land Reform (Scotland) Act (2003) and Scotland's access laws provide exceptional opportunities for recreation and enjoyment and contribute to the social, economic and health values afforded by Scotland's diverse environments and landscapes.

The marine areas of Scotland have been subject to human use for over 10,000 years and it is unlikely that there are any pristine ecosystems left on the Scottish continental shelf (Hughes & Nickell 2009). A wide range of regulating, provisioning and cultural services are provided by Scotland's coastal and marine ecosystems. Fishing is an important activity, long contributing to the viability and sustainability of coastal and island communities around Scotland. However, marine fishing, notably trawling and dredging, have damaged and altered ecosystems in coastal seas around Scotland (Hall-Spencer & Moore 2000a; Gordon 2001) and led to declines in species targeted by fisheries (Greenstreet et al. 1999b, a) as well as others caught as bycatch (Piet et al. 2009). Habitats including maerl bed, oyster bed, file shell, fan shell and tubeworm reef, that form living crusts on the seabed, have been damaged and declined in distribution around Scotland and in extent at sites where they occur (Scott & Moore 1996; University Marine Biological Station Millport 2007; Hughes & Nickell 2009; Moore et al. 2009). Marine areas of Scotland are subject to a wide variety of human uses, including not only fishing but also transportation and renewable and fossil fuel-based energy industries. Impacts of climate change are also apparent in marine ecosystems around Scotland, including a rise in sea surface temperature, rises in sea level and increased ocean acidification (UKMMAS 2010). Marine areas in Scotland are now subject to concerted actions for their conservation, including via legislation through the Marine (Scotland) Act and the application of an ecosystem approach (Greenstreet et al. 2009).

The human population of Scotland has remained relatively stable for the last 60 years and is currently about 5.2 million (**Figure 19.1**). There has been a change in the age structure of the population over time, with an increasing representation of older age groups (**Figure 19.1**). Differences in age structure are also evident between rural areas and the rest of Scotland, rural areas having a lower percentage of population between 15 and 34 and higher proportion of 40–69 year-olds than elsewhere. The average population density is low by global—and UK—standards, at about 65 persons per square kilometre. There are four cities with populations greater than 100,000, and a further 350 towns and villages with more than 1,000 inhabitants. Many of these towns and villages are located within the central belt or around the coast (**Figure 19.2**). One-third of the total population of Scotland live in Edinburgh and Glasgow. The average population density in rural areas is only about 12 persons per square kilometre. The changing age structure, with low population densities in rural areas, presents particular challenges for use and management of resources, especially for island and coastal communities, and for hill and upland areas (Post & Pedersen 2008). There are social and economic issues associated with depopulation, counter-drift migration and relative deprivation in rural, hill and

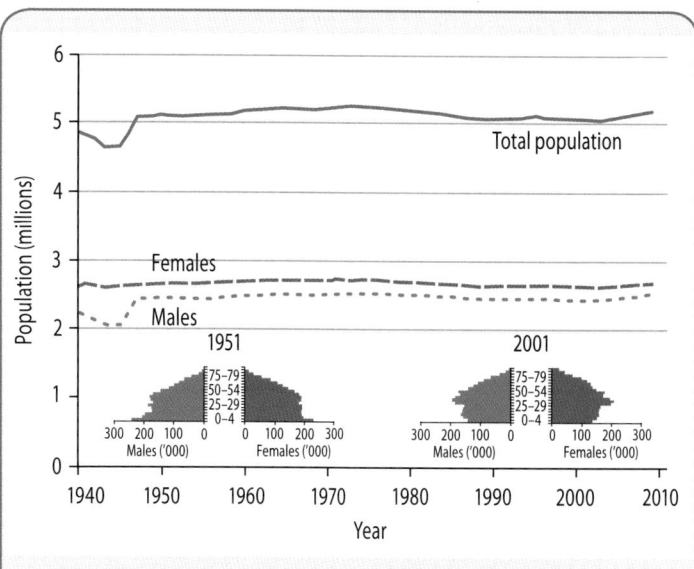

Figure 19.1 Population of Scotland 1940–2009, with population pyramids showing age structure for 1951 and 2001. Source: data from General Register Office for Scotland.

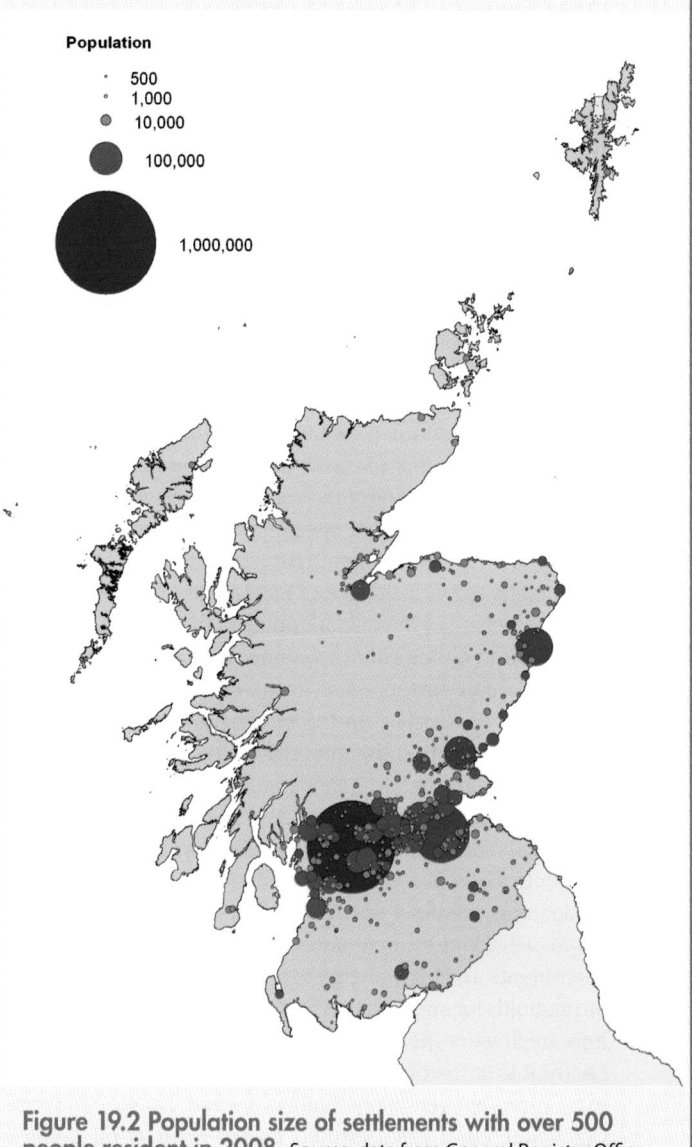

Figure 19.2 Population size of settlements with over 500 people resident in 2008. Source: data from General Register Office for Scotland.

island areas that have an impact on provision of and access to societal services, viability of communities, opportunities for rural development and economic growth, and supply and demand for ecosystem services.

19.3 Biodiversity in Scotland

The diversifying effect of Scotland's varied geological foundations and its position with respect to global atmospheric and oceanic circulations is reflected in its biodiversity resource. The total number of species in Scotland is estimated at about 90,000 (Usher 2002a, b), about 50,400 on land and 39,200 in the seas around Scotland. This total is made up of about 44,100 species of viruses, bacteria and protozoa; 19,184 terrestrial and freshwater invertebrates; 19,069 fungi, algae and bryophytes; 5,527 marine invertebrates; 1,080 vascular plants, 349 marine vertebrates and 310 terrestrial and freshwater vertebrates (Usher 1997, 2002a).

Scotland's biodiversity has been the subject of numerous reviews (Mackey 1995; Usher 1997; Miles *et al.* 1997; Usher 1999, 2002a, b; Mackey 2002; Scottish Biodiversity Forum 2003; Mackey & Mudge 2010). Whilst Scotland's latitude makes it unremarkable in terms of sheer number or global rarity of species, it is remarkable for the unique assemblages of species found in many habitats. For example, nowhere outside Scotland do Atlantic and montane floras co-occur so extensively (Birks 1997). Similarly, the fungal community of Scotland reflects combinations of boreal, Arctic-alpine, oceanic and Lusitanian elements (Watling 1997) and similar patterns are found in taxonomic groups as diverse as bryophytes, lichens and birds (e.g. Thompson *et al.* 1995), with 58% of Europe's bryophyte species found in Scotland (Mackey *et al.* 2001). In the marine environment, a high biodiversity afforded by the coincidence of Lusitanian and boreal/Arctic biogeographic zones in Scotland is further enhanced by the physical and biological heterogeneity created by geological variety, ocean currents and fronts between water masses. This also has its effect in the terrestrial environment, with Scotland supporting the majority of the global populations of Manx shearwaters (*Puffinus puffinus*), northern gannets (*Morus bassanus*), great skuas (*Stercorarius skua*) and grey seals (*Haliochoerus grypus*), and globally important concentrations of a wide range of migratory and wintering wader and wildfowl species (Scottish Biodiversity Forum 2003). In addition, Scotland's rivers, dominated by short catchments and high-energy gravel beds systems, are global strongholds for species such as Atlantic salmon (*Salmo salar*) and freshwater pearl-mussel (*Margaritifera margaritifera*). Lastly, it is in the offshore marine environment that habitats may rank as genuinely highly diverse in global terms. Coldwater coral reefs formed by the hard coral *Lophelia pertusa* may be as rich in biodiversity as some tropical reefs. Similarly, although still poorly studied, deep-sea sediments are likely to be highly species rich and virtually all of the UK resource of these habitats lies off the Western Isles (Matthews *et al.* 1997).

Scotland's topographic diversity also creates biogeographical isolation, whether on its islands, in its lochs or on its montane summits. Endemism and marked genetic and phenotypic distinctiveness within species are therefore marked in Scotland, given its modest land area. The current Scottish Biodiversity List identifies 31 species endemic to Scotland (excluding apomictic plant species), ranging from well-known examples such as the Scottish primrose (*Primula scotica*) and Scottish crossbill (*Loxia scotica*), to a flea (*Ceratophyllus fionnus*) found only from Manx shearwater colonies on Rum, and 11 vascular plants, 10 lichen species, five mosses, and four insects (Mackey & Mudge 2010). Local adaptations within species further add to the genetic component of Scotland's biodiversity (Ennos & Easton 1997). For example, variations amongst island populations of field mice (*Apodemus sylvaticus*) and loch populations of Arctic char (*Salvelinus alpinus*) have been well studied (Hartley *et al.* 1995); recent molecular studies have revealed substantial population genetic structure in water voles (*Arvicola terrestris*) and red grouse (*Lagopus l. scoticus*) between catchments and moors respectively (Piertney *et al.* 1998; Stewart *et al.* 1999); and island forms of several terrestrial bird species, including wren (*Troglodytes troglodytes*), starling (*Sturnus vulgaris*) and song thrush (*Turdus philomelos*), are considered sufficiently distinctive to merit sub-species status (Clugston *et al.* 2001).

Major changes in biodiversity have occurred in Scotland, as elsewhere in the UK, since the 1940s (Rackham 1986; Lovegrove 2007). However, systematic monitoring of biodiversity has only been carried out since the 1960s and 1970s (Marchant *et al.* 1990), when declines in populations became very apparent, for example in birds of prey from the effects of organochlorine pesticides (Ratcliffe 1980) and in native flora from the intensification of agriculture (Perring 1970). Studies of individual species groups, particularly birds, provide evidence of changes since the 19th Century and earlier, e.g. chough (*Pyrrhocorax pyrrhocorax*) (Warnes 1983), crested tit (*Lophophanes cristatus*) (Cook 1982) and others. Recent changes in the distribution of butterflies in Scotland have also been reported (Sutcliffe 2009), four species showing major expansion of their ranges while others have reduced ranges. Usher has reviewed Scotland's coastal biodiversity (Usher 1999) and Scott identified some challenges for development of biodiversity action plans for Scotland's coastline (Scott 1999).

19.3.1 Designated Species and Habitats

In 2004 *Scotland's Biodiversity* (Scottish Executive 2004) was published, a 25-year framework for action to conserve and enhance biodiversity in Scotland. In early 2010 an assessment of biodiversity in Scotland was published (Mackey & Mudge 2010) to coincide with the International Year of Biodiversity.

Overall, Scotland has 65 (38%) of the 169 conservation priority habitat types listed under Annex I of the EU Habitats Directive (Scottish Biodiversity Forum 2003; Scottish Executive 2004), and 82% of the 79 habitats represented in the UK. Over 50% of Scotland's land remains under some form of natural or semi-natural vegetation cover, and Scotland supports examples of 81% of all National Vegetation Classification communities, despite occupying only 35% of the land area of Britain (Miles *et al.* 1997). Amongst the Broad Habitat types to be considered in detail below, Scotland is internationally important for its resource of blanket bog, heather moorland, montane, native woodland and High Nature Value farmland (e.g. machair) habitats. Scotland also holds the UK's largest reedbed, which fringes the lower reaches of the River Tay, the Insh Marshes in the Spey valley, which are the UK's largest continuous area of base-poor fen, and one of Europe's richest surviving concentrations of lowland raised bog (Scottish Biodiversity Forum 2003). Off the coast, some of the finest marine habitats in Europe are in Scottish waters, including estuarine sand and mudflats, coldwater coral reefs, maerl beds, saline lagoons, and deep-sea mud communities (Baxter *et al.* 2008). The Cromarty Firth has the UK's largest known area of dwarf eelgrass (*Zostera noltii*) and the Solway coast contains 10% of the total UK area of saltmarsh (Scottish Biodiversity Forum 2003).

The status of priority species and habitats was reviewed in 2005 and again in 2008 (Mackey & Mudge 2010). Habitats and species that are strongly in decline or particularly vulnerable are identified for targeted action and referred to as biodiversity priority habitats and species. There are 197 UK priority species and 39 priority habitats in Scotland. The summary status of the priority habitats and species is shown in **Figure 19.3**.

Of the 39 priority habitats assessed in 2005 and again in 2008, 17 were stable or increasing, 13 were declining, and the status of nine was unclear or unknown; the overall condition is positive (Mackey & Mudge 2010). Among 41 habitats assessed in 2008, the proportion that were stable or increasing (41%) exceeded those declining (31%; see Mackey & Mudge 2010). Three Priority Habitats of the UK BAP occur only in Scotland (within the UK): serpulid reefs, machair, native pine woods; in 2008, the first two of these were stable and the third increasing. The overall trend for 181 of the 197 priority species in Scotland assessed in 2005 and again in 2008 is negative (Mackey & Mudge 2010). For the 197 priority species assessed in 2008, 74 were stable or increasing, 42

were declining, and the trend was unknown or unclear for a further 77. Three others were lost before or after publication of the BAP and one subsequently was determined not to be a species (Mackey & Mudge 2010; BARS 2011). Among a total of 230 species assessed in 2008, the proportion that were stable or increasing (32%) exceeded those declining or lost (15%; see Mackey & Mudge 2010). The status of priority habitats and species reflects mixed fortunes for BAP species and habitats in Scotland.

Priority habitats and species in Scotland have also been assessed in groups linked to five broad groups of ecosystems (Mackey & Mudge 2010):

Upland: The trend for eight priority habitats associated with Scottish upland ecosystems was positive in 2008. Whereas all the upland priority habitats assessed in 2005 were declining, one had become stable by 2008. The trend for 122 priority species in upland ecosystems was stable and among 13 species assessed in 2008, the proportion that were stable (84%) exceeded those that were declining (8%).

Lowland and farmland: In lowland and farmland ecosystems the trend for 10 priority habitats was stable by 2008. However, of the eight priority habitats assessed in 2008, those declining (63%) exceeded those stable or increasing (39%). The trend for 108 priority species in lowland and farmland ecosystems was divergent, and of 16 priority species assessed in 2008 the proportion that were stable or increasing (32%) was the same as those declining (32%).

Woodland: In woodland ecosystems the trend for seven priority habitats reviewed in 2005 and 2008 was positive and all priority habitats assessed in 2008 were stable or increasing. The trend for 170 priority species in woodland ecosystems is divergent, showing positive and negative elements; of 31 species assessed in 2008, the number stable or increasing (45%) exceeded the number declining or lost (28%).

Freshwater and wetland: In priority habitats associated with freshwater and wetland ecosystems, the trend for nine priority habitats between 2005 and 2008 was stable (no change). Five priority habitats assessed in 2008 showed the proportion that were stable (60%) to be greater than those declining (40%). The overall trend for 75 priority species associated with freshwater and wetland ecosystems was

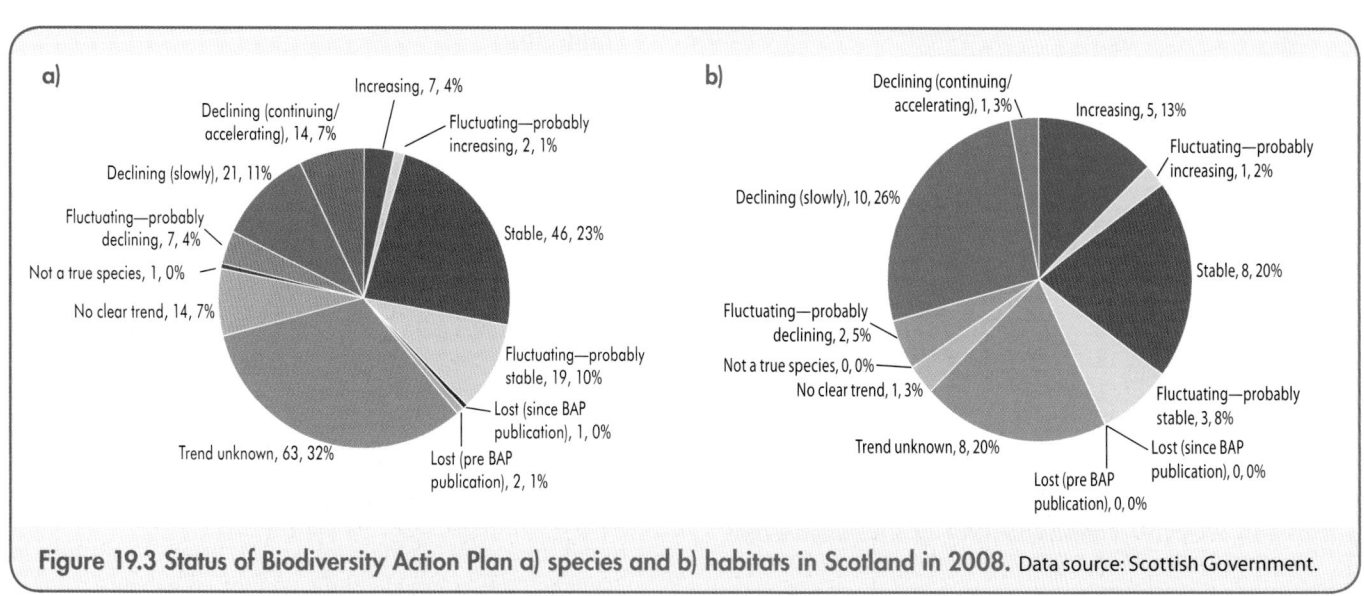

Figure 19.3 Status of Biodiversity Action Plan a) species and b) habitats in Scotland in 2008. Data source: Scottish Government.

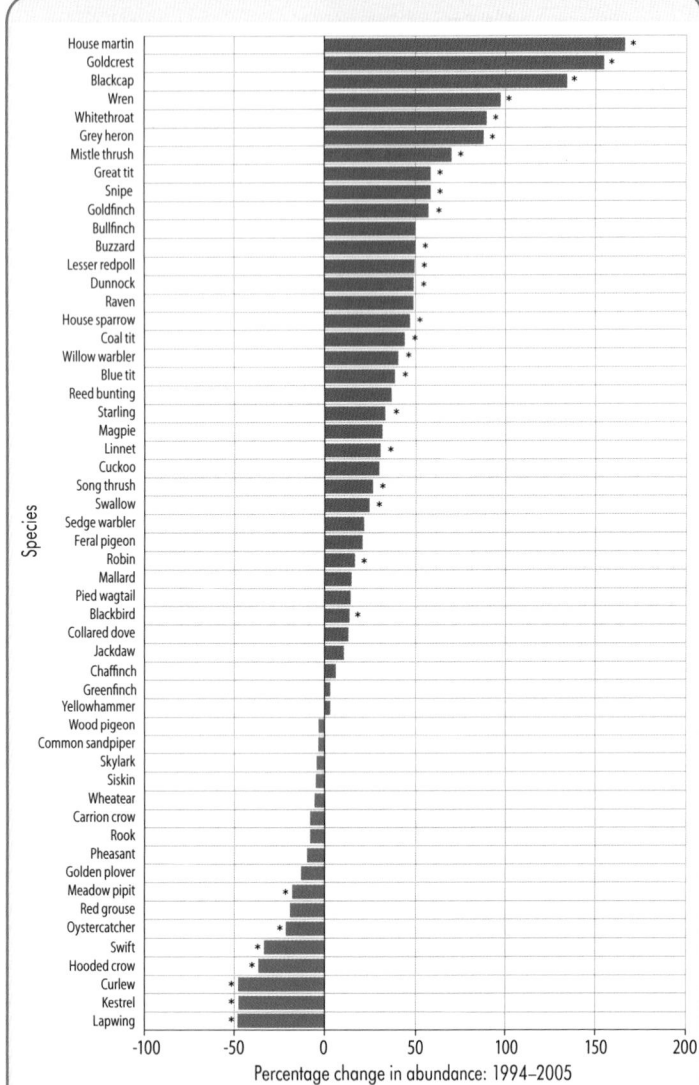

Figure 19.4 Change in the status of widespread breeding land birds in Scotland between 1994 and 2005. Source: data from Raven & Noble (2006). Note: * Identifies species for which population change is statistically significant.

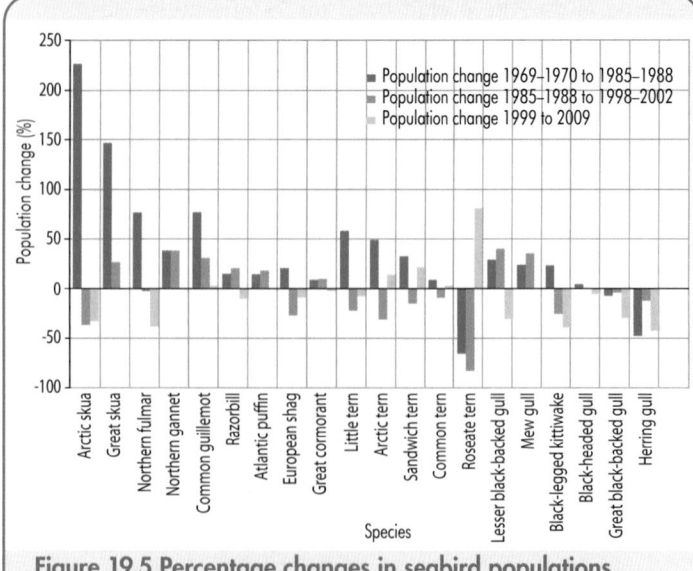

Figure 19.5 Percentage changes in seabird populations between 1969–1970 and 1985–1987 and between 1985–1987 and 1988–2002. Source: data from Mitchell *et al.* 2004.

stable (no change). The proportion that were stable or increasing (41%) exceeded the number declining (25%) in 2008 for the 32 species assessed.

Coastal and marine: Among 26 priority habitats in coastal and marine ecosystems the trend was divergent. Of 11 habitats assessed in 2008, the proportion that were stable (51%) exceeded the proportion declining (38%). The trend for 136 priority species in coastal and wetland ecosystems is positive; those stable or increasing rose from 59% to 66%. Of 28 species assessed in 2008 the proportion that were stable (41%) exceeded those declining (8%).

Although these five groups do not match directly with the eight Broad Habitats used in the UK NEA, they do provide an indication of the status of priority habitats and species across Scotland.

The known trends in populations for well-recorded groups in Scotland similarly are mixed. **Figure 19.4** shows the change in status of widespread breeding land birds in Scotland between 1994 and 2005. Of 54 species studied, 23 showed a statistically significant increase, 7 a statistically significant decrease, and 24 showed no significant change.

Scotland has internationally important populations of breeding seabirds. About 60% of the global population of great skuas, almost 50% of northern gannets, and more than one-third of Europe's Manx shearwaters breed in colonies around Scotland (Mitchell *et al.* 2004). Three seabird surveys have been carried out in Britain, in 1969–1970, 1985–1987 and 1998–2002. Using these data, between 1969 and 1970 and between 1998 and 2002, nine out of 18 seabird species showed a marked increase in their breeding population (i.e. by at least 10%), and five showed a marked decline (Mitchell *et al.* 2004). **Figure 19.5** shows the percentage changes for 18 species of seabird between the dates of the surveys. Only five of the species increased in both the periods between the three surveys, and only seven increased between 1985 and 1987 and between 1998 and 2002.

19.3.2 Designated Areas

The value of the biological, geological and other characteristics of Scotland's ecosystems in the land area is recognised and many areas have been given at least one international, European, national or local designation (**Table 19.1**).

As of 30 November 2008 there were 1,447 Sites of Special Scientific Interest (SSSIs) in Scotland (944 biological, 314 geological, 189 mixed) covering 1,023,000 ha (12.7% of the land area; see **Table 19.1**). Scotland also contributes to the Natura 2000 network as part of the network of protected areas representing the most important wildlife sites in the European Union. Natura 2000 is made up of sites designated as Special Areas for Conservation (SACs) and Special Protection Areas (SPAs). Special Areas of Conservation refer to the European Commission Habitats Directive (Directive 92/43/EEC) and SPAs to the European Commission Birds Directive (Directive 79/409/EEC). There are 239 SACs in Scotland (about 960,000 ha or 9.6% of Scotland's land area) and 153 SPAs (about 1.3 million ha or 13.4% of Scotland's land area, **Table 19.1**). Some of the SACs and SPAs apply to the same area, giving a total of 391 Natura 2000 sites in Scotland. These provide protection for 56 habitats, 79 bird

Type	Number	Area (ha)	Proportion of Scotland's land area (%)
International Designations			
Biogenetic Reserves	2	2,388	0.03
Biosphere Reserves	3	11,445	0.14
European Geoparks	3	804,329	10.02
Ramsar sites	51	313,181	3.90
(Natural) World Heritage Sites	1	24,201	0.01
European Designations			
European Diploma Areas	2	5,848	0.07
Special Areas of Conservation (SAC)	239	962,690	9.61
Special Protection Areas (SPA)	153	1,296,489	13.42
National Designations			
Areas of Special Protection	8	1,518	0.02
Gardens and designated landscapes	386	75,383	0.94
Marine Conservation Areas (MCA)	29	111,895	
National Nature Reserves (NNR)	63	133,746	1.67
National Parks (NP)	2	639,150	7.97
National Scenic Areas (NSA)	40	1,378,358	12.72
Sites of Special Scientific Interest (SSSI)	1447	1,023,152	12.74
SSSI (biological)	944	568,848	7.24
SSSI (geological)	314	34,569	0.44
SSSI (mixed)	189	422,466	5.38
Local Designations			
Country Parks	36	6,481	0.08
Local Nature Reserves (LNR)	57	10,009	0.12
Long Distance Routes (LDR)	5	-	-
Regional Parks (RP)	4	86,160	1.07
Scheduled Ancient Monuments	7,896	17,330	0.22

1,119 km² (see **Table 19.1**). The Marine (Scotland) Act 2010 and the UK Marine and Coastal Access Act include new powers for Scottish Ministers to designate Marine Protected Areas (MPAs) in the seas around Scotland. Marine Protected Areas offer a range of measures to manage and protect Scotland's seas. Under the Marine (Scotland) Act 2010 MPAs can be designated within Scottish territorial waters (inside 12 nm) for conservation of nationally important marine wildlife, habitats, geology and undersea landforms, as Demonstration/Research MPAs to demonstrate or research sustainable methods of marine management or exploitation, and as Historic MPAs for features of historic/cultural importance such as shipwrecks and submerged landscapes. The UK Marine and Coastal Access Act includes equivalent provisions for Scottish Ministers to designate MPAs for the conservation of nationally important marine wildlife, habitats, geology and undersea landforms in offshore waters (outside 12 nm) adjacent to Scotland.

19.4 Condition, Status and Trends in Broad Habitats

The distribution of the Broad Habitat types of Scotland are shown in **Figure 19.6** and the relative proportions are shown in **Table 19.2** and **Figure 19.7**. There are considerable differences between the islands and mainland Scotland in the proportion of different Broad Habitats (see **Table 19.2** and **Figure 19.7**) together with associated land uses and opportunities for land use.

In addition to ecosystem services associated with the Broad Habitats and associated land cover, the ways in which habitats are arranged relative to one another and distributed within different geographic areas also contributes to both the character of Scotland's landscapes and the regional and local nature of ecosystem goods and services that are realised. For example, **Figure 19.8** shows the proportion of each of the Broad Habitats in some of the major river catchments of Scotland, revealing considerable differences across the country. The composition and relative proportion of different habitats, types of land cover and associated land uses within catchment areas, and especially the proportion of arable agriculture, have been found to have a strong correlation with water chemistry in rivers (Wright *et al.* 1991). An understanding of catchment level characteristics is important for river basin management (Ferrier & Jenkins 2010), including flood regulation. Engineering works, especially in urban areas and for sewage management, are also important for maintenance of water quality.

There are a number of general traits that are shared across all the ecosystems represented by the Broad Habitats in Scotland. All cycle nutrients and water and use energy through a complex series of biogeochemical and physical processes. Microbiological communities and processes are among the most important drivers of biogeochemical cycling and energy flow, yet the microbiology of ecosystems

species and 18 other animal species. The majority of SPAs and SACs are also underpinned by SSSI legislation as part of the Nature Conservation (Scotland) Act 2004. An economic assessment of the costs and benefits of Natura 2000 sites in Scotland carried out in 2004 showed that the sites had a national welfare benefit seven times greater than the national costs over a 25-year period (Jacobs 2004).

Although SPAs and SACs can apply to land and marine areas, there are no SACs or SPAs that are entirely in marine areas in Scotland; there are 36 SACs in Scotland with a marine component (Joint Nature Conservation Council 2011). There are 29 Marine Conservation Areas with a total area of

Table 19.2 Amount and proportion of UK NEA Broad Habitat types in Scotland (Mainland, Islands, All Scotland). Source: data derived from the Land Cover Map 2000 (Fuller *et al.* 2002). Note: the area of Woodland in Scotland in 2009 is 17.2% (Forestry Commission 2009).

UK NEA Broad Habitat	Mainland (ha)	%	Islands (ha)	%	All Scotland (ha)	%
Mountains, Moorlands & Heaths	2,887,910	42.2	717,620	69.4	3,605,540	45.7
Grasslands, including Semi-natural Grasslands	1,610,770	23.5	212,680	20.6	1,823,450	23.1
Enclosed Farmland	883,120	12.9	600	0.1	883,720	11.2
Woodlands	1,107,000	16.2	50,490	4.9	1,157,490	14.7
Freshwaters – Openwaters, Wetlands & Floodplains	132,790	1.9	32,710	3.2	165,500	2.1
Urban	186,020	2.7	5,500	0.5	191,530	2.4
Coastal Margins	19,130	0.3	19,200	1.1	38,330	0.4
Total	**6,826,740**		**1,038,800**		**7,865,560**	

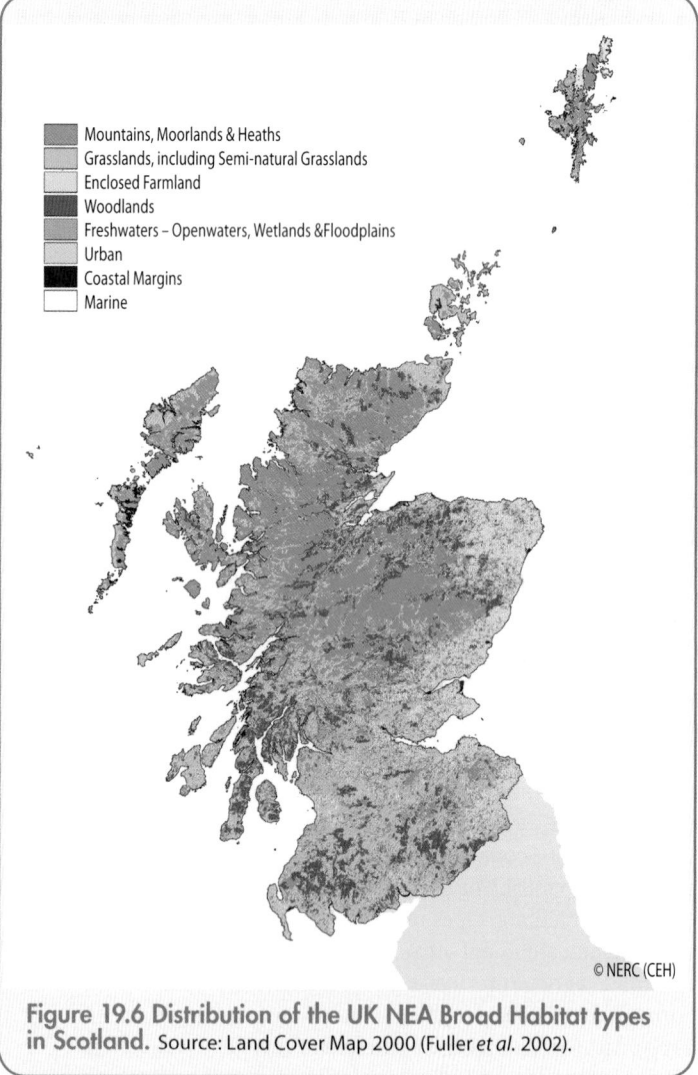

Figure 19.6 Distribution of the UK NEA Broad Habitat types in Scotland. Source: Land Cover Map 2000 (Fuller *et al.* 2002).

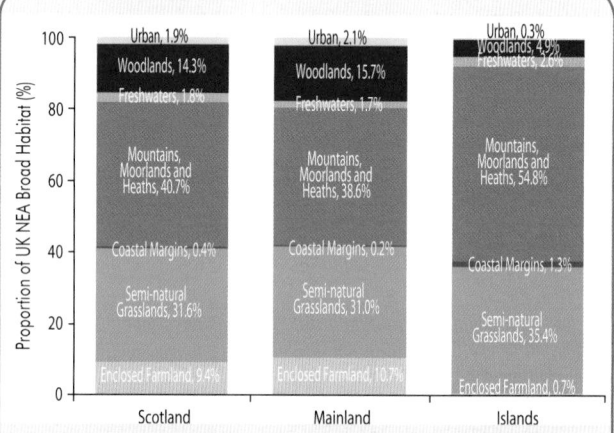

Figure 19.7 Proportion of UK NEA Broad Habitat types in Scotland (All Scotland, Mainland, Islands). Source: data derived from the Land Cover Map 2000 (Fuller *et al.* 2002).

and their associated soils and habitats are among the least studied aspects (Grayston *et al.* 2001; Grayston *et al.* 2004; Aalders *et al.* 2009) with the exception from the upland grassland research at Sourhope (Usher *et al.* 2006). Scotland's ecosystems demonstrate not only the application of environmental processes but also the specific and singular variability of place, time and scale that supports the biodiversity and individual character of places and communities. The influence of human systems is also strongly evident in Scotland. Ecosystems are increasingly documented, studied and understood through a systems view that recognises the importance of human social and economic systems (Aspinall *et al.* 2010). Across the set of ecosystems and habitats considered here, management intensity not only provides a gradient of variation but also provides a good predictor of vegetation type and diversity, as well as consequences of land use change scenarios (Wilson *et al.* 2003).

Associations between the Broad Habitats and major soil groups in Scotland are shown in **Figure 19.9**. The sequences of changes in soils associated with Enclosed Farmland, Semi-natural Grasslands, Woodlands, and Moorland vegetation roughly reflect management intensity. Soil has not been mapped for about 50% of the area of urban land (shown as 'urban' or 'built up area' (bua) in soils maps).

19.4.1 Mountains, Moorlands and Heathlands

Mountains, Moorlands and Heathlands are extensive in Scotland (**Figures 19.6** and **19.10**), which contains a significant area of land at high elevation. Some 30.5% of the land area is above 305 m, 5.8% above 609 m, 3.1% above 700 m and 1.3% above 800 m. There are some 540 distinct tops with 284 over 914 m designated as 'Munros',

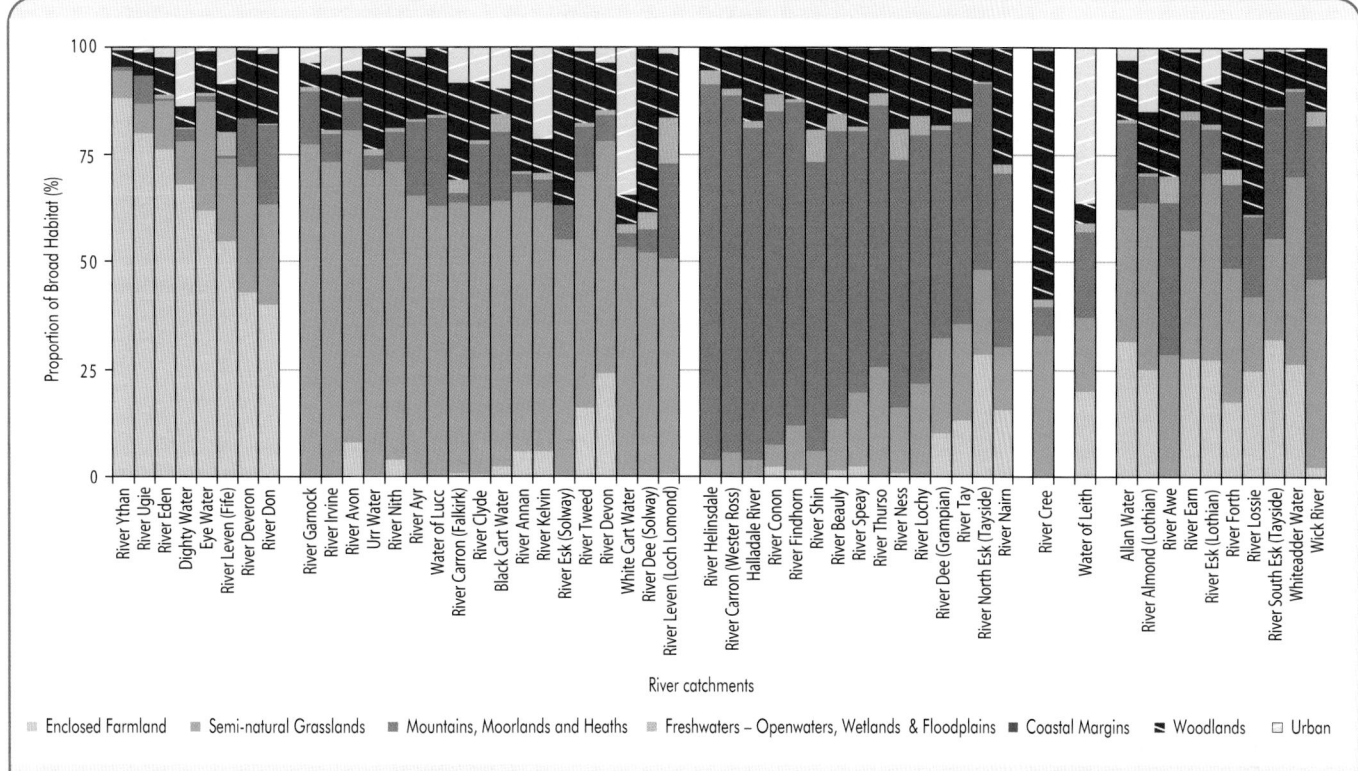

Figure 19.8 Proportion of UK NEA Broad Habitat types in some of the main river catchments in Scotland. Source: derived from the Land Cover Map 2000 (Fuller *et al.* 2002) and spatial data for water catchments in Scotland.

Legend: Enclosed Farmland · Semi-natural Grasslands · Mountains, Moorlands and Heaths · Freshwaters – Openwaters, Wetlands & Floodplains · Coastal Margins · Woodlands · Urban

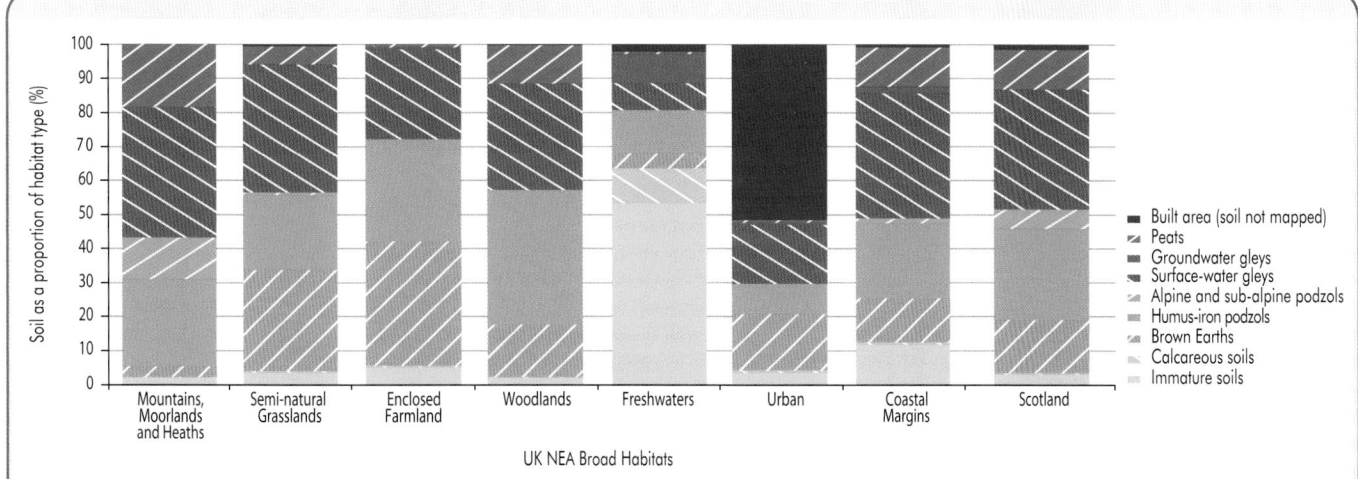

Figure 19.9 Associations between UK NEA Broad Habitat types and major soil groups (based on area of habitats and major soil groups). Source: derived from the Land Cover Map 2000 (Fuller *et al.* 2002) and Major Soil Groups from the 1:250,000 soils map of Scotland (Macaulay Land Use Research Institute).

Legend: Built area (soil not mapped) · Peats · Groundwater gleys · Surface-water gleys · Alpine and sub-alpine podzols · Humus-iron podzols · Brown Earths · Calcareous soils · Immature soils

and over 200 summits between 820 and 914 m designated as 'Corbetts' (Donaldson 1974). The lower elevation limit of the montane area is generally considered to be between 700 and 840 m (McVean & Lockie 1969) and the UK resource of montane habitats is thus heavily concentrated in Scotland.

The vegetation of the high elevation areas is a mix of montane and upland vegetation types including heather moorlands, mires and blanket bog, and poor quality grasslands. Vegetation-environment relationships in upland Scotland show a general pattern that reflects degree of oceanicity and the number of wet days, as well as temperature and other gradients that correlate with geographic location as elevation and latitude (Brown *et al.*

1993; Brown *et al.* 1993). Mountain, Moorland and Heathland habitats cover about 46% of Scotland's land area and are far more extensive than elsewhere in the UK (5% in England, 17% in Northern Ireland and 12% in Wales).

The climatic conditions in Scottish Mountain environments are harsh (Birse & Robertson 1970; Birse & Dry 1970). Winters are extremely cold with significant snowfall. Summers are cool and wet. High wind speeds produce exposed conditions which limit both woody and herbaceous plant growth. Soils are nutrient poor, thin and rocky and, where developed, include a high proportion of humus-iron podzols, alpine and sub-alpine podzols, and surface water gleys, as well as peats (Soil Survey of Scotland

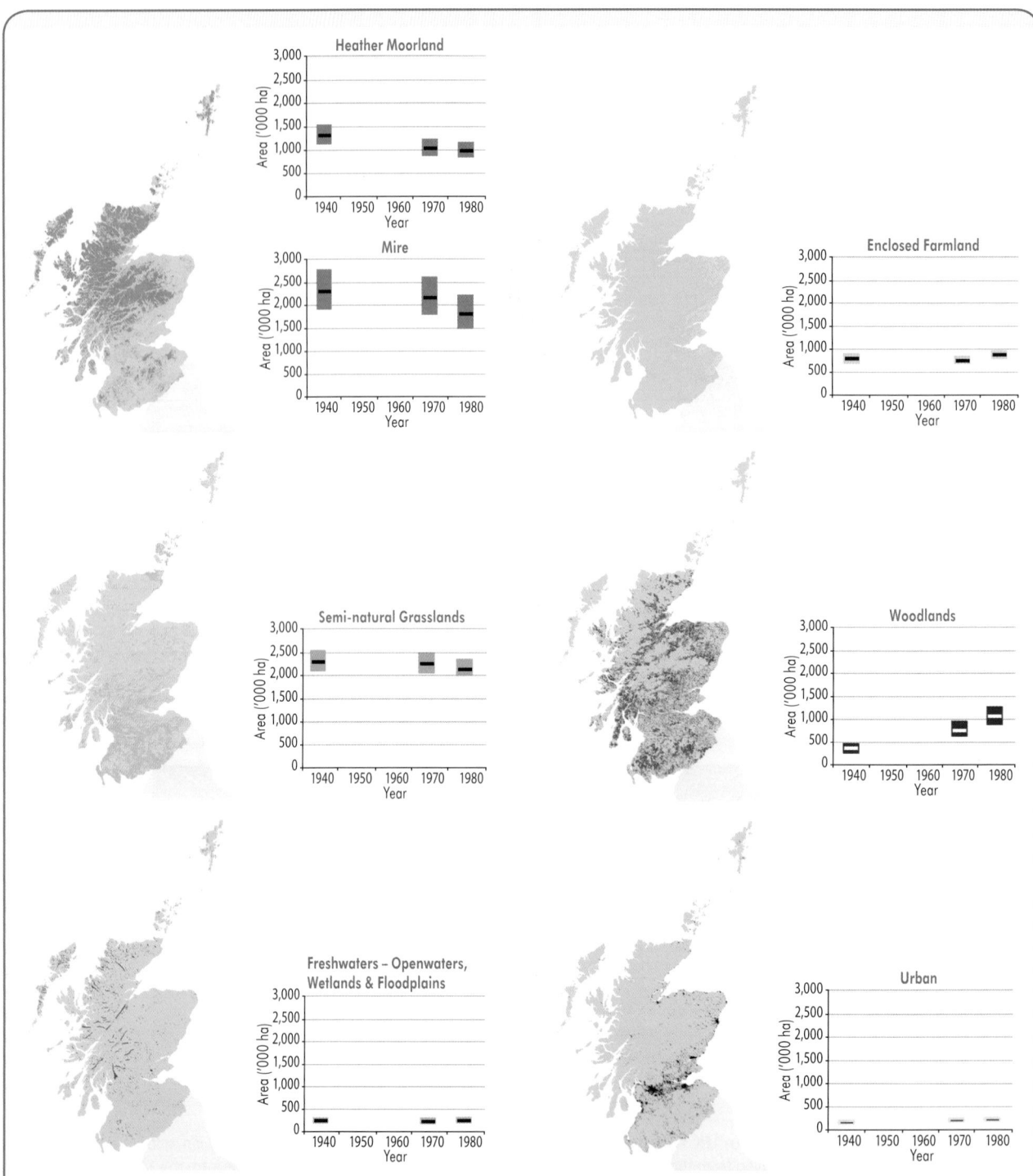

Figure 19.10 Summary of UK NEA Broad Habitats: distribution and change in area between the 1940s and 1980s. The height of the bars on the charts represents the 95% confidence limits around the estimated area of the habitat; the estimated area is shown as a line across the bar. Source: Land Cover of Map 2000 (Fuller *et al.* 2002) and data from the National Countryside Monitoring Scheme (Mackey *et al.* 1998). Countryside Survey data owned by NERC – Centre for Ecology & Hydrology.

1984). Plant growth is slow in these conditions and primary production is low.

A variety of important Montane habitats are found in Scotland, including *Racomitrium* and lichen heaths, plant communities associated with snow beds, mires, and dwarf shrub heaths (Pearsall 1950; McVean & Lockie 1969). *Nardus* grasslands are also present as a result of overgrazing and atmospheric pollution and may replace *Racomitrium* heath (McVean & Lockie 1969).

The Montane habitats of Scotland have several distinctive features (Mackey 1995):

- They are oceanic and southern outliers of communities representative of Arctic-alpine fellfield and mountain tundra environments (Brown *et al.* 1993).
- They contain representative examples of globally rare or local vegetation.
- Their breeding bird communities include both Arctic and temperate species (Thom 1986; Forrester *et al.* 2007), many of which are rare, of international significance, and protected.
- They contain extremely rich and diverse bryophyte and lichen communities, especially within a European context (Thompson *et al.* 1995, Summers *et al.* 1999).

Moorland vegetation includes a range of semi-natural vegetation types dominated by Dwarf Shrub vegetation, especially *Calluna vulgaris*. Moorlands occupy land physically located between the Montane habitats at high elevations, and the Enclosed Farmland, rough grasslands, Woodlands, and Bogs located at lower elevations in Scotland, although in the far north Moorland vegetation is found at or near sea level. Many Moorland areas were formerly covered by woodland, but grazing, mainly since the late 17th Century to develop sheep pasture, and burning, since the 1840s to encourage grouse for shooting, have removed the trees and created the open, heather- and grass-dominated landscapes familiar today (Gimingham 1972). Controlled burning on shooting estates continues to maintain patchworks of heather habitats suitable for grouse (Tharme *et al.* 2001). Grazing by red deer (*Cervus elaphus*) and by sheep also has an impact on Moorland vegetation (Clarke *et al.* 1995; Hester & Baillie 1998; Hester *et al.* 1999; Cuartas *et al.* 2000; Albon *et al.* 2007).

The GB National Vegetation Classification recognises 19 moorland plant communities (Rodwell 1992). Nine of these (**Table 19.3**) are of international importance in Scotland (Mackey 1995).

Heather moorland is associated with nutrient-poor soils and a variety of heather moorland types are recognised (Pearsall 1950; Gimingham 1972). Mires are associated with organic peat soils actively created by their plant communities under wet and cool climatic conditions (Ellis & Tallis 2000; Bragg 2002). Heather moorlands are a product of active land management over the last 200 years, notably by grazing with sheep and, in many areas, by burning, to create habitat for red grouse on sporting estates (Gimingham 1972). Overgrazing and burning exacerbated by drainage of blanket peats for land improvement to increase areas of grassland for grazing, and the expansion of plantation forestry since the 1920s (through direct government action and fiscal support to the private sector) have reduced the area of heather moorland and mire in Scotland since the 1940s (**Figure 19.11**).

The major pressures on Scotland's montane environments arise from grazing, pollution from atmospheric deposition of nitrogen and sulphur, and from climate change that alters the distribution of climatic conditions required by montane biodiversity. Mountains, Moorland and Heathland habitats are also a location for significant leisure activities, hillwalkers being attracted to the highest mountain areas of Scotland. Environmental impacts of these activities include habitat damage, erosion, and disturbance of breeding animals (Gordon *et al.* 2002).

Montane and Moorland plant communities are at risk from increased nitrogen deposition (Woolgrove & Woodin 1996; Britton *et al.* 2005; Britton & Fisher 2007a,b, 2008), climate change (Trivedi *et al.* 2008), overgrazing, especially by red deer and sheep (Albon *et al.* 2007), and increased recreation activity (Bayfield 1973; Sidaway & Thompson 1991; Sidaway 2001).

Atmospheric deposition of nitrogen and sulphates and grazing by sheep reduce the growth of *Racomitrium* and lead to its degradation and replacement by grass-dominated vegetation (van der Wal *et al.* 2003; Britton *et al.* 2005). These changes have been implicated in changes in distribution of dotterel (*Charadrius morinellus*) in Scotland. Dotterel breed on montane heaths dominated by *Racomitrium*, the close juxtaposition of these heaths with montane bogs providing the preferred feeding conditions for both adults and chicks (Galbraith *et al.* 1993). Recent evidence of decline in late-lying snowpack has implications for snowbed communities in montane environments (Bjork & Molau 2007). Similar declines in snowbed communities can be expected in Scotland with changed snowfall patterns (SNIFFER 2006) and earlier snow melt. Snowbed changes can also be expected to have implications for water quality and quantity, and for fish stocks and fishing, as patterns of flow and water temperatures in rivers have changed (Doughty *et al.* 2002; Soulsby *et al.* 2002).

Climate change has implications for all ecosystems in Scotland, not solely for upland ecosystems. Consequences of climate change have been predicted for many species at European, UK and more local scales (Huntley *et al.* 2007). Moreover, climate envelope models have been shown successfully to identify recent changes in bird populations as a function of observed climate changes (Green *et al.* 2008). In Britain, summer temperature has been found to provide the best overall explanation for bird diversity patterns (Lennon *et al.* 2000). Upland species are particularly at risk, as suitable climatic habitat for species that are already located at high elevation may not occur in Scotland under warming conditions (Huntley *et al.* 2007). Detailed ecological understanding of the mechanism through which climate change affects individual upland species remains scarce, but is growing. For example, protracted spring warming has been implicated in the decline of the capercaillie (*Tetrao urogallus*) in Scotland (Moss *et al.* 2001), increased summer temperatures may underlie declines in the British ring ouzel (*Turdus torquatus*) population (Beale *et al.* 2006). There is also now good evidence that future population trends of golden plover (*Pluvialis apricaria*) populations are likely to depend upon interactions between summer rainfall and temperature, their effect on tipulid populations (a key food source for many upland birds), and impact upon plover reproductive success (Pearce-Higgins & Yalden 2004; Pearce-Higgins *et al.* 2010).

Table 19.3 National Vegetation Classification of Moorland habitat plant communities found in Scotland, and that are of international importance.
Source: SNH (2000).

NVC Classification	Community name
H10	*Calluna vulgaris – Erica cinerea*
H12	*Calluna vulgaris – Vaccinium myrtillus*
H16	*Calluna vulgaris – Arctostaphylos uva-ursi*
H21	*Calluna vulgaris – Vaccinium myrtillus – Sphagnum capillifolium*
M15	*Scirpus cespitosus – Erica tetralix*
M16	*Erica tetralix – Sphagnum compactum*
M17	*Scirpus cespitosus – Eriophorum vaginatum*
M18	*Erica tetralix – Sphagnum papillosum*
M19	*Calluna vulgaris – Eriophorum vaginatum*

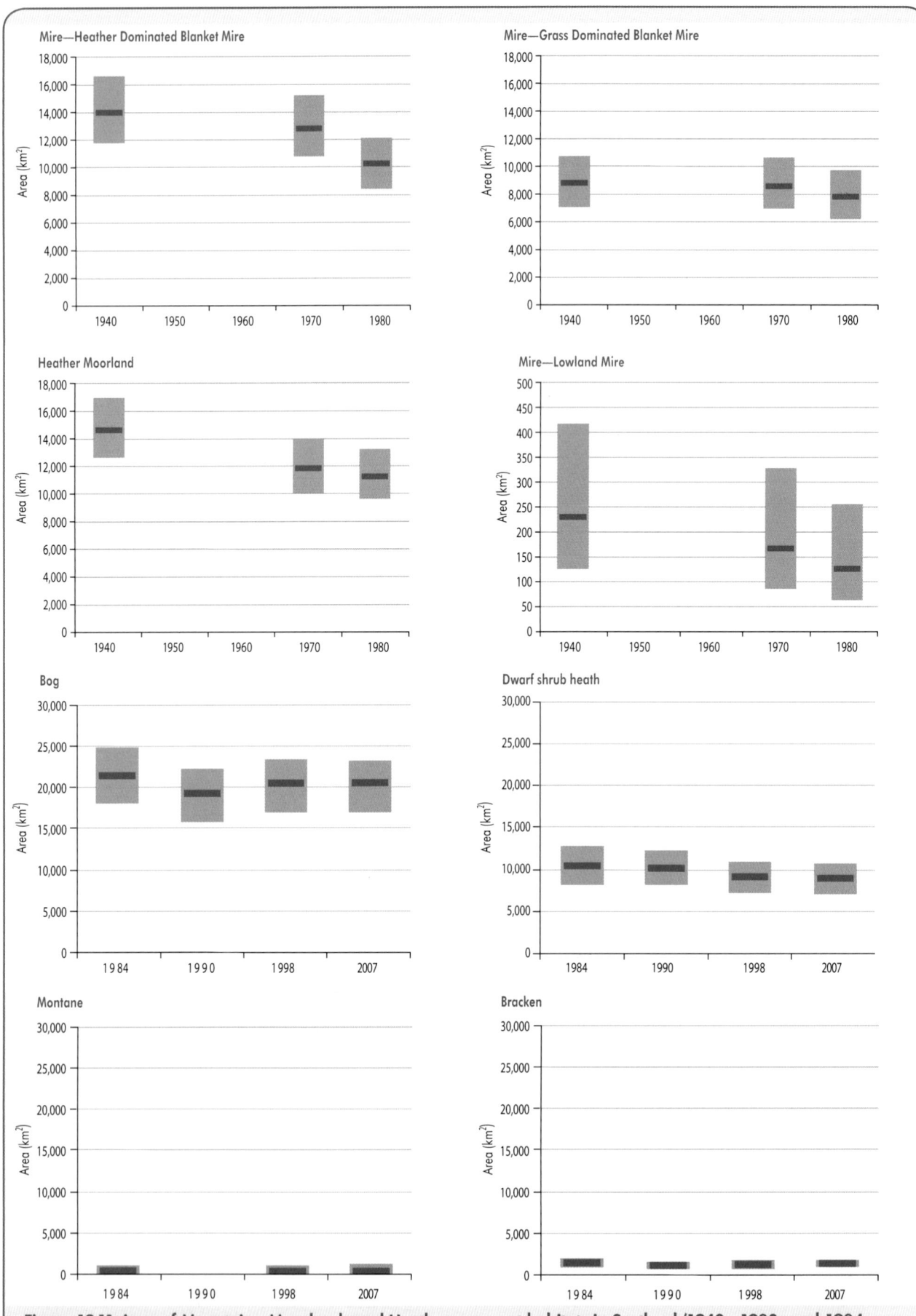

Figure 19.11 Area of Mountains, Moorlands and Heath component habitats in Scotland (1940s–1980s and 1984–2007). The height of the bars on the charts represents the 95% confidence limits around the estimated area of the habitat; the estimated area is shown as a line across the bar. Source: 1940s–1980s: National Countryside Monitoring Scheme (Mackey *et al.* 1998); 1984–2007: Countryside Survey (Norton *et al.* 2009). Countryside Survey data owned by NERC – Centre for Ecology & Hydrology.

Changes in the duration of snow-lie are associated with changes in upland vegetation, especially snowbed plant communities, and have also had an impact on montane animals that depend on prolonged snow. Snow bunting (*Plectrophenax nivalis*) and ptarmigan (*Lagopus muta*), both birds of the Arctic, are found breeding at high elevations in Scotland's mountains. The snow bunting breeding population of Scotland is now estimated at about 50 pairs (Forrester *et al.* 2007), an increase from the very small numbers reported previously (Nethersole-Thompson 1966; Sharrock 1976; Thom 1986).

Upland areas are used for a variety of land uses, and deliver supporting, regulating, provisioning and cultural services. Upland areas act as source areas for human water supply, rainfall draining from gathering grounds being stored in reservoirs and lochs, from where water is piped to Scotland's cities and towns. Much of the uplands also provide rough grazing for livestock. Moorlands provide iconic landscapes supporting a variety of cultural ecosystem services. They can be of high aesthetic value and provide inspiration, 'heather-clad moors', invoking a sense of place, and frequently becoming intimately associated with 'wilderness' (Chapter 5) and with National Parks and National Nature Reserves (NNRs).

Moorland and upland areas are also increasingly attractive for recreation and leisure activities (Chapter 5). A wide variety of recreation and leisure activities take place in Scotland's uplands, including hiking, biking, climbing, skiing, camping, nature viewing, and hunting (fishing, deer-stalking, grouse shooting). These recreational activities provide significant income to local economies, and support employment. Upland ecosystems provide numerous opportunities for diversification in local economies. The high numbers of visits to upland areas can also be expected to have attendant benefits for individual health and well-being.

19.4.2 Semi-natural Grasslands

Grasslands cover about a quarter of Scotland's land area (see **Figure 19.6** and **Figure 19.10**) and are associated with brown earth, humus-iron podzols, and surface-water gley soils (see **Figure 19.9**). The range of associations with different soils reflects the overall variety of grasslands that are found in Scotland. Grassland ecosystems are extensive in upland areas and include 24% of the land area, with an annual average rainfall in excess of 1,500 mm. The extent of grasslands in a river catchment has been shown to have a strong positive association with suspended particulate matter and biologically active phosphorus in river waters downstream, and also to have potential as an indicator of river biogeochemical functioning (Stutter *et al.* 2007). Grasslands are an important habitat for carbon management in Scotland, soils under grassland habitats storing and sequestering carbon. Carbon is lost from grassland soils through a variety of management activities including conversion to arable uses (DECC 2009), and due to liming (Rangel-Castro *et al.* 2004; Foereid *et al.* 2006) and fertiliser application (Jones *et al.* 2005).

The Countryside Survey provides some data on the changing extent of Acid, Neutral and Calcareous Grasslands in Scotland since the 1980s (**Figure 19.12**). Calcareous Grassland is very restricted in extent and there has been some loss of the habitat over the last two decades. In 2007 the Countryside Survey estimated there to be about 26,000 ha, a decline from about 40,000 ha in 1990 (Norton *et al.* 2009). Acid grassland (983,000 ha) and Neutral Grassland (461,000 ha) are both more extensive and show relatively little decline over the period of the Countryside Survey (Norton *et al.* 2009). The data are inconclusive, however, regarding the extent to which there have been changes, as the differences in area estimated by each survey are less than the accuracy with which they are estimated. Better monitoring is needed for very rare and local habitats such as Semi-natural Grasslands in Scotland.

Despite the extent of grasslands in Scotland, Semi-natural Grasslands cover only about 17,800 ha, or less than 1% of the total grassland area of Scotland; they make up only about 8% of the Semi-natural Grasslands of the UK (**Table 19.4**).

Semi-natural Grasslands in Scotland include Calcareous Grassland, Machair[2], and maritime cliff-top grasslands that are associated with exposed conditions but also frequently with grazing. These grasslands are of particular importance, having a rich flora of native grasses and herbs, as well as associated specialised communities of birds, mammals

Table 19.4 Estimate of the extent of Semi-natural Grassland component habitats in Scotland and the UK. Source: UK Biodiversity Action Plan Targets Review (2006); Norton *et al.* 2009. Countryside Survey data owned by NERC – Centre for Ecology & Hydrology.

Biodiversity Action Plan Priority Grassland type	Area in Scotland (ha)	Proportion of Scotland's Semi-natural Grassland priority habitats (%)	Area in UK (ha)	Scotland as proportion of whole UK (%)
Lowland calcareous grassland	761	4.3	40,590	1.9
Lowland dry acid grassland	4,357	24.4	61,650	7.1
Lowland hay meadows	980	5.5	10,520	9.3
Upland hay meadows	27	0.2	897	3.0
Purple moor grass and rush pasture	6,768	37.8	79,390	8.5
Upland calcareous grassland	5,000	27.9	22,640	22.1
Total	**17,893**		**215,687**	**8.3**

2 Note, Machair is discussed in the coastal section of this chapter (19.4.7) and the Coastal Margin chapter of the UK NEA (Chapter 11); in the Semi-natural Grasslands chapter (Chapter 6), discussion is restricted to Acid, Neutral and Calcareous Grasslands.

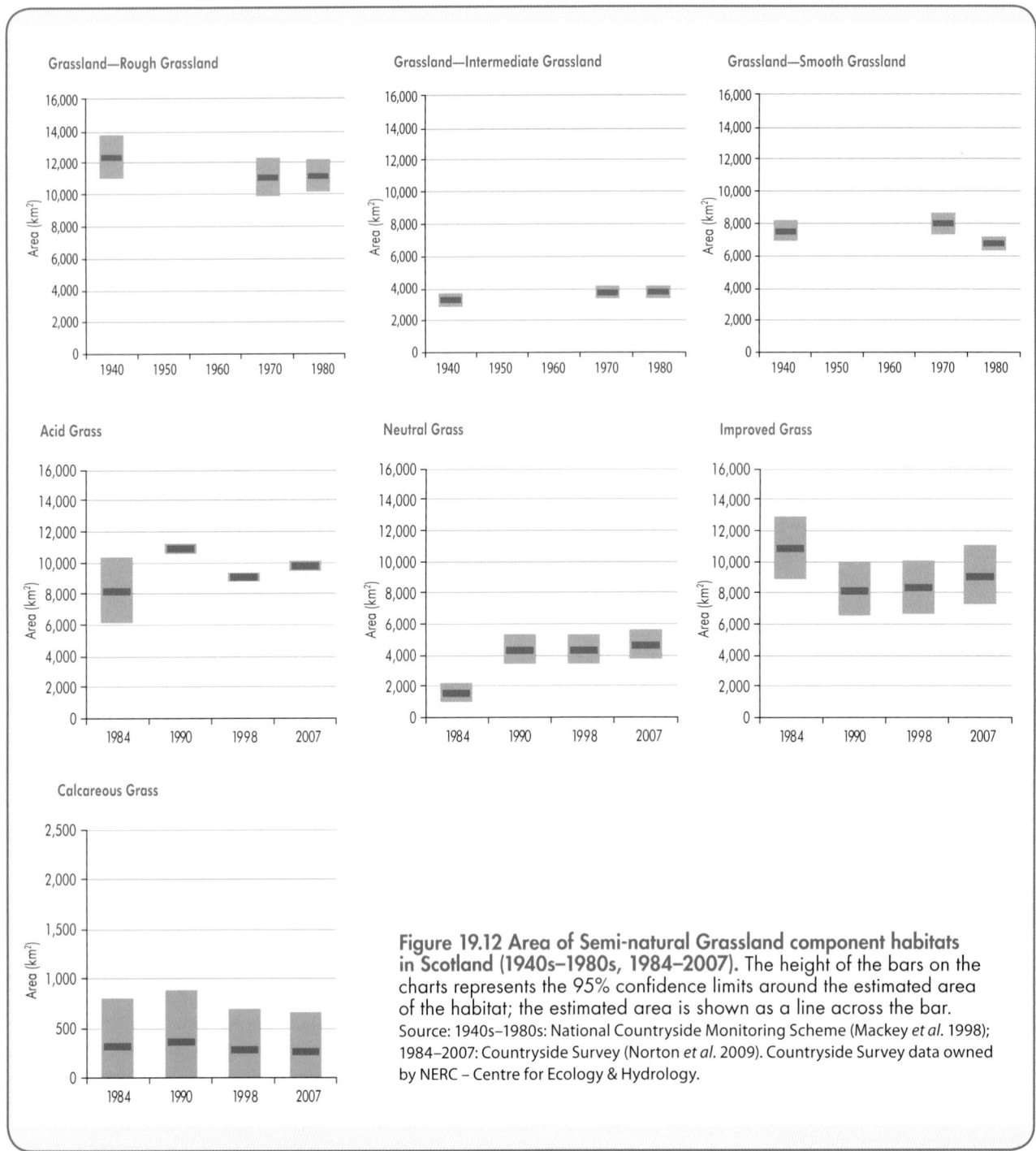

Figure 19.12 Area of Semi-natural Grassland component habitats in Scotland (1940s–1980s, 1984–2007). The height of the bars on the charts represents the 95% confidence limits around the estimated area of the habitat; the estimated area is shown as a line across the bar.
Source: 1940s–1980s: National Countryside Monitoring Scheme (Mackey *et al.* 1998); 1984–2007: Countryside Survey (Norton *et al.* 2009). Countryside Survey data owned by NERC – Centre for Ecology & Hydrology.

and invertebrates. Many of the sub-types of Semi-natural Grassland are of high conservation value and are listed as Priority Habitats in the UK and Scotland Biodiversity Strategy.

Scotland's Semi-natural Grasslands are of international significance for conservation of a variety of flora and fauna, including soil fungal populations that display complex seasonal dynamics (Newton *et al.* 2003). Grazing is an essential part of management of grasslands. Grazing of species-rich grasslands in riparian zones of upland forests has been shown to be important for biodiversity management, retaining high species diversity compared with ungrazed plots (Humphrey & Patterson 2000). Similarly, narrow buffer strips of grassland in riparian areas can increase carabid beetle density (Cole *et al.* 2008).

Scotland's Semi-natural Grasslands also support individual species of high conservation concern. For example, great yellow bumblebees (*Bombus distinguendus*) once widespread across agricultural grasslands, are now almost wholly restricted to unimproved Machair grassland with high floral diversity (Goulson *et al.* 2006), whilst both choughs (*Pyrrhocorax pyrrhocorax*) and corncrakes (*Crex crex*) now have populations that are heavily concentrated in areas where low-intensity grazing systems sustain areas of Semi-natural Grasslands (Whitehead *et al.* 2005; O'Brien *et al.* 2006).

Species diversity is also high in some Semi-natural Grassland types, linked to parent material and soils (e.g. limestone-rich areas and calcareous soils) and particularly to specific management practices. Bird populations of

Semi-natural Grasslands are similarly closely linked to land management practices (Green & Stowe 1993; Stowe *et al.* 1993; Green 1996; Gregory & Baillie 1998; Vickery *et al.* 2001).

The major threats to Semi-natural Grassland habitats include replacement with intensive rotational grassland mixes, which leads to a reduction of their area and fragmentation of remaining areas, intensification through use of fertilisers and pesticides, which reduces the diversity of their flora, and drainage and mechanisation of grassland management, which impacts particularly on associated faunal populations (Vickery *et al.* 2001). The products of intensification in Semi-natural Grassland ecosystems are the more widespread agriculturally improved grasslands, much of whose biodiversity has been lost through drainage, fertilisation, reseeding and grazing. Increasing public pressure also has an impact on Semi-natural Grasslands.

19.4.3 Enclosed Farmland

About 11% of Scotland's land area is arable agriculture, mainly on lower ground (<300 m) in the east of the country (Coppock 1976). There is a marked difference between the mainland of Scotland and the Islands in the extent of arable (see **Table 19.2** and **Figure 19.7**), over 97% of all the arable land in Scotland being on the mainland (Rural and Environment Research and Analysis Directorate 2009c).

The arable areas on islands, which include the Machair, do however contain habitats and species of national and international significance for biodiversity.

A wide variety of agricultural activities are based on Enclosed Farmland land, including cereal production, horticulture, soft fruit, and livestock production (Rural and Environment Research and Analysis Directorate 1939-present; Coppock 1976; Rural and Environment Research and Analysis Directorate 2009b; **Figure 19.13**).

Many of the current patterns of agricultural landscapes in Scotland were established in the 19th Century during enclosure (Gibson 2007). There is a long history of arable agriculture in eastern Scotland, both in the north-east and extending southwards to Lothian (Wood 1931; Symon 1959; Coppock 1976). The production of cereals in these areas has historically been closely linked to meat production (through sheep and cattle fattening) as well as supplying the distilling industry (Coppock 1976; DTZ 2007). There has also been a reduction in the area of fodder crops in the lowlands; this has changed some of the relationships of Scottish agricultural systems, requiring increasing amounts of feed to be purchased.

Crofting also occurs throughout Scotland but especially in the Western Isles, West Coast, Orkney and Shetland Islands, and in the crofting counties. Crofting land is not generally included in the categories of arable land mapped

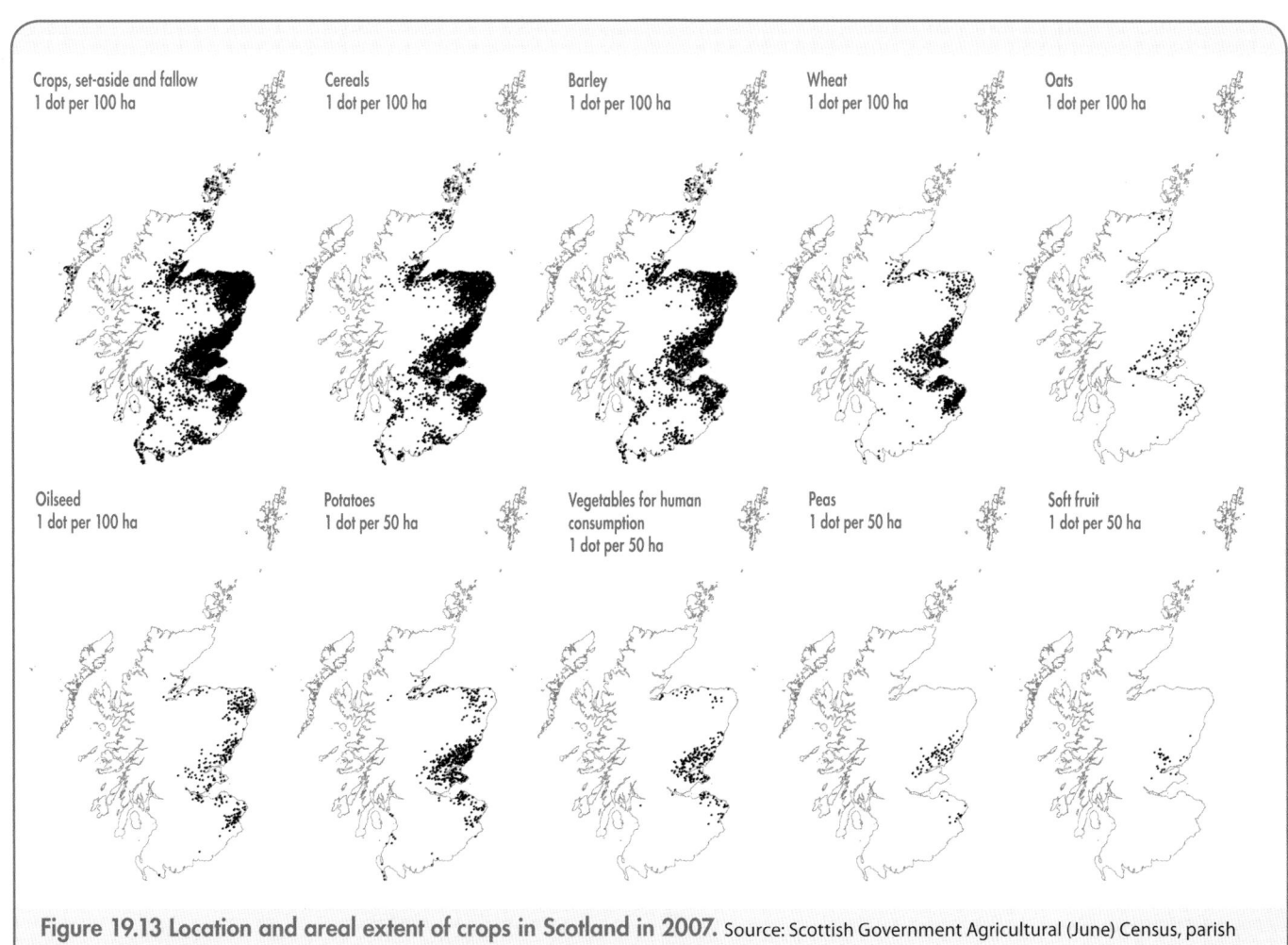

Figure 19.13 Location and areal extent of crops in Scotland in 2007. Source: Scottish Government Agricultural (June) Census, parish summary data 2007.

using air photos or satellite imagery (two of the main sources of synoptic survey data) although it can be recognised in agricultural census data (Rural and Environment Research and Analysis Directorate 1939-present).

Improved grasslands are also an important feature of Scotland's agricultural systems and of lowland and upland landscapes. Grassland expansion in the period following the Second World War (WWII) was intended to increase the fertility and productivity of marginal upland habitats to increase the domestic supply of meat and wool. These grasslands are dominated by relatively few species, including perennial rye-grass (*Lolium perenne*) and white clover (*Trifolium repens*) and continued grazing and occasional reseeding is needed to maintain their nutritional value for livestock. However, despite their lower botanical diversity, agriculturally improved grasslands can, if managed appropriately, still represent important nesting and feeding habitats for some wildlife, including, for example, the important populations of breeding waders that nest and feed on agricultural grasslands in Scotland (O'Brien *et al.* 2002). If active management is removed then most grassland areas will revert to poor fen, moorland, scrub and woodland. Grasslands created by human management of land generally are classified according to soil chemistry and include base-rich, acidic, and neutral grasslands.

The value of Improved grassland for grazing livestock and the productivity of grasses grown under Scottish environmental conditions has led to the creation of extensive areas of Improved grassland pastures across Scotland (**Figure 19.14**). The 1950s and 1960s saw an expansion of Improved grasslands for pasture as other habitats were converted to grassland for sheep and cattle grazing (**Figure 19.15**). Considerable research has been carried out on conversion of upland habitats to grassland, the use of grasslands for animal production and nutrition and the consequences of grazing management for conservation of native flora and fauna. Research shows that re-extensification of grazing over a 16-year period in upland grasslands in Scotland led to slow but continual changes in composition, with some increase in diversity compared to intensive grazing, but productivity did not decline with time (Marriott *et al.* 2009).

Sheep and beef cattle production are the major farming activities in the grass and heather uplands of Scotland. The number of livestock grazed in these habitats is influenced by a variety of factors, not least the availability of winter feed. Flocks of sheep and herds of cattle have been overwintered in the lowlands and have traditionally been fed on turnips and other fodder crops (Coppock 1976). Changes in agricultural practices since Britain joined the Common Market in 1973 have generally resulted in increased specialisation in farming in Scotland and, specifically, lowland areas have increased cereal production while production of fodder crops has declined. This reduces the capacity of lowland

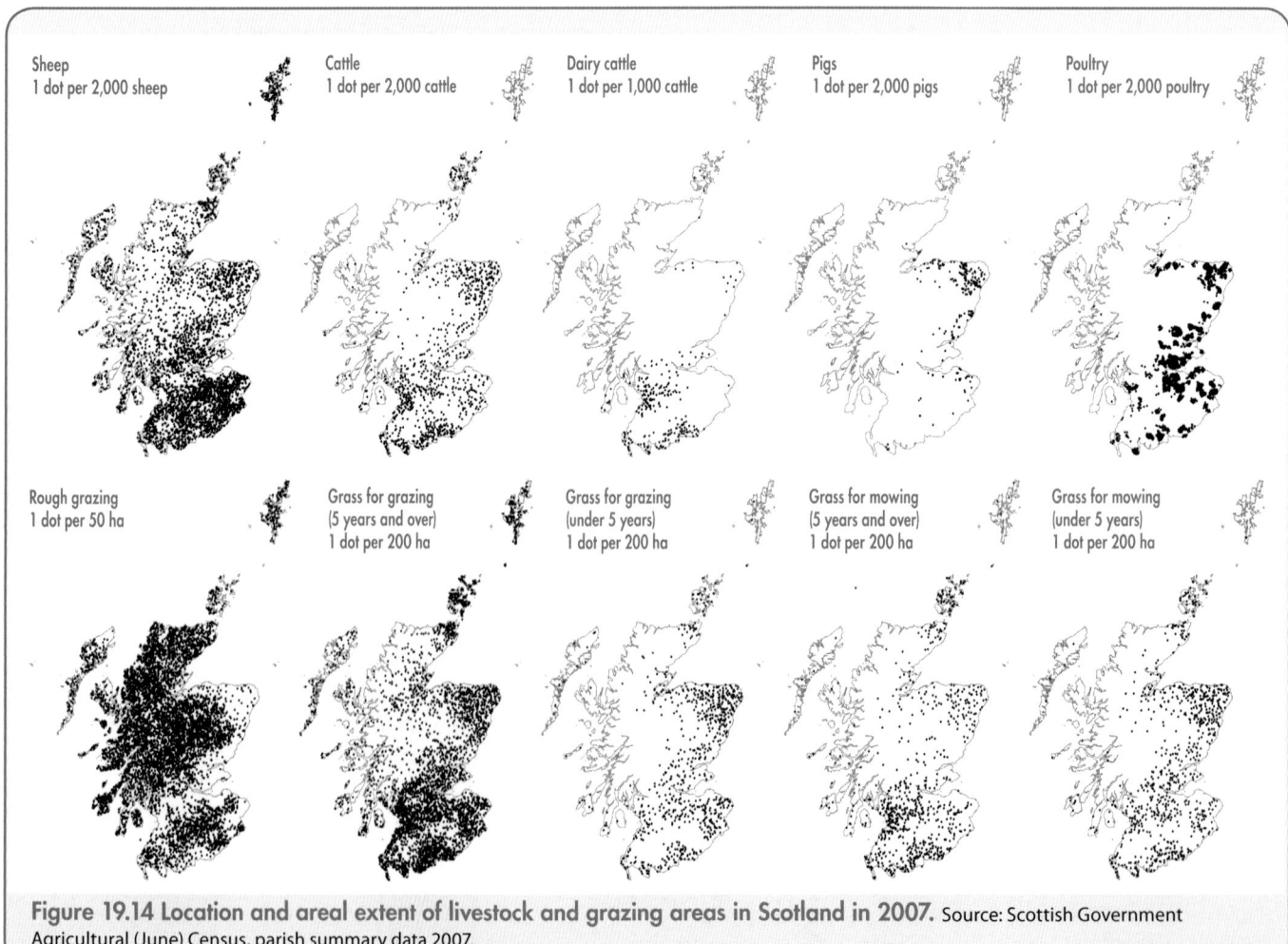

Figure 19.14 Location and areal extent of livestock and grazing areas in Scotland in 2007. Source: Scottish Government Agricultural (June) Census, parish summary data 2007.

areas to support livestock in winter, although much cereal is used as animal feed. The dairy industry has historically been strongest on the grassland pastures of south west Scotland (Wood 1931; Coppock 1976; see **Figure 19.14**).

Synoptic surveys of grassland and change in grassland over time have necessarily mostly used air photos as a data source, despite some inherent difficulties in their use for this purpose. Classification of grasslands on air photos is typically based on the texture of the grassland, which appears clearly in photos, as opposed to the floristic character (Wright & Morrice 1997).

Changes in area of rough, intermediate and smooth grassland are shown in **Figure 19.12**. Rough grassland is the most extensive of the three types. There was a slight reduction between the 1940s and 1980s. Smooth grassland also showed a slight decrease between the 1940s and 1980s, with an increase apparent in the 1970s. Intermediate grasslands have increased in area since the 1940s.

Agricultural areas have been studied as agronomic systems (Clergue *et al.* 2005; Bockstaller *et al.* 2008), and as agri-environmental or agro-ecosystems, developing ecological approaches to understanding agriculture (Ormerod *et al.* 2003). A considerable amount is known about the status, quality, and economic, social and environmental value of agricultural areas. Agricultural development in Scotland has taken place over a sufficiently long time for important species and communities to have become associated with the land use (O'Connor & Shrubb 1986). For example, a number of plant, invertebrate and bird

species are closely associated with habitats produced by specific land management practices and have breeding or feeding cycles and patterns that fit with the traditional land management practices and timing. Changes in agricultural management since the 1940s have had major consequences for these species (Hancock & Wilson 2003; Wilson *et al.* 2009; Wilson 2010), many of which are of conservation concern, e.g. corn bunting (Perkins *et al.* 2008; Watson *et al.* 2009), grey partridge (*Perdix perdix*) (Hancock & Wilson 2002), corncrake (O'Brien *et al.* 2006), and great yellow bumblebee (Goulson *et al.* 2006). Arable systems are generally managed to support mechanisation. They have also seen high inputs of fertilisers and other chemicals to control diseases and pests. In common with other countries, intensive management over the last 60 years has resulted in a decline in traditional arable specialist species which are now rare (Robinson & Sutherland 2002; Hyvonen & Huusela-Veistola 2008). Only species able to exploit the crop itself have benefited from highly intensive production practices. Examples include the growth in wood pigeon (*Columba palumbus*) populations after the introduction of oilseed rape (Inglis *et al.* 1997), and the recovery of populations of wintering geese of high conservation concern through feeding on nutrient-rich crops and grassland (MacMillan *et al.* 2004). Scotland is of international importance for populations of wintering geese. Islay is host to between 60 and 70% of the total Greenland population of barnacle goose (*Branta leucopsis*) and 30% of the total population of Greenland white-fronted goose (*Anser albifrons flavirostris*) (Hallanaro & Söderman

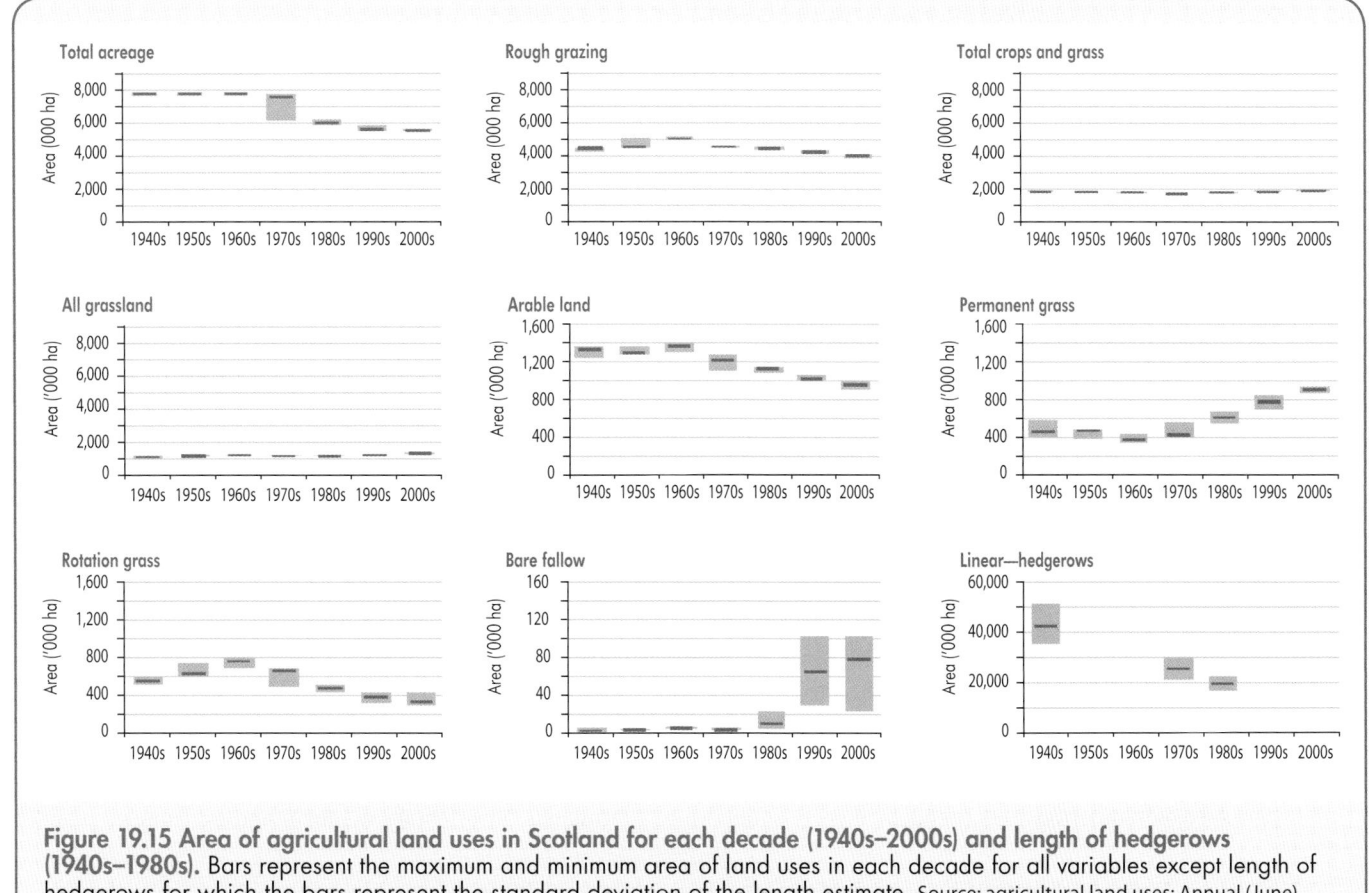

Figure 19.15 Area of agricultural land uses in Scotland for each decade (1940s–2000s) and length of hedgerows (1940s–1980s). Bars represent the maximum and minimum area of land uses in each decade for all variables except length of hedgerows for which the bars represent the standard deviation of the length estimate. Source: agricultural land uses: Annual (June) Agricultural Census tables, 1940–2009, published by the Scottish Government; data on the length of hedgerows from Mackey *et al.* (1998).

2002). Wintering geese feeding on agricultural pastures in Scotland create conflicts with agricultural production (Cope *et al.* 2003), providing challenges for land and conservation management.

Agri-environmental schemes have been shown to contribute to the conservation of avian and insect biodiversity in Scottish agricultural systems (Hancock & Wilson 2003; Parish & Sotherton 2004; Stoate *et al.* 2004; Tiley & Frame 2005; Conway *et al.* 2007; Perkins *et al.* 2008; Perkins *et al.* 2008; Lye *et al.* 2009) though there remain only a few species for which there is evidence that agri-environmental management at current levels of provision has proved capable of reversing losses on a national scale. One example is the corncrake (O'Brien *et al.* 2006) which has benefited from well-targeted management delivered to a high proportion of the population, and backed by good quality advice available to farmers and crofters.

Agricultural areas are also marked by the mosaic of habitats they provide. Field margins constructed of dry stone walls, flagstones or hedgerows not only divide the agricultural area into fields, but also contribute to the appearance of agricultural landscapes. These features and areas may also contribute to wider countryside conservation by providing a 'linear' habitat offering shelter, supporting biodiversity, and maintaining connectivity between habitats in the landscape (Donald & Evans 2006), although better evidence is needed of the circumstances under which this functionality is offered by the cereal margin 'skeleton' of the agricultural landscape (Hodgson *et al.* 2009). The National Countryside Monitoring Scheme and the Countryside Survey both report 'linear' features (see **Figure 19.15**). Lengths of hedgerows in Scotland declined from about 42,500 km in the 1940s to about 19,500 km in the 1980s (Mackey *et al.* 1998). Field boundaries, trees, and copses in an agricultural area provide a suite of ecosystem services that are different from the arable and grassland areas enclosed. Field margins can act as a buffer or filter of runoff, reducing impacts of chemicals and sediments on water quality. Urban trees, small blocks of trees and hedgerow trees are not counted in the carbon storing stock of woodland. As an indication of the extent and potential importance of field margins and trees in agricultural landscapes, the Land Cover of Scotland (1988)[3] (MLURI 1993) mapped 54,484 clumps of trees (outside urban areas) as 'point features' (i.e. less than the 2 ha minimum mapping unit needed to be mapped as an area of woodland) and 12,893 km of linear features composed of trees.

The practice of set-aside, starting in 1988 for two decades (see **Figure 19.15**), has also demonstrated the conservation and functional value and capacity of the mosaic of habitats within agricultural areas for maintenance of biodiversity. In Scotland up to 93,000 ha of land were in set-aside in any one year while the scheme ran (Rural and Environment Research and Analysis Directorate 1939-present). Fields set aside from arable production have been shown to have great value as nesting and foraging habitats for a wide variety of bird species (Sotherton 1988; Henderson *et al.* 2000). This illustrates a more general point that landscapes of even relatively intensive production can maintain substantial biodiversity value if heterogeneity within the cropping system (e.g. diverse, mixed rotations of crops and grassland) and between the cropped areas and patches of non-cropped habitat are used to provide space and time for the life cycles of non-crop organisms (Benton *et al.* 2003). For example, as part of a GB-wide survey of skylarks in 1997 it was found that the highest proportion of skylarks in Scotland occurred where farming systems provided a mix of grazed pasture, winter cereals and spring cereals (Browne *et al.* 2000). Mixed lowland farming systems of eastern Scotland continue to support bird communities that have largely been lost elsewhere in much of the UK as specialisation in arable or grassland enterprises has become more marked.

Throughout the 1940s and early 1950s the area of orchards in Scotland was over 500 ha, but declined steadily to less than 40 ha by the end of the 2000s. The total area of glasshouses also declined from over 100 ha in the 1950s to less than 30 ha by the end of the 2000s. However, there is a growing area of walk-in plastic structures used in agriculture and horticulture in Scotland, although their extent has only been recorded in agricultural statistics since 1982. The total area of glasshouses and walk-in plastic structures is now about 200 ha. Orchards are a particular type of woodland system that provides agricultural output; they not only provide food but may also provide some of the other ecosystem services associated with woodland. Glass/green/plastic houses provide an artificial and highly managed environment for high value foods; they have considerable value in terms of food production although their other environmental impacts are not yet known.

The diversity of species in arable systems has declined over the past 60 years, leading to many of the common weed species of pre-WWII arable agriculture being among present-day threatened species. Wildlife declines, either through change in distribution or abundance or both, are frequently linked to agricultural intensification (Chamberlain *et al.* 1999; Chamberlain *et al.* 2000) or pesticide and fertiliser use (Kleijn & Snoeijing 1997; Henderson *et al.* 2000; Vickery *et al.* 2001; Hart *et al.* 2006). It is recognised that despite their potential negative impact on crop yield and quality, weed species have an important role in maintaining farmland biodiversity (Smart *et al.* 2000). A study of common UK annual weeds, based on their eco-physiological traits, shows potentially beneficial species to have a relatively low competitive ability but high importance for invertebrates and birds (Storkey 2006). Timing of tillage is also important for encouraging (or limiting) plant species with particular life-history and germination traits (Smith 2006). A study of changes in summer numbers of adult corn buntings conducted on farmland from south Angus to central Aberdeenshire showed that following a period of relative stability in 1989–1995, large declines occurred in 1995–1996, 1998–1999 and 2003–2004 (Watson *et al.* 2009). Links between bird numbers on farmlands, invertebrate numbers and agricultural practice

---

3 The Land Cover of Scotland (1988) was produced from medium scale (1:24,000) aerial photography, interpreted using a hierarchical key that distinguished 126 land cover features as points, lines and areas. Mosaic categories, defined as mixtures of two land cover features, were also mapped. Area features were delimited where they were >10 ha for semi-natural vegetation, >5 ha for built up land and >2 ha for woodland.

suggest that agricultural change influences birds through changes in food quality and quantity (Benton *et al.* 2002).

Similarly, the establishment of grassy strips at the margins of arable fields, as part of recent agri-environment schemes, aims to provide resources for native flora and fauna and thus increase farmland biodiversity. Although these field margin interventions are typically targeted at farmland birds and pollinators (Douglas *et al.* 2009), the impact of such management on soil macrofauna has also been shown to be potentially beneficial, particularly if litter-dwelling invertebrates are encouraged by minimising soil cultivation to develop a substantial surface litter layer (Smith *et al.* 2008). Heterogeneity of mixed habitat agricultural landscapes is an important contributor to biodiversity at landscape and catchment scales (Dennis *et al.* 1999; Robinson *et al.* 2001; Benton *et al.* 2003).

Objectives of agri-environment schemes include conservation of biodiversity, an increase in the value of farmland for wildlife, and restoration of natural ecosystem functioning (Woodcock *et al.* 2007; Smith *et al.* 2008, 2009). Set-aside increases bird (Chamberlain *et al.* 1999; Henderson *et al.* 2000; Moorcroft *et al.* 2002) and insect (Carvell *et al.* 2007; Potts *et al.* 2009) abundance, although a need for regional variation in agri-environmental schemes has also been recognised (Robinson *et al.* 2001). To some degree the design of the agri-environmental scheme in Scotland, the Rural Development Contracts, responds to this need in its regional structure.

Arable agriculture is important for regulation of climate and water. The mineral soils of Scotland which dominate arable habitats (**Figure 19.9**) are relatively rich in carbon compared to mineral soils elsewhere in the UK (Section 19.5.2.1). Appropriate management of arable soils is important both for retaining carbon in the soil and for reducing the contribution of arable agriculture to Scotland's greenhouse gas emissions (MacLeod *et al.* 2010).

Arable agriculture contributes to global carbon emissions from diverse sources, including product manufacture and transport, as well as through direct and indirect soil greenhouse gas emissions. Recent assessment of farm survey data from the east of Scotland shows that across all crops and farm types, about 75% of total emissions are from organic and inorganic nitrogen fertiliser use (Hillier *et al.* 2009).

19.4.4 Woodlands

The native forest of Scotland was a western outlier of the transition between European temperate and boreal forests (Barbatti *et al.* 2007). Altitudinal, climatic and latitudinal limits exerted a strong influence on the forest which was dominated by Scots pine (*Pinus sylvestris*) and birch woods. Broad-leaved trees, including oaks, alder, elm and hazel, would have occupied lowland sites. As elsewhere in the UK, this forest was cleared over centuries for timber, charcoal, cultivation and grazing (Smout 2003).

The extent of woodland in Scotland is estimated to have been between 4% and 5% of land area from the 13th Century until the end of the First World War (Smout 2003). The area of Woodland has increased over the last 90 years, partly as a result of governments encouraging reforestation to address domestic shortages of timber. This growth in Woodlands has mostly comprised non-native species in plantation woodlands (**Table 19.5**). Woodlands currently occupy about 17% of Scotland's land area (see **Figures 19.6** and **19.10**).

Despite the overall net increase in total area of Woodlands, the National Countryside Monitoring Scheme showed a decline in Broadleaved (1940s: 150,900 ha, 1980s: 116,400 ha) and Mixed Woodland (1940s: 54,200 ha, 1980s: 34,100 ha). The area of parkland woods appeared to be relatively stable, although at about 7,300 ha (Mackey *et al.* 1998), parkland woods occupy only a small area of Scotland (**Figure 19.16**). The notable increase in the area of commercial conifer plantation forestry took place primarily between the 1940s and 1988 (see **Figure 19.16**).

Commercial plantation forestry uses a variety of introduced species, such as Sitka spruce (*Picea sitchensis*) and lodgepole pine (*Pinus contorta*), that are selected for productivity under the particular climatic, soil and land

Table 19.5 Area of woodland types in Scotland.
Source: Forestry Commission 2003.

	Area ('000 ha)	Proportion of Scotland's forest area (%)	Proportion of area in GB (%)
Conifers			
Scots pine	140	10.9	61.7
Corsican pine	2	0.2	4.3
Lodgepole pine	122	9.5	90.4
Sitka spruce	528	41.3	76.3
Norway spruce	35	2.7	44.3
European larch	9	0.7	39.1
Japanese/Hybrid larch	56	4.4	50.5
Douglas fir	10	0.8	22.2
Other conifer	5	0.4	16.7
Mixed conifer	8	0.6	44.4
Total Conifers	**916**	**71.5**	**65.1**
Broadleaves			
Oak	21	1.6	9.4
Beech	10	0.8	12.0
Sycamore	11	0.9	16.4
Ash	5	0.4	3.9
Birch	78	6.1	48.8
Poplar	0	0.0	0
Sweet chestnut	0	0.0	0
Elm	1	0.1	20.0
Other broadleaves	18	1.4	15.0
Mixed broadleaves	62	4.8	38.8
Total Broadleaves	206	16.1	21.2
Coppice	1	0.1	4.2
Felled	23	1.8	48.9
Open Space	134	10.5	61.8
Total Woodland	**1,281**		**48.1**

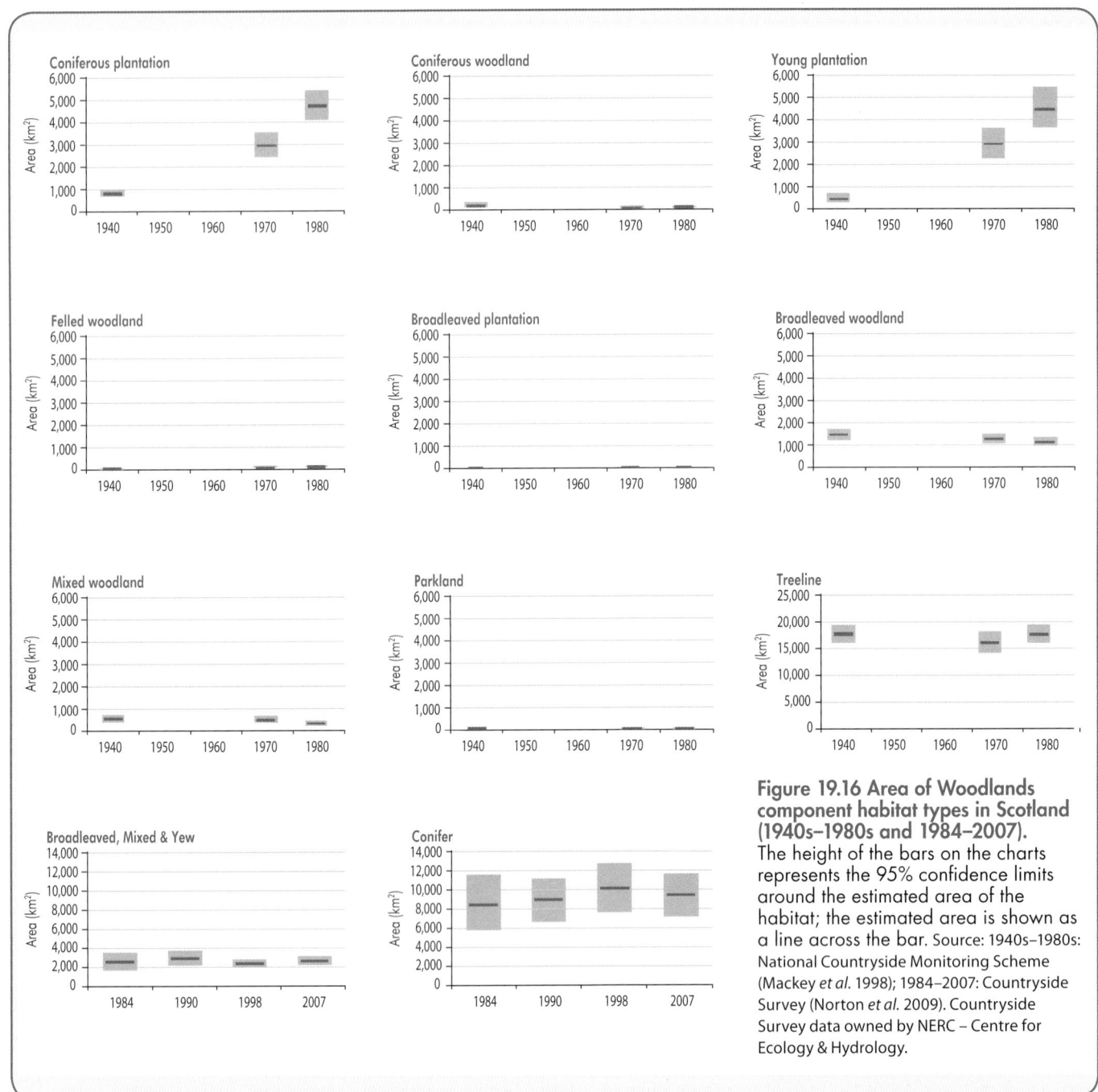

Figure 19.16 Area of Woodlands component habitat types in Scotland (1940s–1980s and 1984–2007). The height of the bars on the charts represents the 95% confidence limits around the estimated area of the habitat; the estimated area is shown as a line across the bar. Source: 1940s–1980s: National Countryside Monitoring Scheme (Mackey *et al.* 1998); 1984–2007: Countryside Survey (Norton *et al.* 2009). Countryside Survey data owned by NERC – Centre for Ecology & Hydrology.

character of planting sites. The species composition of Scotland's forests is shown by the main tree species in **Table 19.5**. The main commercial species planted in Scotland are Sitka spruce, Scots pine, lodgepole pine and Japanese/hybrid larch (*Larix kaempferi*).

Much of the planting since 1940 has taken place on upland moors and grasslands (Robertson *et al.* 2001), with some replacement planting on existing ancient woodland sites. This pattern of planting was controversial as it led to loss of other valued habitats and species (Avery & Leslie 1990). Most recently there has been greater effort to increase forest area using native species, especially Scots pine, and this has led to benefits for biodiversity (Humphrey *et al.* 2003; Humphrey 2005; McIntosh 2006). In addition there has been greater attention to forest design (Anon 2004) including retention of open areas and protection of riparian zones (Quine & Ray 2010).

Table 19.6 shows the area of new planting in Scotland and the UK as a whole for 5-year periods from 1971 to 2006. Between 1976 and 2009 74% of all new planting of UK forests has been in Scotland, increasing the total area under forests by 48,200 ha. The area planted fell dramatically after 1989 (**Figure 19.17**) as a result of the 1988 UK Government Budget that removed tax support for forestry planting. Planting patterns under the pre-1988 tax incentives had previously encouraged planting but preferentially on land that was marginal for forestry (Macmillan 1993); this led to environmental damage and conflict (Warren 2000). Between 1976 and 1989, 87% of the new UK Coniferous and 38% of the UK Broadleaved planting was in Scotland. From 1990 to 2009, 84% of the new Coniferous and 47% of the total UK Broadleaved planting was in Scotland (**Figure 19.18**). In Scotland grant aid for native woodland expansion and improving connectivity of woodlands has recently been

Table 19.6 Area of new planting of woodland in Scotland for 5 year periods from 1971–1976 to 2001–2006.
Source: Forestry Commission 2009.

		5 year period ending 31 March						
		1976	1981	1986	1991	1996	2001	2006
Area in Scotland ('000 ha)	Conifer	148.6	90.9	100.1	94.6	38.3	27.1	11.5
	Broadleaved	0.6	0.8	0.9	9.2	21.0	28.5	19.7
	Total	**149.3**	**91.7**	**100.9**	**103.8**	**5.3**	**55.6**	**31.2**
Area in UK (ha)	Conifer	184.7	108.9	114.3	105.8	45.9	33.0	25.0
	Broadleaved	3.2	2.7	3.8	20.4	45.9	53.3	51.6
	Total	**188.0**	**111.7**	**118.2**	**126.3**	**91.8**	**86.4**	**76.6**
Scotland as proportion of UK total (%)	Conifer	80.5	83.5	87.6	89.4	83.4	82.1	45.7
	Broadleaved	18.8	29.6	23.7	45.1	45.8	53.5	38.2
	Total	**79.4**	**82.1**	**85.4**	**82.2**	**64.6**	**64.4**	**40.8**

brought into the Scottish Rural Development Programme (SRDP).

The UK BAP woodland habitats relevant to Scotland are native pinewoods, upland oakwoods, upland ashwoods, upland birchwoods, wet woodlands, and lowland mixed broadleaved woodlands (Jones *et al.* 2002; Humphrey *et al.* 2006). There are about 148,000 ha of ancient woodland[4] in Scotland (Chapter 8), about 27% of the ancient woodland in the UK. Habitat Action Plans cover the woodland Priority Habitat types in Scotland, including targets for restoration and expansion of the habitats (Humphrey *et al.* 2006). The Countryside Survey records i) native conifer woodland and ii) broadleaf mixed and yew woodland habitats; estimates of their areas have remained 200,000–300,000 ha and 800,000–1,000,000 ha respectively over the duration of the Countryside Surveys (see **Figure 19.16**).

Diseases associated with pests and pathogens are of concern for woodland health and management. Pests and pathogens that are new to woodlands of the UK and Scotland include insects such as the pine-tree lappet moth (*Dendrolimus pini*) which can defoliate Scots pine. The oak processionary moth (*Thaumetopoea processionea*), Asian longhorn beetle (*Anoplophora glabripennis*) and emerald ash borer (*Agrilus planipennis*) are a threat to native broadleaved trees (Chapter 8) although not yet a current threat in Scotland. Pathogens include *Phytophthora ramorum*, which can attack a range of species including Japanese larch (see Brasier 2008; Brasier & Webber 2010), and red band needle blight (*Dothistroma septosporum),* which affects Scots, Corsican (*Pinus nigra subspecies laricio*) and lodgepole pine (Brown & Webber 2008). *Phytophthora lateralis* was found in Scotland for the first time in the UK, killing Lawson's cypress trees in a country park near Glasgow (Chapter 8, Woodlands). Further exotic pests and pathogens may well threaten valued woodland habitats as well as production from managed woodlands. Climate change and other climate-related stresses also influence woodland health (Gregory & Redfern 1998; Green & Ray 2009; Tubby & Webber 2010). Drought stress reduces the resistance of trees to diseases and pests, and wetter spring weather encourages fungal development.

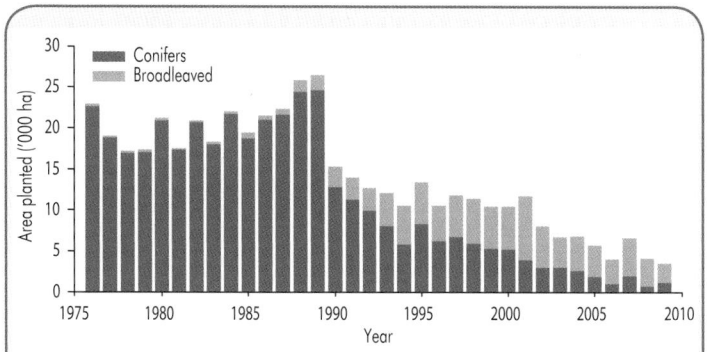

Figure 19.17 Annual area of new Woodlands planting in Scotland, 1976–2009. Source: Forestry Commission (2009).

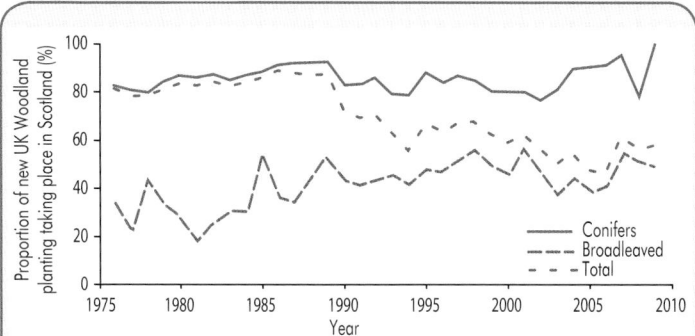

Figure 19.18 Percentage of new UK woodland planting taking place in Scotland, 1975–2009. Source: data from annual Forestry Statistics (Forestry Commission 2009) and the Scottish Government (2011).

As the historic climax vegetation for much of Scotland (Steven & Carlisle 1959), Scots pine forest (Caledonian forest) has a high iconic status. It also has high conservation value as an important habitat in Scotland (Steven & Carlisle 1959; Anderson, Campbell & Prosser 2003) and now receives strong protection and management for biodiversity (Mason *et al.* 2004; Humphrey 2006; McIntosh 2006). The forest type contains many species of conservation value, possibly more than many other habitats[5] (Eggleton *et al.* 2005) and many are iconic species of Scottish wildlife and Priority Species

4 Ancient woodland in Scotland is defined as woodland that has been in continuous existence since 1750 (since 1600 elsewhere in the UK).
5 Habitats compared include: Caledonian forest, closed canopy pine plantation, broadleaved woodlands, riparian woodland, grassland habitats, improved grassland, arable fields.

under the UK BAP. Important species include Scots pine itself, flowering plants such as the twinflower (*Linnaea borealis*), creeping lady's tresses (*Goodyera repensi*), lesser twayblade (*Listera cordata*), chickweed wintergreen (*Trientalis europea*), St. Olaf's candlestick (*Moneses uniflora*), *Pyrola* species, birds and animals such as capercaillie, crested tit, Scottish crossbill (*Loxia scotica*), red squirrel (*Sciurus vulgaris*), pine marten (*Martes martes*) and wildcat (*Felis silvestris silvestris*), and invertebrates, bryophytes and lichens.

19.4.5 Freshwaters – Openwaters, Wetlands and Floodplains

The freshwater ecosystems and natural heritage of Scotland have been regularly and systematically reviewed over the past 50 years (Earp & Eden 1961; Gorrie 1961; Wilson 1961; Maitland *et al.* 1994; Doughty *et al.* 2002) although consistent and comparable data collection on aspects of water ecosystems other than flow have been developed only relatively recently (Doughty *et al.* 2002). In 2007 the Scottish Environment Protection Agency (SEPA) introduced

a single comprehensive monitoring strategy for water bodies in Scotland, building on past data but creating a new monitoring network, using new methodologies and at new locations. Recent past data were summarised in Scotland's Water Environment Review 2000–2006 (SEPA 2006a). Other trends for rivers can be found from analysis of 56 sites since the mid-1970s under the Harmonised Monitoring Scheme (Anderson *et al.* 2010).

Scotland has abundant freshwater resources in lochs and rivers, with 90% of the volume of freshwater in the UK. Important wetland habitats are associated with these water resources. About 2.5% of the surface area of Scotland is freshwater (see **Figure 19.6** and **Figure 19.10**) and relatively little change in area has been recorded over the last 20 years for freshwater habitats (**Figure 19.19**). The total volume of water stored in lochs has been estimated at almost 35 billion cubic metres (m^3) (Lyle & Smith 1994). Scotland's freshwaters are diverse in processes, drainage patterns and riparian and other forms, reflecting geomorphological evolution over long timescales. Their quality is intimately

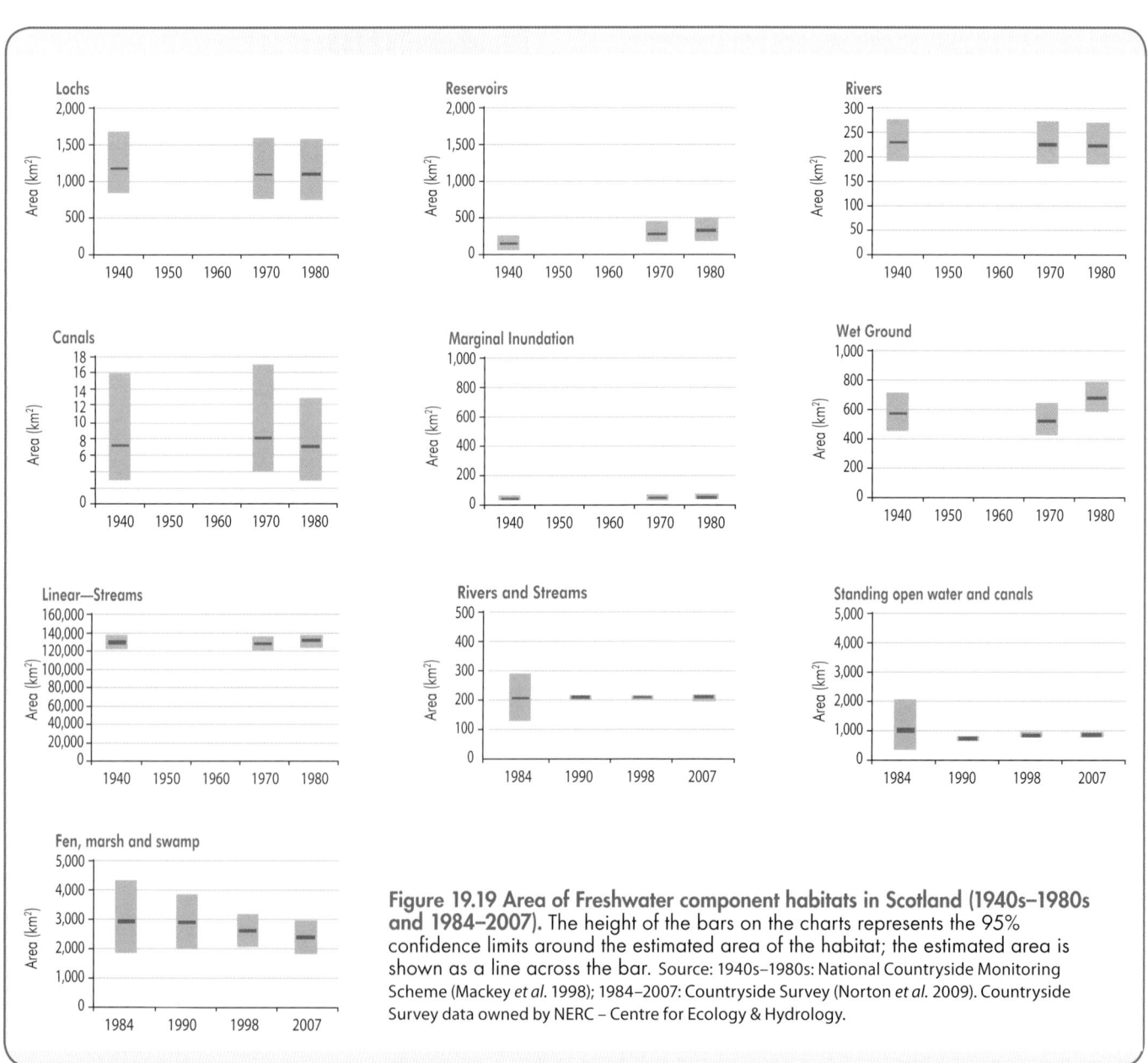

Figure 19.19 Area of Freshwater component habitats in Scotland (1940s–1980s and 1984–2007). The height of the bars on the charts represents the 95% confidence limits around the estimated area of the habitat; the estimated area is shown as a line across the bar. Source: 1940s–1980s: National Countryside Monitoring Scheme (Mackey *et al.* 1998); 1984–2007: Countryside Survey (Norton *et al.* 2009). Countryside Survey data owned by NERC – Centre for Ecology & Hydrology.

linked to the land area of Scotland that they drain. There are also strong influences from topography, bedrock, and rainfall gradients (Werritty *et al.* 1994). Rainfall gradients are most notable from west to east, with over 3,000 mm of rain per year on the western highlands but typically less than 700 mm on the east coast.

There are 170 catchment systems larger than 10,000 ha in area that drain the land of Scotland. The largest of these systems by area, the River Tay system, also has the largest average flow of any river in the UK (167 cubic metres per second (m³/s) at Perth), with a peak discharge in excess of 2000 m³/s (Werritty *et al.* 1994). The typical annual pattern of river flow in Scotland's river shows a maximum volume of runoff in winter.

Climate change is having a major impact on river flows across Scotland (SNIFFER 2006; SEPA 2006b). Scotland has become wetter since 1961, an average increase of rainfall of about 20% having been measured across the country, with a 60% increase in the north and west (SNIFFER 2006). The period of snow cover in Scotland has also decreased over the last 40 years, milder autumn and spring temperatures resulting in later and less snowfall and earlier snowmelt (SNIFFER 2006). These changes have produced a measured increase in mean annual flow in rivers across Scotland since the 1960s and continuing to the present (Curran & Robertson 1991; Doughty *et al.* 2002). There is also an increase in the magnitude of high flow events (SEPA 2006b), particularly on rivers which rise in the west (Black 1996), with corresponding increased risks of flooding.

Annual average temperatures are also increasing in many Scottish rivers (Anderson *et al.* 2010), with implications for river ecology and salmon behaviour and populations. Some of the trends to warmer water may be a consequence of increased urbanisation. Most, however, is considered to be due to warmer air temperatures and the effect is most pronounced in the winter, when widespread warming has been observed (SNIFFER 2006).

Water bodies are affected by all the activities and changes in their catchments (Newson 2002). They can, therefore, monitor and signal environmental changes across whole landscapes (Baron *et al.* 2002). River and loch catchments in Scotland regulate both the quality and quantity of water entering the river and lochs of the freshwater system in Scotland.

Water quality and quantity in rivers, lochs and groundwater are monitored by SEPA. This was previously the responsibility of River Purification Boards. Monitoring methods have changed over time, making direct comparisons of recent and historic classifications problematic. The 2009 publication of River Basin Management Plans for the Scotland (Scottish Government 2009d) and Solway-Tweed River Basin Districts (Scottish Government 2009b) is a major step forward. Water quality is discussed as a regulating service in Section 19.5.2.8.

Climate change forecasts are for wetter, warmer and more seasonal conditions in Scotland. The flow regimes of upland river systems, especially those that depend on snowmelt, can be expected to become modified under a changing climate. Implications of changes in flow regimes of rivers with a major upland component may

include increased periods of drought, but also increased floods and flooding as uplands lose the capacity to store water and moderate flows. There may also be changes in water chemistry and water supply. There will also be implications for salmon and trout production in rivers as water temperatures increase and water chemistry adjusts to new flow regimes. There is already evidence of washout of young salmon fry due to altered hydrological regimes in Scottish rivers.

Functionally intact and biologically complex aquatic ecosystems provide many economically valuable services and long-term benefits to society. Freshwater is used for consumption, irrigation and transport, and contributes to food supply. Freshwater systems contribute to flood control, purification of human and industrial wastes, and as habitat for plant and animal life. In the longer term, freshwater systems provide a capacity to respond to future environmental alterations, such as climate change.

19.4.6 Urban

About 2.5% of the land area of Scotland is Urban, the area of highest numbers and density of population being the Central Belt (see **Table 19.2, Figures 19.6** and **19.10**). About 82% of the population of Scotland lives in cities, towns and villages. Glasgow and the Edinburgh area each have a population exceeding 1 million, and Aberdeen and Dundee each exceed 100,000. In addition to these four major cities there are 52 towns with a population between 10,000 and 100,000, and 115 with a population of between 3,000 and 10,000. There are a further 187 villages with a population between 1,000 and 3,000 (see **Figure 19.2**). The area of Built land increased from about 160,000 ha in the 1940s to about 200,000 ha by the 1980s (**Figure 19.20;** (Tudor *et al.* 1994). Although Urban and Built land are included in the Countryside Survey, the survey focuses on developed land in Britain's rural environment; a new assessment of the extent of urban areas in Scotland is needed.

Urban development changes the nature of ecosystems and ecosystem processes fundamentally. Urbanisation is an intensive and effectively irreversible change (Williams *et al.* 2009). Natural processes of nutrient cycling, and energy and water flow are often replaced by engineering systems. Areas outside of, and geographically remote from, an urban area are required to support the urban population and urban 'ecosystem'. The relationships between urban and non-urban (rural) areas are central to issues of sustainability of human and environmental systems globally, as well as within Scotland and the UK. The physical and attitudinal separation of demand for ecosystem services in Urban areas and the supply of ecosystem goods and services from other land uses elsewhere is an important factor in developing an understanding of the role of ecosystems in supporting human health and well-being.

Urban areas in Scotland contain extensive areas of Greenspace (greenspace scotland 2009). Planning Advice Note 65 (PAN 2008) provides a typology for Greenspace and includes parks, public and private gardens, allotments, civic space, churchyards and cemeteries, and sports areas and playing fields. There are also substantial numbers of roadside and garden trees. Greenspace mapping is in progress for most

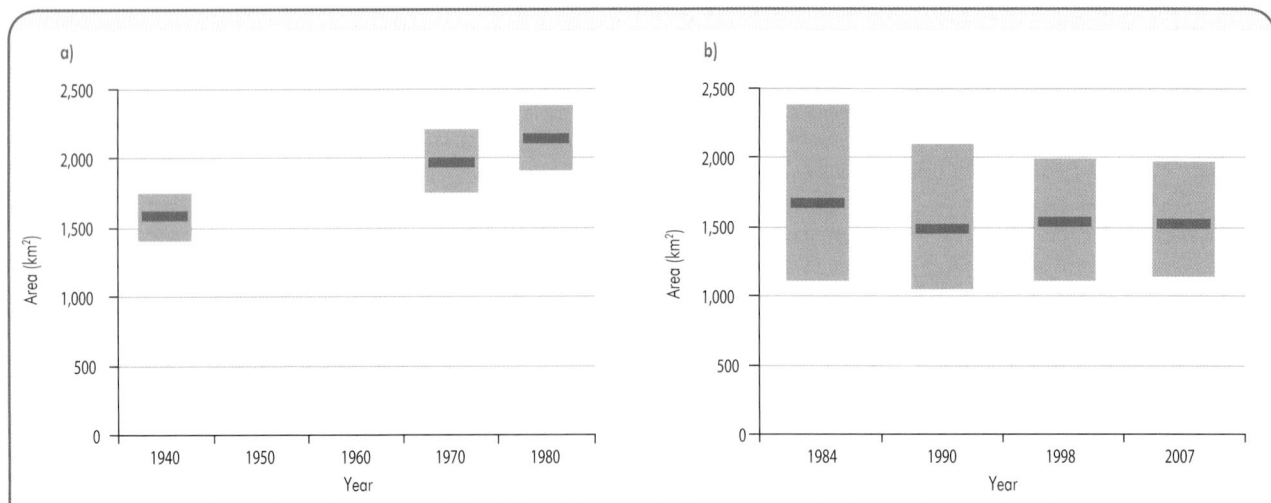

Figure 19.20 Area of a) built land (1940s–1980s) and b) built-up area and gardens in Scotland (1984–2007). Countryside Survey data owned by NERC – Centre for Ecology & Hydrology. The height of the bars on the charts represents the 95% confidence limits around the estimated area of the habitat; the estimated area is shown as a line across the bar. Source: National Countryside Monitoring Scheme (Mackey *et al.* 1998); Countryside Survey (Norton *et al.* 2009).

local authority areas in Scotland following Planning Advice Note 65 (PAN 2008). The 2009 State of Scotland's Greenspace Report (greenspace scotland 2009) describes data from 20 local authorities in Scotland covering 34% of the land area and 70% of the population. These authorities record almost 85,000 ha of Greenspace, 30% of which consists of private gardens (**Table 19.7**). In 2009 there was about 10,800 ha of vacant and derelict land in Scotland (Scottish Government 2010). Scottish Natural Heritage (SNH) has summarised trends in urban Greenspace (SNH 2009). The results show a slowing of

urban built development, a reduction in vacant and derelict land and an expansion of formal recreation land. In 2009 for 171 urban settlements in Scotland, 36,787 ha (25.2%) of the total area is covered by Greenspace policies. Of this 34,555 ha (16.9% of the Urban area) is designated as a protected area (green belt, nature conservation designation or landscape value). Public parks are about 0.8% of the total area of Urban areas (9% of Greenspace); natural/semi-natural Greenspace and green network policies apply to about 10,204 ha (7% of Urban areas).

Table 19.7 Types and percentage of greenspace in Scotland for categories in Planning Advice Note 65. Source: greenspace scotland 2009.

Type of Greenspace	Proportion in Scotland (%)	Description
Private gardens	30%	Areas of land normally enclosed and associated with a house or institution and reserved for private use.
Natural spaces	28%	Areas of undeveloped or previously developed land with residual natural habitats or which have been planted or colonised by vegetation and wildlife, including woodland and wetland areas.
Amenity space	15%	Landscaped areas providing visual amenity or separating different buildings or land uses for environmental, visual or safety reasons and used for a variety of informal or social activities such as sunbathing, picnics or kickabouts.
Sports areas	13%	Large and generally flat areas of grassland or specially designed surfaces, used primarily for designated sports (including playing fields, golf courses, tennis courts and bowling greens) and which are generally bookable.
Public parks and gardens	9%	Areas of land normally enclosed, designed, constructed, managed and maintained as a public park or garden. These may be owned or managed by community groups
Green corridors	3%	Routes including canals, river corridors and old railway lines, linking different areas within a town or city as part of a designated and managed network and used for walking, cycling or horse riding, or linking towns and cities to their surrounding countryside or country parks. These may link greenspaces together.
Cemeteries	1%	Includes churchyards and cemeteries.
Playspace	<1%	Areas providing safe and accessible opportunities for children's play, usually linked to housing areas.
Allotments	<1%	Areas of land for growing fruit, vegetables and other plants, either in individual allotments or as a community activity.
Civic space	<1%	Squares, streets and waterfront promenades, predominantly of hard landscaping that provide a focus for pedestrian activity and can make connections for people and for wildlife.
Other	1%	May be one or more types as required by local circumstances or priorities.

The cities of Glasgow, Edinburgh, Aberdeen and Dundee, and many other settlements, are also on estuaries of major rivers and/or on the coast, this having a strong influence on their character and their changing role in relation to ecosystem services. There is also growing evidence of the importance of urban form for biodiversity and provision of ecosystem services, notably positive relationships between social status of residents and tree cover, and provision of ecosystem services with house type (Tratalos et al. 2007b). As part of Greenspace audits, Councils in Scotland are reviewing biodiversity (greenspace scotland 2009).

Urban areas may provide artificial habitats that have functional similarities to natural ecosystems. Buildings organised along streets may be analogues of cliffs and canyons, and birds roost and nest on building ledges and roofs. Birds are a good indicator of the general state of biodiversity in urban areas because they can occupy a range of urban habitats and are at or near the top of the food chain. There are also long-term data for certain areas. Across Britain total avian species richness as well as data for urban indicator species shows an initial increase followed by a decrease as household density increases (Tratalos et al. 2007a). There are several bird species for which urban roosting and nesting is important, including peregrines (*Falco peregrinus*), feral pigeons (*Columba livia domestic*), gulls and starlings (*Sturnus vulgaris*). In addition to familiar urban birds, a number of seabird and freshwater bird species have colonised Glasgow (Campbell 2008); trends for these species for other cities in Scotland have not been studied.

Gardens and allotments occupy between 6% and 50% of the footprint of major Scottish towns and cities (Birnie et al. 2002; greenspace scotland 2009). Economic, social and environmental services provided by Greenspace in urban areas are beginning to be understood and the benefits through improved health and well-being increasingly recognised (Bell et al. 2008). Several studies of the direct and indirect benefits in Scotland are discussed in the section on cultural services. There are benefits from using gardens and allotments for food production, in terms of both the activity of growing the food and its consumption and increased abundance of pollinators (Andersson et al. 2007). The value of cultural services provided by parks and public gardens is high, largely because of ease of access and use by large numbers of people.

Greenspaces in urban areas also provide a variety of environmental benefits. Air quality can be improved, although more research is needed on types of plants and vegetation that perform best. Noise, the visual intrusion from traffic and flood risk from storm water are all reduced where there are areas of vegetation to intercept or absorb them in urban areas. Urban Greenspaces also provide a diverse habitat, mainly for bird and animal species. Golf courses represent Greenspaces that could be used intentionally for a variety of purposes beyond golf in Scotland; in particular more research could be targeted on management of golf courses to increase their biodiversity

value, for use in reducing noise and flooding, and in providing health and well-being benefits from their green environments.

19.4.7 Coastal Margin and Marine

The Coastal Margin and Marine areas of Scotland are not yet fully documented and are the subject of considerable research and monitoring efforts (Saunders et al. 2002; Baxter et al. 2008; UKMMAS 2010). The state and condition of the coastal and marine areas of Scotland are the subject of a recent report (Baxter et al. 2008), and are an important part of Charting Progress 2, an assessment of the UK's seas, which was published in July 2010 (UKMMAS 2010). A detailed Marine Atlas for Scotland has also been published to provide information for the National Marine Plan (Baxter et al. 2011).

The length of Scotland's coastline[6] has been estimated at 11,803 km (MLURI 1993; SNH 2004a). The area of seabed contained within the 12 nm territorial limit is estimated to be about 88,600 km² (SNH 2004a), about 12% larger than the 78,840 km² (7.9 million ha) land area of Scotland. Extending the territorial limit to the UK Continental Shelf and the 200 nm limit attaches about 470,000 km² of marine area to Scotland (**Figure 19.21**).

Physical, chemical and biological processes and elements of marine ecosystems are strongly interrelated at a range of scales. There is also a strong influence of land-based activities on coastal and marine areas. The offshore environment around Scotland varies in depth from less than 250 m (with an average of approximately 100 m) on the shelf seas to greater than 2,000 m in the deep ocean regions of the Rockall Trough and Faroe-Shetland Channel to the west of the Outer Hebrides and Shetland Isles (Baxter et al. 2008). The shelf seas include the Malin and Hebrides shelf seas, Orkney and Shetland shelf seas, and the North Sea. The shelf seas contain banks (Viking Bank, Stanton Banks) and deep channels. The deep ocean topography is marked by steep ridges (Wyville-Thompson Ridge), seamounts (Anton Dohrn) and banks (Rockall Bank).

Scotland's seas are affected by ocean circulation systems, tidal currents, and freshwater from major rivers. The North Atlantic Current is driven partly by wind and partly by density differences between warmer southern water and cooler northern water. In addition to this surface current, there is a flow of cold water, the Thermohaline Current (or Meridional Overturning Circulation) returning from the Arctic to the Atlantic at depths of below 400–600 m. This flow moves south-eastwards through the Faroe-Shetland Channel and is then diverted westwards by the Wyville-Thompson Ridge into the Rockall Trough. This circulation is of particular interest as it is an important element of climate variability and because there is concern that it may be weakened by global climate change (Higgins & Vellinga 2004; Higgins & Schneider 2005; Kuhlbrodt et al. 2009). The Slope Current is a fast current (15–30 cm per second) that flows northwards along the edge of the continental slope at depths of approximately 400–500 m. This current

---

6 Coastline length is highly dependent on the scale of the data from which it is measured. Estimates of the length of Scotland's coastline range from over 10,000 km to 18,670 km (Angus et al. 2011). The length estimate provide here is based on measurement from 1:25,000 scale Ordnance Survey maps.

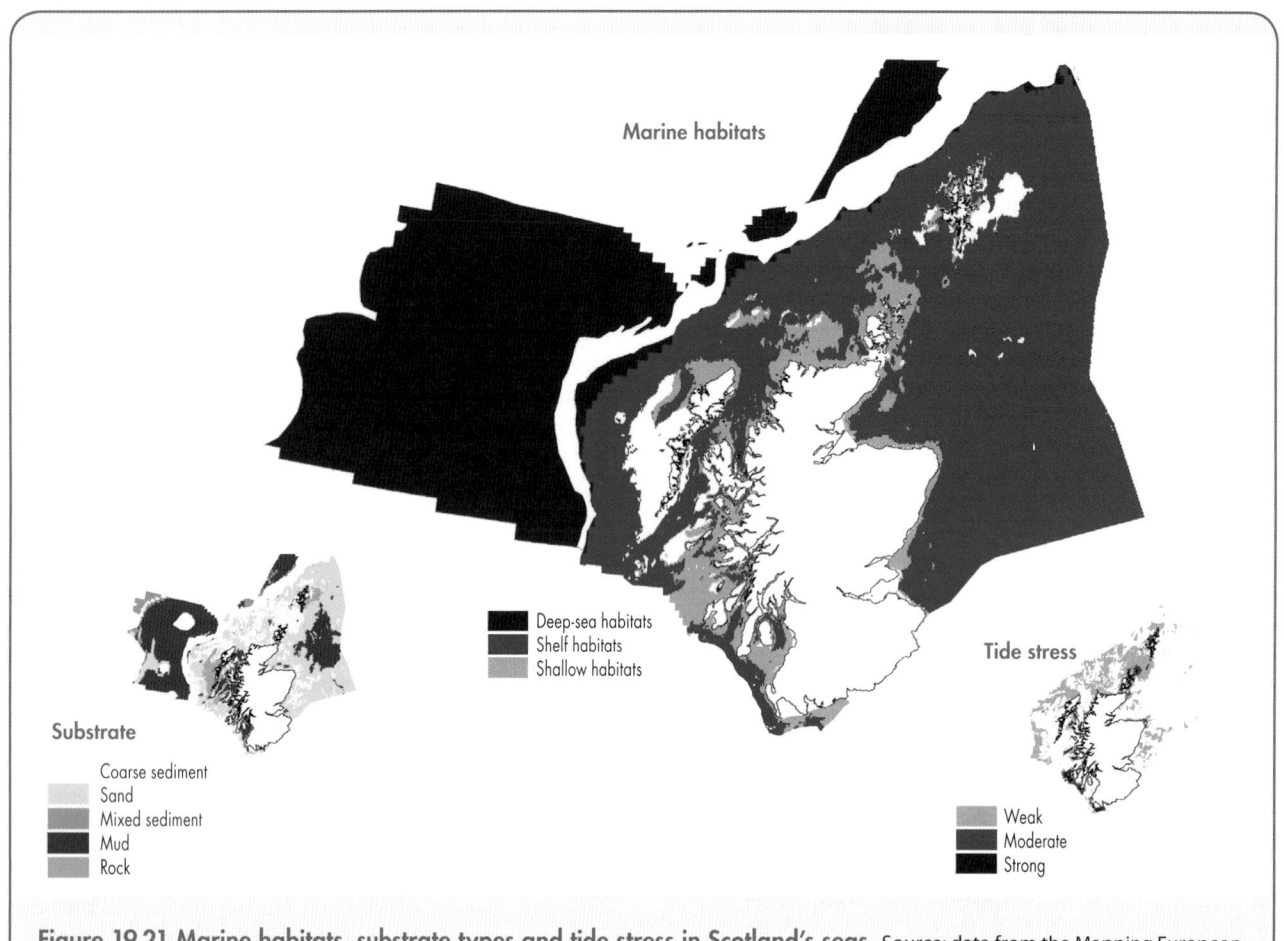

Figure 19.21 Marine habitats, substrate types and tide stress in Scotland's seas. Source: data from the Mapping European Seabed Habitats (MESH) project (http://www.searchmesh.net).

has its source in the Iberian region and part of the North Atlantic Current that reaches the Bay of Biscay; as a result it provides heat, nutrients and plankton to Scotland's waters, influencing fish distribution and feeding (Reid *et al.* 1997; Haugland *et al.* 2006).

A variety of tidal currents affect Scotland. These strong currents are found where the topographic controls constrain water movement and cause mixing within the water column. They are especially apparent around Orkney, Shetland, the Mull of Kintyre, the Hebrides, and in the Pentland Firth. The predominant circulation of water on the west shelf of Scotland is northwards, and is anticlockwise in the North Sea.

Sea temperatures around Scotland are affected both by the local climate and by heat transfer from ocean currents. Sea surface temperatures follow a cycle with a 1-month lag behind atmospheric temperature. In winter, sea temperatures are higher on the west coast than the east. In summer, sea temperatures are warmer in the North Sea on the east than off the West coast.

Salinity in coastal waters is affected by input of freshwater from land and rivers. The waters of the Firths of Solway, Clyde, Moray, Tay, and Forth, and estuaries of smaller rivers, receive considerable freshwater runoff. It is estimated that 73% of the freshwater falling as precipitation in Scotland becomes runoff into the coastal and marine waters of Scotland. West coast sea lochs with a sill at the mouth of the loch, as is characteristic of fjords, may have only limited water exchange with the seas (Hall *et al.* 1996).

Turbidity, a measure of the biological (phytoplankton) and mineral (sediment) suspended solids in water as well as coloured dissolved organic matter, is highest in coastal areas. The Scottish North Sea has local concentrations of suspended sediment that are greater than in the southern North Sea. Turbidity influences the depths at which photosynthesis can take place (Baxter *et al.* 2008).

The effects of salmon farm inputs on pelagic nutrient concentrations and planktonic microbial abundance and biomass were investigated in Loch Fyne on the west coast of Scotland. Ammonium and dissolved organic nitrogen concentrations as well as heterotrophic microbial abundance and biomass were highest nearest to fish farms, suggesting that these and other nutrients derived from the fish farm may be directly or indirectly enhancing heterotrophic microbial activity and that the heterotrophic microbial food web is responsible for processing matter and energy released into the pelagic environment from salmon farms (Navarro *et al.* 2008).

The physical characteristics of the water in the shelf seas have an important influence on the marine ecosystem. The dynamics of currents, tidal flows and water circulation patterns, the supply of sediments and other materials, as well as bathymetry and climatic factors in the seas, all influence the distribution of seabed sediments and the chemical and biological processes operating in the water column. The shelf seabed is variable and includes sediments from mud to rock. The sediments of the seabed in Scotland are sand- and gravel-sized and derive from Quaternary deposits associated with the last glaciation (Baxter *et al.* 2008). Fine, muddy sediments occur nearshore where sediments are supplied by rivers, and offshore in areas where currents and tides are weak, for example at the Witch Ground, Fladen basin, and in the Minch, and at the bed of the deep waters of the Faroe-Shetland Channel and Rockall Trough. There are high concentrations of calcareous seabed material around Orkney and Shetland (Baxter *et al.* 2008).

The Coastal Margin and Marine habitats of Scotland reflect this variability in the physical coastal and marine environment. The Atlantic coast to the west is deeply indented with sea lochs, and with numerous islands, high sea cliffs and rocky skerries. The North Sea coast is predominantly low lying, with sedimentary beaches and fewer cliffs and with extensive firths (Moray, Tay and Forth). Islands form three major archipelagos in Shetland, Orkney and the Western Isles, each with a range of distinctive Coastal Margin habitats (Berry & Johnston 1980; Berry 1985; Boyd & Boyd 1990, 1996). Many of Scotland's islands are home to distinct endemic sub-species (e.g. Shetland *Troglodytes troglodytes zetlandicus,* Fair Isle *T.t. fridariensis,* Hebrides *T.t. hebridensis,* and St. Kilda *T.t. hirtensis* wrens) (Brewer 2001; Aspinall & Aspinall 2011), and the St. Kilda field mouse *Apodemus sylvaticus hirtensis* (Berry & Tricker 1969; Angus 2001), giving Scottish biodiversity another distinctive characteristic.

The coastline of Scotland is made up of a number of characteristic habitat types (**Table 19.8, Figure 19.22**). The

proportion of rocky and shingle coastline is 73.4% of the total, both types being over 80% of the GB total of that type. On sublittoral hard coastline, such as rock and shingle coasts, plant and faunal communities reflect the physiographic nature of the coastline, salinity, wave exposure, and strength of tidal streams and depth (Hiscock 1992). More than two-thirds of the UK area of Sand Dune, Machair and Saline Lagoons are found in Scotland and over 50% of the UK length of Maritime Cliffs and Slopes (Table 19.8b).

Sand Dune systems and Shingle beaches are also important habitat types, not only for breeding birds but also

Table 19.8 Length of Coastal Margin habitats in Scotland.
Source: Ritchie & Mather 1984; Covey 1999; Dargie & Duncan 1999; Dargie 2000; Joint Nature Conservation Council 2011.

Habitat	Length at mean high water mark (km)	Proportion of Scottish Coast (%)	Scottish Coast as proportion of GB Total (%)
Rocky	5,674	48.1	84.6
Shingle	2,992	25.3	82.4
Mixed	1,179	10.0	51.6
Sandy	1,047	8.9	44.5
Saltmarsh	359	3.0	18.3
Muddy	282	2.4	15.7
No intertidal	270	2.3	45.4
Total	**11,803**	**100.0**	**61.0**

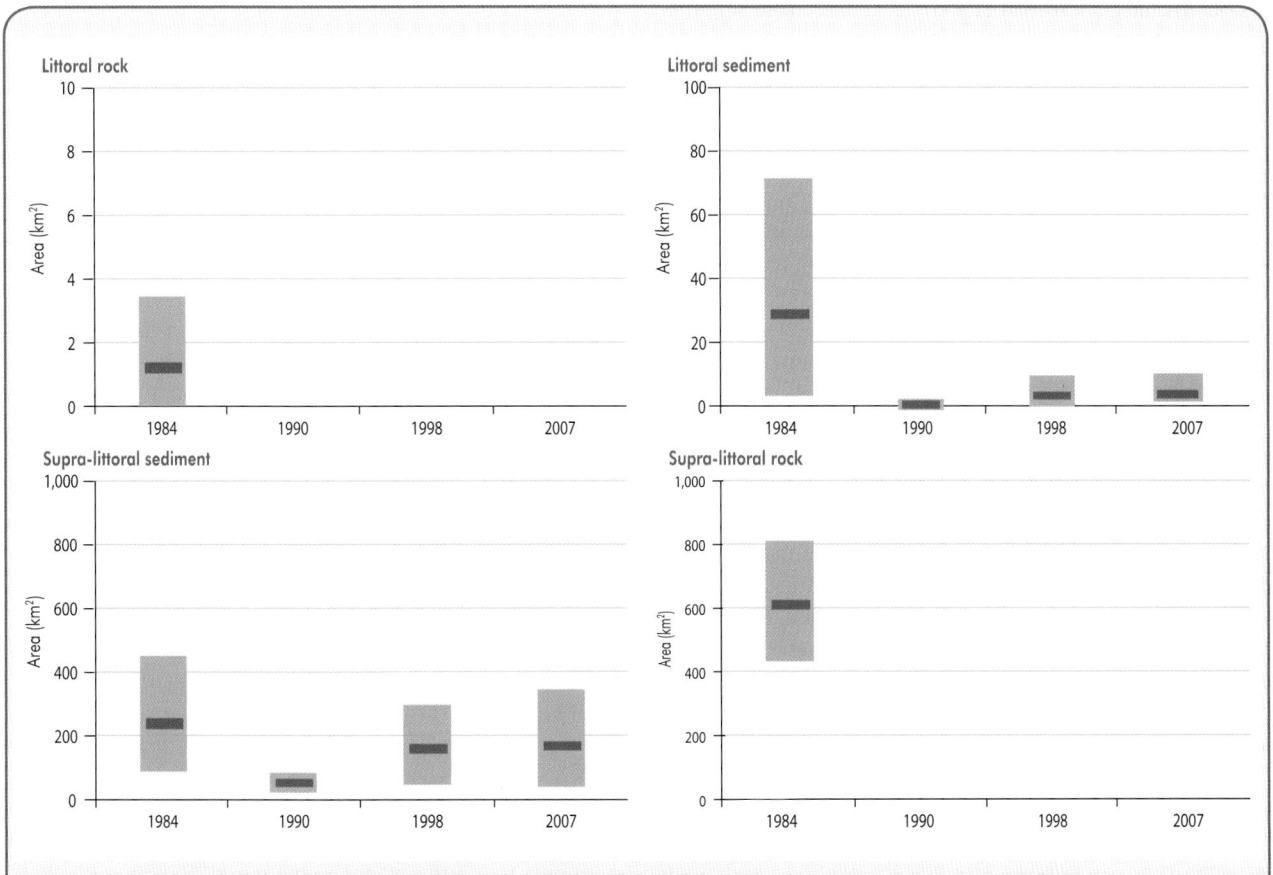

Figure 19.22 Area of Coastal Margin habitats in Scotland (1984–2007). The height of the bars on the charts represents the 95% confidence limits around the estimated area of the habitat; the estimated area is shown as a line across the bar.
Source: Countryside Survey (Norton *et al.* 2009). Countryside Survey data owned by NERC – Centre for Ecology & Hydrology.

for their inherent geomorphological interest and for their function for coastal protection. Similarly, Machair grassland represents a very distinct form of calcareous sand habitat, unique to the west of Scotland and Ireland. Saltmarshes, and intertidal sand and mud flats associated with estuaries, provide important wintering and migration stopover sites for migratory birds.

About 10% of the Hebrides is comprised of coastal Machair, with about 10% of South Uist but up to 33% of Tiree (Mather *et al.* 1975; Boyd & Boyd 1990). This ecosystem is unique to Scotland and Ireland (Hansom & McGlashan 2004) with about 67% of the total being in Scotland (Hanson & Angus 2001). It has been argued that Machair is a cultural as much as a physical or biological phenomenon (Angus 1999). Machair occurs on low-lying coasts comprised of shell sand and has a neutral to basic pH. It is traditionally used for grazing, although there is some cultivation for winter feed. The vegetation is species rich and contains a plant community that is adapted to periodic burial in sand (Owen *et al.* 2004; Kent *et al.* 2005) and with a rich seed bank (Owen *et al.* 2001). The area is also an internationally important nesting area for waders (Boyd & Boyd 1990; Fuller *et al.* 2010), corncrakes (*Crex crex*) (Stowe *et al.* 1993; O'Brien *et al.* 2006), and corn buntings (*Emberiza calandra*) (Wilson *et al.* 2007), and supports remnant populations of several scarce invertebrates now restricted to Semi-natural Grassland (Goulson *et al.* 2006). The survival of Machair is closely linked to continued management using traditional methods (Angus 1999). Use of artificial fertilisers and herbicides, increased stocking densities that increase grazing pressure, or reduction in grazing, all damage Machair and may lead to its loss.

The current estimate of the number of plant and animal species supported in the seas around Scotland is about 6,500 (Baxter *et al.* 2008). This number increases to in excess of 40,000 species if microbial flora are included. The territorial waters within the 12 nm limit support 7 of 9 Marine and 14 of 17 Coastal Margin habitats in Annex I, and nine of 10 marine species listed in Annex II of the European Habitats Directive (SNH 2004a). Northern and western areas of Scotland's seas are of major importance for whales (SNH 2004a).

There are notable seabed habitats and communities around Scotland, many of them being Priority Habitats in the UK BAP, with both species and habitats identified in the Scottish Biodiversity lists. Most have been reduced in extent and their condition damaged by human exploitation (Hughes & Nickell 2009). Seabed habitats are formed by sediments and the biogenic structures created by attached, burrowing, reef-forming and tube-building fauna. The biogenic structures provide important refuges for a high biodiversity of associated species that form the seabed community. The seabed fauna also provides food for fish populations.

Maerl beds (*Rhodophyta*), a Priority Habitat, occur on the west coast and are more frequent in Scotland than in any other European country (Scott & Moore 1996). Maerl beds are important as nursery grounds for scallops and other species (Kamenos *et al.* 2004a, b) but have been reduced and damaged by scallop dredging (Hall-Spencer & Moore 2000b) and salmon farming (Hall-Spencer *et al.* 2006).

Flame shell (*Limaria hians*) beds are recorded along the west coast of mainland Scotland on mixed muddy gravel or sand substrates in moderately strong tidal streams (Hall-Spencer & Moore 2000a; Trigg & Moore 2009; Hughes & Nickell 2009). As for maerl beds, damage to flame shell beds is attributed to scallop dredging (Hall-Spencer & Moore 2000a). *L. hians* nests support a rich fauna of invertebrates and larger animals as well as algae, contributing to total benthic biodiversity (Hall-Spencer & Moore 2000a).

Fan shells (*Atrina pectinata*) are found in mud, sand and gravel habitats along the west and east coasts of Scotland as well as Orkney and Shetland (Woodward 1985) but they are now generally very scarce in UK waters (Solandt 2003). The decline in *A. pectinata* is attributed to habitat destruction and direct damage by bottom trawling and dredging (Hughes & Nickell 2009).

Native oyster (*Ostrea edulis*), a Priority Species, is characteristic of productive estuarine and shallow Coastal Margin habitats on sediments from mud to gravel and where there is shelter from wave action; oysters can form extensive beds (Hughes & Nickell 2009). Oysters in Scotland now occur mainly in small and scattered low density populations around the west coast sea lochs (University Marine Biological Station Millport 2007). However, oysters once were widespread and abundant around Scotland's coast and were an important food from the Mesolithic to the mediaeval period. Oysters supported a commercial fishery by the 18th Century and there are estimates of the Newhaven oyster beds in the Firth of Forth yielding 30 million oysters per year in the first part of the 19th Century (Coull 1996). The decline and disappearance of oysters from Scotland's coastal areas is the result of human over-exploitation (Coull 1996; University Marine Biological Station Millport 2007). Over-exploitation led to the end of the Shetland, Moray Firth and Cromarty Firth oyster fisheries by the late 19th Century and the Orkney and Firth of Forth fisheries by the early 20th Century (University Marine Biological Station Millport 2007; Hughes & Nickell 2009).

In addition to their use as a food, oyster beds potentially also provide important ecosystem services through their impacts on water quality and their contribution to the health of coastal ecosystems through filtration of suspended matter, enhanced nutrient cycling, and creation of habitat for mobile animals. With the extinction of oysters from areas around Scotland these benefits can no longer be achieved, but the potential for beneficial impacts makes restoration of native oyster beds a highly desirable goal for coastal ecosystem management around Scotland (Hughes & Nickell 2009).

Reefs are constructed by a variety of marine organisms including horse mussels (*Modiolus modiolus*), the cold-water coral *Lophelia pertusa*, and the tube-building serpulid worm *Serpula vermicularis*. Serpulid reefs are a Priority Habitat in Scotland. They occur in two known locations, the sea loch Loch Creran, in Argyll (Scottish Biodiversity Forum 2003), and Loch Teacuis (Dodd *et al.* 2009) and are known from only two other places in the world (Baxter *et al.* 2011). Bottom trawling has had a damaging effect on biogenic reefs (UKMMAS 2010). Physical damage from trawling and from storms associated with climate change and sea level rise may combine to reduce the extent of reef habitats (UKMMAS 2010).

Land and marine areas are related, not only along the coast, through runoff and other processes that connect the land and marine environments. The EU Water Framework Directive (WFD), which came into force on 22 December 2000, influences Scottish water policy development and implementation, setting aquatic and wetland natural heritage targets, including for marine areas (Downie & Baxter 2004). Monitoring schemes are required to comply with the WFD regulations. For example, studies in Loch Linnhe in the early 1990s showed low concentrations of dissolved silicon, phosphate and nitrate (Hall *et al.* 1996), the values measured in the loch being considerably lower than those of coastal waters subject to larger anthropogenic burdens.

Designation is one mechanism for addressing issues over the status of habitat and species and concerns of the European Union Habitats Directive (Directive 92/43/EEC). By 2003 there were 430 SSSIs in Scotland with a coastal element, covering an area of some 327,504 ha (see SNH 2004a). However, SSSIs address only the land and intertidal components of the coast.

There are very few marine reserves although SACs (for species and habitats) and SPAs (for wild birds) do cover marine areas (Section 19.3.2). The Habitat Regulations Assessment for the UK Marine Policy Statement was published in 2010 (Defra 2010). This assessment for marine areas is required as part of a Marine Policy Statement under the EU Habitats Directive. The report notes the conservation status of SAC habitats in marine areas of the UK. The UK status for Marine habitats occurring in Scotland is *unknown* for sea caves, *inadequate* for lagoons, and *bad and deteriorating* for seven habitats (estuaries, sub-tidal sandbanks, intertidal mudflats and sandflats, shallow inlets and bays, annual vegetation of drift lines, glasswort and other annuals colonising mud and sand, Atlantic salt meadows) (Defra 2010; Joint Nature Conservation Council 2011); the specific status of these habitats in SACs in Scotland is not separately identified. Pressures on marine habitats include habitat loss and degradation due to infrastructure development on the coast, extraction of oil, gas and marine aggregates, damage from fishing practices, especially bottom-trawling and shellfish dredging, marine pollution, shipping, and pipelines (Defra 2010).

The conservation status of eight SAC Marine Species is *bad* for one species: allis shad (*Alosa alosa*), *inadequate* for two species: the twaite shad (*Alosa fallax*) and common seal (*Phoca vitulina*), *inadequate but improving* for one species: sea lamprey (*Petromyzon marinus*) and *favourable* for four species: bottlenose dolphin (*Tursiops truncatus*), harbour porpoise (*Phocoena phocoena*), grey seal, and otter (*Lutra lutra*). Climate change, marine pollution, human disturbance, fishing practices, invasive species, disease introduction, and changes in hydrological and coastal processes present threats to the long-term survival of these species (Defra 2010).

The condition and status of habitats and species in marine areas around the UK are of significant concern. The lack of information on their specific status and condition around Scotland represents an important knowledge gap.

19.5 Ecosystem Services

19.5.1 Supporting Services

Supporting services provide the foundational processes and functions (primary production, decomposition and nutrient cycling, water cycling on land and in freshwater and the seas, and the formation of soils on land) that are necessary for ecosystems to generate all other services (EASAC 2009).

19.5.1.1 Soil formation

Soils form from weathering of rocks and minerals and accumulation of organic matter; typically soil formation takes many hundreds or thousands of years, as rates of mineral soil formation are in the range of 0.04–0.08 mm per year (mm/yr) (EASAC 2009; Chapter 13). There is no reason to expect soil formation rates to be outside this range in Scotland.

Scotland's soils are diverse and differ markedly from those in the remainder of the UK (Towers *et al.* 2006). The majority have acidic and organic-rich surface layers including large areas of blanket bog up to 8 m thick (Chapman *et al.* 2009). Scotland's soils contribute to nature conservation, biodiversity and carbon storage and make a highly significant contribution to landscape value.

There is considerable variation in depth (and type) of different mineral soils of Scotland. This reflects the variability in the activity of physical, chemical and biological processes that form soil and the interaction of these process with the different soil forming factors (parent material, climate, topography, biota, and land management (Jenny 1941; Ragg 1973). In addition to mineral soils, Scotland has over 700,000 ha of organic peat soils, covering about 10% of the land area (Soil Survey of Scotland 1984). Rates of soil formation in organic peat soils are faster than in mineral soils, and peat depth is estimated to increase at a rate of up to 0.8 mm/yr in actively growing bogs of good status under ideal environmental conditions (Chapter 13). Peats of over 10 m depth have been recorded in Scotland although the mean depth is about 2 m (Chapman *et al.* 2009).

Rates of soil formation expressed as depths translate to stocks of soil and the materials they contain. In Europe the estimated limits of mineral soil formation gives increases in soil of between about 0.3 tonnes per hectare per year (t/ha/yr) and about 1.4 t/ha/yr (Verheijen *et al.* 2009). Soil is lost by erosion, a natural process intensified by land management and land use. In Europe rates of soil erosion for tilled arable land are estimated to be 3 to 40 times greater than the upper limit of soil formation (Verheijen *et al.* 2009). Soils can also be lost through urbanisation as land is sealed from further use by concrete, tarmac or buildings. When last assessed, for the period from 1995 to 2002, conversion of agricultural land to urban uses was occurring in Scotland at a rate of about 1,200 ha/yr (Towers *et al.* 2006).

A peat accumulation rate of 0.8 mm/yr is equivalent to an accumulation rate of carbon of about 0.5 tonnes of carbon per hectare per year (t C/ha/yr), although the average accumulation rate is closer to 0.1 t C/ha/yr. The total peatland carbon stock in Scotland has been estimated to be 1,620 megatonnes of carbon (Mt C) (Chapman *et al.* 2009). In comparison, although using different definitions, notably for depth, of peat, peat soils in England, Wales and Northern Ireland are estimated to contain 296, 116 and 90 Mt C respectively (Bradley *et al.* 2005; Smith *et al.* 2007; Chapman *et al.* 2009).

The current state and trends of Scotland's soil resource have been the subject of a recent review (Towers *et al.* 2006). Soil sealing has a profound effect on the ability of soils to perform other functions and is effectively irreversible. Evidence shows that agricultural land is being developed at twice the rate that it was in the mid-1990s (Towers *et al.* 2006), development occurring on some of Scotland's most versatile and productive soils. Towers *et al.* (2006) found little evidence of serious soil erosion, compaction or other problems related to land management. However, in addition to loss of soil through urbanisation, soils can be damaged. The main factors causing damage to soils in Scotland are intensive management, pollution, reduction in the levels of organic matter, alteration of the nutrient cycle and microbiological biodiversity, as well as climate change including sea level rise (Towers *et al.* 2006).

19.5.1.2 Nutrient cycling

Cycling of nutrients through biogeochemical pathways and processes is a fundamental activity in all ecosystems. Detailed data on different nutrient cycling in different habitats are relatively sparse. Several nutrients are of importance, particularly nitrogen and phosphorus, and carbon is of concern in relation to climate change.

Nitrogen and phosphorus. The two major trends in relation to nitrogen over the period since the 1940s are:
i) atmospheric nitrogen deposition which has enriched many habitats with nitrogen; and
ii) application of inorganic nitrogen fertilisers to agricultural land to maintain soil fertility and increase yields of agricultural crops.

For the UK as a whole, nitrogen deposition often exceeds 25 kg of nitrogen per hectare per year (kg N/ha/yr) although the fate of this nitrogen is uncertain. It is possible that soils in many habitats accumulate the nitrogen in soil organic matter (Phoenix *et al.* 2004) although plants may also sequester the additional nitrogen (Britton & Fisher 2007). Impacts of atmospheric nitrogen deposition are clearly observed in moorland and montane habitats in Scotland and include reduced species richness and reductions in lichen diversity (Britton & Fisher 2007b, 2008) and *Racomitrium* (van der Wal *et al.* 2003).

Inorganic nitrogen fertiliser applications can be at much higher rates than atmospheric deposition. In the Ythan catchment in north-east Scotland, increasing amounts of fertiliser nitrogen were applied annually over the period from the 1960s to 1990s (Domburg *et al.* 1998). By 1994 fertiliser applications were estimated to be equivalent to 194 kg N/ha/yr added to the catchment (Edwards *et al.* 2003). This increase was associated with an approximately threefold increase in surface water nitrate concentrations (Domburg *et al.* 1998), an increase in groundwater nitrate, and river water concentrations exceeding the maximum permitted level of 50 milligrams per litre (mg/l) (11.3 mg/l nitrate nitrogen; see Edwards *et al.* 2003), eutrophication

of the estuary with significant impacts on the distribution and abundance of benthic invertebrates and their shorebird consumers (Raffaelli 1999a, Raffaelli *et al.* 1999), and with consequences for phytoplankton offshore in coastal waters (Balls 1994). The Ythan was designated as Scotland's first Nitrate Vulnerable Zone (NVZ), a mechanism for managing the impacts of nitrogen on the wider environment. The NVZ in the Ythan led to cooperation between farmers and the wider community of the Ythan catchment to protect and restore the river environment (Sang 2008).

In arable habitats nitrogen and phosphorus (as phosphate, slurry, manure and inorganic fertilisers) have been added to land to maintain soil fertility and increase yields (Section 19.5.3.1). The Economic Reports on Scottish Agriculture (SEERAD 2005) record that amounts of nitrogen and phosphorus fertiliser purchased by Scottish agriculture have fallen since the mid-1990s (**Figure 19.23**).

Carbon. Mires and blanket bogs, as peatland areas where organic material is actively developed and stored, are now recognised as an extremely important store of carbon. Recent estimates of the carbon store in peatland in Scotland are 1620 Mt C (Chapman *et al.* 2009). This is equivalent to about 125 times Scotland's (2005) yearly total carbon dioxide emissions (Jackson *et al.* 2008). Scotland's peatlands also have the capacity to accumulate about 0.4 Mt C per year, offsetting about 3% of Scotland's total carbon dioxide emissions. Climate change represents a threat to this store and capacity for carbon sequestration. Increased temperatures will increase decomposition rates, and changes in precipitation leading to summer droughts will not only cause the loss of *Sphagnum*, the species that builds peatlands, but also dry out the peat leading to erosion and increased emission of greenhouse gases (Chapman *et al.* 2009). Projects that block drains in peatland ecosystems can contribute to reversing carbon loss and also improve habitat for biodiversity management (Whittingham *et al.* 2001).

19.5.1.3 Water cycle

Freshwater is vital to human life and societal well-being. The water cycle connects land-based and aquatic habitats and ecosystems and is considered as water stores (soil, groundwater, floodplains, wetlands, lochs and ponds) and fluxes (rainfall, evapotranspiration, river flow) that transfer water between the stores. The health and functional capacity of the water cycle thus depends on complex dynamics that link the land, water and atmosphere. Water quality and quantity are both associated with the water cycle and are discussed in Section 19.5.2.8.

In Scotland precipitation has increased substantially since a dry period in the early 1970s, winter precipitation being notably higher, especially in the western Highlands (SNIFFER 2006). Rainfall seasonality has also changed with wet winters (November–April) increasingly common over the last 30 years. Intensity of rainfall has also increased. Changes in amount and seasonality of precipitation will alter hydrological regimes, the store and fluxes of the water cycle changing the timing and amount of water to accommodate. This changes the pattern of river flow throughout the year and can lead to increases in both flooding and drought. **Figure 19.24** shows the changes in mean daily discharge for winter, spring, summer and autumn for the River Tay for the 1950s to 2000s and for the River Tweed for the 1960s to 2000s. Winter and autumn discharges have increased for the Tay and winter discharge has also increased in the Tweed. The summer discharge appears to show little or no change. Spring discharges are variable from decade to decade although the Tweed appears to show a trend of decreasing discharge while the Tay shows a trend to increased discharge.

Scotland's lochs have been estimated to store almost 35 billion m³ of water (Lyle & Smith 1994). Soils, especially peats, are also a significant store of water; the soils of Scotland are estimated to be able to hold a total of up to 42 billion m³ of water, more than is contained in the lochs.

The water cycle across Scotland is strongly influenced by topography, geographic variation in rainfall, the distribution of vegetation types, and the underlying soils and parent materials. Montane and Moorland habitats, which extend to about 45% of Scotland's land area, include 70% of the land area with an annual average rainfall in excess of 2,000 mm. The large extent of Montane and Moorland vegetation in the uplands of Scotland gives them a particularly important role in relation to climate and the water cycle, including an influence in both water quantity and quality. Upland Montane and Moorland habitats are distributed across the headwaters of many streams and rivers in Scotland; the hydrological characteristics of upland ecosystems can have important influences on both the quantity and quality of streams, rivers and lochs (Soulsby *et al.* 2002). Peatlands are also natural wetlands with a large water storage capacity that can act to moderate peak flows and discharge in rivers and streams, including in areas downstream. Peatlands also act as filters for chemical and particulate deposits, helping to clean water before it enters streams and rivers. Potentially this plays an important role in carbon storage. Increasing losses of dissolved organic carbon are being measured in rivers, particularly during autumn flows, and this is a cause for concern as it indicates that peatland systems possibly are releasing carbon.

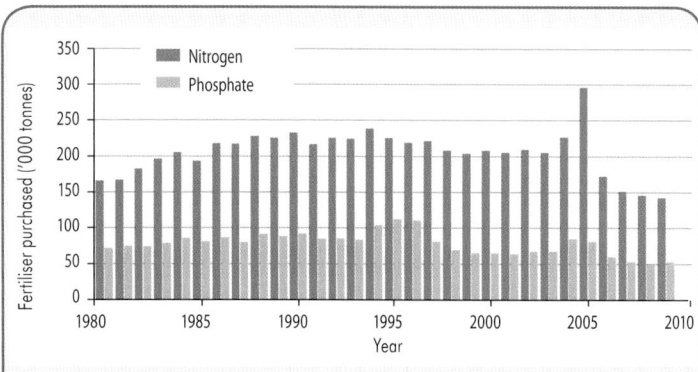

Figure 19.23 Nitrogen and phosphate fertiliser purchased by Scottish agriculture (1980–2009). Source: economic reports on Scottish agriculture, published by the Scottish Government.

19.5.1.4 Primary production

Primary production is the fixation of either atmospheric or aquatic carbon dioxide by plants and algae through the process of photosynthesis. Oxygen is released during photosynthesis, providing a critical component of the earth's atmosphere. A proportion of the carbon dioxide fixed by photosynthetic organisms is retained and the rest is lost in the respiration processes that maintain existing biomass. Gross primary production is the amount of organic carbon fixed. Net primary production is the amount retained after respiration. Net primary production is of greater relevance for ecosystem services because this is the component of primary production that it is available for food and timber harvesting in managed systems (Haberl *et al.* 2004; Haberl 2006), is the foundation of food webs in semi-natural and natural ecosystems, and underpins climate regulation by removing carbon dioxide from the atmosphere.

Primary production is influenced by a range of environmental conditions that affect plants and algae, notably temperature, sunlight duration and intensity, precipitation, and soil conditions including nutrients. Growth of plants is thus strongly seasonal. In grass systems about 50% of total annual production occurs during growth during about 8 weeks over May and June. A second flush of

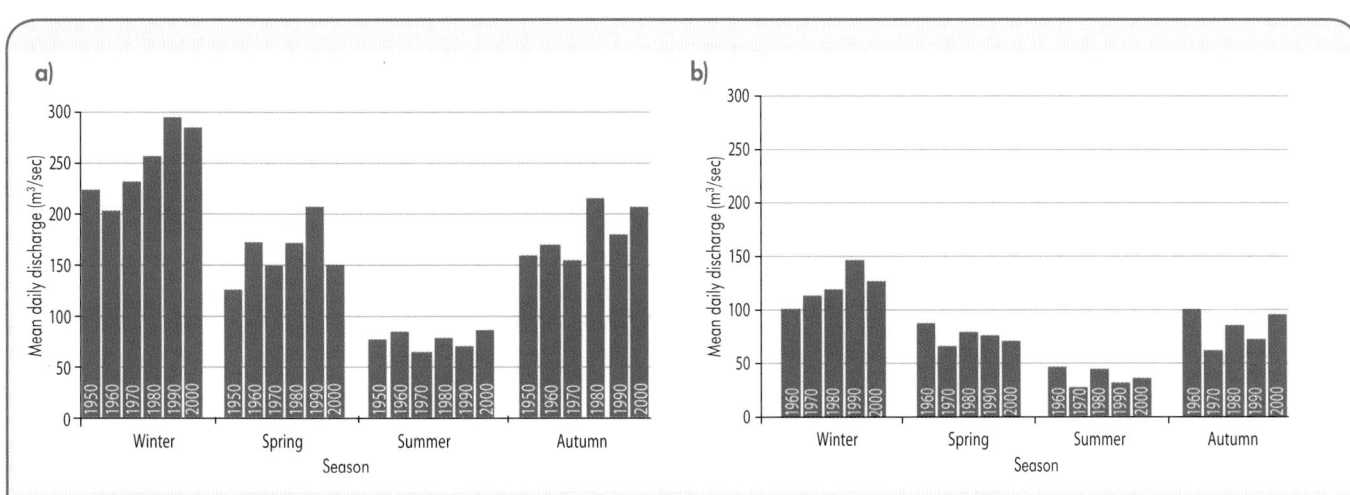

Figure 19.24 Mean daily discharge each decade from: a) the 1950s to the 2000s for the River Tay at Ballathie and b) from the 1960s to the 2000s for the River Tweed at Norham for winter (December–February), spring (March–May), summer (June–August) and autumn (September–November). Source: data provided by the Natural Environment Research Council, National River Flow Archive (NRFA). The Natural Environment Research Council, the Environment Agency, the Scottish Environment Protection Agency and the Rivers Agency (NI) accept no liability for any loss or damage, cost or claims arising directly or indirectly from their use.

growth of about 4 weeks' duration in July/August produces another 25% of total annual production. The remaining 25% of total annual production occurs over about 18 weeks in early spring, mid- and late summer (Hunt 1973).

The productivity of Scotland's coastal and marine areas similarly reflects the complexity of the physical environment. Primary productivity establishes the baseline productivity of the whole marine ecosystem. Estimation of annual primary productivity is important for understanding the function and health of coastal and marine ecosystems, and for understanding the sustainable yields.

Inorganic nutrient (nitrogen, phosphorus, silicon) and trace element (iron, copper) supply in the sunlit layers of the seas influences the amount of primary production that occurs through photosynthesis by phytoplankton, since nutrients and sunlight are required for plant growth. Production based on sources of new nutrients supplied annually to the ecosystem through transport, mixing or atmospheric deposition is termed 'new' production and represents the potential for growth and reproduction of higher trophic levels of the marine ecosystem (Baxter *et al.* 2008). Nutrients available through excretion from herbivores and bacterial decomposition of detritus are termed 'recycled' production, and represent the internal metabolism of the ecosystem itself. Estimates of annual primary new productivity in Scotland's seas over the past five decades (**Figure 19.25**) showed the highest rates to be in the Hebrides (90–170 grams of carbon per square metre per year, gC/m²/y), outer shelf areas in the West of Scotland (60–180 gC/m²/y), North Scotland Coast (60–130 gC/m²/y), and East Shetland (60–150 gC/m²/y). The lowest values were in inshore areas such as the Moray Firth (25–40 gC/m²/y), East Scotland Coast (30–50 gC/m²/y), Minches and Malin Sea (30–90 gC/m²/y), Irish Sea and Clyde (30–100 gC/m²/y), and towards the interior of the North Sea (Fladen Bank 40–70 gC/m²/y, Forties 40–80 gC/m²/y). Planktonic bacterial biomass shows seasonal and geographical variations in the North Sea related to phytoplankton development but with a delay of about 10 days (Billen *et al.* 1990).

Globally, oceans contribute about half of net primary production (Wohlers *et al.* 2009) and Scotland's seas are potentially among the most biologically productive on the planet (SNH 2002, 2004a) and historically one of the richest fisheries (Lucas *et al.* 1961; Coull 1996). Economically, Scotland's seas are also highly productive (Baxter *et al.* 2008; UKMMAS 2010), economic productivity including £2.2 billion of marine related activity and 50,000 jobs (excluding oil and gas) to the Scottish economy (Baxter *et al.* 2008).

Climate change is expected to produce changes in carbon and energy flows within marine systems, altering the timing and magnitude of phytoplankton biomass production (Vargas *et al.* 2009). These changes may reduce the transfer of primary production to higher trophic levels, reducing fish and higher organism populations, and also weaken the ability of the ocean to act as a carbon sink (Wohlers *et al.* 2009). Changes in the distribution of plankton species that can be linked to climate changes are already evident in Scotland's seas. Warm water plankton have shifted their distribution northwards by about 10° latitude, cold water plankton retreating by the same amount (Edwards *et al.* 2007; UKMMAS 2010) linked to warming sea temperatures associated with climate change (Baxter *et al.* 2008).

19.5.2 Regulating Services

19.5.2.1 Climate regulation

Ecosystems regulate climate through biogeochemical effects that operate at regional and global scales, and through biophysical effects that operate at local and regional scales. For example, woodland has direct biophysical impacts on climatic regulation at local scales through effects on microclimate from shelter, shading and changes in evapotranspiration, as well as slowing wind speeds. In urban areas greenspaces may provide local cooling effects that ameliorate urban heat island effects (Bell *et al.* 2008; Gill *et al.* 2008), although wind is considered more of a problem in urban areas in Scotland (Bell *et al.* 2008). Biogeochemical effects arise from ecosystems acting as sources and sinks of greenhouse gases, and as sources of aerosols. Biophysical effects relate to the physical characteristics of ecosystems.

Ecosystems act as both sources and sinks of greenhouse gases depending on their management and condition. **Table 19.9** shows the sources and sinks of carbon dioxide, methane, and nitrous oxide for different land uses and ecosystem types for 1990 and 2007 in Scotland in megatonnes of carbon dioxide (Mt CO_2) equivalent (Mt CO_2e). The main land use and ecosystem sources of greenhouse gases are croplands, settlements and agriculture. In 2007 cropland in Scotland is estimated to have been a source of 6.6 Mt CO_2 and settlements 1.7 Mt CO_2 (12% and 3% respectively of the annual net emissions of 54.4 Mt CO_2 for Scotland in 2007). Agriculture releases carbon dioxide through fuel and agrochemical use, conversion of cropland and soil management, and releases methane and nitrous oxide through enteric fermentation in livestock (methane), manure management and management of agricultural soils (nitrous oxide). The total amounts of

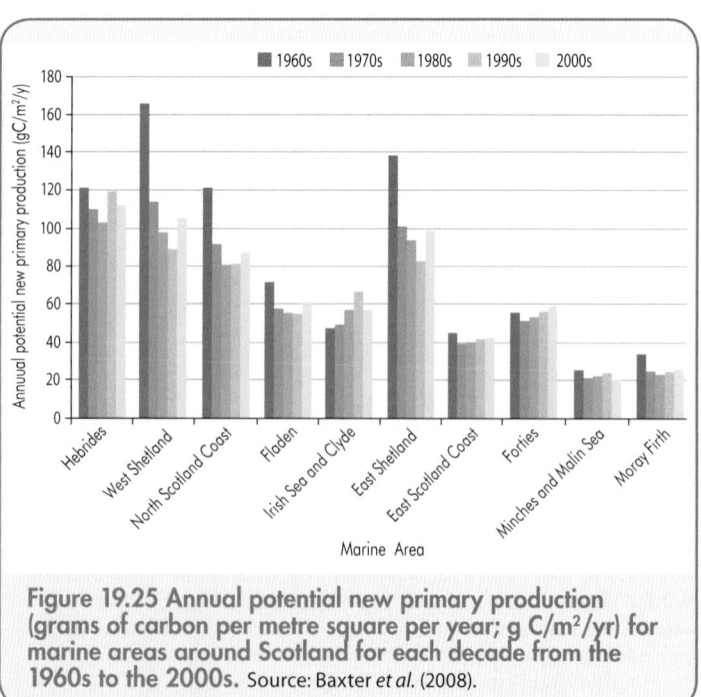

Figure 19.25 Annual potential new primary production (grams of carbon per metre square per year; g C/m²/yr) for marine areas around Scotland for each decade from the 1960s to the 2000s. Source: Baxter *et al.* (2008).

Table 19.9 Greenhouse gas emissions from different land uses in Scotland for 1990 and 2007. All values are in mega tonnes of carbon dioxide equivalents (Mt CO_2e). CO_2: carbon dioxide; CH_4: methane; N_2O: nitrous oxide. Source: Jackson et al. 2009.

	1990			2007		
	CO_2 (Mt CO_2e)	CH_4 (Mt CO_2e)	N_2O (Mt CO_2e)	CO_2 (Mt CO_2e)	CH_4 (Mt CO_2e)	N_2O (Mt CO_2e)
Land uses, land use change and forestry						
Cropland	6.10			6.61		
Settlements	1.77	0.00		1.68	0.00	
Woodland and forestry	-8.30	0.00	0.01	-10.09	0.01	0.00
Grassland	-2.10			-2.65		
Total: Land uses, land use change and forestry	**-2.53**			**-4.45**		
Agriculture						
Soils: nitrogen management			4.91			3.55
Soils: other management	0.26	0.02	0.01	0.19	0.00	0.00
Fuel and agrochemical use	0.90	0.00	0.10	0.73	0.00	0.09
Cropland conversion	3.74			3.78		
Livestock: manure storage		0.38			0.37	
Livestock: enteric fermentation		3.13			2.79	
Total: Agriculture	**4.90**	**3.54**	**5.39**	**4.70**	**3.16**	**3.95**

these gases emitted by agriculture in Scotland have declined from 4.9 Mt CO_2e (carbon dioxide), 3.5 Mt CO_2e (methane) and 5.4 Mt CO_2e (nitrous oxide) in 1990 to 4.7 Mt CO_2e (carbon dixoide), 3.2 Mt CO_2e (methane) and 4.0 Mt CO_2e (nitrous oxide) in 2007 (Jackson et al. 2009). These are reductions of 4.0%, 10.7% and 26.8% over the 1990 total for carbon dixode, methane and nitrous oxide respectively and a total of 14.7% for agriculture in total.

Appropriately managed, Semi-natural Grasslands and Woodlands are important habitats for climate regulation through sequestration and storage of carbon. Grasslands sequester carbon below ground in soils and roots (Leake et al. 2006) while Woodlands add the timber volume as an important carbon store. Both Semi-natural Grasslands and Woodlands currently act as net sinks of carbon dioxide in Scotland (DECC 2009; Jackson et al. 2009). In 2007 Semi-natural Grasslands in Scotland are estimated to have been a net sink for 2.7 Mt CO_2 (Jackson et al. 2009); this is about 5% of the annual net carbon emission of 54.4 Mt CO_2 produced in Scotland in 2007. Woodlands are estimated to have been a net sink for 9.3 Mt CO_2 in Scotland in 2007 (Jackson et al. 2009), about 17% of the annual net carbon emissions.

Peat soils can also act as a sink and store of carbon and thereby contribute to climate regulation. The current rate of carbon fixation for peatland in the UK is difficult to determine but it is likely to between 0.3 Mt C/yr (Chapter 14) and 0.7 Mt C/yr (Cannell et al. 1999). The higher rate is for peatlands that are in good condition. Drainage, agriculture and peat cutting, overgrazing of peatland vegetation and erosion result in loss of carbon from peatlands, estimates of loss in the UK being about 1.0 Mt C/yr (Cannell et al. 1999). Loss of carbon is both to the atmosphere as carbon dioxide and to waters as dissolved organic carbon and particulate organic matter. **Figure 19.26** shows the topsoil organic carbon contents of Scotland's organic and mineral soils.

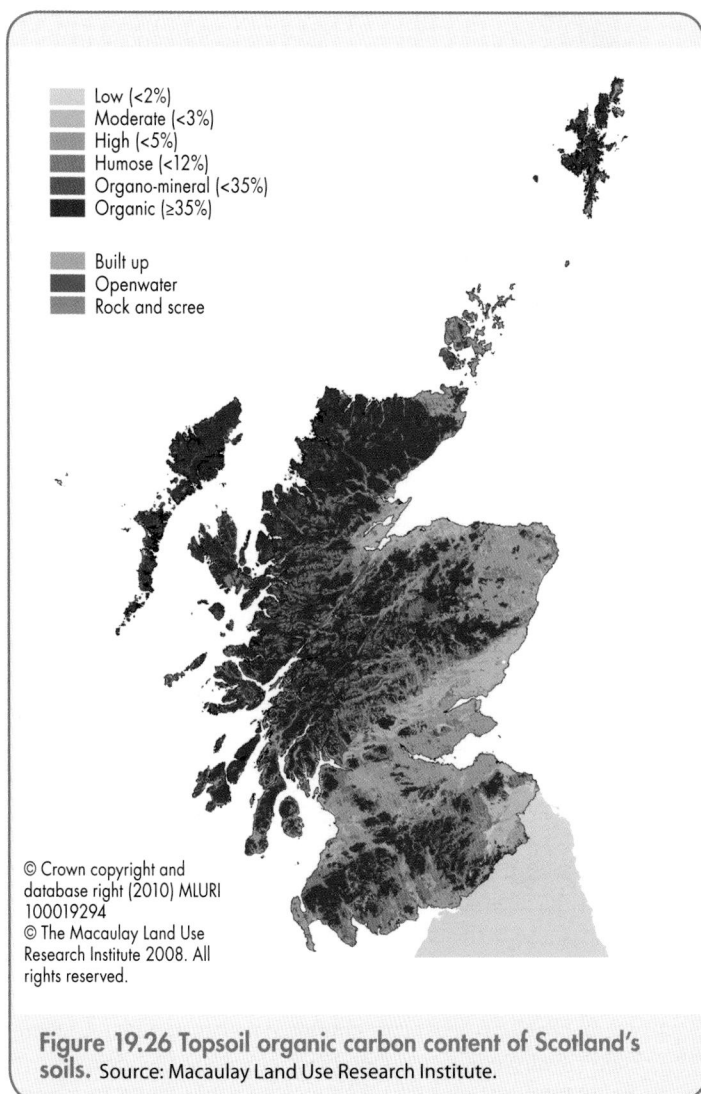

Low (<2%)
Moderate (<3%)
High (<5%)
Humose (<12%)
Organo-mineral (<35%)
Organic (≥35%)

Built up
Openwater
Rock and scree

Figure 19.26 Topsoil organic carbon content of Scotland's soils. Source: Macaulay Land Use Research Institute.

The marine environment, including Scotland's large marine area, also contributes to regulation of global atmospheric carbon. Sea water stores carbon, although it becomes increasingly acidic as carbon dioxide is absorbed (Brierley & Kingsford 2009). Threats to the integrity of marine and coastal ecosystems occur throughout Scotland's seas. Land based activities, notably nitrate enhanced runoff to estuaries, has a direct impact on water quality and sediments, and leads to an increase in mat-forming macro-algae and decreases in invertebrates and shorebirds (Raffaelli 1999a; Raffaelli et al. 1999). The role of decomposition and the composition of the decomposer community in Coastal Margin habitats has important implications for biogeochemical nutrient cycling in estuarine systems (Godbold et al. 2009), but is little studied.

The marine environment, together with the same hemisphere-scaled climate and oceanic factors that influence the nature of Scotland's marine ecosystems (Section 19.4.6), has a considerable influence in regulation of the weather and climate on Scotland's land-based ecosystems. Climate is moderated in summer and winter, marine and coastal influences on weather being particularly apparent.

19.5.2.2 Hazard regulation

Environmental hazards are a function of topographic, geomorphic and weather conditions as well as human activities. Functioning ecosystems help to regulate many of these hazards.

Coastal areas receive natural protection from flooding and erosion by beaches, dunes and salt marshes through natural processes that reduce energy from waves and protect inland areas from seawater. About 12% of Scotland's coastline is experiencing erosion (Masselink & Russell 2008), this representing not only a significant loss of coastal habitat but also reducing the capacity for regulation of coastal hazards. The ability of coastal landforms and habitats to regulate erosion is threatened by sea-level rise, by changes in frequency and severity of storms, and by low sediment availability (de la Vega-Leinert & Nicholls 2008) associated with lack of supply (Hansom 2001; Orford & Pethick 2006) evidenced by coastal steepening (Hansom 2010). Sea-level rise is also apparent in Scotland (Pethick 1999). Recent analysis suggests that isostatic uplift of the Scottish land mass no longer reduces the adverse effects of sea level rise on the Scottish coast. Relative sea level rise rates of between 2.6 and 6.2 mm/yr have been observed in Scotland since 1992 (Rennie & Hansom 2011), higher than the longer-term averages for the 20th Century. The consequences of such rates of relative sea level rise potentially include relocation of coastlines to areas currently well inland. Strategic planning in Scotland will need to address the consequences of more rapidly rising regional relative sea level rises, also recognising that coastal changes associated with sea level rise expected over the next several decades are likely to differ markedly from those in the past (Rennie & Hansom 2011).

Flooding is also increasing in frequency in riparian floodplain areas in Scotland as more intense rainfall events and changed seasonal rainfall patterns (SNIFFER 2006) alter hydrological regimes of catchments. Floodplains are a natural geomorphic response to high flows in rivers.

However, many human activities are located on floodplains, including housing and agriculture. Increasing urbanisation of floodplains is a particular issue. Urbanisation exacerbates flooding by shortening the time for water to reach rivers and increasing the peak flows, which increase the incidence and magnitude of floods (Charlesworth et al. 2003). Locating homes and other buildings in floodplains puts these structures and populations in areas prone to the very severe flooding that the urbanisation exacerbates.

Flooding and erosion of the land surface both add materials and nutrients to water, increasing chemical and physical particulate pollution (Stutter et al. 2008). This also contributes to soil degradation. Erosion in upland Scotland occurs on about 12% of the land area studied (**Table 19.10**). The most significant form of erosion is peat erosion (Grieve et al. 1995), its severity varying geographically with the most severe erosion being in areas of eastern Scotland. Grieve et al. (1995) also found gully erosion of slopes on mineral soils in almost 5% of the area they sampled, particularly in areas with large variation of relief.

Regulation of flood impacts is not only an issue of water quantity, but also is a social and economic issue. Increasingly, attention is being focused on a catchment-wide approach to reducing flood risk. For example, the new Flood Risk Management (Scotland) Act 2009 examines the potential for interventions in upstream land management alongside the more traditional solutions found in engineering and flood defences downstream. This approach places the regulating capacity of wetlands to the fore, with upland bogs, afforested hillsides, floodplain wetlands and valley woodlands all potentially being available to reduce the generation of overland flow, store excess water, and slow the movement of flood waters and sediment downstream. The science behind these practices is still developing, but it may be possible to use improved understanding of freshwater ecosystems and catchment hydrology to manage the risk of increased floods.

19.5.2.3 Disease and pest regulation

The main drivers of disease and pest incidence since 1945 have been agricultural intensification, accidental (and

Table 19.10 Estimated extent of soil erosion in upland Scotland (1988–1989). Source: Grieve et al. 1995.		
Erosion type	Proportion of total sampled area (%)	Ranges amongst 16 regions (Proportion (%) of sampled area)
Eroded peat	6.02	0.47–20.43
Gullied area	4.69	0.00–15.40
Debris flow/cone	0.61	0.00–6.80
Sheet erosion	0.61	0.00–2.71
Landslide	0.08	0.00–0.35
	Density (m/km²)	Ranges amongst 16 regions (m/km²)
Linear gullies	80	0–236
Vehicle tracks	40	0–183
Footpaths	5	

deliberate) introduction of pest and pathogen organisms, and changes in both land and wildlife management (Chapter 14). In future, changes in climate are also likely to become an important driver, as has recently been shown for vector-borne diseases (Purse *et al.* 2007; Lancelot *et al.* 2009; Gilbert 2010). Analysis of Biological Records atlas data for the UK and Scotland showed that at least 12% of the flora of Scotland had changed significantly between the 1930–1960 period and the late 1980s, while introduced species had increased (Rich & Woodruff 1996).

Agricultural intensification with more frequent use of broad spectrum herbicides has resulted in the decline of the traditional weeds at the base of the arable food web but an increase in other species, often crops such as oilseed rape, becoming weeds of different crops (Squire *et al.* 2009). Agricultural intensification with high densities and extensive areas of homogenous crop genotypes provides ideal conditions for both higher incidence of pests and diseases and their spread across the landscape (Matson *et al.* 1997). Similarly, intensification of livestock systems and long-distance transport of animals for slaughter and sale provides conditions in which diseases such as Foot and Mouth Disease can spread rapidly (Gibbens *et al.* 2001). High density salmon farming in fish farms has been shown to have an impact on wild salmon catch and abundance. The survival and abundance of wild salmon and sea trout are reduced in areas with salmon farming, most probably by pathogens, parasites and diseases spreading from the farmed to the wild fish (Ford & Myers 2008).

Climate change may alter the incidence of diseases, pests, pathogens and the various vectors of disease in future. This may allow new diseases and pests to become established as their geographic range expands to include Scotland and conditions within Scotland become more conducive to spread of disease. For example, bluetongue virus, a pathogen of ruminants transmitted by *Culicoides* midges, has spread rapidly across Europe since 1998 and was first detected in Scotland in September 2007. In part, the rate and extent of spread of bluetongue virus was probably underestimated because of the limitations of surveillance methods used (Carpenter *et al.* 2008). It is also possible that the disease is now spread by a wider range of species of *Culicoides* than previously known, for example with ranges throughout northern Europe (Purse *et al.* 2007) including Scotland. There is evidence of new strains of diseases such as bluetongue virus as a response to vaccines used for management of the disease (Carpenter *et al.* 2009). Further climate change could support the establishment of other diseases in Scotland such as African horse sickness, partly through changes in the susceptibility of European midge species to infection (Chapter 14).

Lyme disease, a tick-borne infection, has increased in incidence in Scotland. Changes in the incidence of Lyme disease may be associated with expansion of woodland and scrub habitat, with an increase in deer numbers associated with milder winters and earlier spring linked to climate change. As deer are reproductive hosts for adult ticks (Gilbert 2010), changes in incidence of Lyme disease may also be linked to increased public access to areas of woodland and scrub habitats where deer occur.

Global trade in plants and animals also provides a mechanism for the spread and establishment of diseases and pests (Brasier 2008). *Dickeya dianthicola* is a disease which causes soft rots in potato and is transmitted via infection from a host, soil, and water (Toth & Elphinstone 2009). The disease was reported from the Netherlands in the 1970s and was first found in English seed potatoes in 2001. It has since been recorded in Scotland. Scotland is the centre of the UK seed potato industry and seed certification has been used to protect the Scottish crop. With the arrival of *D. dianthicola* in the UK and Scotland, certification appears insufficient to protect against the disease and research on prevention and treatment is urgently needed.

Dutch elm disease (*Ophiostoma novo-ulmi*) is known for its impact on the UK landscape. Similarly, *Phytophthora ramorum* and *P. kernoviae* are invasive fungal pathogens that are known to cause death in over 130 species of tree and shrub including oak, beech, *Rhododendron* and *Vaccinium*. The disease is also known as Sudden Oak Death for its impact on oak species on the west coast of the USA (Condeso & Meentemeyer 2007; Meentemeyer *et al.* 2008). *Phytophtora* was first recorded in the UK in 2002 and probably spread from garden centres. The pathogen presents a threat to moorland and heathland vegetation in Scotland as it has already been established that it infects *Vaccinium myrtillus* (Beales *et al.* 2009), a common plant in communities associated with heathland habitats and in which other species may also be susceptible.

There are many other diseases of specific plants, crops and animals that are dispersed through the environment and that affect human health and well-being. Lyme disease and a variety of gastrointestinal bacteria from farm animals, notably *Campylobacter* and *Escherichia coli* O157, and protozoan parasites such as *Giardia* species and *Cryptosporidium* species can all infect humans (Smith *et al.* 2006).

The capacity of ecosystems to regulate diseases and pests is thought to depend on different components of biodiversity, including habitat diversity, species richness, host and vector population densities, and genetic diversity (Chapter 14). Relationships between biodiversity and pest and disease regulation remain a significant knowledge gap. Active surveillance programmes are necessary to monitor the incidence of diseases already known to be present but also diseases that may establish themselves in Scotland.

19.5.2.4 Pollination

Pollination is both biotic (mainly bees and other insects) and abiotic (primarily wind). In 2007, crops dependent on insect pollination[7] were grown on about 7.5% (oilseed rape 6.5%) of the total cropped area of Scotland. Consumers are also dependent upon pollination services contributing to imported foodstuffs, since the UK only produces a small proportion of its own pollinator-dependent crop products. The production value of pollinators to Scottish agriculture can be estimated with methods developed by Gallai (Gallai *et*

---

7 Including oilseed rape, berries, currants and orchard fruit.

al. 2009) and is, conservatively, about £43 million per annum (**Table 19.11**); this is about 5% of the value of all crops grown in Scotland or almost 9% of the value of horticulture and crops other than cereals.

Most of the wild plants that make up the vegetation of Semi-natural Grasslands, Mountains, Moorlands, Heathlands, Woodlands, and Coastal Margin habitats are also dependent on pollination. Between 62% and 73% of species are pollination limited (Burd 1994; Ashman *et al.* 2004). At a UK level there has been a greater decline in plants pollinated by bees and hoverflies than in self- or wind-pollinated species (Biesmeijer 2006), while 76% of plants used for forage by bumblebees have decreased in both range and frequency (Carvell *et al.* 2006).

Honeybees (managed bees) and wild pollinators (non-managed bees, bumblebees and hoverflies) have declined over the last 30 years (Goulson *et al.* 2005). Causes of decline include agricultural intensification (Fitzpatrick *et al.* 2007; Potts *et al.* 2009), inappropriate use of agro-chemicals, loss of semi-natural habitat (Goulson *et al.* 2005; Pywell *et al.* 2005), pathogens, and climate change (Williams 2005). Managed colonies of honeybees (*Apis mellifera*) which are used principally to provide honey although also providing pollination services, have declined seriously since 1985 (15% reduction by 2005 (Potts *et al.* 2010). Honeybees are not as effective at pollinating crops (berries, fruit) as wild pollinators (Free 1993). The value of pollination services in non-agricultural ecosystems is not yet known but is likely to be high, not least because these ecosystems provide a reservoir of wild pollinators that are beneficial in all ecosystems.

19.5.2.5 Noise regulation

Noise regulation describes the capacity of an ecosystem to reduce unwanted sounds that can have a negative effect on human well-being and other species. Most studies of the noise environment are conducted in urban areas (Bolund & Hunhammar 1999; Koren & Butler 2006) or in relation to air, road and rail traffic , although noise impacts of wind turbines are also receiving attention on land (Keith *et al.* 2008) and in underwater coastal and marine environments (Gill 2005).

Road construction can lower property prices, a study in Glasgow showing a 0.2% decrease in property price for each decibel increase in road noise (Lake *et al.* 2000). Trees, non-woody vegetation and soil bunds can dampen noise, reducing the decibel levels, especially from road traffic.

In Scotland, maps of noise have been produced that model the noise from traffic at a postcode level in Edinburgh and Glasgow (www.scottishnoisemapping.org/). This is part of Scotland's response to the European Environmental Noise Directive[8] (END). The Directive also requires the relevant authority to draw up action plans to 'reduce noise where necessary' and 'maintain environmental noise quality where it is good'. Models are useful for this but measurements of noise in the environment are limited, especially in rural areas.

19.5.2.6 Soil quality regulation

Maintenance of soil quality is an important regulating service, along with air and water quality. Many of the benefits of soils in storage, capture and release of carbon, nutrients and water have been described under the supporting services of soil formation (Section 19.5.1.1) and nutrient cycling (Section 19.5.1.2) in Supporting services. Soil quality measures the capacity of soils to regulate environmental functions.

The capacity for soil to provide regulating services is related to its function, which is dependent on its physical integrity, chemical composition, the structure and activity of soil biodiversity. The inherent regulating capacity of soil varies with soil type. The capacity of soils to buffer against atmospheric deposition has been used to identify critical loads, notably for acid deposition (Langan & Wilson 1994; Metcalfe *et al.* 1995; Tervet *et al.* 1995).

Indicators of soil quality relevant to regulating services in Scotland have been reviewed for monitoring purposes and to support policy decisions (Aalders *et al.* 2009). Current assessment of soil quality and trends in Scotland depends on large-scale and long-term surveys and experiments such as the National Soils Database for Scotland maintained by the Macaulay Land Use Research Institute and the National Soil Inventory for Scotland.

19.5.2.7 Air quality regulation

Ecosystems can have positive effects on air quality through interception, deposition and removal of pollutants present and transported in the atmosphere. The main atmospheric pollutants of concern are particulate matter, ozone, nitrogen oxides, ammonia and deposition of nitrogen and sulphur. All of these except sulphur deposition can have effects on human health. Ozone also reduces crop and forest yields and can lead to changes in the species composition of vegetation. Nitrogen (nitrogen oxides, ammonia, deposition) can cause eutrophication and acidification of ecosystems, and sulphur causes ecosystem acidification. The percentage of sensitive habitats in Scotland at risk from atmospheric acid and nitrogen deposition from 1996–2007 to 2004–2006 are shown in **Figure 19.27**. Between 40% and 50% of sensitive habitats remain at risk.

Table 19.11 Estimated economic value of pollination services to agriculture in Scotland in 2007. Source: from Agricultural (June) Census data for Scotland (Rural and Environment Research and Analysis Directorate 2009c) using the method of Gallai *et al.* 2009.

Crop	Dependence on Pollinators (%)	Value per annum (£ million)	Value due to pollination per annum (£ million)
Oilseed rape	25	38.40	9.60
Strawberry	45	38.92	17.51
Raspberry	45	15.73	7.08
Blackcurrant	25	3.23	0.81
Orchard Fruit	65–85	4.82	3.62
Protected crops	0–40	33.20	4.98
Total		**207.97**	**43.60**

8 European Parliament and Council Directive for Assessment and Management of Environmental Noise 2002/49/EC.

Atmospheric pollutants are not independent of one another, oxidised nitrogen playing a role in the formation of ozone near the ground surface (Fowler *et al.* 1998). In coastal areas particulate matter is dominated by sodium chloride from the marine environment, while in urban areas local element carbon, soil, ammonium sulphate, ammonium nitrate and organic hydrocarbon dominate (Gibson *et al.* 2009).

The recent trends for atmospheric pollutants in different regions of Scotland are shown in **Figure 19.28**. Particulate matter and sulphur dioxide are decreasing. Ground level ozone and nitrogen dioxide are more variable and show no clear trend. Improvements in air quality are mainly due to reduced anthropogenic emissions.

19.5.2.8 Water quality regulation

The capacity for water quality regulation is related to catchment characteristics and hydrological processes, including plant and microbial nutrient cycling, pollutant input, storage breakdown and transport, buffering of acidity and denitrification. Many habitats, such as grasslands, are important for the regulation of water quality and quantity. Upland grassland regions of Scotland are a main water

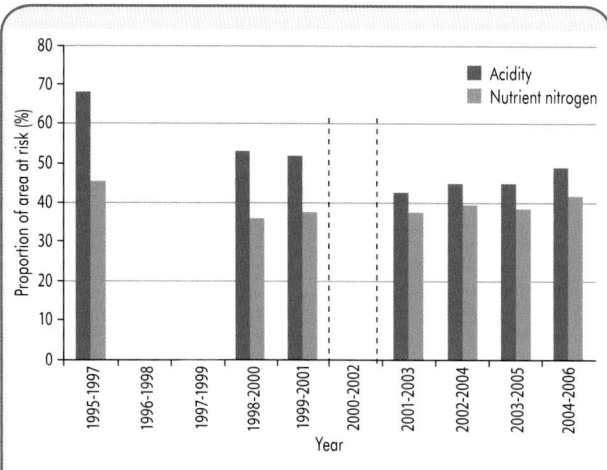

Figure 19.27 Proportion of area of sensitive habitats at risk from acid and nutient nitrogen deposition 1995–1997 to 2004–2006. Source: Centre for Ecology and Hydrology (2011). © NERC (CEH). Three-year averages are used to reduce substantial year to year variability. Deposition data for 1995–1997 to 1999–2001 are based on the same methodology; data for 2001–2003 onwards also include nitric acid and those from 2002–2004 onwards include aerosol deposition of ammonium, nitrate, and sulphate.

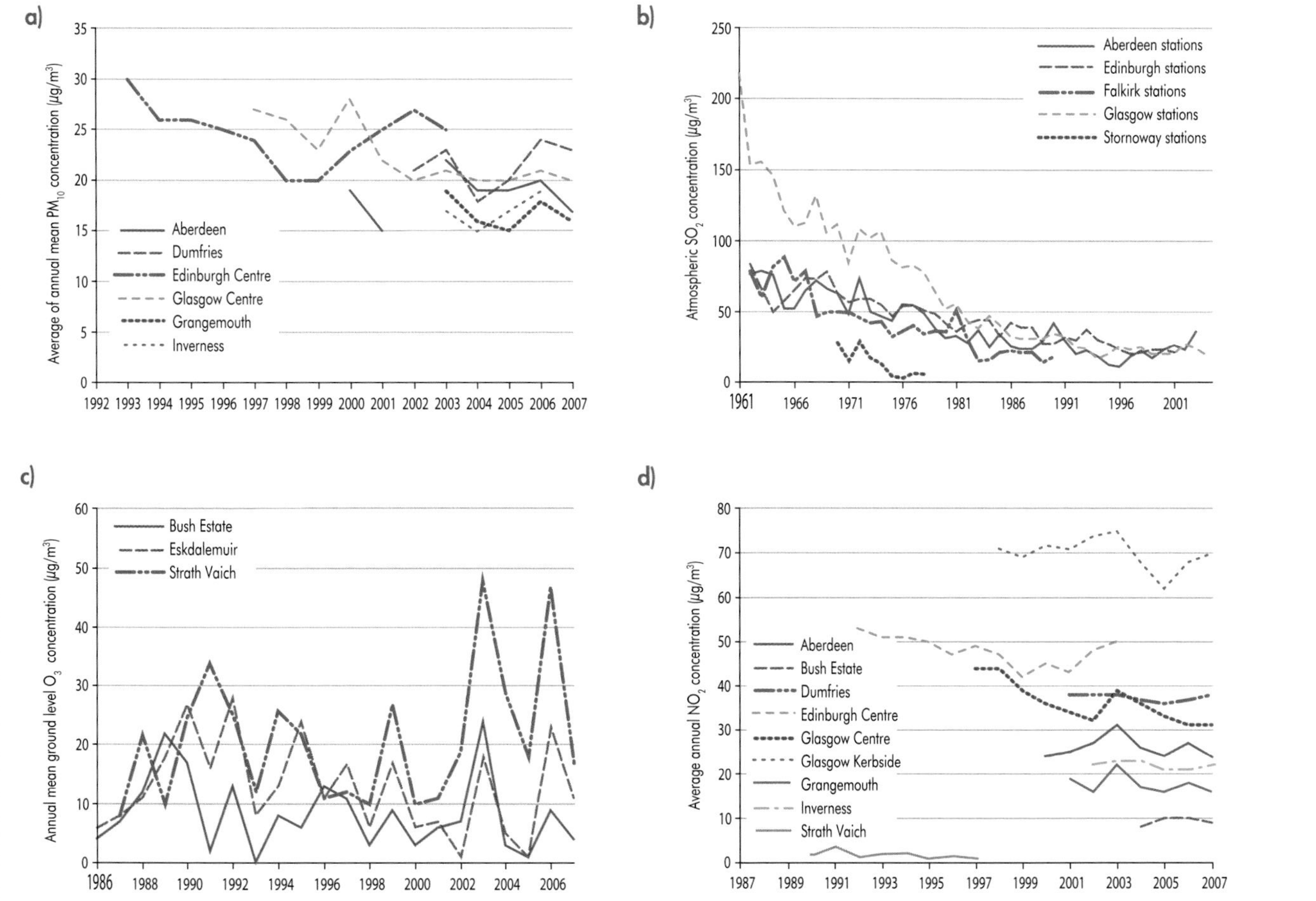

Figure 19.28 Trends in atmospheric pollutants in Scotland: a) particulate matter (PM$_{10}$) concentrations (1992–2007), b) long-term atmospheric sulphur dioxide (SO$_2$) concentrations (1961–2004)*, c) ground-level ozone (O$_3$) concentrations (1986–2007), d) nitrogen dioxide (NO$_3$) concentrations (1987–2007) in micrograms per cubic metre (µg/m^3). Source: UK National Air Quality Information Archive (2011). *Measurements are made using the non-automatic Net Acidity method, expressed as SO$_2$ equivalent. In recent years as ambient levels of SO$_2$ have fallen this method has increasingly tended to overestimate actual SO$_2$.

source, not only locally but also for cities and lowland areas, water falling on and flowing through upland grassland habitats being stored in reservoirs and rivers to support Scotland's piped water supply.

About 65% of the 3,095 water bodies surveyed in Scotland by SEPA achieved good or better ecological status, with rivers at 57%, lochs 66% and groundwater 76%. Diffuse pollution, largely from agricultural sources, and hydromorphological modification of channels and banks (often historic) are the two main reasons for failure to meet good ecological status of water in Scotland. The majority of failing waters are in the Central Belt, despite improvements achieved from better treatment of sewage, closure of polluting heavy industries, and from areas of improved agriculture (Doughty *et al.* 2002).

Until the late 1980s lochs were sparsely monitored, but the current network has improved this situation. One particular aspect of loch waters, acidification of freshwaters by sulphur and nitrogen oxide deposition in the 1970s and 1980s, has seen more focus, and resulted in the establishment of the UK Acid Waters Monitoring Network in 1988 which included six lochs and three stream sites in Scotland. Acidification had marked effects on aquatic food webs. There was a reduction in aquatic invertebrate abundance and diversity, and resultant low reproductive success and population density of predatory species such as dippers (*Cinclus cinclus*) on acidified streams and rivers (Vickery 1991, 1992). The more systematic survey of loch water quality by the UK Acid Waters Monitoring Network led to numerous scientific investigations of causes and changes and the 15-year report from the UK Acid Waters Monitoring Network (Monteith 2003) reveals evidence of biological recovery at some sites and a modest chemical response. Changes in diatom and invertebrate communities at Loch Chon and Loch Grannoch indicate that recovery from acidification is in progress. The general pattern of recovery from acidification was associated with a rapid decline in the deposition of non-marine sulphate (by over 50%) and emissions of nitrogen oxides (by 14%; see Montieth & Evans 2000). It appears that the acid neutralising capacity of lochs is recovering as water improves (Ferrier *et al.* 2001).

When the capacity of an ecosystem's plants and microorganisms to assimilate, buffer and process pollutants, or of soils to sequester them, is exceeded, the ecosystem loses its ability to purify water and water quality associated with the ecosystem is degraded. Drainage can dilute pollutants (e.g. from point sources) to safe levels, store pollutants in (e.g. in lochs and wetlands), or transfer pollutants from the land to the ocean. Estuarine pollution is typically caused by land-based pollution. This is often associated with agricultural activity, for example in the Ythan estuary in north-east Scotland (Domburg *et al.* 1998; Raffaelli 1999b; Raffaelli *et al.* 1999; Raffaelli 2000; Green 2005; Sang 2008), and Firth of Forth (Marsden *et al.* 1997), with petrochemical and other heavy industries in the Forth (Sulaiman *et al.* 1991) and Clyde (Edgar *et al.* 1999), and from sewage in the Tay (Owens & Balls 1997; Reeves & Patton 2005).

Direct long-term monitoring is needed of the ecosystem processes which regulate water quality. Most monitoring is carried out on rivers that drain large, mixed catchments, notably the Harmonised Monitoring Scheme (HMS) including 56 catchments that are a subset of the rivers monitored by SEPA. There are no HMS catchments on islands, nor are there sufficient catchments draining to the west of Scotland in the HMS catchments. The catchments in the HMS are influenced by direct pollutant inputs from agricultural and other land uses.

Catchment monitoring was started by the Scottish River Purification Boards in the mid-1970s and has been continued by SEPA since 1996. Concentrations and fluxes of pollutants have been analysed together for the HMS rivers. Monthly, seasonal and annual trends in physical and chemical parameters of these Scottish rivers are presented in an Atlas of River Water Quality in Scotland (Anderson *et al.* 2010). Physical parameters include river flow, water temperature and suspended sediments; these are affected by changing climate. Suspended sediment is also affected by changing agricultural practice and urban sewage treatment processes. Chemical parameters include Biochemical Oxygen Demand (BOD), ammoniacal nitrogen and total phosphorus concentrations. Biochemical oxygen demand is a broad measure of water quality, high levels of BOD being associated with industrial and sewage pollution. Ammoniacal nitrogen comes from fertilisers, livestock and sewage. High total phosphorus concentrations indicate that a river is affected by sewage, industrial activity or agricultural runoff.

Two opposite trends are apparent in the annual concentration of suspended solids in Scotland. Concentrations are declining in catchments in the centre and south of the country, probably as a result of improvements in sewage treatment and industrial processes. Concentrations are increasing in the north east, possibly related to increased erosion. This pattern is more obvious in trends for spring when the timing of the increase coincides with increased land management activity in rural and agricultural catchments.

Biochemical oxygen demand has declined in almost all rivers in Scotland, although there are possible increasing trends in BOD concentrations in the Water of Leith and the River Tyne. Concentrations of ammoniacal nitrogen are declining in rivers across Scotland, although the River Don shows an increasing trend. The flux of ammoniacal nitrogen shows a different trend, as the trend to increasing flow in many rivers offsets some of the reductions in concentration.

Total phosphorus concentrations are very low in rivers in the north of Scotland and are higher in agricultural and urban areas. High total phosphorus concentrations in summer are linked to sewage effluent, while high concentrations in winter and spring are mainly associated with sediment losses from agricultural catchments. Concentrations of total phosphorus are declining in many urbanised rivers, an improvement in water quality associated with improved sewage treatment and reduced use of phosphate-containing detergents. Increases in total phosphorus flux in summer in some catchments are linked to historical patterns of fertiliser use, increases in the total volume of sewage discharges in northern areas and climate change.

Water quality in upland ecosystems (Montane, Moorlands, Semi-natural Grasslands) is strongly coupled to ecosystem processes, but poorly recorded in standard monitoring regimes. Although upland waters are not subject to agricultural impacts to the same extent as lowland ecosystems, water in upland areas is subject to other environmental pressures, including atmospheric deposition. Upland areas also contain important wetland and aquatic habitats and are a major source of clean drinking water for urban areas. Being relatively unpolluted, water draining the uplands performs a key regulatory service by diluting pollution before it travels downstream in river systems.

A variety of specific ecosystems can also contribute to water quality regulation. Woodlands can help to regulate both water quality and quantity, floodplain woodland contributing to flood control by slowing water velocities and rates of runoff. Freshwater ecosystems also regulate the quality and quantity of water, including flood and drought management.

The main threats to the regulating capacity of freshwater systems in Scotland for water quality, and for flood and drought moderation via water quantity regulation, are land management and land use changes. These include conifer afforestation, although forest management guidelines (Forestry Commission 1993) and modern management practices (Nisbet *et al.* 2002), are a significant improvement. Other land use related issues include diffuse pollution from agriculture, especially nitrate in ground and surface water (Ball *et al.* 2005). Identification of NVZs (Edwards *et al.* 2003), adjustments to management practices (Rode *et al.* 2009) and, potentially, management and modification of forage (Abberton *et al.* 2008), can all contribute to management and reduction of diffuse pollution in freshwaters. Locally, environmental pollution associated with fish farming can damage freshwater ecosystems (Allcock & Buchanan 1994; Bailey-Watts 1994).

The regulating capacity of water systems does not depend solely on land use and other activities in the catchment area. The function of the water ecosystem itself is also of importance (Baron *et al.* 2002). Losses and reductions in native biodiversity associated with pollution events and earlier periods of acidification and pollution (Doughty *et al.* 2002) have altered the biological capacity of rivers and lochs. Fish species have been lost or shown considerable declines (Doughty *et al.* 2002), macro-invertebrates (Fozzard *et al.* 1994) and aquatic flora (Palmer *et al.* 1994) have also declined. There is little evidence of biological recovery of freshwaters from earlier damage (Doughty *et al.* 2002). Alien species and eutrophication are of increasing concern (Holbrook & Hall 2002), particularly the spread of non-native invasive aquatic species such as signal crayfish (*Pacifastacus leniusculus*), and riparian invasives such as Australian stonecrop (*Crassula helmsii*), giant hogweed (*Heracleum mantegazzianum*), Himalayan balsam (*Impatiens grandulifera*) and Japanese knotweed (*Fallopia japonica*). The biological components of freshwater ecosystems are recognised as centrally important elements of system health, contributing to the effectiveness of freshwaters in regulatory services (Palmer 2009; Palmer & Filoso 2009).

19.5.3 Provisioning Services

Provisioning services—the products that we obtain from ecosystems for human use—are very well known in comparison with most other ecosystem services. They include a variety of foods, as well as raw materials for food, fibre, timber and forest products, peat for fuel and horticulture, ornamental resources such as flowers, genetic resources, water and renewable energy. Many of the products making up provisioning services have been recorded on an annual basis for a considerable period. This means that it is possible to track changes in many of the provisioning services of Scotland over time with some accuracy, and in more detail than the other ecosystem services (supporting, regulating and cultural).

19.5.3.1 Food from agriculture

Table 19.12 shows the mean annual value of output for the period 2004–2008 and the mean percentage of agricultural output for the period 2000–2008 for different components of agricultural production in Scotland. Agricultural output is about £1.8 billion for raw materials before further value is added.

Crops. During the 2000s crop production accounted for about 27% of the value of agriculture in Scotland (see **Table 19.12**). The major crops at present are cereals, especially barley and wheat, potatoes, vegetables and soft fruit.

Cereals. Figure 19.29a shows the change in area planted with wheat, barley and oats in Scotland since 1940. Three major changes are clear in this record. First, there has been a considerable decline in the area of oats planted, starting in the 1940s. Second, as the area of oats declined there was an increase in the area of barley to a peak in 1980. Third, there has been an increase in the area of wheat since the 1980s, largely on land previously used for barley. These changes are associated with i) rapid mechanisation of agriculture following WWII; ii) a corresponding decline in the number of agricultural horses as mechanisation replaced horses with tractors for farm work; iii) improved varieties of barley and wheat that are productive under a wider range of environmental conditions in Scotland; iv) changed husbandry methods, including artificial fertilisers, herbicides and pesticides; and v) changes in policy, particularly price support for wheat and barley under the Common Agricultural Policy (CAP) in the 1980s. Additionally there has been an increase in the relative proportion of winter sown barley during the last three decades. This has had a detrimental effect on wintering farmland birds (Tucker 1992; Perkins *et al.* 2008). Retention of winter stubbles in spring sown cereal fields may also be important in reducing soil erosion.

A further characteristic of the changes in planting with cereals in Scotland is that the total area has changed relatively little, even though the balance of wheat, barley and oats has changed dramatically. Despite this relatively constant cropped area, the effective area for crop production has increased in Scotland since the 1940s. Leach (1976) has estimated that about 30% of the area of the oat crop was used to feed the livestock that were used for work on the farms. Mechanisation has meant that land previously used to grow food for horses is now used to produce cereals (wheat and barley) for human uses and as feed for meat production.

Figure 19.29b shows the mean annual yield of wheat, barley and oats since 1940. Oats have increased from an average of about 2 tonnes/ha in the 1940s to 5.5 tonnes/ha since 2000, barley from 2.5 tonnes/ha in the 1940s to 6 tonnes/ha since 2000, and wheat from 2.8 tonnes/ha in the 1940s to over 8 tonnes/ha since 2000. Yields for all three

Table 19.12 Mean annual economic value of agricultural products (2004–2008) and mean percentage contribution of agricultural products to total agricultural output by value (2000–2008). Source: economic reports on Scottish agriculture, Scottish Government.

	Agricultural product	Mean annual value of output between 2004–2008 (£ millions)	Mean annual contribution to total agricultural output (2000–2008) (%)
Cereals			
	Wheat	88.9	4.6
	Barley	178.6	10.6
	Oats	11.4	0.7
	Total: Cereals	**279.7**	**15.9**
Other Crops			
	Potatoes	184.9	8.7
	Fodder crops	9.5	0.5
	Oilseed rape	27.5	1.6
	Total: Other Crops	**501.1**	**26.7**
Horticulture			
	Vegetables for human consumption	86.2	4.1
	Soft fruit	61.5	2.6
	Flowers, bulbs, nursery stock	49.7	2.5
	Total: Horticulture	**197.4**	**9.2**
Livestock			
	Cattle	453.3	28.3
	Sheep	145.6	10.0
	Pigs	59.9	3.5
	Poultry	78.2	4.7
	Total: Livestock	**752.6**	**47.5**
Livestock Products			
	Milk and milk products	265.6	14.4
	Eggs	33.8	1.8
	Clipwool	3.3	0.2
	Total: Livestock Products	**305.9**	**16.6**
	Total: Livestock and Livestock Products	**1058.4**	**64.1**
All Agricultural Products			
	Total: Agricultural Output Value	**1756.9**	

crops have increased as a result of technological changes driven by scientific research, including breeding of new varieties and changed husbandry methods.

Crop production is a function of area planted and yield. **Figure 19.29c** shows the annual production of wheat, barley and oats for Scotland. The annual production of oats has declined from over 800,000 tonnes in the 1940s to less than 120,000 tonnes since 1990. Barley production was 10 times higher in the 2000s than it was in the 1940s (average of 176,000 tonnes in 1940s to 1.8 million tonnes in the 2000s, with a peak in the 1980s of over 2 million tonnes). Wheat increased from 117,500 tonnes in the 1940s to over 800,000 tonnes in the 2000s. In 2009 cropping contributed about 21% of gross agricultural output, the same proportion as in 2000 (22%; Rural and Environment Research and Analysis Directorate 2010). Barley is the leading cash crop in

Scotland, accounting for 10.6% of agricultural output since 2000 (wheat: 4.6%).

Cereals are used for human consumption, for distilling and malting, and for stock feed. In 2007, a report for the Scottish Government noted that about half of the wheat crop and 33% of the barley crop is used for distilling and malting (DTZ 2007). Between 2000 and 2008, 13.8% of wheat, 64.2% of barley, and 13.1% of oats were used as stock feed (1964–1972 figures: wheat 47.6%; barley: 52.2%; oats: 33.7%).

Potatoes. The area planted with potatoes has fallen from a peak of almost 100,000 ha during the later years of WWII to about 30,000 ha since 1990 (**Figure 19.30a**). **Figure 19.30b** shows the increase in potato yields (averaged across seed, early ware, and main crop ware potatoes). The increases in yields have compensated for the decline in area planted such that annual production has been between 1 and 1.4 million tonnes per annum since the 1950s (**Figure 19.30c**). Potatoes contribute between 6 and 10% of the value of agricultural output in Scotland and were the leading cash crop in Scotland until the late 1960s, accounting for 6.7% of agricultural output and 36% of the output from crops in 1965 (Coppock 1976). Between 2000 and 2008 an average of 11% of potato production has been used as stockfeed (1964–1972: 3.5%). Since 2000 potatoes have accounted for 8.7% of agricultural output in Scotland. About 40% of the area planted in potatoes and 46% of the potato crop produced (by weight) consists of seed potatoes.

Oilseed. The area of oilseed rape planted in Scotland since 1982 is shown in **Figure 19.30a**. The area increased rapidly during the 1980s to a peak in the mid-1990s and then declined to around 40,000 ha. Yield of oilseed rape has not increased over time but has remained at about 3–3.5 tonnes/ha (see **Figure 19.30b**) and as a result production reflects the area planted (see **Figure 19.30c**). Since 2000 oilseed rape has accounted for 1.6% of agricultural output.

Table 19.12 shows the relative contribution of wheat, barley, oats, potatoes and oilseed to the value of crop production in Scotland.

Horticulture. In 2009 horticulture contributed about 11% of the gross output of Scottish farming at basic prices, an increase from 6% in 2000 (Rural and Environment Research and Analysis Directorate 2010). Over the period 2000–2008, horticulture has averaged 9.2% of gross output. **Figure 19.31** shows the area of Scotland planted in vegetables for human consumption, soft fruit, and flowers, nursery stock and bulbs from 1940 to present. Increases in the yields of horticultural crops, similar to those for cereals and potatoes, have also been produced over the last 70 years.

The total land area used for growing vegetables for human consumption grew from about 4,000 to 5,000 ha during the 1940s to 1960s, to over 11,000 ha in the 1990s and 2000s. Soft fruit occupies a very small area (about 2,000 ha in the 2000s), the principal area for soft fruit production being based in Perthshire and Angus near Blairgowrie, Dundee and Forfar (Coppock 1976). Despite the small area used, since 2000 soft fruit has accounted for 2.6% of agricultural output.

Flowers, bulbs and nursery stock are grown on a total of less than 1,000 ha of Scotland (see **Figure 19.31**). In 2009, 33 ha of bedding and pot plants as well as nursery stock

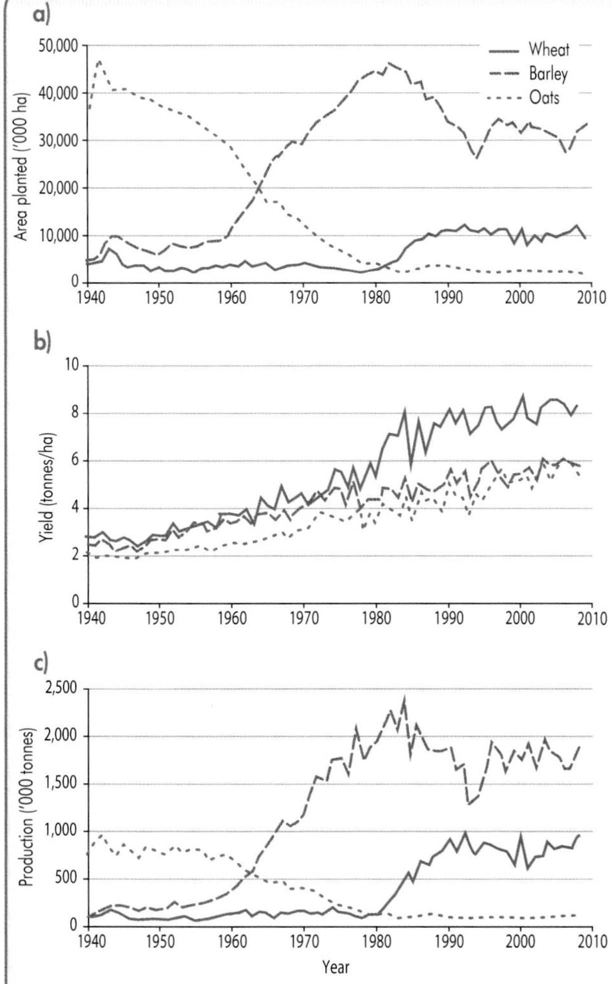

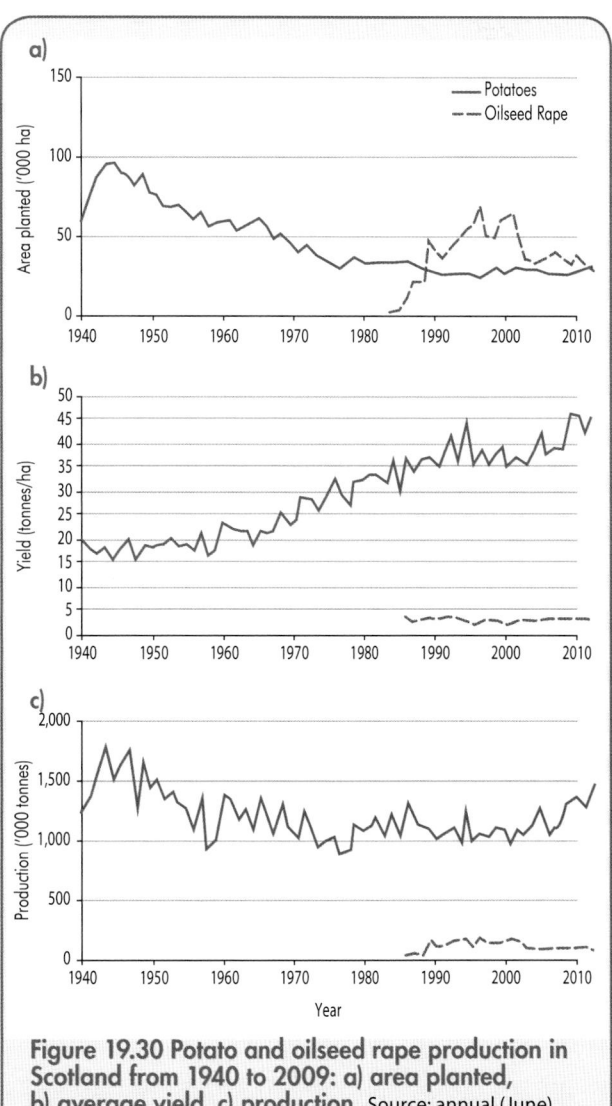

Figure 19.29 Wheat, barley and oat production in Scotland from 1940 to 2009: a) area planted, b) average yield, c) production. Source: annual (June) Agricultural Census tables, 1940–2009, published by the Scottish Government.

Figure 19.30 Potato and oilseed rape production in Scotland from 1940 to 2009: a) area planted, b) average yield, c) production. Source: annual (June) Agricultural Census tables, 1940–2009, published by the Scottish Government.

were grown in glasshouses and plastic structures, making up 18% of the total glasshouse and plastic structure area of 180 ha. Although flowers, bulbs and nursery stock occupy only a small land area, they are high value crops and since 2000 have accounted for 2.5% of agricultural output. The output value of horticultural crops from 2000 to 2009 is shown in **Table 19.12**.

Fodder crops. The area of agricultural Improved Grasslands in Scotland has varied between 950,000 and 1.3 million ha since 1940 (**Figures 19.15** and **19.32**). The decline in grassland between 1940 and 1945 was associated with wartime ploughing to increase domestic crop production. Following WWII the area of Improved Grassland has stayed relatively constant. Despite this, the split between permanent grassland and temporary (rotational) grassland shows contrasting patterns. Permanent grassland increased from between 400,000 and 600,000 ha during the period from the 1940s to 1970s, to about 900,000 ha in the 2000s. Conversely, temporary grassland declined from a maximum area of almost 800,000 ha in the 1860s to under 400,000 ha in the 2000s. The abrupt break in the trends for permanent

and temporary grassland in **Figure 19.32** represents a change in census methodology in 1959 when the distinction between permanent and temporary grass was altered and a question about age of grassland was included in Scotland (Coppock 1976). Prior to 1959 these were distinguished as permanent grass, which was rarely or never ploughed and which was not counted as part of arable land, and temporary (or rotation) grass which was part of agricultural rotations. From 1959 new definitions were used for agricultural grassland (Department of Agriculture and Fisheries for Scotland 1962): grassland of 7 years old and over (treated as equivalent to permanent grass) and grass under 7 years old (treated as equivalent to temporary grass). This change resulted in some grassland being moved from permanent to temporary (Coppock 1971). Later, in 1978, these categories were redefined to grass of 5 years and over and grass of less than 5 years[9]; the change is apparent in **Figure 19.32** in a second abrupt break in the plots for permanent and temporary grassland that occurred in 1979.

The relative extent of grasslands used for mowing and grazing is also shown in **Figure 19.32**. Between 1940 and 1960 about 20% of the grassland was mown, increasing gradually to over 30% between 1970 and the end of the 1990s and then declining to the current 25% by the early 2000s. Mown grasslands provide hay, silage, seed and dry grass (Coppock 1976) and can also be grazed after the grass is mown.

The area of fodder crops is shown in **Figure 19.33**. The marked decline from about 140,000 ha in 1950 to about 20,000 ha in 2009 is clear. The main fodder crop comprises turnips and swedes and the area of these grown is also shown in **Figure 19.33**; the small area of kale/cabbage and vetches/tares is also shown. The area of turnip and swede cropping has declined from about 120,000 ha in 1950 to about 5,000 ha by 2009. Turnips and swedes are used for stock feed. Traditionally the turnip and swede crop has been mostly used as part of a rotation and consumed on the farm where it is grown, being fed to sheep while still in the ground (Coppock 1976). This provides winter food for the sheep, the sheep in turn providing manure to support the fertility of the soils. Fodder crops are also important for conservation of arable weed and wintering farmland bird populations (Hancock & Wilson 2003).

The remarkable decline in the area of fodder crops in the last 70 years reflects increased specialisation farming, especially a reduction in mixed farming, the increasing use of inorganic fertilisers that reduce the reliance on both crop rotations and livestock to maintain fertility of agricultural soils, and increased use of stock feed purchased from other sources, changing methods of livestock production. Since 2000, fodder crops have accounted for 0.5% of agricultural output, a reduction from 2.6% in the 1950s, although since they are often not sold, this underestimates their value to agriculture, particularly when they were more widespread.

Livestock. Livestock are the dominant agricultural product, by value, from Scottish agriculture (Rural and Environment Research and Analysis Directorate 2009a). Livestock contributes 47.5% and livestock products (milk,

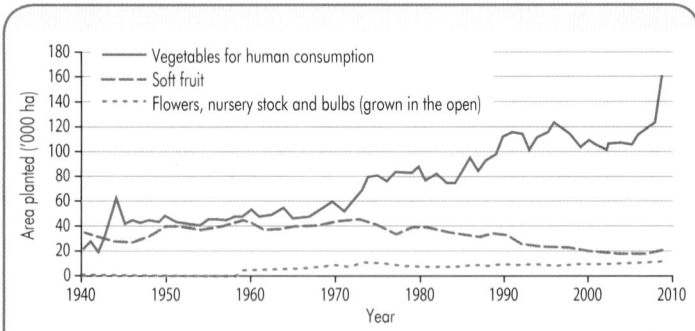

Figure 19.31 Annual area planted with vegetables for human consumption, soft fruit, and flowers, nursery stock and bulbs (grown in the open) in Scotland from 1940 to 2009. Source: annual (June) Agricultural Census tables, 1940–2009, published by the Scottish Government.

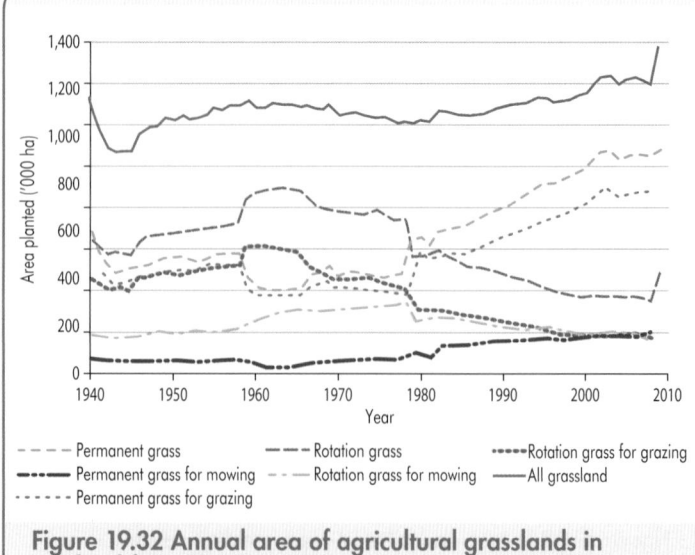

Figure 19.32 Annual area of agricultural grasslands in Scotland from 1940 to 2009. Source: annual (June) Agricultural Census tables, 1940–2009, published by the Scottish Government.

9 For simplicity, permanent and temporary grass are used here to refer to the different classes recorded in the Agricultural (June) Census.

UK National Ecosystem Assessment: Technical Report

milk products, eggs, wool) provide a further 16.6% of annual agricultural output by value. The average annual contribution between 2004 and 2008 was £1,757 million. This is about 64% of Scotland's agricultural output by value. The main products are dairy, meat, eggs and wool.

Some upland vegetation is used to graze cattle and sheep, particularly during the summer months. Rough grazings and deer forest are considered in the agricultural returns for Scotland (the June Census) and recognised for their contribution as grazings for livestock. Not all of the value of livestock production can be allocated to the uplands and livestock production in Scotland is most appropriately considered as an integrated system that uses upland (rough and improved) grazings as well as elements of lowland agriculture, including fodder crops and grain produced in cereal systems (as discussed in this Section above).

Dairy. The number of dairy cattle in Scotland and the milk production from 1940 to present are shown in **Figure 19.34**. The decline in the size of the dairy herd since the 1950s is clearly apparent from 800,000 cattle in the 1950s to 350,000 cattle in the 2000s[10]. Milk production increased rapidly from the 1950s to a peak of over 1,400 million litres in 1980 and remains at over 1,100 million litres per year. Milk and milk products contribute about £266 million to the value of agricultural output, or 14.4% of the total (see **Table 19.12**).

Beef. **Figure 19.35** shows the number of beef cattle and the production of beef from 1940 to present. Numbers of beef cattle increased from about half a million in the 1940s to about 2 million by 1973 and fell since to just over 1 million in the 2000s. The abrupt break in the graph in 1973–1974 is due to a change in allocation of cattle under 1 year old within the census. Beef production generally has increased over the last 70 years. The large decline in 2001 shows the influence of the foot-and-mouth outbreak. Beef production has the largest share of output of Scottish agriculture, with an average value between 2004 and 2008 of £453 million, or 28.3% of value between 2000 and 2008 (see **Table 19.12**).

Sheep. The number of sheep fluctuated widely between about 6 million in 1947 and almost 10 million throughout the 1990s (**Figure 19.36**). Changes reflect severe weather (e.g. the decline associated with the severe winter of 1946–1947), and policy (e.g. the increases of the 1980s associated with introduction of headage payments). Lamb meat production has closely followed the pattern of sheep numbers. Sheep production had an average value between 2004 and 2008 of £146 million, or 10.0% of value between 2000 and 2008 (see **Table 19.12**).

Pigs. The number of pigs varied between about 150,000 in the 1940s to almost 700,000 in the 1970s and 1990s (**Figure 19.37**). The production of pork shows a very similar pattern (**Figure 19.37**) with a maximum of 91,000 tonnes produced in 1998. The value of pork production between 2004 and 2008 averaged £60 million, or about 3.5% of agricultural output during the 2000s.

Poultry. Poultry numbers increased from between 6 and 8 million during the 1940s to about 9 to 10 million in the 1950s and 1960s (**Figure 19.38**). The Agricultural Census records a rapid expansion in the poultry flock in 1970

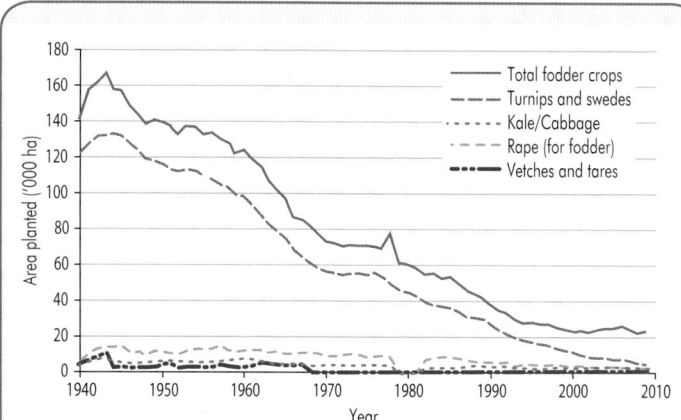

Figure 19.33 Annual area of fodder crops planted in Scotland from 1940 to 2009: total fodder crops, turnips and swedes, kale/cabbage and vetches/tares. Source: annual (June) Agricultural Census tables, 1940–2009, published by the Scottish Government.

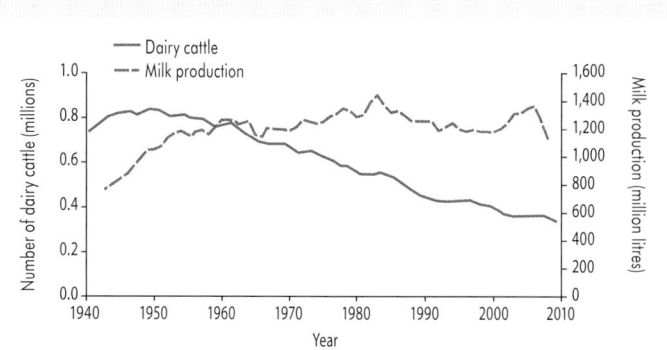

Figure 19.34 Annual numbers of dairy cattle and milk production in Scotland from 1940 to 2009. Source: annual (June) Agricultural Census tables, 1940–2009, and Economic Reports on Scottish Agriculture, published by the Scottish Government.

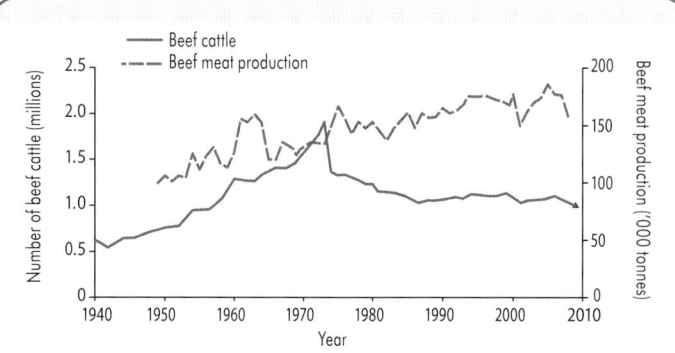

Figure 19.35 Annual numbers of beef cattle and beef production in Scotland from 1940 to 2009. Source: annual (June) Agricultural Census tables, 1940–2009, and Economic Reports on Scottish Agriculture, published by the Scottish Government.

(Department of Agriculture and Fisheries for Scotland 1971). Since the 1970s, poultry numbers have remained between 11.5 and 16 million. The production of chicken meat is also shown in **Figure 19.38**. This has increased rapidly from less than 20,000 tonnes per year in the 1950s and first half of the

10 The data here use the pre-1974 definition of dairy cattle that includes dairy cattle under 1 year old.

1960s to a peak of almost 160,000 tonnes in 1997. During the 2000s the amount of poultry meat produced has declined to about 92,000 tonnes in 2008. Between 2004 and 2008 poultry contributed an average of £78 million to the value of agricultural output, and an average of 4.7% of value between 2000 and 2008 (see **Table 19.12**).

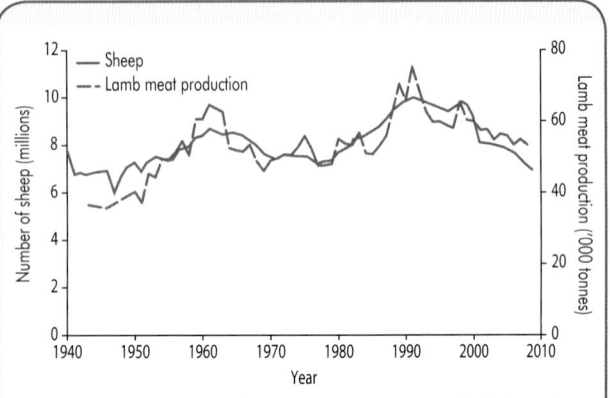

Figure 19.36 Annual numbers of sheep and lamb production in Scotland from 1940 to 2009. Source: annual (June) Agricultural Census tables, 1940–2009, and Economic Reports on Scottish Agriculture, published by the Scottish Government.

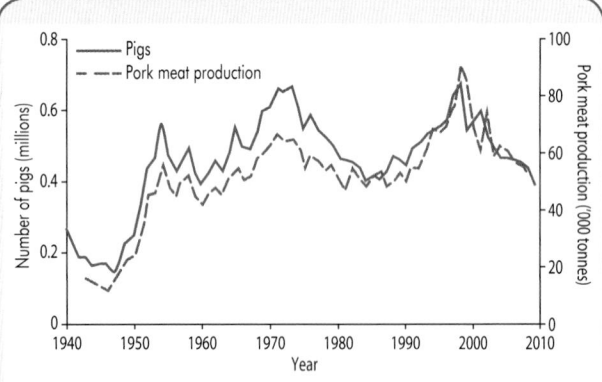

Figure 19.37 Annual numbers of pigs and pork production in Scotland from 1940 to 2009. Source: annual (June) Agricultural Census tables, 1940–2009, and Economic Reports on Scottish Agriculture, published by the Scottish Government.

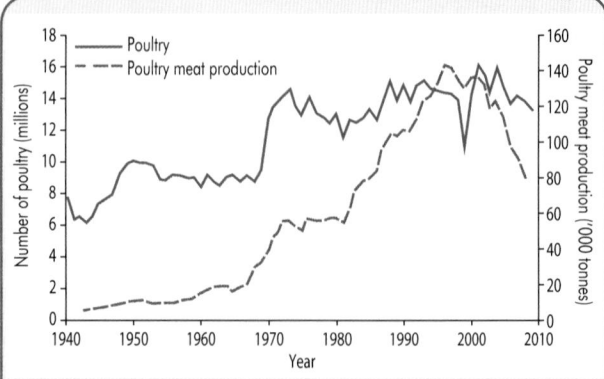

Figure 19.38 Annual numbers of poultry and poultry meat production in Scotland from 1940 to 2009. Source: annual (June) Agricultural Census tables, 1940–2009, and Economic Reports on Scottish Agriculture, published by the Scottish Government.

19.5.3.2 Fibre from agriculture

Plant. Plants appear no longer to be used as a source of fibre, at least not in sufficient quantities to be recorded in census statistics. The area of flax grown during the war years to produce linen was in excess of 2,000 ha, a maximum of 3,560 ha being planted in 1944. Production ceased at the end of WWII.

Animal. Fibre from animals, specifically wool from sheep, has long been a major product derived from Scotland's agriculture. **Figure 19.39** shows the number of sheep (previously discussed) and the production of clipwool since 1940. The amount of wool, fairly obviously, bears a direct relation to the number of sheep. Wool production increased from about 7 million kg of wool in the 1940s to a maximum of 11.5 million kg in 1990 and declined to the 1940s levels again by the end of the 2000s. Between 2004 and 2008 clipwool has provided about £78 million of value to agricultural output, or about 0.2% of value in the 2000s.

19.5.3.3 Fish from marine systems

Coastal and marine ecosystems around Scotland support commercial fisheries. About 5% of the approximately 1,000 species of fish in the north-east Atlantic and North Sea are commercially valuable and the Scottish sea fishing industry has a very long history (Coull 1996). The sea fisheries of Scotland exploit demersal fish (e.g. cod, haddock, whiting, and flatfish) that live near the sea bed, pelagic species (e.g. herring, mackerel, sprats), and shellfish, including scallops, cockles, mussels, lobsters, crabs, and Norway lobster (*Nephrops*). The north-east Atlantic mackerel stock supports the most valuable finfish fishery in UK waters, operating mainly from Scotland. The catch has varied considerably since the 1940s (**Figure 19.40**) as fishing methods have changed, as stocks have declined, and as quotas and other conservation measures have been put in place. The recent increase in the shellfish sea fishery reflects a shift away from offshore demersal fishing for finfish towards fishing inshore waters for Norway lobster (*Nephrops norvegicus*) and other shellfish as well as mixed demersal species (UKMMAS 2010).

The value of the sea fisheries catch to Scotland at landing is shown in **Table 19.13**. During the 2000s the average

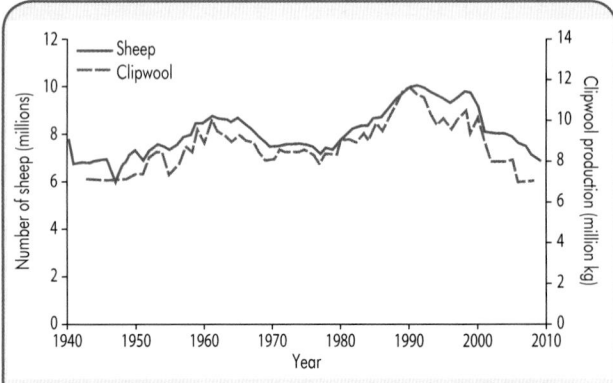

Figure 19.39 Annual numbers of sheep and total clipwool produced in Scotland from 1940 to 2009. Source: annual (June) Agricultural Census tables, 1940–2009, and Economic Reports on Scottish Agriculture, published by the Scottish Government.

UK National Ecosystem Assessment: Technical Report

annual catch has been 314 thousand tonnes, wet fish being 81.3% of the catch by weight. Between 2004 and 2008 the average annual value of the catch was £318 million. Wet fish (demersal and pelagic) contribute 60.7% of the value of the catch, shellfish contributing 30.3%. This is markedly different to the situation in the 1950s when wet fish contributed 96.3% (by value).

Demersal. **Figure 19.40a** shows the total catch of demersal fish landed in Scotland by British vessels since 1940. Cod, haddock and other demersal fish are shown. Between 1940 and the present, cod and haddock have been over half (by weight) of demersal fish landed. 'Other demersal' species include hake, halibut, lemon sole, Dover sole, plaice, skate, whiting, and others.

Two main characteristics of the record of catches are apparent. First, there is a cyclical pattern to the catch, especially of haddock. Second, there has been a decline in the catch since the second half of the 1980s. The cyclical pattern may reflect the increased capacity of fisheries to catch fish and the lack of development of conservation measures that ensure populations remain healthy (Coull 1996). In this case, the cycles may have been a signal of the lack of match between fishery yields and health of fish stocks. The decline in catch of demersal species from the second half of the 1990s represents quotas and other conservation measures that limit the catch in the interests of conservation and management of fish stocks.

The value of the demersal fishery to Scotland is shown in **Table 19.13**. Between 2004 and 2008 the average annual value was £112 million; since 2000 demersal fish have contributed 40.9% of the value of fish caught.

Pelagic. The catch of pelagic fish landed in Scotland by British vessels since 1940 is shown in **Figure 19.40b**. Herring, mackerel and 'other pelagic' species (sprats) are shown. Herring and mackerel have been, on average, 89% (by weight) of pelagic fish landed since 1940. Herring comprised over 90% of the pelagic fish caught (by weight) until 1962; since 2000 they have averaged 30%. The 6-year closure of the herring fishery in the late 1970s and early 1980s as a result of severe depletion of the stock is clearly seen in the figure. Catches since the fishery reopened have been controlled. Mackerel averaged less than 3% of pelagic fish caught each year from 1940 until 1974. The increase in mackerel catch occurred when the herring fishery was closed. Since 2000

mackerel have averaged 54% of the pelagic catch (by weight).

The value of the pelagic fishery to Scotland is shown in **Table 19.13**. Between 2004 and 2008 the average annual value was £74 million; since 2000 pelagic fish have contributed 19.8% of the value of fish caught.

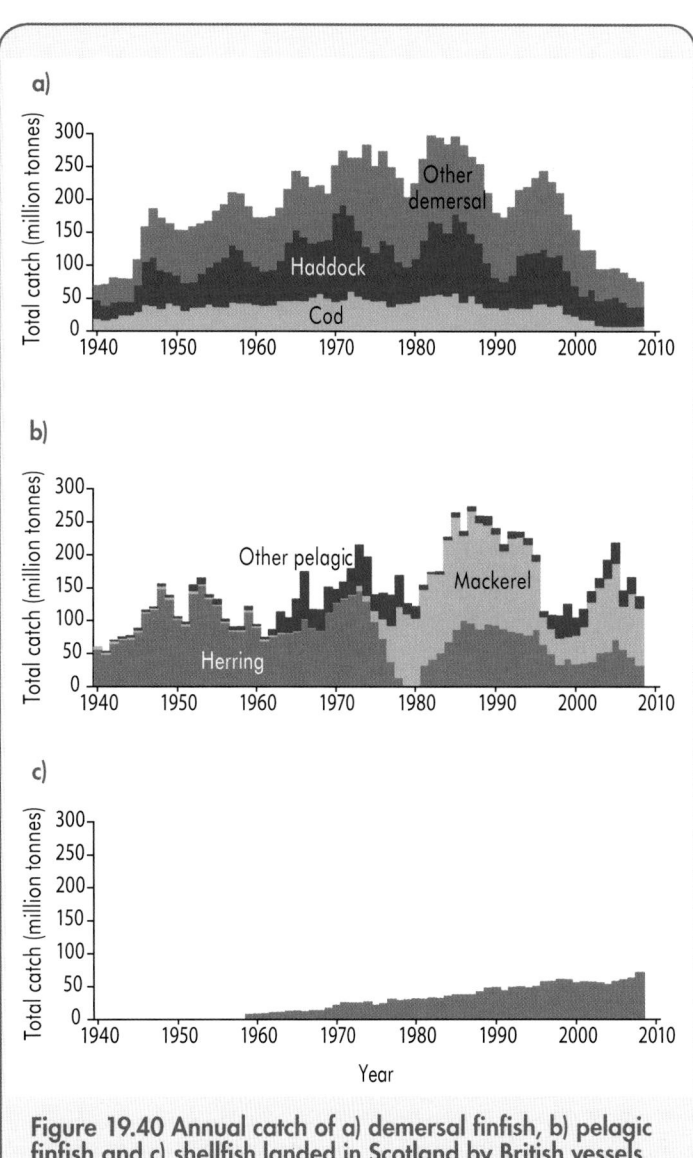

Figure 19.40 Annual catch of a) demersal finfish, b) pelagic finfish and c) shellfish landed in Scotland by British vessels from 1940 to 2009. Source: annual Scottish Sea Fisheries Statistical Tables, 1950–2010, published by the Scottish Government.

Table 19.13 Mean annual weight of fish landed in Scotland by British vessels (2000–2008) and mean annual value of output (2004–2008). Source: Scottish Sea Fisheries Statistics, Scottish Government.

	Mean annual weight of fish landed between 2000–2008 ('000 tonnes)	Mean annual contribution to total weight of fish landed (2000–2008) (%)	Mean annual value of output between 2004–2008 (£ millions)	Mean annual contribution to total value of fish landed (2000–2008) (%)
Demersal	102	32.7	112	40.9
Pelagic	153	48.6	74	19.8
Total wet fish	**256**	**81.3**	**186**	**60.7**
Shellfish	58	18.7	132	39.3
Total Fisheries	**314**		**318**	

Shellfish. The value of the commercial shellfish sea fishery to Scotland is shown in **Table 19.13**. Between 2004 and 2008 the average annual value was £132 million; since 2000 shellfish have contributed 39.3% of the value of fish caught. In 2006 British boats landed 57,280 tonnes of shellfish in Scotland (see **Figure 19.40c**), including 1,203 tonnes of mussels, 8,600 tonnes of scallops, and 29,616 tonnes of *Nephrops*, with a total value of £138 million (Scottish Government 2007).

19.5.3.4 Fish from aquaculture

Provisioning services from marine and coastal ecosystems include inshore mariculture, with finfish and shellfish farming. This is located almost exclusively on the west coast, with Argyll and Bute, and Shetland the main centres of production.

Aquaculture had an annual turnover of £280 million in 2005 (£260 million from farmed salmon, £10 million from rainbow, brown and sea trout, about £2 million from halibut and cod, and £67 million from shellfish). The total value of all fish exports, including from aquaculture, in 2005 was £420 million. This is 60% of all food exports from Scotland by value.

Salmon and trout. Commercial salmon farming started in 1969 and has grown rapidly. **Figure 19.41** shows the annual production of salmon in Scotland from aquaculture since 1989. Production increased rapidly through the 1990s and first half of the 2000s and since 2005 has averaged about 130,000 tonnes. As a representative year, in 2006 131,847 tonnes of Atlantic salmon were produced by 44 companies farming at 252 sites; 11 of these companies produced over 90% of the salmon (Baxter *et al.* 2008). Rainbow trout (7,492 tonnes, of which 2,341 tonnes were from saltwater sites), and brown and sea trout, cod and halibut (total 1,047 tonnes) are also farmed in the coastal environment using cages. In comparison, 272 tonnes of wild Atlantic salmon were caught with fixed engine, net and coble, and rod and line in 2002 (Section 19.5.3.5).

Salmon farming directly employed 1,142 people in 2006. Rainbow trout farming directly employed 143, with other species supporting 92 full-time and 17 part-time jobs.

The use of vaccines and chemicals to control disease and infection of farmed fish, as well as build-up of toxins in the

fish and pollution of the coastal waters present significant management challenges and pollution problems for fish farming in coastal environments (Hansen & Jacobsen 2003; Marshall 2003; Read & Fernandes 2003; Hall-Spencer *et al.* 2006; Telfer *et al.* 2006). Monitoring is also needed to prevent contaminated fish being used in the food chain (Read & Fernandes 2003).

Shellfish. Shellfish farming has also grown rapidly, 173 companies producing 4,594 tonnes of shellfish from 156 sites out of a total of 327 sites in 2006 (Baxter *et al.* 2008). This total included 4,287 tonnes of mussels, 251 tonnes of Pacific oysters (*Crassostrea gigas*), 60 tonnes of queen scallops (*Aequipecten opercularis*), 40 tonnes of scallops and 40 tonnes of native oysters (*Ostrea edulis*). The shellfish sector of aquaculture employs 160 full-time equivalent employees (FTEs), 160 part-time employees and 80 casual workers. There is also indirect employment in processing.

19.5.3.5 Capture of salmon and migratory trout in estuaries and freshwaters

Salmon, sea trout and brown trout are of particular importance in Scottish freshwater fisheries, although data are collected systematically only for salmon and sea trout as these are the two species that have traditionally had the most significant economic value. Salmon occur in almost 400 rivers in Scotland (Baxter & Hutchinson 2002).

Returns of catches since 1952 (Fisheries Research Services 2008), and earlier estimates based on railway company records of salmon shipments (Pyefinch 1961), provide an indication of the extent of the annual catch of salmon and sea trout for the last 60 years (**Figure 19.42**). The annual catch of salmon, by method of catching, since 1952 for Scotland is shown in **Figure 19.43**.

During the 1950s, 1960s and 1970s the average annual number of salmon caught for each decade was in excess of 375,000 fish and 1,400–1,600 tonnes (**Table 19.14**). Since the 1970s there has been a decline in the number and total weight of salmon caught (Baxter & Hutchinson 2002; SNH 2004b). During the 2000s the average annual catch was about 100,000 salmon with an annual average weight of just over 345 tonnes (**Table 19.14**). Some of the decline in

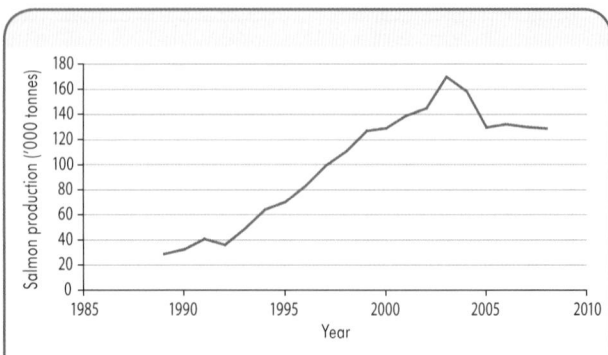

Figure 19.41 Annual production of farmed salmon in Scotland between 1989 and 2008. Source: data derived from Walker 2010. The data are Crown copyright, used with the permission of Marine Scotland Science. Marine Scotland is not responsible for interpretation of these data by third parties.

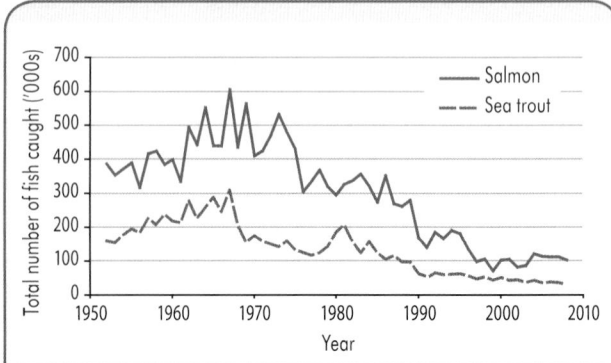

Figure 19.42 Total number of salmon and sea trout caught in estuaries and freshwaters in Scotland between 1952 and 2009. Source: the data used in this figure are Crown copyright, used with the permission of Marine Scotland Science. Marine Scotland is not responsible for interpretation of these data by third parties.

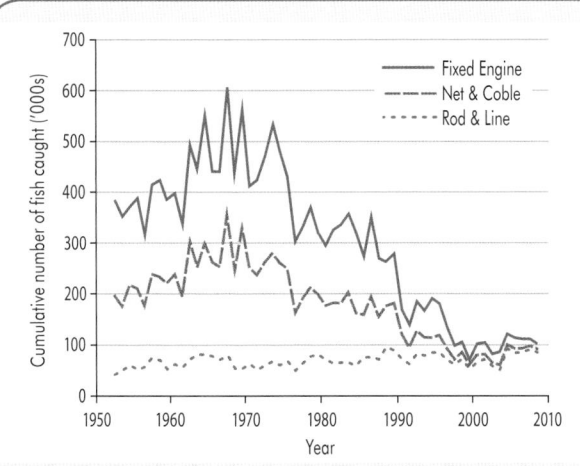

Figure 19.43 Annual catch of Atlantic salmon by method of fishing from 1952 to 2009. Rod and line includes catch and release data. Source: the data used in this figure are Crown copyright, used with the permission of Marine Scotland Science. Marine Scotland is not responsible for interpretation of these data by third parties.

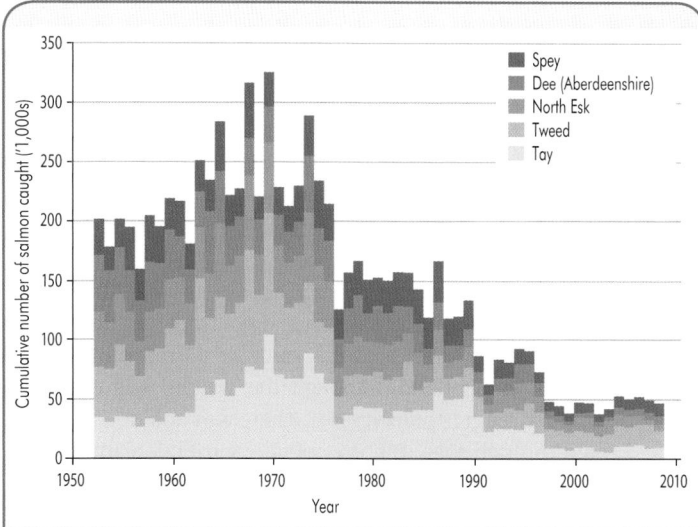

Figure 19.44 Salmon caught in the Tay, Tweed, North Esk, Dee (Aberdeenshire) and Spey between 1952 and 2009. Source: the data used in this figure are Crown copyright, used with the permission of Marine Scotland Science. Marine Scotland is not responsible for interpretation of these data by third parties.

Table 19.14 Mean annual catch of salmon and sea trout for each decade between the 1950s and 2000s by number of fish and weight. Source: the data used in this figure are Crown copyright, used with the permission of Marine Scotland Science. Marine Scotland is not responsible for interpretation of these data by third parties.

Decade	Salmon		Sea Trout	
	Mean annual number caught ('000)	Mean annual total weight (tonnes)	Mean annual number caught ('000)	Mean annual total weight (tonnes)
1950s	379	1,437	192	187
1960s	469	1,691	240	252
1970s	407	1,439	142	146
1980s	306	1,055	136	143
1990s	144	492	55	56
2000s	103	345	39	39

catch can be attributed to the decline of fixed engine and net and coble fishing as netting rights have been bought out (Williamson & Beveridge 1994; Maitland 1994) and fishing effort has decreased (Fisheries Research Services 2008). The rod and line catch has also declined since the 1990s and there are now catch and release schemes in place to conserve declining stocks (**Figure 19.43**).

In 2007, 13,618, 6,279 and 35,581 wild salmon and grilse were reported as caught and retained in fixed engine, net and coble, and rod and line fisheries, respectively; 55,472 wild salmon and grilse were caught and released by the rod fishery (Fisheries Research Services 2008). In total, five salmon rivers have produced over 50% of the total annual catch for Scotland since 1952 (the Tweed, Tay, Spey, Dee, and North Esk). The trends in salmon caught in these rivers are shown in **Figure 19.44**. The trends follow the same pattern as the trends in the data for all Scotland and are also found in many other catchments (**Figure 19.45**).

Sea trout show similar patterns to salmon, with smaller total numbers and total weights caught (see **Figure 19.42**

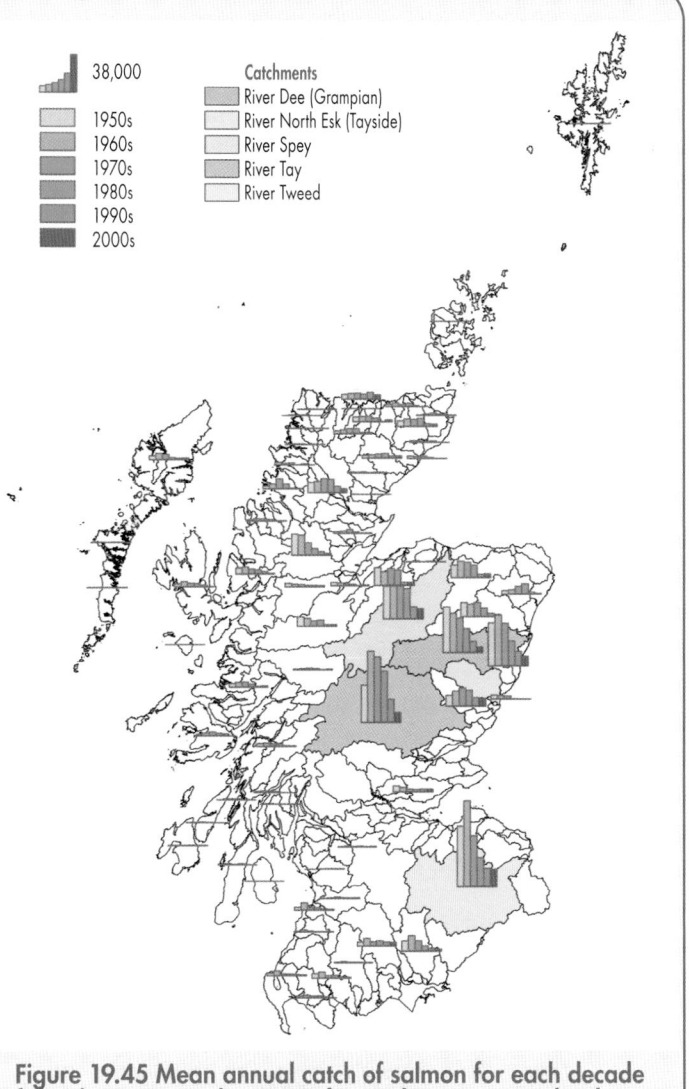

Figure 19.45 Mean annual catch of salmon for each decade from the 1950s to the 2000s for catchments in Scotland. Source: the data used in this figure are Crown copyright, used with the permission of Marine Scotland Science. Marine Scotland is not responsible for interpretation of these data by third parties.

and **Table 19.14**). The pattern of change since the 1950s according to method of fishing (**Figure 19.46**) also reflects the patterns shown by salmon, and for similar reasons. In 2007, 2,671, 2,903 and 10,383 sea trout were reported caught and retained in fixed engine, net and coble and rod and line fisheries, respectively, with another 11,158 sea trout caught and released by rod fisheries (Fisheries Research Services 2008).

Salmon and trout are of high economic value. In the late 1950s the cash value of salmon and sea trout was equivalent to about one-eleventh of the value of all marine wet fish landings in Scotland, although the weight was only one two-hundredth (Pyefinch 1961). There was additional related value through jobs, the economic contribution of angling, and value added to the product. For example, in the 1950s there were 1,600–1,700 people directly employed in the commercial wild (non-farmed) salmon fishery industry, as well as ghillies and water bailiffs. Today there are estimated to be a similar number employed in salmon and sea trout related work (approximately 1,800) of a total of about 2,800 jobs supported by angling. Annual expenditure on salmon and sea trout fishing was £50 million in 1988 and £74 million in 2003 (Scottish Executive 2003). Angling was estimated to be worth about £113 million per annum to the Scottish economy in 2003 (Glasgow Caledonian University & Cogentsi Research International Ltd. 2004). This is additional to the value of the fish.

A 2003 study of rod fisheries for Atlantic salmon, brown, rainbow and sea trout, and pike on the River Spey estimated the capital value of the salmon and sea trout rod fishery as £57 million in the catchment (Butler *et al.* 2009). Some 54,746 angler days were spent on the river, of which 74% were for salmon and sea trout. Angler expenditure was estimated as £12 million per annum (£11 million from salmon and sea trout anglers). With multiplier effects, fisheries contributed £13 million (salmon and sea trout £12 million) to household incomes and 420 FTE jobs (salmon and sea trout 401 jobs). On average this is equivalent to approximately £970 per salmon or sea trout to household incomes. Although the

Spey has a high comparative value measured against other national surveys of angler expenditure, the relative impact of salmon and sea trout in the Spey catchment's economy is among the highest in the country.

19.5.3.6 Game—food from birds and mammals provided from hunting

A wide range of bird and mammal species are hunted in Scotland, field sports providing significant economic income to sporting estates, especially in moorland ecosystems. Sporting estates are estimated to cover some 4.4 million ha or 20% of the land area of Scotland (Slee *et al.* 2009). They are managed by about 8,800 shooting providers and valued at about £130 million per annum (RPA and Cambridge Econometrics 2008). Sporting shooting is estimated to support about 88,000 workers, although most jobs are seasonal or part-time and this is equivalent to about 11,000 full-time jobs; the GVA (gross value added) of sporting shooting was estimated at £240 million (Public and Corporate Economic Consultants 2006a). Land management for hunting is thus important for shaping the appearance of upland landscapes. The Game & Wildlife Conservation Trust has carried out analyses of long-term game bags from across the UK that provide an indication of trends in game birds (Aebischer & Harradine 2007) and mammals (Davey & Aebischer 2008).

Birds. Moorland management using burning is the traditional mechanism for maintaining grouse habitat. There are about 296 grouse shooting moors in Scotland (about two-thirds of the UK total), shooting moors in the Scottish Highlands being about twice the size of southern Scottish and English moors (Chapter 5). The number of grouse shot annually in Scotland has declined, particularly since the mid-1970s (**Figure 19.47**) as management of Moorlands has lessened in intensity and with increased pressure from sheep grazing and afforestation. In Scotland during 2000 about 940 FTE employees were supported by grouse shooting.

A variety of other wild bird species are also hunted. In Scotland there have been long-term increases in bag sizes since 1961 for Canada goose, a number of duck species (wigeon *Anas penelope*, gadwall *Anas strepera*, teal *Anas crecca*, mallard *Anas platyrhynchos*), and some game birds (red-legged partridge *Alectoris rufa*, pheasant *Phasianus colchicus*, woodcock *Scolopax rusticola*); there have been long-term decreases for greylag goose (*Anser anser*), grey partridge and wood pigeon (Aebischer & Harradine 2007). It is not clear whether these changes reflect changes in hunting effort or changes in population sizes. Pheasant and red-legged partridge are commonly bred for hunting, especially in habitats on lower ground.

Mammals. Moorland estates also provide deer stalking. There was an increase in the Game and Wildlife Conservation Trust index of bag density for red deer in the UK between 1961 and 2006, the majority of sites reporting red deer being from Scotland (Davey & Aebischer 2008). Roe deer similarly showed an increase in the index of bag density between 1961 and 2006 in Scotland, increases in the lowlands of Scotland being particularly significant (Davey & Aebischer 2008). Other mammal species hunted include rabbit, mountain (*Lepus timidus*) and brown hares (*Lepus*

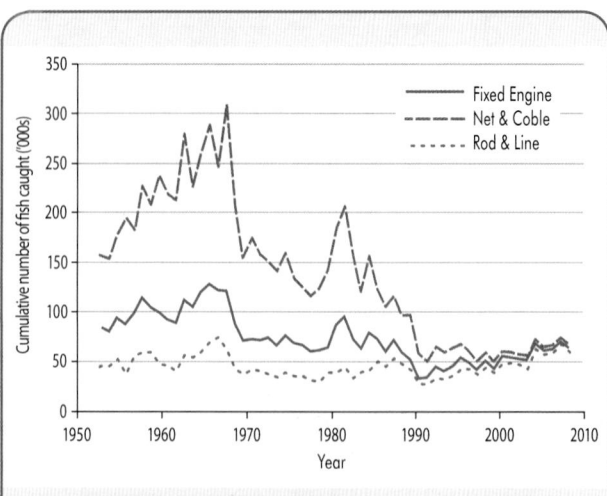

Figure 19.46 Annual catch of sea trout by method of fishing from 1952 to 2009. Source: the data used in this figure are Crown copyright, used with the permission of Marine Scotland Science. Marine Scotland is not responsible for interpretation of these data by third parties.

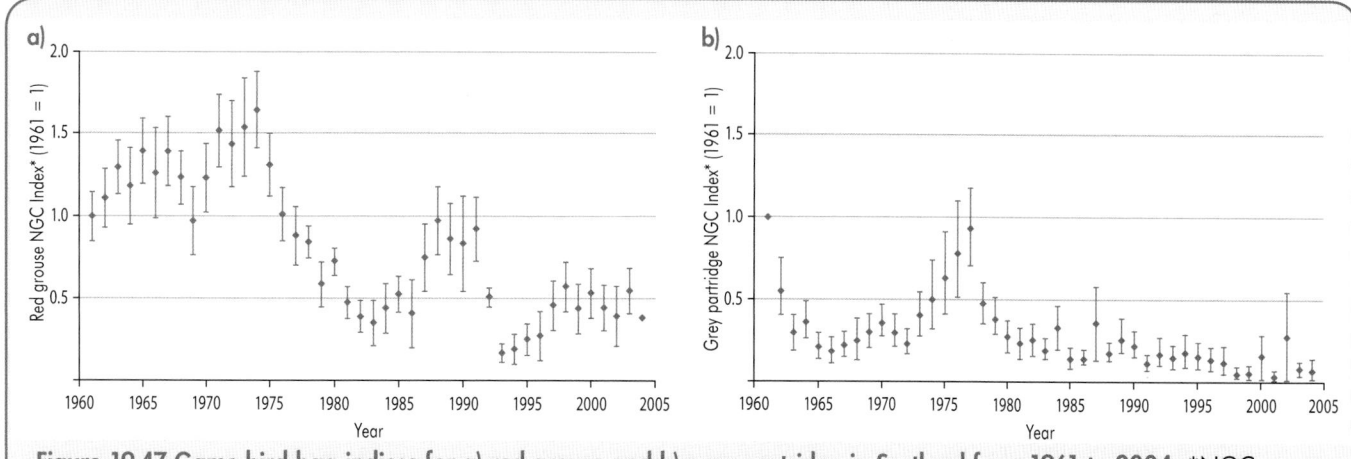

Figure 19.47 Game bird bag indices for a) red grouse and b) grey partridge in Scotland from 1961 to 2004. *NGC index: National Gamebag Census index. Source: data from the Game & Wildlife Conservation Trust's National Gamebag Census (Aebischer & Harradine 2007).

europaeus). Rabbit and brown hare bag densities show a decline over time in Scotland while mountain hare is cyclical (Davey & Aebischer 2008). As in the case of birds, it is not clear whether these changes reflect changes in hunting effort or changes in population sizes.

A 2006 study of the contribution of deer management (for sporting and other purposes) estimated direct and indirect employment at 2,520 FTEs and a GVA of £70 million (Public and Corporate Economic Consultants 2006b). This figure does not include the value of venison and other deer products.

19.5.3.7 Timber and forest products

Timber. Figure 19.48 shows the standing volume of timber harvested in Scotland since 1976. Softwood provides more than 99% of the wood harvested in Scotland. The amount of softwood increased from about 1.1 million m³ (0.93 million tonnes) in 1976 to 6.5 million m³ (5.32 million tonnes) in 2008. Annual hardwood harvests are low and fell from about 109,000 m³ (98 thousand tonnes) in 1976 to about 37,000 m³ (33.6 thousand tonnes) in 2008 (Forestry Commission 2009; Scottish Government 2011). The wood is used for timber and the manufacture of paper products. Although the area felled is often restocked, the harvest has an influence on forest structure and biodiversity by altering the age and structure of woodland areas; there are also impacts on the physical environment through changes to land cover and drainage regimes.

In 2008 the total GVA associated with the Scottish forestry sector was estimated to be about £460 million (£304 million direct, £86 million indirect and £69 million induced[11], (Edwards *et al.* 2009). About 13,200 FTE jobs are also supported (10,300 direct, 1,500 indirect and 1,400 induced). Wood processing is about £111 million of this, forest planting and harvesting contributing about £60 million and £46 million respectively, contributing 3,294 and 2,447 FTE jobs in direct employment (Edwards *et al.* 2009).

Wood products produced domestically. In 2000 there were about 87 sawmills in Scotland processing British timber, of which 56 produced in excess of 1,000 m³ of sawnwood (Forestry Commission 2000). Sawmills consumed some 1.8 million green tonnes of softwoods and produced 989,000 m³ of sawnwood. This is about 44% of GB softwood production. By 2007 over 2.6 million green tonnes of softwood were consumed in Scotland and about 1.5 million m³ of sawn softwood produced (Forestry Commission 2008). Hardwood consumption in Scotland's sawmills in 2000 was about 8,000 m³ of underbark and production about 5,000 m³ (Forestry Commission 2000); this is about 4% of the GB total for hardwoods. In 2007 about 27,000 green tonnes of softwood was sold to bioenergy plants (Forestry Commission 2008). In Scotland in 2007 94% of softwood logs used in larger sawmills came from Scotland, 6% from England (Forestry Commission 2008). Wood biomass is also an important part of renewable energy generation in Scotland.

Christmas trees. Data for Christmas trees grown and sold in Scotland are not available separately from the rest of the UK. The British Christmas Tree Growers Association estimated that about 7.5 million trees were sold in the UK in 2004, of which about 1 million were imported. The imported trees are mainly species that grow less well in the UK. The annual farm gate value of the Christmas trees in the UK is

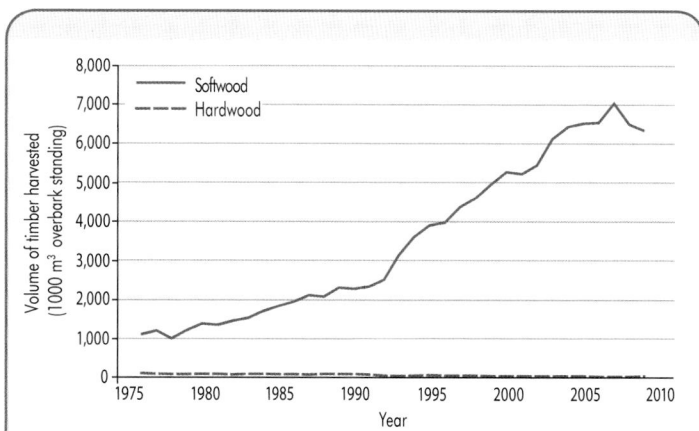

Figure 19.48 Annual volume of softwood and hardwood harvested in Scotland from 1976 to 2009. Source: data from annual statistical reports of the Forestry Commission, and High Level Summary of Statistics: Agriculture, Fisheries and Rural published by the Scottish Government (Scottish Government 2011).

11 Direct GVA arises from employment and activities carried out in forestry. Indirect GVA arises from businesses supplying forestry businesses with goods and services. Induced GVA arises from spending by those who earn their income directly or indirectly from the forestry sector.

about £140 million and the estimated value at retail outlets around double this.

Non-timber forest products (NTFPs). A wide variety of NTFPs are produced and used in Scotland. A survey in 2004 reported over 200 products from 97 vascular plants and 76 fungi and non-vascular species (Emery *et al.* 2006). The survey identified six main types of product: edible (110 species), craft (81 species), beverage (34 species), medicinal (18 species), other, for example toys (10 species) and garden (9 species). The edible category was not only most important as measured in number of species but also in range of products and frequency of uses. Examples of edible products include berries (bramble, raspberry, bilberry, elder, sloe, rowan, rosehips), flowers (elder, nettle), nuts (hazel) and a variety of fungi, notably chanterelle (*Cantharellus cibarius*), boletes (*Boletus* species), field mushroom (*Agaricus campestris*), horse mushroom (*Agaricus arvensis*), hedgehog mushroom (*Hydnum repandum*), puffball (*Lycoperdon* species), giant puffball (*Calvatia gigantea*), parasol (*Macrolepiota procera*), inkcap (*Coprinopsis atramentaria*) and wood blewitt (*Clitocybe nude*). Edible use is dominated by personal consumption of the products, although there is increasing commercial collection and sale of fungi. Craft uses include dyeing of wool as well as production of walking sticks and baskets. Medicinal uses are less common now than in the early- to mid-20th Century (Darwin 1996; Milliken & Bridgewater 2006).

Emery and her colleagues identify a number of benefits beyond the economic value of NTFPs. Collecting provides a sense of physical and emotional well-being and reinforces regular exercise, contributes to collectors' diets, brings beauty into homes, and helps to preserve cultural heritage (Emery *et al.* 2006).

Commercial uses of non-timber forest products focus primarily on edible products. In the late 1990s the total wild mushroom harvest in Scotland was worth approximately £406,000 per year, with 20 jobs directly attributable to the harvest and a further 350 pickers benefiting from casual earnings (Dyke & Newton 1999).

Biochemicals. Biochemicals, with potential uses as flavours, fragrances, nutritional supplements and chemical precursors, can be extracted from a variety of plants and plant materials such as forestry brash. There is scope for commercial exploitation of biochemicals.

19.5.3.8 Peat

Peat has long been used as a resource in Scotland and is cut traditionally by hand and also with large-scale and mechanised methods in commercial cuttings. Peat is used as fuel for heating and also for horticultural compost and in the whisky industry. Peat fires are used in some distilleries to dry the malt, smoke from the fires entering the barley and imparting characteristic flavours and tastes to the whisky. Domestic uses of peat for gardening exceed the demands from the commercial sector, which has sought peat-free substitutes since the late 1990s.

The area of peat extraction has fallen recently. The EU Habitats Directive specifies active raised and blanket bogs as Priority Habitats; as a consequence many of these habitats are designated as SACs and are protected from development.

In 1999 392,000 m³ derived from Scotland were used in GB while by 2008 this had fallen to 265,000 m³ (Chapter 15).

19.5.3.9 Ornamental resources

Plants, animals and minerals are all used for ornamental purposes. Small areas of land are used for commercial production of ornamental plants. For example, in 2007 470 ha were used for growing bulbs, 236 ha for ornamental trees, 12 ha for roses, 7 ha for bedding and pot plants, and 4 ha for other flowers (Rural and Environment Research and Analysis Directorate 2008). There are very limited data for most other uses of ecosystems for ornamental resources.

19.5.3.10 Genetic resources

Very little information is available on the use of genetic resources in Scotland (or the UK). However considerable opportunities exist for use of genetic material, especially from plants. The book *Flora Celtica* (Milliken & Bridgewater 2006) describes the many and varied ways in which plants in Scotland have been and are being used. The role of plant genetic material in relation to medicinal, and diet and nutritional, uses needs further investigation.

19.5.3.11 Water

Population growth in cities and increased connectivity to mains water supplies has increased demands for water, although private water supplies are still used in many rural areas. In Scotland between 1971 and 2001 there was an increase in use of unmetered water supply from about 1.39 mega litres per day (Ml/day) to about 1.88 Ml/day in 2001 (Moran *et al.* 2004). The amount of metered and non-potable water declined from about 0.58 Ml/day to about 0.47 Ml/day over the same period (Moran *et al.* 2004). Average per capita consumption of water in 2001 is about 143 litres per day (l/day); this is forecast to increase to over 149 l/day by 2015 (Moran *et al.* 2004).

The quality of potable water is managed by extensive treatment and quality at consumers' taps has been reported by the Scottish Government Drinking Water Quality Division (Scottish Government Drinking Water Quality Division 2008). Water quality is very high. In 2007, only 577 tests out of 1,600,601 failed to comply with requirements under water quality regulations (Scottish Government Drinking Water Quality Division 2008).

Water resources in Scotland are managed by Scottish Water and SEPA under the Water Resource Planning and River Basin Management Processes. Leakage is a significant component of total consumption in Scotland at about 41% in 2007–2008 (Chapter 15).

19.5.3.12 Renewable energy

Many of Scotland's land, freshwater and marine environments provide the most suitable conditions in the UK for provision of renewable energy. Topographically, Scotland is better suited to low- and medium-head hydropower, and deep valleys in impervious rocks offer good, watertight reservoir sites (Johnson 1994). Hydroelectric power has been generated for over a century, the first significant schemes: Foyers on Loch Ness (1896), Kinlochleven (1909), and Lochaber (1928) being for local use in the production of aluminium (Johnson

1994). The main growth of hydroelectric generation has occurred since the 1940s, following the construction of the high voltage electric transmission grid in the 1930s. Reviews reporting in 1942 (Cooper Committee 1942) and 1962 (MacKenzie Committee 1962), and establishment of the North of Scotland Hydro-Electric Board in 1943 (Anon 1943; North of Scotland Hydro-Electric Board 1944) provided direction and momentum to the development of hydroelectric power. By the end of 1959 the Board had completed 41 separate schemes with a total installed capacity of 866,000 kilowatts (Brown & Hunter 1961). Johnson (Johnson 1994) summarises the contribution of hydropower to electricity generation in Scotland until the early 1990s. Rapid development in the 1960s resulted in about two-thirds of all generation by the North of Scotland Hydro-Electric Board being from hydro, the remainder from coal and oil, by the end of the decade (Johnson 1994). This fell to 25% by 1991–1992 (with 36% from oil and gas, 24% nuclear, 15% coal and other sources). In 2007 hydroelectric generation (other than from pumped storage systems) was 4,697 gigawatt hours (GWh) (11.5% of gross consumption) (Department for Business 2007), virtually identical to the 4,665 GWh (11.4% of gross consumption) generated in 2000.

Hydroelectric power is valuable because it is flexible and rapid in response to demand, and the infrastructure is reliable and readily available. By the 1990s hydropower schemes were being used to meet fluctuations in daytime demands for electricity, nuclear and thermal power plants, delivering a high and constant output (Johnson 1994).

The potential for wind, wave and tidal energy from Scotland's ecosystems has been recognised for many years, as have the technical and economic challenges of generating electricity from these sources (Brown & Hunter 1961). Wind, in particular, has long been recognised as a potential and technically accessible source of electric power (Golding 1955, 1961) although it is only relatively recently that it has begun to be developed and used to a significant extent. Taken together, wind and wave power generated 217 GWh (0.5% of gross consumption) in 2000 compared with 2,644 GWh (6.5% of gross consumption) in 2007 (Department for Business 2007).

Figure 19.49 shows the modelled mean wind speed for Scotland and 2010 distribution of wind farms. Generally the coastal areas have greater potential for wind power generation (Golding 1961) and the coastal and marine environment has been increasingly identified as having possibilities for the generation of wind power in the future.

Wind is, however, relatively unpredictable and this limits the utility of wind as a source of electric power. Wind power is also controversial, often related to public attitudes and landscape aesthetics (Warren & Birnie 2009). Wave and tidal power are more predictable and reliable than wind but have their own technical challenges. The potential of coastal and marine areas around Scotland for wave and tidal power generation have been identified (see **Figure 19.21** for areas of high tidal capacity). Efforts are currently underway to exploit this capacity, partly driven by challenges such as the Saltire Prize that aims to accelerate commercial development of marine renewable energy. The impacts of wave and tidal

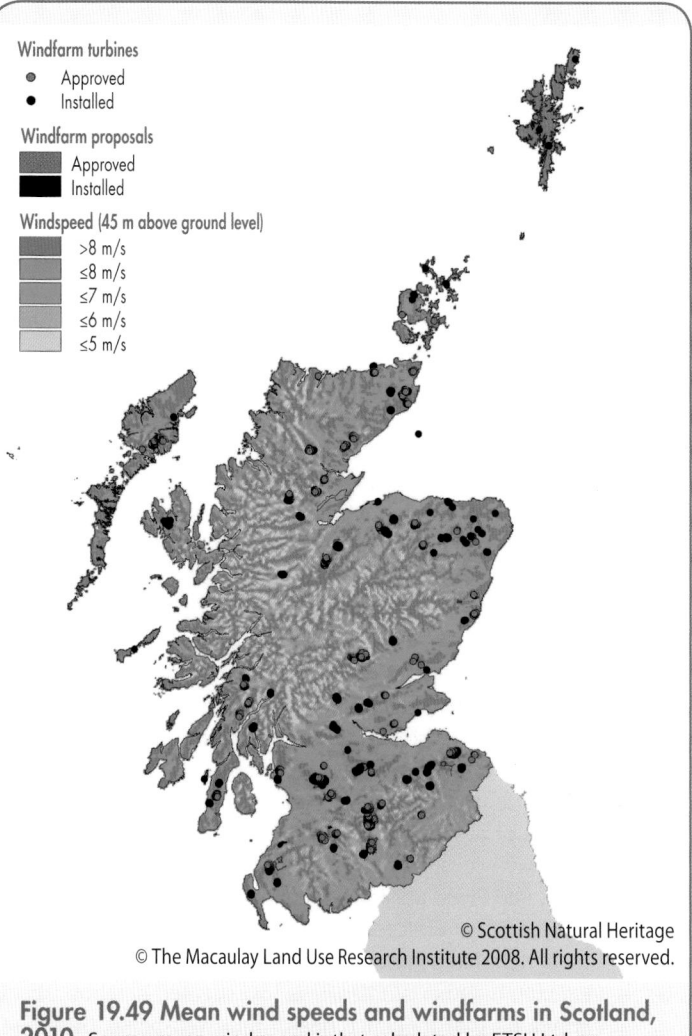

Figure 19.49 Mean wind speeds and windfarms in Scotland, 2010. Source: mean wind speed is that calculated by ETSU Ltd, on behalf of the Department of Trade and Industry, using the NOABL model (Brocklehurst 1997). The outputs were calculated for a resolution of 1 km x 1 km at 45 m above ground level. Windfarms and wind turbine data are from Scottish Natural Heritage.

energy devices on the marine and coastal environment are unknown, particularly the effect of arrays of turbines on seabed and coastal sediments and habitats.

In 2008 Scotland had 2,665 megawatts (MW) of installed renewables capacity. There was also a total of 3,336 MW in schemes not yet constructed but with planning consent (SNH 2008); onshore wind accounted for 3,023 MW of the total. Research for Scottish Enterprise has estimated that the £498 million 623 MW Airtricity Clyde Valley wind farm led to increases of £12 million and £110 million in local and national gross domestic product (GDP) respectively, and creation of 849 jobs throughout the economy (direct, indirect and induced), 246 of these jobs being in the local economy (O'Herlihy & Co. Ltd 2006).

19.5.4 Cultural Services

The UK NEA recognises that cultural services are associated with a variety of environmental settings (geographical and social places) and intimately related to their variety of meanings for people and society. Cultural services and the places to which they are attached are individually established by people and groups.

The assessment of cultural services for Scotland is developed here in relation to two major scales of interest within environmental settings: local places and landscapes/seascapes. These can have geographic and social definitions.

19.5.4.1 Environmental settings: local places

Local places are defined with meaning according to the needs and experiences of individuals. Homes, and local streets and neighbourhoods, define the geographical territories that people experience in their daily activities. At this scale the local environment provides the setting for the cultural services experienced and valued by individuals. There is substantial work in environmental social sciences and in studies of the built environment, health and the humanities that demonstrates the benefits delivered by local places and spaces such as parks, woods, rivers and street trees (Chiesura & de Groot 2003; Chiesura 2004; Andersson 2006; Croucher et al. 2007; van Leeuwen et al. 2010). These elements of the urban system are important in helping individuals to achieve a good quality of life and well-being (Koren & Butler 2006; Fuller et al. 2007). A Scotland-wide study in 2004 revealed that those living in areas with the highest levels of perceived street-level incivilities (such as litter and graffiti) were almost twice as likely to report feelings of anxiety and depression as those who perceived the lowest levels of street-level incivilities (Ellaway et al. 2009). Perceived absence of environmental goods (e.g. safe play areas for children) was associated with anxiety (2.5 times more likely) and depression (90% more likely, Ellaway et al. 2009). Other studies have investigated neighbourhood conditions that influence health and well-being (Braubach 2007) and in a study in Glasgow cleanliness, peacefulness and facilities that encourage exercise and social interaction in urban physical environments were shown to support the health of older people (Day 2008).

19.5.4.2 Environmental settings: landscapes and seascapes

Landscape is formally defined as 'an area, as perceived by people, whose character is the result of the action and interaction of natural and/or human factors' (Council of Europe 2003). Human perception is critical to this definition and illustrates and identifies the changing social context by which landscapes are defined and valued; individuals in Scotland and elsewhere have their own individual appreciation of landscapes. The combined influence of natural and cultural components of landscape has also been applied to the understanding of Scotland's coastal landscapes (Hughes & Macdonald 1999).

Whatever individual agreements or differences there may be over Scotland's landscapes, there are a variety of popular and widely advertised images and meanings of Scottish landscapes that have been developed and used, particularly in the second half of the 20th Century (McCrone et al. 1995). These shape not only the wider perceptions of landscape but also the way landscapes are valued and managed, and the way Scotland is marketed and advertised economically, socially, politically and for trade and visitors. Frequently the images of Scotland's heritage and landscapes are based on scenery, history (especially Celtic history), geography, monuments (notably castles), language and culture, the heritage of Highland clans, and political relations (McCrone et al. 1995) as well as its role in advancing the arts, science and economic and social thinking. These qualities have all been presented as defining a set of distinctively Scottish environmental and social landscapes for decades, as can be seen, for example, in almost any guide to Scotland over the past 70 years (e.g. Meikle 1947; Harvey 1949). All the qualities, individually and collectively, may also provide a sense of place. Archaeological sites, widely and densely distributed throughout Scotland, also provide a sense of place as well as inspiring aesthetically, artistically and in other ways.

There are several designations of landscape character for Scotland. There are 40 National Scenic Areas covering over 1.4 million ha (12.7%) of the land area (**Table 19.1**). National Parks also address the issue of landscape character and the two National Parks in Scotland together include 639,200 ha, about 8% of Scotland. In order to develop understanding of the character of Scotland's landscapes to complement the understanding and knowledge of other aspects of the natural heritage such as conservation of biodiversity, SNH developed Landscape Character Assessment (Hughes & Macdonald 1999; Hughes & Buchan 1999; Bennett et al. 1999). Landscape Character Assessment is combined with Natural Heritage Zones to develop a framework for assessment of the natural heritage that includes landscape (Thin 1999). Similarly the European Environment Agency has developed a Net Landscape Ecological Potential Index[12] (NLEPI) to document the relative quality of natural habitats at a landscape-scale, taking the connectivity and fragmentation of habitat into account (Weber et al. 2008). This is a culturally-determined assessment using both designated areas for both nature and landscape character as evidence of landscape value. **Figure 19.50** shows the distribution of National Parks, National Nature Reserves, Sites of Special Scientific Interest, Special Areas of Conservation, Special Protection Areas and RAMSAR sites in Scotland. These are combined with Broad Habitat types and road data to estimate habitat fragmentation and create a map of net landscape ecological potential. The high potential of the Cairngorm and other mountain and remote upland areas of Scotland is shown in this analysis.

Each of the Broad Habitats, combined with Scotland's geodiversity, contribute to landscape appearance in Scotland. Open habitats such as moorlands and grasslands combine with the topography and geology of Scotland to offer broad views. Coastal Margin habitats are also important and seascapes provide an immediate and important component of Scotland's large-scale and local relationships between people and environment.

---

12 The Net Landscape Ecological Potential is an index that indicates habitat quality at landscape scales including its social component. The index is based on nature conservation and landscape designations. The net landscape ecological potential of a landscape is not the same as its heritage and cultural value of landscape, although high values would often be expected to coincide.

19.5.4.3 Health: physical activity and green exercise

Much of the research on benefits of greenspace and high quality environments has taken place in cities and other urban areas. This is not surprising, since these are the areas in which the majority of the population lives and where green environments are most frequently experienced.

A recent review of international literature for greenspace scotland (Bell *et al.* 2008) provides examples of the health benefits of greenspaces in Urban areas, as do a number of other studies conducted in Scotland, that have already been described (Braubach 2007; Day 2008; Ellaway *et al.* 2009). Elsewhere, studies have been conducted in Scandinavia, the USA and Japan (Kaplan & Kaplan 1989; Frumkin 2001), as well as for the UK as a whole (Mitchell & Popham 2007; Mitchell *et al.* 2009).

Both physical and mental health benefit from engaging with nature in a variety of ways, including simply viewing it, as well as more active pursuits. Exercise (e.g. walking, fishing, and sports such as golf) helps with cardiovascular and respiratory health as well as increasing muscle endurance and improving HDL cholesterol levels. A Finnish study of golfers who walked while playing, rather than using carts, showed health benefits compared to sedentary men (Parkkari *et al.* 2000).

Exercise, especially for children, is more frequent in Urban areas with proximity and access to parks and recreational areas as this increases the opportunity to exercise (Giles-Corti & Donovan 2002; Giles-Corti *et al.* 2005). There is evidence that stress is reduced by both exercise in and views of green environments and that behaviour and cognitive function are improved (Taylor *et al.* 2001).

Greenspaces contribute to social interaction and networking (Hitchings 2010) and have been associated with reduced levels of crime, aggression and violence (Kuo & Sullivan 2001). The aesthetic value of urban areas is improved by greenspaces (Sheets & Manzer 1991). Safety and design of greenspace requires more research.

A number of hedonic valuation studies have shown that greenspace can have a direct effect on property prices and on other public good (e.g. recreation) and social and economic (reduced absenteeism) benefits that are not valued and recognised by markets. For example, proximity to an urban park not only increases property values, but the size of urban parks also substitutes for living space with amenity benefits to residents (Poudyal *et al.* 2009). In Glasgow house prices were shown to be depressed in relation to increasing road noise (Lake *et al.* 2000).

As described Section 19.4.6 Scotland has considerable greenspace in urban areas (Birnie *et al.* 2002; greenspace scotland 2009), and the possible specific benefits of these environments to health and well-being, as well as social and economic aspects of living in Scotland's towns and cities, merit considerable further attention.

19.5.4.4 Leisure, outdoor recreation and tourism

All the Scottish ecosystems provide opportunities for recreation and tourism, including hiking, cycling, skiing and nature viewing. Geoparks and Scotland's geodiversity also offer opportunities for enjoyment of Scotland's landscapes

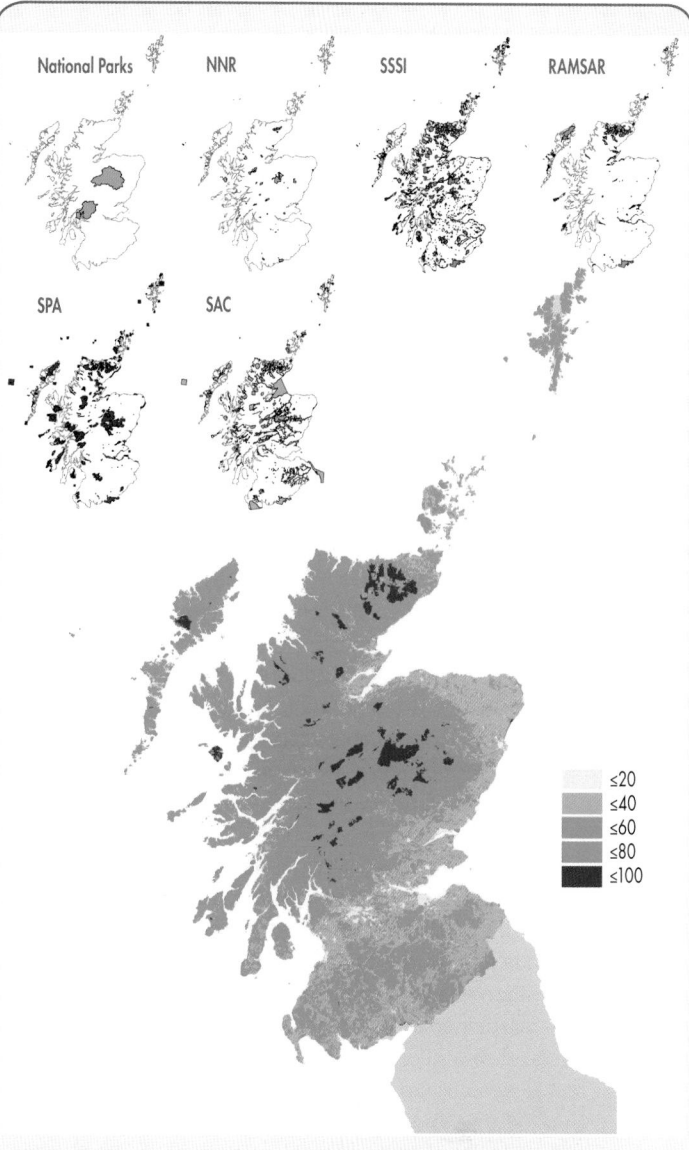

Figure 19.50 Nature conservation designations and Net Landscape Ecological Potential Index (NLEPI) for Scotland. NNR: National Nature Reserve; SSSI: Sites of Special Scientific Interest; SPA: Special Protection Areas; SAC: Special Areas of Conservation. Source: Scottish Natural Heritage. NLEPI calculated for this report.

(Gordon *et al.* 2004; Gordon 2008). Wetlands and water-rich landscapes are an integral part of the character of Scotland's landscapes and provide a sense of place, notably evident in the world famous character and reputation of Scotland's leading salmon and trout fishing rivers (e.g. Tweed, Tay, Spey and others) and lochs. Water-based recreation includes fishing, canoeing, kayaking, nature viewing, jet skiing, water skiing, wind surfing and swimming. Many of these recreational opportunities, but especially fishing salmon and trout, are a major contribution to local economies and communities. Almost all active recreation has benefits for health and well-being, the added benefit of exercise in green environments being found in several studies (Hansmann *et al.* 2007).

As cultural services, recreation and tourism have a high value (measured, for example, as % GVA or by number of jobs). Tourism was worth about 4% GVA to the Scottish economy in 2002 and £4.2 billion in 2006. A recent review of the economic impacts of nature-based tourism in Scotland concluded that overall total visitor spending attributable to nature-based tourism each year is about £1.4 billion with about 39,000 FTE jobs (Bryden *et al.* 2010).

There are between 37 million and 64 million annual recreational and tourism visits to Scottish forests and woodland, respectively. In 2006 this provided some £209 million GVA and sustained approximately 18,000 jobs (Edwards *et al.* 2009). Coastal tourism is also significant in Scotland. In 2002 there were 42 million day visits to the Scottish seaside, spending some £300 million (GB Leisure Day Visits 2004). In 2005 there were 9.2 million overnight visits to the Scottish seaside valued at £481 million (UKTS 2006). The combined value of day and overnight visits in Scotland is likely to be considerable.

Almost half of the adult population in Scotland made at least one visit per week to the outdoors for leisure and recreation purposes in 2007, the same level as was recorded during 2006 (TNS 2009). Additionally, 80% of the adult population claimed to have made at least one trip to the outdoors in the previous 12 months; this is approximately 340 million visits to the outdoors in Scotland during 2007, a 3% increase on the estimate for 2006. In 2004 the average distance travelled for these visits was 26 km; in 2007 it was 18 km. The proportion of visits on foot increased from 50% to 61% and by car decreased from 43% to 31% over the same time interval.

Specific recreational activities also generate considerable use of Scotland's environment as well as jobs and economic income. In 2002–2003 expenditure on recreation in the Highlands and Islands area was estimated to be in excess of £400 million (walkers and mountaineers: £246 million, water sports participants: £90 million, snow sports: £29 million, cyclists: £24 million, equestrianism: £15 million) (George Street Research and Jones Economics 2004). In 2006 it was estimated that sport shooting in Scotland directly employs 5,300 FTEs (about 58,000 paid workers) with 11,000 total FTEs through direct, indirect and induced impacts (Public and Corporate Economic Consultants 2006b). Deer management (for sporting and other purposes) supports 2,520 FTEs and has a GVA of £70 million (Public and Corporate Economic Consultants 2006a). Coarse and game angling supports about 2,800 jobs (salmon and sea trout-related employment is some 65% of the total) and is worth about £113 million per annum (Glasgow Caledonian University & Cogentsi Research International Ltd. 2004). Recreational sea angling supports over 3,100 FTEs and income of over £69 million (Glasgow Caledonian University *et al.* 2009). Golf supports 4,400 jobs and is valued at about £120 million GVA. Scotland regularly hosts the British Open Championship; the Open in Carnoustie in 2007 brought about £15 million to the local community and some £26 million to the Scottish economy (Angus Council 2008). The 2007 Mountain Bike and Trials World Championship at Aonach Mor attracted 30,000 spectators, of which two-thirds were from outside Scotland, and generated £6 million net expenditure in Lochaber and £1.5 million expenditure in Scotland (MLURI *et al.* 2009).

There have been estimates of the economic value of marine wildlife tourism in Scotland. In 1996 about 2,670 full time jobs were supported and revenues of £57 million generated. Tourism expenditure related solely to the east

of Scotland bottlenose dolphin population was estimated to be at least £4 million, providing 202 FTE posts (Davies *et al.* 2010). Whale watching and sea fishing also create employment and income in coastal and marine areas.

19.5.4.5 Heritage: aesthetics and inspiration

The aesthetic and inspirational values of Scotland's land- and seascapes are well known. Their values arise from habitats, topography, geodiversity (Gordon *et al.* 2004; Gordon 2008), expectations of iconic wildlife, and rapidly changing skyscapes associated with Scotland's dynamic weather. There are also clear and obvious links between Scotland's contemporary landscapes and their history that further add to the aesthetic and inspirational services. Together these create a wealth of recognisable local, regional and national identities, many with strong cultural and historical roots, that are regularly exploited in advertising for tourism, recreation, and as part of Scotland's international and domestic brand (McCrone *et al.* 1995). Often these local features are packaged together to create national qualities, for example heritage trees (Rodger *et al.* 2006). Scotland's landscapes are part of an individual and national sense of place, and link the local and landscape-level cultural services. Natural beauty provides inspiration, harmony, peace and feelings of security; land- and seascapes have long been associated with all of these characteristics that contribute to individual and community well-being.

19.5.4.6 Religion and spirituality

Relatively little is known about religious and spiritual values attached to Scotland's ecosystems. Religion and spirituality are two separate but related themes that have strong relevance to human experiences and relations with nature. Religious experience may be linked to specific places, typically churches and cathedrals (Winter & Gasson 1996) but also through their historical status, the stories attached to them and their reputation combined with physical remains or monuments. In Scotland this will include places in cities and towns, but also notable sites such as Iona, Callanish, Maes Howe and others. The attachment this has to ecosystems is limited however, although the landscape setting of these monuments often supports and enhances individual perception of their significance.

More frequently, spirituality as a cultural ecosystem service is associated with local places and landscapes through human attachment to place (Brown & Raymond 2007), often related to notions of wilderness (Habron 1999). This view was pioneered by John Muir (Kocher-Marbaeuf 2008) and Victorian perceptions of the Scottish Highlands (Holl & Smith 2007), and spread through nature writing (e.g. Syse 2007).

19.5.4.7 Biodiversity

In addition to its other roles, biodiversity can also be considered a cultural service. People place considerable value directly on biodiversity itself, through support for different species and groups, and through concern for the existence and health of Scotland's biodiversity. Involvement in biodiversity conservation, membership of biodiversity non-governmental organisations (NGOs) and public attitudes to biodiversity in Scotland are used as biodiversity indicators by SNH (Mackey & Mudge 2010). The total number of conservation volunteers in Scotland increased by 43% between 2005 and 2008 and membership of NGOs increased by 15% between 2007 and 2009 (Mackey & Mudge 2010). More than 70% of adults in Scotland responded positively regarding interest, relevance and concern about Scotland's biodiversity in surveys in 2006 and 2009 (Mackey & Mudge 2010). Two of the 45 National Indicators of the Scottish Government are concerned with biodiversity: i) increase to 95% the proportion of protected nature sites in favourable condition, and ii) biodiversity: increase the index of abundance of terrestrial breeding birds. Progress on these two indicators is indicative of the state of other aspects of Scotland's biodiversity and ecosystems.

19.6 Scotland's Dependence on External Ecosystem Services

Scotland both uses and exports products derived from the services gained from ecosystems, notably, but not solely, from provisioning services. Scotland's landscapes and history are an important part of its brand (McCrone *et al.* 1995). Scotland also imports goods derived from ecosystems outside Scotland's borders, not only elsewhere in the UK and Europe but also from international markets.

Figure 19.51 shows the imports and exports of food and live animals for Scotland for 2009 (HM Revenue and Customs 2010). This gives an indication of the extent to which Scotland is dependent on provisioning services from ecosystems outside Scotland's borders. Value of food and live animals for export was about £937 million while imports were £914 million. Food and live animals are about 8.5% of the total value of imports and 6.2% of the total value of exports for Scotland. Import of beverages was about £155 million while export of beverages was valued at £2.8 billion in 2009. Beverages are 1.4% of the total value of imports and 19.2% of the total value of exports for Scotland. The high export value of beverages is due to Scotch whisky. A higher value of imports than exports occurs for meat and meat preparations, dairy products and eggs, vegetables and fruit, sugar and honey, and feeding stuffs for animals, not including unmilled cereals (see **Figure 19.51**). Fish, crustaceans, molluscs, and aquatic invertebrates make up 60% of Scotland's exports of food and live animals.

19.7 Drivers of Change

A wide range of drivers of change influence the present and future status and condition of habitats and ecosystem services. Drivers operate at a range of organisational scales from local to international. Drivers of change can be considered under five major headings: policy and institutional, economic, demographic, social and cultural, technological, and environmental (Birnie *et al.* 2002; Miller *et al.* 2009). Taken together, these represent a complex suite of interacting forces. Their influence is played out in the way that social and economic systems (individuals, groups, communities, and institutions) respond through decisions and planning (Miller *et al.* 2009), and environmental systems respond via physical, chemical and biological processes. Critically, ways in which social and environmental systems interact also need to be recognised and understood to achieve preferred social, economic and environmental goals (Harris 2002; Hooper *et al.* 2005; Lawton 2007; Slee *et al.* 2009).

Given the importance of agriculture, both crop production and livestock, in terms of both the area of Scotland on which it is carried out and the range of habitats used, the drivers of change in agriculture over the last 70 years have had a major influence on Scotland's ecosystems. Since 1945 the Government has had a strong influence on agriculture through policies and economic drivers. The 1947 Agricultural Act was passed after the end of WWII and was implemented through guaranteed prices for agricultural products and through production grants and subsidies. Subsidies included hill sheep and hill cattle subsidies, calf and beef subsidies, subsidies for lime and fertilisers, and long-term improvement to agricultural infrastructure such as under the Farm Improvement Scheme. All of this support encouraged maximisation of production and, with increased mechanisation and use of artificial fertilisers, pesticides and herbicides developed during the war, led to major structural changes in agriculture as well as extreme impacts on habitats and biodiversity. There was unrestricted entry for agricultural produce to Britain from

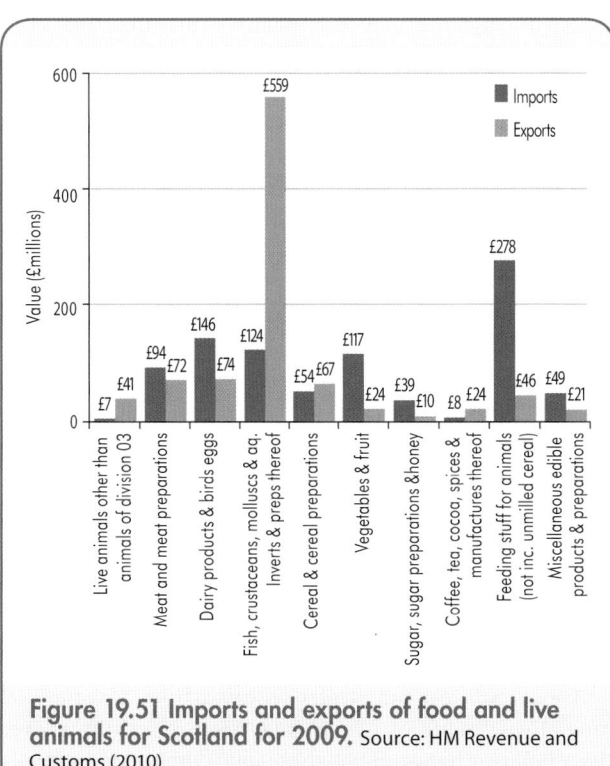

Figure 19.51 Imports and exports of food and live animals for Scotland for 2009. Source: HM Revenue and Customs (2010).

1947 and payments made under price guarantees were thus related to the difference between market prices and the guaranteed prices. During the 1950s the emphasis changed from maximisation of production to economic efficiency of production (Coppock 1971), price guarantees applying to standard quantities of produce. The environmental, economic and structural effects of these changes were similar to those following the 1947 Act. The entry of Britain into the European Economic Community (EEC) in 1973 entrenched the principle of support for farming (Grant 1997). The EEC protected against imports and the vagaries of the world market while inflating prices through buying surplus production into Intervention storage. This provided an impetus for further increasing production. Quotas were introduced from 1984 to reduce over-production. The MacSharry reforms to the CAP in 1991 included set-aside to remove land from cereal production in an attempt to manage production. Set-aside and other agri-environment schemes also improved the environmental impacts of agriculture and help to maintain environmental quality. The wildlife benefits of set-aside have been well studied, especially for birds (Sotherton 1998; Donald et al. 2001; Watson et al. 2009; Whittingham et al. 2009). Ongoing reform of the EU CAP is of critical importance for ecosystem health and provision of ecosystem services.

Policy and economic drivers operate through regulations and incentives and the drivers are apparent in Acts, policies and in designation. Numerous Acts apply directly or indirectly to activities in the ecosystems of Scotland. The National Parks (Scotland) Act 2000 established National Parks in Scotland to conserve and enhance the natural and cultural heritage of the area, promote sustainable use of the natural resources of the area, promote understanding and enjoyment (including enjoyment in the form of recreation) of the special qualities of the area by the public, and promote sustainable economic and social development of the area's communities. As such, this Act provides a legal requirement for management of areas of Scotland that are directly focused on the goals that are informed by ecosystem assessment and that can be implemented using an ecosystem approach (Defra 2007). The Salmon Conservation (Scotland) Act 2001 is directed at conservation of salmon and sea trout, while the Salmon and Freshwater Fisheries (Consolidation) (Scotland) Act 2003 consolidated a variety of Acts related to salmon and freshwater fisheries in Scotland. The Water Environment and Water Services (Scotland) Act 2003 and the Water Services (Scotland) Act 2005 protect the water environment in Scotland, while the Water Industry (Scotland) Act 2002 provides regulations about the quality of drinking water in Scotland. The Nature Conservation (Scotland) Act 2004 addresses conservation of biodiversity, conservation and enhancement of Scotland's natural features, and protection of birds, animals and plants. The Environmental Assessment (Scotland) Act 2005 requires environmental assessment of the impacts of plans and programmes. The Animal Health and Welfare (Scotland) Act 2006 makes provisions for prevention of the spread of disease and for the welfare of animals. The Aquaculture and Fisheries (Scotland) Act 2007 provides regulations related to fish farms. The Flood Risk Management (Scotland) Act 2009 directs the assessment and sustainable management of flood risks related to

European Parliament and Council Directive 2007/60/EC. The Marine (Scotland) Act 2010 provides a mechanism for regulating functions and activities in the Scottish marine area, including the protection of the area and its wildlife. Policies and strategies also directly and indirectly address integrated ecosystem management, including the Scottish Biodiversity Strategy (Scottish Executive 2004), Scottish Forestry Strategy (Forestry Commission Scotland 2006) and Food and Drink Policy (Scottish Government 2009c).

Environmental change, including sea level rise (Richards & Phipps 2007; Rennie & Hansom 2011), climate change (SNIFFER 2006), habitat loss and destruction, and land use changes (Foley et al. 2005), is recognised as a major threat to Scotland's economy (Conway 1998) and ecosystems (Macdonald et al. 1994; Pakeman & Marrs 1996; Conway 1998; Kerr 2000; Milne & Hartley 2001; MacLeod et al. 2005; Wolf & Woolf 2005; SNIFFER 2006; Orr et al. 2008). The Climate Change (Scotland) Act 2009 sets targets for reduction of greenhouse gas emissions, imposes duties related to climate change on public bodies, and requires waste reduction and recycling, and increased energy efficiency. This Act also requires a Land Use Strategy that addresses sustainable land use to be presented to the Scottish Parliament by 31 March 2011.

Designation of habitats as, for example, SSSIs, NNRs and more recently National Parks, as well as under European legislation, also provides a mechanism for management of change in ecosystems.

In Scotland, there are several key contexts and goals/targets that shape the management of environmental systems through their influence on drivers of change. Several of these are enacted in the Scottish Parliament Acts described above. However, contexts and goals are not only internal to Scotland, being developed as a matter of national choice and preference, but are also external, related to international, European or UK objectives and obligations. (Currie 2002) estimates that over 80% of the environmental regulation that affects Scotland is applied through the European Union. Some Acts, for example the Flood Risk Management (Scotland) Act 2009 are a direct response to a European Parliament and Council Directive. Others refer to international conventions. For example, the Nature Conservation (Scotland) Act 2004 refers to the Convention on Biological Diversity (CBD). The Scottish Biodiversity Strategy, as well as ecosystem assessment (as in the UK NEA) and the ecosystem approach are all directly linked to the UN Convention on Biological Diversity, which is a significant international driver.

The Scottish Government National Performance Framework provides a set of specific targets for promoting sustainable economic development for the nation. Many other policies relate to the National Performance Framework and are directly relevant to environmental management and ecosystem goods and services. Some of the current policies and strategies applicable to environmental issues and management in Scotland are listed in **Table 19.15**.

These policies and strategies arise from a variety of imperatives, many of which have been described above. The Climate Change (Scotland) Act addresses Scotland's response to international issues of greenhouse gas reduction

Table 19.15 Current EU, UK and Scottish Government policies and strategies applicable to Scotland.

Agriculture
Common Agricultural Policy Reform (2014)
Animal Health and Welfare Strategy for Great Britain (2005)
Community Action Plan on the Protection and Welfare of Animals 2006–2010
EU Animal Health Law
Farming for a Better Climate Initiative (2009)
Implementation Plan for the Animal Health and Welfare Strategy in Scotland (2003)
Scotland Rural Development Programme 2007–2013 (2008)

Air quality
EU Air Quality Directive

Biodiversity
Scottish Biodiversity Strategy
Review of 2010 Biodiversity Targets
The Economics of Ecosystems and Biodiversity (2010)
Nature Conservation (Scotland) Act 2004
Scottish Soil Framework

Climate Change
Climate Change (Scotland) Act (2009)
Climate Change Adaptation Framework (2009)
Climate Change Delivery Plan (2009)
Land Use Strategy (2011)

Economic development
Government Economic Strategy (2007)
National Planning Framework for Scotland OECD Rural Policy Review. Scotland, UK (2008)
Scottish Government Rural Framework (2010–2011)
Reducing our ecological footprint (Scottish Government Performance Framework Indicator)

Energy
Biomass Action Plan for Scotland 2007
Renewables Action Plan (2009)

Food, diet and health
Healthy Eating, Active Living (2008)
Recipe for Success—The Scottish Food and Drink Policy (2009)

Forestry
Scottish Forestry Strategy (2006)

Marine
The Marine (Scotland) Act 2010
UK Marine Policy Statement: Habitats Regulations Assessment

Waters
Bathing Water Directive
EU Water Framework Directive (2000)
European Nitrates Directive & Nitrate Vulnerable Zone Action Programmes
Flood Risk Management (Scotland) Act (2009)
Scottish Government Vision for Water Industry in Scotland (2010)

---

and both establishes and requires the Land Use Strategy due to be published in 2011. National Food and Drink Policy, Soil Framework Strategy, Scottish and local BAPs, and others, provide specific contexts and policies developed within Scotland to meet its own national objectives. Policies and strategies are also related to EU policies and Directives, such as the Water Framework Directive, Habitats Directive, River Basin Management Planning, that have importance within Scotland.

The suite of drivers listed in **Table 19.16** is common to many of the different issues. A major aspiration among policy-makers is for coordination between these different strategies. This is preferable to addressing each issue singly and in isolation from other issues through a self-standing and independent strategy. It will require systems-based integrative research and new approaches to governance (O'Riordan 2002, 2009). It will also require a commitment to reorient some strategic and policy approaches in order to deliver across a range of concerns in an integrated way. This is needed both to manage Scotland's resources and ecosystems and to tune the various policy instruments to deliver multiple social, economic and environmental benefits. Scotland is well positioned to accomplish this with commitment and motivation among a wide variety of institutions, established social networks on which to develop collaborations and partnerships, and established expertise in public engagement. Successful examples

include Catchment Management Plans (e.g. Dee Catchment Management Plan), Coastal and other partnerships, two National Parks focused on economic, social and environmental development aligned with communities, and many other examples at local, regional and national scales.

In parallel with recent development of policies there have been significant developments in protocols and approaches for getting people more involved in environmental management (Kenyon & Nevin 2001; Quine et al. 2002; Varjopuro et al. 2008; Irvine et al. 2009). These parallel the increasing recognition of the social and economic importance and contribution of healthy and functioning environments. The CBD has developed the ecosystem approach (Defra 2007) as a strategy for integrated management of land, water and living resources to promote conservation, sustainable use, and the fair and equitable sharing of the benefits arising out of the utilisation of resources (United Nations 2000). The Scottish Government and SNH have built on the ecosystem approach for use in Scotland (Mudge & Christie 2009; Aspinall et al. 2010) as a mechanism for developing partnerships and collaborations to foster sound environmental management at local, regional and national scales. The ecosystem approach takes a whole systems view of environment and the different drivers of change, and links this understanding of how environmental systems work with the activities and goals of society.

Table 19.16 Drivers of change influencing Scotland's ecosystems and land systems. Source: Miller *et al.* 2009.

	Driver of change	Examples
Policy and Institutional	Institutions	• Governance arrangements • Designations—approximately 20% Scotland designated with local, national or international conservation designation
	Frameworks	• Planning system, Ecosystem Approach, Environmental Impact Assessment, Strategic Environmental Assessment, Integrated Catchment Management, Coastal Partnerships, River Basin Management, etc.
	Legislation	• Legally binding agreements, for example climate change reduction
	Regulation	• Climate Change (Scotland) Act
	Collaboration	• Coastal Partnerships, Catchment Management Groups, etc
Economic	Grants and payments	• Common Agricultural Policy (CAP) • Common Fisheries Policy (CFP) • Less Favoured Area Support Scheme • Single Farm Payment (SFP) • Scottish Rural Development Programme (SRDP)
	Prices and exchange rates	• Market prices
	Provision of infrastructure (housing and transport)	• Pressures for increasing housing stock • Rural transport (remoteness/accessibility)
Demographic	Demographic change	• Increasing age of population, motivation and behaviours
	Counter drift migration	• Urban to rural; second homes
	Land manager profiles	• i.e. Increasing age, lack of new entrants to many areas of employment in rural economy
Social and Cultural	Changes in decision-maker's motivations	
	Consumer preferences and marketing	
	Heritage	• Approximately 7,500 Scheduled Ancient Monuments, about 46,000 listed buildings, 293 Historic Gardens and Designed Landscapes, occupying 62,000 ha or approximately 0.8% of Scotland
Technological	Reducing costs and economies of scale	
	New products	
	Renewable energy (and landscape impacts)	• Windfarms

Environmental change	Climate change	• Temperature and precipitation
		• Uncertainty in changes in windiness and exposure
		• Changes in agroclimate:
		  o Lengthened growing season
		  o Changed seasonal access to land for machine-based operations
		  o Reduced mountain snowpack
		  o Decline in montane plant communities
		• Rivers:
		  o Rising temperatures of river waters, decrease in baseflow and increase in increase in flash flooding (with consequences for freshwater life - salmonids)
		• Sea-level rise
		• Extreme events: storms, droughts and floods

	Habitat loss, direct physical loss (land conversion)	• Land abandonment, changes in management regime (over grazing and burning), nitrogen deposition (in the uplands), runoff, estuaries , chemical use (pesticides, herbicides, molluscicides, fungicides, fertilizers)
	Invasive non-native species	• Changing geographical distributions of pests and diseases
	Eutrophication of freshwaters and estuaries	• Algal mats • Anoxic zones
	Air quality	
	Wild harvesting	• Marine fish stocks and economics of coastal and fishing communities • Hunting (sporting estates)
	Soil erosion and compaction	• Loss of productivity • Land degradation
	Fate of organic soils and organic matter in soils	• 54% UK soil carbon in Scotland's soils; large areas of organic (peat) soils; inorganic soils of Scotland are carbon-rich

19.8 Consequences of Change for Biodiversity and Human Well-being

There has been considerable change in Scotland's ecosystems and the services they provide over the last 70 years. The delivery of provisioning services, about which more is known than other services, has increased considerably. However, this has not been without significant impacts and consequences for biodiversity and other ecosystem services, although the full impacts and linkages are not well documented. Most of the habitats and ecosystems considered 'natural' and semi-natural have declined in both area and condition. Biodiversity, measured in numbers and abundance of individuals of species, as well as by variety of species, communities and genetic diversity, has shown both declines and increases, although the general long-term trend over the last 70 years is one of decline. There are fundamentally important taxonomic groups for which very little is known (e.g. microflora and microfauna, bryophytes, lichens, invertebrates other than butterflies), including groups for which Scotland has internationally important species (Usher 2002a).

It is apparent that the ecosystems and landscapes of Scotland provide significant ecosystem goods and services and considerable economic benefit to the nation. Provisioning services have a particularly high economic value. Between 2004 and 2008 the average annual total direct value of agriculture, forestry and marine fisheries was about £2.5 billion. In 2008 agriculture was valued at approximately £792 million (Rural and Environment Research and Analysis Directorate 2009a). Forestry (wood production, processing and manufacture) was worth £460 million GVA at 2007–2008 prices. Fisheries also provide high economic value. The pelagic, demersal and shellfish industry in Scotland landed fish valued at around £350 million in 2008 (Scottish Government 2009a).

In addition to the direct value of GDP and GVA in agriculture and forestry, they also provide raw materials for production of many other goods with high value. Revenue from sales and value added in the food and drink industry and other products adds considerably to the total economic value of Scotland's production services. For example, food and drink are worth about an additional £3 billion to GVA. Whisky distillers purchase about £90 million worth of cereals from Scottish suppliers each year, providing an income of about £148 million per year while supporting approximately 7,000 jobs (DTZ Pieda Consulting 2002). Overall, revenue generated from agricultural produce increases the direct value to about £2.3 billion (about 1–2% of GDP and 1.2% of GVA).

A study by the Rural Payments Agency and Cambridge Econometrics and commissioned by SNH assessed the economic output from activities that depend on the natural environment in 2003 at £17.2 billion per annum (11% of total Scottish output). This output supported 242,000 jobs, about 14% of all FTEs in Scotland (RPA and Cambridge Econometrics 2008). About £3.9 billion and 154,000 jobs of these totals were assessed to be from direct impact, maintaining the trend for high quality employment

opportunities related to the natural heritage of Scotland (RSK Era Ltd 2001; Environmental Resources Management Limited 2004).

The role of agriculture and forestry in shaping landscapes and ecosystems in Scotland is perhaps even more important than the economic values. The complexity of the economic and social dependencies of Scotland's society on supporting regulating, provisioning and cultural ecosystem services is revealed in the magnitude and scope of benefits obtained from Scotland's ecosystems and landscapes. The extent of agriculture and forestry land uses in Scotland is about 92% of the land area, and the direct impacts of land management for agricultural and forestry production make the functioning and health of Scotland's ecosystems highly dependent on management for delivery of provisioning services. The impacts on supporting and regulating services are of fundamental importance. Continued loss of habitat, changes in nutrient storage and cycling, climate change and impacts on biological function within habitats have significant consequences for human well-being. In particular, the supporting, regulating and provisioning services that are documented in this report all depend on the continued physical, chemical and biological operation of Scotland's land and marine ecosystems. One of the dominant drivers of change in these ecosystems is resource management.

The value of marine ecosystems includes the direct value from fisheries, sea fisheries almost matching crop production for value and being about half the value of livestock production in Scotland (**Tables 19.12** and **19.13**). Exports add considerably to this value (Section 19.6). The available evidence of the poor status of marine ecosystems (Defra 2010; Baxter *et al.* 2011) is of concern however, and appropriate management is required to ensure the health and long-term sustainable use of Scotland's marine ecosystems and environments.

Only certain cultural services are capable of being valued. However, the economic benefits from nature-based tourism alone, at about £1.4 billion with about 39,000 FTE jobs (Bryden *et al.* 2010), represents a significant value for Scotland.

19.9 Sustainable Management to Enhance Ecosystem Services, Biodiversity and Human Well-being

The diversity of services and their interdependence on ecosystem condition and management suggest that management approaches that focus on achieving multiple objectives are necessary. There are many examples of multiple uses of land and marine areas, and of conflict and apparent incompatibility of uses.

The variety and value of ecosystem services, and delivery of many services from the same ecosystem, management unit or land parcel, indicate that greater attention needs to be paid to multifunctional use of land and water (both fresh and marine). To achieve multiple objectives and to manage for multifunctional land and water uses requires understanding of the integrated nature of ecosystems, and the delivery of services, biodiversity and human well-being. Ecosystem assessment is one first step in this process.

There are already many approaches for the evaluation and management of multiple uses. These include environmental impact assessment and strategic environmental assessment that are used for planning, management and decision making. Both incorporate elements of an integrated understanding of ecosystems. Complementing these systems approaches, there are also approaches that are place-based. Catchment or river basin management develops local approaches to the management of river basins (Gardiner 1994; Ferrier & Jenkins 2010). Examples and guidance on catchment management are available from several sources (Dee Catchment Partnership 2007; Scottish Government 2009b, d). Forestry has adopted integrated approaches such as sustainable forest management (Wang 2004; Sturtevant *et al.* 2007) and ecosystem-based approaches (Schlaepfer 2005; Sayer & Maginnis 2007). Land use planning is also an integrative approach that incorporates linkages between communities and environments in particular places (Lloyd & McCarthy 2000; Lloyd & Peel 2007; Peel & Lloyd 2007). The governance and purposes of Scotland's National Parks makes them test beds and exemplars of community-based integrated planning to achieve multiple goals. Study of their operation and effectiveness would be informative for development of approaches to sustainable management in areas outside the National Park system.

The ecosystem approach, developed under the CBD, deliberately attempts to balance the need to conserve the healthy functioning of ecosystems with the demands placed on resources by society (Defra 2007; Mudge & Christie 2009). The ecosystem approach is set within the context of i) *decisions, plans and policies*, ii) the legal, political, social and economic *contexts* within which decisions are made, iii) the *scope* of an issue and iv) *management, consultative and participatory needs* of society (Aspinall *et al.* 2010). As a strategy for integrated management of land, water and living resources, the ecosystem approach recognises that people, with their diversity, are an integral component of ecosystems.

The ecosystem approach can be implemented through the application of a set of principles and actions (Mudge & Christie 2009; Aspinall *et al.* 2010). Key elements of the ecosystem approach include:

- Participation of people through public agencies, private land managers, voluntary groups, local residents and individuals;
- Understanding a range of management issues related to decision making, including that the ecosystem approach is itself a process that requires management;
- Understanding the scale and dynamics of ecosystems, the way they change, and impact of decisions; and
- Understanding ecosystem functions, goods and services.

This includes understanding ecosystem goods and services from supply and demand perspectives, as well as knowledge of environmental quality and limits.

Independent of the approach used to develop policy-making and management strategies, there is a need to be aware of trade-offs and synergies between ecosystem services. For example, one globally recognised trade-off is between management of arable farming, with the intended and focused delivery of food production as a provisioning service, and an associated reduction in biodiversity and many other services including water quality, pollination and erosion regulation (Benayas *et al.* 2009). Reviewing and valuing all ecosystem services associated with specific land parcels or management activities provides a more comprehensive balance sheet for analysis of trade-offs and synergies. The understanding and evidence that such a balance sheet provides can contribute to achievement of multiple objective and multifunctional management with consequent improvements in social, economic and environmental sustainability.

19.10 Knowledge Gaps

Although a large amount is already known about ecosystem services in Scotland, particularly about provisioning services, there remain significant knowledge gaps. Addressing these gaps will contribute important content to the evidence base for both policy making and management of land and marine ecosystems in Scotland.

19.10.1 Biodiversity

There is a lack of information on status and trends in many important elements of Scotland's biodiversity. Biodiversity includes species, communities and genes, habitats and landscapes, and can be considered in a variety of ways, including by number or by functional relationships (Diaz *et al.* 2007). Work is needed to improve understanding of both the variety of elements and forms of biodiversity itself and the range of relationships between different elements of biodiversity with ecosystem services. For example, mammal and bird species diversity are important cultural services, plant species diversity influences carbon and nitrogen storage in grassland ecosystems (De Deyn *et al.* 2009), functional diversity of soil microorganisms is important for nutrient cycling (Brown 2002; Brussaard *et al.* 2007), and landscape-scale habitat diversity important for flood regulation. Measurement and monitoring of the functional links between biodiversity and supporting and regulating services are also needed to complement the efforts that currently apply to understanding relationships between biodiversity and provisioning and cultural services.

19.10.2 Trends in Ecosystem Services

There are a number of gaps in our knowledge of specific ecosystem services, most notably for supporting, regulating, and cultural services. In particular there is little historic data on the status and contribution of these services in Scotland and how they have changed over time. However, although of some historic and scientific interest, detailed understanding and knowledge of how *all* services have changed over the last 70 years, an aspirational objective of the UK NEA, is neither essential nor necessary for development of contemporary policy and management strategies. In contrast, an improved understanding and awareness of the connections and interdependencies between the many different services will provide a more solid evidence base for policy making and management in future. Further work to measure and monitor these connections and interdependencies, and how they change over time in future, for supporting, regulating and cultural services will be beneficial and informative.

19.10.3 Process-level Understanding

The ecosystem processes that are the basis for sustainable support and delivery of ecosystem services need further study, especially in the context of supporting multiple ecosystem services. The process-level biological, physical and chemical functions of ecosystems, and the roles of biodiversity as both a driver and product of ecosystem processes, require more study. This will improve understanding of the capacity of ecosystems to deliver services and inform analysis of trade-offs and synergies in delivery of ecosystem services. The functional behaviour and capacity of ecosystems to support the range of services documented in this report is currently unknown. Understanding of functional performance is closely linked to process-level understanding; this is a priority for scientific research as ecosystem function has links to ecosystem health, performance, resilience and sustainability. Improved understanding of the resilience and health of all Scotland's ecosystems would be beneficial, but is perhaps most critically needed for Enclosed Farmland and Marine habitats from which raw materials for food are derived. The long-term resilience of farmland ecosystems under high energy-input farming practices is, in particular, not known.

19.10.4 Monitoring and Measurement

Representative information is needed on the status, condition and trends of ecosystems and ecosystem services. There are two areas for development: the measurements made and the monitoring network used.

Considerable information on ecosystems and ecosystem services is already available, although there are a number of specific gaps. Land cover and habitat data are a foundational source of inventory for understanding the status and change in ecosystems. However, the sources of information on the area of ecosystems in Scotland over time have changed, which limits the ability to be confident of measured changes. The measurement of land cover in Scotland and its change from the 1940s to 1980s carried out by the National Countryside Monitoring Scheme (Mackey *et al.* 1998) has not been repeated to provide a recent update during the three decades since the 1980s. The Countryside Survey (Norton *et al.* 2009) does address the period since the 1980s but uses a different sampling strategy and set of data collection protocols and is not directly comparable with the National Countryside Monitoring Scheme. The Land Cover of Scotland (1988) (MLURI 1993) and the more recent Land Cover Maps of Great Britain for 2000 and 2007 were produced from different data sources (aerial photos and satellite imagery) with different scales, using different methods of interpretation (human visual versus automated digital) and with different classifications of land cover. National Forest Inventory and Native Woodlands Survey data are collected by the Forestry Commission; data on habitats are collected by Scottish Natural Heritage, and on water and other aspects of the environment by SEPA. Bringing these datasets, and others, together should support enhanced understanding of the status, condition and trends of Scotland's ecosystems.

In addition to information on ecosystems, ecosystem services need to be measured. Section 19.5 provides a list of candidate ecosystem services. Measures and indices of ecosystem status, condition and trends, and of ecosystem services should together provide an evidence base to monitor the status of uses and human benefits, including well-being, from Scotland's ecosystems, and to assess sustainability at national, regional and possibly also local scales. As part of the development of measures of ecosystem services it will also be necessary to address measurement of the interdependencies between services, as well as trade-offs and synergies.

Looking to the future, there are existing data sources that potentially offer an informative base for the monitoring and measurement of ecosystems and ecosystem services. Notably, the agricultural census collects data for agriculture that may be used as a base for assessment of ecosystem services, although this use would need to operate at a disaggregated level and conform to data protection regulations. Harmonised catchment monitoring schemes and river basin management plans and groups could provide a resource for integrated monitoring of certain ecosystem services and hydrological aspects of ecosystem process and function. The SSSI and other conservation designation networks are currently used as a monitoring system within the SNH Site Condition Monitoring programme. Analysis of the changes at these sites, considered as a whole distributed network, is providing insights into impacts of change across Scotland.

The monitoring of ecosystems and ecosystem services, especially at regional and local scales, needs to be based on a reliable, robust and statistically sound monitoring platform. The development of networks to monitor individual and groups of services is thus necessary for informed understanding of the sustainability of the state, condition and delivery of services into the future. The networks may be based on or link to one or more existing monitoring networks and programmes (e.g. the Environmental Change Network, Harmonised Catchment Monitoring Network, model and monitor farms, weather stations, river gauging stations, water and air quality monitoring sites, Countryside Survey, June Agricultural Census, or other long-term monitoring sites). Alternatively, a dedicated and fit-for-purpose monitoring system for ecosystem services might be designed, rather than basing knowledge on legacy networks of existing systems that have grown organically, with each component designed and site selected either opportunistically or for a particular, different and independent set of purposes.

19.10.5 Spatial and Temporal Scales

The evidence from the UK NEA is that a considerable amount of information is already collected and available for use. However, much of this information is at a national scale. Spatially disaggregated data that can be used regionally and locally would be beneficial. For a number of ecosystem services it would be possible and productive to conduct ecosystem service inventories at sub-national scales. For example, an inventory of ecosystem services could be applied for water catchments or for administrative regions. This would provide not only insights into the contributions of ecosystem services to regional and local economies and communities, but also evidence bases for regional and local decision making. Further, regional and local assessment would serve to raise public awareness of the contribution of ecosystems to economic and social sustainability at scales and for landscapes that are particularly important to residents and other relevant groups. The ecosystem approach provides mechanisms for managing issues that span multiple scales in space and time and for the generation and use of inventories of ecosystem services (Mudge & Christie 2009; Aspinall *et al.* 2010).

19.10.6 Linkages Between Ecosystems

Knowledge gaps also exist concerning the interrelations and interdependencies of ecosystems for delivery of ecosystem services. Ecosystems and habitats create a complex mosaic across Scotland's landscapes and the organisation of ecosystems in space has an influence on biodiversity and ecosystem services (Loreau *et al.* 2003; Pejchar *et al.* 2007; Opdam *et al.* 2009). Many of the issues and uncertainties associated with these landscape and ecological aspects of biodiversity and ecosystem services are allied to issues of scale in space and time. Analysis of the spatial pattern and organisation of ecosystems within landscapes in Scotland has not formed part of this national assessment. For regional and local scales, and for analysis of specific ecosystem services in catchments, administrative areas, or within urban or rural areas, understanding of the spatial organisation and interaction of ecosystems would be required. For management to increase or enhance particular ecosystem services in multifunctional landscapes at local and regional scales it might also be necessary for principles of landscape design to be linked to understanding of pattern and process (Nassauer & Opdam 2008; Lovell & Johnston 2009).

Given the dominantly urban base of the population of Scotland, the functional links between urban populations and communities and rural areas also requires more research, as do the links between land, coastal and marine ecosystems.

19.10.7 Links to Human Well-being

The linkages of ecosystem services to human well-being are only recently becoming recognised and considerable knowledge gaps are clear. The physical and psychological health benefits, and social and economic benefits, of greenspace in urban areas are now beginning to be understood, but the full range of benefits, and their specific values in Scotland, are largely unknown. There is scope for further research to identify the magnitude and impact of greenspace on many aspects of Scotland's population and communities. Medical, psychological and sociological research is needed to address physical and psychological health and well-being, as well as knowledge gaps related to use, access and public attitudes to greenspace. There is also potential for understanding the health benefits of food from locally produced raw materials (provisioning services) through studies of food, diet and health.

Other knowledge gaps include the use and value of natural environments for recreation, leisure and as part of the cultural identity of Scotland's communities, the roles of cultural services in enhancing human well-being in Scotland, and understanding public attitudes to the full range of ecosystem services (Warren & Birnie 2009).

19.10.8 Case Studies

Much of the available information on ecosystem services is at national or other coarse aggregate scale. To improve awareness of the connections between people and ecosystem services, and to develop understanding at landscape and local scales as proposed for cultural services, further work should identify and develop local exemplars of the contribution of biodiversity and ecosystems to ecosystem services and human well-being. This will address knowledge gaps related to societal awareness of dependence on healthy ecosystems.

19.11 Conclusions

Scotland's land, coastal and marine ecosystems sustain an extensive suite of ecosystem services and contribute significantly to human well-being and to the economic and social health of the nation. The environmental foundation (climate, geology, soil, vegetation and other biodiversity, topography/hydrography, management systems) of ecosystems in Scotland is well documented. There is considerable knowledge of the state, condition, trend and dynamics of Scotland's land, coastal and marine ecosystems, although further detailed information is needed, particularly for marine systems around Scotland.

Understanding of the supporting services provided by Scotland's ecosystems is well established, although the trends in these services over time are not well documented. Further work is also needed to establish the resilience of ecosystems to the range of pressures presented by possible environmental changes (e.g. climate change), and the consequences of societal choices and preferences (e.g. for food, landscape and energy). This means understanding ecosystems at the level of the supporting services which reflect fundamental biological and physical processes and underpin delivery of regulating, provisioning and cultural services.

Understanding the role of ecosystems in providing regulating services is similarly well established. Many of the ecosystem services provided by Scotland's ecosystems are well known at an aggregate national scale. Further investigation, and improved documentation, demonstration and awareness of the benefits of regulating services at local and regional scales and for specific communities is needed. The variety and extent of many provisioning services are very well established. Knowledge of some cultural services is well established, but for others, further attention is needed to establish specific examples of their extent and value in Scotland.

Figure 19.52 summarises the relative importance of different habitats and changes within them over the last 20 years in the delivery of final ecosystem services and indicates deterioration in service delivery for many services in all habitats other than Woodlands.

The importance of all habitats for the delivery of ecosystem services is apparent from the colours in the figure. This should not be surprising. All of the habitats and ecosystems of Scotland have been heavily influenced and shaped by human activity over periods of years to centuries. The wild and remote landscapes of Mountain, Moorland and Heathland habitats that dominate upland Scotland are a product of human activity as much as the built urban areas where over 80% of Scotland's population live. The resource management practices used in Scotland's habitats and ecosystems continue to support delivery of considerable levels of ecosystem services to Scotland's population and beyond, while influencing the state and condition of those ecosystems.

The arrows in the figure indicate the general trend of delivery of final ecosystem services from each habitat over the last 20 years. This aspect of the assessment gives cause

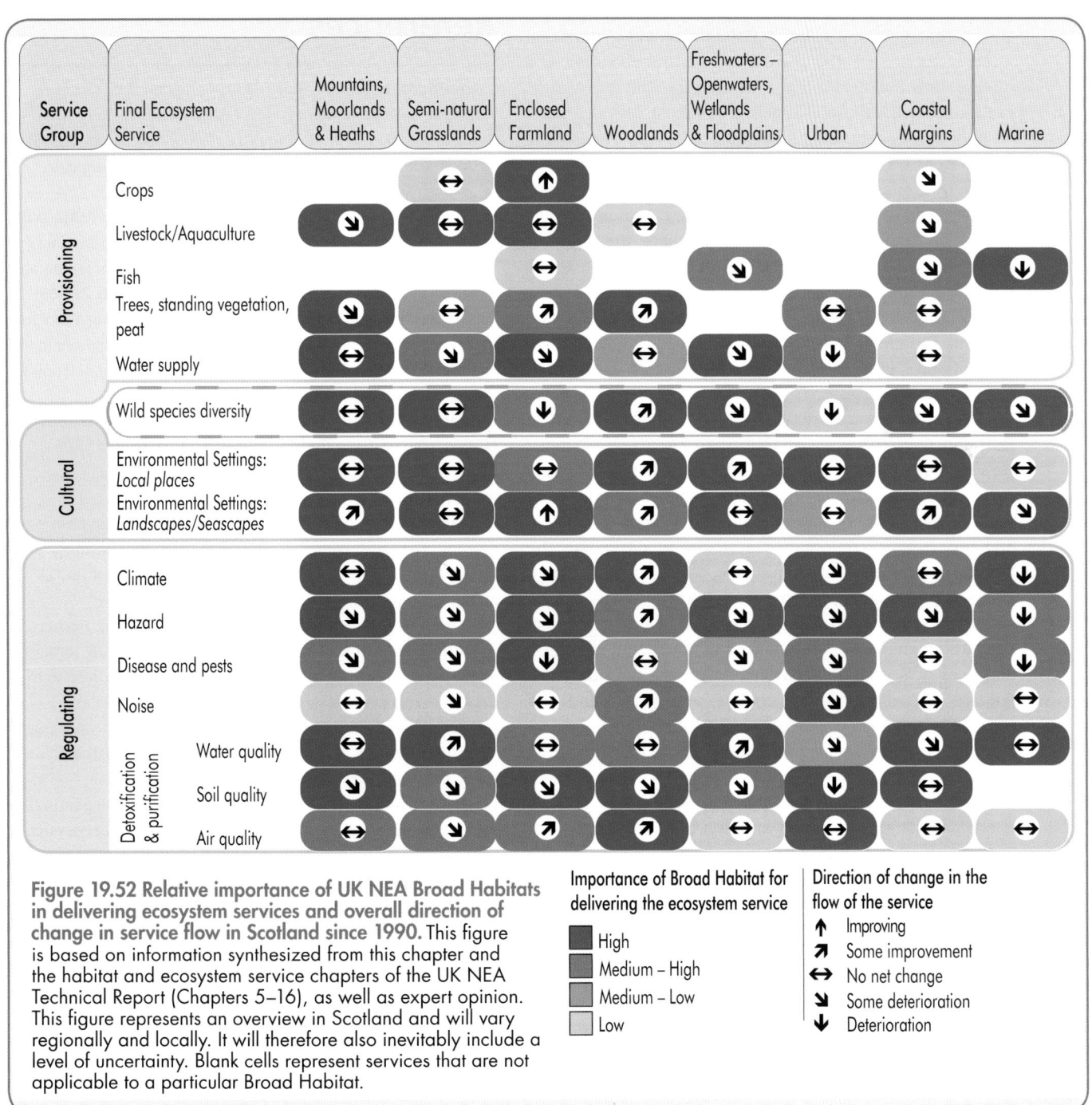

Figure 19.52 Relative importance of UK NEA Broad Habitats in delivering ecosystem services and overall direction of change in service flow in Scotland since 1990. This figure is based on information synthesized from this chapter and the habitat and ecosystem service chapters of the UK NEA Technical Report (Chapters 5–16), as well as expert opinion. This figure represents an overview in Scotland and will vary regionally and locally. It will therefore also inevitably include a level of uncertainty. Blank cells represent services that are not applicable to a particular Broad Habitat.

Importance of Broad Habitat for delivering the ecosystem service
- High
- Medium – High
- Medium – Low
- Low

Direction of change in the flow of the service
- ↑ Improving
- ↗ Some improvement
- ↔ No net change
- ↘ Some deterioration
- ↓ Deterioration

for concern. Of the 103 arrows indicating direction of change in the figure, 45 (43.7%) are towards some deterioration or deteriorating, 41 (39.8%) are showing equivocal changes, and only 17 (16.5%) are showing improvement or some improvement.

The Woodlands habitat shows improving/some improvement trends for eight ecosystem services, four trends that are equivocal, and one trend that shows as deteriorating/some deterioration. All the other habitats each have five to eight trends in service delivery that are deteriorating and/or show some deterioration. Marine and Urban habitats have no ecosystem services showing a trend of some improvement and/or improving; Coastal Margin, Semi-natural Grassland and Mountains, Moorlands and Heaths have a trend of some improvement/improving in only one service each. The assessment of delivery of ecosystem services, where possible over a period of the last 70 years, shows that Scotland's Broad Habitats provide significant levels of service and that there are important economic and other values that derive from this delivery. The assessment in **Figure 19.52** shows that delivery of these services is not without consequences for sustainable delivery, over 80% of the services showing deterioration or equivocal changes.

There is also good knowledge of the role of policies, legislation and regulation, societal preferences and economic drivers on management decisions that shape the future of Scotland's ecosystems. The UK NEA itself demonstrates impacts of policies and other drivers on ecosystem services. The relationships between Scottish national policy and UK and European policies as relative drivers of change in Scotland's land and marine ecosystems merit further attention.

The economic contribution of ecosystem services in Scotland over the past 70 years has been considerable. However, the growth in many of the provisioning services derived from agriculture and marine fisheries has not been without impact on biodiversity and the structure, function and processes of relevant ecosystems. In particular, the long-term resilience of farmland ecosystems under high energy input farming practices is not known.

Scotland has several flagship policies and a number of key Parliamentary Acts that will shape the state, condition and uses of Scotland's ecosystems over the next decades. Policies to address climate change, energy demand and provision, and food and health are all already in place. A land use strategy is to be published at about the same time as the UK NEA.

To contribute to development and delivery of policies related to Scotland's economy and environment, the Scottish Government Rural and Environment Research and Analysis Directorate (RERAD) research programme for 2011–2016 has a theme that directly addresses ecosystem assessment and the ecosystem approach. This will build on the work of the UK NEA, including the economic valuation and scenarios that explore future options for ecosystems and ecosystem services over the next 50 years. Many of the knowledge gaps identified here may be addressed in that programme.

The range, utility and value of ecosystem services obtained from Scotland's ecosystems are considerable. Although many of these services are traded and valued by markets and therefore subject to investment and development, many others are either valued less or not valued at all. Some of the cultural services are not capable of conventional valuation by markets. Many of the services provided by Scotland's ecosystems contribute to economic development; others are critical to health and quality of life. An inclusive and integrated approach to valuing and maintaining the full range of services and benefits enjoyed from Scotland's ecosystems and land- and seascapes can be obtained by attention to multiple services, understanding of trade-offs between services, and by wider awareness and participation in the governance of natural resource management.

References

Aalders, I., Ball, B., Black, H.I.J., Campbell, C.C., Griffiths, B., Hopkins, D., Hough, R.L., Lilly, A., McKenzie, B., Rees, R.M., Sinclair, A., Towers, W. & Watson, C. (2009) Considerations for Scottish soil monitoring in the European context. *European Journal of Soil Science,* **60**, 833–843.

Abberton, M.T., Marshall, A.H., Humphreys, M.W., Macduff, J.H., Collins, R.P. & Marley, C.L. (2008) Genetic improvement of forage species to reduce the environmental impact of temperate livestock grazing systems. *Advances in Agronomy,* **98**, 311–355.

Aebischer, N.J. & Harradine, J. (2007) Developing a tool for improving bag data of huntable bird and other bird species in the UK. The Game Conservancy Trust and the British Association for Shooting and Conservation.

Albon, S.D., Brewer, M.J., O'Brien, S., Nolan, A.J. & Cope, D. (2007) Quantifying the grazing impacts associated with different herbivores on rangelands. *Journal of Applied Ecology,* **44**, 1176–1187.

Allcock, R. & Buchanan, D. (1994) Agriculture and fish farming. The Fresh Waters of Scotland. A National Resource of International Significance. (eds P.S. Maitland, P.J. Boon, & D.S. McLusky). John Wiley and Sons, London. pp. 365–384.

Anderson, H., Futter, M., Oliver, I., Redshaw, J. & Harper, A. (2010) Trends in Scottish river water quality. pp. 178. [online] Available at: <http://www.sepa.org.uk/science_and_research/ data_and_reports/water/scottish_river_water_quality.aspx> [Accessed 28.05.11].

Andersson, E. (2006) Urban landscapes and sustainable cities. *Ecology and Society,* **11(1)**, 34.

Andersson, E., Barthel, S. & Ahrne, K. (2007) Measuring social-ecological dynamics behind the generation of ecosystem services. *Ecological Applications,* **17**, 1267–1278.

Angus Council (2008) The Open 2007: economic impact assessment. Report by the director of Infrastructure Services. [online] Available at: <www.angus.gov.uk/ccmeetings/reports-committee2008/infrastructure/96.pdf> [Accessed 28.05.11].

Angus, S. (1999) The state of the maritime natural heritage: machair in Scotland. Scotland's Living Coastline. (eds J.M. Baxter, K. Duncan, S. Atkins, & G. Lees). The Stationery Office, London. pp. 166–172.

Angus, S. (2001) The Outer Hebrides: moorland and machair. White Horse Press, Harris and Cambridge.

Anon (1943) Hydro-Electric Development (Scotland) Act, Edinburgh.

Anon (2004) The UK Forestry Standard (2nd edition). Forestry Commission GB and Forest Service Northern Ireland, Edinburgh and Belfast.

Ashman, T.L., Knight, T.M., Steets, J.A., Amarasekare, P., Burd, M., Campbell, D.R., Dudash, M.R., Johnston, M.O., Mazer, S.J., Mitchell, R.J., Morgan, M.T. & Wilson, W.G. (2004) Pollen limitation of plant reproduction: Ecological and evolutionary causes and consequences. *Ecology, 85*, 2408–2421.

Aspinall, R.J., Black, H., Blackstock, K., Brown, I., Castellazzi, M., Cooksley, S., Ferrier, R., Gill, E., Gimona, A., Glenk, K., Hastings, E., Hester, A., Langan, S., Matthews, K., Miller, D.R., E., M., Pakeman, R. & Stannard, C.A. (2010) Model Ecosystem Framework Project. Phase 1 Report: A Field Guide to an Ecosystem Approach in Scotland. MLURI, Aberdeen. pp. 87.

Aspinall, S.J. & Aspinall, R.J. (2011) The Fair Isle Wren: population and territory occupancy, 1950–2010. *British Birds.* **104**, 312–324.

Avery, M. & Leslie, R. (1990) Birds and Forestry. A & C Black, Edinburgh.

Bailey-Watts, A.E. (1994) Eutrophication. The Fresh Waters of Scotland. A National Resource of International Significance. (eds P.S. Maitland, P.J. Boon, & D.S. McLusky). John Wiley and Sons, London. pp. 385–411.

Ball, D.F., MacDonald, A.M. & Lilly, A. (2005) Agriculture and diffuse pollution: groundwater nitrate vulnerable zones in Scotland. *Scottish Journal of Geology, 41*, 61–68.

Balls, P.W. (1994) Nutrient Inputs to Estuaries from 9 Scottish East-Coast Rivers–Influence of Estuarine Processes on Inputs to the North-Sea. *Estuarine Coastal and Shelf Science, 39*, 329–352.

Barbatti, A., Corona, P. & Marchetti, M. (2007) European forest types: categories and types for sustainable forest management reporting and policy. European Environment Agency, Copenhagen.

BARS (Biodiversity Action Reporting System) (2011) Biodiversity Action Reporting System. [online] Available at: <http://ukbars.defra.gov.uk/> [Accessed 28.05.11].

Baxter, J. & Hutchinson, P. (2002) The Atlantic Salmon: A case study of Scotland's environment and natural heritage. The State of Scotland's Environment and Natural Heritage. (eds M.B. Usher, E.C. Mackey, & J.A. Curran). The Stationery Office, Edinburgh. pp. 219–234.

Baxter, J.M., Boyd, I.L., Cox, M., Cunningham, L., Holmes, P. & Moffat, C.F. (2008) Scotland's Seas: Towards Understanding their State. Fisheries Research Service, Aberdeen. pp. 174.

Baxter, J.M., Boyd, I.L., Cox, M., Donald, A.E., Malcolm, S.J., Miles, H., Miller, B. & Moffat, C.F. (2011) Scotland's Marine Atlas: Information for the national marine plan. Marine Scotland, Edinburgh. pp. 191.

Beale, C.M., Burfield, I.J., Sim, I.M.W., Rebecca, G.W., Pearce-Higgins, J.W. & Grant, M.C. (2006) Climate change may account for the decline in British ring ouzels *Turdus torquatus. Journal of Animal Ecology, 75*, 826–835.

Beales, P.A., Giltrap, P.G., Payne, A.I.L. & Ingram, N. (2009) A new threat to UK heathland from *Phytophthora kernoviae* on *Vaccinium myrtillus* in the wild. *Plant Pathology, 58*, 393–393.

Bell, S., Hamilton, V., Montarzino, A., Rothnie, H., Travlou, P. & Alves, S. (2008) Greenspace and quality of life: a critical literature review. greenspace scotland, Stirling. pp. 75.

Benayas, J.M.R., Newton, A.C., Diaz, A. & Bullock, J.M. (2009) Enhancement of Biodiversity and Ecosystem Services by Ecological Restoration: A Meta-Analysis. *Science, 325*, 1121–1124.

Bennett, E.M. & Balvanera, P. (2007) The future of production systems in a globalized world. *Frontiers in Ecology and the Environment, 5*, 191–198.

Bennett, S.P., Campbell, L. & Nicol, I. (1999) The use of Landscape Character in development Planning: Two case studies. Landscape Character: Perspectives on Management and Change. (eds M.B. Usher). The Stationery Office, Edinburgh. pp. 13–22.

Benton, T.G., Bryant, D.M., Cole, L. & Crick, H.Q.P. (2002) Linking agricultural practice to insect and bird populations: a historical study over three decades. *Journal of Applied Ecology,* **39**, 673–687.

Benton, T.G., Vickery, J.A. & WIlson, J.D. (2003) Farmland biodiversity: is habitat heterogeneity the key? *Trends in Ecology & Evolution,* **18**, 182–188.

Berry, R.J. & Tricker, B.J.K. (1969) Competition and extinction: the mice of Foula, with notes on those of Fair Isle and St. Kilda. *Journal of Zoology, 158*, 247–265.

Berry, R.J. & Johnston, J.L. (1980) The Natural History of Shetland. Collins, London. pp. 380.

Berry, R.J. (1985) The Natural History of Orkney. Collins, London. pp. 304.

Bibby, J.S., Douglas, H.A., Thomasson, A.J. & Robertson, J.S. (1982) Land Capability Classification for Agriculture. The Macaulay Institute for Soil Research, Aberdeen.

Bibby, J.S., Heslop, R.E.F. & Hartnup, R. (1988) Land Capability for Forestry in Britain. Macaulay Land Use Research Institute, Aberdeen.

Biesmeijer, J.C. (2006) Parallel declines in pollinators and insect-pollinated plants in Britain and the Netherlands. *Science,* **313**, 351–354.

Bignal, E.M. & McCracken, D.I. (1996) Low-intensity farming systems in the conservation of the countryside. *Journal of Applied Ecology, 33*, 413–424.

Billen, G., Joiris, C., Meyerreil, L. & Lindeboom, H. (1990) Role of Bacteria in the North-Sea Ecosystem. *Netherlands Journal of Sea Research, 26*, 265–293.

Birks, H.J.B. (1997) Scottish biodiversity in a historical context. Biodiversity in Scotland: Status, Trends and Initiatives. (eds L.V. Fleming, A.C. Newton, J.A. Vickery, & M.B. Usher). The Stationery Office, Edinburgh. pp. 21–36.

Birnie, R.V., Curran, J., Macdonald, J.A., Mackey, E.C., Campbell, C.D., McGowan, G., Palmer, S.F.C., Paterson, E., Shaw, P. & Schewry, M.C. (2002) The land resources of Scotland: trends and prospects for the environment and natural heritage. The State of Scotland's Environment and Natural Heritage. (eds M.B. Usher, E.C. Mackey, & J.A. Curran). The Stationery Office, Edinburgh. pp. 41–81.

Birse, E.L. & Dry, F.T. (1970) Assessment of Climatic Conditions in Scotland. 1. Based on accumulated temperature and potential water deficit. Macaulay Institute for Soil Research, Aberdeen.

Birse, E.L. & Robertson, L. (1970) Assessment of Climatic Conditions in Scotland. 2. Based on exposure and accumulated frost. Macaulay Institute for Soil Research, Aberdeen.

Bjork, R.G. & Molau, U. (2007) Ecology of alpine snowbeds and the impact of global change. *Arctic Antarctic and Alpine Research, 39*, 34–43.

Black, A.R. (1996) Major flooding and increased flood frequency in Scotland since 1988. *Physics and Chemistry of the Earth, 20*, 463–468.

Boyd, J.M. & Boyd, I.L. (1990) The Hebrides. A Natural History. Collins, London. pp. 416.

Boyd, J.M. & Boyd, I.L. (1996) The Hebrides. A Mosaic of Islands. Birlinn Ltd, Edinburgh. pp. 136.

Bradley, R.I., Milne, R., Bell, J., Lilly, A., Jordan, C. & Higgins, A. (2005) A soil carbon and land use database for the United Kingdom. *Soil Use and Management, 21*, 363–369.

Brasier, C.M. (2008) The biosecurity threat to the UK and global environment from international trade in plants. *Plant Pathology, 57*, 792–808.

Brasier, C.M. & Webber, J.F. (2010) Sudden larch death. *Nature, 466*, 824–825.

Braubach, M. (2007) Residential conditions and their impact on residential environment satisfaction and health: Results of the WHO large analysis and review of European housing and health status (LARES) study. *International Journal of Environment and Pollution, 30*, 384–403.

Brewer, D. (2001) Wrens, Dippers and Thrashers. Christopher Helm, London.

Brierley, A.S. & Kingsford, M.J. (2009) Impacts of Climate Change on Marine Organisms and Ecosystems. *Current Biology, 19*, R602–R614.

Britton, A. & Fisher, J. (2007) NP stoichiometry of low-alpine heathland: Usefulness for bio-monitoring and prediction of pollution impacts. *Biological Conservation, 138*, 100–108.

Brocklehurst, F. (1997) UK Onshore Wind Energy Resources. ETSU report: ETSU-R-99.

Brown, A., Birks, H.J.B. & Thompson, D.B.A. (1993) A New Biogeographical Classification of the Scottish Uplands. 2. Vegetation Environment Relationships. *Journal of Ecology, 81*, 231–251.

Brown, A. & Webber, J. (2008) Red band needle blight of conifers in Britain. Forestry Commission, Edinburgh.

Brown, G. & Raymond, C. (2007) The relationship between place attachment and landscape values: Toward mapping place attachment. *Applied Geography, 27*, 89–111.

Brown, J.G. & Hunter, J.K. (1961) Energy–Resources and Utilisation. Natural Resources in Scotland. Scottish Council (Development and Industry), Symposium at the Royal Society of Edinburgh, 31 October to 2 November 1960. (eds. T. & A. Constable). Edinburgh. pp. 419–434.

Brown, S. (2002) Aspects of soil protozoa on a grassland farm. *European Journal of Protistology, 37*, 359–360.

Browne, S., Vickery, J. & Chamberlain, D. (2000) Densities and population estimates of breeding Skylarks *Alauda arvensis* in Britain in 1997. *Bird Study, 47*, 52–65.

Brussaard, L., de Ruiter, P.C. & Brown, G.G. (2007) Soil biodiversity for agricultural sustainability. *Agriculture Ecosystems & Environment, 121*, 233–244.

Bryden, D.M., Westbrook, S.R., Burns, B.R., Taylor, W.A. & Anderson, S. (2010) Assessing the economic impacts of nature based tourism in Scotland. Scottish Natural Heritage, Inverness. pp. 105.

Burd, M. (1994) Bateman's principle and reproduction: the role of pollinator limitation in fruit and seed set. *Botanical Review, 60*, 83–139.

Butler, J.R.A., Radford, A., Riddington, G. & Laughton, R. (2009) Evaluating an ecosystem service provided by Atlantic salmon, sea trout and other fish species in the River Spey, Scotland: The economic impact of recreational rod fisheries. *Fisheries Research, 96*, 259–266.

Campbell, M.O. (2008) The impact of vegetation, river, and urban features on waterbird ecology in Glasgow, Scotland. *Journal of Coastal Research, 24*, 239–245.

Cannell, M.G.R., Milne, R., Hargreaves, K.J., Brown, T.A.W., Cruickshank, M.M., Bradley, R.I., Spencer, T., Hope, D., Billet, M.E.F., Adger, W.N. & Subak, S. (1999) National inventories of terrestrial carbon sources and sinks: The UK experience. *Climatic Change, 42*, 505–530.

Carey, P.D., Dring, C.M., Hill, M.O., Preston, C.D. & Wright, S.M. (1994) Biogeographical Zones in Scotland. Scottish Natural Heritage, Edinburgh.

Carey, P.D., Preston, C.D., Hill, M.O., Usher, M.B. & Wright, S.M. (1995) An Environmentally Defined Biogeographical Zonation of Scotland Designed to Reflect Species Distributions. *Journal of Ecology, 83*, 833–845.

Carpenter, S., Szmaragd, C., Barber, J., Labuschagne, K., Gubbins, S. & Mellor, P. (2008) An assessment of *Culicoides* surveillance techniques in northern Europe: have we underestimated a potential bluetongue virus vector? *Journal of Applied Ecology, 45*, 1237–1245.

Carpenter, S., Wilson, A. & Mellor, P.S. (2009) *Culicoides* and the emergence of bluetongue virus in northern Europe. *Trends in Microbiology, 17*, 172–178.

Carvell, C., Roy, D.B., Smart, S.M., Pywell, R.F., Preston, C.D. & Goulson, D. (2006) Declines in forage availability for bumblebees at a national scale. *Biological Conservation, 132*, 481–489.

Centre for Ecology and Hydrology (2011) Centre for Ecology and Hydrology. [online] Available at: <http://www.ceh.ac.uk> [Accessed 28.05.11].

Chapman, S.J., Bell, J., Lilly, A. & Donnelly, D. (2009) Carbon stocks in Scottish peatlands. *Soil Use and Management, 25*, 105–112.

Charlesworth, S.M., Harker, E. & Rickard, S. (2003) A review of sustainable drainage systems (SuDS): A soft option for hard drainage questions? *Geography, 88*, 99–107.

Chiesura, A. & de Groot, R. (2003) Critical natural capital: a socio-cultural perspective. *Ecological Economics, 44*, 219–231.

Chiesura, A. (2004) The role of urban parks for the sustainable city. *Landscape and Urban Planning, 68*, 129–138.

Clugston, D.L., Forrester, R.W., MacGowan, R.Y. & Zonfrillo, B. (2001) Scottish list–species and sub-species. *Scottish Birds 22*, 33–49.

Cole, L., Bradford, M.A., Shaw, P.J.A. & Bardgett, R.D. (2006) The abundance, richness and functional role of soil meso- and macrofauna in temperate grassland – A case study. *Applied Soil Ecology, 33*, 186–198.

Cole, L.J., Morton, R., Harrison, W., McCracken, D.I. & Robertson, D. (2008) The influence of riparian buffer strips on carabid beetle (Coleoptera, Carabidae) assemblage structure and diversity in intensively managed grassland fields. *Biodiversity and Conservation, 17*, 2233–2245.

Conway, D. (1998) Recent climate variability and future climate change scenarios for Great Britain. *Progress in Physical Geography, 22*, 350–374.

Cook, M.J.H. (1982) Breeding status of the Crested Tit. *Scottish Birds, 12*, 97–106.

Cooper Committee (1942) Hydro-Electric Development in Scotland. London.

Cope, D.R., Rowcliffe, J.M. & Pettifor, R.A. (2003) Sward height, structure and leaf extension rate of *Lolium perenne* pastures when grazed by overwintering barnacle geese. *Grass and Forage Science,* **58,** 70–76.

Coppock, J.T. (1971) An Agricultural Geography of Great Britain. G. Bell and Sons, Ltd, London. pp. 345.

Coppock, J.T. (1976) An Agricultural Atlas of Scotland. John Donald Publishers Ltd., Edinburgh. pp. 242.

Coull, J.R. (1996) The Sea Fisheries of Scotland: A Historical Geography. John Donald Publishers Ltd, Edinburgh. pp. 308.

Council of Europe (2003) European Landscape Convention. Committee of Ministers of the Council of Europe, Florence 2000.

Covey, R. (1999) The saline lagoon survey of Scotland. Scotland's Living Coastline. (eds J.M. Baxter, K. Duncan, S. Atkins, & G. Lees). TSO, London. pp. 150–165.

Croucher, K., Myers, L. & Bretherton, J. (2007) The links between greenspace and health: a critical literature review. University of York.

Curran, J.C. & Robertson, M. (1991) Water quality implications of an observed trend of rainfall and runoff. *Journal of the Institution of Water and Environmental Management,* **5,** 419–424.

Currie, J. (2002) Scotland's environment: a European opportunity. The State of Scotland's Environment and Natural Heritage. (eds M.B. Usher, E.C. Mackey, & J. Curran). The Stationery Office, Edinburgh. pp. 19–22.

Dargie, T.C.D. & Duncan, K. (1999) The sand dune vegetation survey of Scotland. Scotland's Living Coastline. (eds J.M. Baxter, K. Duncan, S. Atkins, & G. Lees). TSO, London. pp. 136–149.

Dargie, T.C.D. (2000) Sand dune vegetation survey of Scotland: national report. Scottish Natural Heritage, Edinburgh.

Darwin, T. (1996) The Scot's Herbal: the plant lore of Scotland. Mercat Press, Edinburgh.

Davey, P.A. & Aebischer, N.J. (2008) Contract Report: *F90-01-708.* Participation in the National Gamebag Census in the Mammal Surveillance Network. A Report to JNCC for the year 2007/8. The Game and WIldlife Conservation Trust. pp. 56.

Davidson, D.A. & Grieve, I.C. (2006) Relationships between biodiversity and soil structure and function: evidence from laboratory and field experiments. *Applied Soil Ecology,* **33,** 176–185.

Davies, B., Pita, C., Lusseau, D. & Hunter, C. (2010) The value of tourism expenditure related to the East of Scotland Bottlenose Dolphin population. University of Aberdeen and Moray Firth Partnership. pp. 68.

Day, R. (2008) Local environments and older people's health: Dimensions from a comparative qualitative study in Scotland. *Health & Place,* **14,** 299–312.

De Deyn, G.B., Quirk, H., Yi, Z., Oakley, S., Ostle, N.J. & Bardgett, R.D. (2009) Vegetation composition promotes carbon and nitrogen storage in model grassland communities of contrasting soil fertility. *Journal of Ecology,* **97,** 864–875.

de la Vega-Leinert, A.C. & Nicholls, R.J. (2008) Potential implications of sea-level rise for Great Britain. *Journal of Coastal Research,* **24,** 342–357.

DECC (Department of Energy and Climate Change) (2009) UK Greenhouse Gas Inventory, 1990 to 2007: Annual Report for submission under the Framework Convention on Climate Change. Department of Energy and Climate Change, London. pp. 250.

Dennis, P., Young, M.R., Howard, C.L. & Gordon, I.J. (1997) The response of epigeal beetles (Col: Carabidae, Staphylinidae) to varied grazing regimes on upland *Nardus stricta* grasslands. *Journal of Applied Ecology,* **34,** 433–443.

Dee Catchment Partnership (2007) Dee Catchment Management Plan. Dee Catchment Partnership, Aberdeen.

Department for Business (2007) BIS: Department for Business Innovation & Skills. [online] Available at: <http://www.bis.gov.uk/>

Defra (Department for Environment, Food and Rural Affairs) (2007) Securing a healthy natural environment: an action plan for embedding an ecosystems approach. Department for Environment, Food and Rural Affairs, London. [online] Available at: <http://www.defra.gov.uk/wildlife-countryside/natres/eco-actionp.htm> [Accessed 28.05.11].

Defra (Department for Environment, Food and Rural Affairs) (2010) UK Marine Policy Statement: Habitats Regulations Assessment. Department for Environment, Food and Rural Affairs, London. pp. 53. [online] Available at: <http://archive.defra.gov.uk/corporate/consult/marine-policy/100721-marine-policy-hra-report.pdf> [Accessed 28.05.11].

Department of Agriculture and Fisheries for Scotland (1962) Agricultural Statistics. 1959 and 1960. Scotland. Department of Agriculture and Fisheries for Scotland, Edinburgh.

Department of Agriculture and Fisheries for Scotland (1971) Agricultural Statistics. 1970. Scotland. Department of Agriculture and Fisheries for Scotland, Edinburgh.

Diaz, S., Lavorel, S., de Bello, F., Quetier, F., Grigulis, K. & Robson, M. (2007) Incorporating plant functional diversity effects in ecosystem service assessments. *Proceedings of the National Academy of Sciences of the United States of America,* **104,** 20684–20689.

Dodd, J., Baxter, L. & Hughes, D.J. (2009) Mapping *Serpula vermicularis* (Polychaeta: Serpulidae) aggregations in Loch Teacuis, western Scotland, a new record. *Marine Biology Research,* **5,** 200–205.

Domburg, P., Edwards, A.C., Sinclair, A.H., Wright, G.G. & Ferrier, R.C. (1998) Changes in fertilizer and manurial practices during 1960–1990: Implications for N and P inputs to the Ythan catchment, N.E. Scotland. *Nutrient Cycling in Agroecosystems,* **52,** 19–29.

Donald, P.F. & Evans, A.D. (2006) Habitat connectivity and matrix restoration: the wider implications of agri-environment schemes. *Journal of Applied Ecology* **43,** 209–218.

Donaldson, J.C. (1974) Munro's Tables of the 3000 ft mountains of Scotland. The Scottish Mountaineering Trust, Edinburgh. pp. 125.

Doughty, C.R., Boon, P.J. & Maitland, P.S. (2002) The state of Scotland's fresh waters. The State of Scotland's Environment and Natural Heritage. (eds M.B. Usher, E.C. Mackey, & J.A. Curran). The Stationery Office, Edinburgh. pp. 117–144.

Downie, A.J. & Baxter, J.M. (2004) The Water Framework Directive: driving the development of a co-ordinated marine monitoring strategy for Scotland. *Aquatic Conservation-Marine and Freshwater Ecosystems,* **14,** S69–S79.

DTZ (2007) Scottish Primary Food and Drink Produce Processed in Scotland. DTZ, Edinburgh. pp. 87.

DTZ Pieda Consulting (2002) The Economic Impact of the Production of Scotch Whisky, Gin and Vodka in Scotland. A Report for the Scotch Whisky Association, Edinburgh.

Dyke, A.J. & Newton, A.C. (1999) Commercial harvesting of wild mushrooms in Scottish forests: is it sustainable? *Scottish Forestry, 53*, 77–85.

EASAC (European Academies Science Advisory Council) (2009) Ecosystem Services and Biodiversity in Europe. The Royal Society, London.

Edgar, P.J., Davies, I.M., Hursthouse, A.S. & Matthews, J.E. (1999) The biogeochemistry of polychlorinated biphenyls (PCBs) in the Clyde: Distribution and source evaluation. *Marine Pollution Bulletin, 38*, 486–496.

Edwards, A.C., Sinclair, A.H. & Domburg, P. (2003) Identification, designation and formulation of an action plan for a nitrate vulnerable zone: a case study of the Ythan catchment, NE Scotland. *European Journal of Agronomy, 20*, 165–172.

Edwards, D., Elliott, A., Hislop, M., Martin, S., Morris, J., O'Brien, L., Peace, A., Sarajevs, V., Serrand, M. & Valatin, G. (2009) A valuation of the economic and social contribution of forestry for people in Scotland. Forestry Commission Scotland, Edinburgh. pp. 190.

Edwards, M., Johns, D.G., Licandro, P., John, A.W.G. & Stevens, D.P. (2007) Ecological Status Report: results from the CPR survey 2005/2006. pp. SAHFOS Technical Report, 4: 1–8. Plymouth, U.K. ISSN 1744–0750.

Ellaway, A., Morris, G., Curtice, J., Robertson, C., Allardice, G. & Robertson, R. (2009) Associations between health and different types of environmental incivility: A Scotland-wide study. *Public Health, 123*, 708–713.

Emery, M., Martin, S. & Dyke, A. (2006) Wild harvests from Scottish woodlands: social, cultural and economic values of contemporary non-timber forest products. Forestry Commission, Edinburgh. pp. 40.

Ennos, R.A. & Easton, E.P. (1997) The genetic biodiversity of Scottish plants. Biodiversity in Scotland: Status, Trends and Initiatives. (eds L.V. Fleming, A.C. Newton, J.A. Vickery, & M.B. Usher). The Stationery Office, Edinburgh. pp. 135–146.

Environmental Resources Management Limited (2004) The role of the natural heritage in generating and supporting employment opportunities in Scotland. Scottish Natural Heritage, Edinburgh. pp. 74.

Esteban, G.F., Clarke, K.J., Olmo, J.L. & Finlay, B.J. (2006) Soil protozoa–An intensive study of population dynamics and community structure in an upland grassland. *Applied Soil Ecology, 33*, 137–151.

European Environment Agency (2004) High nature value farmland: characteristics, trends and policy challenges. Office for Official Publications of the European Communities, Luxembourg. pp. 32.

Evans, D.M., Redpath, S.M., Elston, D.A., Evans, S.A., Mitchell, R.J. & Dennis, P. (2006) To graze or not to graze? Sheep, voles, forestry and nature conservation in the British uplands. *Journal of Applied Ecology, 43*, 499–505.

Ferrier, R.C., Helliwell, R.C., Cosby, B.J., Jenkins, A. & Wright, R.F. (2001) Recovery from acidification of lochs in Galloway, south-west Scotland, UK: 1979–1998. *Hydrology and Earth System Sciences, 5*, 421–431.

Ferrier, R.C. & Jenkins, A. (2010) Handbook of Catchment Management. John Wiley & Sons Chichester. pp. 540.

Fisheries Research Services (2008) Statistical Bulletin: Scottish salmon and trout catches, 2007. Fisheries Series, No. Fis/2008/1. September 2008.

Fitter, A.H., Gilligan, C.A., Hollingworth, K., Kleczkowski, A., Twyman, R.M., Pitchford, J.W. & Programme, N.S.B. (2005) Biodiversity and ecosystem function in soil. *Functional Ecology, 19*, 369–377.

Foley, J.A., DeFries, R., Asner, G.P., Barford, C., Bonan, G., Carpenter, S.R., Chapin, F.S., Coe, M.T., Daily, G.C., Gibbs, H.K., Helkowski, J.H., Holloway, T., Howard, E.A., Kucharik, C.J., Monfreda, C., Patz, J.A., Prentice, I.C., Ramankutty, N. & Snyder, P.K. (2005) Global consequences of land use. *Science, 309*, 570–574.

Ford, J.S. & Myers, R.A. (2008) A global assessment of salmon aquaculture impacts on wild salmonids. *PLoS Biology 6*, 411–417.

Forestry Commission (1993) Forests and Water Guidelines. Forestry Commission, London.

Forestry Commission (2000) Sawmill Survey 2000. Report on the survey of sawmill consumption and production in Great Britain in 2000. Forestry Commission, London. pp. 28.

Forestry Commission (2003) National Inventory of Woodlands and Trees. Great Britain. Forestry Commission, Edinburgh.

Forestry Commission (2008) Forestry Statistics 2008. Forestry Commission, Edinburgh. pp. 159.

Forestry Commission (2009) Forestry Statistics 2009. Forestry Commission, Edinburgh.

Forestry Commission Scotland (2006) The Scottish Forestry Strategy Forestry Commission Scotland, Edinburgh. [online] Available at: <www.forestry.gov.uk/pdf/SFS2006fcfc101.pdf/$FILE/SFS2006fcfc101.pdf> [Accessed 28.05.11].

Forrester, R., Andrews, I., McInerny, C., Murray, R., McGown, B., Zonfrillo, B., Betts, M., D., J. & Grundy, D. (2007) Birds of Scotland. Scottish Ornithology Club, East Lothian.

Fowler, D., Flechard, C., Skiba, U., Coyle, M. & Cape, J.N. (1998) The atmospheric budget of oxidized nitrogen and its role in ozone formation and deposition. *New Phytologist, 139*, 11–23.

Fozzard, I.R., Doughty, C.R. & Clelland, B.E. (1994) Invertebrates. The Fresh Waters of Scotland. A National Resource of International Significance. (eds P.S. Maitland, P.J. Boon, & D.S. McLusky). John Wiley and Sons Ltd, London. pp. 171–190.

Free, J.B. (1993) Insect Pollination of Crops. Academic Press, San Diego, California.

Frumkin, H. (2001) Beyond toxicity–Human health and the natural environment. *American Journal of Preventive Medicine, 20*, 234–241.

Fuller, R.J., Humphreys, E.M., Wilson, J.D., Hoccom, D.G. & Calladine, J. (2010) Changes in the breeding wader populations of the machair of the Western Isles between 2000 and 2007. *Bird Study 57*, 121–124.

Fuller, R.M., Smith, G.M., Sanderson, J.M., Hill, R.A., Thomson, A.G., Cox, R., Brown, N.J., Clarke, R.T., Rothery, P. & Gerard, F.F. (2002) Land cover map 2000 Module 7 Final Report. Centre for Ecology and Hydrology, Huntingdon.

Galbraith, H., Murray, S., Duncan, K., Smith, R., Whitfield, D.P. & Thompson, D.B.A. (1993) Diet and Habitat Use of the Dotterel *Charadrius morinellus* in Scotland. *Ibis, 135*, 148–155.

Gallai, N., Salles, J.M., Settele, J. & Vaissiere, B.E. (2009) Economic valuation of the vulnerability of world agriculture confronted with pollinator decline. *Ecological Economics*, **68**, 810–821.

Gardiner, J.L. (1994) Sustainable Development for River Catchments. *Journal of the Institution of Water and Environmental Management*, **8**, 308–319.

GB Leisure Day Visits (2004) Great Britain Day Visits Survey 2002–2003. Main Report. TNS Travel & Tourism, Edinburgh. pp. 472.

George Street Research and Jones Economics (2004) Economic impact and development opportunities for outdoor and environment related recreation in the Highlands and Islands. A Report for the Highlands and Islands Enterprise.

Gibbens, J.C., Sharpe, C.E., Wilesmith, J.W., Mansley, L.M., Michalopoulou, E., Ryan, J.B.M. & Hudson, M. (2001) Descriptive epidemiology of the 2001 foot-and-mouth disease epidemic in Great Britain: the first five months. *The Veterinary Record*, **149**, 729–743.

Gibson, R. (2007) The Scottish Countryside: Its Changing Face, 1700–2000. John Donald, Edinburgh. pp. 196.

Gilbert, L. (2010) Altitudinal patterns of tick and host abundance: a potential role for climate change in regulating tick-borne diseases? *Oecologia*, **162**, 217–225.

Giles-Corti, B. & Donovan, R.J. (2002) Socioeconomic status differences in recreational physical activity levels and real and perceived access to a supportive physical environment. *Preventive Medicine*, **35**, 601–611.

Giles-Corti, B., Broomhall, M.H., Knuiman, M., Collins, C., Douglas, K., Ng, K., Lange, A. & Donovan, R.J. (2005) Increasing walking–How important is distance to, attractiveness, and size of public open space? *American Journal of Preventive Medicine*, **28**, 169–176.

Gill, A.B. (2005) Offshore renewable energy: ecological implications of generating electricity in the coastal zone. *Journal of Applied Ecology*, **42**, 605–615.

Gimingham, C.H. (1972) Ecology of Heathlands. Chapman and Hall, London. pp. 266.

Glasgow Caledonian University, Grid Economics & Cogentsi Research International Ltd. (2009) Technical Report: economic impact of recreational sea angling in Scotland. Scottish Government, Edinburgh.

Glasgow Caledonian University & Cogentsi Research International Ltd. (2004) The Economic Impact of Game and Coarse Angling in Scotland. Prepared for the Scottish Executive and Rural Affairs Department.

Godbold, J.A., Solan, M. & Killham, K. (2009) Consumer and resource diversity effects on marine macroalgal decomposition. *Oikos*, **118**, 77–86.

Golding, E.W. (1955) The generation of electicity by wind power. E & F N Spon Ltd., London.

Golding, E.W. (1961) Wind as a source of energy in Scotland: Natural Resources in Scotland. Scottish Council (Development and Industry), Symposium at the Royal Society of Edinburgh, 31 October to 2 November 1960. (eds T & A Constable). Edinburgh. pp. 468–477.

Gordon, J.E., Dvorak, I.J., Jonasson, C., Josefsson, M., Kocianova, M. & Thompson, D.B.A. (2002) Geo-ecology and management of sensitive montane landscapes. *Geografiska Annaler Series A-Physical Geography*, **84A**, 193–203.

Gordon, J.E., Brazier, V. & MacFayden, C.C.J. (2004) Reading the landscapes of Scotland: raising earth heritage awareness

and enjoyment. Natural and Cultural Landscapes–the Geological Foundation. (eds M. Parkes). Royal Irish Academy, Dublin. pp. 227–234.

Gordon, J.E. (2008) "Stone voices": geodiversity, geoparks and cultural landscapes in Scotland. Proceedings of the 7th European Geoparks Conference, Ullapool, September 2007.

Goulson, D., Hanley, M.E., Darvill, B., Ellis, J.S. & Knight, M.E. (2005) Causes of rarity in bumblebees. *Biological Conservation*, **122**, 1–8.

Goulson, D., Hanley, M.E., Darvill, B.E. & Ellis, J.S. (2006) Biotope associations and the decline of bumblebees (*Bombus* spp). *Journal of Insect Conservation*, **10**, 95–103.

Grant, W. (1997) The Common Agricultural Policy. MacMillan Press Ltd, Basingstoke. pp. 244.

Grayston, S.J., Griffith, G.S., Mawdsley, J.L., Campbell, C.D. & Bardgett, R.D. (2001) Accounting for variability in soil microbial communities of temperate upland grassland ecosystems. *Soil Biology & Biochemistry*, **33**, 533–551.

Grayston, S.J., Campbell, C.D., Bardgett, R.D., Mawdsley, J.L., Clegg, C.D., Ritz, K., Griffiths, B.S., Rodwell, J.S., Edwards, S.J., Davies, W.J., Elston, D.J. & Millard, P. (2004) Assessing shifts in microbial community structure across a range of grasslands of differing management intensity using CLPP, PLFA and community DNA techniques. *Applied Soil Ecology*, **25**, 63–84.

Green, R.E. & Stowe, T.J. (1993) The Decline of the Corncrake *Crex Crex* in Britain and Ireland in Relation to Habitat Change. *Journal of Applied Ecology*, **30**, 689–695.

Green, R.E. (1996) Factors affecting the population density of the corncrake *Crex crex* in Britain and Ireland. *Journal of Applied Ecology*, **33**, 237–248.

Green, R.E., Collingham, Y.C., Willis, S.G., Gregory, R.D., Smith, K.W. & Huntley, B. (2008) Performance of climate envelope models in retrodicting recent changes in bird population size from observed climatic change. *Biology Letters*, **4**, 599–602.

Green, S. & Ray, D. (2009) Potential impacts of drought and disease on forestry in Scotland. Forestry Commission, Edinburgh.

greenspace scotland (2009) State of Scotland's Greenspace 2009. greenspace scotland, Stirling. pp. 20.

Greenstreet, S.P.R., Spence, F.E. & McMillan, J.A. (1999a) Fishing effects in northeast Atlantic shelf seas: patterns in fishing effort, diversity and community structure II. Trends in fishing effort in the North Sea by UK registered vessel landings in Scotland. *Fisheries Research*, **40**, 107–124.

Greenstreet, S.P.R., Spence, F.E. & McMillan, J.A. (1999b) Fishing effects in northeast Atlantic shelf seas: patterns in fishing effort, diversity and community structure V. Changes in structure of the North Sea groundfish species assemblage between 1925 and 1996. *Fisheries Research*, **40**, 153–183.

Greenstreet, S.P.R., Holland, G.J., Fraser, T.W.K. & Allen, V.J. (2009) Modelling demersal fishing effort based on landings and days absence from port, to generate indicators of "activity". *ICES Journal of Marine Science*, **66**, 886–901.

Gregory, R.D. & Baillie, S.R. (1998) Large-scale habitat use of some declining British birds. *Journal of Applied Ecology*, **35**, 785–799.

Gregory, S.C. & Redfern, D.B. (1998) Diseases and disorders of forest trees. The Stationery Office, London.

Grieve, I.C., Davidson, D.A. & Gordon, J.E. (1995) Nature, Extent and Severity of Soil-Erosion in Upland Scotland. *Land Degradation and Rehabilitation,* **6**, 41–55.

Griffiths, R.I., Bailey, M.J., McNamara, N.P. & Whiteley, A.S. (2006) The functions and components of the Sourhope soil microbiota. *Applied Soil Ecology,* **33**, 114–126.

Haberl, H., Wackernagel, M., Krausmann, F., Erb, K.H. & Monfreda, C. (2004) Ecological footprints and human appropriation of net primary production: a comparison. *Land Use Policy,* **21**, 279–288.

Haberl, H. (2006) The global socioeconomic energetic metabolism as a sustainability problem. *Energy,* **31**, 87–99.

Habron, D. (1999) Defining the characteristic landscape attributes of wild land in Scotland. Landscape Character: Perspectives on Management and Change. (eds M.B. Usher). The Stationery Office, Edinburgh. pp. 34–40.

Hall-Spencer, J., White, N., Gillespie, E., Gillham, K. & Foggo, A. (2006) Impact of fish farms on maerl beds in strongly tidal areas. *Marine Ecology-Progress Series,* **326**, 1–9.

Hall-Spencer, J.M. & Moore, P.G. (2000a) *Limaria hians* (Mollusca: Limacea): a neglected reef-forming keystone species. *Aquatic Conservation-Marine and Freshwater Ecosystems,* **10**, 267–277.

Hall-Spencer, J.M. & Moore, P.G. (2000b) Scallop dredging has profound, long-term impacts on maerl habitats. *ICES Journal of Marine Science,* **57**, 1407–1415.

Hall, I.R., Hydes, D.J., Statham, P.J. & Overnell, J. (1996) Dissolved and particulate trace metals in a Scottish sea loch: An example of a pristine environment? *Marine Pollution Bulletin,* **32**, 846–854.

Hallanaro, E-L. & Söderman, G. (2002) Nature in Scotland and the Nordic Countrie: Similarities and Differences. The State of Scotland's Environment and Natural Heritage. (eds M.B. Usher, E.C. Mackey, & J. Curran). The Stationery Office, Edinburgh. pp. 23–30.

Hancock, M.H. & Wilson, J. (2002) Winter habitat associations of grey partridge (*Perdix perdix*) in Scotland. *Aspects of Applied Biology,* **67**, 171–178.

Hancock, M.H. & Wilson, J.D. (2003) Winter habitat associations of seed-eating passerines on Scottish farmland. *Bird Study,* **50**, 116–130.

Hansen, L.P. & Jacobsen, J.A. (2003) Origin and migration of wild and escaped farmed Atlantic salmon, *Salmo salar* L., in oceanic areas north of the Faroe Islands. *ICES Journal of Marine Science,* **60**, 110–119.

Hansmann, R., Hug, S.-M. & Seeland, K. (2007) Restoration and stress relief through physical activities in forests and parks. *Urban Forestry & Urban Greening,* **6**, 213–225.

Hansom, J.D. & McGlashan, D.J. (2004) Scotland's coast: Understanding past and present processes for sustainable management. *Scottish Geographical Journal,* **120**, 99–116.

Hansom, J.D. (2010) Coastal steepening around the coast of Scotland: the implication of sea level changes. Scottish Natural Heritage Commissioned Report Series, Edinburgh.

Hanson, J.D. & Angus, S. (2001) Tir a' Mhachair (Land of the Machair): sediment supply and climate change scenarios for the future of the Outer Hebrides machair. Earth Science and the Natural Heritage. (eds J.E. Gordon, & K.F. Lees). The Stationery Office, Edinburgh. pp. 68–81.

Hartley, S.E., Bell, A.A. & Taggart, J.B. (1995) DNA fingerprinting in Arctic charr, *Salvelinus alpinus* (L.): preliminary analyses with multi- and single locus minisatellite probes. *Nordic Journal of Freshwater Research,* **71**, 265–274.

Harvey, G.R. (1949) A Book of Scotland. Adam and Charles Black, London. pp. 216.

Haswell-Smith, H. (1996) Scotland's Islands. Canongate, Edinburgh.

Hillier, J., Hawes, C., Squire, G., Hilton, A., Wale, S. & Smith, P. (2009) The carbon footprints of food crop production. *International Journal of Agricultural Sustainability,* **7**, 107–118.

Hiscock, K. (1992) The Ecology and Conservation of Sublittoral Hard Substratum Ecosystems in Scotland. *Proceedings of the Royal Society of Edinburgh Section B-Biological Sciences,* **100**, 95–112.

Hitchings, R. (2010) Seasonal climate change and the indoor city worker. *Transactions of the Institute of British Geographers,* **35**, 282–298.

HM Revenue and Customs (2010) UK Regional Trade in Goods Statistics. [online] Available at: <https://www.uktradeinfo.com/index.cfm?task=td_regstats&hasFlashPlayer=true> [Accessed 28.05.11].

Holbrook, J. & Hall, J. (2002) Non-native species in Scotland. The State of Scotland's Environment and Natural Heritage. (eds M.B. Usher, E.C. Mackey, & J.A. Curran). The Stationery Office, Edinburgh. pp. 83–87.

Holl, K. & Smith, M. (2007) Scottish upland forests: History lessons for the future. *Forest Ecology and Management,* **249**, 45–53.

Hughes, D. & Nickell, T. (2009) Recovering Scotland's Marine Environment. Dinstaffnage Marine Laboratory, Oban. pp. 68.

Hughes, R. & Buchan, N. (1999) The Landscape Character Assessment of Scotland. Landscape Character: Perspectives on Management and Change. (eds M.B. Usher). The Stationery Office, Edinburgh. pp. 1–12.

Hughes, R. & Macdonald, P. (1999) The landscape character of Scotland's coasts. Scotland's Living Coastline. (eds J.M. Baxter, K. Duncan, S. Atkins, & G. Lees). The Stationery Office, London. pp. 3–14.

Humphrey, J., Quine, C. & Watts, K. (2006) The influence of forest and woodland management on biodiversity in Scotland: recent findings and future prospects. Farming, Forestry and The Natural Heritage. (eds R. Davison, & C.A. Galbraith). TSO Scotland, Edinburgh. pp. 59–75.

Humphrey, J.W. & Patterson, G.S. (2000) Effects of late summer cattle grazing on the diversity of riparian pasture vegetation in an upland conifer forest. *Journal of Applied Ecology,* **37**, 986–996.

Humphrey, J.W., Ferris, R. & Quine, C.P. (2003) Biodiversity in Britain's Planted Forests: Results from the Forestry Commission's Biodiversity Assessment Project. Forestry Commission, Edinburgh.

Humphrey, J.W. (2005) Benefits to biodiversity from developing old-growth conditions in British upland spruce plantations: a review and recommendations. *Forestry,* **78**, 33–53.

Humphrey, J.W. (2006) Ecology and management of native pinewoods: overview of special issue. *Forestry* **79**, 245–247.

Hunt, I.V. (1973) The grass crop. The Organic Resources of Scotland: their nature and evaluation. (eds J. Tivy). Oliver & Boyd, Edinburgh. pp. 122–140.

Huntley, B., Green, R.E., Collingham, Y.C. & Willis, S.G. (2007) A climatic atlas of European breeding birds. Durham University, The RSPB and Lynx Edicions, Barcelona. pp. 521.

Inglis, I.R., Isaacson, A.J., Smith, G.C., Haynes, P.J. & Thearle, R.J.P. (1997) The effect on the woodpigeon (*Columba palumbus*) of the introduction of oilseed rape into Britain. *Agriculture Ecosystems & Environment,* **61**, 113–121.

Irvine, L., Kleczkowski, A., Lane, A.M.J., Pitchford, J.W., Caffrey, D. & Chamberlain, P.M. (2006) An integrated data resource for modelling the soil ecosystem. *Applied Soil Ecology,* **33**, 208–219.

Jackson, J., Li, Y., Passant, N., Thomas, J., Thistlethwaite, G., Thomson, A. & Cardenas, L. (2008) Greenhouse Gas Inventories for England, Scotland, Wales and Northern Ireland; 1990–2006. Report to the Department for Environment, Food and Rural Affairs, The Scottish Government, The Welsh Assembly Government and The Northern Ireland Department of Envrionment. pp. 43.

Jackson, J., Li, Y., Murrells, T., Passant, N., Sneddon, S., Thomas, J., Thistlethwaite, G., Dyson, K. & Cardenas, L. (2009) Greenhouse Gas Inventories for England, Scotland, Wales and Northern Ireland: 1990–2007. Report to the Department for Environment, Food and Rural Affairs, The Scottish Government, The Welsh Assembly Government and The Northern Ireland Department of Envrionment. pp. 76.

Jacobs (2004) An economic assessment of the costs and benefits of Natura 2000 sites in Scotland. Scottish Executive, Environment Group Research Report 2004/05, Edinburgh.

Janvier, C., Villeneuve, F., Alabouvette, C., Edel-Hermann, V., Mateille, T. & Steinberg, C. (2007) Soil health through soil disease suppression: Which strategy from descriptors to indicators? *Soil Biology & Biochemistry,* **39**, 1–23.

Jenny, H. (1941) Factors of Soil Formation. McGraw Hill, New York.

Johnson, F.G. (1994) Hydro-electric generation. The Fresh Waters of Scotland. A National Resource of International Significance. (eds P.S. Maitland, P.J. Boon, & D.S. McLusky). John Wiley and Sons, London. pp. 297–316.

Joint Nature Conservation Council (2011) Joint Nature Conservation Council. [online] Available at: <http://jncc.defra.gov.uk/> [Accessed 24.01.11].

Jones, A.T., Gray, H. & Ray, D. (2002) Strategic application of modelling forest potential: calculating local targets for native woodland habitat action plans in Scotland. *Scottish Forestry,* **56**, 81–89.

Jones, S.K., Rees, R.M., Skiba, U.M. & Ball, B.C. (2005) Greenhouse gas emissions from a managed grassland. *Global and Planetary Change,* **47**, 201–211.

Kamenos, N.A., Moore, P.G. & Hall-Spencer, J.M. (2004a) Nursery-area function of maerl grounds for juvenile queen scallops *Aequipecten opercularis* and other invertebrates. *Marine Ecology-Progress Series* **274**, 183–189.

Kamenos, N.A., Moore, P.G. & Hall-Spencer, J.M. (2004b) Small-scale distribution of juvenile gadoids in shallow inshore waters; what role does maerl play? *ICES Journal of Marine Science,* **61**, 422–429.

Kaplan, S. & Kaplan, P. (1989) The visual environment: public participation in design and planning. *Journal of Social Issues,* **45**, 59–86.

Keith, S.E., Michaud, D.S. & Bly, S.H.R. (2008) A proposal for evaluating the potential health effects of wind turbine noise for projects under the Canadian Environmental Assessment Act. *Journal of Low Frequency Noise Vibration and Active Control,* **27**, 253–265.

Kerr, A. (2000) Managing the risk of climate change in Scotland. *Foresight and Precaution,* **1 and 2**, 545–550.

Kibblewhite, M.G., Ritz, K. & Swift, M.J. (2008) Soil health in agricultural systems. *Philosophical Transactions of the Royal Society B-Biological Sciences,* **363**, 685–701.

Kiemer, M.C.B., Carey, P.D., Palmer, S.C.F. & Roy, D.B. (1998) The biogeographical zones and biodiversity of the coastal waters of Scotland. Scottish Natural Heritage, Edinburgh.

Kocher-Marbaeuf, E. (2008) On the "tracks", "trails" and "paths" of John Muir. *Annales De Bretagne Et Des Pays De L Ouest,* **115**, 111–126.

Krsek, M. & Welllington, E.M.H. (2006) Studies of microbiol community structure and function below ground in a managed upland grassland site at Sourhope Research Station. *Applied Soil Ecology,* **33**, 127–136.

Kuo, F.E. & Sullivan, W.C. (2001) Aggression and violence in the inner city: Effects of environment via mental fatigue. *Environment and Behaviour,* **33**, 543–571.

Lake, I.R., Lovett, A.A., Bateman, I.J. & Day, B.H. (2000) Improving land compensation procedures via GIS and hedonic pricing. *Environment and Planning C: Government and Policy* ,**18**, 681–696.

Leach, G. (1976) Energy and food production. IPC Science and Technology Press Ltd, Guildford. pp. 137.

Leake, J.R., Ostle, N.J., Rangel-Castro, J.I. & Johnson, D. (2006) Carbon fluxes from plants through soil organisms determined by field (CO_2)-C-13 pulse-labelling in an upland grassland. *Applied Soil Ecology,* **33**, 152–175.

Lennon, J.J., Greenwood, J.J.D. & Turner, J.R.G. (2000) Bird diversity and environmental gradients in Britain: a test of the species-energy hypothesis. *Journal of Animal Ecology,* **69**, 581–598.

Lloyd, M.G. & McCarthy, J. (2000) The Scottish parliament, regulation and land use planning. *European Planning Studies,* **8**, 251–256.

Lloyd, M.G. & Peel, D. (2007) Shaping and designing model policies for land use planning. *Land Use Policy,* **24**, 154–164.

Loreau, M., Mouquet, N. & Holt, R.D. (2003) Meta-ecosystems: a theoretical framework for a spatial ecosystem ecology. *Ecology Letters,* **6**, 673–679.

Lovegrove, R. (2007) Silent Fields. Oxford University Press, Oxford. pp. 404.

Lovell, S.T. & Johnston, D.M. (2009) Designing Landscapes for Performance Based on Emerging Principles in Landscape Ecology. *Ecology and Society,* **14**.

Lucas, C.E., Rae, B.B. & Thomas, H.J. (1961) Scottish Inshore Fishery Resources. Natural Resources in Scotland. Scottish Council (Development and Industry), Symposium at the Royal Society of Edinburgh, 31 October to 2 November 1960. (eds T & A Constable Ltd.). Edinburgh. pp. 169–180.

Lyle, A.A. & Smith, I.R. (1994) Standing Waters. The Fresh Waters of Scotland. A National Resource of International Significance. (eds P.S. Maitland, P.J. Boon, & D.S. McLusky). John Wiley and Sons, London. pp. 35–50.

Macdonald, A.M., Matthews, K.B., Paterson, E. & Aspinall, R.J. (1994) The Impact of Climate-Change on the Soil-Moisture Regime of Scottish Mineral Soils. *Environmental Pollution,* **83**, 245–250.

MacKenzie Committee (1962) Electricity in Scotland. Report on the Generation and Distribution of Electricity in Scotland. Scottish Development Department, HMSO, Edinburgh.

Mackey, E.C. (1995) The Natural Heritage of Scotland: an overview. Scottish Natural Heritage, Edinburgh.

Mackey, E.C., Shewry, M.C. & Tudor, G.J. (1998) Land Cover Change: Scotland from the 1940s to the 1980s. The Stationery Office, Edinburgh.

Mackey, E.C., Shaw, P., Holbrook, J., Shewry, M.C., Saunders, G., Hall, J. & Ellis, N.E. (2001) Natural Heritage Trends: Scotland 2001. Scottish Natural Heritage, Perth.

Mackey, E.C. (2002) Scotland in a European context: environmental and natural heritage trends. The State of Scotland's Environment and Natural Heritage. (eds M.B. Usher, E.C. Mackey, & J.A. Curran). The Stationery Office, Edinburgh. pp. 5–22.

Mackey, E.C. & Mudge, G. (2010) Scotland's Wildlife: An assessment of biodiversity in 2010. Scottish Natural Heritage, Inverness. pp. 161.

MacLeod, C.D., Bannon, S.M., Pierce, G.J., Schweder, C., Learmonth, J.A., Herman, J.S. & Reid, R.J. (2005) Climate change and the cetacean community of north-west Scotland. *Biological Conservation,* **124**, 477–483.

MacLeod, M., Moran, D., Eory, V., Rees, R.M., Barnes, A., Topp, C.F.E., Ball, B., Hoad, S., Wall, E., McVittie, A., Pajot, G., Matthews, R., Smith, P. & Moxey, A. (2010) Developing greenhouse gas marginal abatement cost curves for agricultural emissions from crops and soils in the UK. *Agricultural Systems,* **103**, 198–209.

MacMillan, D., Hanley, N. & Daw, M. (2004) Costs and benefits of wild goose conservation in Scotland. *Biological Conservation,* **119**, 475–485.

Macmillan, D.C. (1993) Commercial Forests in Scotland–an Economic Appraisal of Replanting. *Journal of Agricultural Economics,* **44**, 51–66.

Maitland, P.S. (1994) Fish. The Fresh Waters of Scotland. A National Resource of International Significance. (eds P.S. Maitland, P.J. Boon, & D.S. McLusky). John Wiley and Sons, London. pp. 191–208.

Manley, G. (1952) Climate and the British Scene. Collins, London.

Marchant, J.H., Hudson, R., Carter, S.P. & Whittington, P. (1990) Population trends in British breeding birds. British Trust for Ornithology, Tring. pp. 300.

Marriott, C.A., Hood, K., Fisher, J.M. & Pakeman, R.J. (2009) Long-term impacts of extensive grazing and abandonment on the species composition, richness, diversity and productivity of agricultural grassland. *Agriculture Ecosystems & Environment,* **134**, 190–200.

Marsden, M.W., Smith, M.R. & Sargent, R.J. (1997) Trophic status of rivers in the Forth catchment, Scotland. *Aquatic Conservation-Marine and Freshwater Ecosystems,* **7**, 211–221.

Marshall, S. (2003) The incidence of sea lice infestations on wild sea trout compared to farmed salmon. *Bulletin of the European Association of Fish Pathologists,* **23**, 72–79.

Mason, W.L., Hampson, A. & Edwards, C. (2004) *Managing the Pinewoods of Scotland.* Forestry Commission, Edinburgh.

Masselink, G. & Russell, P.A. (2008) Coastal erosion and coastal geomorphology. [online] Available at: <http://www.mccip.org.uk/arc/2007/erosion.htm> [Accessed 28.05.11].

Mather, A.S., Ritchie, W. & Smith, J.S. (1975) Beaches of northern Inner Hebrides. Aberdeen University.

Mather, A.S. & Gunson, A.R. (1995) A review of biogeographical zones in Scotland. Department of Geography, University of Aberdeen.

Matson, P.A., Parton, W.J., Power, A.G. & Swift, M.J. (1997) Agricultural intensification and ecosysytem properties. *Science,* **277**, 504–509.

Matthews, J.B.L., Gage, J.D. & Raffaelli, D. (1997) Marine Biodiversity. Biodiversity in Scotland: Status, Trends and Initiatives. (eds L.V. Fleming, A.C. Newton, J.A. Vickery, & M.B. Usher). The Stationery Office, Edinburgh. pp. 63–76.

McCrone, D., Morris, A. & Kiely, R. (1995) Scotland–the Brand: the making of Scottish Heritage. Edinburgh University Press, Edinburgh.

McIntosh, B. (2006) Native pinewoods in Scotland: perspectives on policy and management. *Forestry,* **79**, 303–307.

McVean, D.N. & Lockie, J.D. (1969) Ecology and Land Use in Upland Scotland. Edinburgh University Press, Edinburgh. pp. 146.

Meikle, H.W. (1947) Scotland. Thomas Nelson and Sons Ltd, Edinburgh. pp. 281.

Miles, J., Tudor, G., Easton, C. & Mackey, E.C. (1997) Habitat diversity in Scotland. Biodiversity in Scotland: Status, Trends and Initiatives. (eds L.V. Fleming, A.C. Newton, J.A. Vickery, & M.B. Usher). The Stationery Office, Edinburgh. pp. 43–56.

Miller, D.R., Schwarz, G., Sutherland, L-A., Morrice, J., Aspinall, R.J., Barnes, A., Blackstock, K., Buchan, K., Donnelly, D., Hawes, C., McCrum, G., McKenzie, B., Matthews, K.B., Miller, D., Renwick, A., Smith, M., Squire, G. & Toma, L. (2009) Changing land use in rural Scotland–drivers and decision-makers. Scottish Government, Edinburgh. pp. 109.

Milliken, W. & Bridgewater, S. (2006) Flora Celtica. Birlinn Limited, Edinburgh. pp. 328.

Milne, J.A. & Hartley, S.E. (2001) Upland plant communities–sensitivity to change. *Catena,* **42**, 333–343.

Mitchell, P.I., Newton, S.F., Ratcliffe, N. & Dunn, T.E. (2004) Seabird populations of Britain and Ireland. T & AD Poyser, London.

Mitchell, R. & Popham, F. (2007) Greenspace, urbanity and health: relationships in England. *Journal of Epidemiology and Community Health,* **61**, 681–683.

Mitchell, R., Gibbs, J., Tunstall, H., Platt, S. & Dorling, D. (2009) Factors which nurture geographical resilience in Britain: a mixed methods study. *Journal of Epidemiology and Community Health,* **63**, 18–23.

MLURI (Macaulay Land Use Reserach Institute) (1993) The Land Cover of Scotland 1988. Final Report. Macaulay Land Use Research Institute, Aberdeen.

MLURI (Macaulay Land Use Reserach Institute), SAC (Scottish Agricultural College) & University of Aberdeen (2009) Project 2: Realising the potential contributions of Scotland's rural land to delivering sustainable economic growth. Scottish Government Social Research, Edinburgh.

Monteith, D.T. (2003) United Kngdom Acid Waters Monitoring Network 15 Year Report. Report to the Department for Environment, Food and Rural Affairs (Contract EPG 1/3/170). Defra, London.

Montieth, D.T. & Evans, C.D. (2000) UK Acid Waters Monitoring Network: 10 year report. ENSIS, London.

Moore, C.G., Bates, C.R., Mair, J.M., Saunders, G.R., Harries, D.B. & Lyndon, A.R. (2009) Mapping serpulid worms reefs (Polychaeta: Serpulidae) for conservation management.

Aquatic Conservation: Marine and Freshwater Ecosystems, 19, 226–236.

Moran, D., Oglethorpe, D., McVittie, A., MacLeod, M. & Aresti, M.L. (2004) Dynamics of Water Use in Scotland. SAC, Edinburgh. pp. 69.

Moss, R., Oswald, J. & Baines, D. (2001) Climate change and breeding success: decline of the capercaillie in Scotland. *Journal of Animal Ecology, 70*, 47–61.

Mudge, G.P. & Christie, M. (2009) Applying an ecosystem approach in Scotland: A framework for action. Scottish Natural Heritage, Edinburgh. pp. 28. [online] Available at: <http://www.snh.gov.uk/docs/C210222.pdf> [Accessed 18.02.11].

Murray, P.J., Cook, R., Currie, A.F., Dawson, L.A., Gange, A.C., Grayston, S.J. & Treonis, A.M. (2006) Interactions between fertilizer addtion, plants and the soil environment: implications for soil faunal structure and diversity. *Applied Soil Ecology, 33*, 199–207.

Nassauer, J.I. & Opdam, P. (2008) Design in science: extending the landscape ecology paradigm. *Landscape Ecology, 23*, 633–644.

Navarro, N., Leakey, R.J.G. & Black, K.D. (2008) Effect of salmon cage aquaculture on the pelagic environment of temperate coastal waters: seasonal changes in nutrients and microbial community. *Marine Ecology-Progress Series, 361*, 47–58.

Nethersole-Thompson, D. (1966) The Snow Bunting. Oliver & Boyd, Edinburgh.

Newson, M.D. (2002) Geomorphological concepts and tools for sustainable river ecosystem management. *Aquatic Conservation-Marine and Freshwater Ecosystems, 12*, 365–379.

Newton, A.C., Davy, L.M., Holden, E., Silverside, A., Watling, R. & Ward, S.D. (2003) Status, distribution and definition of mycologically important grasslands in Scotland. *Biological Conservation, 111*, 11–23.

Nisbet, T.R., Welch, D. & Doughty, R. (2002) The role of forest management in controlling diffuse pollution from the afforestation and clearfelling of two public water supply catchments in Argyll, West Scotland. *Forest Ecology and Management, 158*, 141–154.

North of Scotland Hydro-Electric Board (1944) Development Scheme, North of Scotland Hydro-Electric Board. Prepared, approved and confirmed as required under section 4 of the Hydro-Electric Development (Scotland) Act, 1943.

Norton, L.R., Murphy, J., Reynolds, B., Marks, S. & Mackey, E.C. (2009) Countryside Survey: Scotland Results from 2007. Centre for Ecology and Hydrology. [online] Available at: <http://www.countrysidesurvey.org.uk/outputs/scotland-results-2007> Accessed [28.05.11].

O'Brien, M., Tharme, A. & Jackson, D. (2002) Changes in breeding wader numbers on Scottish farmed land during the 1990s. *Scottish Birds, 23*, 10–21.

O'Brien, M., Green, R.E. & Wilson, J. (2006) Partial recovery of the population of Corncrake *Crex crex* in Britain. *Bird Study, 53*.

O'Connor, R.J. & Shrubb, M. (1986) Farming and Birds. Cambridge University Press, Cambridge. pp. 290.

O'Riordan, T. (2002) Governing for a sustainable Scotland. The State of Scotland's Environment and Natural Heritage. (eds M.B. Usher, E.C. Mackey, & J.A. Curran). The Stationery Office, Edinburgh. pp. 305–320.

O'Riordan, T. (2009) On the Politics of Sustainability of a Long Way Ahead EEAC. The Way Ahead in the Light of the Last Five Years. *Problemy Ekorozwoju, 4*, 155–159.

O'Herlihy & Co. Ltd (2006) Windfarm Construction: Economic Impact Appraisal. A Final Report to Scottish Enterprise. [online] Available at: http://www.scottish-enterprise.com/~/media/SE/Resources/Documents/Sectors/Energy/energy-renewables-reports/windfarm-construction-appraisal.ashx> [Accessed 28.05.11].

Opdam, P., Luque, S. & Jones, K.B. (2009) Changing landscapes to accommodate for climate change impacts: a call for landscape ecology. *Landscape Ecology, 24*, 715–721.

Orr, H.G., Wilby, R.L., Hedger, M.M. & Brown, I. (2008) Climate change in the uplands: a UK perspective on safeguarding regulatory ecosystem services. *Climate Research, 37*, 77–98.

Owen, N.W., Kent, M. & Dale, M.P. (2001) Spatial and temporal variability in seed dynamics of machair sand dune plant communities, the Outer Hebrides, Scotland. *Journal of Biogeography, 28*, 565–588.

Pakeman, R.J. & Marrs, R.H. (1996) Modelling the effects of climate change on the growth of bracken (*Pteridium aquilinum*) in Britain. *Journal of Applied Ecology, 33*, 561–575.

Palmer, M.A., Holmes, N.T.H. & Bell, S.L. (1994) Macrophytes. The Fresh Waters of Scotland. A National Resource of International Significance. (eds P.S. Maitland, P.J. Boon, & D.S. McLusky). John Wiley and Sons Ltd, London. pp. 147–169.

PAN (Planning Advice Note) (2008). Planning Advice Note 65: Planning and Open Space. [online] Available at: <http://www.scotland.gov.uk/Publications/2008/05/30100623/0> [Accessed 28.05.11].

Parkkari, J., Natri, A., Kannus, P., Manttari, A., Laukkanen, R., Haapasalo, H., Nenonen, A., Pasanen, M., Oja, P. & Vuori, I. (2000) A controlled trial of the health benefits of regular walking on a golf course. *American Journal of Medicine, 109*, 102–108.

Pearce-Higgins, J.W., Grant, M.C., Beale, C.M., Buchanan, G.M. & Sim, I.M.W. (2008) International importance and drivers of change of upland bird populations: Drivers of Environmental Change in Uplands. (eds A. Bonn, K. Hubacek, T. Allott, & J. Stewart). Routledge, Oxford. pp. 209–226.

Pearsall, W.H. (1950) Mountains and Moorlands. Collins, London. pp. 312.

Peel, D. & Lloyd, M.G. (2007) Neo-traditional planning. Towards a new ethos for land use planning? *Land Use Policy, 24*, 396–403.

Pejchar, L., Morgan, P.M., Caldwell, M.R., Palmer, C. & Daily, G.C. (2007) Evaluating the potential for conservation development: Biophysical, economic, and institutional perspectives. *Conservation Biology, 21*, 69–78.

Perkins, A.J., Maggs, H.E. & Wilson, J.D. (2008) Winter bird use of seed-rich habitats in agri-environment schemes. *Agriculture Ecosystems & Environment, 126*, 189–194.

Perring, F. (1970) The Flora of a Changing Britain. E. W. Classey Ltd and the Botanical Society of the British Isles. pp. 157.

Petchey, O.L. & Gaston, K.J. (2009) Effects on ecosystem resilience of biodiversity, extinctions, and the structure of regional species pools. *Theoretical Ecology, 2*, 177–187.

Pethick, J.S. (1999) Future sea-level changes in Scotland: options for coastal management. Scotland's Living Coastline. (eds J.M. Baxter, K. Duncan, S.M. Atkins, & R.G. Lees). The Stationery Office, Edinburgh. pp. 45–62.

Phoenix, G.K., Booth, R.E., Leake, J.R., Read, D.J., Grime, J.P. & Lee, J.A. (2004) Effects of enhanced nitrogen deposition and phosphorus limitation on nirtogen budgetrs of semi-natural grasslands. *Global Change Biology,* **9**, 1309–1321.

Piertney, S.B., MacColl, A.D.C., Bacon, P.J. & Dallas, J.F. (1998) Local genetic structure in red grouse (*Lagopus lagopus scoticus*): evidence from microsatellite DNA markers. *Molecular Ecology,* **7**, 1645–1654.

Piet, G.J., van Hal, R. & Greenstreet, S.P.R. (2009) Modelling the direct impact of bottom trawling on the North Sea fish community to derive estimates of fishing mortality for non-target fish species. *ICES Journal of Marine Science.* **66**, 1985–1998.

Post, E. & Pedersen, C. (2008) Opposing plant community responses to warming with and without herbivores. *Proceedings of the National Academy of Sciences of the United States of America,* **105**, 12353–12358.

Potts, S.G., Roberts, S.P.M., Dean, R., Marris, G., Brown, M., Jones, R. & Settele, J. (2010) Declines of managed honeybees and beekeepers in Europe. *Journal of Apicultural Research,* **49**, 15–22.

Poudyal, N.C., Hodges, D.G. & Merrett, C.D. (2009) A hedonic analysis of the demand for and benefits of urban recreation parks. *Land Use Policy,* **26**, 975–983.

Public and Corporate Economic Consultants (2006a) The contribution of deer management to the Scottish economy. Public and Corporate Economic Consultants, Cambridge.

Public and Corporate Economic Consultants (2006b) The Economic and Environmental Impact of Sporting Shooting. [online] Available at: <http://basc.dotadmin.com/media/pacecmainreport.pdf> [Accessed 28.05.11].

Puri, G. & Gordon, J.E. (1998) Soils and sustainability: a natural heritage perspective. *Contaminated Soil 1998,* **1** and **2**, 1–5.

Pyatt, D.G., Ray, D. & Fletcher, J. (2001) An ecological site classification for forestry in Great Britain. Bulletin 124. Forestry Commission, Edinburgh.

Pyefinch, K.A. (1961) Scottish Freshwater Fish. Natural Resources in Scotland. Scottish Council (Development and Industry), Symposium at the Royal Society of Edinburgh, 31 October to 2 November 1960. (eds T & A Constable Ltd, Edinburgh. pp. 163–168.

Quine, C.P. & Ray, D. (2010) Sustainable forestry: which species for which site for which world?: Species Management; Challenges and Solutions for the 21st Century. (eds J. Baxter, & C.A. Galbraith). TSO and SNH, Edinburgh.

Rackham, O. (1986) The History of the Countryside. J. M. Dent & Sons, London.

Ragg, J.M. (1973) Factors in soil formation. The Organic Resources of Scotland: their nature and evaluation. (ed J. Tivy). Oliver & Boyd, Edinburgh. pp. 38–50.

Rapport, D.J. (2007) Sustainability science: an ecohealth perspective. *Sustainability Science,* **2**, 77–84.

Ratcliffe, D. (1980) The Peregrine Falcon. T & AD Poyser, Waterhouses. pp. 416.

Raven, M.J. & Noble, D.G. (2006) The Breeding Bird Survey 2005. British Trust for Ornithology, Thetford.

Read, P. & Fernandes, T. (2003) Management of environmental impacts of marine aquaculture in Europe. *Aquaculture,* **226**, 139–163.

Rennie, A.F. & Hansom, J.D. (2011) Sea level trend reversal: Land uplift outpaced by sea level rise on Scotland's coast. *Geomorphology,* **125**, 193–202.

Rich, T.C.G. & Woodruff, E.R. (1996) Changes in the vascular plant floras of England and Scotland between 1930–1960 and 1987–1988: The BSBI monitoring scheme. *Biological Conservation,* **75**, 217–229.

Richards, L.A.R. & Phipps, P.J. (2007) Managing the impact of climate change on vulnerable areas: a case study of the Western Isles, UK. Landslides and Climate Change: Challenges and Solutions. Proceedings of the International Conference on Landslides and Climate Change, Ventnor, Isle of Wight, UK, 21–24 May 2007. (eds E. Mathie, R. McInnes, H. Fairbank & J. Jakeways). Taylor & Francis. pp. 435–442.

Ritchie, W. & Mather, A.S. (1984) The Beaches of Scotland. Countryside Commission for Scotland, Perth.

Ritz, K., McNicol, W., Nunan, N., Grayston, S., Millard, P., Atkinson, D., Gollottee, A., Habeshaw, D., Boag, B., Clegg, C.D., Griffiths, B.S., Wheatley, R.E., Glover, L.A., McCaig, A.E. & Prosser, J.I. (2004) Spatial structure in soil chemical and microbiological properties in an upland grassland. *Fems Microbiology Ecology,* **49**, 191–205.

Ritz, K., Black, H.I.J., Campbell, C.D., Harris, J.A. & Wood, C. (2009) Selecting biological indicators for monitoring soils: A framework for balancing scientific and technical opinion to assist policy development. *Ecological Indicators,* **9**, 1212–1221.

Robertson, P.A., Park, K.J. & Barton, A.F. (2001) Loss of heather *Calluna vulgaris* moorland in the Scottish uplands: the role of red grouse *Lagopus lagopus scoticus* management. *Wildlife Biology,* **7**, 11–16.

Robinson, R.A., Wilson, J.D. & Crick, H.Q.P. (2001) The importance of arable habitat for farmland birds in grassland landscapes. *Journal of Applied Ecology,* **38**, 1059–1069.

Rode, M., Thiel, E., Franko, U., Wenk, G. & Hesser, F. (2009) Impact of selected agricultural management options on the reduction of nitrogen loads in three representative meso scale catchments in Central Germany. *Science of the Total Environment,* **407**, 3459–3472.

Rodger, D., Stokes, J. & Ogilvie, J. (2006) Heritage Trees of Scotland. Forestry Commission Scotland and The Tree Council, Edinburgh. pp. 256.

Rodwell, J.S. (1992) British Plant Communities. Volume 3: Grasslands and montane communities. Cambridge University Press, Cambridge.

RPA and **Cambridge Econometrics** (2008) The Economic Impact of Scotland's Natural Environment. Scottish Natural Heritage, Edinburgh.

RSE (Royal Society of Edinburgh) (2008) Committee of Inquiry into the Future of Scotland's Hills and Islands. Royal Society of Edinburgh, Edinburgh. pp. 170.

RSK Era Ltd (2001) Quality of Natural Heritage Jobs. Scottish Natural Heritage, Edinburgh. pp. 74.

Rural and **Environment Research** and **Analysis Directorate** (1939–present) Agricultural Census (June). Series of Annual Census data. Scottish Government, Edinburgh.

Rural and **Environment Research** and **Analysis Directorate** (2008) Economic Report on Scottish Agriculture, 2008 Edition. Scottish Government, Edinburgh.

Rural and **Environment Research** and **Analysis Directorate** (2009a) Economic Report on Scottish Agriculture, 2009 Edition. Scottish Government, Edinburgh.

Rural and **Environment Research** and **Analysis Directorate** (2009b) Abstract of Scottish Agricultural Statistics 1982 to 2008. Scottish Government, Edinburgh. pp. 26.

Rural and **Environment Research** and **Analysis Directorate** (2009c) Scottish Agricultural Census Summary Sheets by Geographic Area: June 2008. Scottish Government, Edinburgh. pp. 34.

Rural and **Environment Research** and **Analysis Directorate** (2010) Economic Report on Scottish Agriculture, 2010 Edition. Scottish Government, Edinburgh.

SAC (Scottish Agricultural College) (2008) Farming's Retreat from the Hills. SAC, Edinburgh. pp. 56.

Sang, N. (2008) Informing common pool resource problems: A survey of preference for catchment management strategies amongst farmers and the general public in the Ythan river catchment. *Journal of Environmental Management,* **88**, 1161–1174.

Sayer, J.A. & Maginnis, S. (2007) Forests in Landscapes: Ecosystem Approaches to Sustainability. Earthscan Publications Ltd. pp. 278.

Schlaepfer, R. (2005) Ecosystem approach and Ecosystem Management as the fundaments of Forest Landscape Restoration strategies. EFI Proceedings No. 53, 2005. Forest Landscape Restoration in Central and Northern Europe. (eds. T. Veltheim & B. Pajari). European Forest Institute, Finland. pp. 69–82.

Scott, M. (1999) Biodiversity Action Plans: challenges for Scotland's coast. Scotland's Living Coastline. (eds J.M. Baxter, K. Duncan, S. Atkins, & G. Lees). The Stationery Office, London. pp. 190–199.

Scott, R. & Moore, P.G. (1996) The Status and Distribution of Maerl in Scotland with regard to the EC Habitats DIrective. Desk study prepared for Scottish Natural Heritage by University Marine Biological Station, Millport. pp. 55.

Scottish Biodiversity Forum (2003) Towards a strategy for Scotland's biodiversity: the resources and trends. Scottish Executive, Edinburgh.

Scottish Executive (2003) Statistical Bulletin, Fisheries Series, 2003. Scottish Salmon and Sea Trout Catches, Edinburgh.

Scottish Executive (2004) Scotland's Biodiversity: It's in your hands. A strategy for the conservation and enhancement of biodiversity in Scotland. Scottish Executive, Edinburgh.

Scottish Government (2007) Scottish Sea Fisheries Statistics 2006. Scottish Government, Edinburgh.

Scottish Government (2009a) Scottish Sea Fisheries Statistics 2008. Scottish Government, Edinburgh.

Scottish Government (2009b) The river basin management plan for the Solway Tweed river basin district 2009–2015. Scottish Government, Edinburgh.

Scottish Government (2009c) National Food and Drink Policy for Scotland. Scottish Government, Edinburgh. [online] Available at: <www.scotland.gov.uk/Topics/Business-Industry/Food-Industry/national-strategy> [Accessed 28.05.11].

Scottish Government (2009d) The river basin management plan for the Scotland river basin 2009–2015. Scottish Government, Edinburgh.

Scottish Government (2010) Scottish Vacant and Derelict Land Survey 2009. pp. 41. Scottish Government, Edinburgh.

Scottish Government (2011) High Level Summary of Statistics: Agriculture, Fisheries and Rural. Scottish Government, Edinburgh. [online] Available at: <www.scotland.gov.uk/Topics/Statistics/Browse/Agriculture-Fisheries> [Accessed 18.02.11].

Scottish Government Drinking Water Quality Division (2008) Drinking Water Quality in Scotland 2007. Scottish Government, Edinburgh.

SEERAD (Scottish Executive Environment and Rural Affairs Department) (2005) Economic Report on Scottish Agriculture, 2005 Edition, Edinburgh.

SEPA (Scottish Environment Protection Agency) (2006a) Scotland's Water Environment Review 2000–2006. SEPA, Edinburgh. pp. 93.

SEPA (Scottish Environment Protection Agency) (2006b) State of Scotland's Environment 2006. SEPA, Edinburgh. pp. 198.

Sharrock, J.T.R. (1976) The Atlas of Breeding Birds in Britain and Ireland. British Trust for Ornithology and Irish WIldbird Conservancy. T. & A.D. Poyser, Berhamsted.

Sheets, V.L. & Manzer, C.D. (1991) Affect, cognition and urban vegetation. *Environment and Behaviour,* **23**, 285–304.

Slee, B., Bergman, H., Brown, I., Huband, S., McCracken, D.I., Renwick, A., Sutherland, L-A., Thomson, S. & Reed, M. (2009) Realising the potential contributions of Scotland's rural land to delivering sustainable economic growth. Scottish Government, Edinburgh. pp. 104.

Smart, S.M., Firbank, L.G., Bunce, R.G.H. & Watkins, J.W. (2000) Quantifying changes in abundance of food plants for butterfly larvae and farmland birds. *Journal of Applied Ecology,* **37**, 398–414.

Smith, H.V., Caccio, S.M., Tait, A., McLaughlin, J. & Thompson, R.C.A. (2006) Tools for investigating the envrionental transmission of *Cryptosporidium* and *Giardia* infections in humans. *Trends in Parasitology* **22**, 160–167.

Smith, P., Smith, J., Flynn, H.C., Killham, K., Rangel-Castro, I., Foereid, B., Aitkenhead, M., Chapman, S.B., Towers, W., Bell, J., Lumsdon, D., Milne, R., Thomson, A., Simmons, I., Skiba, U., Reynolds, B., Evans, C., Frogbrook, Z., Bradley, I., Whitmore, A.P. & Falloon, P. (2007) ECOSSE–Estimating carbon in organic soils sequestration and emissions. Scottish Government, Edinburgh.

Smith, R.G. (2006) Timing of tillage is an important filter on the assembly of weed communities. *Weed Science,* **54**, 705–712.

Smout, T.C. (2003) People and Woods in Scotland: A History. Edinburgh University Press, Edinburgh. pp. 244.

SNH (Scottish Natural Heritage) (2000) The Natural Heritage of Scotland: an overview. Scottish Natural Heritage.

SNH (Scottish Natural Heritage) (2002) Natural Heritage Futures: Coasts and Seas. Scottish Natural Heritage, Edinburgh. pp. 40.

SNH (Scottish Natural Heritage) (2004a) Natural Heritage Trends: The Seas Around Scotland. Scottish Natural Heritage. pp. 158.

SNH (Scottish Natural Heritage) (2004b) Natural Heritage Trends. Fresh Waters: Atlantic salmon (*Salmo salar*). Scottish Natural Heritage, Edinburgh. pp. 3.

SNH (Scottish Natural Heritage) (2008) Renewables Trends in Scotland: Statistics & Analysis. Scottish Natural Heritage, Edinburgh.

SNH (Scottish Natural Heritage) (2009) Scottish Natural Heritage Biodiversity Indicator: Extent and Composition of Greenspace. Scottish Natural Heritage, Edinburgh.

SNIFFER (Scotland and Northern Ireland Forum for Environmental Research) (2006) Patterns of Climate Change across Scotland. Scotland and Northern Ireland Forum for Environmental Research, Edinburgh.

Soil Survey of Scotland (1984) Organization and Methods of the 1:250,000 Soil Survey of Scotland. The Macaulay Institute for Soil Research, Aberdeen. pp. 81.

Solandt, J-L. (2003) *Atrina fragilis* (Pennant 1777): a species of conservation concern. *British Wildlife,* **14**, 423–427.

Soulsby, C., Gibbins, C., Wade, A.J., Smart, R. & Helliwell, R. (2002) Water quality in the Scottish uplands: a hydrological perspective on catchment hydrochemistry. *Science of the Total Environment,* **294**, 73–94.

Squire, G.R., Hawes, C., Begg, G.S. & Young, M.W. (2009) Cumulative impact of GM herbicide-tolerant cropping on arable plants assessed through species-based and functional taxonomies. *Environmental Science and Pollution Research,* **16**, 85–94.

Steven, H.M. & Carlisle, A. (1959) The Native Pinewoods of Scotland. Oliver and Boyd, Edinburgh. pp. 368.

Stewart, W.A., Dallas, J.F., Piertney, S.B., Marshall, F., Lambin, X. & Telfer, S. (1999) Metapopulaiton genetic structure in the water vole, *Arvicola terrestris,* in NE Scotland. *Biological Journal of the Linnean Society,* **68**, 159–171.

Storkey, J. (2006) A functional group approach to the management of UK arable weeds to support biological diversity. *Weed Research,* **46**, 513–522.

Stowe, T.J., Newton, A.V., Green, R.E. & Mayes, E. (1993) The Decline of the Corncrake *Crex-Crex* in Britain and Ireland in Relation to Habitat. *Journal of Applied Ecology* **30**, 53–62.

Sturtevant, B.R., Fall, A., Kneeshaw, D.D., Simon, N.P.P., Papaik, M.J., Berninger, K., Doyon, F., Morgan, D.G. & Messier, C. (2007) A toolkit modeling approach for sustainable forest management planning: achieving balance between science and local needs. *Ecology and Society,* **12(2)**, 7. [online] Available at: <http://www.ecologyandsociety.org/vol12/iss2/art7/> [Accessed 28.05.11].

Stutter, M.I., Langan, S.J. & Demars, B.O.L. (2007) River sediments provide a link between catchment pressures and ecological status in a mixed land use Scottish River system. *Water Research,* **41**, 2803–2815.

Stutter, M.I., Langan, S.J. & Cooper, R.J. (2008) Spatial contributions of diffuse inputs and within-channel processes to the form of stream water phosphorus over storm events. *Journal of Hydrology,* **350**, 203–214.

Sulaiman, N., George, S. & Burke, M.D. (1991) Assessment of Sublethal Pollutant Impact on Flounders in an Industrialized Estuary Using Hepatic Biochemical Indexes. *Marine Ecology-Progress Series,* **68**, 207–212.

Sutcliffe, R. (2009) Recent changes in the distribution of some Scottish butterflies and the arrival of new species in Scotland. *The Glasgow Naturalist,* **25**, 5–12.

Sutherland, W.J., Armstrong-Brown, S., Armsworth, P.R., Brereton, T., Brickland, J., Campbell, C.D., Chamberlain, D.E., Cooke, A.I., Dulvy, N.K., Dusic, N.R., Fitton, M., Freckleton, R.P., Godfray, H.C.J., Grout, N., Harvey, H.J., Hedley, C., Hopkins, J.J., Kift, N.B., Kirby, J., Kunin, W.E., Macdonald, D.W., Marker, B., Naura, M., Neale, A.R., Oliver, T., Osborn, D., Pullin, A.S., Shardlow, M.E.A., Showler, D.A., Smith, P.L., Smithers, R.J., Solandt, J.L., Spencer, J., Spray, C.J., Thomas, C.D., Thompson, J., Webb, S.E., Yalden, D.W. & Watkinson, A.R. (2006) The identification of 100 ecological questions of high policy relevance in the UK. *Journal of Applied Ecology,* **43**, 617–627.

Symon, J.A. (1959) Scottish Farming: Past and Present. Oliver and Boyd, Edinburgh. pp. 475.

Syse, K.L. (2007) Gavin Maxwell–The lonely naturalist. *American Studies in Scandinavia,* **39**, 97–109.

Taylor, A.F., Kuo, F.E. & Sullivan, W.C. (2001) Coping with ADD: the surprising connection to green play settings. *Environment and Behaviour,* **33**, 54–77.

Telfer, T.C., Baird, D.J., McHenery, J.G., Stone, J., Sutherland, I. & Wislocki, P. (2006) Environmental effects of the anti-sea lice (Copepoda: Caligidae) therapeutant emamectin benzoate under commercial use conditions in the marine environment. *Aquaculture,* **260**, 163–180.

Tharme, A.P., Green, R.E., Baines, D., Bainbridge, I.P. & O'Brien, M. (2001) The effect of management for red grouse shooting on the population density of breeding birds on heather-dominated moorland. *Journal of Applied Ecolog,y* **38**, 439–457.

Thin, F. (1999) Landscape assessment in the Natural Heritage Zones programme. Landscape Character: Perspectives on Management and Change. (eds M.B. Usher). The Stationery Office, Edinburgh. pp. 23–33.

Thom, V.M. (1986) Birds in Scotland. T & A D Poyser, Calton. pp. 382.

Thompson, D.B.A., Macdonald, A.J., Marsden, J.H. & Galbraith, C.A. (1995) Upland Heather Moorland in Great-Britain–a Review of International Importance, Vegetation Change and Some Objectives for Nature Conservation. *Biological Conservation,* **71**, 163–178.

TNS (TNS Research International) (2009) Scottish Recreation Survey: annual summary report 2007. Scottish Natural Heritage, Edinburgh.

Toth, I. & Elphinstone, J. (2009) *Erwinia chrysanthemi (Dickeya* spp.)–the facts. [online] Available at: <http://www.scri.ac.uk/scri/file/PiP/Erwinia.pdf>

Towers, W., Grieve, I.C., Hudson, G., Campbell, C.D., Lilly, A., Davidson, D.A., Bacon, J.R., Langan, S.J. & Hopkins, D.W. (2006) Scotland's Soil Resource–Current State and Threats. Scottish Government, Edinburgh.

Tratalos, J., Fuller, R.A., Evans, K.L., Davies, R.G., Newson, S.E., Greenwood, J.J.D. & Gaston, K.J. (2007a) Bird densities are associated with household densities. *Global Change Biology,* **13**, 1685–1695.

Tratalos, J., Fuller, R.A., Warren, P.H., Davies, R.G. & Gaston, K.J. (2007b) Urban form, biodiversity potential and ecosystem services. *Landscape and Urban Planning,* **83**, 308–317.

Trigg, C. & Moore, C.G. (2009) Recovery of the biogenic nest habitat of *Limaria hians* (Mollusca: Limacea) following anthropogenic disturbance. *Estuarine Coastal and Shelf Science,* **82**, 351–356.

Tubby, I. & Webber, J.F. (2010) Pests and diseases threatening urban trees under a changing climate. *Forestry,* **83**, 451–459.

Tucker, G.M. (1992) Effects of Agricultural Practices on Field Use by Invertebrate-Feeding Birds in Winter. *Journal of Applied Ecology,* **29**, 779–790.

Tudor, G.J., Mackey, E.C. & Underwood, F.M. (1994) The National Countryside Monitoring Scheme: the changing face of Scotland 1940s to 1970s. Scottish Natural Heritage, Edinburgh.

UK Biodiversity Action Plan Targets Review (2006) Biodiversity Action Plans. [online] Available at: <http://webarchive.nationalarchives.gov.uk/20110303145213/http://ukbap.org.uk/BAPGroupPage.aspx?id=98>

UKMMAS (UK Marine Monitoring and Assessment Strategy) (2010) Charting Progress 2: An assessment of the state of the UK seas. pp. 166.

UK National Air Quality Information Archive (2011). UK-AIR: Air Information Resources. Defra, London. [online] Available at: <http://www.airquality.co.uk> [Accessed 28.05.11].

UKTS (UK Tourism Statistics) (2006) United Kingdom Tourism Statistics 2006. Tourism volumes and values in 2006. Visit Britian, Visit Scotland, Visit Wales, Northern Ireland Tourist Board.

United Nations (2000) United Nations Convention on Biological Diversity. The Convention on Biological Diversity. [online] Available at: http://www.cbd.int/convention/text/> [Accessed 28.05.11].

University Marine Biological Station Millport (2007) Conservation of the Native Oyster (*Ostrea edulis*) in Scotland. Scottish Natural Heritage Commissioned Report No.251 (ROAME No. F02AA408).pp. 186.

Usher, M.B. (1997) Scotland's biodiversity: an overview. Biodiversity in Scotland: Status, Trends and Initiatives. (eds L.V. Fleming, A.C. Newton, J.A. Vickery, & M.B. Usher). The Stationery Office, Edinburgh. pp. 5–20.

Usher, M.B. (1999) Scotland's coastal biodiversity: what, where and when? Scotland's Living Coastline. (eds J.M. Baxter, K. Duncan, S. Atkins, & G. Lees). The Stationery Office, London. pp. 173–189.

Usher, M.B. (2002a) Scotland's biodiversity: trends, changing perceptions and planning for action. The State of Scotland's Environment and Natural Heritage. (eds M.B. Usher, E.C. Mackey, & J. Curran). The Stationery Office, Edinburgh. pp. 257–269.

Usher, M.B. (2002b) Action for Scotland's Biodiversity. The Scottish Executive, Edinburgh.

Usher, M.B., Sier, A.R.J., Hornung, M. & Millard, P. (2006) Understanding biological diversity in soil: The UK's Soil Biodiversity Research Programme. *Applied Soil Ecology,* **33**, 101–113.

van der Wal, R., Pearce, I., Brooker, R., Scott, D., Welch, D. & Woodin, S. (2003) Interplay between nitrogen deposition and grazing causes habitat degradation. *Ecology Letters,* **6**, 141–146.

van Eekeren, N., de Boer, H., Bloem, J., Schouten, T., Rutgers, M., de Goede, R. & Brussaard, L. (2009) Soil biological quality of grassland fertilized with adjusted cattle manure slurries in comparison with organic and inorganic fertilizers. *Biology and Fertility of Soils,* **45**, 595–608.

van Leeuwen, E., Nijkamp, P. & Vaz, T.D. (2010) The multifunctional use of urban greenspace. *International Journal of Agricultural Sustainability,* **8**, 20–25.

Vargas, M., Brown, C.W. & Sapiano, M.R.P. (2009) Phenology of marine phytoplankton from satellite ocean color measurements. *Geophysical Research Letters,* **36**.

Verheijen, F.G.A., Jones, R.J.A., Rickson, R.J. & Smith, C.J. (2009) Tolerable versus actual soil erosion rates in Europe. *Earth-Science Reviews,* **94**, 23–38.

Vickery, J.A., Tallowin, J.R., Feber, R.E., Asteraki, E.J., Atkinson, P.W., Fuller, R.J. & Brown, V.K. (2001) The management of lowland neutral grasslands in Britain: effects of agricultural practices on birds and their food resources. *Journal of Applied Ecology,* **38**, 647–664.

Walker, A.J. (2010) Scottish fish farm production survey: 2009 report. Marine Scotland, the Scottish Government.

Wang, S. (2004) One hundred faces of sustainable forest management. *Forest Policy and Economics,* **6**, 205–213.

Warnes, J.M. (1983) The status of the Chough in Scotland. *Scottish Birds,* **12**, 238–246.

Warren, C. (2000) Birds, bogs and forestry revisited: The significance of the Flow Country controversy. *Scottish Geographical Journal,* **116**, 315–337.

Warren, C.R. & Birnie, R.V. (2009) Re-powering Scotland: Wind Farms and the 'Energy or Environment?' Debate. *Scottish Geographical Journal,* **125**, 97–126.

Watling, R. (1997) Biodiversity of lichenised and non-lichenised fungi in Scotland. Biodiversity in Scotland: Status, Trends and Initiatives. (eds L.V. Fleming, A.C. Newton, J.A. Vickery, & M.B. Usher). The Stationery Office, Edinburgh. pp. 77–88.

Watson, A., Perkins, A.J., Maggs, H.E. & Wilson, J.D. (2009) Decline of Corn Buntings *Emberiza calandra* on east Scottish study areas in 1989–2007. *Bird Study,* **56**, 213–220.

Weber, J.L., Spyropoulou, R., Soukup, T. & Paramo, F. (2008) Net Landscape Ecological Potential of Europe and change 1990–2000. European Environment Agency. pp. 12.

Werritty, A., Brazier, V., Gordon, J.E. & McManus, J. (1994) Geomorphology. The Fresh Waters of Scotland. A National Resource of International Significance. (eds P.S. Maitland, P.J. Boon, & D.S. McLusky). John Wiley and Sons, London. pp. 65–88.

Whitehead, S., Johnstone, I. & Wilson, J. (2005) Choughs (*Pyrrhocorax pyrrhocorax*) breeding in Wales select foraging habitat at different spatial scales. *Bird Study,* **52**.

Whittingham, M.J., Percival, S.M. & Brown, A.F. (2001) Habitat selection by golden plover *Pluvialis apricaria* chicks. *Basic and Applied Ecology,* **2**, 177–191.

Williams, P. (2005) Does specialization explain rarity and decline British bumblebees? A response to Goulson *et al.* *Biological Conservation,* **122**, 33–43.

Williamson, R.B. & Beveridge, M.C.M. (1994) Fisheries and Aquaculture. The Fresh Waters of Scotland. A National Resource of International Significance. (eds P.S. Maitland, P.J. Boon, & D.S. McLusky). John Wiley and Sons, London. pp. 317–332.

Wilson, J.D., Boyle, J., Jackson, D.B., Lowe, B. & Wilkinson, N.I. (2007) Effect of cereal harvesting method on a recent population decline of Corn Buntings *Emberiza calandra* on the Western Isles of Scotland. *Bird Study,* **54**, 362–370.

Wilson, W.L., Abernethy, V.J., Murphy, K.J., Adam, A., McCracken, D.I., Downie, I.S., Foster, G.N., Furness, R.W., Waterhouse, A. & Ribera, I. (2003) Prediction of plant diversity response to land-use change on Scottish agricultural land. *Agriculture Ecosystems & Environment,* **94**, 249–263.

Winter, M. & Gasson, R. (1996) Pilgrimage and tourism: cathedral visiting in contemporary England. *International Journal of Heritage Studies,* **2**, 172–182.

Wohlers, J., Engel, A., Zollner, E., Breithaupt, P., Jurgens, K., Hoppe, H.G., Sommer, U. & Riebesell, U. (2009) Changes in biogenic carbon flow in response to sea surface warming. *Proceedings of the National Academy of Sciences of the United States of America,* **106**, 7067–7072.

Wolf, J. & Woolf, D.K. (2005) Waves and climate change in the Sea of the Hebrides. Proceedings of the Fifteenth (2005) International Offshore and Polar Engineering Conference, Vol 3, Seoul, Korea. 100–107.

Wood, H.J. (1931) An Agricultural Atlas of Scotland. George Gill and Sons Ltd, London. pp. 64.

Woodward, F.R. (1985) The fan-mussel, *Pinna fragilis* Pennant, in Scotland. *The Glasgow Naturalist,* **21**, 63–69.

Woodward, G. (2009) Biodiversity, ecosystem functioning and food webs in fresh waters: assembling the jigsaw puzzle. *Freshwater Biology,* **54**, 2171–2187.

Wright, G.G., Edwards, A.C., Morrice, J.G. & Pugh, K. (1991) North east Scotland river catchment nitrate loading in relation to agricultural intensity. *Chemical Ecology,* **5**, 263–281.

Wright, G.G. & Morrice, J.G. (1997) Landsat TM spectral information to enhance the land cover of Scotland 1988 dataset. *International Journal of Remote Sensing,* **18**, 3811–3834.

Appendix 19.1 Approach Used to Assign Certainty Terms to Chapter Key Findings

This chapter began with a set of Key Findings. Adopting the approach and terminology used by the Intergovernmental Panel on Climate Change (IPCC) and the Millennium Assessment (MA), these Key Findings also include an indication of the level of scientific certainty. The 'uncertainty approach' of the UK NEA consists of a set of qualitative uncertainty terms derived from a 4-box model and complemented, where possible, with a likelihood scale (see below). Estimates of certainty are derived from the collective judgement of authors, observational evidence, modelling results and/or theory examined for this assessment.

Throughout the Key Findings presented at the start of this chapter, superscript numbers and letters indicate the estimated level of certainty for a particular key finding:

1. *Well established:*   high agreement based on significant evidence
2. *Established but incomplete evidence:*   high agreement based on limited evidence
3. *Competing explanations:*   low agreement, albeit with significant evidence
4. *Speculative:*   low agreement based on limited evidence

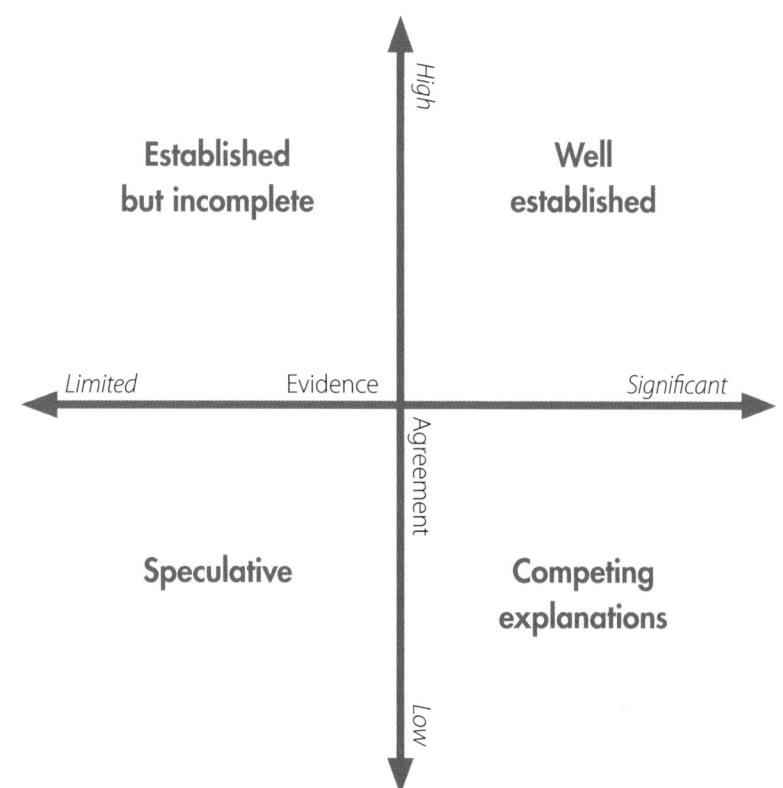

a. *Virtually certain:*   >99% probability of occurrence
b. *Very likely:*   >90% probability
c. *Likely:*   >66% probability
d. *About as likely as not:* >33–66% probability
e. *Unlikely:*   <33% probability
f. *Very unlikely:*   <10% probability
g. *Exceptionally unlikely:* <1% probability

Certainty terms 1 to 4 constitute the 4-box model, while *a* to *g* constitute the likelihood scale.

Chapter 20:
Status and Changes in the UK's Ecosystems and their Services to Society: Wales

Coordinating Lead Author: Shaun Russell
Lead Authors: Tim Blackstock, Mike Christie, Michelle Clarke, Keith Davies, Catherine Duigan, Isabelle Durance, Russell Elliot, Hugh Evans, Charlie Falzon, Peter Frost, Sue Ginley, Neal Hockley, Shelagh Hourahane, Barbara Jones, Laurence Jones, Julia Korn, Peter Ogden, Saskia Pagella, Tim Pagella, Brian Pawson, Brian Reynolds, David Robinson, Bill Sanderson, Jan Sherry, James Skates, Emma Small, Barbara Spence and Clive Thomas

Key Findings

Biodiversity contributes to economic and social prosperity in Wales by underpinning valuable ecosystem services. The annual value of wildlife-based activity to the Welsh economy was estimated as £1.9 billion in 2007 (2.9% of Wales's national output and 3% of employment). These figures do not provide an assessment of the value of biodiversity in terms of its wider provision of ecosystem services to Welsh society. There have been significant changes to biodiversity in Wales over the past 70 years, with some species thriving or recovering from earlier losses, while others have contracted in numbers. Key seabird species have increased during the past 30 years; numbers of wild plants, butterflies of specialist habitats and farmland birds have declined. Honey bees showed a 23% decline in Wales between 1985 and 2005. In common with other countries in Europe, Wales failed to meet its international biodiversity targets in 2010. Fifty-four per cent of Biodiversity Action Plan species were assessed as being in 'unfavourable condition' in 2008, but with considerable variation between species groups. For example, 80% of marine mammals and birds were in favourable or recovering condition, while 80% of amphibians, butterflies and fish were recorded as being in unfavourable condition. In 2005, 59% of Biodiversity Action Plan habitats in Wales were in declining condition. Priority habitats classed as stable or improving increased from 30% in 2002 to 36% in 2008. A rapid review in 2006 judged conservation features at 47% of Welsh Sites of Special Scientific Interest (SSSIs) to be in favourable condition, with 53% in unfavourable condition.

Mountains, Moorlands and Heaths in Wales hold significant amounts of stored carbon, but many protected sites in this broad habitat type are in declining condition. Currently, approximately 60% of designated sites in upland habitats (Mountains, Moorlands and Heaths) are classed as being in unfavourable condition. Climate change, land management and atmospheric deposition of sulphur and nitrogen compounds have all affected the soil systems of Wales's mountain areas. Over 80% of soil carbon stores in Wales are associated with upland and grassland soils. There is a threat of a potential shift from carbon sink to carbon source in the uplands if these areas are not carefully managed for their carbon stores.

The alteration of the composition of lowland Semi-natural Grasslands was one the most rapid and widespread vegetation changes to have taken place in Wales during the 20th Century. Approximately 90% of former unimproved and semi-improved swards were transformed by agricultural management to Improved Grasslands.

About 37.4% of Wales is Enclosed Farmland, consisting of 34% Improved Grassland and 3.4% Arable and Horticultural land. Enclosed Farmland is valuable for provisioning and cultural services in Wales, with potential for greater contributions to supporting and regulating services. But it also imposes important disbenefits in terms of greenhouse gas emissions, diffuse water pollution and losses to biodiversity. There is also evidence that land drainage in Improved Grassland has increased flood risk. Livestock production in Wales is dominated by sheep and cattle farming, with Wales contributing 26% of the total numbers of sheep in the UK (8.2 million) and 11% of the UK total for cattle (1.1 million cows). These provisioning services are heavily supported by subsidy in Less Favoured Areas (80% of the agricultural land area of Wales). Wales imports considerably more food commodities in all categories than are exported, except in the case of animal feedstuffs. This is one indicator of the many ways in which the lifestyles of Welsh citizens rely upon and affect ecosystem services beyond the borders of Wales.

Woodland area in Wales has almost tripled since the early 1900s, and now covers 14% of the country's total land area. In addition, there is a significant tree resource outside Woodlands, in the form of individual trees (15 million live trees) and hedgerows. Forest resources contributed £429 million to the Welsh economy in 2007, and an estimated 8,900 jobs. Woodlands can deliver multiple ecosystem services and the drive for sustainable forest management over the last 25 years appears to have had a positive effect on the trends for many of these services. The Welsh Government is planning the creation of 100,000 ha of new woodland over the next 20 years which, if achieved, will create an additional sink of 1,600,000 tonnes of carbon dioxide equivalent annually by 2040. Despite their limited extent, semi-natural woodlands remain one of the most biodiverse habitats in Wales, with a rich association of rare and priority species. Approximately 5% of Woodlands are SSSIs. However, just 9% of these are considered to be in favourable condition and 25% are classed as being in unfavourable but recovering condition.

Welsh freshwater ecosystems still suffer from an industrial legacy, for example, point sources of metal pollution from mines, but there is evidence of improvement following remediation measures. Biological data suggest deterioration of some rivers from 'very good' to 'good' quality since 1995; reasons are unclear but may link to agricultural activity and phosphorus contamination. Nearly all the major river systems of Wales are regulated by headwater dams and reservoirs installed to provide water supply, flood control and energy generation. Nine ecologically distinct types of lake have been recorded in Wales, out of 11 types found in Britain. The Environment Agency has estimated that one in six properties in Wales (600,000 people in 357,000 properties) is at risk of flooding. The economic risk from flooding to properties and contents was £200 million per annum in 2008. UK climate impact projections suggest that average annual natural river flows could reduce by 10–15% in Wales by 2050, and natural summer river flows could reduce by 50% or more, with implications for flood hazard regulation and water supply.

Five per cent of Wales is classified as Urban habitat. During the past 40 years, activities have taken place to improve the quality of human well-being in the urban environment by expanding greenspace and tree planting, and increasing the numbers of local nature reserves close to urban centres. In 2010, 18 of the 22 local authorities in Wales were working on assessments of the extent and location of accessible natural greenspace in their urban areas.

Sand Dunes, Saltmarsh and Sea Cliffs are the most extensive coastal habitats in Wales and are important for a range of regulating services, including coastal erosion protection. Since 1900, there have been considerable losses of Sand Dune areas to agricultural land claim, forestry and development for housing and tourism. A further 23% of the Welsh coastline is eroding and 28% has some form of artificial sea defence works. In 2007, the sea defence services of Sand Dunes were calculated to be worth between £53 and £199 million in Wales. Seven in every eight hectares of European designated Natura 2000 sites in Wales (0.5 million ha) are Marine areas, reflecting their high importance for conservation. However, 60% of these sites have been classified as being in 'continued or accelerated decline'.

Wales is currently regarded as a net sink for carbon dioxide in the land use, land use change and forestry sector (UNFCC reporting). This is primarily due to the low incidence of land use change in Wales and the relatively young age structure of Welsh forests, rather than the overall stock of carbon held within Welsh soils. Soils represent a significant store of carbon, with 20–30% in the form of peat deposits which occupy 3% of the land area of Wales. Welsh soils hold nine times the amount of carbon that is stored in all vegetation (including forestry). The strength of the forest carbon sink increased from 1990 to 2004, but will start to decline in future as a result of the drop in planting rates over the last 20 years. The total amount of carbon stored in Welsh forests and their soils is equivalent to more than 10 times the annual emissions from industry and services.

Wales records some of the highest rainfall levels in the UK. There are large reserves of surface water in Wales that have long served as sources of supply for the UK more widely. Demands on these reserves from within and outside Wales are likely to increase in the future, under current climate change scenarios.

Provisioning services from agriculture contributed some £418 million or 1.1% to the Welsh economy in 2003. However, the agricultural sector accounts for more than 10% of total employment in Wales and contributes to a wide range of cultural ecosystem service benefits, including landscape values and tourism.

Wales is renowned for its attractive landscapes, with three National Parks and five Areas of Outstanding Natural Beauty covering 24% of the country's land surface. In Wales, 72% of the population has access to woodlands greater than 20 ha in extent within 4 km of their homes. Fifty-eight cultural landscape types are listed in the Register of Landscapes of Historic interest in Wales. However, during the mid-20th Century the distinctive character of the Welsh landscape suffered from intrusive developments related to energy, transport and tourism, and the poor design and location of forest plantations.

A 2001 study estimated that the environment contributed £8.8 billion of goods and services annually to the Welsh economy, 9% of Welsh GDP and one in six Welsh jobs, mainly in the leisure and tourism, agriculture and forestry, water abstraction, conservation and waste management sectors. It also found that the environment is relatively more important to the Welsh economy than it is to the other UK nations.

20.1 Introduction

20.1.1 Scope and Purpose

This chapter provides a snapshot of the major habitat types of Wales, with information about the ecosystem services that these habitats provide. It also discusses drivers of change in these habitats/services, and possible policy responses to achieve the optimum provision of ecosystem services in Wales.

Reference to other chapters of the UK National Ecosystem Assessment (NEA) will provide general and specific information on status and trends in regulating, provisioning, supporting and cultural ecosystem services at the UK level. This chapter aims to highlight aspects that are particular to, and distinctive about, the environment of Wales, through information on:

- condition, status and trends in the Broad Habitats of Wales, and their ecosystem services;
- valuation of the ecosystem services of Wales;
- drivers of change (locally and globally) in habitats and their ecosystem services;
- trade-offs and synergies in the ecosystem services provided by Wales's habitats;
- the relationship between biodiversity and ecosystem service provision in Wales;
- sustainable management options which may enhance ecosystem services provision;
- links between ecosystem services and human well-being; and
- knowledge gaps.

Original contributions to this chapter included more detailed and comprehensive information than could be accommodated within the space limitations for the published UK NEA Wales synthesis. This additional information is archived by the Wales Environment Research Hub (www.werh.org), but has not been subject to the same peer-review process as the condensed synthesis chapter presented here.

20.1.2 Ecosystems in Wales

For the purposes of the UK NEA, eight 'Broad Habitat types' have been recognised, aggregated from the 25 broad habitats recognised in the UK Countryside Survey (Carey *et al.* 2008). The Countryside Survey Technical Report explains how habitats were identified in that study (Maskell *et al.* 2008). The UK NEA Broad Habitat classifications closely match the categories within the UK Land Cover Map 2007, and are also related to UK Biodiversity Action Plan (UK BAP) priority habitats. A table showing the relationships between these classifications is provided in Chapter 2.

The UK NEA Broad Habitat types of 1) Mountains, Moorlands and Heaths, 2) Semi-natural Grasslands, 3) Enclosed Farmland, 4) Woodlands, 5) Freshwaters – Openwaters, Wetlands and Floodplains, 6) Urban, 7) Coastal Margins, and 8) Marine, are mapped for Wales in **Figure 20.1**. Areal statistics for habitats are provided in **Table 20.1**.

20.2 Wales's Land and Sea

The predominantly ancient hard rock geology of Wales, combined with a northerly position in relation to peri-Arctic influences and a westerly situation facing the prevailing rain-bearing Atlantic airflow, has led to an erosion-sculpted landscape of hills/mountains and valleys. Due to the relatively strong relief, river catchments tend to be shorter and steeper than those in England, with rivers that often display 'spate' characteristics.

The climate of Wales is cool temperate, with a regime of cool summers and mild winters, but due to the topography, local climate is strongly influenced by aspect and altitudinal gradients in temperature and rainfall that lead to variation in microclimates.

The post-glacial, 'natural' vegetation of Wales comprised mainly broadleaved deciduous forests in the lowlands and valley sides, with tundra-like heathlands in the uplands. Now, mainly due to human management, the vegetation consists principally of a mosaic of improved grassland, woodland and some cropland in the lowlands, with 'semi-natural' grazing land and some heathland in the uplands.

Of the total amount of land in Wales, 60% is more than 150 m above sea level, and 27% is more than 300 m above sea level. Geology and climate have contributed to the generally low agricultural fertility of Wales's soils, and there are large expanses of substrate with high organic/carbon content, including major deposits of peat. Of the 2.1 million hectares of land in Wales, 1.6 million ha is classed as Less Favoured Area (LFA), of which 1.1 million ha is used for agriculture (69%).

With an area of 2,077,900 ha and a coastline of 2,740 km, no part of Wales is more than 75 km from the coast. The

Table 20.1 Area and percentage cover of UK NEA Broad Habitat types in Wales. Source: Phase 1 Habitat Survey 2004 computed by I. Durance (Cardiff University).

UK NEA Broad Habitat	Total area (ha)	Percentage (%) of terrestrial area	Percentage (%) of total area
Mountains, Moorlands & Heaths	227,735	11	
Semi-natural Grasslands	270,002	13	
Enclosed Farmland	1,066,998	52	
Woodlands	289,216	14	54.86
Freshwaters – Openwaters, Wetlands & Floodplains	22,770	1	
Urban	94,894	5	
Coastal Margins	56,452	3	
Other	34,292	2	
Marine	1,594,175	-	45.14

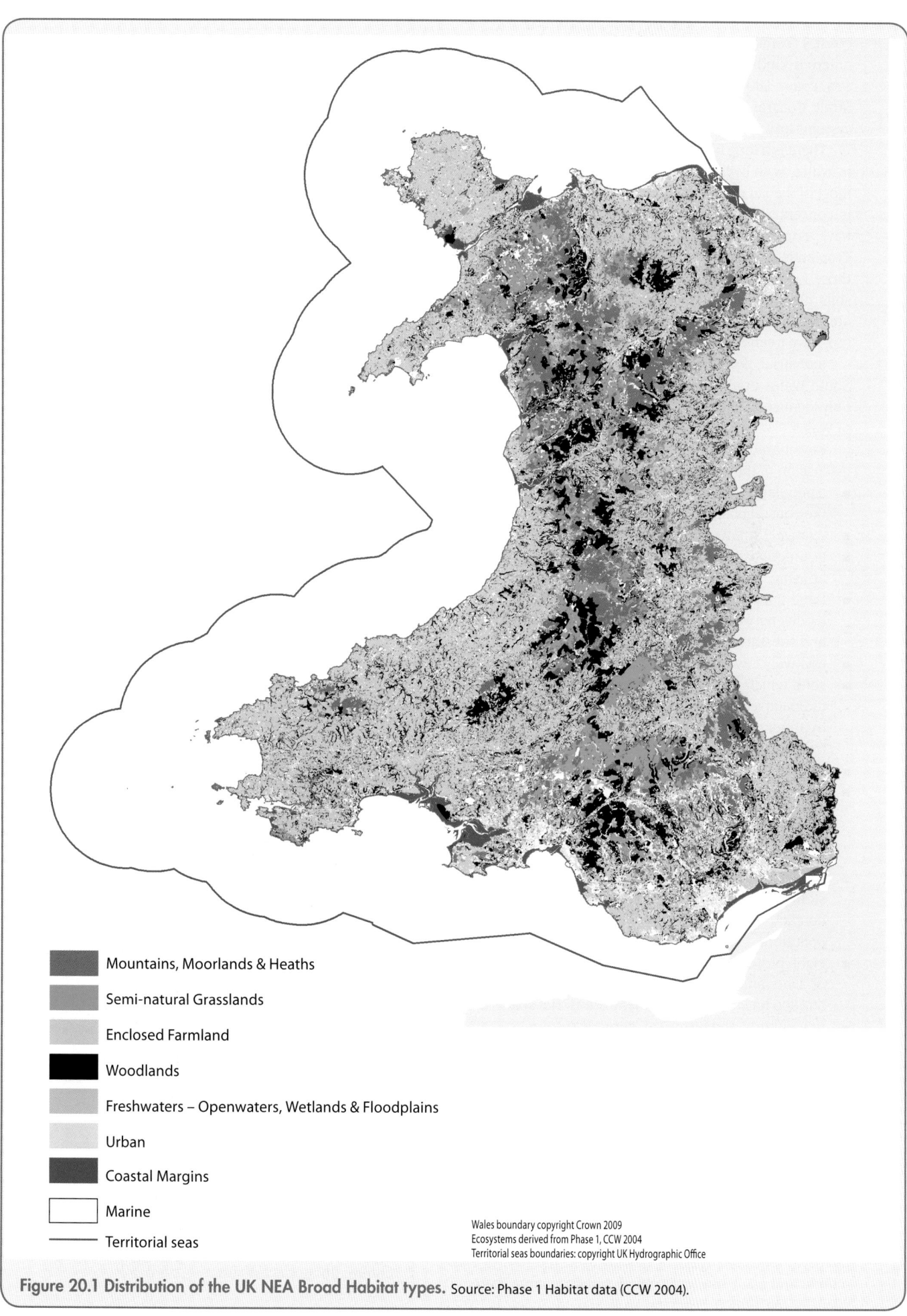

Mountains, Moorlands & Heaths

Semi-natural Grasslands

Enclosed Farmland

Woodlands

Freshwaters – Openwaters, Wetlands & Floodplains

Urban

Coastal Margins

Marine

Territorial seas

Wales boundary copyright Crown 2009
Ecosystems derived from Phase 1, CCW 2004
Territorial seas boundaries: copyright UK Hydrographic Office

Figure 20.1 Distribution of the UK NEA Broad Habitat types. Source: Phase 1 Habitat data (CCW 2004).

coastal configuration of Wales has resulted in several different kinds of distinctive Marine habitats, on the Irish Sea coast, along the Severn Estuary and in the Menai Strait. Coastal scenery also includes impressive Sand Dune systems and spectacular Sea Cliffs.

There is a long history of human occupation and farming in Wales, with livestock rearing the prevailing land use over most of the rural landscape. Intensive pasture management is concentrated in valleys and lowlands, and many farms have associated blocks of unenclosed upland 'sheep-walk'. Croplands are much less prevalent and are largely limited to those lowland zones which have better quality agricultural soils. Semi-natural woodlands and other wildlife habitats are patchy and often degraded, and marine environments, too, have been heavily impacted by human activity.

Industrial development has been most evident in the South Wales Coalfield and north-eastern Wales, but is now only localised. Tourism is a vital component of the economy of Wales.

Key characteristics of Wales that provide the context for discussion of the ecosystem services are therefore:

- a population of 3 million people, mainly concentrated on the coastal plains;
- relatively small cities and towns;
- a unique 'valleys' environment of dense, often old housing, adjacent to semi-natural upland areas;
- large upland tracts often designated for landscape and biodiversity conservation, with high organic soil content and substantial water resources;
- relatively low quality soils for agricultural production;
- soils which have been susceptible to acidification and radioactive contamination, and which, through nutrient treatment, have also contributed to the eutrophication of freshwaters;
- 13–14% of land covered by forest/woodland;
- marine areas with significant biodiversity and potential for expansion of shell fisheries, renewable energy, tourism, etc., but which have been adversely affected by overharvesting in the past;
- a long history of extractive industries, e.g. coal, slate, stone, limestone, metals, which have left a legacy of derelict landscapes, contaminated land and water pollution;
- eight protected landscapes (National Parks and Areas of Outstanding Natural Beauty) in Wales, occupying 507,800 ha, i.e. 24.4% of Wales's terrestrial space; and
- rich cultural and historical/heritage resources.

20.3 Biodiversity in Wales

The landscape and biodiversity of Wales have been shaped by human activity for many centuries. As a result, Wales has a diverse cultural landscape, but human depredation and intensive land management have caused the loss of many animal and plant species. Examples include large mammals such as the brown bear, the wolf and the wildcat, which died out in Wales during the Norman period. Many other species continue to decline (Section 20.3.1) but there are also examples of recovery and successful reintroductions, e.g. the notable case of the red kite (*Milvus milvus*; **Figure 20.2**).

The geographical isolation of the UK and the long history of human activity means that Wales's terrestrial environment has relatively low numbers of native species in global terms. However, the diverse geology, westerly location and oceanic climate of Wales have led to certain groups of organisms showing higher than average abundance and diversity by European standards. There are rich communities of bryophytes (mosses and liverworts), lichens and fungi in Welsh woodlands and montane habitats. The upper reaches of Snowdonia are host to a distinctive arctic-alpine flora which includes species of saxifrage and the Snowdon lily (*Lloydia serotina*). There are several plant species in the lowland vascular flora that are not found elsewhere in Britain, e.g. spotted rock-rose (*Tuberaria guttata*), Radnor lily (*Gagea bohemica*) and yellow Whitlowgrass (*Draba aizoides*) (Perring & Walters, 1990). In the aquatic environment, freshwater fish include economically and culturally valuable trout and salmon species, and the endemic gwyniad (*Coregonus pennantii*) of Lake Bala.

Wales is situated at the boundary of three oceanic/climatic zones (North-east Atlantic, Arctic Boreal, Lusitanian) and is thus richer in marine life than many other European sea-areas. In addition, Wales has a wider range of seabed habitats compared with eastern Britain (the North Sea), and the tidal range is greater than in much of the rest of Europe, leading to higher intertidal diversity. Seventy-five per cent of Welsh coastal waters are of European importance, including several internationally significant seabird colonies. The

Figure 20.2 Red kite at the Gigrin Farm Feeding Centre, Rhayader, Wales. *Photo © Amanda and Phil Ackerman, Bird Photos UK.*

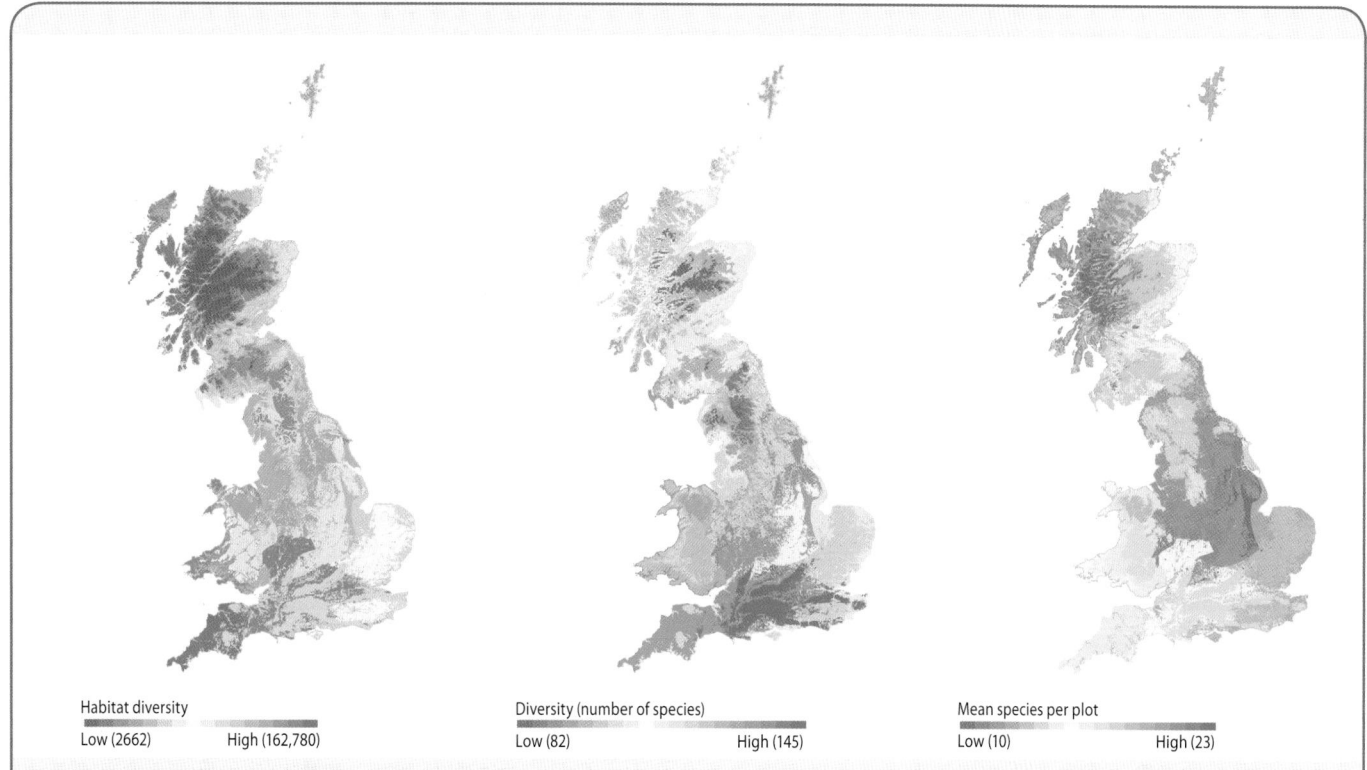

Figure 20.3 Terrestrial habitat complexity/diversity; total species richness per 1 km² and mean species richness per plot, for 1 km² sample plots from the Countryside Survey. Source: Smart *et al.* (2010) with the permission of the NERC Centre for Ecology and Hydrology.

Irish Sea and the south-western approaches are home to an important assemblage of marine animals, including sharks, seals, dolphins, porpoises, jellyfish, crabs and lobsters.

Within a UK setting, Wales has a medium to high terrestrial habitat complexity/diversity and overall species richness, according to the site sample data of the Countryside Survey (**Figure 20.3**). This compares with lower habitat diversity and numbers of species in Scotland and much of lowland England. The south and west of England has, in general, a higher habitat diversity and higher numbers of species compared with Wales.

20.3.1 Biodiversity Trends

The Countryside Survey (Smart *et al.* 2009) showed that plant species richness per sample plot had declined across Wales between 1990 and 2007 (**Figure 20.4**). In particular, there was a reduction in the richness of butterfly larval food plants in all landscape locations sampled, and this appears to be part of a longer-term trend, reflected in Great Britain more widely, that can be traced back to the first survey in 1978. A successional trend in vegetation character was noted, toward more shaded vegetation with fewer species of open ground and larger numbers of taller, more competitive species including trees and shrubs. No large step changes in ecological condition occurred over the 17-year period of the Survey in Wales.

The Countryside Survey also assessed boundary and linear features in the landscape, i.e. hedgerows and walls. Woody linear features (managed hedges and lines of trees and shrubs) made up an estimated 51% of the total length of this landscape feature in Wales in 2007 (England 53%; Scotland 13%). Fences make up 35% of the total length of boundary features in Wales. Walls were evenly distributed

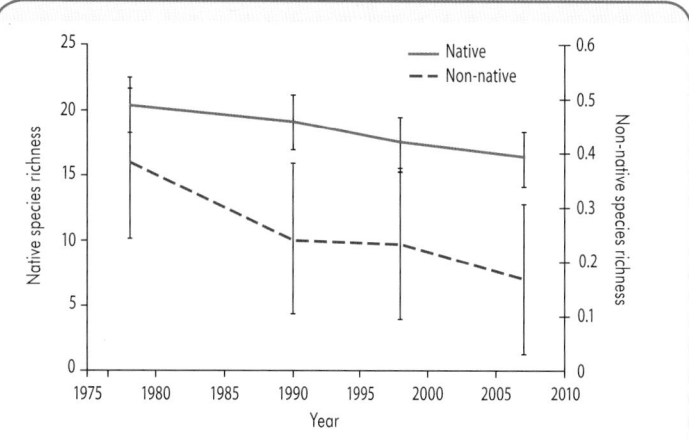

Figure 20.4 Native and non-native plant species richness of repeat survey plots in Wales. Source: Smart *et al.* (2009). Countryside Survey data owned by NERC – Centre for Ecology & Hydrology.

between upland and lowland zones but were more likely to be in poor condition in the uplands. Managed hedgerows saw continuing reduction in length in Wales, reflecting the lower level of hedgerow management across Britain in general. Tree and shrub species richness in Welsh woody linear features was the highest in Britain at 4.2 species per 30 m length, compared with 2.2 in Scotland and 3.7 in England. Forty-four per cent of Welsh hedges were in good structural condition in 2007 according to UK Habitat Action Plan criteria (Smart *et al.* 2009).

In the marine environment, a study for the Countryside Council for Wales by the Marine Life Information Network (MarLIN; Jackson *et al.* 2010) has found varying degrees of habitat diversity (biotope richness) around the coasts of

Wales (**Figure 20.5**). Further studies are required to build up a better picture of species diversity within Welsh marine habitats than exists at present.

In order to assess progress towards UK Biodiversity Action Plan (BAP) targets, Wales has contributed to BAP reporting since 1999. Since 2005 this has largely been through use of the UK Biodiversity Action Reporting System (BARS). Reports were submitted in 1999, 2002, 2005 and 2008. In 1999 and 2002 Wales reported against the UK BAP habitats and species list, in 2005 and 2008 reporting in Wales was against the CRoW Act Section 74 list. Future reporting will be against the NERC Act Section 42 list. Trend data are used to measure progress towards targets and to ascertain whether the status of priority habitats and species is improving, declining or stable. The following section explores trend data from the 2008 BAP reporting round for Wales Section 74 priority habitats and species, and compares these results to the UK data for the same habitats and species.

In Wales, more than half of UK BAP habitats are classed as in 'declining' condition. However, this decline is slowing at many sites and 65% of BAP habitats in Wales can therefore be classed as improving, remaining stable or showing signs that decline is fluctuating or slowing (**Figure 20.6**). A comparison of Wales with the wider UK, for trends in priority species is provided in **Figure 20.7**.

Habitats within the Marine environment exhibit the greatest deterioration, with continued or accelerated decline across 60% of marine habitats compared to only 8% for terrestrial habitats and 33% for freshwater habitats. In non-marine habitats, a more positive picture emerges, with 80% of terrestrial habitats and 66% of freshwater habitats

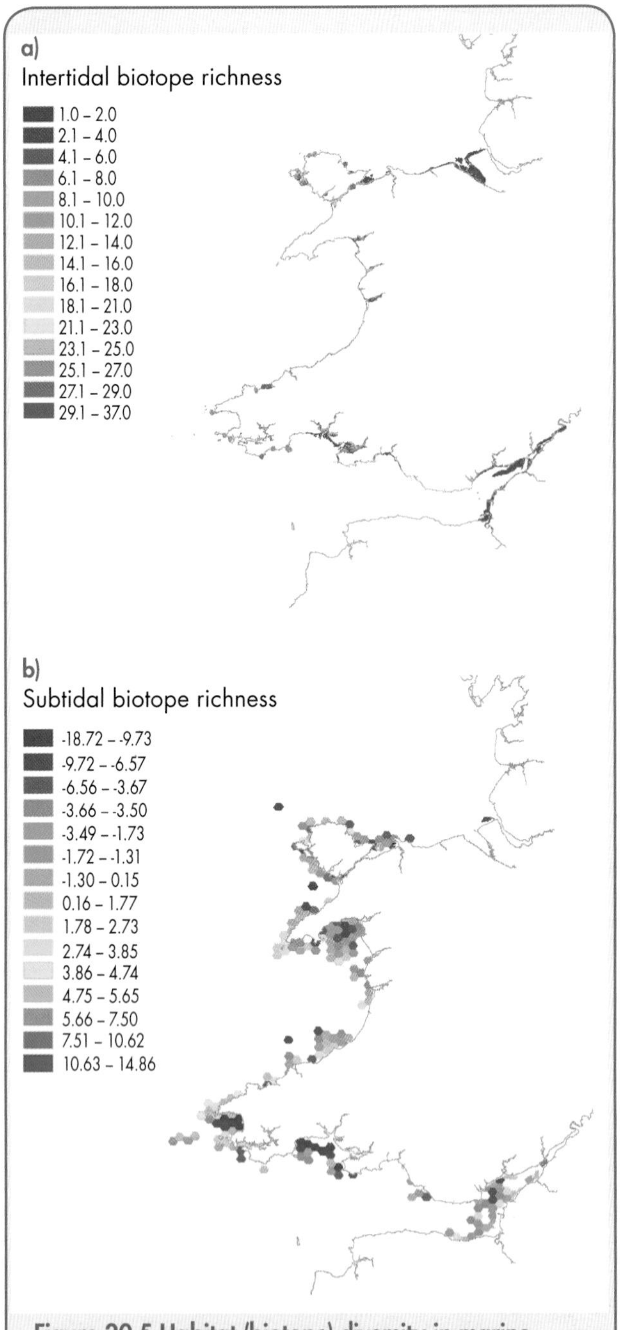

a)
Intertidal biotope richness

1.0 – 2.0
2.1 – 4.0
4.1 – 6.0
6.1 – 8.0
8.1 – 10.0
10.1 – 12.0
12.1 – 14.0
14.1 – 16.0
16.1 – 18.0
18.1 – 21.0
21.1 – 23.0
23.1 – 25.0
25.1 – 27.0
27.1 – 29.0
29.1 – 37.0

b)
Subtidal biotope richness

-18.72 – -9.73
-9.72 – -6.57
-6.56 – -3.67
-3.66 – -3.50
-3.49 – -1.73
-1.72 – -1.31
-1.30 – 0.15
0.16 – 1.77
1.78 – 2.73
2.74 – 3.85
3.86 – 4.74
4.75 – 5.65
5.66 – 7.50
7.51 – 10.62
10.63 – 14.86

Figure 20.5 Habitat (biotope) diversity in marine habitats of Wales. a) intertidal zone; b) subtidal areas. Source: Jackson *et al.* (2010). Crown copyright all rights reserved, Countryside Council for Wales.

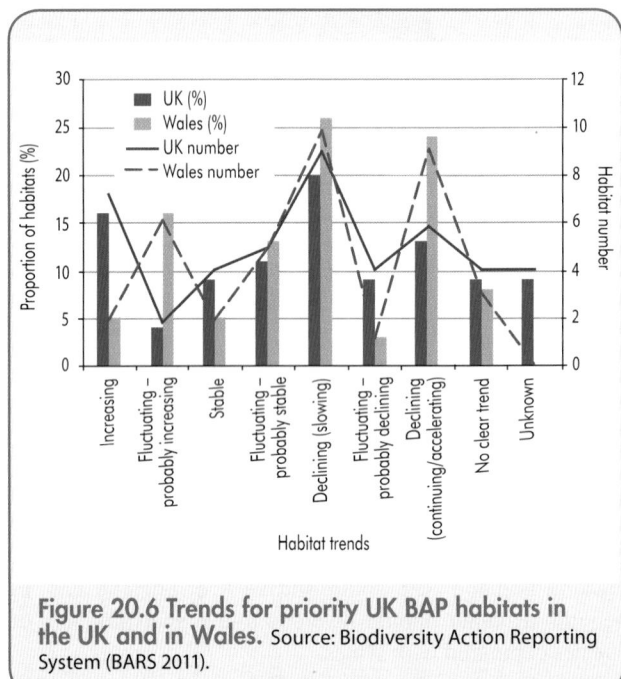

Figure 20.6 Trends for priority UK BAP habitats in the UK and in Wales. Source: Biodiversity Action Reporting System (BARS 2011).

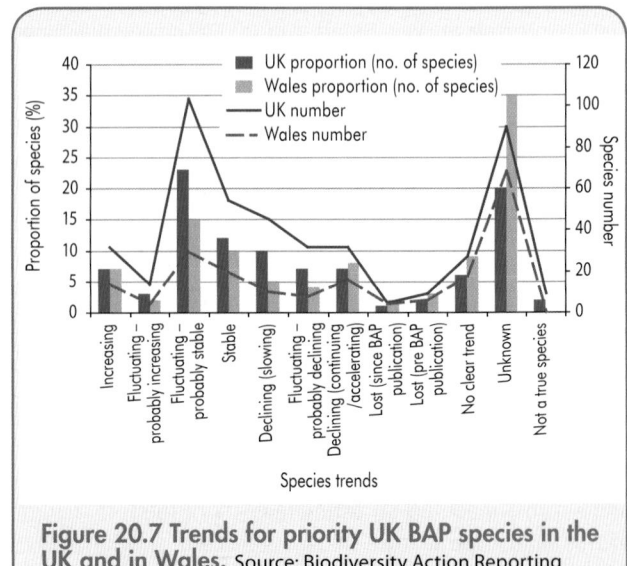

Figure 20.7 Trends for priority UK BAP species in the UK and in Wales. Source: Biodiversity Action Reporting System (BARS 2011).

showing stable or improving conditions, or slowing/ fluctuating declines (BARS 2011).

In Wales, further analysis of the terrestrial habitat data shows that most progress is being made in Woodland, upland and Enclosed Farmland habitats, with 83% of Woodland habitats reported as improving. Of the terrestrial ecosystems, wetlands and coastal habitats show the greatest decline, with 25% of habitats declining at the same or an accelerated rate. For lowland grassland and heathland the decline appears to be slowing, but neither of these habitats is stable or increasing. Similarly, no coastal BAP habitats are recorded as stable or increasing (BARS 2011).

Due to the large number of species which have unknown trends in Wales, it is difficult to compare progress in Wales to progress at the UK level (see **Figure 20.7**). This could mask significant changes in species populations. These data highlight the need for more investment in surveys and monitoring to allow for reliable reporting on BAP and other species trends in Wales.

Figure 20.8 shows trends for Welsh BAP Section 74 species. The three species which are showing a continuing/

accelerating decline are lapwing (*Vanellus vanellus*), curlew (*Numenius arquata*) and golden plover (*Pluvialis apricaria*).

Table 20.2 shows Welsh BAP trend data by taxonomic grouping. Three taxonomic groups (fungi, mammals and marine species) have too few data to derive meaningful conclusions on trends.

Seven taxonomic groups (more than 50% of Section 74 species) show increasing, stable or fluctuating/slowing declines (lichens, mosses and liverworts, stoneworts, vascular plants, invertebrates, fish, amphibians and reptiles). The most notable negative trends are in the birds (34%) and invertebrates (19%). Three groups (with low numbers of reporting species) reported no negative trends, i.e. the stoneworts, fish and amphibians and reptiles. Within the remaining three non-animal groups (mosses and liverworts, lichens and vascular plants), less than 10% of the species are recorded as having a negative trend.

As is apparent from the UK BAP reporting exercise, some species and taxonomic groups have long-term monitoring data and comprehensive trend datasets, while many others are not regularly monitored at all. However, reporting on other groups and from other sources tends to confirm the general picture of species decline and habitat degradation in Wales up to the present day, but with signs of improvement and progress in particular species and habitats. The following indicators are a sample of better-recorded taxonomic groups in Wales.

Wales Environment Strategy Indicator 19b, the Wild Birds Population index, is based on the Breeding Birds Survey carried out by the British Trust for Ornithology and the Royal Society for the Protection of Birds. It shows no clear trend overall, with some groups having increased since 1994 (notably urban birds) while birds of farmed habitats have decreased (see **Figure 20.8**). Based on longer-term data from the Breeding Bird Atlas, 43% of bird species have experienced range decreases between 1968 and 1972 and between 1988 and 1991, with just 17% having increased.

Data produced from the Joint Nature Conservation Committee (JNCC) Seabird Monitoring Programme provide

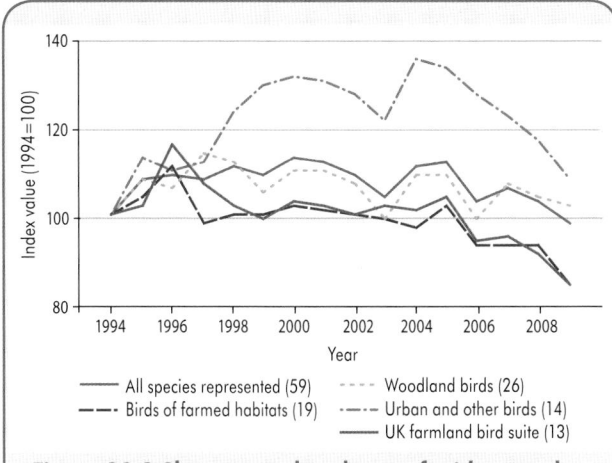

Figure 20.8 Short-term abundance of widespread breeding birds in Wales 1994–2009. Source: Welsh Assembly Government (2010e).

Table 20.2 Wales BAP species trend data by taxonomic grouping (numbers of species). Source: Wales Biodiversity Partnership/ Countryside Council for Wales.

Taxonomic grouping	Increasing	Stable	Declining Slowing/ Fluctuating	Declining Continuing/ Accelerating	Lost/Not Regular Breeder	Trend Unknown	No. of species in assessment
Lichens	0	6	0	0	1	5	12
Fungi	0	0	1	0	0	6	7
Mosses/Liverworts	1	7	0	1	0	3	12
Stoneworts	1	1	0	0	0	1	3
Vascular Plants	1	12	8	2	0	4	27
Fish (excluding marine)	0	1	0	0	0	1	2
Amphibians/Reptiles	2	0	1	0	0	0	3
Invertebrates	5	20	6	6	4	12	53
Birds	2	6	3	4	4	4	23
Mammals (excluding marine)	2	0	1	1	0	7	11
Marine species	1	1	0	4	0	14	20

an annual update on the progress of Welsh seabirds from a network of sites around the Welsh coast. Guillemot (*Urea aalge*), fulmar (*Fulmarus glacialis*) and kittiwake (*Rissa tridactyla*) are used to provide trend indices for Wales. The trend in the seabird population index is recorded as showing a clear improvement, although there is variation year-on-year within the different species populations. The JNCC survey suggests that the three species seem to be faring better in Wales than in the UK as a whole (JNCC 2010a).

The butterfly indicator for Wales has recently been developed by the Centre for Ecology and Hydrology (CEH) and the charity Butterfly Conservation, through the UK Butterfly Monitoring Scheme. Preliminary results indicate similar trends to those found for Scotland (SNH 2009), England and the UK as a whole (Defra 2009a). While generalist species appear to have remained more or less stable, habitat specialists have declined (**Figure 20.9**).

The mean proportion of records of non-native species in samples of birds, mammals, plants and marine life rose by 23% during the period 1990–2007 according to the CEH non-native species indicator. For all taxonomic groups recorded for this indicator, England was the country most affected by non-native species, Wales was intermediate and Scotland was least affected.

20.3.2 Designated Sites

Of the 21,000 km² land and freshwater surface area of Wales, about 30% is protected in special sites for wildlife, scenic beauty or geological value. Twenty-four per cent of terrestrial space (5,078 km²) is included in the eight main protected landscapes of Wales. These are the three National Parks (Snowdonia, Pembrokeshire Coast and Brecon Beacons) and the five Areas of Outstanding Natural Beauty (Gower, Wye Valley, Clwydian Range, Ynys Mon and Llyn Peninsula).

The most important areas for biodiversity in Wales have been mapped by the Countryside Council for Wales (**Figure 20.10**) This work does not include marine Section 42 habitats, some new terrestrial Section 42 habitats, or widespread habitat features such as hedgerows, ponds and veteran trees. Work is ongoing to compare these with spatial mapping of other ecosystem services in Wales, as part of the new Natural Environment Framework initiative (Section 20.10).

In 2006, the Countryside Council for Wales carried out a 'rapid review' of condition in Welsh Sites of Special Scientific Interest (SSSIs). Forty-eight per cent of conservation features at these sites were assessed to a high level of confidence, with 47% of these judged to be in favourable condition and 53% in unfavourable condition.

20.3.3 Drivers of Biodiversity Change

In Wales, habitat fragmentation and biodiversity loss have been caused mainly by changing management and use of land and sea. These changes have been driven largely by development pressures and subsidy regimes that were established to meet the challenges of changing population structures, increasing consumption, technological progress and economic development.

The direct drivers of biodiversity change (and loss) in Wales are similar to those listed for the UK as a whole (Chapter 3) and these include:

- land-use change (particularly agricultural extensification/ intensification and softwood afforestation in Wales);
- pollution;
- exploitation of marine ecosystems, both target species and non-target species;
- climate change; and
- invasive species.

These drivers have led to a loss of connectivity between habitats, and therefore reduced viability of biological communities. These issues are further addressed in Section 20.9 of this chapter, on drivers and consequences of change in habitats and ecosystem services.

Threats for 25 terrestrial habitats were identified for the 2008 BAP reporting round (**Figure 20.11**). These responses also highlight agriculture, climate change, pollution and invasive non-native species as major drivers of biodiversity change in Wales.

20.3.4 Biodiversity Commitments in Wales

In 2001, the EU set itself the target of halting the decline of biodiversity in Europe by 2010 and restoring habitats and natural systems. In April 2002, the Parties to the Convention on Biological Diversity (CBD) committed themselves to achieve, by 2010, a significant reduction in the rate of biodiversity loss at the global, regional and national levels as a contribution to poverty alleviation and to the benefit of all life on Earth. The Welsh Government committed itself to both the EU and global targets, which have been incorporated into national schemes and strategies. In particular, the Environment Strategy for Wales, Outcome 21, aimed for 95% of sites of international importance in Wales to be in favourable condition by 2010. Wales has also adopted the more ambitious target of reversing biodiversity declines by 2026 (Outcome 19 of the Wales Environment Strategy, WAG 2006a).

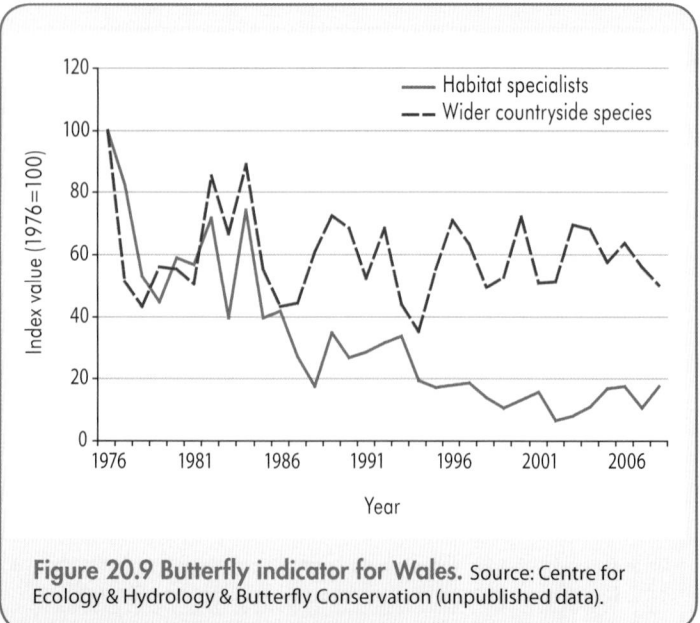

Figure 20.9 Butterfly indicator for Wales. Source: Centre for Ecology & Hydrology & Butterfly Conservation (unpublished data).

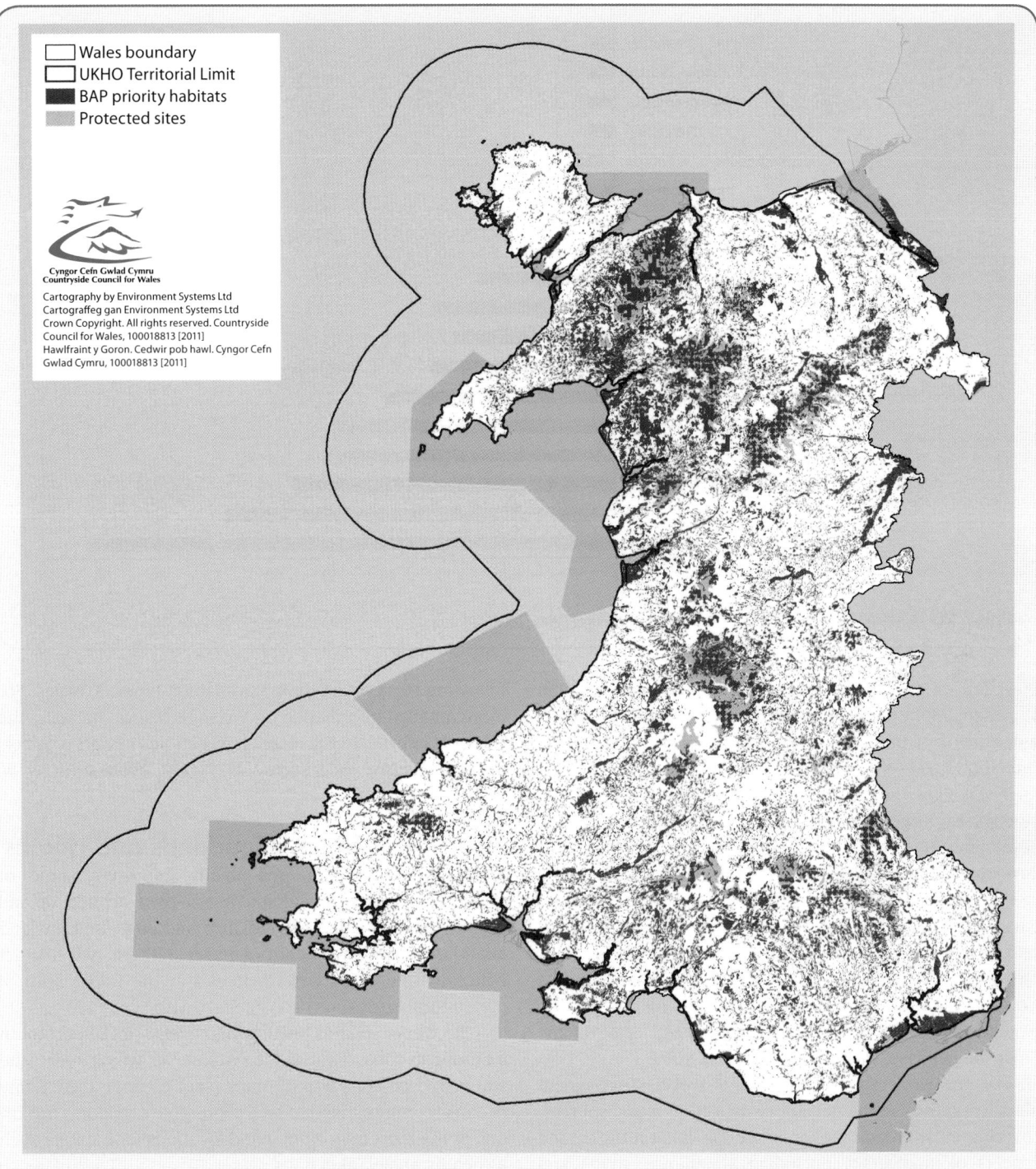

Figure 20.10 Areas of importance for biodiversity in Wales. Protected sites include Sites of Special Scientific Interest, Special Areas of Conservation and Special Protection Areas. Source: Countryside Council for Wales (2010).

In common with other countries and regions of Europe, the Welsh Government has acknowledged its failure to meet the 2010 biodiversity targets and has initiated a programme of responses to address this (see material on the new Wales Natural Environment Framework in Section 20.12). In 2010 the National Assembly for Wales Sustainability Committee also held an inquiry into why Wales had missed its 2010 target to halt the loss of biodiversity. The Committee's report lists 19 recommendations for addressing biodiversity loss in Wales, including driving the ecosystem approach into policy and across all government departments in Wales, focusing more on biodiversity in the wider landscape rather than dependence on protected sites alone, and involving the private sector in biodiversity management through the use of incentives and payments for ecosystem services (National Assembly for Wales Sustainability Committee Inquiry into Biodiversity Loss in Wales, January 2011).

20.3.5 Developing Biodiversity Indicators for Wales

Current 'State of the Environment' assessments are presented biannually in Wales, and they represent the first attempt to systematically monitor Welsh biodiversity within a broader environmental framework. Progress towards

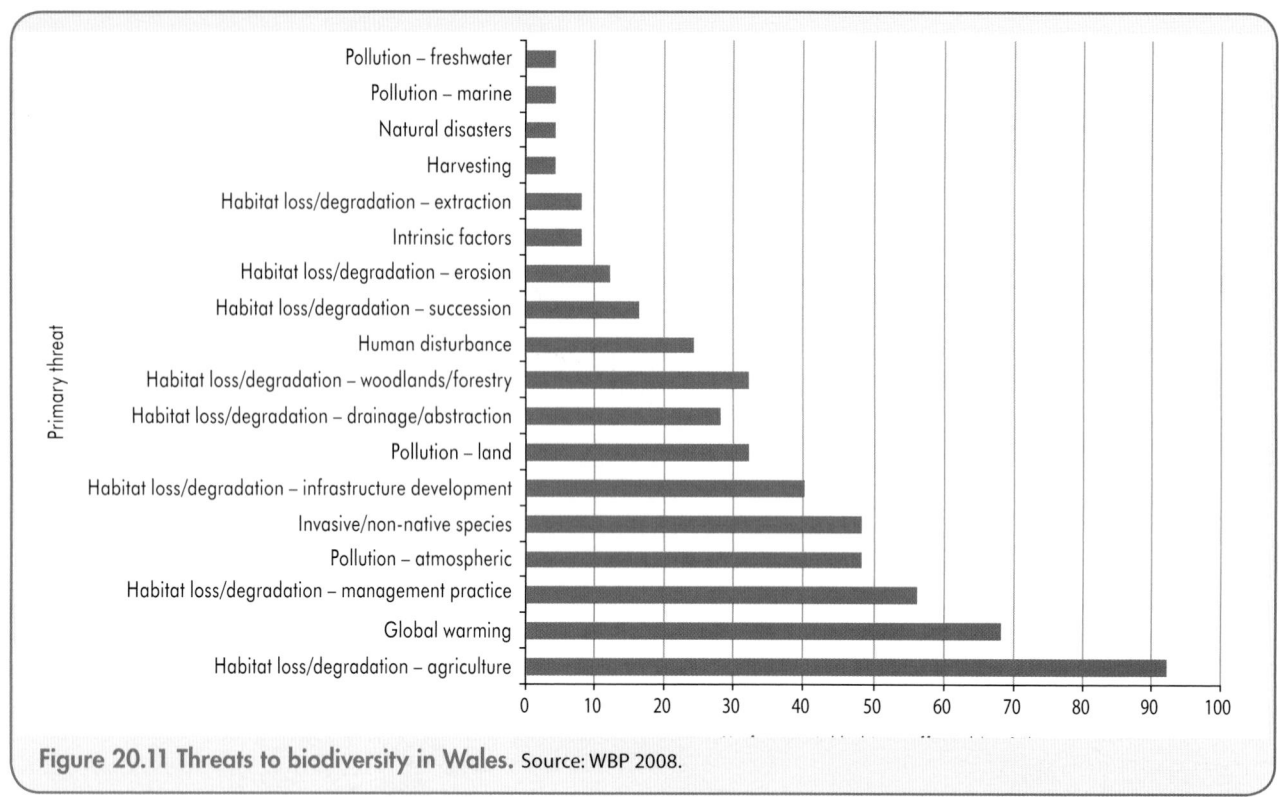

Figure 20.11 Threats to biodiversity in Wales. Source: WBP 2008.

these outcomes is measured using a suite of indicators, but at present, many of the indicators required to make a proper assessment of progress are yet to be defined (Statistical Directorate 2009).

The longer time frame adopted by Wales for its own biodiversity targets, and the fact that it has been late in developing biodiversity indicators, allows it the luxury of developing indicators specifically designed for the task. There is a wealth of biodiversity data collected in Wales, often as part of other UK-wide schemes, but much of this data are not yet presented in the form of Wales-specific measures. It has therefore been proposed to incorporate much of this data into a broad-based suite of indicators that will encapsulate biodiversity status and trends in subsequent State of the Environment assessments (Hockley et al. 2009).

Current work sponsored by the Welsh Government aims to synthesise the necessary data from many sources, covering most broad taxonomic groups, habitat types, and aspects of biodiversity (including abundance, range and diversity), to produce a small number (approximately 2–4) of headline indicators, which will sit atop a hierarchy of sub-indicators, synthesis reports and raw data. At the time of writing the indicators are being reviewed and refined to allow for the incorporation of new information, as and when it becomes available.

20.4 Condition, Status and Trends in Broad Habitats

Habitat specialists from the Countryside Council for Wales and Forestry Commission Wales have contributed the

following sections on the Broad Habitat types of Wales. For more detailed information on Welsh terrestrial habitats, the reader is referred to the recent publication: *Habitats of Wales: a comprehensive field survey 1979–1997* (Blackstock et al. 2010).

20.4.1 Mountains, Moorlands and Heaths

Mountains, Moorlands and Heaths represent some of the least developed land in Wales. They include upland grasslands, heathlands, woodlands and bogs, and lowland heathlands. Lowland heath occurs mainly in two distinct zones: within the coastal belt and at the upper limit of agricultural enclosure.

The Welsh uplands and lowland heaths are important in a European context due to their oceanicity, which affects the status and composition of many plant communities. Some oceanic communities are well represented, making the UK one of the most important world locations for habitats such as heaths and blanket bogs.

Wales does not have the largest stands of moor and heathland, and some areas are in poor condition, but those that remain intact have a heightened importance due to their southerly and westerly location and differing climatic conditions from those experienced further north. This southerly location has also resulted in the Welsh uplands supporting habitats such as montane heath, and arctic-alpine species at their southern limit in the UK. Characteristics typical of the oceanic conditions include the dominance of western gorse in the lowlands, the widespread abundance of purple moor-grass in humid and dry heaths, and the oceanic bryophyte assemblages found in some forms of upland heath.

20.4.1.1 Status, conditions and trends

Two trends are apparent in upland flowering plants and ferns. Rare arctic-alpines such as Snowdon lily and alpine saxifrage

(*Saxifraga nivalis*) remain in a steady state, but many more widespread upland species are significantly threatened. The *New Atlas of the British and Irish Flora* (Preston *et al.* 2002) shows a consistent pattern of range contraction amongst several species which were formerly characteristic of upland Wales, such as mountain pansy (*Viola lutea*) and lesser butterfly orchid (*Platanthera bifolia*).

These factors have produced a suite of Welsh habitats of conservation importance, as listed in the European Habitats Directive. The Countryside Council for Wales Habitat Survey, carried out between 1979 and 1997, remains the best available information source on the characteristics of Mountains, Moorlands and Heaths in Wales (Blackstock *et al.* 2010).

Important ecosystem services provided by the uplands and lowland heathlands of Wales include carbon sequestration in peatland soils, catchment water services including water quantity and quality regulation (important for areas beyond the borders of Wales due to water transfers), nutrient buffering, food and fibre from agriculture and forestry, renewable energy and many cultural services including tourism assets that are highly significant for the Welsh economy (Section 20.5).

Some 127,300 ha (approximately 30%) of the Welsh uplands and lowland heathlands have been designated as SSSIs, of which about 92,149 hectares have also been designated as European Special Areas of Conservation (SACs) or Special Protection Areas (SPAs). The Environment Strategy Action Plan for Wales (WAG 2008a) set a target of ensuring that 95% of international sites were in favourable condition by 2010, with 95% of all SSSIs in favourable condition by 2015 and all sites in favourable condition by 2026. Currently, approximately 60% of upland habitats in Wales are in unfavourable condition, with blanket bog and heath failing at a high percentage of sites. This provides a challenge not only for reaching government targets, but also for the retention of fully functioning habitats and the ecosystem services they provide in the long term, particularly when the potential future effects of climate change are taken into account.

Upland habitats need to be in the best possible condition if they are to be buffered against climate change impacts which are likely to arise in future. Many upland habitats in Wales are near the edge of their range and so could be adversely affected by climate change unless they are robust enough to cope with and adapt to at least some of the effects. This particularly applies to the more montane habitats, of which we have a small but important subset in the UK.

Despite concerns about the effects of climate change, direct land management is still a far more potent force in the uplands at present, particularly sheep grazing which, in addition to its own impact in reducing vegetation cover and replacing heaths, woodland and mires with grassland, also exacerbates other impacts such as pollution and climate change.

Regarding the mitigation of future effects of climate change, the primary concern within Welsh uplands is to secure the existing carbon resource that is locked up within organic and organo-mineral soils. Welsh soils represent a significant store of carbon, currently estimated at 410 million tonnes, of which approximately one-third (121 million tonnes) is in the form of peat (ECOSSE 2007), despite the fact that peat deposits occupy only 3% of the surface area of Wales.

20.4.1.2 Drivers of change

The hotter, drier summers expected with climate change present high risks to organic soils, particularly given the stark warning offered by Holden *et al.* (2006) that many upland peatlands in Wales may already be close to the tipping point between carbon sink and carbon source. Should these soils dry out, peat resources will be oxidised, dissolved organic carbon losses to receiving rivers will increase and carbon dioxide emissions will accelerate. Anticipated increases in winter rainfall will bring other problems, notably increased peat erosion and increased rainwater runoff, leading to downstream flooding.

Modelling of changes in the climatic envelope suitable for peatbogs is underway, but it seems likely that extensive areas of the Welsh uplands will remain suitable for carbon storage and ongoing sequestration in the medium term at least. Management of our finite and comparatively modest peat resource (in proportional land cover terms) is one area where low cost restoration work could make significant contributions in terms of adaptation to climate change. For example, some 36% (25,100 ha) of the Welsh peatland resource is composed of modified bogs within the uplands. Much of this resource is capable of being restored to a condition suitable for long-term protection of the underlying carbon store, whilst a significant subset of this area could also be restored to active peat growth and thus further carbon sequestration. Such restoration would also need to be accompanied by measures designed to ensure that existing high quality areas of bog are well managed and where possible actively growing, and are thus sufficiently buffered against the effects of climate change to continue to function as carbon sinks rather than as sources.

Heathlands occur on organic and organo-mineral soils and therefore play a vital role in carbon storage, particularly in the uplands and in lowland wet and humid heaths. Carbon is also stored above ground in the heather biomass with estimates varying from 200 g C/m² to 1,325 g C/m² (Farage *et al.* 2009). Both lowland and upland heath are managed by regular burning, which can result in a net loss of carbon. However, careful burning practices over long burning rotations (15–20 years) can reduce the losses of carbon attributed to burning to less than 10% of the total losses of carbon from the system (Farage *et al.* 2009).

Compared to active peatland, the level of organic matter accumulation in grassland soils is likely to be small at the level of the individual land unit. But, given the extent of acid- and *Molinia-* dominated marshy grasslands in the uplands, these may still contribute significant carbon storage potential in aggregate. By contrast, fertiliser applications, compaction (leading to increased rainwater runoff), drainage and even the poaching of wet ground associated with stock feeding sites and gates may all lead to emissions of carbon and other greenhouse gases, which exceed the capacity of vegetation-soil combinations to absorb and store carbon and may even cause them to act as sinks.

Woodlands absorb and store carbon dioxide, but carbon balances in woodland are complicated by interactions with soil and the ultimate fate of the timber crop. Conifers planted on peatlands (within Wales there are some 12,000 ha of such plantations) cause the soil to dry out, oxidising the peat and releasing carbon dioxide. Recent research has shown that whilst in the short-term the clearance of plantations on peat soils increases the level of greenhouse gas emissions, over several decades the subsequent carbon sequestration within newly restored bogs will offset losses within acceptable timescales (Colls 2006).

Native broadleaved woodland cover in the Welsh uplands is very low, with many woodlands used for shelter for grazing animals, and consequently regeneration is absent or very limited. Natural tree lines are practically non-existent and most woodlands have sharp boundaries protected by fencing.

Evidence is now beginning to emerge of a change in grazing regimes on a number of upland SSSIs/SACs. Prior to the 2003 Common Agricultural Policy (CAP) reforms, the most commonly reported problem on such sites was that of overgrazing. Whilst this is still very much an issue on large parts of many upland SSSIs, some landholders are now reducing or even removing stock from all or part of their holdings. This is a development which has the potential to help both land managers and government achieve best use of the Welsh uplands, but which could also have detrimental effects if abandonment, rather than active management, takes place.

Trends in the uplands have led to a failure to achieve early BAP and government biodiversity targets, so there is a need to develop large-scale initiatives to target particular areas for appropriate conservation management, to restore upland woodland and scrub and the natural altitudinal succession of vegetation, extend priority habitats and restore degraded stands. The new Natural Environment Framework for Wales will help address these issues by putting the ecosystem approach at the centre of government action on development and land management in Wales.

In lowland heathlands the trend has been towards neglect and abandonment, as small and fragmented sites became more difficult and less economic to manage by grazing and burning. Other drivers include increasing recreational pressure on the coastal belt, which results in farmers withdrawing grazing from these sites to avoid conflict between livestock and people (PCNP 2003). In the long-term, lowland heathland like other semi-natural habitats will remain threatened as long as it exists in small, isolated and scattered patches. Emphasis needs to be given to the re-creation of lowland heathland and associated semi-natural habitats to provide more extensive units of ecologically functional semi-natural vegetation.

20.4.2 Semi-natural Grasslands

Over most of the rural land surface of Wales, sheep and other livestock rearing is the major land use and much of the vegetation is grassy. In the lowlands, improved rye-grass (*Lolium perenne*)/white clover (*Trifolium repens*) grasslands and silage crops prevail, and during the 20th Century these extensively replaced semi-natural swards that were formerly used for grazing and hay crops. The much diminished Semi-natural Grasslands are rich in species, including many that are only poorly represented in other habitats and do not ascend into the uplands. Fragmentation of species-rich grasslands and other habitats has led to isolation and concern that there will be local extinction of component taxa in surviving fragments over time (Kuussaari *et al.* 2009).

In the sheep-walk country of the open moorlands, above the upper level of enclosure, Semi-natural Grasslands cover considerable areas of the major hills and mountains. These grasslands are mostly developed over shallow acid soils and are likely to have increased in extent, at the expense of Dwarf Shrub Heath and other habitats, as sheep numbers increased during the last century.

Sources of data presented in this short account on the extent and composition of Welsh grassland include two major field surveys undertaken by the Countryside Council for Wales. These are the Habitat Survey of Wales and the associated Lowland Grassland Survey of Wales. The surveys were largely undertaken during the period 1979–2004, and provide data on the distribution and abundance of Welsh habitats and lowland grassland plant communities; full accounts have recently been published (Blackstock *et al.* 2010; Stevens *et al.* 2010).

20.4.2.1 Status, conditions and trends

The relative amounts of unimproved, semi-improved and improved dry grasslands in Wales are summarised in **Table 20.3**. In the lowlands, the floristic composition of semi-improved swards on dry soils is somewhat intermediate between the rarer species-rich unimproved grasslands and the lush, green Improved Grasslands that now cover approximately half of the land surface of Wales. This is reflected in community composition. The highly productive improved grasslands are heavily dominated by bred strains of rye grass and white clover; semi-improved swards have more species but mostly belong to one community; unimproved swards have a range of communities on differing soil types, with many more species, up to 64 per 4 m^2 in calcareous pastures, up to 61 per 4 m^2 in Neutral Grassland, up to 55 per 4 m^2 in acidic grasslands and up to 59 per 4 m^2 in marshy grasslands. Examples of specialist plant species, more or less confined to the unimproved or Semi-natural Grasslands in the lowlands and often becoming scarce over many parts of their range, are shown in **Table 20.3**; such grasslands also host a wide variety of grassland fungi, invertebrates and other taxonomic groups. In many cases such species now occur in somewhat isolated stands; the distribution of crested dogstail/knapweed (*Cynosurus-Centaurea*) neutral pastures and meadows, for instance, in Wales is plotted in **Figure 20.12**, which reveals the thin scatter and patchy distribution of remnant fragments.

Also included in **Table 20.4** are wet or marshy grasslands that are mainly found on shallow peats, peaty gleys and related soil types; these are a distinctive component of the Welsh land cover in a European context (Blackstock *et al.* 1998). Forty per cent of the UK's 'rhos' habitat (unimproved, damp heathland pasture) is found in Wales.

In the uplands, by contrast, there are large stands of semi-natural dry grasslands composed of relatively few communities. Major dominant species include common bent (*Agrostis capillaris*), sheep's fescue (*Festuca ovina*), purple moor-grass and mat grass (*Nardus stricta*). There are fewer uncommon grassland species than in the lowlands, but such swards are used by a range of bird species, including uncommon species such as chough (*Pyrrhocorax pyrrhocorax*) and the well-known carrion-feeders buzzard (*Buteo buteo*), red kite (*Milvus milvus*) and raven (*Corvus corax*).

Important in the Welsh context is the ffridd (or coedcae) zone. This zone does not belong to any one broad habitat type, but instead refers to a mix of vegetation communities found on the often uncultivated valley sides; bridging the uplands and lowlands of Wales. The Brecon Beacons National Park Authority website states, "Its primary characteristic is a collection of various habitats (a diverse mixture of grass and heathland with bracken, scrub (often hawthorn and gorse) or rock exposures and it may also include flushes, mires, streams and standing water)" (BBNPA, 2011) In most instances, ffridd cannot be effectively farmed due to steepness or the rocky condition of the ground. The ffridd zone is noted for its dynamic nature due to a long history of changing cycles of management. Because of its situation at the boundary of lowland and upland habitats, the future management of ffridd may have important implications for biodiversity and the delivery of regulating services in Wales.

20.4.2.2 Drivers of change

Sheep and, to a lesser extent, beef rearing are the major forms of farming in Wales, with dairying and crop production now more localised. Many farms in the upland heartlands have land extending from the valley bottoms into the uplands, with the mountain flock overwintering in the lowlands or off-farm, although sheep are also on the hills during winter in some parts of Wales. Semi-natural Grasslands formerly played a fundamental role along this altitudinal gradient, providing summer grazing and hay crops in lowland enclosures; nowadays these have been very widely replaced by productive rye-grass grasslands that provide grazing and silage for winter food, and a much enhanced level of meat production. It is now common to find that remnant examples

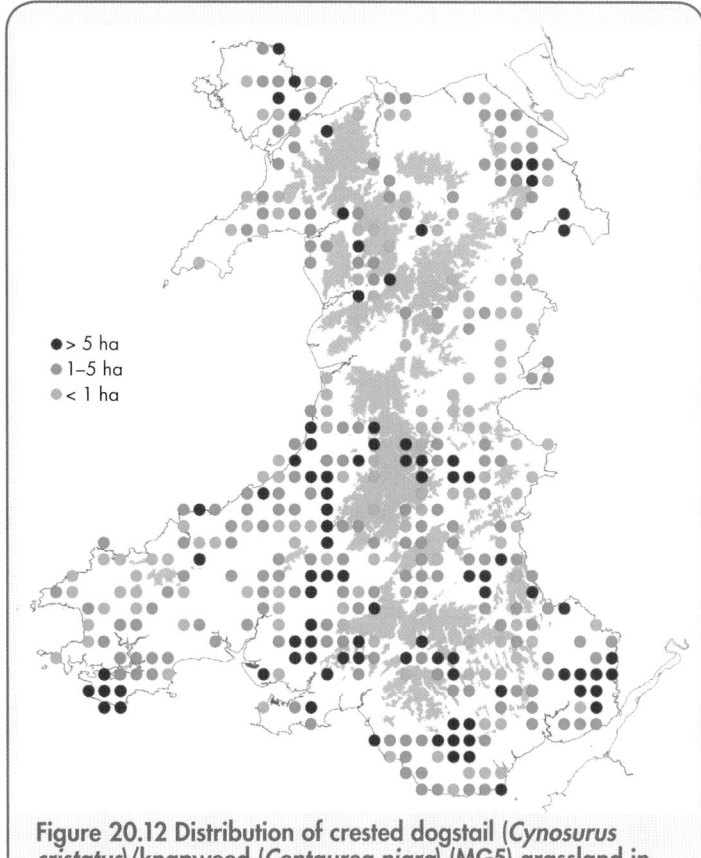

Figure 20.12 Distribution of crested dogstail (*Cynosurus cristatus*)/knapweed (*Centaurea nigra*) (MG5) grassland in Wales. Source: Stevens *et al.* (2010).

Legend:
● > 5 ha
● 1–5 ha
● < 1 ha

of Semi-natural Grasslands have become neglected and overgrown. While these grasslands still prevail in the uplands, this change in grassland composition in the lowlands has come at the cost of heavy fertiliser application and land drainage works in many locations.

Soil conditions in lowland grasslands have shown changes in the soil microbial community that have implications for nutrient management and carbon storage. Soils associated with low nutrient input semi-natural dry grassland have a relatively high fungal to bacterial biomass ratio compared to Improved Grassland (e.g. Bardgett & McAlister 1999), with fungi-rich soils appearing to retain

Table 20.3 Extent and community diversity of grasslands in Wales. Source: Blackstock *et al.* (2010).

	Extent (ha)	Number of component communities
Lowlands		
Improved	1,012,700	2
Semi-improved	53,400	3
Unimproved dry	22,100	4 (acid), 3 (neutral), 6 (calcareous)
Marshy	35,300	7
Uplands		
Improved	14,000	2
Semi-improved	5,400	2
Unimproved dry	108,700	5 (acid), 2 (calcareous)
Marshy	29,200	3

Table 20.4 Examples of plant species strongly associated with semi-natural lowland grasslands in Wales. Source: Stevens *et al.* (2010).

Acid grasslands	Neutral grasslands
Radnor Lily (*Gagea bohemica*) Upright Clover (*Trifolium strictum*) Wood Bitter-vetch (*Vicia orobusv*)	Dyer's Greenweed (*Genista tinctoria*) Green-winged Orchid (*Orchis morio*) Greater Butterfly Orchid (*Platanthera chlorantha*) Great Burnet (*Sanguisorba officinalis*)
Calcareous grasslands	**Marshy grasslands**
Soft-leaved Sedge (*Carex montana*) Dwarf Mouse-ear (*Cerastium pumilum*) Hoary Rock-rose (*Helianthemum oelandicum*) Spiked Speedwell (*Veronica spicata*)	Whorled Caraway (*Carum verticillatum*) Meadow Thistle (*Cirsium dissectum*) Blunt-flowered rush (*Juncus subnodulosus*) Wavy St John's-wort (*Hypericum undulatum*)

nitrogen more effectively (e.g. de Vries *et al.* 2006; Gordon *et al.* 2008). Soil carbon pools may also be increased in grasslands with legumes such as birdsfoot trefoil (*Lotus corniculatus*) and white clover (e.g. de Deyn *et al.* 2009), and grassland management has potential to enhance carbon sequestration in agricultural landscapes (Smith *et al.* 2008); marshy grasslands on peaty soils are likely to be particularly significant in this respect.

The ecosystem services provided by Semi-natural Grasslands include carbon and nutrient storage, and regulation of water quantity and quality through mediation of drainage regimes. These aspects are dealt with in more detail in Section 20.5.2.

Alteration of the composition of lowland grasslands is one the most rapid and widespread vegetation changes that has taken place in Wales during the 20th Century. Grasslands of different types were mapped across Wales over several years up to 1934/1935 by staff of the Plant Breeding Station at Aberystwyth (Davies 1936). Although the classification employed differs from that of the recent surveys, a comparative assessment by Stevens *et al.* (2010) indicates that some 90% of former unimproved and semi-improved swards have been transformed by agricultural management to Improved Grasslands. Such changes in grassland habitats are likely to have profound implications for the specialist biodiversity associated with Welsh lowland grasslands. The rate of loss of Semi-natural Grasslands in lowland Wales has been dampened by protection in conservation sites and agri-environment schemes, but such measures were too late to curtail the major post-war transformation.

Changes in the extent of upland Semi-natural Grassland have not been assessed, but the cover is likely to have increased during the last century, especially at the expense of Dwarf Shrub Heath. An inventory of heath on upland moorland in 1990–1991 (Bardgett *et al.* 1995) found a considerable amount of degraded heath which was attributed in part to overgrazing by sheep. This is corroborated by the findings of the Habitat Survey of Wales, which recorded a high proportion of heathland in grass-heath mosaics (Blackstock *et al.* 2010).

Modification of the composition of Welsh grasslands has taken place during a period of substantial increases in the number of sheep in Wales from about 4 to 11 million between 1950 and 1990 (Fuller & Gough 1999). More recently there has been a decline, and sheep numbers recorded in 2007 totalled almost 9 million (WAG 2009a).

Further widespread impacts on the composition of Welsh Semi-natural Grasslands are also likely to have come about through atmospheric deposition, particularly of nitrogen and sulphur, and associated acidification and eutrophication. Changes in community composition have been found with nitrogen manipulation experiments (Cunha *et al.* 2002), and there is evidence of a decline in acidic grassland species diversity associated with nitrogen deposition in Britain more generally (Stevens *et al.* 2004).

20.4.3 Enclosed Farmland

Agriculture is the predominant land use over much of the land surface of Wales, and it plays a major role in the management of natural resources and the provision of ecosystem services, particularly the provisioning services that result from agricultural production.

Including commons, agricultural land occupied some 1.64 million ha or 79% of Wales in 2008. Of this, permanent grassland and arable crops accounted for 1.163 million ha or nearly 71% of the total agricultural area (WAG 2009a). Not all of this can be regarded as Enclosed Farmland, however, since whilst much permanent grassland has been improved, a large proportion remains in a semi-natural state (Smart *et al.* 2009). According to the methods used, there remains scope for considerable variation in the estimated area of Enclosed Farmland. For example, Improved Grassland was estimated by the Countryside Survey of 2007 as covering 731,000 ha or 34% of Wales, a much higher proportion than any other country in the UK apart from Northern Ireland (Smart *et al.* 2009). By contrast, the Habitat Survey of Wales (HSW) which was completed in 1997, records the total area of improved grassland (virtually all of which, by its very nature, must be enclosed) as being 1,026,700 ha (Habitat Survey of Wales, 2008). These variations are likely to arise from the use of different definitions of improved grassland, rather than any fundamental change in the extent of this habitat between the mid-1990s and 2007.

According to the Countryside Survey (Smart *et al.* 2009), Enclosed Farmland can be defined as comprising Improved Grassland, Arable land and Horticultural crops. In 2007, the total area of Enclosed Farmland was estimated at 804,000 ha or some 40% of Wales (Smart *et al.* 2009). In comparison to the other terrestrial habitats, Enclosed Farmland varies enormously from one part of Wales to another. For example, there are considerable differences between parts of Pembrokeshire and the Brecon Beacons in terms of recreation activity, nitrogen dioxide emissions and hedgerow morphology. Enclosed Farmland has more or less intrinsic value for many ecosystem services by virtue of its scale and proximity to other habitats. In much of the Welsh uplands there is a more intimate interaction between Enclosed Farmland and the semi-natural habitats that surround it, whilst in the lowlands, the interactions are primarily with rivers, streams and woods.

Wales's National Parks and Areas of Outstanding Natural Beauty are famed for their mountainous scenery, coastal views and extensive woodlands, but all of these features interconnect with a matrix of Enclosed Farmland where field boundaries, streams, woodlands, farm buildings and a wide range of historic features contribute substantially to the overall quality of the landscape. In addition, many of the more spectacular elements of protected landscapes can only be accessed by using the roads, tracks or public footpaths that are part of the Enclosed Farmland mosaic.

Within Wales, Improved Grassland predominates in the lowlands and the upland fringes, whilst semi-natural rough grazings and woodlands occupy most of the uplands (WAS 2008). Arable land is largely confined to the lowlands and occupies less than 10% (162,000 ha) of the total agricultural area (Habitat Survey of Wales 2008). Pembrokeshire, Gower, South Glamorgan, Eastern Powys and Eastern Clwyd have significant areas of intensive arable cultivation, with smaller areas present in Ceredigion, the Lleyn Peninsula and Anglesey. A relatively small amount of arable land is occupied by cereals, potatoes and horticulture (42,898 ha) representing less than 3% of the agricultural area. Part of the arable area is devoted to oilseeds (2,820 ha) and livestock feeds such as maize (18,632 ha) or forage crops, but the majority is occupied by improved grasslands of less than 5 years old (95,034; Habitat Survey of Wales 2008). Many of these grasslands will continue to be reseeded on a regular basis and will have been defined as improved grassland during the Habitat Survey of Wales (Blackstock *et al.* 2010).

The optimal zones for agricultural production are related to climatic and soil conditions. High altitudes, acid soils and impeded drainage have prevented arable cropping and grassland intensification over large parts of Wales. The LFA designation identifies those areas where farming is most difficult, with the Severely Disadvantaged Area (SDA) closely aligned with the most mountainous and upland areas. The current LFA (which includes both the SDA and the Disadvantaged Area or DA) covers approximately 80% of the total agricultural area of Wales.

Soil conditions suitable for cultivation and sufficiently fertile to support arable crops are described as falling within Agricultural Land Classes Grade 1–3 (**Figure 20.13**). In these areas, crops are a frequent component of the landscape. Grasslands that are regularly reseeded (i.e. less than 5 years old) are relatively more frequent across Grades 1–4.

20.4.3.1 Status, conditions and trends

According to the annual Welsh Agricultural Census, the total area of agricultural land has decreased since 1994, with a reduction of 45–50,000 ha occurring in 1999 (Smart *et al.* 2009). Within this total agricultural area, the relative

proportions of the different types of farmland have also changed (Smart *et al.* 2009):

- Permanent grassland increased steadily from 55% in 1994 to 62% in 2008.
- Rough grazing decreased steadily from 29% in 1994 to 23% in 2008.
- Temporary grassland decreased steadily from 9% in 1994 to 5% in 2008.
- Total tillage has mostly remained stable at around 4%, but a significant increase of 4,300 ha (66%) was detected in the upland zone between 1998 and 2007.

Livestock rearing is a major component of agriculture throughout rural Wales. Whilst rough grazings play a major role, in particular within the sheep sector, the bulk of Welsh agricultural production takes place on enclosed land. This not only accounts for 70% of the agricultural area, but is also considerably more productive. Agriculturally improved grasslands characterised by various strains of rye-grass and white clover now predominate. During the course of the 20th Century, these highly productive crops have largely replaced the once much more characteristic semi-natural pastures and hay meadows. In particular, much of the land formerly used for hay cropping is now devoted to the production of silage. This is used for stock feed over the winter period along with concentrates and occasional forage crops.

20.4.3.2 Drivers of change

Data on the long-term trends (1867–2002) in agricultural land use and livestock numbers are presented in Section 20.5.3 on provisioning services. Towards the end of the last century, arable crops covered about 300,000 ha or 20% of the agricultural area, with cereals accounting for over half of this and the remainder consisting of roots, brassicas, peas and beans (Ashby & Evans 1944). Crops were grown for domestic consumption as well as for feeding livestock such as horses. Towards the end of the 19th Century, however, it became possible to import livestock feed. This allowed a movement away from mixed farms and towards greater specialisation. In general, the importance of crops declined and the area of land under grass increased. By the late 1930s the area of crops had reduced markedly. Despite a brief surge as more land was ploughed during the Second World War (WWII), the switch from arable to grassland accelerated from 1947 onwards, especially as horses were replaced by tractors. Crops now account for only 3% of the agricultural land area according to the Habitat Survey of Wales (Blackstock *et al.* 2010).

Information on hedgerows and walls, which are important ecological and cultural features of farmland in Wales, is provided in the sub-section on biodiversity trends in Section 20.3.

There are some 68,000 ha of farm woodlands, both conifer and broadleaved, comprising some 4% of the total area of agricultural holdings in Wales (WAS 2008). Recent woodland and agricultural schemes have helped to increase the area of Woodland (**Figure 20.14**) which has been fenced to control access by livestock, but extensive areas of semi-natural broadleaved woodland remain heavily grazed, in particular by sheep. Whilst this can bring benefits to birds such as

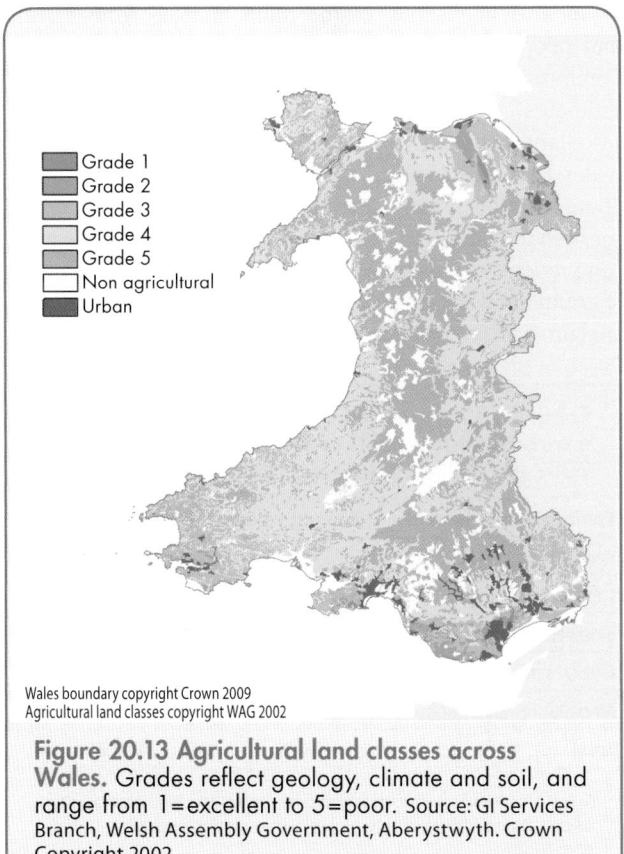

Grade 1
Grade 2
Grade 3
Grade 4
Grade 5
Non agricultural
Urban

Wales boundary copyright Crown 2009
Agricultural land classes copyright WAG 2002

Figure 20.13 Agricultural land classes across Wales. Grades reflect geology, climate and soil, and range from 1=excellent to 5=poor. Source: GI Services Branch, Welsh Assembly Government, Aberystwyth. Crown Copyright 2002.

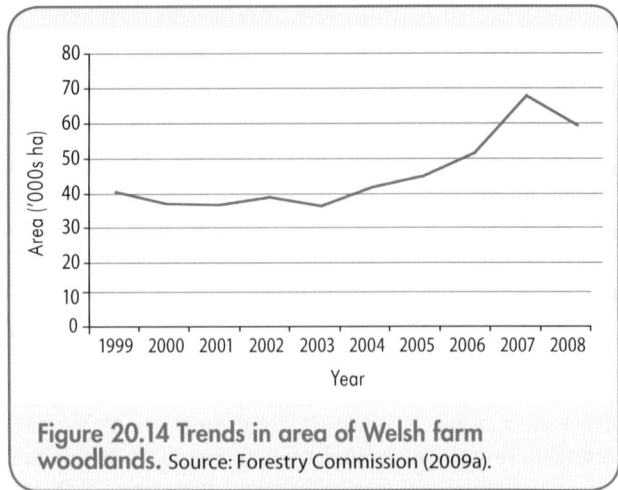

Figure 20.14 Trends in area of Welsh farm woodlands. Source: Forestry Commission (2009a).

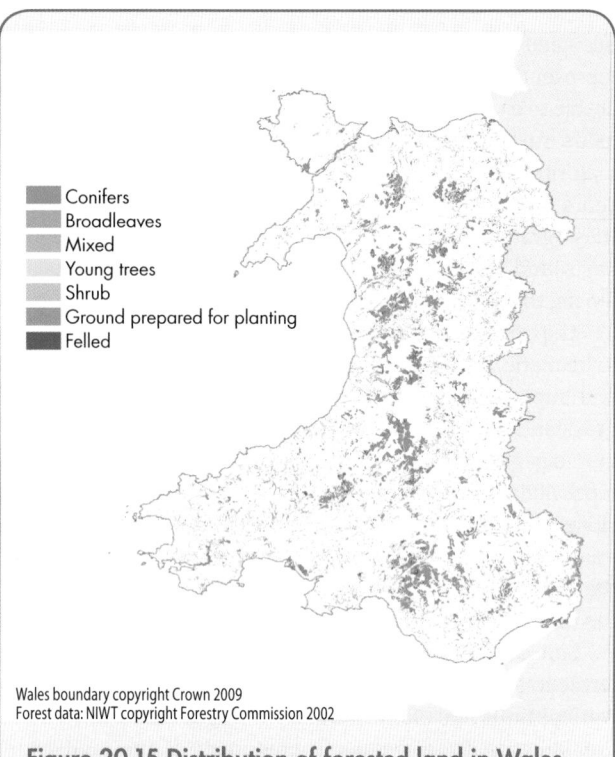

Wales boundary copyright Crown 2009
Forest data: NIWT copyright Forestry Commission 2002

Figure 20.15 Distribution of forested land in Wales, derived from National Inventory of Woodland and Trees (NIWT) (areas of tree cover with a crown density of, or likely to achieve, at least 20%, a minimum width of 50 metres and a minimum area of 2 ha). Source: Forestry Commission (2003).

the pied flycatcher (*Ficedula hypoleuca*) which are more common in heavily grazed oak woodlands, uncontrolled levels of grazing seem likely to inhibit regeneration of trees and shrubs, representing a long-term threat to the continued survival of these habitats. However, in 2007, the Countryside Survey reported on changes in a number of sample plots between 1971 and 2001 and found that the basal area of trees and shrubs had increased, numbers of tree seedlings had decreased and the abundance of open habitats and signs of recent management had all decreased. These changes were also accompanied by a decrease in the number of species of ground flora and a shift toward more shade-tolerant understorey plants (Countryside Survey 2007). As a result, current advice on woodland management focuses on trying to ensure the right level of grazing is used, rather than attempting to exclude livestock altogether.

20.4.4 Woodlands

"Trees...Nothing can compete with these larger-than-life organisms for signalling the changes in the natural world." (Deakin 2007).

Woodlands cover approximately 14% of the land area of Wales (**Figure 20.15**). They provide an important range of ecosystem services and associated goods and benefits such as timber, soil protection, amenity and biodiversity. The climate of Wales has a strong maritime influence that, over time, has led to the development of a number of distinctive cool temperate native forest types, which are a subset of those found in continental Europe (Barbatti *et al.* 2007). There is considerable variation in composition in response to climatic gradients and soil type. Distinctive Atlantic woodlands dominated by oak, also known as upland oak woodlands, are widespread throughout Wales, currently accounting for about half of the semi-natural woodland cover. Other native woodland types in Wales include upland mixed ash woodlands, which represent 25% of the semi-natural woodlands, wet woodlands of alder, willow and birch, lowland beech and yew confined to South Wales, and on the heavier soils, lowland mixed broadleaved woodland of oak, ash and elm. Climatic constraints have influenced the development of woodland management in Wales, permitting a wide range of potential temperate species to be considered for use, and imposing other constraints such as wind, rather

than fire, as a dominant abiotic disturbance factor (Quine & Gardiner 2006).

Biodiversity is one of the main benefits from forests that people (70–80% of respondents) recognise (Forestry Commission 2009b) and has been included as part of estimates of the non-timber values associated with woodland. The environmental benefits of woodlands in Wales have been valued at £34 million (Read *et al.* 2009). There have been some attempts to assess the value of the services provided by woodlands and forests. One of the most comprehensive was by Willis *et al.* in 2002. The assessment of annual and capitalised social and environmental benefits are summarised in **Table 20.5**.

Table 20.5 Annual and capitalised social and environmental benefits of forests in Wales (£ millions, 2002 prices). Source: Read *et al.* (2009).

Environmental benefit	Annual value	Capitalised value
Recreation	13.84	395.40
Landscape	7.25	207.14
Biodiversity	4.00	28.57
Carbon sequestration	9.19*	262.57
Air pollution absorption	0.04*	1.13
Total	**34.32**	**894.81**

* An approximation, since carbon sequestration, and probability of death and illness due to air pollution, varies over time (Read *et al.* 2009).

20.4.4.1 Status, conditions and trends

The area of woodland in Wales began to increase following the First World War when, in 1919, the Forestry Commission was formed. The Forestry Commission began acquiring land and planting it mainly with conifers, to build up a strategic reserve of timber so that Britain would no longer have to rely on imports in times of war. The first trees to be planted by the Forestry Commission in Wales were in Llantrisant in 1921. The Second World War (1939–1945) put further pressure on our woodlands, despite all the planting in the previous years. Concern over losses and degradation of ancient and native woodland in the decades after WWII led to the development of policies for the protection of key sites (e.g. National Nature Reserves (NNRs), first designated in 1951, and SSSIs, first designated in 1981), and latterly for the protection, management and expansion of priority woodland habitats (Kirby 2003; Latham *et al.* 2005; UKBAP 2006; section 2). The latest estimate (Finch *et al.* 2008) is that there are currently 109,556 ha of native woodland in Wales (5.2% of Wales's land surface) comprising 81,000 ha semi-natural woodland and 29,000 ha of planted native woodland. This is 38% of the total woodland cover in Wales.

Different regimes of woodland management have evolved, reflecting woodland type, markets, and labour availability and affordability. In the latter part of the 20th Century, there was an almost complete cessation of traditional coppice management systems in native woodlands (Buckley 1992). Commercial plantations were, and in many cases still are, managed on an even-aged basis, with large-scale felling of stands at economic maturity to maximise timber production. In recent decades there has been a major shift in forestry policy and practice with the adoption of the principle of Sustainable Forest Management (SFM) for multiple benefits (Mason 2007). Woodlands are increasingly managed as a resource for people (recreation, amenity, well-being) and wildlife as well as timber and other wood products.

Woodlands in Wales vary in nature and character, with a very uneven spatial distribution of the principal woodland types. All Welsh woodland has been modified by management to some extent. According to the FRA (Global Forest Resource Assessment) 2005 definitions, there are no areas of primary woodland left in Wales. The majority of woodland area is classed as productive plantation with the next largest category, modified natural, representing 28.7% of the woodland area. Each of these categories delivers a somewhat different set of ecosystem services. In Wales only 1.6 % of land surface (and 12% of woodland) is ancient and semi-natural, and thus of the highest value for nature conservation (**Table 20.6**). However, native woodland (6% of land surface and 45% of woodland) is one of the most species-rich habitats in Wales, and non-native woods also have some biodiversity value. About 210 (39%) of the Section 42 species of principal importance for conservation of biological diversity in Wales either rely on woodland habitats, or could potentially be affected by silvicultural operations.

The major concentrations of Coniferous Woodland are located on the poorer soils in upland Wales. These woodlands are generally not close to major towns except for in the Valleys of South Wales where large areas of woodland are found close to sizeable centres of population. The vast majority of Wales's ancient semi-natural woodland and native woodlands are small and fragmented, often unmanaged, and generally set within an intensively managed agricultural landscape. There are some significant areas of ancient semi-natural woodland in South East Wales, particularly in the Wye Valley. Forty-four per cent of woodland over 2 hectares in extent is owned by or leased to the Forestry Commission, and responsibility for the management of the remaining 56% of woodland is in other ownership (NIWT 2002).

A significant amount of the tree resource in Wales is outside woodlands, in the form of individual trees and hedgerows (approximately 15.33 million live trees and 64 thousand dead trees in Wales; NIWT 2002). No data are available on trends in the area of urban woodland or numbers of urban trees in Wales.

The UK NEA Broad Habitat 'Woodlands' is based on the UK BAP broad habitat definitions, as also used by the UK-wide Countryside Survey (Countryside Survey 2007) with slight variation. Two woodland component habitats are recognised: Coniferous Woodland and Broadleaved Mixed and Yew Woodland. Within these categories, further priority habitats are recognised, with five of these being found in Wales. In addition about a quarter of the UK BAP priority species are associated with woodland or tree habitats to varying degrees. The NERC Act 2006, Section 42 List, includes 152 species which are associated with woodlands in Wales.

Tree cover of one sort or another is considered to have dominated the landscape in Wales in the pre-Neolithic period, although there are disputes as to how much of this

Table 20.6 Extent of woodland in Wales ('000s hectares). Source: Forestry Commission (2009a) with data on ancient woodland derived from Pryor & Peterken (2001) and the National Inventory of Woodlands and Trees, Forestry Commission (2003).

| Woodland Type | Conifer | | Broadleaf | | Total Woodland |
	Area ('000 ha)	Proportion (%) of total woodland	Area ('000 ha)	Proportion (%) of total woodland	Area ('000 ha)
PAWS* 1997	17	6	11	4	
ASNW* 1997	-	-	34	12	
Total in 2009	**156**	**55**	**128**	**45**	**284**

* Ancient woodland is woodland that has been in continuous existence since 1600; ASNW (ancient semi-natural woodland) is both ancient and semi-natural; PAWS (plantation on an ancient woodland site) is ancient but not semi-natural – and may be covered with broadleaf or conifer species.

was closed high forest and how much was a more open wooded system (Vera 2000; Rackham 2003; Hodder *et al.* 2005, 2009). The post-glacial history of native woodland in Wales (as in the rest of the UK) is largely one of loss, degradation and fragmentation (Rackham 1986; Watts *et al.* 2005). It is thought that a significant proportion of the country's woodland biodiversity was conserved through the retention of ancient broadleaved woodland (accounting for approximately 1% of the land area).

Forest cover in Wales declined through the Middle Ages, reaching an all-time low of 4.2% around the beginning the 20th Century. Since that period woodland area in Wales has almost tripled and currently amounts to 284,000 ha, representing approximately 14% of the total land area (Forestry Commission 2009a). This compares with a global woodland cover average of 30% and the EU average of 37% (FAO Forest Resource Assessment). The increase in woodland cover in Wales parallels a similar trend in Europe (World Resources Institute 2003). Notable woodland planting by private estate owners in Wales began in the late 17th and 18th Centuries, but substantial re-afforestation efforts began in the 20th Century (Smout 2002; Linnard 2000). Successive governments attempted to address the shortage of timber (compounded by wartime fellings) by encouraging the creation of large plantations of non-native conifer species. There was considerable criticism of planting on upland habitats (Avery 1989) and on existing ancient woodland sites (NCC 1984; Humphrey & Nixon 1999) due to loss of valued habitats, and pace of change in upland areas. This, and other changes, such as those relating to government taxation policy, has led to a dramatic decrease in the last 20 years of new planting of conifers, although they continue to be used extensively in replanting (restocking).

By contrast, over this period there has been an increase in the area of native woodland and use of broadleaved tree species through planting or natural regeneration. On river and stream banks, a clear on-going successional trend is observed, consistent with a marked increase in cover of trees and shrubs, and continuing reductions in species richness, especially of butterfly larval food plants (Countryside Survey 2007).

The restoration in tree cover has resulted particularly from the afforestation of marginal grazing land in the uplands— the main driver for expansion being timber production—and this underpins the current dominance of conifers, which comprise 55% of woodlands in Wales. However, the amount of broadleaved woodland has also increased, so that by 2009 broadleaf cover stood at 45% (see **Table 20.6**). This reflects

changes in forestry policy since the mid-1980s which have sought to increase the range of services that woodlands can provide (including biodiversity, regulating services and cultural services). In this period the overall rate of increase in woodland cover slowed (the increase in the 5 years to 2006 being only 15% of that in the 5 years to 1976). There was a shift towards expansion of broadleaved/native woodland rather than coniferous woodland (Forestry Commission 2003), and usually in smaller blocks (**Table 20.7**).

One of the key aims of Woodlands for Wales, the Welsh Government's strategy for woodlands and trees (WAG 2009b), is to increase the diversity of woodlands. Ancient and semi-natural/native woodlands, a particular concern from a biodiversity perspective (Peterken 1977), have declined due to losses to agriculture and to a lesser extent to development; and in addition, there was widespread planting of conifer species on ancient woodland sites between 1900 and the 1980s (at least 17,000 ha; Spencer & Kirby, 1992; Roberts *et al.* 1992). This was followed by a concerted effort to restore these woodland areas to native species (approximately 5,000 ha between 2000 and 2010; Forestry Commission 1985; Defra/Forestry Commission 2005; ODPM 2005; Goldberg *et al.* 2007). Individual sites do, however, still come under threat.

Despite recent reductions in pollutant emissions, nitrogen deposition and ozone levels are still above 'critical loads' for habitats such as Atlantic oak woodlands with sensitive ground flora and epiphytic lichens. It is well established that wild herbivores, including deer, have increased in Wales over at least the past 30 years, with impacts on tree regeneration, woodland structure, species diversity and timber quality. Woodland ageing has led to increased shading and loss of structural diversity and may have contributed to the decline of some woodland birds. Increased shading is also caused by lack of management. Where woodlands cover a sufficiently large area there will be a range of woodland types and age structure with associated variation of flora and fauna which will be able to move between and into gaps, sustaining complex ecosystem dynamics and resulting in greater biodiversity. However, most Welsh woodlands are small and may consist of stands of one or just a few tree species. In these, the process of stand development can have the effect of displacing ground flora to the edge of the woodland, and with little scope for moving to adjacent suitable habitat, some species may be lost to the site either temporarily or permanently.

Historic management patterns of thinning, small-scale felling and coppicing have in the past mitigated the shading effect by removing a proportion of canopy trees, accelerating the environmental partitioning process and producing a more diverse stand structure. In small woodlands where such management has ceased or never commenced, woodland ecosystems have lost many important functions and remain sub-scale and less diverse than their full potential would allow. Deforestation of other woodland types does takes place to restore open habitats that were afforested during the 20th Century. For instance, Forestry Commission Wales is working to restore deep peat habitats on the Government Woodland Estate and to date, 900 ha of conifers have been removed to achieve this. There is less

Table 20.7 New woodland creation ('000s hectares) in Wales; five year totals over an 18 year period ending March 31st. Source: Forestry Commission (2009a).

Woodland type	1976	1981	1986	1991	1996	2001	2006	2009
	'000 hectares							
Conifer	12.9	6.8	5.6	3.0	0.5	0.7	0.0	0.0
Broadleaved	0.1	0.2	0.3	1.1	2.0	2.1	1.9	0.7
Total	**12.9**	**6.9**	**5.9**	**4.1**	**2.5**	**2.7**	**1.9**	**0.7**

information on changes in the numbers and extent of small clumps and individual trees (Forestry Commission 2003). These include a high proportion of veteran trees, for which the UK has a particular responsibility/reputation in Europe (Woodland Trust 2009). These declined in the post-war period (e.g. Peterken & Allison 1989) as a consequence of agricultural intensification.

In broadleaved woodlands, evidence from the Countryside Survey (2007) and Kirby et al.(1998) suggests that three key changes have taken place over the last 20 years. 1) Increasing shadiness, reductions in open space and increases in deadwood: primarily due to the ageing of woodlands planted in the 20th Century, but also following limited silvicultural interventions in broadleaved woods over the last 60 years. This has led to increases in shade-tolerant plants including bramble, with concurrent reductions in the species richness of ground flora (particularly butterfly food species). 2) Increasing density of the 0.5–4 m shrub layer. Amar et al (2010) suggest that over the last century Welsh woodlands have typically experienced increased levels of grazing by stock, followed in the last 20 years by a reduction in grazing pressures as government policy has encouraged stock exclusion. The increasing shrub layer may further shade out the ground flora and lichens on lower trunks of trees as well as competing with the veteran trees (Read 2000). 3) An increasing 'generation gap' whereby sites with mature or veteran trees frequently lack younger generations to replace them.

For at least the last 30 years, grey squirrel and deer populations have increased in Wales (Ward 2005) and now constitute a major limitation on natural regeneration (Fuller & Gill 2001). The apparently increasing threats (Broadmeadow et al. 2009) to mature trees from disease (Dutch Elm Disease, alder dieback, ash dieback, various syndromes affecting oak, new strains of Phytophthora affecting a broad range of trees, etc.) makes a lack of replacement trees even more acute.

The condition of Coniferous Woodlands has also changed. There is increased diversity of structure with the maturing of coniferous forests, plus the impacts of deliberate restructuring of plantations through smaller felling coupes and gradual transformation of forests in Wales from clear felling to continuous cover (Mason 2007). Over the last decade, efforts to identify areas to be left as stream corridors, and to remove dense conifer shading and open out stream sides, are likely to have significantly increased invertebrate abundance and numbers of trout where water quality is suitable.

A landscape connectivity indicator has recently been developed (Watts & Handley 2010) to reflect the constraints that different landscapes may place on the dispersal of species from one patch of habitat to another. This has been applied to Countryside Survey 2007 data for the purposes of biodiversity reporting. Preliminary results indicate a decline in Wales in the functional connectivity of woodlands within the landscape. The declines appear to be largely due to the increasing hostility to species dispersal of landuse types that separate woodland patches, for example by the intensification of agricultural practice. Efforts are underway to encourage native woodland planting in key network zones via the Better Woodlands for Wales grant scheme. The

trends identified are likely to continue to be significant in the short to medium term. The future may pose a different set of threats to woodland condition.

20.4.4.2 Drivers of change

Over the last century, the key drivers of change in Welsh woodlands have been:

a) Government policy: The last century saw a major shift from a policy of large-scale woodland planting (early 1900s to 1980s) generally, with timber production as a single objective, to a focus on multipurpose forestry and little increase in woodland cover (1980s to present) where forest design and management have aimed to provide a balance of ecosystem services. In particular, there have been significant increases in the provision of recreation facilities, a restructuring of wooded riparian zones, a large-scale redesign of woodland shapes in the landscape, and a recent reduction in the reliance on clear felling.

b) Endogenous ageing of woodlands: The ageing of conifer and broadleaved woodlands planted in the 20th Century has led to significant changes in ecosystem delivery through a combination of active management and natural processes.

c) Reduction in use of home-grown hardwood fibre: There has also been ageing of the broadleaved woodland resource due to reductions in silvicultural intervention (e.g. for firewood, tan bark, pit props and charcoal making).

To a lesser extent, invasive species, pests and diseases, pollution and rising energy prices have also been drivers of change.

In future, the key drivers of change are likely to be:

a) Implementation of the Welsh Government's Woodlands for Wales Strategy. This 50-year strategy, published in 2001 and revised in 2009, recognises the role of woodlands and trees in delivering social, economic and environmental benefits. It promotes the design and management of woodlands to provide a wide and balanced range of ecosystem services. Government and market incentives for planting to deliver more benefits such as carbon sequestration (or to a lesser extent, flood risk mitigation). These could lead to a major increase in planting rates, and also affect the way that existing woodlands are managed.

b) Projections about the probable impacts of climate change. These are likely to drive change in silvicultural practice in order to increase the resilience of the woodland resource. Efforts are already underway to diversify woodland structures and to alter the variety of tree species planted. A changing climate is likely to increase the number of outbreaks of pests and diseases (e.g. Phytophthora species), and the levels of windthrow and drought.

c) Rising energy prices. These are likely to further encourage planting and management of broadleaved woodland for woodfuel, and may also impact on the way conifer plantations are created and managed.

Detailed discussion of drivers is provided in the UK-level chapter on Woodlands (Chapter 8). It includes coverage of climate change, land use change, economic forces, woodland fragmentation and loss, pollution (e.g. nitrogen deposition and ozone levels), biotic pressures due to herbivores, pests and invasive species, and the ageing of the woodland stock in Wales.

20.4.5 Freshwaters – Openwaters, Wetlands and Floodplains

Wales has some of the most dynamic fluvial systems in Britain. An average annual total of 3,000 mm of rainfall falls on Snowdonia, the wettest part of the country. The geological foundation of the region is mainly hard rock with limited underground water storage capacity. Generally, rainfall is quickly channelled into rivers, which are very responsive to changes in weather. In addition, lakes and wetlands act as surface reservoirs supplementing river flows. Over 20 major river systems drain the total surface area of Wales (2,077,000 ha).

Welsh rivers have a distinctive westward- or eastward-flowing biogeography (distribution of plants and animals). Westward rivers are dominated by salmonid species, while eastward rivers often have a more diverse assemblage, including several coarse fish species. Plant communities dominated by bryophytes and a range of vascular plants tolerant of fast flows and base-rich conditions are found in the south-east, e.g. Wye and Usk. River plant assemblages in the westward-flowing rivers have a diverse bryophyte flora adapted to the shaded, base-poor conditions. There is also a distinctive plant community adapted to acid, low-nutrient conditions in the headwaters.

20.4.5.1 Status, conditions and trends

Change in freshwater habitat. An Environment Agency dataset has shown that Wales has some of the best quality river habitat in England/Wales. River invertebrate distribution reflects the 'River Continuum Concept' (Vannote *et al.* 1980), responding to physical and chemical factors and varying across riffle-pool (shallow-deep) sequences. There is no distinctly Welsh river invertebrate fauna, but many species are of conservation importance and some are on the brink of extinction within the region, e.g. freshwater pearl mussel (*Margaritifera margaritifera*). In headwaters, invertebrate community composition is strongly influenced by calcium and pH composition.

Lakes located along rivers reflect the environmental gradient from upland acid waters to lowland, often more nutrient-rich conditions. Geographic location has a major influence on lake biology in Wales, with the most obvious distinction occurring between lowland and upland environmental conditions. The upland, natural lakes of glacial origin usually have nutrient-poor, acid, clear, or peat-stained waters. Their stony and exposed shorelines are a challenging environment favouring stress-tolerant, low-growing rosette vegetation (plants with a rosette of leaves held flat to the ground). Invertebrate communities are dominated by insect taxa—mayflies, stoneflies, some beetles—with simple food webs based on algal growths and fine detritus.

Lowland lake systems have a higher degree of niche diversity, with a variety of submerged and floating plant forms and greater range of physiological tolerance. Abundant and diverse assemblages of invertebrates are found, including leeches, snails, crustaceans and insects, with the more complex food web based on well-developed plant beds.

The biodiversity of Welsh lakes is comparable to that found in England and Scotland, but the range of lake types is high for a small region, with nine out of 11 of the UK's ecological lake types recorded in Wales according to the JNCC lake classification (Duigan *et al.* 2007).

Welsh fens are important by virtue of their extent, diversity and quality, and they present a microcosm of the range of variation found within British fens. There is an estimated 6,200 ha of fen habitat occurring in Wales, encompassing approximately 2,700 ha of basin, valley and floodplain mire and 2,100 ha of flush vegetation in the lowlands, together with approximately 1,400 ha of swamp (figures from the Lowland Habitats Survey of Wales 1987–1997 and the RSPB Inventory of Welsh Reedbeds 1993, 1995).

There is an estimated 460 ha of Welsh reedbed, amounting to approximately 10% of the total UK cover of this habitat (some 5,000 ha), and the notable concentrations in some Welsh local BAP areas represent an important western UK stronghold. Wales supports a total of 1,700 ha of lowland blanket bog, of which 1,200 ha is modified bog, which reflects the extent to which this habitat has undergone modification. Grazing marshes and floodplain grasslands are widespread in lowland Britain, covering an estimated total area of 300,000 ha; however, only a small proportion of this is semi-natural grassland. A total of 54,600 ha of grassland habitat types have been recorded within coastal levels and floodplain landscapes in Wales, within a Countryside Council for Wales inventory of Welsh grazing marsh and floodplain sites. There is a continuously changing assemblage of birds moving into and around Wales and a substantial proportion are dependent on freshwater and wetland habitats. For example, the red-breasted merganser (*Mergus serrator*) and goosander (*Mergus merganser*) have successfully colonised, osprey (*Pandion haliaetus*) have returned and nested near the River Glaslyn since 2004, while some species have noticeably shifted their distribution away from the coast.

The otter (*Lutra lutra*) is one of the largest predators found in fresh waters and wetlands in Wales. Historic population declines have been attributed to the use of toxic pesticides but recovery remains slow, with numbers and the distribution range of otters below previous levels (Environment Agency, 2004). Rivers are especially important to a diversity of bat species, as feeding/roosting areas and flyway connections. Mink introduction has been linked with water vole decline. However, Welsh rivers have also served as isolated refuges for imperilled species, such as the polecat (*Mustela putorius*).

The Welsh fish fauna has a preponderance of diadromous types (species that migrate between the sea and fresh water). The populations of salmon, shad and lampreys (*Lampetra planeri*) are of particular conservation importance in a European context. Welsh rivers have 32 resident fish species, including eight non-natives. Brown trout are common in upland lakes, and Welsh lakes also support the most southern populations of Arctic charr (*Salvelinus alpines*) and gwyniad in Britain.

Freshwater ecosystems in Wales are undergoing serious environmental degradation from a variety of human pressures including pollution, sedimentation, extractive fisheries, invasive/non-native species introduction and water regulation. The majority of freshwater features within designated sites in Wales are in unfavourable or declining condition according to European survey criteria (**Figure 20.16**). The Countryside Survey (2007) found that species richness within sampled watercourses (primarily headwaters) did not change between 1998 and 2007 and the physical characteristics of watercourses improved.

Condition of rivers. Upland Welsh freshwater ecosystems are very vulnerable to acid deposition due to a combination of local acid sensitivity (base-poor rocks and soils), large volumes of rainfall containing sulphur and nitrogen oxides, and local land use practices. In particular, over 20% of the highest altitude catchments in Wales (over 200 m) are afforested by exotic conifers that increase local sulphur and nitrogen deposition, thereby increasing the contribution of acids and metals. Over half of Wales's stream length—around 12,000 km—was impacted by acidification making this the single largest pollution problem (Firth *et al.* 1995; Stevens *et al.* 1997). Ecosystem structure and function in acidified streams has been altered, including reductions in salmonid and dipper populations (Ormerod & Jüttner 2009).

Condition of lakes. It is estimated that there are almost 570 lakes (over 1 ha) in Wales and 47,000 smaller ponds and wetland pools (2007) increased from 40,000 in 1998. However, only 5% of ponds were classified as being in 'good' condition at the time of the Countryside Survey in 2007 (**Figure 20.17**). The majority of Welsh lakes are of glacial origin and located in the mountains of north and mid-Wales. Several shallow lake ecosystems in Wales have switched from clear-water, plant-dominated ecosystems to phytoplankton-dominated lakes, or are exhibiting symptoms of a trend in this direction (e.g. Langorse Lake; Anglesey Lakes; Bosherston). Records of toxic blue-green algal blooms are increasing (e.g. Llyn Padarn, 2009; Llyn Tegid , since 1995).

Condition of reservoirs. Nearly all the major river systems in Wales are regulated by headwater dams and reservoirs installed for water supply, flood control and energy generation, which have caused hydromorphological modification of lakes and river courses (**Figure 20.18**). Reservoir development became an Anglo-Welsh political issue in the 1960s, with the displacement of the Welsh-speaking Capel Celyn community to create Lyn Celyn

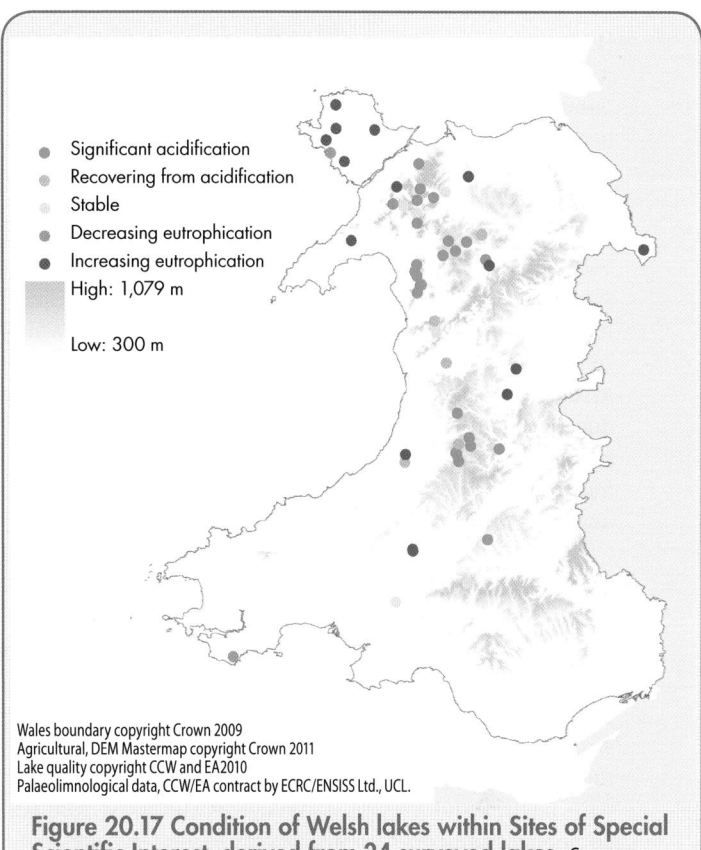

Wales boundary copyright Crown 2009
Agricultural, DEM Mastermap copyright Crown 2011
Lake quality copyright CCW and EA2010
Palaeolimnological data, CCW/EA contract by ECRC/ENSISS Ltd., UCL.

Figure 20.17 Condition of Welsh lakes within Sites of Special Scientific Interest, derived from 24 surveyed lakes. Source: CCW 2010.

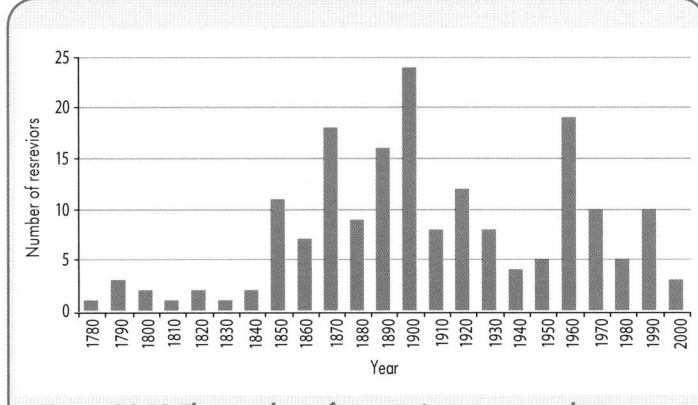

Figure 20.18 The number of reservoirs constructed per decade in Wales from 1780 to 2010. Source: based on Environment Agency data (statistics derived by the Countryside Council for Wales).

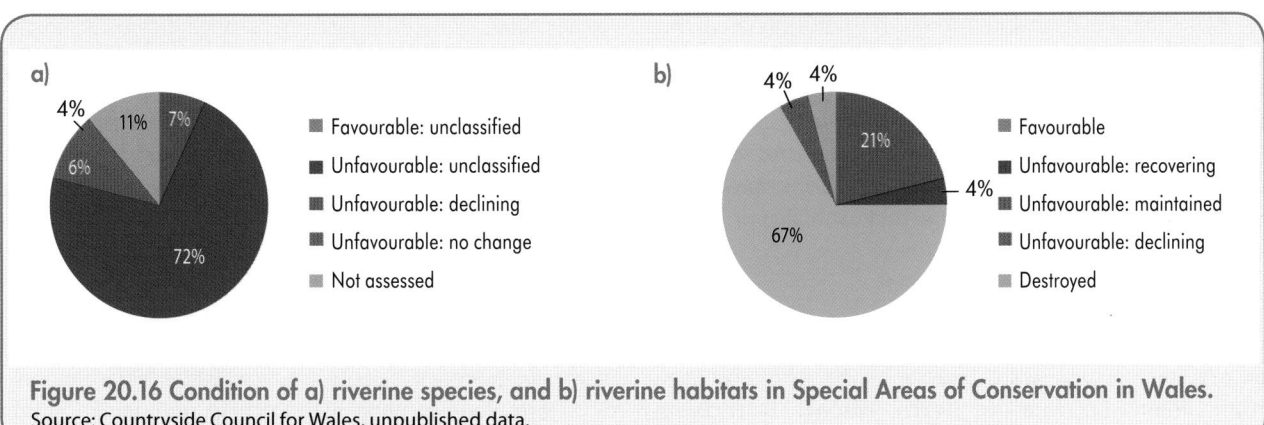

Figure 20.16 Condition of a) riverine species, and b) riverine habitats in Special Areas of Conservation in Wales. Source: Countryside Council for Wales, unpublished data.

(1965) as a water supply for Liverpool, and resistance to impoundments in the Clywedog valley in the 1970s. Two hundred-and-three reservoirs are now listed in the public register of reservoirs in Wales, but 11 of them are less than 1 ha in extent. One hundred and ninety-two reservoirs greater than 1 ha in area represent 33.86% of Welsh lakes. In 2010, over 799,709,824 m³ of fresh water was contained within Welsh reservoirs. There may be further demands for reservoir construction as climate change increasingly impacts water availability and security in England and Wales. As Wales develops the ecosystem approach to governance as embodied in its new Natural Environment Framework, questions are certain to arise regarding the trade-off between maintenance of natural freshwater ecosystems and human demands on the environment where riverine, lake and reservoir resources are concerned.

Condition of floodplains. Some of the most valuable and productive agricultural land in Wales is strongly associated with floodplains. As a result, floodplain habitat is scarce, with 60% contained within just 10 river systems. Welsh river floodplain habitat is seriously degraded and fragmented, largely due to agricultural intensification and flood defence structures (Jones et al. 2009). Agricultural grassland is the most extensive land cover within Welsh floodplains, with neutral and marshy grassland as the most common component of semi-natural habitat. Secondary woodland, swamp, fen, bog and standing water also occur, with a wide diversity of floristic communities dependent on low-intensity farming in floodplains. Flood defence structures protect and isolate neighbouring areas from inundation, especially in urban environments. For example, almost the entire length of the River Taff is channelised with reinforcement and embankments for flood control (Dobson et al. 2009). This, coupled with conversion to improved grassland, upland forestry, general agricultural intensification, non-native species and urbanisation has degraded floodplain habitat across Wales.

More than 75% of Welsh-designated conservation sites (SSSIs /SACs/SPAs) contain water-dependent features. The Countryside Council for Wales is responsible for ensuring protection of these designated interests on six major river systems and over 140 lakes. Approximately 320 wetland SSSIs depend upon groundwaters, and 35 sites depend upon critical water level management. Between 50 and 75% of the land area of Wales is within the catchments of these rivers, lakes and wetlands.

Water and aquatic habitats form a key naturally occurring habitat network, and some river stretches have also been recognised for their fluvial geomorphological features, as part of the Geological Conservation Review. These sites (approximately 20) serve as illustrations of the evolution of the Welsh landscape, its cover landforms, processes, channel features, channel change and examples of human impact.

20.4.5.2 Drivers of change

A direct policy driver of change in Welsh freshwater ecosystems is, and will continue to be, the European Water Framework Directive (WFD). Through River Basin Management Plans working at the catchment level, the WFD is emphasising a more holistic approach to freshwater management that takes account of the wide range of ecosystem services that Welsh freshwater habitats provide.

Climate change is set to have a major influence on Welsh freshwater ecosystems, and changing patterns in water quantity and temperature are already discernible in Wales. In Llyn Brianne streams for example, winter temperatures have increased over the last 25 years by 1.4–1.7°C, causing changes in invertebrate populations (Durance & Ormerod 2007). Declines in Wye salmon and trout populations are also being linked to hotter, drier summers (Clews et al. 2010; Ormerod & Jüttner 2009). Welsh streams are adapted to large-scale 'gradual' climatic phenomena such as the North Atlantic Oscillation (Bradley & Ormerod 2001; Briers et al. 2004; Ness et al. 2004), so native species with less capacity for internal temperature control tend to dominate assemblages. They are therefore more vulnerable to climate change impacts that are likely to result in more sudden changes in local stream environments (Ormerod & Jüttner 2009).

Upland waters in the UK and Wales that were damaged by acid rain are beginning to recover. Between 1984 and 1995, average pH across streams in the Welsh Acid Waters Survey increased on average by 0.2 pH, while sulphate concentrations fell by around 16% (Stevens et al. 1997). Biological recovery is lagging behind chemical trends (because some streams remain chronically acid, while others are still affected by acid episodes), with acid-sensitive species still occurring only sporadically in recovering streams, and representing only a fraction of the species previously lost (Bradley & Ormerod 2002; Ormerod & Durance 2009). The true extent of acidification in Wales is under-recorded by routine Environment Agency monitoring and there are potential adverse consequences for key conservation sites, e.g. the River Wye (Ormerod & Jüttner 2009; Lewis et al. 2007).

Nutrients from diffuse and point sources and other forms of pollution are responsible for a decline in the health of freshwater ecosystems across Wales. Pollution may take the form of a short-term event/incident or may be a persistent influence over a longer period of time. Phosphorus and nitrate values are limiting the number of rivers which can be considered to be in 'good' condition. Significant slippage of rivers (700–800 km) from 'very good' to 'good' biological quality has taken place in Wales from around 1995 onward. The reasons are unclear but may be linked to diffuse pollution from agricultural sources (Ormerod & Jüttner 2009). Phosphate measurements indicate decreasing levels, but nitrate levels are remaining constant (Ormerod & Jüttner 2009). Agricultural runoff has been identified as a particular problem in mid-Wales and sheep dip impacts are of concern, particularly in west Wales. In 2000–01, sheep dip residues were found at 86–92% of Welsh survey sites, with cypermethrin responsible for most water quality failures. Reduced invertebrate abundance has been linked to sheep dip impacts in the upper Teifi (Rutt 2004, Environment Agency Technical Memo unpublished) and Johnes et al. (2007) have shown how agricultural developments and increased livestock densities across Wales have probably more than doubled phosphate loadings and trebled nitrate loadings to river catchments.

Industrial contamination. Welsh freshwater ecosystems are still suffering from an industrial legacy but there is evidence of improvement following remediation interventions, with over 50 metal mine locations having remediation strategies in place (Environment Agency 2002). The Afon Goch ('Red River'), which drains the currently inactive copper mine on Parys Mountain, Anglesey, has been described as one of the most acid- and metal-contaminated streams in the UK (Boult *et al.* 1994). Abandoned coal mines release acid, sulphate-rich water, often with negative effects on biota (Ormerod & Jüttner 2009). The most recent Welsh review identified 90 mine discharges and 60 km of Welsh rivers suffering clear biological impacts at around 70% of the sites sampled. The Afon Pelenna wetlands were constructed (1995–1999) to remediate an acid-mine discharge, and the abundances of invertebrates, trout and river birds have recovered, despite occasional episodes of pollution (Wiseman *et al.* 2004). There has also been ecological recovery in the Welsh Valley Rivers, with salmon returning to the Ebbw, the Rhymney, the Taff and the Rhondda.

20.4.6 Urban

The urban feature type of the Ordnance Survey Strategic dataset (1:250,000 scale) shows that 117,373.6 ha or 5.64% of Wales may be classified as Urban. However the Land Cover Map (LCM 2000) classifies only 4.1% of Wales as urban habitat. Depending on methods for mapping areas, the estimate tends to range between approximately 3–6% urban cover. Although a relatively small total area, the urban centres are mainly concentrated in the south Wales valleys and coastal strip and along the north Wales coast. Stevens *et al.* (2002) concluded that there were no national level statistics on annual loss of land to development in Wales and no consistent, nationwide schemes for gathering the necessary data. They noted that while planning policy tended to protect better quality agricultural land, protection of land with less agricultural value, but possibly greater ecological importance, was inadequate and therefore at greater risk of loss.

20.4.6.1 Status, conditions and trends

The definition for an urban space in Wales is where the population size is over 3,000 (Countryside Agency 2004). The extent of non-built land in urban Wales is unclear and the breakdown of that land by type is also unknown. The Countryside Council for Wales LANDMAP system can only provide data on land use in non-built parts of urban areas outside Cardiff and Swansea—our largest cities. Similarly, the Countryside Survey excludes all 1 km squares which are found to be more than 75% built-up, effectively excluding major urban areas from that survey.

However, the Countryside Survey showed that the extent of the Built-up Areas and Gardens habitat type was estimated to have increased by 14,700 ha between 1998 and 2007. This increase was evenly spread between the uplands and lowlands. In survey squares, half of the increase was new buildings and the remainder included gravel workings, caravan parks, gardens and extensions to the boundaries of farmyards and outbuildings. Eighty-six per cent of the mapped increase replaced Improved or Neutral Grassland or boundary and linear features (Smart *et al.* 2009).

In Welsh planning policy guidance (WAG 2009c), open space is classified as follows:

"Parks and gardens; natural and semi-natural urban greenspaces; green corridors; outdoor sports facilities; amenity greenspace; provision for children and young people; allotments, community gardens and urban farms; cemeteries and churchyards; accessible areas of countryside in the urban fringe; civic spaces and water". However, habitats in Urban areas also include building surfaces (walls, roofs, etc.) and the newly defined UK BAP priority habitat: open mosaic habitats on previously developed land (OMHoPDL). The criteria and definitions for OMHoPDL are available in the recently updated UK BAP Priority Habitats Description report (Maddock 2008). Gwent Wildlife Trust used an experimental survey methodology and an earlier version of the habitat definition to discover 640 potential OMHoPDL sites within Gwent, covering an area of 1909.35 ha. Of these, 115 (946.14 ha) were considered to have high or medium/high potential to meet the priority habitat criteria. They were able to extrapolate a 'best guess' estimate of 13,128 ha for the extent of this habitat in Wales (Gwent Ecology 2010).

In 2010, 18 of the 22 local authorities in Wales were working on complete assessments of the extent and location of accessible natural greenspace in their urban areas (**Table 20.8**). Because these assessments provide information to assist in improving public health they do not classify greenspace by habitat type. However, a desk-based analysis conducted across the five local authorities in the Heads of the Valleys area indicated that of the 104,800 ha total area assessed, 37,900 ha were classed as greenspace, but on average only 55% of people in the area lived within a 400 m walk of greenspace judged to be accessible and natural (exeGesIS 2007, unpublished data).

Many authorities are planning for networks of greenspace in their Local Plans, and Wales has recently introduced its first formal green belt on 2,536 ha of land between Cardiff and Newport.

Gardens are an important component of Urban areas and the Biodiversity in Urban Gardens (BUGS II) project assessed the extent and characteristics of gardens in five cities across the UK. The research revealed that of the 9,080 ha within the urban boundary of Cardiff, 2,100 ha or 16.2% could be defined as private gardens (Loram 2007).

The extent of urban woodlands in Wales, as a percentage of the total Urban area, is 13.1% (LCM 2000), the highest in the UK. In 2009, 76% of the Welsh population were assessed as having access to woodlands over 20 ha within 4 km of their home (Woodland Trust 2010).

Many Local Nature Reserves (LNRs) are in or adjacent to urban areas (CCW 2003). The Countryside Council for Wales keeps records of the area of all LNRs upon which it is consulted—**Figure 20.19**. Despite the overall area being inflated by one large rural LNR (Traeth Llafan, Gwynedd, declared an LNR in 1979), there has been a steady increase in the extent of LNRs in Wales. Whilst this does not reflect a change in habitat type within or around urban areas in Wales, it does show increasing protection for habitats considered to be of educational or conservation importance.

Table 20.8 Accessible Natural Greenspace Standards by local authorities in Wales from 2007 to 2010. Source: WAG (2010a).

Local Authority	Extent (ha) of accessible natural greenspace per 1,000 population	Proportion (%) of the population			
		Living within 300 m walk of any accessible natural greenspace	Living within 2 km of 20 ha site	Living within 5 km of 100 ha site	Living within 10 km of 500 ha site
Isle of Anglesey	-	-	-	–	–
Gwynedd	-	-	-	–	–
Conwy	-	-	-	–	–
Denbighshire	188	34	89	79	43
Flintshire	-	-	-	-	-
Wrexham	68	56	90	87	96
Powys	-	-	-	-	-
Ceredigion	-	-	-	-	-
Pembrokeshire	-	-	-	-	-
Carmarthenshire	109	24	24	32	38
Swansea	-	-	-	-	-
Neath Port Talbot	4	60	-	-	-
Bridgend	58	67	48	91	98
Vale of Glamorgan	-	-	-	-	-
Rhondda Cynon Taff	52	27	83	100	94
Merthyr Tydfil	95	57	98	100	100
Caerphilly	52	51	98	100	99
Blaenau Gwent	84	65	100	100	100
Torfaen	64	76	76	97	99
Monmouthshire	95	76	93	93	100
Newport	74	75	95	97	100
Cardiff	11	68	100	100	100

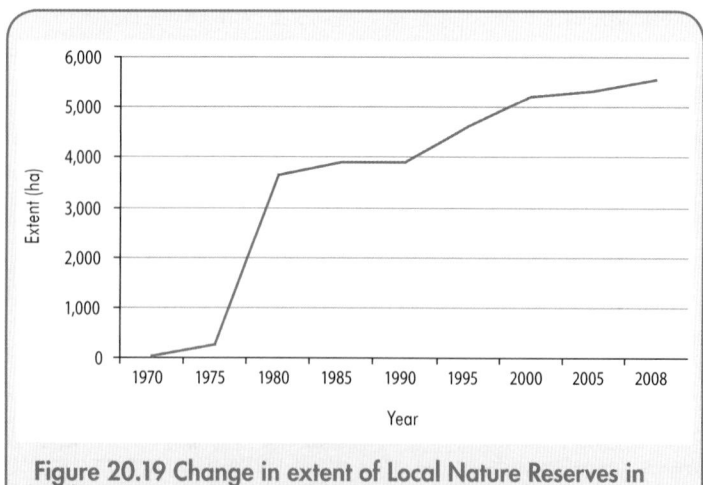

Figure 20.19 Change in extent of Local Nature Reserves in Wales. Source: Countryside Council for Wales, unpublished data.

Several bird species are strongly associated with human settlements, including the house sparrow (*Passer domesticus*), swift (*Apus apus*), starling (*Sturnus vulgaris*) and collared dove (*Streptopelia decaocto*). The British Trust for Ornithology Breeding Bird Survey (British Trust for Ornithology, pers. comm.) shows the following percentage population change for these species in Wales between 1995 and 2007:

- House sparrow: 71% increase
- Collared dove: 51% increase
- Swift: 43% decline
- Starling: 51% decline.

However, these results are not exclusively from urban Wales as there are only 16 survey tetrads in villages, towns and cities, so further monitoring work is required to develop a clear picture of these species in the urban setting in Wales. The UK BAP has associated the lapwing with OMHoPDL because of its tendency to nest on larger areas of post-industrial wasteland. The great crested newt (*Triturus cristatus*) is particularly associated with ponds in urban areas, and the large pond at Stryd Las in north Wales is a notable breeding site which has been given SSSI status for the protection of this species.

The UK BAP also associates Species Action Plans for the following animals with OMHoPDL: slow worm (*Anguis fragilis*), common lizard (*Lacerta vivipara*), adder (*Vipera berus*), grass snake (*Natrix natrix*), and common toad

(*Bufo bufo*). Open mosaic habitats on previously developed land provide open areas in which reptiles may bask for thermoregulation and rubble piles which may serve as hibernacula. Fish-free ponds and water bodies in which amphibians may breed may also be available. Some plant species are also highly associated with human settlements where walls mimic natural cliff habitats. The Dalmatian bellflower (*Campanula portenschlagiana*) is now red listed in its original habitat in the Balkans but thrives on urban walls in the UK as a garden escape—with Llanelli as a notable location in Wales. Because of the year-round damp climate in western Wales, the wall flora of human settlements is particularly diverse compared to the rest of Europe (Gilbert 1996).

Soil contamination is an additional threat posed by industrial development, urbanisation and mineral extraction, which can particularly affect biological processes of soil formation. Wales has a long history of mining and heavy industry, resulting in a significant legacy of soil contamination. For example, there are 1,300 mine sites where discharges to water are known to occur (EAW 2002). Although abandoned mines are generally perceived to pose an environmental risk, there are several sites designated as SSSIs because of the unique ecosystems that have developed on them.

A baseline desk study assessment of contaminated and derelict land in Wales was undertaken in 1988 (EAU 1988). It indicated that there were 752 potentially contaminated sites covering 3,721 ha of contaminated land and 10,900 ha (0.5% of the land area of Wales) of derelict land. The Welsh Office Environmental Advisory Unit (EAU) report (1988) and the review by Stevens *et al.* (2002) both acknowledged the limitations of the assessment, due to the relative rapidity of urban and industrial land-use change (e.g. factory closures, redevelopment) and the dynamic nature of the legislation at the time due to the introduction of the Pollution Prevention and Control Act 1999 and the 1990 Environmental Protection Act. Subsequently, 122 sites were designated in Wales under Part 2A of the Environmental Protection Act (1990) between 2001 and the end of March 2007 (Environment Agency 2009). Of these, four had been fully remediated by the end of March 2007. However, Part 2A excludes many wastes and some receptors and so may not represent the full extent of contaminated soils in Wales.

Soils in the built environment can provide the same range of services as in any other environment (Wood *et al.* 2005), but soil can also be degraded and destroyed by construction of buildings and infrastructure. If the population of Wales continues to grow and there is a focus of economic activity in the built environment, pressure on soil from urbanisation will increase. However, the scope for future urban development in Wales is constrained by the topography of the country and the infrastructure. Future development may, therefore, put more pressure on soils in the coastal margins, estuaries and river floodplains of Wales. These are likely to be vulnerable to impacts from climate change such as sea level rise and more frequent storm surges (Farrar & Vaze 2000), so that a complex picture emerges for future scenarios of urban development in Wales and for the threat to soil formation.

20.4.6.2 Drivers of change

Air quality declines and sealing of surfaces due to increased vehicle ownership, and loss of greenspace due to the selling-off of parks, gardens and allotments in the UK in general, are likely to have been mirrored in urban areas of Wales. Large gardens are increasingly sold as development plots for housing and front gardens are converted to parking space, which usually involves paving or otherwise sealing the ground surface. Loram (2007) has estimated that front gardens represent 26% of the total garden area for an average city. Applying this to the total garden area of Cardiff, then 5.46 km² of the urban area of that city is front garden (Loram et al. 2007). If this were all to be paved over for parking then the amount of permeable surface available for the absorption of rainfall would fall by around 6%.

20.4.7 Coastal Margins

The Coastal Margins comprise five component habitats in Wales; the sixth, Machair, is found only in Scotland and Ireland. Sand Dunes, Saltmarsh and Sea Cliffs are the most extensive, and each covers around 12% of the UK resource (**Table 20.9**). Sand Dunes are found all along the coasts of Wales. Sites such as Newborough, Kenfig and Merthyr Mawr are among the largest in the UK. These west coast sites are particularly important for their invertebrate biodiversity (Howe *et al.* 2010), and for their dune slacks, holding 68% of the UK resource of rare early successional (sd13 and sd14) dune slack communities (JNCC data).

20.4.7.1 Condition, status and trends

As with the rest of the UK, considerable loss of sand dune area has occurred due to agricultural land claim, golf courses and development for housing and tourism, primarily along the North Wales coast, and due to forestry in north, mid- and south Wales. Losses are probably comparable to the UK figure of 30% loss since 1900 (Delbaere 1998). Habitat quality has also declined, with most dunes becoming overstabilised since 1945 (Rhind *et al.* 2001, 2008), Morfa Dyffryn being the notable exception.

Saltmarsh is also found all around Wales, with the largest extents in the Dee estuary in North Wales and the Severn estuary in South Wales. Estuarine saltmarsh occurs mostly on sandy substrate in macrotidal estuaries. The area in

Table 20.9 Area of Coastal Margins UK NEA component habitats in Wales, and as proportion of UK total. Trends in habitat condition (SACs/SSSIs): = stable, ↓ weak decline, ↓↓ strong decline, ↔ trend equivocal, ? trend unknown. Source: Table 11.2, Chapter 11 of the UK NEA.

Coastal Margins component habitats	Area (ha)	% of UK total	Trend
Sand Dunes	8,101	11.3	↓
Saltmarsh	5,800	12.7	?
Shingle	109	1.9	↓
Sea Cliffs	522*	12.9	↓
Coastal Lagoons	37	0.7	=

* Cliffs are measured as length (km).

Wales has been reduced landward by land claim for industry and agriculture, but in the larger estuaries such as the Dee, habitat has extended seaward due to vegetative colonisation of mudflats. The net change in area since 1945 is uncertain.

Some Coastal Lagoons have probably been lost in Wales historically, as was the case in England in the mid-20th Century, but there is little documentary evidence. Hard flood defence structures may hinder the development and evolution of coastal lagoons and lead to further losses, especially when compounded with climate change effects. The Countryside Council for Wales has developed new monitoring tools and baselines that are contributing to the management of Welsh lagoonal habitats (Stringell *et al.* in press), the reporting of Conservation Status, and potentially reporting for the European Water Framework Directive also.

Hard rock Sea cliffs occur predominantly in South West Wales and the Lleyn Peninsula, while soft rock cliffs have a slightly wider distribution around the Welsh coast. It is assumed that the length of cliff is largely unchanged. However, cliff habitat quality has declined since 1945, not so much due to armouring, but due to agricultural encroachment at the cliff-top and reductions in grazing and traditional forms of management, leading to excess scrub development. Welsh Shingle comprises less than 2% of the UK resource but locally important examples occur, e.g. Dinas Dinlle in north Wales and Freshwater West in Pembrokeshire. There are 13 Coastal Lagoons in Wales, less than 1% of the UK total lagoon area. These are predominantly small sea inlets and artificial sluiced pools. Changes in area since 1945 and predicted changes to 2060 are unknown. However, of the terrestrial ecosystems, wetlands and coastal habitats show the greatest decline, with 25% of habitats declining at the same or accelerated rate (Wales Biodiversity Partnership 2008, unpublished data).

20.4.7.2 Drivers of change

Major drivers of change in the Welsh Coastal Margin habitats include changing tourism patterns and interests, land use demands, as discussed above, climate change, nitrogen deposition and sea-level rise. Background levels of nitrogen deposition on the Welsh coast are currently around 10 kg nitrogen per hectare per year (Jones *et al.* 2005, 2008) but have doubled since 1945. This increase is likely to have reduced plant species diversity and, with climate change, has altered soil processes in coastal habitats (Jones *et al.* 2008). Climate change is likely to have major impacts on dune slacks, by reducing water tables (Clarke & Sanitwong 2010). Isostatic adjustment (coastal lifting or depression since the ice-age) is more or less balanced in Wales, but sea-level rise will have impacts on Welsh coastal margin habitats, with a sea-level rise of 26.3 cm predicted for Cardiff by 2060 under a medium emissions scenario (Lowe *et al.* 2009), and steepening of beach profiles observed in Wales (Saye & Pye 2007). Seaward habitat losses will cause coastal squeeze where habitats are unable to migrate inland.

20.4.8 Marine

The coastline of Wales borders the Irish Sea and the Celtic Sea. Its length has been estimated at 2,120 km (2,740 km including the islands of Holyhead and Anglesey; Frost 2010).

Marine designated sites in Wales total more than half a million hectares. Seven in every eight hectares of Welsh Natura 2000 sites are in the marine environment, reflecting the high conservation importance afforded to marine habitats in Wales.

20.4.8.1 Status, conditions and trends

The condition of the Marine areas of Wales is the subject of a recent report (UKMMAS 2010; **Figure 20.20**). Typically, there are good data for coastal areas but generally less data for offshore habitats. The last synoptic assessment of European marine Special Areas of Conservation (SACs) in Wales was in 2007 and showed that about half the features of these SACs were in unfavourable condition and that their future prospects (in status assessments) were, in general, not likely to improve in the short term.

The majority of factors contributing to environmental degradation in Welsh waters have recently been re-emphasised by the Charting Progress 2 (UKMMAS 2010) process. The major factors identified as affecting marine habitats in Wales are: fisheries, coastal development, non-native species introductions and climate change.

Condition of Intertidal Rock. The spatially most widespread pressure in Intertidal Rock habitats is that of shore collecting of winkles and other shellfish from moderately wave-exposed shores and collecting of bait from beneath boulders. These activities result in disturbance of the substratum and the associated biological communities, as well as removal of the target species, but in relatively small numbers at the majority of intertidal habitats. The Countryside Council for Wales is currently monitoring the effects of this kind of pressure in the boulder shores of the Menai Straits.

Estuarine rock habitat is consistently under threat from coastal development and riverine inputs, causing habitat loss and damage, local changes in water movement (hydrology) and increased siltation. The introduction of additional non-native species and continual spread of established non-

Habitat	Status	
	Celtic Sea	Irish Sea
Intertidal rock	↓	↓
Intertidal sediments	↓	↓
Subtidal rock	↔	↔
Shallow subtidal sediments	*	↔
Shelf subtidal sediments	*	↔
Deep-sea habitats	↓	habitat not present

↑ Improvement
↓ Deterioration
↔ Stable
* No trend information available

Many problems
Some problems
Few or no problems

Figure 20.20 The health and biodiversity of Welsh Marine habitats. Source: adapted from UKMMAS (2010).

native species, particularly in conjunction with the effects of climate change, present a long-term threat to Welsh estuarine rocky habitats that is currently most evident in the south-western regions of the UK. The invasive non-native wireweed (*Sargassum muticum*) was first found in Pembrokeshire in 1998 and has since been tracked by the Countryside Council for Wales Phase 1 Intertidal survey, monitoring work and incidental recording as it spread to Cardigan Bay, the Llyn, the Menai Strait and the west coast of Anglesey (Brazier *et al.* 2007). It is now widespread in Wales and of particular concern because it can outcompete local species, including red and brown seaweeds.

In intertidal rocky habitats throughout Wales the impact of climate change is evident with regard to species succession. The northward progression in Wales of the toothed topshell (*Osilinus lineatus*) illustrates how some marine species are quick to take advantage of warmer sea surface and air temperatures, whilst other species show little or no shift in distribution, presumably due to the different driving forces and influences on the species (Mieszkowska *et al.* 2006; Mieszkowska 2010).

Condition of Intertidal Sediment. The key pressure responsible for changes to Intertidal Sediment, relative to former natural conditions across Wales, is habitat loss, predominantly resulting from historical land claim, with concomitant hydrological changes. This pressure has particularly affected intertidal sediment habitats in estuaries. Coastal squeeze of intertidal sediment habitats due to rising sea levels and the presence of immobile coastal defence structures is likely to continue to cause habitat loss. This may result in certain habitat types (particularly saltmarsh communities) becoming increasingly scarce. Other pressures, while not resulting in very widespread change across *all* the communities that comprise Intertidal Sediment, are considered to impact significant proportions of individual habitats within Wales.

Contamination by hazardous substances is likely to have impacted the species composition of some upper estuary sediments in Wales. For example, Milford Haven and some parts of other estuaries may be impacted by organic and nutrient enrichment. The invasive species common cord-grass (*Spartina anglica*) has colonised areas of upper mudflat and pioneer Saltmarsh communities within the Wales and the wider Irish Sea regions, in some cases leading to replacement of these communities by dense, monotypic swards, and thereby modifying the habitat.

Where bait digging, particularly among sheltered muddy gravels, and the collection of cockles occur with sufficient intensity in or adjacent to sensitive communities, composition of these environments has been altered. For example, a Countryside Council for Wales-commissioned study in Milford Haven has found over 30,000 bait dug holes in sheltered muddy gravel and mudflat habitats. This activity is widespread and intensive in the waterway. Some areas get little, or in some cases, no chance to recover. This work will inform a bait digging management scheme.

It is also worth noting that unexplained mass mortalities of cockles (currently under investigation by the Environment Agency) have occurred in the Burry Inlet in the last few years. Countryside Council for Wales evidence shows that the inlet is no longer able to support the number of wading birds for which the Special Protection Area was notified in 4 out of the last 5 years (Sanderson *et al.* 2010).

The distribution of some Intertidal Sediment habitats, particularly of saltmarshes, intertidal mudflats, intertidal seagrass beds and annual vegetation of driftlines on shingle, has been reduced compared to their historic distribution due to various impacts, including land reclamation, coastal development and disease (UK BAP 2006; JNCC 2010).

Condition of Subtidal Rock. Subtidal rocky habitats harbour rich benthic communities that have altered little over the years at the scale of regional seas. Most rocky habitats have largely avoided significant physical damage as their complex topography can damage many types of mobile fishing gear and these fisheries tend to avoid such habitats where possible. Current trends in static gear effort measured at Skomer Marine Nature Reserve may make a reassessment necessary of the potential for damage from static gear, such as lobster pots, at specific sites. Fishing effort has increased by 400% in this area since 2001, with a trend away from single pots towards strings that affect a greater area of seabed and are more prone to dragging during recovery.

Biogenic reefs such as those built by horse mussels (*Modiolus modiolus*) are easily damaged by physical disturbance, and some reefs within the regional sea have been permanently lost (although this is not known to be the case yet in Wales). Examples of illegal heavy fishing activities have been recorded adjacent to horse mussel reefs by Countryside Council for Wales monitoring (Robinson 2007), highlighting the need for adequate enforcement. Nevertheless, the Countryside Council for Wales's annual monitoring work has shown that the ancient horse mussel reef in Pen Llyn, the largest such biodiversity hotspot left in the Irish Sea, has been maintained since the designation of the SAC and the inception of the 'Modiolus Box' closed area (Lindenbaum *et al.* 2008).

The invasive carpet seasquirt (*Didemnum vexillum*) has caused substantial harm to biodiversity and economic damage around the world. It was discovered on pontoons and ropes in the marina in Holyhead harbour in 2008 (the only location in the UK at the time), and the Welsh Government funded a Countryside Council for Wales eradication attempt in the marina, which was successful. Unfortunately, the gap between identifying the invader and starting the eradication (13 months) appears to have allowed it to spread to other areas in the harbour (still to be confirmed). This highlights the need for appropriate rapid responses when dealing with invasive non-native species.

There is very little information on the effects of contaminants or increases in nutrient concentrations or siltation on reef habitats, but damage on the open coast, at least, is believed to be small. Although available evidence suggests that the damaging effects of invasive non-native species in Wales are very limited, this is probably the greatest threat to subtidal reefs in the future.

Condition of Shallow Subtidal Sediment. Many of the activities in shallow subtidal sediments can cause damage in small, localised areas (e.g. aggregate extraction). Damage or change in the structure and function of the habitat due to fishing activities is potentially the most damaging and widespread activity in the Regional Seas around Wales. However, the degree of impact will depend on the type of gear used, intensity and the sensitivity of the community. Intensive beam trawling and scallop dredging have significant effects on both the structure and function of many habitats. The Countryside Council for Wales has recorded cases where illegal fishing has impacted Shallow Subtidal Sediment habitats in SACs in 3 of the last 4 years. One case in Tremadog Bay has impacted 77 ha of muddy gravel habitat that was formerly rich in invertebrate species.

Maerl is one of the most sensitive of the sub-habitats in the component habitat of Shallow Subtidal Sediments. Wales has only one maerl bed, which is located in Milford Haven. This bed is approximately 1.5 km², of which only 0.5 km² still contains live maerl. Baseline monitoring has been established. Spatial mapping of the sea bed enabled the establishment of a statutory exclusion zone in 2009 for shellfish dredging.

Seagrass beds are also affected by localised pressures such as anchor chain damage, siltation and nutrient enrichment. Unpublished Countryside Council for Wales surveys using volunteer divers show impacts from moorings and anchors on a seagrass bed in Pen Llyn a'r Sarnau SAC. This evidence is being used to seek less damaging alternatives. At Skomer Marine Nature Reserve, successive surveys have shown improvements in the spread and abundance of seagrass since management of anchoring was introduced in the form of buoyed 'no anchoring' areas

and the provision of visitor moorings adjacent to, but outside the seagrass bed. Improved water clarity may also have contributed to this, however.

Indicator 22c of the Wales Environment Strategy is the number of fisheries, assessed annually by the International Council for the Exploration of the Sea (ICES) and the Sea Fisheries Committees, to be in safe biological condition, based on stock assessments, fish catches and catch per unit effort. It helps to assess which species are within 'safe biological limits' or suffering reduced reproductive capacity, and to decide upon fishing quotas (total allowable catch). **Table 20.10** shows the current status of selected fish stocks based on these analyses.

Marine Management Organisation and UK Sea Fisheries annual statistics give landings into Welsh ports, but not necessarily of catches which have been sourced from Welsh waters. More information on Welsh fisheries is provided in this chapter's section on provisioning services.

20.5 Ecosystem Services

Ecosystem services are the outputs of ecosystems from which people derive benefits, including goods and services. The UK NEA follows the categorisation of ecosystem services adopted in the Millennium Ecosystem Assessment, namely: Supporting Services (primary ecological functions) and Final Ecosystem Services (Regulating, Provisioning and Cultural services; Section 2.2). These services are discussed here in relation to their role and importance in Wales.

20.5.1 Supporting Services

Supporting services include the underlying ecological processes of soil formation, nutrient cycling, the water cycle, primary production, decomposition, etc. These fundamental supporting services tend to be generic across the UK and the reader is therefore referred to the main UK NEA chapter on supporting services for further information. Some aspects of supporting services that are relevant to Wales are summarised below.

Not all the factors and influences on soil formation discussed by Bardgett *et al.* (this volume) have equal importance within the Welsh geographical context, and therefore, particular attention is given here to soil formation as a supporting service. Considerable studies on soils, of relevance for Wales and the wider UK, have also been carried out by the Government's CEH research station based in Bangor, North Wales.

20.5.1.1 Soil formation

The soil is a multifunctional resource without which land is infertile, barren and unable to support vegetation. The soils of Wales are the foundation of the land-based economy and have a strong influence on the Welsh landscape (**Figure 20.21**). The diversity of the vegetation and the quality and flows of Welsh rivers reflect the range of climate and soil conditions found in Wales. The sustainability of these services, along with

Table 20.10 State of selected Welsh commercial marine fish species in the Celtic Sea and the Irish Sea. Source: Irwin & Thomas (2010).

Species	Total Allowable Catch (TAC) Advisory 2010 (% increase/decrease on 2009 TAC)	Stock Assessment
Celtic Sea		
Cod	*	Status unknown for 2009 but in 2008 stocks were viewed as at risk of suffering reduced reproductive capacity
Plaice	*	Stocks at risk of suffering reduced reproductive capacity
Sole	Decrease – 15%	Stocks at full reproductive capacity and being harvested sustainably
Haddock	*	Status unknown
Irish Sea		
Cod	Decrease – 25%	Status unknown for 2009 but in 2008 stocks were viewed as suffering reduced reproductive capacity
Plaice	Increase – 12%	Stocks at full reproductive capacity and being harvested sustainably
Sole	Decrease – 20%	Stocks suffering reduced reproductive capacity
Haddock	*	Status unknown

* No data available, management plan under construction.

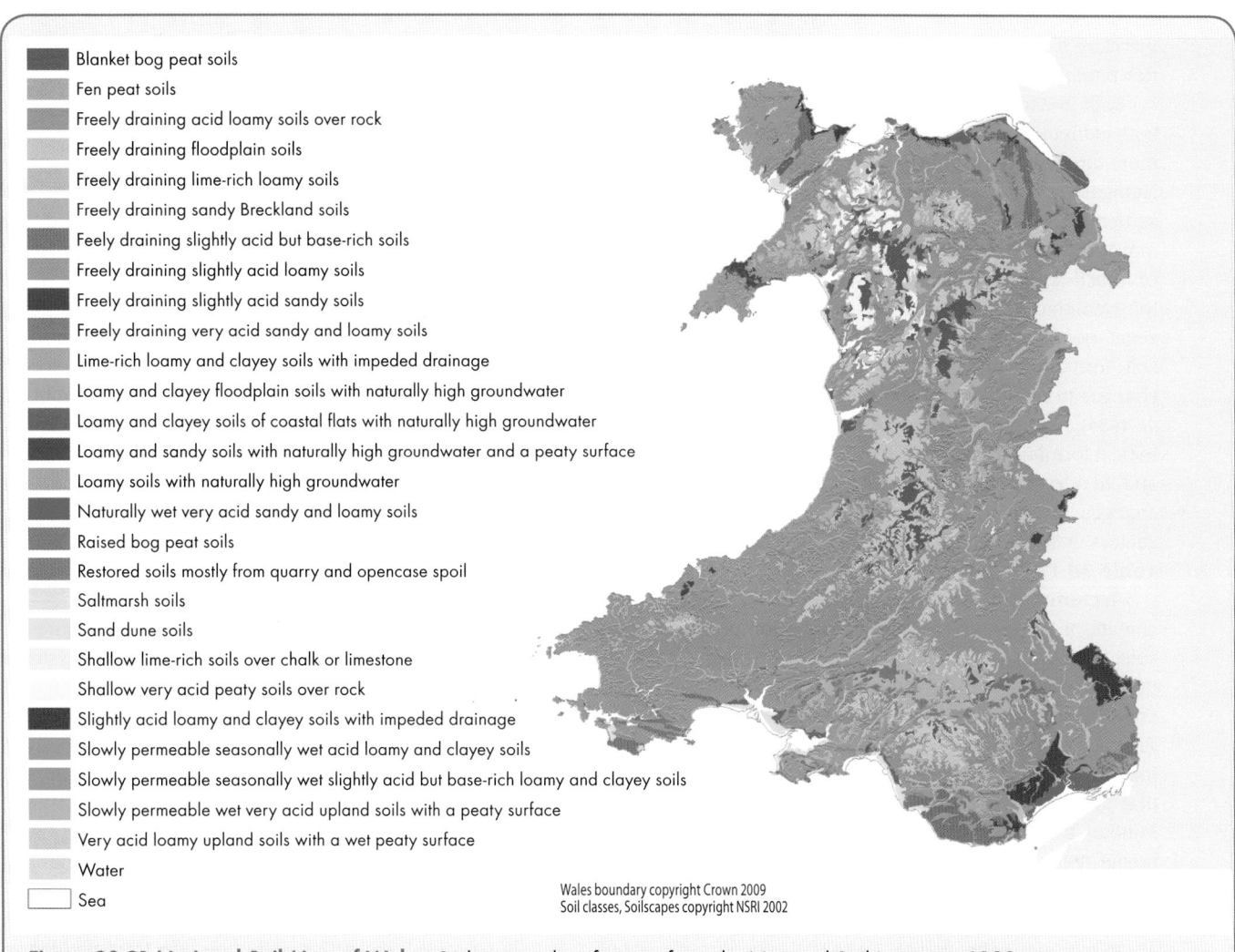

Blanket bog peat soils
Fen peat soils
Freely draining acid loamy soils over rock
Freely draining floodplain soils
Freely draining lime-rich loamy soils
Freely draining sandy Breckland soils
Feely draining slightly acid but base-rich soils
Freely draining slightly acid loamy soils
Freely draining slightly acid sandy soils
Freely draining very acid sandy and loamy soils
Lime-rich loamy and clayey soils with impeded drainage
Loamy and clayey floodplain soils with naturally high groundwater
Loamy and clayey soils of coastal flats with naturally high groundwater
Loamy and sandy soils with naturally high groundwater and a peaty surface
Loamy soils with naturally high groundwater
Naturally wet very acid sandy and loamy soils
Raised bog peat soils
Restored soils mostly from quarry and opencase spoil
Saltmarsh soils
Sand dune soils
Shallow lime-rich soils over chalk or limestone
Shallow very acid peaty soils over rock
Slightly acid loamy and clayey soils with impeded drainage
Slowly permeable seasonally wet acid loamy and clayey soils
Slowly permeable seasonally wet slightly acid but base-rich loamy and clayey soils
Slowly permeable wet very acid upland soils with a peaty surface
Very acid loamy upland soils with a wet peaty surface
Water
Sea

Wales boundary copyright Crown 2009
Soil classes, Soilscapes copyright NSRI 2002

Figure 20.21 National Soil Map of Wales. Soilscapes classification from the National Soil Inventory 1998. Source and copyright: NSRI (2009).

the capacity to retain or lose carbon, depends significantly on soil management (Stevens *et al.* 2002).

Soil-forming processes are discussed in the UK context by Bardgett *et al.* (this volume) and are not repeated here. However, there are several key factors that have specifically influenced, and continue to affect, soil formation in Wales. These include the following:

- Almost complete glaciation of the landscape, ending around 12,000 years ago. This left a fresh land surface for soil development; soils in Wales are therefore relatively young by world standards.
- A moist, cool climate; low thermal energy results in low weathering rates but high rainfall leads to high leaching rates.
- Hard, mostly acid bedrock and superficial deposits resulting in a particular suite of acid, base-depleted loamy soils (**Table 20.11**).
- High relief and steep slopes which control soil formation through their effects on hydrology and climate.
- Predominantly low intensity land management including extensive agriculture dominated by grazing, forestry and significant areas of protected (conservation) land.

The coastal fringes of Wales tend to be the exceptions to these general principles. Here the land is at lower altitude and

Table 20.11 The major soil groups of Wales. Source: data from Rudeforth *et al.* (1984); Stevens *et al.* (2002).

Major soil group	Extent in Wales (% cover)	Description
Terrestrial raw soils	<0.1	Very young soils with only a superficial organo-mineral layer
Raw gley soils	0.2	Unripened young soils of saltmarshes
Lithomorphic soils	2.2	Shallow soils without a weathered subsoil
Pelosols	0.1	Clayey 'cracking' soils
Brown soils	30.2	Loamy, permeable soils with weathered subsoil
Podzolic soils	32.3	Acid soils with brightly coloured iron-enriched subsoil
Surface-water gley soils	24.7	Loamy and clayey seasonally waterlogged soils with impermeable subsoil
Ground-water gley soils	3.4	Soils associated with high seasonal groundwater
Man-made soils	0.4	Restored soils of disturbed ground
Peat soils	3.4	Soils in deep peat
Unclassified land (urban)	3.0	

therefore warmer, drier and often underlain by more base-rich parent materials, making the soils more productive.

Soils in Wales have a long history of influence by humans, both indirectly through management of native vegetation and more directly through agricultural practice. With significant changes in climate throughout the period of human settlement it is not always possible to isolate the effects of man's influence (Stevens *et al.* 2002). However, clearance of much upland deciduous woodland in Wales during the Neolithic period led to the development of heathland vegetation, accompanied by a transition from brown earth soil formation processes to podzol conditions, due to changes in microclimate and nutrient cycling (Rudeforth *et al.* 1984). Organic matter accumulated on wetter sites leads to peat formation. Agricultural management in the lowlands and, to a lesser extent, in the uplands, has led to significant changes in soil hydrology, fertility, acidity and structure. Factors influencing soil formation in Wales are given in **Table 20.12**.

Accumulation of soil organic matter. The cool, wet climate of Wales encourages the formation of organic-rich soils including peats and organo-mineral soils such as humic gleys, humic rankers, podzols, stagnohumic gleys and stagno-podzol soil groups (ECOSSE 2007). Collectively, they account for over 20% of the land surface and are an important repository for carbon. Recent estimates suggest that for Wales, peats account for 121.3 Mt C and organo-mineral soils a further 74.5 Mt C to the base of the soil profile (ECOSSE 2007). Using the most recent Countryside Survey data (Emmett *et al.* 2010), the amount of soil carbon stored across all broad habitat types in Wales to a depth of 15 cm has been estimated at 159 Mt C. It is important to note when comparing these figures that the Countryside Survey estimate is for 0–15 cm depth and includes data from a wide spectrum of soils, including those with relatively low organic matter content (less than 8% loss on ignition), whilst the estimating carbon in organic soils, sequestration and emissions (ECOSSE) estimate is restricted to organic-rich soils, but extends to the base of the soil column.

The rate at which the soil carbon store is changing in Wales is the subject of considerable debate, with apparently contradictory results from two major UK surveys: the National Soil Inventory (Bellamy *et al.* 2005) and the Countryside Survey 2007 (Emmett *et al.* 2010). Work is ongoing to understand and resolve these differences.

Soil mineral weathering. During the 1970s and 1980s there was a focus of research interest in Wales to determine chemical weathering rates for the Lower Palaeozoic sedimentary rocks that make up the bulk of the Cambrian Mountain chain (see, for example, Adams *et al.* 1971; Day *et al.* 1980; Hornung *et al.* 1987; Reynolds *et al.* 1987). A variety of techniques was employed, leading to estimated rates of surface lowering for Lower Palaeozoic greywackes in Wales of between 2 and 5 mm per 1,000 years, equivalent to 0.06 to 0.14 tonnes per hectare per year of bedrock under steady state conditions.

In the mid-1980s and 1990s, there was renewed interest in the weathering release of base cations for these systems because of its importance in the neutralisation of acid rain and for setting critical loads to protect ecosystems from acidification (Langan *et al.* 1996). Empirically derived weathering rates have been assigned to the major soil associations in Wales as part of the national critical load mapping exercise (Hornung *et al.* 1995; Figure 1 empirical critical loads map for Wales), but these values are largely based on expert judgement underpinned by relatively few experimentally determined quantitative data. Concerns have also arisen about the acidifying effects of plantation conifer forests established on large areas of base-poor, acid sensitive soils and associated depletion of soil calcium reserves by repeated forestry cycles (Reynolds & Stevens 1998).

Table 20.12 Key factors affecting soil formation as a supporting service in Wales. + Positive, - Negative. Source: Stevens *et al.* (2002); EAU (1988).

| Factor | Influence on soil formation service | Importance in Welsh context | | State of knowledge on status and change |
		Geographical	Functional	
Accumulation of soil organic matter	+	Relatively large spatial coverage of organic-rich soils with significant carbon store	Regulation of carbon fluxes	Several estimates of stock; conflicting data on change
Soil mineral weathering	+	Large area of 'acid' geology and soils with low weathering rates	Neutralisation of acidity; sustainability of forestry and agriculture	Limited quantitative data from site specific studies; extensive empirical data
Erosion	–	High relief, steep slopes and high rainfall	Loss of productivity, siltation of water courses and reservoirs	Some data on extent of erosion, particularly for uplands, few data on erosion rates
Structural degradation (compaction)	–	Large areas of extensive grazing on seasonally wet vulnerable soils	Increased flood risk; loss of productivity	Few quantitative data (Stevens *et al.* 2002), some semi-quantitative surveys of soil structural condition
Urbanisation (soil sealing) and contamination	–	Urban and industrial centres are focused in south Wales and northern coastal fringe; extensive historical legacy from mineral exploitation throughout much of Wales	High risk of degradation or total loss of soil resource; risk to ecological and human health	Baseline of 1988 data (EAU 1988); need for audit of current status following changes in legislation

There is currently renewed interest in quantifying soil formation processes and loss rates in the context of the 'critical zone' concept defined as the soil-plant system from 'bedrock to tree top' (Richter & Mobley 2009). The Plynlimon catchments in mid-Wales are now part of an international network of critical zone observatories (CZEN 2011) and a pan-European project (SoilTrEC 2010), which is intended to provide platforms for collaborative research into processes and rates of soil formation and loss across gradients of climate, geology and land management.

Urbanisation and removal of soil overburden during mineral extraction have major impacts on soil formation (Section 20.4.6). Loss of soil to urbanisation eliminates many of its functions, although significant areas may remain in an amenity role within parks, gardens and verges, etc., where soil can perform an important hydrological function for infiltration of runoff. The importance of soil management is well recognised in the planning process for mineral extraction in Wales (NAW 2000), with an emphasis on progressive restoration to eliminate the need for soil storage.

20.5.1.2 Nutrient cycling

The nutrient status of soils and waters underpins the delivery of regulating and provisioning services in particular. Trace elements are no more or less important in Wales than in the rest of the UK, although there are pockets of trace minerals in rocks and soils that influence farm animal nutrition in parts of Wales, and sources of contamination related to metalliferous mining that also effect local water quality in some areas (see section on regulating services). Major nutrients such as nitrogen and phosphorus show some differences in Wales compared to other areas of the UK.

Nitrogen levels tend to be greater in soils of high organic content in woodlands and wetlands than in agricultural soils. There is also a spatial trend in relation to climate and land use, with a greater amount of nitrogen being found in the soils of the uplands and the more westerly parts of Britain, including Wales (Emmet et al. 2010).

Statistics for the past 20 years published by the Environment Agency (2008; Chapter 13, Figure 13.7b) suggest a decline in phosphate concentrations in the higher rainfall, livestock-rearing areas of western Britain.

Much of Wales is more acidic than England due to the higher rainfall and its leaching effects, and the presence of more organic soils in the uplands and the west. In common with the rest of the UK, however, soil acidity has decreased in Wales as a result of emissions controls that have curbed air pollution in the past 40 years. These trends appear to be related particularly to the decline in sulphate deposition that occurred over this period, which in most cases was accompanied by increases in rainfall pH (Morecroft et al. 2009; Chapter 13, Figure 13.10a).

20.5.1.3 The water cycle

The hydrological cycle encompasses rainfall, water storage in soil, groundwater, lakes, etc., evaporation and transpiration from water surfaces, soil and plant leaves, and river flows to the ocean. With its westerly Atlantic location, Wales shows some of the highest rainfall values recorded in the UK. This rainfall varies widely, with the highest average annual totals recorded in the central upland region from Snowdonia in the north to the Brecon Beacons in the south. Snowdonia is the wettest area, with average annual totals exceeding 3,000 mm, comparable to those in the English Lake District or the western Highlands of Scotland. In contrast, places along the coast and closer to the border with England are drier, receiving less than 1,000 mm per year (UK Met Office; Chapter 17, Figure 17.2).

The cooler and cloudier conditions in Wales, compared to the rest of southern Britain, lead to lower levels of evaporation and transpiration and more humid conditions. Coupled with less fertile soils, this favours pastoral agriculture over arable tillage. The more humid conditions also favour crops that are less susceptible to blight and other fungal infections than those commonly planted in eastern Britain.

There are large reserves of surface water in Wales that have long served as sources of supply for the UK more widely. Demands on these reserves from within and outside Wales are likely to increase in the future, under current scenarios for climate change in north-western Europe.

The relatively high rainfall and steep and varied topography of Wales leads to rivers that are more variable in runoff than those in England. This 'flashiness' has increased in some watercourses in Wales over the past century, for example the River Wye (**Figure 20.22**). The long-term catchment experiment at Plynlimon on the headwaters of the River Severn has provided a record of rainfall and runoff over the past 40 years in Wales for Britain's largest river (Chapter 13, Figure 13.14).

20.5.1.4 Primary production

Plant photosynthesis and primary production processes in the terrestrial habitats of Wales mirror those of other cool temperate zones where agricultural land use has predominated for millennia, and so the information contained in the main UK chapter regarding primary production supporting services applies in general to Wales also (Chapter 13).

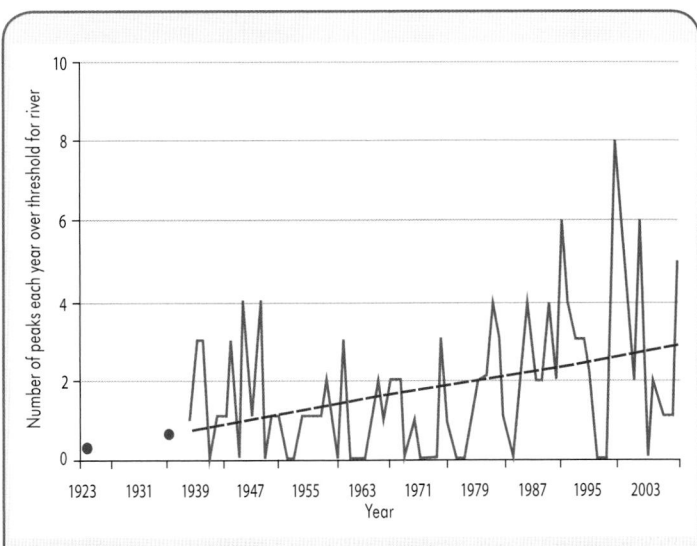

Figure 20.22 Flood events in the River Wye from 1923 to 2003. Source: Environment Agency (2005). Contains Environment Agency information © Environment Agency and database right.

Photosynthetic activity of terrestrial vegetation is influenced by seasonal factors, cloud cover and complexity of vegetation formations (e.g. multi-storey woodland). Areas of photosynthesis inferred from remote sensing, tend to show higher values in the better-vegetated lowland pastures and woodlands of Wales (**Figure 20.23**). In common with other regions of the world, biological primary production tends to decrease with altitude, so that the lowest primary productivity occurs mainly in upland habitats. Managing land to enhance primary productivity in Wales, by tree planting and conserving estuarine areas for example, could therefore contribute to important synergies with other ecosystem services (e.g. climate and water quality regulation).

Photosynthesis and primary productivity, as indexed by chlorophyll levels, are relatively high in Welsh Marine habitats when compared to other offshore zones of the British Isles. This is due, in part, to the shallow waters and lower rates of mixing in the semi-enclosed Irish Sea marine environment.

20.5.2 Regulating Services

Regulating services are the benefits accruing to humankind through the regulation of ecological processes by ecosystems. Regulating services include those ecological processes that influence water quality and quantity, pollination, climate regulation, severity and frequency of hazards, soil quality,

noise, air quality and diseases and pests. The regulating services provided by ecosystems are extremely diverse. There can be a range of different indicators within each service (e.g. the various components of water quality such as acidity, pollutants and sediment levels).

20.5.2.1 Climate regulation

Biogeochemical mechanisms through which ecosystems regulate climate. Ecosystems regulate climate by acting as sources and sinks of greenhouse gases, and as sources of aerosols. It is well established that Wales has large amounts of carbon locked up in its forests, peatlands, grasslands and soils (114 Mt C in vegetation; 9,838 ± 2,463 Mt C in soils). Welsh soils hold nine times the amount of carbon than is stored in all vegetation (including forestry), with over 80% of this carbon associated with upland and grassland soils (Farrar *et al.* 2003). The amount of carbon stored in Welsh soils is currently estimated at 410 million tonnes. Soil carbon densities are greatest in semi-natural habitats (Mountains, Moorlands and Heaths, Semi-natural Grassland, Freshwaters – Openwaters, Wetlands and Floodplains) and Woodlands (including peat soils) and lower under Enclosed Farmland and Urban habitats (**Figure 20.24**). Approximately one-third (121 Mt) of Welsh soil carbon is in the form of peat (ECOSSE 2007), although peat deposits occupy only 3% of the area of Wales. This large carbon store needs to be well managed to ensure

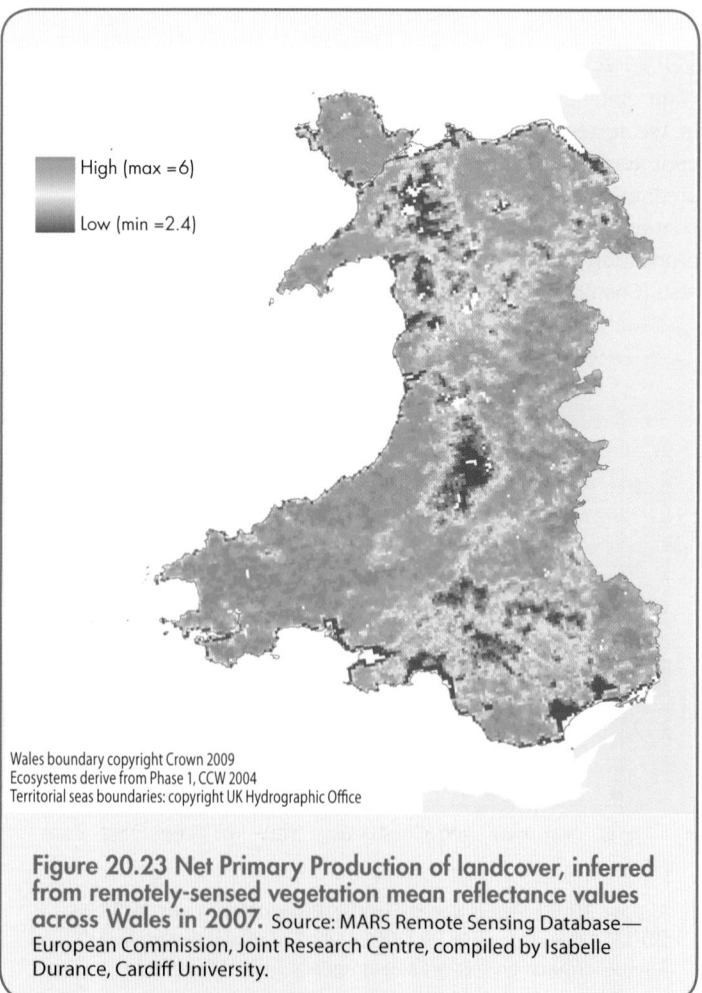

Wales boundary copyright Crown 2009
Ecosystems derive from Phase 1, CCW 2004
Territorial seas boundaries: copyright UK Hydrographic Office

Figure 20.23 Net Primary Production of landcover, inferred from remotely-sensed vegetation mean reflectance values across Wales in 2007. Source: MARS Remote Sensing Database—European Commission, Joint Research Centre, compiled by Isabelle Durance, Cardiff University.

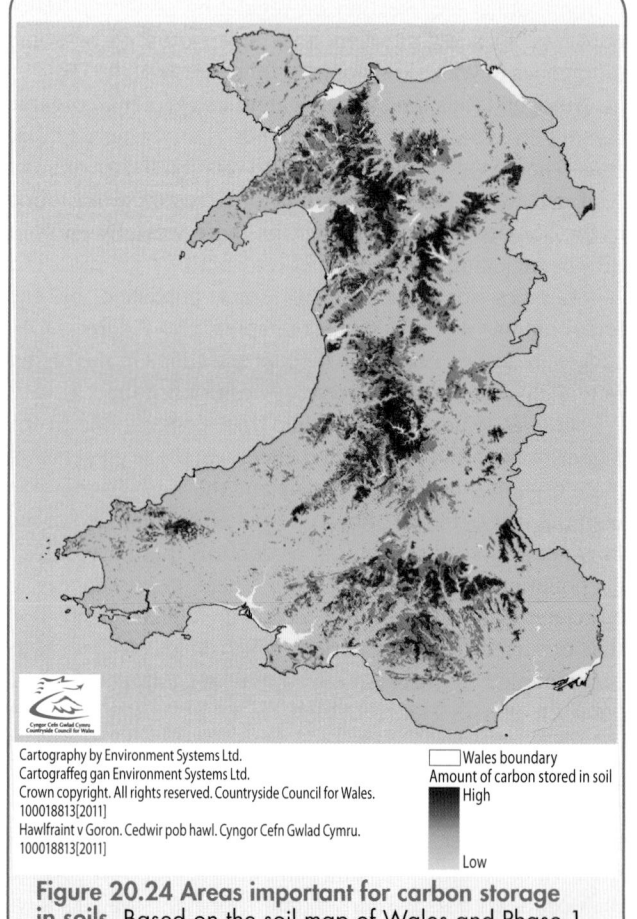

Cartography by Environment Systems Ltd.
Cartograffeg gan Environment Systems Ltd.
Crown copyright. All rights reserved. Countryside Council for Wales.
100018813[2011]
Hawlfraint v Goron. Cedwir pob hawl. Cyngor Cefn Gwlad Cymru.
100018813[2011]

Wales boundary
Amount of carbon stored in soil
High
Low

Figure 20.24 Areas important for carbon storage in soils. Based on the soil map of Wales and Phase 1 vegetation data. Source: CCW (2010).

losses do not accelerate and that the processes adding to this soil carbon store (usually incomplete decomposition of organic material in nutrient-poor, acidic and/or anaerobic/waterlogged conditions) are maintained. It has been calculated that a 1% per annum loss of stored soil carbon would increase Welsh net carbon emissions by 25% (Farrar et al. 2003).

The primary concern for mitigating the future effects of climate change within the Welsh uplands is to secure the existing carbon resource that is locked up within organic and organo-mineral soils. The Countryside Council for Wales suggest that Welsh peatlands may currently be sequestering an additional 5,588–10,406 tonnes of carbon per annum. Whilst a significant figure, this is dwarfed by the 121 million tonnes already stored as peat.

The total carbon stock in Welsh forests (including their soils) is approximately 140 Mt carbon dioxide equivalent (CO_2 e). The total carbon stored in Welsh forests and their soils is equivalent to more than 10 times the annual emissions from industry and services in Wales. Currently, 57 Mt CO_2 e of the carbon stock is in the trees themselves, but the greatest amount of carbon (80 Mt CO_2 e) is stored in the soils, particularly heathland and blanket bog. The soil carbon content is often a function of the soil type and therefore the primary management implication is the long-term sustainability of this carbon stock. The strength of the forest carbon sink in Wales increased between 1990 and 2004. However, projections show that within a decade, woodlands in Wales will become an annual emissions source, not a sink, as a result of the falloff in planting rates (Dyson et al. 2009).

Trees outside woodlands (on field margins and in hedgerows) also sequester carbon, although this has received very little research attention. A report measuring holistic carbon footprints for lamb and beef farms in the Cambrian Mountains Initiative (Taylor et al. 2010) suggested that woodlands and isolated trees both offer potential to sequester more carbon on farms. An extra 1 ha of woodland on the farms in the study could increase annual sequestration rates by up to 12%, while planting 50 isolated trees could increase sequestration rates by up to 5%. The report also suggested that a change in hedge cutting regimes could also offer some carbon sequestration.

In March 2010 the Welsh Assembly Government announced a programme to create 100,000 ha of new woodland over the following 20 years. This initiative would create an additional major sink of 1,600,000 t CO_2 e annually by 2040, with a net sink of 1,200,000 t CO_2 e, and an additional fuel wood potential of 1.4 terawatt-hour per year

by 2030–2040, offsetting emissions of a further 350,000 t CO_2 e of fossil fuels (Land use climate change report to WAG, March 2010).

Data on soil carbon densities for Coastal Margin habitats are not readily available for Wales but are expected to be significant, although limited in extent. It is well established, but with incomplete evidence, that Marine ecosystems provide extensive carbon stores and uptake significant amounts of atmospheric carbon dioxide. In the longer term, rising carbon dioxide concentrations in seawater may lead to increased acidification of Marine environments. This could have a negative impact on hard-shelled marine organisms (e.g. molluscs, crustaceans, various plankton species), as their ability to produce calcium carbonate shells may decrease, and consequently this will affect their associated food webs (IPCC 2007; MCCIP 2008).

There is an important knowledge gap associated with quantification of the climate regulation services provided by Coastal Margins, Marine and Urban ecosystems in Wales.

Fluxes of vapour and gases from the land surface are important in regulating atmospheric concentrations of greenhouse gases, which include water vapour, carbon dioxide, nitrous oxide and methane. Welsh soils are considered to be a net sink of carbon dioxide under land use, land use change and forestry activities; unlike the soils of England, which are a net source. This is primarily due to the low incidence of land use change in Wales and the relatively young age structure of Welsh forests, rather than the overall stock of carbon held within Welsh soils.

Jackson et al. (2009) gave the UK distribution of regional net greenhouse gas emissions in 2005, expressed in terms of global warming potentials, as: England 78%; Scotland 8.3% and Wales 7.7%. Trends for gas emissions in Wales are provided in **Table 20.13**.

Agriculture currently contributes 11% of total greenhouse gas emissions in Wales, primarily in the form of methane and nitrous oxide. Carbon dioxide released by agriculture (1 Mt per year) contributes around 2% of total Welsh greenhouse gas emissions. Most of this arises from the conversion of pasture to cropland. There is relatively little empirical data available on carbon sequestration of soils under grazed grassland, and existing data suggest a range of possible sequestration rates.

Methane and nitrous oxide emissions from agriculture represent around 67% and 84% respectively of all anthropogenic emissions in Wales. Some 90% of the Welsh agricultural methane emissions are derived from enteric fermentation in cattle and sheep (Baggott et al. 2005), although many of these livestock will spend a large part

Table 20.13 Greenhouse gas emissions for Wales (megatonnes carbon dioxide equivalent): carbon dioxide, methane and nitrous oxide. Source: data from Jackson et al. (2009).

Greenhouse gases	1990	1995	1998	1999	2000	2001	2002	2003	2004	2005	Change (%) 1990–2005
Carbon dioxide	43.3	40.7	42.9	44.4	46.5	43.9	37.5	38.7	42.4	41.7	-4%
Methane	7.7	6.6	6.0	5.8	5.6	5.1	4.9	4.7	4.7	4.5	-41%
Nitrous oxide	3.7	3.6	3.9	3.7	3.5	3.4	3.3	3.3	3.3	3.4	-8%

of their lives on rough pasture. By contrast, the majority of nitrous oxide emissions result from the cultivation practices used on enclosed land.

Aggregated emission trends indicate that agriculture and waste disposal are declining as sources. This is largely due to reductions in livestock numbers and decreases in fertiliser application rates, leading to a fall in the levels of methane and nitrous oxide respectively.

Biophysical mechanisms through which ecosystems regulate climate. Whereas biogeochemical effects tend to operate at the regional/global scale, biophysical effects operate at a more local or regional scale. These local effects also assist in the avoidance of climate stress. Woody ecosystems, for example, provide localised benefits such as shade and shelter. A driver behind much of the hedgerow and farm woodland management in Wales is provision of shelter for livestock, and here, factors such as the roughness of vegetation will have an impact on wind speeds and air moisture content. Recent studies have begun to quantify the wider ecosystem service benefits of farmland shelter planting in the Welsh context, e.g. the Pontbren study in mid-Wales.

20.5.2.2 Hazard regulation

Hazard regulation implies three principle vulnerabilities in the UK context—coastal protection, erosion protection and flood regulation. There are strong links between the regulation of flooding and erosion, as interventions designed to manage the movement of water across the landscape will be likely to have an impact on both services.

Coastal protection. It is estimated that 23% of the Welsh coast (compared with 30% in England, 20% in Northern Ireland and 12% in Scotland) is experiencing erosion (Masselink & Russell 2007). Erosion of these areas represents a significant loss of important habitat.

In localised areas, there has been damage to Saltmarsh vegetation and there have been changes to sediment structure, as a result of removal of natural beach-cast materials (together with litter) during mechanical beach-cleaning operations. Microscopic plastic particles are now known to be widespread in marine sediments as a result of wear and tear of discarded plastics. There are also concerns about elevated pollutants such as polychlorinated biphenyls (PCBs) and endocrine-disrupting chemicals that may affect species through bioaccumulation (e.g. Mato *et al.* 2001; Thompson *et al.* 2004).

Erosion protection. The most comprehensive data on soil erosion in Wales exist for upland soils. In a Defra-funded study, the spatial extent of erosion assessed at 155 field sites showed that 43% of these sites contained eroded soil (Harrod *et al.* 2000; McHugh 2002a,b). Most erosion was measured on peat soils, with decreasing amounts of erosion observed on wet, peaty mineral soils, wet mineral soils and dry mineral soils. Upland soil erosion occurred uniformly throughout Wales. At 75% of sites, animals and humans were responsible for initiating erosion, and for maintaining bare soil at 77% of the sites (McHugh 2002b). Unfortunately, the 5 km sampling grid used for the Defra study excluded arable fields, which tend to be smaller in Wales than those in England. The study did not, therefore, provide quantitative data for Welsh arable sites. Erosion was measured at 28 lowland grassland sites in Wales (Harrod 1998). Five of these sites displayed erosion, with a total eroded soil volume of 0.16 m³. It was concluded that soil erosion was not a significant process on established enclosed grassland. In a separate study in the Llafar catchment, Ford (2000) showed that while the extent of bare and poached ground was relatively small as a percentage of the catchment area, 75% of bare soil features were within 40 m of fluvial systems, thereby increasing the likelihood of soil loss to the river network.

Information on erosion rates is limited, and derives mainly from studies in the Plynlimon catchment and at Llanbrynmair (Francis & Taylor 1989; Collins *et al.* 1997). These data show that erosion tends to be highly episodic, and that rates can be high in response to specific land management activities, e.g. ploughing, forest harvesting, etc., if the correct precautions are not taken.

Landslides contribute to surface erosion in Wales. Classic, major landslides are not common, but rockfalls and peat slides occur in mountainous areas, although they are not usually a major threat to population centres. Sudden, catastrophic events have occurred in the South Wales coal fields. In 1966, 144 people were killed at Aberfan following a coal tip slide. Failure to restore habitats to fully functioning ecological conditions leads to an increased likelihood of landslides and debris flows following extreme rain events. These can cause disruption to rail and roads and expense to the public purse. Erosion in the uplands also increases the amount of peat (and carbon) in source supplies of drinking water, causing it to become peat-coloured and involving the water companies in considerable treatment costs.

Flood regulation. *Riverine floods.* Survey work in the Upper Severn catchment (Holman *et al.* 2003) identified areas of soil structural degradation as a potential contributory factor in the flooding of Shrewsbury in 2000. Flood risk management research at Pontbren in mid-Wales has studied the influence of upland land management on soil structure and flood risk in considerable detail (Marshall *et al.* 2009; Wheater *et al.* 2010). This research has shown how sheep grazing on heavy textured soils can change soil structure and hydrology (Carroll *et al.* 2004) and suggests that strategically planted linear tree features can be used to improve soil structure and alleviate flood risk (Jackson *et al.* 2008; Marshall *et al.* 2009).

The soil's ability to act as a sponge is important in influencing whether rainfall infiltrates the substrate or runs off the surface (**Figure 20.25**). Increasing soil bulk density is commonly linked to inappropriate management of agricultural land or soil-sealing by impermeable surfaces which will increase storm runoff and peak flows in watersheds. However, the Countryside Survey, at its current sampling intensity (Emmett *et al.* 2010), has shown no change in bulk density for soils across a range of Welsh habitats, nor has there been any observed increase in carbon levels which are also linked to increased infiltration.

Climate change is likely to increase the frequency of extreme weather events in the future. Within the Welsh uplands, the targeted establishment of woodland in plantations on valley sides, or as part of a network of farm hedgerows and shelterbelts, would help to reduce flood risks by increasing the rate at which rainwater percolates into the

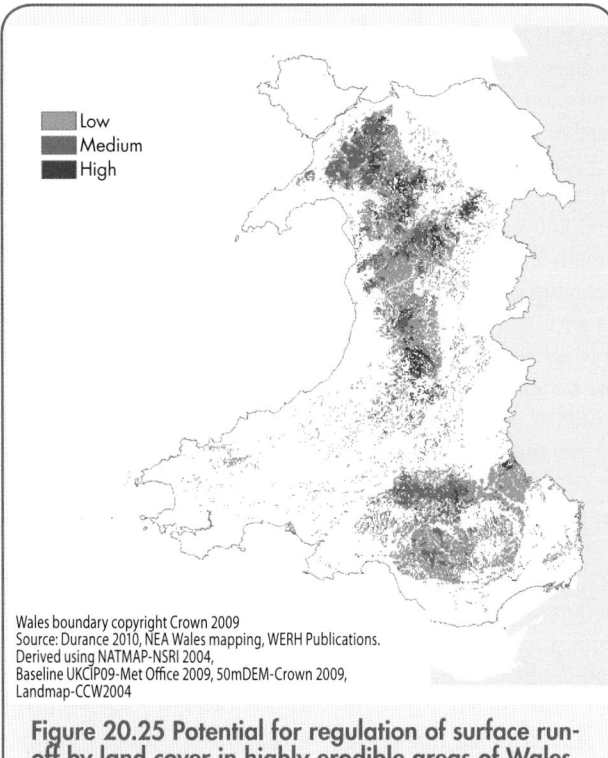

Low
Medium
High

Wales boundary copyright Crown 2009
Source: Durance 2010, NEA Wales mapping, WERH Publications.
Derived using NATMAP-NSRI 2004,
Baseline UKCIP09-Met Office 2009, 50mDEM-Crown 2009,
Landmap-CCW2004

Figure 20.25 Potential for regulation of surface run-off by land cover in highly erodible areas of Wales. Run-off regulation potential modelled by Isabelle Durance, Cardiff University, using values for rainfall pattern, slope and soil texture. Source: Wales Environment Research Hub unpublished data.

soil and slowing down the rate at which it reaches nearby watercourses.

In the lowlands, the establishment of floodplain woodland and the maintenance of grazing marshes can also provide increased water storage capacity at times of heavy rainfall. At first sight this could appear to be an uneconomic use of high grade agricultural land which is scarce in Wales, especially if only the potential timber values are taken into account. In the wider context, however, it might be preferable to accept some localised reduction in food production capacity, in the interests of reducing the risks, for example, to urban infrastructure. Under the ecosystem approach that is central to the thinking behind the new Natural Environment Framework for Wales, there is likely to be greater demand for targeted planting of woodland, establishment of wetlands, etc., in the most effective locations for the delivery of ecosystem services, thereby leading to multiple benefits to humans and the environment.

Investment in green infrastructure of this type usually requires action at a scale larger than that of the individual farm or forestry business. Reduction of flood risk and provision of improved water storage are best undertaken at the catchment scale. This is likely to require greater cooperation between private landowners and land managers than has been usual in the past.

In downstream and at-risk areas, Wales has adopted a policy that promotes Sustainable Drainage Systems (SuDS; WAG 2010d). This integrated approach aims to reduce flood risk, minimise diffuse pollution, maintain or restore natural flow regimes and enhance amenity in urban areas. However, uptake of the SuDS schemes is at a relatively early

stage and has so far been patchy across local authority areas in Wales.

Coastal floods*.* Wales has approximately 2,740 km of coastline, and flood risk is highest along the low-lying zones of the North Wales coast, and at Llanelli, Port Talbot, and the Severn Estuary in the south (Farrar & Vaze 2000). The Towyn flood of 1990 affected 2,800 homes between Pensarn and Rhyl. Given changes in population, predictions of sea-level rise due to climate change and possible increases in storm surge events, it is likely that coastal flooding will increase over the next 90 years. The economic impact will depend upon infrastructure development and levels of affluence in the coastal regions. Erosion of natural flood defences, such as dunes and wetlands, makes Welsh coasts more susceptible to risk.

20.5.2.3 Disease and pest regulation

Disease and pest regulation are primary/intermediate ecosystem services which affect human health and well-being directly, or through effects on the provision of final ecosystem services such as crops and livestock, food and fibre. This regulating service relates largely to the role of ecosystems in regulating the incidence of insect and fungal pests and pathogens. (All the UK NEA Broad Habitat types are home to diseases and pests, and to natural predators of those pests.)

In Woodland habitats there are increasing impacts of grey squirrels on the regeneration of native tree species, some instances of disease outbreak (e.g. Dutch Elm Disease) and increasing impacts of invasive species (e.g. Japanese knotweed). There has also been a significant presence of invasive trees species e.g. *Rhododendron ponticum* (L.). Although this rhododendron possesses attractive flowers, it has few other attributes that can offset the negative impact it has on invaded sites. It has been shown to reduce the numbers of earthworms, birds and plants, and reduce the regenerative capacity of a site, leading to a reduction in the biodiversity of the area.

Information on disease and pest regulation is poor. Independent data for Wales regarding disease regulation are not currently available as they are included with statistics for England. The reader is therefore referred to the analysis in Chapter 13 of the UK report.

20.5.2.4 Pollination

The production function value of biotic pollination as a contribution to UK crop market value in 2007 was £430 million, comprised of: England, £367 million; Northern Ireland, £19 million; and Scotland, £43 million. Unfortunately, figures for Wales are unknown at present, as data are not collected due to the relatively small amount of arable crops in Wales compared to other parts of the UK. However, insect pollinators are known to be essential for the maintenance of many vegetation types across all the terrestrial habitats of Wales, and the valuation of pollination services in Wales is therefore an important area for future research. This is particularly so because, although honey bees are the most common pollinators of commercial field crops across the UK, they have shown a 23% decline in Wales between 1985 and 2005, with this trend continuing at present (Klein *et al.* 2007; Potts *et al.* 2010).

20.5.2.5 Noise regulation

Moderation of sounds by ecosystems is a regulating service, but natural sound may also be considered as a cultural service, sometimes beneficial, and at other times a disservice (unwanted sound). Noise regulation is of particular significance in urban settings and vegetation is well known to have a capacity for noise abatement in Urban habitats and along transport corridors, for example. There are no readily available data on the relationship between urban tree density and noise regulation; this service is discussed in more detail in the section on Urban habitats in Wales.

20.5.2.6 Soil quality regulation

This regulating service is closely linked to soil formation (a supporting service) and erosion regulation—discussed above. There is no statutory soil monitoring programme within the UK at present. The Countryside Survey report for Wales (Smart *et al.* 2009) is the most thorough compilation of results indicating changes in Welsh soils for broad habitats. In Wales, soil pH has shown a significant increase under Improved Grassland; and an increase in Neutral Grassland; however, no change was observed in Acid Grassland. Soil carbon acts as a surrogate measure for soil organic matter content, which is a vital intermediate regulating service, particularly in terms of its impact on nutrient retention and cycling, and its physical effect on structure which regulates gas and water fluxes. Since the 1970s, topsoil carbon content has shown no significant change in soils under most semi-natural habitats. The carbon stock in the Arable and Horticultural component habitat is considered to be approximately 33 tonnes per hectare in Wales, lower than the same habitats in England and Scotland (Smart *et al.* 2009). However, the carbon stock in Improved Grassland is approximately 62 tonnes per hectare, comparable with the GB level. Wales, with a large amount of upland area and high rainfall, is vulnerable to soil erosion. The habitats and ground cover provide important protection for the soil surface and prevent erosion.

20.5.2.7 Air quality regulation

The main air pollutants of concern, which are considered under the national Air Quality Strategy (Defra 2007) and in international policy evaluation, are particulate matter, ozone, nitrogen oxides, ammonia and the deposition of nitrogen and sulphur. In Wales, acid deposition has been a major issue. Between 1987 and 2005, there was an 80% reduction in UK sulphur dioxide emissions; over the same period, non-marine sulphur deposition to Wales declined by 72%. Non-marine sulphur deposition is predicted to decrease by a further 40% of 2004–06 values by 2020, assuming full implementation of emission controls. There was little change in total nitrogen oxides loading to Wales between 1987 and 1997, despite a 25% reduction in UK nitrogen oxides emissions over this period. Subsequently there was a further 10% decline in deposition between 1997 and 2005. Over the same period, UK nitrogen oxides emissions decreased by 26%. Deposition of ammonia changed little between 1987 and 2005. No emissions data are available prior to 1990, but UK emissions declined by about 14% between 1997 and 2005, whilst in Wales the corresponding decline in deposition was 8%. For all pollutants, there is evidence to suggest non-linearity in the relationship between UK-level emission reductions and deposition in Wales which needs further investigation.

Each year in Wales, existing urban trees absorb between 45 and 73 megatonnes of particulates and between 91 and 165 megatonnes of sulphur dioxide (Small 2009). The health effects of this pollution absorption are significant, delaying deaths and preventing hospital admissions related to air quality causes, and these benefits could be enhanced through further urban tree planting. Willis *et al.* (2003) valued the benefits at £124,998 for each death avoided by 1 year due to PM10 (air pollution with particle diameters of less than 10 microns) and sulphur dioxide absorption by trees, and at £602 for an 11-day hospital stay avoided due to reduced respiratory illness, totalling an annual value of £0.04 million in Wales in 2002.

Vegetation in urban areas can reduce particulate air pollution, with woodland removing three times more than grassland (NUFU 2005). Rough Wood in Walsall was estimated to remove 50 kg of dust pollution per hectare per year (NUFU 1999). The Welsh Assembly Government has determined that there is a risk that PM10 levels in the Neath-Port Talbot area will be exceeded (WAG 2009d) and the local authority is working with the steel maker Corus to plant trees to help intercept particulate air pollution (WAQF 2008).

20.5.2.8 Water quality regulation

Water quality is strongly linked to ecosystem processes in the Welsh uplands. These areas are subject to a range of environmental pressures, particularly acidification. Upland waters and wetland habitats are a major source of clean drinking water. Being relatively unpolluted, water draining the uplands performs a key regulatory service by diluting pollution that enters river systems further downstream. These services are strongly linked to flow rates.

In terrestrial systems, the quality of water is heavily influenced by the ecosystems it interacts with. Freshwater habitats such as fens, bogs and riparian woodlands provide important filtering services. Management activities, particularly within enclosed agriculture systems, have a strong influence on quality water. The extent to which these various habitats provide a benefit will be dependent on the number of people or properties potentially affected in a given location. In addition to surface water systems, groundwater systems in Wales are also important sources of public water supply. These systems are also heavily influenced by land management activities.

Forestry Commission Wales's Forest Design Plans for the government woodland estate take account of riparian areas and include changes to tree cover and species choice when areas of trees are felled adjacent to rivers. Large-scale riparian management projects include the WoodLIFE Ravine project in the Wye Valley, the government-funded Riverine project and the Environment Agency Fishing Wales Objective 1 project. Strict adherence to UK Forestry Standard (UKFS) Forests and Water Guidelines is currently considered sufficient to address the contribution of forests to acidification in Wales.

Water quality monitoring by national environmental agencies is mainly targeted at rivers draining larger, mixed catchments. Chemical General Quality Assessments, which measure organic pollution, showed that 95% of Welsh rivers were of good chemical quality in 2008, compared to only 86% in 1990 (Defra 2009b; **Figure 20.26; Figure 20.27**). This sign of improvement is corroborated by the Countryside Survey for Wales (Smart *et al.* 2009). The most commonly recorded reason for water quality degradation is nutrient enrichment (eutrophication). Concentrations of phosphates were high (greater than 0.1 milligrams per litre) in 8% of rivers in Wales, by length, but show declines since 1980. Nitrates cause eutrophication in coastal waters and can impair drinking water quality. Work presented by Pretty *et al.* (2003) for the UK showed that the incidence of algal blooms per water body, per decade was highest in Wales, with a value of 1.6 from 1990 to 1999. Nitrate levels remain generally stable, after increasing in the 1990s, with a small decline since 2000. Indicators of organic pollution (biological oxygen demand and ammoniacal nitrogen) have declined in Wales since the 1980s, leading to improved water quality survey results for these factors (Figure 14.6, Chapter 14).

Acidification of surface waters is an important aspect of water quality in Wales, with implications for aquatic ecosystems and salmonid fisheries. Statistics for freshwaters in Wales show that in 1986–88 nearly 80% of sites exceeded critical levels for total acid deposition. This figure reduced by 30% over the next 20-year period, so that just over half the total number of Welsh sites exceeded critical levels in 2002–

4. Under the reduced emissions scenario predicted for 2020, 70% of sites will be receiving total acid deposition loadings that are less than the critical load. As would be anticipated, the amount by which deposition exceeds the critical load at individual sites also diminishes over time. In 2002–4 there were no sites exceeded by more than 2.0 kilogram equivalents of element per hectare per year (keq/ha/yr) and only five sites are expected to fall into the 1.0–2.0 keq/ha/yr category by 2020.

Environment Agency monitoring of acidification in Wales has shown that surface waters are beginning to recover chemically, with increases in pH and acid neutralising capacity (ANC) observed at sampling sites, along with reductions in sulphate and aluminium concentrations. The rate and extent varies spatially throughout Wales, depending on site conditions and local atmospheric deposition. There is evidence that episodes of adverse chemical conditions are still occurring, but their severity is reducing. However, the episodes are still sufficient to inhibit and slow biological recovery. The majority of freshwater sites that exceed critical limits lie in north Wales, along the Cambrian Mountains and in the Brecon Beacons, reflecting the combined effects of high deposition loading and acid-sensitive fresh waters. This distribution does not change significantly over time.

Dissolved organic carbon (DOC) concentrations in upland waters have increased, suggesting that soil carbon stocks may be destabilising in response to climate change (see Evan *et al.* 2007) However, these increases may also be associated with recovery from acidification in peatlands and agricultural intensification in managed systems.

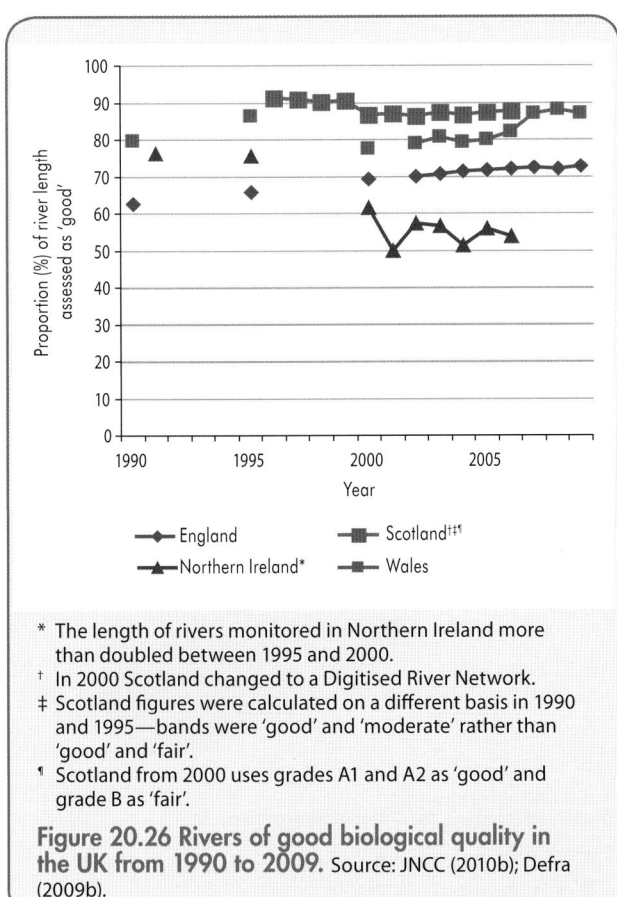

* The length of rivers monitored in Northern Ireland more than doubled between 1995 and 2000.
† In 2000 Scotland changed to a Digitised River Network.
‡ Scotland figures were calculated on a different basis in 1990 and 1995—bands were 'good' and 'moderate' rather than 'good' and 'fair'.
¶ Scotland from 2000 uses grades A1 and A2 as 'good' and grade B as 'fair'.

Figure 20.26 Rivers of good biological quality in the UK from 1990 to 2009. Source: JNCC (2010b); Defra (2009b).

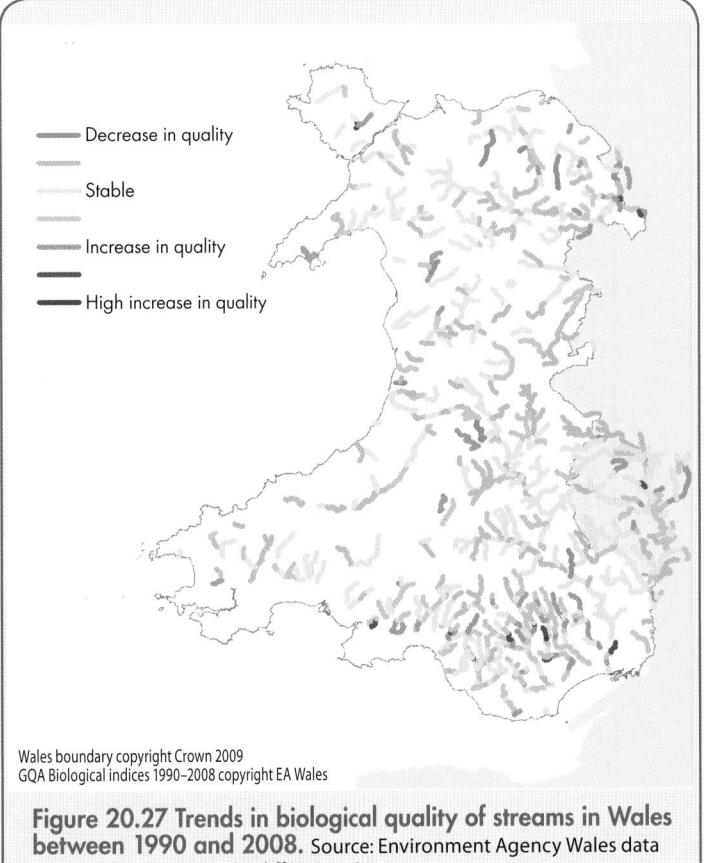

Wales boundary copyright Crown 2009
GQA Biological indices 1990–2008 copyright EA Wales

Figure 20.27 Trends in biological quality of streams in Wales between 1990 and 2008. Source: Environment Agency Wales data mapped by I Durance, Cardiff University.

Seasonal changes in precipitation due to climate change are likely to affect species in estuaries, although this has not yet been recorded. The predicted higher winter rainfall on western UK coasts, including Wales, may result in higher flows of fresh water extending further down estuaries, which may lead to contamination and eutrophication as well as sustained reductions in salinity. At the same time, drier summer periods will see the influence of marine water moving upstream, a trend likely to be exacerbated by increased abstraction from watercourses (MCCIP 2008).

20.5.3 Provisioning Services

In this section the focus is on documenting the trends in the supply of goods provided directly to humans by Welsh ecosystems, and understanding how this service has interacted with UK NEA Broad Habitats. Long-term data sets do not exist for all ecosystem goods in Wales and where they do exist for the UK, it is not always possible to disaggregate them for Wales.

20.5.3.1 Food from agriculture

Enclosed Farmland makes a substantial contribution to Welsh food production and the Welsh economy. Unfortunately, statistics for enclosed land alone are not available, owing to the interconnected way in which improved land and unenclosed rough grazing are still used throughout the year across much of rural Wales. The situation is further complicated by the routine use of winter housing on many beef and sheep farms in Wales. Nevertheless, it is clear that Enclosed Farmland contributes substantially to livestock production in Wales. Indicative figures for overall production in 2005 were 4.22 million lambs (30% of UK total) and 137,000 cattle. Welsh slaughtering resulted in 76,600 tonnes of sheep meat and 44,000 tonnes of beef in 2005 (Hybu Cig Cymru 2007). Enclosed land also underpins Welsh dairy and arable

production, as well as the smaller horticulture, poultry and pig meat sectors. The total numbers of holdings of each farm type are summarised in **Table 20.14**.

The high percentage of land above 150 m altitude in Wales (60%), and the predominance of peaty and gley soils with relatively low fertility and limited agricultural potential, result in 76% of Wales being classified as Less Favoured Area (LFA; see Section 20.2 and Figure 20.31). This has had a profound influence on the history and economy of Wales, and soil management regimes and conditions will continue to play a fundamental role in provisioning and other ecosystem services for Wales in the future.

Twenty-three per cent of land in Wales is classified in the Disadvantaged Area (DA) and 56% in the Severely Disadvantaged Area (SDA)—**Figure 20.28**. Most of the holdings in these areas are eligible for compensatory allowances (amounting to £25.1 million in 2010) from the Tir Mynydd agri-environment scheme (Farming Facts and Figures, WAG 2010b). This programme supports livestock production in the less productive farming areas.

Figure 20.29 charts long-term trends in the areas of different agricultural land uses in Wales since 1867, and **Table 20.15** shows more detailed information on changes in agricultural activity since 1998.

Livestock. The number of adult sheep and lambs in Wales increased substantially from 4 million to 11 million during the period between 1950 and 1990 (Fuller & Gough 1999). Since 2000, however, numbers have steadily declined, with the total population of sheep and lambs standing at just over 8.5 million in 2008 (**Figure 20.30**). Cattle numbers have remained relatively stable, declining by 11% from 1.3 million cattle and calves in 1999 to 1.2 million in 2007 (**Figure 20.31**). The total number of holdings with dairy cows has declined over the same period from 4,596 to 3,835 whilst the total number of dairy animals has fallen from 278,533 to 234,081 (WAS 2008). It should be borne in mind,

Table 20.14 Welsh holdings by farm type. Source: data from Welsh Assembly Government (WAG 2010b).

Farm type	Holdings 2009 (number)	Share of total (%)
Cattle and sheep (LFA)	11,425	29.3
Cattle and sheep (lowland)	2,169	5.6
Dairy	2,094	5.4
Mixed*	796	2.0
Cereal	394	1.0
Pigs and poultry	361	0.9
Horticulture	332	0.9†
General cropping	148	0.4
Other types‡	2,394	6.1
Minor holdings¶	3,771	9.7
Dormant holdings	15,140	38.8
Total number of holdings	39,024	

* Combination of cropping and various types of livestock
† Although it represents a low area, horticulture represents a potential high value
‡ Mainly grass and forage or specialist horses
¶ Holdings with small amounts of agricultural activity.

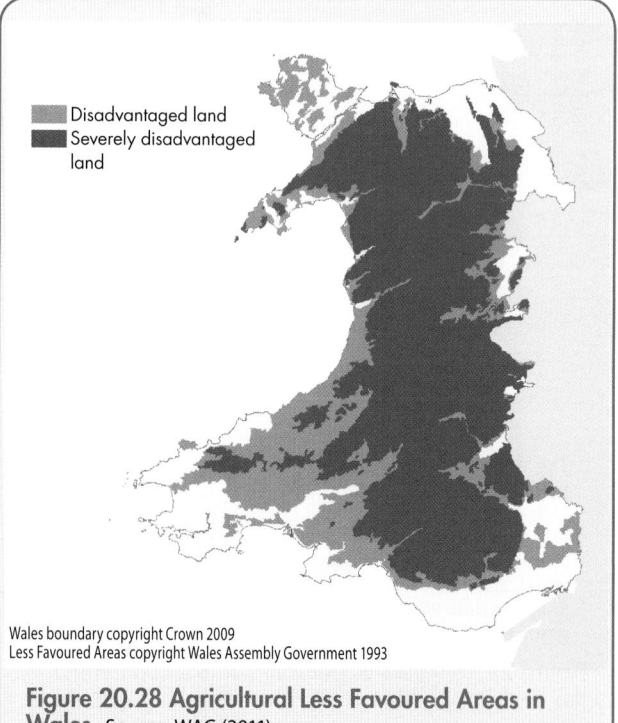

Disadvantaged land
Severely disadvantaged land

Wales boundary copyright Crown 2009
Less Favoured Areas copyright Wales Assembly Government 1993

Figure 20.28 Agricultural Less Favoured Areas in Wales. Source: WAG (2011).

UK National Ecosystem Assessment: Technical Report

however, that such statistics mask substantial changes in both the distribution and the nature of agricultural activity. For instance, the number of farms describing themselves primarily as dairying operations has declined by 43% over the period from 1997 to 2007 (WAS 2008). Similarly, sheep numbers have reduced more slowly in mid-Wales than is the case in the north and the south (probably due to there being fewer alternative land uses available in central Wales), whilst a pronounced shift to larger, more productive breeds is evident in the beef and dairy industries as well as in the sheep sector.

In 2003, agriculture contributed some £418 million or 1.1 % to Welsh Gross Value Added (GVA). If direct subsidies are excluded, the agricultural contribution falls to less than 1.0% (Welsh Assembly Government 2008). Whilst this figure appears modest, the industry also provides substantial downstream benefits through the multiplier effects associated with the processing and supply industries, which provide more than 10% of total employment (calculated as full-time equivalents) in many parts of rural Wales. Agriculture is therefore relatively more important within the economy of rural Wales, contributing 3.2% of GVA in 2003, in comparison to 0.3% across the rest of Wales (Welsh Assembly Government 2008).

Crops. Towards the end of the 19th Century, arable crops covered about 300,000 ha or 20% of the agricultural area of Wales, with cereals accounting for over half of this

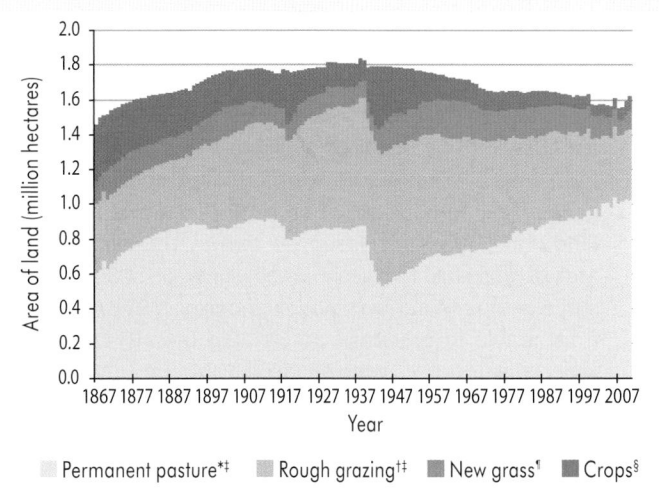

* Permanent pasture is grassland aged at least 5 years.
† Rough grazing sole rights rough grazing excluding use of common land
‡ The distinction between permanent pasture and rough grazing is made by the farmer.
¶ New grass is grassland less than 5 years old.
§ Crops is mainly cereals but includes all other crops for human consumption or for stockfeed.

Figure 20.29 Land on Welsh farm holdings from 1867 to 2007. Results are taken from the Welsh Agricultural Survey at June each year and exclude common land (around 180,000 hectares in 2007). Source: WAG (2010f).

Table 20.15 Changes in land area of Welsh agricultural activities since 1998. Source: WAG (2010f).

Land area	1998	2008	2009	2010	Change 2009–2010
	('000 ha)				(%)
Total agricultural area	1,677	1,635	1,670	1,710	2
Total area on agricultural holdings	1,497	1,455	1,489	1,529	3
Total crops	72	74	82	85	4
Total vegetables/fruits/ horticulture	1	1	1	1	0
Permanent grassland	927	1,017	1,027	1,021	-1
Grass under 5 years old	141	87	88	103	17
Sole rights rough grazing	298	200	213	230	8
All other land (including farm woodland)	58	76	78	90	15
Common rough grazing	180	180	180	180	0

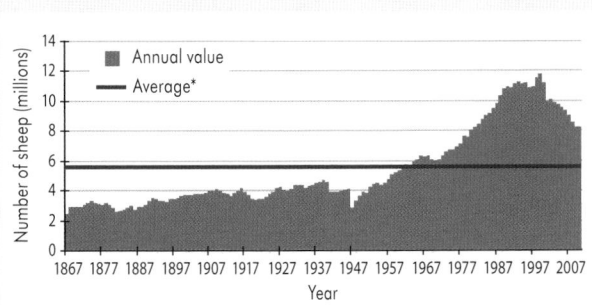

* The average figure shows the annual average over the period 1867 to 2010.

Figure 20.30 Total number of sheep and lambs in Wales from 1867 to 2007. Results are taken from the Welsh Agricultural Survey at June each year. Figures include all sheep and lambs of both sexes and all ages. Source: WAG (2010f).

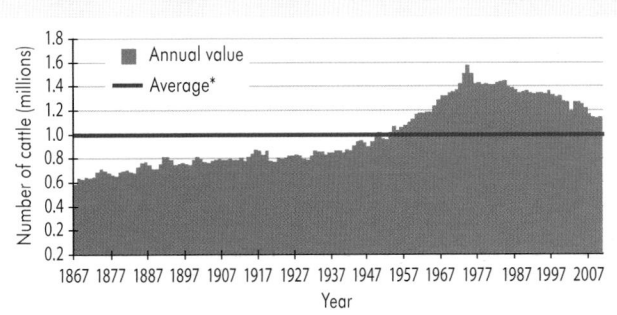

* The average figure shows the annual average over the period 1867 to 2010.

Figure 20.31 Total number of cattle and calves in Wales from 1867 to 2008. Results from 1867 to 2003 are taken from the Welsh Agricultural Survey in June each year. Results from June 2004 onwards are based on data from the Cattle Tracing System. Figures include all cattle and calves of both sexes and all ages, and animals used for dairy and beef purposes. Source: WAG (2010f).

and the remainder consisting of roots, brassicas, peas and beans (Ashby & Evans 1944). Crops were grown for domestic consumption as well as for feeding livestock such as horses. At the end of the 19th Century, however, livestock feed began to be imported, which led to a movement away from mixed farms and towards greater specialisation. In general, the importance of crops declined and the area of land under grass increased, so that by the late 1930s the area of crops had reduced markedly in Wales. Despite a brief surge as more land was ploughed during WWII, the switch from arable to grassland accelerated from 1947 onwards, especially as horses were replaced by tractors. In Wales, the area of cereals and total crops dropped significantly from 198,000 ha in 1940 to 83,000 ha in 2009. Crops now account for only 3% of the agricultural land area (Blackstock et al 2010). Substantial amounts of forage maize are grown in Wales, but the exact figures are not readily available.

It is important to remember that the production of food in Wales does not directly relate to the consumption of food by Welsh citizens. Some food items are produced in Wales and exported, while other foodstuffs consumed in Wales are imported from overseas, e.g. tropical fruits. The UK exported 94,500 tonnes of sheep meat in 2009 and imported 115,000 tonnes. Only 4% of Welsh lamb output is consumed in Wales and recent food price increases have served to underline the interconnectedness of Wales with the global food market.

20.5.3.2 Fibre from agriculture

Plants. There is a small amount of hemp and flax production in Wales, but exact figures are unavailable. Projects to help promote hemp and flax agronomy have been undertaken as part of farm diversification in Wales, e.g. Project Cywarch a Llîn at the Bangor University Henfaes Research Farm.

Animal. Fleece production in Wales is predominantly from sheep, with very small quantities of mohair and cashmere from goats (**Table 20.16**).

Table 20.16 Trends in wool production in Wales.
*Cash payments to producers by the British Wool Marketing Board. Source: data from Welsh Government Agricultural Statistics annual reports, 2007–2010.

	Total fleece wool production (million kg)	Valuation of clip to producers (£ million)*
1998–1999	12.1	5.3
1999–2000	11.5	4.9
2000–2001	10.9	5.1
2001–2002	9.5	4
2002–2003	9.7	4.3
2003–2004	9.5	4.9
2004–2005	9.7	4.9
2005–2006	10.0	4.7
2006–2007	8.8	2.7
2007–2008	8.0	2.7

Biomass and biofuels. Welsh woodlands (within the Woodlands and Enclosed Farmland UK NEA Broad Habitats) provide logs, chip, pellets and charcoal for domestic and commercial consumption in Wales. There is currently no data available on total amounts produced. However, the wood fuel market has become buoyant recently, due to increases in energy prices, cold winters and an interest in reducing carbon dioxide emissions. There is potential for Welsh woodlands to provide more wood fuel in the future, particularly through harvesting a greater proportion of the hardwood increment. The demand for fuel from woodlands is likely to continue to rise and it is possible that demand could outstrip domestic supply, leading to an increase in imports (Clubb & Tansley 2010).

Most of the Welsh hardwood harvest of 0.024 million tonnes is used for domestic firewood. However, this is dwarfed by the amount of softwood from conifers that is used in the three large biomass plants in Wales (approximately 0.56 million tonnes), most of which is imported. The commercial woodchip market accounts for approximately 0.3 million tonnes a year (Mike Pitcher, pers. comm.).

20.5.3.3 Fish from Marine systems

Offshore. Approximately 30% of landings of marine species from UK vessels occurred in England and Wales during survey years 1994 and 2008, with 68% and 63% landing in Scotland in those 2 years. Over 50% of the UK's shellfish landings occurred in England and Wales during the same periods. Marine Management Organisation and UK Sea Fisheries annual statistics give landings into Welsh ports, but they are not necessarily catches which have been sourced from Welsh waters (**Table 20.17**).

Inshore. The inshore fleet is mainly comprised of boats fishing within 6nm of the shore. These craft work out of 33 recognised ports across Wales, primarily targeting bass, crabs, scallops, lobsters, prawns, brill, turbot, plaice, rays and cod. Complete historical data are not readily available for the Welsh inshore fleet, which mainly comprises small vessels (craft less than 15 m long are not legally obliged to report their catches nationally or to the European Commission).

Shellfish. Shellfish production is important to the Welsh fishing industry. Mussels (*Mytilus edulis*) make up the bulk of production; live, fresh produce is primarily exported to Europe. Production rose from 8,000 tonnes in 2001 to 16,000 tonnes in 2008; Wales is the UK leader in seabed mussel production (WAG 2008c). There is currently a niche market for oyster (*Ostrea edulis*) production in Wales (less than 20 tonnes per year). Scallops, clams and abalone are potential new species for cultivation, again for the niche market. Shellfish cultivation in Wales was valued at approximately £12 million in 2005.

20.5.3.4 Inland fisheries

Commercial fishing for salmon, sea trout and eels, which spend part of their lifecycle at sea, and part in estuaries and rivers, is still practised around the coast and rivers of Wales, but is declining (**Figure 20.32**). Traditional methods of fishing for these species are recognised as having a heritage value.

Table 20.17 Weight and value of species (categorised by demersal, pelagic and shellfish) landed into three major Welsh ports and as a total for Wales. Source: reprinted from Welsh Assembly Government (WAG 2008c).

Port	Milford Haven		Holyhead		Bangor		Total for Wales	
	Weight (tonnes)	Value (£ '000)	Weight (tonnes)	Value (£ '000)	Weight (tonnes)	Value (£ '000)	Weight (tonnes)	Value (£ '000)
Demersal								
2003	1,753	3,144	414	531	-	-	2,302	3,956
2006	1,737	3,653	190	270	-	-		
Pelagic								
2003	14	10	-	-	-	-	14	10
2006	4	2	-	-	-	-		
Shellfish								
2003	471	900	2,939	1,456	-	-	6,796	6,771
2006	597	1,843	2,617	1,901	5,129	193*		
Total								
2003	**2,238**	**4,053**	**3,353**	**1,987**	-	-	**9,112**	**10,737**
2006	**2,238**	**5,498**	**2,807**	**2,170**	**5,129**	-		

* Value of 4,965 tonnes of mussels unknown.

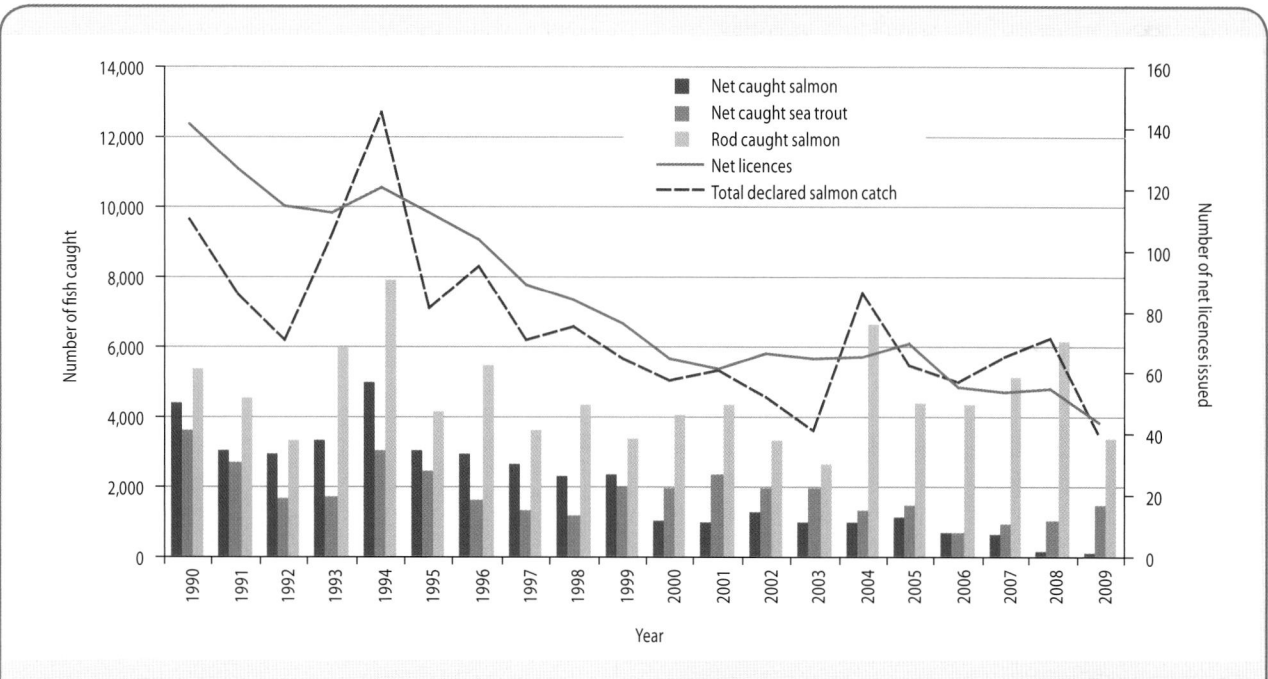

Figure 20.32 Trends in declared catches of salmon (net, rod and total) and net-caught sea trout between 1990 and 2006 in Wales. Source: WAG 2008c with updated data provided by the Environment Agency. © Environment Agency and database right.

20.5.3.5 Game—food from birds and mammals provided by hunting

Interest in both farmed and wild caught (hunted) meat has grown in recent years (Mintel Game and Exotic Meat Report 2007) and there are now three approved game meat-handling establishments in Wales (Food Standards Agency data). No specific data on volumes or value of this niche market in Wales were available for inclusion in this study.

20.5.3.6 Timber and forest products

Timber. From a peak in 2003, there has been a decline in recent years to 1.1 million green tonnes of coniferous timber harvested annually in Wales, representing 76% of annual increment (**Figure 20.33**). A further 0.024 million tonnes of hardwood are produced from broadleaves, mostly for wood fuel. This is about 5% of annual increment, and current policy is to increase this proportion further, although there are market and attitudinal barriers to harvesting more of the Welsh hardwood stand at present.

Total consumption of wood products increased from 1999 to 2007, but dropped in 2008 (Forestry Commission 2009a). Use of home-produced and imported timber in construction could increase in future because of its potential to substitute for products such as concrete and

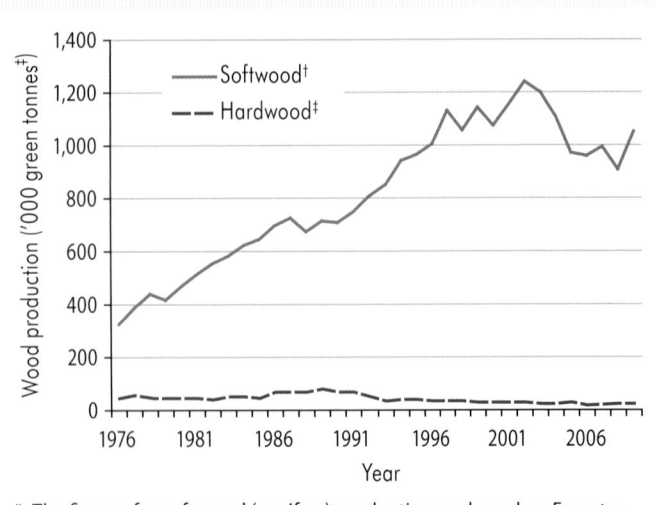

* The figures for softwood (conifers) production are based on Forestry Commission (FC) administrative records and on trends reported by the largest harvesting companies.
† The figures shown for hardwood (broadleaved) production are estimates, based on reported deliveries to wood processing industries and FC administrative records.
‡ One green tonne is equivalent to approximately 0.98 m^3 underbark softwood or 0.88 m^3 underbark hardwood, and to approximately 1.22 m^3 overbark standing softwood or 1.11 m^3 overbark standing hardwood.

Figure 20.33 Timber harvested from woodlands in Wales from 1976 to 2009. Source: Environment Agency Wales data mapped by I Durance, Cardiff University.

brick which involve higher emissions (Southey *et al.* 2009).

The gross value added to the Welsh economy in forestry and primary wood processing was in the region of £400 million in 2007, and 9,000 people were employed in these activities.

Non-timber forest products, ornamental and genetic resources. In common with the rest of the Britain (Chapter 15), there are very limited data on non-timber forest products, ornamental and genetic resources in Wales. There is increasing interest in wild-harvested products, and foraging for wild foods is now promoted in Wales as a tourism activity (Visit Wales website accessed March 2011). However, no information on volumes or trends in these activities were available for this study.

20.5.3.7 Water

The topography and climate of Wales combine to provide a relatively high supply of water in many parts of Wales. Water moves through catchments—and interacts to a greater or lesser extent with all the terrestrial habitats. Agriculture and land use clearly play important roles in delivering high quality water resources.

Assessments of the availability of water resources for licensing are conducted by the Environment Agency as part of Catchment Abstraction Management Strategies (CAMS). **Figure 20.34** shows the amounts abstracted in Wales in 2008. Abstractions in Wales were 40% greater in 2007 than in 1995. The major reasons for abstraction related to electricity supply and represented 75% of total Welsh abstractions. Abstractions for water supply represented 18% of Welsh abstractions, and these had increased over 1995 levels. Not all of the water abstracted for this use is consumed in Wales

as there are considerable transfers to English regions. For example, the Elan valley supplies an average 360 million litres of water a day to Birmingham.

The Environment Agency has identified significant pressures on the water environment in parts of Wales. Only 46 of the 100 surface water CAMS units in Wales currently have water available that can be licensed for abstraction without restrictions at low flows. Additionally, 16 CAMS units are currently over-licensed or over-abstracted, meaning that existing abstractions could be adversely impacting the environment, particularly during times of low flow. Levels of leakage in Wales have declined to 23.5% of total water supplied. There has been an increase in the average consumption of water, from 148 litres per person per day in 2001 to 152 litres per person per day in 2009.

The amounts of available water are increasingly likely to be affected by climate change. Current research suggests that by 2050, river flows in winter may rise by 10–15% due to changes in rainfall patterns. However, river flows in the summer and early autumn could reduce by over 50%, and by as much as 80% in some places. These patterns would result in a drop in total annual average river flow of up to 15% (Environment Agency 2008). Projections for housing growth in Wales forecast the numbers of homes in Wales to increase by 20% to 1.48 million by 2026 (WAG 2006b).

Effect of woodland cover on supply of potable water. After large increases in forest cover in the uplands of Wales during the 20th Century, some deforestation has occurred with the purpose of restoring open upland habitats (approximately 4,000 ha in the last 10 years). Forest cover is known to reduce the availability of water supply, and Willis (2003) estimated that it would cost £35.4 million per year if water companies had to replace all the water 'lost' to forest

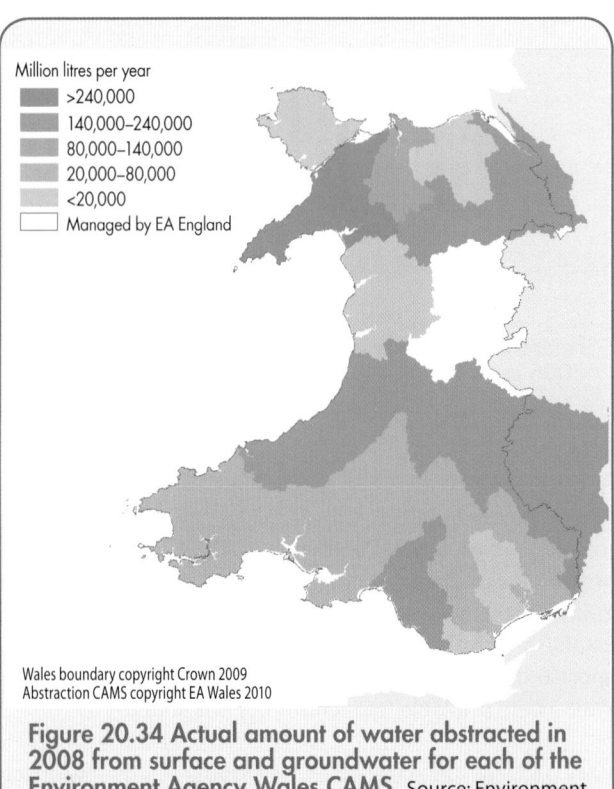

Wales boundary copyright Crown 2009
Abstraction CAMS copyright EA Wales 2010

Figure 20.34 Actual amount of water abstracted in 2008 from surface and groundwater for each of the Environment Agency Wales CAMS. Source: Environment Agency Wales data mapped by I Durance, Cardiff University.

cover in Wales. However, whilst hydrologists point to the theoretically large impact of forestry on water availability, British water companies currently internalise the impact of forest cover in water supply costs (Willis 2002).

20.5.4 Cultural Services

"Mae'r dolydd blodeuog o dan gysgod Pen-y-Fâl, Powys yn adlewyrchu'r canrifoedd o ofalaeth a greodd dirweddau amrywiol Cymru."

"The flower-rich meadows under the shadow of Sugar Loaf Mountain, Powys, testify to the centuries of stewardship which have created the variety of landscapes of Wales".
Caring for the Historic Landscapes—CADW (2007, p2)

This section focuses on aspects of habitats and cultural services which relate to human well-being in Wales. It aligns with the conceptual basis of the UK NEA main chapter on cultural services (Chapter 16), including the New Economics Foundation's 'Five Ways to Well-being', namely: being active, connecting, learning, giving and taking notice. It is qualitative in its approach, since it does not attempt to estimate volumes of ecosystem products or services. It is mainly based on policy and strategy documents related to the promotion and optimisation of cultural services in Wales. Academic material is covered in more detail in the UK-level chapter on cultural services.

The cultural services addressed here comprise: tourism and recreation, education, tradition and language, sense of place and community development, spiritual and religious services, and aesthetic and inspirational services. There is considerable overlap and convergence between these various services; for example, culture and language have fundamental links to the services associated with a sense of place and community development, and are intimately associated with the perception of and responses to landscape and nature. Initiatives and projects that are planned to conserve and enhance awareness in one area will have implications and benefits for others.

The following sections discuss each cultural aspect and identify the key ecosystem services and opportunities associated with it.

20.5.4.1 Tourism and recreation

Wales has a wide variety of habitats which display a range of aspects from gently undulating lowlands and vales, to upland 'wilderness' areas, rugged mountains and sweeping or dissected coastlines. These offer a significant range of types and levels of physical activity for residents and visitors alike. As well as the main benefits of physical and mental challenge, health and well-being offered by recreation in these habitats, many outdoor activities also create opportunities for developing a greater awareness and understanding of the natural environment.

The economic and social benefits arising from countryside recreation are now widely acknowledged. Walking in Wales alone has been estimated as being worth over £500 million per annum to the Welsh economy. The

Foot and Mouth Disease outbreak in 2001 demonstrated that trips to the countryside by local residents and visitors make a huge contribution to rural areas (**Table 20.18**). During the outbreak, the economic losses to UK businesses dependent on tourism were estimated as ranging from £2.7 billion to £3.2 billion.

Direct tourism spend in Wales was estimated at £753 million per year averaged across 2006–2008 (UKTS 2009). The Tourism Satellite Account for Wales, compiled by Cardiff Business School for Visit Wales, estimated that the wider impact of tourist spend on the Welsh economy was an estimated £4.2 billion in 2007, with direct support of 78,000 full-time equivalent jobs. The report found that 50% of tourist spending in Wales is by day trip visitors, 32.5% by longer-stay UK holidaymakers, 8% by international visitors and 6% by business tourists.

A major current driver of rural tourism is the Wales Rural Development Plan, which uses European Convergence funds to support farm diversification into visitor services and niche activities such as green tourism and wildlife-watching. Wales also has strategies that aim to increase well-being and healthy lifestyles through physical activity and sports for a wide range of Welsh people. Examples of this include support for the national long distance footpaths, cycle routes and the Wales Coastal Path.

The value of recreational angling to Wales is now estimated at more than £100 m (WAG 2008b, p39). Lakes, rivers and seas are being targeted for the expansion of recreational services. Environment Agency Wales is aiming for a substantial increase in water-related leisure activities by 2013, including an increase in recreational angling. Typical of such initiatives is the Get Hooked on Fishing (GHOF) strategy, which is developing a range of angling-related local projects in Wales. In 2009 the first such scheme was launched in Flintshire, coordinated by the local Neighbourhood Watch Association,

Table 20.18 Welsh Outdoor Recreation Survey summary.
Source: data from Countryside Council for Wales and Forestry Commission Wales (CCW & FCW 2009).

Types of activity	Proportion of visits (%)	Places visited	Proportion of visits (%)
Short walks	35	Local parks	15
Dog walking	31	Woodlands or forests	14
Long walks	28	Roadside pavements	12
Hill walking	14	Hills/moorland	11
Visits to playgrounds	11	Farmland	8
Wildlife watching	11	Rivers/lakes/canals	8
Sightseeing	10	Local open space	8
Running	6	Beaches	7
Informal games	5	Other coastline	6
Picnicking	4	The sea	2
Road/off road cycling	3		
Horse riding	3		
Other	3		

with additional schemes planned for the Anglesey/Gwynedd area, Brynmawr and Neath.

Information on tourism earnings for the Welsh seaboard is given in the section on the Coastal Margins in Wales. In line with European directives on coastal waters, it is planned that there will be 100 blue/green coast award beaches and nine blue flag marinas in Wales by 2015, all of which are likely to contribute to increased visitor numbers to this habitat.

Tourism to rural Wales frequently focuses on opportunities for a range of landscape and wildlife-related activities. The existence of a mosaic of healthy habitats is therefore important for the tourist experience, and for the biodiversity that these land-/seascapes support. The Government recognises the potential for growth in wildlife-related tourism and the fact that this form of tourism relies on the good condition of the ecosystems on which it depends:

> "Increased development of the wildlife tourism sector could have considerable 'knock-on' benefits, including increases in conservation activity, particularly if it occurs alongside additional associated investment in the protection and management of Wales's wildlife resource". (CCW 2007).

Wales's national tourism strategy, Achieving our Potential 2006–2013, is supported by regional strategies and sectoral tourism policies, such as the Wales Coastal Tourism Strategy, the Green Sea Development Strategy 2006–2015 and specific initiatives such as the Brecon Beacons National Park and Powys Green Tourism Scheme 2009 and Wild and Green Tourism (Powys Rural Development Plan).

An example of a major initiative which is based on ecosystem service principles, and which has been designed to develop, expand and enhance the tourism potential of the South Wales valleys, is the Valleys Regional Park project (VRP), see **Figure 20.35**. This scheme aims to create a mosaic of high-quality countryside recreation and heritage amenities including country parks, urban parks, greenspaces, upland commons, reservoirs, lakes, canals, nature reserves and river corridors, as well as historic sites and visitor attractions, all linked together by an extensive rights of way network, trails, tramways and cycle routes. Fundamental to the VRP approach is the concept of cross-sector and cross-boundary collaboration between 40 organisations, focusing on an ecosystem services approach to maximise the wider opportunities afforded by the environment. The project will cover an area of over 200,000 hectares which is home to over 1 million people (nearly one-third of the Welsh population). Part of the programme is focusing on maximising the economic opportunities offered by the environment for business through the ecosystem services approach.

Wales has a 33,000 km network of public rights of way. Local Authority survey data for 2008/9 showed that 49.26% of routes were classed as 'easy to use' and the overall picture is one of gradual improvement since 2002/3 when the Wales average was 43.7%. Nevertheless, the current position means that just over half the public rights of way in Wales are still not easy to use according to the performance measures used by Local Authorities. This is likely to significantly affect the ability of walkers to access areas of open country and coastline.

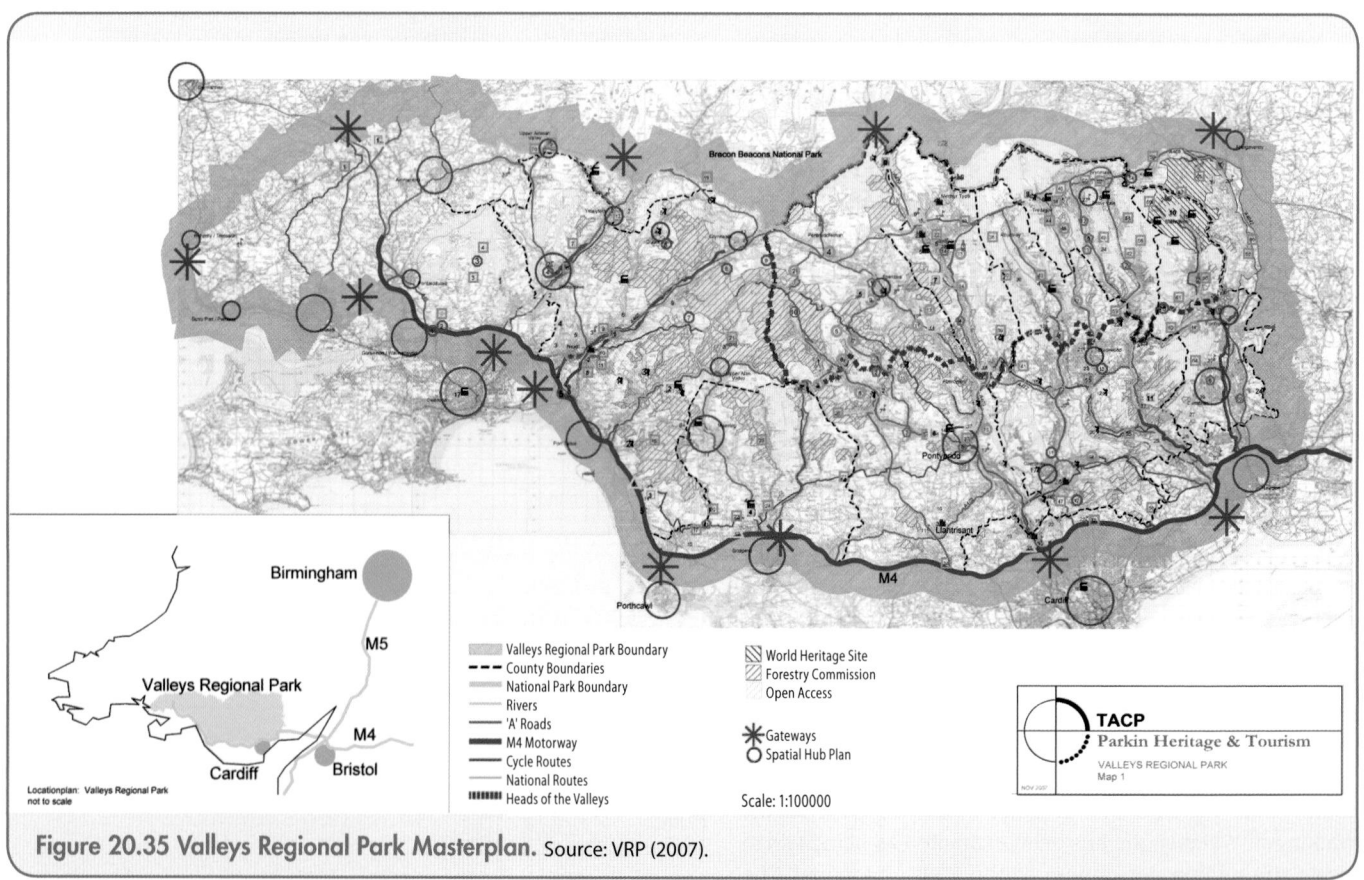

Figure 20.35 Valleys Regional Park Masterplan. Source: VRP (2007).

The impact of land management on public rights of way can be significant and can lead to problems such as poor surface condition (caused by ploughing, livestock trampling, etc.) as well as obstruction (growth of surface vegetation, installation of fence lines and deterioration of gates and stiles). The potential exists for significantly reducing problems on public rights of way, thus improving both accessibility and quality of experience by users as well as bringing associated cost benefits to the public sector.

Welsh tourism and recreation strategies target walking as a main activity to attract visitors to Wales. Research in 2001 showed that 74% of trips to Wales by UK holidaymakers involved walking as an important component of their visits. The Welsh Coastal Tourism Strategy 2008 indicates that 68% of people cite walking as their main activity when visiting Wales, and the Welsh Outdoor Recreation Strategy 2009 states that 86% of all outdoor activity involves walking (see **Table 20.18** above).

The health benefits of walking are well known and the importance of outdoor physical activity in relation to health and well-being has been recognised by the National Institute for Clinical Excellence (NICE) in its guidance on physical activity and the environment:

"Ensure public open spaces and public paths are maintained to a high standard. They should be safe, attractive and welcoming to everyone."(NICE 2008, p8).

20.5.4.2 Education

Education and ecological knowledge can be derived from all the other cultural ecosystem services covered here. Learning is both 'giving and taking notice', and is encountered either through formal or informal education or through site-specific interpretation.

Schools use the ecosystems of Wales, urban greenspaces, LNRs, the woodland estate, etc., for many educational activities as part of the National Curriculum. Colleges and Universities rely on Welsh habitats for training in many fields, including countryside management, agriculture, marine science, geology, hydrology, heritage and outdoor sports. Many continuing and further education activities also focus on the learning opportunities presented by the Welsh environment, and Wales is well served by a range of field centres, which include the UK's only residential Environmental Studies Centre entirely owned and managed by a National Park Authority (Plas Tan-y-Bwlch in Snowdonia).

Urban wildlife habitats also score highly for education services because urban farms, Learning through Landscapes schemes, school eco-projects and wildlife gardens provide a variety of hands-on educational experiences that are embedded in the formal curriculum. The Enclosed Farmland habitat also offers educational opportunities through schemes such as the Schools Food and Farming Initiative.

20.5.4.3 Tradition and language

Some ecosystem services have acquired cultural status through their association with human stories, legend and myth. These services are especially important in Wales because of the significance of the Welsh language, which has often preserved and enshrined local and particular aspects of ecosystems. Welsh words and terms define specific elements or aspects of biodiversity, traditional skills and agricultural/marine products and practices. The Welsh language is also firmly associated with unique literary responses to ecosystem services.

Such services and products are reflected in a variety of cultural and creative initiatives and opportunities, including events such as eisteddfodau; agricultural and breed society shows, countryside and community events, and heritage and interpretation projects in Wales. An example is Iaith Pawb, the action plan for a bilingual Wales, which not only aims to implement policy and law on culture and language, but also has a specific brief to conserve and develop links between the language and its traditional connections to wildlife and the landscape of Wales.

Bwrlwm Eryri is a cultural landscape initiative launched in 2005 and led by the Snowdonia National Park Authority, which aims to encourage communities and organisations to become involved in recording and safeguarding the Park's cultural heritage and to promote greater awareness, understanding and enjoyment of this rich resource amongst residents and visitors (SNPA 2010). Cymdeithas Edward Llwyd has a programme of over 100 walks every year, focusing on different aspects of the natural and historical life of Wales. The online facility Llên Natur gives access to current information about biodiversity, with sections on traditional lore associated with various habitats. It also provides access to nature terminology in the Welsh language.

Cultural and historic features of the landscapes of Wales have been recorded by government initiatives such the Register of Landscapes of Historic Interest in Wales (Cadw, Countryside Council for Wales, ICOMOS UK) and the Historic Landscape Characterisation Project (Cadw, Countryside Council for Wales and four Welsh Archaeological Trusts). Cultural and traditional/historical landscape features are also evaluated alongside geological, habitat/biodiversity and visual/sensory criteria, and are held in a nationally consistent data set and Geographical Information System (LANDMAP), which assists with planning decisions in Wales (CCW 2009).

There are nearly 5,000 Scheduled Ancient Monuments in Welsh woodlands and the relative lack of ground disturbance, for example by tilling, contributes to the preservation of these features of the historic environment. However, Willis *et al.* (2003) were unable to assign a monetised benefit to the archaeological resources of Wales.

20.5.4.4 Sense of place and community development

There is a significant relationship between ecosystem goods associated with tradition and those that reinforce a sense of place and community development in Wales. Recently, there has been a growing emphasis on local products, animal breeds, foods and crafts, and how they can be used to regenerate and animate the local rural economy. Food festivals, farmers' markets, farm tourism, local energy provision, traditional building with local materials and 'sustainable livelihood' projects are typical manifestations of this. The fish festivals of Anglesey, Llŷn, Aberaeron and Pembrokeshire, for example, derive their distinctive character from the provisioning services of the marine environment and its cultural relationship to local human communities.

There are several schemes in Wales which demonstrate how underlying ecosystem services can contribute to community development and an enhanced sense of belonging and commitment to regions and localities. The four Welsh Landscape Partnership schemes supported by the Heritage Lottery Fund are focused on: 1) moorland/heathland habitat (Heather and Hillforts—Clwydian Hills); 2) a coastal/farmland area (Llyn); 3) the semi-natural upland grassland of the area around Blaenavon (Forgotten Landscapes); and 4) the river valley of the Tywi (Afon yr Oesoedd). The purpose of these projects is to create interaction between nature conservation and agricultural initiatives, traditional culture, communities and educational/interpretive programmes.

The Communities and Nature programme (CAN) is administered by the Countryside Council for Wales and aims to: "generate increased economic growth and sustainable jobs … by enabling a wider range of Wales' residents to benefit … from the country's environmental qualities, particularly its landscape and wildlife".

Wales's Geoparks and the Eco Dyfi project in the UNESCO Biosphere Reserve in West Wales, are further examples of the way in which ecosystem goods and services are being used to stimulate social and economic development and local community engagement.

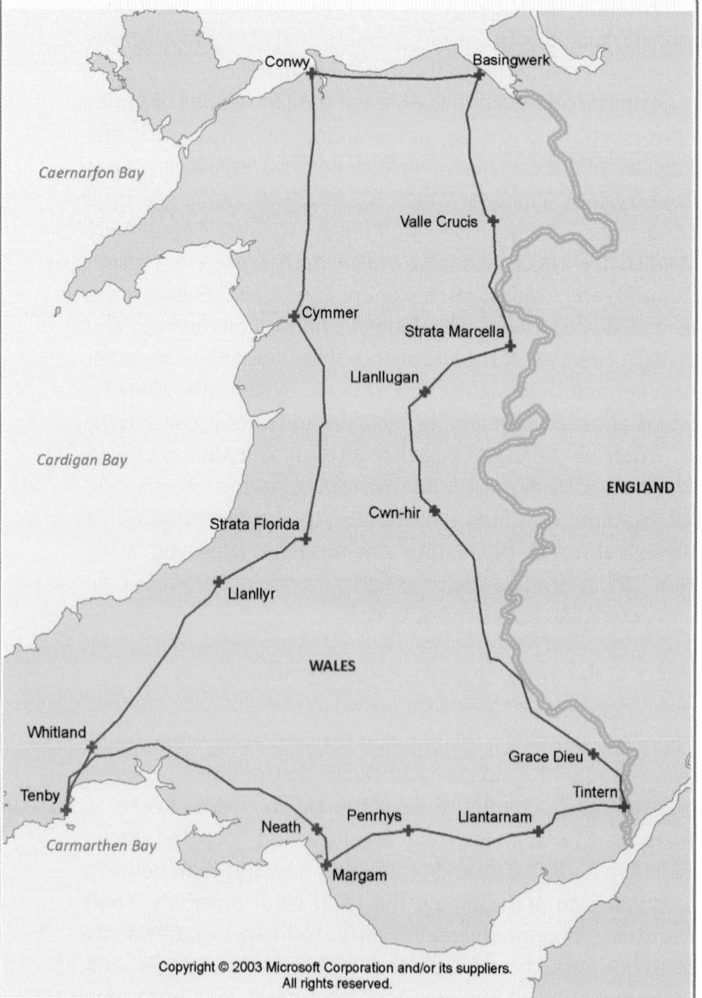

20.5.4.5 Spiritual and religious services

Ecosystem features associated with spiritual and religious feelings, include landscape features linked to deities or to human experiences such as renewal, healing and burial. Some of these elements form a bridge between Christian and pagan beliefs, and holy sites in Wales are often linked to more than one religion. In some instances, large landscape features such as mountains, lakes or rivers are recognised for their connections with mythical figures, with the power of a deity or as entrances to another world.

Just as droving routes are an important feature of the working landscape, so pilgrimage routes offer opportunities for an experience of landscape that is marked out by religious elements such as holy wells and churchyards, or sacred trees and stones. One example is the Cistercian Way, which is a long distance footpath, begun in 1998, linking sites associated with Cistercian monasticism in Wales (**Figure 20.36**). Cistercian monasteries were often sited in remote places with a sense of wildness and isolation, and were closely linked to the natural environment through practical (farming) and spiritual (meditation) activities. Corpse routes were used to take coffins across a mountain, usually when returning a person to their home village after death. Such spirit paths and ancient trackways are best preserved in upland areas, partly because they have not been overlain with roads or other development.

The spiritual and religious aspects of ecosystem services are of interest to many more people than the members of practising faith communities. Urban churchyards and cemeteries are often valued as wildlife havens and for conservation projects, e.g. the Gwent Wildlife Trust's Living Churchyards project. Sacred sites and church trails also offer opportunities for special-interest tourism.

Wales's heritage organisation, Cadw, includes in its cultural heritage initiative, a theme dedicated to the 'spiritual and inspirational'. The intention of this programme is to: "… connect individual heritage sites with other heritage attractions and with the local community and the surrounding area, as well as to link to broader interpretive stories and themes".

There is a strong religious or sacred element in two of the Welsh Landscape Partnership projects. Death and Religion—an exploration of the Sacred Sites and Landscapes of the Tywi Valley, is a main theme for the Afon yr Oesoedd (River through Time) project; and in the Llyn Peninsula, churches and sacred wells mark out the ancient pilgrimage route to Ynys Enlli (Bardsey Island). Bardsey is also an NNR and SSSI. It has 350 species of lichen and 10–16,000 breeding Manx shearwaters (*Puffinus puffinus*).

20.5.4.6 Aesthetic and inspirational services

Aesthetic services and benefits are intensely personal, but there tends to be consensus concerning the link between habitats such as mountains and the sea, and the positive aesthetic experiences that they offer. The aesthetic characteristics of the Welsh landscape have been analysed

Figure 20.36 Route of the Cistercian Way. Source: The Cistercian Way (2011).

and mapped by the Countryside Council for Wales, and the evaluations are held in the 'visual and sensory' layer of the LANDMAP database. The project considered the physical attributes of landform and land cover, the visible patterns and distribution of landscape features and their interrelationships. Allowance was also made for auditory and olfactory (hearing and smell) signatures of landscape.

Figure 20.37, taken from the LANDMAP inventory, rates much of upland and coastal Wales as of high aesthetic value, with some areas classed as outstanding. This coincides with the observation that habitats and ecosystems of wild, lonely and dramatic places tend to elicit some of the strongest aesthetic responses, including motivations to conserve and protect such places.

However, individual aesthetic experiences may also arise from familiarity or from sensory detail in intimate and unexpected places. Details of form, colour and texture may be valued and provide inspiration and contemplation in places that are far from 'natural'. Such places might include the surprisingly rich local biodiversity of abandoned land in an urban setting, or the 'patchwork quilt' of farmed landscapes.

Outside of the flagship protected areas, examples of culturally important landscapes are found throughout Wales. Anglesey is thought to have one of the highest densities of Neolithic remains anywhere in Europe (GeoMon website accessed March 2011). Prehistoric field systems have survived in large parts of North and South West Wales where stone is plentiful, much of the land marginal and where it has been uneconomic to clear away redundant boundaries. Areas on the Historic Register exhibiting this type of cultural landscape include the Lower Conwy Valley, North Arllechwedd, Ogen Valley, Dinorwig and Ardudwy, Preseli, St David's Peninsula, Pen Caer and Strumble Head.

The Gwent Levels preserve clear evidence of successive periods of human activity in reclaiming land from the sea since Roman times. Rhossili Vale in the Gower peninsula demonstrates a traditional mediaeval strip farming system, and other such open farming systems have become 'fossilised' in later enclosure patterns at Wrexham Maelor, the Vale of Clwyd, Lleyn and Manorbier.

20.5.4.7 Case study—cultural services of Welsh Woodlands

Trees and woodlands are highly valued by people in Wales for their historic and cultural values and as places for quiet recreation. Woodland is cited as one of the most popular destinations for countryside visits—around 12 million day visits per year in Wales—and public opinion survey data show an increasing use of rural and urban woodlands for exercise and recreation, including walking, jogging, cycling and horse riding, with concomitant health benefits (Forestry Commission 2009b).

Welsh woodlands host a number of world-renowned mountain biking centres. United Kingdom tourism figures, averaged for 2006–2008, showed that mountain biking generated a tourism spend of over £18 million per year in the Welsh economy (UKTS 2009).

Walking is an activity undertaken by the majority (60%) of day visitors to woodlands in Wales (TNS 2004). Willis

Outstanding
High
Moderate
Low
Unassessed

Wales boundary copyright Crown 2009
LANDMAP overall scenic value copyright CCW 2003

* The LANDMAP Visual & Sensory evaluation identifies those landscape qualities that are perceived through the senses. It deals with the individual physical attributes of landform and land cover, as well as their visual patterns of distribution and sensory characteristics, and the relationships between them in a particular area, for example:
Scenic Quality: The area will have accessibly-viewed scenes which are of a picturesque quality, demonstrating aesthetically-pleasing elements in composition.
Integrity: The area should be generally unspoilt by large-scale, visually intrusive or other inharmonious development.
Character: The area should have a distinctive and common character including topographic and visual unity and a clear sense of place.
Rarity: The area should exhibit features or qualities that are both rare/representative and valuable for any other Visual & Sensory criteria.
LANDMAP Visual and Sensory Guidance. [online] <http://landmap.ccw.gov.uk/methodology/> [Accessed 13.07.2011].

Figure 20.37 Visual and sensory evaluation of Wales, LANDMAP landscape values. *Source: copyright Countryside Council for Wales (CCW 2003).

et al. (2003) attribute a total annual recreational value for Welsh forests of £13.84 million. A number of internationally significant events are staged in woodlands, generating significant economic input to the local and national economies. For example, the Wales Motor Rally GB brought £7 million into the Welsh economy in 2004, including £3.8 million in short-term visitor expenditure (Econactive 2005).

In Wales, 22% of the woodland area has open public access, some of which is secured under the Countryside and Rights of Way Act, mainly through the dedication of the Forestry Commission's public estate, voluntary and public bodies. Seventy-two per cent of the Welsh population have access to woods greater than 20 ha within 4 km of their home, but only 17% have access to woods greater than 2 ha within 500 m. There are a number of initiatives to encourage people to use woodlands for benefits relating to their health and well-being. The Forestry Commission Wales is working in partnership with Coed Lleol (the Smallwoods Association initiative in Wales) in two Regeneration Areas—the Heads of the Valleys and Aberystwyth. Here, the focus will be specifically on groups with, or at risk of developing, chronic illness. Expansion of access to woodlands for walking/ cycling, education and social/community activities is taking place, but more woodland is needed within or near to urban areas if the educational opportunities and benefits to well-being are to be more widely available.

There was a perceived 'loss of connection' between people and local woodlands during the 20th Century, but during the last 10 years there has been an increase in the number of community woodland groups to 138, and a significant increase in the number of educational and recreational visits to the forest estate. The Forestry Commission Wales encourages local people to use the Assembly Government Woodland Estate for such activities, and there are now 140 Forest Schools in Wales, set up to promote outdoor learning for school children. The Forestry Commission Wales Education Strategy supports a range of other local community and social forestry initiatives that include educational benefits, e.g. Coed Lleol, Llais y Goedwig, Cyd Coed and Forest School Wales.

Woodlands can contribute to the protection of cultural artefacts and archaeological remains beneath them, providing a link with the past. Welsh forests contain nearly 1,000 Scheduled Ancient Monuments, and a much larger but unknown number of sites of archaeological interest. Forests can help protect such evidence from disturbance, unless events such as catastrophic windthrow occur.

Trees and woodlands increase the diversity of landscape character. They provide a sense of place in key locations and form the major components of many landscapes, such as the hanging oakwoods of North Wales. There is some association between perceptions of landscape value and woodland characteristics: for example, woodland type (broadleaves tend to be more favoured than conifers), tree age (large, old trees tend to be favoured over younger ones), openness (valued more than dense, closed areas) and diversity (mixtures and variation valued over uniformity; Willis *et al.* 2003). These authors and others have explored ways of expressing preferences in value terms via willingness-to-pay calculations, deriving an annual value of £7.25 million for Welsh forests, attributable largely to their landscape characteristics and attractions (Willis *et al.* 2003).

Concluding remarks. Cultural ecosystem services are prized by the people of Wales, for personal, social and economic reasons. They also form an internationally important patrimony that deserves careful nurturing and protection in a global context.

"I am aware when I'm walking here that there is much more to the landscapes of Wales than fine views—the landscape, its geology and the society which grew out of the geology are all part of the same thing, and it is important that we do not forget that link. The fact that the mountains and the slate rocks were created in the first place has had a dramatic influence on Wales and its people". Lord Dafydd Elis Thomas, Presiding Officer of the Senedd—Welsh Assembly, in: I Care for Wales...do you? (CPRW 2004, p10–11).

20.6 Status and Trends in the Ecosystem Services of Wales

Figure 20.38 provides an assessment of the relative importance of ecosystems in Wales for the delivery of specific ecosystem services, and the direction of change in these services over the past 20 years. The assessment is based on the expert judgement of contributors to the Wales synthesis chapter of the UK NEA, but cannot be regarded as definitive, due to generalisation, differing opinions and gaps in knowledge. There are issues with combining a range of differing component habitats into the UK NEA Broad Habitat types, and complex trends into a single direction of travel. However, as with the equivalent diagrams in the UK NEA section on ecosystem service trends at the UK level, **Figure 20.38** helps to highlight positive and negative areas of ecosystem management and health over the past 20 years, and forms a good basis for discussion and planning of response options for sustainable management of ecosystem services in the future.

20.7 Valuation of Wales's Ecosystem Services

Where studies exist, monetary values have been given in preceding sections for ecosystem services in Wales. These include provisioning services such as agriculture, fisheries and forestry, tourism and the wildlife economy. The Valuing Our Environment study of 2001 (Countryside Council for Wales and the National Trust) estimated that the environment contributed £8.8 billion of goods and services annually to the Welsh economy; 9% of Welsh GDP; one in six Welsh jobs and wages worth £1.8 billion to the people of Wales. The report found that jobs that are strongly dependent on the environment and ecosystem services are mainly in the leisure and tourism, agriculture, water abstraction, conservation and waste management sectors. It also found that the environment is relatively more important to the Welsh economy than is the case for the other UK nations. This study relied on conventional economic measures of financial worth and did not attempt to place a value on many of the services that have been addressed in the present study. The reader is referred to the UK NEA chapter on valuation for further information (Chapter 22). Studies on the valuation of Welsh ecosystem services have been identified as a priority workstream within the Welsh Assembly Government's new Natural Environment Framework, and are being carried forward in parallel with the spatial mapping of ecosystem services in Wales.

Evidence of the value of biodiversity and ecosystems to human society in Wales is still developing. The value of wildlife-based activity to the Welsh economy was investigated in 2007 and the final report, Wildlife Economy Wales (CCW 2007) found that there was:

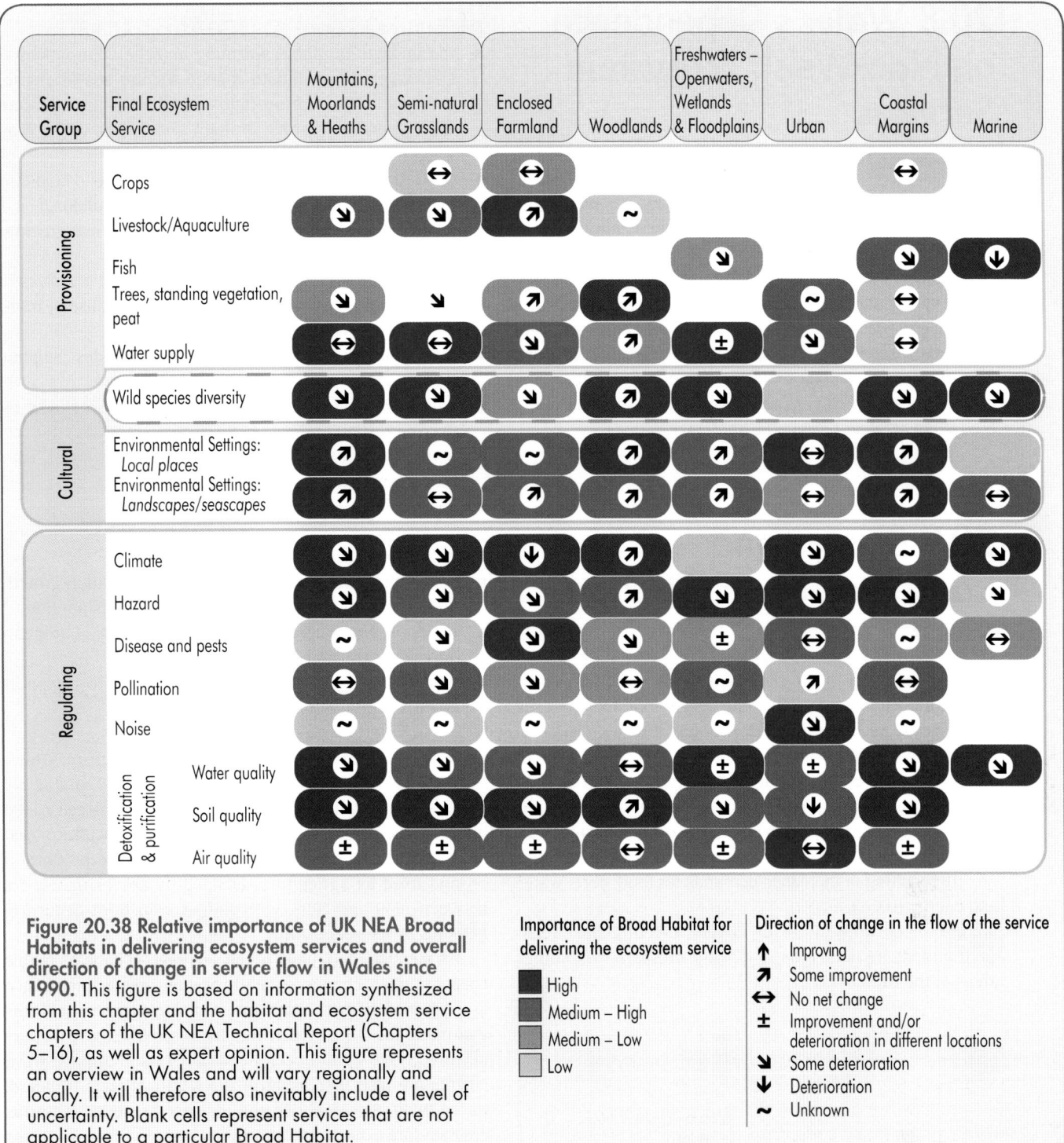

Figure 20.38 Relative importance of UK NEA Broad Habitats in delivering ecosystem services and overall direction of change in service flow in Wales since 1990. This figure is based on information synthesized from this chapter and the habitat and ecosystem service chapters of the UK NEA Technical Report (Chapters 5–16), as well as expert opinion. This figure represents an overview in Wales and will vary regionally and locally. It will therefore also inevitably include a level of uncertainty. Blank cells represent services that are not applicable to a particular Broad Habitat.

Importance of Broad Habitat for delivering the ecosystem service

- High
- Medium – High
- Medium – Low
- Low

Direction of change in the flow of the service

- ↑ Improving
- ↗ Some improvement
- ↔ No net change
- ± Improvement and/or deterioration in different locations
- ↘ Some deterioration
- ↓ Deterioration
- ~ Unknown

- total output of £1,936 million with a direct output value of £1,426 million;
- total employment of 31,766 (full-time equivalents);
- total GVA of £894.9 million; and
- total income to labour of £478.5 million.

This indicates that wildlife-related activities in Wales could be contributing 2.9% of Wales's national output, 3% of employment, 2.2% of GVA and 2.6% of incomes. Much of the output is driven by or linked strongly to wildlife-related public services, hospitality/retail and agriculture-related activities, with all other linked sectors making relatively smaller contributions. However, these figures only refer to wildlife-related conventional economic activity and they do not provide an assessment of the value of biodiversity as a whole through the provision of ecosystem services to Welsh society. More information on the value of biodiversity in the wider UK is provided in Chapter 22 (Norris *et al.*) and further discussion of the role of biodiversity in Wales is included in the sections on habitats and ecosystem services.

20.8 Wales's Dependence on Non-Welsh Ecosystem Services

The Stockholm Environment Institute has calculated the average Welsh person's ecological footprint as equivalent to 5.16 global hectares (Welsh Assembly Government Sustainable Development Indicator). This is the equivalent of 'three-planet living' for the average Welsh citizen. Data shows that Wales imports considerably more foodstuffs in all categories than it exports, except in the case of animal feedstuffs (**Figure 20.39**). This is just one indicator of the way in which the lifestyles of Welsh citizens rely upon, and will impact upon, ecosystem services beyond the borders of Wales.

20.9 Drivers and Consequences of Change

A broad definition of drivers of change is: "any natural or human-induced factor that directly or indirectly causes a change in an ecosystem" (MA 2005). The UK NEA has adopted this definition and a modified classification of direct and indirect drivers. Direct drivers are those which directly impact on biodiversity and ecosystems, e.g. land use and climate change. Indirect drivers are those which influence the direct drivers of change, e.g. economic and population growth resulting in increased demands for food, fibre, water and energy (UK NEA 2011).

The range and nature of drivers affecting the Welsh environment are numerous, and many are shared with other areas of the UK.

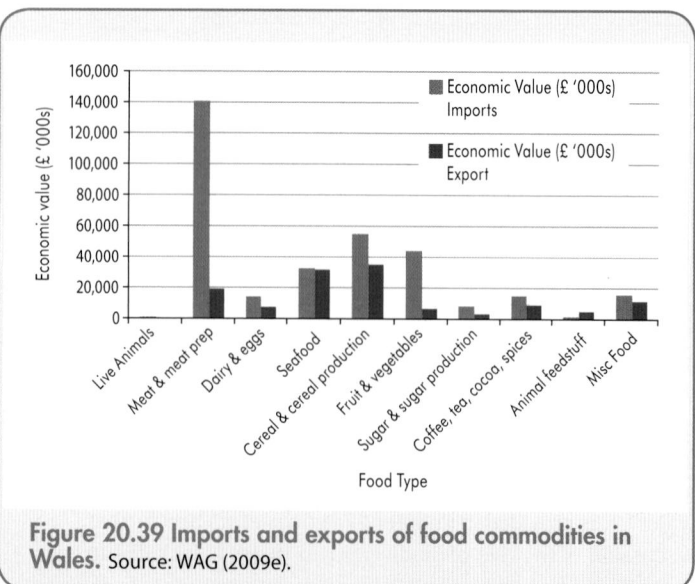

Figure 20.39 Imports and exports of food commodities in Wales. Source: WAG (2009e).

Direct drivers include:

- the impacts of global warming and the environmental consequences of climate change such as sea-level rise, changes in temperature and precipitation and extreme events such as storms, drought and floods, which may trigger irreversible changes of state in systems;
- habitat destruction—direct physical loss due to land-use conversion by the plough, the axe and the bulldozer;
- habitat degradation—due to neglect, overgrazing, fertiliser and pesticide use;
- non-native species—alien introductions and invasives;
- eutrophication—on land mainly due to fertilisers; more complex sources in fresh water and the sea;
- air quality—e.g. particulates, nitrogen oxides, sulphur dioxide, etc.;
- wild harvesting—e.g. damage to marine fish stocks by overharvesting and by-catch effects;
- toxic chemicals—pollutants and new substances with little-known effects, e.g. nanoparticles; and
- soil erosion and compaction.

Indirect drivers include:

- social and demographic change, e.g. population growth and movement, increased affluence and consumption;
- national and supra-national policies, e.g. European agricultural subsidies; and
- competition for financial resources to support environmental initiatives.

Land use has been a major driver of change in Wales. According to Swetnam (2007) between 1930 and 2008 England and Wales saw "an increase in forestry, the intensification and spatial polarisation of agriculture, and the expansion of urban areas". In England the proportion of land used by agriculture declined by approximately 7% between 1950 and 2008, with similar reductions occurring in Wales (Angus *et al.* 2010).

As mentioned in many of the sections on habitats in this chapter, climate change is likely to assume greater importance as a driver of change in the future. Satellite altimetry indicates that increases of 3.36 ± 0.41 mm/yr in sea level have already occurred (1993–2007; Beckley *et al.* 2007), and average wave heights are also increasing in the North Atlantic (Gulev & Hasse 1999). Sea-level rise and increased severity of storms are therefore expected to affect the Coastal Margins of Wales through increased flood events, for example.

Population increase brings about added pressures through demands for services, infrastructure development, production of waste, etc. According to the Welsh Assembly Government, the population of Wales is projected to increase by 11% to 3.3 million in 2031. Tourism as a major industry in Wales is expected to add to this pressure on the environment.

A key instrument of governance in Wales is the Welsh Assembly Government's Sustainable Development Scheme—the One Wales, One Planet agenda—which sets out sustainable development as the central organising principle for the delivery of Welsh Assembly Government policy making. It emphasises the importance of living within environmental limits, developing economic resilience and promoting social justice. The Wales Environment Strategy and the new Natural Environment Framework for Wales are key parts of the One Wales, One Planet agenda. The principle delivery mechanism for these Strategies is the Wales Spatial Plan, which has the potential to apply the ecosystem approach. Examples of policy instruments and levers in Wales are shown in **Table 20.19.**

The following factors have affected natural resource management in Wales in the past, and will influence responses to environmental change and societal needs in the future:

Conflicting political forces which have determined the use of Wales's natural resources, e.g. local needs, national legislation and the requirements of different European Directives.

- The legacy of habitat and resource fragmentation, and the consequent loss of connectivity resulting from patterns of land use driven by previous development pressures and subsidy regimes.
- The tradition of working independently and micro-managing land at a farm scale, rather than collectively at the landscape scale.
- The extensification, and even abandonment, of areas of upland Wales, and the lack of manpower in rural areas to undertake sustainable forms of natural resource management activity.
- The reduction in the area of woodlands in active management and the limited successes in bringing small private woodlands into sustainable woodland management regimes.
- The differences in attitude among different segments of the population in regard to competition for space on land and sea, for the production of different goods and services, e.g. food, fibre, renewable energy, water, public amenity, etc.

Drivers are discussed in more detail in relation to individual habitats in the relevant sections above (20.4) and within the main UK Synthesis Chapter.

20.10 Options for Sustainable Management

Ecosystem services and the ecosystem approach are assuming increasing importance in governance, economics, planning and land management globally (TEEB 2010; Volans 2010) and locally in Wales (Glastir 2010; Natural Environment Framework 2010). Pathways for ecosystem management at the UK level are addressed in the UK NEA main chapter on response options. Further discussion is provided here, on how Wales can achieve the greatest benefit from the management of its own 'critical environmental resources'. The following factors offer necessary context for this discussion:

- Wales has a range of particular social and economic problems, e.g. 22.7% of the population suffer long-term illness and there are areas of high social deprivation.
- The health/social budget in Wales accounts for about 35% of the grant received from the UK Government. Spend per head on environmental protection is low, yet the contribution the environment makes to the economy is high (see section on valuation of ecosystem services).
- The Sustainable Development Scheme and the new Natural Environment Framework imply a re-orientation of government policy and an integrated approach to the management of natural resources in Wales. This also implies prioritisation and tailoring of incentives for ecosystem service management through policy levers and fiscal measures.
- There is a desire to promote a transition to more locally integrated and sustainable economies which reflect high environmental standards, but which also provide added security for both local food and energy supplies.
- There has been an emergence of risk-based regulations to protect the integrity of critical environmental resources on which public goods and services depend.

Table 20.19 Examples of policy instruments and levers in Wales. Source: CCW, March 2011:			
Level/Strategy	**Policy instrument or lever**		
EU	EU Common Agricultural Policy and Fisheries Policy	EU Territorial Cohesion	EU Directives (Water Framework; Species; Habitats; Air Quality; Strategic Environmental Assessment, etc.)
UK	UK Government National Policy Statements	UK Marine Policy Statement, Energy Policy	UK Biodiversity Action Plan
One Wales	One Wales – Programme for Government	One Wales: One Planet Sustainable Development Scheme	Wales Spatial Plan
Local	Local Development Plans	National Park and AONB Plans	National Park and AONB Plans
Sectoral	Sectoral programmes – Economic Renewal; Rural Development Programme; National Infrastructure Plan; Wales Transport Strategy	Sectoral programmes – Climate Change Strategy; Waste Strategy; Wales Environment Strategy; Natural Environment Framework; Woodlands for Wales	Other sectoral plans, e.g. Health; Education; Farming; Food and Countryside; Sport; Social Care; Fisheries Strategy; Coastal Zone Strategy
Other	Town and Country Planning consents	Protected area designations; management agreements	Grant aid, e.g. Glastir agri-environment scheme

- There are signs of the appearance of new technologies to help reduce the carbon footprint of rural development, especially agricultural activities.
- There is a large amount of land in rural Wales which is of limited value for high intensity agricultural production.
- There has been a wide range of agricultural and environmental management initiatives in Wales with challenges for the degree of strategic coordination between them, for management and evaluation, and for the level of 'buy-in' among stakeholders in these schemes.
- There is already a relatively large area of land in Wales under environmentally focused forms of stewardship (including the National Parks and Areas of Outstanding Natural Beauty). The public and political appetite for protection of further areas of land and seascape for ecosystem services delivery is as yet unknown.
- There has been a public motivation to protect traditional family farm structures and the associated approaches to traditional livestock husbandry.
- There has been inadequate recognition of the connectivity between terrestrial and marine ecosystems, and these realms have traditionally been regarded as two independent resources for management purposes.

Considerable work has been carried out by the scenarios assessment team for the UK NEA, and the reader is referred to Chapter 25 of the UK NEA report for information that is relevant to the UK and Wales in general. Assessments have not yet been carried out at the country level (England, Scotland, Wales and Northern Ireland) during the NEA process, but the UK-level work provides a valuable conceptual framework for the planning of response options within the nations.

A sample of response narratives is given below, for some but not all of the sectors of the Welsh 'natural economy', namely: soils, the uplands, urban habitats, coastal margins and fisheries. For information on scenarios and potential response options in agricultural habitats in Wales, the reader is referred to the detailed treatment in the recent report on Land Use and Climate Change in Wales (Wyn Jones *et al.* 2010).

20.10.1 Soil Management in Wales

The sustainable management of soils in Wales has to take account of the nature and distribution of land use within the country which results from its particular combination of hilly topography, ancient geology and moist, cool climate. Agricultural land use is dominated by extensive livestock grazing. Twenty per cent of Wales's grassland and 25% of woodland occur on 95% of the organo-mineral and peat soils in Wales (Jones & Emmett 2009). Therefore, sustainable management of soil carbon, for example, has to use measures appropriate to these two land-use types. In a review of mitigation options for greenhouse gas emissions from Welsh agriculture, Jones & Emmett (2009) concluded that forestry (increased tree planting) and better management of improved grasslands had the greatest capability for locking up atmospheric carbon in soils and reducing nitrous oxide emissions. Unimproved grassland and bogs also need to be managed sustainably in order to preserve the large amounts of carbon stored in these soils and to prevent them from becoming an enhanced source of carbon dioxide.

Within Wales, the Welsh Soils Action Plan (WAG 2008a) and Woodland for Wales strategy (WAG 2009b) provide a policy framework for addressing sustainable soil management. Glastir (WAG 2010c), the new agri-environment scheme for Wales, provides farmers with financial incentives for appropriate soil management alongside other requirements for farm payments. Within the planning sector, recommendations have been made to review the Technical Advice Notes (TANs) which guide planning policy so that soil-related issues are specifically included (Stevens *et al.* 2002); the TANs in place for mineral extraction were considered a good model to follow. The effects of transboundary air pollution on UK soils has also been reviewed recently (RoTAP, 2010) and emission control legislation formulated at the European level will continue to be the main management tool. Thus, a number of policy instruments already exist in Wales to promote sustainable soil management. However, there is a requirement for appropriate soil monitoring in Wales to measure whether policies are successful and to identify areas of continuing concern.

20.10.2 Management of the Welsh Uplands

The success of agri-environment schemes in the uplands of Wales has been partly limited by the inability to effectively target management at key habitats, or to secure agreements across common land. Common land accounts for a large proportion of upland habitats and includes some of the most biologically degraded areas in Wales. Current legislation covering common land and its unique governance structures presents particular difficulties in terms of achieving agreement over the right approach to land management, but will be a major consideration in addressing many of the issues affecting the uplands of Wales in the future.

There is a continuous demand for a range of different land uses in the uplands of Wales, raising concerns about potential future conflicts. Trade-offs will have to be made when seeking to reconcile multiple objectives. For example, the methane emitted by livestock is, by volume, 21 times more effective than carbon dioxide in trapping thermal infrared radiation, but grazing is still the most cost-effective means of maintaining many of the habitats characteristic of the Welsh uplands. Careful management of the timing, types and numbers of stock animals used, with low levels of grazing designed to increase biodiversity value, could help optimise the condition of Welsh upland habitats (e.g. partial substitution of cattle for sheep flocks). Such management could also help to tackle problems of soil compaction and erosion, water runoff and downstream flooding/pollution which are current on a number of the 'drier' upland sites in Wales.

Consideration might be given to the withdrawal of 'traditional' agricultural management in some sensitive areas. The end result need not necessarily involve 're-wilding', but the adoption of alternatives to the current pattern of management might include minimal intervention in some places, with judicious use of grazing animals in others, and not necessarily with food production as the primary purpose. The challenge will be to plan where such approaches could best be applied, taking into account market forces, the need to manage ecosystem services and the increasing demand for recreational access.

A developed framework for the conservation of the Welsh uplands would help to highlight where it is most important to conserve particular habitats, and would act as a guide to inform decision making on land management. Knowledge of where it might be regionally most important to expand and restore woodland or species-rich grassland, for example, would ease decision making at any particular site. Larger sites will have a greater range of possibilities for habitat conservation measures. This approach is outlined in The Countryside Council for Wales's Upland Framework (Jones 2007), which attempts to convert the conservation objectives for statutory upland sites into a long-term vision of the actual vegetation that would exist on these sites if the objectives were fully realised.

20.10.3 Urban Environments

The provision and management of greenspace in towns and cities has often been reactive and opportunistic. In order to deliver a 'full basket' of ecosystem services, the provision of urban greenspace should be planned according to evidence of need. The Countryside Council for Wales Accessible Natural Greenspace Toolkit (CCW 2006) provides a model which can be followed to determine the need for a particular suite of ecosystem services (using clear, evidence-based standards) and for determining the areas where greenspace could most usefully be situated, taking other demands into account. The toolkit then provides a methodology to determine deficiencies or over-provision, and suggested policy responses to remedy any deficiencies. Such responses may include allowing development on greenspace where it is over-supplied in order to release funds to acquire land where greenspaces are lacking.

Sustainable Drainage Systems (SuDS) is a more integrated approach to urban drainage and has been adopted as policy in Wales (Prosper 2002). Traditional drainage design has typically been based upon the principle of removing surface waters in urban areas as quickly and conveniently as possible, usually via an existing watercourse or soakaway. This can contribute to an increased likelihood of flooding and diffuse pollution during high rainfall events. The SuDS approach takes into account the aesthetic and biodiversity potential of urban watercourses and drainage systems, while contributing to increases in water quality and natural replenishment of groundwater and watercourses.

20.10.4 Management of the Welsh Coastal Margins

Built infrastructure constrains the natural evolution of the coast and may locally lead to a build-up of sediments among intertidal rocky habitats, potentially leading to smothering (muds), scouring (sands) and/or a reduced photic zone (depth at which sunlight can penetrate to allow photosynthesis to occur) as a result of greater suspended sediment loads in the water column. Construction of piers, breakwaters and harbours (largely historic) within and at the mouths of estuaries throughout Wales have reduced wave exposure and changed the hydrology of rocky habitats within such estuaries. Construction may locally impact biological communities on estuarine rocky habitats. Coastal infrastructure is generally considered a poor surrogate for intertidal rocky shores, in terms of the diversity and abundance of colonising species, and reduced structural complexity of the surface available for colonisation (Moschella et al. 2005).

Managed realignment, or roll-back, has primarily been applied to saltmarshes in England, but is increasingly being considered in Wales and for other habitats (Pye et al. 2007). Managed realignment can help to maintain the extent of Coastal Margin habitats threatened by sea-level rise, and the ecosystem services they provide. Artificial re-mobilisation of over-stabilised or reclaimed habitats may rejuvenate dynamic natural processes with the aim of restoring the dynamic processes which allow Coastal Margin habitats to self-adjust to changing environmental conditions, with long-term benefits for biodiversity (Garbutt et al. 2006; Jones et al. 2010b).

In general therefore, sustainable management should take into account the uniqueness and non-replaceability of the existing ecosystem services of Coastal Margin habitats in Wales, and aim to enhance or maintain their specific characteristics, rather than replicating services provided better elsewhere.

20.10.5 Fisheries Management in Wales

The Wales Fisheries Strategy (2008c) identified several modes for improving ecosystem service provision in the marine environment while minimising the impact of fisheries and maximising human gain from this service. One major cross-sector challenge for sustainable fisheries development is the issue of economic headroom or scope for growth. Some of the key approaches outlined in the strategy (WAG 2008c) are outlined below:

- The centralisation of research and technological development activities to ensure that infrastructures are in place and that these activities are coordinated and responsive to the needs of the ecosystems and species, fisheries industry, regulators and the public.
- Greater capitalisation of under-utilised species such as mackerel and sprats (although levels should be monitored) and further investment in shoreside handling/holding and transport facilities to ensure greater economic returns from existing targeted species.
- Greater provision of training for commercial fisheries workers to promote sustainable practices, with significant emphasis on conservation awareness and safety in the workplace.

20.11 Knowledge Gaps and Research Capacity

20.11.1 Knowledge Gaps

An assessment of research needs in relation to the Wales Environment Strategy has been carried out by the Wales Environment Research Hub (WERH 2009). Several hundred specific research questions were identified by scientists and policy makers across Wales, and the reader is referred to the cited document for details of these findings (WEHR 2009).

A set of general research questions were raised in relation to response options for dealing with environmental pressures, and by implication, ecosystem services in Wales, namely:

- Research is needed to address issues of unsustainable resource use that impact on Wales, and pressures that originate from within and beyond our borders. We need to more closely define requirements for sustainable living in urban and rural contexts in Wales, including a full environmental costing of our current development framework. Carbon footprints need to be gauged and the potential for organisational and personal carbon accounting explored in the Welsh context.
- Further research is needed on the environmental implications of a balanced energy mix and a sustainable transport system for Wales. Additional studies are also required of water budgets, waste minimisation and local environmental quality, including air pollution and greenspace in Welsh urban environments.
- Further research is also required to develop and refine sustainable farming practices in light of CAP reform and climate change, and to tackle the environmental, health and social consequences of food, fibre and fuel production within and beyond our borders.
- Ongoing scientific assessments are needed of the impacts of development and environmental change on the biodiversity and landscapes of Wales, including the role of habitat connectivity in planning for 'networked regions'. More studies are needed of our important but relatively neglected Marine habitats, with research to underpin truly sustainable fisheries and the understanding of climate change impacts in our coastal seas. Further knowledge is also needed of Welsh soils, particularly the impacts of climate change on our soils with high organic carbon content (peatlands).
- Sustained observations are essential in Wales, for key environmental parameters that impact on ecosystems and human health, and are predictive of environmental progress and sustainability. This includes research to refine the suite of indicators for the Wales Environment Strategy and the Natural Environment Framework. Locally-relevant research into human behaviour and societal change is also crucial if we are to successfully understand and equitably address the environmental and developmental challenges facing Wales.

In relation to ecosystem services and land management, general questions raised by the review included:

- What is the current knowledge and understanding of ecosystem services in Welsh society?
- How should our thinking evolve on incorporation of the value of ecosystems and their services into national accounts and local decision making?
- How can we spatially map ecosystem services and determine weights for individual services when assessing ecosystem health and deciding on land-use interventions?

Research is needed on the following specific problems within the Enclosed Farmland habitat and the agriculture sector more widely in Wales:

- Reducing methane emissions from extensive livestock grazing.
- Reducing nitrogen oxides emissions from cultivation.
- Enhancing carbon sequestration within arable soils and Improved Grassland.
- Improving the management of Improved Grassland to reduce flood risks and pollution of watercourses.
- Developing cultivation techniques that enhance biodiversity whilst at the same time reducing greenhouse gas emissions.
- Developing the use of crop residues and other waste products for energy production.

To wisely apportion resources for sustainable land management and agri-environment schemes in Wales, further information is needed on optimum stock/crop ratios under climate change scenarios, tree and hedge planting regimes for catchment water quantity and quality management, and field boundary management prescriptions for biodiversity enhancement, etc.

Knowledge gaps in Marine and Coastal Margins habitats include:

- accurate estimates of change in extent and condition of the Coastal Margins habitat over time;
- management options required to respond to sea-level rise; in particular, how to apply roll-back or managed realignment to Coastal Margin habitats other than Saltmarsh;
- better knowledge, including mapping, of the Welsh subtidal habitat and its ecosystem services; and
- quantification of the links between marine biodiversity and ecosystem functioning to better understand the effects of human impacts on Marine ecosystems in Wales.

20.11.2 Research Capacity

There is a broad range of research into ecosystem services going on currently in Wales. The website of the Wales Environment Research Hub (www.werh.org) contains links to environmental science research groups at the Universities, and a map of long-term field experimental sites in Wales. The Centre for Ecology and Hydrology (CEH) has a good skills base and infrastructure for conducting ecosystem studies, but insufficient capacity to carry out the increased level of research and long-term monitoring studies that will be required for a robust evidence base if Wales and the wider UK are to pursue new governance models founded on the ecosystem approach.

Examples of current CEH ecosystem studies in Wales include work at the following sites:

- Conwy: 'carbon catchment'—soils for climate regulation
- Clocaenog: climate manipulation experiment—soils for carbon storage
- Lake Vrynwy: climate regulation, nutrient cycling, waste filtration
- Plynlimon: soils for water quality and fibre production
- Pontbren: sustainable management of farm grasslands for multiple services

- Berwyn: restoration of peatland for multiple services.

Wales has good capacity for marine research in its universities and, currently, in the Countryside Council for Wales. The universities are assisting the Welsh Assembly Government with planning for marine conservation zones, and The Countryside Council for Wales has carried out many marine assessments on which management decisions have been based.

20.11.3 Spatial and Temporal Scales, and Linkages Between Ecosystems

There are several initiatives to map the spatial distribution of ecosystem services in Wales, including the mapping of ecological connectivity being carried out by The Countryside Council for Wales. **Figure 20.40** shows an example of broadleaved woodland habitat functional networks as predicted by least-cost modelling, a method developed by The Countryside Council for Wales in collaboration with Forest Research (Watts *et al.* 2005; Latham *et al.* 2008).

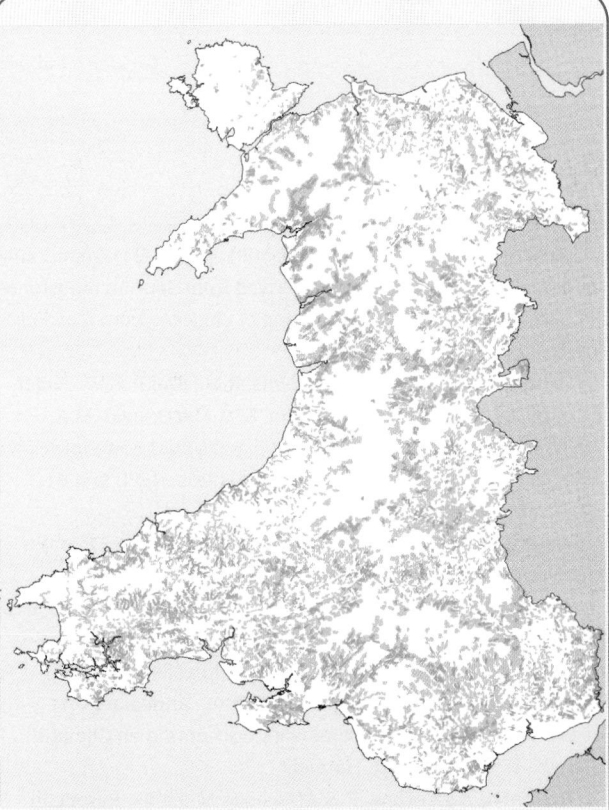

Figure 20.40 Broadleaved woodland habitat networks in Wales, as predicted by least-cost modelling (Latham *et al.* 2008). Networks comprise woodland and areas of other habitats around them that species may use to move between woodland patches; actual woodland boundaries are not shown. **Dark green** areas are core networks for species demanding a large minimum habitat area and with low dispersal ability; **light green** areas are networks for species with a low minimum habitat area and moderate dispersal ability. Many species will lie between these extremes. Source: CCW (2009). Map is © Crown copyright. All rights reserved. Countryside Council for Wales, 100018813 [2007].

A further programme of research in The Countryside Council for Wales, in collaboration with Environmental Systems Ltd of Aberystwyth, has mapped the following ecosystem services in Wales:

- Areas important for carbon storage in soils
- Areas important for carbon storage in vegetation
- Areas important for carbon storage (in soil or vegetation)
- Potential factors contributing to high surface water runoff
- Areas potentially contributing to the regulation of surface water runoff
- River catchments and flood risk areas
- Agricultural intensity
- Range of fishing activities
- Areas important for current renewable energy provision
- Areas with potential for additional renewable energy provision
- Areas important for current fibre provision
- Recreation resources: legally accessible resource
- Promoted areas and routes
- Outdoor recreation opportunities and health deprivation.

Further evidence gathering to support decision making for ecosystems management is being pursued through the workstreams of the Wales Natural Environment Framework, and through work in other government agencies, non-governmental organisations and the Universities in Wales. However, cutbacks in funding for state environment-related agencies, pressures on university budgets, and 'belt tightening' by private citizens, which in turn affects what NGOs and voluntary organisations can contribute, are all likely to impact on environmental evidence gathering and environmental action in Wales. It will be particularly important not to let austerity measures adversely affect long-term environmental monitoring programmes that provide the benchmarks and trend information on which future policy and practice will be based. Such information is crucial to the ecosystem approach and will become more so as environmental change impacts Welsh society and land/seascapes over the coming years.

20.12 Conclusions

The Wales synthesis has found and presented information relevant to Wales for five of the key questions addressed by the UK NEA:

- What are the status and trends of the UK's ecosystems and the services they provide to society?
- What are the drivers causing changes in ecosystems in the UK and their services?
- What is the current public understanding of ecosystem services and the benefits they provide?
- How can we secure and improve the continued delivery of ecosystem services?
- How have we advanced our understanding of the influence of ecosystem services on human well-being and what are the knowledge constraints on more informed decision making?

However, knowledge gaps and/or lack of capacity at the Wales level, have made it difficult to provide adequate answers to the remaining five questions:

- How do ecosystem services affect human well-being, who and where are the beneficiaries, and how does this affect how they are valued and managed?
- Why should we incorporate the economic values of ecosystem services into decision making?
- How might ecosystems and their services in the UK change in the future under plausible futures?
- What are the economic implications of the different plausible futures?
- What provisioning services upon which the UK depends are not provided by UK ecosystems?

As mentioned above, research is already going on to address some of these uncertainties, e.g. spatial mapping of ecosystem services by Environment Systems (Aberystwyth) for The Countryside Council for Wales and the Wales Environment Research Hub, and valuation of ecosystem services as part of the economics workstream of the Welsh Assembly Government's Natural Environment Framework. Work is also continuing on the ecological footprint of Wales and our reliance on external/global ecosystem services. Scenarios work at the Wales level is desirable as follow-up to the first phase of the UK NEA, and there are still large gaps in our understanding of the effects of ecosystem service changes on human well-being and the distribution of these effects in Wales. This area of research will require a cross-disciplinary collaboration between social scientists, economists and environmental scientists, if answers are to be found to the complex questions of human motivation and behaviour that will underpin our personal and policy responses to sustainable management of ecosystem services in the future.

The Welsh Assembly Government is already moving to address these issues and has begun to: "radically rethink how it manages and protects its living environment ... in order to achieve the best environmental and economic outcomes" (WAG 2010c). The Living Wales policy initiative is establishing a Natural Environment Framework for governance in Wales, based on the ecosystem approach. This policy initiative retains sustainable development as a central organising principle through which all polices will be developed and delivered, and by means of which, natural capital will be conserved or enhanced.

"The policy implies a new contract between environmental managers and regulators, industry and commerce, and the public. It is intended to result in better decision making about the use of land and water, that reflects all the costs and benefits to society, so as to promote healthier environments and the conservation of wildlife and environmental assets, while allowing developments in the right places. It recognises the value and importance of the efforts of every individual contributing to a healthy environment, and it aims for prosperous livelihoods, where the provision of public goods and services is well rewarded and where nature thrives. Larger, connected and diverse habitats will allow full ecological functionality and adaptation to climatic change, while Welsh rivers lakes and seas should sustain healthy fisheries through good regulation that benefits everyone now and into the future. A simpler regulatory system is envisioned, based on the assessment of risk to the ecosystem and clearer guidance on what should be avoided, and a more integrated system of environmental management will be pursued, which is administratively simple, cost-effective but fully protective of Welsh environmental assets. Wales aims to be the first country to explicitly embed the ecosystem approach into governance and grass roots action, based on sound scientific evidence." (WAG 2010c).

The UK NEA has come at the right time to provide an, albeit as yet incomplete, evidence base for the Natural Environment Framework policy and governance initiative in Wales. It serves to highlight, after centuries of scientific endeavour, just how much is known about the environment of Wales and the wider UK, but also how much we still need to discover about the complexities and interconnections between ourselves and our natural surroundings, if we are to manage our relationship with ecosystems wisely in the future.

References

Adams, W.A., Evans, L.J. & Abdulla, H.H. (1971) Quantitative pedological studies on the soils derived from Silurian mudstones. III Laboratory and in situ weathering of chlorite. *Journal of Soil Science*, **22**, 158–165.

Amar, A., Hewson, C.M., Thewlis, R.M., Smith, K.W., Fuller, R.J., Lindsell, J.A., Conway, G., Butler, S. & MacDonald, M.A. (2006) What's happening to our woodland birds? Long-term changes in the populations of woodland birds. RSPB and BTO, Sandy and Thetford.

Ashby, A.W. & Evans I.L. (1944) The Agriculture Of Wales And Monmouthshire. Gwasg Prifysgol Cymrv, Cardiff

Avery, M.I. (1989) Effects of upland afforestation on some birds of the adjacent moorland. *Journal of Applied Ecology*, **26**, 957–966.

Baggott, L., Brown, L., Rand, M. & Murrells, T.P. (2005) UK greenhouse gas inventory, 1990 to 2003: annual report for submission under the Framework Convention on Climate Change. AEA Technology, Harwell.

Barbatti, A., Corona, P. & Marchetti, M. (2007) European forest types: categories and types for sustainable forest management reporting and policy. EEA Technical Report No 9/2006. European Environment Agency, Copenhagen.

Bardgett, R.D., Marsden, J.H. & Howard, D.C. (1995) The extent and condition of heather on moorland in the uplands of England and Wales. *Biological Conservation*, **71**, 155–161.

Bardgett, R.D. & McAlister, E. (1999) The measurement of soil fungal: bacterial biomass ratios as an indicator of ecosystem self-regulation in temperate meadow grasslands. *Biology and Fertility of Soils*, **19**, 282–290.

BARS (Biodiversity Action Reporting System) (2011) Biodiversity Action Reporting System, Defra. [online] Available at: <http://ukbars.defra.gov.uk/default.asp> [Accessed: 15.07.11].

BBNPA (Brecon Beacons National Park Authority) (2011). Environment – Biodiversity pages, Brecon Beacons National Park Authority [online] Available at: <www.breconbeacons.org/environment/bd-in-the-bbnp/the-uplands/ffridd> [Accessed 23.05.11].

Bellamy, P.H., Loveland, P.J., Bradley, R.I., Lark, R.M. & Kirk, G.J.D. (2005) Carbon losses from all soils across England and Wales 1978–2003. *Nature*, **437**, 245–248.

Blackstock, T.H., Stevens, D.P., Stevens, P.A., Mockridge, C.P. & Yeo, M.J.M. (1998) Edaphic relationships among *Cirsio-Molinietum* and related wet grassland communities in lowland Wales. *Journal of Vegetation Science*, **9**, 431–444.

Blackstock, T.H., Howe, E.A., Stevens, J.P., Burrows, C.R. & Jones, P.S. (2010) Habitats of Wales. University of Wales Press, Cardiff.

Bradley, D.C. & Ormerod, S.J. (2001) Community persistence among upland stream invertebrates tracks the North Atlantic Oscillation. *Journal of Animal Ecology*, **70**, 987–996.

Bradley, D.C. & Ormerod, S.J. (2002) Long-term effects of catchment liming on invertebrates in upland streams. *Freshwater Biology*, **47**, 161–171.

Brazier, P., Birch, K., Brunstrom, A., Bunker, A., Jones, M., Lough, N., Salmon, L. & Wyn, G. (2007) When the tide goes out. The biodiversity and conservation of the shores of Wales – results from a 10 year intertidal survey of Wales. Countryside Council for Wales.

Briers, R.A., Gee, J.H.R. & Geoghegan, R. (2004) Effects of the North Atlantic Oscillation on growth and phenology of stream insects. *Ecography*, **27**(6), 811–817.

Broadmeadow, M.S.J., Webber, J.F., Ray, D. & Berry, P.M. (2009) An assessment of the likely future impacts of climate change on UK forests. Combating climate change – a role for UK forests (D.J. Read, P.H. Freer-Smith, J.I.L. Morison, N. Hanley, C.C. West & P.R. Snowdon), pp. 67–98. The Stationery Office, Edinburgh.

Buckley G.P. (1992) Ecology and management of coppice woodland. Chapman & Hall, London.

CADW (2007). Caring for Historic Landscapes. CADW (Welsh Assembly Government Historic Environment Service) Cardiff.

Carey, P.D., Wallis, S., Chamberlain, P.M., Cooper, A., Emmett, B.A., Maskell, L.C., McCann, T., Murphy, J., Norton, L.R., Reynolds, B., Scott, W.A., Simpson, I.C., Smart, S.M. & Ullyett, J.M. (2008) Countryside Survey: UK Results from 2007. NERC/Centre for Ecology & Hydrology, 105pp. (CEH Project Number: C03259).

Carroll, Z.L., Bird, S.B., Emmett, B.A., Reynolds, B. & Sinclair, F.L. (2004) Can tree shelterbelts on agricultural land reduce flood risk? *Soil Use and Management*, **20**, 357–359.

CCW (Countryside Council for Wales) (2003) A place for nature at your doorstep: The role of Local Nature Reserves. Countryside Council for Wales, Bangor.

CCW (Countryside Council for Wales) (2006) Providing Accessible Natural Greenspace in Towns and Cities: A Practical Guide to Assessing the Resource and Implementing Local Standards for Provision in Wales. 2006 CCW, Bangor.

CCW (Countryside Council for Wales) (2007) Wildlife Economy Wales': An Economic Evaluation Scoping Study. Countryside Council for Wales and Environment Agency. [online] Available at: <http://www.environment-agency.gov.uk/static/

documents/Research/wildlifewales_wb_1823119.pdf> [Accessed 16.03.11].

CCW (Countryside Council for Wales) (2009) Communities and Nature Project Handbook. Countryside council for Wales. [online] Available at: <http://www.ccw.gov.uk/enjoying-the-country/communities-and-nature.aspx> [Accessed 15.04.11].

CCW (Countryside Council for Wales) (2010) Sustaining Ecosystem Services for Human Well-being; Mapping Ecosystem Services. CCW Report, Environment Systems Ltd, Aberystwyth.

CCW & FCW (Countryside Council for Wales & Forestry Commission Wales) (2009) Welsh outdoor recreation survey 2008. First release: headline results. [online] Available at: <http://www.ccw.gov.uk/enjoying-the-country/idoc.ashx?docid=11b3a3ac-e98b-4f02-9ebc-6d4a7b357b8a&version=-1> [Accessed 12.04.11].

Clarke, D. & Sanitwong Na Ayutthaya, S. (2010) Predicted effects of climate change, vegetation and tree cover on dune slack habitats at Ainsdale on the Sefton Coast, UK. *Journal of Coastal Conservation*, **14**, 115–126.

Clews, E., Durance, I. & Ormerod, S. (2010) Juvenile salmonid populations in a temperate river system track synoptic trends in climate. *Global Change Biology*, **16**(12), 3271–3283.

Collins, A.L., Walling, D.E. & Leeks, G.J.L. (1997) Sediment sources in the Upper Severn catchment: a fingerprinting approach. *Hydrology and Earth System Sciences*, **1**, 509–521.

Colls, A. (2006) The carbon consequences of habitat restoration and creation. PhD thesis, Tyndall Centre.

Countryside Agency (2004) Rural and Urban Area Classification 2004, An Introductory Guide. Defra, ONS, ODPM and the Welsh Assembly Government. [online] Available at: <www.statistics.gov.uk/geography/downloads/Rural_Urban_Introductory_Guidev2.pdf> [Accessed 16.03.11].

Countryside Survey (2009) England Results from 2007. NERC/Centre for Ecology & Hydrology, Department for Environment, Food and Rural Affairs, Natural England.

CPRW (Campaign for the Protection of Rural Wales) (2004) Campaign for the Protection of Rural Wales. [online] Available at: <http://www.cprw.org.uk> [Accessed 16.03.11].

Cunha A., Power, S.A., Ashmore, M.R., Green, P.R.S., Haworth, B.J. & Bobbink, R. (2002) Whole ecosystem nitrogen manipulation: an updated review. JNCC Report 331, Peterborough.

CZEN (Critical Zone Exploration Network) (2011) CZEN Home. [online] Available at: <http://www.czen.org/> [Accessed 15.04.11].

Davies, W. (1936) The grasslands of Wales – a survey. A survey of the agricultural and waste lands of Wales (ed R.G. Stapledon), pp13–107. Faber & Faber, London.

Day, M.J., Leigh, C. & Young, A. (1980) Weathering of rock discs in temperate and tropical soils. Z. *Geomorph*, **35**, 11–15.

De Deyn, G.B., Quirk, H., Zou, Y., Ostle, N. & Bardgett, R.D. (2009) Vegetation composition promotes carbon and nitrogen storage in model grassland communities of contrasting soil fertility. *Journal of Ecology*, **97**, 864–875.

De Vries, F.T.E., Hoffland, N. van Eekeren, N., Brussaard, L. & Bloem, J. (2006) Fungal/bacterial ratios in grasslands with contrasting nitrogen management. *Soil Biology and Biochemistry*, **38**, 2092–2103.

Deakin, R. (2007) Wildwood: a journey through trees. Hamish Hamilton.

Defra (Department for Environment, Food and Rural Affairs)/Forestry Commission (2005) Keepers of time: a statement of policy for England's ancient and native woods. Bristol and Cambridge. [online] Available at: <www.forestry.gov.uk/pdf/anw-policy.pdf/$FILE/anw-policy.pdf> [Accessed 14.03.11].

Defra (Department for Environment, Food and Rural Affairs) (2007) Air Quality Strategy, England Scotland, Wales and Northern Ireland. CMD Paper No.7169. [online] Available at: <http://www.defra.gov.uk/environment/quality/air/airquality/strategy/documents/air-qualitystrategy-vol1.pdf> [Accessed 14.03.11].

Defra (Department for Environment, Food and Rural Affairs) (2009a) UK Biodiversity Indicators in Your Pocket 2009. Measuring progress towards halting biodiversity loss. Defra, London. [online] Available at: <http://jncc.defra.gov.uk/pdf/Biyp_2009.pdf> [Accessed: 15.05.11]. Supporting data available from Joint Nature Conservation Committee at www.jncc.gov.uk/biyp

Defra (Department for Environment, Food and Rural Affairs) (2009b) River Water Quality Indicator for Sustainable Development–2008 results. Statistical Release Ref. 203/09. [online] available at: <http://archive.defra.gov.uk/evidence/statistics/environment/inlwater/download/pdf/20100907ns.pdf> [Accessed: 15.05.11].

Delbaere, B.C.W. (1998) Facts and figures on European biodiversity; state and trends 1998–1999. European Centre for Nature Conservation, Tilburg, The Netherlands.

Durance, I. & Ormerod, S.J. (2007) Climate change effects on upland stream macroinvertebrates over a 25-year period. *Global Change Biology*, **13**, 942–957.

Duigan, C., Kovach, W. & Palmer, M. (2007) Vegetation Communities of British Lakes: a revised classification. *Aquatic Conservation: marine and freshwater ecosystems*, **17**, 147–173.

Dyson, K.E., Thomson, A.M., Mobbs, D.C., Milne, R., Skiba, U., Clark, A., Levy, P.E., Jones, S.K., Billet, M.F., Dinsmore, K.J., van Oijen, M., Ostel, N., Foereid, B., Smith, P., Matthews, R.W., Mackie, E., Bellamy, P., Rivas-Casado, M., Jordan, C., Higgins, A., Tomlinson, R.W., Grace, J., Parrish, P., Williams, M., Clement, R., Moncrieff, J. & Manning, A. (2009) Inventory and Projections of UK Emissions by Sources and Removals by Sinks due to Land Use, Land Use Change and Forestry, Annual Report, July 2009. Centre for Ecology & Hydrology, University of Aberdeen, Forest Research Alice Holt, National Soil Resources Institute, Agri-Food & Biosciences Institute, Queen's University Belfast, University of Edinburgh. [online] Available at: <http://ecosystemghg.ceh.ac.uk/docs/2009/Defra_Report_2009.pdf> [Accessed: 20.05.11].

EAU (Environmental Advisory Unit) (1988) Survey of Contaminated Land in Wales. Environmental Advisory Unit, Welsh Office. ISBN 0 86348 8285.

EAW (Environment Agency Wales) (2002) Metal Mines Strategy for Wales. Environment Agency Wales, Cardiff.

Econactive (2005) An evaluation of the 2004 Wales Rally of Great Britain. A report for the Welsh Development Agency. WAG, Cardiff.

ECOSSE (Estimating Carbon in Organic Soils, Sequestration and Emissions) (2007) ECOSSE – Estimating carbon in organic soils, sequestration and emissions. Scottish Executive Environment and Rural Affairs Department and Welsh Assembly Government. Scottish Executive, Edinburgh.

Emmett, B.A., Reynolds, B., Chamberlain, P.M., Rowe, E., Spurgeon, D., Brittain, S.A., Frogbrook, Z., Hughes, S., Lawlor, A.J., Poskitt, J., Potter, E., Robinson, D.A., Scott, A., Wood, C. & Woods, C. (2010) Countryside Survey: Soils Report from 2007. Technical Report No. 9/07 NERC/Centre for Ecology & Hydrology 192pp. (CEHProject Number: C03259).

Environment Agency (2002) Metal Mines Strategy for Wales. Environment Agency Wales, Cardiff.

Environment Agency (2004) Otter Survey of Wales 2002. Environment Agency, Bristol.

Environment Agency (2005) The Climate is Changing: Time to Get Ready. Environment Agency, Bristol.

Environment Agency (2008) Summer river flows could more than halve by 2050 due to climate change. National Press Office Release 4 Oct 2008. Doc Reference 92/2008. [online] Available at: <http://www.environment-agency.gov.uk/news/94724.aspx?page=8&month=10&year=2008> [Accessed 15.04.11].

Environment Agency (2009) Dealing with contaminated land in England and Wales. A review of progress from 2000–2007 with Part 2A of the Environment Protection Act. Environment Agency, Bristol.

Environment Agency (2010) Water Resources in England and Wales – current state and future pressures. [online] Available at: <http://publications.environment-agency.gov.uk/PDF/GEHO1208BPAS-E-E.pdf> [Accessed: 15.07.11].

Evans, C.D., Freeman, C., Cork, L.G., Thomas, D.N., Reynolds, B., Billett, M.F., Garnett, M.H. & Norris, D. (2007) Evidence against recent climate-induced destabilisation of soil carbon from C-14 analysis of riverine dissolved organic matter. *Geophysical Research Letters*, **34**, 7.

exeGesIS (2007) Heads of the Valleys Greenspace Provision Report September 2007. exeGesIS Spatial Data Management, Brecon. [online] Available at: <http://www.rhondda-cynon-taf.gov.uk/en/relateddocuments/publications/developmentplanning/evidencebase/eb50-headsofthevalleysgreenspaceprovisionreport.pdf> [Accessed: 19.05.11].

Farage, P., Ball, A., McGenity, T.J., Whitby, C. & Pretty, J. (2009) Burning management and carbon sequestration of upland heather moorland in the UK. *Australian Journal of Soil Research*, **47**(4), 351–361.

Farrar, J.F. & Vaze, P. (eds) (2000) Wales: Changing Climate, Challenging Choices. A scoping study of climate change impacts in Wales. Technical Report to the National Assembly for Wales, Cardiff.

Farrar, J., Freeman, C. & Jones, D.L. (2003) Wales' Carbon – managing climate change. Countryside Council for Wales Commissioned Report. Bangor University, Institute of Environmental Sciences.

Finch, P., Gilbert, J., Peace, A. & West, V. (2008) Native woodland area and HAP type from NIWT I. Forestry Commission Wales, Wales.

Ford, B.A. (2000) Aerial photographic assessment and proposed remediation of particulate sediment transport bonded phosphorus sources in the Afon Llafar catchment, mid-Wales. MSc Thesis, Cranfield University.

Forestry Commission (1985) The Policy for Broadleaved Woodland. Forestry Commission, Edinburgh.

Forestry Commission (2003) National Inventory of Woodlands and Trees. Great Britain. Forestry Commission, Edinburgh.

Forestry Commission (2009a) Forestry Statistics 2009. [online] Available at: <http://www.forestry.gov.uk/pdf/ForestryStatistics2009.pdf/$FILE/ForestryStatistics2009.pdf> [Accessed 16.03.11].

Forestry Commission (2009b) Public opinion of forestry 2009, UK. Forestry Commission, Edinburgh.

Forestry Commission (2011) Forestry Statistics (2011) [online] Time series data for wood production (roundwood removals), for 1976 to 2010 (provisional) [online] Available at: <http://www.forestry.gov.uk/forestry/infd-7aql5b> [Accessed 13.07.2011].

Francis, I.S. & Taylor, J.A. (1989) The effect of forestry drainage operations on upland sediment yields: a study of two peat-covered catchments. *Earth Surface Processes and Landforms* **14**, 73–83.

Frost, M. (2010) Charting Progress 2 Feeder Report: Healthy and Biologically Diverse Seas. UK Marine Monitoring and Assessment Strategy (UKMMAS), Defra. [online] Available at: <http://chartingprogress.defra.gov.uk/chapter-3-healthy-and-biologicaly-diverse-seas> [Accessed 19.01.11].

Fuller, R.J. & Gough, S.J. (1999) Changes in sheep numbers in Britain: implications for bird populations. *Biological Conservation*, **91**, 73–89.

Fuller, R.J. & Gill, R.M.A. (2001) Ecological impacts of deer in British woodland. *Forestry* **74**, 193–299.

Gilbert, O. (1996) Rooted in stone – The natural flora of urban walls. English Nature, Peterborough.

Goldberg, E.A., Kirby, K.J., Hall, J.E. & Latham, J. (2007) The ancient woodland concept as a practical conservation tool in Great Britain. *Journal of Nature Conservation*, **15**, 109–119.

Gordon, H., Haygarth, P.M. & Bardgett, R.D. (2008) Drying and rewetting effects on soil microbial community composition and nutrient leaching. *Soil Biology & Biochemistry,* **40**, 302–311.

Gray, N. (1986) Woodland management for pheasants and wildlife. David & Charles, Newton Abbott.

Gwent Ecology (2010) Gwent Brownfield Baseline Survey 2010. Gwent Ecology (Gwent Land Management Ltd), Monmouth.

Harrod, T.R. (1998) A systematic approach to national budgets of phosphorus loss through soil erosion and surface runoff at National Soil Inventory (NSI) nodes. Defra, London.

Harrod, T.R., McHugh, M., Appleby, P.G., Evans, R., George, D.G., Haworth, E.Y., Hewitt, D., Hornung, M., Housen, G., Leekes, G., Morgan, R.P.C. & Tipping, E., (2000) Research on the quantification and causes of upland erosion. Soil Survey and Land Research Centre report JX4118E. The Ministry of Agriculture, Fisheries and Food.

Hockley, N., Farrar, J., Gibbons, J.M., Hearn, S.M., Jones, J.P.G. & Kaiser, M. (2009) Biodiversity Indicators for Wales. Welsh Assembly Government, Cardiff.

Hodder, K.H., Bullock, J.M., Buckland, P.C. & Kirby, K.J. (2005) Large herbivores in the wildwood and modern naturalistic grazing systems. English Nature, Peterborough.

Hodder, K.H., Buckland, P.C., Kirby, K.J. & Bullock, J.M. (2009) Can the pre-Neolithic provide suitable models for re-wilding the landscape in Britain? *British Wildlife*, **20**(supplement), 4–15.

Holden, J., Chapman P., Hubacek K., Kay P. & Warburton J. (2006) Vulnerability of Organic Soils in England and Wales, DEFRA Project SPO532. [online] Available at: <http://www.geog.leeds.ac.uk/fileadmin/downloads/school/people/academic/j.holden/organic_soils.pdf> [Accessed 16.03.11].

Holman, I.P., Hollis, J.M., Bramley, M.E. & Thompson, T.R.E. (2003) The contribution of soil structural degradation to catchment flooding: a preliminary investigation of the 2000 floods in England and Wales. *Hydrology and Earth System Sciences*, **7**, 754–765.

Hornung, M., Reynolds, B., Stevens, P.A. & Hughes, S. (1987) The use of stream solute budgets for estimating weathering rates and period of soil development in a small mid Wales catchment. Report to the Welsh Soils Discussion Group, no.24, 135–143.

Hornung, M., Bull, K.R., Cresser, M., Hall, J.R., Langan, S.J., Loveland, P. & Smith, C. (1995) An empirical map of critical loads of acidity for soils in Great Britain. *Environmental Pollution*, **90**(3), 301–310.

Howe, M.A., Knight, G.T. & Clee, C. (2010) The importance of coastal sand dunes for terrestrial invertebrates in Wales and the UK, with particular reference to aculeate Hymenoptera (bees, wasps & ants). *Journal of Coastal Conservation*, **14**(2), 91–102.

Humphrey, J.W. & Nixon, C.N. (1999) The restoration of upland native oakwoods following removal of conifers: general principles. *Scottish Forestry*, **53**(2), 68–76.

Hybu Cig Cymru (2007) The Situation and Outlook to 2020 for the Welsh Beef and Sheep Industry. TSO. [online] Available at: <http://www.official-documents.gov.uk/document/hc0607/hc06/0641/0641_ii.pdf> [Accessed 15.04.11].

IPCC (Intergovernmental Panel on Climate Change) (2007) Climate Change 2007: Mitigation of Climate Change. Contribution of Working Group III to the Fourth Assessment Report of the Intergovernmental Panel on Climate Change (eds B. Metz, O.R. Davidson, P.R. Bosh, R. Dave, L.A. Mayer). Cambridge University Press, Cambridge, UK and New York, NY, USA.

Irwin, C. & Thomas, B. (2010) UK Sea Fisheries Statistics. Marine Management Organisation – A National Statistics Publication.

Jackson, B.M., Wheater, H.S., McIntyre, N.R., Chell, J., Francis, O.J., Frogbrook, Z., Marshall, M., Reynolds, B. & Solloway, I. (2008) The impact of upland land management on flooding: insights from a multiscale experimental modelling programme. *Journal of Flood Risk Management,* **1**, 71–80.

Jackson, J., Li, Y., Murrells, T., Passant, N., Sneddon, S., Thomas, J., Thistlethwaite, G., Dyson, K. & Cardenas, L. (2009) Air Quality Pollutant Inventories for England, Scotland, Wales and Northern Ireland: 1990–2007. [online] Available at: <http://uk-air.defra.gov.uk/reports/cat07/0910211141_DA_AQ_Inventory_Report_2007_maintext_Issue1.pdf> [Accessed 16.03.11].

Jackson, E.L., Langmead, O., Evans, J., Wilkes, P., Seeley, B., Lear D. & Tyler-Walters, H. (2010) Mapping Marine Benthic Biodiversity in Wales. CCW Contract Science Reports Report No: 913, 88pp, Countryside Council for Wales, Bangor.

JNCC (Joint Nature Conservation Committee) (2010a) Main Results of the 2008 UK Biodiversity Action Plan Reporting Round, Published by JNCC on behalf of the UK Biodiversity Partnership. [online] Available at: <www.jncc.defra.gov.uk/biyp> [Accessed 15.07.11].

JNCC (Joint Nature Conservation Committee) (2010b) Biological river quality. UK Biodiversity Indicators [online] Available at: <http://jncc.defra.gov.uk/page-4250> [Accessed 04.05.11].

Johnes, P.J., Foy, R., Butterfield D. & Haygarth, P.M. (2007) Land use scenarios for England and Wales: evaluation of management options to support 'good ecological status' in surface freshwaters. *Soil Use and Management* **23**, 176–194.

Jones, M.L.M., Pilkington, M.G., Healey, M., Norris, D.N., Brittain, S.A., Tang, S.Y., Jones, M. & Reynolds, B. (2005) Determining a nitrogen budget for Merthyr Mawr sand dune system. CEH Project No: C02352NEW, CCW Contract Number FC 72-02-59. Countrside Council for Wales.

Jones, M.L.M., Sowerby, A., Williams, D.L. & Jones, R.E. (2008) Factors controlling soil development in sand dunes: evidence from a coastal dune soil chronosequence. *Plant and Soil*, **307**, 219–234.

Kirby, K.J., Reid, C.M., Thomas, R.C. & Goldsmith, F.B. (1998) Preliminary estimates of fallen dead wood and standing dead trees in managed and unmanaged forests in Britain. *Journal of Applied Ecology*, **35**, 148–155.

Kirby, K.J. & Goldberg E.G. (2003) Ancient woodland: guidance material for local authorities. English Nature, Peterborough.

Klein, A.M., Vassiere B.E., Care, J.H., Steffan-Dewanter, I., Cunnigham, S.A., Kremen, C. & Tscharntke, T. (2007) Importance of pollinators in changing landscapes for world crops. *Proceedings of the Royal Society of Biological Sciences*, **274**, 303–313.

Kuussaari, M., Heikkinen, R.K., Helm A., Krauss, J., Lindburg, R., Öckinger, E., Pärtel, M., Pino, J., Roda F., Stefanescu, C., Teder, T., Zobel, M. & Steffan-Dewenter I. (2009) Extinction debt: a challenge for biodiversity conservation. *Trends in Ecology and Evolution*, **24**, 654–571.

Langan, S.J., Reynolds, B. & Bain, D.C. (1996) The calculation of base cation release from mineral weathering in soils derived from Palaeozoic greywackes and shales in upland UK. *Geoderma,* **69**, 275–285.

Latham, J., Miller, H., Mountford, E.P., Kirby, K.J. & Ioras, F. (2005) Country Report – United Kingdom. COST Action E27 – Protected Forest Areas in Europe – Analysis and Harmonisation (PROFOR) – Reports of Signatory States (eds J. Latham, G. Frank, O. Fahy, K. Kirby, H. Miller & R. Stiven), pp 399– 413. BFW, Vienna.

Latham, J., Blackstock, T.H. & Howe, E.A. (2008) Ecological connectivity in Wales: planning action to help terrestrial biodiversity respond to habitat fragmentation and climate change. CCW Staff Science Report No. 08/7/1. Countryside Council for Wales.

LCM (Land Cover Map) (2000) Land Cover Map Countryside Survey 2000. CSLCM, Centre for Ecology and Hydrology. National Environment Research Council. Project Code T02083j5/C00878.

Lewis, B.R., Juttner, I., Reynolds, B. & Ormerod, S.J. (2007) Comparative assessment of stream acidity using diatoms and macroinvertebrates: implications for river management and conservation. *Aquatic Conservation–Marine and Freshwater Ecosystems*, **17**(5), 502–519.

Lindenbaum, C., Bennell, J.D., Rees, E.I.S., McClean, D., Cook W., Wheeler, A.J. & Sanderson, W.G. (2008) Small-scale variation within a *Modiolus modiolus* (Mollusca: Bivalvia) reef in the Irish Sea: I. Seabed mapping and reef morphology. *Journal of the Marine Biological Association of the UK*, **88**(1), 133–141.

Linnard, W. (2000) Welsh Woods and Forests: A History. Gomer Press, Llandysul, Wales.

Loram, A., Tratalos, J., Warren, P.H. & Gaston, K.J. (2007) Urban domestic gardens (X): the extent & structure of the resource in five major cities. *Journal of Landscape Ecology*, **22,** 601–615.

Lowe, J.A., Howard, T.P., Pardaens, A., Tinker, J., Holt, J., Wakelin, S., Milne, G., Leake, J., Wolf, J., Horsbaugh, K., Reeder, T., Jenkins, G., Ridley, J, Dye, S. & Bradley, S. (2009) UK Climate Projections Science report: Marine and Coastal Projections. Met Office Hadley Centre, Exeter, UK.

Maddock, A. (ed.) (2008) Biodiversity Reporting and Information Group (BRIG). UK Biodiversity Action Plan; Priority Habitat Descriptions, UK Biodiversity Partnership. [online] Available at: <http://www.ukbap.org.uk/library/UKBAPPriorityHabitatDescriptionsRevised20100730.pdf> [Accessed 14.02.11].

Marshall, M.R., Francis, O.J., Frogbrook, Z.L., Jackson, B.M., McIntyre, N., Reynolds, B., Solloway, I., Wheater, H.S. & Chell, J. (2009) The impact of upland land management on flooding: results from an improved pasture hillslope. *Hydrological Processes*, **23**, 464–475.

Maskell, L.C., Norton, L.R., Smart, S.M., Carey, P.D., Murphy, J., Chamberlain, P.M., Wood, C.M., Bunce, R.G.H. & Barr, C.J. (2008) Field Mapping Handbook. CS Technical Report No. 1/07. Centre for Ecology and Hydrology.

Mason, W.L. (2007) Changes in the management of British forests between 1945 and 2000 and possible future trends. *Ibis*, **149**, 41–52.

Masselink, G. & Russell, P. (2008) MCCIP Annual Report Card 2007–2008 Scientific Review – Coastal Erosion and Coastal Geomorphology. Marine Climate Change Impacts Partnership.

Mato, Y., Isobe, T., Takada, H., Kanehiro, H., Ohtake, C. & Kaminuma, T. (2001) Plastic resin pellets as a transport medium for toxic chemicals in the marine environment. *Environmental Science Technology* **35**, 318–324.

MA (Millennium Ecosystem Assessment) (2005) Millennium Ecosystem Assessment Synthesis Report. Island Press, Washington.

MCCIP (Marine Climate Change Impacts Partnership) (2008) Marine climate change impacts: annual report 2007–2008. Marine Climate Change Impacts Partnership. [online] Available at: <http://www.mccip.org.uk/media/3007/arc2007.pdf> [Accessed 16.03.11].

McHugh, M. (2002a) Arable and upland NSI erosion resurvey. Defra project SP0407.

McHugh, M. (2002b) Upland soil erosion data analysis. Defra project SP0407.

Mieszkowska, N., Kendall, M.A., Hawkins, S.J., Leaper, R., Williamson, P., Hardman-Mountford N.J. & Southward, A.J. (2006) Changes in the range of some common rocky shore species as a response to climate change. *EMBS Special Issue. Hydrobiologia*, **555**(1), 241–251.

Mieszkowska, N. (2010) MarClim Annual Welsh Intertidal Climate Monitoring Survey 2008. Countryside Council for Wales. CCW Science Report No 921.

Mills, J., Gibbon, D., Dwyer, J., Short, C. & Ingram, J. (2006). Identification of delivery mechanisms for Welsh top-tier agri-environment schemes. CCW Policy Research Report No 06-15.

Mitchell, R.J., Campbell, C.D., Chapman, S.J., Osler, G.H.R., Vanbergen, A.J., Ross, L.C., Cameron, C.M. & Cole, L. (2007) The cascading effects of birch on heather moorland: a test for the top-down control of an ecosystem engineer. *Journal of Ecology*, **95**, 540–554.

NAW (National Assembly of Wales) (2000) Minerals Planning Policy Wales. National Assembly of Wales. [online] Available at: <http://wales.gov.uk/docrepos/40382/epc/planning/403821/403828/MPPW.pdf?lang=en> [Accessed 16.03.11].

NCC (Nature Conservancy Council) (1984) Nature Conservation in Great Britain. Nature Conservancy Council, Peterborough.

NICE (National Institute for Health and Clinical Excellence) (2008) Promoting or supporting built and natural environments that encourage and support physical activity. National Institute for Health and Clinical Excellence [online] Available at: <http://www.nice.org.uk/nicemedia/pdf/PH008guidance.pdf> [Accessed: 19.05.11].

NIWT (National Inventory for Woodlands and Trees) (2002) National Inventory for Woodlands and Trees, Wales. Forestry Commission, Edinburgh.

NSRI (National Soils Resources Institute) (2009) Soilscapes mapping [online] Available at: http://www.landis.org.uk/soilscapes/ [Accessed 07.03.11].

NUFU (National Urban Forestry Unit) (1999) Trees and woods in towns and cities: how to develop local strategies for urban forestry. National Urban Forestry Unit, Wolverhampton.

NUFU (National Urban Forestry Unit) (2005) Trees matter: bringing lasting benefits to people in towns. National Urban Forestry Unit, Wolverhampton.

ODPM (Office of the Deputy Prime Minister) (2005) Planning Policy Statement 9: Biodiversity and geological conservation. ODPM, London.

Ormerod, S.J. & Durance, I. (2009) Restoration and recovery from acidification in upland Welsh streams over 25 years. *Journal of Applied Ecology*, **46**, 164–174.

Ormerod, S.J. & Jüttner, I. (2009) Pollution effects on Welsh rivers: a damaged past, an uncertain future? The Rivers of Wales (eds D.D. Williams & C.A.), pp. 181–203. Backhuys Publishers, Leiden.

PCNP (Pembrokeshire Coast National Park) (2003) Conserving the coastal slopes 1999–2002. Pembrokeshire Coast National Park.

Perring, F. & Walters, S.M. (1990) Atlas of the British Flora. BSBI Publications, Melksham.

Peterken, G.F. (1977) Habitat conservation priorities in British and European woodland. *Biological Conservation*, **11**, 223–236.

Peterken, G.F. & Allison, H. (1989) Woods, Trees and Hedges: a Review of Changes in the British Countryside. Focus on Nature Conservation 22. Nature Conservancy Council, Peterborough.

Potts, S.G., Roberts, S.P.M., Dean, R., Marris, G., Brown, M., Jones, R. & Settele, J. (2010) Declines of managed honeybees and beekeepers in Europe. *Journal of Apicultural Research*, **49**(1), 15–22.

Preston, C.D., Pearman, D.A. & Dines, T.D. (2002) New Atlas of the British and Irish flora. Oxford University Press, Oxford.

Pretty, J.N., Mason, C.F., Nedwell, D.B., Hine, R.E., Leaf, S. & Dils, R. (2003) Environmental Costs of Freshwater Eutrophication in England and Wales. *Environmental Science & Technology*, **37**(2), 201–208.

Pryor, S. & Peterken, G.F. (2001) Protected Forest Areas in the UK. WWF, Godalming.

Quine, C.P. & Gardiner, B.A. (2006) Understanding how the interaction of wind and trees results in windthrow, stem breakage and gap formation. Plant disturbance ecology: the process and the response (eds E.A. Johnson & K. Miyanishi), pp. 103–155. Academic Press (Elsevier), New York.

Rackham, O. (1986) The history of the countryside. Dent, London.

Rackham, O. (2003) Ancient woodland (revised edition). Castlepoint Press, Dalbeattie.

Read, H.J. (2000) Veteran tree management handbook. English Nature, Peterborough.

Read, D.J., Freer-Smith, P.H., Morison, J.I.L., Hanley, N., West, C.C. & Snowdon, P.R. (eds) (2009) Combating climate change – a role for UK forests. The Stationery Office, Edinburgh.

Reynolds, B., Hornung, M. & Stevens, P.A. (1987) Solute budgets and denudation rate estimates for a mid-Wales catchment. *Catena*, **14**, 13-23.

Reynolds, B. & Stevens, P.A. (1998) Assessing soil calcium depletion following growth and harvesting of Sitka spruce plantation forestry in the acid sensitive Welsh uplands. *Hydrology and Earth System Sciences*, **2**, 345-352.

Rhind, P.M., Blackstock, T.H., Hardy, H.S., Jones, R.E. & Sandison, W. (2001) The evolution of Newborough warren dune system with particular reference to the past four decades. Coastal dune management, shared experience of European conservation practice (eds J. Houston, S.E. Edmondson, P.J. Rooney), pp. 345–379. Liverpool University press, Liverpool.

Rhind, P.M., Jones, R. & Jones, M.L.M. (2008) Confronting the impact of dune stabilization and soil development on the conservation status of sand dune systems in Wales. Proc. International conference on management and restoration of coastal dunes, Santander, Spain (ICCD 2007). Universidad de Cantabria.

Richter, D. & Mobley, M.L. (2009) Monitoring earth's critical zone. *Science*, **326**, 1067–168.

Roberts, A.J., Russell, C., Walker, G.J. & Kirby, K.J. (1992) Regional variation in the origin, extent and composition of Scottish woodland. *Botanical Journal of Scotland*, **46**, 167–189.

Robinson, L.A. (2007) Review of Sidescan Sonar Results from North Llyn. Bangor, CCW Marine Monitoring Report No: 50.

Rudeforth, C.C., Hartnup, R., Lea, J.W., Thompson, T.R.E. & Wright, P.S. (1984) Soils and their use in Wales. Soil Survey of England and Wales Bulletin No. 11. Harpenden.

Sanderson, W.G., Stillman, R.A., Moore, T.J.J.R. & Murphy, M.D. (2010) Cockle 'die offs' and conservation in an internationally important estuary system. Case study in Habitats Chapter of Charting Progress Feeder Report Defra.

Saye, S.E. & Pye, K. (2007) Implications of sea level rise for coastal dune habitat conservation in Wales, UK. *Journal of Coastal Conservation*, **11**, 31–63.

Smart, S.M., Allen, D., Murphy, J., Carey, P.D., Emmett, B.A., Reynolds, B., Simpson, I.C., Evans, R.A., Skates, J., Scott, W.A., Maskell, L.C., Norton, L.R., Rossall, M.J. & Wood, C. (2009) Countryside Survey: Wales Results from 2007. NERC/Centre for Ecology & Hydrology, Welsh Assembly Government, Countryside Council for Wales, pp. 94 (CEH Project Number: C03259).

Smart, S., Dunbar, M.J., Emmett, B.A., Marks, S., Maskell, L.C., Norton, L.R., Rose, P. & Simpson, I.C. (2010) An integrated assessment of countryside survey data to investigate ecosystem services in Great Britain. Technical Report No. 10/07 NERC/ Centre for Ecology & Hydrology 230pp. (CEH Project Number: C03259).

Smith, P., Martino, D., Cai, Z., Gwary D., Janzen H., Kumar, P., McCarl, B., Ogle, S., O'Mara, F., Rice, C., Scholes, B., Sirotenko, O., Howden, M., McAllister, T., Pan, G., Romanenkov, V., Schneider, U., Towprayoon, S., Wattenbach, M. & Smith, J. (2008) Greenhouse gas mitigation in agriculture. *Philosophical Transactions of the Royal Society B,* **363**, 789–813.

Smout, T.C. (ed) (2002) People and woods in Scotland: a history. Edinburgh University Press, Edinburgh.

SNH (Scottish Natural Heritage) (2009) Scotland's Biodiversity Indicators. [online] Available at: <http://gateway. snh.gov.uk/pls/htmldb_cagdb1/snhlive.tai_disp_template_pkg. display_main_page> [Accessed 16.03.11].

SNPA (2010). Snowdonia National Park Management Plan 2010–2015 p.31. Snowdonia National Park Authority. Penrhyndeudraeth, Wales.

SoilTrEC (2010) The Challenge. [online] Available at: <http://www.soiltrec.eu/> [Accessed 15.04.11].

Southey, E., Taylor, G., Livesey, K. & Tickell, F. (2009) Potential of forest products and substitution for fossil fuels to contribute to mitigation. In UK Forests and Climate Change Report.

Spencer, J.W. & Kirby, K.J. (1992) An inventory of ancient woodland for England and Wales. *Biological Conservation,* **62**, 77–93.

Statistical Directorate (2009) State of the Environment, 2008. Welsh Assembly Government, Cardiff.

Stevens, P.A., Ormerod, S.J., & Reynolds, B. (1997) Final report on the acid waters survey of Wales. Volume 1, Main Text. Institute of Terrestrial Ecology, Bangor.

Stevens, P.A., Reynolds, B., Emmett, B.A., Thompson, T.R.E., Loveland, P.J., Jarvis, S.C., Haygarth, P., Thomas, H.R., Owen, D-H., Roberts, R. and Marsden, T. (2002) Critical Appraisal of State and Pressures and Controls on the Sustainable Use of Soils in Wales. Final Report to Welsh Assembly Government and Environment Agency, Centre for Ecology and Hydrology.

Stevens, C.J., Dise, N.B., Mountford, J.O. & Gowing, D.J. (2004) Impact of nitrogen deposition on the species richness of grasslands. *Science,* **303**, 1876–1879.

Stevens, D.P., Smith, S.L.N., Blackstock, T.H., Bosanquet S.D.S. & Stevens, J.P. (2010) Grasslands of Wales: a survey of lowland species- rich grasslands, 1987–2004. University of Wales, Cardiff Press.

Stringell, T.B., Skates, L.R., Bamber, R.N., Nikitic, C. & Sanderson, W.G. (In press) Assessment and management in a variable lagoon MPA: the use of control charts. *Aquatic Conservation: Marine and Freshwater Ecosystems.*

Taylor, R., Jones, A. & Edwards-Jones, G. (2010) Measuring holistic carbon footprints for lamb and beef farms in the Cambrian Mountains Initiative (unpublished Report, Bangor University).

The Cistercian Way (2011). The Cistercian Way [online] Available at: <http://cistercian-way.newport.ac.uk/> [Accessed: 13.07.2011].

Thompson, R.C., Olsen, Y., Mitchell, R.P., Davis, A., Rowland, S.J., John, A.W.G., McGonigle, D. & Russell A. E. (2004) Lost at sea: where is all the plastic? *Science,* **304**, 838.

UKBAP (UK Biodiversity Action Plan) (2006) The UK Biodiversity Action Plan: Highlights from the 2005 reporting round. Defra, London. [online] Available at: <http://www.ukbap. org.uk/genpagetext.aspx?id=104> [Acccessed 16.03.11].

UKMMAS (UK Marine Monitoring and Assessment Strategy) (2010) Charting Progress 2: The State of UK Seas. Published by the Department for Environment Food and Rural Affairs on behalf of UKMMAS. TSO, London. 166pp. ISBN 9780112432937. Available at: <http://chartingprogress.defra.gov. uk/resources> [Accessed 06.06.10].

UK NEA (UK National Ecosystem Assessment) (2011) The UK National Ecosystem Assessment: Synthesis of Key Findings. UNEP-WCMC, Cambridge.

UKTS (United Kingdom Tourism Survey) (2009) United Kingdom Tourism Survey. WAG, Cardiff.

Vannote, R.L., Minshall, G.W., Cummins, K.W., Sedell, J.R. & Cushing, C.E. (1980) "The River Continuum Concept". *Canadian Journal of Fisheries and Aquatic Sciences,* **37**, 130–13.

Vera, F.M.W. (2000) Grazing Ecology and Forest History. CABI Publishing, Oxford.

VRP (Valleys Regional Park) (2007) Valleys Regional Park Master Plan 2007 [online] <http://www.thevalleys.org.uk/ vrp.html> [Accessed 13.07.11].

Ward, A.I. (2005) Expanding ranges of wild and feral deer in Great Britain. *Mammal Review,* **35**, 165–173.

WAG (Welsh Assembly Government) (2006a) Environment Strategy for Wales. Welsh Assembly Government, Cardiff.

WAG (Welsh Assembly Government) (2006b) National Housing Strategy for Wales. Welsh Assembly Government, Cardiff.

WAG (Welsh Assembly Government) (2008a) Environment Strategy Action Plan 2008–2011. Welsh Assembly Government, Cardiff.

WAG (Welsh Assembly Government) (2008b) Coastal Tourism Strategy. Visit Wales, Cardiff.

WAG (Welsh Assembly Government) (2008c) Wales Fisheries Strategy. Welsh Assembly Government, Cardiff.

WAG (Welsh Assembly Government) (2009a) Welsh agricultural statistics 2008. Welsh Assembly Government, Cardiff.

WAG (Welsh Assembly Government) (2009b) Woodlands for Wales: the Welsh Assembly Government strategy for woodlands and trees. Welsh Assembly Government, Cardiff.

WAG (Welsh Assembly Government) (2009c) Welsh Assembly Government, Planning Policy Wales, TAN 16: Sport, Recreation and Open Space. **(Welsh Assembly Government)**

WAG (Welsh Assembly Government) (2009d). An Independent Review of Monitoring Measures Undertaken in Neath Port Talbot in Respect of Particulate Matter (PM10). Welsh Assembly Government, Cardiff.

WAG (Welsh Assembly Government) (2009e) Wales Imports and Exports Statistics. StatsWales. [online] Available at: <http://statswales.wales.gov.uk/index.htm> [Accessed: 01.07.11].

WAG (Welsh Assembly Government) (2010a) Accessible Natural Greenspace Standards by local authority in Wales, 2007 – 2010. Countryside Council for Wales survey. StatsWales. [ONLINE] <Available AT: http://statswales.wales.gov.uk/index. htm> [Accessed 15.05.11].

WAG (Welsh Assembly Government) (2010b) Farming facts and figures, Wales 2010. [online] Avaliable at: <http://

wales.gov.uk/docs/statistics/2010/100518farmfact2010en.pdf>
[Accessed 12.04.11].

WAG (Welsh Assembly Government) (2010c) A Living
Wales – a new framework for our environment, our countryside
and our seas. Consultation Document 15 September 2010. Welsh
Assembly Government, Cardiff.

WAG (Welsh Assembly Government) (2010d) Planning
Policy Wales, Edition 3. Welsh Assembly Government, Cardiff.

WAG (Welsh Assembly Government) (2010e) Statistics
for Wales, State of the Environment Report 14th December 2010.
Welsh Assembly Government, Cardiff.

WAG (Welsh Assembly Government) (2010f) June 2010
Survey of Agriculture and Horticulture: Results for Wales SDR
188/2010 [online] Available at: <http://wales.gov.uk/docs/statist
ics/2010/101117sdr1882010en.pdf> [Accessed on 20/06/11].

WAG (Welsh Assembly Government) (2011) Map of land
classified as the less favoured area in Wales [online] Available
at: <http://wales.gov.uk/topics/environmentcountryside/
farmingandcountryside/maps/lfamap/?lang=en> [Accessed
16.05.11].

WAQF (Welsh Air Quality Forum) (2008) Welsh Air
Quality Forum 2008 Seminar: Updated Local Authority Air
Quality Guidance & Effective Action. [online] Available
at: <http://www.welshairquality.co.uk/documents/
seminars/213081104_6_Neath_Port_Talbot.pdf> [Accessed
16.03.11].

Ward A.I. (2005) Expanding ranges of wild and feral deer in
Great Britain. *Mammal Review* **35**, 165–173.

WAS (Welsh Agricultural Statistics) (2008) Welsh
Agricultural Statistics. Statistics for Wales. Welsh Assembly
Government. [online] Available at: <http://wales.gov.uk/docs/
statistics/2009/090513was08ency.pdf> [Accessed 18.05.11].

Watts, K., Humphrey, J.W., Griffiths, M., Quine, C.P. & Ray, D.
(2005) Evaluating biodiversity in fragmented forest landscapes:
principles. Forestry Commission Information Note. 73. Forestry
Commission, Edinburgh.

Watts, K. & Handley, P. (2010) Developing a functional
connectivity indicator to detect change in fragmented
landscapes. *Ecological Indicators,* **10**, 552–557.

WBP (Wales Biodiversity Partnership) (2008) Threats to
biodiversity in Wales. Biodiversity Action Plan Reporting 2008.

WERH (Wales Environment Research Hub) (2009).
Environment Strategy for Wales – Review of Research Needs
pp1–54. Wales Environment Research Hub, Bangor.

Wheater, H.S., McIntyre, N, Jackson, B.M., Marshall, M.R.,
Ballard, C., Bulygina, N.A.S., Reynolds, B. & Frogbrook, Z. (2010)
Multiscale impacts of land management on flooding. Flood Risk
Science and Management (eds G. Pender, C. Thorne, I. Cluckie, H.
Faulkner), Blackwell Publishing.

Williams, N.S.G., Schwartz, M.W., Vesk, P.A., McCarthy,
M.A., Hahs, A.K., Clemants, S.E., Corlett, R.T., Duncan, R.P.,
Norton, B.A., Thompson K. & McDonnell M.J. (2009) A conceptual
framework for predicting the effects of urban environments on
floras. *Journal of Ecology,* **97**, 4–9.

Willis, K.G., Garrod, G., Scarpa, R., Powe, N., Lovett, A.,
Bateman, I.J., Hanley, N. & Macmillan, D.C. (2003) The social
and environmental benefits of forests in Great Britain. Forestry
Commission, Edinburgh.

Wood, G.A., Kibblewhite, M.G., Hannam, J.A., Harris, J.A.
& Leeds-Harrison, P.B. (2005) Soil-based services in the built
environment. A report prepared for the Department of the
Environment, Food and Rural Affairs, National Soil Resources
Institute. Cranfield University, Cranfield.

Woodland Trust (2009) Ancient Woodlands: a guide for
woodland owners and managers. Woodland Trust [online]
Available at: <http://www.woodlandtrust.org.uk/en/aboutus/
publications> [Accessed: 18.05.11].

Woodland Trust (2010) Space for People: targeting action
for woodland access. Woodland Trust. [online] Available at:
<http://www.woodlandtrust.org.uk/en/about-us/publications/
key-publications/space-for-people/Documents/space-for-
people-summary.pdf>[Accessed 16.03.11].

Wyn Jones, G. (2010) Land Use Climate Change
Report. Report for the Welsh Assembly Government.
[online] Available at: <http://wales.gov.uk/docs/drah/
publications/110214luccgLreport%20finalv2.pdf> [Accessed:
15.05.11].

Chapter 21:
UK Dependence on non-UK Ecosystem Services

Coordinating Lead Author: Tony Weighell

Key Findings*

The UK is increasingly drawing on the services of overseas ecosystems to support its own economic growth. The UK's landmass cannot provide all the ecosystem services required to support the national economy. Access to overseas ecosystem services, particularly for the supply of biomass (for food, fibre and bioenergy), is essential. This dependence makes the protection of the long-term functionality of these overseas ecosystems an economic imperative for the UK.

National consumption of minerals and fossil fuels reflects economic cycles. Domestic biomass consumption does not; its steady growth within the UK's economy over the last 40 years has primarily been related to population size[1]. With domestic production relatively stable, growth in the use of biomass by the UK's economy has been supported by a growth in imports, starting from 1980 and peaking in 2002[1]. Recently, imported biomass flow appears to have stabilised at approximately 50 million tonnes per year (t/yr), but population growth and the implementation of new bioenergy policies will increase future national demand for biomass, including imports.

[1] well established

Approximately one third of the biomass used by the UK comes from overseas according to Environmental Accounts prepared by the Office for National Statistics. This data indicates an annual biomass flow through the economy of 150 million tonnes based on domestic production of approximately 100 million tonnes (from agriculture, forestry and fisheries) and imports of 50 million tonnes. Exports are 20 million tonnes, so net annual biomass consumption by the UK economy is approximately 130 million t/yr, which is equivalent to 2.1 t/capita.

Total overseas land requirement for biomass exported to the UK was approximately 14 million hectares (ha) in 2008[2]. The domestic productive area in the UK is about 20 million ha. Provision of food (for human or animal consumption) and forest products (timber, pulp and paper) accounts for 90% of this land use impact and the remaining 10% is related to bioenergy crops.

[2] established but incomplete evidence

The majority of the overseas biomass utilised by the UK's economy comes from the Palearctic Realm (including the EU and wider Europe) and has a land requirement of 8.5 million ha[2]. In 2008, the estimated land requirement in the Neotropical Realm (South America) to supply biomass to the UK was approximately 2.4 million ha. Approximately 1.3 million ha was required in both of the Nearctic (North America) and Oceania Realms. Imports from the Afrotropical Realm (Sub-Saharan Africa) are relatively insignificant with a land use impact of only 300,000 ha in 2008.

[2] established but incomplete evidence

Approximately 10 million of the UK's 14 million ha of overseas land use impact can be assigned to four individual biomes[2]. Boreal Forest Taiga and Temperate Broadleaf and Mixed Forest biomes are key suppliers with a land use impact of approximately 3 million ha in each. Impacts in the Boreal Forest biome occur primarily through import of timber products; the impacts in the Temperate Forest biome are due to the provision of food chain biomass for human or animal consumption. Land use impact elsewhere affects less than 2 million ha in both the Temperate Grasslands of North and South America and Tropical/Sub-tropical Broadleaf Forests of South America and South East Asia.

[2] established but incomplete evidence

---

* Each Key Finding has been assigned a level of scientific certainty, based on a 4-box model and complemented, where possible, with a likelihood scale. Superscript numbers and letters indicate the uncertainty term assigned to each finding. Full details of each term and how they were assigned are presented in Appendix 21.1.

In 2008, almost 90% of domestic biomass consumption involved food chain material for human or animal use. Thus the national food requirement will be a key driver of future UK biomass demand as population continues to grow. If current consumption and waste patterns persist, and domestic production remains stable, food requirements will drive increased import demand for food chain biomass in direct proportion to population growth[2]. Food chain imports are likely to rise from the current 35 million tonnes to almost 50 million tonnes in 2030[2]. This demand is likely to be mitigated by waste reduction and increased domestic production[2]. Effective demand mitigation would stabilise the overseas land use requirement associated with UK food imports at the current level of approximately 10 million ha.

[2] established but incomplete evidence

As the UK implements renewable energy policies, biomass demand for heat and power production will increase significantly in the next decade, exceeding the UK's domestic biomass capacity before 2020[3]. As much as 27 million t/yr of additional biomass imports is very likely to be required to feed this one industry, potentially creating an additional overseas land requirement of 7–10 million ha by 2020, after which demand is very likely to stabilise if renewable targets remain unaltered[3].

[3] competing explanations

There is significant scope for moderating the UK's biomass import demand and its associated overseas impacts. A combination of increased domestic biomass production and food waste reduction could make significant contributions to reducing both. If biomass import demand is unmitigated by increased domestic production and reduced waste, the overseas land use requirement is likely to almost double from the current 14 million ha to 26 million ha by 2030, and continuing to increase with population growth thereafter[3]. Mitigated through increased domestic production and reduction in waste, this land use requirement could be limited to approximately 20 million ha, and potentially held at this level from 2020 onwards.

[3] competing explanations

The use of biomass Material Flow Analysis provides a framework for reporting on UK trends in biomass use: the measurement of pressures exerted on overseas ecosystems and the basis for formulating domestic and international policy initiatives. The framework allows identification and quantification of the UK's overseas biomass dependencies, including the spatial distribution of material sources. A suite of nationally important indicators can be used for reporting. The framework also identifies potential ecosystem impacts of imported biomass imports. The links between the indirect and geographically distant socioeconomic drivers of ecosystem change operating in the UK and the direct drivers of ecosystem change on the ground in countries supplying the UK economy are made explicit. The need for, and potential benefits arising from, domestic polices to minimise the overseas impacts of UK biomass consumption are made equally explicit.

Measuring the UK's use of biomass and combining these measurements with other data permits the drivers for national biomass consumption to be identified along with the global locations which supply this material. Empirical assessment of biomass flows and qualitative assessment of how and where pressures may be exerted does not, in itself, mean that negative ecosystem impacts are occurring, but serves to identity where and how they may occur. Detailed case-by-case sustainability analyses will be needed to determine if the pressures are acceptable on social, economic and ecological grounds, and if they are being effectively managed. Such analysis needs to be undertaken to determine the resilience of the ecosystems concerned and the appropriate thresholds below which we can safely continue to exploit specific systems. Given the economic dependence of the UK's economy on these overseas ecosystems, it is in the national interest to ensure that we, and other countries, identify and operate within these limits.

21.1 Scope and Purpose of this Chapter

The natural environment provides the UK's economy and population with food, energy, construction materials and water. These demands may cause ecosystem degradation and have the potential to impair long-term delivery of the ecosystem services on which the country depends. Current consumption patterns ensure that the landmass of the UK and the surrounding territorial waters cannot provide all of the services required to support the national economy. This is particularly true for the national consumption of biomass (food, fibre and bioenergy) where one third of the biomass utilised by the UK is currently sourced from outside the country. Access to the provisioning services of overseas ecosystems is, therefore, essential to ensure the security of food supply (Defra 2006, 2009), and will be necessary to meet the national renewable energy targets in the future.

The UK National Ecosystem Assessment (UK NEA) analyses historical trends and evaluates alternative futures for the landscape of the UK until 2060. This chapter uses an empirical approach to look at the dependence of the UK economy on imported biomass. This dependence is described and quantified in terms of the material goods imported into the UK from non-UK ecosystems. The source ecosystems are identified at the scale of Biogeographical Realm and Biome. Available knowledge on biomass flows and consumption and national population trends are combined with an empirical assessment of the future implications of new bioenergy policies to produce credible projections for national biomass consumption up to 2030. Secondary measurements of land and water requirement to produce specific biomass streams can be estimated and used to identify how the use of imported biomass may be translated into ecosystem impacts.

This focus on the UK's dependency on the provisioning services (tangible goods) provided by various biomass streams does not imply that the other services provided by non-UK ecosystems have no value. The UK's population makes use of the tourism and cultural benefits of overseas ecosystems, but these benefits do not represent an economic necessity or dependence. Nor are these services, or the climate regulation services upon which we are all dependent, amenable to straightforward measurement and impact assessment.

Measuring the UK's dependence on overseas ecosystems by analysing the material goods they provide does not mean that provisioning services can be valued directly on the basis of goods entering our national ports. The market price of these materials at their time of entry into the UK is not a true measure of the value of the ecosystem services underpinning the production of these goods (Bateman 2010). Therefore, this chapter does not attempt to value the goods and services provided by overseas ecosystems, but quantifies key dependencies on them, and identifies potential impacts that may arise from them. The Material Flow Analysis (MFA) techniques described and used in this chapter provide a general framework for sustainability analysis and policy development. These techniques have the capacity to enable the identification and development of effective policy responses to possible overseas ecosystem service degradation attributable to the UK's use of imported provisioning services.

Material Flow Analysis identifies where and how ecosystem dependencies exist (defining the eco-political context), and the *potential* scale and nature of impacts that may arise from such dependencies. Determining the *actual* scale and nature of these impacts will require location specific analysis. By describing and quantifying biomass flows from overseas ecosystems into the UK, MFA can, in this case, focus sustainability analysis in key areas of the world and in key ecosystems. The MFA framework also provides qualitative information on how ecosystem impacts may occur. These include pressure for land use change, water use, and pollution of water or soils. The quantitative and qualitative framework provides the basis for appropriate policy responses within the UK, both in the domestic and global context. To be effective in managing the UK's impact on overseas ecosystems, the level of deployment of these policies will be critical. Policies to comprehend and manage the UK's impact on overseas ecosystems need to be location-specific and designed to address particular impact categories.

Material Flow Analysis does not provide a direct measure of specific impacts of the UK's economy on overseas ecosystems. In its review of UK material flows the Office for National Statistics (ONS) reflects that: "There is increasing policy interest in the relocation of production as it disguises the global impact of the UK economy" (ONS 2005). What MFA does is to define where in the world these impacts are being relocated to, and how they are may be expressed if not properly managed. Defining these global pressure points is the essential first step to developing and promoting policies to avoid, or mitigate, these impacts.

Projections beyond 2030 have not been attempted in this chapter because the numerical basis for such projection (particularly population trends and the consequences of policies governing biomass supply and demand) cannot be reasonably extended beyond this date. However, the projections presented suggest that the next 20 years are critical in terms of the policy actions needed to ensure sustainable use of overseas ecosystems. If current policy initiatives are successful, the UK's use of provisioning services from non-UK systems could be stabilised by 2030. Subsequent economic and population growth could be detached from a continued growth in demand for overseas biomass supplies and the associated impacts. If these policies fail, our inability to ensure efficient biomass use within the UK's economy, coupled with continued population growth, will lead to an unsustainable growth in demand for imported biomass. The overseas ecosystems upon which we currently rely, and others which may come 'on stream' in the future, are unlikely to cope with this demand from the UK and other global economies. The chapter presents:

- a description of the data available on biomass flow through the UK's economy and how this can be used to analyse imports flows;
- a baseline position using 2008 data to describe and quantify the nature of biomass imported into the UK, its

geographical and ecosystem origins, and an estimated land use requirement;

- an historical analysis of biomass imports to identify trends and socio-economic drivers of biomass use;
- projections of future biomass use by the UK's economy up to 2030, and the potential associated overseas land use impacts.

21.2 Imported Biomass: Quantifying the Dependency Between Domestic and Global Ecosystems

The national environmental accounts published by ONS quantify material flows through the economy using a set of high level indicators that reflect domestic production of raw materials (fossil fuels, minerals and biomass), imports, and national consumption (ONS 2010). Set alongside indicators of total material use are a complimentary set of biomass measurements (**Table 21.1**), which can be used to quantify biomass flows through the economy including monitoring of biomass imports.

21.2.1 Imported Biomass
Over one third of the 150 million tonnes of biomass available to the UK economy is imported. Trade data (gathered by HM Revenue & Customs) provide the basis for a set of indicators to quantify and map the biomass links between the UK and overseas ecosystems. These include potential 'primary' and 'secondary' indicators. Primary indicators are direct measurements that form part of the existing national statistical database, can be used in an unmodified form, and have long-term value for monitoring trends. Secondary indicators are derived directly from primary statistical data through some form of transformation, or are primary statistics judged to have less value (due to special considerations) for long-term trend analysis.

21.2.2 Mass (Weight) of Imported Biomass as a Primary Indicator
Trade statistics provide the basis for:
- the quantification of the long-term contribution of imported biomass to the UK's economy in relation to domestic production and exports;
- the identification and quantification of the UK's main imported biomass commodities and development of a 'profile' of the UK's biomass imports;
- and profiling of the UK's regional suppliers of biomass at the global level to identify and quantify regional suppliers of key commodities.

Trade data (**Box 21.1**) provides a set of robust numerical indicators to monitor the UK's use of primary production sourced from overseas ecosystems. Gathered according to

standard international procedures, this data can be used to identify long-term trends in national use of all forms of biomass, and to identify and monitor key commodity flows (see Giljum 2009 for a European perspective). It can also be combined with other information to project future use. Spatial analysis is possible through the use of this data to identify national or regional suppliers of biomass to the UK and the ecosystems that are providing this service.

21.2.3 Secondary Measurements: Land Use, Water Use and Monetary Value
Secondary biomass indicators based on the UK's national trade data are:

- *Land requirement to produce imported biomass*—by recording mass, commodity type and country of origin, trade data can be combined with country-specific crop yield data to estimate the land area required to produce imported biomass commodities. This is distinct from ecological footprinting which integrates biomass and energy demands with waste generation to estimate total land requirements for production and disposal (WWF 2010). Ecological footprinting reports using a standardised unit:the global hectare. Land requirement is reported in actual hectares (ha).
- *Biomass market price*—the UK's Overseas Trade Statistics report the recorded monetary value of imported biomass in Pounds Sterling Biomass value is regarded as a secondary measurement because the changing value of Sterling and commodity prices through time make it less valuable as a long-term indicator than mass (weight) data. This data does, however, provide a useful economic dimension to this form of analysis, emphasising the economic importance of imported biomass, and, by extension, the source ecosystems, to the UK economy. In 2008 the total value of these imports was approximately £50 billion (HMRC 2010a).
- *Embedded (virtual) water associated with biomass imports*—primary data on biomass weight and type permits the calculation of the amount of water required to produce biomass supplied to the UK through imports (Hoekstra & Chapgain 2008). This measurement is linked directly to the primary statistics on import mass, but is a derivative of this data and is, therefore, of limited use for long-term analysis. Approximately 66% of the UK's water demand is met by overseas sources, three quarters of which is due to the production of agricultural biomass (WWF 2008; **Box 21.2**).

Trade data on UK biomass imports provides a suite of potential indicators for mass flow, economic analysis and the assessment of potential ecosystem impacts of biomass production overseas. These indicators can be utilised for time-series or geographical analysis. This chapter presents a new analysis of the overseas land use requirement arising from biomass imports, but only summarises already published assessments of the UK overseas water requirement. The value of land and water use indicators is their relevance to the provision of ecosystem goods and services, and to specific drivers of biodiversity loss such as land use change and increased water stress.

Table 21.1 Material and Biomass Flow Indicators. Source: ONS (2005, 2010b)

Total material flow indicator	Equivalent biomass flow indicator
Domestic Extraction—the sum of materials (minerals, fossil fuels, biomass) taken from the UK environment.	**Domestic Biomass Extraction**—the sum of primary biomass taken from the UK marine and terrestrial environment.
Direct Material Input—primary resources extracted from the UK environment plus imports. Direct Material Input represents the *gross* use of raw materials by the UK economy.	**Domestic Biomass Input**—biomass extracted from the UK environment plus biomass imports.
Domestic Material Consumption—is Direct Material Input less the mass of goods exported from the UK.	**Domestic Biomass Consumption**—Domestic Biomass Input less biomass exported.
Imported Material—mass of primary resources (minerals, fossil fuels, biomass) imported into the UK.	**Imported Biomass Input**—mass of biological material imported into the UK. Can be used at aggregated level (total imported biomass) or for specific commodity groups.

Box 21.1 Imported biomass: data available, data codes and import profiling.

Reporting on UK import flows follows international guidelines and employs a hierarchical coding system that allows biomass imports to be classified and recorded on the basis of a single to eight digit coding system. Single digit codes provide a high level summary; eight digit coding provides very specific commodity data. For example, code 15111010 represents the precisely defined *'Crude palm oil for technical or industrial uses (excluding for manufacture of foodstuffs)'*.

The UK HM Revenue & Customs database records commodity code, commodity type, volume (kilogrammes), value (Pounds Sterling) and country of dispatch for each import category. Detailed coding provides the ability to analyse import data for specific commodities of interest.

This chapter focuses on the use of five trade data groups defined by single digit codes and 26 associated (two digit) commodities. Two digit coding classifies biomass imports into the following groups:

- **Food and live animals** (Code 0)—over 50% of UK biomass imports fall into this category including meat, cereal, animal feedstuffs and vegetable commodities.
- **Beverages and tobacco** (Code 1)—a minor commodity group within which only tobacco is classed as biomass for this analysis.
- **Crude materials** (Code 2)—includes the oilseeds, wood pulp and cork/wood commodities.
- **Animal and vegetable oils and fats** (Code 4)—includes palm oil, soya and rapeseed oils.
- **Manufactured goods** (Code 6)—a miscellaneous group of processed biomass commodities, paper products being most significant.

Taken together, these groupings provide the basis for high level analysis of import flows in this chapter, including the graphical profiling of the UK's biomass imports in terms of volume and category (**Figure 1**).

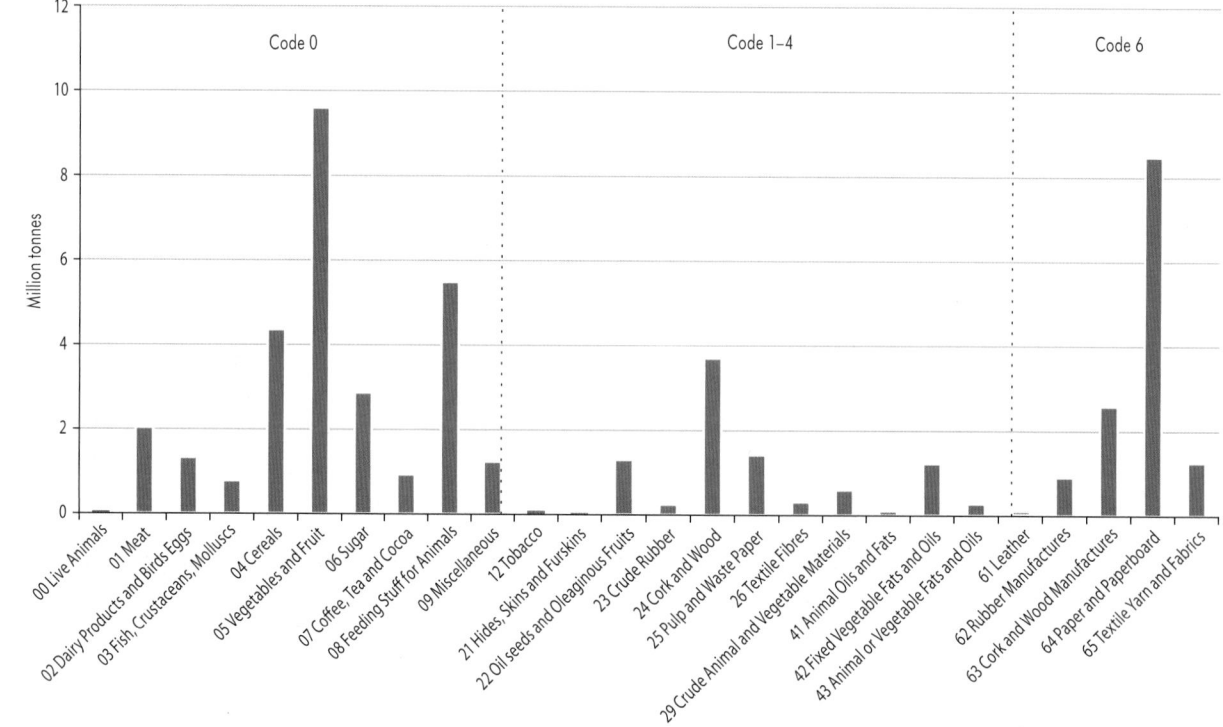

Figure 1 Commodity profile of UK biomass imports in 2008. Source: data from HMRC (2010b).

21.3 Domestic Pressures on Global Ecosystems

The link between the UK's economy and the provision of biomass from overseas ecosystems can be quantified and analysed in an eco-political context (described in terms of ecological and political boundaries). Dependencies can be defined, and the ways in which the UK is adding to pressures on specific global ecosystems can be identified, providing a framework for developing appropriate domestic and international policies to eliminate or manage these pressures.

21.3.1 Ecosystems

Spatial patterns of biodiversity can be expressed in varying levels of geographical and ecological detail. This chapter follows the approach adopted by the Millennium Ecosystem Assessment (MA 2005a) and uses 'Biogeographical Realms' and 'Biomes' as the geographical units for analysis of the UK's links to overseas ecosystems. These ecological units fall within political boundaries, so a useful framework for policy development requires an eco-political analysis.

The geographical analysis presented in this chapter is designed to provide this eco-political context and is undertaken on three levels, two biogeographical and one political:

- The Biogeographic Realm, the eight large spatial regions in which ecosystems share broadly similar characteristics and evolutionary history and roughly correspond to the continents (**Figure 21.1**). Global Biogeographic Realms display variations in the extent of the change to their component ecosystems, face different drivers for change and may be amenable to different strategies for managing these drivers.

- The Biome, the 13 major terrestrial global biological communities (**Figure 21.2**) classified according to the predominant vegetation, and characterised by adaptations of organisms to that particular environment.

- National sources of biomass imports, as recorded in the UK trade database (HMRC 2010b), allowing specific trade partners to be identified and categorised according to biomass trade relationships. Any international UK policies to manage the overseas impacts of its material consumption will be implemented at a national level and will be deployed in the context of agricultural, environmental and other frameworks.

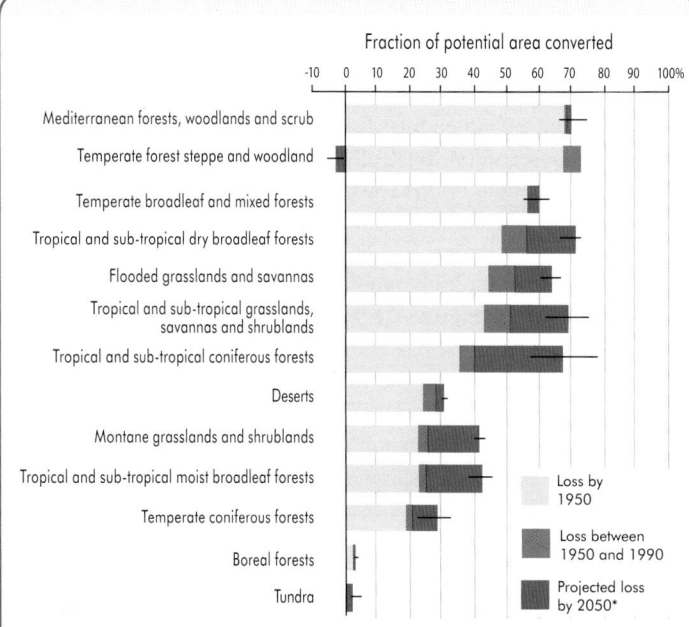

*According to the four MA scenarios. For 2050 projections, the average value of the projections under the four scenarios is plotted and the error bars (black lines) represent the range of values from the different scenarios.

Figure 21.2 Principal global biomes and their status. Source: MA (2005a).

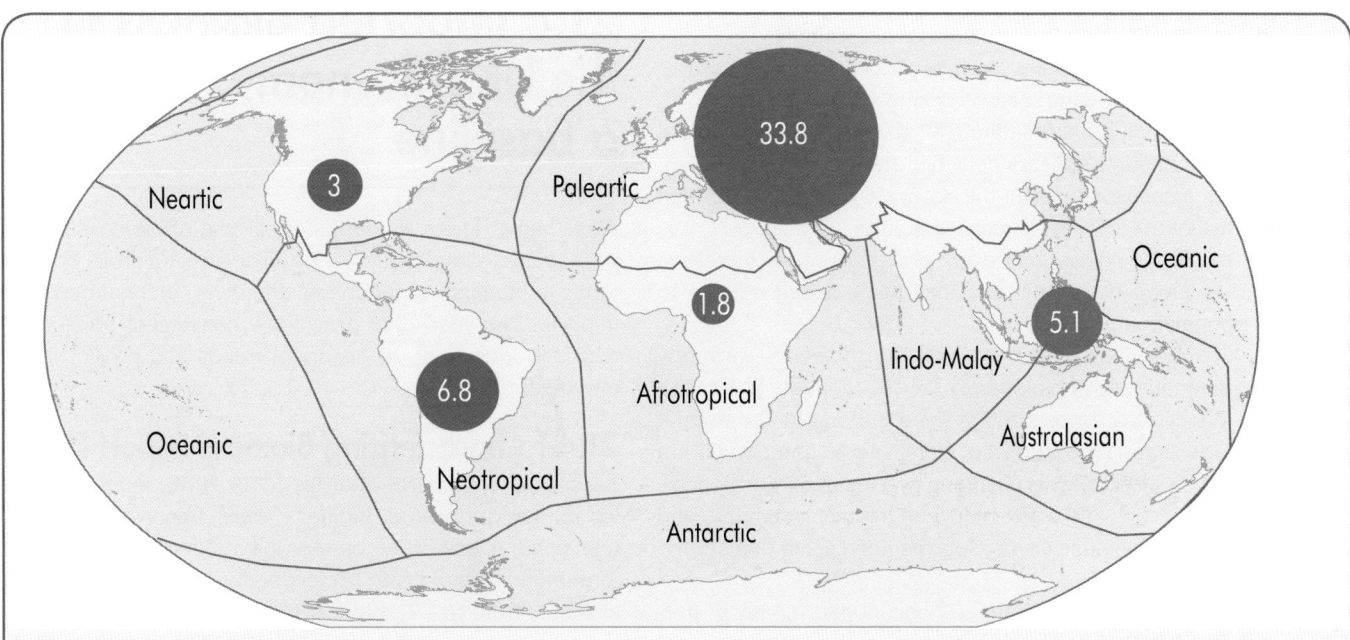

Figure 21.1 Source of biomass (millions of tonnes) imported into the UK by Biogeographical Realms in 2008. Source: data from HMRC (2010b); underlying map based Olson *et al.* (2004).

21.3.2 Pressures and Drivers

Changes within global ecosystems are primarily a result of indirect anthropogenic drivers, the most significant of which are related to demographic and economic changes. Population growth and relocation (urbanisation) are major factors, along with changing consumption patterns associated with increasing per capita income. These indirect drivers have resulted in an absolute increase in global consumption of ecosystem services and goods, and also an increase in per capita consumption. These indirect drivers are linked to a set of direct drivers of ecosystem degradation (and biodiversity loss) which include habitat change, climate change, impacts of invasive alien species, overexploitation and pollution.

The original extent of many of the terrestrial global biomes (on which this chapter focuses) is uncertain because of deforestation, agricultural expansion and urbanisation. The original boundaries can be estimated by reference to soil and climate conditions, the results of which infer significant changes in all of the major biomes: 20–50% of nine out of the 14 biomes have been converted to croplands (MA 2005a; **Figure 21.2**). This pressure for conversion is increasing as global demand for food and other biomass rises, emphasising the role of provisioning services at the expense of the other ecosystem services and biodiversity. The MA predicts that habitat loss due to land use change will cause continued decline in local and global taxa, and states that this decline is a cross-border issue driven by both local and global pressures. The expected increase in the UK's use of global ecosystem services, particularly its use of biomass, will add to these pressures.

The MA highlights the potential for socioeconomic factors (consumption patterns, population changes, policies and economic cycles) to have positive or negative effects on the functioning of ecosystem provisioning services and on the supporting services underpinning them. The capacity of these socioeconomic drivers to impact on ecosystem function reinforces the need to understand the nature of these links and to formulate policies accordingly.

The UK contributes to global ecosystem pressures through the following socioeconomic drivers:

- *Economic growth*—although UK domestic material consumption appears detached from economic growth (as measured by GDP) the economy has grown through use of overseas resources (ONS 2010).
- *Increasing population*—over the past 30 years, increased UK biomass consumption has been closely related to population growth.
- *Changing patterns of biomass consumption*—currently the main use of biomass by the UK economy is for food (either directly or through contributions to the animal food chain). The pattern of biomass consumption within the UK's economy is changing as a result of new policies on recycling and waste reduction (reducing demand) and use of renewable energy sources (increasing demand).

The capacity to measure UK economy biomass use, combined with other data examining the drivers for national biomass consumption, allows an assessment to be made of the effects of these UK domestic drivers on overseas ecosystems. Population growth and changes in national wealth and patterns of biomass use can be translated into a strategic overview of where (in which countries and ecosystems) these pressures will be felt and through what specific mechanisms. Empirical assessment of biomass flows and qualitative assessment of how and where pressures may be exerted does not, in itself, mean that negative ecosystem impacts are occurring, but serves to identity where and how they may occur. Detailed sustainability analysis on a case-by-case basis will be needed to determine if the pressures within the identified ecosystems are acceptable on social, economic and ecological grounds, and if they are being effectively managed. Such analysis needs to be undertaken to determine the resilience of the ecosystems concerned and appropriate thresholds below which we can safely continue to exploit specific systems (Bateman 2010; Turner 2007).

The MFA approach used here provides a framework for such sustainability work by providing:

- *An eco-political location (in terms of country and ecosystem) where pressures are occurring*—demonstrating the UK's dependencies on specific regions/countries and the need to focus sustainability analysis on these areas.
- *The basis for a numerical measure of land and water requirements for biomass production in each eco-political region*—permitting quantification of pressure exerted through these demands, indicating the scale of potential associated impacts and the extent to which pressure is being exerted on individual ecosystems.
- *A strategic overview of the mechanisms through which ecosystem impacts may occur in specific regions*—analysis of commodity types originating from individual regions permits specific associated environmental pressures to be identified, providing a screening mechanism to direct sustainability analysis.

21.4 Imported Biomass in the UK's Economy: 2008 as a Baseline

This chapter looks at the historical use of biomass by the UK's economy, and makes some basic forward projections in terms of biomass requirements and their potential overseas impacts. The year 2008 provides a convenient point from which to look back on historical trends and project these into the future.

21.4.1 Characterising Biomass Import Flows

According to the ONS analysis (ONS 2010), approximately 52 million tonnes of biomass were imported in 2008, representing one third of the 154 million tonnes of the total biomass input into the economy (**Figure 21.3**). Data available from HM Revenue & Customs allows UK biomass imports to be profiled according to their characteristics. Imports cover the full range of biomass groups from unprocessed raw materials (primarily foodstuffs) to highly processed items such as textiles and manufactured wood products. Almost 70% of imported biomass is food chain material, either for direct human consumption or animal feed, with fruit and vegetables, animal feed and cereals dominating (**Box 21.1**; **Figure 21.4**). Non-food imports are primarily forest products such as cork, wood and paper.

21.4.2 Biofuels: a Special Case

To comply with the EU Renewable Energy Directive, the UK will need to achieve a 10% substitution of transport fuels with biofuels by 2020. The UK used approximately 1 million tonnes of biofuels in 2008. Over 80% of this fuel was biodiesel sourced from soya, oilseed rape and palm oil (RFA 2009), the remainder being bioethanol primarily sourced from sugarcane.

Trade data on biomass does not directly record biofuel imports, which are described under several industrial classifications and customs codes, but the UK Renewable Fuels Agency (RFA) monitors the use of biofuels in the UK, including imports. Currently, most biofuels used in the UK come from primary crops, rather than recycled materials, so have a land use requirement. With over 80% of biofuels being imported (RFA 2010), much of this requirement falls overseas: the total overseas land use requirement for the UK's use of biofuels was estimated at 1.3–1.4 million ha in 2008 (RFA 2009; JNCC 2009). In addition to volumetric data, the RFA records data on source country and crop, allowing source biome to be deduced for most of the imported supply (JNCC 2009).

The bias towards biodiesel use by the UK transport sector skews overseas land use impacts to those areas producing oilseed rape, palm oil and soya: Germany, Malaysia and Indonesia, and the Americas respectively. Plant oil and, therefore, biofuel yield per hectare varies considerably for the three principal biodiesel source crops. Soya is the most important single biodiesel feedstock for the UK. It has the lowest yield per hectare, however, so the high relative use of this crop results in over 60% of the land use pressure arising from UK biofuels use occurring in the 'Americas', specifically the USA, Argentina and Brazil.

21.4.3 UK Biomass Imports: Sources and Land Requirements

The UK's biomass imports, including bioethanol and biodiesel fuels, amounted to approximately 52 million tonnes of primary materials in 2008. As agricultural or forest products, or their derivatives, these imports can be expected to have a land use requirement for their production. More than 98% of these imports are sourced from five Biogeographical Realms (**Figure 21.1**; **Table 21.2**), with an estimated total land use footprint of 14 million hectares. Of this footprint, 90% arises from the provision of agricultural products for food and forest products, and the remaining 10% from bioenergy crops.

The UK's trade relationships are dominated by its links to the EU which, along with Russia and other European neighbours, supplied 34 million tonnes of biomass to the UK economy in 2008: 65% of the country's total biomass imports. Therefore, the majority of the land use footprint associated with biomass imports (approximately 8.5 million ha) falls in the Palearctic Realm (**Figure 21.1**).

Tropical regions provide a further 26% of the UK's biomass imports, with the remaining material coming from North America. The Neotropical region of South America provides 2.4 million ha of land to support UK biomass consumption, which is approximately equal to the total contribution from the Nearctic (North American) and Oceania Realms combined (**Box 21.3**). In addition to its land demand, the UK also has a significant South American water footprint (**Box 21.2**).

Analysed at the global biome level, approximately 10 million ha of land use footprint can be assigned to five individual biomes (**Table 21.3**): Boreal Forest Taiga, Temperate Broadleaf and Mixed Forest, Temperate Grasslands, Mediterranean Forest and Tropical/Sub-tropical Broadleaf Forest. The processed nature of some of the biomass imported into the UK prevents simple analysis of source biome and land use requirements, and the estimates presented here represent minimum figures. European Boreal Forest Taiga and Temperate Broadleaf and Mixed Forest biomes are key providers, the former for timber products and the latter for food chain biomass. Outside these areas,

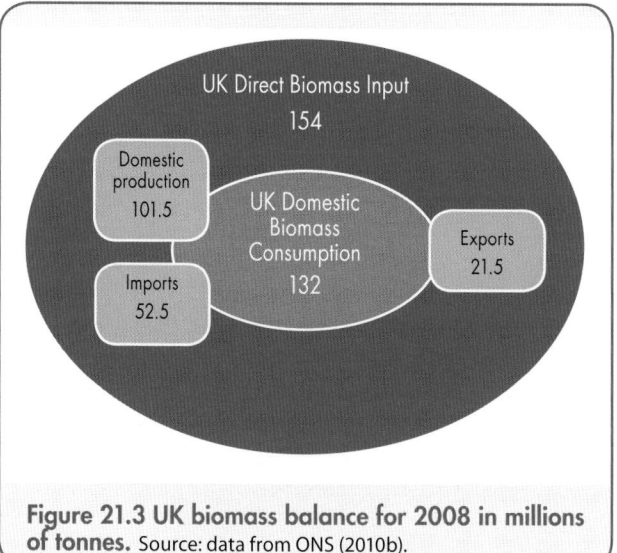

Figure 21.3 UK biomass balance for 2008 in millions of tonnes. Source: data from ONS (2010b).

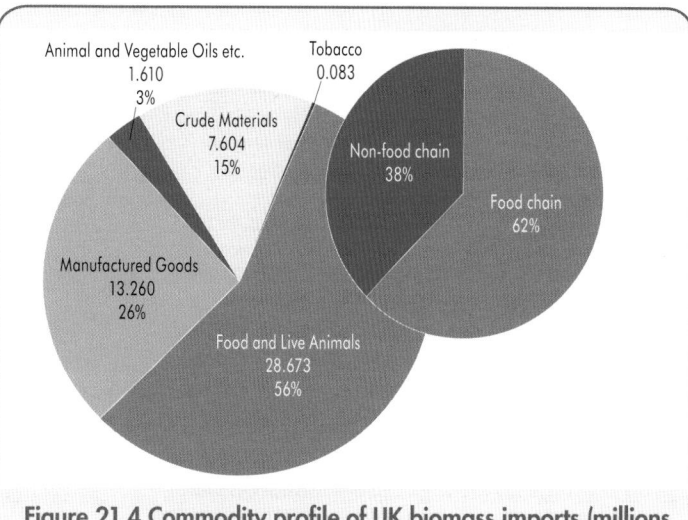

Figure 21.4 Commodity profile of UK biomass imports (millions of tonnes/percentage) in 2008. Source: data from HMRC (2010b).

Table 21.2 Estimated land requirement (in millions of ha) in global Biogeographical Realms to provide biomass imported to the UK. Land area estimates based on detailed analysis of imported biomass commodity flows, country/region- and crop-specific biomass yields. Due to rounding of numbers column totals may not match cell figure totals. See JNCC (2009) for details of biofuels analysis.

Realms	Agricultural and forest products area	Biofuels area	Total area
Palearctic	8.3	0.2	8.5
Nearctic	0.7	0.6	1.3
Oceania	1.3	0.0	1.3
Neotropical	1.9	0.5	2.4
Afrotropical	0.3	0.0	0.3
Total	12.5	1.4	13.9

Table 21.3 Estimated land requirement (in millions of ha) in global Biomes to provide biomass imported to the UK. Land area estimates based on detailed analysis of imported biomass commodity flows, country/region- and crop-specific biomass yields. Not all biomass imports can be assigned to a specific biome. See JNCC (2009) for details of biofuels analysis.

Biomes	Agricultural and forest products area	Biofuels area	Total area
Boreal Forest Taiga	3.3	0	3.3
Temperate Broadleaf and Mixed Forest	3.1	0.2	3.3
Temperate Grasslands	0.6	1.1	1.7
Mediterranean Forest	0.1	0.0	0.1
Tropical/Sub-Tropical Broadleaf Forest	1.7	0.1	1.8
Total	8.8	1.4	10.2

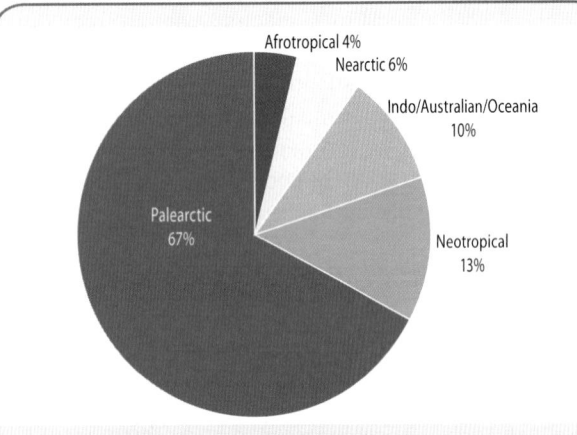

Figure 21.5 Source of UK-imported biomass by Biogeographical Realm (as per Figure 21.1) in 2008.
Source: data from HMRC (2010a).

the land use footprint is almost identical in Temperate Grasslands and Tropical/Sub-tropical Broadleaf Forest. Impacts on Temperate Grassland are due to both food chain and biofuels provision, with soya-based products being the key commodity in both cases.

There are regional and national differences in the global agricultural systems providing biomass to the UK. These differences, due to climatic and economic factors, are reflected in the 'profiles' of their biomass commodity exports. South America (Neotropical Realm) and Sub-Saharan Africa (Afrotropical Realm) have biomass supply profiles skewed towards basic (unprocessed) raw materials. Sub-Saharan Africa is an immature region that has large areas of largely unconverted ecosystems with relatively low agricultural yields which supply basic commodities within national boundaries or to regional neighbours. Provision of basic foodstuffs is the primary concern. Value-added biomass

Box 21.2 The UK's overseas water demand.

Whereas two thirds of the UK's biomass comes from domestic sources, the situation with national water demand is reversed, and only one third of the water we use actually comes from the UK (WWF 2010). The bulk of UK water demand—75% of the total national usage of 102 billion cubic metres per year (Gm³/yr)—is associated with the production of agricultural commodities (**Figure 1**). Industrial products require 24 Gm³/yr and household water use is only 3.3 Gm³/yr. Of the 75 Gm³/yr agricultural water demand, 46 Gm³/yr (61%) is an external demand being provided by overseas ecosystems to produce biomass for UK consumption, of which over 70% is from arable crops. In respect of agricultural water use in general, and crop production in particular, overseas water demand significantly exceeds that imposed on domestic supplies.

According to WWF: "Most of the products that make up the UK's EWF (external water footprint) originate from Brazil, France, Ireland, Ghana and India." Brazil, through provision of soybeans, coffee and livestock products, is responsible for 9% of this external water demand, reaffirming the strong link between the UK and South America through import of agricultural commodities.

Combined with the land requirement to produce imported biomass described in this chapter, this water demand represents a quantifiable link between the UK's economy and overseas ecosystems (Hoekstra & Chapgain 2008), and is one basis for monitoring the impacts of UK biomass imports in space and time.

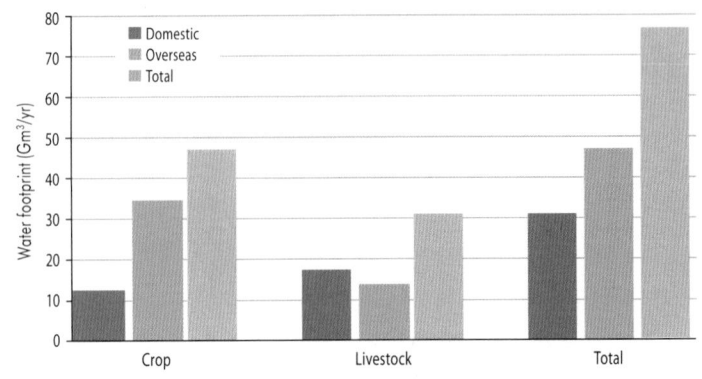

Figure 1 UK water usage (in billion cubic metres per year).
Source: data from WWF (2008).

The UK imported 6 million tonnes of biomass from Central and South America in 2008, with soya and fruit/vegetables representing almost 70% of these imports (**Figure 1**). Based on crop and country-specific yield data, it is estimated that approximately 2.4 million ha were required to grow these materials.

■ Soya products for human and animal feed had a land use requirement of 1.2 million ha in 2008. An additional 500,000 ha requirement also arose from the use of soya-based biodiesel. To put this in context, van Gelder *et al.* (2008) estimate that approximately 12 million ha of South American land were required to supply the whole of the EU with soya products in 2007.

■ Brazil and Argentina are the UK's two dominant trade partners in the region, providing at least 4 million tones of biomass from 1.62 million ha of land, principally though their supply of soya-based commodities. This land requirement is equivalent to the agricultural land area within Wales. There is a strong dependency between UK food, agricultural and bioenergy sectors and soya supplies from South America.

■ Approximately 60% of biomass sourced from South America can be assigned to specific biomes. Whilst this is only an approximation of the geographical origin of these materials, it demonstrates the importance of two key biomes within the region, specifically Temperate Grasslands, lying exclusively in Argentina, and Tropical Broadleafed Forests, primarily within Brazil but with some small contributions from Ecuador and Colombia.

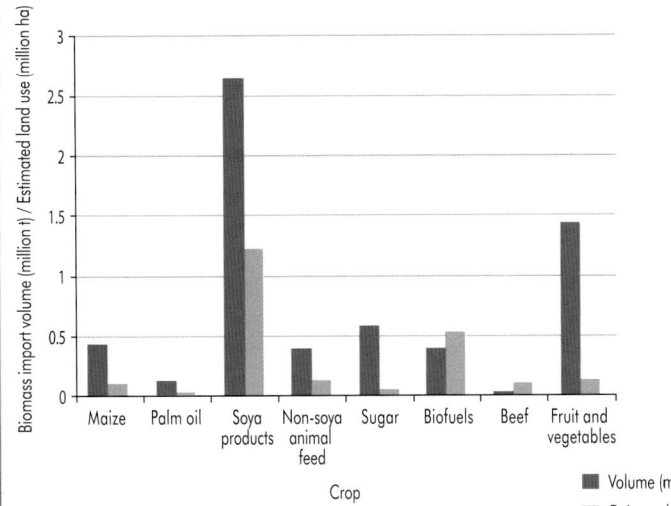 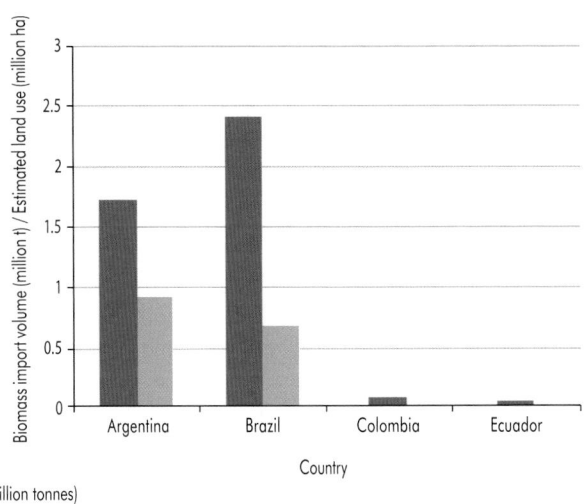

Figure 1 UK biomass import volumes (in millions of tonnes) and estimated land use (in millions of hectares) for South America (Neotropical Realm) in 2008: a) principal biomass imports and land use requirement, and b) total biomass volumes and land use requirement in four key regional countries. Source: ONS for import biomass volumes, HMRC (2010a)

products are a small element in these economies due to the lack of the industrial infrastructure to undertake processing. Long distance exports from such regions are limited.

Some regions, or nation states within regions, are moving away from basic raw materials (including tropical beverages such as tea and coffee) and exporting higher value dairy, meat and horticultural products (FAO 2007). South America shows the beginnings of a transition from being a supplier of basic raw materials to providing more processed biomass materials.

21.5 Trends in UK Consumption of Biomass

Material Flow Analysis provides the basis for tracking the history of biomass use by the UK economy over a 40-year period. Combining data on biomass use with other data provides an insight into the role of biomass in the UK economy and the key drivers underpinning supply and demand.

21.5.1 Background

Over the last 200 years, the UK's economy has moved from a mixture of services, manufacturing and biomass-based activities (farming, forestry and fisheries) to an economy based on the service sector (**Figure 21.6**). The extent to which ecosystem services, such as the use of primary productivity, support a service-based economy are not always obvious, and the shift from an agricultural to a service-based economy can be interpreted as a process that reduces pressures on ecosystems (MA 2005a). This is based on the assumption that services are less demanding on ecosystem products. The decline in agricultural contributions to the economy is only relative, the contributions from the other sectors simply outgrowing biomass-based activities. Reporting of relevant statistics also understates this sector, recording many food-related activities under industrial classifications rather than agriculture.

Biomass remains an undervalued contributor to developed economies, one which is currently being re-evaluated (BTF 2005; Svetlana & Vinterbäck 2009). Furthermore, long-term analysis shows 'Domestic Biomass Consumption' (**Table 21.1**) in the UK to be virtually recession-proof (**Figure 21.7**) and related primarily to population size. This contrasts with mineral and fossil fuel consumption patterns which reflect

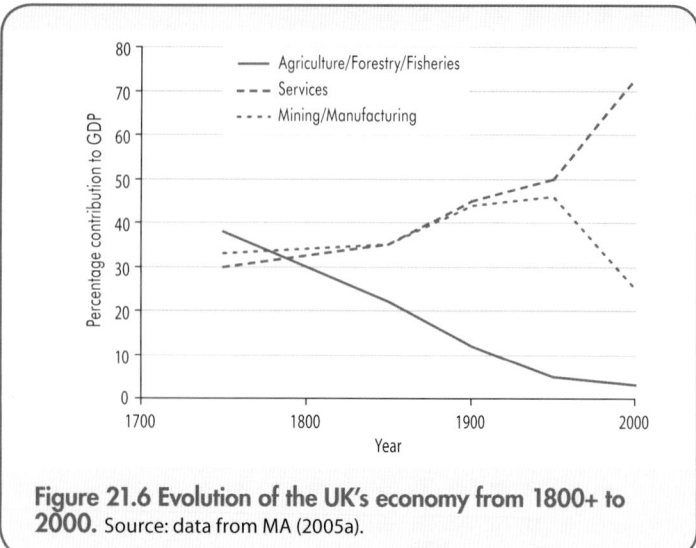

Figure 21.6 Evolution of the UK's economy from 1800+ to 2000. Source: data from MA (2005a).

major recessions that typically reduce mineral consumption (due to contraction in the construction sector) and fuel use. Trend analysis also shows that steady economic growth since 1990 has not been matched by an increase in consumption of domestic natural resources ('Domestic Material Consumption') but over the same period imports have risen. In the words of the Office for National Statistics this suggests that "*t*hat some of the environmental impacts associated with consumption are being transferred abroad" (ONS 2010). The growing import flows, including a steady increase in biomass imports, contrasts with the relatively steady domestic biomass production (**Figure 21.8**) making it clear that the UK is drawing increasingly on the primary production of overseas ecosystems.

21.5.2 Drivers of UK Biomass Demand

Between 1970 and 2002, when consumption peaked, the UK net consumption of biomass, allowing for domestic production, imports and exports, increased by 4.5%. Analysis of primary statistical data on material flows and trade allows demand and supply side drivers for UK biomass consumption to be determined.

21.5.2.1 Population growth

A growing and changing population increases overall consumption and modifies patterns of consumption through changing levels of affluence and degrees of urbanisation (MA 2005a). Increased population size inevitably draws on more, and a greater variety of, ecosystem services. Analysis of UK population growth and Domestic Biomass Consumption shows a strong relationship during the period 1970 to 2002. This relationship is reflected in both an absolute growth in national biomass consumption during this period and an increase in per capita consumption (**Figure 21.9**; **Figure 21.10**). This analysis shows that Domestic Biomass Consumption peaked at 137 million tonnes in 2002, before dropping to 131 million in 2008. Per capita consumption of biomass also increased up to 2002, peaking at 2.31 tonnes (t) per person.

The change in the population/consumption relationship which occurred early in the 21st Century (and was not related to any economic downturn) appears to represent

a fundamental shift in consumption pattern (**Figure 21.9**; **Figure 21.10**). Whilst consumption of food products, including animal feed, has continued to increase during the last decade, there has been a decline in timber imports which probably reflects increased reuse and recycling of available timber as a result of legislation designed to reduce material going to landfill.

21.5.2.2 Food demand

In 2008, the UK's agricultural system contributed approximately 92 million tonnes of biomass into the food chain, supplemented by 35 million tonnes of imported human and animal foods (ONS 2010). Allowing for food exports of 13 million tonnes, the net 'food chain' biomass utilised by the UK population was approximately 114 million tonnes, 87% of the Domestic Biomass Consumption. Biomass consumption in the UK is, therefore, currently driven primarily by food demand.

Annual surveys of the food purchasing and consumption patterns of the UK's population provide detailed statistics on diet (Defra 2008). Actual food consumption is recorded

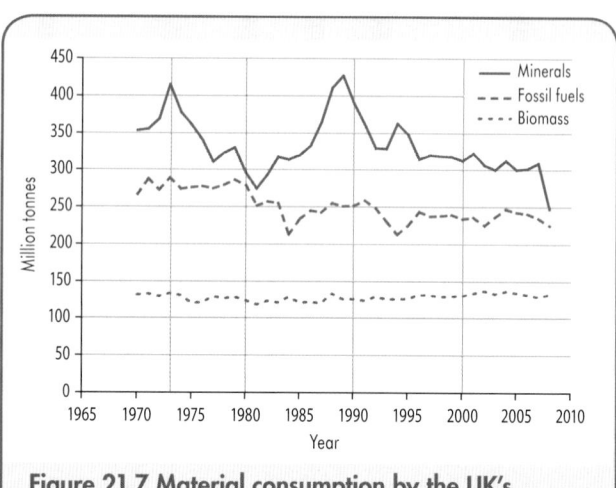

Figure 21.7 Material consumption by the UK's economy from 1970 to 2008. Source: data from ONS (2010b).

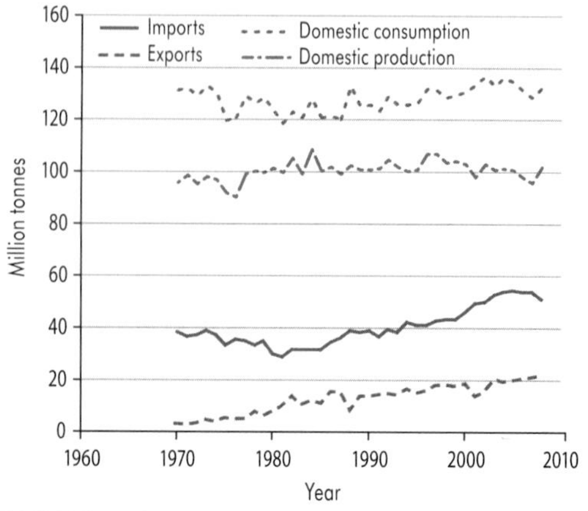

Figure 21.8 UK biomass flows from 1970 to 2008. Source: based on data from ONS (2010b).

UK National Ecosystem Assessment: Technical Report

as 0.36 t/person/yr, a total national consumption of 22.1 million tonnes. The relationship between food actually consumed and material entering the food chain to support this consumption indicates a ratio of at least 1:5—for every tonne of food consumed there is an underpinning biomass volume of at least 5 tonnes[1].

21.5.2.3 Forest products demand

Food chain biomass dominates the flow and use of biomass in the UK; most of the remainder (including 34% of imported biomass) is classified as forest products such as timber, paper and wood pulp. Current national demand for wood fibre is approximately 12 million t/yr (Confor 2010) representing 0.3 t/capita. Domestic production from UK forest systems has remained relatively constant at 8–9 million t/yr since 2000, but annual imports of timber have declined by over 4 million tonnes from a peak of 10 million t/yr in 2004 (HMRC 2010b).

21.5.2.4 Energy

The UK government has adopted a renewable energy policy which makes provision for substitution of fossil fuels by biomass for the supply of liquid transport fuels, heat energy and electricity. There is also renewed interest in the capacity of the UK's landscape to produce biomass (BTF 2005). Current biomass demand for energy purposes is focused primarily on supplying liquid biofuels as partial replacements for petrol and diesel (Section 21.4.2). In 2008, the bioenergy sector was responsible for only 1.5% of the country's import biomass demand through the use of liquid biofuels (RFA 2010). Demand for biofuels is growing, however (Booth *et al.* 2009; Confor 2010), and the increasing use of biomass for heat and power generation will ensure that this sector has a major impact on future UK biomass demand (Section 21.6).

21.5.3 Biomass Supply

The UK currently utilises approximately 150 million tonnes of biomass per year, of which 130 million tonnes represents actual domestic consumption, and the remaining balance is exported. The balance between domestic supply and imported materials has shifted slowly through time, with UK production (Domestic Biomass Extraction; **Table 21.1**) being relatively constant in the long-term but imports steadily increasing (**Figure 21.8**).

21.5.3.1 Domestic Supply

Since the late 1970s, UK domestic biomass production from agriculture, horticulture and forests has averaged 100 million t/yr, varying between 94–104 million tonnes (**Figure 21.8**). The additional contribution from domestic marine fisheries is less than 1 million t/yr and has been excluded from this analysis. Terrestrial biomass production in the UK comes from three sources: grasslands and agricultural harvests together provide approximately 92 million tonnes of biomass, complimented by 8 million tonnes of timber, primarily from

coniferous woodland. A slow decline in domestic biomass output began in 2000, reflecting low profitability in the agricultural sector, but this trend was sharply reversed in 2008 as commodity prices rose, indicating that the UK agricultural system has the capacity to increase output in response to market forces (JNCC 2011).

21.5.3.2 Biomass Imports

The relatively steady domestic biomass supply contrasts with growth in biomass imports from 1980 through to a peak in 2002 (**Figure 21.8**). Post 2002, a different pattern of consumption emerged, reflecting greater reuse of some biomass, particularly timber products (Section 21.5.2.1). Biomass imports stabilised at around 52–54 million tonnes for several years, but data for 2009 indicate a further drop in imports of biomass, down to 47.6 million tonnes. This reduction reflects a continuing decline in imports of forest products and a small (1.2 million tonnes) drop in food chain imports which follows consumer response to price increases in 2008.

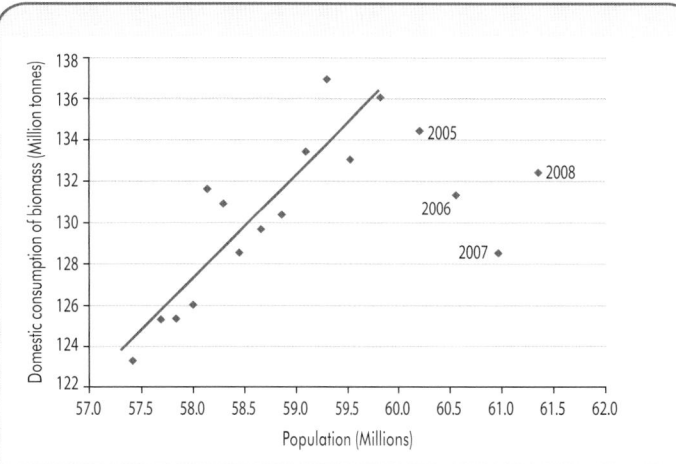

Figure 21.9 Relationship between domestic biomass consumption and UK population size. Source: data from ONS (2010a & b).

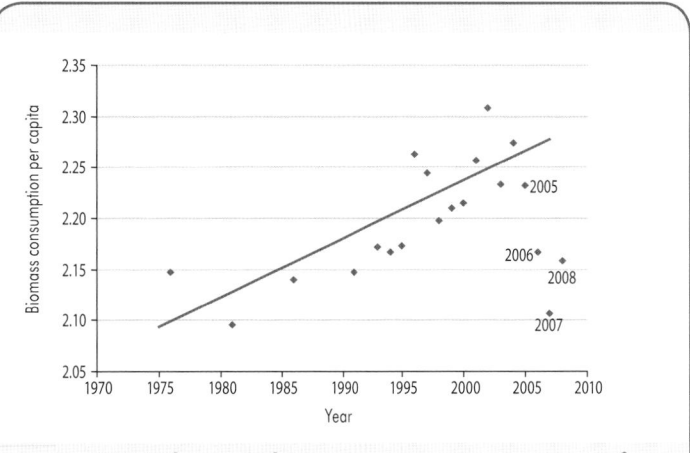

Figure 21.10 Change in biomass consumption per capita from 1975 to 2008. Source: data from ONS (2010a & b).

---

1 This ratio is based on biomass volumes recorded in government statistics (imported biomass statistics, domestic agricultural production data and food consumption patterns), but does not take into account the significant amount of unused waste biomass associated with domestic and overseas agricultural systems that support the UK food chain. Estimates of these hidden flows suggest that the true ratio is closer to 1:10.

21.6 Future Biomass Demand—Projecting to 2030

An analysis of the historical links between biomass consumption and population size in the UK, combined with an assessment of the future biomass demand likely to result from the new national renewable energy policies, permits assessments to be made of future biomass import demand. The implications of these projections for future UK biomass imports can be described in terms of material flows and overseas land use requirements.

21.6.1 Assumptions

The UK's historical use of biomass has been driven primarily by food consumption, with over 85% of the national biomass demand supporting the food chain. The use of biomass for other purposes, such as construction and bioenergy, has been less important in terms of biomass volumes, but new renewable energy policies will significantly increase the demand for biomass for heat and power generation. Biomass heat and power facilities with significant capacity, and currently under construction or in the planning stage, are principally located on the coast to ensure access to adequate biomass feedstocks. As these facilities come on-line over the next few years, the demand for imported biomass will significantly increase[2] (Confor 2010).

Numerical projections of potential biomass demand up to 2030 are possibly based on population growth forecasts and an assessment of the impact of energy policy. Population growth and the nature of the UK and global policy landscape beyond 2030 are less clear, and forecasts would be more subjective and less valuable in the context of this assessment. Furthermore, the projections presented here suggest that if appropriate biomass demand mitigation measures are implemented in the next decade, imported biomass demand could be stabilised by 2030.

The projection of imported biomass demand up to 2030, and associated overseas land use requirements (**Figure 21.11**; **Figure 21.12**), illustrates population-driven food chain demand augmented by the growing demand for biomass for energy, and is based on the following:

- Up to 2030, there will be a steady population growth, reaching 70.5 million by that date (ONS 2010).
- A *maximum* imported food chain demand up to 2030 has been estimated based on a relatively constant domestic production of approximately 95 million t/yr combined with a 'consumption as usual' model. This implies current patterns of biomass usage continue with a food chain biomass[3] demand of 1.86 t/capita/yr.
- A *minimum* imported food chain demand up to 2030 has been estimated based on a progressive increase in domestic production, achieving a 10% increase by

2030 equivalent to an additional 10 million t/yr. This is coupled with a progressive reduction in food chain waste based on a 50% waste reduction by 2030[4].

- A steady increase in biofuels consumption up to 2020, but a rapid implementation of broader bioenergy policies with an associated abrupt increase in demand for solid biomass (Confor 2010).

21.6.2 Implications: Material Flows

Future biomass demand in the UK, and the associated import requirements, will be determined by two principal factors: food and energy demand. Population growth and new renewable energy policies will increase absolute demand for biomass. This increasing import demand could be mitigated by successful implementation of waste reduction strategies and increased domestic biomass production, both of which would help reduce biomass imports.

The key conclusions in respect of these projections in terms of biomass imports are:

- Unmitigated food consumption will result in a linear increase in food chain biomass import demand in direct proportion to population growth, resulting in an increase from the current 35 million tonnes food chain import to almost 50 million tonnes in 2030 (**Figure 21.11**).
- Food chain biomass import demand can be mitigated by waste reduction (see WRAP 2010) and increased domestic production, potentially reducing total food chain demand by approximately 15 million tonnes by 2030. Such mitigation measures could effectively compensate for the underlying increased food demand arising from population growth.
- In the absence of mitigation, total imported biomass demand will rise rapidly in the next decade due to steady population increase and an abrupt increase in the use of biomass for energy production (**Figure 21.11**).

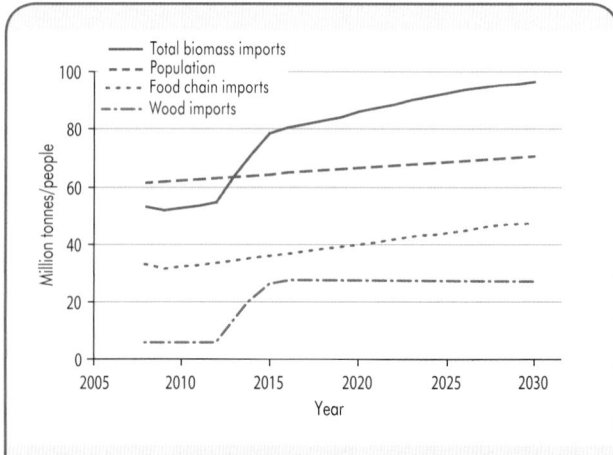

Figure 21.11 Possible UK biomass imports to 2030 based on current food consumption patterns and bioenergy policies. Source: Confor (2010) and ONS (2010a).

---

2 Two facilities planned for Tyneside and Teesside, and due to be commissioned in 2013, will use 4 million tonnes of imported woodchips a year. These facilities alone will increase the UK's imported biomass demand by almost 8%.
3 All forms of biomass supporting the human food chain, including direct input for human consumption and animal feed.
4 This total biomass saving is based on the 5:1 ratio of food consumption to underpinning biomass.

21.6.3 Implications: Overseas Land Use Impacts

Potential land requirements to supply future biomass imports are estimated on the basis of an average yield value for UK biomass imports in 2008[5].

The impacts of a growing future demand for imported biomass, in terms of overseas land use requirement, are likely to be as follows:

- If biomass import demand is unmitigated by increased domestic production and reduced waste, the overseas land use requirement could double from the current 14 million ha to 28 million ha by 2030. However, if appropriately mitigated, this land use requirement could be limited to approximately 20 million[6].

- Additional national biofuels demand (mostly imported) will create a land use requirement of at least 5 million ha by 2020 if current consumption patterns persist, most of which will be in South America (Argentina) through the supply of soya-based biodiesel. There may be an increase in imports from Sub-Saharan Africa and associated growth in footprint in that region. Sugarcane ethanol and palm oil diesel have higher energy yields per unit of land area, so the overseas land requirement could be mitigated by switching to greater use of these fuels[7].

- If current food consumption patterns continue, and domestic production remains unchanged, the import demand will grow significantly, creating an additional overseas land demand of approximately 5 million ha to support UK food consumption.

- Modified food consumption patterns, particularly a reduction in waste throughout the whole food chain, could mitigate the increased demand from a growing population, and the overseas land use impact could be held close to the existing level of 10 million ha.

- The UK's demand for biomass for energy alone (driven by government policy to generate power and heat from biomass) will potentially create an additional 7 million ha global pressure on overseas ecosystems by 2020.

These simplified projections illustrate the potential effects, in terms of biomass demand and overseas land use, which could arise from continued population growth and the implementation of new bioenergy policies in the UK. Given current domestic policies and global trends, it is highly likely that a combination of factors, including increased agricultural yields in the UK and overseas and food waste reduction, will exert a downward pressure on food import demand. Bioenergy policies will exert a contrary pressure, increasing demand. The elementary projections presented here illustrate that significant opportunities exist to reduce biomass imports and the associated overseas impacts that come with population growth. They also illustrate the policy drivers that will increase import demands and their associated impacts.

21.6.4 Projections of Overseas Biomass Demand in the Context of the UK NEA

The UK NEA recognises the role of direct and indirect drivers on ecosystem function. The implications of changing circumstances within UK society, and the changing roles of these drivers for national ecosystems, are examined through a set of UK NEA scenarios for the year 2060. As with the UK domestic landscape, the causal links between the evolution of UK society and the associated impacts on overseas ecosystems are complex. This chapter simplifies the analysis by reference to the key overseas ecosystem service upon which the UK's economy is dependent (the supply of biomass), the use of which is driven by food consumption and, increasingly, energy-related demand. At both strategic or details levels, the biomass material flow streams are easy to quantify and can be used to identify key direct drivers putting pressure on ecosystems.

As with the main UK NEA scenarios (Chapter 25), an understanding of current states and past trends has been used to develop simple plausible projections of biomass import demand and the associated overseas land use requirement (**Figure 21.11**; **Figure 21.12**). The land use projections show high and low case scenarios up to 2030. The higher case assumes no change in current consumption patterns or policies on bioenergy. It also assumes global sources can supply demand. The lower case assumes that import demand can be moderated through a combination of increased domestic biomass production and a reduction in biomass waste arising in the food chain. Given the numerical nature of these biomass and land use demand projections they have not been extended beyond 2030 because the population projections and policy developments that underpin them become increasingly uncertain beyond that date.

Each of the UK NEA scenarios has implications for the future balance to be struck between reliance on domestic

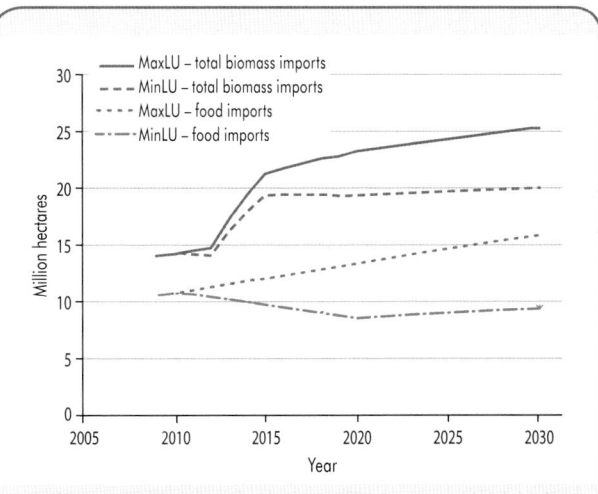

Figure 21.12 Projected overseas land use requirement to supply the UK with imported biomass under high and low import scenarios. MaxLU = maximum land use; MinLU = minimum land use.

---

5 Calculated as 3.7 t/ha average biomass yield across all biomass import categories based on a detailed analysis of UK biomass imports and country-specific yields.

6 Resulting in a balance between the use of UK and overseas land area to support the UK economy: 20 million ha at home and 20 million ha overseas.

7 Data available in late 2010 on the use of biofuels in the UK suggests that this is already happening with increased national use of bioethanol as a fossil fuel substitute.

biomass production and imports. The six UK NEA scenarios describe the end state of each storyline rather than a timeline for each. The biomass import projections in this section do not extend beyond 2030. However, it can be argued that, given current rates of change in biomass use and consumption patterns, policy initiatives adopted to manage biomass imports over the next two decades will effectively determine domestic and global landscapes in later years.

The high case biomass impact trajectory presented here could result from either of the *'Green and Pleasant Land'* or *'World Market'* UK NEA scenarios. The former involves a preservationist attitude to the UK's own landscape, meeting increased demand for food and energy biomass primarily from overseas sources. The *World Market* scenario, although not seeking to protect the UK's landscape to the same extent, allows free markets to determine the source of the UK's biomass with little regard for environmental issues. Import demand grows considerably under this scenario.

The low case impact trajectory could reflect a conscious decision by the UK to be more self-reliant, or be imposed by a need to fall back on our own resources through lack of access to world markets for political or technical reasons. The former, free choice, situation is embodied in the *'Local Stewardship'* UK NEA scenario, where self-sufficiency is a key concept and both exports and imports are minimised. The *'National Security'* scenario describes a situation where global food supplies may be limited through climate change or other factors such as the breakdown of free trade with food exporters limiting outward flows or supplying preferred clients through unilateral agreements that exclude the UK. Under this scenario biomass imports are limited by supply.

Underpinning all of the UK NEA scenarios, and the simple projections of this chapter, is the key question of population growth within the UK over the coming decades. The six UK NEA scenarios are built around population storyline attributes involving a UK population that varies from 65 million (slightly more than today) to 75 million by 2030. The direct link between biomass consumption through the food chain and population size makes this driver critical.

21.7 UK Dependence on Overseas Ecosystems: a Monitoring, Evaluation and Policy Framework

Policy on sustainable consumption and production in the UK, as outlined in Securing the Future (HMSO 2005), identifies the need for reliable indicators of the impact of the UK economy on other countries, including the measurement of resource use. This strategy advocates the use of indicators that are:

- comparable with those used internationally and other national accounts;

- capable of reporting on national, EU and global trends;
- and capable of measuring the overseas impact of UK material consumption.

The strategy stresses that domestic policies to monitor and modify material consumption should be complemented by following through on our international commitments to spread good practice and maintain political pressure for change. The use of a biomass material flow framework provides the basis for reporting on UK, EU and global trends in biomass use, measurement of impacts on overseas ecosystems, and the formulation of domestic and international policy initiatives.

21.7.1 Biomass Material Flow Analysis as a Framework for Measuring and Reporting on National, EU and Global Trends

The biomass flow framework allows the UK's use of specific biomass commodities from individual eco-political regions (countries, biomes) to be quantified and monitored in time and space. Monitoring can focus on strategic analysis of major commodity groups or focus on individual commodities, total global flows or individual regions. Biomass flow analysis can highlight key commodities coming out of individual eco-political regions and link directly to socioeconomic drivers within the UK's economy such as population growth, food consumption patterns and bioenergy policies.

Key variables for measuring and reporting on biomass consumption by the UK's economy are summarised in **Table 21.1** and **Figure 21.13**. The important characteristics of these indicators are that they:

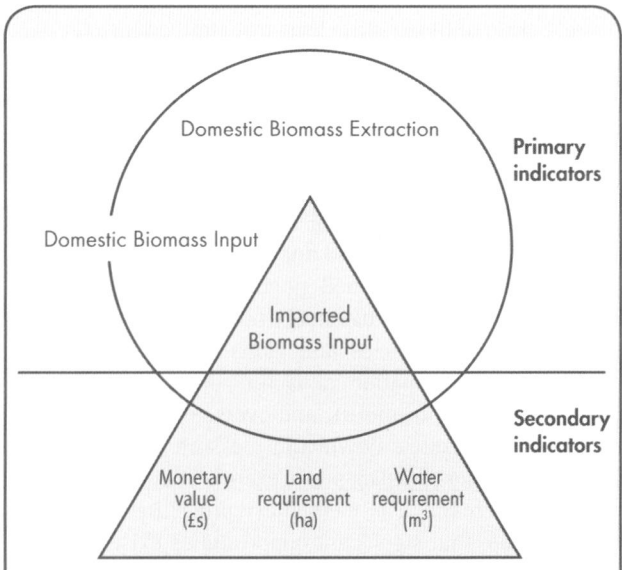

Figure 21.13 Total biomass available to the UK economy 'Domestic Biomass Input') comprises domestic extraction plus imports. These material flows are directly recorded (as mass) and provide a set of Primary Indicators of UK biomass supply. Secondary Indicators, derived from mass flow data, can be generated including the monetary value of biomass flows and the land or water required for biomass production.

- are based on published data that have been gathered consistently over long time periods;
- are easily understood by policy makers;
- are themselves statistical data and can be related to other economic and demographic statistics, notably GDP and population statistics;
- provide information about the changes in biomass imports in time and space.

The UK is one of many countries placing demands on overseas ecosystems. The MFA approach, based on freely available data gathered according to international standards, allows international biomass flows to be quantified, and the demand created by the UK's consumption to be placed in context. For example, the UK's import of South American soya products in 2008 is recorded as approximately 3 million tonnes (almost 6% of all biomass imports) with an estimated land use impact of 1.7 million ha. This is in the context of a total EU soya-based land use impact in the region of 12 million ha (Profundo 2010).

Monitoring the flow of biomass out of specific ecosystems and into the UK and other economies provides a direct measure of our dependencies (**Figure 21.14**) on these systems and the means to report on national, EU and global trends. The data available data makes clear which countries and which ecosystems we are dependent upon.

21.7.2 Biomass Material Flow Analysis as a Framework for Measuring the Overseas Impact of UK Material Consumption

Primary indicators of biomass use can be combined with other information to derive a measure of the overseas impacts of this aspect of our material consumption. In the case of agricultural and managed forest systems, the pressure we are applying to overseas ecosystems can be measured in terms of water demand and land required to produce the biomass that is imported into the UK. For 'harvested' commodities, such as fish and hardwoods, this analysis is not applicable, and the ecosystem pressures can only be expressed in terms of volume (mass) of biomass being extracted from individual eco-political areas.

Quantitative analysis of the land and water required to sustain imported biomass supply provides the context for identification and assessment of specific environmental pressures which our economy may be causing overseas (**Figure 21.14**). Knowledge of the specific characteristics of biomass streams ('crop type') permits specific associated environmental pressures to be identified.

In general terms these pressures are:
- *agricultural/forestry frontier expansion or agricultural intensification* to meet increasing demand for biomass; land use requirement estimates indicate where such pressures may be increased through UK biomass imports.

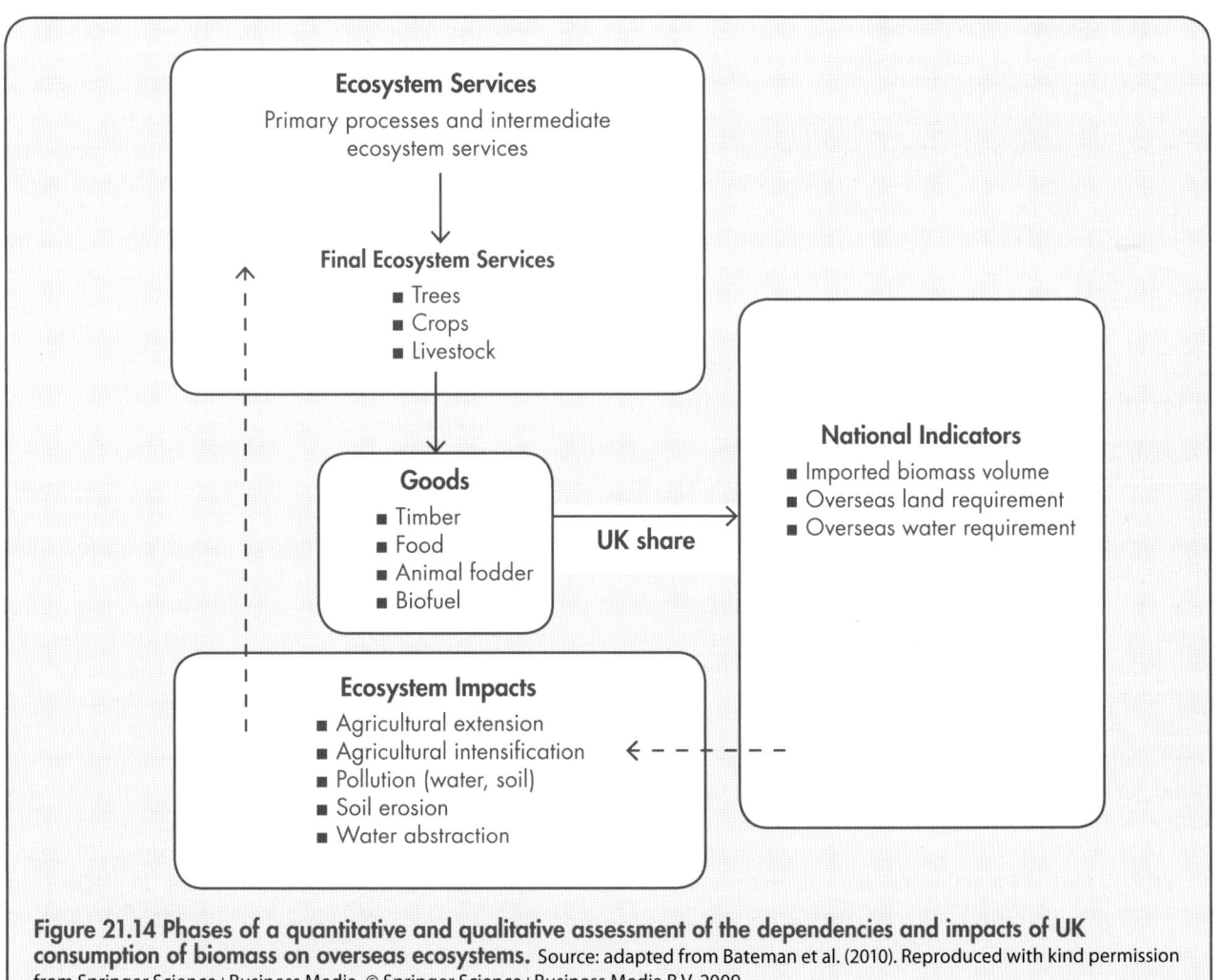

Figure 21.14 Phases of a quantitative and qualitative assessment of the dependencies and impacts of UK consumption of biomass on overseas ecosystems. Source: adapted from Bateman et al. (2010). Reproduced with kind permission from Springer Science+Business Media. © Springer Science+Business Media B.V. 2009.

- *water abstraction*—UK overseas water use due to biomass production can be quantified for agricultural commodities and related to existing, or predicted, water stress in source ecosystems with the potential to impact on wetlands, river systems, etc.
- *pollution*—arising from use of agrichemicals and potentially affecting soil and water.
- *soil degradation*—through erosion or impairment of function (pollution, reduction in organic matter, soil biodiversity, etc.).
- *use of invasive alien species*—crop species for food, bioenergy or wood fibre potentially displacing indigenous populations.

The biomass analysis framework discussed here allows the UK (or any other economic unit) to undertake two important actions. Firstly, to identify and quantify its overseas biomass dependencies, including the spatial determination of where material is being sourced from. Secondly, to determine the nature of potential ecosystem impacts that may arise from use of imported biomass imports. The framework allows us to determine what we are importing, where it comes from and how impacts may be occur. By integrating material flow data with other socioeconomic information, we can also understand why the demand is occurring.

The biomass framework provides the basis for a three-stage process for sustainability analysis of UK use of overseas ecosystems, specifically:

- Primary analysis of biomass material flows into the UK to monitor use and trends;
- Secondary analysis to derive a measure of overseas ecosystem pressures in terms of land and water use;
- Tertiary sustainability analysis focusing on key global pressure points, key commodities and the direct impacts recognised through the framework to assess the resilience of the ecosystems supplying the UK with biomass.

21.7.3 Biomass Material Flow Analysis as a Framework for Policy Implementation

Through its ability to enable monitoring of biomass flows through the economy, and focus sustainability analysis in critical areas, this framework provides a basis for developing forward looking policies. These policies should be designed to minimise our overseas impacts and maximise biomass security, whilst ensuring the long-term sustainable use of the ecosystems upon which the country depends. This can include current dependencies and those which MFA projections suggest may develop in the future.

The analysis presented here suggests that there are a small number of current pressure points where detailed sustainability analysis of particular commodity production should be carried out. Approximately 60% of the overseas land requirement to supply imported biomass falls within the UK's EU partners and the adjacent European countries. As a member of the EU, the UK participates in policy

development to protect the European landscape and, therefore, is already engaged in mitigating the impacts of its biomass imports from these areas. It can be argued that the impact occurring in North America (less than 10% of the total) is either effectively managed or beyond the influence of UK policies. This leaves the three tropical regions (South America, Sub-Saharan Africa and Oceania) which provide almost 30% of the UK's overseas land requirement and where significant changes are occurring to natural environments; it is here that the UK should actively engage in mitigating its impacts. In terms of biomes outside the EU, Argentinean Temperate Grasslands and Brazilian and Asian Tropical Broadleafed Forests are the key ecological units supplying food and biofuels to the UK (**Table 21.2**; **Table 21.3**) and merit immediate attention.

Looking forward, potential increases in imports of palm oil from Ecuador and Colombia into the UK will affect tropical forests in these areas. Additional pressure is likely to be exerted on Brazil and Argentina through increased food, animal feed and biofuels imports, including biodiesel from soya and ethanol from sugarcane. Increased biomass for bioenergy use is expected to be met from Baltic and South American forest sources. As a global supplier of biomass, Sub-Saharan Africa remains a giant-in-waiting. As well as helping to monitor impacts on existing global pressure points, biomass flow analysis, including the routine use of indicators, can also act as an early warning system, showing where new pressure points are emerging.

Geographical identification of key areas now providing biomass to the UK's economy, or likely to supply it in the future, provides the basis for targeted international policies designed to protect the long-term functioning of the ecosystems vital to the UK's national interest. Technical assistance, financial aid and political dialogue are all options to achieve this objective. These could be executed through bilateral actions between the UK and its key overseas suppliers and dialogues with other significant global consumers for traded biomass. Increasing domestic biomass production through appropriate policies can also be used to moderate overseas demand.

These 'supply side' policies to influence the means of biomass production can be complemented by domestic 'demand side' policies which influence UK consumption. Biomass flow analysis suggests that more effective national use of biomass, particularly through reducing waste within the food chain, can significantly affect biomass demand, including imports[8]. Domestic ecological footprinting of the UK's material consumption shows that whilst "the food supply chain is complex, food footprints can be reduced and success will have a major impact" (Dawkins *et al.* 2008). The ecological footprint of food consumption in the UK has been reviewed by Frey and Barnett (2007) and in a global context by the MA (MA 2005b). New analysis for this chapter of the UK NEA demonstrates the potential benefits of reducing food waste, in particular the reduction in import demand and attendant reduction in overseas ecosystem impacts. In addition to reducing biomass demand throughout the food chain and the

---

8 Food waste reduction implies that food which would have been wasted would not be purchased, reducing total demand.

land required to produce this biomass, significant reductions in energy use and greenhouse gas emissions would result.

Monitoring material flows of biomass out of a particular ecological unit (at Realm, Biome or Ecosystem scale) says nothing, in itself, about the capacity of a system to continue to supply these materials into the future. This will depend upon the resilience of the systems concerned, and their ability to withstand the stresses imposed and to continue to provide the services we need from them. We need to identify which of the systems that we are dependent on are resilient, and which are not. Judgements also need to be made in the context of safe minimum standards where conventional economic decisions prevail (i.e to continue to exploit) until a threshold value/tipping point is identified (Turner 2007). Beyond this point, the onus shifts to a presumption of protection. We need to know which ecosystems we depend upon are close to their tipping points and why.

This chapter focuses on the UK as the consuming entity but MFA can also be undertaken at the regional level (WWF 2006), highlighting regional differences in per capita consumption of food and fuel. The dependence of individual regional economies, or individual citizens, on overseas biomass production can be estimated and used for regional sustainability analysis and policy development. For example, based on per capita consumption of imported biomass, Scotland currently depends upon approximately 4.5 million tonnes of imported biomass per year, or 1.2 million ha of overseas land. Material flow analysis can follow policy initiatives down to the appropriate regional level at which actions may be most effective.

The value of biomass to the UK and global economy is currently being re-evaluated (BTF 2005; Booth *et al.* 2009; Openshaw. 2010). The recognition that biomass for energy production is relevant to developed economies and is not just a third world resource is leading to ambitious renewable energy strategies in the developed world (Svetlana & Vinterbäck 2009). These strategies will dramatically increase demand for biomass use in the production of transport fuels, heat and electricity. Global demand for food is increasing, reflecting population growth and increased global incomes. Continued national population growth will inevitably increase demand for human food and animal feed within the UK. As a result of the food and bioenergy drivers, biomass will take a more prominent role in the UK's economy in the future. The UK's obvious dependence on the primary productivity of overseas ecosystems makes it imperative that we take steps to ensure the long-term productivity of these systems. Routine monitoring and analysis of imports flows, and the formulation of policies to ensure long-term productivity, are, therefore, in the national interest.

References

Bateman, I., Mace, G., Fezzi, C., Atkinson, G. & Turner, K. (2010) Economic Analysis for Ecosystem Service Assessments. *Environmental and Resource Economics.* DOI 10.1007/s10640-010-9418-x.

Booth, E., Walker, R., Bell, J., McCracken, D., Curry, J., Knight, B., Smith, J., Gottschalk, P. & Biddle, A. (2009) An assessment of the potential impact on UK agriculture and the environment of meeting renewable feedstock demands. National Non-Food Crops Centre. Sac Consulting, UK.

BTF (Biomass Task Force) (2005) Report to Government. [online] Available at: <http://www.defra.gov.uk/foodfarm/growing/crops/industrial/energy/biomass-taskforce/pdf/btf-finalreport.pdf> [Accessed 01.02.11].

Confor (Confederation of Forest Industries) (2010) Wood fibre availability and demand in Britain 2007 to 2025. [online] Available at: <http://www.confor.org.uk/Upload/Documents/37_WoodFibreAvailabilityDemandReportfinal.pdf> [Accessed 01.02.11].

Dawkins, E., Paul, A., Barrett, J. Minx, J. and Scott, K. (2008) Wales' Ecological Footprint—Scenarios to 2020. Stockholm Environment Institute, Sweden. [online] Available at: <http://wales.gov.uk/topics/sustainabledevelopment/publications/ecofootprint/?lang=en> [Accessed 19.01.11].

Defra (Department of Food and Rural Affairs) (2006) Food security and the UK. An evidence and analysis paper. Food Chain Analysis Group, Defra, London.

Defra (Department of Food and Rural Affairs) (2008) Family Food in 2007. National Statistics, Defra. Crown, London.

Defra (Department of Food and Rural Affairs) (2009) UK Food security assessment: our approach. Defra, London.

Frey, S. & Barnett, J. (2007) Our health, our environment. The Ecological Footprint of what we eat. International Ecological Footprint Conference, Cardiff.

FAO (Food and Agriculture Organization) (2007) The State of food and agriculture. Food and Agriculture Organization of the United Nations, Rome.

Giljum, G. (2009) How to measure Europe's resource use. Sustainable Europe Research Institute, Austria.

HMRC (Her Majesty's Revenue & Customs) (2010a) UK Regional Statistics, UK Trade Information. [online] Available at: <https://www.uktradeinfo.com> [Accessed 19.01.11].

HMRC (Her Majesty's Revenue & Customs) (2010b) Overseas Trade Statistics (OTS) Data, UK Trade Information. [online] Available at: <https://www.uktradeinfo.com/index.cfm?task=data> [Accessed 19.01.11].

HMSO (Her Majesty's Stationery Office) (2005) Securing the Future: delivering UK sustainable development strategy, Command Paper 6467. Parlimentary Publications.

Hoekstra, A.Y. & Chapgain, A.S. (2008) Globalisation of water. Sharing the Planet's freshwater resources. Blackwell Publishing, Oxford.

JNCC (Joint Nature Conservation Committee) (2009) The global biodiversity footprint of UK biofuels consumption. [online] Available at: <http://www.jncc.gov.uk/pdf/Biofuelsfootprint%20(2).pdf> [Accessed 01.02.11].

JNCC (Joint Nature Conservation Committee) (2011) The global land use impact of the United Kingdom's biomass consumption. [online] Available at:<http://www.jncc.gov.uk/page-4353> [Accessed 02.02.11].

MA (Millennium Ecosystem Assessment) (2005a) Ecosystems and Human Well-being: Biodiversity Synthesis. World Resources Institute, Island Press, Washington, D.C.

MA (Millennium Ecosystem Assessment) (2005b) Global Assessment Reports: Volume 1: Current State & Trends. Chapter 8: Food. Island Press, Washington D.C.

Olson, D.M., Dinerstein, E., Wikramanayake, E.D., Burgess, N.D., Powell, G.V.N., Underwood, E.C., D'amico, J.A., Itoua, I., Strand, H.E., Lamoreux, J.F., Wettengel, W.W., Hedao, P., Kassem, K.R. (2004). Terrestrial Ecoregions of the World: a new map of life on earth. *BioScience*. **51**: 933–938. Subsequently modified and extended at UNEP-WCMC (2011).

ONS (Office for National Statistics) (2005) UK Material flow review. Office for National Statistics, London.

ONS (Office for National Statistics) (2010a) 2008-based National Population Projections. Office for National Statistics, Newport.

ONS (Office for National Statistics) (2010b) Environmental Accounts 2010. Office for National Statistics, Newport.

Openshaw, K. (2010) Can biomass power development? International Institute for Environment and Development, London.

RFA (Renewable Fuels Agency) (2009) Renewable Fuels Agency 2008/09 Annual Report to Parliament on the Renewable Transport Fuel Obligation. The Stationary Office, London.

RFA (Renewable Fuels Agency) (2010) RFA Quarterly Report 9: 15 April 2010–14 July 2010.

Svetlana, L. & Vinterbäck, J. (2009). Global potential of sustainable biomass for energy. Report 013. SLU, Swedish University of Agricultural Sciences Department of Energy and Technology, Sweden. [online] Available at: <http://www.worldbioenergy.org/system/files/file/WBA_PP-1_100122final10.pdf> [Accessed 02.02.11].

Turner, K. (2007) A Pluralistic Approach to Ecosystem Services Evaluation. CSERGE Working Paper EDM 10–07. Economic and Social Research Council, Norwich.

Van Gelder, J.W., Kammeraat K & Kroes, H (2008) Soy consumption for feed and fuel in the European Union. Profundo, Netherlands.

WRAP (Waste and Resource Action Programme) (2010) Waste arisings in the supply of food and drink to households in the UK. Oakdene Hollins Research and Consulting.

WWF (2006) Counting consumption. CO_2 emissions, material flows and Ecological Footprint of the UK by region and devolved country. WWF-UK, Surrey.

WWF (2008) UK Water Footprint: the impact of the UK's food and fibre consumption on global water resources. WWF-UK, Surrey. [online] Available at: <http://assets.panda.org/downloads/wwf_uk_footprint.pdf> [Accessed 02.02.11].

WWF (2010) Living Planet Report 2010 Biodiversity, biocapacity and development. WWF, Switzerland.

Appendix 21.1 Approach Used to Assign Certainty Terms to Chapter Key Findings

This chapter began with a set of Key Findings. Adopting the approach and terminology used by the Intergovernmental Panel on Climate Change (IPCC) and the Millennium Assessment (MA), these Key Findings also include an indication of the level of scientific certainty. The 'uncertainty approach' of the UK NEA consists of a set of qualitative uncertainty terms derived from a 4-box model and complemented, where possible, with a likelihood scale (see below). Estimates of certainty are derived from the collective judgement of authors, observational evidence, modelling results and/or theory examined for this assessment.

Throughout the Key Findings presented at the start of this chapter, superscript numbers and letters indicate the estimated level of certainty for a particular key finding:

1. *Well established:* high agreement based on significant evidence
2. *Established but incomplete evidence:* high agreement based on limited evidence
3. *Competing explanations:* low agreement, albeit with significant evidence
4. *Speculative:* low agreement based on limited evidence

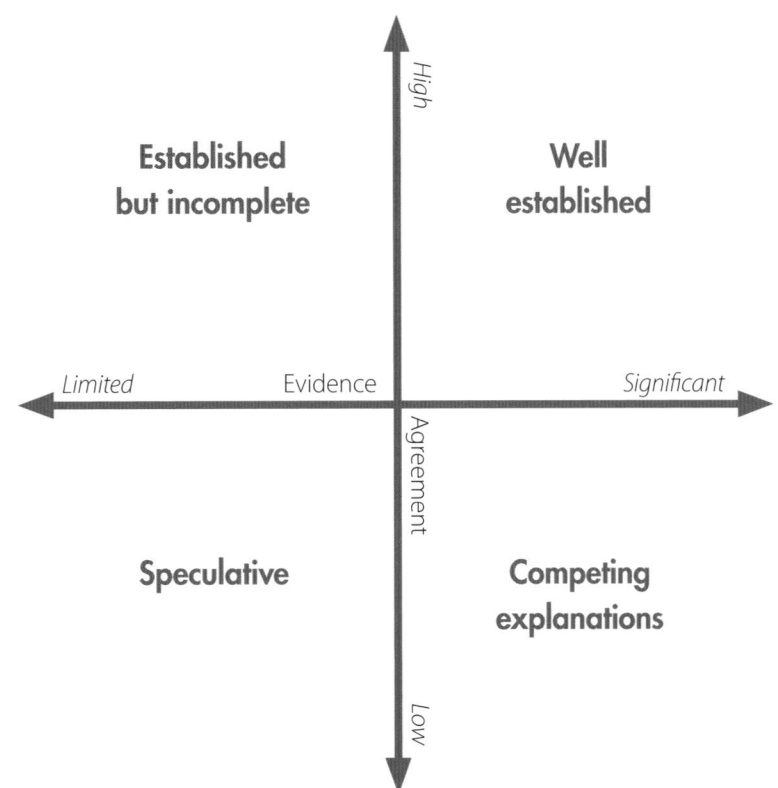

a. *Virtually certain:* >99% probability of occurrence
b. *Very likely:* >90% probability
c. *Likely:* >66% probability
d. *About as likely as not:* >33–66% probability
e. *Unlikely:* <33% probability
f. *Very unlikely:* <10% probability
g. *Exceptionally unlikely:* <1% probability

Certainty terms 1 to 4 constitute the 4-box model, while *a* to *g* constitute the likelihood scale.

Chapter 22:
Economic Values from Ecosystems

Coordinating Lead Author: Ian J. Bateman
Lead Authors: David Abson, Nicola Beaumont, Amii Darnell, Carlo Fezzi, Nick Hanley, Andreas Kontoleon, David Maddison, Paul Morling, Joe Morris, Susana Mourato, Unai Pascual, Grischa Perino, Antara Sen, Dugald Tinch, Kerry Turner and Gregory Valatin
Contributing Authors: Barnaby Andrews, Viviana Asara, Tom Askew, Uzma Aslam, Giles Atkinson, Nesha Beharry-Borg, Katherine Bolt, Matt Cole, Murray Collins, Emma Comerford, Emma Coombes, Andrew Crowe, Steve Dugdale, Helen Dunn, Jo Foden, Steve Gibbons, Roy Haines-Young, Caroline Hattam, Mark Hulme, Mallika Ishwaran, Andrew Lovett, Tiziana Luisetti, George MacKerron, Stephen Mangi, Dominic Moran, Paul Munday, James Paterson, Guilherme Resende, Gavin Siriwardena, Jim Skea, Daan van Soest and Mette Termansen
Economic Advisory Panel: Sir Partha Dasgupta, Brendan Fisher, Karl-Göran Mäler, Steve Polasky and Kerry Turner

Key Findings

The contribution that ecosystem services make to the national economy in terms of a sustained flow of income is very substantial. The continued maintenance of this natural capital stock is critically important for the future prospects of a thriving 'green' economy. The sustainable development goal will not be achievable without a more efficient and effective management of ecosystems encompassing economic appraisal principles and practice.

It is clear that a body of theoretically sound methodologies now exists for the valuation of most (if not all) ecosystem service flows (i.e. the flow of values which ecosystems deliver to individuals). This methodology is consistent with the Conceptual Framework of the UK National Ecosystem Assessment (Chapter 2) and has been clarified in supporting papers (see Bateman *et al.* 2011a). This methodology extends, but is consistent with, standard decision analysis principles set down by HM Treasury and is expected to be highly compatible with the aims and objectives of the forthcoming Environment White Paper.

In line with standard economic analysis, the methodology that has been developed rejects attempts to estimate the total value of ecosystem services. Many of these services are essential to continued human existence and total values are therefore underestimates of infinity. However, real world decisions typically involve incremental changes and require choices between options. Our economic analysis therefore examines the value of observed trends and feasible, policy-relevant changes. It also adopts a precautionary approach, given the uncertainties shrouding the necessary and sufficient conditions for continued 'healthy', functioning ecosystems under the pressures of environmental change.

Our economic analysis provides a bridge from the ecosystem habitat focus of the natural science elements of the UK National Ecosystem Assessment (UK NEA) to consideration of the goods and services those ecosystems provide and the values these yield to individuals. The analysis has highlighted the considerable value provided by a broad range of ecosystem service flows (see Table 22.27 for a summary). These include: the contribution of ecosystem services to the production of both terrestrial and marine foods; the direct and indirect use value of biodiversity in underpinning and delivering ecosystem services; timber production; carbon sequestration, storage and greenhouse gas (GHG) flux; water quality and quantity; inland and coastal flood protection; pollution remediation; energy and raw materials; employment; sporting and game; landscape values and the amenity value of nature; the amenity value of the climate; the amenity value of urban greenspace; environmental education and knowledge; the health effects of the environment; and recreation and tourism. Collectively, this service flow makes a vital contribution to the wealth and well-being of the UK. While information gaps mean that we cannot estimate values for all services, those values that are reported are substantial and underline the vital role which the natural environment plays in supporting current human wealth creation and well-being and in offering the foundations for a sustainable future economy.

The detailed ecosystem service valuations presented in the main body of this chapter are broadly categorised into those that assess past trends and those that consider likely future scenarios. Considering the first category, there has been relatively little work which has adjusted for the value of manufactured and human capital in ecosystem service-related output values. This means that many of the estimates in this category are liable to overstate the contribution of ecosystem services to resultant values. Nevertheless, ecosystem inputs are often vital to the production of such goods and accepting this caveat, we highlight the following examples for the UK:

- The value of UK fish landings is about £600 million per annum (p.a.), while that of aquaculture (fish and shellfish farming) is around £350 million p.a..
- Biodiversity pollination services are estimated at £430 million p.a.
- Willingness to pay (WTP) estimates of the non-use (existence) value of terrestrial biodiversity range from £540 million to £1,262 million p.a. and for marine biodiversity, estimates of around £1,700 million p.a. have been reported. However, as noted below, there is debate regarding such estimates. Legacy values are around £90 million p.a.
- Timber values are just under £100 million p.a.
- The water quality benefits of inland wetlands may be as high as £1,500 million p.a., while planned river quality improvements may generate values up to £1,100 million p.a. However, climate change-induced losses of water availability are valued at £350 million to £490 million p.a..
- The costs associated with changing agricultural land use to reduce nutrient loadings into rivers are substantially smaller than the benefits which consequent reductions in diffuse water pollution would bring (however, the former costs are concentrated within rural communities, while benefits are distributed across a mainly urban society).
- The amenity value of all wetland types, including coastal, is around £1.3 billion p.a.
- Renewable fuels currently meet 3% of UK energy demand and 7% of electricity generation.
- Marine-based biotic raw materials are worth £95 million p.a.
- The UK aggregates industry is worth £4,800 million p.a., of which more than £100 million comes from the marine environment.

- The environment generates substantial **educational benefits** each year.
- The total value of **net carbon sequestered** currently by UK woodlands is estimated at £680 million p.a.
- There are also **substantial costs** arising from activities which deplete ecosystem services. For example, considering the previous result regarding carbon sequestration by woodlands, this is completely negated by **GHG emissions** from UK agriculture, which are currently around £4,300 million p.a. Similarly, the average annual **cost of flooding** is about £1,400 million, although this can rise as high as £3,200 million in extreme years. These costs need to be added to WTP to avoid intangible costs of £120 million p.a.

Moving to consider valuations based upon future trends and scenarios, this draws upon new work undertaken for the UK NEA, most of which isolates the role of changes in ecosystem –and wider environmental – services in the estimation of values. Highlights here include the following:

- **Changes in climate services are likely to have marked impacts upon agricultural land use,** although the value implications of these changes will vary across the country. Forecast increases in temperature and shifts in rainfall patterns may well improve the agricultural potential of currently challenging upland areas, resulting in increases in incomes in much of upland England, Northern Ireland, Scotland and Wales. Impacts upon lowland areas, including most of southern England, depend crucially upon changes in technology such that under current forecasts, incomes are liable to decline in these areas. However, it is likely that this will stimulate technological change which would alter predictions for these areas.
- The **increase in agricultural productivity** in upland Britain is **likely to stimulate a corresponding rise in agricultural carbon emissions** in those areas. Full economic costing of these emissions would cancel out a substantial portion of the benefits of higher agricultural outputs.
- Changes in land use will have a **significant impact upon biodiversity**. Indicators such as the number of farmland bird species suggest that at best, agricultural land use changes will have a neutral effect, while at worst, there is the likelihood of local extinctions.
- **Ecosystem services have a major impact upon outdoor recreation values.** There are over 3,000 million recreational visits p.a. generating a social value in excess of £10,000 million p.a. (see details in Chapter 26). The recreational value of ecosystems varies not only with their type but, more significantly, with their location. Economic valuation shows that a modestly sized, physically identical, nature recreation site can generate values of between £1,000 and £65,000 p.a., depending purely upon location.
- **Urban greenspace amenity values** range from losses of £1,900 million p.a. to gains of £2,300 million p.a., depending on the policy context.
- Again, there are also substantial costs arising from activities which deplete ecosystem services. For example, **climate change is likely to increase the frequency and intensity of flooding events,** with annual costs rising to more than £20,000 million (in 2010 prices) by 2060 under extreme scenarios.

We conclude our key messages with two caveats. First, while we report values for a wide array of ecosystem services, there are limits to the ability of economics to capture all values associated with ecosystem services. In particular, this applies to certain shared social values, especially those which are not evident in observable behaviour. An example of this might be **the spiritual value of the environment**, especially where this is linked solely to the knowledge of pristine or intact environments (this issue is addressed more fully in Chapter 16). Related to this, while we have included estimates of the use-related values of biodiversity, **there is debate regarding our ability to derive robust monetary estimates of the non-use (existence) value of biodiversity.** Currently these can only be estimated using stated preference methods. While such methods fit conventional economic principles for non-market environmental goods for which individuals hold well-formed economic preferences, commentators are not in agreement as to whether preferences for the non-use (existence) value of biodiversity conform to these requirements. While **some argue that stated preference valuation methods are applicable, and can include collective value estimations via group-based elicitation methods, others reject this and instead argue for natural science determined strategies for safeguarding biodiversity** (possibly including biodiversity offsets), **with economic assessments being confined to cost-effectiveness analysis of competing strategies.**

Our second caveat recognises that **a vital area for future investigation is the incorporation of stocks of natural resources into economic analyses. This is essential in order to ensure that ongoing and future flows of ecosystem service values are sustainable.** While theoretical approaches to the economic valuation of stocks are established (Bateman *et al.* 2011a), there is a significant dearth of information on the size of stocks and, equally importantly, how they may deplete as economic activity changes. The potential for thresholds beyond which stocks might more rapidly deplete, or even collapse, needs to be recognised along with the potential for imperfect restoration or irreversible loss. **Addressing this problem requires the establishment of an integrated decision analysis and support community, uniting different disciplines of the natural sciences with economists, risk analysts and other social scientists.** Although initial moves to establish such a community are underway (see www.valuing-nature.net/), it remains in its infancy and further development of such intellectual capital is a clear requirement if the UK is to move towards ensuring efficient, sustainable and equitable management of the natural environment.

22.1 Introduction

In keeping with the UK National Ecosystem Assessment (UK NEA) Conceptual Framework set out in Chapter 2, in this chapter we move from consideration of ecosystem types and the services they provide, to focus instead upon the contribution which these services make to human well-being. Specifically, this chapter presents an economic assessment of this contribution following the methodology set out for the UK NEA in Bateman *et al.* (2011a), which in turn rests upon a wealth of prior literature covering the application of economic analysis to ecosystem assessments. Given the diverse audience addressed by the UK NEA, we open this chapter with an overview of that methodology, the key issues which it addresses, and its limitations. The remainder of the chapter presents a summary of the published literature focused on the economic analyses of ecosystem service values, combined with new analyses which have been prepared partly or wholly for the UK NEA initiative. The new material covers the following topics: the value of environmental legacy giving (Section 22.3.3.2); a meta-analysis[1] of wetland ecosystem values (Section 22.3.3.1, 22.3.6 and 22.3.8); the health effects of broadly defined UK habitats (Section 22.3.16); the CSERGE (Centre for Global and Economic Research on the Global Environment) land use change model (Section 22.3.17.2, 22.3.17.3 and 22.3.17.4); carbon storage modelling for the UK (Section 22.3.18.2); the value of agricultural climate regulation (Section 22.3.18.3 and 22.3.18.4); cost-effective biodiversity conservation (Section 22.3.19); education and environmental knowledge (Section 22.3.15); informal recreation (Section 22.3.20.1); urban greenspace amenity (Section 22.3.21); and the amenity value of nature (Section 22.3.14). Space limitations mean that full details of these analyses cannot be presented within this chapter and the reader is directed to the UK NEA website (http://uknea.unep-wcmc.org/) for detailed reports compiled by the UK NEA Economics team (Abson *et al.* 2010; Beaumont *et al.* 2010; Dugdale, 2010; Fezzi *et al.* 2011; Hulme & Siriwardena 2010; Maddison, 2010; Morling *et al.* 2010; Morris & Camino, 2010; Mourato *et al.* 2010; Perino *et al.* 2010; Sen *et al.* 2010; Termansen *et al.* 2010; Tinch, 2010; Tinch *et al.* 2010; and Valatin & Starling 2010).

Note that this chapter deliberately adopts a broad remit, considering not only biotic ecosystem services (those involving living organisms), but also encompassing a brief overview of certain abiotic services of the natural environment, such as renewable energy. It also briefly considers wider issues such as raw material, energy and ecosystem-related employment. This is to illustrate the flexibility of the approach adopted and through this, to argue for a wider application of this approach beyond purely biotic ecosystem services. We recognise that these additional discussions go beyond the remit of other analyses in the UK NEA, but feel that they constitute a useful case for the extension of the principles underpinning the ecosystem services approach, contributing to a possible harmonising of methods across all related fields of decision making. The literature review (Section 22.3) also contains links to financial value data and their interpretation in the natural science chapters of the UK NEA (Chapters 4–16). Appendix 22.1 further broadens its scope to consider the macroeconomic implications of adopting the ecosystem service approach to decision analysis and policy formation.

Overall, the chapter makes the case that ecosystems and their services are economically very significant at the national scale (see **Table 22.27** for a summary). The conservation and efficient management of the natural capital stock and the flows of value that ecosystems represent can provide a solid foundation for a sustainable and thriving 'green' economy. Equally, inefficient management and overexploitation of natural capital may well inhibit future prospects for sustainable growth (by imposing unnecessary costs) over the medium- to long-term future. A full recognition of the wealth of services provided by ecosystems can also underpin efforts to improve well-being (e.g. health, cultural heritage and diversity, social cohesion) in society at large. Long-term economic growth prospects will be substantially conditioned by both natural and social capital stock/flow maintenance.

22.2 Methodological Summary[2]

The crucial role which managed and unmanaged natural systems play in underpinning economic activity and human well-being is of growing concern as evidence mounts of the increasing pressures being placed upon such systems by human activity (GEF 1998; Chapin *et al.* 2000; Koziell 2001; MA 2005; CBD 2006; Loreau *et al.* 2006). One reflection of that concern is the recent undertaking of major assessments of the status of the services provided by ecosystems (see, for example, MA 2005 or TEEB 2010[3]). Economic analysis is an

---

1 A meta-analysis entails the combined re-analysis of previous studies.
2 This section draws heavily upon Bateman *et al.* (2011a).
3 In response to review requests, we can contrast the UK NEA with the studies undertaken under The Economics of Ecosystems and Biodiversity (TEEB) initiative. While TEEB considers the global value of certain ecosystem services, the UK NEA, as its name implies, focuses almost exclusively upon the UK. Each has its own specific advantages. TEEB is intended to support international negotiations within the global-political sphere and has a particular interest in the relationship between ecosystem services and poverty. However, the complexity of global environmental issues and the lack of valuation and other data at a worldwide level mean that the empirical focus of TEEB is necessarily confined to a selection of services, notably: the carbon storage value of forests; fisheries; and coral reefs. In contrast the national level focus of the UK NEA permits a more comprehensive assessment of relevant ecosystem services and focuses upon practical decision making. The restriction of the NEA to the UK also avoids some (if not all) of the more extreme data and knowledge gaps which inevitably arise across the global context. However, in many respects the fundamental principles of both TEEB and the UK NEA are similar. Both recognise that "successful environmental protection needs to be grounded in sound economics" (TEEB 2010, p.3) and attempt to move from previous considerations of total value to more policy-relevant assessments of the marginal value of ecosystem-related goods and the benefits generated from alternative strategies for change.

increasing feature of such undertakings and has prompted a rapidly expanding literature regarding the implementation of such analyses (see, for example, Bockstael *et al.* 2000; Balmford *et al.* 2002; De Groot *et al.* 2002; Howarth & Farber 2002; Heal *et al.* 2005; Barbier 2007; Boyd & Banzhaf 2007; Wallace 2007; Finnoff & Tschirhart 2008; Fisher *et al.* 2008, 2009; Mäler *et al.* 2008; Tschirhart 2009; Liu *et al.* 2010; Turner *et al.* 2010; Bateman *et al.* 2011a). This literature forms the methodological basis of the economic analysis conducted for the UK NEA. Some of the concerns raised by critics of the economic approach to ecosystem services assessment (O'Neil 2001; Sagoff 2011) are also addressed in this chapter.

Ecosystem service assessments and accompanying economic analyses can be roughly divided into two types.[4] 'Sustainability analyses' typically assess the stocks of natural assets,[5] while 'programme evaluation' analyses seek to ascertain the value of the flow of ecosystem services provided by those assets. Each type of analysis has its various uses. For example, sustainability analyses may inform macro-level policy formation while programme evaluations might be used to support calculations underpinning payments for ecosystem services (Defra 2010b). However, both require information regarding the value of ecosystem services and it is this task which forms the focus of the economic analysis conducted for the UK NEA, leaving the assessment of natural asset stock levels mainly for future consideration.[6] This is not an entirely satisfactory situation. Arguably, the focus on flows rather than stocks is perfectly acceptable provided that we are operating safely above any thresholds below which stocks (and hence the sustainability of flows) might collapse. Even when this is not the case, flow analyses can be perfectly acceptable, provided that the values used reflect the long-term stream of benefits to society and incorporate the value of any depletion of stocks (such assessments are properly termed 'shadow values').[7] However, there is a lack of data on and understanding of threshold levels for different stocks of services. In the absence of that information, analysis of ecosystem flow values is, it is argued, a major improvement

over conventional decision making, but work on thresholds is an important future supplement to that analysis. It is not accepted that the complete absence of economic monetary data in ecosystem management and decision making is an acceptable situation (for contrary perspectives, see O'Neil 2001 and Sagoff 2011). The underpinning of the economic analysis conducted for the UK NEA is provided by the Conceptual Framework set out in Chapter 2. Within it, at any given point in time, an ecosystem is defined by its structure and processes. These processes are inherently complex and any attempt to value both the primary supporting services (say the weathering processes which lie at the heart of soil formation) and higher processes (such as the contribution of soil quality to food production) risks the possibility of generating double counting errors. Therefore Fisher *et al.* (2008, 2009) argue that economic analyses should focus upon the 'final ecosystem services' which are the last link in the chain of natural processes which contribute to human well-being by inputting to the production of goods.[8] Our use of the term 'goods' goes well beyond the common conception of market-priced items to include non-market contributors to well-being, be they physical or non-physical (pure experiential) objects.[9] While some of these goods come straight from the natural world without the intervention of humans (e.g. the visual amenity of beautiful natural landscapes), many other items (e.g. intensive food production) require some inputs of manufactured or other human capital. In the latter cases it is vital to isolate the contribution of the natural environment to the production of those goods, as failing to do so ignores human and manufactured capital inputs and so risks overstating the value of ecosystem services and undermining the credibility of such analyses.[10] Once isolated, economic analyses seek to assess this value in monetary terms, applying methods which are summarised in Section 22.2.1. However, as acknowledged in the Conceptual Framework of the UK NEA (Chapter 2), not all of the benefits derived from ecosystem services are necessarily amenable to economic valuation

4　We are grateful to Sir Partha Dasgupta for highlighting this distinction and suggesting these terms.

5　Much of the empirical literature concerning sustainability analyses has focused upon assessing historic development paths through adjustments of national income accounts (Bartelmus 2001, 2008; UN 2003; Hamilton & Ruta 2009). An underpinning theoretical framework for sustainability analyses is provided through the notion of 'Comprehensive Wealth', which considers the ecological stocks from which all ecosystem service flows are generated and corresponding economic values derived (Dasgupta & Mäler 2000; Arrow *et al.* 2007; Mäler *et al.* 2008; Dasgupta 2009). See also Turner (1999) on the notion of the 'primary' or 'glue' values that healthy, functioning ecosystems possess.

6　Both the natural science and economic analysis bases for sustainability analyses are less developed than that for flow valuations. In particular, accurate sustainability analyses require an understanding not only of the scale of stocks and rates of depletion but also of any threshold effects (points beyond which further depletion may result in accelerated reductions in stocks which may be imperfectly reversible, hysteretic (i.e. reversible but only when the rate of depletion is first very substantially lowered; see references listed for further discussion, or completely irreversible; see Brock & Starrett, 2003; Mäler *et al.* 2003; Rockström *et al.* 2009). In the review presented in Bateman *et al.* (2011a) we consider three potential strategies for incorporating sustainability concerns into economic appraisals of projects and programmes: i) assessment of how future depletion of ecosystem stocks might increase the marginal social value of corresponding services (see also: Gerlagh & van der Zwann 2002; Hoel & Sterner 2007; Sterner & Persson 2008; Pascal *et al.* 2009); ii) incorporation of the insurance value of maintaining ecosystem resilience (see Mäler 2008; Mäler *et al.* 2009; Walker *et al.* 2010) and iii) the use of safe minimum standards as a means of preserving stocks of ecosystem assets (see Farmer & Randall 1998; Randall 2007). To date none of these analyses have been conducted within the UK and this is one of the empirical foci of the recently established Valuing Nature Network (www.valuing-nature.net/), which seeks to bring together natural scientists, economists, other social scientists and the policy community to improve the valuation of ecosystem service flows, facilitate sustainability analyses and incorporate these various assessments within decision-making protocols.

7　Note that the use of such shadow values is also fundamental to sustainability analyses such as green accounting exercises (see, for example, Dasgupta 2009; Hamilton & Ruta 2009; and Mäler *et al.* 2009).

8　Of course, there is a potential problem here if the primary value and hence sustainability of supporting systems is ignored and only the value of final ecosystem services is considered; hence our earlier discussions of the need for ancillary sustainability analyses.

9　So a beautiful woodland landscape generates amenity views which are a good to the outdoor walker as much as a piece of timber is a good to the home improver. As this example illustrates, some goods are mutually exclusive of others.

10　This is achieved by examining how production of goods varies as inputs of final ecosystem services and other capital are varied at different rates. Natural variation across different areas and across time will often provide a good source of such data (see discussion in Bateman *et al.* 2011a).

(examples include environmentally related social norms which condition, for example, symbolically important landscapes or the spiritual value of the natural world). The debate over the individual value and collective value distinction and the use of non-monetary assessment methods are described in Chapter 16.

22.2.1 Valuing Ecosystem Services

The value of some change in the provision of a good is, within economic analyses, assessed in terms of the change in well-being that it generates; this value is often referred to as a 'benefit' ('cost') if it raises (lowers) well-being. Note that we draw a sharp distinction between the terms 'good' and 'benefit' to highlight the fact that the same good can generate very different benefit values depending on its context (e.g. location) and timing of delivery. For example, considering the spatial context of a good, a woodland situated on the edge of a major city will generate much greater recreational benefits than a physically identical woodland situated in a remote area.[11] Note also that some goods generate instrumental 'use value' (e.g. the value of timber to a carpenter), while others deliver 'non-use value' (e.g. the knowledge that biodiversity is being conserved even if the person expressing that value does not observe the species concerned).

In considering the task of valuing ecosystem services an important distinction needs to be drawn between the terms 'value' and 'price'. That they are not, in fact, equivalent is easy to demonstrate. Consider a walk in a local park. The market price of such recreation is likely to be zero as there are no entrance fees and anyone can simply walk in. However, the very fact that people do indeed spend their valuable time in parks shows that this is not a zero value good. In fact the price of a good is simply that portion of its value which is realised within the marketplace. Now in some cases, price may be a perfectly acceptable approximation to value, particularly where all the inputs to the production of a good are privately owned, that good is produced in a competitive market,[12] and where there is not large-scale intervention by governments or other authorities.[13] Indeed, even when these latter distortions do arise, economists can often adjust for their influence. However, as the park recreation example shows, market price can, in some cases, be a poor approximation of value. Indeed, this divergence can often be substantial and is a characteristic of many of the goods produced by the natural environment.

Economists have developed a variety of methods for estimating the value of goods whose market prices are either imperfect reflections of that value or non-existent. These methods are designed to span the range of valuation challenges raised by the application of economic analyses to the complexity of the natural environment. Application guidelines are discussed in detail through a variety of reviews[14] and **Table 22.1** provides only a brief summary of the available techniques.

It was noted earlier that market prices can, in some cases, provide an acceptable starting point for valuation (e.g. Cairns 2002). However, adjustment should always be made to correct for market distortions such as taxes and subsidies (which are effectively merely transfers from one part of society to another) as well as for non-competitive practices (Freeman 1991; Dasgupta 2009; Nicholson *et al.* 2009). Related to this approach is the factor input or production function method (see Barbier 2000, 2007; Freeman 2003; and Hanley & Barbier, 2009). As discussed previously, this examines the contribution of all of the inputs used to produce a good in terms of the value they add.[15] This approach can be applied to a range of market (consumption) goods, but has also been used for valuing regulatory and 'protection' goods (examples of the latter including flooding and extreme weather protection).[16] All of these approaches infer values by examining linkages with (adjusted) market-priced goods. This tactic is also used in the examination of potential value losses in terms of avoided damage costs or behaviour and expenditure intended to avert such damages.[17] However, we have excluded the use of restoration or replacement costs as a proxy for the value of ecosystem services. Although there are a few interesting examples of such studies, such as the study of the New York City drinking water source in the Catskills Mountains discussed by Chichilinsky & Heal (1998), many economists consider that such methods should be used with caution (Ellis & Fisher 1987; Barbier 1994, 2007; Heal 2000; Freeman 2003), due to the suspicion that restoration or replacement costs may bear little resemblance to the values they approximate.[18] That said, in cases where cost-benefit assessment is not feasible (say, because of a lack of robust benefit estimates), not required (for example, because of regulations requiring compensatory offsetting shadow projects), or even not permitted (say, because of legislation requiring certain actions), then cost information becomes a vital informational input to cost-effectiveness analyses.[19]

---

11 Of course biodiversity might be inversely related to urban proximity. Analysing such trade-offs is the essence of environmental economics.
12 Typically, the less competitive a market, the more any individual producer can exert pressure upon price.
13 Interventions such as government subsidies or taxation can distort prices from their competitive market levels.
14 See, for example, Champ *et al.* (2003), Bateman *et al.* (2002a), Freeman (2003), Pagiola *et al.* (2004), Heal *et al.* (2005), Kanninen (2006), Barbier (2007), Bateman (2007), and Hanley & Barbier (2009).
15 Examples of production function-based valuations of ecosystem services include: multi-purpose woodlands (Bateman *et al.* 2003; Boscolo & Vincent 2003; Nalle *et al.* 2004); marine nutrient balance (Gren *et al.* 1997; Knowler & Barbier 2005; Smith 2007), pollination (Ricketts *et al.* 2004); power generation (Considine & Larson 2006); fisheries (Rodwell *et al.* 2002; Sumaila 2002; Barbier 2003, 2007); watershed protection (Kaiser & Roumasset 2002; Hansen & Hellerstein 2007).
16 Examples include the storm protection values of mangroves in Thailand (Barbier 2007) and hurricanes along the US Atlantic and Gulf coasts (Costanza *et al.* 2008).
17 Note that the averting behaviour method could also be viewed as a variant of the revealed preference approach discussed subsequently.
18 Note that we are not rejecting the use of costs within the process of determining values. For example, cost-based payment vehicles are a standard element of many stated preference willingness to pay studies. Costs may also be useful indicators of value where variations in the level of costs can be related to the level of purchases of such services (again revealing values). Rather what we are cautioning against is the inference that costs can directly approximate benefits in the absence of these further data and analyses.
19 Cost-effectiveness analyses compare alternative options for delivering a specified outcome with the most efficient option typically being preferred.

Table 22.1 Various valuation methods applied to ecosystem services. Source: Bateman *et al.* (2011a).

Valuation method	Value types	Overview of method	Common types of applications	Examples of ecosystem services valued	Example studies
Adjusted market prices	Use	Market prices adjusted for distortions such as taxes, subsidies and non-competitive practices.	Food; forest products; Research & Development benefits.	Crops; livestock; multi-purpose woodland.	Godoy *et al.* (1993); Bateman *et al.* (2003)
Production function methods	Use	Estimation of production functions to isolate the effect of ecosystem services as inputs to the production process.	Environmental impacts on economic activities and livelihoods, including damage costs avoided, due to ecological regulatory and habitat functions.	Maintenance of beneficial species; maintenance of arable land and agricultural productivity; support for aquaculture; prevention of damage from erosion and siltation; groundwater recharge; drainage and natural irrigation; storm protection; flood mitigation.	Ellis & Fisher (1987); Barbier (2007)
Damage cost avoided	Use	Calculates the costs which are avoided by not allowing ecosystem services to degrade.	Storm damage; supplies of clean water; climate change.	Drainage and natural irrigation; storm protection; flood mitigation.	Kim & Dixon (1986); Badola & Hussain (2005)
Averting behaviour	Use	Examination of expenditures to avoid damage.	Environmental impacts on human health.	Pollution control and detoxification.	Rosado *et al.* (2000).
Revealed preference methods	Use	Examines the expenditure made on ecosystem-related goods, e.g. travel costs for recreation; hedonic (typically property) prices in low noise areas.	Recreation; environmental impacts on residential property and human health.	Maintenance of beneficial species; productive ecosystems and biodiversity; storm protection; flood mitigation; air quality; peace and quiet; workplace risk.	See Bockstael & McConnell (2006) for the travel cost method and Day *et al.* (2007) for hedonic pricing.
Stated preference methods	Use and non-use	Uses surveys to ask individuals to make choices between different levels of environmental goods at different prices to reveal their willingness to pay for those goods.	Recreation; environmental quality; impacts on human health; conservation benefits.	Water quality; species conservation; flood prevention; air quality; peace and quiet.	See Carson *et al.* (2003) for contingent valuation and Adamowicz *et al.* (1994) for discrete choice experiment approach.

The methods described above might appear straightforward. However, this is somewhat deceptive. Recall that the task of the economist is to estimate the value of goods in terms of the welfare they generate, rather than simply their market price. As mentioned, it is only under a set of fairly restrictive assumptions that we can take market price as a direct estimate of value (recall the park recreation example) and the adjustment process from the former to the latter is far from straightforward. However, even this route becomes impassable for goods which are devoid of market prices such as outdoor, open-access recreation, or peace and quiet. Revealed preference methods provide an approach to the valuation of goods such as these where an individual can only enjoy some non-market environmental good through the consumption of some market-priced private good. Here, economists make use of the 'weak complementarity' concept introduced by Mäler (1974) to examine how much individuals are prepared to spend on

the private good in order to enjoy the environmental good, thereby revealing the value of the latter. A number of variants of the revealed preference approach exist. For example, the travel cost method examines the expenditure and time that individuals are prepared to give up to visit environmental recreation areas. Similarly, the hedonic property price method typically examines the premium which people are prepared to pay in order to purchase houses in areas of higher environmental quality (e.g. quieter, less polluted neighbourhoods, and locations near parks). By controlling for other determinants (e.g. the number of bedrooms in a property), such purchases reveal the values people hold for these environmental goods.[20]

While revealed preference techniques tend to be applicable to a relatively narrow range of goods, stated preference approaches such as contingent valuation and discrete choice experiment methods (see **Table 22.1**) should, in theory, be applicable to a wide range of ecosystem service goods,[21] and

---

20 Notice that the hedonic property price approach examines the value of a flow of services as capitalised within house prices. A related approach is to model the relationship between the price of land and its attributes. Examples of such 'Ricardian' analyses include Mendelsohn *et al.* (1994), Schenkler *et al.* (2005), Seo *et al.* (2009) and Fezzi *et al.* (2010b). While revealed preference methods have been widely applied, they have various drawbacks and limitations. They often require a number of assumptions to hold as well as copious amounts of data and intensive statistical analysis.

21 The stated preference literature is vast but for a few examples focused upon ecosystem services: Naylor and Drew (1998), Rolfe *et al.* (2000), Hearne & Salinas (2002), Carlsson *et al.* (2003), Hanley *et al.* (2003), Huybers & Bennett (2003), Othman *et al.* (2004), Naidoo & Adamowicz (2005), Banzhaf *et al.* (2006), and Luisetti *et al.* (2011a,b).

typically they are the only option available for estimating non-use values.[22] Such methods are defensible in cases where respondents have clear prior preferences for the goods in question or can discover economically consistent preferences within the course of the survey exercise. Where this is not the case, elicited values may not provide a sound basis for decision analysis. Such problems are most likely to occur when individuals have little experience, or poor understanding, of the goods in question (Bateman *et al.* 2008 2010a).[23] Therefore, while stated preferences may provide sound valuations for many goods, the further we move to consider indirect use and pure non-use values, the more likely we are to encounter problems.

While a number of solutions have been proposed for the problem of valuing low experience, non-use goods (Christie *et al.* 2006; Bateman *et al.* 2009b), we have to consider those cases where such values cannot be established to any acceptable degree of validity. The question of what should be done in such cases has generated much debate, but one approach is the adoption of 'safe minimum standards' to ensure the sustainability of resources (such as the continued existence of species) which are not amenable to valuation (Farmer & Randall, 1998). This would not negate the need for economic analysis, which would still play an important role in the identification of cost-effective approaches to ensuring the maintenance of sustainable ecosystems.[24]

While much of the valuation literature consists of original research conducted for a variety of purposes, real world policy decisions often face time and resource constraints which preclude the undertaking of new field studies. To remedy this, a substantial literature has developed examining techniques for transferring values from original source to new policy situations. The value transfer literature embraces a number of approaches.[25] The simplest technique is to search for a prior source valuation study which addresses a good and context which approximates that of the policy application and apply the value from the former to the latter.[26] This simple approach, often referred to as mean value transfer (because typically it is the average value which is transferred) is defensible, provided that source and policy good and context are highly similar. However, the limitations of source valuation studies mean that this is often not the case. In such cases, one option is to attempt to adjust the source values by incorporating differences between the source and policy contexts (e.g. differences in good characteristics, changes in valuing populations and their characteristics, different use costs or substitute/complement availability). One approach to such adjustment is to undertake a meta-analysis of results from previous studies, relating values to the characteristics of those studies and the goods and contexts valued. Such an analysis typically yields a regression model linking values to the characteristics captured in the available source data. As shown by Brander *et al.* (2006), the analyst can then apply the characteristics of a particular policy case to this model to estimate the relevant value.[27] An alternative approach to adjusting from source to policy values is to undertake a set of prior studies specifically designed to capture the effect of factors known to influence values, such as variation in the level of ecosystem service or changes in the spatial location of those services. Data from these studies are then analysed to yield a transferable, spatially explicit value function. The characteristics of any policy relevant site can then be fed into this model to estimate its corresponding value.

22.2.2 Total and Marginal Values

While the literature on ecosystem service valuations is developing rapidly, it highlights a variety of caveats regarding the application of such methods. Of these, one of the most serious problems facing the effective and robust valuation of ecosystem services is that there are gaps in our understanding of the underpinning science relating those services to the production of goods.[28] In addition, there is

---

22   Notice that we deliberately eschew the term 'intrinsic value'. The word 'intrinsic' is defined by the Merriam-Webster dictionary as 'belonging to the essential nature or constitution of a thing'. Therefore the intrinsic value of, say, an endangered British bird such as the bittern (*Botaurus stellaris*) (Eaton *et al.* 2009) belongs to the bittern and is not reliant in principle on human perception. Of course, humans can and do hold values for bitterns. These can include the use value held by birdwatchers and the non-use values which a wider group hold for the continued existence of the bittern as a species. However, these are anthropocentric rather than intrinsic values. Some would argue for notions of human-assigned intrinsic values (e.g. Hargrove 1992) but from a conventional economic perspective, many so-called 'intrinsic' values would instead be reclassified as non-use existence values. True intrinsic values (e.g. the value of the bittern to the bittern) could be protected by a property rights approach which makes it illegal to harm the species concerned. However, in reality such rules are more likely to be enacted and maintained when they are actually supported by anthropocentric non-use values. The issue of how far society is prepared to go to protect so-called sacrosanct rights is an interesting topic of ongoing heated debate.
23   A related problem is where variants of the stated preference approach provide survey respondents with heuristic cues (simple rules of thumb) regarding response strategies (Bateman *et al.* 2009b).
24   A related strategy, the implementation of offsetting compensatory 'shadow' projects validated for their ecological suitability (Klassen & Botterweg 1976; Pearce *et al.* 1990; FR 1995), would also generally require cost-effectiveness analyses. For an example of a cost-effective approach to species preservation, see Bateman *et al.* (2009c) and contrast this to the highly variable stated preference values for these projects given in Bateman et al. (2010a).
25   Examples of value transfers (sometimes called benefit transfers, although this is confusing as these techniques can also be applied to costs) and related meta-analyses for environmental goods include Desvousges *et al.* (1992); Bergland *et al.* (1995); Carson *et al.* (1996); Downing & Ozuna (1996); Brouwer & Spaninks (1999); Brouwer *et al.* (1999); Brouwer (2000); Barton (2002); Bateman & Jones (2003); Muthke & Holm-Mueller (2004); Ready *et al.* (2004); Brouwer & Bateman (2005); Johnston *et al.* (2005, 2006); Moeltner *et al.* (2007); Navrud & Ready (2007); Zandersen *et al.* (2007); Leon-Gonzalez & Scarpa (2008); Lindhjem & Navrud (2008); Johnston & Duke (2009); TEEB (2009, 2010); and Bateman *et al.* (2010c, 2011b).
26   Transfer databases such as The Environmental Valuation Reference Inventory (EVRI) have been developed to assist the search process for such applications.
27   Although it is important that such meta-analyses take into account any effect exerted upon values by the choice of valuation methodology in the source studies (see Bateman & Jones 2003).
28   Two problems are particularly highlighted: i) the availability of quantified data on changes in the provision of services over time and space under different scenarios; ii) quantified understanding of the interactions between ecosystems and their services, particularly under novel general stressors such as global climate change. These issues will require concerted action and high degrees of collaboration between the natural and social sciences.

a paucity of valuation studies and available data regarding the values of these goods. A further complex, yet important, aspect of the ecosystem service valuation problem is that even when overall stocks are at or above sustainable levels, the size of any given stock of natural assets may affect the value of changes in associated service flows. This can be illustrated in part through reference to the highly cited study by Costanza *et al.* (1997), which attempted to provide value estimates for the total stock of all ecosystem services globally. While that paper very substantially raised awareness of the application of economics to ecosystem assessments, particularly within the natural science community, the focus upon valuing total stocks has been criticised on a number of grounds (e.g. Heal *et al.* 2005).[29] In particular, very few policy decisions relate to total losses of ecosystem services. Instead, most decisions concern incremental, often relatively modest changes in natural assets and their service flows. Economic valuation of such changes requires an initial understanding of the value of changing a single unit of a stock. Economists refer to this as the 'marginal' value of the ecosystem service in question. Of course, if the value of a marginal unit is constant, then it is straightforward to go from valuing a single unit to valuing whatever number of units a given policy will create or destroy. However, an interesting phenomenon is that for many goods and services, marginal values will change with the total size of the stock, even when the overall stock level is above sustainable levels. **Figure 22.1** illustrates the relevant point here by contrasting the two cases: the first concerning the marginal benefit (i.e. the per unit value) of reducing climate change by increasing carbon storage; the second showing the marginal benefit of increasing the area of recreational greenspace. In both cases, we postulate a situation where there is a policy which changes land use so as to increase the provision of both carbon storage and land for recreation (e.g. through the creation of woodlands, which in turn generate both carbon storage and recreational visits).

Figure 22.1a shows a (virtually) constant level for the marginal value of carbon storage throughout the range of feasible projects within the UK. This reflects the simple fact that, using existing technologies whereby the bulk of terrestrial carbon storage is held in living biomass and soils, the UK is simply not big enough to capture sufficient carbon to significantly reduce the problem of climate change to the level where the marginal benefits of further carbon capture change. Only if carbon sequestration were to be undertaken on a truly global scale would it begin to significantly affect the potentially damaging effects of climate change and hence reduce the marginal value of further carbon capture. Here then, the total benefit value of the envisioned provision change is estimated by multiplying the (constant) marginal benefit of carbon capture by the increase in provision between the baseline and alternative scenario.

A more complex situation is shown **Figure 22.1b**, which concerns increases in the area of recreational land. Within any given area, while an initial provision of recreational land may be highly valued, once that is provided, further (marginal) units of such land in that area generate progressively lower increases in recreational value.[30] This pattern of diminishing marginal values is a characteristic of many goods (even carbon capture would exhibit such a pattern once climate change began to be significantly ameliorated).

The two parts of **Figure 22.1** also reflect the role of location in determining values. While the benefits of storing a tonne of carbon are spatially unconstrained (all individuals gain from this good), the benefits of increasing the size of a given recreational area are highly spatially confined, being disproportionately captured by those who live near to the site. This of course means that locating recreational sites near to population centres can substantially increase their value. Bateman *et al.* (2006) discuss the concept of 'distance decay' in such values. Note also that this raises the possibility of localised losses of stocks occurring even when regional, national or global stocks are maintained. This is likely to generate high spatial specificity in marginal values.

Figure 22.1b also illustrates why it may be unwise to attempt to estimate the total value of ecosystem stocks rather than the value of specified changes. A total value would be given by summing all of the values underneath the marginal value curve back to a level of zero provision. However, such a situation (e.g. the disappearance of all recreational land) may be highly unlikely to occur. Equally

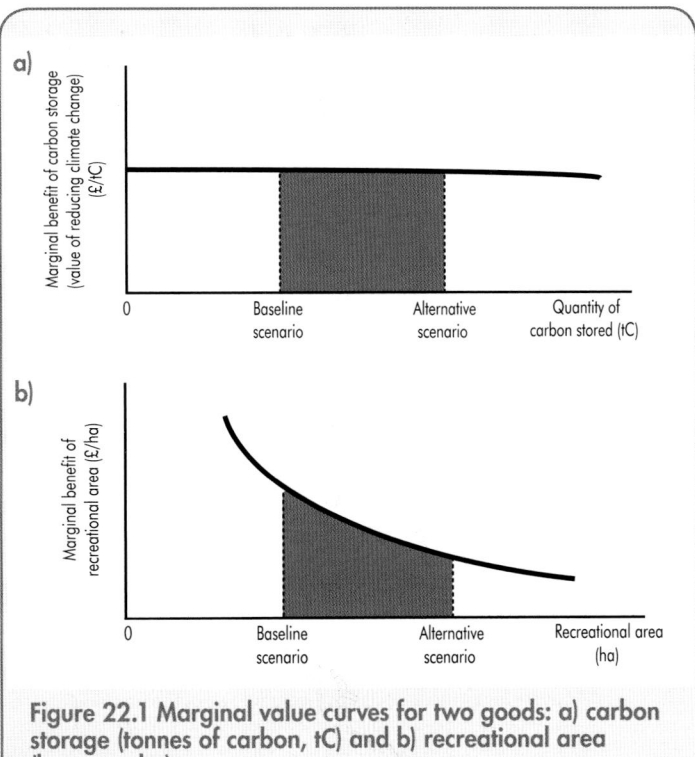

Figure 22.1 Marginal value curves for two goods: a) carbon storage (tonnes of carbon, tC) and b) recreational area (hectares, ha).

29 Note that while they do not provide solutions to these problems, Costanza *et al.* (1997) are aware of these issues and raise these within the discussion of their findings.
30 The Brander *et al.* (2006) meta-analysis of wetland valuation studies provides an example of such a case with per hectare values diminishing as the overall size of a wetland area increases.

importantly, it moves the calculation through areas of the marginal value curve which are entirely unsupported by data. Extrapolation out of the range of existing data is likely to generate unreliably high values.[31] One common alternative to this approach is to use the current level of marginal benefits and hold this constant for the calculation of total values. However, just as the former approach is likely to generate overestimates of value, this latter method ignores the shape of the marginal value curve and is liable to lead to underestimates of total value. Both options are unattractive and unnecessary. The focus upon changes in value between feasible, policy-relevant scenarios is much more useful for decision purposes. Accordingly, this is the approach adopted for the UK NEA, which argues that for the valuation of any good we require:

i) understanding of the change in provision of the good under consideration (i.e. the change in the number of units being provided) given changes in the environment, policies and societal trends;

ii) a robust and reliable estimate of the marginal (i.e. per unit) value; and

iii) knowledge of how ii) might alter as i) changes.

22.2.3 Discounting

So far in our discussions we have said nothing of the additional complications which arise where benefits and/or costs do not all occur in the present period but instead arise at some future time. This raises the issue of 'discounting': the process by which economic analyses reflect the preferences of individuals by reducing the present-day value of future costs and benefits, with this reduction increasing in intensity the further into the future we go.

The discounting procedure is based upon both theoretical and empirical arguments that individuals have a preference for receiving benefits sooner rather than later. This means that social values encapsulate within them conceptions of the impact of changes in the stock of all assets (including natural assets) upon intergenerational well-being. However, both the form and rate of the discounting procedure are the subject of intense and very long-standing controversy.[32] A critical element of this debate centres on whether, in selecting the social discount rate, a descriptive or prescriptive approach should be used (IPCC 1996; Dietz et al. 2007; Stern 2007). Put another way, should investments in natural assets be appraised purely in the light of information about preferences for the future as revealed in actual economic decisions, or is there room for the practitioner to make alternative moral judgments such as support for intergenerational equity?[33]

Interestingly, recent discussions surrounding discounting have also broken new ground with the growing recognition that some environmental problems, such as climate change, are truly 'non-marginal' in the sense that this problem could end up shifting the global development path, say with 'business as usual' emissions of greenhouse gases (GHGs)[34] possibly leading to considerably lower future consumption levels than now (Hoel & Sterner 2007; Weitzman 2007; Dietz 2010). Indeed, the corresponding notion that the socially appropriate discount rate for short-term effects might differ from that relevant to long-term impacts (such as climate change) has caught hold in official practical guidance (e.g. HM Treasury 2003).[35] This results in the concept of time-varying discounting, where discount rates fall for more delayed costs and benefits (i.e. giving them greater emphasis in present values than if the short-term rate were maintained throughout an assessment).

22.2.4 Principles of Economic Analysis for Ecosystem Service Assessments: A Summary and Illustration

The methodology discussed so far in Section 22.2 allows us to define four key principles for the economic analysis of ecosystem services: *integration, valuation, efficiency,* and *distribution.* In this final discussion before presenting the key economic research undertaken for the UK NEA, we briefly

31 Note that it may indeed be that large reductions in a resource will involve losses of value which are very high. However, such reductions may begin to take analyses beyond the realm of marginal changes within which conventional economic assessments typically reside. A significant complication to this arises where we consider local rather than regional or national assessments. A given reduction in a resource might be nationally marginal but locally non-marginal, especially in areas with low stocks of the resource in question. A further issue is the possible non-marginal cumulative effects of individually marginal changes. This further emphasises the need, stressed at the outset of this chapter, to supplement consideration of the value of flows with stock assessments. This becomes even more important for resources with non-linear depletion paths, i.e. those which exhibit threshold effects whereby further exploitation leads to a rapid acceleration in stock depletion (e.g. when long-term overfishing suddenly breeches the capacity of the stock to replenish itself, leading to population crashes). Further complications include the problem of hysteresis in attempts to replenish depleted stocks. This arises for resources for which rates of exploitation have to be massively reduced before any recovery of stock levels begin. The extreme case here is when there is irreversible depletion of a stock. This irreversibility may be either physical or economic, the latter referring to cases where the costs of restoration become prohibitive. These issues are overviewed by Bateman et al. (2011a).

32 This is nowhere more evident than in the debate surrounding the recent Stern Review on the economics of climate change (Stern 2007). Subsequent argument has focused on the evidence that underpinned the central conclusion of the Review that "the benefits of strong, early action far outweigh the economic costs of not acting" (page VX). In particular, the focus of much of this discussion has been on the way in which this conclusion was driven by choices made in setting the social discount rate (that rate which is relevant for decisions made on behalf of, and reflecting the wishes of, society – it differs and is typically markedly lower than the market discount rate which reflects private investment decisions), including all of the fundamental reasons for discounting: pure time preference, the utility value of future increments in consumption and the extent to which it can be assumed that future consumption will be higher than consumption today (see, for example, Dasgupta 2007, Nordhaus 2007, Weitzman 2007).

33 Stern (2007) adopts a strong intergenerational equity position (and also addresses the problem of potentially non-marginal effects) through a very low discount rate giving a relatively high weight to future costs and benefits. However, Nordhaus (2007) and Weitzman (2007) argue that there is little evidence that such an approach is reflected in people's actual behaviour and choices and, thus, the empirical evidence suggests that the pure rate of time preference should take a higher value. Resolving such debates is far from straightforward and entails questions on which, to quote Beckerman & Hepburn (2007) "reasonable minds may differ" (p198).

34 When talking about GHG emissions the term carbon (or tonnes of carbon) is often used as shorthand for carbon dioxide (CO_2) or the equivalent of other GHGs (CO_2e) in the atmosphere. For the sake of expediency we will follow this convention here.

35 For a variety of views on the discounting debate see Groom et al. (2005), Dietz & Hepburn (2010) and Dasgupta (2001).

expand upon these principles before illustrating them via a couple of case studies.

Integration. The bedrock of an economic analysis of ecosystem services has to be an architecture of highly integrated natural science and economic modelling. Clearly, one cannot value any ecosystem service if the basic relationships determining the provision of that service are not understood and embedded within the analysis. This analysis needs to embrace the variation in the quantity and quality of ecosystem services across differing locations (spatial heterogeneity). This often arises as a result of underlying variation in the natural environment across different areas.

Valuation. While financial analysts are solely interested in the prices of marketed goods, true economic analyses value the full gamut of goods and services which contribute to human well-being, irrespective of whether or not those drivers of welfare are traded in markets. Appropriate application of the valuation methods summarised above allows the analyst to move from decisions which are dominated by market prices to ones which are supported and informed by social values. Again, marginal values may differ between locations, for example in response to changes in the quality of ecosystem services in different areas. Importantly, spatial variation can substantially affect the level of demand for a given service (e.g. demand for recreation sites will change with proximity to population centres) and this needs to be reflected in the aggregate value of changes in the supply of ecosystem services.

Efficiency. Efficient use of resources is always desirable, but especially so in times of austerity. Economic assessments are crucial when identifying efficient options for resource use as they allow the decision maker to compare across alternative options. Where resources are constrained, efficiency analysis allows the identification of optimal investments in ecosystem service provision in terms of their net benefits (benefits minus costs).

Distribution. Although many economic analyses apply an efficiency-based rule that the option offering the highest net benefit should generally be recommended, decision makers need to know about which groups gain or lose from these alternatives. Concerns regarding the perceived equity of different policy options will often play a major role in determining which alternative is adopted. Economic analyses have the potential to contribute significantly to such decisions if they are extended to assess the incidence of benefits and costs across society, both now and at future points in time.[36]

A brief illustration of these methodological principles and techniques is provided by considering a case study concerning the issue of land use change (Section 22.3.17). Drawing on Bateman *et al.* (2002b, 2003) and Bateman (2009), we consider an economic analysis of a potential change from farmland to woodland in Wales. The policy motivation for such an analysis comes from the fact that farming receives a higher rate of public subsidy than woodland, and that while most agricultural outputs have market prices (however imperfect), this is not true of various of the major benefits of woodland (notably open-access recreation and carbon storage). This raises the possibility of a welfare-inefficient situation in which we have a relative excess of farmland as opposed to woodland that justifies policy interest in such an analysis.

Given our first principle of economic analysis for ecosystem service assessment, the underpinning requirement of any such study is to ensure that we have an integrated understanding of the natural environment and the economic forces which dictate the possible agricultural and woodland uses for the full study area. This requires the integration of a long time series of highly detailed, spatially explicit information from across the study area. These data capture variation across time and space, encompassing issues such as local changes in soil characteristics and slope, fertiliser application and labour inputs, as well as more macro-level variables such as temperature, rainfall, the price of outputs and inputs, and subsidy levels. These data are brought together within integrated environmental-economic models which embrace both the physical and economic considerations required for informed decision making.

Figure 22.2 illustrates the outputs of such an environmental–economic analysis through a series of maps, all but the last of which show the annual social value of the various benefit streams which arise from the land use decision under consideration (while a separate analysis allows a contrast with the private values which determine land use in the absence of any policy intervention).[37] The first map in **Figure 22.2** shows the social value of agricultural output.[38] This is derived from an integrated environmental-economic model which reflects the highly heterogeneous nature of Wales, as shown in the relatively low values in the central upland areas, where poor soils and low temperature limit productivity, and the comparatively higher values in areas such as the lowland south west, where excellent soils and warm, moist conditions produce excellent yields.

Our second principle of economic analysis is now brought into play as we reject simple market prices in favour of estimating social values by adjusting prices to reflect subsidies and other transfers. A similar integrated analysis underpins the woodland timber values illustrated in the second map. Here, integrated models incorporating natural environment factors (such as tree species, soils, slope, topographic shelter, aspect), together with economic determinants (such as planting regime, management, genetic improvement), are combined to determine timber yield and, through further analysis, its social value (again based upon

---

36 While agricultural values are typically given in annual terms, for ease of comparison the long term discounted net present value of woodland has been annualised. For details of this and the private values of land use, see Bateman *et al.* (2003).

37 Official guidelines given in HM Treasury (2003) discuss both conventional and distributionally adjusted cost-benefit analyses. Although we consider distributional issues within our analysis of urban greenspace values (Section 22.3.21), generally there is a paucity of cost-benefit consideration of such concerns, suggesting that this may be a fruitful area for future research.

38 There are multiple agricultural sectors with the highest value dairy farming sector being illustrated here. For a comparison across sectors and between the social and private (farm gate) value of agriculture see Bateman *et al.* (2003).

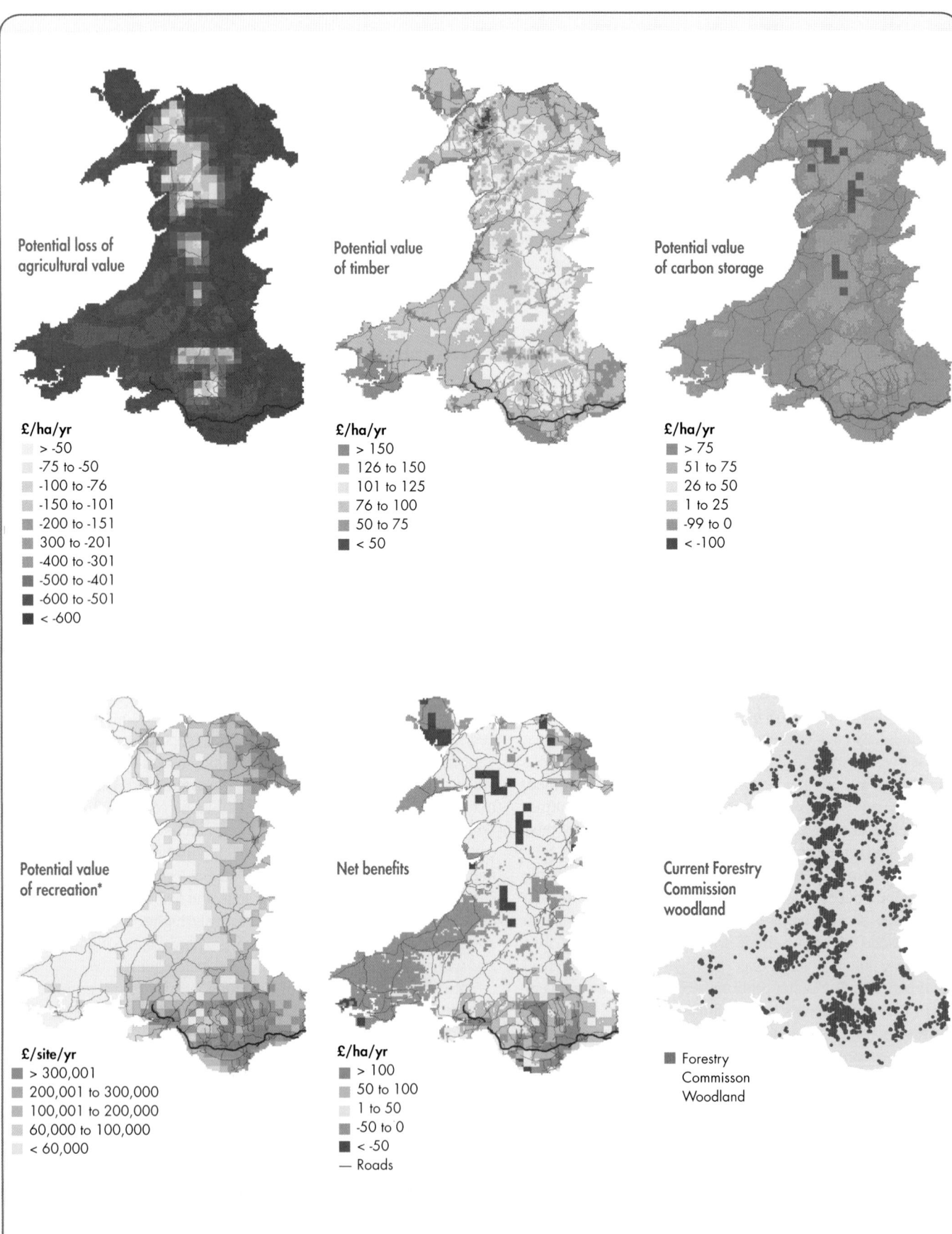

Figure 22.2 Economic values that would arise from a change of land use from farming to multi-purpose woodland in Wales (£ per year). *Unlike other values which are on a per hectare basis, the recreation is valued using one site per 5 km grid; this captures the fact that once a woodland site is established the per hectare recreational value of establishing a second site is not constant but diminishes significantly and to err on the side of caution we take that marginal value as being zero. Source: adapted from Bateman *et al.* (2002, 2003) and Bateman (2009) and reproduced with permission from Elsevier © (2009).

adjusted market prices). These values echo those of the agricultural sector, being higher in more favourable, lowland locations. Notice that the map covers the entire non-urban extent of Wales, indicating the timber values that would be achieved in each location, irrespective of its present use.

The third map of **Figure 22.2** illustrates net carbon storage values, combining the effects of both above- and below-ground biomass, soil carbon gains and losses and the effects of post-felling carbon emissions across different species and end uses. Whereas both of the previous value streams (agricultural produce and timber) involved adjusted market prices, here social values for carbon sequestration are taken from the literature on the value of avoiding damaging climate change (although the official UK policy value could be used as an alternative to this). Note that the values follow a generally similar pattern to those of timber, except for some very significant negative values in peatland areas (highlighted later in **Figure 22.2**) where the planting of forests dries out wetlands and results in net carbon release rather than storage.

The fourth map in **Figure 22.2** illustrates the value of recreation which would be generated through the establishment of woodlands. Here, the initial modelling phase requires information on the travel patterns of recreationists so as to capture the influence of population distribution and road infrastructure upon likely demand for visits to woodlands in differing locations. Values might be obtained through either revealed or stated preference methods or through some meta-analyses or value transfer exercise (as in this case). While the agricultural, timber and carbon storage values described previously all exhibit reasonably constant marginal values (as per **Figure 22.1a**), this is not the case for recreation, which is likely to exhibit diminishing marginal values (as per **Figure 22.1b**). So, in any given area, while an initial woodland area might generate substantial marginal recreation benefits, planting further woodland in the same area will yield lower marginal benefits.[39]

The fifth map of **Figure 22.2** summarises all previous analyses by detailing the net benefits arising from a move from agriculture into woodland. Here the green areas indicate locations where woodland provides a higher shadow value than agriculture, while yellow and purple areas indicate locations where agriculture provides a higher value. It is interesting to note that the areas which generate the highest shadow values from conversion into woodland are in the north east and south east, a result which reflects the high populations in these areas and consequent elevated recreational values arising from afforestation. In contrast, the most negative shadow values from such conversion are shown by the purple areas corresponding to upland peats where afforestation causes major losses of soil carbon. This then provides the analysis of efficient resource allocation, which is our third principle of economic analysis for

ecosystem service assessments. It shows that there should be a major reshaping of land use in Wales which would introduce woodlands into lowland urban fringe areas.

This also provides the basic information for the consideration of distributional issues, which is our final principle for such economic analyses. One can see that the major beneficiaries of any such change would be urban populations. Whether or not this would be accompanied by losses for the rural farming community depends crucially upon how such change is implemented. Given that this change allows for net social gains, there is clearly scope for implementation via incentives; in effect, compensating farmers for facilitating such change. Given the massive ongoing reorganisation of the European Union Common Agricultural Policy (CAP), which gives great emphasis to the natural environment and the provision of ecosystem services, there is clearly scope here to avoid the inequity of one relatively small group losing out to provide benefits to the majority. However, economic analysis can only provide the raw information for such decisions, which are ultimately political.

The geographic distribution of net benefit shadow values is in sharp contrast with the actual distribution of forests shown as the dark green areas in the final map. The latter is driven primarily by market forces alone and hence ignores the carbon sequestration and recreational values and fails to adjust to the social values of farming and timber shown at the start of this figure. On the basis of market prices only being considered, agriculture outperforms woodland in all lowland areas, pushing forestry up the hill to low productivity areas where land prices are lower. This results in a distribution of woodland which is in marked contrast to its true social value; a finding which underlines the importance of using integrated environmental-economic analyses as the basis for decision making.

22.2.5 Methodological Summary

As Section 2 has shown, there is a growing research and policy interest in the application of economic analysis within ecosystem service assessments as a guide for decision making. Such analyses have to deal with the complexities of both the natural world and individual preferences and values for the goods to which it contributes. They are most applicable when decision contexts are framed in such a way as to highlight the welfare gains and losses stimulated by marginal changes in the provision of ecosystem services. Such changes are typically spatially explicit, providing an argument against straightforward aggregation valuation exercises. They must also be carefully scrutinised from an interdisciplinary perspective for the possible presence of threshold effects. A number of methods have been developed to address these complexities, and these form the tools employed within the various economic analyses presented

---

39 Similarly, existing forests constitute recreational substitutes for subsequent woodlands, lowering the marginal values of the latter (see, for example, Jones *et al.* 2010). In effect, while the map shown is valid for any initial decision and helps guide the optimal location for land use change, the analysis needs to be repeated after any such change to allow for these substitution effects. However, automation of this analysis makes this a straightforward operation. Note that in reality many ecosystem service goods exhibit non-linear marginal value functions. The marginal recreational values of a tiny woodland may be trivial and can initially increase with size but eventually exhibit declining marginal values. The same is likely to be true of landscape amenity benefits although this may well not coincide with the function for recreation i.e. the optimal size of woodland for recreation will differ from that for landscape amenity and the objective for the decision maker will be to maximise the overall net benefit.

in Section 22.3. Section 22.3 is organised so as to present reviews of previously published literature in Section 22.3.1 to 22.3.14. The remainder Section 22.3 (i.e. Section 22.3.15 to 22.3.21) presents valuation work specifically conducted for the UK NEA.

22.3 Ecosystem Service Valuations

The UK NEA Economics team undertook a wide-ranging review of ecosystems services derived for all UK natural habitats, considering the goods these generate and, where possible, their resultant values. These are, wherever possible, estimates of economic value. But where full economic valuation is unavailable simpler financial costings are included in order to give an indication of market impacts. Full details are given in the UK NEA economic reports referred to in Section 22.1; some financial/economic information is also included in a number of the UK NEA ecosystem science chapters (Chapter 5 to Chapter 16). In addition, work on the CSERGE SEER (Social and Environmental Economic Research) programme was accelerated to provide the analyses of agricultural food production, recreation, bird biodiversity (with the British Trust for Ornithology) and urban greenspace amenity.[40] This work is outlined in Section 22.3.15 to 22.3.21.

22.3.1 Non-agricultural Food Production

22.3.1.1 Marine food production[41]
The Marine environment plays a major role in food production. **Figure 22.3** details the weight and value of total landings of pelagic and demersal finfish and shellfish into the UK by domestic and foreign vessels from 1938 to the present day.

Noting the uneven time axis of **Figure 22.3**, we can observe a marked decline in landings throughout the second half of the 20th Century to a more stable trend in recent years. Although landings have clearly declined over the period shown, this has been only marginally reflected in prices, which are influenced by readily available imports and the introduction of alternative fish species over time. This has meant that the value of landings has roughly tracked their weight, falling from £1,465 million/yr in 1938 (in 2008 prices) to £596 million in 2008. While much of this is due to the inputs of the natural environment, a lack of data meant that it was not possible to separate out ecosystem services from other inputs to the value of fish.

One area that has seen considerable expansion is the farming or culturing of aquatic organisms (fish, molluscs, crustaceans and plants). Collectively known as aquaculture, this sector has increased dramatically in the UK, with the financial value of fish and shellfish farming rising by 132% over the period 2000–2006 (CEFAS 2008). In 2007, turnover from finfish farming in the UK was £327 million, while shellfish farming generated £23 million (Saunders 2010; CEFAS 2008).

The sustainability of UK fish stocks. The steadily growing influence of EU fisheries policies means that the landings data do not reflect the size and sustainability of UK fish stocks. With regard to stock analysis and sustainable extraction level, 18 species of finfish are routinely monitored and used to create a sustainability index for marine finfish stocks around the UK. This is not representative of the UK fisheries provisioning service, but does provide useful data for discussion, and also highlights the lack of UK-wide species stock data. Armstrong & Holmes (2010) report that for 2008, 50% of assessed UK stocks were at full reproductive capacity and were being harvested sustainably, an increase from 5% to 15% in the 1990s, and from 20% to 40% in 2000. While this is a positive trend, a number of scientifically assessed UK stocks continue to be fished at levels considered to be unsustainable, the majority are fished at rates well above the values expected to provide the highest long-term yield, and a number of other commercially important species remain unassessed due to inadequacies in the available data.

As fish stocks have declined, there has been an increase in the levels of human and technological inputs to substitute for the decreasing natural capital (i.e. fish) to maintain landings. Indeed, Thurstan et al. (2010) report that despite changes in the size of the fishing fleet, technological advancements, and improvements in fishing efficiency, UK bottom trawl landings per unit of fishing power (LPUP) have reduced by 94% over the past 118 years. The authors suggest that this decrease in LPUP reflects a decrease in fish stocks and indicates that fish catch globally has only remained stable in recent years because of an increase in fishing effort.

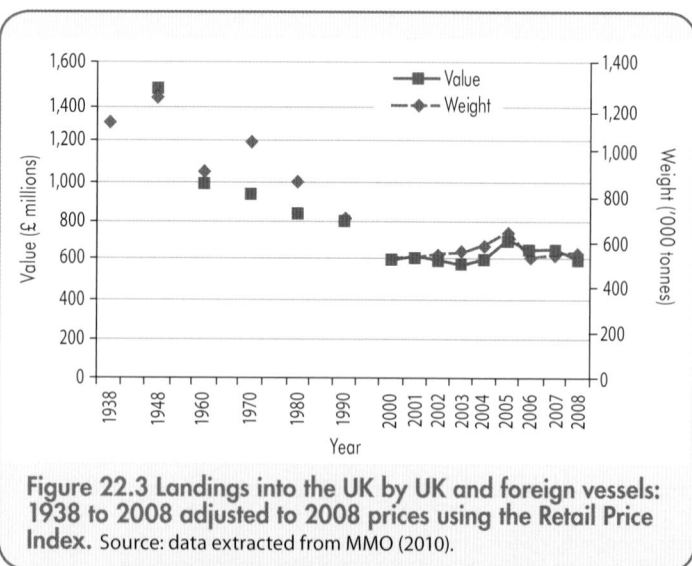

Figure 22.3 Landings into the UK by UK and foreign vessels: 1938 to 2008 adjusted to 2008 prices using the Retail Price Index. Source: data extracted from MMO (2010).

40 Social and Environmental Economic Research (SEER) into Multi-Objective Land Use Decision Making. Funded by the Economic and Social Research Council (ESRC); Funder Ref: RES-060-25-0063. The UK NEA and SEER objectives are coincident in several respects and so the latter was rescheduled to help inform the former. The work on urban greenspace amenity was conducted in collaboration with Grischa Perino, Barnaby Andrews and Andreas Kontoleon.
41 This Section draws on Beaumont et al. (2010).

Aquaculture is a financially significant and growing sector (Chapter 12; Chapter 15). In 2007, turnover from finfish farming in the UK was £327 million, while shellfish farming generated £28 million (CEFAS 2008). Marine aquaculture contributes around 21% of the finfish and shellfish supplied to the fish processing sector (CEFAS 2008). The UK fish processing sector in total generated a financial gross value added flow of £490 million in 2007, within which aquaculture contributed around £105 million. A full economic assessment of the marine food production sector is not available, but it would need to account for, among other things, the externalities (e.g. possible impacts of pollution, effects on wild populations) of fish farming and not just its financial, value added contribution.

Given the complexity of the social and natural drivers affecting fisheries, it is very difficult to make any future projections beyond the next few years, and even these are prone to significant error. It is, however, widely agreed that the demand for fish will increase globally, although fish consumption rates within the EU are expected to remain stable. Wild capture fish landings are expected to show limited or no growth (and may even decline as many stocks are overexploited), with the increased demand for fish protein being met through aquaculture. An additional variable is climate change, which has been shown to alter fish community structure through changes in distribution, migration, recruitment and growth (Walther et al. 2002).

In order to move from the simple accounting approaches outlined above to a true economic analysis, we need to introduce the concept of a resource 'rent'. For fisheries, this is the difference between the total costs faced by those who fish and the total revenues arising from fish landings.[42] As exploitation rates are increased, so this resource 'rent' declines. In a recent study, Cunningham et al. (2010) estimate the annual rent earned by Britain's fishing fleet at around £50 million per annum (p.a.) (although they acknowledge that this estimate is highly uncertain). However, the same authors claim that a reduction in fishing effort would both reduce total costs and allow stocks and hence total revenue to recover, such that annual rents might increase more than ten-fold.[43] Up until the latter part of the last century, UK fisheries were effectively open-access resources and as such, highly susceptible to the 'tragedy of the commons' (Hardin 1968) problem of overexploitation. Unfortunately, the excess fishing capacity built up historically still persists to some degree, resulting in excess fishing effort reducing rents. Cunningham et al. (2010) argue for a shift to a 'wealth'-based approach in which rental values are optimised by reducing excess capacity. This would fit well with a move towards sustainable management of natural stocks and the service flows they generate.

22.3.1.2 Woodland-related food production[44]

There is a burgeoning national (e.g. RS 2003) and international (e.g. Marshall et al. 2006) literature on the issue of recognising (and increasingly valuing) non-timber forest products (NTFP). In essence, NTFP include all the products obtainable from forest other than timber. While internationally this can include a very wide variety of products, within the UK the major value streams focus around wild foods such as mushrooms, berries and certain wild animals, of which one of the major groups is the variety of deer which now use woodland as a major habitat.

Six species of deer are currently found in the wild in the UK. Although data on UK deer populations and their change over time is generally sparse and approximate (see Hunt 2003; Ward 2005; Ward et al. 2008; Dolman et al. 2010), there is general agreement that wild deer populations have been increasing and now approach around 1.5 million animals (Spence & Wentworth 2009). Deer are associated with a range of ecosystem services, including recreational values associated with wildlife viewing (see subsequent discussions). They are also associated with various costs, including negative impacts on wood production (although estimates range from negligible costs up to £57 per ha; White et al. 2004), damage to gardens, and road accidents (Langbein 2006; Langbein & Putnam, 2006). However, increasing deer populations have led to a rise in culling and a consequent increase in UK venison supplies. No firm data are available on the annual value of this service flow, but one estimate from 2004 puts it at over £24 million p.a. (Tinch et al. 2010), although this primarily refers to stalking rather than venison values. A further £5 million p.a. in venison revenue is generated through the culling of deer by shooting estates purely for purposes of population control. The future value of this service is more difficult to forecast as, while culling has roughly doubled over the past 25 years to around 60,000 annually in Scotland, so venison prices have declined by almost 75% over the same period (MacMillan & Phillip 2010). Note, however that this is due in part to increasing import penetration (Munro 2003; MacMillan & Phillip 2010).

22.3.2 Biodiversity: Use Values[45]

The Convention on Biological Diversity (CBD 1992) defines what is commonly referred to as biodiversity as "the variability among living organisms from all sources including, *inter alia*, terrestrial, marine and other aquatic ecosystems and the ecological complexes of which they are part; this includes diversity within species, between species and of ecosystems" (Article 2, p.5). This definition has subsequently been broadened to embrace the diversity (a measure of variation between genes, species and ecosystems),

---

42 Note that total costs include what is termed 'normal profits', i.e. those that would be made if the fishery was being overexploited to the point where total revenues declined to equal total cost.

43 Cunningham et al. (2010) estimate that British fish stocks have the potential to produce resource rents in the order of £573 million p.a. Using a discount rate of 9% they estimate that the capitalised value of such rents would be £6.4 billion. Such inefficient over-exploitation is a characteristic of global fisheries. The World Bank & FAO (2009) 'Sunken Billions' report estimates that the difference between the potential and actual net economic benefits from marine fisheries is in the order of $50 billion per year; equivalent to more than half the value of the global seafood trade.

44 This Section draws in part from Valatin & Starling (2010).

45 This Section draws in part from Morling et al. (2010).

composition and relative abundance of living things. This complexity of definition is mirrored by the diverse roles of biodiversity within ecosystem services. Within this section we consider the variety of use-related values generated by biodiversity, while Section 22.3.3 considers non-use values.

Use values can be subdivided into two broad types:

- The role of biodiversity in the direct delivery of ecosystem services.
- The role of biodiversity in underpinning ecosystem service delivery.

We discuss each of these in turn below.

22.3.2.1 The role of biodiversity in the direct delivery of ecosystem services

Pollination, fertilisation and pest reduction effects upon food production. Evidence on the relationship between biodiversity and ecosystem service delivery is mixed. However, while some studies show little association (Anderson *et al.* 2008; Naidoo *et al.* 2008), in the greater number of experiments to date, increased rates of the ecosystem processes underlying ecosystem services are associated with increased numbers of species (Hooper *et al.* 2005; Hector & Bagchi 2007). In a recent meta-analysis of 446 studies of the impact of biodiversity on primary production, 319 of which involved primary producer manipulations or measurements, Balvanera *et al.* (2006) found that there is "clear evidence that biodiversity has positive effects on most ecosystem services" and, specifically, that there is a clear effect of biodiversity on productivity. Most of the evidence for this association is drawn from overseas. For example, Ricketts *et al.* (2004) estimated that pollination services to coffee plantations in Costa Rica can be worth up to nearly USD\$400/ha/yr (approximately £220/ha/yr at 2004 rates), or about 7% of farm income. However, evidence for the UK is scarce. An exception is provided by research for the UK NEA (outlined in Chapter 14) that estimates 20% of the UK cropped area comprises pollinator-dependent crops and note that a high proportion of wild, flowering plants depend on insect pollination for reproduction. This is considered a conservative estimate of the value of pollinators to UK agriculture of £430 million p.a. (see also POST 2011).[46] Similarly Bianchi *et al.* (2006) review the considerable evidence regarding the pest control services of biodiversity, noting that this appears highest in diverse landscapes. Valuations of this service are not provided, but appear potentially substantial.

As our brief discussion of threshold effects indicates, evidence of a valuable stock of ecosystem services, such as pollination, need not necessitate any policy action unless there is reason to believe that this stock is under threat. Certainly, there is evidence that proximity of semi-natural habitats is correlated with pollinator visits to crops (Tinch 2010). Furthermore, there has been an extremely large contraction of semi-natural and natural habitats (since the 1930s, some

97% of enclosed Neutral and Calcareous Grasslands in the UK have been lost; Fuller 1987). However, the evidence that this contraction has resulted in any fall in agricultural productivity in less clear. That is not to say that we are not close to a tipping point, but further high spatial resolution research is required looking at the mosaic of different land cover types before a definite assessment of any threshold effects becomes clear. Until then we are unable to say how much of the above pollination value might be at threat.

Maintaining genetic diversity. Maintaining crops' wild relatives, rare breeds and landraces offers potential benefits to domesticated crops as well as insurance-type values. While there is a range of potential benefits to conserving such genetic diversity and international examples suggest that associated values can be substantial (Poysa 1993; Newton *et al.* 2010), the only evidence available from the UK to demonstrate the marginal values associated with their conservation are internal Department for Environment, Food and Rural Affairs (Defra) estimates in respect of the Millennium Seedbank (pers comm., Mallika Ishwaran, Defra 2011; taken from Defra's Spending Review business case). Here, under various assumptions,[47] the value of genetic material in species in the seedbank likely to be extinct by 2050 gives a return of 26:1 on investment.

Bioprospecting. If biodiversity harbours potentially valuable species or compounds as yet undiscovered, bioprospecting may be an economically rewarding activity. Consequently, bioprospecting focuses on the world's biodiversity hotspots. The marginal pharmaceutical value of a species is estimated to be moderate or small in biodiversity hotspots. Some commentators suggests that terrestrial values for the UK are likely to be relatively small (Morling *et al.* 2010), although marine values might be more substantial (Lloyd-Evans 2005). However, recent work from the Joint Nature Conservation Committee (JNCC 2011) provides at least one example of potentially significant terrestrial bioprospecting values in the form of treatments for Alzheimer's Disease being derived from daffodils (*Narcissus pseudonarcissus*) and snowdrops (*Galanthus nivalis*). Given that treatment of dementia costs the UK economy £23 billion/yr (JNCC 2011), the potential value of such ecosystem services is clearly highly substantial and worthy of further investigation.

Biodiversity-related recreation. The direct appreciation of wildlife can generate substantial benefits, as evidenced by the widespread participation in activities such as birdwatching and the high price paid for certain flower bulbs from wild stock (e.g. snowdrops). These may be valued through observed behaviour (e.g. applying the travel cost method to valuing nature watching trips or estimating values through membership fees). The issue of recreation is addressed in Section 22.3.20. While that analysis examines evidence of habitat-related variation in recreation values, we acknowledge that this can only provide a relatively weak proxy for any biodiversity element in these values.

---

46 See also the Insect Pollinators Initiative: www.bbsrc.ac.uk/web/FILES/PreviousAwards/pollinators-biesmeijer.pdf. The UK agricultural sector as a whole was worth £6.6 billion in 2009 and approximately 20% of the UK's cropped area comprises pollinator dependent crops (pers comm., Mallika Ishwaran, Defra, 2011).

47 These are: that all seeds are equally likely to be stored, and go extinct; that all seeds are equally likely to be those contributing to the economic markets depending on genetic resources; that the seedbank at Millennium Seedbank at Kew Gardens holds the only examples of seeds if they do go extinct; that extinction rates are those given by the Millennium Ecosystem Assessment (MA 2005).

22.3.2.2 The role of biodiversity in underpinning ecosystem service delivery

Morling et al. (2010) argue that there is evidence to suggest that increased rates of the ecosystem processes underlying ecosystem services are associated with increased numbers of species or genes. There are also a number of examples where simplification of ecosystems has potentially led to a net loss of services. However, valuation of such services requires an understanding of the following concepts:

- The infrastructure, or primary, value of biodiversity is related to the fact that some combinations of ecosystem structure and composition are necessary to ensure the 'healthy' functioning of the system.

- The insurance hypothesis states that enhanced biodiversity insures ecosystems against declines in their functioning because the more species there are, the greater the guarantee that some will continue to function, even if others fail.

- The resilience hypothesis may be characterised as an ecosystem's flexibility to reconfigure itself in the face of external shocks. It suggests that biodiversity per se may also have economic benefits if species richness enables an ecosystem, currently in a desirable state, to resist or recover from perturbations.

While there is evidence from both terrestrial and marine ecosystems that lends support to the insurance and resilience hypotheses (Morling et al. 2010; Beaumont et al. 2010), there is little information with which to quantify the magnitude of these values within the UK or the habitats and services for which they are most applicable. Empirical research is limited by gaps in our understanding of the underpinning science and a consequent lack of relevant data alluding to the primary value of ecosystems.

22.3.3 Biodiversity: Non-use Values[48]

While there is substantial anecdotal evidence of non-use (existence and bequest) values associated with maintaining biodiversity, the estimation of associated values is somewhat problematic.[49] Unlike use values, we cannot observe behaviour regarding non-use values, neither are they reflected in productivity. Some commentators have argued that a lower boundary estimate of values might be provided by the payments provided by policies designed to promote biodiversity. Certainly such amounts are substantial and usually related to opportunity costs (e.g. the profits forgone by farmers when they agree to take on biodiversity schemes). For example, payments of £280/ha are available for additional Semi-natural Grasslands (Morling et al. 2010), while the Rural Development Plan for England (which is a development of the CAP agri-environmental schemes) will run from 2007 to 2013 with a budget of £3.9 billion. However, the use of public policy costs as a proxy measure

of biodiversity values has to be handled with caution, with the potential circularity of the valuation process being recognised. Given this, some would argue for the application of estimates of individual preference, with the most common approach to assessing the non-use value of biodiversity being via stated preference studies.

22.3.3.1 The Non-use Value of Biodiversity: Stated Preference Estimates

Stated preference (SP) valuations of what are principally non-use benefits typically fail to provide values at a UK level. However, one exception is the assessment of the benefits associated with the Environmental Stewardship scheme provided by Boatman et al. (2010); also see Christie et al. (2008). Unfortunately, results are reported for the joint bundle of both wildlife and landscape benefits and seem likely to also include elements of perceived use value. However, accepting that this cannot all be assigned to non-use biodiversity value and that it only applies to agricultural land within the Stewardship scheme (although this is likely to be a large proportion of farmland), nevertheless the UK-level sums estimated are substantial, ranging from £540 million to £1,262 million p.a. with a mid-range estimate of £845 million p.a. (all adjusted to 2010 prices). More recently Christie et al. (2010) estimate the value of the UK Biodiversity Action Plan (BAP) at £1,366 million p.a. Mallika Ishwaran, Defra (pers comm., 2011) contrasts this with a BAP cost estimate of £564 million p.a. (GHK Consulting 2010) to yield a benefit:cost ratio for conserving biodiversity of approximately 2.5:1.

Further national level SP estimates for terrestrial biodiversity include a value of £320 million p.a. to prevent the decline of nine bird species in the UK (Foster et al. 1998) and an estimated biodiversity value for British forests of £480 million p.a. (Willis et al. 2003; all values adjusted to 2010 prices). Leaving the terrestrial environment, McVittie & Moran (2010) use an SP analysis to estimate a UK value for halting the ongoing loss of marine biodiversity (through the introduction of a UK-wide marine conservation zone) of £1,714 million p.a. The same authors note that this benefit value easily outweighs the associated costs of such a scheme. Arguably, one of the areas where biodiversity non-use values have been most closely studied using SP methods is in relation to wetlands, to which we now turn.

Meta-analysis of stated preference estimates of biodiversity non-use values: the case of wetlands.[50] The perceived high cost of undertaking SP research, while in itself a subject of some controversy, has resulted in a considerable number of meta-analysis and related studies seeking to draw out generic findings and valuations from the literature.[51] One of the sources of ecosystem services most frequently subject to such analyses is wetland habitats (see Brouwer et al. 1999; Woodward & Wui 2001; Brander et al. 2006, 2008).

---

48 This Section draws in part from Morling et al. (2010).

49 As their names suggest, existence value is that benefit which individuals gain from the pure knowledge that some entity (e.g. some species) will continue to exist, while bequest value is associated with passing on a stock of benefits to others (typically future generations although one might include present others here). Note that neither value category involves direct use of the resource by the valuing individual, hence they are 'non-use' values.

50 This Section draws on Morris & Camino (2010).

51 The costs of any study, SP or otherwise, should always be assessed in cost-benefit terms taking into account the value of extra information they provide.

Wetlands deliver a number of important ecosystem service-related goods and so a single meta-analysis can provide a range of valuation estimates relevant to the UK NEA. Morris & Camino (2010) conclude that the recent meta-analyses of wetland valuation provided by Brander *et al.* (2008) provide the most appropriate value transfer function for valuation of UK wetland goods. The Brander *et al.* (2008) study draws upon 264 valuations from 78 European sites. Morris & Camino's (2010) reworking of the Brander *et al.* (2008) meta-analysis provides values for five ecosystem service-related goods:

- Biodiversity
- Water quality improvement
- Surface and groundwater supply
- Flood control and storm buffering
- Amenity and aesthetics.

For completeness, we present valuations for all of these goods within **Table 22.2**, although only biodiversity values are discussed here, with other values being discussed subsequently in this chapter.

Table 22.2 is divided into separate assessments for inland and coastal wetlands, reflecting the finding that in all cases, values for the latter exceed those for the former. Considering biodiversity values, these were principally non-use and are expressed as additions over a default value for wetlands which do not provide significant biodiversity habitat. Therefore, considering inland wetlands, the first result reported indicates that on average the meta-analysis of SP valuations estimates that a wetland which affords good quality biodiversity habitat generates a value of £454/ha/

yr more than one which does not offer such habitat. The second column calculates the total annual value of these (mainly) non-use biodiversity values on the assumption that all UK inland wetlands provide good quality biodiversity habitat. While this is clearly an upper bound assumption, it is true that most wetlands are indeed highly biodiverse areas (note that Morris & Camino (2010) considerably extend this analysis by calculating total values for UK inland and coastal wetlands, disaggregating these down to individual country levels and supplementing them with detailed case studies). However, this only tells us about the status quo situation, not the value arising from changes induced by policy or other drivers. To assess this we require a marginal value for a change in the area of such biodiverse wetlands. This is provided in the third column of each block of values. In both cases we see, as expected, that the value of such a marginal hectare of wetland is lower than the average value. This reflects the diminishing marginal values associated with increases in almost any good, including biodiversity. It is these values, of £304/ha of inland wetland and £1,866/ha of coastal wetland, which should be applied to any proposed change in the area of these habitats. As noted, we discuss the other values given in this table subsequently.

Stated preference estimates of the non-use value of biodiversity: caveats. The SP literature therefore suggests that the non-use value of biodiversity is substantial. However, some reservations can be identified regarding the use of SP methods for estimating these non-use values. Arguably, an invalid critique is that such studies can yield values which may be inconsistent with natural science assessments of what is required for sustainability. Stated preference studies reveal

Table 22.2 Estimated average, total and marginal values for specified ecosystem service-related goods provided by inland and coastal wetlands in the UK.* Source: Morris & Camino (2010).

Wetland type	UK Inland Wetlands			UK Coastal Wetlands		
No. of sites[†]	1,519			693		
Total area (hectares; ha)	601,550			274,613		
Ecosystem service-related goods	Total value of service assuming it is present in all UK inland wetlands[‡] (£ million/yr)	Average value of service where present (addition to default value)[¶] (£/ha/yr)	Marginal value of service when provided by an additional hectare of new wetland[§] (£/ha/yr)	Total value of service assuming it is present in all UK coastal wetlands[‡] (£ million/yr)	Average value of service where present (addition to default value)[¶] (£/ha/yr)	Marginal value of service when provided by an additional hectare of new wetland[§] (£/ha/yr)
Biodiversity	273	454	304	1,275	2,786	1,866
Water quality improvement	263	436	292	1,245	2,676	1,793
Surface and groundwater supply	2	2	1	514	16	12
Flood control and storm buffering	366	608	407	1,534	3,730	2,498
Amenity and aesthetics	204	339	227	1,081	2,080	1,394

* Values are area-weighted estimates for all UK inland wetland sites using the Brander *et al.* (2008) benefit function and CORINE land use data sets. All values are given in (£, 2010) prices.
† Data on the number and area of wetlands are drawn from the European CORINE Land Cover Maps (Morris & Camino 2010).
‡ Default total value of the existing inland wetland stock, assuming that none of the ecosystem services in the table apply, is £182 million/year for UK inland wetlands and £509 million/year for UK coastal wetlands.
¶ Default average values (where all of the ecosystem services specified in this table do not apply) are £303/ha/year for UK inland wetlands and £1,856/ha/year for UK coastal wetlands.
§ The per hectare value of services associated with additional new wetlands is lower than the average per hectare value of existing wetlands. This reflects the diminishing marginal value of additional wetlands.

the unsurprising result that individuals attach much higher values to charismatic megafauna such as larger mammals or familiar birds rather than small reptiles and amphibians (Morse-Jones *et al.* 2010). Similarly, habitats yielding high amenity values, such as water meadows, are valued more than, say, mudflats (Bateman *et al.* 2009a). Of course, from a natural science perspective, lowly amphibians and mudflats might form a vital element in the food and habitat webs which ultimately support those animals which are considered of greater value. This, however, is not a problem which can be laid at the door of SP techniques; rather, these appear to be reasonable representations of preferences which may have little to do with sustainability requirements.

A more pertinent critique is that SP assessments assume that, at the point of expressing willingness to pay (WTP) amounts, the SP respondent comprehends biodiversity goods in the same absolute sense that they would comprehend everyday goods. While SP studies can certainly enhance comprehension through the provision of appropriate information,[52] there is evidence that in some biodiversity and animal welfare valuation studies respondents may not have the stable preferences required for economic valuations (see, for example, Bateman *et al.* 2008), resulting in stated values which are malleable (Loomes & Sugden 2002) and may not provide robust evidence regarding true underlying WTP (Cameron 1992; Harrison 1995; Kahn *et al.* 2001; Christie 2007).[53] Morris & Camino (2010) discuss at length the caveats that need to be borne in mind when working with meta-analyses of SP valuations. A more fundamental critique of the applicability of all economic approaches within this area is given by Craig *et al.* (1993).[54]

22.3.3.2 The non-use value of biodiversity: legacy values

While there is no ideal measure of the non-use value of biodiversity, an alternative to SP studies is provided by examining actual payments for non-use-related wildlife conservation.[55]

Pearce (2007) notes that private donations to charities are relatively small (in part because of the transaction costs individuals face in banding together), and instead focuses upon UK overseas expenditure on biodiversity of roughly £65 million p.a. (at 2010 prices). However, the policy-led determination of such amounts means that they cannot be taken as a robust estimate of values. A more robust, although very much lower bound source of individualistic valuations, is provided by examining legacies to environmental

charities. Legacies can be argued to represent a pure non-use value: individuals leaving a charitable bequest to an environmental organisation in a will, for the purposes of supporting their conservation activities, will not experience the benefits of this work.

Mourato *et al.* (2010) examine the value of legacies to the largest environmental charities in the UK: The National Trust, the Royal Society for the Protection of Birds (RSPB), and the National Trust for Scotland. Atkinson *et al.* (2009) estimate that in 2007, only 6% of all deaths in Britain resulted in a charitable bequest (with this percentage rising considerably with the size of the estate). But despite the relatively small proportion of estates leaving a charitable bequest, legacies are a major source of income for charities. In 2008/09, charitable giving by individuals was almost £6 billion to the top 500 fundraising charities (Pharoah 2010). Legacies represent almost one-quarter of this total (£1.4 billion), with almost three-quarters of charities reporting income from legacies. Although environmental charities rank seventh in terms of total fundraised income, they rank fourth in terms of legacy income (within the top 500 charities in the UK) after cancer, animals and general social welfare charities. Legacy income is an important source of revenue for environmental charities, comprising almost 30% of all their fundraising income. Overall, the total legacy income earned by environmental charities in 2008/09 was £97 million, which represents 7% of all charitable legacies (Pharoah 2010).

Table 22.3 details the top five environmental charities according to the fundraised and legacy income they earned in 2008/09. Three of these charities (The National Trust,

Table 22.3 Fundraised and legacy income of top five environmental charities (2008/09). Source: data extracted from Pharoah (2010).

Environmental charity	Legacy income (£ million and % of total fundraised income)		Total fundraised income (£ million)	Rank within top 500 charities
The National Trust	42.8	44%	97.8	12
Royal Society for the Protection of Birds	26.6	41%	64.9	16
WWF UK	8.1	22%	37.4	32
The Woodland Trust	8.2	40%	20.6	58
National Trust for Scotland	4.0	21%	18.8	61

52 Note that an association between the information provided and SP values is not an indication of bias in the latter values; indeed, we would expect such a link and observe this in everyday values (Munro & Hanley 1999). Furthermore, different forms of what is objectively the same information can substantially hamper or enhance its comprehension (Bateman *et al.* 2009b). However, what is not consistent with economic theory is where values based upon the same information vary purely because of the way that questions are framed (Loomes & Sugden 2002).

53 Note that much of the existing literature does not conform to best practice guidelines (e.g. Bateman *et al.* 2002a) and therefore cannot be taken as clear evidence of the non-applicability of stated preference methods for valuing non-use values for biodiversity.

54 We are grateful to Nigel Cooper for highlighting this critique.

55 In lieu of biodiversity values, Morling *et al.* (2010) consider the cost of managing biodiversity on the strong assumption that the political biodiversity targets and legal mechanisms that have been brought in to support biodiversity are a reflection of public preferences. Annual costs for the UK at 2010 prices are as follows: Biodiversity Action Plans = £837 million (although this contrasts the previously cited BAP cost estimate of £564 million p.a. given by GHK Consulting (2010); additional costs for protected areas = £217 million; marine biodiversity costs = £63 million. This gives a total UK cost for these biodiversity initiatives of £1,117 million p.a. However, the assertion that policy spending is a good indicator of underlying benefit values is a very strong assumption and may well not hold. Given this, we do not argue that this should be taken as a robust indicator of non-use biodiversity value.

RSPB and WWF UK) rank within the top 50 largest charities in the UK. Environmental legacy income is considerable, with the National Trust attracting the largest number of legacies, constituting some 44% of their total fundraised income at almost £43 million (Pharoah 2010). Had donors intended their legacy income to be spent on National Trust countryside, RSPB reserves or National Trust for Scotland countryside, we would have been able to estimate a legacy-based non-use value of around £219/ha of National Trust countryside, £190/ha of RSBP reserve and £53/ha of National Trust for Scotland's Scottish countryside for 2008/09, respectively. However, donors' preferences about the allocation of their legacies are not known and these figures are therefore liable to overstate the environmental component of these legacies. That said, further analysis suggests that for the two largest environmental charities (National Trust and RSPB) the total value of annual legacies has increased significantly over the last two decades and the proportion of estates leaving a legacy to environmental causes has risen, even in the light of falling death rates.

Legacies are interesting proxies for non-use values in that they are observable in the market and not reliant upon SP data. But clearly, they capture only one element of environmental non-use values, i.e. those that are reflected in the marketplace at the time of death. Further research is needed to ascertain the magnitude of the non-use values that are not reflected in the market. Moreover, there are major knowledge gaps in our analysis. In general, very little is known about charitable bequests in the UK. Data on charitable bequests, estates and demographic characteristics of donors is not easily accessible, particularly for analysis over time. Equally, comprehensive data on charitable giving over time, from the perspective of the recipient organisations, and covering a wide range of organisations, is not freely available.

22.3.4 Timber Production

The total quantity of wood produced in the UK has risen substantially over the past three decades, more than tripling since the mid-1970s to over 8 million green tonnes currently, as Coniferous Woodlands planted in the 20th Century have matured. Forecasts suggest that UK softwood production from existing woodlands will continue to rise over the next decade, and then decline until the mid-2050s (Valatin & Starling 2010). However, during the same period, world softwood timber prices have collapsed from £35/tonne in the early 1970s to about £12/tonne at present (all at 2010 prices). This appears to follow a longer term downward trend. Given that domestically produced wood accounts for under one-fifth of the total used in Britain, there does not seem to be a purely timber-based case for a domestic forest sector on social value grounds (although clearly there is a private financial case for such production and a reduction of imports may reduce transport-based GHG emissions). However, the case is much stronger when we consider the wider values

of UK woodland in relation to ecosystem services, with recreation and carbon storage values being particularly substantial and both exceeding timber values (recreation and carbon storage values are considered subsequently in this chapter). The increasing significance of such ecosystem service values in the case of broadleaved woodland is reflected in a halving of hardwood production since the mid-1970s, reflecting a shift in management objectives by state sector bodies including the Forestry Commission away from timber production and towards the provision of multiple ecosystem services.

22.3.5 Carbon Storage and Greenhouse Gas Flux: Marine and Coastal Margins[56]

22.3.5.1 Coastal Margins

Biomass and sediments in Coastal Margins and the Marine environment raise the potential for sequestration or release of GHGs. In the case of Coastal Margin habitats, carbon sequestration is primarily provided by Sand Dunes, Saltmarsh and uncultivated Machair, although carbon sequestration rates are not available for the latter. The second half of the 20th Century has seen a reduction in the area of both Sand Dunes and Saltmarsh in the UK, with the former falling most rapidly. These trends are expected to continue through the first half of the present century and overall, are expected to result in declines in sequestration within UK Sand Dunes of more than 80,000 tonnes of carbon dioxide per year (tCO_2/yr) and within Saltmarshes of around 35,000 tCO_2/yr.[57]

Applying the Department of Energy and Climate Change (DECC 2009) carbon sequestration values (which are based on avoided damage costs calculations as discussed in Section 22.2.1) to these estimates allows us to derive marginal (per ha) values for changes in storage within these coastal land categories. Wide variations in storage capacity estimates mean that for Sand Dunes, these values range from £32/ha/yr to just over £240/ha/yr, whereas the higher sequestration capacities of Saltmarsh yield values ranging from £60/ha/yr to around £620/ha/yr. Combining these marginal values with data on expected changes in areas for each habitat type yields suggests that in 2010 UK Sand Dunes will sequester carbon at a rate of nearly £8 million p.a. Despite the expectation that the area of sand dune will reduce over the next half century, the roughly six-fold increase in the planned DECC carbon sequestration value between 2004 and 2060 means that by 2060, UK Sand Dunes are expected to sequester nearly £40 million of carbon p.a. (in 2010 prices).[58] A similar pattern arises with UK Saltmarsh, with a shrinking area being offset by a rising carbon price to yield an increasing annual value. Annual values for carbon sequestration in UK Saltmarsh are expected to rise from just under £11 million in 2010 to over £63 million p.a. in 2060 (again at 2010 prices). The spatial distribution of these values is uneven, with most Sand Dune sequestration occurring in Scotland, and the majority of carbon fixing by

---

56 This Section draws in part from Beaumont *et al.* (2010).

57 Sand Dune estimates from data and forecasts for the period 1900–2060 (Jones *et al.* 2010). Saltmarsh estimates from data and forecasts for the period 1945–2060 (Jones *et al.* 2004, 2008, 2010; Beaumont *et al.* 2010).

58 The stock of carbon in Coastal Margin vegetation and soils is estimated to be at least 6.8 megatonnes of carbon. However, there are insufficient data to determine how this may change.

Saltmarsh arising in England.[59] A reorientation of coastal protection and defence policy in recent years has meant that a number of new saltmarshes have been created on the eastern coast of England. Economic assessments of this so-called managed realignment policy are presented later in this chapter. **Table 22.4** summarises the various results concerning Coastal Margin sequestration of carbon.

22.3.5.2 Carbon sequestration in Marine habitats

The Marine habitat plays a significant role in the global carbon cycle although, as detailed in Chapter 12, there are minimal data readily available to quantify the extent of this role, or indeed even the total stock of carbon stored within the Marine habitat. What is clear is that, at any point in time, large amounts of carbon are stored in marine phytoplankton (Davis 2007). **Figure 22.4** details estimates of the historical levels of this storage in UK shelf seas from 1961, together with a forecast out to 2050. Analysis suggests that there may be some growth in forecast levels, but that, at present, there is no clearly significant trend. However, even if this were proven, it would not illuminate whether or not there is any net change in carbon storage over time. For marine carbon to be considered permanently sequestered it must either sink to the deep ocean, via the 'biological carbon pump', or be buried in the benthic environment. The UK waters assessed in this analysis are primarily shallow shelf seas and the currents in these waters mean that it is unlikely that the carbon fixed by primary productivity in UK waters will be transported to the deep oceans. It is also unlikely that the carbon will be buried in the benthic environment as the carbon is more likely to be labile (subject to change), and therefore more accessible and likely to be 'processed' and kept within the marine ecosystem. That said, the massive

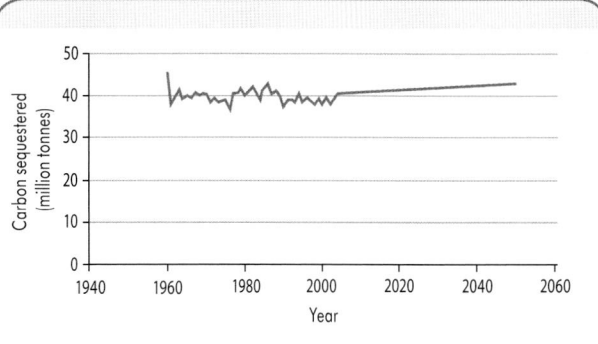

Figure 22.4 Estimated carbon sequestration by marine phytoplankton in UK shelf seas, 1961–2050.*
Source: Beaumont *et al.* (2010); time series to 2004 based on Momme Butenschön (unpublished data); projection to 2050 based on Rob Holmes (unpublished data). * Forecast based upon the IPCC (2007) Business as Usual scenario (the special Report Emissions Scenario AIB).

levels of carbon involved in these processes suggests that further research into the processes and any underlying trends may be worthwhile.

22.3.6 Water Quantity and Quality[60]

Freshwater habitats, comprising open waters, wetlands and floodplains, provide a range of ecosystem services associated with the provisioning and regulation of water quantity and quality. In turn, they generate a range of final goods, including for example public water supply, water for habitats, recreation, amenity and heritage.[61] These aspects of freshwater ecosystems are also considered in other sections of this chapter.

22.3.6.1 Water quantity

The freshwater ecosystem regulates the provision of water for human use. Water is vital to life and hence it is not meaningful to try and put finite estimates on its total value. However, at least in the UK, there is no feasible scenario in which a total value for water would be needed for decision making. Instead economic analysis focuses upon feasible marginal changes in supplies.

About 22 billion cubic metres (m³) of water are abstracted in the UK each year, 52% from rivers and lakes, 11% from groundwater and about 37% from tidal waters (mainly used for cooling; EA 2009e; SEPA 2004). Of the 13 billion m³/yr extracted from non-tidal sources in England and Wales, about half is used for public water supply. A further third is used for electricity power generation. Industry takes about 10% and aquaculture and amenity about 9%. Spray irrigation accounts for less than 1% of total abstraction, but this is concentrated in the relatively dry Anglian water region in summer. Total reported abstraction quantities have remained more or less constant over the last 15 years (EA 2010).

Prices charged for abstraction do not reflect the full value of water, either in its natural state or in any particular

Table 22.4 Summary of the quantity and value of Coastal Margin carbon storage (tonnes of carbon dioxide; tCO₂). Values assessed as avoided damage costs in 2010 prices. Source: Beaumont *et al.* (2010).

Units	Estimates
Quantities (t CO₂/yr)	Sand Dunes: decrease of 80,168 tCO₂ /yr
	Saltmarsh: decrease of 34,774 tCO₂/yr
Marginal values (£/ha/yr)*	Sand Dunes: sequestration value £32.25–241.49/ha/yr
	Saltmarsh: sequestration value £60.63–622.30/ha/yr
National (UK) values (£/yr)	Sand Dunes: 2010: £7.98 million/yr; 2060: £39.13 million/yr (an increase of £31.15 million/yr)
	Saltmarsh: 2010: £11.93 million/yr; 2060: £63.22 million/yr (an increase of £51.29 million/yr)
	2010: Value of carbon dioxide sequestration: £268/ha
	2060: Value of carbon dioxide sequestration: £1,420/ha

* These marginal values imply a total UK stock value from Sand Dunes, Saltmarsh and Machair of £1,282 million in 2010 prices. However, given that changes to this entire area are not credible, this is not a policy relevant value.

---

59 Calculated using the mid-range carbon price and mid-range sequestration rate.
60 This Section draws in part from Morris & Camino (2010).
61 See Table 9.1 in Chapter 9.

applications. Rather, they reflect the cost of managing the licensing system and there is concern that this leads to inefficient use. Water prices vary from £0.003 to £0.06/m³ for abstracted raw water, through to £1.50/m³ for metered, treated, potable water piped to households. These cost-based prices grossly underestimate the very considerable consumer surplus that water users enjoy over and above the prices paid for this essential good.

The Scottish Government provides the most comprehensive assessment of water values and these are thought to be broadly indicative for the UK in general (SEPA 2004; Moran & Dann 2008).[62] As demonstrated in **Table 22.5**, the value of water varies considerably between uses. The marginal value for treated water ranges from £0.50/m³ to £1.20/m³. For raw water, the marginal value for irrigation water ranges between £0.23/m³ and £1.38/m³ for the Scottish case, comparable with values well in excess of £1.5/m³ for irrigated potato and salad crops in eastern England (Knox *et al.* 1999; Morris *et al.* 2004). Marginal values for raw water vary considerably according to industrial processes, highest where high water quality is required for the chemicals industry and whisky manufacturing. The energy sector shows relatively low marginal values for water used for cooling but for large throughputs. The value of water for hydropower is particularly sensitive to assumptions about the economic price of energy and the cost of alternative sources. **Table 22.5** also shows the relative use of abstracted water across the sectors, but it is not clear whether the estimates are entirely comparable between the countries of the UK.

Fresh water has a value *in situ* in the natural environment, supporting the range of services referred to elsewhere in this chapter, such as biodiversity, recreation and property values. A survey in southern England of household WTP to leave water in the environment in situations where abstraction could lead to environmental damage produced an estimate of £0.30/m³ per day in 2010 prices (Jacobs 2008).

However, while natural habitats are obviously the source of such supplies, it is unclear how these are liable to change and what the implications are for water provisioning. For example, Tinch *et al.* (2010) note that mountainous areas are major providers of water but there is no clear association between changes in the natural environment in these areas and water supply levels. Rather, the major contributors to variation in water quantity supplies in such regions are due to human and manufactured capital inputs such as damming. Such values cannot readily be attributed to ecosystems. They can, however, indicate the value of services provided by Freshwaters where their supply, for a variety of reasons, is limited.

There is concern about how development pressures, exacerbated by climate change, could affect the capacity of Freshwater ecosystems to provide sufficient water for people. Reduction in the amount of water available for abstraction could result in i) the loss of value from some water uses and/or ii) extra costs of providing water from alternative sources or adopting water saving technologies. 'Unsecured' sources such as for irrigation and industrial/mineral washing are likely to be most vulnerable to variations in supply. This may justify additional expense of securing water by, for example, winter storage reservoirs. High value uses of water, such as those associated with public water supply, clearly justify relatively high investment to improve water security.

Table 22.5 Estimates of the value of water use.* Source: water value use data is from SEPA (2004); valuation assumptions and estimated abstraction data for Scotland is from Moran & Dann (2008); estimated abstracted data for England and Wales is from the Environment Agency (2010). Note the abstraction estimates are not comparable. Amounts of water in cubic metres (m³).

Sector	Water value in use for Scotland (2004 prices)	Valuation assumptions: MV (marginal values); AV (average values); TV (total values)	Estimated abstraction in Scotland (million m³/year)	Estimated abstraction in England and Wales (million m³/year)
Households (treated water)	50–120 pence/m³	MV for treated water only, based on WTP[†] estimate	876	6,038
Agriculture–irrigation	23–138 pence/m³	MV based on value added	57	72 (+19 for non-irrigation uses)
Aquaculture	0.126 pence/m³	AV assumes avoided cost of waste disposal	1,582	1,203
Salmon angling	£175/day	TV benefit transfer estimate	-	-
Industry	4–37.5 pence/m³ (e.g. 16 pence/m³ paper and pulp industries; 35 pence/m³ chemical industries)	MV benefit transfer from Canadian industry study	675 chemicals, food, textiles and paper	1,151
Energy	0.049–0.817 pence/m³	MV comparative cost of alternative energy sourcing: coal, gas, windpower	23,755 hydro throughput; Non-hydro 3,783 including tidal	4,012 non-tidal 6,672 tidal

* All monetary values derived from Scottish data.
† Willingness to pay.

62 One unpublished yet interesting contrast is provided by NERA economic consultants for Thames Water which estimates the value of lost output in London from water-use restrictions during the 2000 droughts at around £174 million a day. This impact would be expected to increase as a result of climate change where, under a medium emissions scenario, summer mean precipitation in the south east is expected to fall by 23%, creating the imperative for more efficient water management.

Measures to secure water for nature conservation may be justified, especially in protected areas. Failure to restrict abstraction in the face of declining Freshwater resources would compromise the non-market ecosystems services referred to elsewhere in this chapter.

In the long term, the economic value of freshwater provisioning will reflect the costs of achieving an appropriate balance of the demand for and supply of water. On the demand side, the Environment Agency reports that measures such as compulsory metering to reduce household water consumption by a target of 15% (from 150 to 130 litres/day) could cost between £1.40 and £1.6/m³ (EA 2009e). By comparison, options to enhance freshwater supply appear more expensive, namely surface and ground water development (£1–£5/m³), reservoirs (£3–£10/m³) and desalinisation (£4–£8/m³). A detailed review of water supply options (Mott MacDonald 1998), however, estimated incremental average costs for reservoir development ranging between £0.21/m³ and £1.36/m³ of water delivered in a given year in 2010 prices, assuming a 50% annual utilisation rate.

Increased investments may be required in future in order to avoid pressures on Freshwater habitats associated with changes in climate and/or demographics.[63] A moderate climate change scenario could reduce water available for immediate abstraction by 10% by 2060, equivalent to about 1.4 billion m³/yr for the UK at current levels of abstraction. Assuming water storage and transfer costs of between £1.0 and £1.5/m³ for large-scale provision, securing this amount of water would cost about £1.4 to £2.1 billion/yr for the whole UK population. (This assumes that there are similar abstraction rates across the nation, equivalent to about £23 to £35/yr/capita of population affected). These investment costs could be higher if the climate change impact is greater and the growth in water demand is unconstrained. While these figures do not estimate the value of water services provided by Freshwater ecosystems, they indicate the equivalent cost of securing water supplies for

use while maintaining the non-market ecosystem services of rivers, lakes and aquifers. In some cases, investments in supply enhancement and regulation may also achieve environmental enhancement.

One assessment of the potential marginal value of changes in ecosystems upon water supply is provided by Morris & Camino (2010). **Table 22.6** details estimates of average, total and marginal values for surface and groundwater supply provided by inland and coastal wetlands in the UK. However, while these are significant, amounting to more than £0.5 billion p.a., the marginal values associated with expansions of wetlands appear relatively minor. It is noted that inland wetlands, particularly, help to reduce variations in water flows and levels.

22.3.8.2 Water quality

Water quality is a major determinant of the capacity of the Freshwater ecosystems to provide a range of market and non-market services. It is important here to distinguish between the total value of water quality and the value of a marginal change in quality. As discussed below, the quality of most water bodies in the UK is moderate to good, according to the EU Water Framework Directive (WFD) classification. Much of the discussion below refers to a change in quality around the current position, recognising the significant ongoing measures to protect water quality by the water industry and others. Clearly, a major deterioration in the quality of a freshwater body could result in complete loss of some ecosystem services and final goods, such as drinking water, irrigated crops, bathing and fishing, or require major expenditure to mitigate the consequences of loss of quality. Within the limits of the available information, the assessment here focuses on selected marginal changes from the current situation, mostly associated with the WFD.

Market benefits associated with water quality. The quality of water that is abstracted and used will obviously affect a range of market benefits for particular sectors and groups such as water companies, those involved in

Table 22.6 Estimated average, total and marginal values for surface and groundwater supply provided by inland and coastal wetlands in the UK.* All values are given in £, 2010 prices. Source: Morris & Camino (2010).

Ecosystem service-related goods	No. of sites[†]	Total area (ha)	Average value of service where present (addition to default value)[‡] (£/ha/year)	Total value of service assuming it is present in all UK inland/coastal wetlands[¶] (£ million/year)	Marginal value of service when provided by an additional hectare of new wetland[§] (£/ha/year)
UK inland wetlands	1,519	601,550	2	2	1
UK coastal wetlands	693	274,613	16	514	12

* Values are area-weighted estimates for all UK inland wetland sites using the Brander *et al.* (2008) benefit function and CORINE land use data sets.

† Data on the number and area of wetlands were drawn from the European CORINE Land Cover Maps (Morris & Camino 2010).

‡ Default average values (where all of the ecosystem services specified in this table do not apply) are £303/ha/yr for UK inland wetlands and £1,856/ha/yr for UK coastal wetlands.

¶ In contrast, the default total value of the existing inland wetland stock, assuming that none of the ecosystem services in the table apply, is £182 million/yr for UK inland wetlands and £509 million/yr for UK coastal wetlands.

§ The per hectare value of services associated with additional new wetlands is lower than the average per hectare value of existing wetlands. This reflects the diminishing marginal value of additional wetlands.

63 For example, the Environment Agency forecast change in water demand for England and Wales for the 2050s ranging from -4% through to +35% according to different scenarios: www.environment-agency.gov.uk/research/library/publications/40731.aspx.

commercial fisheries and those providing recreation and tourism services (Entec 2008; University of Brighton 2008). Household drinking water supplies are routinely treated to bring them up to potable standards. Both common sense and empirical studies have confirmed the massive health benefits of such treatment. Ecosystems contribute to these benefits by improving water quality through natural processes such as the filtration services provided by healthy soils. That said, it is argued that the economic benefits of such services should be measured in terms of a reduction in treatment costs rather than attempting any estimation of the benefits of avoided ill health.

Assessment of the avoided remediation costs of water purification which may come about by environmental improvement is complicated, as necessary information is typically considered as confidential by private water utilities (Andrews 2003; Knapp 2005). However, Lovett *et al.* (2006) draw upon work by the Environment Agency (EA 2002) and Pretty *et al.* (2003) to provide a lower bound estimate of the annual cost of treating UK drinking water to meet EU nitrate standards of at least £13 million and note that this is expected to rise further in the future. A more recent report published by UK Water Industry Research (UKWIR 2004) summarises the costs incurred by the UK water supply industry in response to a range of groundwater quality problems (arising from nitrates, pesticides and other chemicals, salinity, metals, bacteria and so on) during the years 1975–2004. Total capital (CAPEX) and operating (OPEX) expenditure associated with these problems is estimated at £754 million (2003 prices). In addition, Lovett *et al.* (2006) estimate capital expenditure by water companies to reduce nitrate levels in ground and surface water of about £300–£400 million during the Fourth Asset Management Plan (AMP4) investment period ending in 2009, although the authors again note the difficulties of obtaining accurate costing data from a privatised water industry. Working from these and other sources, Lovett *et al.*(2006) estimate costs of around £8/person/yr to treat nitrate problems in affected areas.

Further variations in treatment costs can arise at a local level if specific issues arise due to ecosystem influences. Numerous natural habitats such as upland and peatland areas contribute both positively and negatively to water quality, and hence to the costs and benefits accruing to water users. In particular, the management of peatlands can influence water colouration. Colour problems due to run-off of dissolved organic carbon have increased over the last 20–30 years. The practice of moorland 'gripping' (digging and enlarging drainage ditches) may have contributed to this problem. Avoided cost calculations can be made of the benefits of reducing colouration problems by blocking drains to reduce peat wastage. These will vary on a catchment-to-catchment basis and are not known at a national level. However, one study showed benefits from avoided costs of treatment were around £5 million over 10 years. As we note subsequently, these are likely to be dwarfed by the non-market benefits of avoiding such problems as discolouration.

While information is incomplete, the evidence which is available suggests that the direct market benefits associated with the incremental changes in water quality to be achieved under the WFD are unlikely to be significant in total. They are also difficult to estimate at a national level using available data (Defra 2010a). It is noted, however, that a major loss of water quality would seriously compromise the market-based services provided by freshwater ecosystems and for some purposes, would be similar to a curtailment in water supply.

Non-market benefits associated with water quality. Turning to consider the non-market values of water quality in rivers and lakes, these are typically estimated by examining the benefits associated with improving quality back to natural levels (i.e. in effect, these are estimates of the value of losses currently being experienced under present lower quality).[64]

In a major study undertaken for Defra as part of their preparations to implement the WFD, NERA Economic Consulting use a mixture of contingent valuation and choice experiment methods to estimate the value that households in England and Wales ascribe to water quality as it affects biodiversity (in terms of fish and other aquatic life), aesthetic quality (viewing, clarity, smell, insects) and recreation (suitability for providing relaxation, recreational activities in and near streams) (NERA 2007). Estimates of WTP for water quality varied according to the methods of elicitation,[65] with mean WTP thought by NERA (2007) to lie between £45 and £168 per household p.a. for improving water quality in 95% of rivers and lakes to 'good quality standards'. Allocation of values across different levels of improvement is given in **Table 22.7**, which also reports aggregate benefits across England and Wales of £1,140 million p.a. The greatest proportion of extra benefits is associated with improvements from moderate to good water quality. This reflects not only the greater share of water bodies in this improvement category but also, as expected, the relatively high values for improvements in more populous areas.

Drawing on the preceding analysis, the Environment Agency has compiled estimates of the benefits of improvements in water quality per kilometre for the main river basins in England and Wales. Average benefits are £15.6/km, £18.6/km and £34.2/km for improvements that lift water quality from low to medium, from medium to high and from low to high respectively. Benefits per kilometre are much greater than these average values in river basins with higher population densities.

Another perspective on freshwater quality is given by the estimated annual equivalent expenditure of £1.1 billion/yr (in 2008 prices) to meet WFD quality targets over the next 43 years through to 2052. Reflecting pressures and vulnerabilities, most of this expense is associated with supporting water abstraction and discharges (£889 million/yr), habitat and fisheries (£160 million/yr), urban drainage and reservoir safety (£91 million/yr) and agricultural pollution (£57 million/yr).

---

64 There are actually four theoretically acceptable economic measures of welfare change: WTP for a gain; WTP to avoid a loss; willingness to accept compensation to forgo a gain; willingness to accept compensation for a loss. Terminology and theoretical and empirical comparison of measures is explored by Bateman *et al.* (2000).
65 For a discussion of WTP elicitation effects see Bateman *et al.* (1995).

Table 22.7 Non-market benefits associated with improvements in water quality in rivers and lakes in England and Wales in 2009. Source: Morris & Camino (2010).

Initial quality status of water bodies: rivers and lakes	Benefit of planned improvement in water quality to be achieved in the period 2009–2015 (£ million/yr)	Remaining benefits associated with achieving Good quality status post 2015 (£ million/yr)	Total benefits of improvement to Good quality status (£ million/yr)	Distribution of extra benefits of water quality improvement by class (%)
Moderate	46.4	720	766.4	67%
Poor	26.3	273.8	300.1	26%
Bad	9.1	55.7	64.8	6%
Not known	0.7	8.1	8.8	1%
Total			**1,140.0**	**100%**

It is recognised that the preceding figures do not indicate the value of the total benefits of non-market goods associated with freshwater quality. Rather, they indicate in broad terms the expected benefits of services associated with achieving given increments in water quality about current quality levels, and a (potential) revealed willingness to incur costs to obtain these incremental benefits. Neither do they tell us about WTP to avoid the loss of non-market benefits if there were considerably lower standards of water quality in UK Freshwaters, other than suggesting that these are likely to be very significant.

One attempt to consider both the benefits and costs of changes in water quality is provided through the work of Fezzi *et al.* (2008, 2010a) and Bateman *et al.* (2010b). Fezzi *et al.* (2008) draw on the prior work of Cuttle *et al.* (2007) to consider the costs of a variety of measures to reduce farm diffuse nutrient pollution of waterways (the agricultural sector being the principle source of such pollution). Fezzi *et al.* (2008) estimate that measures such as lowering livestock dietary nitrogen and phosphorus intakes could increase farm costs by up to £46/cow p.a. (due to the need to find alternative foodstuffs) and reduce revenues by as much as 8% (in the poultry sector where cuts in nutrient intake reduce productivity). Fezzi *et al.* (2010a), extend this work to develop an integrated hydrological-economic analysis combining data from the Farm Business Survey with models of nutrient leaching and in-stream processes. This enables them to estimate the indirect costs to farms of changing activities in order to reduce their diffuse nutrient pollution. The effectiveness of competing strategies was assessed in terms of both nutrient loading and in-stream concentrations, with the latter being more relevant to the ecological impacts central to policies such as the WFD. While Fezzi *et al.* (2008) estimate that mean costs of reducing nutrient pollution via a 20% reduction in fertiliser application exceeded more than £100/ha in the worst affected sector (dairy), Fezzi *et al.* (2010a) show (in a study of a catchment within the Humber Basin) that alternatives such as the targeted conversion of arable areas into grassland could more than halve the impact of pollution reductions upon farm incomes.

Of course, the costs associated with reducing water pollution need to be set against the benefits. Bateman *et al.*

(2010b) build on the prior work of Fezzi *et al.* (2010a), to conduct a benefit valuation study in the Humber Basin. Data were collected from more than 2,000 households detailing their outdoor recreational behaviour across the year. By recording both the trip outset and destination locations, a travel cost analysis was conducted to examine the influences upon trip choice. Focusing upon water-based recreation, Bateman *et al.* (2010b) show that, after controlling for other determinants as diverse as travel time, the presence of local pubs, and recreational facilities, significantly more visits are made to rivers with higher water quality.[66] Bateman *et al.* (2010b) relate this model to the level of improvement in river water quality that was shown by Fezzi *et al.* (2010a) to be feasible through farm land use change. They estimate that in the study area considered (the Aire catchment which covers much of Leeds, most of Bradford and areas upstream of the confluence with the River Calder), the benefits of improving water quality to pristine levels (as defined under the WFD) were of the order of £12.5 million p.a. This was contrasted with the costs of land use change in the Humber catchment assessed by Fezzi *et al.* (2010a) of just over £5.5 million p.a. Given the considerable excess of benefits over costs in this case, it would seem likely that such a scheme would pass most assessments. However, there is a distributional issue to be addressed here, in that the costs of such a scheme would impact upon a small rural sector of society, whereas the benefits would be dispersed across the mainly urban population of visitors. Clearly, there is the potential for a compensated trade-off leading to social gain here. However, without such compensation the potential for inequality is obvious.

A further cost-benefit result can be approximated by contrasting the costs associated with combating discolouration problems with the benefits derived from such actions. Bateman & Georgiou (2010) report findings from a contingent valuation study of such benefits, showing that average WTP per household, in order to avoid one day of discolouration problems, was £5.40. Comparison with costs presented previously suggests that such schemes are likely to pass cost-benefit tests.

Turning away from rivers, wetlands are also a major provider of water quality improvement benefits through their ability to recycle nutrients. **Table 22.8** uses a value transfer

---

66 Interestingly this is not a simple linear relation; potential visitors are indifferent to variation at the lower end of the quality scale. In other words, there is a lower threshold which water quality must exceed before visitor numbers increase. Thereafter the relationship is approximately linear, with increases in water quality leading to higher visitor numbers.

Table 22.8 Estimated average, total and marginal values for water quality improvements provided by inland and coastal wetlands in the UK.* All values are given in £, 2010 prices. Source: Morris & Camino (2010).

Ecosystem service-related goods	No. of sites[†]	Total area (ha)	Average value of service where present (addition to default value)[‡] (£/ha/year)	Total value of service assuming it is present in all UK inland/coastal wetlands[¶] (£ million/year)	Marginal value of service when provided by an additional hectare of new wetland[§] (£/ha/year)
UK inland wetlands	1,519	601,550	436	263	292
UK coastal wetlands	693	274,613	2,676	1,245	1,793

* Values are area-weighted estimates for all UK inland wetland sites using the Brander *et al.* (2008) benefit function and CORINE land use data sets.

[†] Data on the number and area of wetlands were drawn from the European CORINE Land Cover Maps (Morris & Camino, 2010).

[‡] Default average values (where all of the ecosystem services specified in this table do not apply) are £303/ha/yr for UK inland wetlands and £1,856/ha/yr for UK coastal wetlands.

[¶] In contrast, the default total value of the existing inland wetland stock, assuming that none of the ecosystem services in the table apply, is £182 million/yr for UK inland wetlands and £509 million/yr for UK coastal wetlands.

[§] The per hectare value of services associated with additional new wetlands is lower than the average per hectare value of existing wetlands. This reflects the diminishing marginal value of additional wetlands.

function to estimate average, total and marginal values for water quality improvements provided by inland and coastal wetlands in the UK. These can be substantial, amounting to £1,500 million p.a. Notice, however, that the marginal values associated with expansions of wetlands are significantly lower than present average benefits, reflecting the diminishing marginal benefits of increases in such resources.

Clearly, Freshwater ecosystems play a central role in supporting human welfare. They are also a focal point for conflicts that arise when there are competing human demands for water as an essential natural resource. The analysis here (and that covered in other sections of this chapter that deal with water-related benefits such as biodiversity, recreation and amenity) is known to be incomplete in terms of the full identity and valuation of benefits. For such a critical resource, data on the value of water resources and related services appear fragmented and incomplete, in spite of the very considerable advances made recently under the WFD. This is an important area of work for the future.

22.3.7 Flood Protection: Inland[67]

Ecosystems can play a major role in flood control. Approximately £1 billion/yr is spent on flood risk management (EA 2009a,b). However, in recent years, flooding has become more problematic in the UK (Pitt 2008). In the UK as a whole, probably over 5 million properties are exposed to low to moderate probability of river and coastal flooding (between 0.5% and 1.3% chance of flooding each year) and the average annual cost of flooding in the UK is about £1.4 billion (EA 2009a,b). However, extreme flooding events can generate much higher costs, with the 2007 floods in England resulting in estimated costs of £3.2 billion (Chatterton *et al.* 2010) with two-thirds of this being borne directly by households and businesses. This leads to a strong case for investment in flood defences, both natural and man-made, with Defra's Spending Review suggesting an average benefit-cost ratio of 8:1 (pers. comm., Mallika Ishwaran, Defra, 2011).

Direct intangible impacts on flood victims include stress and health risks. A survey of households (RPA & FHRC 2004) showed a weighted average WTP of £200/household/yr to avoid the intangible costs associated with a 1% per year chance of flooding, equivalent to a present value sum of about £5,000 over 50 years. Evidence from the 2007 floods suggests this is probably an underestimate. There are currently about 600,000 households in the UK at serious risk of flooding (FFCD 2004). This equates to a WTP to avoid intangible costs of £120 million/yr.

The link between ecosystems and flooding can be demonstrated via two examples. First, the climate can be seen as an ecosystem service and hence, deterioration in the climate should be seen as a relevant value for the UK NEA. Second, changes to the extent and management of certain terrestrial habitats can lead to flooding-related values, whether benefits or costs.

Climate change could double numbers of households exposed to serious risk for the UK by 2060 (EA 2009d). Looking forward to 2080, the Foresight Future Flooding Project (FFCD 2004) identified a possible increase in the annual river and coastal flood damage costs to property of £14–£19 billion (in 2004 prices) under future consumption-oriented scenarios in the absence of additional measures to control flood risk (**Table 22.9**). This is equivalent to about £17–£23 billion in 2010 prices: or about £11–£17 billion/yr in 2060 (the UK NEA time horizon), assuming a linear increase in damage cost over time. Incremental flood damage costs were estimated at £0.5–£3.8 billion for 2080 and £0.4–£3.4 billion in 2060 (all figures at 2010 prices) under sustainability oriented scenarios, reflecting a combination of reduced flood probability and damage costs. Additional costs were identified for urban flooding unconnected with river and coastal sources.

Climate-induced increases in flood damage will also impact upon agricultural land. The average cost of a flood occurring at any time within a given year on intensively farmed Grade 1 agricultural land (£1,220/ha) is much higher than on extensively grazed grade 4 land (£160/ha), with costs rising for summer flooding (Posthumus *et al.* 2009). Where flooding results in permanent abandonment, land prices of up to £15,000/ha can apply (Defra 2009; RICS 2010).

67   This Section draws in part from Morris & Camino (2010).

There are about 1.34 million hectares of agricultural land at risk of flooding in England and Wales, of which 62% are liable to flooding by rivers only, 23% by sea only and 15% by both. About 421,500 ha currently benefit from flood defences in England and Wales, of which 70,000 ha (17% of total) are grade 1 and 2, and 424,000 benefit from coastal defences, of which 158,000 ha (37%) are grade 1 and 2. About 1.28 million hectares in England and Wales also benefit from pumped drainage to avoid either flooding or waterlogging; over 90% of this land is used for agriculture, and one-third is located in the Anglian region.

An assessment of land use, estimated flood damage costs, and flood return periods in years for defended and undefended areas of England and Wales (Roca *et al.* 2010) shows that flood defence reduces expected annual damage costs from river flooding by £5.2 million, and from coastal flooding by £117.7 million. These estimates, however, undervalue the considerable associated benefits of land drainage and the management of water levels for farming. Estimates are not available for other parts of the UK at the time of writing.

Land use management clearly impacts upon the probability of flooding of adjacent or downstream property, although robust national estimates of associated values are not available. Nevertheless, some wetland values are available. While Tinch *et al.* (2010) argue that the ability of peatlands to act as flood buffers may be overstated, European evidence suggests that wetlands can be a major provider of flood control values, depending on their location. **Table 22.10** employs findings from a value transfer model to provide estimates of average, total and marginal values for these benefits, as provided by inland wetlands in the UK. These are substantial, although the marginal values associated with expansions of wetlands are somewhat lower than present average benefits, reflecting the diminishing marginal benefits of increases in such resources.

22.3.8 Flood Protection: Coastal

The majority of UK coastal defence is provided by the natural environment, with only 18% protected by defence works and artificial beaches. Of course, much of this natural defence can effectively be omitted from decision making where there is no significant danger of flooding (e.g. high, non-eroding cliffs). While this provides a clear flood defence value, effectively we can treat such defences as infinite

Table 22.9 Estimated annual economic flood damage to residential and commercial properties for the UK under current (2000) and future (2080) scenarios according to Foresight Flood Defence (2004 prices). Source: FFCD (2004).

Flood source	Current flooding costs Year 2000 (£ million/yr)	Costs under consumption-oriented scenarios* (£ million/yr)	Costs under sustainability oriented scenarios[†] (£ million/yr)
River and coastal	1,088	15,175–20,600	1,508–4,820
Intra-urban	270	5,100–7,900	740–1,870
Total	1,358	20,275–28,500	2,248–6,690

* National Enterprise and World Market scenarios.
[†] Local Stewardship and Global Sustainability scenarios.

and any value calculations as mere mental gymnastics. However, there are many other areas of the country where topography means that there is a real risk of sea flooding. Here the natural environment can provide a very valuable service.

In assessing the net annual value of any flood defence option one needs to consider three factors:
i) the frequency of any flooding which will occur under this option (virtually no defence scheme is perfect);
ii) the damage that would occur in any such flood; and
iii) the costs of building (where appropriate) and maintaining that flood defence option.

Consideration of items i) and ii) allow estimation of the expected flood damage under a defence option. This can then be added to the defence costs given at iii). One could then repeat the analysis for a situation in which the defence disappears. Obviously, this reduces maintenance and other costs, but is likely to increase the damage costs. If the latter outweighs the former, there is a case for retaining that defence, although one would then wish to consider further defence options, typically opting for the one which yields the largest net benefits relative to other options.

While there are numerous case studies of local defence schemes, to date there is no national level assessment that would allow a comparison of natural versus man-made defence values (Beaumont *et al.* 2010). Indeed, even at a more

Table 22.10 Estimated average, total and marginal values for inland flood control provided by wetlands in the UK.* All values are given in £, 2010 prices. Source: Morris & Camino (2010).

Ecosystem service-related goods	No. of sites[†]	Total area (ha)	Average value of service where present (addition to default value)[‡] (£/ha/yr)	Total value of service, assuming it is present in all UK inland wetlands[¶] (£ million/yr)	Marginal value of service when provided by an additional hectare of new wetland[§] (£/ha/yr)
UK inland wetlands	1,519	601,550	608	366	407

* Values are area-weighted estimates for all UK inland wetland sites using the Brander *et al.* (2008) benefit function and CORINE land use data sets.
[†] Data on the number and area of wetlands were drawn from the European CORINE Land Cover Maps (Morris & Camino 2010).
[‡] Default average values (where all of the ecosystem services specified in this table do not apply) are £303/ha/yr for UK inland wetlands.
[¶] In contrast, the default total value of the existing inland wetland stock, assuming that none of the ecosystem services in the table apply, is £182 million/yr for UK inland wetlands.
[§] The per hectare value of services associated with additional new wetlands is lower than the average per hectare value of existing wetlands. This reflects the diminishing marginal value of additional wetlands.

local level, with the exception of managed realignment scheme assessments (Turner et al. 2007; Luisetti et al. 2011a), studies tend to focus not on the net benefits of natural versus built defences, but instead simply on the cost of the latter, arguing that these costs are saved when natural defences are used. For example, King & Lester (1995) estimate that an 80 m wide saltmarsh can save from £2,600 to £4,600 per metre of seawall that does not have to be constructed. Obviously, such costs do not reflect the net benefits of different defence options.

Although no national estimates of the value of Coastal Margin ecosystems for flood defence currently exist, there are examples in the literature of methods that could be applied if such a study were to be undertaken. Penning-Roswell et al. (2010) and Defra (2009) provide some damage-cost analysis and Eftec (2010) considers the use of value transfers. However, a key requirement for such valuation would be a quantitative assessment of flood risk for the entire UK coastline. This seems a useful direction for future research. Such an approach could draw on the method of Costanza et al. (2008), who estimate the spatial value of coastal wetlands for hurricane protection. Through a two-step regression analysis, they explore the relationship between hurricane damage, wind speed and wetland area, and combine this with data on annual hurricane frequency to derive an estimate of the annual value of wetlands to hurricane protection. Unfortunately, however, they do not compare the values calculated to other forms of coastal defence.

Building on the meta-analysis of SP studies undertaken by Brander et al. (2006), Morris & Camino (2010) show that wetlands are a major provider of coastal storm surge protection benefits. **Table 22.11** provides estimates of average, total and marginal values for these benefits as provided by coastal wetlands in the UK. These are substantial, at more than £1.5 billion/yr. While the marginal values associated with expansions of wetlands are somewhat lower than present average benefits, reflecting the diminishing marginal benefits of increases in such resources, these are, nevertheless, still highly significant values. This underlines the argument that in many cases, coastal wetlands yield storm protection values which exceed the opportunity cost of not converting such areas to agricultural production.

Coastal saltmarshes can provide a range of services in addition to carbon storage and have more recently been utilised as a component in a new, more flexible approach to

coastal erosion and flood management strategy. So-called 'managed realignment' schemes have been designated to replace/augment hard engineering coastal defences on the east coast of England. Economic cost-benefit appraisal of a selection of managed realignment schemes indicates that such investments may be efficient; however, their spatial location is critically important, both in terms of the ecosystem services generated and the human beneficiaries. While there are 'win-win' policy opportunities, managed realignment is not sustainable as a generic solution to the complex problem of 'defending' Coastal Margins under the threat of climate change.

Managed realignment typically involves the deliberate breaching of existing sea defences, with the land behind them consequentially being flooded. Such projects result in the creation or restoration of saltmarshes, which, it is claimed, may provide a sustainable flood defence approach to dissipating wave energy. Such 'soft' defences allow the intertidal habitat to naturally move inland, thereby creating opportunities for biodiversity enhancement, amenity and recreation (i.e. a diversity of ecosystem services). Note, however, that this will of course be dependent on how successfully saltmarsh communities can re-establish.

A number of appraisals of potential or implemented managed realignment schemes have been reported in the literature. For example, a case study of the Alkborough Flats in the Humber estuary (Everard 2009; also Chapter 11) aimed to both reduce flood risk and provide physical compensation for habitat lost elsewhere in the estuary. The Environment Agency argues that this case study shows that, given the value of the ecosystem services generated following an ecosystem restoration, managed realignment innovations can result in 'win-win' solutions. One of the key results of the report is that the annual loss of food production (opportunity cost of realignment) was compensated for by the higher value of fibre related to the sale of rare breed genetic stock sheep and cattle farmed on the reclaimed marshes. The economic value of commercial fishing was also considered to be a potentially significant research gap. The valuation approach followed in this case study differs from that used by Turner et al. (2007) and Luisetti et al. (2011a,b) to value similar schemes around the Humber and Blackwater estuaries respectively (see below). For the Alkborough Flats case study, supporting services and regulatory services were assessed as being

Table 22.11 Estimated average, total and marginal values for storm buffering and flood control provided by coastal wetlands in the UK.* All values are given in £, 2010 prices. Source: Morris & Camino (2010).

Ecosystem service-related goods	No. of sites[†]	Total area (ha)	Average value of service where present (addition to default value)[‡] (£/ha/yr)	Total value of service, assuming it is present in all UK inland wetlands[¶] (£ million/yr)	Marginal value of service when provided by an additional hectare of new wetland[§] (£/ha/yr)
UK coastal wetlands	693	274,613	3,730	1,534	2,498

* Values are area-weighted estimates for all UK inland wetland sites using the Brander et al. (2008) benefit function and CORINE land use data sets.
† Data on the number and area of wetlands were drawn from the European CORINE Land Cover Maps (Morris & Camino 2010).
‡ Default average values (where all of the ecosystem services specified in this table do not apply) are £1,856/ha/yr for UK coastal wetlands.
¶ In contrast, the default total value of the existing inland wetland stock, assuming that none of the ecosystem services in the table apply, is £509 million/yr for UK coastal wetlands.
§ The per hectare value of services associated with additional new wetlands is lower than the average per hectare value of existing wetlands. This reflects the diminishing marginal value of additional wetlands.

worth just under £1 million p.a. (excluding possible flood regulation function value), and included in the aggregated gross benefit calculation. While a full investigation of the whole services production and delivery 'system' is to be commended, there is a risk of double counting problems due to the addition of both supporting service values and the value of those services they support.

Published research has highlighted the fact that managed realignment policy needs to be appraised across a more extensive spatial and temporal scale than has been the case in the traditional scheme-by-scheme coastal management system. Whole estuaries or multiple coastal cells should be treated as a single 'project' encompassing a number of realignment sites. Although in some estuaries along the English east coast some experimental managed realignment schemes have already been implemented, the approach continues to be controversial because previously reclaimed coastal land (usually agricultural land) is sacrificed in order to reduce the threats of coastal erosion and flooding (RCEP 2010). The value of agricultural land may increase over time as food security concerns rise up the political agenda.

A best practice appraisal approach first requires the identification of all sites that are likely to generate low opportunity costs and the minimum of social justice or ethical concerns. In this policy context it is feasible to apply an efficiency-based cost-benefit analysis, with the expectation that this may provide decisive information for policy choice (Randall 2002; Turner et al. 2007). It is also necessary to demonstrate, as was the case in the Blackwater case study (Luisetti et al. 2011a,b) and in analyses completed in the Humber estuary (Turner et al. 2007), that there has been no reduction in the level of protection (vis-à-vis hard defences) where new saltmarshes were put in place.

In their study of managed realignment on the Blackwater estuary, Luisetti et al. (2011a,b) provide economic values for the sites considered and examine issues of location and ecosystem services. They show three important results: i) that the values of users or potential users of the area are higher than those of non-users; ii) that the values held by both groups decay with increasing distance from the managed realignment site; and iii) that values increase with the size of the proposed wetland, but at a declining rate (a result echoing the diminishing marginal values mentioned in our methodological overview—Section 22.2.2). These relationships mean that the value of any managed realignment site will not be constant, but will vary according to location. Factors i) and ii) mean that a site located nearer to population centres is likely to generate higher values than an otherwise comparable site located in some remote place. Factor iii) means that we cannot use simple constant per hectare values to estimate the value of such schemes. However, all of these factors are in line with expectations and can be quantified, providing that a sufficient number of high quality, comparable valuation studies are undertaken. This requires study designs which are specifically orientated towards the production of generalised and transferable value functions.

Although studies such as Luisetti et al. (2011a,b) show that some realignment schemes and soft defences can pass economic analyses, for many stretches of coastline, hard defences will continue to be required for the foreseeable future because of the scale and significance of the economic and social assets that are at risk. This means that we cannot claim that managed realignment will always offer 'win-win' solutions. Although general principles for analysis can be identified, the costs and benefits of differing options will vary by location and will require individual consideration.

22.3.9 Pollution Remediation

Tinch et al. (2010) argue that habitats such as Mountains, Moorlands and Heaths may provide a substantial pollution remediation service, noting that they assimilate air pollutants such as sulphur dioxide and nitrogen oxides. Similarly, in Chapter 8 it is noted that woodlands and trees can intercept pollution from point sources, and capture diffuse pollution (including both ground and atmospheric pollution), thereby helping to reduce ambient concentrations and limit the spread of pollutants. One of the few studies to value such pollution remediation services in the UK is Powe & Willis (2004) who state, for example, that trees in Britain absorb 0.4–0.6 million tonnes of particulates (PM_{10}) a year. They include an estimate of the annual value of pollution remediation services by Britain's trees (associated both with absorption of particulates and of sulphur dioxide) of £0.9 million. Based upon associated net health benefit (reduced morbidity and mortality) estimates, the latter is closely related to other types of health benefits considered subsequently.

It seems likely that ecosystem service values for pollution remediation are substantial. Yet there was little evidence available on the value of these services or how they may vary due to habitat change. It seems likely, therefore, that this is an area which requires further research.

22.3.10 Energy and Raw Materials

22.3.10.1 Energy

The focus of the UK NEA has been upon biotic ecosystem services and their value. However, there is no reason why the principles of the ecosystem services approach should not be extended to embrace the wider contribution of the natural environment to human well-being, and indeed, such extension is argued for elsewhere (Bateman et al. 2011a). Two areas of extension seem to be of particular importance for consideration within a future expanded assessment: energy and abiotic raw materials.

The energy contribution of the natural environment is likely to expand globally in line with development needs. Fossil fuels currently dominate global energy markets. Market prices represent a good starting point for estimating the underlying economic value of fossil fuel extraction, but adjustments may need to be made for subsidies, taxes and the exercise of market power. The latter is particularly important in global oil markets. The market value of UK consumption of fossil fuels was £112 billion in 2009 (DECC 2010), of which £35 billion comprises tax and duties. Fossil fuels met 90% of UK energy demand in 2009 (DECC 2010). Two concerns are typically highlighted in consideration of fossil fuels: externalities and sustainability. The externality issue is particularly pertinent in respect of the contributions of fossil fuels to global climate change through atmospheric emissions of carbon dioxide and other GHGs. Clearly, the costs associated with such emissions must be considered within any economic analysis of such services, and these impose a substantial penalty on fossil fuels. Fossil fuel extraction and use also give rise to a range of other environmental externalities associated with air pollution, water use and the disposal of solid wastes. The sustainability issue arises because fossil fuels are physically non-renewable. However, this highlights the fact that we are looking at the maintenance of services rather than the physical constitution of any given asset. So we might run down conventional oil reserves yet maintain the service of energy provision by increasing stocks of alternative energy resources.

This brings us to consider renewable energy sources such as solar, wind and wave power and energy crops. After a slow start, the deployment of renewable energy is starting to expand rapidly. Renewables met 3% of UK energy demand in 2009 and 7% of electricity generation needs. Estimating the value of the renewable contribution is complicated by the level of subsidy associated with the Renewables Obligation and, more recently, Feed-in Tariffs for smaller generation.[68] The current value of renewable energy supply is dwarfed by that of fossil fuels. However, the supply of renewables will grow considerably if policy ambitions and forecasts are realised. For example, a recent study predicts large rises in demand for wood fibre in the UK over the period 2007–2025, mainly due to government policies and incentives to encourage the use of woodfuel (JCC 2010). Overall renewable fuels are typically associated with very low levels of externality and are inherently sustainable, making them attractive options for long-term development.

Of course, a further alternative energy source is provided by nuclear power, which supplied 17% of the UK's electricity generation needs in 2009 (DECC 2010). While providing a low emission alternative to fossil fuel, the nuclear power sector raises unique issues regarding risk and long-term waste storage and decommissioning costs.[69]

22.3.10.2 Raw materials

The annual value of marine-based biotic raw materials, including fish meal, fish oil and seaweed, is estimated to exceed £95.1 million p.a. (2010 prices). The value of non-biotic services arising from the Marine environment is huge, as summarised in **Table 22.12**. However, these are not investigated in detail in this report as they are not 'true' ecosystem services, and have been well documented elsewhere (Pugh 2008; Saunders 2010).

Terrestrial abiotic resources are also generally excluded from analyses, although they are of substantial value. For example, the UK aggregates industry is worth in the region of £4.8 billion annually and is almost exclusively supplied by natural resources. However, one resource that was considered was the value of peat extraction for supply to gardeners and horticulturalists. UK production fell from about 1.8 million m³ in 2001 to 0.94 million m³ in 2009. However, while this most

Table 22.12 Review of UK per annum values of abiotic commercial activities occurring in the Marine and Coastal Margin environments. GVA = gross value added; n/r = not reported.

Marine and Coastal Margin services	Pugh (2008) (GVA, £ million)*	Saunders et al. (2010) (£ million, 2008)
Oil and gas	19,845	36,814
Aggregates	114	31
Cooling water	n/r	100
Salt	n/r	4
Ship and boat building	1,223	n/r
Marine equipment and materials	3,268	n/r
Marine renewable energy	10	62
Construction	228	n/r
Shipping operations	3,399	7,100
Ports	5,045	n/r
Navigation and safety	150	n/r
Cables	2,705	n/r
Business services	2,086	n/r
Licence and rental	90	n/r
Defence	2,814	300

* Price base varies from 2004 to 2006. See Beaumont et al. (2010) for details.

recent output was worth about £9.7 million p.a., it resulted in the release of about 400,000 tonnes of carbon dioxide, which had an external cost of around £20 million using a DECC price in 2009 of £50 per tonne of carbon dioxide. Given this net social cost, there is a policy target for ending the use of peat in gardening products by 2020.

22.3.11 Employment

While it is certainly the case that large numbers of jobs are connected to ecosystem services, the argument that these should be counted as a distinct and robust economic benefit of such services is less clear cut. The economic approach to appraising benefit values rests upon considering trade-offs and in the case of employment benefits, the key issue concerns the opportunity costs of alternative employment. A good example of this thinking is provided by the case of forestry.

It has been argued that creating jobs in forestry is a good way to stem the ongoing trend of rural depopulation and combat the psychological and other economic costs of rural unemployment. However, numerous studies have suggested that forestry is a relatively expensive and inefficient method of providing rural employment, particularly when compared to agriculture (HM Treasury 1972; Laxton & Whitby 1986; NAO 1986; Evans 1987; Johnson & Price 1987). Therefore, while forestry expansion might be justified on a number of grounds, employment does not appear to be one of them. Such conclusions have been disputed by noting that since the 1990s,

---

68 DECC Feed-In Tariffs support small scale (less than 5 MW), low carbon electricity generation schemes, while the Renewables Obligation mandates the partial use of low carbon energy options such as wind and biomass sources.

69 Construction, containment and disposal emissions mean that this cannot be described as a zero-emission option, although clearly, carbon release is far lower than for fossil fuels.

employment in forestry has been falling and productivity rising (Thompson 1990; FICGB 1992; FC 2001). However, coincident rises in the efficiency of the most likely alternative form of rural employment, agriculture, means that the economic case for arguing that there is a major employment benefit from ecosystem services remains to be proven.

A stronger argument may well be made in terms of the benefits of ecosystem service-related employment in terms of cultural and social cohesion in marginalised and remote rural communities. For example, in 2005 more than 31,500 people were employed in the fish catching, processing and aquaculture sector in the UK, with many of these jobs located in remote coastal regions of Scotland, Wales and south-west England. While some of this employment might be transferred to other sectors if fisheries were to decline further, previous experience of translocations from remote communities dominated by single industries suggests that there are genuine net benefits in this respect. Similar arguments can be made regarding upland farming, remote forestry, employment on grouse moors and the like. An in-depth analysis would be required to estimate such benefits in economic terms and find out whether there is any robust linkage to ecosystem service levels. However, ultimately it may well be that the magnitude of any such values is dependent, in considerable part, not only upon the individuals concerned but also upon wider social preferences regarding the maintenance of such remote rural communities and the landscapes they work. While the case for conventional economic appraisal rests on the criterion of efficiency, employment and related social impacts raise equity and social justice concerns, which will be important components of the policy- and decision-making process.

22.3.12 Game and Associated Landscape Values

A substantial area of UK moorlands, most noticeably in Scotland, is managed for shooting. While ecosystem services are clearly an important input to be considered in the valuation of such activities, data are not available to permit us to isolate the value of such services separately from the human capital and other inputs required to generate sporting activities. However, it is unlikely that net values are substantial. As an example, while gross expenditure on grouse shooting in Scotland is estimated at between £5.8 and £12.6 million (FAI 2010, adjusted to 2010 prices), only 43% of Scottish sporting estates actually make a profit (Tinch et al. 2010). Valatin & Starling (2010) estimate mean stalking revenues of up to £3/ha (2010 prices) for English woodlands, based upon data for Forestry Commission land, although they recognise that these may be somewhat higher in Scotland.[70]

An economic assessment of an undertaking should consider all of its externalities, positive and negative. Clearly blood sports excite strongly negative passions amongst some in society. However, proponents point out that much lowland woodland, especially in England, has been maintained as such precisely because of sporting interests and so provides vital wildlife habitat which would not be economically sustainable without sporting revenues. Indeed, many in the blood sport fraternity argue that positive contributions to biodiversity are provided not only in terms of habitat but also directly through the culling of what are now considered pest species such as deer and therefore they are a necessary substitute for the historic loss of top predators such as wolves that previously kept deer densities in check. Similarly, the management of Mountain, Moorland and Heath habitats for grouse shooting is a direct driver of the open landscapes which are valued by many in society. This example can be extended further through allied management practices such as heather burning and raptor control to highlight the complexity of issues that are raised by grouse moor management practices. It is interesting that many of these habitats, including the agricultural areas which dominate the majority of the UK, yield landscapes which are in fact not natural, but are perceived as such by a population accustomed to such environments. This raises an interesting point that what people value about landscapes is in part dictated by what is familiar, rather than simply some innate preference.

22.3.13 Amenity Value of the Climate[71]

As noted previously, there are no constraints against (and good reasons for) extending the principles of the ecosystems service approach to the wider set of benefits and costs which are provided by the environment. Hence, we here consider the extent to which the climate delivers amenity benefits or disbenefits quite separately from the other impacts it is likely to deliver.

Whilst the case for the existence of a relationship between climate and well-being seems clear, in practice the nature of that relationship is liable to be complex. People may feel happier inhabiting warmer climates or indeed find that they need to spend less in order to achieve the same level of well-being. But this change in temperature may influence other determinants of well-being such as prices, incomes and even ecosystem availability, especially if these changes are not locally confined but global, as seems very likely to be the case. Therefore, as in the case of urban greenspace amenity, we are faced with a potentially complex set of highly correlated goods which cannot readily be untangled. Given this, all we can reasonably do is to value a subset of the possible impacts of climate change and furthermore, stop short of attributing the relationship between climate and value to particular causes, for example the reduction of heating expenditure or the existence of particular landscapes.

It may not be immediately apparent how climate fits conceptually within the ecosystem services framework. This, however, is readily understood by noting that households combine marketed and environmental goods in order to produce 'service flows' of direct value to themselves. Climate is an input to the households' production functions in the same way that pollination services, genetic diversity and indeed climate are inputs to agriculturalists' production functions.

---

70 Inspection of shooting offers on the Shooting4All website (www.shooting4all.com) suggest current rental values are in the region of £20/ha/yr although these can vary substantially according to location and site quality. Comparison with values quoted by Crockford et al. (1987) suggests that these have not varied greatly in real terms for some time.
71 This Section draws on Maddison (2010).

Most valuations of climate amenities have been undertaken through revealed preference studies, mainly considering property purchases across very varied climates.[72] Such hedonic pricing studies typically relate large numbers of house sale records to characteristics of the properties concerned, their access to facilities and workplaces, local neighbourhood and environmental conditions. By including climate variables in the analysis and examining how these are related to variation in house prices, a valuation of climate amenities can be obtained. By using spatial variation in climate as an analogue for future climate, such exercises assume perfect adaptation. The phrase 'perfect adaptation' means that households have made all cost-effective adjustments. The question is whether it is reasonable to assume that households are able to adapt perfectly over the period in question. If not, any benefits will be overestimated and any costs underestimated.

While such studies have been conducted for Great Britain (GB), and are discussed below, revealed preference methods do face a practical challenge when applied within the GB context. Although GB is characterised by different climates, these differences are much less pronounced than in many countries. However, for the purposes of revealed preference valuation, this more restricted range of climates is not helpful as, ideally, the analyst wishes to observe behaviour under a wide variety of conditions. Therefore most revealed preference analyses of climate amenity values have been conducted in large, climatically diverse countries such as the USA. Imprecision is likely to be a greater problem in a GB study. Consequently, the literature has recently been extended to consider a first life-satisfaction analysis of global climate amenity values. Here, survey respondents are asked to place their life satisfaction typically on a 1–10 scale. By analysing the impacts which income has upon life satisfaction and contrasting these with the impacts of other factors, including climate, trade-offs between money and climate can be inferred and valuations obtained.

The relevant international literature indicates two important characteristics of the resultant valuations; first, that they possess wide ranges of uncertainty, and second, that the central and upper end of those ranges include some very high values. Both of these characteristics are present within estimates of the value of climate amenity in GB. The finding that such values have the potential to be very high is not surprising, given the ubiquity of the climate. That the range of value estimates is very wide is a less desirable aspect of the literature, but again not surprising given our previous comments on the relatively restricted range of climatic conditions in GB (although the weather changes frequently, in global terms the range of climates experienced nationally is relatively small).

Accepting the above caveats, the literature reports both a revealed (hedonic pricing) and life-satisfaction preference assessment of climate amenities in GB under a common scenario: Intergovernmental Panel on Climate Change (IPCC) A1B under which there is rapid global economic growth, especially in developing nations (IPCC 2007). While this scenario is expected to generate major damages and economic losses at a global scale, and these and more direct effects may very adversely impact upon well-being in the UK, in terms purely of climate amenity alone, both studies suggest that the most probable change in climate associated with the A1B emissions scenario will bring significant benefits to the population of GB.

Results from the revealed preference study (based upon observed behaviour) suggest that climate amenity benefits in GB, averaged over the time period 2030–2059, are just over £21 billion p.a. These gains are estimated using the current climate as a counterfactual, that is, it represents the value of such a change in climate if it occurred today. The life-satisfaction approach, while detecting major welfare losses in many countries of the world, also predicts that global warming will actually generate climate amenity benefits within GB which, calculated in the same manner as previously, are estimated at just over £69 billion p.a. (equivalent to £1,130/person/yr) by 2030–2059. This analysis, however, suggests that richer societies care less about the climate and that as temperatures exceed those expected for 2030–2059, they will eventually result in losses rather than benefits.[73]

It is important to bear in mind that these estimates only consider climate amenities and their findings and have to be offset against the potentially very significant losses which could impact upon GB due to the international impacts of climate change, and the impact on prices and incomes. Neither do these estimates account for extreme events associated with changes in the distribution of climate variables, or, as noted, the short-run costs of adaptation. It is not possible to argue that climate change is a 'good thing' for GB based on analysing only a subset of the impacts and holding everything else constant.

22.3.14 The Amenity Value of Nature[74]

There is a long tradition of using hedonic pricing studies to estimate the value of a wide range of environmental amenities and disamenities as they are reflected in local property prices (Sheppard 1999). Using this approach, a novel study was undertaken for the UK NEA to estimate the amenity value associated with proximity to habitats, designated areas, heritage sites, domestic gardens and other natural amenities. The analysis considered over 1 million housing transactions from across England for the period 1996–2008. Information on sales prices and the internal

---

72 Hedonic studies simultaneously examine differences in wage rates paid to workers in different areas. An alternative revealed preference approach is applied by Maddison (2003), who examines household expenditures across areas with differing climates, considering how much individuals have to pay to modify their environments where they are adverse (e.g. heating and cooling costs). Arguably, this will only yield a lower bound assessment of climate amenity values, as a number of the benefits of pleasant climates will not be reflected in these expenditures.

73 Studies have shown that survey respondents tend to overestimate the beneficial impacts on their well-being which warmer climates will have (more precisely, they fail to allow for the extent to which they are likely to adapt to new situations; see Schkade & Kahneman 1998). However, this should not be a problem for the life satisfaction approach, which does not directly ask respondents for their perceptions of future or different environments, but rather assessed whether satisfaction scores differ across groups, including those exposed to different climates. However, as with any analysis, the potential for correlation between climate and some related factor cannot be entirely ruled out.

74 This Section draws upon Mourato et al. (2010).

characteristics of these houses (e.g. property type, floor area, tenure, age, number of bathrooms, number of bedrooms) was combined with data on their proximity to a variety of built environment facilities (e.g. distance to transport infrastructure, distance to the centre of the local labour market, local school quality, land area of ward, population density) and natural environment characteristics including:

- the proportion of the local area classified as Marine and Coastal Margins; Freshwaters – Openwaters, Wetlands and Floodplains; Mountains, Moorlands and Heaths; Semi-natural Grasslands; Enclosed Farmland; Coniferous Woodland; Broadleaved Mixed and Yew Woodland; Urban areas; and inland bare ground;
- the proportion of the local area which is made up of private gardens, greenspace and water features;
- the proportion of green belt and National Park land in the census ward in which a house is located; and
- the distance to various natural and environmental amenities, such as coastline, rivers, National Parks and National Trust properties.

While internal characteristics such as house size and number of bedrooms or proximity to places of work, have a major influence on the price of a property, the analysis showed that, after allowing for these, the local environment exerted highly significant effects on house prices; in other words, homeowners reflect their values for better environments through the amounts they are prepared to pay for houses which enjoy higher levels of environmental quality. In this manner, the hedonic pricing technique allows us to see the prices that homeowners implicitly pay for those environmental improvements. Because these 'implicit prices' are amounts that homeowners pay at the time of purchase, they reflect the stream of benefits purchasers expect to receive into the future rather than just the benefits obtained during the purchase year (i.e. they are capitalised present values). However, these are not perfect indicators of value as they reflect not only individuals' underlying values but also the conditions of the local housing market. It might be that in some areas there is a good supply of high quality environments, while in others there is not; this may not change people's value for such environments, but it will alter the implicit price they have to pay to enjoy these benefits in differing areas.[75] Nevertheless, these implicit prices represent a major advance over making decisions without any such information on the benefits of better environments and the disamenity of degraded areas.

Table 22.13 summarises these 'implicit prices' of environmental amenities in England. Results for all of England (column 1) reveal that many of the land use and land cover variables are highly statistically significant in influencing house prices and represent quite large implied economic effects. Domestic gardens, greenspace and areas of water within the census ward all attract a similar positive price premium, with a 1 percentage point increase in one of these land use shares increasing house prices by around 1%. Translating these into monetary implicit prices indicates capitalised values of around £2,000 for these land

use changes at the mean transaction price of £194,000. Regarding land cover shares (within 1 km squares) there is a strong positive effect from i) Freshwaters – Openwaters, Wetlands and Floodplain locations, ii) Broadleaved Mixed and Yew Woodland, iii) Coniferous Woodland and iv) Enclosed Farmland, with a 1 percentage point increase in the share of these types of land cover attracting house price premiums of 0.4% (on average £768), 0.19% (£377), 0.12% (£227) and 0.06% (£113) respectively.

We find that increasing distance from natural amenities such as rivers, National Parks or National Trust sites is associated with a fall in house prices. It is easy to misinterpret these relationships by extrapolating them outside the sample from which they were estimated. However, a simple example indicates the magnitude of some effects. So, while the data is not accurate enough to allow analysis of precisely what can be seen from any given house, moving from a property near to (but without a direct view of) a river to one, say, 1 km away, will lower the price of otherwise identical properties by some 0.9% (or, on average, £1,750). Clearly, homeowners place substantial values upon such environmental amenities.

We can use this analysis to predict the house price differentials that can be attributed to variations in the level of environmental amenities across England. This is achieved by effectively ignoring (holding constant) differences in house types and non-environmental characteristics across areas and only looking at the impact on house prices arising from variations in environmental quality. The resulting predictions therefore show the variation in prices around the mean in England as a result of environmental quality. These are mapped in **Figure 22.5**, with those areas in which environmental quality has the strongest positive impact on house prices being shaded in green, while negative impacts are shown in purple. Given that the mean house price in 2008 was just under £200,000, then this implies that in areas of the highest environmental amenity values, implicit prices were up to £68,000 higher than might be expected on average. Annualised over a long time horizon, this is equivalent to nearly £2,000/yr at the Treasury discount rate. These highest values are seen in areas such as the Lake District, Northumberland, the North York Moors, the Pennines, Dartmoor and Exmoor.

Returning to **Table 22.13**, columns 2–4 show the implicit prices (capitalised) for grouped Government Office Regions in England. These are derived from separate regression models for each regional group sample, with reported implicit prices based on the mean 2008 house price in each sample (reported in the last row of the table). Looking across these columns, although the results are qualitatively similar, it is evident that there are differences in the capitalised values and significance of the various environmental amenities according to region. While the ward land use shares of gardens, greenspace and water have remarkably similar implicit prices across regions, a notable difference is the greater importance of National Park designation in the Midlands regions (the Peak District and Broads National Parks), but lesser importance of National Trust sites. It is also evident that the value of Freshwater,

---

75 A few studies have extended their analyses from implicit prices to underlying values. For example, Day *et al.* (2007) provide estimates of the underlying benefits of reducing road and rail noise in urban locations.

Table 22.13 Implicit prices by region (£, capitalised values).[†] Statistically significant results are indicated by: ***p<0.01, **p<0.05, *p<0.10. Source: Mourato et al. (2010).

	All England	London, South East and West	Midlands and East	North, North West and Yorkshire
Ward share of[‡]				
Domestic gardens	1,970***	1,769***	1,955***	2,487***
Greenspace	2,020***	2,068***	1,200***	1,773***
Water	1,886***	1,794***	1,179***	1,911***
Domestic buildings	4,242***	4,796***	610	2,292**
Other buildings	5,244***	5,955***	2,858***	4,593
Green belt	41	19	81	17
National Park	94	-184*	256***	131
Ward area (+10 km square)	0.017***	0.034***	0.013**	0.009***
Distance to[¶]				
Coastline	-275	-56	-94	-348
Rivers	-1,751*	-2,446	-2,711***	-884
National Parks	-461***	-348**	-188	-782***
Nature reserves	-143	-1,322	632	-402
National Trust properties	-1,347***	-3,596***	-212	-1,117***
Land cover share in 1 km square[§]				
Marine and Coastal Margins	70	138	53	58
Freshwaters – Openwaters, Wetlands and Floodplains	768***	1,332***	36	233
Mountains, Moorlands and Heaths	166	-155	-258	832***
Semi-natural Grasslands	-27	6	-32	-191**
Enclosed Farmland	113***	123***	32	71**
Coniferous Woodland	227*	305***	307	-131
Broadleaved Woodland	377***	495***	412***	240*
Inland bare ground	-738***	-1,055***	-111	-479**
Sample size	1,013,125	476,846	341,527	194,752
Mean house price 2008	£194,040	£243,850	£181,058	£158,095

† The table reports implicit prices evaluated at regional mean prices. The analysis covers a sample of housing transactions in England, 1996–2008. Variables which are not of focal interest are considered in the analysis but omitted from the table (e.g. the impact of extra bedrooms).

‡ 'Ward share of' shows the implicit prices for a 1 percentage point increase in the share of land in a specified use in the census ward containing the property. For gardens, greenspace, water, domestic and other buildings the omitted category is 'other land uses'.

¶ 'Distance to' variables shows the implicit prices associated with an increase of 1 km to the specified amenity.

§ 'Land cover share in 1 km square' shows implicit prices for a 1 percentage point increase in the share of the specified land cover in the 1 km square containing the property (≈ 10,000 m² within nearest 1 million m²). Omitted category is 'Urban'.

Wetlands and Floodplain locations is driven predominantly by London and the south of England. Coniferous woodland attracts value in the regions other than the north, but Broadleaved woodland attracts a positive premium everywhere. Although Mountain, Moorland and Heath cover had no significant effect on prices in England as a whole, we see that it attracts a substantial positive premium in those locations where this land cover is predominantly found, i.e. the north, North West and Yorkshire.

Further restricting the sample to major metropolitan regions (not shown in **Table 22.13**) leads to a pattern of results that is broadly similar to those discussed above for England. Some effects become more significant, particularly those related to distance to coastline, rivers and National Parks and, as might be expected, green belt designation becomes more important. The results indicate implicit prices amounting to around £5,800 for houses in green belt locations (although these are much higher in some areas), which offer access to cities, coupled with tight restrictions on housing supply.

While there are limitations to this analysis (discussed in Mourato et al. 2010), overall we conclude that there is substantial value attached to a number of natural habitats, designations, heritage sites, private gardens and local environmental amenities. While there is evidence of some substantial differences across regions, generally the underlying preferences for these amenities seems robust and may well be broadly transferable across the UK.

One limitation with the hedonic pricing approach is that it only reflects values which are embodied within property prices. A concern, then, is that this may underestimate the amenity and landscape aesthetics value of more remote environments. Certainly some of the latter value will be captured within our prior assessments of outdoor recreation values. But still there is the risk that some values, especially residual non-use benefits, may be omitted. There is a clear need for an integrated assessment which addresses such omissions in a coherent framework which also avoids double counting. In the meantime we are forced to rely upon a mixture of assessments which risk both of these problems. Accepting that this may be an issue, there is nevertheless considerable evidence of amenity and aesthetic landscape values associated with various ecosystems. As a purely illustrative example of such benefits, **Table 22.14** provides estimates of average, total and marginal values for these as provided by inland and coastal wetlands in the UK. These are substantial, potentially amounting to roughly £1.3 billion p.a. Marginal values associated with expansions of Wetlands are also significant, although somewhat lower than present average benefits, reflecting the diminishing marginal benefits of increases in such resources.

Clearly there is a concern regarding the potential for overlap and hence double counting between the estimates provided by Mourato *et al.* (2010) and those from Morris & Camino (2010). However, ignoring these different sources would risk significant underestimation of ecosystem service benefits. In short, these values appear very substantial, yet there is a need for an integrated assessment of these benefits.

22.3.15 Education and Environmental Knowledge[76]

Engaging with nature can lead to increased environmental knowledge. A novel accounting study of the investment value of environmental knowledge was undertaken for the UK NEA.[77] Given the importance of such knowledge within the education process, this study focused on environmental knowledge accumulation within the formalised education system for school-age children. Specifically, we consider two types of ecological knowledge experience related respectively to indoor and outdoor learning: i) the environmental knowledge embodied in successful student outcomes in GCSE and A-level examination in geography and biology,

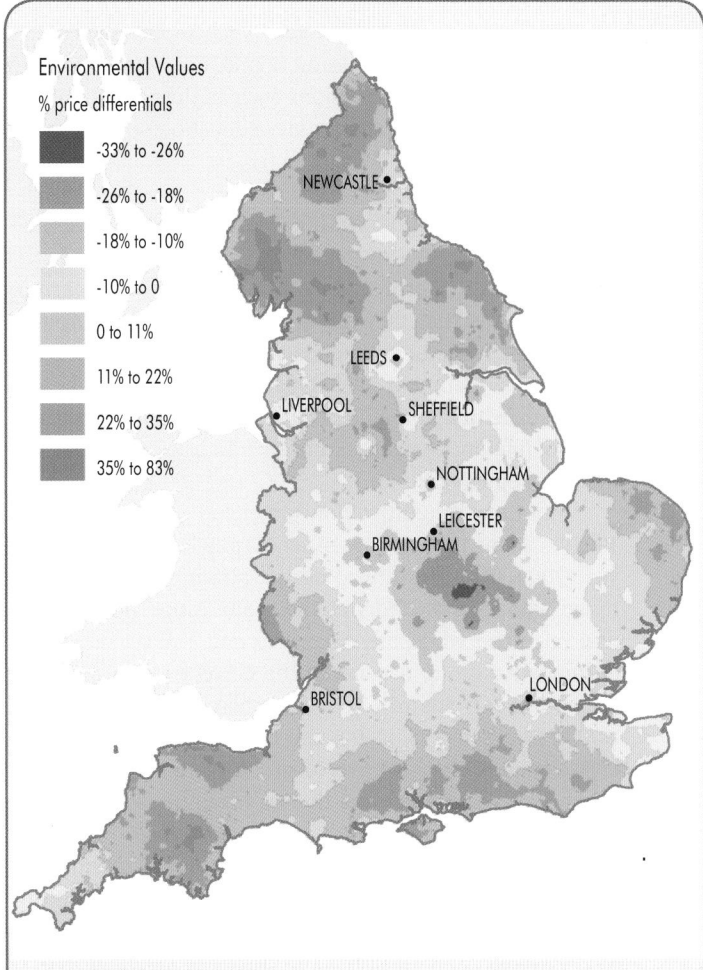

Figure 22.5 Geographical distribution of environmental value (predicted price differentials from property value regressions). Percentage price differentials are based on log price differentials, and correspond to maximum percentage differentials relative to the national mean price level. Source: Mourato *et al.* (2010).

at the end of the school year 2009/10, in England; and, ii) nature-related school trips, taking place outside the school, as well as 'citizen science' projects taking place within (and

Table 22.14 Estimated average, total and marginal values for amenity and aesthetics provided by inland and coastal wetlands in the UK.* All values are given in £, 2010 prices. Source: Morris & Camino (2010).

Ecosystem service-related goods	No. of sites[†]	Total area (ha)	Average value of service where present (addition to default value)[‡] (£/ha/yr)	Total value of service, assuming it is present in all UK inland/ coastal wetlands[¶] (£ million/yr)	Marginal value of service when provided by an additional hectare of new wetland[§] (£/ha/yr)
UK inland wetlands	1,519	601,550	339	204	227
UK coastal wetlands	693	274,613	2,080	1,081	1,394

* Values are area-weighted estimates for all UK inland wetland sites using the Brander *et al.* (2008) benefit function and CORINE land use data sets.
† Data on the number and area of wetlands were drawn from the European CORINE Land Cover Maps (Morris & Camino 2010).
‡ Default average values (where all of the ecosystem services specified in this table do not apply) are £303/ha/yr for UK inland wetlands and £1,856/ha/yr for UK coastal wetlands.
¶ In contrast, the default total value of the existing inland wetland stock, assuming that none of the ecosystem services in the table apply, is £182 million/yr for UK inland wetlands and £509 million/yr for UK coastal wetlands.
§ The per hectare value of services associated with additional new wetlands is lower than the average per hectare value of existing wetlands. This reflects the diminishing marginal value of additional wetlands.

76 This Section draws in part from Mourato *et al.* (2010).
77 As noted by one reviewer, this method has not to date been subjected to rigorous academic peer review and so is offered with that caveat in mind.

around) school grounds. Obviously, such an assessment can at best provide only a very lower bound investigation of such values and important omissions such as the contribution of ecosystem services to the tertiary education sector require further analysis.

22.3.15.1 Environmental knowledge embodied in successful student outcomes

An economic interpretation of environmental learning experiences is that they are one element of the output of the education sector and hence, per the pioneering work of Jorgenson & Fraumeni (1989, 1992), an investment in human capital. Core to that method is the calculation of the present value of (lifetime) earnings from spending an additional year in formal education.

Mourato *et al.* (2010) follow Jorgenson & Fraumeni (1989, 1992) to define three groups of school pupils for the academic year 2009/10: i) those who do not attain qualifications; ii) those who attain GCSEs in the grade range from A to C and iii) those who pass A-level exams.[78] Assuming initial earnings for group i) being at the current minimum wage for 16–18-year-olds of £3.64/hour then, following Dearden (1999), Dearden *et al.* (2000) and Blundell *et al.* (1999, 2004), it is assumed that, relative to group i), the wage rate for group ii) is 15% higher and that of group iii) is 22% higher. Numbers in each group are taken from ONS (2009).[79] Using these data and assuming a retirement age for all groups of 68 (reflecting expected changes in this age), we estimate future earnings from age 16 for group i), from age 17 for group ii) and from age 19 for group iii) assuming incomes growth of 1.5%. Present values of these income streams are calculated using a HM Treasury discount rate of 3.5%.

We then seek to identify the environmental component of this educational attainment and its value. We focus on geography and biology as the fields of study where, at school level, there is formal evidence of significant environmental components to the curriculum, either in guidelines provided by national curricula and/or official examination boards. Determining the precise weight that ecological education

has in these studies is clearly contentious and subject to variation across schools. Nevertheless, on the basis of consulted documentation (AQA 2009, 2010; Edexcel 2008a,b), we assume that the weights reflecting the ecological components to be the following: GCSE geography = 0.15; GCSE biology = 0.25; GCSE (basic) science = 0.08; A-level geography = 0.15; and A-level biology = 0.25.

Results are provided in **Table 22.15**. The left-hand side of the table gives the number of students accomplishing specified examination outcomes. The right-hand side gives corresponding values. These are the product of pupil numbers and the 'adjusted' present values for representative individuals achieving the relevant qualifications (as estimated above) in 2010. Our tentative findings indicate that the annual value of environmental knowledge embodied in successful student outcomes in (relevant) GCSE and A-level examinations at the end of the academic year 2009/10 is substantial, at just over £2.1 billion. However, some caution is needed in interpreting these results. The data that we provide cannot be interpreted as the net benefit of the production of environmental knowledge (i.e. relative to other forms of education). Ours is purely an accounting framework that attempts, in a very approximate way, to identify some portion of the environmental component of school education. Nevertheless, we would argue that the findings are instructive, not least in indicating, in explicit terms, that the value of this environmental knowledge is possibly substantial.

22.3.15.2 Environmental knowledge embodied in nature-related school trips

Environmental education also occurs outside the classroom and Mourato *et al.* (2010) consider case studies of both school trips to UK nature reserves and a national 'citizen-science' project as follows:

- There is no central record of the number of school trips to nature reserves and related environmental resources annually. However, during the 2009/10 school year just over 50 RSPB reserves played host to nearly 2,000 school trips involving over 57,000 students and staff. Valuations of travel costs and travel time suggest an economic expenditure value ranging from just under £850,000 to just over £1.3 million for these trips alone.

- Taking the RSPB Big School Birdwatch as one example of a citizen science project, in 2010 some 75,500 people participated (69,101 children and 6,275 adults) from 1,986 schools. Utilising a similar methodology to the previous case study gives a value of this time of about £375,000 or £188 per participating school.

Neither of these case studies provide true economic valuations of educational benefits concerned, reporting instead just the 'cost of investment' involved in these undertakings. Nevertheless, assuming that these undertakings were deemed to be value for money, such costs should provide a lower

Table 22.15 The annual value of environmental knowledge in GCSE and A-level attainment for school leavers in 2010.*
Source: Mourato *et al.* (2010).

	Candidates ('000)		Value of environmental knowledge (£ million/yr)		
	GCSE	**A-level**	**GCSE**	**A-level**	**Total**
Geography	118.2	29.2	426.9	134.7	561.6
Biology	110.2	52.7	663.4	405.9	1,069.2
Science	258.4	n/a	497.8	n/a	756.2
Total	486.8	81.9	1,588.1	540.6	2,128.7

* The values refer to successful candidates who would have received their results in these GCSEs and A-levels in the summer of 2010.

---

78 Those attaining higher educational qualifications (containing environmental knowledge in our accounting year) are not considered in this analysis as it stands. However, inclusion of this further increment in ecological knowledge, in principle, could be incorporated as a further (net) investment.

79 Note that these need not equate to labour market participation figures.

bound minimum of the values concerned. This suggests that there may be a substantial underlying value within the much larger number of total school trips and citizen science projects undertaken each year.

22.3.16 Health[80]

Environmental quality and proximity to natural amenities is increasingly being recognised as having substantial effects on physical and mental health, both directly and indirectly (e.g. Bird 2004). Broadly this can happen in three ways. First, the absence of environmental quality can directly impact upon human health. Second, natural settings can act as a catalyst for healthy behaviour, leading, for example, to increases in physical exercise, which affect both physical and mental health (Pretty *et al.* 2007; Barton & Pretty 2010). Third, simple exposure to the natural environment, such as having a view of a tree or grass from a window, can be beneficial, improving mental health status (Pretty *et al.* 2005) and physical health (Ulrich 1984). Health outcomes in this respect can be disaggregated into two categories: reductions in mortality and reductions in morbidity (including physical and mental health).

The focus upon ecosystem services underpinning the UK NEA means that the major emphasis of our analysis is upon the second and third pathways mentioned above. However, some consideration of the direct impact of poor environmental quality upon health is worthwhile, if only for completeness. A key example of such a pathway is the issue of air quality. The chronic health effects of particulate matter alone is estimated to cost around £15 billion per year (IGCB 2010).[81] In comparison, action to address this cost can be highly cost effective. For example the latest vehicle emission standards are estimated to reduce the value of this health impact by around £1 billion annually at a cost of around £350 million p.a. (IGCB 2010).[82] A second example is the issue of noise which is estimated to incur health costs of around £2 billion p.a. (and wider costs of a further £5–£7 billion[83]; IGCB(N) 2010). Here the costs of noise mitigation measures vary substantially according to local circumstances but in many areas the benefit:cost ratio is strongly positive (pers comm., Mallika Ishwaran, Defra 2011).[84]

Returning to our ecosystem focus, Mourato *et al.* (2010) conducted a preliminary investigation of the valuation of the impacts of marginal changes in the provision of natural habitats and greenspaces on physical and mental health. They address both of the pathways identified above: i) health improvements arising from additional exercise created by the provision of natural habitats and green settings; and ii) health benefits arising from more passive forms of contact with nature such as viewing nature or being within natural spaces.

22.3.16.1 Value of the health benefits of green exercise

Willis (2005) identifies three key steps in the valuation of the health benefits of 'created exercise' due to additional provision of greenspace: i) measuring the physical and mental health impact of exercise; ii) valuing the health benefits of exercise; and iii) estimating the probability of additional exercise with changes in greenspace. Mourato *et al.* (2010) analyse each in turn.

The only exercise that should be directly attributed to the provision of natural settings is what Willis (2005) calls 'created exercise', i.e. exercise which would not have occurred otherwise. Exercise which would have occurred anyway in another setting (e.g. the gym or urban pavements) should not be included in the calculations as it is not truly additional. It is, however, very difficult to identify created exercise. The following calculations follow the Willis (2005) approach and attempt to focus on created exercise under a scenario whereby changes in countryside and parks management lead to an additional reduction of 1 percentage point in the numbers of sedentary people in the UK. Reduction in sedentary life and increase in exercise lead to a number of proven health benefits which include reductions in mortality and morbidity due to: i) coronary heart disease (CHD); ii) colo-rectal cancer; iii) stroke; and iv) stress, anxiety and depression (morbidity only). We obtained up-to-date data on mortality and morbidity for CHD, colo-rectal cancer, stroke and depression. The change in excess cases of morbidity and mortality from these conditions associated with a 1 percentage point reduction in sedentary behaviour are then calculated. This is valued using the theoretically correct WTP approach (e.g. Krupnick 2004; Pearce *et al.* 2006), based on the trade-offs that individuals would make between health and wealth, to estimate the economic value of these health impacts. For mortality, government estimates of the value of a preventable fatality (VPF) of £1,589,800 (DfT 2007) are used; for morbidity the value used for CHD prevention is based on the Department for Transport's (DfT 2007) value for a slight injury (£13,769), while the stroke prevention value is based on its value for a serious injury (£178,640). The value for cancer prevention is taken from Hunt & Ferguson (2010) and reflects the existence of a 'dread' factor associated with diseases that are long and painful (£288,304). Finally, the value for reduction of mental illness is based on Morey *et al.*'s (2007) estimate of WTP to eliminate depression (£5,343).

Estimates of the value of health benefits arising from a 1 percentage point reduction in the sedentary population are discussed in detail by Mourato *et al.* (2010). These show that a change in natural habitats that causes a 1 percentage point reduction in sedentary behaviour would provide a

---

80   This Section draws on Mourato *et al.* (2010).
81   For comparison, the health costs of obesity are estimated at £10 billion p.a. (pers comm., Mallika Ishwaran, Defra 2011).
82   Furthermore, tackling climate change can deliver significant synergies in terms of knock-on air quality benefits. Defra (2011) presents evidence showing that the synergy benefits of optimizing for climate change and local air quality objectives to 2050 have a net present value of around £24 billion.
83   The cost of the levels of noise prevailing in 2010 is estimated at between £7billion–£9billion p.a.—an amenity cost of £3–5 billion, health cost of £2 billion and productivity losses of £2 billion (IGCB(N) 2010).
84   Source states that, even if only amenity values are considered then benefit:cost ratio can reach as high as 8:1 is some areas.

total benefit of almost £2 billion p.a. (using WTP-based values), across the three physical conditions (CHD, colorectal cancer and stroke) and the mental health condition considered (stress, anxiety and depression). However, if all people over 75 years are excluded from the analysis (on the basis that they are less able or likely to be physically active), then the benefits fall to just over £750 million. Given this, the key question left to answer is: if a green living environment does indeed provide an incentive to be physically active, how much true additional exercise is created with the extra provision of greenspaces that would not have taken place otherwise? Unfortunately, there are large gaps in knowledge in this area, as environmental attributes appear to be among the least understood of the known influences on physical activity. There is a limited body of evidence that appears to suggest patterns of positive relationships between some environmental attributes and physical activity, such as walking or cycling. Reviews by Humpel et al. (2002), Owen et al. (2004) and Lee & Maheswaran (2010) show that the aesthetic nature of the local environment, the convenience of facilities (such as footpaths and trails) and accessibility of places to walk to (such as parks and beaches) are often associated with an increased likelihood of certain types of exercise orientated walking. However, several other studies found no link between recreational physical activity and greenspace provision. A recent large-scale study of nearly 5,000 Dutch people by Maas et al. (2008) found that the amount of greenspace in people's living environment has little influence on their level of physical activity. Given this, Mourato et al. (2010) find no conclusive evidence on the strength of the relationship between the amount of greenspace in the living environment and the level of physical activity. This would suggest that, at the present time, it is not possible to accurately value the health benefits of created exercise due to additional provision of greenspace. However, this is a rapidly developing field. For example, recent research by Coombes et al. (2010) shows that those who live within 500 m of accessible green space are 24 per cent more likely to meet recommended levels of physical activity. Figures from the Department of Health suggest that better access to open spaces could reduce healthcare costs by over £2 billion per year (pers comm., Mallika Ishwaran, Defra, 2011). While such cost savings cannot be taken as valid estimates of the benefit of such health improvements, nevertheless they serve to underline the substantial nature of likely values.

22.3.16.2 Valuing the health and well-being benefits of exposure to nature

There is now a substantial body of evidence suggesting the existence of a wide range of health and well-being benefits associated with greenspace over and above those induced by increased exercise. In a recent review, Lee & Maheswaran (2010) reports associations between contact with greenspace and a variety of psychological, emotional and mental health benefits, reduced stress and increased quality of life. This has led to a recent linkage between the economics of happiness and environmental economics (Welsch 2009). Moreover, research spanning more than two decades suggests that mere views of nature, compared to most urban scenes lacking elements of the natural environment, appear to have positive influences on emotional and physiological states, providing restoration from stress and mental fatigue (Ulrich 1986; Kaplan 2001) and even improve recovery following operations in hospital (Ulrich 1984). These health benefits of non-exercise-related exposure to nature are likely to be substantial and pervasive, given the lack of substitutes and the size of the population potentially affected.

Mourato et al. (2010) use novel techniques, including a newly commissioned geo-located survey, to estimate the physical and mental health effects associated with UK ecosystem types, domestic gardens, managed areas and other natural amenities. Data were collected by a web survey during August 2010. A total of 1,851 respondents completed the survey. Measures of general and physical health were obtained,[85] including assessments of the impact of health upon personal utility (broadly speaking, the individual's well-being). These were then related to indicators of the local environmental characteristics such as the ecosystem types describing the physical land cover within a 1 km radius of the respondent's home location (such as woodland, freshwater, farmland or mountains) and direct questions regarding views of greenspaces and water from the respondent's home, frequency of use of domestic gardens, of open countryside, and of non-countryside greenspaces such as parks, recreation grounds and cemeteries, as well as distance to various natural and environmental amenities, such as coastline, rivers, National Parks and National Trust properties. A wide variety of further information was gathered to allow for differences between gender, age, qualifications, work status, religiosity and income as well as house prices and postcodes.

Analysis of these various data detected positive links between proximity of the home to specific habitat types and the health-related utility score, although such links were not observed between habitat types and simple aggregate physical and emotional health indicators. There appear to be strong, positive relationships between green views from the home and emotional well-being and health utility. Specifically, having a view of greenspace from one's house increases emotional well-being by 5% and the general health utility score by about 2%; regular use of gardens and greenspaces has a similar positive effect on well-being. Using a garden weekly, or more often, increases physical functioning and emotional well-being by around 3.6% and the heath utility score by 2.7%; Similarly using non-countryside greenspace monthly, or more frequently, increases physical functioning and emotional well-being by 3.4% and 2.6% respectively, and the heath utility score by 1.8%. Furthermore, an increase in 1% of the area of freshwater, farmland and broadleaved woodland within a 1 km radius of the home increases health utility by 0.3%,

---

85 The RAND SF-36 Health Survey was employed (see Brazier et al. 2002). This is the leading general health measure, comprising 36 survey items, with standardised administration and item scoring to produce several validated sub-scales. The 'physical functioning' and 'emotional well-being' subscales were used as outcome variables.

0.1% and 0.1% respectively. **Table 22.16** summarises these effects. However, it is important to note once again that the associations we have estimated cannot be interpreted as causal effects. There may be variables omitted from the models that cause changes in both the dependent and explanatory variables, and/or the dependent variable may itself be a cause of some explanatory variables.

The final column in **Table 22.16** reports tentative values of the health changes estimated above. The general health measure used by Mourato *et al.* (2010) is capable of detecting changes in health in a general population (Hemmingway *et al.* 1997). As such, it may be possible to use our survey results to tentatively estimate the monetary value of the health benefits associated with increasing the number of people making monthly visits to greenspaces and having views of grass, or associated with increasing particular types of land cover. To achieve this, Mourato *et al.* (2010) first relate the health index used in their survey to Quality Adjusted Life Year (QALY) measures associated with the environmental changes of interest. Quality Adjusted Life Years are measures of health benefits that combine length of life with quality of life, where quality of life is assessed on a scale where 0 typically represents death and 1 represents full health (Drummond *et al.* 1997). There is an emerging literature attempting to empirically estimate the value of QALYs (e.g. Jones-Lee *et al.* 2007; Mason *et al.* 2009; Tillig *et al.* 2009; Baker *et al.* 2010). Although there is currently no consensus about what the monetary value of a QALY is or how to calculate it (Willis 2005; Tilling *et al.* 2009; Donaldson *et al.* 2011), one approach involves deriving a 'value of a life year' from existing empirical estimates of the VPF (Jones-Lee *et al.* 2007). Of particular interest to us is a special case of this approach proposed very recently by Mason *et al.* (2009), that consists of estimating the value of a QALY based only on quality of life changes. The Mason *et al.* (2009) study is based on UK figures and provides a value

for the prevention of a non-fatal injury, from which they in turn estimate monetary values of a QALY ranging from £6,414 to £21,519. Given that the environmental changes being considered are likely to have impacts mostly on quality of life (rather than on life expectancy), these seem to be the most appropriate values to use.

The last column of **Table 22.16** contains the very tentative results of the calculation outlined above. It shows the estimated annual health benefits associated with having a view of nature, using the garden often, visiting greenspaces regularly and increasing the proportion of broadleaved woodland, freshwater and farmland cover. We note that these figures are indicative only, are subject to many assumptions as described above, and should therefore be treated with caution.

22.3.16.3 Direct impacts of climate change upon health[86]

In its report on the health impacts of climate change, the Department of Health estimates that under a medium to high scenario, climate change might, by the 2050s, reduce the number of cold-related deaths by up to 20,000 whilst increasing the number of heat-related deaths by 2,800 (POST 2004; Department of Health 2008). We can value these net avoided deaths by applying the UK official value of statistical life (£1.1 million in 2008 prices) to obtain a benefit estimate of £18.9 billion. However, such estimates need to be treated with some caution. First, many of those whose deaths would be averted would be elderly, with a short remaining life expectancy because of pre-existing conditions. Second, some studies present evidence to support the use of declining values for preventing fatalities in such circumstances.[87] Finally, climate change is likely to be far more erratic than just a simple increase in temperature, and this variability requires a sophisticated treatment of likely impacts which calls for extensions beyond the present work.

Table 22.16 Health changes and contact with nature: summary findings.* Source: Mourato *et al.* (2010).

Explanatory variable	Difference in explanatory variable	Associated health differences			
		Physical functioning (%)	Emotional well-being (%)	Health utility score (%)	Tentative annual value per person (£)
Having a view over greenspace from your house	No view → any view	–	+5.0	+2.1	135–452
Use of own garden	Less than weekly → weekly or more	+3.5	+3.7	+2.7	171–575
Use of non-countryside greenspace	Less than monthly → monthly or more	+3.4	+2.6	+1.8	112–377
Local freshwater, wetlands and floodplains	+1% within 1 km of the home (+3.14 out of 314 ha)	–	–	+0.3	20–68
Local enclosed farmland	+1% within 1 km of the home (+3.14 out of 314 ha)	–	–	+0.1	4–12
Local broadleaved/mixed woodland	+1% within 1 km of the home (+3.14 out of 314 ha)	–	–	+0.1	8–27

* Based on analyses of data for England and Wales.

86 This Section draws on Maddison (2010).
87 Aldy & Viscusi (2007) find an inverted U-shaped relationship between age and the value of statistical life.

22.3.17 Agricultural Food Production

22.3.17.1 Introduction and overview

The natural environment clearly plays a major role in agricultural food production. However, when undertaking an economic analysis of agricultural ecosystem services we need to control for the contribution to food values which also comes from other inputs such as machinery, labour and chemical fertilisers. To ignore the latter would be to implicitly assume that ecosystem services are the only inputs to agricultural food production and so significantly overestimate the value of those services and undermine the validity of our analysis.[88] One way to avoid this problem is to examine the change in value of agricultural output when we vary a given ecosystem service by some marginal (unit) amount, holding all other inputs constant.[89] Within reason,[90] we can then use these findings to estimate the impacts of whatever multiple unit change in ecosystem services is of policy interest. Again within limits, we can extend this approach to also consider cases where more than one ecosystem service changes at the same time.[91]

Given this methodology, an obvious initial question concerns which ecosystem services might be of interest to decision makers. Obviously, even the most self confident of policy makers will not be interested in the impacts upon agriculture of changing the elevation of an area. Indeed, there are a number of ecosystem services which are likely to stay fairly constant into the future and are therefore of limited policy interest. However, one obvious source of potentially significant variation in pertinent ecosystem services is climate change.[92] We examine two of the key effects of climate change upon agriculturally significant ecosystems services: variations in temperature and precipitation.

Our analysis draws upon the newly compiled, highly spatially disaggregated datasets embracing temporal variation across a long time series. Economic theory is drawn upon to construct new behavioural models of land use decision making. These predict how farm land use varies, not only because of factors such as the prices of goods, costs of manufactured inputs and changes in agricultural policy but also with the farm's environmental characteristics, including temperature and precipitation.

The model is validated through standard comparisons of actual versus predicted measures. Here we deliberately omit some of the data available to us, for example by dropping observations on land use in the most recent years of our dataset. We feed the remaining data into our analysis and produce a model of the factors determining land use. We then use that model to predict land use in the omitted years. These predictions are compared with the actual land use in those omitted years. The error between our predictions and what actually happened gives us a very robust insight into the reliability of our model. If, as we show later is indeed the case, we find our model to be highly reliable, we can use all of the available data to improve it even more and feel justified in using that model to examine what would happen if circumstances changed—within reason. This latter caveat is important. Any analysis that draws upon data from the past cannot be reliably applied to totally different future conditions, that is we cannot push the model too far outside the range of prior observations. However, our ambition of using it to examine the impacts of predicted climate change has a good claim to being robust in this respect. Because we build our model using data from right across the full extent of GB (including the generally warm and dry South East and the typically colder and wetter North West) and across many years (including both warm and cold periods), then this information embraces much (although not all) of the range of climatic conditions predicted for at least the first half of the present century.[93]

One caveat that we do acknowledge is that, due to time constraints, the analysis presented here does not adjust from market prices to underlying values. To do so requires allowances to be made to remove market imperfections such as those brought about by subsidies and other interventions. This is likely to reduce the size of estimates reported here, an issue which should be kept in consideration throughout this analysis and that conducted for agricultural values within Chapter 26.

22.3.17.2 The CSERGE land use model

Recent research within the SEER project based at the Centre for Social and Economic Research on the Global Environment (CSERGE), University of East Anglia, develops a new model of agricultural land use which is particularly suitable for the ecosystem service assessment conducted under the UK NEA. Below we briefly overview the model specification and the data used for estimation, and summarise the main

---

88 These manufactured and human capital inputs could be reassigned to other uses. Therefore the loss of some portion of ecosystem services could in part be compensated for by reassigning the former capital to other ends. Note, however, that this offsetting compensation should ideally be valued by examining the 'opportunity cost' value (i.e. the value that this non-ecosystem capital could generate if applied to the next best alternative use).

89 Of course, basic microeconomics shows that if one factor of production changes (e.g. the level of some ecosystem service) then it is likely that it will be cost-beneficial to alter other inputs. However, ignoring this substitution gives us an insight into the value of that initial input.

90 Recall from our methodological summary that marginal values are typically robust for some ranges but can change substantially if we consider very large alterations in circumstances (e.g. the marginal value of a 1% reduction in water availability might provide a perfectly good basis for valuing more substantial losses up to a point, but eventually a further change in water availability starts to have a very different impact on food production). This is why marginal values cannot be used to estimate the total value of ecosystem services.

91 Similarly, any combined change in ecosystem and man-made inputs can be assessed. However, it should be pointed out that there are real limits to the state of natural science understanding regarding what may happen when large numbers of ecosystem services all change simultaneously, particularly in the context of an overarching stressor such as climate change.

92 Elsewhere in this chapter we consider several of the indirect effects which agriculture has upon other ecosystem services such as carbon storage, water quality and biodiversity. An issue which is flagged for future consideration is the problem of soil erosion.

93 This is particularly true for most areas of the country where climate predictions are that conditions in, say, the north and west will become more similar to those of the south and east. Obviously the region which will most noticeably move into new climatic territory (i.e. not captured in UK data from the past) will be the South East and so arguably our model is less robust there.

results. For a more detailed discussion of the methodology, see Fezzi & Bateman (in press).

Theoretical basis and statistical modelling. The model is rooted in basic economic theory (Chambers & Just 1989), which is used to link profit-seeking behaviour by farmers to their consequent land use.[94] The model considers the full range of possible outputs which GB farmers have produced to date, the prices of those outputs,[95] the cost of inputs and the existing policy regime including incentives, disincentives and constraints. The model also incorporates detailed descriptions of the physical environmental characteristics of each farm. All of these data are collected at a very detailed spatial resolution with information on outputs being held at a 2 km grid square and other data held at the finest resolution available. The analysis then seeks to examine how changes in these factors across space (all of GB) and time (dating back to the late 1960s) result in farms allocating different shares of their available land to different activities. Care is taken to allow for the likelihood that many of the relationships underpinning farm land use decisions are interrelated and non-linear. The model building procedure uses statistical estimation techniques which allow for this complex set of relationships and the nature of the underlying data. It also estimates all land use decisions simultaneously, to mimic the decision process of the farmer who considers all farm land and all output options together when determining the land use for the farm.

Data sources. The data used for this analysis integrates multiple sources of information dating back to the late 1960s to assess the financial, policy and environmental drivers of land use change. Collected on a 2 km grid square (400 ha) basis, these data cover the entirety of England, Wales and Scotland, and encompass, for the past 40 years: i) the share of each land use and the numbers of livestock, ii) environmental and climatic characteristics, and iii) policy and other drivers. However, data on yields and profits are not available at the disaggregated level required by this analysis. While we could overcome this problem by moving the analysis to a less disaggregated level at which such information is available (and indeed do so in other work —see Fezzi *et al.* 2010b), this would reduce the accuracy with which we could understand the impact of variations in ecosystem services upon agricultural land use. Given that this is the main purpose of the present exercise, we retain the highly detailed spatial basis of this land use analysis and use secondary data to assign money values to these uses.

Data on agricultural land use and livestock numbers for each 2 km (400 ha) grid square for the whole of GB were taken for 17 unevenly spaced years between 1969 and 2006.[96] This yields roughly 60,000 grid-square records each year, giving about 1 million records in total. This allows us to explicitly model six of the agricultural land use types as defined in the Agricultural Census: cereals (including wheat,

barley and oats); oilseed rape; root crops (potatoes and sugar beet); temporary grassland (grass being sown every 3 to 5 years and typically part of an arable crop rotation); permanent grassland (grassland maintained perpetually without reseeding); and rough grazing. Together, these account for more than 88% of the total agricultural land in GB. We include the remaining area in an 'other' land category encompassing horticulture, other arable crops, woodland on the farm, set-aside, bare, fallow and all other land (e.g. ponds, paths). In addition to the above, the model also allows us to estimate three rates of livestock intensity for dairy and beef herds and flocks of sheep.

For each 2 km grid square we consider a detailed specification of the environmental factors influencing farmers' decision making. For each grid square, we represent climate through Met Office data on i) average temperature in the growing season (April–September) and ii) accumulated rainfall during the growing season. Other data on environmental characteristics included soil depth to rock, volume of stones, various categories of soil texture (fine, medium fine, medium, coarse, peaty), mean altitude, and a measure of slope for the agricultural land in the square. Met Office values are taken from 5 km grid square climatic averages for the period 1961–1990 as calculated from the monthly data available from the Met Office website (www.metoffice.gov.uk) and interpolated to 2 km to match with our land use data. This is the same baseline used by the UKCIP09 (www.ukcip.org.uk) to derive climate change scenarios. Soil characteristics are derived from the 1 km raster library of the European Soil Database (van Liedekerke *et al.* 2006), which we aggregate at a 2 km level. Altitude and high slope (greater than 6 degrees) were both derived via geographical information system (GIS) analysis of the Ordnance Survey, Digital Terrain Model.

Policy determinants which in some way alter agricultural prices or costs were directly incorporated into the model. Area designations such as Nitrate Sensitive Areas (NSAs), Environmentally Sensitive Areas (ESAs) and National Parks were incorporated by denoting the area in each 2 km square under each scheme.

It should be noted that NSAs are voluntary, being established in 1990 and extended in subsequent years. These were introduced in order to test the effects of farming practices on nitrate levels in aquifers, as well as to reduce nitrate levels in selected groundwaters used for public water supply. ESAs were introduced in 1987 and have undergone various extensions in subsequent years. They were launched to safeguard and enhance areas of particularly high landscape, wildlife or historic value. Participation in ESA schemes is also voluntary, and farmers receive monetary compensation for engaging in environmentally friendly farming practices, such as converting arable land to permanent grassland, and establishing hedgerows. Many National Parks were established in the 1950s with some

---

94 We freely acknowledge the evidence of non-profit motivated behaviour discussed by Pike (2008) and others. However, our model draws upon a long time series of data from across the country. Analysis shows that, over such long time periods and after allowing for lags in response times, a profit maximising assumption provides a strong fit to the data on observed behaviour and land use choices.

95 Prices obviously have a highly significant impact on agricultural land use. For an insight into how these have changed in real terms from the middle of the last century see Tinch *et al.* (2010).

96 These data are derived from the June Agricultural Census as available online from EDINA (www.edina.ac.uk). Note that in 2005 and 2006 only Welsh data are available. No more recent data were available. Descriptive statistics for each land use and livestock numbers are given by region and nationally in Fezzi *et al.* (2011).

extensions in the 1980s. Farms located within the boundaries of National Parks can benefit from direct payments if they manage their land by environmental planning and undertake low-intensity activities.

Results. The analysis provides a set of equations describing the share of each of the six land uses (plus the 'other' agricultural land) and the number of each of the three types of livestock in each 2 km square. Details of these equations are given in Fezzi & Bateman (in press), but in summary these show that both land use and livestock numbers are determined by agricultural prices, input costs, a variety of policy measures, and a large number of physical environmental conditions on farms, including those temperature and precipitation variables affected by climate change.

Validation and extension to all of the UK. Our analysis is tested using a comparison of predicted with actual values, as outlined previously. This is undertaken for all land use types and livestock numbers. Formal statistical testing shows that the model performance is highly satisfactory. **Figure 22.6** illustrates two of these comparisons, showing actual and predicted shares of cereals and rough grazing in 2004. Even though some minor differences can be seen (e.g. the model somewhat overpredicts cereals in the English Midlands and underpredicts cereals in Eastern Scotland) the two comparisons show essentially the same spatial patterns of land use. It should be noted that the actual data is somewhat 'blocky', with abrupt changes in recorded cereal between grid squares. This is due to data being gathered at parish level and subsequently allocated to grid squares. The predicted values avoid this problem.

Therefore, we now have a model which provides robust estimates of land use change based upon observations from the past 40 years and across the entirety of GB. Note, however, that data were not available on farm performance in Northern Ireland. Nevertheless, the range of environments and circumstances in our model encompass those observed within Northern Ireland and therefore, we can extend our analysis to the whole of the UK by applying the relationships estimated for GB to data detailing the physical environment of Northern Ireland.

22.3.17.3 Valuing ecosystem services: the impact of climate change

As outlined above, by examining those agricultural ecosystem services most likely to be altered by climate change we estimate how farm outputs will vary and hence assess the value of those services.[97] The UK Climate Impacts Programme (UKCIP) (www.ukcip.org.uk) provides the most up-to-date predictions regarding future climate in the UK. Importantly, the most recent UK Climate Projections (UKCP09) are spatially explicit, being presented at a 25 km grid square resolution. Such data is inherently compatible with our spatially explicit model of agricultural land use.

For the purposes of valuing ecosystem services, we examine the impacts on the value of agricultural production of the UKCIP09-predicted changes in monthly average minimum temperature, maximum temperature and precipitation in the growing season (from April to September). Predictions are taken up to the end point of the UK NEA analysis in 2060 and show temperatures increasing and growing season precipitation falling over this period. For further sensitivity, we consider predictions calculated under both the low and high GHG emission scenarios set out by the IPCC.[98] Obviously, trends are somewhat more extreme under the higher emission scenario.

As an illustration of the UKCP09 trends, **Figure 22.7** shows precipitation in the growing season in 2004 and 2040. Similarly, **Figure 22.8** repeats this analysis for temperature (measured as growing season average). Inspection of these figures shows that rainfall is reduced over time, particularly in the eastern and central parts of England. In contrast, temperatures increase noticeably over time in all areas.

Land use change predictions. By feeding the UKCP09 climate predictions into our model, we obtain predictions of the change in land use in each 2 km grid square across

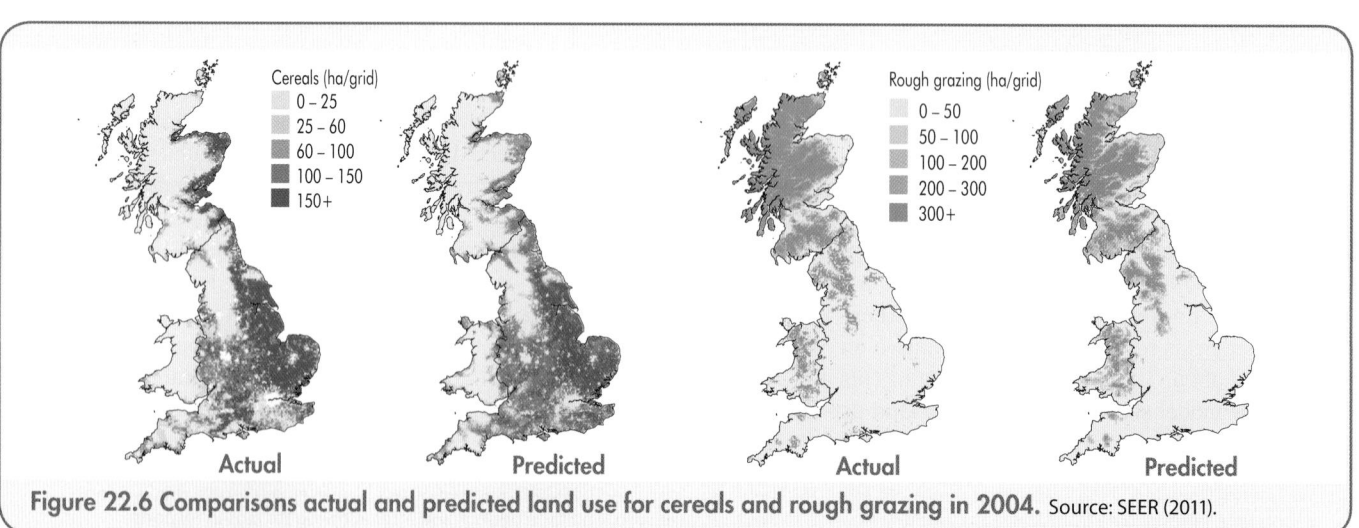

Figure 22.6 Comparisons actual and predicted land use for cereals and rough grazing in 2004. Source: SEER (2011).

---

97 A point of debate here concerns precisely which service we are valuing here. Fezzi *et al.* (2010b) argue that climate services are under assessment, with their value being reflected in the induced variation in food production. Another reviewer has argued that pure provisioning service (food production) is being valued.
98 These correspond respectively to the SRES B1 and the SRES A1FI in the IPCC Special Report on Emissions Scenarios (Nakicenovic *et al.* 2000).

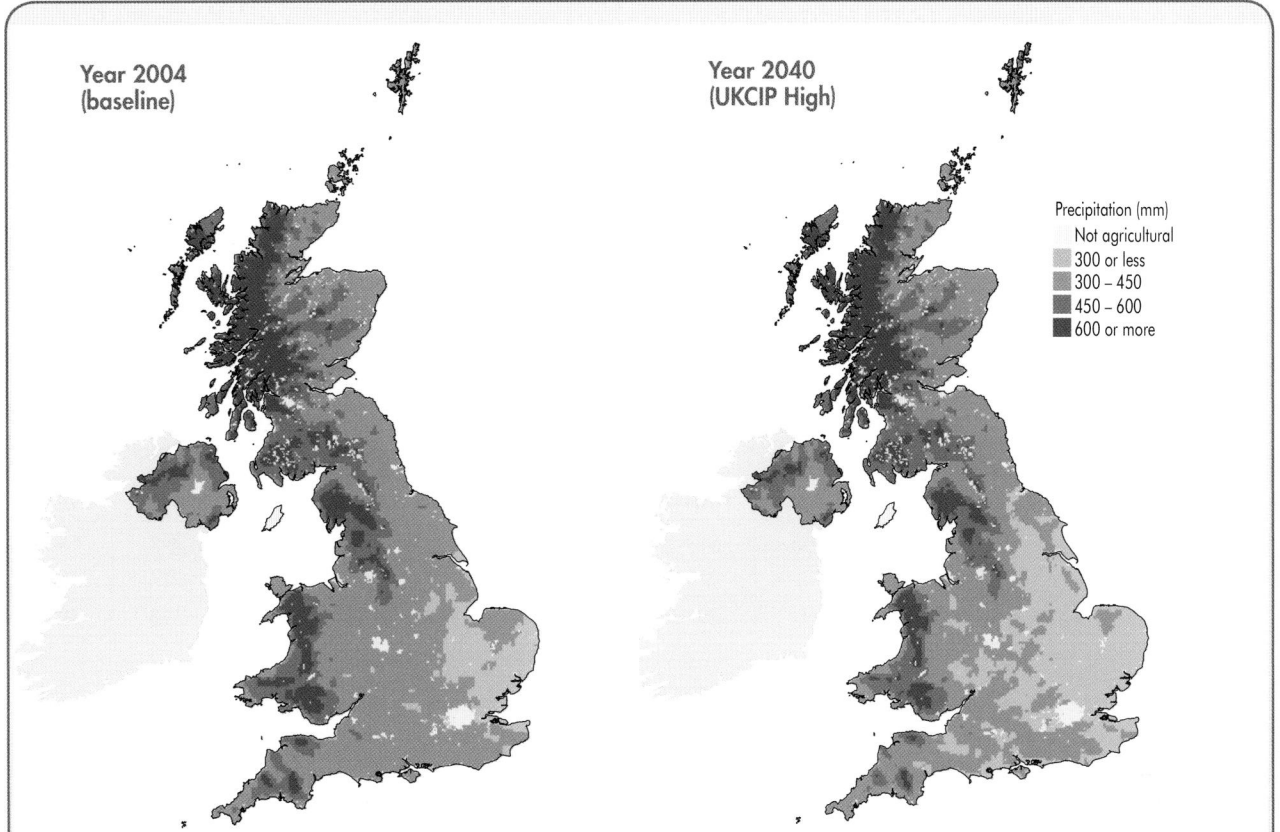

Figure 22.7 Precipitation in the growing season (April–September) in 2004 and UKCIP projections for 2040 under an IPCC high emissions scenario. Source: UKCP09 (http://ukclimateprojections.defra.gov.uk/content/view/868/531/).

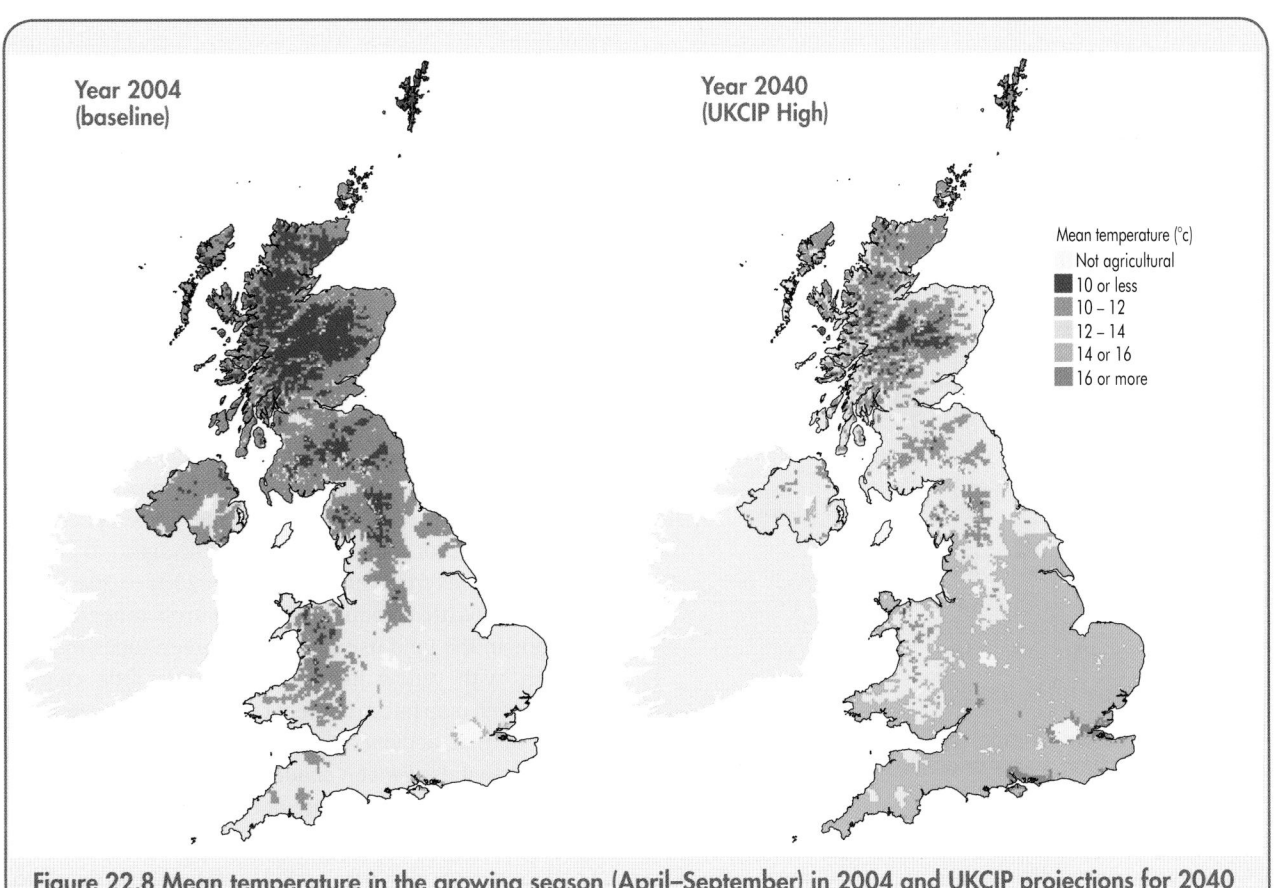

Figure 22.8 Mean temperature in the growing season (April–September) in 2004 and UKCIP projections for 2040 under an IPCC high emissions scenario. Source: UKCP09 (http://ukclimateprojections.defra.gov.uk/content/view/868/531/).

Table 22.17 Average predicted land uses and livestock intensities in Great Britain (2004–2060) under both low and high emission climate change scenarios. *Land use cells*: upper value is average hectare per 2 km grid square (400 ha); lower value (in parentheses) is the percentage of the square. *Livestock cells*: average number of head per 2 km grid square (400 ha). Source: SEER (2011).

Year	Land use						Livestock		
	Cereals	Oilseed rape	Root crops	Temporary grass	Permanent grass	Rough Grazing	Dairy	Beef	Sheep
Low emission scenario									
2004	61.1 (15.3)	7.4 (1.9)	0.7 (0.2)	19.4 (4.9)	85.1 (21.3)	98.2 (24.6)	28.7	90.8	535.8
2020	47.9 (12.0)	4.4 (1.1)	1.0 (0.3)	21.0 (5.3)	110.6 (27.7)	74.3 (18.6)	49.4	84.3	524.5
2040	41.2 (10.3)	3.4 (0.9)	1.1 (0.3)	22.3 (5.6)	113.5 (28.4)	71.0 (17.8)	55.2	75.6	498.4
2060	36.8 (9.2)	2.8 (0.7)	1.3 (0.3)	22.8 (5.7)	110.4 (27.6)	72.7 (18.2)	57.2	67.3	473.8
High emission scenario									
2004	61.1 (15.3)	7.4 (1.9)	0.7 (0.2)	19.4 (4.9)	85.1 (21.3)	98.2 (24.6)	28.7	90.8	535.8
2020	48.5 (12.1)	4.5 (1.1)	1.0 (0.3)	21.0 (5.3)	110.8 (27.7)	74.9 (18.7)	48.8	86.1	530.0
2040	37.8 (9.5)	2.9 (0.7)	1.2 (0.3)	22.8 (5.7)	113.6 (28.4)	72.4 (18.1)	57.3	72.4	488.5
2060	21.7 (5.4)	1.3 (0.3)	1.4 (0.4)	26.1 (6.5)	107.0 (26.8)	84.3 (21.1)	65.7	55.6	431.8

the UK. Taking the UK as a whole, descriptive statistics for predicted levels of the different land uses and livestock intensities are reported in **Table 22.17**. These figures suggest declines over time in some farmland uses, most notably amongst cereals and rough grazing, the latter being of some concern regarding associated biodiversity values. Interestingly, the area of a broad category of 'other farmland', which encompasses farm woodland, vegetables and other arable crops, is foreseen to increase more or less steadily over time. This may reflect the creation of climatic conditions suitable for the cultivation of new or currently marginal crops. Turning to consider livestock, the marked increase in permanent grassland is accompanied by a rise in numbers of dairy cows but a decline in beef livestock, although the reduction in rough grazing sees a fall in sheep

numbers. Considering the various grassland types together implies a substantial increase in dairy stock intensities, a substantial decline in beef stocking and a more modest decline in sheep stocking densities. While the changes in the dairy sector would appear counter-intuitive considering the recent trends in the livestock sector (with dairy, beef and sheep stocks falling by as much as 25% in the past 10 years) we must recall that these scenarios describe the impact of climate change *ceteris paribus*. In other words, trends in husbandry practices, technology and other economic and social factors are not taken into account. It may well be that if current trends do persist into the future then these may overpower the impacts of climate change.

The relative trends in these UK level predictions are summarised in **Figure 22.9**, which describes the percentage of total UK agricultural land allocated to each land use type under each climate scenario. As can be seen, notable trends include a decline in cereals offset by an increase in permanent grassland.

Although national figures are of obvious importance, they disguise a number of marked regional trends in which a given activity will increase in prevalence in one area while declining in another. The highly disaggregated and spatially explicit nature of our model is ideally suited to such analysis. **Figure 22.10** details the spatial distribution of changes in our main agricultural land uses over time. For simplicity, we map results just for the high emissions scenario, reporting these for changes from our base year of 2004 to 2020, 2040 and 2060. Maps are coloured such that purple tones indicate reductions in the land use shown and green tones indicate increases, with yellow indicating relatively little change. Note that each map has a different range relating to predicted changes in that activity. However, as these ranges differ between activities, a given shade of colour for one activity does not refer to the same amount in a different activity.[99]

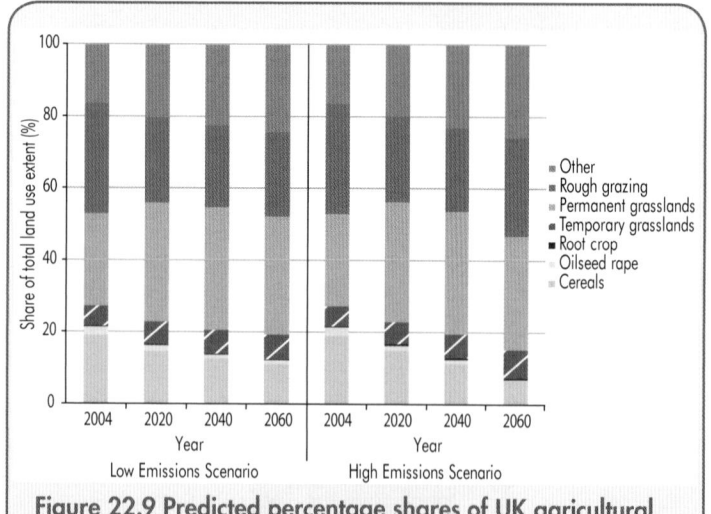

Figure 22.9 Predicted percentage shares of UK agricultural land use under two climate scenarios. Baseline year is 2004. Source: SEER (2011).

99 It is effectively impossible to determine a single colour scale which works for all activities yet still highlights the sensitivity of changes in each individual activity. To see this, contrast the maps for rough grazing, which embrace a range of ±100 ha, with that for temporary grassland, which ranges from –5 ha to +20 ha, figures which barely span two of the categories for the former activity.

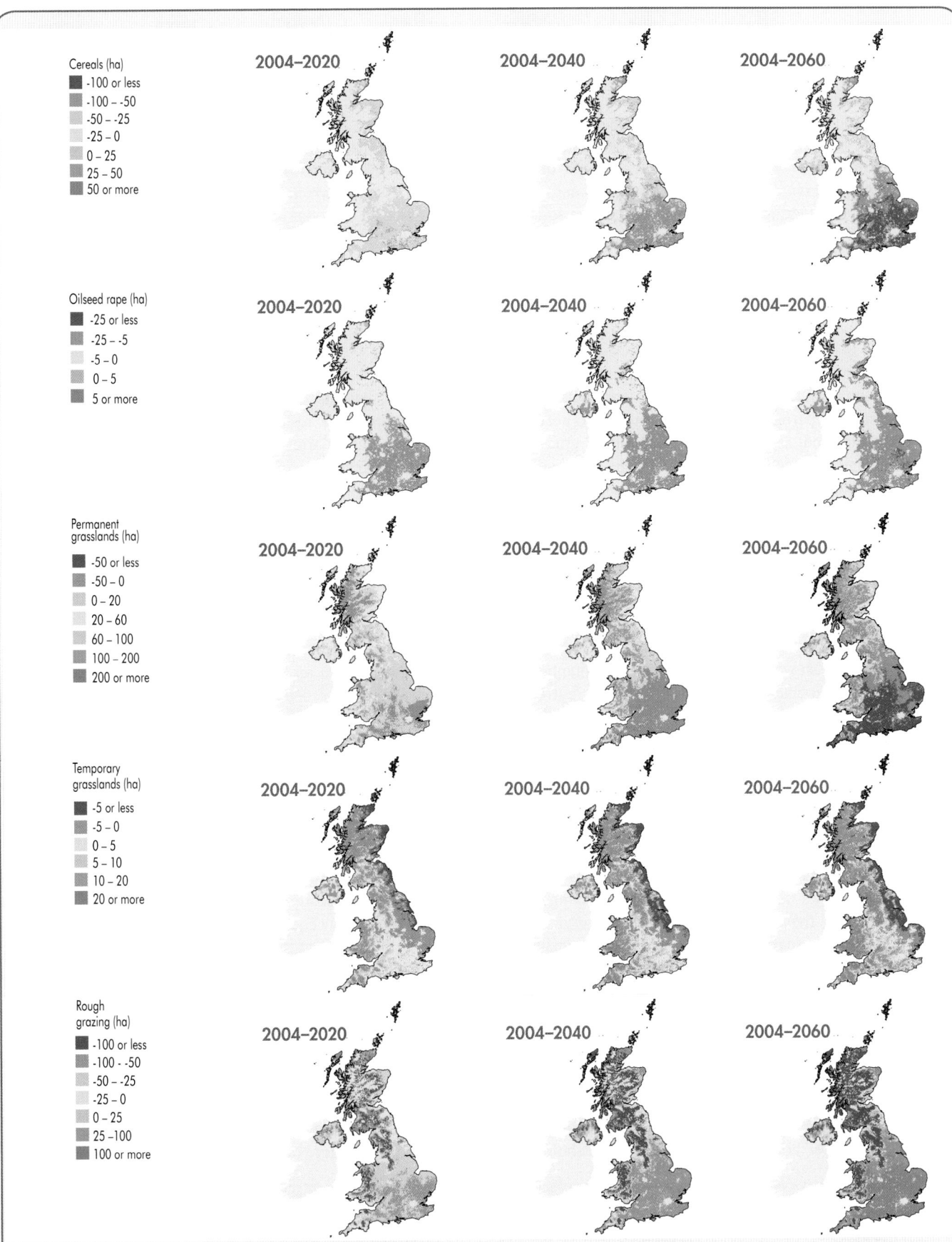

Figure 22.10 Predicted changes in land use from the base year 2004 to three future dates (2020, 2040 and 2060) under the UKCIP high emission climate change scenario (changes shown as the number of hectares (ha) per 2 km grid square). For each of the maps, the colour scheme ranges from dark purple, indicating the largest reductions, to dark green, indicating the largest increases, with yellow indicating relatively little change. Note that each map has a different upper and lower bound indicating the absolute changes but, as these ranges differ for each activity, the same shade of colour means different things across maps. Source: SEER (2011).

When interpreting **Figure 22.10** it is important to note that each land use type is mapped using its own category scale. This is necessary, as a single scale could not capture the quite diverse absolute differences in changes between land use types. However, this does mean that any given colour for one land use does not have the same meaning for another. Nevertheless, within each land use we can readily observe trends in losses and gains across different areas. Considering the first row of maps, we see a marked reduction in cereals in south and east England as climate change brings with it problems of droughtiness in this area. However, this is somewhat offset by an increase in cereals in eastern Scotland as the same processes reduce problems of cold and waterlogging in that area. Another interesting trend is provided by the contrast of changes in temporary and permanent grasslands (third and fourth rows) and rough grazing (final row). Here we see a marked switch from rough grazing to permanent grassland in Wales, north-western England and Scotland (with temporary grassland also increasing in the former two areas). As discussed in more detail subsequently, trends such as the predicted increase in rough grazing in the south-east of England should be treated with caution as they correspond to the area of the country where predicted climates rise most above historical trends and hence out of the range of data.

Figure 22.11 shows the changes in predicted livestock numbers in England and Wales in 2020, 2040 and 2060 compared to the base year (2004). Echoing the rise of grasslands shown previously, the overall number of dairy cows is expected increase substantially, particularly in Northern Ireland, England and Wales and lowland areas of Scotland. Beef cattle and sheep are predicted to generally increase in less extreme upland areas such as Wales and the Borders, but to decline across most of England as lands become more suitable for more profitable undertakings.

When combined, the results for land use and livestock intensity mapped in **Figure 22.10** and **Figure 22.11** predict the profile of farm activities across the period to 2060. This in turn allows us to calculate the implied changes in value induced by these changes in ecosystem services through that period. Ideally, we would use prices adjusted for all subsidies and interventions. However, if we assume that these are relatively marginal shifts, an approximation to that value can readily be obtained by applying the farm gross margin (FGM) value of each output, where FGM is simply the difference between per unit farm revenue and associated variable costs for a given activity.[100] While gross margins are heavily influenced by subsidy levels (see Tinch *et al.* 2010; Bateman *et al.* 2003), examining changes in those margins (i.e. holding subsidies constant) should provide

some indication of underlying shifts in values. **Figure 22.12** illustrates changes in FGM across the UK as evaluated using baseline (2004) prices and (for contrast) the low emissions scenario.[101]

Figure 22.12 shows some interesting trends in FGM.[102] In particular, there is a clear north–south trend, with strong increases in the north and small decreases in the driest areas of the south, which progressively become more and more significant with the warming and the drop in precipitation. However, assumptions concerning the response of farmers to these circumstances mean that we have some doubts that the forecast loss for the south east of England will arise to the extent predicted, if at all. We now turn to consider these and related caveats.

22.3.17.4 Caveats

Several caveats need to be taken into account when considering the results produced by this analysis. Firstly, the model scenarios are not predictions of the future, but rather represent the impact of climate change *ceteris paribus*, i.e. keeping all other drivers of land use and agricultural production fixed to their baseline levels (year 2004). Therefore, for example, market prices and government involvement (subsidies, levies, milk quotas) are assumed to stay constant. However, changes in both prices and agricultural policies can be expected to take place in the future. For example, global warming could cause major shifts in the supply of all the main agricultural products, while the growth of developing economies such as China and India could have significant implications for demand. Also, UK policies are likely to change, in accordance with the ongoing reforms of the CAP.

Considering our measure of financial impacts, FGM, two important limitations need to be acknowledged. Firstly, since FGM is defined as the difference between revenues and variable costs, all farm fixed costs (e.g. machinery, buildings, rent) are not included in the analysis. Secondly, conversion costs are also not included. In other words, all changes in land use and FGM refer to equilibrium conditions, but do not take into account possible costs encountered in order to reach these new equilibriums.

It is important to note that the UKCP09 scenarios, particularly those relating to periods furthest into the future, include climatic conditions for some areas of the country (notably the South East and south coast of England) which are considerably above those experienced for any length of time over the past 40 years. Therefore these conditions lie outside the range of data used to estimate the model. For this reason, the results have to be interpreted cautiously. In particular, since the model uses farmers' past behaviour to predict their future response, it cannot include the impact of

---

100 While FGM is a very widely applied measure within the field of agricultural economics, it lacks the simple link to welfare of a measure such as profit. However, as noted earlier, farm profit data are not available on the disaggregated regular grid of the agricultural census data used for this analysis. The CSERGE SEER project is currently examining possibilities for supplementing this analysis with data from the Farm Business Survey which would address this problem. A further issue concerns the extent to which these shifts are marginal. Again, this is a topic of ongoing research.

101 FGM forecasts for 2004 are taken from Fezzi *et al.* (2010a) as follows: cereals = £290/ha, root crops = £2,425/ha, oilseed rape = £310/ha, dairy = £576/head, beef = £69/head, sheep = £9.3/head. Appendix 1 of Fezzi *et al.* (2011) provides an analysis of the variation in these estimates induced by changes in agricultural prices for different outputs. This shows that such variation can alter absolute FGM values considerably, although the overall spatial pattern in changes remains the same as that illustrated in Figure 22.11.

102 Note that the trends here are significantly different to those shown in various of the valuations of scenarios reported in Chapter 26. In the analysis reported in the present chapter the only driver of change is shifts in the climate, yielding the patterns illustrated in Figure 22.12. However, in Chapter 26 multiple drivers of change are acting simultaneously producing, in many cases, quite different patterns of response.

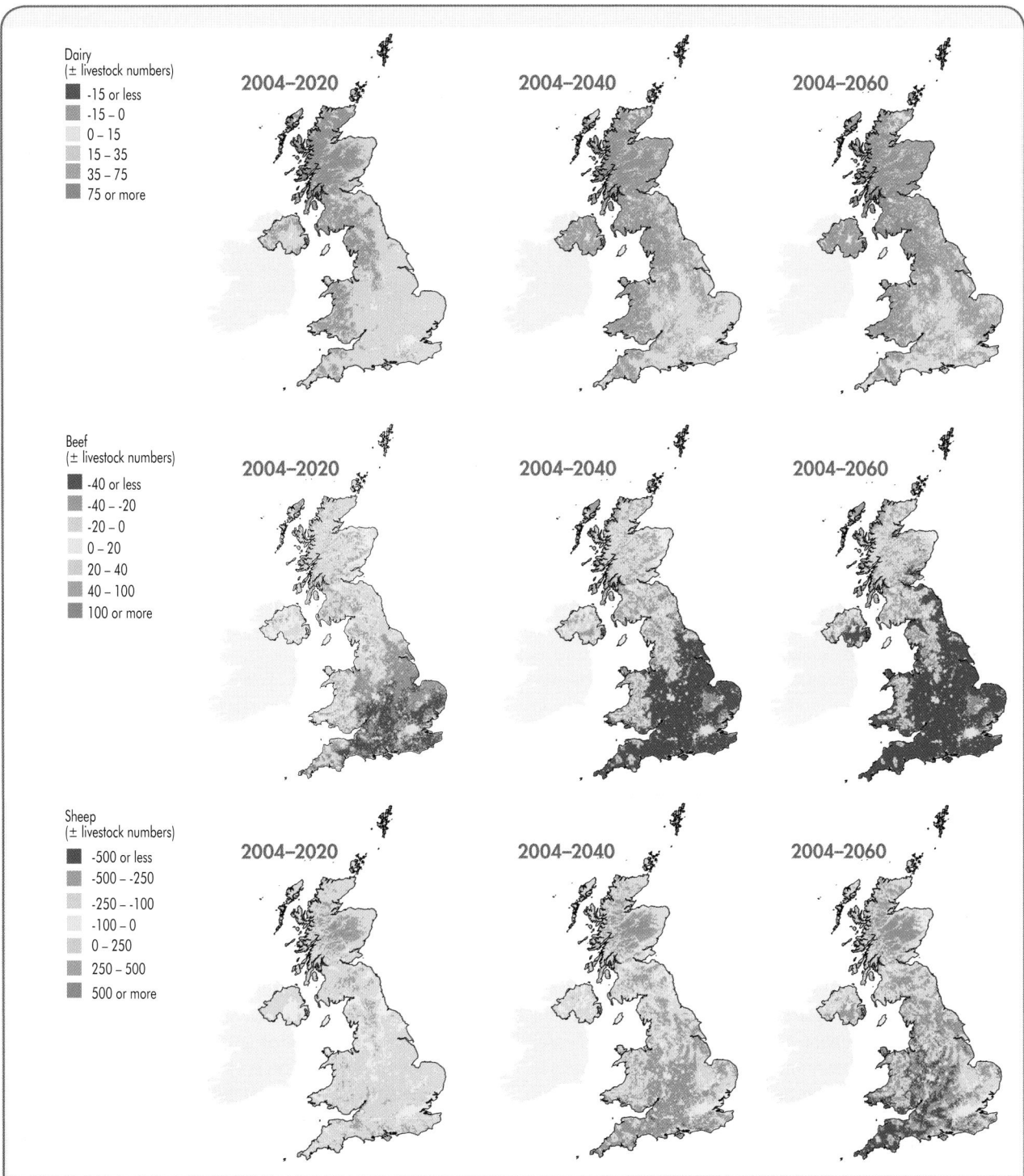

Figure 22.11 Predicted changes in livestock numbers from the base year 2004 to three future dates (2020, 2040 and 2060) under the UKCIP high emission climate change scenario (changes shown as the number of head of livestock per 2 km grid square). For each of the maps, the colour scheme ranges from dark purple indicating the largest reductions, to dark green indicating the largest increases, with yellow indicating relatively little change. Note that each map has a different upper and lower bound indicating the absolute changes but, as these ranges differ for each activity, the same shade of colour means different things across maps. Source: SEER (2011).

introducing new crop types which have not been significantly present in UK farmland in the past (e.g. outdoor tomatoes, vineyards). This relates to a further caveat concerning technological innovation. Although our model includes a time trend which provides some indication of technical progress, this is not assumed to change. Taking these factors together, the predictions for the warmest areas are subject to the highest degree of uncertainty and the results for the most extreme scenarios (e.g. 2060 high emissions) for these areas should be interpreted cautiously. Conversely, however, the results for the north of England, Wales, Scotland and Northern Ireland should be more robust.

Our analysis focuses on the impact of changes in temperature and precipitation, and not on other things that might be affected by climate change. For example, Mendelsohn & Dinar (2009) and others suggest that

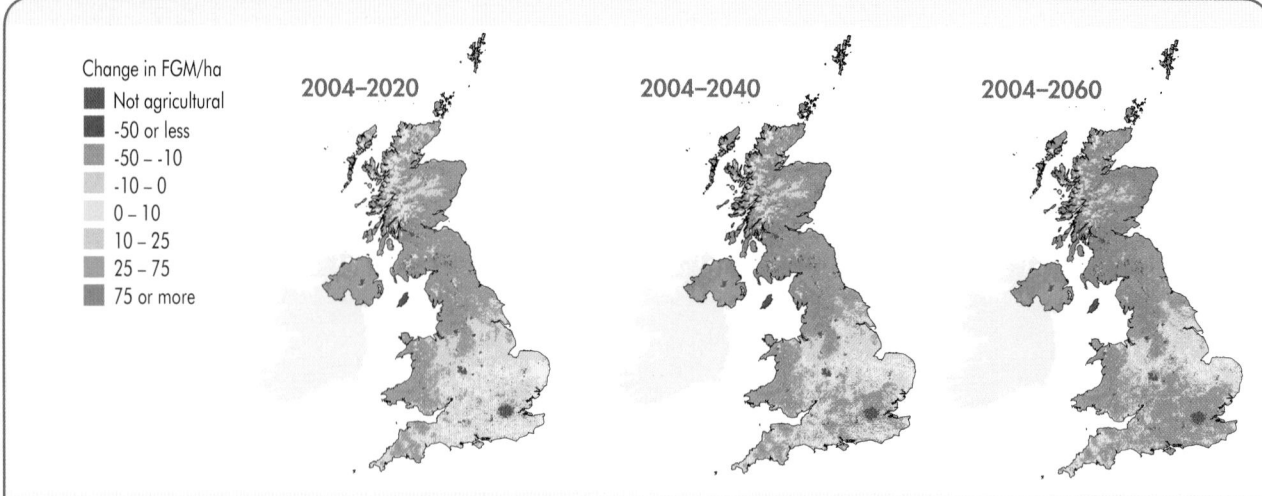

Figure 22.12 Valuation of climate ecosystem services: the impact of climate change (UKCIP low emission scenario) upon UK farming calculated as the induced change in annual farm gross margin (FGM) per hectare (ha) compared to its level in 2004. Source: SEER (2011).

increased carbon dioxide fertilisation may increase crop yields. However, there may be a trade-off between quantity and quality, as the projected increase in crop growth is offset by a decline in nutritional value (Jablonski *et al.* 2002). Another factor which is likely to change in the future is pollination. Current research (e.g. Potts *et al.* 2010) indicates a significant decline in pollination ecosystem services in recent years. Among the most important drivers are land use change, with the consequent loss and fragmentation of habitats increasing, pesticide application, environmental pollution and climate change. This could have a significant impact on yields. Furthermore, there is a growing body of evidence to suggest that climate change may modify (and generally exacerbate) crop disease patterns in ways that are, to date, still poorly understood (Harvell *et al.* 2002).

22.3.17.5 Agricultural food production: conclusions

The analysis develops a novel, spatially explicit model for estimating changes in agricultural land use as a result of changes in any combination of policy, price or environmental drivers. A detailed spatially and temporally variable dataset is compiled and applied to this model to yield estimates of farm land use under analyst-controlled scenarios. The UKCIP09 climate change predictions are applied to this model, and land use change impacts are estimated. These are in turn employed to calculate farm gross margin estimates of the value of changes in ecosystem provisioning services.

Our analysis remains incomplete, yet findings to date suggest that changes in ecosystem inputs induced by climate change will have a substantial influence upon the gross margins generated by farm food production. Interestingly, climate change seems likely to generate both positive and negative impacts across different part of the UK. These patterns include a new north–south divide, reversing the characteristic direction of that inequality, with the winners in this case being in northern areas and losers being in areas of the south of England.

22.3.18 Carbon Storage and Annual Greenhouse Gas Emissions: Terrestrial[103]

22.3.18.1 Introduction

Regulation of the carbon cycle and emissions of GHGs has become an increasingly important element of contemporary land use decision making, both in the UK and globally. The inclusion of land use choices and land management activities as an integral part of assessments of climate regulation services is important for several reasons. Climate is a key determinant of land use, and climate change would be expected to result in regional shifts in land use. Different land uses are, in turn, associated with varying regulation capacity, and land use change might therefore itself lead to increases or decreases in GHG emissions. Finally, land management can be tailored to differing land use so as to manipulate the potential for GHG mitigation. Given that agriculture accounts for 10–12% of the total global anthropogenic emissions of GHG (Smith *et al.* 2007), the potential for such mitigation is clearly substantial.

An interesting example of how land use change can affect carbon storage is illustrated by the case of forestry. Estimates show total net carbon sequestration by UK woodlands planted after 1921 rising from 2.4 million tonnes of carbon dioxide (Mt CO_2) in 1945 to a peak of 16.3 Mt CO_2 in 2004, subsequently falling to 12.9 Mt CO_2 in 2009 (Valatin & Starling 2010). Over the period 2001–2009 these estimates imply annual mean net sequestration rates of around 5.2 tCO_2/ha across all UK woodlands (with an additional 0.3 tCO_2/ha net increase in carbon storage in harvested wood products). If assumed permanent (e.g. because of future woodland expansion) and valued at the DECC (2009) central social value of carbon estimate of £53/tCO_2 in 2009, the estimates suggest that the total value of net carbon sequestered annually by UK woodlands increased five-fold from £124 million in 1945 to £680 million in 2009 (at 2010

---

103 This Section draws in part from Abson *et al.* (2010) and Valatin & Starling (2010).

prices). It would also imply a mean value per hectare of the carbon sequestered annually by UK woodlands (£239/ha) of more than triple the mean value for softwood production (£66/ha) and of the order of 10 times the value of hardwood production (£7–£25/ha) in 2009. Forecasts of net carbon sequestration based upon the continuation of current rates of woodland creation indicate a drop of more than half in net carbon sequestration by woodlands from 2010 to 2028. When combined with changes in carbon storage in harvested wood products, the forecasts show combined net sequestration falling from 14.5 Mt CO_2 in 2010 to a minimum of 2.5 Mt CO_2 in 2034, before gradually rising to 3.3 Mt CO_2 by 2050 (Valatin & Starling 2010) However, recent analysis for the Read Report (Matthews & Broadmeadow 2009) suggests an additional 12 Mt CO_2 to 15 Mt CO_2/yr could be sequestered in 2060, were a programme of enhanced afforestation of an additional 23,200 ha a year adopted. Although apparently much more valuable than the timber produced by UK woodlands, carbon sequestration nevertheless remains a largely non-market value, with little incentive at present for private landowners to increase provision of this ecosystem service (or to maintain existing carbon storage).[104] This may in part be addressed through the Woodland Carbon Code which is currently being developed by the Forestry Commission to help stimulate emerging markets for carbon sequestration in the UK.

In addition to forest, peatland is an interesting example of a land use which provides climate regulating services. Of course, while carbon stocks held by peatland may be significant, where land use remains stable the flow values may be negligible. So, for example, around 40% of UK soil carbon is found within Mountain, Moorland and Heath habitats (Tinch et al. 2010), much of which are peatlands, while Natural England (NE 2010a) estimate that some 6,700 ha of peatland stores around 584 Mt C, equivalent to about 2.14 billion tonnes of carbon dioxide equivalents (CO_2e). However, most of this is stored in stable conditions. That said, estimated emissions from peatlands are currently about 2.48 Mt CO_2e/yr (Tinch et al. 2010). This is equivalent to about £130 million/yr at DECC's 2010 price for carbon dioxide.

So where land use changes, so does the level, and hence the value, of its climate regulation service. The analysis presented here considers how these climate regulation services will alter as climate change induces shifts in UK agricultural land use. The analysis outlines the assumptions made to estimate this value, based on the predicted climate change associated with the UKCIP low and high GHG emission scenarios (UKCIP 2009) for the years 2004, 2020, 2040 and 2060. These are the same predictions used in the agricultural analysis presented earlier in this chapter, and the changes in land uses are drawn from the outputs of the CSERGE agricultural land use model (Fezzi & Bateman in press). This has an important benefit in that it allows us to simultaneously assess both the agricultural and carbon

storage values associated with the UKCIP climate change predictions.

The analysis includes both estimates of changes in potential equilibrium carbon stocks (i.e. that level of carbon that can feasibly be stored) and changes in the annual flow of GHGs associated with the shifts in modelled land use patterns in the Enclosed Farmland Broad Habitat. The stock estimates for the modelled Enclosed Farmland land use patterns are based on i) the carbon stored in, above and below ground vegetation and ii) the potential equilibrium soil organic carbon (SOC) levels of the soils under those land use patterns. The flow estimates are based on the annual GHG emissions from farm activities (including energy usage, emissions from fertilisers and livestock) and the annual SOC emissions or accumulations resulting from changes in land use. All impacts are converted to carbon dioxide equivalents.

Land uses in the Enclosed Farmland Broad Habitat include cereals, oilseed rape, root crops (sugar beet and potatoes), temporary grassland, permanent grassland, rough grazing, on-farm woodland[105] and other agricultural land uses (including horticulture, and bare/fallow land). This document first presents an analysis relating to changes in the capacity to store carbon, then an analysis of the changes in annual emissions resulting from changes in land use and associated land management. Finally, we provide an economic valuation of the changes in climate regulation given specified climate change scenarios. Uncertainty in the valuation estimates is assessed by comparing results using the two main approaches to carbon pricing: social cost of carbon and the marginal abatement costs of carbon.

22.3.18.2 Changes in the UK terrestrial capacity to store carbon

An analysis was conducted of the change in carbon stocks, including changes in SOC and vegetative carbon stocks (full details in Abson et al. 2010). It is important to note that the analysis provides information about potential long-term equilibrium estimates, while in reality carbon stocks are dynamic as they are subject to changes in growth and decomposition rates driven by climate and land management. The results of the analysis give a total UK estimate of vegetative carbon stocks for the baseline year (2004) of 134 Mt C, of which 77% is stored in woodland. This compares with Milne et al.'s (2001) estimate of 113.8 ±25.6 Mt C for GB of which 80% was estimated to be stored in woodland. Vegetative carbon stocks are relatively evenly spread across the UK, with the highest stocks in wooded areas such as Thetford forest and southern Scotland.

While the vegetative stock of carbon is substantial, it is dwarfed by that in soils (Bradley et al. 2005). The analysis suggests that 50% of the carbon stocks in the UK's terrestrial ecosystems are found in Scotland (2,365 Mt C), with a further 37% (1,755 Mt C) in England, 7% (338 Mt C) in Wales and 6% (292 Mt C) in Northern Ireland. The highest stocks are found

---

104 This depends upon the permanence assumption and whether the carbon substitution benefits of using the wood harvested are also included in the comparison.

105 On-farm woodland is subsumed within an 'other land' category in the Fezzi & Bateman (in press) model. However, because of the importance of woodland in regulating climate, this land use is separated out in the present analysis, but it is assumed that its extent remains unchanged within the UK NEA Scenario timelines (see Chapter 25).

in the upland peat areas of northern England, Northern Ireland and Scotland.

Next we model how the land use change predicted under the UKCIP low and high GHG emission scenarios will affect the equilibrium carbon stock for the UK. Here it should be noted that SOC may take many years to reach new equilibrium levels after land use change (particularly in organic soils), therefore the potential equilibrium stock estimates do not represent the actual stocks in the analysis year, but rather they indicate the potential equilibrium stocks associated with the modelled land use configuration for that analysis year. Under these scenarios, only the Fens in the East of England and small areas of the north-east Scottish Highlands show a consistent increase in carbon stocks, this being due to a reduction in intensive cereal production on organic soils. There are significant reductions in potential equilibrium carbon stocks in the lowland agricultural regions of southern England in both the low and high emissions scenarios, these losses being most pronounced in the high emissions scenario towards the end of our analysis period (2060). Conversely, the largest reductions in carbon stocks occur in the SOC stored in peatland and upland areas of the UK. Overall patterns are broadly similar across the high and low emissions scenarios, although potential equilibrium stocks decline more rapidly in southern regions and under the high emissions scenario. Land use change in Scotland is predicted to most dramatically reduce the potential equilibrium carbon stocks, with a decrease in stocks (relative to the present day) of approximately 37% (113 tonnes C/ha) for the 2060 land use configuration in both scenarios. This change in stock is due to increases in arable and improved grassland activities on peat and other soils with a high SOC. The total reduction in potential UK equilibrium carbon storage from the baseline year to 2060 is 1,381 Mt C for the low emissions scenario and 1,560 Mt C for the high emissions scenario; this would equate to total carbon dioxide emissions of approximately 5,064 Mt CO_2e and 5,719 Mt CO_2e respectively. For comparison, the total UK emissions of GHGs in 2008 has been estimated as 628.5 Mt CO_2e (DECC 2008).

22.3.18.3 Changes in UK land-based greenhouse gas emission flows

Four major sources of GHG emissions were considered when estimating changes in annual GHG emission flows:

i)   The indirect emissions due to energy use from farmland activities such as tillage, sowing, spraying, harvesting and the production, storage and transport of fertilisers and pesticides. Per hectare estimates of GHG emissions for typical farming practices were applied to each type of land use in order to map these emissions across the UK.

ii) Emissions of nitrous oxide and methane from livestock, including beef cattle, dairy cows and sheep through the production of manure and enteric fermentation.

iii) Direct emissions of nitrous oxide emissions from artificial fertilisers.

iv) Annual flows of carbon from soils due to land use changes. For example, permanent grassland converted

from arable farming will be accumulating SOC, while permanent grassland on land that was previously under rough grazing may be losing SOC. For the baseline year (2004) annual flows of SOC were only estimated for organic (peat) soils as there is insufficient data on land use change prior to the baseline to accurately model changes in SOC in non-organic soils. In the analyses of subsequent years (2020, 2040 and 2060), SOC flows due to land use change in both organic and non-organic soils are included in the annual GHG emission estimates. In both UKCIP low/high emissions scenarios there are considerable changes in annual emissions.

We estimate that the annual GHG emissions from Enclosed Farmland for the baseline year (2004) to be 48 Mt CO_2e (approximately 9% of UK net GHG emissions for that year) with emissions from enteric fermentation and the direct release of nitrous oxide from both artificial fertilisers and the application of farmyard manure representing the biggest sources of GHG emissions from Enclosed Farmland in the UK.[106] **Figure 22.13** maps the distribution of changes in farmland emissions across the UK for three time periods under two climate change scenarios. In general, results suggest that emissions will fall in the lowland areas of England and increase in more upland areas. These trends echo the shifts in land use expected for those areas, with the latter areas seeing increases in livestock numbers and in arable and horticultural production, leading to increased emissions of methane and nitrous oxide. These trends are exacerbated by the potentially large rise in GHG emissions from the conversion of peatland from rough grazing and semi natural grassland into improved grassland.

Considering **Figure 22.13**, while spatial patterns are more pronounced under elevated climate change, overall predicted emissions from agriculture are similar for both scenarios, with aggregate emissions differing by only 4% on average between the two scenarios. In the UK, GHG emissions from Enclosed Farmland are estimated to increase from 2.14 tonnes CO_2e/ha/yr in 2004 to 2.33 tonnes CO_2e/ha/yr in 2060 under the UKCIP low emissions scenario, and to rise to 2.21 tonnes CO_2e/ha/yr in 2060 under the high emissions scenario. There are effectively two opposing land use dynamics identified by the model, increasing carbon intensities (per hectare) of agriculture in the north and decreasing carbon intensities in the south. Aggregate UK GHG emissions under the high emissions scenario are slightly lower than for the low emissions scenario, due to greater carbon reductions in the south by 2060 under the high emissions scenario. These land use changes equate to an aggregate increase in UK GHG emission from agriculture of approximately 11% between 2004 and 2020 under both emissions scenarios. Trends then peak with annual changes in GHG emissions remaining relatively stable between 2020 and 2040 for both scenarios (with an approximate increase in emissions of 10% from the baseline year). Towards the end of the analysis period trends begin to improve somewhat, with 2060 annual GHG emissions being 8.9% higher than the baseline for the low emissions scenario

106 Official estimates for the GHG emissions from UK agriculture for 2004 range from 44.5 Mt CO_2e (Defra 2007) to 51.7 Mt CO_2e (DECC 2008), with the differences in the two estimates in part due to different definitions of what represents a GHG emission from agriculture.

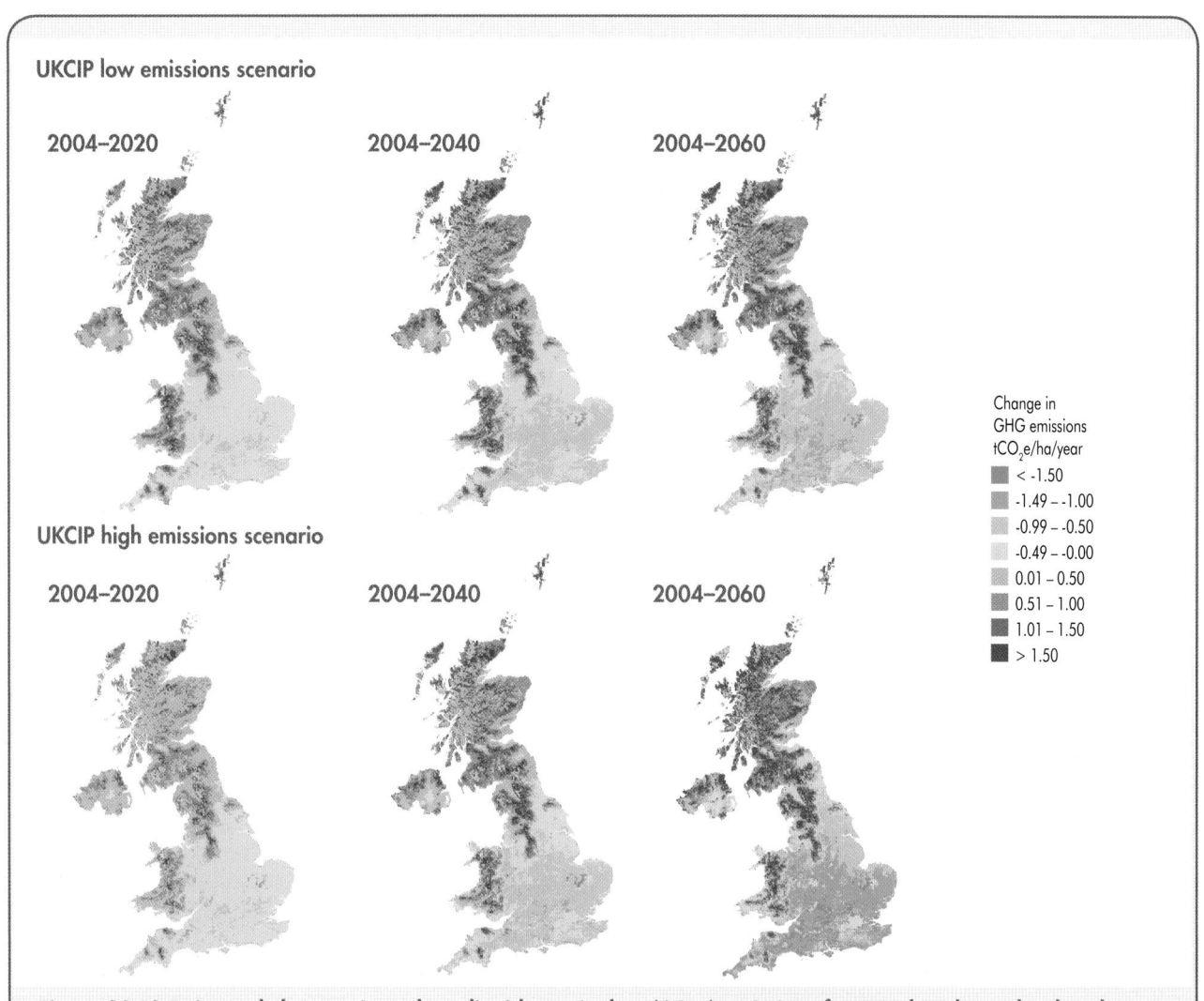

UKCIP low emissions scenario

2004–2020 2004–2040 2004–2060

UKCIP high emissions scenario

2004–2020 2004–2040 2004–2060

Change in
GHG emissions
tCO₂e/ha/year
■ < -1.50
■ -1.49 – -1.00
■ -0.99 – -0.50
■ -0.49 – -0.00
■ 0.01 – 0.50
■ 0.51 – 1.00
■ 1.01 – 1.50
■ > 1.50

Figure 22.13 Estimated changes in carbon dioxide equivalent (CO₂e) emissions from Enclosed Farmland under two UKCIP climate scenarios. GHG = greenhouse gas; t = tonnes; ha = hectare. Source: Abson *et al*. (2010).

and 3.2% higher than the baseline year for the high emissions scenario. The reduction in aggregate GHG emissions between 2040 and 2060 is largely driven by a climate-induced switch to less intensive land uses, resulting in reductions in fertiliser usage and consequent nitrous oxide emissions, with concurrent increases in SOC due to a reduction in tillage on non-organic soils. All in all, while most southern regions see significant drops in GHG emissions, northern regions see increasing emissions due to increased livestock numbers and a shift to more intensive land uses (primarily improved grassland and arable production) as the climate makes these new land uses economically viable. Additionally, it is worth noting that while in the baseline year net GHG emissions from UK peat soils are estimated at 3.76 Mt CO₂e/yr, these increase to 7.67 Mt CO₂e/yr by 2060 (high emissions scenario), with Scotland accounting for almost half of these emissions, due mainly to land use changes from rough grazing to permanent grasslands.

Contrasting the spatial pattern of changes in carbon flux with the distribution of shifts in agricultural values presented in Section 22.3.17.3 (see **Figure 22.11** and **Figure 22.12**), we can see the duality of effects which climate change is expected to bring in these respects. The increases in temperature and shifts in rainfall patterns

brought about by climate change will result in a shift towards relatively more intensive agriculture in upland Britain (**Figure 22.11**). While this will generate increases in farm income in parts of upland Britain (**Figure 22.12**), the present analysis shows that this will also be synonymous with increased emissions in such areas (**Figure 22.13**).

22.3.18.4 The value of agricultural climate regulation

Providing estimates on the value of non-market GHG emissions is problematic (particularly when the estimates are for future emissions) for two main reasons. First, climate science is complex and we do not yet have a definitive relation between emissions and climate change. Moreover, there is considerable uncertainty regarding the relationship between climate change and its impacts on the economy, dependent as those impacts are on socio-technological responses to changes in the climate. Second, when forecasting carbon values, the societal cost associated with the emission of an additional tonne of carbon is dependent on how many tonnes of carbon have previously been emitted (and abated), the eventual concentrations at which carbon dioxide is stabilised in the atmosphere, and the emissions trajectory adopted to achieve this stabilisation (DEFRA 2007). As such, future carbon prices are depend upon the emission and climate scenarios upon which they are based. The issues of carbon pricing are further complicated by the choice of methodology used to construct these prices. There are two main approaches to carbon pricing: the social cost of carbon (SCC); and the marginal abatement cost of carbon (MACC). We apply two separate price functions to investigate the sensitivity of results to the choice of carbon value. The UK government's official non-market MACC prices from DECC (2009) are applied to both climate scenarios. However, for comparison we also apply an endogenous SCC price derived from Stern (2007). Stern's (2007) business as usual price is applied to the UKCIP high emissions scenario and the atmospheric concentration of 550 parts per million CO_2e price is applied to the UKCIP low emissions scenario. For the DECC prices, the carbon prices for each point in the scenarios are based on a linear interpolation of the prices provided by DECC (2009).[107] **Table 22.18** details the prices arising from these various strategies. All prices are in 2009 values.

The prices provided in **Table 22.18** are used in **Table 22.19** to estimate the total annual cost of GHG emissions from UK agriculture for the predicted land uses under the two UKCIP climate scenarios. Annual costs of carbon emissions from agriculture are predicted to increase from £2.1 billion p.a. in 2004 to £14.0 billion in 2060 under the UKCIP low emissions scenario, based on the DECC price function and to £4 billion under Stern's price function. While some of this steep increase in costs is due to the predicted 8.8% increase in GHG emissions from agriculture, it is largely driven by the increase in the predicted price of carbon.

By calculating the difference between the estimated cost of emissions for the baseline year (2004) and those for the modelled land uses in 2020, 2040 and 2060 we identify the impact of predicted future land use change on the value of carbon regulating service provided by UK agriculture. **Figure 22.14** presents a regional analysis of the relative change in annual carbon costs (per hectare) of climate-driven land use change in the UK. This is achieved by comparing the carbon costs associated with the baseline and predicted land uses for a given year (2020, 2040, 2060) at that year's DECC carbon price. While agriculture remains a net emitter of GHGs for all regions of the UK, land use changes are predicted to results in relative decreases in costs per hectare of emissions in southern regions of the UK (compared to the emissions associated with the baseline land uses) and relative increases in costs in northern regions. For example, in 2060 the average cost of GHG emissions from agriculture in the East of England are predicted to be approximately £300/ha lower than if the baseline land use patterns had been retained, while in Scotland the cost of carbon for agriculture in Scotland is predicted to be £250/ha higher due to changing land uses.

Table 22.18 Greenhouse gas pricing for non-market greenhouse gas in the UKCIP scenarios. Source: Abson et al. (2010).

Year	DECC* ($£/tCO_2e$[†])	STERN 550 ppm[‡] stabilisation ($£/tCO_2e$[†])	STERN BAU[¶] ($£/tCO_2e$[†])
2004	44.00	25.47	88.38
2020	60.00	34.96	121.32
2040	135.00	51.95	180.28
2060	265.00	77.20	267.89

* Department of Energy and Climate Change.
[†] Tonnes of carbon dioxide equivalents.
[‡] Parts per million.
[¶] Business As Usual.

Table 22.19 Estimated total annual costs of UK agricultural greenhouse gas emissions. Source Abson et al. (2010).

Carbon price function	2004 (£ million)	2020 (£ million)	2040 (£ million)	2060 (£ million)
DECC* low emissions scenario	2,134	3,261	7,334	14,000
Stern low emissions scenario	1,235	1,900	2,822	4,078
DECC* high emissions scenario	2,134	3,141	7,121	13,265
Stern high emissions scenario	4,286	6,352	9,509	13,409

* Department of Energy and Climate Change.

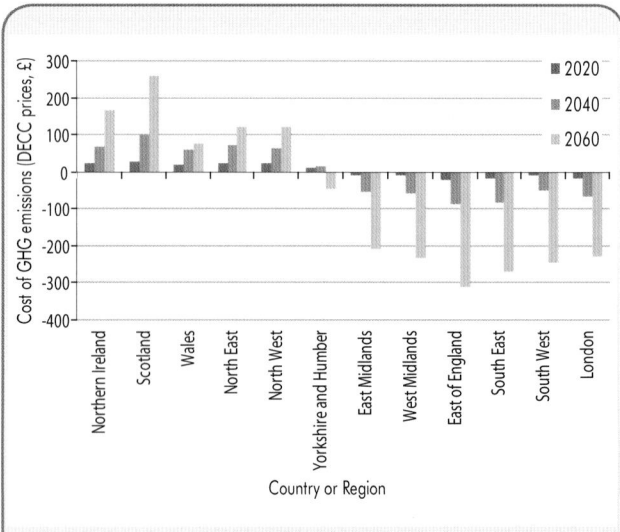

Figure 22.14 Predicted impact of land use change on the cost of greenhouse gas (GHG) emissions (Department of Energy and Climate Change (DECC) prices) from agriculture in the UK under the UKCIP high emissions scenario, compared to estimated costs in the baseline year (2004). Source: Abson et al. (2010).

107 Stern's (2007) prices were converted from US dollars using the long-term exchange rate ($/£) of 1.61 and assumed to increase by 2%/yr in real terms. All prices are in 2009 values, calculated using the treasury gross domestic product (GDP) deflator (HM Treasury 2010). Where £/tonne of carbon (£/tC) were reported, a standard conversion ratio of 44/12 was used to convert to CO_2e.

Table 22.20 Regional analysis of cost from agricultural greenhouse gas emissions per hectare (ha) (based on Department of Energy and Climate Change (DECC) prices). Source: Abson et al. (2010).

	Baseline 2004 (£/ha/yr)	UKCIP low emissions scenario			UKCIP high emissions scenario		
		2020 (£/ha/yr)	2040 (£/ha/yr)	2060 (£/ha/yr)	2020 (£/ha/yr)	2040 (£/ha/yr)	2060 (£/ha/yr)
Northern Ireland	140	217	501	980	213	497	1,007
Scotland	86	154	363	735	144	361	774
Wales	89	155	355	660	142	335	615
North East	102	167	385	758	163	384	737
North West	129	204	470	907	197	459	895
Yorkshire Humber	98	146	325	614	144	317	547
East Midlands	85	107	219	385	107	206	305
West Midlands	91	116	238	414	116	224	319
East of England	90	101	203	356	101	191	233
South East	74	80	158	261	83	144	175
South West	108	143	302	523	139	279	404
London	54	54	111	179	59	101	100
UK total	**94**	**144**	**324**	**618**	**139**	**314**	**585**

Table 22.20 presents a regional analysis of the total cost of annual per hectare emissions of GHG from Enclosed Farmland based on the DECC (2009)-MACC price function for the two UKCIP emissions scenarios. Whereas **Figure 22.14** identifies the relative carbon costs of changing land uses (the change from the baseline in carbon emissions multiplied by the carbon price for a given year), **Table 22.20** presents absolute costs (i.e. those based on the total emissions in a given year multiplied by the price in that year). Therefore **Table 22.20** differs from **Figure 22.14** in that it considers the value of a particular set of emissions at a particular point in time. For example, under the high emissions scenario Scotland is predicted to see a nine-fold increase in the cost of agricultural GHG emissions, rising from £86/ha/yr in 2004 to £774/ha/yr in 2060, yet Scottish agricultural GHG emissions are predicted to increase by around 50%. The majority of the nine-fold increase in absolute carbon costs is driven by a six-fold increase in predicted GHG prices between 2004 and 2060. Using the DECC price function under the high emissions UKCIP scenario, the highest cost from carbon in Enclosed Farmland will be in Northern Ireland (£1,007/ha/yr) and the lowest (excluding London) will be in the southeast of England (£175/ha/yr). On average, the cost of carbon emissions from Enclosed Farmland in the UK is predicted to increase by £491/ha/yr from 2004 to 2060.

22.3.19 The Non-use Value of Biodiversity: Towards Cost-effective Provision of Sustainable Populations

We have highlighted a variety of caveats regarding both the use of stated preferences and legacies as estimates of biodiversity non-use values. Furthermore, we recognise that certain non-use motivations such as ethical or spiritual concerns may not transfer well into a monetary valuation paradigm (see discussions in Chapter 16). These uncertainties add to the challenges facing natural science models of biodiversity relationships within and across species and habitats under a context of general climate change and anthropocentric pressures. Given this, a risk averse strategy might be to allow policy in this area to be guided by precautionary standards for biodiversity conservation, with economic assessment being focused upon the cost-effective provision of those standards (Bateman et al. 2009b). The UK NEA analysis seeks to provide an initial indication of such a strategy. The SEER project undertook two complementary studies of bird diversity (taken as an indicator of biodiversity as per HMG 2007),[108] both of which are presented below. In Chapter 26, these biodiversity assessment models are applied to a number of different scenarios for the future of Great Britain. A range of economic values are also assessed for each of these scenarios. By contrasting these values with the biodiversity implications of each scenario, the decision maker can observe the costs of attaining different levels of biodiversity. This cost-effectiveness approach provides a useful guide for decision making in situations where the full monetary benefits of a value stream (here biodiversity) cannot be reliably established.

Preparing for cost-effectiveness analysis 1: Modelling breeding bird diversity as a function of land cover.[109] Birds have the highest public profile amongst the UK's biodiversity and are high in the food chain, so are widely considered to be good indicators of wider ecosystem health. They are also better monitored than any other group in the UK. It has been demonstrated that birds can be sensitive to land use change;

---

108 Note that the Public Service Agreement referred to here (HMG 2007) is currently suspended pending replacement under the forthcoming White Paper on the Environment.
109 This Section draws from the work of Hulme & Siriwardena (2010).

indeed, changes in farming practices have contributed to a 53% decrease in the England farmland bird index between 1966 and 2009 (Defra 2010c). Most of this decline occurred during the 1970s and 1980s; since then numbers have continued to fall, but at a more modest pace. Birds are, therefore, the best available means by which to assess the biodiversity implications of land use change, including that envisioned through scenarios developed under the UK NEA.

UK land use information derived from the CEH Land Cover Map 2000 (Fuller *et al.* 2002) was matched with bird data from the British Trust for Ornithology (BTO) Breeding Bird Survey (BBS) which assesses widespread, terrestrial bird species at the 1 km Ordnance Survey grid square level (further details being given in Risely *et al.* 2010). For this analysis, BBS annual data from 1995 to 2006 provided a large database centred upon the date of the land use data, although note there is no census data available for 2001 due to access restrictions arising from the foot-and-mouth outbreak. Species recorded on an average of fewer than 40 squares/yr were omitted,

leaving 96 bird species recorded across a sample of 3,468 1 km grid squares across Britain.[110]

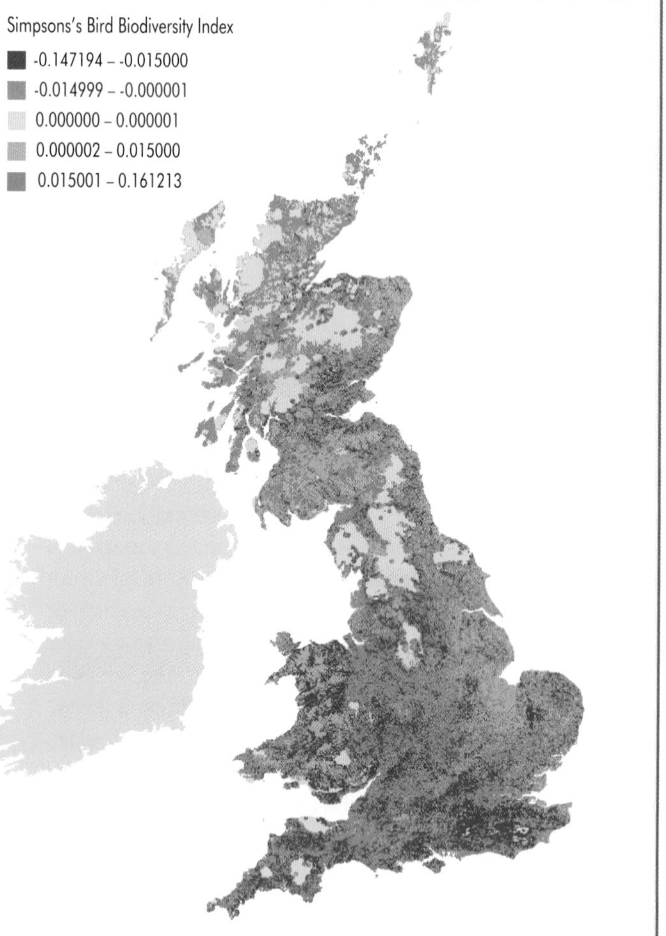

The composition of the bird community represented by the presence and abundance of the bird species in each survey square was summarised using Simpson's Diversity Index (see Hulme & Siriwardena 2010), calculated for each square across all years within the study period in which that square was surveyed. This index provides a simple summary of diversity which has high values where many species are present and are equally abundant. The variation in diversity was analysed with respect to land use (from the CEH Land Cover Map 2000) using standard techniques (generalised linear models and model averaging) to produce statistically sound results. The land cover classes used were chosen to match those included within the UK NEA Scenarios (Chapter 25): Coastal Margins, Freshwaters – Openwaters, Wetlands and Floodplains, arable and horticultural land, improved grassland, Semi-natural Grasslands, broadleaved woodland, coniferous woodland, upland habitats and Urban habitats.

Diversity across the whole of the UK was predicted at the 1 km grid square level from the land use predictions for each of the UK NEA Scenarios. While results indicated that there is significant unexplained variation in bird diversity and that, at a UK scale, it is regional geographic drivers such as altitude which provide the strongest determinants of bird viability, nevertheless all land cover variables except for coastal habitats and inland water cover were shown to have significant effects on diversity. Given that, obviously, influences such as altitude are constant across time, it is this strong relationship between diversity and land use which is of greatest importance to policy makers.

For illustrative purposes, the changes in diversity predicted under the UK NEA *World Markets* (high emissions) Scenario for the whole of Britain is presented in **Figure 22.15** (details of all scenarios are given in Chapter 26 and in Hulme & Siriwardena 2010). As can be seen, the *World Markets High* scenario is predicted to have significant positive and negative impacts in the absolute diversity index, which, depending on the area of the country under consideration, decreases by as much as 0.131 (e.g. south-east England) and increases by up to 0.040 (e.g. Scottish Borders area).[111] As a general guide, changes of this magnitude represent the loss or gain of around one locally scarce species from a low diversity (e.g. upland) square or a change in abundance of approximately 5–20% of a common species in a higher diversity square (e.g. lowland, with a matrix of woodland, farmland and gardens). It is important to note, therefore, that all the variation shown in **Figure 22.15** represents only minor changes in species number and abundance, not wholesale changes in communities.

Notwithstanding the limited extent to which *absolute* diversity is predicated to change, there are clear local differences in relative effects. These will each reflect the influences of changes in the areas of habitats associated with particular bird communities, as well as variation in the

Simpsons's Bird Biodiversity Index

- -0.147194 – -0.015000
- -0.014999 – -0.000001
- 0.000000 – 0.000001
- 0.000002 – 0.015000
- 0.015001 – 0.161213

Figure 22.15 Predicted change in bird diversity (Simpson's Diversity Index) under the UK NEA *World Markets* (high emissions) Scenario. Source: Hulme & Siriwardena (2010).

110 This will ignore the occurrence of some rare, conservation-priority birds, but both reflects the species range that is monitored adequately by the survey and will produce an index that better reflects broad ecosystem health, rather than unrelated factors that often influence the distribution of rare species.

111 The numbers mapped in Figure 22.15 are changes in the absolute Simpson's diversity index between the baseline model for Land Cover in the year 2000 and the predictions under the World Market scenario.

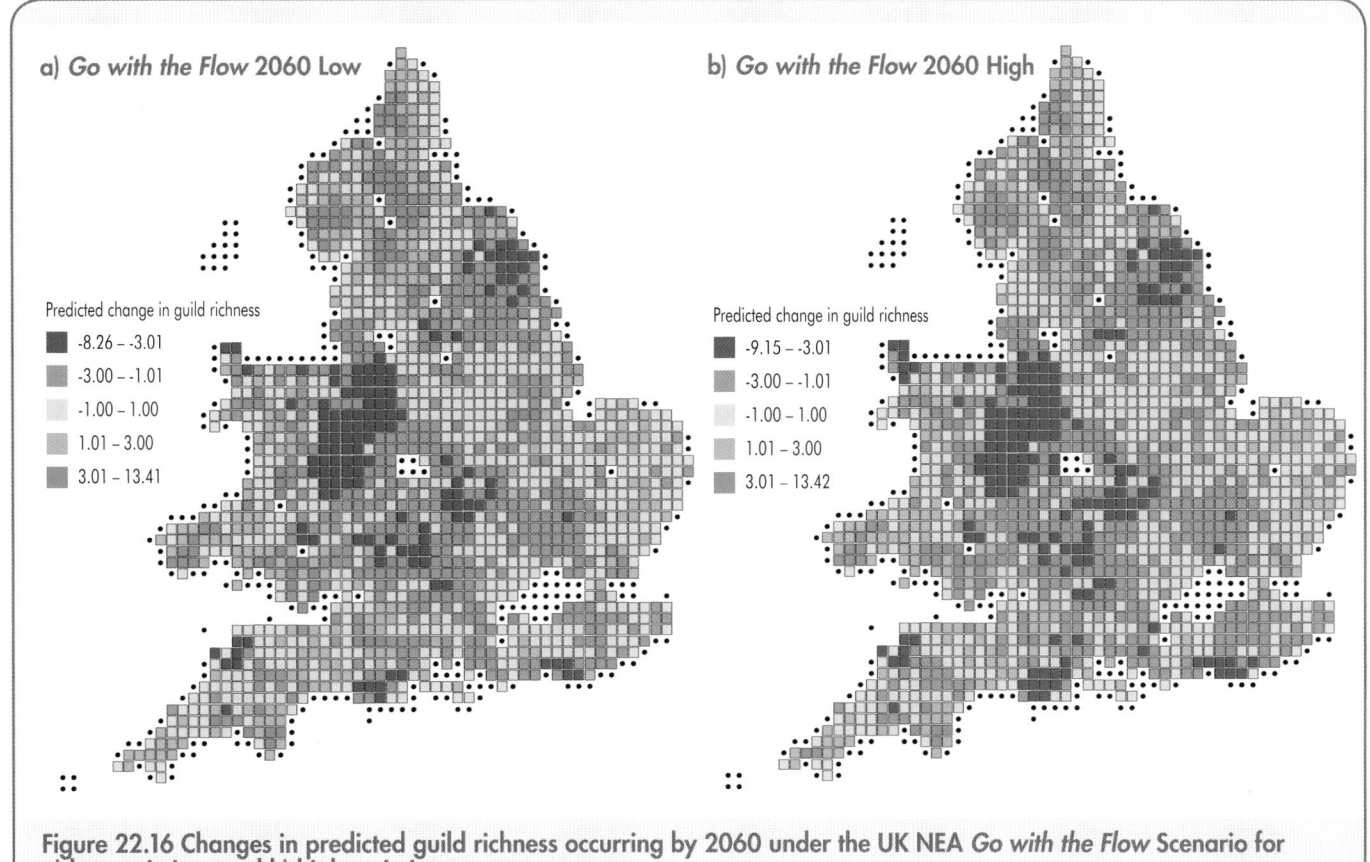

Figure 22.16 Changes in predicted guild richness occurring by 2060 under the UK NEA *Go with the Flow* Scenario for a) low emissions and b) high emissions. Source: Dugdale (2010).

presence or abundance of species that tend to benefit from the juxtaposition of multiple habitats within a landscape. Interpretation of the detail of any given scenario requires close examination of the habitat changes predicted for specific local areas. Overall, however, the greater the land use change, the larger the impact (both positive and negative) upon bird diversity. However, patterns of change are patchy, reflecting the highly heterogeneous British countryside and the highly uneven distributions of birds revealed by bird atlas surveys (e.g. Gibbons *et al.* 1993).

The changes in land cover (linked to an increased overseas ecological footprint) in the *World Markets High* Scenario lead to expectations of decreases in diversity, especially in the southern half of the UK. Importantly, overall changes in diversity may also mask important impacts on individual species. For example, increases in deciduous upland woodlands are likely to impact adversely on the species currently located in the areas where such planting occurs, but increase the representation of currently common lowland species. Note, however, that all the changes in diversity per se are still predicted to be small in absolute terms.

There are a number of important limitations to the data and model interpretations which are discussed in detail by Hulme & Siriwardena (2010). However, in principle, such a modelling approach is well suited to analysis of economic cost-effectiveness. That said, the analysis reported above uses a wide focus across most UK bird species, whereas it is farmland birds which have exhibited the sharpest declines over the past 40 years (Chapter 4). Therefore we complement

112 This Section draws from the work of Dugdale (2010).

the above analysis with a focused consideration of just the latter group.

Preparing for cost-effectiveness analysis 2: habitat association modelling for farmland birds.[112] Chapter 4 of the UK NEA highlights the plight of UK farmland birds as the group which has exhibited the sharpest falls in population numbers over recent decades, declining some 47% between 1970 and 2008. A focused analysis of such birds was undertaken using a methodology which was completely compatible with that used to predict agricultural land use developed by Fezzi & Bateman (in press) as discussed in 22.3.17.2. Such compatibility ensures that any land use change scenario can be simultaneously assessed in terms of both its agricultural impact (including measures of associated values) and its consequences for farmland birds. This compatibility allows the decision maker to investigate a wide variety of policy options from multiple perspectives. For example, we can use this joint modelling approach to provide cost-effectiveness analyses of land use change measures in terms of both financial and bird biodiversity impacts.

The present analysis of farmland birds proceeded by developing habitat association models for 19 bird species that belonged to the same guild (i.e. set of species with similar dietary requirements as assessed via consumption of seeds and invertebrates during the breeding season). The predicted change in guild richness in 10 km squares in England and Wales was calculated using a baseline richness taken from *The New Atlas of Breeding Birds in Britain and*

Ireland (Gibbons *et al.* 1993). Spatially referenced data on agricultural land use were then obtained from the 1988 Agricultural Census (the same data source as used in the Fezzi & Bateman (in press) farm land use model). Other land uses such as woodland were derived from the CEH Land Cover Map 1990, while urban outlines were obtained from standard Ordnance Survey sources.

Statistical regression analyses (detailed in Dugdale 2010) confirmed that the percentage of each 10 km square utilised for cereals, temporary grassland, coniferous woodland and urban use along with the mean altitude were all found to be highly significant predictors ($p<0.001$) of guild richness. The resulting models allow us to examine the consequences for guild richness under any desired land use scenario. **Figure 22.16** maps the changes in bird guild richness under the UK NEA *Go with the Flow* low and high emissions Scenarios. Patterns are broadly similar across the two scenarios, confirming our previous results that show that, under the *Go with the Flow* Scenario, the switch from low to high emissions makes relatively little difference. Analysis of summary statistics indicates that on average, both scenarios predict an overall decline in guild richness, with this being marginally more severe under the high emission case. However, the maps highlight that the main effect is in terms of spatial heterogeneity, with upland areas generally seeing an increase in farmland birds and the English Midlands and Welsh borders suffering the most significant declines.

Preparing for cost-effectiveness analysis 3: summary. The contrast in findings between analyses 1 and 2 underlines the importance of considering more than one measure of biodiversity when considering policy in this area. While analysis 1 suggested that upland areas would see a decline in overall bird diversity, analysis 2 shows that the reverse holds for farmland birds, with guild richness in upland England and Wales increasing.

Both analyses are constructed to be entirely compatible with the agricultural land use and valuation modelling undertaken by Fezzi & Bateman (in press) and reported earlier in this chapter (Section 22.3.17.2). In Chapter 26 we contrast the biodiversity impacts of a variety of future scenarios with monetary values for key ecosystem service-related goods. By comparing across scenarios, the decision making can observe the trade-off between economic values and biodiversity offered under each scenario. Such a cost-effectiveness analysis is a significant aid to decision making in the absence of full reliable monetary values for all benefit streams.

22.3.20 Recreation and Tourism

22.3.20.1 Outdoor informal recreational day trips[113]

Introduction. Outdoor recreation forms one of the major leisure activities for the majority of the population. According to the most recent figures (NE 2010b) even just focusing upon English recreational behaviour, there are some 2,858 million visits made p.a., with direct expenditure of some £20.4 billion p.a. This suggests that the true value of these visits is substantially higher than this sum. Considering the location of these visits, research undertaken for the England Leisure Visits Survey (ELVS 2006) report shows that, "during a 12 month period 64% of adults had visited a town/city with 62% visiting a seaside town/city, 59% visited the countryside and 37% had visited the seaside coast. Across England as a whole, 40% had visited a wood/forest in the past year. A quarter (25%) of people had visited a stretch of inland 'water with boats' whilst just under one-fifth (18%) had taken a trip to 'water without boats'" (p.8). Clearly, outdoor visits generate substantial value and it is likely that changes to the natural environment would affect those values in ways which should be considered within policy- and decision-making institutions.

While the majority of outdoor recreation involves informal activities such as walking, nature watching and picnicking, some more distinct activities deserve mention. For example, angling is a major pastime, with about 1 million licensed anglers in England and Wales, although an estimated 2.6 million people go fishing each year. Other notable distinct activities include inland waterway recreation (O'Gorman *et al.* 2010) and bird watching. Licensed anglers fished a total 30 million days during 2005, about 26 million for coarse fishing and 4 million for game (salmon and trout) fishing (EA 2009c). Recreational fishing involves estimated expenditures of about £1,000 million/yr[114] in England and Wales, associated with the equivalent of 37,000 full-time jobs. The economic gross value added from an extra 1,000 days of coarse fishing is estimated at £15,000–19,000, varying according to region (EA 2009c).

The CSERGE SEER model. While specific activities are clearly important, it is general, informal activities which form the bulk of ecosystem service-related recreation. Here one of the major problems facing assessment is that the outdoor recreation values generated by any given resource are likely to vary substantially, depending upon spatial context. Put simply, the same resource located in different areas will generate very different numbers of visits and values. This means that any attempt to simplify the recreation decision-making process to the level of assuming a set value for a resource, irrespective of its location, is unlikely to be reliable.

In order to overcome this difficulty and provide the foundations of a general tool for recreation planning and decision making, as well as generating valuations for the UK NEA, the CSERGE SEER project developed and implemented a novel methodology for combining the spatial analytic capabilities of a GIS with new data and econometric analyses to model how the distribution of natural environment and urban resources interact with population distribution to determine recreational visit flows. This new methodology was applied to the Monitor of the Engagement with the Natural Environment (MENE) which was recently released

113 This Section draws principally from Sen *et al.* (2010) and the CSERGE SEER project, although many of the supporting documents prepared for the UK NEA economic chapters (Chapter 22 and Chapter 26) discuss recreation issues. We would like to thank the Monitor of the Engagement with the Natural Environment (MENE) teams at Natural England, Defra and the Forestry Commission, Luke Brander at IVM Amsterdam, the UK NEA Economics group members, Natural England and their contractor, TNS, for sharing their valuable data with us.
114 To clarify; this statement refers to expenditure, not to net economic value in terms of WTP.

by Natural England, Defra and the Forestry Commission. This is a major new database intended to provide baseline and trend information on how people use the natural environment in England. It provides an unrivalled source of data and our present analysis is, as far as we are aware, the first major empirical use of MENE.

The methodology developed for this analysis consists of three elements:

i) A site prediction model (SPM): Normally, the location of existing and proposed recreation sites is known. However, the economic analysis of the UK NEA Scenarios described in Chapter 26 extends to future worlds where such locations are not known. To address this problem, for the scenario analysis alone we need a way of predicting the likely location of recreational sites in new variations of the world. The SPM achieves this by taking information from MENE on the location of outdoor recreational sites and examining how these are related to: the type of natural resources at that site, the distribution of the population around that site, and travel times from that population to the site. While the location of sites is known for England via MENE, this model also allows us to predict the location of sites for the rest of the UK. This avoids reliance upon secondary sources which are liable to omit informal recreation sites which are not officially recorded as such, but may generate a large proportion of overall trip numbers.

ii) A trip generation function (TGF): This models the factors determining the number of visits from each UK Census Lower Super Output Area (LSOA) to any given recreational site.[115] The analysis takes information on the location of both LSOAs and sites. We incorporate measures of the environmental characteristics of sites (which could be taken either directly from MENE or from the predictions of the previous model) and their surroundings so as to assess their attractiveness to potential visitors. We also examine the accessibility of environmental characteristics within and around LSOA outset locations, so assessing the availability of substitutes which may divert potential visitors away from any given site. Allowance is also made for the population of each LSOA and its socioeconomic and demographic make-up, as this may affect people's propensity to undertake visits.

iii) A valuation meta-analysis (VMA): Once we know where sites are located and the number of visits to each of those sites, we now seek to value those visits. This stage in the study re-analyses nearly 200 previous estimates of the value of a recreational visit, examining the influence of the environmental characteristics of visited sites and differences in the methods used to generate those value estimates.

Once the SPM has been estimated using data for England taken from MENE, it is then used to generate a predicted number of potential recreational sites in each 5 km square cell. This model is then extrapolated to all of Great Britain allowing for variation in transport infrastructure, population distribution and habitat type. The only assumption made in this extrapolation is that, allowing for those factors, it is assumed that attitudes towards issues such as distance are roughly consistent across the country. The TGF is then used to estimate the predicted number of visits per week to a site in each of the 5 km cells. By weighting that estimate by the number of sites per cell (as predicted by the SPM) we begin to get a sense of the spatial distribution of visits. However, adjustments have to be made for the sampling strategy of the MENE survey. The survey is well designed for extrapolation purposes, with households from all areas of the country being sampled at all periods across the year, thus avoiding spatial and temporal biases. However, of course only a subset of households can be interviewed, and even these are just asked about the trips they make during a 1-week period, with just one of these being selected at random for detailed study including outset and destination data. Any extrapolation process therefore has to make allowance for all of these sampling characteristics. As the potential for grossing up errors is substantial in such exercises (Jones *et al.* 2002), adjustments were calibrated by official estimates of the total annual number of outdoor visits to all sites. Once this adjustment is made, we obtain our estimate of the predicted number of visits to each 5 km cell allowing for both the number of sites and number of visits to those sites.

The final step of our assessment is to value these predicted visits. Our meta-analysis allows the value of a visit to vary according to the habitat type characteristics of the visited site. We assume that these characteristics can be proxied by information on the physical environment of the 5 km cell into which a site falls. This allows us to generate a site-specific value per person per visit for each trip. Multiplying this by the predicted number of trips to each site in that cell allows us to estimate its annual recreational value. This obviously varies according to the natural environment of the area, the availability of substitutes, the transport infrastructures and the distribution and characteristics of the population in and around that area. The resulting recreational value is therefore highly spatially explicit, reflecting variation in all of these factors. This provides a useful input to decision making, allowing the efficient allocation of scarce resources, which is particularly necessary in times of austerity. Furthermore, these values can be aggregated up across any desired spatial unit up to and including country level to provide an estimate of total annual recreational value under a given scenario. Analyses of policy change or future scenarios can then be undertaken by applying our SPM, TGF and VMA models to the various land use and population distributions envisioned under those policies or scenarios. **Figure 22.17** provides a schematic overview of the methodology developed in this analysis.

115 LSOAs are small areas of around 400–600 households which, particularly in urban areas, means that the influence of location upon visits can be accurately modelled. We used population-weighted LSOA centroids as the outset point for our analysis. Further details regarding LSOAs are available at: www.neighbourhood.statistics.gov.uk/dissemination/Info.do?page=aboutneighbourhood/geography/superoutputareas/soa-intro.htm. For our modelling of Scottish outset areas we used the Census Data Zone (DZ) unit. A preliminary analysis using Northern Ireland Super Output Area (SOA) data was undertaken, but as this would not have been ready for when the UK NEA went to print, it was not completed.

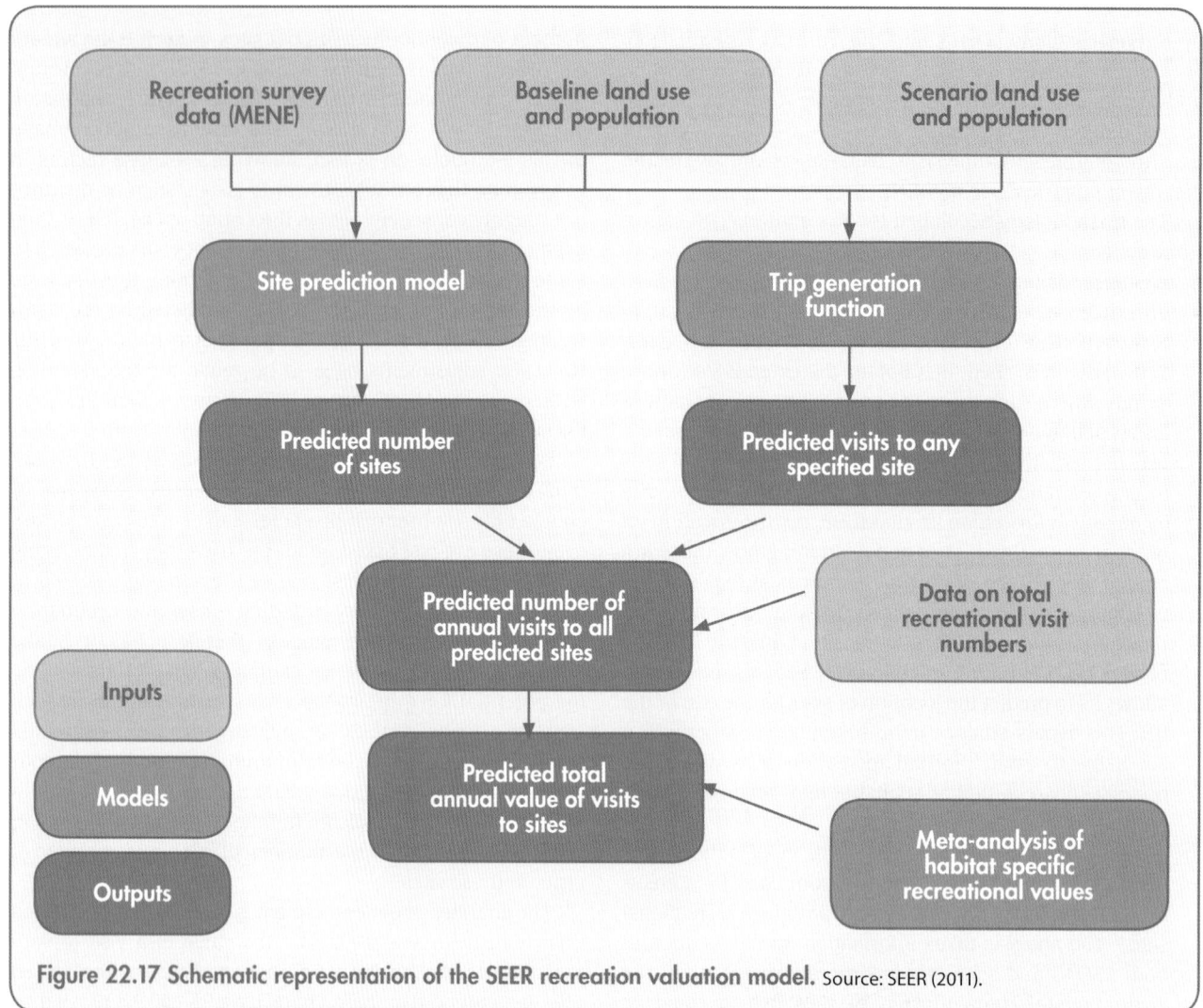

Figure 22.17 Schematic representation of the SEER recreation valuation model. Source: SEER (2011).

The analysis allows us to estimate where recreational sites are located, how many visits they will generate and the value of those visits. Importantly, for decision-making purposes, the models allow us to vary policy-relevant elements of the analysis to examine their impacts on recreational values. So, for example, we can examine how new land use scenarios would alter the environmental characteristics of potential sites, making them more or less attractive to visitors and enhancing or degrading the value of any visits made. Furthermore, because of the spatially explicit nature of this analysis, models can readily be linked to other grid-referenced data or analyses so that, for example, we can investigate how changes in the CAP might alter farm incomes and land use (as discussed in Section 22.3.1) and then feed these outputs into the present analysis to examine consequent impacts upon recreational behaviour and values. Further linkages to elements such as water pollution and biodiversity indicators (e.g. bird populations) are an inherent part of the SEER programme of research.

In the present chapter we describe the full SPM, TGF and VMA models. We illustrate their operation through a case study of just a single (although substantial and highly heterogeneous) area. In Chapter 26 this remit is extended to consider all of GB under the full range of population and land use change Scenarios developed by the UK NEA.

Initial data preparation. The intention of this analysis was to produce a decision analysis tool which would not require perpetual reanalysis or updating and should, once constructed, be relatively easy to query by decision makers. However, the model construction phase of the analysis is necessarily data intensive so as to incorporate the complexity of the real world and those locational factors which determine the ways in which recreational values vary across space.

The most crucial and novel source of spatially explicit data used in the analysis was MENE. The data for MENE were provided by a year-long, in-house, face-to-face survey. Respondents were asked about the number of visits that they had made seven days prior to the day of their interview. One of these trips was then randomly selected by the interviewer and the respondent was asked to give detailed information regarding this visit, including the location of the destination. This was then recorded alongside the outset location, providing the vital information required for this analysis. Survey results from MENE were published in September 2010 (NE 2010b) and have been used for economic analysis for the first time in this report.

The methodology developed for this study was applied not only to England where the survey data were gathered, but throughout Great Britain.[116] A description of the methodology underlining the GIS-based calculation of locational and travel time variables is provided in Sen *et al.* (2010). In summary this entailed the following steps:

- Respondent home and visited site locations were obtained.
- The environmental characteristics for both the visited site and its surroundings were defined.
- A GIS was used to calculate travel times via the entire road network between all potential outset points (LSOAs) and both potential and actual destination sites.
- Potential substitute sites were defined, including measures of the density of different land use and habitat types around each potential outset point.
- Socioeconomic and demographic variables describing each LSOA were obtained.

From an original dataset of 48,514 respondents, 5,305 were omitted due to incomplete locational information and a further 751 were omitted as they were on holiday during the interview period (only day trippers were considered in our analysis) leaving a final sample size of 42,458 respondents.[117]

An analysis of potential 'edge-effects' was undertaken, to examine whether those who live on the land borders of England appeared to have lower than expected visit rates due to visits to locations outside England being truncated. This analysis indicated that a small number of respondents (approximately 150 people) were affected in this way and these were omitted from further analysis. Of the remainder, some 27,593 did not take a visit during the seven days preceding the survey, although these were retained within our subsequent analysis to adjust model estimates for these valid zero visit observations. From the MENE survey, 8,292 distinct destination sites were identified, each having a 1 km square grid reference. **Figure 22.18** maps the location of LSOA outset areas and destination sites.

The environmental characteristics of sites were defined by linking their 1 km square grid cell locations to habitat proportions derived from the 25 m resolution UK-wide Land Cover Map 2000 data (Fuller *et al.* 2002).[118] This dataset was used for its coverage and availability. Habitat categories here were: i) broadleaved woodland; ii) coniferous woodland; iii)

Figure 22.18 Distribution of a) day trip visitor outset locations and b) destination sites in England. LSOA = UK census lower super output area.

116 There is an implicit assumption here that the preferences of English respondents can be generalised across the UK. While we see no clear cultural case against this assumption, one concern is whether the environmental characteristics of England embrace the diversity of the UK. Generally this is not thought to be a problem. Perhaps the weakest element of this assumption is in regard to mountains. England contains a considerably lower density of such environments and does not contain any of the high peaks of Wales and none of the major mountains of Scotland. Obviously it would be ideal to have comparable data from all UK nations. However, perhaps surprisingly, information on both outset and destination location is not collected in surveys other than MENE. Note that while our application considers all of GB, it could readily be applied throughout the UK or further afield, provided that sufficient data are available.

117 Subsequent investigations further restricted our analysis to the more than 90% of day trip journeys with a one-way duration of 60 minutes or less. This restriction was imposed to avoid the very large number of zero visit outset locations imputed when we permit our analysis to allow day trip visits from any outset to any destination across the entire country.

118 LCM2000 is provided by the Centre for Ecology and Hydrology (CEH), Wallingford, UK. The procedure used by the SEER project employs a substantially greater degree of spatial accuracy than that used in the UK NEA Scenarios. As a result of this, the SPM and TGF models reported in the present chapter had to be re-estimated using the simplified land use map employed by the UK NEA Scenarios team before they could be applied to value those scenarios (see Chapter 26). However, the models reported in this chapter are based upon our preferred, high spatial accuracy, approach.

coast (littoral and supra littoral); iv) Enclosed Farmland; v) freshwater body; vi) Mountains, Moorlands and Heaths; vii) estuary (sublittoral); viii) Semi-natural Grassland; and ix) urban and suburban (see details in Sen *et al.* 2010). Percentages of each habitat type in each 1 km square cell were calculated and used to define sites for the SPM estimation. For prediction across GB, habitat proportions were calculated at a 5 km grid square resolution.

Travel times between outset and destination locations were calculated for all of GB, predominantly using the Ordnance Survey Meridian road network. Average road speeds were taken from Jones *et al.* (2010). These discriminate between road types (motorway, A-road, B-road and minor road), as well as between urban and rural contexts. The road network was converted into a regular grid of 100×100 metre cells, with each cell contained a value corresponding to travel-time-per-unit distance. Allowances for locations off the regular road grid were made using adjustments for walking speed (Jones *et al.* 2002). The resultant travel time map was used to calculate the minimum travel time between any outset location and any destination site.[119] An example of the resulting travel time surface for just one destination is given in **Figure 22.19**.

The number of visits to a specific site from a given outset location will be lower when that outset area is well served by other local substitute sites. Ignoring the impact of substitutes is likely to inflate the attractiveness of more distant sites. To allow for this, the availability of substitute resources around each potential outset location across the country was assessed. This was achieved by defining circular areas around each LSOA and calculating the percentage of each land use and habitat type in that area.[120] This measure of substitute availability was then included within the TGF. The radius of these circles was varied and the analysis repeated to identify the optimal size of the surrounding area for capturing this substitution effect.[121]

Previous research suggests that visit rates vary across LSOAs, depending in part upon the socioeconomic and demographic characteristics of those areas (Jones *et al.* 2010). To allow for this possibility, such characteristic data were obtained for all LSOAs from the UK Census with income variables being obtained from Experian data.[122] Comparable statistics for the rest of Great Britain were also obtained for predictive purposes.

As noted above, we expect that the probability of recreational sites being located in an area is in part a function of the size and distribution of the local population. To include this factor within the SPM, a spatially weighted measure of the population around any point was calculated

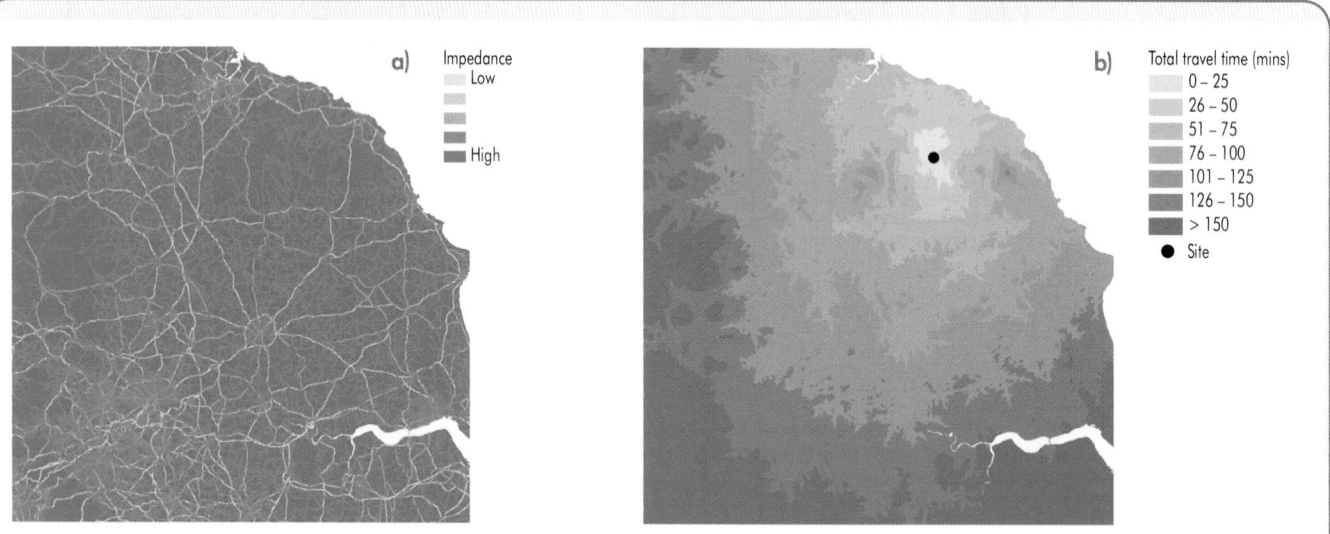

Figure 22.19 Impedance surface (a) and estimated travel time bands (b) for potential outset locations around a single recreational visit site near to Pickering in the North York Moors. Source: SEER (2011).

---

119 Essential simplifications for the SPM analysis were that all visitors are assumed to start their journey from the population-weighted centroid of their home LSOA and to travel using the shortest time route to their chosen destination site, the location of which is taken to be the geometric centroid of the 1 km grid square containing that site. A similar approach was used for the TGF analysis although here, 5 km grid square centroids were used for the location of destination sites. Bateman *et al.* (1996, 1999) show that actual and GIS predicted routes are highly correlated and the latter provides a strong predictor of the former for modelling purposes. The calculations needed for this analysis were undertaken using the 'Cost Distance' (impedance surface) command in ESRI ArcGIS.

120 Zonal Statistics ++, a module of the 'Hawth's Tools' plug-in for ArcGIS (Beyer 2004), was used to count the cells entirely within the search radius that were of a particular substitute type. These were converted into percentages of the total circle area (25 m cells entirely within the search radius).

121 Radii of 1, 2.5, 5 and 10 km were used for defining substitution availability measures around outset locations. Resultant measures were used within a variety of model specifications including travel time from the population-weighted centroid of each LSOA to the nearest substitute site and interactions between travel time and the proportion of the above circles taken up by substitutes. An AIC criterion (Akaike 1974) comparison of different models indicated that a measure of the density of each land use/habitat type within a 10 km radius of the LSOA population-weighted centroids provided the best fit to the MENE visitation data.

122 This of course assumes that LSOA statistics can be used as valid estimates for the households interviewed in the MENE survey. Note that UK Census 2001 data were used for all socio-demographic variables but that the 2009 Experian data on income was employed. Experian data is held at MIMAS, University of Manchester.

by first taking a 1 km grid square map of population and aggregating this up to the 5 km grid used by that model. Population from outside any 'focal' 5 km square are likely to have a non-zero but diminishing probability of visiting a site in that cell. As there is no theoretical guidance regarding the form of this relationship, it can be determined through purely empirical means. To investigate this we first define a population weight (w) as the following inverse power function:

$$w = \frac{1}{d^y}$$

Where w = population weight
d = distance from focal cell[123]
y = empirically determined exponent

As can be seen, w is defined so that populations at a greater distance from a given location site have a diminishing impact on the probability of that location being a recreational site. The larger the value of the exponent (y) then the faster this diminishment occurs. Empirical analysis suggested that a good fit to the data on actual site locations could be found by an SPM containing two versions of this weight, the first with $y=1$ and the second with $y=2$. This was improved by constraining values of w lower than 0.125 to be zero. **Figure 22.20** illustrates the resultant weight functions.

Analysis 1: the site prediction model (SPM). The first element of our analysis seeks to predict the likely location of recreational sites. While this is not needed where the location of existing or planned recreational sites are known, this is required both for extrapolation of our analysis beyond the base-data area of England, and to apply the model to the new worlds envisioned within the UK NEA Scenarios.

Two broad factors were postulated as determinants of recreational site location:

- the nature of any potential destination site (e.g. its environmental and land use characteristics); and
- the availability of population around that site.

The data drawn from across the entirety of England provide a good deal of variation in both of these dimensions (see details in Sen *et al.* 2010). Analysis of competing model specifications resulted in our best-fitting SPM as reported in **Table 22.21**. This takes Enclosed Farmland as the base land use category such that the coefficients on other land uses show their influence relative to that base case.

Because of the (negative binomial) form of the model the coefficients cannot be directly interpreted as marginal effects. However, their signs do allow simple interpretation of the direction of their effects. To interpret the coefficients on the land use variables we need to recall that these show the differences in effect from the baseline which is set as Enclosed Farmland. Given this, a positive coefficient shows a land use or habitat which is more likely to yield recreational sites than does Enclosed Farmland (and the opposite applies for negative coefficients). This means that coastal, freshwater, Semi-natural Grassland, estuary, broadleaved woodland and even Urban areas yield a higher number of recreation sites than Enclosed Farmland. One

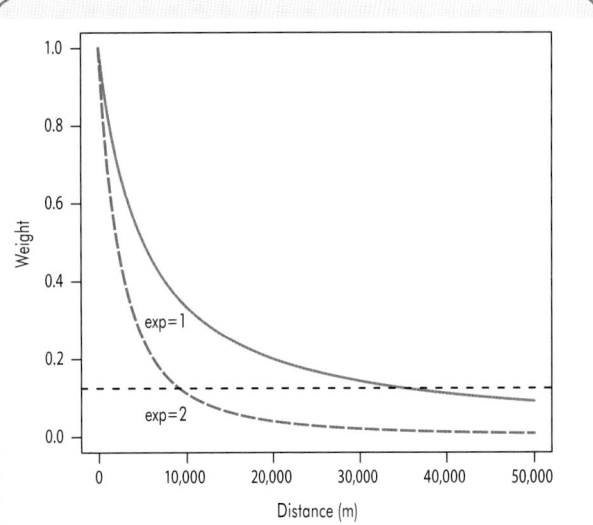

Figure 22.20 Weight function relating population to the probability of recreational sites over increasing distance to that potential site. Exponent (exp) values of 1 and 2 and dotted line indicating cut-off value of 0.125 are empirically determined.

Table 22.21 Site probability model: predicting the number of recreation sites visited in England in each 5 km square using a negative binomial model with robust standard errors. Base category land use is Enclosed Farmland. Statistically significant results are indicated by: *p<0.05, **p<0.01, ***p<0.001. Source: Sen *et al.* (2010) and the SEER (2011) project.

Dependent Variable[†]	Coefficients	t-statistic	p-value
% of coast in cell	0.00769**	2.603	0.009
% of freshwater in cell	0.0651***	6.128	<0.0001
%of semi-natural grass in cell	0.00545**	3.151	0.002
% of mountains & heath in cell	-0.0149***	-4.949	<0.0001
% of estuary and ocean in cell	0.0134***	12.27	<0.0001
% of urban area in cell	0.0543***	32.07	<0.0001
% of coniferous forests in cell	-0.00631	-1.461	0.144
% of broadleaved forests in cell	0.0267***	10.24	<0.0001
weighted population density (y=1)[‡]	0.000000417***	5.541	<0.0001
weighted population density (y=2) [‡]	-0.00000486***	-9.103	<0.0001
Constant	-0.805***	-20.62	
Log alpha	-0.644***	-12.22	
Observations[¶]	5,497		

[†] Dependent variable is number of visited MENE sites in a 5 km cell.
[‡] The variables 'weighted population density (y=1)' and 'weighted population density (y=2)' refer to transformations of the weight function (w) described previously with exponent (y) values of 1 and 2 respectively.
[¶] The number of observations refers to the number of 5 km square grid cells in England on which the estimation was based. This is less than the number of sites in the MENE dataset due to multiple sites falling within the same grid square.

123 Distance (d) was defined as d = (centroid distance from focal cell centroid (in metres)+ 5,000)/5,000 giving a maximum weighting of 1 for the population of the focal cell.

clear exception is Mountains, Moorlands and Heaths. Again this is in line with expectations as, while such habitats yield high quality recreational experiences (as evidenced in our subsequent TGF and VMA analyses), they are characterised by few access points relative to their size. Interestingly, coniferous forests were insignificantly different from Enclosed Farmland in terms of site probability, a result in stark contrast to the positive and significant effects found for broadleaved woodland. The weighted population density variables indicate a positive and significant but marginally diminishing impact on the expected count of recreational sites.[124]

The estimated site prediction model described above is used to generate a predicted count of potential recreational sites in each 5 km square cell of GB. This count is then divided by the total predicted count of sites for GB to generate a weight for each cell. This figure can then be used in conjunction with the output from our TGF to estimate the number of visits to each cell.

Analysis 2: the trip generation function (TGF). The combination of large numbers of potential outset points and visit sites generates a dataset of more than 4 million observations for analysis within our TGF. The function predicts the number of visits made from each outset location (defined as each LSOA within 60 minutes (one-way travel) of a potential site), to any given recreational site (whether observed or predicted from the SPM) as a function of: the travel time to the site; the accessibility of other potential substitute recreational areas near to outset locations; socioeconomic and demographic characteristics of population in the outset area; and the land use and habitat characteristics of the potential destination site (see Sen *et al.* 2010 for summary statistics on these variables). **Table 22.22** reports our best-fitting TGF.

Examining the relationships captured in the TGF we see that by far the most powerful predictor of visits from an outset area to a potential visit site is the travel time involved. Here the highly significant negative coefficient shows that as travel time increases, so the number of visits falls. This is an important finding as it underlines the vital importance of space in optimal decision making; location is a major driver of value. The impact of the availability of substitutes is also strongly in line with prior expectations, with all substitutes working to reduce visits to more distant sites with the exception of mountains where (as discussed previously) access to sites is limited by the available road infrastructure relative to the size of such areas.[125]

A set of variables is included in the TGF to describe the attractiveness of land use and habitat type across different

potential visit sites. By specifying all site habitat variables to contrast with a baseline of Enclosed Farmland we see that most of the habitat types exert a positive impact upon visits (i.e. they are considered more attractive than enclosed farmlands). Mountains, coasts, freshwater sites and Woodlands exert significant positive effects in attracting visitors. Notice that while mountainous outset locations are associated with a low substitute availability effect, nevertheless they have a positive effect as destinations for visits from other areas.

A set of socioeconomic and demographic variables pertaining to the population in the outset area are also included in the TGF. We observe significantly higher levels of engagement in recreation from retired and richer populations and lower engagement amongst ethnic groups. This latter result highlights the importance of government initiatives to broaden the engagement of ethnic groups in recreational activities.

The estimated TGF allows us to predict the number of visitors who would arrive at a site located in any given 5 km square cell of GB. However, as we have already seen from our SPM analysis, the distribution of sites across the country is far from uniform. Therefore, by multiplying the predictions of visit counts in a given cell (from the TGF) by the expected number of sites in that cell (from the SPM analysis) we obtain an estimate of the total number of visits in each grid square which is fully adjusted for the characteristics and location of that cell. The resulting spatial distribution of predicted visits can readily be mapped for decision support purposes or aggregated up to any desired area including country or GB level. However, we now need to allow for the fact that the characteristics of sites may influence the value of any predicted visits. For this we turn to our VMA model.

Analysis 3: the valuation meta-analysis (VMA). The literature on the valuation of outdoor recreation activities is substantial and a review revealed some 193 value estimates within 98 relevant studies. A meta-analysis of these findings related valuations to both the resources they were concerned with and to various variables describing the type of studies and populations used to provide those estimates. To improve comparability across studies, all the value estimates from non-UK studies were adjusted using purchasing power parity data and all estimates were converted to common pound sterling (2009) prices. Sen *et al.* (2010) detail summary statistics for all variables and **Table 22.23** presents the estimated VMA model. [126]

The estimated model detailed in **Table 22.23** conforms well to prior expectations. Most of the methodological variables are statistically insignificant, which suggests that the framing issues observed in many individual studies may

---

124 In detail, the implications of the specified weighting function are as follows: i) In centres of high population the value for the inverse square weighted population (y=2) is greater than for the inverse linear weighting (y=1) such that the site probability is reduced; ii) In areas outside but near to high population centres the inverse linear weighted population (y=1) is greater than the inverse square weighted population (y=2) such that the site probability is increased; iii) In areas away from high population centres the inverse linear weighted population is slightly greater than inverse square weighted population such that the site probability weight is slightly increased. However, the weight has to be considered in conjunction with the distribution of population before its combined impact upon site probability can be determined. This combined effect is best demonstrated in Chapter 26 where we see that, as expected, the probability of sites declines markedly away from areas of higher population densities.

125 Note that the 'other marine' category does not include coast and generally picks up the effect of less accessible marine areas. But this is insignificantly different from the Enclosed Farmland base category.

126 The mode in Table 22.23 is estimated using OLS with Huber-White-standard errors to adjust for the presence of significant heteroskedasticity. This was insignificantly different from a cluster robust model allowing for the fact that the meta-analysis dataset consist of some studies which report multiple value estimates.

be less of a problem when studies are pooled within a meta-analysis. Interestingly, although the SPM highlighted that mountain areas provided a lower density of recreational sites (a finding reflecting the TGF's low substitution availability offered in mountainous outset areas), the VMA model suggests that those visits that are made to such areas yield relatively high per visit values (a result which chimes with the TGF's attractiveness of mountains as destinations).

Case study. The methodology developed here is flexible and readily applied to a variety of policy questions. In Chapter 26 we apply the method to valuing the variety of changes envisioned in the UK NEA Scenarios. However, the approach can also be applied to more commonplace decision contexts such as the simple question of how to optimise the recreation value generated by a limited budget. Such a question is addressed here so as to demonstrate the versatility of the methodology.

Our illustration considers a simple scenario in which a policy maker has the funds to convert a single area of farmland into recreational forest and wants to know where best to locate that forest. For this simple illustration we bypass the site prediction model (SPM), which is mainly of use when we seek to transfer findings outside England to the rest of the UK (a stage considered in Chapter 26). Therefore we omit this stage and pass straight on to applying our TGF.

The estimated TGF reported in **Table 22.22** shows that Woodland is significantly more attractive to recreational visitors than Enclosed Farmland (the base case for that model). However, the strong influence of travel time shows that both land uses become relatively less attractive the further away a site is from an outset location. This is illustrated in **Figure 22.21**, which shows the predicted visitor rates for each of these land uses at different travel times.

Figure 22.21 demonstrates not only that Woodlands attract more visitors than Enclosed Farmland, but also that there is a strong distance decay in these visit rates. This means that the location of sites will significantly determine the number of visitors they attract. We apply our methodology to examine how the recreational values created by converting Enclosed Farmland to Woodland will vary depending upon the location of that conversion. For simplicity we illustrate this by considering the consequences of placing our new forest in ten randomly chosen locations across the North Humberside area illustrated in **Figure 22.22**. If we were undertaking a formal review of such a scheme then this process would be iterated for all potential sites across the entire area (a process which is rapid and straightforward given modern computing speeds) so as to identify the optimal location for such a scheme.

For each of the randomly chosen land use conversion sites we calculate the various substitution measures needed for the TGF. These are added to data on site characteristics and the socioeconomic and demographic variables included in that model. Applying our TGF visit rates to each location, first under its present agricultural land use and then under Woodland, we can estimate the change in visit numbers generated by the land conversion policy. The final stage of our analysis is to use our VMA model to value predicted visits to each site under first Enclosed Farmland and then Woodland.

Table 22.22 Trip generation function: predicting visit numbers from an outset location to a site destination estimated using a Multilevel Poisson regression model. Statistically significant results are indicated by: *p<0.05, **p<0.01, ***p<0.001. Enclosed Farmland is taken as the base case for both the 'substitute availability' and 'site' characteristic variables. Source: Sen et al. (2010) and the SEER (2011) project.

Variable	Coefficient	t-statistic
Travel time from a LSOA/DZ to a site[†]	-0.0594***	-106.3
Coast substitute availability[‡]	-0.0115***	-4.156
Urban substitute availability[‡]	-0.0211***	-32.99
Freshwater substitute availability[‡]	-0.0633***	-5.109
Grassland substitute availability[‡]	-0.0225***	-10.16
Woodland substitute availability[‡]	-0.0168***	-8.446
Other marine substitute availability[‡]	0.000710	0.738
Mountain substitute availability[‡]	0.0148***	3.725
% of coast in site[†]	0.00940***	6.504
% urban in site[†]	-0.00219***	-4.464
% of freshwater in site[†]	0.0102***	4.220
% of grasslands in site[†]	0.00158	1.343
% of woodlands in site[†]	0.00286**	2.948
% of estuary and ocean in site[†]	-0.0156***	-11.89
% of mountain and heath in site[†]	0.0226***	10.54
% non-white ethnicity[†]	-0.00580***	-6.537
% retired[†]	0.00642***	3.678
Median household Income[†]	0.00000874***	9.414
Total population of outset area[†]	0.000225***	5.899
Constant	-3.195***	-37.84
Insig2u[¶]		
Constant	-0.737***	-21.76
Observations	4,141,089	

[†] The site characteristic variables are the number of visits from a specified small area Census unit (Lower Super Output Area (LSOA) in England and Wales; Census Data Zone (DZ) in Scotland) to a specified site.

[‡] The substitute availability variables are calculated as the percentage of a specified land use type within a 10 km radius of the outset point.

[¶] log sigma2u = natural logarithm of the variance of the random intercept term in the multilevel model. The random intercept term captures the unobserved heterogeneity between the different sites.

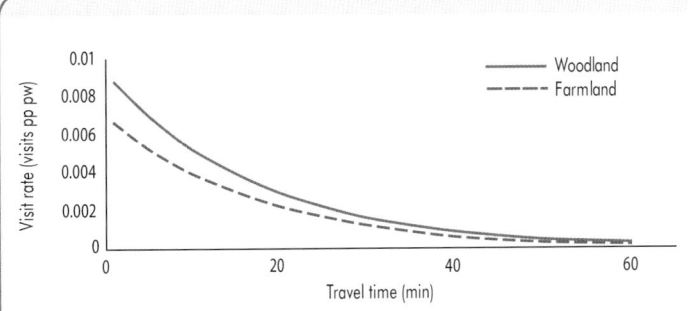

Figure 22.21 Trip Generation Function predictions: travel time impacts on visit rate for woodland and farmland sites. Visit rate calculated per person per week (pp pw). Source: Sen et al. (2010) and SEER (2011).

Table 22.23 Valuation meta-analysis (VMA) model of recreational value estimates (£, 2009 prices). Model estimated using Ordinary Least Squares with Huber-White standard errors to adjust for heteroskedasticity[†]. R^2 (adjusted) = 0.75; Statistically significant results are indicated by: *$p<0.10$, **$p<0.05$, ***$p<0.01$, ****$p<0.001$

Variable[†]	Variable definition	Coefficient	t-statistic
Good characteristics [¶]			
Mountains & heathlands	1 if recreational site valued is mountain or heath; 0 otherwise	1.771*	1.834
Grasslands, farm & woods	1 if recreational site valued is grasslands, farm and woodlands; 0 otherwise	0.579*	1.886
Freshwater, marine & coastal	1 if recreational site valued is freshwater, marine & coastal; 0 otherwise	0.222	0.763
Designated site	1 if recreational site holds some official designation; 0 otherwise	0.0225	0.121
Study characteristics [§]			
Published	1 if study published in peer-reviewed journal or book; 0 otherwise	0.133	0.468
Survey year	Discrete variable: 1 = published in 1975, to 29 = published in 2008	0.0360	1.364
Log sample size	Logarithm of sample size	-0.493**	-2.143
In-person interview	1 if survey mode is in-person; 0 otherwise	0.130	0.469
Use value only	1 if use value study; 0 otherwise	0.372*	1.787
Substitutes considered	1 if substitute sites included in the valuation study; 0 otherwise	-0.117	-0.570
Valuation unit [§]			
Per household per year	1 if value in terms of per household per year; 0 otherwise	2.825****	8.583
Per person per year	1 if value in terms of per person per year; 0 otherwise	2.090****	6.251
Other valuation unit	1 if value in terms of per household/ person, per day/ month; 0 otherwise	2.101****	4.648
Valuation method [††]			
RPM & mixed valuation	1 = revealed preference or mixed valuation methods; 0 otherwise	1.494**	2.335
Open-ended format	1 = stated preference using open-ended WTP elicitation format; 0 otherwise	-0.363*	-1.838
Payment vehicle tax	1 = payment vehicle is a tax; 0 otherwise	0.351	1.316
Study country characteristics			
Log of population density	Population density of state/country in which the site is located	0.360	1.206
Non-UK countries[‡‡]	1 = study conducted overseas; 0 otherwise (UK)	1.193***	3.215
Constant		-0.110	-0.123
Observations		193	

[†] This was insignificantly different from a cluster robust model allowing for the fact that the meta-analysis dataset consist of some studies which report multiple value estimates.
[‡] Dependent variable is logarithm of recreational value (willingness to pay or consumer surplus) (£, 2009).
[¶] Omitted land use base case = urban environments.
[§] Base case for valuation units is per person per visit.
[††] Base case for valuation method is close-ended stated preference methods.
[‡‡] Non-UK countries considered: North America, Western Europe, Australia and New Zealand.

Table 22.24 presents results from this illustrative analysis. As can be seen, in each of the ten locations considered, the number of visits increases when the land is converted into Woodland. However, the magnitude of this change and the value they generate varies very substantially across locations. Site P9 yields the highest increase in value from this change in land use while site P4 provides the lowest value. Clearly, the incorporation of spatial variation into decision making is a vital aid to efficient resource allocation, particularly in a time of austerity.

Under a cost-effectiveness analysis this would conclude our assessment. However, a full economic cost-benefit analysis would supplement this recreational value with the other market and non-market benefits generated and set this against the costs of each scheme in each location. Because costs such as the loss of agricultural output values will also

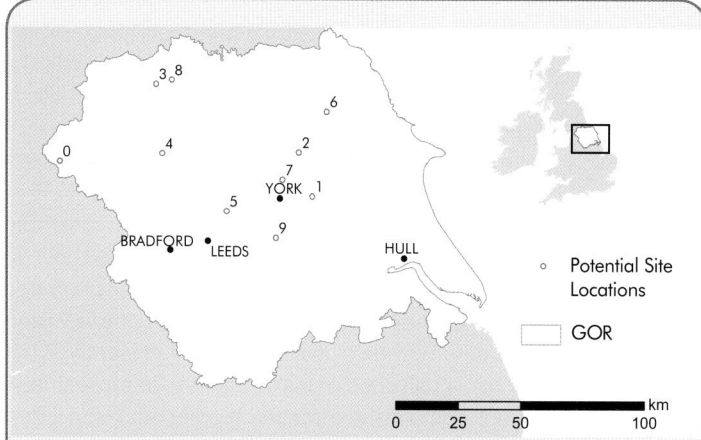

Figure 22.22 Location map for ten randomly assigned land use change locations. GOR = Government Office Region. Source: Sen *et al.* (2010) and the SEER (2011) project.

Table 22.24 Predicted increase in recreational visits and valuations at alternative sites following conversion from farmland to woodland (£/yr, 2010 prices). Source: Sen *et al.* (2010) and the SEER project (2011).

Site No. →	P0		P1		P2		P3		P4	
Description	Very remote site but near to rural A-road		Close to York		A little remote and with substitutes like P7 nearer to York		Slightly further from Middlesbrough than site P8		Very remote and with no nearby major roads	
Travel bands (min)	Extra visits (p.a.)	Value of extra visits (£ p.a.)	Extra visits (p.a.)	Value of extra visits (£ p.a.)	Extra visits (p.a.)	Value of extra visits (£ p.a.)	Extra visits (p.a.)	Value of extra visits (£ p.a.)	Extra visits (p.a.)	Value of extra visits (£ p.a.)
1	0	0	0	0	0	0	0	0	0	0
5	0	0	0	0	0	0	0	0	0	0
10	0	0	195	643	0	0	0	0	0	0
20	162	537	541	1,788	0	0	595	1,967	0	0
30	241	796	3,159	10,444	90	298	451	1,492	0	0
40	201	664	602	1,991	251	830	1,004	3,318	33	111
50	931	3,076	1,042	3,445	875	2,891	958	3,168	28	92
60	709	2,342	1,671	5,523	290	957	822	2,719	67	222
Total	**2,243**	**7,414**	**7,210**	**23,834**	**1,506**	**4,977**	**3,831**	**12,664**	**129**	**425**
Site No. →	P5		P6		P7		P8		P9	
Description	Midway between York & Leeds with good road links		Remote site but near to rural A road		Very close to York		Quite near Middlesbrough but no main road link		Midway between York & Leeds with excellent motorway links	
Travel bands (min)	Extra visits (p.a.)	Value of extra visits (£ p.a.)	Extra visits (p.a.)	Value of extra visits (£ p.a.)	Extra visits (p.a.)	Value of extra visits (£ p.a.)	Extra visits (p.a.)	Value of extra visits (£ p.a.)	Extra visits (p.a.)	Value of extra visits (£ p.a.)
1	0	0	0	0	0	0	0	0	165	545
5	0	0	261	862	0	0	0	0	130	431
10	0	0	292	965	584	1,930	0	0	0	0
20	1,028	3,398	271	894	2,705	8,942	866	2,862	1,948	6,438
30	3,581	11,836	361	1,194	2,046	6,764	301	995	4,574	15,119
40	4,601	15,209	402	1,327	719	2,378	1,389	4,590	4,852	16,039
50	4,643	15,349	996	3,291	1,740	5,752	968	3,199	4,718	15,595
60	2,183	7,215	590	1,949	1,914	6,326	1,091	3,608	3,372	11,148
Total	**16,036**	**53,008**	**3,171**	**10,483**	**9,708**	**32,092**	**4,614**	**15,253**	**19,759**	**65,315**

vary spatially, it is not necessarily the case that the site which generates the highest recreational value is necessarily the optimal location for such land use conversion. Nevertheless, given the prevailing shadow value of agriculture it seems very likely that many of these sites, if chosen, would pass benefit-cost tests (although note that there is a substitution effect here; once one new site is created this forms a substitute for, and lowers the value of, any other proposed site in the vicinity—our methodology can readily be automated to permit the capture of such effects within the decision analysis system). Why then do such sites not presently exist? This is, in part, a reflection of market failure; at present land users are not compensated for the recreational and other non-market benefits they provide and hence such services are, from a social optimality perspective, under-supplied. It is the task of government to address such market failures through incentives or other mechanisms (including the removal of market imperfections and distortions which, perversely, often reinforce the problems of missing markets for environmental goods).

22.3.20.2 Outdoor tourism

The UK tourism industry is a major contributor to the economy, yielding a direct value of £52 billion p.a. (roughly 4.0% of gross domestic product (GDP)) in terms of businesses providing tourism-related goods and services, with a substantially larger sum being claimed as an indirect contribution through supporting businesses in the supply chain (VB 2010). Estimates of the number of visits by overseas residents to the UK vary from 20 million p.a. (ONS 2010) to 30 million p.a. (Visit Britain 2010) although there is closer agreement on their related spending at about £16 billion (ONS 2010; VB 2010).

It is unclear to what extent these sums might be attributed to ecosystem services, or to what extent variation in those services might change this expenditure and what the underlying economic values might be.[127] Nevertheless, given the size of expenditures involved and the likelihood of ecosystem service contributions to such values, this would appear to be an area worthy of further investigation.

22.3.21 Urban Greenspace Amenity[128]

22.3.21.1 Introduction and overview

While the natural science assessments of the UK NEA consider Broad Habitats and the ecosystem services they provide (Chapters 4–16), the economic analysis focuses upon the goods and values that those services offer. However,

a problem arises when we consider habitats which yield sets of goods, the amounts of which are highly correlated together. This is the case for urban greenspace which yields multiple ecosystem related goods such as recreation, visual aesthetics, reductions of air and noise pollution, all of which tend to be highly correlated (i.e. larger parks generally provide more opportunities for recreation, more visual amenity and better levels of noise and pollution reduction than do smaller parks).[129] In such situations it is very difficult to separate out the effect of any one individual good upon people's well-being, and hence individual valuation becomes problematic.[130] In such cases, we are instead forced to value the collective bundle of correlated goods and tend to refer to this bundle through the shorthand of the habitat name. However, we should not forget that it is these goods, rather than the habitat from which they are derived, that we are valuing. That said, one of the convenient features of the urban greenspace amenity bundle of goods is that, within reason, it does not duplicate values estimated elsewhere. For example, it excludes the benefits of private gardens and the values of rural recreation, both of which we consider in Section 22.3.14. Indeed rather than resulting in a net over-estimate of values, a lack of data meant that our analysis is liable to underestimate values, as we omit items such as the impact of urban greenspace on the reduction of downstream flooding risks. The values presented should therefore be treated as lower bound estimates. Double counting should, therefore, not be a major issue here. Any possibility of overlap between the three categories of greenspace designation, and which might lead to some overstatement of values are discussed by Perino *et al.* (2010).

The analysis developed the following methodology:

i) A meta-analysis of previous urban greenspace valuation studies was undertaken, with particular emphasis being placed upon the spatial location of study households in relation to various categories of urban greenspace including city parks, the urban/rural fringe and informal greenspace. The meta-analysis provides value functions, quantifying how values vary with proximity to the former two types of urban greenspace and the percentage cover in a 1 km square of the latter.

ii) A set of UK urban centres, ranging from relatively small cities like Norwich to major conurbations like Glasgow, were spatially analysed using GIS techniques. This analysis provided information on the proximity of each household in the city to urban greenspaces in that city and the percentage cover of informal greenspace in the household's vicinity.[131]

---

127 Some habitat specific estimates are available. For example, Beaumont *et al.* (2010) report that UK seaside tourism is valued at £17 billion annually. However, such a value appears at odds with other estimates. (ONS 2005, 2006). Other habitats generate more modest expenditures, such as the £3 million spent annually upon skiing in Scotland (Tinch *et al.* 2010), although here the link with ecosystem services such as climate are clearly easier to demonstrate and, reflecting this, visitor numbers have fluctuated with the weather (Tinch *et al.* 2010). While there is clearly a dearth of detailed research into this issue, the size of sums involved suggests that this might be a fitting subject for further investigation.

128 This Section draws on Perino *et al.* (2010). We thank Olena Talavera for excellent research assistance.

129 Of course there are exceptions and as we show subsequently in this section, there is no reason to suppose a linear relationship between the size of a park and the benefits it offers.

130 This problem is not always insurmountable. For example, Day *et al.* (2007) manage to collect enough information to generate separate valuations for different sources of noise. However, this typically takes very substantial amounts of data (in the latter case more than 10,000 observations were used) and this level of information was not available in the case of urban parks.

131 Note that proximity measurements were taken from the centroid of each full postcode, although as these typically contain just 20 households, any error induced by this assumption should be minor. This caveat applies throughout this Section.

iii) These data were then fed into the value functions obtained from our meta-analysis to estimate values for each greenspace category. Summing these together gave a total urban greenspace value for the status quo configuration of urban greenspace.

iv) Changes in urban greenspace were then obtained from the UK NEA Scenarios team (Chapter 25). By inputting these scenarios into the value functions and contrasting findings with those for the status quo, we can estimate the change in values induced under each of these scenarios. We consider two of these scenarios in detail within this chapter and the full set of UK NEA Scenarios are considered in Chapter 26.

v) By considering the characteristics of those cities assessed in detail, and comparing these to all Urban areas across Great Britain, value estimates were obtained for all cities. These were summed to obtain a national estimate of the value of changes in urban greenspace under each scenario.

22.3.21.2 Meta-analysis of urban greenspace valuation studies

A meta-analysis is essentially a study of studies through which prior research is assessed together, typically using quantitative methods. A review of the relevant literature (see Perino *et al.* 2010) produced a set of five studies that value benefits associated with urban greenspace in UK cities, from which 61 marginal valuations were extracted[132]. These studies embraced three different valuation methods, namely hedonic pricing (two studies giving 37 values), contingent valuation (two studies providing six values) and expert interviews (one study yielding 18 values). Analysis showed that these studies covered a wide variety of circumstances, including areas both close to and distant from both small and large areas of urban greenspace.

Meta-analysis (reported in full by Perino *et al.* 2010) of the valuations gleaned from the literature showed that the value of urban greenspace declined with increasing distance from the valuing household and increased with the size of the greenspace in question.[133] Both of these are marginally diminishing effects such that, for example, as the size of greenspace doubles so its value increases, but by less than double. This reflects a basic finding characteristic of virtually all goods, whether related to ecosystem services or not.

The valuation functions estimated from the meta-analysis were then applied to estimates of distance to, and size of, urban greenspaces for the set of UK cities subjected to spatial analysis, and estimates of resultant values for the status quo were obtained.

22.3.21.3 Scenario analysis methods

The UK NEA Scenario team provided a variety of future visions of UK cities. We use two of these: *Go with the Flow* and *Green and Pleasant Land* to illustrate the method developed for valuing urban greenspace amenity. Values are assessed by comparing outcomes under each scenario with present day situations. **Table 22.25** presents relevant aspects of these scenarios as specified by the UK NEA Scenario team.

The changes envisioned in these scenarios were implemented for our sample of UK cities using a set of simple assumptions. Changes in urban area were assumed to occur evenly around the perimeter of a city and a similar procedure was adopted for changes to the size (and hence location) of existing greenspaces. Increases in population were allocated so as to preserve the relative densities observed at present. The scenario descriptions supplied specify the state of the world in 2060 but do not provide any details about the period in between. Therefore the assumption was made that changes are spread evenly across the 50 years considered.

Under these assumptions, each of the scenarios was applied to each of the cities considered within our spatial analysis. This alters the size of each urban greenspace and its distance to each household. Feeding this data into the meta-analysis model allows us to calculate the change in value generated under each scenario for each household p.a. As these values are spread over a 50-year time horizon we apply standard HM Treasury (2003) discounting rules to obtain their present value.[134] Values for an example city are presented in Perino *et al.* (2010). However, in the present chapter we focus upon the implications of this analysis at the national level.

22.3.21.4 Scenario values for Great Britain[135]

Given that the smallest city considered in our analysis was Norwich, we are wary of over-extrapolating our values for urban greenspace, and hence restrict ourselves to considering urban centres with populations in excess of 50,000. The

Table 22.25 Urban dimensions of two UK NEA Scenarios: *Go with the Flow* and *Green and Pleasant Land*.

Scenario name	Change in urban area (%)	Change in urban population (%)	Change in formal urban greenspace area (%)	Change in informal urban greenspace area (%)
Go with the Flow	3.0	32.2	36.2	0.0
Green and Pleasant Land	0.0	21.7	38.9	5.4

132 While there is a wider international literature, this introduces problems associated with translations across economic and cultural contexts from countries which may have very different availability of such greenspace. All of these factors will influence values, making the pooling of estimates problematic unless a large number of observations are available to control for these various influences.

133 Ideally we would have wished to base these analyses upon travel times rather than distances. Indeed this is the approach taken in the valuation of recreation work where both outset and destination locations were available. However, such information was not available for the urban greenspace analysis.

134 Note that there is a degree of inconsistency here in that the HM Treasury discounting rules are based on the assumption of a 2% average growth rate of the UK economy while the UK NEA Scenarios adopt growth rate assumptions varying from 0.5% (Local Stewardship scenario) to 3% (Nature@Work scenario).

135 We restrict our analyses to GB, as comparable data for Northern Ireland were not available.

general reasoning behind this restriction is that for smaller towns, urban greenspace plays a lesser role in the provision of many related ecosystem services as, by their very nature, most households live relatively close to rural areas.

As the analysis did not have access to data allowing the measurement of distance from all urban households to all greenspaces in each city across Britain, a simpler extrapolation was undertaken. This sought to characterise each small census area (lower super output area or LSOA) in each of the cities in our spatial analysis in terms of their local area income and population density as well as larger scale measures of the size of city in which they were based. A simple regression model then related the median urban greenspace value in each LSOA under each scenario to these characteristics. These characteristics are known for all LSOAs in every urban area across Britain and so the model allows us to produce an estimate of how each scenario will change the value of urban greenspace (relative to the present day situation) as experienced in every urban LSOA. Summing across all these areas gives

us our national level estimate of the value changes induced under each scenario.

Figure 22.23 details the spatial distribution of changes in the discounted value of urban greenspace across GB under the *Go with the Flow* Scenario (**Figure 22.23a**) and the *Green and Pleasant Land* Scenario (**Figure 22.23b**). The maps illustrate that per household changes in benefits are highest in the centres of large conurbations. However, what is more important is the nature and scale of these changes. The *Go with the Flow* scenario leads to a worrying reduction in urban greenspace amenity values as large increases in urban extent and population and static informal greenspace overwhelm the relatively modest increases in formal city park areas. In contrast, under the *Green and Pleasant Land* Scenario urban greenspace values increase as more modest changes in urban population and extent are complemented by relatively large increases in both formal and informal areas of greenspace.

By summing the values estimated for each urban LSOA we can obtain GB-level estimates of the change in urban greenspace amenity values under each scenario.[136] These are

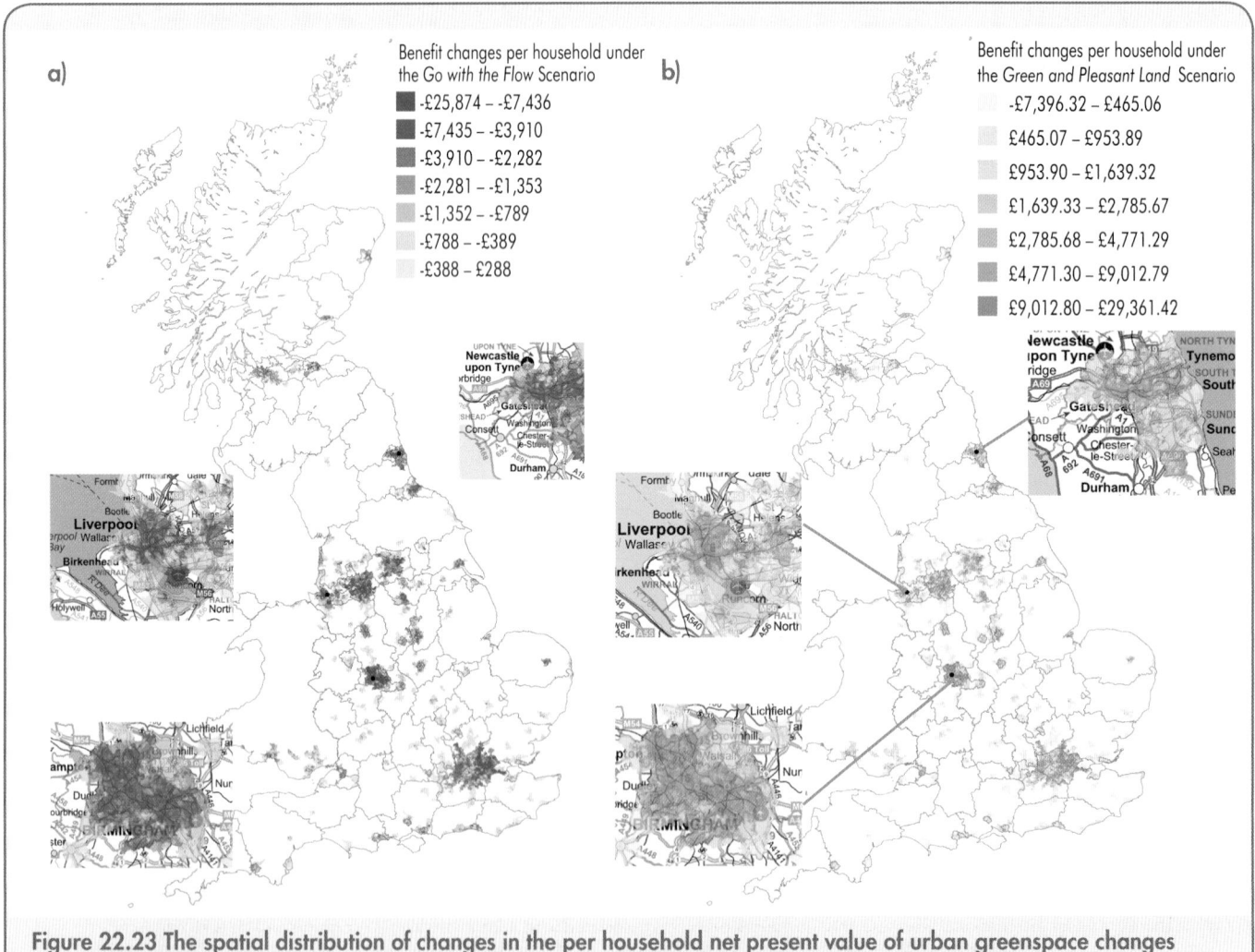

Figure 22.23 The spatial distribution of changes in the per household net present value of urban greenspace changes across Great Britain under a) the *Go with the Flow* Scenario and b) the *Green and Pleasant Land* Scenario. Source: Perino *et al.* (2010) and the SEER (2011) project. © Crown Copyright/database right 2010. This work is based on data provided through EDINA UKBORDERS with the support of the ESRC and JISC and uses boundary material which is copyright of the Crown and the Post Office.

136 These are calculated for the 15.2 million urban households living in the areas included in the extrapolation. This is, of course, an underestimate of total values, as those living outside these areas may well also hold values for improvements in urban parks (reflecting their actual or potential use of those parks and any non-use values).

Table 22.26 Changes in the value of urban greenspace in Great Britain and per household under two UK NEA Scenarios, each compared with the present day situation. Source: Perino *et al.* (2010) and the SEER (2011) project.

Assessment unit	Assessment period	Go with the Flow Scenario	Green and Pleasant Land Scenario
Great Britain	2010–2060 (discounted value)	£-55 billion	£66 billion
Great Britain	Per annum (annualised equivalent)	£-1.94 billion	£2.32 billion
Average urban household	2010–2060 (discounted value)	£-3,600	£4,400
Average urban household	Per annum (annualised equivalent)	£-128	£152

detailed in **Table 22.26** as discounted present values for the entire period (2010–2060) and their annualised equivalents. Average values for each urban household considered in the analysis are also reported.[137]

Table 22.26 summarises the findings of **Figure 22.23** showing us the magnitude of losses under *Go with the Flow* and the potential gains under *Green and Pleasant Land*. Average annual impacts upon household welfare are a loss of nearly £130 under the former scenario and a gain of just over £150 p.a. under the latter. While such changes might appear rather modest, when aggregated across the majority of British households that live in urban areas, they generate substantial welfare changes of the order of roughly £2 billion p.a.

22.4 Summary and Conclusions

This chapter provides a summary of findings from the detailed economic reports compiled for the UK NEA (see Section 22.1).

The chapter opened with a summary of the methodology underpinning economic analyses of ecosystem services (further details of which are found in Bateman *et al.* 2011a). This clarified that the main focus of the UK NEA economic analysis was to examine the value of ecosystem service flows. This is a substantial advance upon conventional financial analyses which focuses upon market-priced goods to the exclusion of the many non-market values generated by ecosystem services. Nevertheless, an early

caveat concerned the recognition that there is inadequate understanding of the sustainability of many ecosystem services and that awareness of potential thresholds beyond which our use of natural resources is unsustainable is a priority for future research. It is clear from the evidence presented that ecosystems provide a very substantial stock of economic value and that ecosystem services represent a significant flow of economic value at the national level.

The methodological summary introduced what we hope will be seen as a simple terminology to help common understanding of the ecosystem service concept across economists and other social scientists, all areas of the natural sciences (not just the biological sciences which have traditionally dominated ecosystem concepts) and decision makers. Because of the potential for error and double counting, if we try to value all of the interlocking relationships which make up the complexity of the natural world, the economic focus is upon those 'final ecosystem services' which are the last link in the chain of natural processes which contribute to human well-being by inputting to the production of 'goods'. Our use of the term 'goods' goes well beyond the common conception of market-priced items to include non-market contributors to well-being, be they physical or non-physical (pure experiential) objects. While some of these goods come straight from the natural world without the intervention of humans (e.g. the visual amenity of beautiful natural landscapes), others require some inputs of manufactured or other human capital (e.g. intensive food production). We also discussed the need to adjust our assessment of ecosystem service values for these other capital inputs and the fact that while economics can value most goods, non-monetary methods are an important complement for assessing those which are not amenable to economic appraisal.

The majority of our methodological summary considered the transition from goods to their value. We made the distinction between prices and values and noted that the latter can arise in both use and non-use contexts. Our summary reviewed the variety of economic valuation methods which have been developed, showing the differing situations in which each is most appropriate. Reference has also been made (in this chapter and a number of the natural science chapters— e.g. Chapter 12) to various financial value estimates that exist, for example tourism day visit expenditure, specific recreation expenditure and employment creation, related to ecosystem services. While these data are useful in order to signify the importance of such services, they are not economic values and cannot be aggregated with the latter.

Another area which we also emphasised was the key distinction between the total and marginal value of a resource. While total values are arguably of importance for highlighting the overall contribution and importance of ecosystem services to human well-being, they are of little help in the decision-making process, which is very rarely concerned with, say, the total loss of a resource, but rather focuses upon the trade-offs involved in alternative options.

---

137 Per household rather than per hectare values are reported, because the value of a hectare of urban greenspace is highly dependent on its location (driven, for example, by the number of households living close by). Furthermore, the extrapolation procedure is based on household information, since data on urban greenspace are not available at sufficient detail at the level of Great Britain.

For these latter decisions, what is needed is an assessment of how an increase or loss of a unit of the resource will affect well-being. Such unit or 'marginal' values can then be used within analyses of trade-offs to allow the decision maker to determine the best use of available resources[138]. This led us to a simple prescription for such analyses: that they should i) understand the change in provision of the good under consideration; ii) know its marginal value; and iii) understand how ii) might alter as i) changes.

Our methodological summary then continued via a brief discussion of decision making for delayed costs and benefits through the process of discounting before a case study illustrated the four guiding principles of economic analysis for ecosystem service assessment:

i) Integration of natural sciences and economic assessments of the relationships determining the provision of ecosystem service;
ii) Valuation of the benefits of all welfare-bearing goods, including those either directly or indirectly provided by ecosystem services;[139]
iii) Efficient use of resources; and
iv) Distributionally aware decision making.

The rest of the chapter applied these tools and principles across the wide gamut of goods which ecosystem services either directly or indirectly provide. The detailed ecosystem service valuations presented in the main body of this chapter can be broadly categorised into those that assess past trends and those that consider likely future scenarios.

Considering the first category, there has been relatively little work which has adjusted for the value of manufactured and human capital in ecosystem service-related output values. This means that many of the estimates in this category are liable to overstate the contribution of ecosystem services to resultant values. Nevertheless, ecosystem inputs are often vital to the production of such goods and accepting this caveat, **Table 22.27** gives a summary of the variety of value estimates provided by this chapter.

22.4.1 Integrated Valuations

A number of the economic valuation exercises undertaken for the UK NEA were designed to integrate together so that policy makers could readily examine the impact of a given impetus for change across multiple impacts. An example of this is given in the integration of work undertaken by the CSERGE SEER project at the University of East Anglia, the British Trust for Ornithology and the University of Leeds. Here the CSERGE SEER Land Use Model was used to estimate the impact of combinations of market forces, policy shifts and environmental change (especially the UKCIP climate change scenarios). The resulting shifts in land use were used both directly to produce valuation estimates in terms of farm gross margin changes, and indirectly as the basis for predicting consequent changes in bird diversity (as an indicator of biodiversity) and carbon storage. Ongoing work under the SEER project will add in further integrations to examine linked issues such as the impact of this land use change upon recreation.

Table 22.27 Summary of UK NEA ecosystem service valuations.

Section	Good	Valuation method*	Valuations
22.3.1.1	Marine food production	Market prices[†]	■ The value of UK fish landings is around £596 million p.a., while that of aquaculture (fish and shellfish farming) is around £350 million annually. However, there is insufficient data to isolate ecosystem contribution from manufactured capital inputs.
22.3.1.2	Woodland-related food production	Market prices	■ Venison valued at over £24 million p.a.
22.3.2.1	Pollination services	Production function method	■ £430 million p.a.
	Maintaining genetic diversity	Production function method	■ No values currently available
	Bioprospecting	Production function method	■ No values currently available
22.3.3.1	Biodiversity: non-use values	Stated preference[‡]	■ Terrestrial biodiversity: £540 million to £1,262 million p.a. (mid-range estimate £845 million p.a.) ■ Inland wetlands: £273 million p.a. (marginal value = £304/ha p.a.) ■ Coastal wetlands: £1,275 million p.a. (marginal value = £1,866/ha p.a.) ■ Marine biodiversity: £1,714 million p.a.
22.3.3.2	Biodiversity: non-use values	Revealed preferences (legacy values)	■ £89.7 million p.a.[¶]

138 Of course, such analyses have to be aware of the danger of incremental losses—hence our stress on the need for understanding of thresholds and their consequences for resource sustainability. However, it is also true that an economic marginal analysis which ensures no net loss of environmental stocks must de facto be sustainable.

139 As noted before, there is a role for non-monetary assessment of those goods which cannot be robustly valued through economic analyses.

Table 22.27 continued. Summary of UK NEA ecosystem service valuations.

Section	Good	Valuation method*	Valuations
22.3.4	Timber production	Market prices	■ 8 million green tonnes p.a. @ £12/tonne = £96 million p.a. ■ Softwood production = £66/ha; hardwood production = £7 to £25/ha. No allowance made for manufactured capital inputs.
22.3.5.1	Carbon storage and GHG flux: Marine and Coastal Margins	DECC values	■ Marginal (and total) values for coastal margin carbon storage (sand dune marginal sequestration value = £32 to £241/ha p.a.; saltmarsh marginal sequestration value = £61 to £622/ha p.a.). UK emissions from all lost coastal margins rise by £82 million/year by 2060 (mainly due to increase in DECC carbon storage value).
22.3.5.2	Carbon storage and GHG in Marine and Coastal Margins	DECC values	■ Carbon storage in marine habitats potentially substantial but unquantified.
22.3.6	Water quality and quantity	Market prices, cost savings and stated preferences	■ Water quality improvements would lead to some cost reductions in the costs of potable water supplies although commercial confidentiality means that the scale of these benefits is unclear. ■ The costs associated with changing agricultural land use to reduce nutrient loadings into rivers are substantially smaller than the benefits which such changes would bring. However, the former costs are concentrated within rural communities while benefits are distributed across a mainly urban society. ■ Water quality benefits of inland wetlands approximately £290/ha p.a.; coastal wetlands approximately £1,790/ha p.a. Total value up to £1.5 billion p.a. ■ Potential benefits of improvements to river water quality up to £1.1 billion p.a. Average benefits are £15.6/km, £18.6/km and £34.2/km for improvements that lift water quality from low to medium, from medium to high and from low to high respectively. ■ Climate change losses upon UK water availability are estimated at £350–490 million p.a.
22.3.7	Flood protection: inland	Market priced cost savings	■ Climate change induced increases in flooding costs range up to £23 billion p.a. depending upon strategy. ■ Marginal value of flood defence from wetlands = £407/ha p.a.
22.3.8	Flood protection: coastal	Stated preference	■ Marginal value of coastal flood protection by wetlands £2,498/ha p.a. Total value up to £1.5 billion p.a.
22.3.9	Pollution remediation	n/a	■ No valuations currently available.
22.3.10	Energy and raw materials	Market prices	■ Fossil fuels currently meet 90% of UK energy demand. Market price £112 billion p.a. (of which £35 billion tax and duties). Renewables meet 3% of UK energy demand and 7% of electricity generation (nuclear power = 17%). ■ Marine-based biotic raw materials = £95 million p.a. UK aggregates industry worth £4.8 billion p.a. of which up to £114 million p.a. comes from the marine environment.
22.3.11	Employment	n/a	■ Economic benefits unquantified. Potentially substantial cultural and social cohesion benefits.
22.3.12	Game and associated landscape values	Market prices	■ Woodland game revenues up to £3/ha p.a. Thought to be higher for Scottish sporting estates.
Section	**Good**	**Valuation method***	**Valuations**
22.3.13	Amenity value of the climate	Revealed preference and life satisfaction	■ £21 billion p.a. to £69 billion p.a.
22.3.14	Amenity value of nature	Hedonic pricing, stated preference	■ Significant positive effects on house prices from increases in local greenspace, rivers and freshwater, wetlands, woodland, farmland, National Parks, National Trust sites. High environmental amenity valued at around £2,000 p.a. per household. Geographical distribution of environmental values mapped for England. ■ Marginal amenity value of inland wetlands = £230/ha/yr; coastal wetlands = £1,400/ha p.a. Total wetland amenity value up to £1.3 billion p.a.

Table 22.27 continued. Summary of UK NEA ecosystem service valuations.			
22.3.15	Education and environmental knowledge	Wage rate assessments, travel and time cost valuations	▪ Environmental knowledge embodied in higher qualifications valued at £2.1 billion p.a. ▪ School trips to just 50 nature reserves valued at £1.3 million p.a.
22.3.16	Health	Stated preference	▪ Value of health benefits of green exercise not quantified. Tentative assessments of health changes arising from a variety of contacts with nature provided, ranging from around £10/person p.a. for a marginal increase in woodland within 1 km of the person's home to around £300/person p.a. for views of greenspace from the person's home. ▪ Climate change is likely to have health impacts and on balance, the direct effects are likely to be positive (the reduction in cold-related deaths outweighs the increase in heat-related deaths). This ignores the indirect effects arising due to climate-induced global economic change.
22.3.17	Agricultural food production	Production function method	▪ Land use model developed from data from the 1960s to the present day. Relates land use and farm gross margin (£/ha) to a variety of ecosystem services and manufactured inputs. Distributions of marginal values mapped at a 2 km square resolution (see discussions in Section 22.4.1 of integrated valuations). Example valuations examine changes in climate ecosystem services induced by climate change from the present day to 2060. Most values vary from (mainly lowland) losses of £50/ha p.a. to (mainly upland) gains of £75/ha p.a.
22.3.18	Carbon storage and annual GHG emissions: terrestrial	Department of Energy Climate Change (DECC) and Stern report values	▪ Mapped distributions of the marginal value (£/ha p.a.) of changes in carbon dioxide equivalent (CO_2e) emissions under each of the agricultural land use change scenarios (from Section 22.3.1). Emissions rise in uplands and fall in lowland areas. Monetised using DECC and Stern carbon storage valuations. ▪ UK-wide valuations for agricultural greenhouse gas (GHG) emissions (i.e. costs) estimated for all of the UK ranging from £4,286 million p.a. in 2004 to £13,409 million p.a. in 2060 (both calculated using Stern values for the UKCIP high emissions scenario). ▪ Specific examples: Within the above costs, emissions from peatlands are estimated at £130 million p.a. Total value of net carbon sequestered (i.e. benefits) annually by UK woodlands = £680 million (marginal value = £239/ha p.a.).
22.3.19	Biodiversity: non-use values	Cost-effective provision of biodiversity indicator species[§]	▪ Maps of the change in bird diversity under each of the agricultural land use change scenarios.
22.3.20	Recreation and tourism	Travel and time cost valuations, stated preferences, meta-analysis	▪ English recreation: 2,858 million visits p.a. with direct expenditure of £20.4 billion p.a. (UK-wide values may exceed £30 billion p.a. In addition, foreign visitors spend £16 billion p.a. in the UK). Economic valuation shows that physically identical nature recreation sites can generate values of between £1,000 p.a. and £65,000 p.a. depending upon location.
22.3.21	Urban greenspace amenity	Meta-analysis of hedonic pricing, stated preference and expert assessments	▪ Valuations vary from losses of £1.9 billion p.a. to gains of £2.3 billion p.a. depending on policy scenario.

* Where no studies are currently available, this column refers to potentially applicable methods.
† See caveats and cited texts in the methodological summary regarding caveats surrounding the use of market prices in economic analyses.
‡ See Section 22.3.2.1 for caveats and reservations regarding stated preference estimates of non-use biodiversity values.
¶ Based upon leagues to just the top five environmental charities: The National Trust; the Royal Society for the Protection of Birds (RSPB); WWF UK; The Woodland Trust; National Trust for Scotland. See caveats in Section 22.3.3.2; this is very much a lower bound estimate of non-use value.
§ As discussed in the Section 22.3.19, this is not a valuation method. Rather it provides estimates of the cost of efficient provision of desirable biodiversity outcomes.

22.4.2 Final Conclusions

We do not pretend that the list of goods assessed in this chapter is complete or that those assessments themselves are definitive. Furthermore, time constraints have precluded more than a cursory consideration of the uncertainties surrounding many of the assessments presented here. However, we would suggest that the economic analysis presented here provides at least a useful initial step for better informing the way in which decisions are made in the UK (and indeed internationally). We believe that the principles and direction which the present analysis adopts are a contribution to the longer term aim of ensuring the sustainability of human society through a recognition of the need to live within our means and work with, rather than against, nature. Given the very large financial and economic values (stock and flows) that are provided by healthy functioning ecosystems, future economic development can best be sustained through policy directed at the safeguarding of the natural capital that ecosystems represent. Proper long-term management of ecosystems can lay the foundations for a thriving 'green' economy and an improving level of general well-being in society as social capital stocks are nurtured in parallel.

References

Abson, D.J., Termansen, M. Aslam, U. & Pascual, U. (2010) Valuing regulating services (climate regulation) from UK terrestrial ecosystems. The Economics Team of the UK National Ecosystem Assessment, School of Earth and Environment, University of Leeds and Department of Land Economy, University of Cambridge.

Adamowicz, W., Louviere, J. & Williams, M. (1994) Combining revealed and stated preference methods for valuing environmental amenities. *Journal of Environmental Economics and Management,* **26**(3), 271–292.

Akaike, H. (1974) A new look at the statistical model identification. *IEEE Transactions on Automatic Control* **19** (6): 716–723. doi:10.1109/TAC.1974.1100705. MR0423716.

Aldy, J. & Viscusi, K. (2007) Age differences in the value of statistical life. RFF Discussion Paper 07-05. Resources for the Future, Washington D.C.

Anderson, B., Armsworth, P., Eigenbrod, F., Thomas, C., Gillings, S., Heinemeyer, A., Roy, D. & Gaston, K. (2008) Spatial covariance between biodiversity and other ecosystem service priorities. *Journal of Applied Ecology,* **46**(4): 888–896.

Andrews, K. (2003) United Kingdom: financial and cultural constraints. Governance of Water-related Conflicts in Agriculture: New Directions in Agri-environmental and Water Policies in the EU (eds F. Brouwer, F. Heinz & T. Zabel), pp. 151–166. Kluwer Academic, Dordrecht, The Netherlands.

AQA (2010) *GCE AS and A level specification: Geography.* [online] Available at: <http://store.aqa.org.uk/qual/gce/pdf/AQA-2030-W-SP-10.PDF> [Accessed 10.03.11].

AQA (2009) *GCE AS and A level specification: Biology.* [online] Available at: <http://store.aqa.org.uk/qual/gce/pdf/AQA-2410-W-SP.PDF> [Accessed 10.03.11].

Armstrong, M. & Holmes, I. (2010) An indicator of sustainability for marine fin-fish stocks around the UK: 1990–2008, Centre for Environment, Fisheries and Aquaculture Science, Lowestoft, UK.

Arrow, K.J., Dasgupta, P., Goulder, L.H., Mumford, K. & Oleson, K. (2007) China, the U.S. and sustainability: Perspectives Based on Comprehensive Wealth. Stanford Working Paper, Stanford University, Stanford.

Atkinson, A., Backus, P. & Micklewright, J. (2009) Charitable bequests and wealth at death in Great Britain. Working Paper A09/03. University of Southampton, Southampton.

Badola, R. & Hussain, S.A. (2005) Valuing ecosystem functions: an empirical study on the storm protection function of Bhitarkanika mangrove ecosystem India. *Environmental Conservation,* **32**(1), 85–92.

Baker, R., Bateman, I.J., Donaldson, C., Jones-Lee, M., Lancsar, E., Loomes, G., Mason, H., Odejar, M., Prades, J.L.P., Robinson, A., Ryan, M., Shackley, P., Smith, R., Sugden, R. & Wildman, J. (2010) Weighting and valuing quality-adjusted life-years using stated preference methods: preliminary results from the Social Value of a QALY Project. *Health Technology Assessment,* **14**(27), 1–161.

Balmford, A., Bruner, A., Cooper, P., Constanza, R., Farber, S., Green, R.E., Jenkins, M., Jefferis, P., Jessamy, V., Madden, J., Munro, K., Myers, N., Naeem, S., Paavola, J., Rayment, M., Rosendo, S., Roughgarden, J., Trumper, K. & Turner, R.K. (2002) Economic reasons for conserving wild nature. *Science,* **297**, 950–953, DOI: 10.1126/science.1073947.

Balvenera, P., Pfisterer, A.B., Buchmann, N., He J-S, Nakashizuka, T., Raffaelli, D. & Schmid, B. (2006) Quantifying the evidence for biodiversity effects on ecosystem functioning and services. *Ecology Letters,* **9**, 1146–1156.

Barbier, E.B. (1994) Valuing environmental functions: tropical wetlands. *Land Economics,* **70**, 155–173.

Barbier, E.B. (2000) Valuing the environment as input: applications to mangrove-fishery linkages. *Ecological Economics,* **35**, 47–61.

Barbier, E.B. (2003) Habitat-fishery linkages and mangrove loss in Thailand. *Contemporary Economic Policy* **21**(1), 59–77.

Barbier, E.B. (2007) Valuing ecosystem services as productive inputs. *Economic Policy,* **22**, 177–229.

Bartelmus, P. (2001) Accounting for sustainability: greening the national accounts. Our Fragile World, Forerunner to the Encyclopedia of Life Support Systems, vol. II (ed M.K. Tolba), pp. 1721–1735. Eolss Publishers, Oxford.

Bartelmus, P. (2008) Quantitative economics: how sustainable are our economies? Springer Science and Business Media, Secaucus, NJ and Heidelberg.

Barton, D.N. (2002) The transferability of benefit transfer: contingent valuation of water quality improvements in Costa Rica. *Ecological Economics,* **42**, 147–164.

Barton, J. & Pretty, J. (2010) What is the best dose of nature and green exercise for improving mental health? A multi-study analysis. *Environmental Science & Technology,* **44**(10), 3947–3955.

Bateman, I.J., Langford, I.H., Turner, R.K., Willis, K.G. & Garrod, G.D. (1995) Elicitation and truncation effects in contingent valuation studies, *Ecological Economics,* **12**(2):161–179. DOI: 10.1016/0921-8009(94)00044-V

Bateman, I.J., Garrod, G.D., Brainard, J.S. & Lovett, A.A. (1996) Measurement, valuation and estimation issues in the travel cost method: A geographical information systems approach. *Journal of Agricultural Economics*, **47**(2), 191–205.

Bateman, I.J., Brainard, J.S., Garrod, G.D. & Lovett, A.A. (1999) The impact of journey origin specification and other measurement assumptions upon individual travel cost estimates of consumer surplus: a geographical information systems analysis. *Regional Environmental Change*, **1**(1), 24–30.

Bateman, I.J., Langford, I.H., Munro, A., Starmer, C. & Sugden, R. (2000) Estimating the four Hicksian measures for a public good: a contingent valuation investigation. *Land Economics*, **76**(3), 355–373.

Bateman, I.J., Carson, R.T., Day, B., Hanemann, W.M., Hanley, N., Hett, T., Jones-Lee, M., Loomes, G., Mourato, S., Özdemiroglu, E., Pearce, D.W., Sugden, R. & Swanson, J. (2002a) Economic Valuation with Stated Preference Techniques: A Manual. Edward Elgar Publishing, Cheltenham.

Bateman, I.J., Jones, A.P., Lovett, A.A., Lake, I. & Day, B.H. (2002b) Applying geographical information systems (GIS) to environmental and resource economics. *Environmental and Resource Economics*, **22**(1–2) 219–269. DOI: 10.1023/A:1015575214292.

Bateman, I.J. & Jones, A.P. (2003) Contrasting conventional with multi-level modelling approaches to meta-analysis: An illustration using UK woodland recreation values. *Land Economics*, **79**(2), 235–258.

Bateman, I.J., Lovett, A.A. & Brainard, J.S. (2003) Applied Environmental Economics: a GIS approach to cost-benefit analysis. Cambridge University Press, Cambridge.

Bateman, I.J., Day, B.H., Georgiou, S. & Lake, I. (2006) The aggregation of environmental benefit values: welfare measures, distance decay and total WTP. *Ecological Economics*, **60**(2), 450–460. DOI:10.1016/j.ecolecon.2006.04.003.

Bateman, I.J. (2007) Valuing preferences regarding environmental change. The SAGE handbook of environment and society (eds J. Pretty, A. Ball, T. Benton, J. Guivant, D. Lee, D. Orr, M. Pfeffer & H. Ward), pp.155–171. Sage, London.

Bateman, I.J., Burgess, D., Hutchinson, W.G. & Matthews, D.I. (2008) Contrasting NOAA guidelines with Learning Design Contingent Valuation (LDCV): preference learning versus coherent arbitrariness. *Journal of Environmental Economics and Management*, **55**, 127–141.

Bateman, I.J. (2009) Bringing the real world into economic analyses of land use value: incorporating spatial complexity. *Land Use Policy*, **26S**, S30–S42. DOI:10.1016/j.landusepol.2009.09.010

Bateman, I.J., Day, B.H., Jones, A.P. & Jude, S. (2009a) Reducing gains/loss asymmetry: a virtual reality choice experiment (VRCE) valuing land use change. *Journal of Environmental Economics and Management*, **58**, 106–118. DOI:10.1016/j.jeem.2008.05.003.

Bateman, I.J., Coombes, E., Fisher, B., Fitzherbert, E., Glew, D. W. & Naidoo, R. (2009b) Saving Sumatra's species: combining economics and ecology to define an efficient and self-sustaining program for inducing conservation within oil palm plantations, CSERGE Working Paper EDM-2009-03. Centre for Social and Economic Research on the Global Environment, University of East Anglia, Norwich.

Bateman, I.J. & Georgiou, S. (2010) The socioeconomic consequences of climate change for the management of water resources. The impact of climate change on European lakes (ed D.G. George), pp. 437–452. Springer, Amsterdam.

Bateman, I.J., Binner, A., Coombes, E., Day, B.H., Ferrini, S. Fezzi, C., Hutchins, M. & Posen, P. (2010a) Integrated and spatially explicit modelling of the economic value of complex environmental change and its knock-on effects, presented at the 4th World Congress of Environmental and Resource Economists (WCERE2010), Montreal, Canada, 28 June–2 July, 2010.

Bateman, I.J., Fisher, B., Fitzherbert, E., Glew, D. & Naidoo, R. (2010b) Tigers, markets and palm oil: market potential for conservation. *Oryx*, **44**(2), 230–234. DOI:10.1017/S0030605309990901.

Bateman, I.J., Brouwer, R., Cranford, M., Hime, S., Ozdemiroglu, E., Phang, Z. & Provins, A. (2010c) Valuing environmental impacts: practical guidelines for the use of value transfer in policy and project appraisal. Main Report. The Department for Environment, Food and Rural Affairs, Economics for the Environment Consultancy (eftec), London.

Bateman, I.J., Mace, G.M., Fezzi, C., Atkinson, G. & Turner, R.K. (2011a) Economic analysis for ecosystem service assessments. Special issue on 'Conservation and human welfare: economic analysis of ecosystem services' (Guest Editors: Brendan Fisher, Steve Polasky and Thomas Sterner). *Environmental and Resource Economics*, **48**(2), 177–218. DOI 10.1007/s10640-010-9418-x.

Bateman, I.J., Brouwer, R., Ferrini, S., Schaafsma, M., Barton, D.N., Dubgaard, A., Hasler, B., Hime, S., Liekens, I., Navrud, S., De Nocker, L., Šceponaviciute, R. & Semeniene, D. (2011b) Making benefit transfers work: deriving and testing principles for value transfers for similar and dissimilar sites using a case study of the non-market benefits of water quality improvements across Europe. *Environmental and Resource Economics*. DOI 10.1007/s10640-011-9476-8.

Beaumont, N., Hattam, C., Mangi, S., Moran, D. van Soest, D., Jones, L. & Tobermann, M. (2010) Economic analysis of ecosystem services provided by UK Coastal Margin and Marine Habitats, Final Report. The Economics Team of the UK National Ecosystem Assessment. Plymouth Marine Laboratory, Plymouth.

Beckerman, W. & Hepburn, C. (2007) Ethics of the discount rate in the Stern Review on the Economics of Climate Change. *World Economics*, **8**, 187–210.

Bergland, O., Magnussen, K. & Navrud, S. (1995) Benefit transfer: testing for accuracy and reliability. Comparative environmental economic assessment (eds R.J.G.M. Florax, P. Nijkamp & K.G. Willis), Edward Elgar, UK.

Beyer, H.L. (2004) Hawth's analysis tools for ArcGIS. [online] Available at <http://www.spatialecology.com/htools> [Accessed 15.08.10].

Bianchi, F.J.J.A., Booij, C.J.H. & Tscharntke, T. (2006) Sustainable pest regulation in agricultural landscapes: a review on landscape composition, biodiversity and natural pest control. *Proceedings of the Royal Society B*, **273**, 1715–1727. DOI:10.1098/rspb.2006.3530

Bird, W. (2004) Natural fit: can greenspace and biodiversity increase levels of physical activity? Royal Society for the Protection of Birds. [online] Available at: <http://www.rspb.org.uk/Images/natural_fit_full_version_tcm9-133055.pdf> [Accessed 14.03.11].

Blundell, R., Dearden, L., Meghir, C. & Sianesi, B. (1999) Human capital investment: the returns from education and training to the individual, the firm and the economy. *Fiscal Studies*, **20**(1), 1–23.

Blundell, R., Dearden, L. & Sianesi, B. (2004) Evaluating the impact of education on earnings in the UK: models, methods and results from the NCDS. Centre for the Economics of Education Working Paper CEE DP 47, London School of Economics, London.

Boatman, N., Willis, K.G., Garrod, G. & Powe, N. (2010) Estimating the wildlife and landscape benefits of environmental stewardship: final report. Defra and Natural England. The Food and Environment Research Agency, York, and the Centre for Research in Environmental Appraisal and Management, Newcastle University, Newcastle.

Bockstael, N.E., Freeman, A.M. III, Kopp, R.J., Portney, P.R. & Smith, V.K. (2000) On measuring economic values for nature. *Environmental Science and Technology, ***34**, 1384–1389.

Bockstael, N.E. & McConnell, K.E. (2006) Environmental and resource valuation with revealed preferences: a theoretical guide to empirical models, the economics of non-market goods and services: Volume 7. Springer, Dordrecht.

Boscolo, M. & Vincent, J.R. (2003) Nonconvexities in the production of timber, biodiversity, and carbon sequestration. *Journal of Environmental Economics and Management, ***46**, 251–268.

Boyd, J. & Banzhaf, S. (2007) What are ecosystem services? The need for standardized environmental accounting units. *Ecological Economics*, **63**, 616–626.

Bradley, R.I., Milne, R., Bell, J., Lilly, A., Jordan, C. & Higgins, A. (2005) A soil carbon and land use database for the United Kingdom. *Soil Use and Management*, **21**, 363–369.

Brander, L.M., Florax, R.J.G.M. & Vermaat, J.E. (2006) The empirics of wetland valuation: a comprehensive summary and a meta-analysis of the literature. *Environmental and Resource Economics*, **33**, 223–250. DOI 10.1007/s10640-005-3104-4.

Brander, L.M., Ghermandi, A., Kuik, O., Markandya, A., Nunes, P.A.L.D., Schaafsma, M. & Wagtendonk, A. (2008) Scaling up ecosystem services values: methodology, applicability and a case study. Final Report, EEA. Fondazione Eni Enrico Mattei. [online] Available at: <http://www.feem.it/userfiles/attach/2010471736364NDL2010-041.pdf> [Accessed 14.03.11].

Brazier, J., Roberts, J. & Deverill, M. (2002) The estimation of a preference-based measure of health from the SF-36. *Journal of Health Economics*, **21**, 271–292.

Brock, W. & Starrett, D. (2003) Managing systems with non-convex positive feedback. *Environmental and Resource Economics*, **26**, 575–602.

Brouwer, R. & Spanninks, F.A. (1999) The validity of environmental benefits transfer: further empirical testing. *Environmental and Resource Economics, ***14**(1), 95–117.

Brouwer, R., Langford, I.H., Bateman, I.J. & Turner, R.K. (1999) A meta-analysis of wetland contingent valuation studies. *Regional Environmental Change*, **1**(1), 47–57.

Brouwer, R. (2000) Environmental value transfer: state of the art and future prospects. *Ecological Economics*, **32**, 137–152.

Brouwer, R. & Bateman, I.J. (2005) Benefits transfer of willingness to pay estimates and functions for health-risk reductions: a cross-country study. *Journal of Health Economics*, **24**, 591–611. DOI:10.1016/j.jhealeco.2004.09.004.

Cairns, R.D. (2002) Green accounting using imperfect, current prices. *Environment and Development Economics*, **7**(2), 207–214.

Cameron, T.A. (1992) Non-user resource values. *American Journal of Agricultural Economics, ***74**(5), 1133–1137.

Carlsson, F., Frykblom, P. & Lijenstolpe, C. (2003) Valuing wetland attributes: an application of choice experiments. *Ecological Economics, ***47**, 95–103.

Carson, R.T., Flores, N.E., Martin, K.M. & Wright, J.L. (1996) Contingent valuation and revealed preference methodologies: comparing the estimates for quasi-public goods. *Land Economics*, **72**, 80–99.

Carson, R.C., Mitchell, R., Hanemann, W.M., Kopp, R., Presser, S. & Ruud, P. (2003) Contingent valuation and lost passive use: damages from the Exxon Valdez oil spill. *Environmental and Resource Economics*, **25**(3), 257–286.

CBD (United Nations Convention on Biological Diversity) (1992) Handbook of the Convention on Biological Diversity; 3rd edition, United Nations, New York.

CBD (United Nations Convention on Biological Diversity) (2006) Global Biodiversity Outlook 2. Secretariat of the Convention on Biological Diversity, Montreal.

CEFAS (Centre for Environment, Fisheries & Aquaculture Science) (2008) Shellfish News 26, Autumn/Winter 2008. [online] Available at: <http://www.cefas.defra.gov.uk/publications/shellfish-news/shellfish-news-issue-no-26,-autumnwinter-2008.aspx?RedirectMessage=true> (Accessed 10.03.11).

Chambers, R.G. & Just R.E. (1989) Estimating multi-output technologies. *American Journal of Agricultural Economics*, **71**, 980–995.

Champ, P.A., Boyle, K. & Brown, T.C. (eds) (2003) A primer on non-market valuation. The economics of non-market goods and services. Volume 3. Kluwer Academic Press, Dordrecht.

Chapin, F.S. III, Zavaleta, E.S., Eviner, V.T., Naylor, R.L., Vitousek, P.M., Reynolds, H.L., Hooper, D.U., Lavorel, S., Sala, O.E., Hobbie, S.E., Mack, M.C. & Díaz, S. (2000) Consequences of changing biodiversity, *Nature*, **405**, 234–242. DOI:10.1038/35012241.

Chatterton, J., Viavattene, C., Morris, J., Penning-Rowsell, E. & Tapsell, S. (2010) The costs of the summer 2007 floods in England. Science Project SC070039, Environment Agency. [online] Available at: <http://publications.environment-agency.gov.uk/pdf/SCHO1109BRJA-e-e.pdf> [Accessed 10.03.11].

Chichilnisky, G. & Heal, G.M. (1998) Economic returns from the biosphere. *Nature,* **391**, 629–630.

Christie, M., Hanley, N., Warren, J., Murphy, K., Wright, R. & Hyde, T. (2006) Valuing the diversity of biodiversity. *Ecological Economics,* **58**, 304–317.

Christie, M. (2007) An examination of the disparity between hypothetical and actual willingness to pay using the contingent valuation method: the case of red kite conservation in the United Kingdom. *Canadian Journal of Agricultural Economics*, **55**(2), 159–169.

Christie, M., Fazey, I. & Hyde T (2008) Economic valuation of the benefits of the UK Biodiversity Action Plan: Phase 1 report. Defra, London.

Christie, M., Hyde, T., Cooper, R., Fazey., I, Dennis, P., Warren, J., Gibbons, J., & Hanley, N. (2010) An economic evaluation of the ecosystem service benefits of the UK

Biodiversity Action Plan. Report to Defra, Institute of Biological, Environmental and Rural Sciences. Aberystwyth University.

Cole, M.A. & Elliott, R.J.R. (2007) Do environmental regulations cost jobs? An industry-level analysis of the UK. *The B.E. Journal of Economic Analysis and Policy,* **7**, Article 28.

Cole, M.A., Elliott, R.J.R. & Okubo, T. (2010) Trade, environmental regulations and industrial mobility: an industry-level study of Japan. *Ecological Economics,* **69**, 1995–2002.

Considine, T.J. & Larson, D.F. (2006) The environment as a factor of production. *Journal of Environmental Economics and Management,* **52**, 645–662.

Coombes, E., Jones, A.P. & Hillsdon, M. (2010) The relationship of physical activity and overweight to objectively measured green space accessibility and use. *Social Science & Medicine,* **70**(6): 816–822. DOI: 10.1016/j.socscimed.2009.11.020.

Costanza, R., d'Arge, R., Groot, R.D., Farber, S., Grasso, M., Hannon, B., Limburg, K., Naeem, S., O'Neill, R.V., Paruelo, J., Raskin, R.G., Sutton, P. & Belt, M.V.D. (1997) The value of the world's ecosystem services and natural capital. *Nature,* **387**, 253–260.

Costanza, R., Pérez-Maqueo, O., Martinez, M.L., Sutton, P., Anderson, S.J. & Mulder, K. (2008) The value of coastal wetlands for hurricane protection. *Ambio,* **37**, 241–248.

Craig, P., Glasser, H. & Kempton, W.K. (1993) Ethics and values in environmental policy. *Environmental Values,* **2**, 137–157.

Crockford, K.J., Spilsbury, M.J. & Savill, P.S. (1987) The relative economics of woodland management systems. Occasional Paper No.35. Oxford Forestry Institute, Oxford.

Cunningham, S., Neiland, A., Bjorndal, T., Gordon, D., Bezabih, M., Hatcher, A., McClurg, T. & Goodlad, J. (2010) The potential benefits of a wealth-based approach to fisheries management: an Assessment of the potential resource rent from UK Fisheries, Defra Project MF 1210. IDDRA Ltd., Portsmouth.

Cuttle, S.P., Macleod, C.J.A., Chadwick D.R., Scholefield, D., Haygarth, P.M., Newell-Price, P., Harris, D., Shepherd, M.A., Chambers, B.J. & Humphrey, R. (2007) An inventory of measures to control diffuse water pollution from agriculture, Defra. ADAS and IGER, London.

Dasgupta P. & Mäler, K.-G. (2000) Net national product, wealth, and social well-being. *Environment and Development Economics,* **5**(1), 69–93.

Dasgupta, P. (2001) Human well-being and the natural environment. Oxford University Press, Oxford.

Dasgupta, P. (2007) Comments on the Stern Review's economics of climate change. *National Institute Economic Review,* **199**, 4–7.

Dasgupta, P. (2009) The welfare economic theory of green national accounts. *Environmental and Resource Economics,* **42**(1), 3–38. DOI: 10.1007/s10640-008-9223-y.

Davis, C.E. (2007) An economic valuation of the marine gas and climate regulation service and the bioremediation of wastes provided by the biodiversity of the Isles of Scilly. Unpublished MSc Thesis, University of Plymouth, Plymouth.

Day, B.H., Bateman, I.J. & Lake, I. (2007) Beyond implicit prices: recovering theoretically consistent and transferable values for noise avoidance from a hedonic property price model. *Environmental and Resource Economics,* **37**(1), 211–232. DOI: 10.1007/s10640-007-9121-8.

de Groot, R.S., Wilson, M.A. & Boumans, R.M.J. (2002) A typology for the classification, description and valuation of ecosystem functions, goods and services. Special issue on the dynamics and value of ecosystem services: integrating economic and ecological perspectives. *Ecological Economics,* **41**, 393–408.

Dearden, L. (1999) Qualifications and earnings in Britain: how reliable are conventional OLS estimates of the returns to education? IFS Working Paper W99/7. Institute for Fiscal Studies, London.

Dearden, L., McIntosh, S., Myck, M. & Vignoles, A. (2000) The returns to academic and vocational qualifications in Britain. Centre for the Economics of Education, London School of Economics, London.

DECC (Department of Energy and Climate Change) (2008) 2008 final UK greenhouse gas emissions: data tables. Department of Energy and Climate Change, London.

DECC (Department of Energy and Climate Change) (2009) Carbon valuation in UK policy appraisal: a revised approach. Department of Energy and Climate Change, London.

DECC (Department of Energy and Climate Change) (2010) Digest of UK energy statistics 2010. Department of Energy and Climate Change, London. [online] Available at: < <http://www.decc.gov.uk/assets/decc/statistics/publications/dukes/348-dukes-2010-printed.pdf> [Accessed 13.03.11].

Defra (Department for Environment, Food and Rural Affairs) (2007) UK Greenhouse gas inventory, 1990 to 2005. Defra, London.

Defra (Department for Environment, Food and Rural Affairs) (2009) Appraisal of flood and coastal erosion risk management. Department for Environment, Food and Rural Affairs, London. [online] Available at: <http://archive.defra.gov.uk/environment/flooding/documents/policy/guidance/erosion-manage.pdf> [Accessed 10.03.11].

Defra (Department for Environment, Food and Rural Affairs) (2010a) Overall impact assessment for the Water Framework Directive (2000/60/EC). [online] Available at: <http://archive.defra.gov.uk/environment/quality/water/wfd/documents/RIA-river-basin-v2.pdf> [Accessed 10.03.11].

Defra (Department for Environment, Food and Rural Affairs) (2010b) Payments for ecosystem services: a short introduction. Department for Environment, Food and Rural Affairs, London.

Defra (Department for Environment, Food and Rural Affairs) (2010c) Wild populations: farmland birds in England 2009. Statistical release. [online] Available at: <http://nds.coi.gov.uk/content/detail.aspx?NewsAreaId=2&ReleaseID=414756&SubjectId=2> [Accessed 10.03.11].

Defra (Department for Environment, Food and Rural Affairs) (2011) Air pollution: action in a changing climate. Department for Environment, Food and Rural Affairs, London. [online] Available at: <http://www.defra.gov.uk/publications/2011/04/13/pb13378-air-pollution/> [Accessed 18.02.11]

Department of Health (2008) Health effects of climate change in the UK 2001/2002. Department of Health/Health Protection Agency, HMSO, London.

Desvousges, W.H., Naughton, M.C. & Parsons, G.R. (1992) Benefit transfer: conceptual problems in estimating water quality benefits using existing studies. *Water Resources Research,* **28**(3), 675–683.

DfT (Department for Transport) (2007) 2005 Valuation of the benefits of prevention of road accidents and casualties.

Highways Economics Note No. 1. Department for Transport, London.

Dietz, S., Anderson, D., Stern, N., Taylor, C. & Zenghelis, D. (2007) Right for the right reasons: a final rejoinder on the Stern Review. *World Economics*, **8**, 229–58.

Dietz, S. (2010) High impact, low probability? An empirical analysis of risk in the economics of climate change. Unpublished manuscript, London School of Economics, London.

Dietz, S. & Hepburn, C. (2010) On on-marginal cost-benefit analysis. Grantham Research Institute on Climate Change and the Environment, London School of Economics and Political Science. Mimeo, London.

Dolman, P., Fuller, R., Gill, R., Hooton, D. & Tabor, R. (2010) Escalating ecological impacts of deer in lowland woodland. *British Wildlife*, **21**(4), 242–254.

Donaldson, C., Baker, R., Mason, H., Jones-Lee, M., Lancsar, E., Wildman, J., Bateman, I.J., Loomes, G., Robinson, A., Sugden, R., Pinto Prades, J-L., Ryan, M., Shackley, P. & Smith, R. (2011) The social value of a QALY: raising the bar or barring the raise? *BMC Health Services Research*, **11** (8). [online] Available at: <http://www.biomedcentral.com/1472-6963/11/8> [Accessed 12.02.11].

Downing, M. & Ozuna, T. (1996) Testing the reliability of the benefit function transfer approach. *Journal of Environmental Economics and Management,* **30**, 316–322.

Drummond, M., O'Brien, B., Stoddart, G. & Torrance, G. (1997) Methods for the economic evaluation of health care programmes (2nd ed). Oxford University press, Oxford.

Dugdale, S. (2010) Habitat association modelling for farmland birds. The Economics Team of the UK National Ecosystem Assessment. CSERGE, University of East Anglia.

EA (Environment Agency) (2002) Agriculture and natural resources: benefits, costs and potential solutions. Environment Agency, Bristol.

EA (Environment Agency) (2009a) Flooding in England. Environment Agency, Bristol .

EA (Environment Agency) (2009b) Flooding in Wales. Environment Agency, Cardiff.

EA (Environment Agency) (2009c) Economic evaluation of fishing. Science Report SC050026/SR2, Environment Agency, Bristol.

EA (Environment Agency) (2009d) Investing for the Future. Flood and Coastal Risk Management in England. Environment Agency, Bristol.

EA (Environment Agency) (2009e) Water for people and the environment: water resources strategy for England and Wales. Environment Agency, Bristol. [online] Available at: <http://publications.environment-agency.gov.uk/pdf/GEHO0309BPKX-E-E.pdf> [Accessed 10.03.11].

EA (Environment Agency) (2010) Estimated Water Abstraction for England and Wales. Environment Agency, Bristol.

Eaton, M.A., Brown, A.F., Noble, D.G., Musgrove, A.J., Hearn, R., Aebischer, N.J., Gibbons, D.W., Evans, A. & Gregory, R.D. (2009) Birds of conservation concern 3: the population status of birds in the United Kingdom, Channel Islands and the Isle of Man. *British Birds*, **102**, 296–341.

Ederington, J., Levinson, A. & Minier, J. (2005). Footloose and pollution free. *Review of Economics and Statistics*, **87**, 92–99.

Edexcel (2008a) Specification GCE geography. [Online] Available at: <http://www.edexcel.com/migrationdocuments/

GCE%20New%20GCE/UA024843%20GCE%20Geography%20 Issue%203%20210510.pdf> [Accessed 10.03.11].

Edexcel (2008b) Specification GCE Biology. [Online] Available at: <http://www.edexcel.com/migrationdocuments/GCE%20 New%20GCE/UA024831%20GCE%20in%20Biology%20Issue%20 4%20250510.pdf> [Accessed 10.03.11].

Eftec (2010) Flood and coastal erosion risk management: economic valuation of environmental effects, handbook for the Environment Agency for England and Wales. [online] Available at: <http://publications.environment-agency.gov.uk/pdf/ GEHO0310BSFH-e-e.pdf>

Ekins, P., Summerton, P., Thoung, C. & Lee, D. (in press) A major environmental tax reform for the UK: results for the economy, employment and the environment. *Environmental and Resource Economics*.

Ellis, G.M. & Fisher, A.C. (1987) Valuing the environment as input. *Journal of Environmental Management,* **25**, 149–156.

ELVS (England Leisure Visits Survey) (2006) England Leisure Visits 2005. English Nature, Wetherby, West Yorkshire.

Entec (2008) Potential market benefits of the Water Framework Directive, Report for Defra, Entec, London.

Evans, A. (1987) The growth of forestry and its effects upon rural communities in North East Scotland: the case of Strathdon. *Scottish Forestry*, **41**, 310–313.

Everard, M. (2009) Ecosystem services case studies. Science Report SCHO0409BPVM-E-E. Environment Agency, Bristol.

Everett T., Ishwaran, M., Ansaloni, G.P. & Rubin, A. (2010) Economic growth and the environment. Defra evidence and analysis series, Paper 2, DEFRA, London. [online] Available at: <http://www.defra.gov.uk/publications/files/pb13390-economic-growth-100305.pdf> [Accessed 28.03.11]

FAI (Fraser of Allander) (2010) Fraser of Allander Economic Commentary, **34**(2). University of Strathclyde, Scotland.

Farmer M.C. & Randall A. (1998) The rationality of a safe minimum standard. *Land Economics*, **74**, 287–302.

FC (Forestry Commission) (2001) Forestry facts and figures. Forestry Commission, Edinburgh.

Fezzi, C., Rigby, D., Bateman, I.J., Hadley, D. & Posen, P. (2008) Estimating the range of economic impacts on farms of nutrient leaching reduction policies. *Agricultural Economics*, 39, 197–205.

Fezzi, C., Hutchins, M., Rigby, D., Bateman, I.J., Posen, P. & Hadley, D. (2010a) Integrated assessment of Water Framework Directive Nitrate Reduction Measures. *Agricultural Economics*, **41**, 123–134.

Fezzi, C., Bateman, I.J. & Schlenker, W. (2010b) The Ricardian Approach with panel data and flexible functional forms: an additive mixed model applied to English and Welsh farmland values. Presented at the 4th World Congress of Environmental and Resource Economists (WCERE2010), Montreal, Canada, 28 June–2 July, 2010.

Fezzi, C., Bateman, I.J., Askew, T., Munday, P. Pascual, U., Sen, A. & Coombes, E. (2011) Enclosed Farmland 1: provisioning services. The Economics Team of the UK National Ecosystem Assessment. CSERGE, University of East Anglia, Norwich.

Fezzi, C. & Bateman, I.J. (in press) Structural agricultural land use modeling for spatial agro-environmental policy analysis, *American Journal of Agricultural Economics*.

FFCD (Foresight Flood and Coastal Defence) (2004) Foresight Future Flooding, Department of Trade and Industry (DTI). [online] Available at: <http://www.bis.gov.uk/foresight/

our-work/projects/published-projects/flood-and-coastal-defence> [Accessed 10.03.11].

FICGB (Forestry Industry Committee of Great Britain) (1992) The forestry industry year-book 1991–92. Forestry Industry Committee of Great Britain, London.

Finnoff, D. & Tschirhart, J. (2008) Linking dynamic economic and ecological general equilibrium models. *Resource and Energy Economics*, **30**(2), 91–114. DOI: 10.1016/j.reseneeco.2007.08.005.

Fisher, B. & Turner, R.K. (2008) Ecosystem services: classification for valuation. *Biological Conservation*, **141**, 1167–1169.

Fisher, B., Turner, R.K., Zylstra, M., Brouwer, R., de Groot, R., Farber, S., Ferraro, P., Green, R., Hadley, D., Harlow, J., Jefferiss, P., Kirkby, C., Morling, P., Mowatt, S., Naidoo, R., Paavola, J., Strassburg, B., Yu, D. & Balmford, A. (2008) Ecosystem services and economic theory: integration for policy-relevant research. *Ecological Applications*, **18**(8), 2050–2067.

Fisher, B., Turner, R.K. & Morling, P. (2009) Defining and classifying ecosystem services for decision making. *Ecological Economics*, **68**(3), 643–653.

Foster, V. & Mourato, S., Tinch, R., Ozdemiroglu, E. & Pearce, D.W. (1998) Incorporating external impacts in pest management choices. Bugs in the system: redesigning the pesticide industry for sustainable agriculture (eds B. Vorley & D. Keeney). Earthscan, London.

FR (Federal Register) (1995) Federal guidance for the establishment, use and operation of mitigation banks. *Federal Register*, **60** (228), 58605–58614.

Freeman, A. III (1991) Valuing environmental resources under alternative management regimes. *Ecological Economics*, **3**, 247–256.

Freeman, A. III (2003) The measurement of environmental and resource values: Theory and methods, 2nd ed. Resources for the Future, Washington, D.C.

Fuller, R.M. (1987) The changing extent and conservation interest of lowland grasslands in England and Wales: a review of grassland surveys 1930–1984. *Biological Conservation*, **40**, 281–300.

Fuller, R.M., Smith, G.M., Sanderson, J.M., Hill, R.A. & Thomson, A.G. (2002) The UK Land Cover Map 2000: construction of a parcel-based vector map from satellite images. *Cartographic Journal*, **39**, 15–25.

GEF (Global Environment Facility) (1998) Valuing the global environment: actions and investments for a 21st Century. GEF, Washington D.C., USA.

Gerlagh, R. & van der Zwaan, B.C.C. (2002) Long-term substitutability between environmental and man-made goods. *Journal of Environmental Economics and Management*, **44**, 329–345.

GHK Consulting (2010) Update of the UKBAP costs and funding data – NE0111. GHK Consulting, Plymouth.

Gibbons, D.W., Reid, J.B. & Chapman, R.A. (1993) The new atlas of breeding birds in Britain and Ireland: 1988–1999. T. & A.D. Poyser, London.

Godoy, R., Lubowski, R. & Markandya, A. (1993) A method for the economic valuation of non-timber forest products. *Economic Botany*, **47**, 220–233.

Gren, I.M., Elofsson, K. & Jannke, P. (1997) Cost-effective nutrient reductions to the Baltic Sea. *Environmental and Resource Economics*, **10**, 341–362.

Gray, W.B. & Shadbegian, R.J. (2003). Plant vintage, technology, and environmental regulation. *Journal of Environmental Economics and Management*, **46**, 384–402.

Groom, B., Hepburn, C., Koundouri, P. & Pearce, D.W. (2005) Declining Discount Rates: The Long and the Short of it. *Environmental and Resource Economics*, **33**, 445–93.

Hamilton, K. & Ruta, G. (2009) Wealth accounting, exhaustible resources and social welfare. Themed Issue: Advances in the theory and practice of environmental accounting. *Environmental and Resource Economics*, **42**(1), 53–64.

Hanley, N., MacMillan, D., Patterson, I. & Wright, R. (2003) Economics and the design of nature conservation policy: A case study of wild goose conservation in Scotland using choice experiments. *Animal Conservation*, **6**, 123–129.

Hanley, N. & Barbier, E.B. (2009) Pricing nature: cost-benefit analysis and environmental policy-making. Edward Elgar, London.

Hansen, L. & Hellerstein, D. (2007) The value of the reservoir services gained with soil conservation. *Land Economics*, **83**(3), 285–301.

Hardin, G. (1968) The Tragedy of the Commons. *Science*, **162**(3859), 1243–1248.

Hargrove, C. (1992) Weak anthropocentric intrinsic value. *The Monist*, **75**, 183–207.

Harrison, G.W. (1995) The measurement and decomposition of non-use values: a critical review. *Environmental & Resource Economics*, **5**(3), 225–247.

Harvell, C.D., Mitchell, C.E., Ward, J.R., Altizer, S., Dobson, A.P., Ostfeld, R.S. & Samuel, M.D. (2002) Climate warming and disease risks for terrestrial and marine biota. *Science*, **296**(5576), 2158–2162. DOI:10.1126/science.1063699.

Heal, G. (2000) Valuing ecosystem services. *Ecosystems*, **3**(1), 24–30.

Heal, G.M., Barbier, E.B., Boyle, K.J., Covich, A.P., Gloss, S.P., Hershner, C.H., Hoehn, J.P., Pringle, C.M., Polasky S., Segerson, K. & Shrader-Frechette, K. (2005) Valuing ecosystem services: toward better environmental decision making. The National Academies Press, Washington D.C.

Hearne, R.R. & Salinas, J. (2002) The use of choice experiments in the analysis of tourist preferences for ecotourism development in Costa Rica. *Journal of Environmental Management*, **65**, 153–163.

Hector, A. & Bagchi, R. (2007) Biodiversity and ecosystem multifunctionality. *Nature*, **448**, 188–190.

Hemingway, H., Stafford, M., Stansfeld, S., Shipley, M. & Marmot, M. (1997) Is the SF-36 a valid measure of change in population health? Results from the Whitehall II study. *BMJ*, **315**(7118), 1273–1279.

HMG (Her Majesty's Government) (2007) PSA delivery agreement 28: secure a healthy natural environment for today and the future. HMSO, Norwich.

HM Treasury (1972) Forestry in Great Britain: an interdepartmental cost/benefit study. HMSO, London.

HM Treasury (2003) The green book: appraisal and evaluation in central government. The Stationery Office, London. [online] Available at <http://greenbook.treasury.gov.uk/>.

HM Treasury (2010) UK Gross Domestic Product (GDP) deflators. HMSO, London.

Hoel, M. & Sterner, T. (2007) Discounting and Relative Prices. *Climatic Change*, **84**, 265–280.

Hooper, D., Chapin, I., Ewel, J., Hector, A., Inchausti, P., Lavorel, S., Lawton, J., Lodge, D., Loreau, M., Naeen, S., Scmid, S., Seta, H., Symstad, H., Vandermeer, A. & Wardle, D. (2005) Effects of biodiversity on ecosystem functioning : a consensus of current knowledge. *Ecological Monographs*. **75**, 1–33.

Howarth, R.B. & Farber, S. (2002) Accounting for the value of ecosystem services. *Ecological Economics*, **41**, 421–429.

Hulme, M. & Siriwardena, G. (2010) UK National Ecosystems Assessment: breeding bird diversity as a function of land cover. The Economics Team of the UK National Ecosystem Assessment. British Trust for Ornithology, Thetford.

Humpel, N., Owen, N. & Leslie, E. (2002) Environmental factors associated with adults' participation in physical activity: a review. *American Journal of Preventative Medicine,* **22**(3), 188–99.

Hunt, J.F. (2003) Impacts of wild deer in Scotland: how fares the public interest? Report for WWF Scotland and RSPB Scotland.

Hunt, A. & Ferguson, J. (2010): A review of recent policy-relevant findings from the environmental health literature. Working Party on National Environmental Policies, Organisation for Economic Co-operation and Development (OECD). ENV/EPOC/WPNEP(2009)9/FINAL. [online] Available at: <http://www.oecd.org/officialdocuments/displaydocumentpdf?cote=env/epoc/wpnep(2009)9/final&doclanguage=en>

Huybers, T. & Bennett, J. (2003) Environmental management and the competitiveness of nature-based tourism. *Environmental and Resource Economics*, **24**, 213–233.

IGCB (Interdepartmental Group on Costs and Benefits) (2010) Valuing the overall impacts of air pollution. Defra, London.

IGCB(N) (Interdepartmental Group on Costs and Benefits Noise Subject Group) (2010) Noise & health: valuing the human health impacts of environmental noise exposure report. Defra, London. [online] Available at: <http://archive.defra.gov.uk/environment/quality/noise/igcb/documents/igcn-noise-health-response100707.pdf>

IPCC (intergovernmental Pannel on Climate Change) (1996) Climate change 1995: economic and social dimensions of climate change. Cambridge University Press, Cambridge.

IPCC (Intergovernmental Panel on Climate Change) (2007) Contribution of Working Groups I, II and III to the Fourth Assessment Report of the Intergovernmental Panel on Climate Change. IPCC Fourth Assessment Report: Climate Change 2007 (eds R.K. Pachauri & A. Reisinger), pp. 104. IPCC, Geneva, Switzerland.

Jablonski, L.M., Xianzhong, W. & Curtis, P.S. (2002) Plant reproduction under elevated CO_2 conditions: a meta-analysis of reports on 79 crop and wild species. *New Phytologist*, **156**, 9–26.

Jacobs (2008) Environmental accounts for agriculture in the UK 2008. Defra, London.

JCC (John Clegg Consulting) (2010) Wood fibre availability and demand in Britain, 2007 to 2025. Report prepared for Confor, UKFPA and WPIF by John Clegg Consulting Ltd, with support from The Forestry Commission: [online] Available at: <http://www.confor.org.uk/Upload/Documents/37_

WoodFibreAvailabilityDemandReportfinal.pdf> [Accessed 14.03.11].

JNCC (Joint Nature Conservation Committee) (2011) Treating Alzheimer's disease with daffodils. Joint Nature Conservation Committee. [online] Available at: <http://www.jncc.gov.uk/page-5721> [Accessed 10.03.11].

Johnson, J.A. & Price, C. (1987) Afforestation, employment and depopulation in the Snowdonia National Park. *Journal of Rural Studies*, **87**(3), 195–205.

Johnston, R.J., Besedin, E.Y., Iovanna, R., Miller, C.J., Wardwell, R.F. & Ranson, M.H. (2005) Systematic variation in willingness to pay for aquatic resource improvements and implications for benefit transfer: a meta-analysis. *Canadian Journal of Agricultural Economics,* **53**, 221–48.

Johnston, R.J., Ranson, M.H., Besedin, E.Y. & Helm, E.C. (2006) What determines willingness to pay per fish? A meta-analysis of recreational fishing values. *Marine Resource Economics,* **21**, 1–32.

Johnston, R.J. & Duke, J.M. (2009) Willingness to pay for land preservation across states and jurisdictional scale: implications for benefit transfer. *Land Economics,* **85**(2), 217–237.

Jones, A.P., Bateman, I.J. & Wright, J. (2002) Estimating arrival numbers and values for informal recreational use of British woodlands. Forestry Commission, Edinburgh.

Jones, A.P., Wright, J., Bateman, I.J. & Schaafsma, M. (2010) Estimating arrival numbers for informal recreation: a geographical approach and case study of British woodlands. *Sustainability*, **2**(2), 684–701. DOI: 10.3390/su2020684.

Jones, M.L.M., Wallace, H.L., Norris, D., Brittain, S.A., Haria, S., Jones, R.E., Rhind, P.M., Reynolds, B.R. & Emmett, B.A. (2004) Changes in vegetation and soil characteristics in coastal sand dunes along a gradient of atmospheric nitrogen deposition. *Plant Biology,* **6**(5), 598–605.

Jones, M.L.M., Sowerby, A., Williams, D.L. & Jones, R.E. (2008) Factors controlling soil development in sand dunes: evidence from a coastal dune soil chronosequence. *Plant and Soil,* **307**(1–2), 219–234.

Jones-Lee, M., Loomes, G. & Spackman, M. (2007) Human costs of a nuclear accident: final report. Health and Safety Executive. [Online] Available at: <http://www.hse.gov.uk/economics/research/humancost.pdf> [Accessed 10.03.11].

Jorgenson, D. & Fraumeni, B. (1989) The output of the education sector. Output measurement in the service sector (ed Z. Griliches). National Bureau of Economic Research/ University of Chicago Press, Chicago.

Jorgenson, D. & Fraumeni, B. (1992) Investment in education and US economic growth. *Scandinavian Journal of Economics,* **94**(supplement), S51–70.

Kahn, J.R., O'Neill, R. & Stewart, S. (2001) Stated preference approaches to the measurement of the value of biodiversity. Valuation of biodiversity benefits: selected studies. Organisation for Economic Co-operation and Development (OECD), Paris.

Kaiser, B. & Roumasset, J. (2002) Valuing indirect ecosystem services: the case of tropical watersheds. *Environment and Development Economics,* **7**, 701–714.

Kanninen, B. (ed.) (2006) Valuing environmental amenities using stated choice studies: a common sense approach to theory and practice. The economics of on-market goods and services: volume 8. Springer, Dordrecht.

Kaplan, R. (2001) The nature of the view from home: psychological benefits. *Environment & Behavior, 33*, 507–542.

Kim, S.-H. & Dixon, J.A. (1986) Economic valuation of environmental quality aspects of upland agricultural projects in Korea (eds J.A. Dixon & M.M. Hufschmidt). Economic valuation techniques for the environment: a case study workbook. Johns Hopkins Press, Baltimore.

King, S.E. & Lester, J.N. (1995) The value of saltmarsh as a sea defence. *Marine Pollution Bulletin, 30*, 180–189.

Klassen, L. & Botterweg, T.H. (1976) Project evaluation and intangible effects – a shadow project approach. Environmental Economics: Volume 1 – Theories (ed P. Nijkamp). Martinus Nijhoff, Leiden.

Knapp, M.F. (2005) Diffuse pollution threats to groundwater: a UK water company perspective. *Quarterly Journal of Engineering Geology, 38*, 39–51.

Knowler, D. & Barbier, E.B. (2005) Managing the Black Sea anchovy fishery with nutrient enrichment and a biological invader. *Marine Resource Economics, 20*, 263–285.

Knox, J.W., Morris, J., Weatherhead, E.K., & Turner, A.P. (1999) Mapping the financial benefits of spray irrigation and potential financial impact of restrictions on abstraction: a case study in Anglian Region. *Journal of Environmental Management, 58*, 45–59.

Koziell, I. (2001) Diversity not adversity: sustaining livelihoods with biodiversity. International Institute for Environment and Development and Department for International Development (DFID), England.

Krupnick, A.J. (2004) Valuing health outcomes: policy choices and technical issues. Resources for the Future, Washington DC.

Langbein, J. (2006) National deer-vehicle collisions project, England, 2003–2005. The Deer Initiative, Wrexham.

Langbein, J. & Putnam, R.J. (2006) National deer-vehicle collisions project, Scotland, 2003–2005. The Deer Initiative, Wrexham.

Laxton, H. & Whitby, M.C. (1986) Employment in forestry in the Northern Region. The Countryside Commission, University of Newcastle upon Tyne.

Lee, A. & Maheswaran, R. (2010) The health benefits of urban green spaces: a review of the evidence. *Journal of Public Health*, 33(1):1–11

Leon-Gonzalez, R. & Scarpa, R. (2008) Improving multi-site benefit functions via Bayesian model averaging: a new approach to benefit transfer. *Journal of Environmental Economics and Management, 56*(1), 50–68.

Lindhjem, H.L. & Navrud, S. (2008) How reliable are meta-analyses for international benefit transfers? *Ecological Economics, 66*, 425–435.

Liu, S., Costanza, R, Farber, S. & Troy, A. (2010) Valuing ecosystem services. *Annals of the New York Academy of Sciences,* **1185**, 54–78. DOI: 10.1111/j.1749-6632.2009.05167.x

Lloyd-Evans, L.P.M. (2005) A study into the prospects for marine biotechnology development in the United Kingdom. Volume 1: Strategy. Foresight Marine Panel. [online] Available at: <http://www.bis.gov.uk/files/file10469.pdf> [Accessed 14.03.11].

Loomes, G. & Sugden, R. (2002) Cautions, caveats and future directions. Economic valuation with stated preference techniques: a manual (eds I.J. Bateman, R.T.Carson, B. Day, W.M. Hanemann, N. Hanley, T. Hett, M. Jones-Lee, G. Loomes, S.

Mourato, E. Özdemiroglu, D.W. Pearce, R. Sugden & J. Swanson). Edward Elgar Publishing, Cheltenham.

Loreau, M.A., Oteng-Yeboah, M.T.K. Arroyo, D. Babin, R. Barbault, M. Donoghue, M. Gadgil, C. Häuser, C. Heip, A. Larigauderie, K. Ma, G. Mace, H. A. Mooney, C. Perrings, P. Raven, J. Sarukhan, P. Schei, R.J. Scholes & R.T. Watson, (2006) Diversity without representation. *Nature,* **442**, 245–246. DOI:10.1038/442245a.

Lovett, A.A., Hiscock, K.M., Dockerty, T.L., Saich, A., Sandhu, C., Johnson, P.A., Sünnenberg, G. & Appleton K.J. (2006) Assessing land-use scenarios to improve groundwater quality: a Slea catchment study. Science Report – SC030126/SR. Environment Agency, Bristol.

Luisetti, T., Turner, R.K., Bateman, I.J., Morse-Jones, S., Adams, C. & Fonseca, L. (2011a) Coastal and marine ecosystem services valuation for policy and management: managed realignment case studies in England. *Ocean and Coastal Management, 54*, 212–224.

Luisetti, T., Bateman, I.J. & Turner, R.K. (2011b) Testing the fundamental assumption of choice experiments: are values absolute or relative? *Land Economics,* **87**, 284–296.

MA (Millennium Ecosystem Assessment) (2005) Ecosystems and human well-being: synthesis. Island Press, Washington, D.C.

Maas, J., Verheij, R., Spreeuwenberg, S. & Groenewegen, P. (2008) Physical activity as a possible mechanism behind the relationship between green space and health: a multilevel analysis. *BMC Public Health,* **8**, 206.

MacMillan, D.C. & Philip, S. (2010) Can economic incentives resolve conservation conflict: the case of wild deer management and habitat conservation in the Scottish highlands. *Human Ecology,* **38**(4), 485–493.

Maddison, D. (2003) The amenity value of climate: the household production function approach. *Resource and Energy Economics,* **25**, 155–175.

Maddison, D. (2010) Economic assessment of the amenity value of the UK climate. The Economics Team of the UK National Ecosystem Assessment, University of Birmingham, Birmingham.

Mäler, K.G. (1974) Environmental economics: a theoretical inquiry. Resources for the Future, Baltimore.

Mäler, K.G., Xepapedeas, A. & de Zeeuw, A. (2003) The economics of shallow lakes. *Environmental and Resource Economics,* **26**, 603–624.

Mäler, K.G. (2008) Sustainable development and resilience in ecosystems. *Environment and Resource Economics,* **39**(1), 17–24.

Mäler, K.G., Aniyar, S. & Jansson, Å., (2008) Accounting for ecosystem services as a way to understand the requirements for sustainable development. *PNAS,* **105**(28), 9501–9506. DOI:/10.1073/pnas.0708856105.

Mäler, K.G., Aniyar, S. & Jansson, Å. (2009) Accounting for ecosystems. *Environmental and Resource Economics,* **42**, 39–51.

Marshall, E., Rushton, J., Schreckenberg, K., Arancibia, E., Edouard, F. & Newton, A. (2006) Practical tools for researching successful NTFP commercialization: a methods manual. The United Kingdom Department for International Development (DFID) for Project R7925. Forestry Research Programme, UNEP-WCMC, Cambridge.

Mason, H., Jones-Lee, M. & Donaldson, C. (2009) Modelling the monetary value of a QALY: a new approach based on UK data. *Health Economics, 18*, 933–950.

Matthews, R.W. & Broadmeadow, M.S.J. (2009) The potential of UK forestry to contribute to government's emissions reduction commitments. Combating climate change – a role for UK forests: an assessment of the potential of the UK's trees and woodlands to mitigate and adapt to climate change (eds D.J. Read, P.H. Smith, J.I.L. Morison, N. Hanley, C.C. West & P. Snowdon), pp. 139–161. The Stationery Office, Edinburgh.

McVittie, A. & Moran, D. (2010) Valuing the non-use benefits of marine conservation zones: an application to the UK Marine Bill. *Ecological Economics*, 70, 413–424.

Mendelsohn, R., Nordhaus, W.D. & Shaw, D. (1994) The impact of global warming on agriculture: a Ricardian Analysis. *The American Economic Review, 84*(4), 753–771.

Mendelsohn, R. & Dinar, A. (2009) Climate change and agriculture: an economic analysis of global impacts, adaptation and distributional effects, Edward Edgar, Cheltenham.

Milne, R., Tomlinson, R.W. & Gauld, J. (2001) The land use change and forestry sector in the 1999 UK greenhouse gas inventory. Annual report for DETR Contract EPG1/1/160. UK Emissions by sources and removals by sinks due to land use land use change and forestry activities (ed. R. Milne), pp. 11–59.

MMO (Marine Management Organisation) (2010) United Kingdom Sea Fisheries Statistics Archive. Available at: <http://www.marinemanagement.org.uk/fisheries/statistics/annual_archive.htm> [Accessed 12.11.10].

Moeltner, K., Boyle, K.J. & Paterson, R.W. (2007) Meta-analysis and benefit transfer for resource valuation-addressing classical challenges with Bayesian modelling. *Journal of Environmental Economics and Management, 53*(2), 250–269.

Moran, D. & Dann, S. (2008) The economic value of water use: implications for implementing the Water Framework Directive in Scotland. *Journal of Environmental Management, 87*, 484–496.

Morey, E., Thacher, J. & Craighead, W. (2007) Patient preferences for depression treatment programs and willingness to pay for treatment. *Journal of Mental Health Policy and Economics, 10*(2), 87–99.

Morling, P., Comerford, E., Beaumont, N., Bolt, K., van Soest, D. & Vause, J. (2010) Economic assessment of biodiversity ecosystem services. The Economics Team of the UK National Ecosystem Assessment, RSPB, Sandy, Bedfordshire.

Morris, J., Weatherhead, E.K., Knox, J., Vasilieou, K., de Vries, T., Freeman, D., Leiva, F. & Twite, C. (2004) Irrigation: The Case of England and Wales. (eds J. Burbel & C.G. Martin), The Sustainability of European Irrigation under Water Framework Directive and Agenda 2000. Office for Official Publications of the European Communities, Luxembourg.

Morris, J. & Camino, M. (2010) Economic assessment of Freshwater, Wetland and Floodplain ecosystem services. UK National Ecosystem Assessment, Cranfield University, Cranfield.

Morse-Jones, S., Bateman, I.J., Kontoleon, A., Ferrini, S., Burgess, N. & Turner, R.K. (2010) Testing the theoretical consistency of started preferences for tropical wildlife conservation. GSERGE Working paper EDM 10-02. [online] Available at: <http://www.cserge.ac.uk/sites/default/files/edm_2010_02.pdf> [Accessed 14.03.11].

Mott MacDonald (1998) Review of costs to balance water supply and demand. Report No. 48550/WSD/02B, August 1998. Ofwat, Birmingham.

Mourato, S., Atkinson, G., Collins, M., Gibbons, S., MacKerron, G. & Resende, G. (2010) Economic assessment of ecosystem related UK cultural services. The Economics Team of the UK National Ecosystem Assessment, London School of Economics, London.

Munro, A. & Hanley, N. (1999) Information, uncertainty and contingent valuation. Valuing environmental preferences (eds I.J. Bateman & K.G. Willis.), Oxford University Press, Oxford.

Munro, R. (2003) Report on the deer industry in Great Britain, 2002. Report for Defra. Defra, London.

Muthke, T. & Holm-Mueller, K. (2004) National and international benefit transfer testing with a rigorous test procedure. *Environmental and Resource Economics, 29*, 323–336.

Naidoo, R. & Adamowicz, W.L. (2005) Biodiversity and nature-based tourism at forest reserves in Uganda. *Environment and Development Economics, 10*, 159–178.

Naidoo, R., Balmford, A., Costanza, R., Fisher, B., Green, R. E., Lehner, B., Malcolm, T. & Ricketts, T. (2008) Global mapping of ecosystem services and conservation priorities. *Proceedings of the National Academy of Sciences USA, 105*(28), 9495–9500.

Nalle, D.J., Montgomery, C.A. Arthur, J.L. Polasky, S. & Schumaker, N.H. (2004) Modeling joint production of wildlife and timber. *Journal of Environmental Economics and Management, 48*(3), 997–1017.

NAO (National Audit Office) (1986) Review of the Forestry Commission's objectives and achievements. Report by the Comptroller and Auditor General. HMSO, London.

Navrud, S. & Ready, R. (eds) (2007) Environmental value transfer: issues and methods. Springer, Dordrecht, The Netherlands.

Naylor, R. & Drew, M. (1998) Valuing mangrove resources in Kosrae, Micronesia. *Environment and Development Economics, 3*, 471–490.

NE (Natural England) (2010a) England's Peatlands: carbon storage and greenhouses gases. Natural England, Peterborough.

NE (Natural England) (2010b) Monitor of Engagement with the Natural Environment: the national survey on people and the natural environment – Technical Report NECR050. Natural England, Sheffield.

NERA (NERA Economic Consulting) (2007) The benefits of Water Framework Directive Programmes of Measures in England and Wales, Final Defra, CRP Project 4b/c. NERA, London.

Newton, A.C., Akar, T., Baresel, J.P., Bebeli, P.J., Bettencourt, E., Bladenopoulos, K.V., Czembor, J.H., Fasoula, D.A., Katsiotis, A. , Koutis, K., Koutsika-Sotiriou, M., Kovacs, G., Larsson, H., Pinheiro de Carvalho, M.A.A. Rubiales, D., Russell, J., Dos Santos J.M.M. & Vaz Patto, M.C. (2010) Cereal landraces for sustainable agriculture: a review. *Agronomy for Sustainable Development, 30*, 237–269.

Nicholson, E., Mace, G.M., Armsworth, P.R., Atkinson, G., Buckle, S., Clements, T., Ewers, R.M., Fa, J.E., Gardner, T.A., Gibbons, J., Grenyer, R., Metcalfe, R., Mourato, S., Muûls, M., Osborn, D., Reuman, D.C., Watson, C. & Milner-Gulland, E.J. (2009) Priority research areas for ecosystem services in a changing world. *Journal of Applied Ecology, 46*, 1139–1144.

Nordhaus, W.D. (2007) A review of the Stern Review on the economics of climate change. *Journal of Economic Literature, 45*, 686–702.

O'Gorman, S., Bann, C. & Caldwell, V. (2010) The benefits of inland waterways (2nd Edition). Defra and IWAC, Jacobs Engineering , London.

O'Neil, J. (2001) Is it time to bury the ecosystem concept? *Ecology*, **82**, 3275–3284.

ONS (Office for National Statistics) (2005) Regional trends 37: tourism, 1991 and 2001. Office for National Statistics, London.

ONS (Office for National Statistics) (2006) Regional trends 39: 2006 edition. Office for National Statistics, London.

ONS (Office for National Statistics) (2009) Regional trends. Office for National Statistics, London.

ONS (Office for National Statistics) (2010) Travel and tourism. Office for National Statistics, London. [online] Available at: <http://www.statistics.gov.uk/cci/nugget.asp?id=352> [Accessed: 14.03.11].

Othman, J., Bennett, J. & Blamey, R. (2004) Environmental management and resource management options: a choice modelling experience in Malaysia. *Environment and Development Economics*, **9**, 803–824.

Owen, N., Humpel, N., Leslie, E., Bauman, A. & Sallis, J. (2004) Understanding environmental influences on walking review and research agenda. *American Journal of Preventive Medicine,* **27**(1), 67–76.

Pagiola, S., Ritter, K.V.& Bishop, J.T. (2004) How much is an ecosystem worth? Assessing the economic value of conservation. The World Bank, Washington D.C.

Pascal, U., Muradian, R., Gómez-Baggethun, E., Armsworth, P., Brander, L., Cornelissen, H., Farley, J., Loomes, J., Martinez-López, B., Pearson, L., Perrings, C., Polasky, S. & Verma, M. (2009) Valuation of ecosystems services: methodology and challenges. Review of The Economics of Ecosystems and Biodiversity. European Commission/ UNEP/ BMU, Germany.

Pearce, D.W., Barbier, E.B. & Markandya, A. (1990) Sustainable development: economics and environment in the Third World. Earthscan, London.

Pearce, D.W., Atkinson, G. & Mourato, S. (2006) Cost-benefit analysis and the environment: recent developments. OECD, Paris.

Pearce, D.W. (2007) Do we really care about biodiversity? *Environmental and Resource Economics*, **37**(1), 313–333. DOI: 10.1007/s10640-007-9118-3.

Penning-Roswell, E., Viavattene, C., Pardoe, J., Chatterton, J., Parker, D. & Morris, J. (2010) The benefits of flood and coastal risk management: a handbook of assessment techniques – 2010. Flood Hazard Research Centre, Middlesex University, London.

Perino, G., Andrews, B., Kontoleon, B. & Bateman, I.J. (2010) Economic assessment of ecosystem services provided by UK Urban habitats. The Economics Team of the UK National Ecosystem Assessment, University of East Anglia, Norwich.

Pharoah, C. (2010) Charity market monitor 2010: tracking the funding of UK Charities. CaritasData, London.

Pike, A. (2008) Understanding behaviours in a farming context: bringing theoretical and applied evidence together from across Defra and highlighting policy relevance and implications for future research. Defra Agricultural Change and Environment Observatory Discussion Paper. Defra, London.

Pitt, M. (2008) Learning lessons from the 2007 Floods. Cabinet Office, London.

Porter, M. & van der Linde, C. (1995). Toward a new conception of the environment-competitiveness relationship. *Journal of Economic Perspectives*, **9**, 97–118.

POST (The Parliamentary Office of Science and Technology) (2004) UK health impacts of climate change. Postnote 232, The Parliamentary Office of Science and Technology, London.

POST (Parliamentary Office of Science & Technology) (2011) Biodiversity offsetting. Postnote 369, Parliamentary Bookshop. [online] Available at: <http://www.parliament.uk/business/publications/research/post/pubs/>

Posthumus, H., Morris, J., Hess, T., Neville, D., Philips, E. & Baylis, A. (2009) Impacts of the summer 2007 floods on agriculture in England. *Journal of Flood Risk Management*, **2**(3), 1–8.

Potts, S.G., Biesmeijer, J.C., Kremen, C., Neumann, P., Schweiger, O., & Kunin, W.E. (2010) Global pollinator declines: trends, impacts and drivers. *Trends in Ecology and Evolution*, **25**, 345–353.

Powe, N.A. & Willis, K.G. (2004) Mortality and morbidity benefits of air pollution (SO_2 and PM_{10}) absorption attributable to woodland in Britain. *Journal of Environmental Management*, **70**, 119–128.

Poysa, V. (1993) Use of *Lycopersicon cheesmanii* and *L. chmielewskii* to increase dry matter content of tomato fruit. *Canadian Journal of Plant Sciences,* **73**, 273–279.

Pretty, J.N., Mason, C.F., Newdwell, D.B., Hine, R.E., Leaf, S. & Dils, R. (2003) Environmental costs of freshwater eutrophication in England and Wales. *Environmental Science & Technology*, **37**, 201–208.

Pretty, J., Peacock, J., Sellens, M. & Griffin, M. (2005) The mental and physical health outcomes of green exercise. *International Journal of Environmental Health Research,* **15**(5), 319–337.

Pretty, J., Peacock, J., Hine, R., Sellens, M., South, N. & Griffin, M. (2007) Green exercise in the UK countryside: effects on health and psychological well-being and implications for policy and planning. *Journal of Environmental Planning & Management,* **50**(2), 211–31.

Pugh, D. (2008) Socio-economic indicators of marine related activities in the UK economy. The Crown Estate, London

Randall, A. (2002) Benefit-cost considerations should be decisive when there is nothing more important at stake. Economies, ethics and environmental policy (eds D. Bromley & J. Paavola) Blackwell, Oxford.

Randall, A. (2007) Benefit-cost analysis and a safe minimum standard. Handbook of sustainable development (eds G. Atkinson, S. Dietz, E. Neumayer). Edward Elgar, Cheltenham.

RCEP (Royal Commission on Environmental Pollution) (2010) 28th Report: adapting institutions to climate change. The Stationary Office, London.

Ready, R., Navrud, S., Day, B., Dubourg, R., Machado, F., Mourato, S., Spaninks, F. & Vázquez Rodriquez, M.X. (2004) Benefit transfer in Europe: How reliable are transfers between countries? *Environmental and Resource Economics*, **29**, 67–82.

RS (Reforesting Scotland) (2003) Non-timber forest products. [online] Available at: <http://www.reforestingscotland.org> [Accessed 14.03.11].

Ricketts, T.H., Daily, G.C., Ehrlich, P.R. & Michener, C.D. (2004) Economic value of tropical forests to coffee production. *Proceedings of the Natural Academy of Sciences,* **101**(34), 12579–12582.

RICS (Royal Institution of Chartered Surveyors) (2010) Rural market survey. [online] Available at: <http://www.rics.org/ruralmarketsurvey> [Accessed 14.03.11].

Risely, K., Baillie, S.R., Eaton, M.A., Joys, A.C., Musgrove, A.J., Noble, D.G., Renwick, A.R. & Wright, L.J. (2010) The Breeding Bird Survey 2009. BTO Research Report 559. British Trust for Ornithology, Thetford.

Roca, M., Bast, H., Panzeri, M., Hess, T. & Sayers, P. (2010) Developing the evidence base to describe the flood and coastal erosion risk to agricultural land in England and Wales. Defra R&D Technical Report, FD2634/TR. HR Wallingford Ltd, Wallingford.

Rockström, J., Steffen, W., Noone, K., Persson, A., Chapin, F.S.III, Lambin, E. F., Lenton, T. M., Scheffer, M., Folke, C., Schellnhuber, H.J., Nykvist, B., de Wit, C.A., Hughes, T., van der Leeuw, S., Rodhe, H., Sorlin, S., Snyder, P.K., Costanza, R., Svedin, U., Falkenmark, M., Karlberg, L., Corell, R.W., Fabry, V.J., Hansen, J., Walker, B., Liverman, D., Richardson, K., Crutzen, P. & Foley, J.A. (2009) A safe operating space for humanity. *Nature,* **461**(7263), 472–475. dx.doi.org/10.1038/461472a.

Rodwell, L.D., Barbier, E.B., Roberts, C.M. & McClanahan, T.R. (2002) A model of tropical marine reserve-fishery linkages. *Natural Resource Modeling,* **15**(4), 453–486.

Rolfe, J., Bennett, J. & Louviere, J. (2000) Choice modelling and its potential application to tropical rainforest preservation. *Ecological Economics,* **35**, 289–302.

Rosado, M.A., Cunha-e-Sa, M.A., Ducla-Soares, M.M. & Nunes, L.M. (2000) Combining averting behavior and contingent valuation data: an application to drinking water treatment. FEUNL Working Paper No. 392. [online] Available at: <http://ssrn.com/abstract=880458> [Accessed 14.03.11].

RPA (Rural Payments Agency) & FHRC (Flood Hazard Research Centre) (2004) The appraisal of human related intangible impacts of flooding. R&D Technical Report FD2004/TR. Defra, London.

Sagoff, M. (2011) The quantification and valuation of ecosystem services. *Ecological Economics,* 70, 497–502.

Saunders, J. (ed) (2010) Charting Progress 2 Feeder Report: Productive Seas. UKMMAS (2010), Defra. [online] Available at: <http://chartingprogress.defra.gov.uk/productive-seas-feeder-report-download> [Accessed 14.03.11].

Schenkler, W., Hanemann, W.M. & Fisher, A. (2005) Will US agriculture really benefit from global warming? Accounting for irrigation in the hedonic approach. *American Economic Review,* **95**, 395–406.

Schkade, D. & Kahneman, D. (1998) Does living in California make people happy? A focusing illusion in judgments of life satisfaction. *Psychological Science,* **9**, 340–346.

SEER (Social and Environmental Economic Research) (2011) Social and Environmental Economic Research (SEER) into Multi-Objective Land Use Decision Making. CSERGE, University of East Anglia.

Sen, A., Darnell, A., Bateman, I.J., Crowe, A., Munday, P., Foden, J., & Coombes, E. (2010) Economic assessment of the recreational value of ecosystems in Great Britain. The Economics Team of the UK National Ecosystem Assessment, CSERGE, School of Environmental Sciences, University of East Anglia.

Seo, N., Mendelsohn, R., Dinar, A., Hassan, R. & Kurukulasuriya, P. (2009) A Ricardian analysis of the distribution of climate change impacts on agriculture across agro-ecological zones in Africa. *Environmental and Resource Economics,* **43**(3), 313–332.

SEPA (Scottish Environment Protection Agency) (2004) An economic analysis of water use in the Scotland river basin: summary report. Scottish Environment Protection Agency, Edinburgh.

Sheppard, S. (1999) Hedonic analysis of housing markets. Handbook of Regional and Urban Economics, Edition 1, Volume 3, Chapter 41 (eds P.C. Cheshire & E.S. Mills), Elsevier.

Smith, M.D. (2007) Generating value in habitat-dependent fisheries: the importance of fishery management institutions. *Land Economics,* **83**, 59–73.

Smith, P., Martino, D., Cai, Z., Gwary, D., Janzen, H., Kumar, P., McCarl, B., Ogle, S., O'Mara, F., Rice, C., Scholes, B. & Sirotenko, O. (2007). Agriculture. Climate change 2007: mitigation. Contribution of Working Group III to the Fourth Assessment Report of the Intergovernmental Panel on Climate Change (eds B. Metz, O.R. Davidson, P.R. Bosch, R. Dave, & L.A. Meyer). Cambridge University Press, Cambridge, United Kingdom and New York, NY, USA.

Spence, L. & Wentworth, J. (2009) Wild deer. *Postnote,* **325**, 1–4.

Stern, N. (2007) The economics of climate change: the Stern review. Cambridge University Press, Cambridge.

Sterner, T. & Persson, U.M. (2008) An even Sterner review: introducing relative prices into the discounting debate. *Review of Environmental Economics and Policy,* **2**(1), 61–76.

Stiglitz, J., Sen, A. & Fitoussi, J.P. (2009) Report by the Commission on the Measurement of Economic Performance and Social Progress. [online] Available at: <http://www.stiglitz-sen-fitoussi.fr/documents/rapport_anglais.pdf>

Sumaila, U.R. (2002) Marine Protected Area performance in a model of a fishery. *Natural Resource Modeling,* **15**(4), 439–451.

TEEB (The Economics of Ecosystems and Biodiversity) (2009) The Economics of Ecosystems and Biodiversity for national and international policy makers. [online] Available at: <www.teebweb.org> [Accessed 14.03.11].

TEEB (The Economics of Ecosystems and Biodiversity) (2010) The Economics of Ecosystems and Biodiversity: mainstreaming the economics of nature: a synthesis of the approach, conclusions and recommendations of TEEB. Progress Press, Malta.

Termansen, M., Abson, D.J., Pascual, U. & Aslam, U. (2010) Enclosed Farmland 3: climate regulation. The Economics Team of the UK National Ecosystem Assessment, University of Leeds, Leeds.

Thompson, J. (1990) Forest employment survey 1988–89. Occasional Paper 27, Forestry Commission, Edinburgh.

Thurstan, R.H., Brockington, S. & Roberts, C.M. (2010) The effects of 118 years of industrial fishing on UK bottom trawl fisheries. *Nature Communications.* **1**, Article 15, DOI: 10.1038/ncomms1013.

Tilling, C., Krol, M., Tsuchiya, A., Brazier, J., van Exel, J. & Brouwer, W. (2009) Measuring the value of life: exploring a new method for deriving the monetary value of a QALY. HEDS Discussion Paper 09/14. University of Sheffield, Sheffield.

Tinch, D. (2010) Economic assessment of ecosystem services provided by UK Semi-Natural Grasslands (SNG). The Economics Team of the UK National Ecosystem Assessment, University of Stirling, Stirling.

Tinch, D., Hanley, N. & Beharry-Borg, N. (2010) Economic assessment of ecosystem services provided by UK Mountains, Moorlands and Heaths (MMH). The Economics Team of the UK National Ecosystem Assessment, University of Stirling, Stirling.

Tschirhart, J. (2009) Integrated ecological-economic models. *Annual Review of Resource Economics,* **1**, 381–407.

Turner, R.K. (1999) The place of economic values in environmental valuation. Valuing environmental preferences: theory and practice of the contingent valuation method in the US, EU, and developing countries (eds I.J. Bateman & K.G. Willis). Oxford University Press, Oxford.

Turner, R.K., Burgess, D., Hadley, D., Coombes, E.G. & Jackson, N. (2007) A cost-benefit appraisal of coastal managed realignment policy. *Global Environmental Change,* **17**, 397–407.

Turner, R.K., Morse-Jones, S. & Fisher, B. (2010) Ecosystem valuation: a sequential decision support system and quality assessment issues. *Annals of the New York Academy of Sciences,* **1185**, 79–101.

UKCIP (UK Climate Impacts Programme) (2009) UK climate projection: briefing report. Met Office Hadley Centre, Exeter, UK.

UKWIR (UK Water Industry Research) (2004) Implications of changing groundwater quality for water resources and the UK water industry. Phase 3: financial and water resources impact, Report 04/WR/09/8. UK Water Industry Research, London.

Ulrich, R. (1984) View through a window may influence recovery from surgery. *Science,* **224**, 420–421.

Ulrich, R. (1986) Human responses to vegetation and landscapes. *Landscape and Urban Planning,* **13**, 29–44.

United Nations (UN) (2003) The handbook of national accounting: integrated environmental and economic accounting 2003. United Nations, New York.

UNEP (United Nations Environment Programme) (2011). Towards a Green Economy: Pathways to Sustainable Development and Poverty Eradication.

University of Brighton (2008) Collaborative research programme on river basin management planning economics. Valuation of recreational benefits of improvements in water quality – potential benefits and data requirements. University of Brighton, Brighton.

Valatin, G. & Starling, J. (2010) Economic assessment of ecosystem services provided by UK Woodlands. The Economics Team of the UK National Ecosystem Assessment, Forest Research.

van Liedekerke M., Jones A. & Panagos P. (2006) ESDBv2 Raster Library – a set of rasters derived from the European soil database distribution v2.0. European Commission and the European Soil Bureau Network, CD-ROM, EUR 19945 EN.

VB (Visit Britain) (2010) How tourism supports the British economy. Visit Britain, London.

Walker, B., Pearson, L., Harris, M., Mäler, K.G., Li, C.Z., Biggs, R. & Baynes, T. (2010) Incorporating resilience in the assessment of inclusive wealth: an example from South East Australia. *Environmental and Resource Economics,* **45**, 183-202. DOI 10.1007/s10640-009-9311-7.

Wallace, K.J. (2007) Classification of ecosystem services: problems and solutions. *Biology Conservation,* **139**, 235–246.

Walther, G.R., Post, E., Convey, P., Menzel, A., Parmesan, C., Beebee, T.J.C., Fromentin, J.-M., Hoegh-Guldberg, O. & Bairlein, F. (2002) Ecological responses to recent climate change. *Nature,* **416**, 389–395. DOI:10.1038/416389a.

Ward, A.I. (2005) Expanding ranges of wild and feral deer in Great Britain. *Mammal Review,* **35**(2), 165–173.

Ward, A., Etherington, T. & Ewald, J. (2008) Five years of change. *Deer,* **14**(8), 17–20.

Weitzman, M. (2007) A review of the Stern review on the economics of climate change. *Journal of Economic Literature,* **45**, 703-24.

Welsch, H. (2009) Implications of happiness research for environmental economics. *Ecological Economics,* **68**(11), 2735–2742. DOI:10.1016/j.ecolecon.2009.06.003.

White, C.L., Smart, J.C.R., Bohm, M., Langbein, J. & Ward, A.I. (2004) Economic impacts of wild deer in the East of England. Forestry Commission, Edinburgh. [online] Available at: < http://www.forestry.gov.uk/newsrele.nsf/WebPressReleases/C923BC1A0C24036780256E12005A4A6C> [Accessed 14.03.11].

Willis, K.G., Garrod, G., Scarpa, R., Powe, N., Lovett, A., Bateman, I.J., Hanley, N. & Macmillan, D. (2003) The social and environmental benefit of forests in Great Britain, Forestry Commission, Edinburgh.

Willis, K.G. (2005) Chapter 3: Measuring health impacts in economic terms. Economic benefits of accessible green spaces for physical and mental health: scoping study. Final Report. CJC Consulting, The Forestry Commission. [online] Available at: <http://www.forestry.gov.uk/pdf/FChealth10-2final.pdf/$FILE/FChealth10-2final.pdf> [Accessed 14.03.11].

Woodward, R.T. & Wui, Y.S. (2001) The economic value of wetland services: a meta-analysis. *Ecological Economics,* **37**(2), 257–270.

World Bank & FAO (Food and Agriculture Organization) (2009) The sunken billions: The economic justification for fisheries reform. The International Bank for Reconstruction and Development/The World Bank, Washington DC. [online] Available at: <http://go.worldbank.org/MGUTHSY7U0>

Zandersen, M., Termansen, M. & Jensen, F.S. (2007) Testing benefits transfer of forest recreation values over a twenty-year time horizon. *Land Economics,* **83**(3), 412–440.

Appendix 22.1 The Economic Case for the Sustainable Management and Use of Natural Capital

Natural capital and the various services it provides contribute to economic activity and human welfare in two general ways:

■ Directly as an input to production; for example, through the provision of fossil fuels, minerals and the contribution of sectors such as farming, forestry and fishing to economic activity.

■ Indirectly through its productivity-enhancing effects on other factors of production; for example, through better human health outcomes from improved local air quality and provision of greenspaces; by providing a sink for waste generated as a by-product of economic activity; and the mitigation of some of the risks posed by climate change such as from flooding.

Some of the contributions of natural capital have a market value, and are at least partly reflected in measures of economic activity such as Gross Domestic Product (GDP). However, while GDP and similar measures reflect the value of goods and services provided through the market, they exclude others that are not provided through the market, but nevertheless facilitate economic activity and contribute to overall human welfare.

Natural capital also contributes to wider societal well-being; for example, through the non-material benefits people obtain from ecosystems such as from aesthetic enjoyment and recreational services. Well-being is a multidimensional concept including a range of objective and subjective factors. For example, the Commission on the Measurement of Economic Performance and Social Progress (Stiglitz *et al.* 2009) identified the key dimensions of well-being to include:

i)   material living standards (income, consumption and wealth);
ii)   health;
iii) education;
iv)   personal activities including work;
v)   political voice and governance;
vi)   social connections and relationships;
vii) environment (present and future conditions);
viii) and insecurity, of an economic as well as a physical nature.

The Commission notes that "all these dimensions shape people's well-being, and yet many of them are missed by conventional income measures." (Stiglitz *et al.* 2009; p15). Thus, the contribution of the natural environment to society's overall well-being needs to be considered alongside its contribution to economic growth and welfare.

Securing future economic prosperity and well-being requires ensuring the availability of natural capital, and the services it provides, into the future. However, markets alone will be unable to deliver sustainable management and use of natural capital. The value of the goods and services provided by natural capital are, at best, imperfectly priced into economic decisions to produce and consume. This leads to overuse of such resources and their depletion and/or degradation beyond economically efficient levels. For example, without policy intervention, a firm releasing pollutants into the atmosphere does not pay the full cost to society of the negative health effects resulting from its actions. This leads to higher levels of production (and pollution) than if the firm faced the full higher cost of such resource use.

Correcting for this 'market failure' will improve the overall (allocative) efficiency of the economy and ensure that environmental goods and services are not consumed beyond their economically efficient level. However, the sustainable management and use of natural capital requires consideration of some additional attributes unique to natural capital, namely:

■ Finite limits or critical thresholds beyond which non-linear and/or irreversible changes may occur; for example, 'source limits' in fish stocks and top soil where breaching the threshold could lead to a change or collapse in the ecosystem.

■ Services provided by natural capital may not be readily substitutable by other types of capital; for example, technology and produced capital could not easily substitute for the ecosystem services provided by the ozone layer.

Declining levels of some natural assets can be consistent with environmentally sustainable growth as long as adequate investments are made in other types of capital. However, to the extent that the services provided by natural assets have critical thresholds, or cannot be substituted for by other goods and services, maintaining a minimum stock of these assets needs to be considered.

Policy action is required in order to ensure that natural capital is managed and used sustainably, both in terms of ensuring the efficient level of natural capital and of protecting key natural assets. Environmental policy of this nature should achieve its environmental objectives without significant adverse macroeconomic impacts (acknowledging that some sectors could disproportionately benefit or lose out in the process), particularly if implemented through cost-effective interventions (or package of interventions) and using market instruments wherever possible.

Indeed, fears surrounding the macroeconomic impacts resulting from a strengthening of environmental policy are not borne out by the economics literature. A large number of studies have examined the impact of environmental regulation costs on different aspects of industrial competitiveness (for instance, on trade and foreign direct investment patterns and on productivity and employment levels) for a range of economies including the UK (Gray & Shadbegian 2003; Ederington *et al.* 2005; Cole & Elliott 2007; Cole *et al.* 2010; Ekins *et al.* in press). These studies have generally found no, or only very limited, evidence that environmental regulation costs adversely influence industrial competitiveness. While these studies tend to focus on the impact on competitiveness of pollution abatement costs, rather than the costs of correctly pricing natural capital more broadly, their findings provide some indication of the potential impacts of these latter costs.

Possible reasons for the lack of evidence of macroeconomic impacts associated with environmental regulations include: the fact that the most pollution-intensive firms tend to be physically capital intensive and, hence, less suited to relocation to (or displacement by) low regulation, labour-intensive economies; the fact that pollution regulation costs form only a small proportion of a firm's total costs even within pollution intensive firms; and the possibility that a strengthening of environmental regulations can actually stimulate innovation in firms, which may at least partially offset the cost of complying with these regulations (the so-called Porter hypothesis; Porter & van der Linde 1995). Related to this latter point, a recent report by the United Nations Environment Programme (UNEP) provides further evidence of the potential economic benefits of 'green investment' by indicating that investment of this nature can enhance economic growth by stimulating certain industries and, crucially, by reducing environmental risks (UNEP 2011). It is obviously vital that the costs of failing to reduce such risks are taken into account when quantifying the overall economic costs of environmental policy. If natural capital is not adequately protected its depletion and degradation is likely to have negative effects on growth and welfare through the loss of inputs to production (such as reduced availability of clean water), the loss of assets which contribute to resilience of business and communities (such as reduced flood risk management), or through negative effects on well-being (such as the loss of biodiversity and associated recreation services). The management of environmental risks seem likely to be key to maximising both well-being and economic growth over the long-term.

Chapter 23:
Health Values from Ecosystems

Coordinating Lead Author: Jules N. Pretty
Lead Authors: Jo Barton, Ian Colbeck, Rachel Hine, Susana Mourato, George MacKerron and Carly Wood

Key Findings*

Observing nature and participating in physical activity in greenspaces play an important role in positively influencing human health and well-being[1]. 'Green exercise', comprising of activity in green places (in the presence of nature), is associated with positive health outcomes, which exceed those experienced from exercising in environments lacking nature[a].

[1] *well established*
[a] *virtually certain*

Ecosystems provide three generic health benefits: i) direct positive effects on both mental and physical health[2]; **ii) indirect positive effects** which facilitate nature-based activity and social engagement (by providing locations for contact with nature, physical activity and social engagement), all of which positively influence health, and provide a catalyst for behavioural change in terms of encouraging the adoption of healthier lifestyles (improving life pathways, activity behaviour, consumption of wild foods)[2]; **iii) a reduction in the threats of pollution and disease vectors** to health via a variety of purification and control functions, such as local climate regulation, noise reduction, and scavenging of air pollutants[b].

[2] *established but incomplete*
[b] *very likely*

Ecosystems can be a direct provider of threats to human health[1]. These threats include infectious agents (e.g. *Lyme borreliosis*, Cryptosporidium, Plasmodium that cause malaria); physical threats from wild animals (although this is not generally a factor in the UK), domestic livestock and dogs; pollutants or contaminants from plants (e.g. bracken spores, volatile organic compounds (VOCs), pollen); elemental threats through extremes of temperature or UV radiation.

[1] *well established*

All eight UK NEA Broad Habitats contribute to all three positive and the one negative class of health-related ecosystem services[2]. However, there is limited evidence to indicate that habitats with more biodiversity have a greater effect on health, even though they may encourage greater use[c]. The UK NEA Broad Habitat that has received the greatest empirical study in terms of its effects on health is Urban, mainly because the presence of greenspace is clearly a contrast to the majority of the built environment.

[2] *established but incomplete evidence*
[c] *likely*

Local greenspaces or nearby natural habitats are vital for all individuals[3]. There is a clear link between the amount of accessible greenspace and psychological well-being. The more frequent the visits to nearby green spaces, the lower the incidence of stress[c].

[3] *competing explanations*
[c] *likely*

Access to nature can encourage participation in physical activity (green exercise)[2]: individuals with easy access to nature are three times as likely to participate in physical activity and, therefore, are 40% less likely to become overweight or obese.

[2] *established but incomplete evidence*

Green exercise in all habitats results in significant improvements in both self-esteem and mood[1]; however, those habitats with open water produce a significantly larger degree of improvements in mental well-being[b]. The greatest effects for self-esteem and mood occurred within the first five minutes of activity. The improvement in both of these measures appears to be larger in green settings compared to exercising in areas lacking nature[1]. The greatest health outcomes are experienced by those with mental health problems, suggesting that exercise in ecosystems can be therapeutic for specific cohorts of people.

[1] *well established*
[b] *very likely*

Nature-dominated drives increase recovery from stress[2]. Commuters both recover quicker from stress and reduce the likelihood of experiencing future stresses after nature-dominated drives, compared to urban-dominated drives.

[2] *established but incomplete evidence*

There is a growing use of 'green care' in many contexts in the UK, including therapeutic horticulture, animal-assisted therapy, ecotherapy, green exercise therapies and wilderness therapy[2]. Green care produces health, social and educational benefits, but these have not yet been widely evaluated[3].

[2] *established but incomplete evidence*
[3] *competing explanations*

---

* Each Key Finding has been assigned a level of scientific certainty, based on a 4-box model and complemented, where possible, with a likelihood scale. Superscript numbers and letters indicate the uncertainty term assigned to each finding. Full details of each term and how they were assigned are presented in Appendix 23.1.

Recent experience using smartphones (*Mappiness*) has shown increased happiness levels are associated both with vigorous outdoor pursuits, such as sports, running and exercise, and walking and hiking, and with less energetic activities, such as gardening, birdwatching and nature-watching[2]. On average, respondents are happiest outdoors and least happy indoors, and report intermediate happiness levels when in a vehicle. All green or natural habitat types were linked with higher happiness levels than the continuous urban environment.

[2] *established but incomplete evidence*

Experiencing nature has been demonstrated to have a significant positive impact upon heart rate and blood pressure[2]. Green settings have a relaxing effect on autonomic functions, thus decreasing heart rate and blood pressure measurements. Green settings lead to a greater increase in parasympathetic nervous system activity and a greater decrease in sympathetic nervous activity than built environments[c].

[2] *established but incomplete evidence*
[c] *likely*

Humans depend on exposure to the sun for the synthesis of adequate amounts of vitamin D; a lack of vitamin D absorption, or vitamin D deficiency, is associated with a number of health problems[2]. Concerns over skin cancer, combined with a decrease in the opportunities for people to access green places, is reducing exposure to sunlight and, therefore, contributing to the development of chronic diseases[b]. Sensible exposure to sunlight for approximately 5–10 minutes three times per week helps to protect against the development of skin cancer and is highly likely to be beneficial to physical health.

[2] *established but incomplete evidence*
[b] *very likely*

Green settings offer opportunities for the building of social capital, which, in turn, benefits health[2]. The presence of trees and grass in urban areas also has a substantial effect upon social engagement and neighbourhood ties. Areas with trees and grass encourage individuals to utilise outdoor space and increases the likelihood of social interaction. Green places can also increase social engagement and interaction through conservation activities and initiatives. By protecting nature, individuals can obtain social contact and derive value from being in the presence of nature[b].

[2] *established but incomplete evidence*
[b] *very likely*

Ecosystems provide wild foods which can have a direct effect on health[1]. Today, wild foods act as a supplement to purchased foods, as opposed to providing the sole means of nutrition, and interest in wild foods is growing.

[1] *well established*

Ecosystems not only affect immediate health and well-being, but also affect health throughout life[2]. Healthy behaviours may be followed as a direct result of an individual's surroundings, although there is no guarantee of uptake. If 1% of the sedentary population moves to a healthy pathway, 1,063 lives and £1.44 billion will be saved each year. The earlier this shift occurs during life, the greater the impact upon health and society[3].

[2] *established but incomplete evidence*
[3] *competing explanations*

Contact with nature at any age can derive a whole number of benefits for physical and mental health, **contact with nature during youth can directly impact upon healthy adult behaviours[2].** Research indicates that the frequency of visits to green places during childhood significantly correlates to the number of visits during adulthood. A lack of experience of nature as a child may directly result in a lack of contact during adulthood.

[2] *established but incomplete evidence*

23.1 Ecosystems and Health

23.1.1 Overview

The term 'health' is generally taken to incorporate physical health, mental or emotional health, social health, spiritual health, lifestyle and functionality. The World Health Organization's definition of health is still the most widely cited and states that: "health is a state of complete physical, mental and social (individual) wellbeing, and not merely the absence of disease or infirmity" (WHO 1948). A universal definition of 'well-being' is not available, as many sources interpret it differently. However, well-being is generally considered in a broader context, and Defra (2007) has collaborated with other government departments and stakeholders to develop a shared understanding of the meaning of well-being within a policy context (Defra 2007; **Box 23.1**).

Ecosystems comprise a multifaceted set of relationships between the living organisms, resources (including plants, animals, fish, birds and microorganisms, water sources, soil, rocks, minerals and the local atmosphere) and habitats of an area, which function together as a unit. Ecosystem services support our health and well-being in a variety of ways. These include the provision of resources for basic survival, such as clean air, water and genetic resources for medicines, along with the provision of raw materials for industry and agriculture. However, ecosystem services also contribute to better mental and physical well-being by providing accessible urban and rural spaces for recreation and interaction with nature. Both observing natural ecosystems and participating in physical activity in greenspaces play an important role in positively influencing human health and well-being (**Table 23.1**).

It is well-known that regular physical activity improves both physical and mental health (CDC 1996; DH 2005a; Foresight 2007; Sandercock *et al.* 2010), and can improve the survival of the elderly and their quality of life (Lim & Taylor 2005). There is also increasing evidence to show that exposure to nature and greenspace positively affects health and well-being (Maas *et al.* 2006; Pretty *et al.* 2006; Van den Berg *et al.* 2007; Hansen-Ketchum *et al.* 2009; Barton & Pretty 2010). Thus 'green exercise'—physical activity undertaken in green places in the presence of nature—leads to positive health outcomes (**Table 23.1**). Green exercise has been shown to be more effective than comparable activities (which reflect the exercise component only) undertaken indoors (Thompson Coon *et al.* 2011). Participating in physical activity in green settings is associated with decreased feelings of tension, confusion, anger and depression, while exhibiting greater feelings of revitalisation (Thompson Coon *et al.* 2011). Outdoor experiences are rated as more restorative (Hug *et al.* 2009) and more effective in improving mood and vitality (Ryan *et al.* 2010). In comparison, indoor activity is associated with increased frustration, anxiety, anger and sadness (Teas *et al.* 2007). Research shows that health benefits arise in all urban and rural ecosystems tested, ranging from deep wilderness to domestic gardens and allotments, and including open countryside, forests, woodlands, national or country parks, nature or wildlife reserves, urban parks, grasslands, hills and valleys.

Existing research studies can be grouped into one of two prevailing categories. The first involves experimental research which has predominantly focused on stress reduction and attention restoration, often by inducing stress within the experimental setting. These types of studies often administer pre- and post-intervention measures to assess the immediate short-term health benefits of active or passive exposure to natural and urban ecosystems. They often take place within a controlled setting to limit confounding variables and attempt to isolate the ecosystem as the key variable influencing health measures. The second type comprises epidemiological research studies which primarily report correlations between ecosystem use and health benefits. However, the difficulty with this type of analysis is that it is very challenging to establish causality and often relationships can only be described, not explained. Although these associations regularly emerge from such experiments, determining causality is not straightforward and further research is required to establish any direct cause-effect relationships. Demonstrating a link between ecosystems and health is not the same as proving that exposure to ecosystems produces positive health outcomes. Yet evidence of causality would provide a powerful argument for a change in existing policies. Although interpretation of the causal structure of these relationships is challenging due to the complexity of the system, it remains an important finding in its own right.

Ecosystems provide three generic health benefits (**Figure 23.1**):

i) Direct positive effects
   a) Mental health (Kaplan 2001; Pretty *et al.* 2005; Pretty *et al.* 2007).
   b) Physical health (Laumann *et al.* 2003; Kampman *et al.* 2007; Pretty *et al.* 2007)

ii) Indirect positive effects
   a) Facilitating nature-based activity and social engagement (by providing locations for contact with nature, physical activity and social engagement), all of which positively influence health (Coley *et al.* 1997; Kuo *et al.* 1998; Ward Thompson 2002).
   b) Providing a catalyst for behavioural change in terms of encouraging the adoption of healthier lifestyles (improving life pathways, activity behaviour and the

---

Box 23.1 Shared understanding of well being. Source: Defra (2007).

"Well being is a positive physical, social and mental state; it is not just the absence of pain, discomfort and incapacity. It requires that basic needs are met, that individuals have a sense of purpose, that they feel able to achieve important personal goals and participate in society. It is enhanced by conditions that include supportive personal relationships, strong and inclusive communities, good health, financial and personal security, rewarding employment, and a healthy and attractive environment. Government's role is to enable people to have a fair access now and in the future to the social, economic and environmental resources needed to achieve wellbeing. An understanding of the effect of policies on the way people experience their lives is important for designing and prioritising them."

Table 23.1 The health and well-being benefits of contact with nature.

Health and well-being benefit	Evidence
Provides opportunities for 'green exercise' and associated improvements in self-esteem and/or mood	Hartig *et al.* (1991), Ulrich *et al.* (1991), Hartig *et al.* (1996), Hartig *et al.* (2003), Van den Berg *et al.* (2003), Morita *et al.* (2006), Pretty *et al.* (2005), Hine *et al.* (2007), Pretty *et al.* (2007), Barton *et al.* (2009), Barton & Pretty (2010), Bowler *et al.* (2010)
Reduces stress	Parsons (1991), Ulrich *et al.* (1991), Lohr *et al.* (1996), Rubinstein (1997), Parsons *et al.* (1998), Hartig *et al.* (2003), Laumann *et al.* (2003), Fredrickson & Branigan (2005)
Promotes ecological knowledge	Pilgrim *et al.* (2007), Pilgrim *et al.* (2008), Pretty (2011)
Fosters social bonds	Kawachi *et al.* (1997), Takano *et al.* (2002), Ward & Thompson (2002), Brugha *et al.* (2003), Barton *et al.* (2011), Pretty (2011)
Reduces levels of crime and violence	Kuo & Sullivan (2001a), Kuo & Sullivan (2001b)
Provides outdoor classrooms	Kaplan & Kaplan (1989), Kahn & Kellert (2002)
Delivers cognitive benefits	Berman *et al.* (2008), Hansen-Ketchum *et al.* (2009)
Influences behavioural choices	Kuo *et al.* (1998a), Maas *et al.* (2006), Mitchell & Popham (2008), Barton *et al.* (2011)

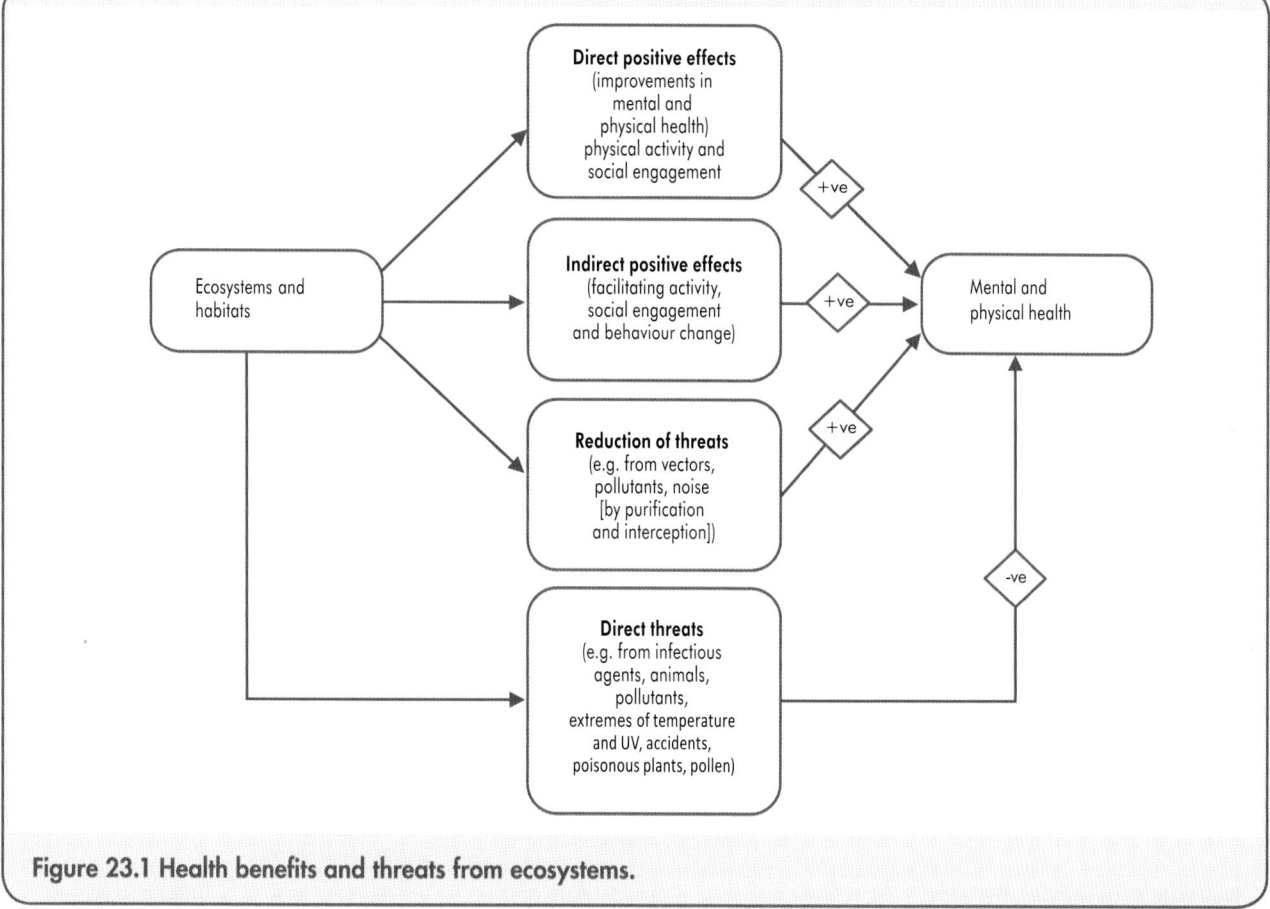

Figure 23.1 Health benefits and threats from ecosystems.

consumption of wild foods) (Wells & Lekies 2006; Pretty *et al.* 2009).

iii) Reducing the threats and incidence of pollution and disease vectors via a variety of purification and control functions such as local climate regulation, noise reduction and scavenging of air pollutants (Morecroft *et al.* 1998; Pitcairn *et al.* 1998; Bignal *et al.* 2004).

However, ecosystems can also be a direct source of threats to human health including: infectious agents (e.g. *Lyme borreliosis*, *Cryptosporidium* species, *Plasmodium* species that cause malaria); physical threats from animals, pollutants or contaminants from plants (e.g. bracken spores,

volatile organic compounds (VOCs), pollen); and elemental threats through extremes of temperature or UV radiation (Frumkin *et al.* 2004).

Health outcomes depend on the types of ecosystems and the services they provide, as well as the choices people have and decisions they make. If individuals do not engage with the natural world, either by observation or undertaking physical activity in green settings (including urban greenspace), then they will not derive the specific mental or physical health benefits nature can provide. Such choices are affected by location of dwelling, proximity of, and access to, nature, and individual choices and environmental behaviours (DH & DCSF 2009).

Access to nature often varies according to cohort demographics. For example, wealthier individuals are able to access certain places more readily because they own a car; it is common for the most biodiverse ecosystems not to be served by public transport, which excludes the poorest individuals and other minority groups. Thus, access is dependent on the socioeconomic characteristics of the potential beneficiaries and not solely on the ecosystem qualities. Yet having access to nearby greenspace can eradicate the health inequality levels in areas of deprivation (Mitchell & Popham 2008). This highlights the importance of providing health-promoting, accessible greenspaces to reduce socioeconomic health inequalities.

Behaviours can also influence correlative relationships identified between ecosystem exposure and health outcomes, which contributes to the challenge of interpreting the causal structure. In effect, health outcomes of ecosystems are not independent of people's demographics, choices and behaviours. Health benefits are, therefore, a function of the ecosystem type, ease of access to nature and frequency of use of green places.

23.1.2 Health Benefits According to UK NEA Broad Habitats

All eight UK NEA Broad Habitats contribute to all three positive and the one negative class of health-related ecosystem services. However, there is limited empirical evidence to indicate that habitats with more biodiversity have a greater effect on health (Fuller *et al.* 2007). One UK study has shown positive associations between urban greenspace species richness and improved well-being (Fuller *et al.* 2007), although the authors acknowledge the challenge of deciphering causality. There is also empirical evidence to indicate that, after rehabilitation, Urban greenspace attracts more users, providing a greater health service (Barton *et al.* 2009; Barton & Pretty 2010). In a similar way, it could be hypothesised that habitats with greater biodiversity or particular rare or distinctive species (e.g. nature reserves, Sites of Special Scientific Interest (SSSIs)) may attract more visitors and, therefore, deliver a greater aggregate health benefit; this hypothesis would fit with the findings of Fuller *et al.* (2007).

The UK NEA Broad Habitats provide potential places for people to engage in physical activity (green exercise) and social interaction. If these habitats are used, they would have positive direct effects on health, and reduce threats from disease vectors, pollutants and noise; but they could potentially provide a variety of direct threats to health (**Table 23.2**). The provision of positive health benefits is dependent not only on the intrinsic biological characteristics of the ecosystems, but also on location. An ecosystem which is close to a densely populated area will provide many more health benefits than a physically identical ecosystem in a remote area, because it is accessible to more individuals.

Table 23.2 Health-related ecosystem services (positive and negative) from the eight UK NEA Broad Habitats.

UK NEA Broad Habitats	Health-related ecosystem services			
	Provide places for physical activity and social engagement	Direct positive effects on health	Reduce threats from disease vectors, pollutants, noise	Direct threats to health
Mountains, Moorlands and Heaths	Considerable provision; access generally good	Considerable provision; wild foods	Purification of water and air	Bracken, accidents, temperature extremes
Semi-natural Grasslands	Considerable provision; access often limited	Considerable provision; wild foods	Purification of water and air, flood regulation	Zoonoses and vectors, livestock accidents
Enclosed Farmland	Limited access except by footpaths and bridleways	Considerable provision; wild foods from hedgerows	Purification of water and air, flood regulation	Zoonoses and vectors, livestock accidents
Woodlands	Considerable provision; access generally good	Considerable provision; wild foods	Purification of water and air, flood regulation, climate regulation (shading and cooling)	Pollen-causing asthma, VOCs, Lyme disease
Freshwaters – Openwaters, Wetlands and Floodplains	Considerable provision; access generally good	Considerable provision; wild foods from fishing	Purification of water and air	Waterborne diseases (*Cryptosporidium*, Weil's disease), red tides from eutrophication, accidents
Urban*	Considerable provision; access limited	Provision where access is available from homes and workplaces; foods from domestic gardens and allotments	Purification of water and air, interception of noise and water, reduction of heat island effect	Accidents
Coastal Margins	Considerable provision; access generally good	Considerable provision; wild foods (birds, shellfish, samphire)	Sea defences	Red tides, accidents
Marine	Limited access	Limited provision (as limited access)	Limited	Accidents

*Urban greenspace includes, for example, parks, gardens, allotments, street trees; does not include the built environment.

Therefore, the aggregate health benefit is not solely reliant on type of habitat, but ease of access.

The UK NEA Broad Habitat that has received the greatest empirical study in terms of its effects on health is Urban, mainly because the presence of nature and greenspace is clearly a contrast to most of the built environment. In addition, the majority of people reside in urban areas and are, therefore, more able to access Urban habitats. Some 3.5% of England is urbanised (428,000 hectares), and these environments contain 52,000 hectares of greenspace in the form of parks, allotments, city and community farms, cemeteries, golf courses, nature reserves, street trees and green roofs (not counting private gardens) (CABE 2010).

23.2 Direct Positive Effects on Mental Health

23.2.1 Observing Ecosystems

The importance of observing nature is becoming increasingly recognised. Viewing nature through a window can help to increase recovery from mental fatigue and improve mental well-being (Kaplan 1992; Maller et al. 2006). Natural views in hospitals help to increase recovery from illness (Diette et al. 2003), while access to nature in the workplace is associated with lower levels of perceived stress and greater job satisfaction (Kaplan & Kaplan 1989; Maller et al. 2006; Hine et al. 2007). Furthermore, research suggests that prison inmates whose cell has a view of nature have a lower frequency of stress and psychological symptoms when compared to those inmates who lack such a view (Moore 1982). The view from the home is also known to be important (Kaplan 2001; Taylor et al. 2002). For children, green views have a positive effect on cognitive thinking and concentration, while also aiding self-discipline (Taylor et al. 2002).

The positive effect of viewing nature even occurs if the view is not of living nature; pictures of nature can also elicit improvements in mental well-being (Pretty et al. 2005). Several studies have compared the effects on mental well-being of viewing photographic scenes of both nature and built environments. The results suggested that the natural scenes, especially those depicting water, had a more positive effect on measures of emotional well-being such as sadness and happiness, than viewing built environments (Ulrich 1981). Indeed, viewing built environments led to a decline in attention and interest. In 2005, Pretty et al. (2005) examined the mental health benefits of viewing urban and rural scenes while performing physical activity. Participants took part in five exercise conditions: exercise only; exercise while viewing unpleasant urban scenes (cityscapes lacking greenspaces); exercise while viewing pleasant urban scenes (buildings with surrounding nature); exercise while viewing pleasant rural scenes; and exercise while viewing unpleasant rural scenes (landscapes spoilt with rubbish, abandoned cars, or pipes carrying effluents). The results indicated that all exercise conditions led to a significant improvement in self-esteem;

however, the unpleasant conditions reduced the positive effects of the physical activity, while the pleasant conditions led to the greatest improvements. The improvement for both urban and rural scenes was comparable, highlighting the importance of urban nature. Mood was also significantly affected by viewing the different scenes. Both the urban and rural pleasant conditions led to significant reductions in fatigue and tension, and a significant increase in vigour. Pleasant urban scenes also led to a significant decrease in depression. Both urban and rural conditions can improve mental well-being; however, those scenes that depict threats to the natural environment lead to a reduction in self-esteem and mood (Pretty et al. 2005).

Parsons et al (1998) reported similar results when reviewing the literature on commuter stress in car drivers and the effect of the surrounding environment. The evidence indicated that commuters who participated in nature-dominated drives experienced quicker recovery from stress, and a reduction in the likelihood of experiencing subsequent stress, than those who took part in an urban-dominated drive (Parsons et al. 1998).

23.2.2 Contact with Nearby Nature

Local greenspace and accessible nature are vital for all individuals, whether it is an urban park or an area of rural wilderness (Barton & Pretty 2010). Being in the presence of 'nearby nature' (whether or not it is incidental to some other activity, such as walking to work or sitting on a bench) plays an important role in human well-being (Pretty et al. 2005; Hine et al. 2007). Research suggests that there is a link between the amount of accessible greenspace and psychological well-being (Takano et al. 2002; De Vries et al. 2003), as contact with nature can help individuals to recover from stress, protect them from further stress and improve concentration (Maller et al. 2002). Furthermore, the more frequent the visits to nearby natural spaces, the lower the incidence of stress (Grahn & Stigsdotter 2003).

Nearby nature is also important for the mental well-being of children (Kaplan & Kaplan 1989; Thomas & Thompson 2004; Ward Thompson et al. 2008). Evidence suggests that the well-being of children is closely linked to their ability to access natural settings close to their homes (Thomas & Thompson 2004). Wells (2000) conducted a longitudinal study with children of low-income urban families and assessed the effects of nature on their cognitive functioning. When the families were relocated to houses with more nearby nature they had higher levels of cognitive functioning and their ability to direct attention continued for several months after moving. However, these findings should be treated with caution because it could be argued that these types of families were able to select these types of preferred homes. Therefore, cause and effect can be difficult to disentangle and decipher (Wells 2000).

In addition, Wells and Evans (2003) found that children with easy access to nature were more able to cope with stressful life events and were generally less stressed individuals than those in urban habitats lacking greenspace (Wells & Evans 2003). However, the issue of cause and effect is still indeterminate as it remains unclear whether having contact with nature aids the development of stress-coping mechanisms which are used in later life; whether nearby nature provides the opportunity for stress recovery and replenishes attentional fatigue; whether greenspace provides the opportunity to play with other children (social contact); or whether it is a combination of many factors. However, access to nature during youth is of great importance, particularly as childhood experiences of nature predict contact during adulthood (Ward Thompson *et al.* 2008).

In health care settings, gardens are of particular importance to mental well-being (Ulrich 2002). Gardens in hospitals have a number of positive effects on individuals by helping them to feel more relaxed and able to cope, reducing stress, and improving mood (Cooper-Marcus & Barnes 1995; Whitehouse *et al.* 2001). Even short visits of five minutes in duration to these gardens have been demonstrated to have a positive effect on the mental well-being of patients (Cooper-Marcus & Barnes 1995; Whitehouse *et al.* 2001).

23.2.3 Green Exercise

Natural ecosystems can provide an environmental setting for green exercise (Pretty *et al.* 2005; Bowler *et al.* 2010). Both physical activity and exposure to nature have separately been demonstrated to provide benefits for mental well-being, thus, by combining the two, green exercise has synergistic health benefits (Pretty *et al.* 2003; Pretty *et al.* 2005; Pretty *et al.* 2007; Hine *et al.* 2007; Peacock *et al.* 2007; Barton *et al.* 2009; Barton & Pretty 2010; Barton *et al.* 2011). For instance, walking in greenspaces is more effective at enhancing self-esteem and mood than walking indoors, suggesting a greater amalgamated health benefit than either component provides alone (Mind 2007; Peacock *et al.* 2007).

Pretty *et al.* (2007) examined the psychological health benefits of participating in ten different green exercise activities (including walking, fishing, horse riding, cycling and conservation activities) in four different regions in the UK. The results of the study found that green exercise led to significant improvements in self-esteem and mood, especially in the mood subscales of anger, confusion, depression and tension (Pretty *et al.* 2007). Furthermore, improvements in self-esteem and mood were not affected by the type, intensity or duration of the exercise, or by the different regions themselves (Pretty *et al.* 2007).

Barton *et al.* (2009) examined the mental well-being effects of walking in four UK national heritage sites (Dunwich Heath, Suffolk; Flatford Mill, Suffolk; Hatfield Forest, Essex; Wicken Fen, Cambridgeshire). In line with the results produced by Pretty *et al.* (2007), both self-esteem and overall mood were significantly enhanced as a result of participating in the green exercise (Barton *et al.* 2009). Furthermore, feelings of anger, confusion, depression, fatigue and tension were reduced as a result of the green exercise, while feelings of vigour were increased (Barton *et al.* 2009). However, in contrast to the results of Pretty *et al.* (2007), the study suggested that there was a relationship between the duration of the green exercise and the degree of improvements in mental well-being: participants walking for the longest period of time displayed the greatest improvements in mood (Barton *et al.* 2009).

Barton and Pretty (2010) undertook a meta-analysis on the mental health outcomes of many different types of green exercise in different habitats, for varying lengths of time, and by different age cohorts and gender. Habitats included woodland, forests, watersides, urban green areas, farmland and natural habitats, and the activities included walking, horse riding, sailing and gardening (Barton & Pretty 2010). Green exercise in all habitats resulted in significant improvements in both self-esteem and mood; however, those habitats with open water produced a significantly larger degree of improvement in mental well-being. Furthermore, self-esteem and mood was most improved during the first five minutes of activity, but this effect gradually deteriorated if the exercise lasted between 10 minutes and half a day (Barton & Pretty 2010). Nevertheless, the effectiveness of the green exercise in improving mental well-being increased again if the activity lasted for a whole day. The results are in contrast to those produced by Pretty *et al.* (2007), implying a need for further research in this area.

The meta-analysis also revealed that the effectiveness of the green exercise was influenced by its intensity (Barton & Pretty 2010). For self-esteem, light intensity exercise produced the greatest improvements, with the effects deteriorating as the intensity of exercise increased; a similar response was noted for mood. However, the lowest effect on either measure was seen during moderate exercise; the effects increasing once again for vigorous exercise.

With regards to the different age cohorts of participants, the meta-analysis revealed that the fewest health outcomes occurred for the elderly, while the greatest health outcomes were experienced by those with mental health problems, suggesting that exercise in ecosystems can be therapeutic for specific cohorts of people (Barton & Pretty 2010).

Essentially, the evidence implies that there is a synergistic health benefit from exercising in areas containing nature (including urban greenspace) compared to exercising in urban areas lacking nature or indoor environments. All types of habitat are beneficial, from experiences in deep wilderness to gardening in local allotments. The optimal dose of green exercise may be dependent on many variables, but it is clear that both urban and countryside habitats can provide the ideal setting to facilitate activity and afford greater health benefits.

23.2.4 Green Care

'Green care' is an inclusive term for many complex and diverse nature-based interventions that use nature and the natural environment as a framework in which to create health and well-being benefits for vulnerable groups of people (Sempik *et al.* 2010). Green care has emerged from the idea that contact with nature could be effective in therapeutic applications (**Figure 23.2**) (Pretty 2006; Peacock *et al.* 2007; Hine *et al.* 2008a). In the UK, there is a growing movement towards green care in many contexts ranging from social and therapeutic horticulture, animal-assisted interventions, ecotherapy, green exercise therapies as a treatment option, and care farming (Sempik *et al.* 2003; Sempik 2007; Hine *et al.* 2008a). Green care is different to green exercise in that it is used as a therapy or intervention for specific groups, such as psychiatric patients, people with learning disabilities, disaffected youth and several other at-risk populations, while green exercise is more of a therapeutic experience (Pretty

2006; Hine *et al.* 2008a). The aim of green care is to produce health, social and educational benefits (Hine *et al.* 2008a).

There are six key types of green care options:

i) **Social and therapeutic horticulture** is defined as "participation by a range of vulnerable people in groups and communities whose activities are centred around horticulture and gardening. It is distinct from domestic gardening because it operates in an organised and formalised environment" (Sempik *et al.* 2003; Samson & Pretty 2005). Social and therapeutic horticulture has been demonstrated to promote psychological well-being and has also been utilised in the treatment of disease.

ii) **Animal-assisted interventions** involve the use of animals in the rehabilitation and social care of humans (Kruger & Serpell 2006; Bokker 2006). Companion animals can also play a therapeutic role for people with psychiatric disorders, physically ill people, those with emotional disorders, the elderly and children (Fine 2006). Like human relationships, animal-human relationships can help to buffer against stress responses and illness (McNicholas & Collis 2006).

iii) **Care farming** is defined as the therapeutic use of agricultural landscapes and farming practices (Hassink 2003; NCFI 2011) and its use is increasing both within the UK and Europe (Hine *et al.* 2008a). On care farms, components of either the whole or part of the farm environment are utilised to provide health, social or educational care services through a supervised, structured programme of farming-related activities. Results from studies into the mental health benefits of

these care farms within the UK have found that their use can result in significant improvements in both self-esteem and mood, with significant alterations in all mood factors (Pretty 2006; Peacock *et al.* 2007; Hine *et al.* 2008a).

iv) **Green exercise therapy** is defined as facilitated green exercise activities. Evidence suggests that these activities may have therapeutic applications (Pretty *et al.* 2007; Peacock *et al.* 2007); for example, they may provide an effective treatment for mild to moderate depression through reconnection with nature and the positive mental health benefits that come hand in hand with this (Samson & Pretty 2005; Pretty *et al.* 2007). Currently, approximately 21% of general practitioners use exercise as a therapy in the treatment of mental disorders (Mental Health Foundation 2009). Green exercise therapy may be even more effective than exercise alone and could, therefore, be utilised as an alternative or complimentary treatment therapy to antidepressants (Samson & Pretty 2005).

v) **Ecotherapy** encompasses all nature-based methods aimed at the re-establishment of human and ecosystem reciprocal well-being (Sempik *et al.* 2010). Contact with natural ecosystems enhances physical, psychological and social health for people, communities and ecosystems. Ecotherapy encourages reconnection with nature and therefore facilitates behavioural and social changes which can directly influence mental health and well-being (Burls 2008).

vi) **Wilderness therapy** is described as an "experiential programme (e.g. Outward Bound) that takes place in wilderness or a remote outdoor setting" (Conner 2007). It

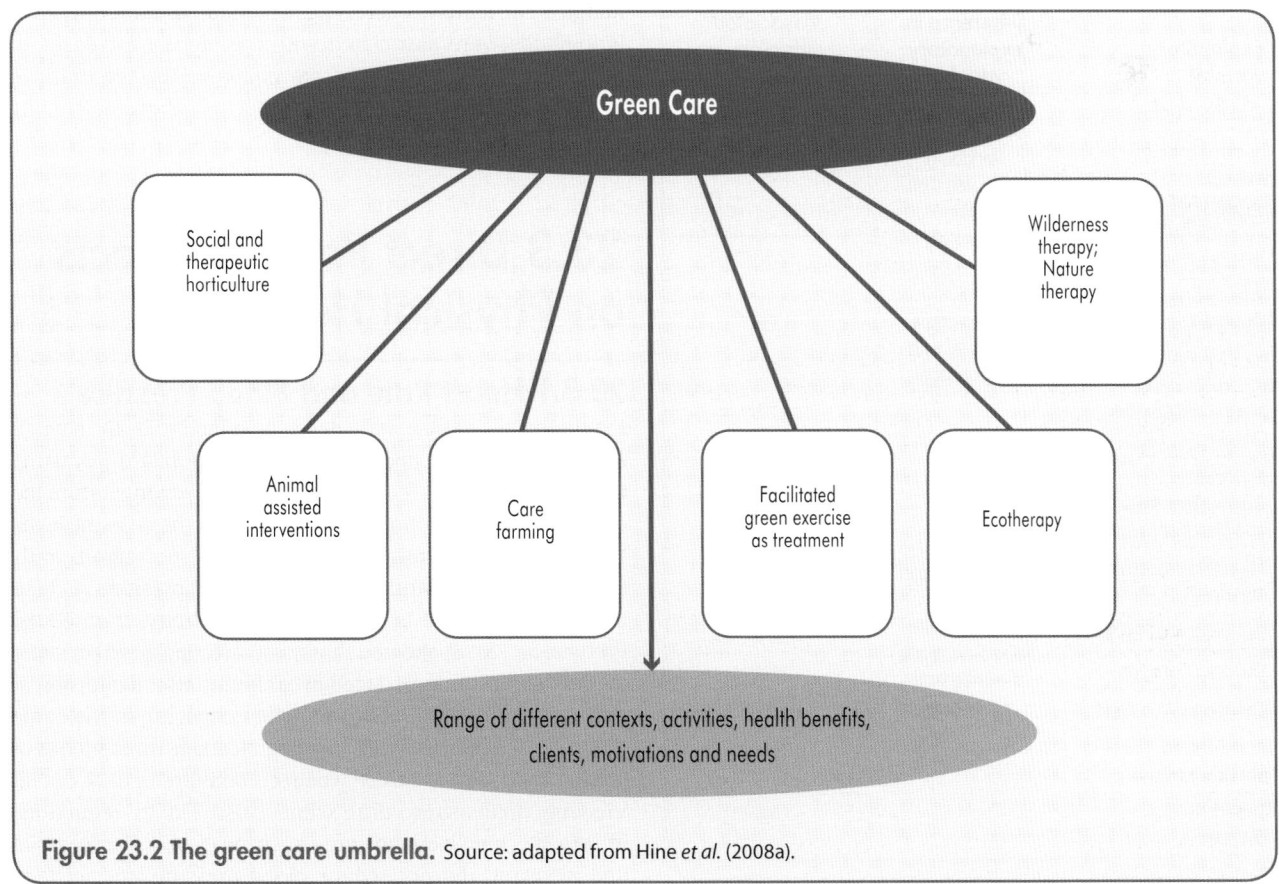

Figure 23.2 The green care umbrella. Source: adapted from Hine *et al.* (2008a).

has been widely used in the USA for many years, but is a relatively new concept in the UK and is most commonly used for adolescents with behavioural problems (Pretty *et al.* 2009) and adults with mental health issues (Hine *et al.* 2011). Programmes provide healthy exercise and diets, group and individual therapy sessions, and separate participants from daily negative influences, placing them in a safe outdoor environment. Evidence regarding the benefits of wilderness therapy has indicated that it can facilitate behaviour change, address problem behaviours, improve mental well-being and self-esteem, reduce Body Mass Index (BMI) and provide opportunities for emotional growth (Moote & Wadarski 1997; Hans 2000; Russell & Phillips-Miller 2002; Samson & Pretty 2005; Russell 2006; Conner 2007; Hine *et al.* 2009; Bharucha & Pretty 2010; Godfray *et al.* 2010; Hine *et al.* 2011).

23.2.5 *Mappiness* Research for Well-being

Subjective well-being is related to happiness and has become increasingly important to economists (Layard 2005; Dolan *et al.* 2008; Frey 2008; Mourato & MacKerron 2010; MacKerron & Mourato 2011). The established influences on happiness include income (positively correlated with subjective well-being); the incomes of others, rivalry (negative) and/or ambition (positive); an individual's own lagged income;

and reduced responses due to habituation (negative). Further factors include unemployment; separation, divorce and widowhood; and poor health (all negatively correlated). Social capital indicators and relational goods are important, such as membership of interest groups or friendly relations with neighbours; trust; and belief in a god (all positively correlated). Important environmental quality parameters include climate, noise, air quality, and access to greenspaces. Mourato and MacKerron (2010) investigated well-being in the UK by using a satellite geo-located, large-scale, smartphone-based Experience Sampling Method study (*Mappiness*) to explore links between instantaneous mood states and the immediate environment.

On average, respondents were happiest outdoors and least happy indoors, and reported intermediate happiness levels when in a vehicle. Increased happiness levels were associated both with vigorous outdoor pursuits, such as 'sports, running and exercise' and 'walking and hiking', and with less energetic activities such as 'gardening' and 'birdwatching and nature watching'. High energy pursuits, such as sports, running and exercise, were associated with a 6% increase in happiness, and more contemplative activities, such as nature watching, were linked with a 3% increase in happiness. Respondents were happiest when neither at home nor at work, least happy at work, and reported intermediate happiness when at home. When outdoors, higher happiness levels were associated with higher temperatures, while rain and wind are linked to lower happiness. Importantly, there was a clear link between being outdoors in particular habitat types and happiness levels. Almost all habitat types (with the exception of inland bare ground) were linked with higher happiness levels than urban habitats. Marine and Coastal Margins, Mountains, Moorlands and Heaths, and Coniferous Woodlands were associated with the highest increases in happiness. The key findings from *Mappiness* are summarised in **Table 23.3**.

Table 23.3 Summary findings from an analysis of subjective well-being (Mappiness). Significance: *** p < 0.001, ** p < 0.01, * p < 0.05, + p < 0.1. Source: MacKerron & Mourato *et al.* (2011); Mourato & MacKerron *et al.* (2010).

Explanatory variable	Difference in explanatory variable	Associated difference in happiness response
Walking, hiking	Not doing compared with doing this activity	+2.6%***
Sports, running, exercise		+6.1%***
Gardening, allotment		+2.5%***
Birdwatching, nature watching		+2.9%**
Outdoors	Being indoors compared with being outdoors	+1.4%***
Marine and Coastal Margins	Being outdoors in 'continuous urban' land cover compared with being outdoors in the listed land cover type	+5.2%***
Freshwater – Openwaters, Wetlands and Floodplains		+1.7%+
Mountains, Moorlands and Heaths		+4.0%**
Semi-natural Grasslands		+1.2%**
Enclosed Farmland		+2.1%***
Coniferous Woodland		+4.5%***
Broad-leaved/Mixed Woodland		+2.3%***
Suburban/rural developed		+1.0%***

23.3 Direct Positive Effects on Physical Health

23.3.1 Heart Rate and Blood Pressure

Experiencing nature has been demonstrated to have a significant impact upon heart rate and blood pressure. Laumann *et al.* (2003) demonstrated that viewing nature led to a significant reduction in heart rate from the baseline level. However, viewing urban landscapes did not significantly reduce the participants' heart rate. Blood pressure is also reduced as a result of viewing nature (Pretty *et al.* 2005). Pretty *et al.* (2005) showed that mean arterial blood pressure (MABP) significantly reduced five minutes after exercising at a moderate intensity. However, when engaging in the same intensity of exercise while viewing pleasant rural scenes, a greater reduction in MABP was recorded (Pretty *et al.* 2005). Viewing unpleasant rural scenes also led to reductions in MABP; but viewing urban scenes, both unpleasant and pleasant, did not reduce blood pressure and, in fact, increased the measurements relative to the exercise-only control. Thus, viewing nature can have a relaxing effect on autonomic functions (the unconscious regulation of internal bodily activity), decreasing heart rate and blood pressure measurements (Laumann *et al.* 2003; Pretty *et al.* 2005). Spending time in green settings leads to a greater increase in parasympathetic nervous system activity (the slowing of autonomic functions at rest) and greater decrease in sympathetic nervous activity (accelerated functions associated with the fight-or-flight response) than spending time in urban settings (Li *et al.* 2007).

23.3.2 Encouraging Physical Activity

Nature can encourage participation in physical activity: individuals with easy access to nature are three times more likely to participate in physical activity than those with poorer access and, therefore, 40% less likely to become overweight or obese (Wells *et al.* 2007; Bowler *et al.* 2010). The issue of cause and effect is difficult to identify as individuals may choose to live near habitats which facilitate activity if they enjoy exercising in greenspaces. Therefore, this cohort may engage in more activities simply because they chose to reside close to that type of habitat, rather than adopting new active behaviours because greenspace became accessible. However, by encouraging physical activity through participation in green exercise, such habitats can provide a whole number of physical health outcomes.

Physical activity can reduce the risk of developing Cardiovascular Disease and the associated risk factors, such as hypertension, high blood lipids and elevated blood pressure, and can also reduce the likelihood of developing Type 2 Diabetes (Blair & Connelly 1996; Biddle *et al.* 2004; DH 2004). Furthermore, individuals who regularly partake in green exercise are less likely to become overweight or obese, and may also have better bone health and a reduced risk of developing Osteoporosis (Biddle *et al.* 2004; DH 2005b). Thus, the natural environment supports physical health through the provision of opportunities for exercise (Wells *et al.* 2007).

Urban habitats are less encouraging of physical activity than other habitat types and often restrict access to nature (Wells *et al.* 2007). Urban design and planning sometimes reduces opportunities for individuals to participate in physical activity, contributing to large increases in physical inactivity and the prevalence of overweight and obese individuals (Wells *et al.* 2007). Nonetheless, urban parks promote healthy living for residents of Urban habitats by encouraging participation in green exercise activities such as walking and cycling (Ross 2000; Berrigan & Troiano 2002; Craig *et al.* 2002; Handy *et al.* 2002; Parks *et al.* 2003). In the UK, urban parks attract 2.5 billion day visits per year (DLTR 2002), so as urban sprawl continues, the importance of access to nearby nature is paramount. Urban life exposes people to many stressors, such as traffic noise, crowding and fear of crime (Van den Berg *et al.* 2007), and often access to nature and greenspace is limited or of poor quality. The type of nature close to where people live and work, in the form of parks, gardens, tree-lined streets, communal squares and allotments, is strategically important for the quality of life of urban dwellers and for the sustainability of towns and cities

(Chiesura 2004). Hence, individuals need easy access to nature and greenspace, as these encourage physical activity and result in a number of benefits for physical health.

23.3.3 Vitamin D and Latitude

Humans depend on exposure to the sun for the synthesis of adequate amounts of vitamin D. Some 90% of the human requirement for vitamin D comes from the sun (Hollick 2005; Kampman *et al.* 2007). Ultraviolet B (UVB) radiation is absorbed by dehydrocholestrol in the skin, which is transformed and further converted to vitamin D3. This is then metabolised by the liver to its active form (Hollick 2005). Outdoor contact with nature allows humans to absorb the vitamin D required in the human body. However, a lack of vitamin D absorption, or vitamin D deficiency, is associated with a number of health problems.

Vitamin D deficiency can lead to poor bone health, increasing the likelihood of the development of diseases such as Osteoporosis and Osteomalacia. Vitamin D deficiency has also been associated with the development of Rickets in children. Furthermore, a lack of vitamin D can lead to cancer cell growth, an increased risk of heart failure and Cardiovascular Disease, Arthritis and Type 1 Diabetes (Hollick 2005; Kampman *et al.* 2007). In a study following children from age 1 into adulthood, those individuals who received adequate vitamin D decreased their risk of developing diabetes by 80% (Hollick 2005; Kampman *et al.* 2007).

Latitude can also have an impact upon physical health. Areas at high latitudes have been associated with a reduced risk of developing Multiple Sclerosis and also a reduced risk of developing cancer (Hollick 2004; Kampman *et al.* 2007). However, Norway appears to be an exception to this finding. This is likely to be the result of increased summer outdoor activities in childhood, which have been demonstrated to protect against Multiple Sclerosis (Hollick 2004). Contact with nature and sunlight are essential to physical health. However, concerns over skin cancer, combined with the reduction in the opportunity to access nature, are reducing exposure to sunlight and contributing to the development of chronic diseases (Hollick 2004)(Hollick, 2004). Sensible exposure to sunlight for approximately 5–10 minutes three times per week helps to protect against the development of skin cancer and is highly likely to be beneficial to physical health (Hollick 2004).

23.3.4 Recovery from Illness and Immunity

Access to nature can also aid recovery from illness (Kaplan 2001). A study revealed that hospital patients with a view of nature from their hospital room recovered from surgery and illness faster than those who had a view of a built environment (Maller *et al.* 2006). They spent less time in hospital and nursing staff also reported fewer negative comments in their medical records. Furthermore, those patients with a view of nature required fewer painkillers for their illness and had less post-operative complications. A similar pattern was noted in prison environments: those inmates with a natural view from their cell reported a lower frequency of stress symptoms, including digestive illness and headaches, and had an overall reduced number of sick calls (Moore 1982; West 1985). Access to nature can also help to reduce the requirements of the health care services (Kaplan 2001).

There is evidence to suggest that some habitats may help to enhance immunity to disease (Li *et al.* 2007; Park *et al.* 2010). Spending time in a forest environment has been demonstrated to increase natural killer T cell activity, a vital component in the rejection of tumours and cells infected by viruses. Contact with forest environments also increase levels of perforin, a substance found in the presence of natural killer T cells, and granulysin which destroys infected body cells (Park *et al.* 2010). Additionally, studies have noted an increase in the induction of intracellular anti-cancer proteins in subjects that spend time in forest environments (Park *et al.* 2010).

23.4 Indirect Positive Effects

23.4.1 Facilitating Nature-based Activity

Access to nature, via any of the three levels of engagement (view from the window; functional engagement; active participation), can help to facilitate nature-based activity. If nature is within close proximity, there are health benefits from simply viewing it through a window (Ulrich 1984; Pretty *et al.* 2005), being in its presence (De Vries *et al.* 2003), or actively taking part in green activities and wilderness trails (Davis-Berman & Berman 1989; Hartig *et al.* 2003; Pretty *et al.* 2007). Research suggests that individuals who are readily able to access greenspaces, whether they are vast areas of wilderness or urban parks, are three times more likely to participate in physical activity than those that cannot access it so easily (Wells *et al.* 2007; Bowler *et al.* 2010). Furthermore, the nature-based activities associated with the two latter levels of engagement can, in turn, lead to a number of health benefits. Activities such as walking, gardening, fishing, hunting and horse riding not only provide those health benefits associated with contact with nature, but also provide benefits through participation in physical activity (Pretty *et al.* 2007; Barton & Pretty 2010).

23.4.2 Facilitating Social Engagement

High levels of social capital can have a direct effect on markers of individual and community well-being (Kawachi *et al.* 1997; Pretty & Ward 2001; Wood & Giles-Corti 2008). Social capital captures the idea that social interaction and social norms are an important part of the basis for sustainable livelihoods and communities (Pretty & Ward 2001). Levels of social interaction can be directly influenced by the availability of greenspace (Coley *et al.* 1997; Ward Thompson 2002). Modern Urban habitats lacking greenspace tend to restrict social contact as individuals are not attracted to their surrounding environments so tend to stay indoors, away from others (Coley *et al.* 1997). However, urban greenspace, in the form of parks, streets and allotments, can facilitate social contact and give rise to stronger neighbourhood ties (Coley *et al.* 1997; Kuo *et al.* 1998; Ward Thompson 2002). Evidence suggests that the presence of trees and grass in urban areas encourages individuals to utilise outdoor space, increasing the likelihood of social interaction. The higher the number of trees and vegetation in an area, the more people that use it and the more time they spend within it (Coley *et al.* 1997; Kuo *et al.* 1998). Urban parks give individuals the opportunity to meet new people—an opportunity that is not so readily provided elsewhere in modern society (Ward Thompson 2002).

Social engagement and interaction can also be increased through participation in outdoor conservation and development activities and initiatives (Pretty & Smith 2004; Parliamentary Office of Science and Technology 2007). These activities can connect people through groups and networks, and build stronger communities, particularly in Urban areas where greenspace such as woodlands are generally declining (Pretty & Smith 2004; Parliamentary Office of Science and Technology 2007). By protecting nature, individuals can obtain social contact and derive value from being in the presence of nature (Pretty & Smith 2004).

23.4.3 Providing Wild Foods

Ecosystems provide wild foods that can have a direct effect on health. For many thousands of generations, farmers, hunter-gatherers, fishers and foragers have utilised, managed and amended wild foods from their surrounding habitats in order to provide a source of nutrition for themselves and others (WHO 2005; Bharucha & Pretty 2010). Historically, wild plants and food were the sole source of nutrition for hunter-gather and forager cultures, and so, have long-standing cultural value as well.

Today, wild foods help to link people to local habitats and increase social engagement, thus impacting upon health. The Food and Agriculture Organization of the United Nations estimates that one billion people use wild foods in their diet at some time during a typical year (Aberoumand, 2009). In many parts of the world, wild foods remain important to health: the mean use of wild foods by agricultural and forager communities in 22 countries of Asia and Africa (36 studies) is 90–100 species per location (Bharucha & Pretty 2010). In the UK, however, they now tend to be no more than a supplement to purchased foods (Bharucha & Pretty 2010). Yet older generations can still recall when the wild harvest had a critical nutritional value and products ranged from autumn berries and nuts, to rabbits, wildfowl and birds' eggs.

The use of wild foods and the prevalence of traditional ecological knowledge appear to be declining in industrialised countries (Mabey 1996; Pilgrim *et al.* 2008). In New Zealand, however, more than 60 species are still in common use, largely because of traditions of Māori groups. These include muttonbird (sooty shearwater, *Puffinus griseus*), seagull, possum, rabbit, deer, wild pig, goat, salmon, trout, eel, watercress, sea lettuce, gorse and many berries (Newman & Moller 2005; Stephenson & Moller 2009). In the Wallis Lake catchment, Australia, 88 species are in general use (Gray *et al.* 2005). In the swamps of Louisiana, USA, large numbers of people still hunt and fish regularly for their own food (Roland 2006). With regards to Europe, Pieroni (1999) suggests that the geographical isolation of the upper Serchio Valley in Tuscany has "permitted a rich popular knowledge to be maintained", and, as a result, gastronomic traditions have survived from pre-Roman times: 120 species still form a well-preserved pharmacopoeia of food and medicine (Pieroni 1999). In other regions of continental Europe, wild food use persists: 123 edible species are still used in Spain (Tardio *et al.* 2003); and in many Mediterranean countries, wild foods are still prevalent enough to be considered an important part of local diets (Leonti *et al.* 2006).

In the UK, wild foods remain an important cultural link to certain habitats. Wildfowling was very common in coastal communities, for example, until the mid-20th Century (Tennyson 1949; Wentworth Day 1949, 1950), and duck decoys were an important source of both food and income during the 18th Century (Heaton 2001). At their height, there were 29 duck decoys in Essex, 14 in Suffolk and 26 in Norfolk, and each could harvest 5,000 birds per year. The last working duck decoy in East Anglia closed in 1968. Yet wildfowling remains an important activity and food for small groups in coastal areas (Pretty 2011). In some communities, the wild harvest remains a significant cultural event. For example, for generations men from the fishing village of Ness on the Isle of Lewis, Scotland, have travelled 60 km each August to the island of Sula Sgier to gather young gannets (*Morus bassanus*) (Pretty 2011). Some 2,000 of these *guga* (Gaelic for young gannet) are collected from nests on the rock faces and killed; they are later salted and stored for local consumption as the meat is a highly valued. There is no evidence that the gathering has any adverse effect on the overall population of the gannet colony.

There is some evidence that wild foods are now receiving greater prominence in butchers and supermarkets, with venison (deer), rabbits and game becoming increasingly available and being purchased. In the UK, deer numbers are increasing because of growing woodland cover, warmer winters, improved urban habitat management, and the development of more golf courses. Over the past 20 years, the area of woodland in the UK has increased by 600,000 hectares to some 2.6 million hectares, and there are now thought to be 500,000 roe (*Capreolus capreolus*), 360,000 red (*Cervus elaphus*) and 100,000 fallow (*Dama dama*) deer, along with 50,000 muntjac (*Muntiacus reevesi*), sika (*Cervus Nippon*) and Chinese water (*Hydropotes inermis*) deer. Due to their grazing habits, which can decimate plant growth, in many habitats, numbers of deer have to be controlled, and this provides a ready source of venison. Such hunting and shooting also brings income and people into the countryside.

In addition, each year, some 20 million pheasants (*Phasianus colchicus*) and 400,000 mallards (*Anas platyrhynchos*) are raised and released for shooting in and around woodlands and wetlands in the UK. It has been shown that landowners who both hunt and maintain gamebird stocks conserve 7% of their farms as woodland, whereas those who do neither keep less than 1% as woodland (Oldfield *et al.* 2003).

23.4.4 Providing a Catalyst for Behaviour and Lifestyle Change

Contact with nature not only affects immediate health and well-being, but also health throughout life. Life courses and pathways, through which all lives are shaped, can be mapped out into a 'funnel'. **Figure 23.3** represents the two extreme pathways, healthy A and unhealthy B. However, there are numerous pathways that lie in between, consisting of varied configurations and patterns of behaviours (Pretty *et al.* 2009).

In pathway A, the healthy pathway, people tend to live longer and have a better quality of life (Pretty *et al.* 2009). This increase in life expectancy and quality of life is a direct result of increased levels of physical activity, a greater connection to people and society, contact with nature, and the consumption of healthy foods (Pretty *et al.* 2009). These healthy behaviours may be followed as a direct result of an individual's surrounding environment. The ability to access green settings has been demonstrated to encourage contact with nature and participation in physical activity, both of which encourage the adoption of other healthy lifestyle choices such as social engagement and consumption of healthy foods (Wells *et al.* 2007; Pretty *et al.* 2009; Bowler *et al.* 2010). The availability of greenspace is, therefore, critical to healthy behaviours. On the healthy pathway, individuals have a better level of mental health, engage with nature regularly, are more resilient to stress, are members of social groups and keep learning (Foresight 2008; Pretty *et al.* 2009).

By contrast, the second life course in **Figure 23.3**, pathway B, is the unhealthy pathway. In this pathway, individuals have a lower life expectancy and a poorer quality of life, resulting from inactive and sedentary behaviour, disconnection from society and people, a lack of connection with nature, and the consumption of energy-dense and unhealthy foods (Pretty *et al.* 2009). Individuals on the unhealthy pathway also have more stressful jobs, a lower socioeconomic status, live in areas where active travel is difficult, and have an increased likelihood of being mentally ill, overweight or obese (Foresight 2007; Pretty *et al.* 2009).

In an increasingly urbanised society, the likelihood of following this pathway is becoming increasingly likely. As urban areas continuously grow and diffuse into rural areas, individuals rely heavily on cars for transportation, and are separated from neighbouring communities (Pretty *et al.* 2009). In modern human history, inactivity, disengagement from nature, consumption of unhealthy foods and social isolation are common behaviours. Urban areas do not provide vast opportunities for physical activity or active transport (e.g. cycling), and greenspace is continuously decreasing (Biddle *et al.* 2004; Louv 2005; Pretty *et al.* 2007; Pretty *et al.* 2009). The unhealthy behaviours encouraged by more modern urban environments are resulting in poor health and well-being (Pretty *et al.* 2009) and some environments may be considered as obesogenic (Foresight, 2007).

Although an individual may spend some time on a particular life pathway, it is possible to change behaviour and take an alternative pathway (Pretty *et al.* 2009). Individuals may move to a more healthy pathway as a direct result of adopting healthy behaviours that require spending time outdoors. For example, an individual may take part in a wilderness trail or activity away from their normal environment, but may continue to have contact with nature even when the trail has finished. This change in behaviour may also lead them towards the adoption of other healthy

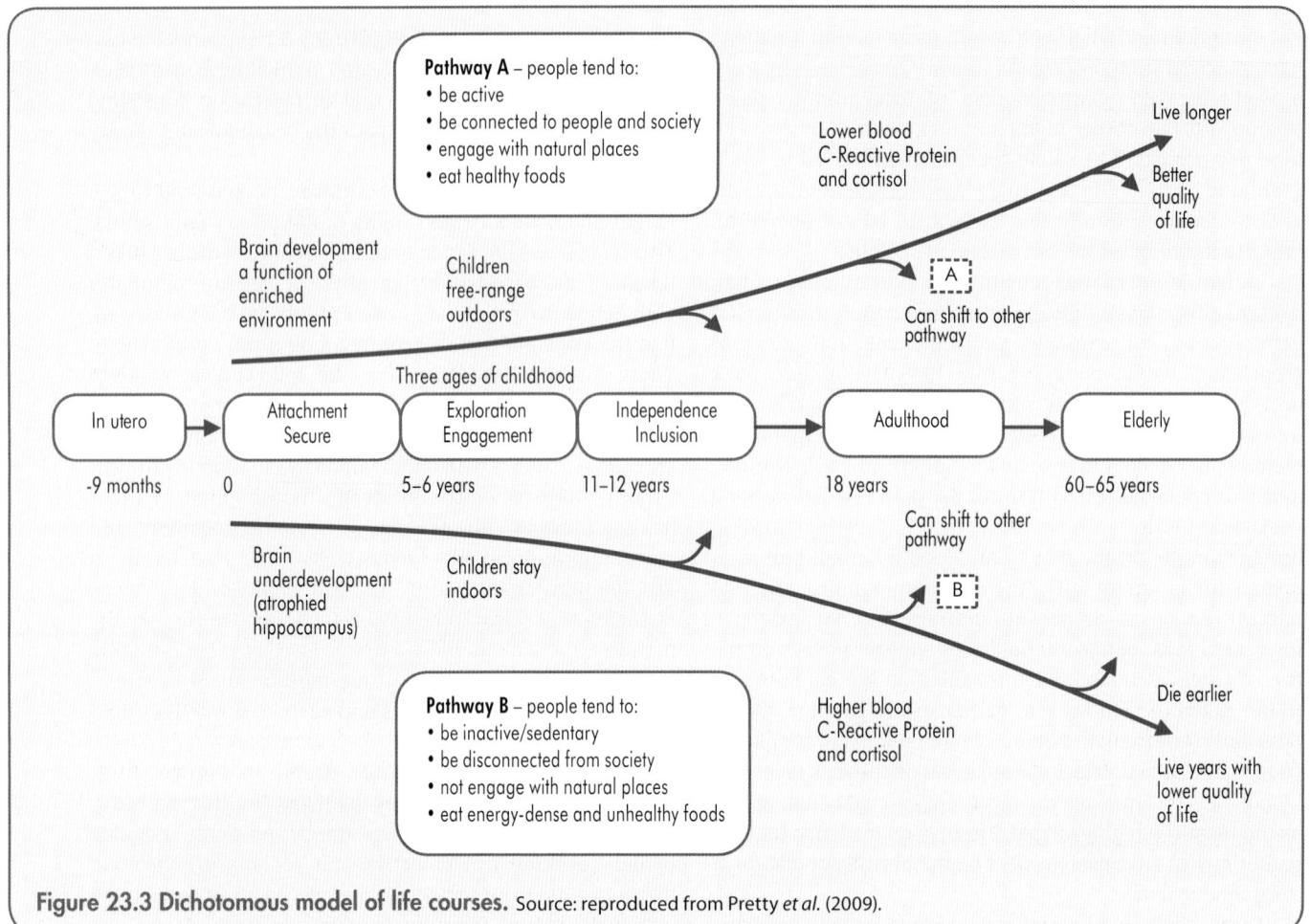

Figure 23.3 Dichotomous model of life courses. Source: reproduced from Pretty *et al.* (2009).

behaviours, such as physical activity. However, individuals may also move from a healthy to an unhealthy pathway as a result of a particular experience. Yet resilient individuals, who regularly perform physical activity and have contact with nature, are more likely to be able to cope with these stressful life events and will, therefore, continue on the healthy pathway (Pretty *et al.* 2009).

By moving from an unhealthy to a healthy pathway, individuals will experience significant improvements in quality of life and well-being. Furthermore, this shift will save society approximately £2,423 per person per year in health care costs (Pretty *et al.* 2009). Indeed, if just 1% of the sedentary population moves to a healthy pathway, 1,063 lives and £1.44 billion will be saved each year (NICE 2009). The earlier this shift occurs during life, the greater the impact will be upon health and society.

23.4.5 Childhood Experience and Behaviour

Experience of nature during childhood can impact upon adult behaviour and life pathways. Although contact with nature at any age can derive a whole number of benefits for physical and mental health, contact with nature during youth can directly impact upon healthy adult behaviours. Research indicates that the frequency of visits to green places during childhood significantly correlates to the number of visits during adulthood (Ward Thompson *et al.* 2008; Pretty *et al.* 2009). Therefore, a lack of experience of nature as a child

may directly result in a lack of contact during adulthood. Being disconnected from nature is characteristic of an unhealthy life pathway and may reduce the opportunities for adopting other healthy behaviours (Pretty *et al.* 2009).

Contact with nature during childhood can also influence environmental attitudes and behaviours during adulthood. Evidence suggests that children who participated in nature-based activities before the age of 11 are much more likely to express pro-environment attitudes and engage in pro-environment behaviours (**Figure 23.3**). Experience during childhood can, therefore, have a significant impact upon an individual's attitude towards the environment, a factor that could potentially impact upon environmental conservation (Wells & Lekies 2006).

Despite the evidence that adults who have high levels of contact with nature during youth have an increased likelihood of adopting a healthy life pathway and exhibiting environmentally friendly behaviours (Wells & Lekies 2006; Pretty *et al.* 2009), opportunities for the children of today to play and engage in green settings are continually diminishing. Less than 10% of children ever play in natural areas, compared to the 40% of today's adults who did so as children. Children are spending less time outdoors than they used to, and have a reduced understanding of the natural environment (Louv 2005; Bird 2007). If the children of today continue to be disconnected from nature, it is increasingly likely that they will embark on an unhealthy life pathway throughout their lives and, hence, have a reduced quality of life and life expectancy (Pretty *et al.* 2009).

23.4.6 Epidemiological Studies

Epidemiological studies often show associations between the proximity of greenspace to the home and positive health outcomes (Maas *et al.* 2006; Mitchell & Popham 2007, 2008). A direct link between the amount of accessible local greenspace and health has been evidenced using large-scale epidemiological studies in Japan, Netherlands and Sweden, which we have reviewed here (Takano *et al.* 2002; De Vries *et al.* 2003; Grahn & Stigsdotter 2003).

In Tokyo, Japan, tree-lined streets, parks and other greenspaces play a key role in the increased longevity of residents, and decrease the risk of mental health issues (Takano *et al.* 2002). A longitudinal study compared access to local greenspaces within walking distance of home and mortality rates in elderly people over a period of five years. After controlling for demographic and socioeconomic variables, Takano *et al.* (2002) found that, out of 3,100 Tokyo citizens born between 1903 and 1918, 71% were still alive in 1992, and that the probability of their living for an additional five years was linked to their ability to walk in a local park or tree-lined street (Takano *et al.* 2002). However, the issue of causality is not clear as it is possible that the more affluent individuals, who often live longer anyway, represented those who lived in the greener neighbourhoods (Adams & White 2003).

In the Netherlands, self-reported health data from over ten thousand Dutch urban residents was correlated with national environmental data characterising the type and quantity of blue and green spaces present in their neighbourhood. Socioeconomic and demographic characteristics were controlled for selection effects and the study reported that people living in greener neighbourhoods enjoyed better general health (De Vries *et al.* 2003). The type of greenspace did not seem to alter effectiveness; the total amount of greenspace in the living environment seemed to be the most relevant predictor. However, environmental characteristics were separated into neighbourhoods, and all individuals within that particular area were classed as having equal access to greenspaces. This measure does not acknowledge that exposure to greenspace may vary considerably between residents of the same neighbourhood and that durations of exposure may also differ.

In a Swedish study, Grahn and Stigsdotter (2003) examined the relationship between the use of urban greenspaces and health, and found that the level of self-reported stress showed significant relationships with the proximity of urban greenspaces, the frequency of visits to those greenspaces, and the duration of the stay. The findings implied that the more frequent the visits, the lower the incidence of stress-related illnesses. Having access to a public or privately owned garden adjacent to their place of residence was another principal factor, which has implications for both policy and urban landscape planning (Maas *et al.* 2006; Mitchell & Popham 2007, 2008).

Perceived neighbourhood 'greenness' is also strongly associated with better mental and physical health (Sugiyama *et al.* 2008). Respondents who perceived their neighbourhood as highly green were 1.37 and 1.60 times more likely to have better physical and mental health respectively, in comparison with those who perceived it as low in greenery. The degree of species richness in urban greenspaces has also been positively associated with the psychological well-being of visitors (Fuller *et al.* 2007), emphasising the importance of locally managed biodiversity in providing a sense of place and an object for reflection.

Despite these findings, it is also important to acknowledge potential selection or causation mechanisms (De Vries *et al.* 2003). Selection processes would suggest that healthy people move to green surroundings (selective migration), whereas causation mechanisms would imply that living in green environments promotes good health and well-being. So do green environments make people healthier and affect individual behaviour, or do those particular areas attract healthy people? If a person resides in a green area, do they spend more time being physically active outdoors? Even if the natural environment did not affect physical activity patterns, would the health of those living in greener surroundings improve solely from the increased exposure to nature? Although all of these studies have attempted to address the possibility of selective migration, it cannot be categorically ruled out. The studies are also cross-sectional in nature, as opposed to longitudinal. Cross-sectional studies are valuable and provide a good starting point (Wells *et al.* 2007) by establishing relationships among correlates or covariates (Bauman *et al.* 2002). However, longitudinal studies are necessary to establish causality, which is an important outcome for informing policy and practical recommendations. Although longitudinal studies are time intensive, the advantage of exploring causality makes them a creditable goal.

23.5 Reducing the Incidence of Pollution and Disease Vectors

Ecosystems provide important services by reducing threats to health through purification, dampening and consumption functions. Processes include local climate regulation, noise reduction, scavenging of air pollutants and the control of vectors of disease.

23.5.1 Air Purification Through the Reduction of Pollution

Ambient air pollution has long been implicated as a contributor to adverse health effects. The House of Commons Environment Audit Committee reported that up to 50,000 people a year in the UK may be dying prematurely because of air pollution (Defra 2007). The Government's 2007 Air Quality Strategy estimates that the health impact of particulate matter alone costs the UK between £8.5 billion and £20.2 billion a year (Defra 2007). This is very likely to be an underestimate as it ignores the impact on morbidity, costing only mortality. In addition, air pollution has wide-ranging environmental impacts including loss of biodiversity, reduced crop yields and contributing to climate change.

Rehdanz and Maddison (2008) found that perceived levels of air pollution are negatively related to well-being in Germany. Welsch (2006) examined average well-being in relation to average air pollution values, and found significant negative associations in each case. Brereton *et al.* (2006) and Ferreira & Moro (2010) working with individual-level data on air pollution and other Environmental Quality parameters in Ireland, also found negative associations between air pollution and well-being; and MacKerron & Mourato (2010) arrived at the same conclusion using air pollution data for London.

Numerous studies have shown how ecosystems can play a significant role in reducing air pollution.

Rowe (2010) recently reviewed the use of green roofs to reduce pollution. He concluded that they have significant potential to reduce air pollution directly and emissions indirectly. The major hurdle to their widespread utilisation is the considerable cost barrier between green and conventional roofs (Rowe 2010).

Urban forests can either reduce air pollution by increasing dry deposition, or increase it through emissions of enhanced biogenic volatile organic compound (BVOC), which can act as precursors of secondary air pollutants. Many reports have shown that trees in urban areas provide a significant contribution to the reduction of air pollutants (Yang *et al.* 2005; Nowak 2006; Escobedo & Nowak 2009). Escobeda *et al.* (2011) argue the forests should be managed within the parameters of urban sustainability and, at the same time, promoted to policy makers and citizens as a means of mitigating pollution, so they can be used to improve human quality of life throughout the cities of the world (Escobedo *et al.* 2011).

There is little guidance on optimum locations in which to plant trees in urban areas. In New York, locations for tree planting have used indicators such as hospitalisation and asthma rates (Grove *et al.* 2006). This earlier work has now been developed into a planting priority index that spatially considers air pollution concentrations, human population density and tree cover. On the other hand, the placement of trees may also increase pollution concentrations at street levels, especially in valleys where they impact on the dispersion processes (Buccolieri *et al.* 2009).

On a global scale, BVOCs emitted from vegetation are more reactive than, and exceed, anthropogenic VOCs. Emission rates of BVOCs are strongly dependent upon temperature, so it is expected that they will increase in the future as a result of climate change. Emissions also vary from species to species, so selective planting of low-emitting species may be beneficial. Donovan *et al.* (2005) developed an urban tree air quality score that ranks trees in order of their potential to improve air quality. They concluded that pine, larch and silver birch had the greatest potential to improve air quality. In contrast, if planted in large numbers, oaks, willows and poplars had the potential to decrease air quality downwind (Donovan *et al.* 2005).

23.5.2 Interception of Noise and Water

In recent years, noise pollution has become an increasingly important environmental problem which can have adverse effects on human health (Ozer *et al.* 2008). Traffic-generated noise is one of the main sources of noise pollution, with excessive noise from roads, air traffic and railways in urban areas commonly resulting in stress (den Boer & Schroten 2007; Ozer *et al.* 2008). Habitats containing trees and shrub vegetation have been demonstrated to be particularly effective at providing barriers to noise in urban settings (Frumkin *et al.* 2004; Ozer *et al.* 2008; Ernstson *et al.* 2010; Fitter *et al.* 2010). Research has also demonstrated that the presence of vegetation can significantly reduce noise levels from urban motorways (Ozer *et al.* 2008). Furthermore, green belts have been suggested to be effective tools for the mitigation of traffic-generated noise (Pathak *et al.* 2011). However, the specific characteristics of the vegetation should be considered as the crown width, height and density of plants, and the position of their leaves against the direction of the noise, may influence their effectiveness (Ozer *et al.* 2008). The vegetation must also be tolerant to air pollutants from motorised transport (Pathak *et al.* 2011).

Vegetation is important for the interception of water in Urban habitats (Cornell University 2009). Large cities and towns are often covered with hard surfaces that do not allow for the absorption of water. During storms or times of high rainfall, this can result in high levels of surface water. This excess water often runs into sewer systems causing them to overflow into rivers and lakes, washing pollutants into them. The presence of trees and other vegetation can reduce this problem by lessening the surface water and enhancing water absorption via the soil. Vegetation can also transpire water from their leaves. The presence of vegetation in urban ecosystems is, therefore, of great importance as it can help to reduce flooding and prevent the pollution of rivers and lakes (Cornell University 2009).

23.5.3 Mitigation of the Heat Island Effect

The heat island effect is a well-established phenomenon of large urban settlements; the temperature difference between London and the surrounding suburbs, for example, can be as large as 9°C (Kolokotroni & Giridharan 2008). It is known that urban greenspace mitigates this effect (Gill *et al.* 2007). Trees also filter and take up air pollutants, including oxides of nitrogen and sulphur and particulates (Beckett *et al.* 1998; Tiwary *et al.* 2009). The current 7% tree cover in the West Midlands reduces air concentrations of PM_{10} (particulates >10 micro-metres) by 4% (McDonald *et al.* 2007). Trees and other vegetation also intercept noise by absorbing reflected and laterally transmitted noise.

23.6 Direct Threats to Human Health

This section does not consider the toxicants, pollutants or contaminants introduced into the environment as a result of human activity or management. Those classes of compounds with known effects on human health include some pesticides, air pollutants, endocrine disruptors, PCBs, heavy metals, radionuclides, asbestos, aliphatics (e.g. vinyl chloride, formaldehyde), and oils (Conway & Pretty 1991; Frumkin 2005; Pretty 2005). The effects of some of these threats to health are dampened or mitigated by specific ecosystems.

Ecosystems themselves, however, can be a direct provider of threats to human health, and it is these threats that we are reviewing here. They include infectious agents (e.g. *Lyme borreliosis*, *Cryptosporidium* species, malaria, cholera, *cyclospora cayetanensis*, *campylobacter* species and *leptospirosis* species); physical threats from wild animals (though not generally a factor in UK), domestic livestock and dogs; pollutants or contaminants from plants (e.g. bracken spores, VOCs, pollen); elemental threats through extremes of temperature or UV radiation; and accidents (Frumkin *et al.* 2004).

There are a wide variety of pathogens in water that comprise threats to health including *Escherichia coli* and *Salmonella*, *Campylobacter*, *Giardia* and *Cryptosporidium* species. Some of these come from natural sources, such as (waterbirds and wild animals, and some come from human sources. Vector-borne diseases involve the transmission of infectious agents (viruses, bacteria and parasites) by blood-sucking arthropods such as mosquitoes. A number of such diseases have emerged for the first time, or resurged, as significant public health threats during the past 25 years. These include Lyme Disease, Dengue Fever and the more serious Dengue Haemorrhagic Fever, Yellow Fever, Japanese Encephalitis, West Nile Virus, Alkhurma Virus, a subtype of Kyasanur Forest Disease, Venezuelan Equine Encephalitis, Epidemic Polyarthritis (Ross River Virus), Barmah Forest Virus, Rift Valley Fever, Oropouche Fever, California Encephalitis and Crimean-Congo Haemorrhagic Fever (Watson *et al.* 2005).

Lyme Disease, involving the infection of humans following a tick bite, has become a significant public health problem in the USA, and has recently increased within the UK. The Health Protection Agency now estimates that there are 1,000–2,000 cases of Lyme Disease in the UK each year. The ticks that cause Lyme Disease are commonly found in woodland and heathland areas because these types of habitats have a high number of tick-carrying animals such as deer and mice. Parts of the UK that are known to have a particularly high population of ticks include Exmoor, the New Forest, the South Downs, parts of Wiltshire and Berkshire, Thetford Forest in Norfolk, the Lake District, the Yorkshire Moors and the Scottish Highlands (NHS 2011b). The tick population is highest in late spring and early summer.

A further threat to human health arises from natural VOCs. These air pollutants originate from vegetation, such as oak and maple, but can also be anthropogenic in origin (Steinbrecher *et al.* 2008). The main natural VOCs are isoprene and terpene, and large forests can emit 50 kg/km² daily at the height of the growing season (Behr & Johnen 2008). Natural VOCs emitted by such habitats can contribute significantly to the formation of tropospheric ozone, which has negative health consequences (AQEG 2009).

Another threat to human health arises from noise intruding on ecosystems and consequently affecting well-being. The sources of noise pollution are mainly from transport. Van Pragg & Baarsma (2005) investigated aircraft noise around Amsterdam Schiphol airport and found that experienced noise nuisance was negatively related to well-being, although direct noise measures were not significant.

Climate also has an effect on human health. Redhanz & Maddison (2005) assessed climate parameters across 67 countries and found that greater well-being was associated with a higher mean temperature during cold months and a lower mean temperature during hot months. In addition, Brereton *et al.* (2006) found that higher well-being in Ireland was related to lower wind speeds, but higher rainfall.

In addition to the direct effects of climate on well-being, climate change is predicted to have a substantial future impact as altered conditions allow the spread and development of new vector-borne and waterborne diseases (Watson *et al.* 2005). It is not clear whether this will bring vectors that affect human health, but the livestock disease, Bluetongue Virus, has now become established in the UK since its arrival from the continent via migrating adult midges taking advantage of warmer conditions. Airborne allergens may also be significantly influenced by climate change. It has been shown that pollen counts rise with increasing temperatures (Tamura *et al.* 1997; Anhlholm *et al.* 1998). In addition, increased atmospheric carbon dioxide results in enhanced production of pollens from species such as ragwort (*Senecio jacobea*) (Ziska & Caulfield 2000). The recent comprehensive assessment by the Health Protection Agency (DH & HPA 2008) has concluded that outbreaks of malaria in the UK are likely to remain rare, but that there is still the possibility that more effective vectors (different species of mosquito) may arrive in the UK as the climate becomes more suitable for them. Tick-borne diseases are expected to become more common, but this is more likely to be due to changes in land use and leisure activities than to climate change. The likelihood that tick-borne encephalitis will become established in the UK is very low.

Finally, there are some natural sources of radiation in the UK (e.g. radon from granite rocks in south-west England and Scotland) that constitute significant natural threats to health.

23.7 Methods for Establishing Health Values

23.7.1 Questionnaire-based Measures for Mental Health

Table 23.4 summarises the main instruments in use for measuring mental health arising from exposure to nature. Many different methods are available, but **Table 23.4** comprises a list of the most commonly applied tools from key studies identified in earlier sections. This list is indicative rather than exhaustive.

23.7.1.1 Self-esteem

Self-esteem is commonly accepted as a key indicator of emotional stability and, therefore, is a contributor to mental well-being, quality of life and survival (Huppert & Whittington 2003). An individual's level of self-esteem has implications for health behaviours, motivations and lifestyle choices. High levels of self-esteem are associated with healthy behaviours, such as healthy eating and physical activity, and also stress resilience and life satisfaction (Torres & Fernandez 1995; Fox 2000). Low self-esteem is closely linked to mental illness and the absence of psychological well-being, with symptoms including depression, trait anxiety, suicidal ideation and a sense of hopelessness (Fox 2000).

Rosenberg's Self Esteem Scale (RSE) is the most widely used and popular self-esteem measure (Rosenberg 1965). It is a standardised tool used in health psychology and is regarded as the standard against which other measures of self-esteem should be compared (Rosenberg 1965). The RSE scale consists of ten statements concerning how an individual views themselves, and requires a response of 'strongly agree', 'agree', 'disagree' or 'strongly disagree' for each (Rosenberg 1965). The scale's conservative measure, superior reliability and validity is widely acknowledged, and these qualities have been demonstrated with many different sample groups (Fox 2000): its use has been validated for adolescent, adult and elderly populations. The RSE has been used in a wide range of green exercise studies, predominantly in the UK (Pretty *et al.* 2005; Peacock *et al.* 2007; Pretty *et al.* 2007; Peacock *et al.* 2008; Barton *et al.* 2009; Barton & Pretty 2010; Barton *et al.* 2011).

23.7.1.2 Mood states and/or emotion

Mood is defined as "the subtle subjective state or feelings of a person at any given moment" (Hull 1991). It is an integral component of daily life and has a strong influence on feelings of happiness, being able to appreciate the moment, coping with stressful situations and general quality of life (Berger *et al.* 2002). Mood states are known to influence long-term health by both direct (immune system) and secondary (lifestyle choices) pathways.

The **Profile of Mood State (POMS)** standardised short form questionnaire is the primary instrument for measuring mood due to its sensitivity to mood changes in many settings (McNair *et al.* 1971; Biddle 2000; Biddle *et al.* 2000). The POMS questionnaire comprises six subscale mood components: five negative and one positive. These are 'anger-hostility', 'confusion-bewilderment', 'depression-dejection', 'fatigue-inertia', 'tension-anxiety' and 'vigour-activity' (McNair *et al.* 1971). There are five words to represent each of the six subscales and respondents are requested to indicate the degree to which they are experiencing the particular mood state by selecting 'not at all', 'a little', 'moderately', 'quite a bit' or 'extremely' (McNair *et al.* 1971). The POMS questionnaire has been regularly used to assess short-term and acute mood changes in individuals after they have participated in nature-based activities in the UK (Pretty *et al.* 2005; Peacock *et al.* 2007; Pretty *et al.* 2007; Peacock *et al.* 2008; Barton *et al.* 2009; Barton & Pretty 2010; Barton *et al.* 2011).

The **Zuckerman Inventory of Personal Reactions (ZIPERS)** is a broad state affect test that assesses feelings on five factors: 'fear arousal', 'positive affect', 'anger/aggression', 'attentiveness' and 'sadness' (Zuckerman 1977; Ulrich 1981; Hartig 2003). The respondents indicate the extent to which the statements describe how they feel at that precise moment using a five-point scale (1=not at all to 5= very much) (Zuckerman 1977; Hartig 2003). The ZIPERS has been used in a large number of studies examining the effect of restorative environments, mainly in the USA (Ulrich 2002; Hartig 2003).

Anxiety is a mood or emotional state that includes feelings of apprehension, tension and nervousness (Spielberger 1970). The **Spielberger State-Trait Anxiety Inventory (S-STAI)** and the **S-STAI six item short version** are used to assess anxiety (Spielberger 1970; Diette *et al.* 2003). The S-STAI is a self-report questionnaire which requires participants to indicate whether they are feeling calm, tense, upset, relaxed, etc. Participants respond on a four-point scale using either

Table 23.4 Summary of mental health measures.

Questionnaire title	Mental health measure	Number of items/ Factors on questionnaire	Examples of ecosystem studies in which they have been utilised
1. Rosenberg's Self Esteem Scale	Self-esteem	10 items	Pretty *et al.* (2005), Peacock *et al.* (2007), Pretty *et al.* (2007), Barton *et al.* (2009), Barton & Pretty (2010), Barton *et al.* (2011)
2. Profile of Mood State Questionnaire	Mood	6 factors (30 items)	Van den Berg *et al.* (2003), Pretty *et al.* (2005), Peacock *et al.* (2007), Pretty *et al.* (2007), Peacock *et al.* (2008), Barton *et al.* (2009), Barton & Pretty (2010), Barton *et al.* (2011)
3. The Zuckerman Inventory of Personal Reactions	Emotion and mood	5 factors	Ulrich (1981), Ulirich *et al.* (1991), Honeyman (1992), Hartig *et al.* (1996), Ulrich (2002), Hartig *et al.* (2003)
4. Spielberger State-Trait Anxiety Inventory	Anxiety	20 items	Diette *et al.* (2003)
5. The Lewis Stressful Life Events Scale	Stress	20 item scale	Wells & Evans (2003)
6. The General Health Questionnaire	Mental well-being	28-item and 12-item questionnaires	Pretty *et al.* (2005)
7. The Rutter Child Behaviour Questionnaire	Psychological distress, behavioural problems, anxiety and depression	26 items	Wells & Evans (2003)
8. The Global Self-worth Scale	Perception of mental well-being	6 items	Wells & Evans (2003)

'not at all', 'somewhat', 'moderately' or 'very much so' (Spielberger 1970; Diette *et al.* 2003). The scores are summed and normalised to a scale with scores ranging from 20 to 80: 20 represents a low level of anxiety and 80 represents a high level (Diette *et al.* 2003).

The Lewis Stressful Life Events Scale is used to assess the frequency of stressful life events (Lewis *et al.* 1984) and was originally tested and developed on children in the USA (Wells & Evans 2003). The scale consists of 20 items each concerning a stressful life event. The respondent is asked to indicate the degree to which they experience this stressful life event using 'a lot', 'sometimes' or 'never' (Lewis *et al.* 1984; Wells & Evans 2003). Examples of items on the scale include "how often were you picked on or made fun of by other kids?" and "How often did you fight or argue with your parents?". The method has been used to explore relationships between access to nature and the ability to cope with stressful life events (Wells & Evans 2003).

23.7.1.3 Overall mental well-being

The *General Health Questionnaire (GHQ)* is the industry standard for measuring psychological health and provides an overall indication of psychological state (Chisholm *et al.* 1975; Goldberg 1978). There are several versions of the GHQ including a 28-item and 12-item version (Goldberg *et al.* 1997). Questions are scored using a three-point Likert scale, with variation in their meaning according to the question itself (Goldberg 1978; Goldberg *et al.* 1997). The 12-item version has been demonstrated to be robust and to work as well as the longer, 28-item version (Goldberg *et al.* 1997). On the 12-item version, the questionnaire scores range from a minimum of 0 to a maximum of 36. A score of 0 represents an excellent state of mental health, while a score of 36 represents a poor state of mental health (Pretty *et al.* 2005). Although this tool is commonly used in mental health research, it has only been used sparingly to assess the health values of contact with nature.

The *Rutter Child Behaviour Questionnaire* is used to assess psychological distress, including symptoms of behavioural disorders, anxiety and depression (Rutter *et al.* 1970; Boyle & Jones 1985; Wells & Evans 2003). The questionnaire is a standardised, widely used instrument that is commonly used in non-clinical populations. The questionnaire consists of 26 items that are responded to on a three-point scale by the child's mother (0=does not apply, 1=applies somewhat, 2=certainly applies) (Wells & Evans 2003). Items on the scale include phrases such as my child "often appears unhappy" and "bullies other children". This instrument has been used to explore relationships between access to nature and the ability to cope with stressful life events (Rutter *et al.* 1970; Boyle & Jones 1985; Wells & Evans 2003).

The *Global Self-Worth Scale* is used to assess children's perception of mental well-being (Harter 1982). The scale assesses three domains of self-competence, including social, cognitive and physical domains, and also assesses general self-worth (Harter 1982). The scale includes six items with statements such as "some kids like the kind of person that they are but other kids often wish they were someone else" (Wells & Evans 2003). The respondent responds to each statement using either 'really true' or 'sort of true' (Wells & Evans 2003).

23.7.1.4 Mappiness methods

A custom iPhone application ('app') and accompanying back-end data server have been developed by (Mourato & MacKerron 2010). Recruitment of participants is opportunistic, relying mainly on media coverage and snowballing via Twitter. After downloading the app to their devices, participants provide basic demographic and health-related information, confirm settings, and give their informed consent in order to register. Participation is anonymous: no name, address, or other contact information is requested. Participants receive simple feedback, charting their happiness in different contexts, and can take part in the study for as long (or short) a period as they wish. Following registration, participants receive a notification (beep) on their device between one and five times a day, at their own choice. The notifications come at a random moment during hours agreed by the participant. The default frequency is twice a day, and the default hours are 8am–10pm. Each notification prompts the participant to open the app and to briefly report how they are feeling and, in broad terms, whom they are with, where they are and what they are doing. Respondents report the extent to which they feel 'Happy', 'Relaxed' and 'Awake' on a sliding visual analogue scale.

23.7.2 Physiological and Questionnaire-based Methods for Assessing Physical Health

The majority of the research assessing the health benefits of exposure to nature has predominantly used mental health measures. However, to establish an overall health value we also need to address the impact upon physical health indices such as heart rate, blood pressure, skin conductance and/or cortisol (stress hormone). Some authors have started exploring the impact on natural killer T cell activity and other key hormones to progress the research to a cellular level (Li *et al.* 2007).

23.7.2.1 Body Mass Index and Waist to Hip Ratio

Body Mass Index (BMI) is a simple index of weight:height that has been widely used to estimate body fat and to classify adults as underweight, overweight and obese for several decades (Keys *et al.* 1972; WHO 2011; NHS 2011a; NIH 2011). It is defined as the weight in kilograms divided by the square of the height in metres (kg/m^2). It has been used by the World Health Organization as the standard for recording obesity statistics since the early 1980s and is seen as a useful estimation of risk for diseases that can occur with more body fat. The higher the BMI calculation, the greater the risk for certain health issues such as Cardiovascular Disease , high blood pressure, Type 2 Diabetes, gallstones, breathing problems and certain cancers (NIH 2011). Although controversies over the use of BMI for medical diagnosis remain, it is generally accepted for individuals with an average body composition (WHO 1995). Classification of BMI scores are: <18.5 = underweight; 18.5–24.99 = normal; 25–29.99 = overweight and >30 = obese. Some studies have monitored changes in BMI over time as a result of participation in green exercise activities (Hine *et al.* 2011).

Others have explored the relationship between BMI and the mental health benefits experienced through nature-based activity (Pretty *et al.* 2005).

Waist to Hip Ratio (WHR) is a simple and useful measure of fat distribution and is a tool that helps determine overall health risk (NHS 2011a). People with more weight around their waist are at greater risk of lifestyle-related diseases, such as Cardiovascular Disease and diabetes, than those with weight around their hips. The classification of risk as defined by waist to hip ratios is as follows: for men: <0.95=low risk; 0.96–1.00=moderate risk; >1=high risk; and for women: <0.80=low risk; 0.81–0.85=moderate risk; >0.85=high risk. The norms for adults are 0.84 for males and 0.72 for females. Waist circumference is measured with a measuring tape around the narrowest circumference between pelvis and thorax (or two-finger width above navel) and hips are measured from the side at the level of the maximal protuberance of buttocks.

23.7.2.2 Blood pressure

Blood pressure is an important marker of cardiovascular health: particularly high levels are associated with Cardiovascular Disease and cerebrovascular events (HEW 2004). **Manual and digital sphygmomanometers** are most commonly utilised to assess blood pressure and are applicable in a variety of settings (O'Brien *et al.* 2001). They are simple to use and provide a quick assessment of blood pressure. However, the accuracy of the manual monitor is largely influenced by the assessor itself and should only be used by experienced individuals (O'Brien *et al.* 2001). Assessing blood pressure change pre and post nature-based interventions provides an indication of recovery, and many studies have used this approach to compare exposure to natural environments and urban areas lacking nature (Ulrich 1981; Ulrich *et al.* 1991; Parsons *et al.* 1998; Pretty *et al.* 2005). A **portapres** is used to measure blood pressure and can provide a beat-by-beat assessment for up to 24 hours (O'Brien *et al.* 2001). This would allow researchers to explore the longer-term impact of exposure to nature on blood pressure over a 24-hour period and introduce ambulatory monitoring rather than one-off measures. The portapres gives waveform measurements similar to intra-arterial recordings. However, this method can lead to various inaccuracies which may only be fixed by correction factors and digital monitors (O'Brien *et al.* 2001).

23.7.2.3 Heart rate and Heart Rate Variability (HRV)

Heart rate and heart rate variability (HRV) are important markers of autonomic nervous system activity and are contributors to cardiovascular health, especially as there is a significant relationship between the autonomic nervous system and cardiovascular mortality (Treiber *et al.* 1989; Task Force 1996). **Heart Rate monitors** are commonly utilised to assess heart rate as they are applicable in both laboratory and field settings (Treiber *et al.* 1989). Heart rate monitors consist of a chest strap and a wristwatch. The chest strap is fitted around the subject's chest to detect a heart rate reading; this reading is transmitted to the wristwatch which stores and monitors heart rate for a selected time period (Treiber *et al.* 1989). While heart rate monitors are easy to use in both laboratory and field settings, there is some concern with regards to their accuracy (Treiber *et al.* 1989). Heart rate monitors have been used to assess experiences both in greenspaces and in urban areas lacking nature in a few studies (Ulrich *et al.* 1991; Parsons *et al.* 1998; Pretty *et al.* 2005).

Electrocardiograms (ECGs) are also used to assess heart rate and are considered to provide much more reliable results than heart rate monitors (Treiber *et al.* 1989). Not only do ECGs provide an overall measure of heart rate, but they also provide a measure of heart rate variability: beat-by-beat variation in heart rate (Task Force 1996; Martini 2006). Three electrodes are placed at different points on the body's surface and connected to a computer (Martini 2006). The computer generates a graph of each heart beat cycle, which is made up of several different features including a P-wave, QRS complex and T-wave. If a portion of the heart has been damaged, for example by a heart attack, the ECG will detect abnormalities in the normal heart beat cycle (Task Force 1996; Martini 2006). Although useful in laboratory studies using pictures of natural scenes and urban scenes lacking nature or greenspace (Ulrich *et al.* 1991), this method would have limited applicability in field settings.

23.7.2.4 Cortisol

Cortisol is a biomarker of psychosocial stress. Cortisol levels gradually increase within a few minutes of stress stimulation and reach peak concentrations 10–30 minutes after stress cessation (Foley & Kirschbaum 2010). Cortisol levels are commonly measured through saliva. A piece of absorbent cotton is placed in the mouth for approximately 1–2 minutes and placed in a test tube. The saliva sample can then be frozen and stored for later analysis of cortisol concentration (Foley & Kirschbaum 2010; Park *et al.* 2010). However, when cortisol is measured via samples of saliva, it is only possible to determine free cortisol levels (the concentration of those cortisol particles not bound to protein) (Foley & Kirschbaum 2010).

Blood samples can also be taken to measure cortisol levels. Unlike salivary samples, blood serum samples can provide both a measure of free cortisol levels and total cortisol (Foley & Kirschbaum 2010). However, blood-sampling is a more intrusive method. Exploring changes in cortisol profiles following participation in longer-term nature-based interventions is currently being considered for future research. Very few studies have analysed cortisol levels (Hartig *et al.* 1996) in relation to contact with nature, but investigating this stress hormone could potentially inform future calculated health values.

23.7.3 Questionnaire-based Methods for Establishing Connectedness to Nature

23.7.3.1 Connectedness to nature

Connectedness to nature is an important predictor of ecological behaviour and subjective well-being and has been demonstrated to be related to an increase in awareness of environmental issues and environmentally friendly behaviour (Hine *et al.* 2008b). The **Connectedness to Nature Scale (CNS)** is a standardised and validated questionnaire which is a 'new measure of individuals' trait feelings of being emotionally connected to the natural world' (Mayer & McPherson Frantz 2004). Thirteen questions are scored on a scale ranging from one to five, with five indicating the maximum level of connectedness to nature. The CNS score is calculated by adding the scores for each question and dividing by thirteen to give an overall score between one and five (Mayer & McPherson Frantz 2004). The CNS has been utilised to assess short term changes in connectivity following green exercise activities (Peacock *et al.* 2008; Hine *et al.* 2011).

23.7.3.2 Nature relatedness

Nature relatedness describes an individual's level of connectedness with the natural world and comprises the cognitive, affective and physical connection we have with nature (Nisbet *et al.* 2009; Nisbet 2011). The **Nature Relatedness Scale** is a relatively recent scale (2008) designed to measure an individual's level of connectedness with the natural world. The scale consists of 21 items rated on a five-point Likert scale, from 1 (disagree strongly) to 5 (agree strongly). Items 2, 3, 10, 11, 13, 14, 15 and 18 are reverse-scored. A total nature relatedness scale score is created by adding the total score and dividing by 21. Scores range from one to five, with a high score endorsing a cognitive, affective and physical connection with nature (Nisbet *et al.* 2009).

The Nature Relatedness Scale also has three subscales: 'self', 'perspective' and 'experience'. A score can be created for each subscale by averaging the items within that subscale. Again, scores again range from one to five, with high scores endorsing the subscale. The self subscale measures "an internalized identification with nature, reflecting feelings and thoughts about one's personal connection to nature"; the perspective subscale measures "an external, nature-related worldview, a sense of agency concerning individual human actions and their impact on all living things"; and the experience subscale measures "a physical familiarity with the natural world and the level of comfort with and desire to be out in nature" (Nisbet *et al.* 2009). This measure is now starting to be used in ecosystem and health research.

23.8 Conclusions

The findings of this chapter suggest that attention could be given to developing the use of green exercise as a therapeutic intervention (Hine *et al.* 2009; Haubenhofer *et al.* 2010); that planners and architects should improve access to greenspace (green design); and that children should be encouraged to spend more time engaging with nature and be given opportunities to learn in outdoor settings (green education). Some of the substantial mental health challenges facing society (Foresight 2008; HSE 2008), and physical challenges arising from modern diets and sedentary lifestyles (Wanless 2002; Wanless 2004; DH 2005a; Sport England 2006; Wells *et al.* 2007; NICE 2008; DH & DCSF 2009; NICE 2009), could be addressed by increasing physical activity in green settings. If children are encouraged

and enabled to undertake more green exercise, then they are more likely to have active exposure to nature embedded in their lifestyle as adults and they will reap the associated health benefits.

Future research needs to address the issue of causality to convince policy makers of the health benefits derived from exposure to nature. Therefore, existing measures need to be integrated within longitudinal population studies such as the British Household Panel Survey. There remains a lack of longitudinal studies within the existing literature, especially exploring changes from childhood to adulthood. Introducing this type of time-series research would also allow a comparison with financial costings to infer value for money and identify causal effects of the environmental intervention. Although the existing evidence base concerning the restorative properties of nature and its role in reducing stress and replenishing attention fatigue is strong, the duration and frequency of exposure required to prevent stress-related illness in the long-term is not fully understood. Thus, longitudinal studies would ensure the key question concerning long-term motivation and sustained behaviour change was addressed, which has important consequences for public health.

References

Adams, J. & White, M. (2003) Health benefits of green spaces not confirmed. *Journal of Epidmiology and Community Health,* **57**, 312.

Anhlholm, J.U., Helander, M.L. & Savolainen, J. (1998) Genetic and environmental factors affecting the allergenicity of birch (*Betula pubescens* ssp. *czerepanovii* [Orl.] Hämet-ahti) pollen *Clinical and Experimental Allergy,* **28**, 1384–1388.

AQEG (Air Quality Expert Group) (2009) Ozone in the United Kingdom. Defra, London.

Barton, J., Hine, R. & Pretty, J. (2009) The health benefits of walking in greenspaces of high natural and heritage value. *Journal of Integrative Environmental Sciences,* **6**, 261–278.

Barton, J. & Pretty, J. (2010) What is the best dose of nature and green exercise for improving mental health? A multi-study analysis. *Environmental Science and Technology,* **44**, 3947–3955.

Barton, J., Griffin, M. & Pretty, J. (2011) Exercise, nature and socially interactive based initiatives improve mood and self-esteem in the clinical population. *Perspectives in Public Health,* In press. DOI: 10.1177/1757913910393862.

Bauman, A.E., Sallis, J., Dzewaltowski, D. & Owen, N. (2002) Toward a better understanding of the influences on physical activity: The role of determinants, correlates, causal variables, mediators, moderators and confounders. *American Journal of Preventive Medicine,* **23**, 5–14.

Beckett, K.P., Freer-Smith, P.H. & Taylor, G. (1998) Urban woodlands: their role in reducing the effects of particulate pollen. *Environmental Pollution,* **99**, 347–360.

Behr, A. & Johnen, L. (2008) Myrcene as a natural base chemical in sustainable chemistry: A critical review. *ChemSusChem,* **2**, 1072–1095.

Berger, B.G., Pargman, D. & Weinberg, R.S. (2002) Foundations of exercise psychology. Fitness Information Technology, Morgantown.

Berrigan, D. & Troiano, R.P. (2002) The association between urban form and physical activity in US adults. *American Journal of Preventive Medicine,* **23**, 74–79.

Bharucha, Z. & Pretty, J. (2010) The roles and values of wild foods in agricultural systems. *Philosophical Transactions of the Royal Society,* **365**, 2913–2926.

Biddle, S., Fox, K. & Boutcher, S. (2000) Physical activity and psychological well-being. Routledge, London.

Biddle, S.J.H. (2000) Emotion, mood and physical activity. Physical activity and psychological well-being. (eds S.J.H. Biddle, K.R. Fox, & S.H. Boutcher). Routledge, London. pp. 63–87.

Biddle, S.J.H., Gorely, T. & Stensel, D.J. (2004) Health-enhancing physical activity and sedentary behaviour in children and adolescents. *Journal of sports sciences,* **22**, 679–701.

Bignal, K., Ashmore, M. & Power, S. (2004) Ecological effects of diffuse air pollution from road transport. English Nature, Peterborough.

Bird, W. (2007) Natural Thinking. Investigating the links between the Natural Environment, Biodiversity and Mental Health. A report for the Royal Society for the Protection of Birds, Bedfordshire.

Blair, S.N. & Connelly, J.C. (1996) How much physical activity should we do? The case for moderate amounts and intensities of physical acitvity. *Research Quarterly for Exercise and Spor* ,**67**, 193–205.

Bokker, E.A.M. (2006) Effects of interactions between humans and domesticated animals. In Hassink, J. and van Dijk, M. (eds.), Farming for Health. Green-Care Farming Across Europe and the United States of America, Wageningen: Springer Dordrecht.

Bowler, D.E., Buyung-Ali, L.M., Knight, T.M. & Pullin, A.S. (2010) A systematic review of evidence for the added benefits to health of exposure to natural environments. *BMC Public Health,* **10**, 456–466.

Boyle, M. & Jones, S. (1985) Selecting measures of emotional and behavioural disorders of childhood for use in general populations. *Journal of Clinical Psychology and Psychiatry,* **26**, 137–159.

Brereton, F., Clinch, J.P. & Ferreira, S. (2006) Environmental amenities and subjective well-being: testing the validity of hedonic pricing. School of Geography, University College, Dublin.

Brugha, T., Morgan, Z., Bebbington, P., Jenkins, R., Lewis, G., Farrell, M. & Meltzer, H. (2003) Social support networks and type of neurotic symptom among adults in British households. *Psychological Medicine,* **33**, 307–318.

Buccolieri, R., Gromke, C., Di Sabatino, S. & Ruck, B. (2009) Aerodynamic effects of trees on pollutant concentration in street canyons. *Science of the Total Environment,* **407**, 5247–5256.

Burls, A. (2008) Seeking nature: A contemporary therapeutic environment. *Therapeutic Communities* **29**.

CABE (Commission for Architecture and the Built Environment) (2010) Managing green spaces: seven ingredients for success. CABE, London.

CDC (Centres for Disease Control) (1996) Physical activity and health. A report of the Surgeon General. US Department of Health and Human Services, Centres for Disease Control and Prevention, National Centre for Chronic Disease Prevention and Health Promotion, Washington, D.C. [online]

Available at: <http://www.cdc.gov/nccdphp/sgr/contents.htm> [Accessed 04.05.11].

Chiesura, A. (2004) The role of urban parks for the sustainable city. *Landscape and Urban Planning,* **68**, 129–138.

Chisholm, D.M., Collis, M.L., Kulak, L.L., Davenport, W. & Gruber, N. (1975) Physical activity readiness. *British Columbia Medical Journal,* **17**, 375–378.

Coley, R.L., Kuo, F.E. & Sullivan, W.C. (1997) Where does community grow? The social context created by nature in urban public housing. *Environment and Behaviour,* **29**, 468–494.

Conner, M. (2007) What is wilderness therapy and a wilderness program? [online] Available at: <http://www. wilderness-therapy.org/Wilderness/WhatIsWilderess.htm> [Accessed 18.09.10].

Conway, G.R. & Pretty, J. (1991) Unwelcome harvest: agriculture and pollution. Earthscan, London. pp. 645.

Cooper-Marcus, C. & Barnes, M. (1995) Gardens in healthcare facilities: Uses, therapeutic benefits and design recommendations. The Centre for Health Design, Inc., California. [online] Available at: <http://www.healthdesign.org/sites/default/files/Gardens%20in%20HC%20Facility%20Visits.pdf> [Accessed 04.05.11].

Cornell University (2009) Urban silviculture research and education project: ecosystem services of urban trees. Cornell University, Cooperative Extensive, New York City.

Craig, C.L., Brownson, R.C., Cragg, S.E. & Dunn, A.L. (2002) Exploring the effect of the environment on physical activity: A study examining walking to work. *American Journal of Preventive Medicine,* **23**, 36–43.

Davis-Berman, J. & Berman, D.S. (1989) The wilderness therapy programme: An empirical study of its effects with adolescents in an outpatient setting. *Journal of Contemporary Psychotherapy,* **19**, 271–281.

De Vries, S., Verheij, R.A., Groenewegen, P.P. & Spreeuwenberg, P. (2003) Natural environments – healthy environments? An exploratory analysis of the relationship between greenspace and health. *Environment and Planning A,* **35**, 1717–1731.

Defra (Department for Environment, Food and Rural Affairs) (2007) Sustainable development indicators in your pocket 2007: An update of the UK Government Strategy Indicators Defra, London. [online] Available at: <http://collections.europarchive.org/tna/20080530153425/http://www.sustainable-development.gov.uk/progress/data-resources/documents/sdiyp2007_a6.pdf> [Accessed 04.05.11].

den Boer, L.C. & Schroten, A. (2007) Traffic noise reduction in Europe: Health effects, social costs and technology and policy options to reduce road and rail traffic noise. CE Delft: Solutions for environment, ecology and technology, Delft, The Netherlands. [online] Available at: <http://www.ce.nl> [Accessed 04.05.11].

DH (Department of Health) (2004) Choosing Health? A consultation on action to improve people's health. National Health Service, London. pp. 1–12. [online] Available at: <http://www.dh.gov.uk/assetRoot/04/07/57/54/04075754.pdf> [Accessed 04.05.11].

DH (Department of Health) (2005a) Public Health White Paper. Choosing Health: Making healthy choices easier. Department of Health, London. [online] Available at: <http://webarchive.nationalarchives.gov.uk/+/www.dh.gov.uk/en/Publicationsandstatistics/Publications/

PublicationsPolicyAndGuidance/DH_4094550> [Accessed 04.05.11].

DH (Department of Health) (2005b) Choosing activity: A physical activity action plan. Department of Health, London.

DH & DCSF (Department of Health & Department for Children and Young People) (2009) Healthy Lives, Brighter Futures: The strategy for children and young people's health. Department of Health, Department for Children, Schools and Famlies, London. [online] Available at: <http://www.dh.gov.uk/prod_consum_dh/groups/dh_digitalassets/documents/digitalasset/dh_094397.pdf> [Accessed 04.05.11].

DH & HPA (Department of Health & Health Protection Agency) (2008) Health effects of climate change in the UK 2008: An update of the Department of Health report 2001/2002. Department of Health, London. pp. 124.

Diette, G.B., Lechtzin, N., Haponik, E., Devrotes, A. & Rubin, H.R. (2003) Distraction therapy with nature sights and sounds reduces pain during flexible bronchoscopy. A complementary approach to routine analgesia. *Chest Journal,* **123**, 941–948.

DLTR (Department for Transport, Local Government and the Regions) (2002) Green Spaces Better Places: Final report of the Urban Green Spaces Taskforce. Department for Transport, Local Government and the Regions, London. [online] Available at: <http://www.communities.gov.uk/documents/communities/pdf/131015.pdf> [Accessed 04.05.11].

Dolan, P., Peasgood, T. & White, M. (2008) Do we really know what makes us happy? A review of economic literature on the factors associated with subjective well-being. *Journal of Economic Psychology,* **29**, 94–122.

Donovan, R.G., Stewart, H.E., Owen, S.M., MacKenzie, A.R. & Hewitt, C.N. (2005) Development and application of an urban tree air quality score for photochemical pollution episodes using the Birmingham, UK area as a case study. *Environmental Science & Technology,* **39**, 6730–6738.

Ernston, H., Barthel, S., Andersson, E. & Borgstrom, S.T. (2010) Scale-crossing brakers and network governance of urban ecosystem services: the case of Stockholm. *Ecology and Society,* **15**, 28.

Escobedo, F.J. & Nowak, D.J. (2009) Spatial heterogeneity and air pollution removal by an urban forest. *Landscape and urban planning,* **90**, 102–110.

Escobedo, F.J., Kroeger, T. & Wagner, J.E. (2011) Urban forests and pollution mitigation: Analyzing ecosystem services and disservices. *Environmental Pollution*, In press.

Ferreira, S. & Moro, M. (2010) On the use of subjective well-being data for environmental valuation. *Environmental and Resource Economics,* **46**, 249–273.

Fine, A.H. (2006) Handbook on animal-assisted therapy. Academic Press, San Diego.

Fitter, A., Elmqvist, T., Haines-Young, R., Potschin, M., Rinaldo, A., Setala, H., Stoll-Kleemann, S., Zobel, M. & Murlis, J. (2010) An assessment of ecosystem services and biodiversity in europe. Ecosystem Services. (eds R.M. Harrison, & R.E. Hester). The Royal Society of Chemistry, London. pp. 1–28.

Foley, P. & Kirschbaum, C. (2010) Human hypothalamus-pituitary-adrenal axis responses to acute psychological stress in laboratory settings. *Neuroscience and Biobehavioural Reviews,* **35**, 91–96.

Foresight (2007) Tackling obesities: Future choices. Government Office of Science, London.

Foresight (2008) Mental health: Future challenges. Government Office of Science, London.

Fredrickson, B.L. & Branigan, C. (2005) Positive emotions broaden the scope of attention and thought-action repertoires. *Cognition and Emotion,* **19**, 313–332.

Frey, B. (2008) Happiness: A revolution in economics. MIT Press, Cambridge, Massachusetts.

Frumkin, H., Frank, L. & Jackson, R. (2004) Urban sprawl and public health: Designing, planning and building for healthy communities. MIT Press, Cambridge, Massachusetts.

Frumkin, H. (2005) Environmental health: From global to local. Jossey Bass, San Fransisco.

Fuller, R.A., Irvine, K.N., Devine-Wright, P., Warren, P.H. & Gaston, K.J. (2007) Psychological benefits of greenspace increase with biodiversity. *Biology Letters,* **3**, 390–394.

Fox, K. (2000) The effects of exercise on self-perceptions and self-esteem. Physical Activity and Psychological Well-Being. (eds S. Biddle, K. Fox, & S. Boutcher). Routledge, London. pp. 88–117.

Gill, S., Handley, J., Ennos, A. & Pauleit, S. (2007) Adapting cities for climate change: The role of the greenspace. *Built Environment,* **33**, 115–133.

Godfray, C.J., Beddington, J.R., Crute, I.R., Haddad, L., Lawrence, D., Nuir, J.F., J., P., Robinson, S., Thomas, S.M. & Toulmin, C. (2010) Food security: The challenge of feeding 9 billion people. *Science,* **327**, 812–818.

Goldberg, D.C. (1978) Manual of the General Health Questionnaire. NFER Publishing, Windsor.

Goldberg, D.P., Gater, R., Sartorius, N., Ustun, T.B., Piccinelli, M., Gureje, O. & Rutter, C. (1997) The validity of two versions of the GHQ in the WHO study of mental illness in general health care. *Psychological Medicine,* **27**, 191–197.

Grahn, P. & Stigsdotter, U.A. (2003) Landscape planning and stress. *Urban Forestry & Urban Greening,* **2**, 1–18.

Gray, M.C., Altman, J.C. & Halasz, N. (2005) The economic value of wild resources to the indigenous community of the Wallis Lakes Catchment. Blackie and Son, London.

Grove, J.M., O'Neil-Dunne, J., Pelletier, K., Nowak, D.J. & Walton, J. (2006) A report on New York cities prsent and possible urban tree canopy. University of Vermont, Burlington.

Handy, S.L., Boarnet, M.G., Ewing, R. & Killingsworth, R.E. (2002) How the built environment affects physical activity: Views from urban planning. *American Journal of Preventive Medicine,* **23**, 64–73.

Hans, T.A. (2000) A meta-analysis of the effects of adventure programming on locus of control. *Journal of Contemporary Psychotherapy,* **30**, 33–60.

Hansen-Ketchum, P., Marck, P. & Reutter, L. (2009) Engaging with nature to promote health: New directions for nursing research. *Journal of Advanced Nursing,* **65**, 1527-1538.

Harter, S. (1982) The perceived competence scale for children. *Child Development,* **53**, 87–97.

Hartig, T., Mang, M. & Evans, G.W. (1991) Restorative effects of natural environment experiences. *Environment and Behaviour,* **23**, 3–26.

Hartig, T., Book, A., Garvill, J., Olsson, T. & Garling, T. (1996) Environmental influences on psychological restoration. *Scandinavian Journal of Psychology,* **37**, 378–393.

Hartig, T. (2003) Guest Editor's Introduction: Restorative Environments. *Journal of Environmental Psychology, 23*, 103–107.

Hartig, T., Evans, G., Jamner, L.D., Davis, D.S. & Garling, T. (2003) Tracking restoration in natural and urban field settings. *Journal of Environmental Psychology, 23*, 109–123.

Hassink, J. (2003) Combining agricultural production and care for persons with disabilities: a new role of agriculture and farm animals. Farming and Rural Systems Research and Extension. Local identities and Globalisation (eds A. Cirstovao, & L.O. Zorini). Fifth IFSA European Symposium, 8-11 April 2002. Florence, Wageningen University, Netherlands. pp. 332–341.

Haubenhofer, D.K., Elings, M., Hassink, J. & Hine, R. (2010) The devlopment of green care in Western European countries. *Explore, 6*, 106–111.

Heaton, A. (2001) Duck Decoys. Shire Books, Buckinghamshire.

HEW (US Department of Health Education and Welfare) (2004) Role of blood pressure in cardiovascular morbidity and mortality. Progress in Cardiovascular Diseases, **17**, 5–24.

Hine, R., Peacock, J. & Pretty, J. (2007) Green spaces: Measuring the benefits, drawing on case studies from the East of England. Report for the National Trust. University of Essex, Colchester. [online] Available at: <http://www.nationaltrust.org.uk/main/w-green-_lungs.pdf> [Accessed 04.05.11].

Hine, R., Peacock, J. & Pretty, J. (2008a) Care Farming in the UK: evidence and opportunities. University of Essex, Colchester.

Hine, R., Peacock, J. & Pretty, J. (2008b) Evaluating the impact of environmental volunteering on behaviours and attitudes to the environment. Report for BTCV Cymru. University of Essex, Colchester.

Hine, R., Pretty, J. & Barton, J. (2009) Research project: Social, psychologlical and cultural benefits of large natural habitat and wilderness experience: A review of current literature. Report for the Wilderness Foundation. University of Essex, Colchester.

Hine, R., Wood, C., Barton, J. & Pretty, J. (2011) The mental health and well-being effects of a walking and outdoor based theapy project. A report for Discovery Quest. University of Essex, Colchester.

Hollick, M.F. (2004) Sunlight and vitamin D for bone health and prevention of autoimmune diseases, cancers and cardiovascular disease. *American Journal of Clinical Nutrition*, **80**, 1678S–1688S.

Hollick, M.F. (2005) Vitamin D: Important for prevention of osteoporosis, cardiovascular heart disease, type 1 diabetes, autoimmune diseases, and some cancers. *Southern Medical Association,* **98**, 1024–1027.

Honeyman, M.C. (1992) Vegetation and Stress: A comparison study of varying amounts of vegetation in countryside and urban scenes. The Role of Horticulture in Human Well-Being and Social Development: A National Symposium. (eds D. Relf). Timber Press, Portland. pp. 143-145.

HSE (Health and Safety Executive) (2008) Self-reported work-related stress and workplace injuries in 2006–07. National Statistics Publication, London.

Hug, S.M., Hartig, T., Hansmann, R., Seeland, K. & Hornung, R. (2009) Restorative qualities of indoor and outdoor exercise settings as predictors of exercise frequency. *Health and Place*, **15**, 971–980.

Hull, R.B. (1991) Mood as a product of leisure: Causes and consequences. Benefits of Leisure (eds B.L. Driver, P.J. Brown, & G.L. Peterson). Venture Publishing, Inc, State College, Pennsylvania. pp. 249–262.

Huppert, F. & Whittington, J. (2003) Evidence for the independence of positive and negative wellbeing: Implications for quality of life assessment. *British Journal of Health Psychology,* **8**, 107–122.

Kahn, P.H. & Kellert, S.R. (2002) Children and nature: Psychological, sociocultural and evolutionary investigations. MIT Press, Cambridge, Massachusetts.

Kampman, M.T., Wilsgaard, T. & Mellgren, S.I. (2007) Outdoor activities and diet in childhood and adolescence relate to MS risk above the Arctic Circle. *Journal Of Neurology*, **254**, 471–477.

Kaplan, R. & Kaplan, S. (1989) The experience of nature: A psychological perspective. Cambridge University Press, Cambridge.

Kaplan, R. (1992) The psychological benefits of nearby nature. The role of horticulture in human well-being and social development: A National Symposium. (eds D. Relf). Timber Press, Portland. pp. 125–133.

Kaplan, R. (2001) The nature of the view from home. *Journal of Environment and Behaviour*, **33**, 507–542.

Kawachi, I., Kennedy, B., Lochner, K. & Prothrow-Smith, D. (1997) Social capital, income inequality and mortality. *American Journal of Public Health*, **87**, 1491–1498.

Keys, A., Aravanis, C., Blackburn, H., Van Buchem, F.S., Buzina, R., Djordjevic, B.S., Fidanza, F., Karvonen, M.J., Menotti, A., Puddu, V. & Taylor, H.L. (1972) Coronary heart-disease: Overweight and obesity as risk factors. *Annals Internal Medicine*, **77**.

Kolokotroni, M. & Giridharan, R. (2008) Urban heat island intensity in London: An investigation of the impact of physical characteristics on changes in outdoor air temperature during the summer. *Solar Energy*, **82**, 986–998.

Kruger, K.A. & Serpell, A. (2006) Animal-assisted interventions in mental health. Academic Press, San Diego.

Kuo, F.E. & Sullivan, W.C. (2001a) Environment and crime in the inner city: Does vegetation reduce crime? *Journal of Environment and Behaviour*, **33**, 343–367.

Kuo, F.E. & Sullivan, W.C. (2001b) Aggression and violence in the inner city: Effects of environment via mental fatigue. *Environment and Behaviour*, **33**, 543–571.

Kuo, F.E., Sullivan, W.C., Coley, R.L. & Brunson, L. (1998) Fertile ground for community: Inner-city neighbourhood common spaces. *American Journal of Community Psychology* **26**, 823–851.

Laumann, K., Gärling, T. & Stormark, K.M. (2003) Selective attention and heart rate responses to natural and urban environments. *Journal of Environmental Psychology, 23*, 125-134.

Layard, R. (2005) Happiness. Allen Lane, London.

Leonti, M., Nebel, S., Rivera, D. & Heinrich, M. (2006) Wild gathered food plants in the European Mediterranean. *Economic Botany*, **60**, 130–142.

Lewis, C.E., Siegel, J.M. & Lewis, M.A. (1984) Feeling bad: Exploring sources of distress among pre-adolescent children. *American Journal of Public Health*, **74**, 117–122.

Li, Q., Morimoto, K., Nakadai, A. & *al, e.* (2007) Forest bathing enhances human natural killer activity and expression of anti-cancer proteins. *International Journal of Immunopathology and Pharmacology,* **20**, 3–8.

Lim, K. & Taylor, L. (2005) Factors associated with physical activity among older people: A population-based study. *Preventive Medicine,* **40**, 33–40.

Lohr, V.I., Pearson-Mims, C.H. & Goodwin, G.K. (1996) Interior plants may improve worker productivity and reduce stress in a windowless environment. *Journal of Environmental Horticulture,* **14**, 97–100.

Louv, R. (2005) Last child in the woods: Saving our children from nature-deficit disorder. Algonquin Books, North Carolina.

Maas, J., Verheij, R.A., Groenewegen, P.P., De Vries, S. & Spreeuwenberg, P. (2006) Green space, urbanity, and health: How strong is the relation? *Journal Epidemiology Community Health,* **60**, 587–592.

Mabey, R. (1996) Flora Britannica. Sinclair-Stevenson, London. pp. 480.

MacKerron, G. & Mourato, S. (2011) Mappiness: Quantifying wellbeing in relation to environment across space and time. European Association of Environmental and Resource Economists 18th Annual Conference, 29 June - 2 July, Rome.

Maller, C., Townsend, M., Brown, P. & St Leger, L. (2002) Healthy Parks Healthy People: The health benefits of contact with nature in a park context. Deakin University and Parks Victoria, Melbourne, Australia. [online] Available at: <http://www.parkweb.vic.gov.au/resources/mhphp/pv1.pdf> [Accessed 04.04.11].

Maller, C., Townsend, M., Pryor, A., Brown, P. & St Leger, L. (2006) Healthy Nature Healthy People: 'contact with nature' as an upstream health promotion intervention for populations. *Health Promotion International,* **21**, 45–54.

Martini, F.H. (2006) Fundamentals of anatomy and physiology. Pearson Education Inc.

Mayer, F.S. & McPherson Frantz, C. (2004) The connectedness to nature scale: A measure of individuals' feeling in community with nature. *Journal of Environmental Psychology,* **24**, 503–515.

McDonald, A.G., Bealey, W.J., Fowler, D., Dragosits, U., Skiba, U., Smith, R.I., Donovan, R.G., Brett, H.E., Hewitt, C.N. & Nemitz, E. (2007) Quantifying the effect of urban tree planting on concentrations and deposition of PM_{10} in two UK conurbations. *Atmospheric Environment,* **41**.

McNair, D.M., Lorr, M. & Droppleman, L.F. (1971) EdITS manual for the Profile of Mood States. Educational and Industrial Testing Service, San Diego, California.

McNicholas, J. & Collis, G.M. (2006) Animals as social supports: Insights for understanding animal assisted therapy. Elsevier, San Diego.

Mental Health Foundation (2009) Moving on up. Mental Health Foundation, London.

Mind (2007) Ecotherapy: The green agenda for mental health. Mind week report, May 2007. Mind, London.

Mitchell, R. & Popham, F. (2007) Greenspace, urbanity and health: Relationships in England. *Journal of Epidemiology and Community Health,* **61**, 681-683.

Mitchell, R. & Popham, F. (2008) Effect of exposure to natural environment on health inequalities: An observational population study. *The Lancet,* **372**, 1655–1660.

Morita, E., Fukuda, S., Nagano, J., Hamajima, N., Yamamoto, H., Iwai, Y., Nakashima, T., Ohira, H. & Shirakawa, T. (2006) Psychological effects of forest environments on healthy adults: Shinrin-yoku (forest-air bathing, walking) as a possible method of stress reduction. *Public Health,* **121**, 54–63.

Moore, E.O. (1982) A prison environment's effect on health care service demands. *Journal of Environmental Systems,* **11**, 17–34.

Moote, G.T. & Wadarski, J.S. (1997) The acquisition of life skills through adventure-based activities and programmes: A review of the literature. *Adolescence,* **32**, 143–167.

Morecroft, M.D., Taylor, M.E. & Oliver, H.R. (1998) Air and soil microclimates of deciduous woodland compared to an open site. *Agricultural and Forest Meterology,* **90**, 141–156.

Mourato, S. & MacKerron, G. (2010) Cultural services and subjective wellbeing. London School of Economics and Political Science, London.

NCFI (National Care Farming Initiative) (2011) National Care Farming Initiative (UK). [online] Available at: <http://www.ncfi.org.uk> [Accessed 18.09.10].

Newman, J. & Moller, H. (2005) Use of Matauranga (Maori traditional knowledge) and science to guide a seabird harvest: Getting the best of both worlds? *Senri Ethnological Studies,* **67**, 303–321.

NHS (National Health Service) (2011a) National Health Service choices. [online] Available at: <http://www.nhs.uk/Tools/Pages/Healthyweightcalculator.aspx> [Accessed 16.01.11].

NHS (National Health Service) (2011b) Lyme disease. [online] Available at: <http://www.nhs.uk/conditions/Lyme-disease> [Accessed 23.01.11].

NICE (National Institute for Health and Clinical Excellence) (2008) Physical activity and the environment. National Institute for Health and Clinical Excellence, London.

NICE (National Institute for Health and Clinical Excellence) (2009) Promoting physical activity for children and young people. National Institute for Health and Clinical Excellence, London.

NIH (National Institute of Health) (2011) National Institute of Health (US). [online] Available at: <http://www.nhlbi.nih.gov/health/public/heart/obesity/lose_wt/risk.htm> [Accessed 23.01.11].

Nisbet, E., Zelenski, J. & Murphy, S. (2009) The Nature Relatedness Scale: Linking indivduals connection with nature to environmental concern and behaviour. *Environment and Behavior,* **41**, 715–740.

Nisbet, E. (2011) Nature Relatedness Research. [online] Available at: <http://chat.carleton.ca/~enisbet/nature_relatedness_research.htm> [Accessed 15.02.11].

Nowak, D.J. (2006) Air pollution removal by urban trees and shrubs in the United States. *Urban Forestry & Urban Greening,* **4**, 115–123.

O'Brien, E., Waeber, B., Parati, G., Staessen, J. & Myers, M.G. (2001) Blood Pressure measuring devices: Recommendations of the European Society of Hypertension. *British Medical Journal,* **322**, 531–536.

Oldfield, T.E.E., Smith, R.J., Harrup, S.R. & Leader-Williams, N. (2003) Field and sports conservation in the UK. *Nature,* **423**, 531–533.

Ozer, S., Irmak, A. & Yilmaz, H. (2008) Determination of roadside noise reduction effectiveness of *Pinus Sylvestris L.* and *Populus Nigra L.* in Erzurum, Turkey. *Noise and Water Inception,* **144**, 191–197.

Park, B.J., Yuko, T., Tamami, K., Takahide, K. & Yoshifumi, M. (2010) The physiological effects of Shinrin-yoku (taking in the forest atmosphere or forest bathing): Evidence from field experiments in 24 forests across Japan. *Environmental Health and Preventive Medicine, 15*, 18–26.

Parks, S.E., Housemann, R.A. & Brownson, R.C. (2003) Differential correlates of physical activity in urban and rural adults of various socioeconomic backgrounds in the United States. *Journal of Epidemiology and Community Health, 57*, 29–35.

Parliamentary Office of Science and Technology (2007) UK trees and forests. Postnote, London.

Parsons, R. (1991) The potential influences of environmental perception on human health. *Journal of Environmental Psychology, 11*, 1–23.

Parsons, R., Tassinary, L.G., Ulrich, R.S., Hebl, M.R. & Grossman-Alexander, M. (1998) The view from the road: Implications for stress recovery and immunization. *Journal of Environmental Psychology, 18*, 113–139.

Pathak, V., Tripathi, B.D. & Mishra, V.K. (2011) Evaluation of anticipated peformance index of some tree species for green belt development to mitigate traffic generated noise. *Urban Forestry & Urban Greening, 10*, 61–66.

Peacock, J., Hine, R. & Pretty, J. (2007) Got the Blues, then find some Greenspace: The mental health benefits of green exercise activities and green care. Report for Mind. University of Essex, Chesterton.

Peacock, J., Hine, R. & Pretty, J. (2008) The Turn Around 2007 Project. Report for the Wilderness Foundation. University of Essex, Colchester.

Pieroni, A. (1999) Gathered wild foods in the upper valley of the Serchio River (Garfagnana), Central Italy. *Economic Botany, 53*, 327–341.

Pilgrim, S., Smith, D. & Pretty, J. (2007) A cross-regional assessment of the factors affecting ecoliteracy: Implications for policy and practice. *Ecological Applications, 17*, 1742–1751.

Pilgrim, S.E., Cullen, L.C., Smith, D.J. & Pretty, J. (2008) Ecological knowledge is lost in wealthier communities and countries. *Environmental Science and Technology, 42*, 1004–1009.

Pitcairn, C.E.R., Leith, I.D., Sheppard, L.J., Sutton, M.A., Fowler, D., Munro, R.C., Tang, S. & Wilson, D. (1998) The relationship between nitrogen deposition, species composition and foliar nitrogen concentrations in woodland flora in the vicinity of livestock farms. *Environmental Pollution, 102*, 41–48.

Pretty, J. & Ward, H. (2001) Social capital and the environment. *World Development, 29*, 209–227.

Pretty, J., Griffin, M., Sellens, M. & Pretty, C. (2003) Green Exercise: Complementary roles of nature, exercise and diet in physical and emotional well-being and implications for public health policy. CES Occasional Paper 2003-1, pp. 38.

Pretty, J. & Smith, D. (2004) Social capital in biodiversity conservation and management. *Conservation Biology, 18,* 631–638.

Pretty, J. (2005) The pesticide detox. Earthscan, London.

Pretty, J., Peacock, J., Sellens, M. & Griffin, M. (2005) The mental and physical health outcomes of green exercise. *International Journal of Environmental Health Research, 15*, 319–337.

Pretty, J. (2006) From green exercise to green care: A new opportunity for farming in the UK? University of Essex, Colchester.

Pretty, J., Hine, R. & Peacock, J. (2006) Green Exercise: The benefits of activities in green places. *The Biologist, 53*, 143–148.

Pretty, J., Peacock, J., Hine, R., Sellens, M., South, N. & Griffin, M. (2007) Green exercise in the UK countryside: Effects on health and psychological well-being and implications for policy and planning. *Journal of Environmental Planning and Management, 50*, 211–231.

Pretty, J., Angus, C., Bain, M., Barton, J., Gladwell, V., Hine, R., Pilgrim, S., Sandercock, G. & Sellens, M. (2009) Nature, childhood, health and life pathways. Interdisciplinary Centre for Environment and Society Occasional Paper 2009-02. University of Essex, Colchester, UK. pp. 1–30.

Pretty, J. (2011) This luminous coast. Full Circle Editions, Saxmundham.

Rehdanz, K. & Maddison, D. (2005) Climate and happiness. *Ecological Economics, 52*, 111–125.

Rehdanz, K. & Maddison, D. (2008) Local environment quality and life-satisfaction in Germany. *Ecological Economics, 64*, 787–797.

Roland, G. (2006) Atchafalaya Houseboat. Louisiana State University Press, Baton Rouge.

Rosenberg, M. (1965) Society and the adolescent self-image. Princeton University Press, Princeton, New Jersey.

Ross, C.E. (2000) Walking, exercising and smoking: Does neighbourhood matter? *Social Science and Medicine, 51*, 265–274.

Rowe, D.B. (2010) Green roofs as a means of pollution abatement. *Environmental Pollution*, 1–11.

Rubinstein, N.J. (1997) The psychological value of open space. The Benefits of Open Space. (eds L.W. Hamilton). The Great Swamp Watershed Association, New Jersey.

Russell, K.C. & Phillips-Miller, D. (2002) Perspectives on the wilderness therapy process and its relation to outcome. *Child and Youth Care Forum, 31*, 415–437.

Russell, K.C. (2006) Brat camp, boot camp, or...? Exploring wilderness therapy program theory. *Journal of Adventure Education and Outdoor Learning, 6*, 51–68.

Rutter, M., Tizard, J. & Whitmore, K. (1970) Education, health and behaviour. Longmans, London.

Ryan, R.M., Weinstein, N., Bernstein, J., Warren Brown, K., Mistretta, L. & Gagne, M. (2010) Vitalizing effects of being outdoors and in nature. *Journal of Environmental Psychology, 30*, 159–168.

Samson, C. & Pretty, J. (2005) Environmental and health benefits of hunting lifestyles and diets for the Innu of Ladrador. *Food Policy, 31*, 528-533.

Sandercock, G., Voss, C., McConnell, D. & Rayner, P. (2010) The cardiorespiratory fitness of affluent English children are largely independent of changes in body mass index. *Archives of Disease in Childhood, 95*, 46–47.

Sempik, J., Aldridge, J. & Becker, S. (2003) Social and therapeutic horticulture: Evidence and messages from research. University of Loughborough. Centre for Child and Family Research, Reading, UK. pp. 60.

Sempik, J. (2007) Researching social and therapeutic horticulture for people with mental ill-health: A study of methodology. Thrive in association with the CCFR (Centre for Child and Family Research), Loughborough University, Leicestershire, UK.

Sempik, J., Hine, R. & Wilcox, D. (2010) Green care: A conceptual framework. A report for the working group on the health benefits of green care. COST Action. Loughborough University, Leicestershire, UK.

Spielberger, C.D. (1970) State-Trait Anxiety Inventory. John Wiley & Sons, Inc., New Jersey.

Sport England (2006) Active People Survey 2005/6. Sport England, London.

Steinbrecher, R., Smiatek, G., Koble, R., Seufert, G., Theloke, J., Hauff, K., Ciccioli, P., Vautard, R. & Curci, G. (2008) Intra- and inter-annual variability of VOC emissions from natural and semi-natural vegetation in Europe and Neighbouring countries. *Atmospheric Environment, 43*, 1380–1391.

Stephenson, J. & Moller, H. (2009) Cross-cultural environmental research and management. *Journal of the Royal Society of New Zealand, 39*, 139–149.

Sugiyama, T., Leslie, E., Giles-Corti, B. & Owen, N. (2008) Associations of neighbourhood greenness with physical and mental health: Do walking, social coherence and local social interaction explain the relationships? *Journal of Epidemiology and Community Health, 62*, e9.

Takano, T., Nakamura, K. & Watanabe, M. (2002) Urban residential environments and senior citizens' longevity in megacity areas: The importance of walkable green spaces. *Journal of Epidemiology and Community Health, 56*, 913–918.

Tamura, Y., Kobayashi, Y., Watanabe, S. & Endou, K. (1997) Relationship of pollen counts of Japanese cedar to weather factors in Isehara City, Kanagawa. *Nippon Jibi Inkoka Gakkai Kaiho, 100*, 326–331.

Tardio, J., Pascual, H. & Morales, R. (2003) Wild food plants traditionally used in the province of Madrid, Central Spain *Economic Botany, 59*, 122–136.

Task Force (1996) Heart rate variability: standards of measurement, physiological interpretation and clinical use. Task force of the European Society of Cardiology and the North American Society of Pacing and Electrophysiology. *Circulation, 93*, 1043–1065.

Taylor, A.F., Kuo, F.E. & Sullivan, W.C. (2002) Views of nature and self-discipline: Evidence from inner city children. *Journal of Environmental Psychology, 22*, 49–64.

Teas, J., Hurley, T., Ghumare, S. & Ogoussan, K. (2007) Walking outside improves mood for healthy postmenopausal women. *Clinical Medicine: Oncology, 1*, 35–43.

Tennyson, J. (1949) Suffolk Scene. A book of description and adventure. Blackie and Son, London.

Thomas, G. & Thompson, G. (2004) A child's place: Why environment matters to children. Green Alliance / Demos Report, London.

Thompson Coon, J., Boddy, K., Stein, K., Whear, R., Barton, J. & Depledge, M.H. (2011) Does participating in physical activity in outdoor natural environments have a greater effect on physical and mental wellbeing than physical activity indoors? A systematic review. *Environmental Science & Technology, 45*, 1761–1772.

Tiwary, A., Sinnett, D., Peachey, C., Chalabi, Z., Vardoulakis, S., Fletcher, T., Leonardi, G., Grundy, C., Azapagic, A. & Hutchings, T.R. (2009) An integrated tool to assess the role of new planting in PM_{10} capture and the human health benefits: a case study in London. *Environmental Pollution, 157*, 2645–2653.

Torres, R. & Fernandez, F. (1995) Self-esteem and the value of health as determinants of adolescent behaviour. *Journal of Adolescent Health Care, 16*, 60–63.

Treiber, F.A., Musante, L., Hartdagan, S., Davis, H., Levy, M. & Strong, W.B. (1989) Validation of a heart rate monitor with children in laboratory and field settings. *Medicine and Science in Sports and Exercise, 21*, 338–342.

Ulrich, R.S. (1981) Natural versus urban scenes: Some psychophysiological effects. *Journal of Environment and Behaviour, 13*, 523–556.

Ulrich, R.S. (1984) View through a window may influence recovery from surgery. *Science, 224*, 420–421.

Ulrich, R.S., Simons, R.F., Losito, B.D., Fiorito, E., Miles, M.A. & Zelson, M. (1991) Stress recovery during exposure to natural and urban environments. *Journal of Environmental Psychology, 11*, 201–230.

Ulrich, R.S. (2002) Health benefits of gardens in hospitals. Conference for Plants for People – International Exhibition. Florida, United States of America.

van den Berg, A.E., Koole, S.L. & Van der Wulp, N.Y. (2003) Environmental preference and restoration: (How) are they related? *Journal of Environmental Psychology, 23*, 135–146.

van den Berg, A.E., Hartig, T. & Staats, H. (2007) Preference for nature in urbanised societies: Stress, restoration and the pursuit of sustainability. *Journal of Social Issues, 63*, 79–96.

van Praag, B.M.S. & Baarsma, B.E. (2005) Using happiness surveys to value intangibles: The case of airport noise. *The Economic Journal , 115*, 224-226.

Wanless, D. (2002) Securing our future health: Taking a long-term view. HM Treasury, London. <http://www.hm-treasury.gov.uk/Consultations_and_Legislation/wanless/consult_wanless_final.cfm> [Accessed 04.04.11].

Wanless, D. (2004) Securing good health for the whole population. HM Treasury, London.

Ward Thompson, C. (2002) Urban open space in the 21st Century. *Landscape and Urban Planning, 60*, 59–72.

Ward Thompson, C., Aspinall, P. & Montarzino, A. (2008) The childhood factor: Adult visits to green places and the significance of childhood experience. *Environment and Behaviour, 40*, 111–143.

Watson, R.T., Patz, J., Gubler, D.J., Parson, E.A. & Vincent, J.H. (2005) Environmental health implications of global climate change. *Journal of Environmental Monitoring, 7*, 834–843.

Wells, N.M. (2000) At home with nature: effects of "greenness" on children's cognitive functioning. *Environment and Behaviour, 32*, 775–795.

Wells, N.M. & Evans, G.W. (2003) Nearby nature: A buffer of life stress among rural children. *Environment and Behaviour, 35*, 311–330.

Wells, N.M. & Lekies, K.S. (2006) Nature and the life course: Pathways from adulthood nature experience to adult environmentalism. *Children Youth and Environments, 16*, 1–24.

Wells, N.M., Ashdown, S., Davies, E.H.S., Cowett, F.D. & Yang, Y. (2007) Environment, design and obesity. Opportunities for interdisciplinary collaborative research. *Environment and Behaviour, 39*, 6–33.

Welsch, H. (2006) Environment and happiness: Valuation of air pollution using life satisfaction data. *Ecological Economics, 58*.

Wentworth Day, J. (1949) Coastal Adventure. Harrap, London.

Wentworth Day, J. (1950) Marshland Adventure. Harrap, London.

West, M.J. (1985) Landscape views and stress response in the prison environment. Department of Landscape, Architecture. University of Washington, Seattle.

Whitehouse, S., Varni, J.W., Seid, M., Cooper-Marcus, C., Ensberg, M.J., Jacobs, J.R. & Mehlenbeck, R.S. (2001) Evaluating a children's hospital garden environment: Utilisation and consumer satisfaction. *Journal of Environmental Psychology, 21,* 301–314.

WHO (World Health Organization) (1948) Preamble to the Constitution of the World Health Organization as adopted by the International Health Conference. 19–22 June 1946, New York, United States of America.

WHO (World Health Organization) (1995) Physical Status: The use and interpretation of Anthropometry. WHO, Geneva.

WHO (World Health Organisation) (2005) Ecosystems and human well-being. Health synthesis. WHO, Geneva.

WHO (World Health Organisation) (2011) BMI database website. [online] Available at: <http://apps.who.int/bmi/index.jsp?introPage=intro_3.html> [Accessed 16.02.11].

Wood, L. & Giles-Corti, B. (2008) Is there a place for social capital in the psychology of health and place? *Journal of Environmental Psychology, 28,* 154–163.

Yang, J., McBride, J., Zhou, J. & Sun, Z. (2005) The urban forest in Beijing and its role in air pollution reduction. *Urban Forestry & Urban Greening, 3,* 65–78.

Ziska, L.H. & Caulfield, F.A. (2000) Rising CO_2 and pollen production of common ragweed, a known allergy-inducing species: implications for public health. *Australian Journal of Plant Physiology, 27,* 893–898.

Zuckerman, M. (1977) The development of a situation-specific trait-state test for the prediction and measurement of affective responses. *Journal of Consulting and Clinical Psychology, 45,* 513–523.

Appendix 23.1 Approach Used to Assign Certainty Terms to Chapter Key Findings

This chapter began with a set of Key Findings. Adopting the approach and terminology used by the Intergovernmental Panel on Climate Change (IPCC) and the Millennium Assessment (MA), these Key Findings also include an indication of the level of scientific certainty. The 'uncertainty approach' of the UK NEA consists of a set of qualitative uncertainty terms derived from a 4-box model and complemented, where possible, with a likelihood scale (see below). Estimates of certainty are derived from the collective judgement of authors, observational evidence, modelling results and/or theory examined for this assessment.

Throughout the Key Findings presented at the start of this chapter, superscript numbers and letters indicate the estimated level of certainty for a particular key finding:

1. *Well established:*   high agreement based on significant evidence
2. *Established but incomplete evidence:* high agreement based on limited evidence
3. *Competing explanations:*   low agreement, albeit with significant evidence
4. *Speculative:*   low agreement based on limited evidence

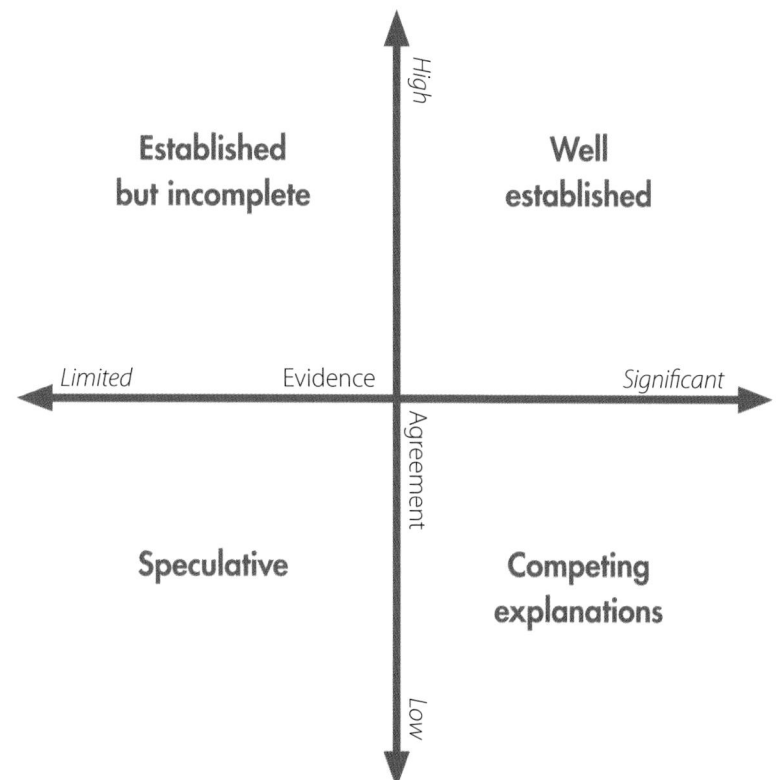

a. *Virtually certain:*   >99% probability of occurrence
b. *Very likely:*   >90% probability
c. *Likely:*   >66% probability
d. *About as likely as not:*   >33–66% probability
e. *Unlikely:*   <33% probability
f. *Very unlikely:*   <10% probability
g. *Exceptionally unlikely:*   <1% probability

Certainty terms 1 to 4 constitute the 4-box model, while *a* to *g* constitute the likelihood scale.

Chapter 24:
Shared Values for the Contributions Ecosystem Services Make to Human Well-being

Coordinating Lead Authors: Robert Fish, Jacquelin Burgess, Andrew Church and Kerry Turner

Key Findings

Ecosystem assessment requires a consideration of shared values. Valuing the contribution that ecosystem services make to human well-being cannot be reduced to individual preferences and motivations alone. Ecosystem services have collective meaning and significance. Whether individuals choose to regard themselves as isolated beings driven to satisfy their own needs and desires before taking account of others' needs, or whether they see themselves as wanting to moderate their rights to maximise their own satisfaction because they have shared responsibility for collective well-being, is a matter of context and philosophical perspective.

Shared values concern the values people hold for ecosystem services as 'citizens'; that is as 'social beings' capable of expressing preferences for ecosystem services not simply in terms of individual costs and benefits, but in terms of social rights and wrongs. An important dimension of shared values is, therefore, consideration of the ethical arrangements which guide society's concern for nature, place and landscape, and includes issues of altruism and existence value, as well as aesthetic considerations.

The reliability and legitimacy of decision-making processes that flow from ecosystem assessment depends on the explicit recognition of shared values. This is particularly the case when trade-offs have to be made between utilitarian, ethical and aesthetic dimensions of change. In order to ensure public trust and confidence when reaching difficult decisions, decision-makers need to be able to demonstrate knowledge and understanding of the shared values individuals and social groups attribute to their interactions with the natural world.

Consideration of shared values within ecosystem assessment and decision-making requires a more interpretative approach to valuation. The primary focus is on qualitative expressions of value for ecosystem services. Evidence for these values may be explored textually, such as through the interpretation of documents and media, but also via group discussion, learning and deliberation. As such, there is a natural overlap between these techniques and non-monetary forms of valuation. However, the use of deliberation within decision-making can also be used to link social values to quantitative and monetary valuation techniques. The key techniques are 'deliberative monetary valuation' and 'participatory multi-criteria analysis'.

There is an overall need for theoretical and methodological plurality in how we assess the value of ecosystem services for human well-being. Just as there are quite different grounds on which judgments of value can be communicated and inferred for ecosystem services, so too are there many different ways in which values can be formally recorded and assigned significance. Both individual and collective values have validity in their own right to ecosystem assessment and corresponding processes of decision-making. Hybrid valuation techniques, such as deliberative monetary valuation and participatory multi-criteria analysis, hold much promise for systematic and integrated treatment of utilitarian, ethical and aesthetic considerations, although they remain at an experimental stage.

24.1 Introduction

The UK NEA Conceptual Framework (Chapter 2) emphasises the need for holistic valuation of ecosystem services. It is explained that within economic analysis the conventional focus is on assessing the monetary value of environmental goods to individuals. While this approach is fundamental to the analysis of the UK NEA, the Conceptual Framework recognises that this is not an exhaustive way of thinking about ecosystem services in the context of valuation. Holistic valuation implies the need for theoretical and methodological plurality in how we think about the importance of ecosystem services to human well-being. One important facet of this, which is the focus of this chapter, is the need to give due recognition to shared values for ecosystem services. In general terms, this dimension of the valuation debate concerns the way ecosystem services are assigned collective meaning and significance by citizens, that is, values for services that cannot be reduced to individual preferences and motivations alone. The purpose of this chapter is to consider the analytical and methodological dimensions of incorporating such shared values into ecosystem assessment alongside the conventional focus of inferring what individuals are prepared to pay for a given environmental good.

The chapter begins by revisiting some of the general arguments made in Chapter 2 regarding distinctions within economic analysis between individual and collective forms of valuation. It then goes on to consider how traditions of work within the humanities and social sciences may make sense of shared values in the context of valuation. A general distinction is drawn between interpretive methods based on analysing cultural texts, and those that involve directly interacting with people. Against this background, the chapter describes how novel methodological tools are now emerging from within ecological economics that may be used to derive monetary values for ecosystem services through collective (group-based) discussion and deliberation. These tools may be used to enhance the credibility of individual values for ecosystem services by overcoming weaknesses within conventional contingent valuation techniques; but more importantly, in the context of this chapter, they may also bring collective (social 'willingness to pay') values to bear directly upon valuation. The chapter then considers how complementary (non–monetary) values for ecosystem services can also be elicited by linking deliberative forums to multi-criteria approaches. This provides a further way of acknowledging shared values within ecosystem assessment and is important given wider philosophical problems that tend to arise when embedding ethical and aesthetic considerations into economic analysis. Finally, the chapter considers the status of shared values in the context of scenario-building, which is another important dimension of analysis within the UK NEA (Chapter 25).

24.2 Incorporating Shared Values: General Rationale

Ecosystem services valuation is an emerging area of policy appraisal where there is debate about the extent to which the full range of costs and benefits of marginal changes in provision can be quantified. Given the inherent complexity of nature, a number of different dimensions of nature-based value can be discerned and evaluated in various ways. These include: in monetary terms via economic analysis and the concept of Total Economic Value (TEV), where TEV = use value + non-use value; in biophysical and geochemical terms via natural science; and in cultural terms via the more interpretive social sciences, arts and humanities. Each of these dimensions of nature-based value has validity in its own domain.

Environmental philosophers have constructed a generic value typology with four categories: 'anthropocentric instrumental value' which maps closely onto the economic concepts of use and most of non-use values; 'anthropocentric intrinsic value', a culturally dependent concept expressing ethical and aesthetic principles of human stewardship of nature and which requires humans to ascribe intrinsic value to non-human nature—the economist's concept of 'existence value' can overlap into this value category. The other two value categories, 'non-anthropocentric instrumental value' and 'non- anthropocentric intrinsic value', are less directly relevant to ecosystem policy appraisal unless a radical ethical position is accepted as the societal norm, which is currently not the case (Hargrove 1992).

Within the TEV framework, the distinction is drawn between 'use' and 'non-use' values. Non-use value, such as existence value, derives from individuals who feel a benefit from knowing that, for example, an ecosystem and/or its component parts does exist, and will continue to exist, somewhere on the planet. The economic valuation literature has yet to reach a comprehensive consensus on whether use and non-use value can be formally distinguished using standard welfare economic measures. The use of survey-based methods, such as Contingent Valuation (CV) and Choice Modelling Experiments (CME), to elicit monetary expressions of existence values is still open to debate on the grounds of validity and reliability (Bateman *et al.* 2002; Sagoff 2011).

The conventional economic assumptions about human motivations and behaviour can be seen as quite restrictive. For example, findings from behavioural economics and psychology are extending the somewhat limited understanding within environmental economics of cognitive behaviour and the influence of networks of agents (individuals, groups, institutions and governments) on environmental values (Gowdy 2007; Welsch & Kuhling 2008; Rauch 2010). It seems that 'bequest' motivations (i.e. the requirement to pass on, over generational time, an 'environment' which can yield at least a constant set of 'opportunities'), existence value motivations and altruistic motives may all be relevant and real in certain environmental loss contexts.

Analysts disagree over how to interpret this set of possibly overlapping motivations and behaviours. Some see the welfare effect as an individualised 'warm glow' effect connected to the act of giving, while others insist that 'pure altruism' is required for existence value and can be recognised. The debate is further complicated by consumer-citizen distinctions (Sagoff 1988): individuals may assume either a utility-maximising (consumer) or common good, 'other regarding' (citizen) role in responding to CV surveys. As citizens, individuals may hold social preference values and motivations which may be best elicited through participation in some kind of collective or public forum.

If one accepts the position (as in conventional Cost-Benefit Analysis [CBA]) that only individual preferences yield 'real' values to be taken into account in the policy process and that individual behaviour is dominated by self-interest and self-regarding motives, then only a restricted version of existence value (contaminated by the 'warm glow' effect) is possible. Thus, value estimates derived from CV surveys will not necessarily indicate 'true' economic value derived from public goals such as the ecosystem service gain/loss under test. If, on the other hand, one is persuaded that citizen-type motivations and behaviour can be recognised, then other motives and social preferences—'true altruism'—exist. In the latter case, it is necessary to consider the adoption of techniques which offer opportunities for wider public and stakeholder participation, using methods which encourage dialogue and debate to arrive either at consensus about which bequest and existence values can be elicited, or agreement to differ in which the reasons for divergence are clarified.

When focusing on anthropocentric instrumental and intrinsic value in nature, it is important to note that the former value concept is usually interpreted in economic analysis in terms of an individual person (or sometimes aggregated household) and their preferences and motivations. The latter value concept, however, can also be viewed in a collective way such that motivations and preferences can be assigned to social groups, and may be culturally transmitted and assimilated over time as social norms. These shared values may not be captured adequately through monetary valuation, but they are important. Shared values demonstrate that human well-being (a richer concept than that of human welfare) and quality of life is a function of satisfying individual 'wants', but also the fulfillment of a variety of social, health-related, and cultural collective needs.

It is also important to acknowledge that ecosystem services classifications and approaches may lead to the 'commodification' of ecosystems, with the danger of consequent policy and management failure. Such failure would manifest itself in terms of an over-concentration on those ecosystem services and benefits of direct and indirect use/non-use to humans, with the risk of overexploitation and system change or collapse. Where the value of whole environmental systems is concerned, conventional economic valuation (restricted to the flow of service benefits) may not be sufficient. It is important to assess and conserve the structural and process/functional value of 'healthy' evolving ecosystems despite the formidable uncertainties surrounding likely thresholds for system change. The fundamental life-support services provided by ecosystems are clearly valuable, and the focus on the flow of assigned ecosystem benefit values is not meant to deny this. Healthy ecosystems, anchored to a sufficient configuration of structure and process, have 'prior' value (labelled 'primary', 'glue' or 'infrastructure' value) in the sense that the continued existence of the system's integrity determines the flow of all the instrumental and intrinsic values related to final ecosystem services and benefits. So total system value is always greater than total economic value (Gren *et al.* 1994; Turner *et al.* 2003). **Figure 24.1** summarises the arguments presented so far.

The fundamental challenge, identified in Defra's (2007) 'Introductory Guide to Valuing Ecosystem Services', is how to ensure policy appraisals fully capture the benefit provided to society by ecosystem provisioning, regulating, supporting and cultural services, as well as the costs of the impacts of policies on those services. One element of this challenge is to ensure that every value-producing technique used as evidence in an ecosystem services policy appraisal process is reliable and capable of generating results which are recognised to have validity. Such assurance is dependent on a number of factors including the integrity and defensibility of data from the natural sciences relating to the primary value of the ecosystem. This is difficult given issues of spatial and temporal scale, uncertainty, non-linearity and thresholds. Furthermore, ensuring the quality of knowledge about the multiple benefits of ecosystem services (provisioning, regulating, supporting and cultural services) is difficult since it requires the evaluation of evidence produced under different philosophical, theoretical and methodological assumptions.

Standards used to judge qualitative evidence will not be applicable to quantitative data, and *vice versa*. This presents significant difficulties for economic valuation of ecosystem services if the argument above is accepted, i.e. collective benefit-values are not the same as individual benefit-values. Measurement of the latter does not ensure the former are adequately captured, which may lead to distortions in the appraisal process. Developing an impact assessment methodology able to integrate monetary and non-monetary valuation approaches may assist in resolving this issue.

In Defra's (2007) Introductory Guide to Valuing Ecosystem Services it is argued that "the choice is not a case of either economic or non-economic valuation but of using a combination of both, as required by the context of the decision". It may be the case that the context of the decision would call for engagement with a broad range of stakeholders in an ecosystem services valuation, but there may be time, financial and practical constraints which place limits on what might be possible. Full-scale participatory and deliberative processes require levels of resource that may only be available to central government.

In summary, if society is simply the sum of isolated individuals, their wants and needs are, if not infinite, many

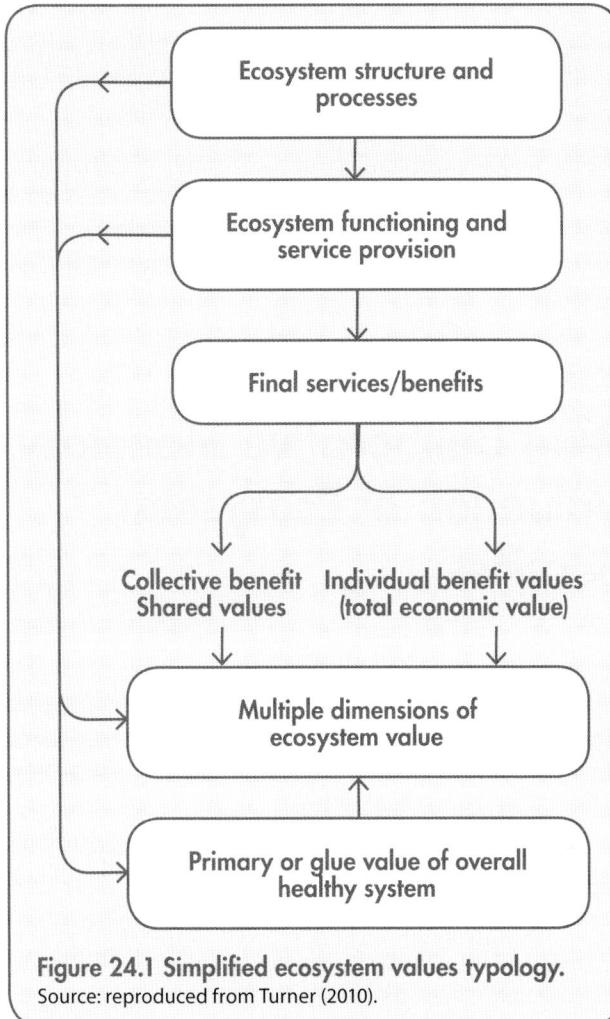

Figure 24.1 Simplified ecosystem values typology.
Source: reproduced from Turner (2010).

The boxes in the figure read:

Ecosystem structure and processes

Ecosystem functioning and service provision

Final services/benefits

Collective benefit Shared values

Individual benefit values (total economic value)

Multiple dimensions of ecosystem value

Primary or glue value of overall healthy system

examining these, though it would be misleading to suggest that there is a corpus of research explicitly registering its concerns as 'non-monetary assessments of the shared value of ecosystem services'. Work is placed within a variety of theoretical and disciplinary registers.

An important focus has been analysis of cultural texts: television, magazines, cinema, art and literature, official documentation and so forth (Burgess *et al.* 1991; Anderson 1997; Davies 2000; Fish 2007). As Turner (2010) explains, such texts are integral to an understanding of collective/ cultural values about change. From the perspective of ecosystem services, interpretative analysis of cultural texts can help make explicit what would otherwise remain tacit assumptions regarding the aesthetic, ethical and utilitarian dimensions of ecosystem worth.

Shared values for the natural world have also been explored by surveying people. Surveys of individuals represent a basic approach with many variants: quantitative and qualitative; extensive and intensive; structured and semi-structured. For instance, a recent study of cultural ecosystem services in marine landscapes by Gee and Burkhard (2010) used an extensive postal questionnaire to explore, in part, the aesthetic controversies surrounding offshore windfarm development in the German North Sea. In contrast, Dougill *et al.* (2006) used an intensive round of face to face semi-structured interviews with key informants to build an understanding of priorities for a socially valued landscape: the Peak District in England. There is voluminous literature within academic and public policy discourse utilising such survey methodologies to explore how people value and benefit from environmental settings under threat or change.

Since shared values are, by definition, a product of social and cultural interaction, it has also been common to provide contexts in which these values can be negotiated and articulated in group settings. The practice of bringing small groups of people together to share their feelings, experiences and values for local nature and greenspace developed in the mid 1980s in the UK with the Greenwich Open-Space project (Harrison *et al.* 1987; Burgess *et al.* 1988a,b,c). The commonest metaphor used in people's talk about why urban parks and greenspace mattered was that outdoor settings were 'a gateway to a better world', valued for the multiple contributions they made to community well-being. Studies of 'talk' were combined in the 1990s and 2000s with more novel ways of observing what people actually did when out in the natural world and interacting with living nature (Burgess 1995; Hinchliffe *et al.* 2005; Wild Ennerdale Partnership 2006). Since the landmark Royal Commission for Environmental Pollution report (RCEP 1998), such studies have been complemented by the use of a range of participatory and deliberative techniques which aim to introduce environmental values into decision-making processes in ways that are not reductive, i.e. shared values have not been reduced/reconfigured into statistical, questionnaire answers.

The general term we can use to convey the idea of shared (group-based) valuation of ecosystem services is 'deliberative valuation'. By deliberation we follow Stern and Fineberg (1996) in referring to a process by which: 'people

and diverse. If resources are scarce (relative or absolute), then CBA and its economic efficiency-based social welfare function is relevant to, and very useful for, public policy choice-making. Furthermore, given that all policy choices are made by humans, some conception of 'preferences' and their human motivation lie behind any environmental policy. Yet many would contend that collective society is more than the aggregation of individuals, other social welfare functions have validity and that techniques such as CBA tend to overlook issues of distribution, equity, fairness and justice (Sagoff 1988). They would dispute the economic (new welfare) explanation of how preferences are determined and would not agree that self-interest is the only 'rational' motivation. There are 'other regarding' preferences towards humans and other entities in nature.

24.3 Methodologies for Examining Shared Values

Shared values for the natural world are expressed through environmental discourses, practices and institutions. There is, in principle, considerable diversity in methodologies for

confer, ponder, exchange views, consider evidence, reflect on matters of mutual interest, negotiate, and attempt to persuade each other. Deliberation includes both consensual communication processes and adversarial ones'.

In a methodological sense, deliberation is grounded in 'talk' and the process of in-depth discussion around a particular topic or theme, ideally sustained over an extended period of time. Deliberation provides for the qualitative expression of values for ecosystem services through the sharing of information, ideas and experiences between citizens. Like other methodologies that use qualitative approaches (such as a semi-structured interview), the focus is on gaining an understanding of why people think and feel the way they do. The formative output of a deliberative process is a well-reasoned group argument about the topic or theme under investigation. Since deliberation primarily expresses the values people hold about ecosystem services through 'words', there is a natural overlap between deliberative techniques and non-monetary forms of valuation.

As Turner *et al.* (2010) argue, through a group valuation process individuals are encouraged to: 'extend beyond their own personal welfare so that the resulting values, judgments will reflect a more complete and socially equitable assessment of the issue at hand'. Nonetheless, it would be an oversimplification to suggest that the valuation of ecosystem services is divided into two competing strands: either deliberative non-monetary values for 'other regarding' citizens or non-deliberative monetary values for 'self-regarding' individuals. In practice, these procedures can be coupled together in novel analytical-deliberative ways:

- Firstly, there is a body of novel work emerging that is combining Stated Preference (SP) methods with deliberative processes to elicit 'Willingness to Pay/Accept Values' (WTP/A)—so called 'Deliberative Monetary Valuation' (DMV). Not only can these techniques use shared values to inform individual motivations and preferences towards ecosystem services, but they are also giving rise to new value expressions based on an aggregate social value for change, or 'social willingness to pay';
- Secondly, there are methodologies emerging that allow non-monetary values to be expressed in quantitative terms and considered alongside monetary valuation as part of a deliberative process—so called 'Deliberative Multi-criteria Analysis' (DMCA). The process involves

scoring and weighting a range of monetary and non-monetary criteria to provide an integrated and systematic assessment of priorities for decision-making.

The methodological pluralism needed for holistic valuation is, therefore, leading to more hybridised models of assessment. In Sections 24.4 and 24.5 we provide an overview of these DMV and DMCA techniques including some examples of recent work.

24.4 Deliberative Monetary Valuation of Ecosystem Services

In general terms, the development of DMV techniques reflect economists' concerns to strengthen the validity of monetary values elicited through standard SP methods. There are a number of general parameters and principles guiding DMV (Spash 2008; Turner *et al.* 2010):

- Individuals are provided with detailed information about the issues which they are asked to discuss and formally deliberate on.
- Group settings for DMV may take the form of an in-depth group discussion or may include more elaborate techniques, such as the use of 'citizens' jury' in which deliberation is based on exposure to information provided by 'expert witnesses'.
- Through group discussion and exposure to information, individuals 'learn' about the issue. Preference construction is therefore part of the process.
- Through learning in a deliberative setting, individuals are encouraged to understand an issue in terms beyond their personal welfare, so that the resulting valuation reflects a more complete and socially equitable assessment.

There are four key types of DMV exercise which can be considered alongside the conventional contingent valuation survey (**Table 24.1**). A fundamental distinction within DMV

Table 24.1 Survey-based and deliberative monetary valuation: key variations. Source: reproduced from Fish *et al.* (2011).

Valuation Objective	Individual benefit values: Individual willingness to pay/accept		Collective benefit values: Social willingness to pay/accept		
Engagement Level	**Survey**	**Deliberative monetary valuation (Group-based)**			
Techniques	Questionnaire/ interview format—(Optional quality check via one-off focus group)	In-depth discussion/ workshop	Citizens' Jury, in-depth discussion group or workshop	In-depth discussion/ workshop	Citizens' Jury, in-depth discussion group or workshop
Value expression	**Individuals** express a value for what they **personally**—would pay/ accept	**Individuals** express a value for what they **personally**—would pay/accept	**Groups** express a value for what they believe **individuals** should pay/ accept	**Individuals** express a value for what they believe **society** should pay/accept	**Group** expresses a value for what they believe **society** should pay/accept

is whether the process is designed to elicit the same values as the conventional SP technique (i.e. individual WTP/A estimates), or those based on an aggregate social value for change (i.e. social WTP/A estimates). Both of these pathways have variants dictated by whether it is a group or an individual expressing the WTP/A values. In a methodological sense, it is worth noting that, in situations where the focus is on a group expressing a WTP/A value, practitioners of the DMV will be able to use a citizens' jury technique in addition to more standard group discussion formats. This is because the citizens' jury is, by design, concerned with group judgments. This opportunity is, therefore, precluded for DMV where participants are expressing values for what they (individually) believe they or society should pay/accept.

24.4.1 Individual Willingness to Pay/Accept Through Group Deliberation

As a review by Spash (2008) shows, most DMV studies are attempting to increase the validity of individuals' utility WTP/A measure by using, before assessment, a deliberative process to improve: knowledge of the 'good'; scientific uncertainties; as well as the range of issues likely to impact on successful implementation of the proposal,. This approach to DMV has two dimensions. Either DMV involves individuals expressing a value for what they would personally pay/accept following a group discussion, or the group makes a collective judgment of what they believe individuals should pay/accept.

In both cases the deliberative element brings a social learning dimension to the process. Determining what individuals should pay/accept is based on some explicit or implicit negotiation of shared values. In instrumental terms, combining SP techniques with group interaction is understood to provide for a richer understanding of what is being asked of individuals and help overcome the difficulties that respondents can experience when trying to understand the elements of a hypothetical market presented to them in a survey format. Such practical benefits have been noted in a study of wild goose conservation in Scotland by Macmillan et al. (2002). The research involved individuals stating their individual WTP/A values in a group context. The authors suggest the process allowed misunderstandings and gaps in understanding to be resolved and, therefore, respondents could make more informed or rational decisions.

A further recent experiment of the influence of deliberation on individual WTP/A values examined the mitigation of carbon dioxide emissions and was conducted by social psychologists in the USA (Dietz et al. 2009). The mitigation measure focused upon was the sequestering of carbon dioxide through the planting of trees—a regulating ecosystem service. Individuals were asked to state WTP/A values, firstly through a private (mailed) survey and, secondly, after a structured, small-group discussion. Among the findings, the process revealed that, compared to mailed survey respondents, the deliberative group respondents considered a greater number, and a broader range, of issues in making their responses, ranging from the nature of underpinning scientific evidence surrounding global warming to the location of tree planting. Of particular interest, the data do not support a simple

distinction between individual and social values. Rather, 'the survey mode frames the WTP question in terms of a charitable contribution or a consumer purchase... [whereas] group discussion frames the question as a public policy problem' (ibid.). Individuals ask different questions of themselves and others depending on the two ways of thinking about the task. In 'survey mode' they adopt an economic orientation: 'how much do I support this cause?' and 'how much could I afford to contribute?' The authors' report 66% of survey respondents thought about the positive attributes of the mitigation proposal, while 50% also considered personal financial issues in their WTP. By contrast, in group deliberation mode, 'they thought and acted like policy-analysts' (ibid.), asking different questions, including: is climate change a real problem? How will the proposed policies work? Would there be better ways to achieve the outcome? Respondents commented on implementation issues (94%), alternative solutions (54%) and scientific evidence (45%). Personal financial issues were only mentioned by roughly one third of the sample. One conclusion from the study is worth quoting in full:

"In terms of estimating societal WTP, the data show that even a simple simulation of societal discussion can change the way people think in considering their preferences for environmental improvements. Thus, societal WTP calculated from a CV survey early in the history of public debate on an environmental issue may yield different results from what would be found later on, because the societal debate may change the way people see the issue and the kinds of values they see as being at stake. The results also suggest that the same environmental improvement, presented in association with different policies for achieving it, may yield different estimates of societal WTP. ...These possibilities deserve investigation in future experiments that manipulate both the mode of presentation (individual vs. group deliberation) and the policies offered for achieving the same environmental objective". (ibid.).

The consumer-citizen distinction, first drawn by Sagoff (1988) to describe the two roles that individuals might adopt in responding to questions about environmental valuation, finds expression in what were described in Section 24.3 as 'self-regarding' or 'other regarding' perspectives. As Dietz et al. (2009) conclude: "[E]ven minimal group discussion seems to prompt citizens to think in terms of public values—the appropriate kind of thinking for public policy decisions—rather than in terms of individual considerations, such as charitable contributions, that dominated when responding to a standard CVM survey".

24.4.2 Social Willingness to Pay/Accept Through Group Deliberation

The two alternative options for DMV take a quite different perspective, which are more closely in keeping with the arguments made in Section 24.2. In these cases, the deliberative model involves individuals being asked to determine an 'aggregate social value of an environmental change' (Spash 2008). In other words, through facilitated deliberation, participants are able to debate the pros and cons of a suggested course of action, including its scientific, economic and policy justifications, to determine value for what they believe society should pay/accept. The distinction between the options lies in the way the social willingness to pay/accept values are formally delivered: DMV is designed either to elicit individual views regarding the aggregate social value of a proposed course of action, or the group stating an aggregate social WTP/A.

This approach to valuation remains only weakly exemplified in practice. A useful example is provided by Gregory and Wellman (2001) who developed a process of groups' stating social willingness to pay values as part of estuary management in the Tillamook Bay catchment, north-western Oregon. This is a valued landscape supporting diverse living resources including shellfish, runs of salmon and trout, groundfish, and numerous bird species. It is integral to the local and regional economies that are largely based on natural resources such as forestry, agriculture, tourism and recreation, and commercial fishing. The principal focus of the work was an evaluation of the consequences of three ecosystem management options in terms of their associated environmental and economic consequences: limiting livestock access to streams; protecting and restoring tidal wetlands; and upgrading forest management roads. Each option was associated with a specific cost or benefit to society for additional land purchases.

The overall valuation process involved five small group sessions consisting of 89 local residents drawn randomly from utility ratepayers. Participants were asked to select the most desirable actions and asked if they would be 'willing to have society pay' additional money (US$ millions) in added taxes to implement the policy option. As a result, the researchers were able to place a lower (US$ 3,000) and upper (US$ 5,000) boundary on the social value for each additional acre of protected salmon habitat. The data were then used by Tillamook Bay National Estuary Project managers to decide whether or not it was worthwhile to purchase marginal farmland at US$ 3,000–5,000 per acre to attempt to restore the full range of ecological services. These results show strong support for adopting a structured group decision process to both clarify trade-offs among different policy objectives and derive meaningful social estimates of the economic value of ecosystem goods and services.

24.5 Non-monetary Expressions of Shared Values

Deliberative techniques are able to inform shared valuations of ecosystem services where monetisation is considered difficult or felt to be inappropriate. The potential for qualitative expressions of value through techniques such as interviews, focus groups and discussion forums have already been noted in above (24.3). A further additional technique

is 'Multi-criteria Analysis' (MCA). Within decision-making this technique allows otherwise unvalued criteria to be considered alongside monetised costs and benefits through a more formal process of weighting and scoring. The use of participatory and deliberative techniques is considered central to the application of a MCA process.

In general terms, MCA encompasses a range of techniques for assessing decision problems characterised by a large number of diverse attributes. They are designed to address the difficulties that decision-makers have in handling complex information in a consistent way. The common feature of all MCA techniques is that they break a decision problem down into its component objectives and then develop and apply criteria to measure the performance of options and/or actions against those objectives.

Application of MCA across government is already the subject of formal guidance (CLG 2009) and, in environmental research more generally, is an area of recent innovation. According to Proctor and Drechsler (2006), the key four key technical steps of MCA involve:
i) Identifying the alternatives or options that are to be investigated in coming to a decision;
ii) Determining a set of criteria by which to rank these alternatives;
iii) Establishing preferences or weights for the various criteria;
iv) Undertaking an aggregation procedure by which the criteria-specific rank orders are aggregated into a single 'compromise' rank order.

An important part of this fourth step is to conduct sensitivity and robustness analyses in order to examine how different preferences affect the outcome of the aggregation and how robust the compromise rank order is with respect to deviations in the preferences. The ultimate outcome of this process, which may take several iterations, is a preferred option, or set of options.

Multi-criteria Analysis does not constitute a participatory process in and of itself, although when applied properly, it involves working with experts and stakeholders. A range of deliberative and participatory forms of MCA have been developed in recent years. The approach essentially varies in terms of who participates in the process and the degree to which they are involved in different stages of the process. So, for instance, key variants include:

- **Multi-criteria Mapping** (MCM) is an interview-based MCA technique focused on specialists and professional representatives. This approach is appropriate to the appraisal of policies, programmes or projects in the context of an ecosystem approach where interested and affected stakeholders have well-established knowledge and viewpoints on the issue in question, but where the performance of policy options is uncertain and underlying value judgments are contested (Stirling & Mayer 2001).
- **Stakeholder decision analysis** (SDA) is a group-based MCA focused on involving specialists and professional representatives. The standard SDA method involves 10 to 15 professional stakeholders coming together in repeat deliberative workshop processes to inform the MCA. The

chief advantage of SDA over MCM is that it introduces a group learning and dynamic to the MCA process. (Burgess 2000).

■ **Deliberative Mapping** (DM) is a group-based MCA which opens the process up to members of the public as well as specialists and professional representatives. The technique rests on integrating the approaches of SDA and MCM. This approach is best used in situations of greater risk and public controversy (Burgess *et al.* 2007).

Despite these variants, all of the approaches exhibit the basic structure of MCA. They integrate formal quantitative multi-criteria techniques with participatory and deliberative techniques, as well as providing qualitative evidence of the reasoning and judgments underlying valuations (Stagl 2007).

24.6 Shared Values and Scenario-building

An important further approach linked to group-based work, and which is especially pertinent for embedding social values for ecosystem services into policy and decision-making, is scenario-building. (Alcamo 2001; Börjeson *et al.* 2006; Bishop *et al.* 2007; O'Neill *et al.* 2008; Wilkinson & Eidinow 2008).

As Bradfield *et al.* (2005) observe, while scenarios have been used extensively, a number of methodological issues remain unresolved. They note that there are many conflicting definitions, principles and ideas about scenarios that exist in the literature, with terms such as 'planning', 'thinking', 'forecasting', 'analysis' and 'learning' all variously employed in describing what scenarios might be used for. The tension between the forecasting and learning perspectives is, it seems, particularly acute.

Although there are many differences of approach among those who use scenario tools, perhaps one common or unifying assumption is that they are not predictions about the future. Rather they are a set of conceptual tools that enable people to collectively deal with a particular type of problem that involves high uncertainty and complexity. According to Zurek and Henrichs (2007), in these circumstances, scenarios can help stakeholders by:

■ structuring choices by revealing their possible long-term consequences;

■ support strategic planning and decision-making by providing a platform for thinking through the implications of various options in the face of future uncertainties; and,

■ facilitating participation in the strategic development process by allowing the voicing of conflicting opinions and different world views.

In terms of a practical approach, scenario construction can legitimately try to:

■ 'look forward' and seek to identify what kind of future might unfold under different assumptions about the key drivers of change; or alternatively

■ 'backcast' from some desired set of goals, thus allowing people to think through the conditions that might realise these objectives.

O'Neill *et al.* (2008) have recently set out some of the issues surrounding the development and use of scenarios that throw particular light on their relationship to processes of social valuation in deliberative settings. They argue that one important theme that has emerged from recent debates is the tension between two contrasting perspectives on the role of scenarios, namely scenarios as 'products' and scenarios as 'processes'. The notion of scenarios as products relates to more model-based approaches to capturing different futures. The emphasis is on the technical representation of social values for, and about, change. In contrast, the process perspective emphasises the relationship between scenario-building and social learning.

There are a number of corresponding ways in which we can evaluate the value of scenario-building as a tool for decision-making. This issue has been considered by Hulme and Dessai (2008) who looked at the 'predictive success' of scenarios alongside two other potential outcome measures, namely 'decision success' and 'learning success'. These commentators emphasise just how misleading it can be, in scientific terms, to regard scenarios as prophetic devices. Problems with such a perspective include the fact that, by looking to predictive success, we often try, inappropriately, to make a judgment about which scenario from a family of scenarios is 'better' or more 'accurate', when the actual outcomes are within the plausible or probability range of many of them. Thus, they emphasise that 'decision' and 'learning' success are perhaps more useful measures of the efficacy of the scenario approach, with the latter probably being the best.

For Hulme and Dessai (2008), 'decision success' is measured according to whether the decisions based on a scenario-building exercise were 'good ones'. A key test, they suggest, is whether the scenario exercise allowed the full range of uncertainties surrounding an issue to be considered by the decision-makers. However, while this perspective is perhaps more useful than one based on prediction, it is also problematic. These authors argue that measures based on 'decision success' only make sense if we move away from judging decisions by some kind of retrospective analysis of outcomes, and look at the robustness of the decision-making processes themselves; this seems to involve notions of learning and capacity-building.

Although difficult to measure, the extent to which scenario-building leads to effective social learning is, according to Hulme and Dessai (2008), the most appropriate test of the success of such studies. The measure is closer to the original intention of scenario studies, which was to introduce alternative and multiple views of possible futures into discussions about future strategies and plans. Learning success is, they suggest, also more lasting than 'product outcomes' which can rapidly become outdated as the relationship between the science, society and policy communities evolves. As Garb *et al.* (2008) argue, providing we recognise that scenarios shape and embed their social contexts, they can be used effectively as decision support tools.

Scenarios are an important dimension of the UK NEA (Chapter 25). The focus is on understanding and valuing the consequences of different plausible futures, with a corresponding assessment of implications for policy and decision-makers. While the UK NEA scenarios were not designed to be linked to a deliberative social valuation process, they are designed to serve a general social learning purpose. The wider methodological point, however, is that scenarios are a useful technique for participative process because they can provide a context in which people can begin to explore what kinds of values they hold about particular environmental features or characteristics, and what kinds of change might be considered socially acceptable.

24.7 Conclusion

According to Turner *et al.* (2010), ensuring the "correct and appropriate application of economic valuation techniques, alongside other valuation methods" is a key element of reconciling—or least understanding—the types of trade-off that may occur between the different values we hold for ecosystem services. Capturing and acknowledging these values within ecosystem assessment and corresponding decision-making processes implies the need for methodological plurality: just as there are quite different grounds on which judgments of value can be communicated and inferred for ecosystem services, so too, there are many different ways in which values can be formally recorded and assigned significance.

This chapter has emphasised that consideration of shared values is one important component of moving towards more pluralistic approaches to valuation. Economic analyses that infer monetary values for ecosystems services based on individual—'self-regarding'—preferences are recognised to be philosophically and analytically restrictive. There is a need to consider 'other regarding' motivations towards humans and other entities in nature. As Wilson and Howarth (2002) have suggested, ecosystem services are: "inherently objects of ethical and normative concern...what is done to them can be discussed not simply in terms of individual costs and benefits, but in terms of social rights and wrongs".

The practical process of incorporating shared values into ecosystem assessment and wider decision-making involves recognition of the validity of more qualitative and interpretative approaches to valuing ecosystem services. The emphasis on deliberation and participation is particularly important in the context of decision-making processes that flow from ecosystem assessment. The consideration of values for ecosystem services in a deliberative context provides a basis upon which both synergies and just trade-offs between practical courses of action can be identified and explored—for instance, between utilitarian, ethical and aesthetic concerns. In an important sense, exploring shared values in a deliberative setting can help expose the wider politics in which decisions about ecosystem services occur, and can lead to more informed, citizen-led outcomes.

While such approaches have integrity in their own right, the development of integrated platforms for ecosystem assessment and valuation is likely to be a design feature of decision support tools in the future. Hybrid tools that bring together quantitative and qualitative, monetary and non-monetary, and individual and shared values for future change remain a logical aspiration for decision-makers wishing to take an holistic approach to the management of ecosystem services. Future experimentation in the promising, but by no means fully developed, techniques of 'deliberative monetary valuation' and 'deliberative multi-criteria analysis' will be an important part of developing an holistic approach.

References

Alcamo, J. (2001) Scenarios as tools for international environmental assessments. European Environment Agency, Copenhagen.

Anderson, A. (1997) Media, Culture and the Environment. UCL, London.

Bateman, I.J., Carson, R.T., Day, B., Hanemann, M., Hanley, N., Hett, T., Jones-Lee, M., Loomes, G., Mourato, S., Ozdemiroglu, E., Pearce, D.W., Sugden, R. & Swanson, J. (2002) Economic Valuation With Stated Preference Techniques: A Manual. Edward Elgar, Cheltenham.

Bishop, P., Hines, A. & Collins, T. (2007) The current state of scenario development: An overview of techniques. *Foresight,* **9**, 5–25.

Börjeson, L., Höjer, M., Dreborg, K., Ekvall, T. & Finnveden, G. (2006) Scenario types and techniques: Towards a user's guide. *Futures,* **38**, 723–739.

Bradfield, R., Wright, G., Burt, G., Cairns, G. & Van Der Heijden, K. (2005) The origins and evolution of scenario techniques in long range business planning. *Futures,* **37,** 795–812.

Burgess, J., Limb, M. & Harrison, C.M. (1988a) Exploring environmental values through the medium of small groups. Part one: theory and practice. *Environment and Planning A,* **20**, 309–326.

Burgess, J., Limb, M. & Harrison, C.M. (1988b) Exploring environmental values through the medium of small groups. Part two: illustrations of a group at work. *Environment and Planning A,* **20**, 457–476.

Burgess, J., Harrison, C.M. & Limb, M. (1988c) People, parks and the urban green: a study of popular meanings and values for open spaces in the city. *Urban Studies,* **25**, 455–473.

Burgess, J., Harrison, C. & Maiteny, P. (1991) Contested meanings: the consumption of news about nature conservation. *Media, Culture and Society,* **13**, 499–519.

Burgess, J. (1995) Growing in Confidence: Understanding People's Perceptions of Urban Fringe Woodlands. Countryside Commission, Cheltenham.

Burgess, J. (2000) Situating knowledges, sharing values and reaching collective decisions: the cultural turn in environmental decision-making. Cultural Turns/Geographical Turns: Perspectives on Cultural Geography (eds I. Cook, D. Crouch, S. Naylor & J.R. Ryan), pp 273–287. Prentice Hall, London.

Burgess, J., Stirling, A., Clark, J., Davies, G., Eames, M., Staley, K. & Williamson, S. (2007) Deliberative mapping: a novel analytic-deliberative methodology to support contested science-policy decisions. *Public Understanding of Science,* **16**, 299–322.

CLG (Department for Communities and Local Government) (2009) Multi-criteria analysis: a manual. CLG, London.

Davies, G. (2000) Science, observation and entertainment: competing visions of postwar British natural history television, 1946–1967. *Cultural Geographies,* **7**, 432–459.

Defra (Department for Environment, Food and Rural Affairs) (2007) Introductory Guide to Valuing Ecosystem Services. Defra, London.

Dietz, T., Stern, P.C. & Dan, A. (2009) How deliberation affects stated willingness to pay for mitigation of carbon dioxide emissions: an experiment. *Land Economics,* **85**, 329–347.

Dougill, A.J., Fraser, E.D.G., Holden, J., Hubacek, K., Prell, C., Reed, M.S., Stagl, S. & Stringer, L.C. (2006) Learning from Doing Participatory Rural Research: Lessons from the Peak District National Park. *Journal of Agricultural Economics,* **57**, 259–275.

Fish, R. (ed) (2007) Cinematic Countrysides. University Press, Manchester.

Fish, R., Burgess, J., Chilvers, J., Footitt, A., Haines-Young, R., Russel, D., Turner, K. & Winter, D.M. (2011) Participatory and Deliberative Techniques for Embedding an Ecosystems Approach into Decision Making. Full Technical Report. (NR0124). Department for Environment, Food and Rural Affairs, London.

Garb, Y., Pulver, S. and VanDeveer, S. (2008) Scenarios in society, society in scenarios: toward a social scientific analysis of storyline-driven environmental modeling. *Environmental Research Letters,* **3**, 045015 (8pp).

Gee, K. & Burkhard, B. (2010) Cultural ecosystem services in the context of offshore wind farming: A case study from the west coast of Schleswig-Holstein. *Ecological Complexity,* **7**, 349–358.

Gowdy, J.M. (2007) Towards an experimental foundation for B-C analysis. *Ecological Economics,* **63**, 649–655.

Gren, I.-M., Folke, C., Turner, K. & Bateman, I. (1994) Primary and secondary values of wetland ecosystems. *Environmental and Resource Economics,* **4**, 55–74.

Hargrove, E. (1992) Weak Anthropocentric Intrinsic Value. *The Monist,* **75**, 183–207.

Harrison, C.M., Burgess, J. & Limb, M. (1987) Nature in the city: popular values for a living world. *Journal of Environmental Management,* **25**, 347–362.

Hinchliffe, S., Kearnes, M.B., Degen, M. & Whatmore, S. (2005) Urban wild things: a cosmopolitical experiment. *Environment and Planning D,* **23**, 643–658.

Hulme, M. & Dessai, S. (2008) Predicting, deciding, learning: can one evaluate the 'success' of national climate scenarios? *Environmental Research Letters,* **3**, 045013 (7pp).

Macmillan, D.C., Philip, L., Hanley, N. & Alvarez-Farizo, B. (2002) Valuing the non-market benefits of wild goose conservation: a comparison of interview and group-based approaches. *Ecological Economics,* **43**, 49–59.

O'Neill, B., Pulver, S., VanDeveer, S. & Garb, Y. (2008) Where next with global environmental scenarios? *Environmental Research Letters,* **3**, 1–4.

Proctor, W. & Drechsler, M. (2006) Deliberative multicriteria evaluation. *Environment and Planning C: Government and Policy,* **24**, 169–190.

Rauch, J.F. (2010) Does network theory connect to the rest of us? *Journal of Economic literature,* **48**, 980–986.

RCEP (Royal Commission for Environmental Pollution) (1998) Setting Environmental Standards. RCEP, London.

Sagoff, M. (1988) The economy of the earth. Cambridge University Press, Cambridge.

Sagoff, M. (2011) The quantification and valuation of ecosystem services. *Ecological Economics,* **70**, 497–502.

Spash, C.L. (2008) Deliberative monetary valuation and the evidence for a new value theory. *Land Economics,* **84**, 469–488.

Stagl, S. (2007) Rapid Research and Evidence Review on Emerging Methods for Sustainability Valuation and Appraisal. Sustainable Development Research Network, London.

Stern, P. & Fineberg, H.V. (1996) Understanding Risk: Informing Decisions in a Democratic Society. National Academy Press, Atlanta.

Stirling, A. & Mayer, S. (2001) A novel approach to the appraisal of technological risk: a multicriteria mapping study of a genetically modified crop. *Environment and Planning C: Government and Policy,* **19**, 529–555.

Turner, R.K., Paavola, J., Cooper, P., Farber, S., Jessamy, V. & Georgiou, S. (2003) Valuing nature: lessons learned and future research directions. *Ecological Economics,* **46**, 492–510.

Turner, K. (2010) A Pluralistic Approach to Ecosystem Services Evaluation. CSERGE Working Paper EDM 10-07. The Centre for Social and Economic Research on the Global Environment (CSERGE), Norwich, UK.

Turner, R.K., Morse-Jones, S. & Fisher, B. (2010) Ecosystem valuation: a sequential decision-support system and quality assessment issues. *Annals of the New York Academy of Sciences,* **1185**, 79–101.

Welsch, H. & Kuhling, J. (2008) Using happiness data for environmental valuation: issues and applications. *Journal of Economic Surveys,* **23**, 385–406.

Wild Ennerdale Partnership (2006) Wild Ennerdale Stewardship Plan. Forestry Commission, National Trust and United Utilities, Cumbria, UK.

Wilson, M.A. & Howarth, B. (2002) Discourse-based valuation of ecosystem services: establishing fair outcomes through group deliberation. *Ecological Economics,* **42**, 431–443.

Wilkinson, A. & Eidinow, E. (2008) Evolving practices in environmental scenarios: a new scenario typology. *Enviromental Research Letters,* **3**, 045017 (11pp).

Zurek, M. & Henrichs, T. (2007) Linking scenarios across geographical scales in international environmental assessments. *Technological Forecasting and Social Change,* **74**, 1282.

Chapter 25:
The UK NEA Scenarios: Development of Storylines and Analysis of Outcomes

Coordinating Lead Author: Roy Haines-Young
Lead Authors: James Paterson and Marion Potschin
Contributing Authors: Alister Wilson and Gary Kass

Key Findings

Storylines

The six UK National Ecosystem Assessment (UK NEA) scenarios have been developed to gather insight into how ecosystem services and human well-being might change under a range of plausible futures. The UK NEA scenarios explore how emerging driving forces might combine to create different socio-political and economic conditions in the future and describe different ways the world might look in 2060.

Green and Pleasant Land is a scenario in which the conservation of biodiversity and landscape are dominant driving forces. Although society recognises the intrinsic value of biodiversity, the push for conservation is essentially cultural: the UK is well enough off that it can choose how it looks after its own backyard. Society's choice is to preserve its natural assets and the countryside is a highly managed cultural landscape, with policy focused on protecting, maintaining and improving its aesthetic appeal. The drive for conservation has led to a greater emphasis on habitat restoration and recreation and, consequently, a reduction in productive farmland. The approach has boosted tourism and leisure, which has increased its contribution to the UK economy. In general, conservation of biodiversity and preservation of landscape sit hand in hand, but the continued pressure of climate change on some habitats and ecosystems means this is an area of growing social—and perhaps economic—conflict.

Nature@Work is a scenario where population growth and the adoption of new technologies are dominant driving forces. Maintaining and enhancing the output of ecosystem services in response to climate change is a key priority and society accepts that trade-offs are necessary to achieve it. Conservation of habitats and species remains desirable, but not at the expense of wider benefits—and the introduction of non-native species to provide food, energy, shade or habitat conversion (e.g. Semi-natural Grasslands to Woodlands) are commonplace if they promote ecosystem-based adaptations that enhance society's resilience to climate change. Society takes a pragmatic view that values nature for what it provides or does and accepts the need to create multifunctional landscapes to maintain ecosystem services and quality of life. 'Balanced service provision' is key and many ecosystem services are the result of careful evaluation of the trade-offs through scientific and community review.

The *World Markets* scenario is driven by the push for economic growth through the complete liberalisation of trade. International trade barriers have dissolved, agriculture subsidies have disappeared and farming is industrialised and large-scale. Consumption in society is high, which results in greater resource use and more imports. Competition for land is high, and this, coupled with the reduced rural and urban planning regulations on housing, agriculture and industry, means that biodiversity is often the loser. Technological development in all industries is mainly privately funded and is burgeoning. Food production has benefited from technological development and intensification and food is cheap and plentiful, but mostly of low quality. Land and sea are mainly seen as resources for exploitation and there is little effort to manage them sustainably. Fish stocks have plummeted and some species have been become locally extinct; most fish eaten in the UK is imported from Asia now. The UK's coastal areas are changing in response to the increasing demand for ecosystem services. The east coast is the prime location of the desalination plants that have been built to meet the high demand for water. Coastal areas elsewhere accommodate the network of power plants and gas pipeline stations that are required now that domestic fossil fuel energy production is declining and imports of gas have increased. The UK's expanded nuclear industry is financed by the private sector and supplies of other ecosystem services are increasingly being privatised as well.

The *National Security* scenario is driven primarily by increasing global energy prices that force most countries to seek greater self-sufficiency and efficiency in many of their core industries. This is not an easy transition for the UK and it relies on a heavy government hand in setting policy for ecosystem service provision and in creating a competition-free environment for industry within the UK. Trade barriers and tariffs have been increased to protect jobs and livelihoods, and immigration is tightly controlled. Technological development is state funded and many industries (including agriculture) are subsidised. Food, fuel, timber and mineral resources are prioritised over the conservation of biodiversity. Protectionism is a necessary response to the challenges posed by climate change rather than a source of conflict between nations, and trade continues where it can. Nevertheless, life is uncomfortable and people work hard to get by. Economic growth is low and every last resource in the UK is utilised for the provision of services. This has led to the reopening of many coalmines, greater protection of the UK's fisheries and the conversion of previously non-productive land to farming. Resource consumption is curbed and society is less profligate and more sustainable—though perhaps out of economic necessity as much as environmental concern.

The *Local Stewardship* scenario is driven by similar external pressures to *National Security*, but society has made a more conscious effort to reduce the intensity of economic activity and the high levels of consumption that were a characteristic of the early years of the century. People understand the need to think and act differently and want to be responsible for managing resources for the future. Political power has been devolved and many major issues are decided at a regional or local level (except crucial national aspects like defence). Local timber and energy production is encouraged and there is great pride in the varied local food products. Consumption has reduced to more sustainable (and healthy) levels and societal equity fits alongside environmental equity. People are motivated to live in low carbon economies, and consequently travel less and depend more on their own locality for food and leisure activities. Technology supports sustainability and its development and is driven by a mix of private innovation and government funding. Alternative economies such as LETS (Local Exchange Trading Systems) schemes are popular. Increased local specialisation means that the UK is now less homogenised—landscapes are more distinctive and local economies vary considerably. Economic growth is slow but the economy is stable.

Go with the Flow describes a scenario in which the dominant sociopolitical and economic drivers acting on the UK at the end of 2010 continue. In this sense it is not a 'do-nothing' storyline, but a projection of current approaches. Thus pursuing environmental improvement is important in this world, but society and industry are reluctant to adopt many global or national environmental policies that would lead to radical change. Progress towards a low-carbon economy and better environmental standards across industry and society is therefore slow and bumpy. Although there has been a marked improvement in the delivery of all ecosystem services, with a gradual shift away from provisioning services to regulating and cultural services, the battle between socioeconomic forces and environmental improvement continues. For now, access to ecosystem services is managed, but some regions (such as the South East, for example) are increasingly unable to meet their own needs and rely on other parts of the UK.

Drivers

The combined effects of the major indirect drivers of change (demographic, sociopolitical, economic, scientific and technological, and cultural and religious) differ according to each scenario, and this results in both increases and decreases in ecosystem function and processes. Indirect drivers form the backbone of each of the storylines, which explore how assumptions about the size and scale of their impact might influence the more immediate causes of change (direct drivers), such as climate and land management. The storylines are, as far as possible, evidence-based in terms of the assumptions made about the potential impacts of the various drivers on ecosystem services. Climate change has been explored for two levels of impact ('high' and 'low'), based on UKCIP09 (Murphy *et al.* 2009) data. The impacts (both direct on species, natural and semi-natural ecosystems and human behaviour) and responses (mitigation and adaptation) are major points of variation within the storylines, and result in a range of different outcomes for many ecosystem services.

The storylines differ in terms of the assumptions made about the size of the UK population in 2060, levels of immigration and emigration, and geographical distribution of people within the country. The population in 2060 is assumed be around 65 million for *Green and Pleasant Land* and *Local Stewardship*, but between 75 and 77 million for *Go*

with the Flow and World Markets. Nature@Work sits in the middle with around 67 million.

One of the ways in which the differences brought about by the direct and indirect drivers can be seen in the consequence for the UK's overseas 'environmental footprint'. This allows the UK's ecosystem service use and provision to be viewed in a global context. The footprint is highest for *World Markets, Green and Pleasant Land* and *Go with the Flow*, intermediate for *Nature@Work* and *National Security*, and lowest for *Local Stewardship*.

Biodiversity and Ecosystem Services

Three key direct drivers affect biodiversity in the scenarios: land use change, pollution and climate change. The state of biodiversity in 2060 reflects the prevailing societal attitudes of each of the storylines: *Green and Pleasant Land, Nature@Work, Local Stewardship* and *Go with the Flow* are characterised by more environmentally benign perspectives, compared to *World Markets and National Security.*

The storylines take different approaches, too, in their focus on different aspects of biodiversity and ecosystem character. In *Green and Pleasant Land* a more static 'preservationist' attitude seeks to conserve native flora and fauna as well as cultural landscapes. In contrast, in *Local Stewardship,* and particularly in *Nature@Work,* a more dynamic view of ecosystems is taken, and adaptability is considered more important than the degree of 'nativeness'; novel ecosystems composed of non-native species develop or are created if they provide the requisite suite of ecosystem services.

Land Cover Responses

Mountains, Moorlands and Heaths

The extent of Mountains, Moorlands and Heaths does not change radically from today, and remains around 18% of the national land area. The largest changes are associated with *Local Stewardship,* in which an extensive programme of coniferous afforestation is needed to meet local demand for resources; this results in the loss of some Mountain, Moorland and Heath habitats. On the whole, however, mountain habitats remain the least human-influenced ecosystem for the other storylines, although they are enhanced in *Nature@ Work, Green and Pleasant Land* and *Local Stewardship.*

The main drivers affecting this habitat change slightly from the current day. Grazing pressure is reduced substantially in Green and Pleasant Land, Nature@Work, Local Stewardship and Go with the Flow in response to indirect driver pressures (environmental attitudes). The two climate change scenarios do not differ substantially in regard to land cover change in Mountains, Moorlands and Heaths. However, the human response to climate change does vary across the storylines (e.g. the adoption of wind farms, or the maintenance of flood alleviation programmes). Agricultural land use shifts due to a warmer and drier climate, and results in some loss of this habitat type. More radical approaches to land use planning and population pressures in the World Markets storyline also lead to a loss of habitat to housing and other development.

Ecosystem service provision from Mountains, Moorlands and Heaths changes not only in quantity but in type across the storylines. In some, a focus on regulating services is stressed (*Nature@Work*); others highlight the need to maintain provisioning services (*National Security*) or cultural services (*Green and Pleasant Land*). Despite these habitats being a major source of drinking water, this service is not protected and maintained in *World Markets* or *National Security*, resulting in the need to source water from coastal desalination systems. Soil carbon is maintained and conserved in *Nature@Work, Green and Pleasant Land, Local Stewardship* and *Go with the Flow*. The multifunctional aspect of Mountains, Moorlands and Heaths are particularly developed and maintained in the *Nature@Work* storyline—provisioning, cultural and regulating services are kept in balance.

Semi-natural Grasslands

The huge loss of Semi-natural Grasslands in the 20th Century is partially addressed by restoration programmes in four of the storylines (*Green and Pleasant Land, Nature@Work, Local Stewardship* and *Go with the Flow*). Further declines in *World Markets* and *Local Stewardship* occur, due to pressure from other land uses such as agriculture, forestry and development. An increase in recreation and the maintenance of soil carbon are two of the main service gains in the four storylines that include restoration programmes, but other, more localised services include provisioning (use of traditional and local livestock grazing for high quality meat).

Enclosed Farmland

Enclosed Farmland continues to be a dominant land cover type in all six storylines. However, its importance as a provider of multiple ecosystem services does vary considerably between them. In *Local Stewardship*, food production is of prime importance and little regard is given to other ecosystem services; in *World Markets*, whilst Enclosed Farmland cover declines, a switch to greater intensification and industrial agricultural models increases productivity (with deleterious outcomes for regulating and cultural services). In contrast, *Nature@Work* seeks to improve productivity through technology and sustainable management techniques in order to maintain other ecosystem services too (e.g. soil carbon). *Green and Pleasant Land* and *Local Stewardship* adopt a low-input agricultural model which seeks to conserve a range of ecosystem services (although provisioning declines). *Go with the Flow* takes a middle-ground approach with better environmental standards than today, but also greater productivity. Energy production in farmland is also a dominant driver in *Local Stewardship*, and to a lesser degree in *Nature@Work*.

The drivers affecting Enclosed Farmland in the future are mainly fourfold: population pressure from the UK (fuelling demand), global economic forces (the degree to which it is easy to import food from overseas rather than producing it indigenously), technology (further management improvements and crop/livestock breeding) and societal (the adoption of environmental considerations). These three factors shape the approach to farm production and management in the six storylines. The higher population storylines (*World Markets, Local Stewardship* and *Go with the Flow*) maintain high food production; however in the case of *World Markets*, food imports are also high. *Green and Pleasant Land* also requires large food imports to offset the smaller area used as farmland and the demands of a high population. In contrast, *Local Stewardship*, with a relatively low population and a greater emphasis on local food production, has very low import requirements. *Nature@Work* seeks to balance food production for home demand by adopting sustainable but high output management.

The attitude towards the environment is also largely played out in the approach to meat production in each of the storylines. Where environmental concerns are high (*Nature@Work, Green and Pleasant Land*), improved grassland cover for livestock production declines dramatically as society demands greater land use efficiency for its protein demands (e.g. through legume crops such as soybeans). In contrast, the *World Markets* storyline moves further towards low-quality meat production, based on the use of intensive methods. *Local Stewardship* also maintains low input livestock production for environmental reasons: as a result, the landscape becomes more heterogeneous and there is an enhancement of farmland biodiversity.

Woodlands

The area of woodland in 2060 increases in all the storylines except *World Markets*, reflecting its importance in delivering multiple ecosystem services, but the emphasis given to broadleaved and conifer woodland is different. Where provisioning services are important (*Local Stewardship*) an emphasis is placed on species with high yield class (conifers sourced from around the world); this is also the case in *Nature@Work*, but it is balanced by a need to increase broadleaved cover for other reasons (recreation, biodiversity). *Go with the Flow* and *Local Stewardship* create new forest area through planting native species; this is also the case in *Nature@Work*, except for areas that have become unsuitable for native species through climate change—in these instances, more adaptable congeners from southern Europe are used.

Management of woodland is also an important driver affecting ecosystem service provision, and sustainable woodland management is the norm for *Green and Pleasant Land, Nature@Work, Local Stewardship* and *Go with the Flow*. As a consequence, biodiversity, carbon stocks, flood alleviation, and opportunities for recreation, as well as timber and non-timber forest production, are enhanced. In contrast, the high-tech silvicultural approach to timber production in Local Stewardship does have negative consequences for a range of other services (soil quality, recreation, biodiversity).

Woodland cover also expands in areas close to and within major conurbations, because multiple ecosystem service benefits can be derived from locating forests there. This is a particular pattern in *Nature@Work*, as woodlands are created to provide cultural benefits as well as flood alleviation; a further benefit is derived from shade provision in hotter summers in the high climate change scenario.

Freshwaters – Openwaters, Wetlands and Floodplains

Freshwater cover increases or remains the same in all the storylines, but for different reasons. In the more environmentally benign storylines, restoration of old, traditional wetland and riverine habitats is a major policy focus—this has cross-benefits for biodiversity and recreation as well as improving flood mitigation, erosion regulation and water quality. Land cover adjacent to riverine habitats also benefits from conversion (often from Improved Grassland or Arable) to wetland grazing or marshland. This pattern is further enhanced in the high climate change scenario, partly due to greater winter flood pressures. In *World Markets* and *Local Stewardship*, freshwater expansion still occurs in the high climate change scenario, but is mainly due to land abandonment resulting from a lack of investment or a lack of willingness to adapt to a higher incidence of flooding. The consequences of major wetland drainage programmes in the 19th and 20th Centuries are partially amended.

Freshwater habitats continue to provide multiple ecosystem services in most of the storylines. In some (*Local Stewardship*), the renewal of traditional practices is carried out (greater emphasis given to using local fish for food supplies). Better quality riverine systems result in greater recreational usage too.

Urban

The land cover of urban areas in the UK remains fairly constant in all the storylines except two: in *World Markets*, a large population increase (domestic and from immigration) and a reduction in planning restrictions results in major urban sprawl, with a greater concentration in the South East. In contrast, *Local Stewardship*, a storyline with a static population and a slight return to primary industry, results in a pattern or counter-urbanisation which provides an opportunity for urban greening and 'softening'.

The development of greenspace in urban areas is a common theme for *Nature@Work*, *Green and Pleasant Land*, *Go with the Flow* and *Local Stewardship*. This is either through creating parks, gardens or open spaces (*Green and Pleasant Land*, *Go with the Flow*) but also through the creation of green areas with a focus on food production as well as recreation (allotments, permaculture gardens and urban farms in *Nature@Work* and *Local Stewardship*).

The management of water in urban areas is also considered important. In *Nature@Work*, *Green and Pleasant Land* and *Go with the Flow*, rivers, lakes and ponds are restored, protected, re-channelled and managed to ensure connectivity for wildlife (through towns and cities), whilst recreational opportunities and flood mitigation are improved.

Climate change is a major driver of change in urban areas for all six storylines. This may just be witnessed through an increase in urban street tree planting or maintaining garden cover (*Go with the Flow*, *Local Stewardship*) but is also seen through the adoption of vegetated roof cover to increase cooling (*Nature@Work*, *Green and Pleasant Land*, *Local Stewardship*).

Coastal Margins

Coastal Margin habitats remain constant or increase slightly in all the storylines except for *World Markets*. In this scenario, Coastal Margin habitats come under pressure from industrial expansion in the form of ports, petrochemical and desalination plants, tourism, and housing in the south.

Better management of coastal habitats does occur in *Nature@Work*, *Green and Pleasant Land* and *Local Stewardship*, all of which adopt an ecosystem approach to planning and management. A particular emphasis is placed on geomorphological processes as well as biodiversity. A dynamic view of habitat change is taken in *Nature@Work*, which recognises the importance of working with natural processes; habitats are allowed to 'migrate' and, where appropriate, coastal inundation is encouraged.

Marine

Marine ecosystems have contrasting outcomes in the six storylines. The most exploitative are *World Markets* and *Local Stewardship*, which have echoes of the 'Tragedy of the Commons' in relation to fish stocks and the use of marine minerals. In *Green and Pleasant Land*, the Marine ecosystem is given due conservation protection but is also valued as a source of recreation. In *Local Stewardship* a regional management approach to the sea is adopted and the sustainable fishing of unfashionable species is encouraged to offset declines in the traditional seafood species. The most holistic approach to marine management occurs in *Nature@Work*, which stresses the importance of conserving all marine ecosystem services.

In the marine sector, the *World Markets* storyline continues the most harmful human activities prevalent today (e.g. trawl fisheries, aggregate extraction, coastal defences, ports and coastal developments). Some of these activities are also adopted by other storylines (offshore wind farms by *Nature@Work* and *Local Stewardship*; trawl fisheries by *Local Stewardship*).

Sea-level rise caused by climate change will lead to the loss of some coastal habitat in all the storylines. However, this is particularly evident in the *World Markets* storyline because it assumes no serious effort to adapt.

Comparing Ecosystem Services Across the Scenarios

A comparison of the sustainability of ecosystem service outputs was made for each scenario by counting the number of services that appeared to be increasing, stable or declining under the assumptions of each storyline. This indicative analysis showed that while current policy approaches, as characterised in *Go with the Flow*, were likely to lead to some improvements in ecosystem service output, the UK can make significant gains where policy takes the approach outlined in three scenarios: *Green and Pleasant Land*, *Nature@Work* and *Local Stewardship*. In each of these, the majority of services appeared to show improving trends, compared to the present where a more mixed picture has been reported. By contrast, *World Markets and National Security* showed significant losses compared to the present and *Go with the Flow*.

The comparison between scenarios described here is exploratory and further work is needed to develop the evidence base describing how changes in the various direct drivers impact on service output for the major habitat types. Nevertheless, despite the preliminary nature of the analysis, two important insights emerge that should be explored more deeply. The first is that quantitative comparison between storylines shows that the difference in ecosystem services outputs between the high and low climate change versions of each scenarios are smaller than the difference observed between different scenarios. It may be, therefore, that future changes in land use could have as much impact on ecosystem services as the direct effects of climate change.

The second is that none of the scenarios which show significant gains in ecosystem service outputs over *Go with the Flow*, such as *Green and Pleasant Land, Nature@Work* and *Local Stewardship,* share enough similarity that we can infer a single set of characteristics that lead to improving or more balanced service outputs. Equally, none of the scenarios which show significant losses over *Go with the Flow* (*World Markets* and *National Security*) are similar enough to highlight a specific or core policy risk that needs to be addressed. This suggests that there are no simple policy solutions which can deliver improved ecosystem service output. A better understanding of the way in which changes in habitat condition affect service output, and the relative importance of the different habitats in terms of service output, are two important gaps in knowledge that need to be addressed before these important policy questions can be resolved.

25.1 Introduction

The UK National Ecosystem Assessment (UK NEA) has shown that over the last 50 years there have been major changes in the way we have used the land and sea, with considerable impacts on ecosystem services. Although we have increased the output of our provisioning services from sectors such as agriculture, land use change and pollution have had major impacts on many biodiversity groups in the UK and the ability of many ecosystems to deliver important services. The climate and water regulation services provided by many terrestrial ecosystems in the UK have diminished in the 20th Century. In the marine sector, the sustainability of food provision has been under threat because of overexploitation and the impacts of fishing activities on other marine ecosystem services. The pressures on the marine space have also been growing with the expansion of renewable energy, recreation and port activities.

What will happen if these trends continue? Are present policy approaches sufficient to reverse them? What would the world look like in 2060 if we gave greater priority to ecosystem services or if we had to face an uncertain world where national security was the main issue? These are some of the questions the UK NEA scenario work has explored. To help answer them six storylines have been developed:

- *Green and Pleasant Land* is a future where high economic growth has focused more on secondary and tertiary industries, while primary industry has continued to decline. As a result, development pressures in rural areas decline, making space for 'beautifying' the countryside. This has many positive benefits for biodiversity.

- *Nature@Work* is a version of today, but with a very strong emphasis on maintaining ecosystem services through all sectors in the UK. It is inherently about resolving trade-offs between ecosystem services and sustaining multifunctional ecosystems. Indeed, in this world, sustainability is the underlying principle across all sectors of society.

- *World Markets* is a vision of unfettered economic growth and trade. Trade barriers disappear, imports increase, and environmental perspectives are given little weight. As a result, the countryside becomes more developed.

- *National Security* shares many characteristics with *World Markets* but is different in one key area, namely that it is strongly focused on self-sufficiency and economic protectionism.

- *Local Stewardship* presents a slower pace of life and a determined move towards a low-impact, low resource-use society. In this world there have been major shifts in values and attitudes compared to today.

- *Go with the Flow* offers a vision of how the UK might evolve if we continue with current socioeconomic and environmental policies. It is not a base-line because people continue to see the need for changes; the problem is that visions are often blurred and compromise reigns as we continue to 'muddle through'.

Section 25.2 explains how the scenarios were developed and Section 25.3 examines how ecosystems and their services in the UK might change under each of these futures, what the effects might be on human well-being and who might be affected most. The conceptual framework used for the UK NEA (Chapter 2) describes more fully the context for the scenarios work. In building the scenarios there has been no attempt to predict the future, or to construct a set of policy choices. Rather, the task has been to use current knowledge of ecosystems and ecosystem services to explore how they might respond under different assumptions about the processes driving change over the next 50 years.

There are many issues that surround the methods used to construct scenarios, and questions about methodology are important in terms of judging the success of any scenario exercise (Ash *et al.* 2010). However, rather than beginning by explaining the particular approaches used in the UK NEA, this discussion is postponed until the end of this chapter. In Sections 25.4, 25.5 and 25.6 we reflect critically on what was attempted and how the work can be taken further.

25.2 Developing the UK NEA Storylines

25.2.1 Identifying the Focal Questions

The process by which scenarios were developed in the Millennium Ecosystem Assessment (MA 2005) was a deliberative one (**Table 25.1**). It involved a dialogue between the research and user communities to define objectives, to determine the scope of the exercise, and to identify the particular issues that scenarios would be used

Table 25.1 Procedure used for developing scenarios in the MA. Source: Alcamo *et al.* (2006).

Phase I: Organisational steps
1. Establish a scenario guidance team.
2. Establish a scenario panel.
3. Conduct interviews with scenario end users.
4. Determine the objectives and focus of the scenarios.
5. Devise the focal questions of the scenarios.
Phase II: Scenario storyline development and quantification
6. Construct a zero-order draft of scenario storylines.
7. Organise modeling analyses and begin quantification.
8. Revise zero-order storylines and construct first-order storylines.
9. Quantify scenario elements.
10. Revise storylines based on results of quantifications.
11. Revise model inputs for drivers and re-run the models.
Phase III: Synthesis, review, and dissemination
12. Distribute draft scenarios for general review.
13. Develop final version of the scenarios by incorporating user feedback.
14. Publish and disseminate the scenarios.

to explore. This same broad approach was used for the UK NEA, but it was modified in detail to take account of specific national needs and other relevant scenario work that has been published since the MA was completed.

A key step in any scenario work that is part of an ecosystem assessment is the identification of a set of 'focal questions' (**Figure 25.1**). There are always a large number of issues that could be included in such an exercise and many possible futures that may be envisaged, each with complex and competing trade-offs between ecosystem services and spatially differentiated responses to the various drivers of change. However, a focus on the issues that are of most interest to users can help constrain the exercise. As Carpenter *et al.* (2006, p5) have observed, 'Scientific assessments are most helpful to decision makers when the intended users are active in the assessment process and, especially, when the users directly help shape the questions that the assessments will answer'. Involvement of users also helps to establish credibility and legitimacy, as well as saliency of the storylines that are developed (Rounsevell & Metzger 2010).

Thus, to gain an insight into the needs of potential users of the UK NEA, a web-based survey was undertaken, designed to identify a set of focal questions around which scenarios might be constructed (for a more detailed analysis see Moore *et al.* 2010). The approach was piloted in a focus group with people interested in the UK NEA before the material went online. In total, 72 people were invited to contribute to the web survey. The target population consisted of UK NEA user and client groups, members of the UK NEA expert panel, and the lead authors of the UK NEA chapters. The website was open for 50 days in the second quarter of 2010. Thirty-six individuals made a return and altogether they posed 71 questions. A preliminary review suggested that marine issues were potentially under-represented, and so a further 13 questions were added following a telephone

conference with the UK NEA Marine Group later in 2010. In total 149 distinct questions were identified from the initial focus group, the online survey and the later consultations (**Appendix 25.1**).

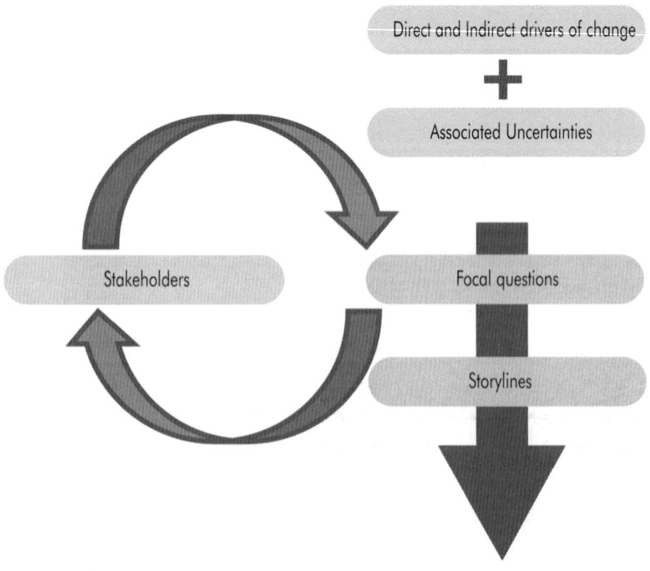

Since the number of people who took part in the consultation was small, and the group was self-selecting, it is not clear how representative the consultees were of the wider scientific and policy communities in the UK. Nevertheless, their views are useful in highlighting some of the areas that potential users of the UK NEA wanted to consider. Many of the people involved had seen some of the early results from the UK NEA analysis of current state and trends, and so their questions often referred to specific issues that were beginning to arise from the assessment. As an insight into the concerns of people likely to use the results of the Assessment, the survey results were therefore valuable.

The survey results suggested that there was particular interest in the impacts of the main drivers of change being considered by the UK NEA (Chapter 3), such as climate, policy (e.g. CAP), population growth, management, global markets and trade. Surprisingly, the issue of technological change garnered the fewest responses; this contrasts with the assumption that technology will be a major driver in many published scenario studies, and with the close attention that it has often been given. When asked about ecosystem services, most respondents expressed an interest in seeing provisioning and regulating services explored; cultural services were cited less frequently. Thus there were a greater number of questions about energy, food, water, and carbon-related ecosystem services. However, while topics such as biodiversity, leisure and recreation were cited less frequently, questions about cross-cutting issues affecting the balance or trade-offs between all ecosystem services did receive a good deal of attention.

A number of the focal questions provided in the survey were useful in defining the contrasts and dichotomies that the UK NEA scenarios might explore. Thus, for example, one consultee asked: 'What happens if you implement all the sustainable management options posed in the various habitat chapters in the UK NEA?'. Another asked: 'What will be the consequences of recasting biodiversity targets in terms of ecosystem services?'. Questions of this kind were particularly helpful in defining the potential 'geometry' of the UK NEA scenarios; that is, the set of contrasts around which the storylines could be constructed and the outcomes that would emerge under different assumptions. They suggested, for example, that the set of scenarios might include one in which biodiversity issues were prioritised (this later became *Green and Pleasant Land*), compared to one in which a more utilitarian view of nature was dominant (this later formed the basis of *Nature@Work*).

Policy-related questions posed by the consultees provided further material that suggested other potential storylines. For example, questions like *'How could CAP reform help delivery of services other than "provisioning" from farmland?'* led to the consideration of scenarios that differed in terms of the type and strength of policy interventions; thus storylines might contrast 'regulated' and 'unregulated' worlds. A further avenue to explore suggested by the responses was

Figure 25.1 The role of stakeholders and focal questions in building the UK NEA scenarios.

the effect of external global actors and market forces on the UK's future. Here, questions like *'What would 70% food security mean for the UK's ecosystems?'* were extremely useful in suggesting a security-related storyline (later to become the *National Security* scenario) that might be contrasted with one in which trade operated with few barriers (to become *World Markets*) or a future like today (later to become *Go with the Flow*). Another version of a less regulated world to emerge from the material and later discussions was one in which more 'place-based' or 'fine-grained' responses dominated (this became *Local Stewardship*).

From the outset the UK NEA work programme recognised that different conditions and concerns may exist between England, Scotland, Wales and Northern Ireland. In terms of the UK NEA scenario development, it was also considered important that any potential contrasts between outcomes or issues in the four countries should be explored. However, the focal questions collected through the survey were largely 'UK-centric'. Just one respondent mentioned cross-country relationships in a question related to the water sector, and only one other was interested in *'how different amounts of habitat per nation affect what is important'*. These results were not interpreted to mean that significant differences between the four countries do not exist, but rather that further dialogue was needed. It was felt that this could be done by constructing the scenarios at the UK level and exploring the implications for the separate administrations at a later stage.

Climate change was clearly an important issue for many respondents, while some were specifically interested in comparisons across different climate futures, as implied by: *'What would be the impact of a specific set of UK climate change predictions ... on the continued delivery of provisioning and regulating services across a range of UK broad ecosystems?'*, or more specifically: *'What are the implications of climate change and a growing population on the availability of water for agriculture?'*. However, many consultees accepted some level of climate change as a given. They were mostly interested in the ways in which other drivers might impact on emissions or what the implications different emissions reduction strategies might have in different environmental, social or economic contexts, as in: *'How can we integrate climate adaptation strategies, energy needs and waste management together with maintenance of quality habitats to ensure continuity of ecosystem regulation?'*, or *'Are semi-natural grasslands becoming more or less productive in terms of meat and milk production per unit of greenhouse gas emissions?'* and *'What are the implications of any trends observed for emissions of greenhouse gas from grassland and the efficiency of milk and meat production?'*.

The conclusion drawn from the way the questions about climate change were framed was that in any set of scenarios, the differences between 'low' and 'high' climate change versions of each narrative might be worth considering, to explore how sensitive different types of future might be to different climate trajectories. However, given that the storylines are only considering the next 50 years, it was decided that they must start from the assumption that whatever we do now as a society will not have much effect on the climate over this period. Given the time lag between mitigation activity and climate response, it was decided that

the most useful things to consider would be how different mitigation or adaptation strategies might play themselves out in these different types of future, or how different policies or trends in other areas might support or undermine them.

25.2.2 Other Scenario Studies

In designing the UK NEA scenarios it was considered important that the work should take account of the other relevant national or international studies. These included FORESIGHT Land Use (FLUF 2010), UKCIP (Hulme *et al.* 2002), the scenario work undertaken in the marine sector (Pinnegar *et al.* 2006; FEUFAR 2008), the recent initiatives by Natural England (Creedy *et al.* 2009) and the Environment Agency's Scenarios 2030 (Environment Agency 2009). It was felt that considerable effort had already gone into these other studies and the wider community were probably already familiar with many of the assumptions and outcomes, and that there should be some explanation of how the UK NEA scenarios related to them. Thus, in parallel to the survey of user needs, a review of these other studies was made to examine if they could be used to help answer the kinds of questions being asked in the UK NEA, or whether their approach might be helpful in developing narratives or analytical approaches. Two aspects were looked at most closely: the extent to which ecosystem service trajectories were dealt with implicitly or explicitly by the studies; and, whether the studies could be used to help develop plausible projections of the major drivers of change being considered by the UK NEA. From initial consultations and a review of recent literature, 21 scenarios studies were identified as relevant to the kinds of issue being considered in the UK NEA, or were useful in methodological terms.

Table 25.2 summarises some of the key features of the studies included in the review (for a more detailed analysis see Paterson *et al.* 2010). It suggests that there is considerable diversity in thematic breadth, with some studies quite general in scope (e.g. covering a range of environmental issues), while others are more focused around particular topics (e.g. agriculture or water use). Insights about the drivers of change that have been proposed as the framework for the UK NEA were found to be one of the major strengths of the set of studies identified (see Chapter 3). Nearly all of them use the five main indirect drivers proposed as a focus for the UK NEA, namely: sociopolitical; economic; science and technological; cultural and religious; and demographic. Of these, cultural and religious drivers were probably the least frequently considered, but are still adopted by 70% of the studies. The three dominant direct drivers considered were climate change (in 100% of scenarios), resource consumption (95%) and land use change (80%). Biotic drivers (e.g. invasive species) were only dealt with in about 40% of the studies. **Table 25.2** suggests that the European and global scenarios also tend to be broader in their remit than the UK or sub-national studies, although there are some exceptions, such as the nationally focused work of Natural England (Creedy *et al.* 2009). There are also differences in the time horizon considered, with global and European studies tending to look further into the future. Those with a national or regional focus tended to look at developments over the next 50 years.

Table 25.2 Key aspects of the scenarios reviewed for the UK NEA. Ql=Qualitive, Qn=Quantitative.

Scenario exercise	Main focus	Timeline	Data	Uses five main indirect drivers?	Outlines habitat impacts	Ecosystem Services
SRES	Climate change, economic development	2100	Ql, Qn	Yes	0	No
MA	Ecosystem Services		Ql, Qn	Yes	8	Yes
Foresight Futures	Environment	2020	Ql, Qn	2	8	Yes
Foresight Futures Land Use	Land use change	2060	Ql	Yes	6	Yes
UKCIP socio-economic	Climate change	2050	Ql, Qn	Yes	6	No
UKCIP Climate change	Climate change	2050	Ql, Qn	4	0	No
AFMEC Marine	Marine	2040	Ql, Qn	Yes	1	brief discussion
Net Benefits	Fisheries	2025	Ql, Qn	4	1	brief discussion
Natural England 2060	Environment	2060	Ql	4	7	brief discussion
EA Water Resources	Water	2050	Ql	Yes	0	brief discussion
UNEP 3rd GEO	Environment	2040	Ql, Qn	Yes	6	No
WCS Futures of the Wild	Biodiversity	2030	Ql, Qn	4	6	No
ELME	Marine	2040	Ql, Qn	4	1	No
EEA Prelude	Environment	2035	Ql, Qn	Yes	4	No
PSI BESEECH	Urban, climate change	2050	Ql, Qn	4	1	No
Global Scenarios Group	Environment	2050	Ql	Yes	4	No
ACCELERATES	Agriculture	2050	Ql, Qn	4	1	No
ATEAM	Climate change	2080	Qn	4	4	Yes
EURURALIS	Land use, environment	2030	Ql, Qn	Yes	5	Yes
ALARM	Biodiversity	2050	Ql, Qn	4	4	Yes
ESPON	Geopolitics & planning	2030	Ql, Qn	Yes	4	No

Table 25.3 Approximate correspondence between Global, European and British scenarios. Scenarios included in analysis: [1]Office Science and Technology (2003); [2]UKCIP (2001); [3]EA (2001); [4]Hulme *et al.* (2002); [5]Pinnegar *et al.* (2006); [6]Prime Minister's Strategy Unit (2004); [7]Creedy *et al.* (2009); [8]EA (2009); [9]Dahlstrom & Salmons (2005); [10]UNEP & RIVM (2003); [11]Langmead *et al.* (2007);

NEA	Foresight Futures[1]	UKCIP Socio-economic scenario[2]	EA water demand scenario[3]	UKCIP Climate Change Scenario[4]	AFMEC Marine Scenario[5]	Net Benefits[6]	Natural England[7]	EA Water Resources Strategy for England & Wales[8]	PSI BESEECH[9]	UNEP 3rd GEO Four Scenarios for Europe[10]	ELME European Lifestyle & Marine Ecosystem[11]
	UK	UK	UK	UK	UK	UK	UK	UK	UK	Europe	Europe
Nature @ Work / *Local Stewardship*	Global Commons	Global Commons	Gamma	Low Emissions	Global Commons	Green World	Connect for Life	Sustainable behaviour	Global Responsibility	Sustainability First	Global Communi(ty)
Green & Pleasant Land	Local stewardship	Local Stewardship	Delta	Medium-Low Emissions	Local Stewardship	–	Keep it Local	Local Resilience	Local Stewardship	Policy First	Local Responsib(ility)
Go with the Flow / *National Security*	Provincial Enterprise	Fortress Britain	Alpha	Medium-High Emissions	Fortress Britain	Fortress-Europe	Succeed through Science	Innovation	National Enterprise	Security First	Nationa(l) Enterpris(e)
World Markets	World Markets	World Markets	Beta	High Emissions	World Markets	Market-World	Go for Growth	Uncontrolled Demand	World Markets	Markets First	World Mark(ets)

A comparison between the storylines used in the different studies is shown in **Table 25.3**, which groups them according to whether they are mainly UK focused, or whether they have a global or European perspective. The approach used to construct this table is based on the one used by Pinnegar *et al.* (2006), who summarised the correspondences between storylines used in the different scenario studies relevant to their work. **Table 25.3** uses this framework to cross-reference the various narratives, but extends it to a wider range of studies. While some interpretation was needed to make the associations between the storylines of the different studies, the conclusion drawn by Pinnegar *et al.* (2006) about a similarity of structure between studies, seems to be borne out. The use of a contrasting 'two axis' model was common. Nearly all the scenario studies followed a fairly generic pattern of differentiation with four basic storylines: a free-market model (corresponding to the SRES A1 scenario; MA Global Orchestration); a national security model (SRES A2, MA Order From Strength); a sustainable or green vision model (SRES B1, MA Techno-Garden); and a local stewardship model (SRES B2, MA Adaptive Mosaic, Cork *et al.* 2006b; Nakicenovic *et al.* 2009).

Our review of other scenario studies also looked at the way they dealt with ecosystem services and how they mapped on to the focal questions identified in our user survey. The MA provided the most complete treatment of future ecosystem services, but while it offered a broad context in which the UK could be set, it was not clear how the storylines would translate to the UK scale, or how they would lead to contrasting outcomes across the UK if they were viewed as simply driving change from outside. In this respect, the recent study by Natural England (Creedy *et al.* 2009) was more useful in giving guidance about the way in which differences in scales of action and commitment to the environment may play themselves out at national scales. However, this study did not look at issues in Scotland, Wales or Northern Ireland, and so it was difficult to use this directly as a framework for the UK NEA.

The Foresight Land Use Study (FLUF 2010) used three scenario narratives which differed considerably from those of the MA and other studies. They were formed by pairwise combinations of the degree of adaptation to environmental change, the degree of societal resistance to change, and concentration of people and economic activity within the UK. Like the Natural England study, the sustainable management and restoration of ecosystem services was covered by the scenario narratives, but a detailed analysis on the implications for particular services and habitats was not made. However, both this and the Natural England Study did make a useful, detailed analysis of the drivers of social, economic and environmental change, and so provided valuable background for the UK NEA work; Land Use Foresight, for example, produced a rich body of peer-reviewed material on the impact of land use change on ecosystems (see Beddington 2009) and this has been used here to help define projections for different drivers and to understand their potential impact on land cover and ecosystem services.

[12]Volkery (2007); [13]Audsley *et al.* (2006); [14]Rounsevell *et al.* (2006); [15]Westhoek *et al.* (2006); [16]Settele *et al.* (2010); [17]European Observation Network for Territorial Development & Cohesion (2007); [18]Nakicenovic *et al.* (2009); [19]Cork *et al.* (2006a); [20]Wildlife Conservation Society (2007) and [21]Raskin *et al.* (2002).

EEA PRELUDE[12]	ACCELERATES[13]	ATEAM[14]	EU-Ruralis[15]	ALARM[16]	ESPON[17]	SRES	MA[19]	WCS Futures of the Wild[20]	Global Scenarios Group[21]
Europe	Europe	Europe	Europe	Europe	Europe	Global	Global	Global	Global
Big crisis—Europe of Cohesion	B1	B1	Global co-operation	SEDG	–	B1	Techno-garden	Connecting the dots	(Great Transitions) New Sustainability
Evolved Society—Europe of Harmony	B2	B2	Regional Communities	BAMBU	Cohesion oriented future	B2	Adaptive-mosaic	The New Zoogenesis	(Great Transitions) Eco-communalism
Lettuce Surprise U—Europe of Innovation	A2	A2	Continental Markets	–	–	A2	Order-from-Strength	Bad to Better	(Barbarization) Fortress World
									(Barbarization) Breakdown
Great Escape—Europe of Contrasts	A1	A1	Global Economy	GRAS	Competitiveness oriented future	A1	Global Orchestration	While the World Warms	(Conventional Worlds) Market Forces
Clustered Networks—Europe of Structure									(Conventional Worlds) Policy Reform

The conclusion to emerge from the review of other studies was that none of existing sets of storylines could be used in their entirety for the UK NEA because they either did not consider ecosystem services in sufficient depth or because their focus did not map on to the concerns expressed in the user survey. The conventional 2x2 axis structure, that juxtaposed global/local and reactive/proactive futures, seemed particularly unhelpful in exploring the nuances between alternative green futures that emphasised biodiversity priorities on the one hand and ecosystem services on the other. The other studies also did not seem to fully capture the issues of risk and security identified by the users and, especially, the differing impacts of alternative climate change trajectories. The review suggested that a different configuration of scenarios was probably needed for the UK NEA.

25.2.3 Creating the UK NEA Scenarios Using a Morphological Analysis

The results of the user survey and the review of existing scenario studies were brought together by means of a 'morphological analysis'. Morphological analyses are useful for investigating the relationships between multiple quantifiable and qualitative factors. They have been used widely in developing scenarios because they provide a simple way of representing the links between drivers and the storylines (Godet 2000; Ritchey 2010). They are also a good way of mapping out clearly the assumptions embodied in the different scenario narratives.

The method involves constructing a matrix that links key factors or issues to alternative future trajectories (**Box 25.1**). The columns of the matrix are the direct and indirect drivers that need to be considered in the scenario exercise, such as climate change, food supply or land use. The rows set out different potential trends for each driver, and thus the range of conceivable or plausible futures that might be considered. Different scenarios can then be constructed by linking cells horizontally in the matrix, each strand forming a distinct scenario based on our understandings of how drivers might be associated or causally connected.

A 'full' morphological analysis includes a number of steps, involving users and experts working through the matrix to check the range of projections defined for each driver, and to agree which combination of drivers go together in a plausible way to define a distinct storyline. The timetable for the UK NEA prevented such an extended process of consultation, and so material from the existing scenario studies that included the drivers being considered by the UK NEA was used to define the projections in the matrix. This material was supplemented with information extracted from the draft UK NEA chapters on current state and trends, that was available in mid-2010. The desk study was completed by mapping on to the matrix the storylines implied from the user survey, focusing particularly on how they might be differentiated by different intensities and combinations of drivers.

Using the morphological approach, six draft storylines were created: *Green and Pleasant Land*, *Nature@Work*,

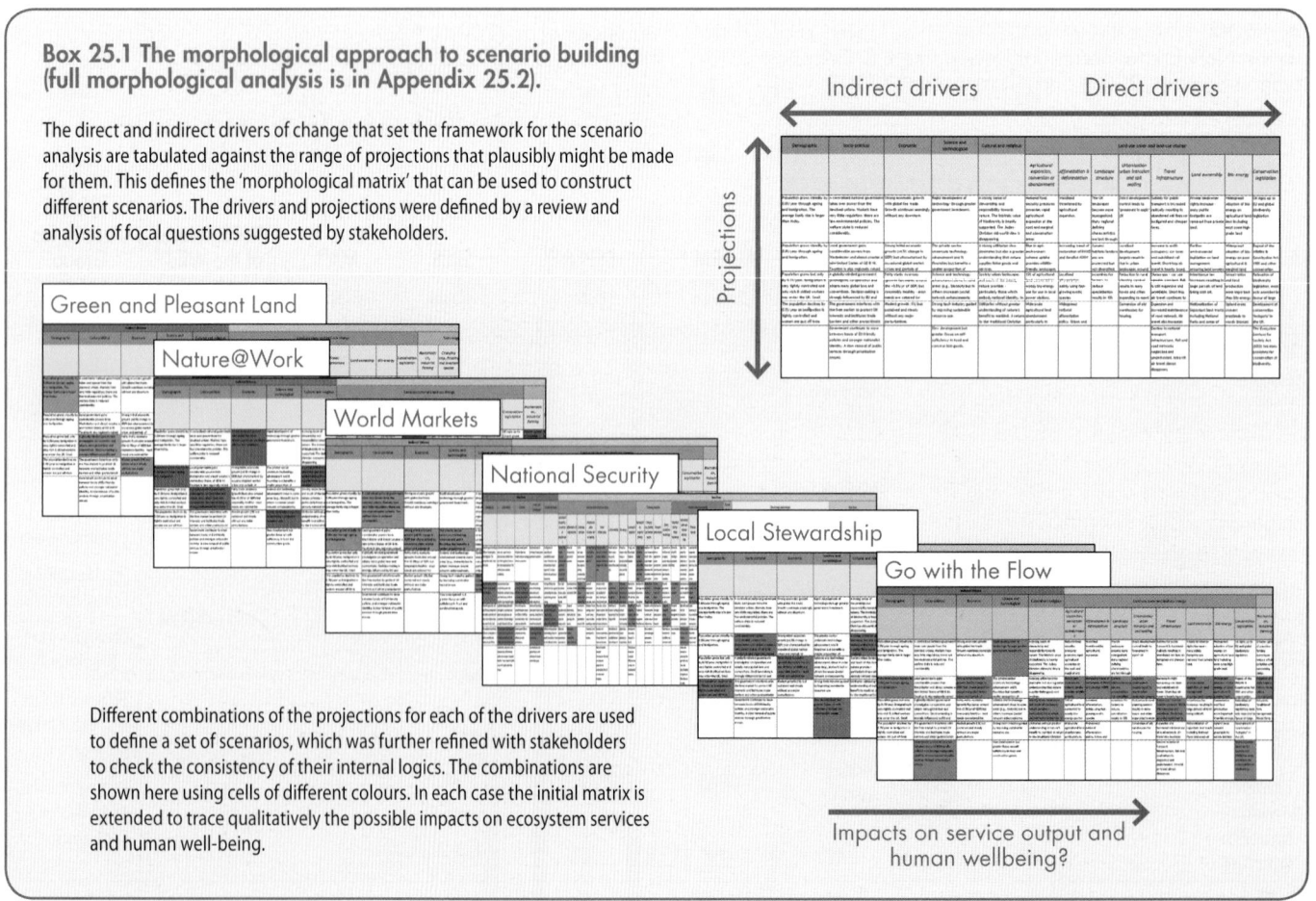

Box 25.1 The morphological approach to scenario building (full morphological analysis is in Appendix 25.2).

The direct and indirect drivers of change that set the framework for the scenario analysis are tabulated against the range of projections that plausibly might be made for them. This defines the 'morphological matrix' that can be used to construct different scenarios. The drivers and projections were defined by a review and analysis of focal questions suggested by stakeholders.

Different combinations of the projections for each of the drivers are used to define a set of scenarios, which was further refined with stakeholders to check the consistency of their internal logics. The combinations are shown here using cells of different colours. In each case the initial matrix is extended to trace qualitatively the possible impacts on ecosystem services and human well-being.

National Security, *World Markets*, *Local Stewardship and Go with the Flow*. Two different levels of response to climate change for each storyline were created using the simplified UKCIP-09 Low and High Emissions Scenarios for 2050–2079. This was done by setting up contrasts in the matrix for change in mean annual temperature and change in summer precipitation; these two variables were selected because both are important drivers of change for a range of habitats.

The morphological analysis made it possible to go beyond the traditional 2x2 set of dichotomous axes to create a set of scenarios that showed a greater degree of differentiation in ecosystem service output that met more of the expectations of the stakeholders. Thus, the six scenarios allowed a comparison between a set of future worlds where societies' ideological grounding is more nuanced and complex than, say, a green storyline versus a free market one. It also enabled all storylines to more easily encapsulate 'good' and 'bad' aspects, and so avoid the implication that one was to be preferred or regarded as potentially more desirable than the others. The full morphological analysis for the six scenarios is given in **Appendix 25.2**.

25.3 The UK NEA Scenarios

25.3.1 Scenarios: Representing their Internal Logics

The drafts of each storyline and their climatic variants were first reviewed at a full-day meeting by UK NEA stakeholders and experts interested in scenario issues. The narratives were refined and taken forward into four full-day meetings with stakeholders from the four countries, where they were further reviewed and criticised. These discussions, all of which took place in 2010, covered a range of topics from the more general conceptual and philosophical aspects of scenario building through to the plausibility and implications of the draft scenarios themselves. The broader methodological issues will be considered in the last part of this chapter. Here the focus is on the scenarios themselves, their assumptions and implications that seem to follow for ecosystem services and well-being.

The morphological framework used to draft the storylines was valuable both in showing how storylines differed in terms of the projections for the various drivers of change, and in developing the logic that linked these changes through to the output of ecosystem services. This latter step, and questions about the robustness of the reasoning that connects the drivers and ecosystem outputs, is clearly critical to judging the success of the whole exercise. Thus it is important to consider it further here.

For a scenario exercise to be convincing scientifically, the reasoning that connects assumptions about changes in the key drivers to ecosystem outputs should be evidence-based. Although scenarios attempt to look to the future and describe worlds very different from today's, the ecosystem responses have to be credible in biophysical or socioeconomic terms; that is, they need to be broadly consistent with what we know about ecosystems and how they behave at present. This is generally achieved by using either process-response models or empirical relationships that would allow drivers and ecosystem services to be quantified, and some kind of input-output analysis made. The need to 'quantify' scenarios is, for example, a key point in the approach developed out of the MA experience (Ash *et al.* 2010); quantification is seen as a way of increasing the transparency of the arguments that underpin the deductions developed around different storylines. Unfortunately, the UK NEA material on current state and trends provided few models or empirical relationships of the type needed. Certainly none appeared to exist that deals with the balance between different types of service output, or trade-offs under different sets of assumptions at the UK scale.

Thus, the initial phase of scenario development had to employ a more qualitative approach for deducing the impacts of the different combinations of drivers that defined the six storylines. This was done initially by extending the morphological analysis to include the likely consequences for the UK NEA habitats and services that were implied by the projections for the drivers assumed under each narrative. To take account of the lack of modelling tools we have, however, sought to make the logic that underpins our deductions as clear as possible by also using a rule-based approach that describes how the major land cover types being considered by the UK NEA would change under the different storylines.

For each storyline we considered how the major land cover types would change in different types of location, and represented these quantitatively as a set of land cover transition matrices. These matrices could be used to change the present pattern of land cover in ways that were consistent with each narrative. The major factors influencing change were considered to be altitude, the density of ancient and semi-natural woodlands, landscape designation, and proximity to urban areas, agricultural land quality, and climate (temperature and precipitation). The influences that each of these factors is assumed to have on land cover under each scenario are described in **Table 25.4**. The use of these transition matrices allowed some of the qualitative assumptions that underpin the scenarios to be represented quantitatively—not as a way of making modelled predictions of future patterns of land cover, but to describe more clearly the spatial assumptions made about the location and magnitude of change implied by the particular storylines. It was felt that the land cover projections produced by this analysis allowed the plausibility of the scenarios to be more easily tested.

The approach used to make projections for the different scenarios had another advantage: it allowed the economic valuation of ecosystem services to be used to examine the implications of the six scenarios in monetary terms. Many of the models used to estimate the present value of services are based on an understanding of the stocks of different types of land cover and their geographical distribution (Chapter 22). Thus, land cover mapping, coupled with other assumptions about population and economic growth, enabled marginal differences in the values for some services to be estimated

Table 25.4 Factors assumed to affect land cover change and their impacts in each scenario.

Criteria	Variable	Effect	Green and Pleasant Land (GPL)	Nature@Work (N@W)	World Markets (WM)
Altitude	Upland	Land >250 m asl; in northern Scotland upland can be almost down to down to sea level though	Decline in arable (AR), improved grassland (IG), conifer and urban (UR) to enhance the landscape biodiversity and aesthetics. Broadleaf wood, semi-natural grassland and upland habitats all increase as a result.	Similar patterns to GPL although as well as improving biodiversity many of the land cover changes are designed to alleviate flood (> broadleaf wood (BL) and semi-natural grassland) or improve regulating ecosystem services.	Arable increases slightly although IG declines as animal production becomes more crop-based. Slight decline in BL & semi-natural grassland to make way for urban growth. Upland habitats decrease slightly due to some conversion to UR. High Climate Change (CC) increases freshwater as winter flooding becomes difficult and too expensive to manage (the rest to semi-natural grassland).
Altitude	Lowland	<250 m	Almost identical patterns to upland (and for the same reasons). Agriculture declines in the UK but is compensated for by much larger imports.	Similar to above although improved grassland declines even more due to it being an inefficient use of land and less meat consumption in the UK. Broadleaf also increases more. Arable declines slightly.	AR increases as a result of a decline in IG (livestock indoors) and a greater need for crop-based animal feed. Semi-natural grassland declines also, some is lost to AR, some to UR. Overall, UR growth is the major lowland winner in the south east and most other land use lose some to it.
Woodland potential	ASNWHigh	Area of land with a density of ASNW† or PAWS‡ >5% of cover in a 10 km grid squares	A slightly higher expansion of new woodland near areas of high ASNW but overall new woodland planting is important in both low and high density areas for landscape as well as biodiversity reasons.	ASNWHigh significantly increases broadleaf woods for conservation/ ecological reasons (and results in lower conifer).	Broadleaf woodland stays constant or declines slightly with no ASNW effect on changes. Woodland is abandoned and unmanaged. Some loss to UR growth. High climate change kills back some vulnerable woods like beech in south.
Woodland potential	ASNWLow	<5% per 10 km grid squares			
Urban influence	Near	Land within 5 km or urban boundary	Distance to urban areas does not have a huge influence on land cover transitions (no Urban growth so not an issue).	Distance to urban areas does not have a huge influence on land cover transitions except for small urban growth near existing urban areas.	Near urban is generally converted to urban regardless of land cover type. General spread of urban sprawl.
Urban influence	Far	Land further than 5 km from urban boundary			
Landscape designation	Park	Land within National Park or AONB¶	An important factor which affects changes to semi-natural habitats (increases more in Parks) and productive cover types (decreases less outside parks).	Park designation significantly increases broadleaf woods for conservation reasons (and results in lower conifer).	Park designation has very little consequence for land cover change. In some areas, urban area may increase in Parks as the rich want to live in beautiful areas.
Landscape designation	NotPark	Land outside National Park or AONB¶			
Agricultural Land Classification (ALC)	High	ALC - grades 1 & 2	ALC 1+2 loses less productive land from arable and improved grassland to others (but still does) than 3, 4 & 5. The lowest grade soils gain more in conifers.	High ALC soil that is arable and does not transfer to other land uses as it is important to maintain the most productive land for food. Medium and Low ALC significantly increase broadleaf and semi-natural grassland.	The best soil is protected for arable (ALC 1, 2 and high 3); other soils are more likely to be converted to urban if close to urban areas. Some poor soils will be converted to conifer in from arable or improved grassland or upland habitats.
Agricultural Land Classification (ALC)	Med	ALC - grades 3a & 3b			
Agricultural Land Classification (ALC)	Low	ALC - grades 4 & 5			
Change in temperature	Hi - North	Areas of UK likely to experience a mean change in summer temperature of +3°C	Higher temperatures will affect some land cover types—arable suffers a slight loss with little adaptation capacity (semi-natural grassland gains here). Broadleaf woods also suffer slightly as beech and some oak woods cannot cope with climate change in southern UK.	Warmer areas in south of UK sill reduce agricultural production slightly although N@W loses less AR than others because it is better adapted to climate change. Generally speaking, in N@W, the difference between Low and High climate change is very small.	Very little adaptation capacity in WM; High climate change reduces arable area in south (abandoned to semi-natural grassland or southern hemisphere conifers). Some broadleaf woods suffer and is converted to conifer.
Change in temperature	Hi - South	Areas of UK likely to experience a mean change in summer temperature of +4°C			

Storyline

National Security (NS)	Local Stewardship (LS)	Go with the Flow (GF)
Food and timber production very important and conifer cover increases considerably as does arable. Slight decline in improved grassland due to a move towards more efficient food production (i.e. crop-based protein). Broadleaf wood also slightly increases at the expense of semi-natural grassland and upland habitats. High CC reduces arable area in uplands and more is switched to improved grassland.	Semi-natural grassland and broadleaf woods two main winners here. Food production is very important but is managed sustainably and extensively hence the transition to more semi-natural habitats. Upland stays constant but is managed more sustainably.	Slight increases in broadleaf woods, semi-natural grassland and upland habitats reflecting the continuing pattern of 'softening' landscapes through agri-environment schemes and other conservation grant-aided programmes.
Arable and conifers increase considerably as does arable. Decline in improved grassland due to a move towards more efficient food production (i.e. crop-based protein). BL woods also slightly increases at the expense of semi-natural grassland. High CC reduces arable area in south and more is switched to drought-tolerant conifer.	Similar to above although improved grassland declines slightly (and more under High climate change). Main underlying factor behind land cover changes is a lower demand for food (low population, less waste)—as a result, semi-natural grassland increases (but is used for livestock production too). Loss of arable due to less demand for food.	Continuation of current agri-environment policy— slight loss of arable to semi-natural grassland and broadleaf woods. Continued conversion of PAWS conifer to broadleaf woods. Loss of improved grassland as more livestock reared indoors and requires arable crop land. Slight increase in urban as population continues to rise.
Increase in broadleaf woods and huge increase in conifer with little regard to presence or absence of ANSW. ALC is a more important factor here.	Biodiversity is very important in this storyline, as are timber and non-timber forest products hence increase in traditional native woodland types near existing ANSW woods. Increases in High climate change to replace arable which struggles with heat and drought.	Presence of ASNW increases likelihood of new broadleaf woods to improve biodiversity value.
Generally, proximity to urban has little effect on other land cover changes.	No influence on land use transitions except for increase in arable (for local peri-urban food production).	Near urban is more likely to become urban; rural areas generally protected from housing development.
Park designation has very little consequence for land cover change. Recreation and conservation not important in this storyline.	Has major influence - Park areas protect semi-natural grassland and broadleaf and both increase at expense of arable and improved grassland.	National Parks etc. continue to maintain strict planning laws. Conversions of arable and improved grassland to semi-natural grassland and broadleaf occurs, as does some to freshwater habitats.
Major determinant factor on arable—the best land is kept or converted to arable even ALC 3 is protected. Maximising yield is paramount.	High ALC soils are kept as arable; lower ALC soils more likely to become broadleaf woods and semi-natural grassland throughout UK. Some Medium ALC soils will become improved grassland to increase farmland heterogeneity.	High ALC soils are kept arable; lower ALC soils more likely to become broadleaf woods and semi-natural grassland through UK.
High climate change temperatures reduce arable production in south east; adaptation capacity (e.g. drought resistant crops) not as prevalent as in N@W); switch to conifer or improved grassland in these circumstances.	Reduces arable but increases native wood planting (not beech or other climate change intolerant species). Some improved grassland is converted to semi-natural grassland because it is more climate change tolerant.	Loss of arable and improved grassland as High climate change impacts make growing crops more difficult. Some degree of adaptation but not enough to see small transition to either water, broadleaf woods or semi-natural grassland.

Criteria	Variable	Effect	Green and Pleasant Land (GPL)	Nature@Work (N@W)	World Markets (WM)	
Change in precipitation	-40%	Areas of UK likely to experience a mean change in summer precipitation of -40%	Similar effects as temperature changes on arable and broadleaf wood (drought compounds heat affect).	Drier areas in south of UK sill reduce agricultural production slightly although N@W loses less arable than others because it is better adapted to climate change. Generally speaking, in N@W, the difference between Low and High climate change is very small.	As for temperature changes.	
	-30%	Areas of UK likely to experience a mean change in summer precipitation of -30%				
	-20%	Areas of UK likely to experience a mean change in summer precipitation of -20%				
Inland flood risk*	Significant	The chance of flooding in any year is >1.3% (1 in 75)	The higher risk will remove more agricultural land than low risk; GPL is not the best at coping with flood and is characterised by the loss of arable and improved grassland and an increase in broadleaf woods (floodplain woods) and semi-natural grassland.	N@W is the best adapted to vagaries of climate change including flood; but, while the best ALC soils will be protected from flood and kept arable lower quality arable is best given over to broadleaf woods or semi-natural grassland to improve other ecosystem services.	WM spends little effort mitigating flood and even low risk will lose land cover to water; this is compounded more in High climate change.	
	Moderate	The chance of flooding in any year is 1.3% (1 in 75) or less but >0.5% (1 in 200)				
	Low	The chance of flooding each year is 0.5% (1 in 200) or less				
Sea level	None	No risk of flooding	Land under risk of flooding increases considerably as the flood risk increases. All land covers lose, particularly urban areas. Flood defence is not a high priority as the prevailing view is to let nature take its course. High climate change impacts increases risk.	Land under risk of flooding increases considerably as the flood risk increases. All land covers lose space but N@W takes sea defence seriously if land has high ecosystem service value. In some areas, managed retreat is utilised. High climate change impacts increases risk.	Only high value urban areas are protected; most other land cover types will have increasing risk of conversion to sea as little is spent on flood defence.	
	Low	Medium risk of flooding (land where a 15 cm rise of sea level)				
	Significant	Significant risk of flooding (land within 45 cm)				

* Note: due to data limitations, the impacts of flooding were only considered in the qualitative projections for each scenario, and were not included in making
† Ancient Semi-natural Woodland. ‡ Plantation on Ancient Woodland Site. ¶ Area of Outstanding Natural Beauty.

between scenarios (Chapter 26). It has also allowed the marginal changes in value to be calculated using today's situation as a baseline.

Box 25.2 describes the way in which the transition matrices were employed; the method involved a set of Bayesian belief networks that expressed the probability of landscape change in different situations. For the land cover analysis, *Land Cover Map 2000* of Great Britain was used to represent the 'current condition'[1]. The transition matrices were used to change the mix of land cover in each 1 km x 1 km cell of the Ordnance Survey National Grid for each scenario according to the assumptions set out in **Table 25.4**. Unfortunately, a comparable approach could not be used to look at changes in the marine space, and so only qualitative projections could be made for these ecosystems. The effectiveness of the methods used for making the mapped projections of future land and sea cover will be reviewed more fully in the last part of this chapter.

25.3.2 The UK NEA Scenarios: Key Contrasts

There are a number of contrasts between the six UK NEA scenarios related to the outcomes for land cover, ecosystem services, social equity and governance. All share the common characteristics of a decline in the availability of global resources and an ageing UK population. They also include some level of technological innovation, although there are differences in the sectors involved. **Figure 25.2** provides an overview and **Table 25.5** gives a more detailed account of their major assumptions and the differences between them. **Table 25.6** documents the assumed differences between the narratives for the population and its geographical distribution.

In terms of the contrasts between the scenarios, there are differences in: the levels of consumerism (assumed to be high in *World Markets, National Security* and *Go with the Flow*); the strength of community cohesion (higher in *Green*

1 Land Cover Map 2007 was not available at the time of the UK NEA analysis; the analysis was not made for Northern Ireland because a full set of context data were not available. The effects of flood were also not undertaken for GB because of the unavailability of data.

UK National Ecosystem Assessment: Technical Report

Storyline		
National Security (NS)	**Local Stewardship (LS)**	**Go with the Flow (GF)**
As for temperature changes. Drier conditions more likely to result in arable converting to conifer woods.	As for temperature changes.	Loss of arable and improved grassland as High climate change impacts make growing crops more difficult.
Flood control is important for food or timber producing land. High risk areas will lose to water but for moderate or low every effort is made to protect arable. Some loss of urban to water too.	Increased flood risk is seen as an opportunity to return land to grazing marsh or floodplain woods rather than hindrance. Conversion of arable, improved grassland to broadleaf woods and semi-natural grassland rises with increased flood risk.	Housing development in floodplains is protected though afforestation projects (hence in high flood risk areas some degree of arable and improved grassland to broadleaf woods).
As with inland flood risk— arable near coast is protected more than urban.	Managed retreat is fully accepted by society, loss of arable and improved grassland occurs.	Some managed retreat in coastal areas away from urban zones—loss of some arable and improved grassland.

ojections for land cover based on the construction of a set of transition matrices.

and *Pleasant Land, Nature@Work* and *Local Stewardship*); interdependence with other countries (higher in *World Markets, Go with the Flow* and *Green and Pleasant Land*) or autonomy (higher in *Nature@Work, National Security* and *Local Stewardship*); the UK's overseas ecological footprint (higher for *World Markets, Go with the Flow and Green and Pleasant Land*); landscape heterogeneity (higher in *Green and Pleasant Land, Nature@Work* and *Local Stewardship*); and habitat fragmentation (higher in *World Markets, National Security and Go with the Flow*), as well as response to climate change through mitigation and adaptation efforts (higher in *Nature@Work, Green and Pleasant Land* and *Local Stewardship*).

The development of the built environment also differs between the storylines. In *World Markets, Nature@Work* and *Go with the Flow* there is a strong south-east UK focus, while in *Green and Pleasant Land* and *National Security*, development is concentrated in existing urban areas throughout the UK. Transport and mobility also vary: in *World Markets, Go with the Flow* and *National Security* it is assumed that there is a greater dependence on fossil fuels, air and car travel and

continued investment and expansion of the road network; in *Green and Pleasant Land*, car use stays high but no new roads are built; in *Nature@Work* and *Local Stewardship* the whole transport system is more sustainable, low-cost flights are less frequent, cycling and walking to work is easier and alternative fuels like electricity and hydrogen are promoted.

A comparison of the results from the analysis of the land cover changes using the transition matrix approach is shown in **Figure 25.3**, and **Figure 25.4** gives a breakdown by country. These figures only show the net change and do not show the spatial shifts that might be anticipated; thus the impacts of the scenarios on land cover may look more similar than they otherwise are. These more detailed changes are examined below. For each scenario the projection for the high and low climate variants are shown, together with the proportions of the different land cover types for 2000. Differences between the six scenarios are evident in terms of the proportion of Enclosed Farmland, which declines compared to the present for *Green and Pleasant Land, Nature@Work, Local Stewardship* and *Go with the Flow*. In contrast, Woodland cover expands under each

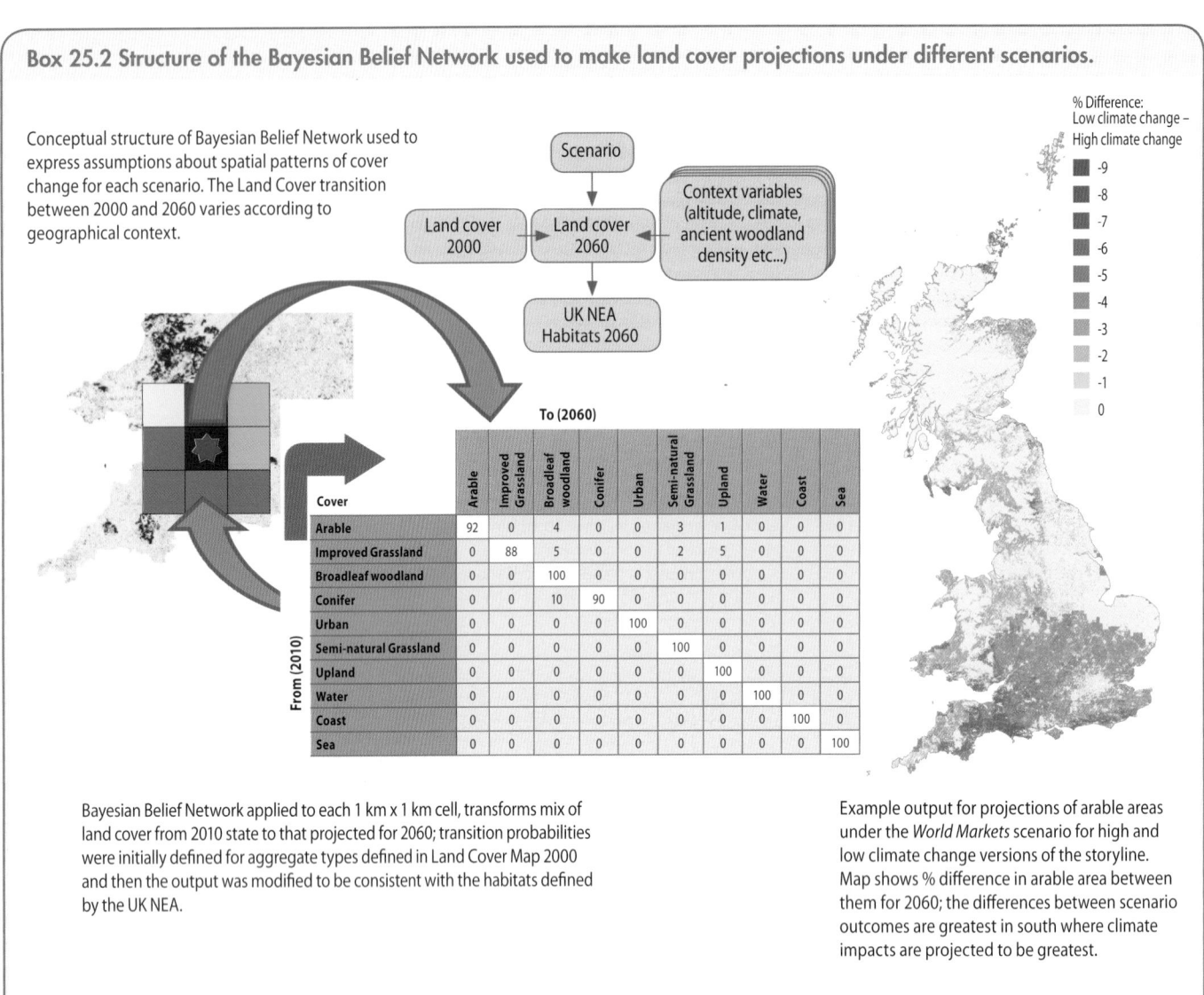

Box 25.2 Structure of the Bayesian Belief Network used to make land cover projections under different scenarios.

Conceptual structure of Bayesian Belief Network used to express assumptions about spatial patterns of cover change for each scenario. The Land Cover transition between 2000 and 2060 varies according to geographical context.

Scenario → Land cover 2060
Land cover 2000 → Land cover 2060
Context variables (altitude, climate, ancient woodland density etc...) → Land cover 2060
Land cover 2060 → UK NEA Habitats 2060

% Difference:
Low climate change – High climate change

-9, -8, -7, -6, -5, -4, -3, -2, -1, 0

To (2060)

From (2010) \ Cover	Arable	Improved Grassland	Broadleaf woodland	Conifer	Urban	Semi-natural Grassland	Upland	Water	Coast	Sea
Arable	92	0	4	0	0	3	1	0	0	0
Improved Grassland	0	88	5	0	0	2	5	0	0	0
Broadleaf woodland	0	0	100	0	0	0	0	0	0	0
Conifer	0	0	10	90	0	0	0	0	0	0
Urban	0	0	0	0	100	0	0	0	0	0
Semi-natural Grassland	0	0	0	0	0	100	0	0	0	0
Upland	0	0	0	0	0	0	100	0	0	0
Water	0	0	0	0	0	0	0	100	0	0
Coast	0	0	0	0	0	0	0	0	100	0
Sea	0	0	0	0	0	0	0	0	0	100

Bayesian Belief Network applied to each 1 km x 1 km cell, transforms mix of land cover from 2010 state to that projected for 2060; transition probabilities were initially defined for aggregate types defined in Land Cover Map 2000 and then the output was modified to be consistent with the habitats defined by the UK NEA.

Example output for projections of arable areas under the *World Markets* scenario for high and low climate change versions of the storyline. Map shows % difference in arable area between them for 2060; the differences between scenario outcomes are greatest in south where climate impacts are projected to be greatest.

of these narratives. Urban cover (i.e. all developed land) is largest under *World Markets,* while the cover of Semi-natural Grasslands and Mountains, Moorlands and Heaths appears greatest in extent under *Green and Pleasant Land, Nature@ Work* and *Local Stewardship.* This analysis appears to show that the differences between scenarios are greater than the difference between the high and low climate change variants of each scenario, although it should be noted that the data need to be interpreted with caution.

25.3.3 Green and Pleasant Land

25.3.3.1 Origin
This storyline arose from two main influences: the popularity of a green storyline in many of the published scenarios and a demand from the survey of focal questions to include biodiversity or landscape elements. A number of additional focal questions helped to refine it, e.g. *'How would reversing habitat fragmentation affect ecosystem services?'*, and *'What are the implications of a continuing growth in leisure use in the countryside?'.* Originally the emphasis was more on biodiversity underpinning national and regional policies. However, feedback from the discussion sessions with country groups resulted in this storyline developing a more

preservationist aspect, albeit one that emphasised the importance of biodiversity. While *Green and Pleasant Land* may appear to be a 'green' storyline, the heavy dependence on overseas ecosystem services to maintain a high quality of life in the UK tends to contradict this. The underlying theme is one of enhancing cultural services in the UK at a cost to others. Whilst attaining this sometimes benefits regulating services, it also involves trade-offs with provisioning services. As a consequence we see declines in the area of more intensively managed Enclosed Farmland, for example, and expansion in semi-natural habitats.

25.3.3.2 Rationale
The preservationist attitude that characterises this scenario comes about because the UK can afford to look after its own backyard without diminishing standards of living. The countryside is a managed and cultural space, and the focus is on trying to maintain, protect and improve its aesthetic appeal. Consequently, tourism and leisure are boosted by this drive, and their share of overall UK GDP increases. This is helped by the reduced popularity of many late-20th Century destinations because of climate change (e.g. France, Spain and Italy). The changes in key drivers gradually result in a greener countryside—this comes

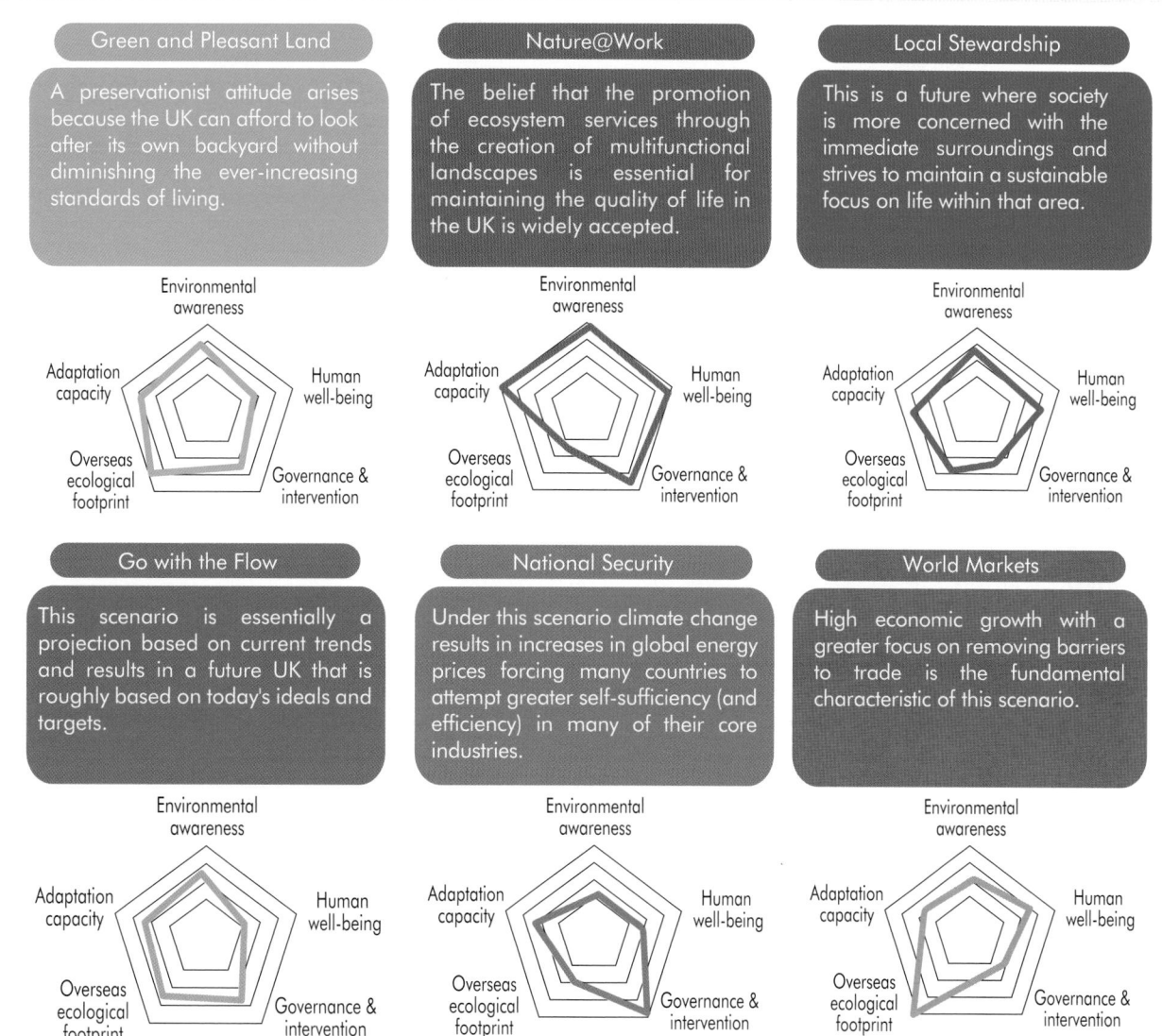

Figure 25.2 An overview of the six scenarios developed for the UK NEA. All share the common characteristics of a decline in global resource availability and an ageing UK population but five contrasting socio-economic aspects are highlighted. The largest ring in the spider diagram demonstrates the highest level of each aspect. Environmental awareness describes the level of appreciation and concern for conservation and sustainability issues in society, for example recycling; Human well-being relates to the standards of health provision, education, employment, freedom, human rights and happiness; Governance and intervention describes how much the state uses political authority and institutional resources to manage society; Overseas ecological footprint is a measure of demand on the earth's resources overseas (resulting from imports of biomass and energy and exports of waste products); Adaptation capacity relates to societies' ability and willingness to cope with the impacts if climate change.

about through a reduction in productive farmland (more is converted through agri-environment schemes to Semi-natural Grassland and Woodland). Climate adaptation for biodiversity is also a dominant driver of land use change, resulting in greater connectivity between semi-natural landscapes and a softening of the landscape. There is also a greater emphasis on habitat restoration and recreation in areas with existing high levels of biodiversity (e.g. areas with high concentrations of ancient semi-natural woodland). The drive towards conservation is so strong that even the best quality agricultural land is occasionally targeted for agri-environment schemes.

Climate change is a high priority under this scenario because it is recognised that not only could it affect habitats (and hence landscapes), but also the economy. This is

reflected in numerous adaptation programmes, which are frequently biodiversity focused, or use biodiversity as a means of delivering other adaptation aims.

In general, landscape preservation coincides with biodiversity conservation, although one major source of conflict is between the importance of recognising habitat and ecosystem change and the maintenance of landscape character. A range of legislation has enabled higher levels of protection for landscape and biodiversity, and the UK has willingly adopted many EU environmental directives and often gone further with UK legislation. Biodiversity and landscape conservation legislation is underpinned by a strong emphasis on these issues in the education system, and is also backed up by a well-funded body of advisory and research groups (government and NGO).

Table 25.5 Key storyline attributes for the UK NEA scenarios.

		Green and Pleasant Land	Nature@Work	World Market	National Security	Local Stewardship	Go with the Flow
Global scenarios	*World overview*	Continued expansion of global free-market enterprise alongside further increases in global environmental standards.	Continued expansion of global free-market enterprise alongside further increases in global environmental standards.	Massive expansion and adoption of free market enterprise globally. Stronger faith in technological solutions to environmental problems.	Global resources are in short supply hence the need to focus on home-grown production and sustainable use.	Global free-market enterprise slows down; further increases in global environmental standards.	Continued expansion of global free-market enterprise alongside further increases in global environmental standards.
	Global Energy Resource	Moderate	High	Low	Very Low	Low	Moderate
	Global Energy Price	High	Moderate	High	Very High	High	Moderate
	Global Biofuel Consumption	High	Moderate	Very high	Moderate	Low	Moderate
	Global Agricultural production	High, adapted to climate change.	High, adapted to climate change.	Medium, loss to climate change but extensive use of biotechnology.	Low, loss to climate change.	Medium, some adaptation to climate change.	High, some to climate change.
	World Food Prices (FAO Food Price Index - 2002–2004=100)	540	360	340	560	450	350
Socio-economic context	*Governance*	National	National with strong EU (& global) influence.	National but small government.	Strong national. Outside the EU.	Local decision rule.	EU and National, increase in private sector control of public services.
	Institutional & governance factors	Private property mixed with public owned National Parks etc.	Land with key ecosystem services is public. Many land owners become 'stewards'.	Government backs away and lets markets run free.	Very strong national government. Less power with local authorities and EU.	National Government underpins localism. Local government more important (think Cantons)	Move towards more privatisation of public services. Continued love/hate relationship with EU.
	Research & Development investment	1.5% GDP	3% GDP	2.0% GDP	1.9% GDP	1.4% GDP	1.5% GDP
	GDP growth of UK	2% increase since 2010	3% increase	2% increase, but numerous crashes.	1% increase	0.5% increase, but sustainable.	1.5% increase. Pattern of recession and boom.
	UK Population	65 million	68 million; many new immigrants from southern EU escaping climate change.	77 million; nearly 30% ethnic minority	70 million	65 million	75 million; 24% ethnic minority.
	Regional factors	SE* dominates finance and service industry. Other regions boost tourism and tech development.	Greater spread of GDP across regions. Renewed urban and rural areas.	London and SE* dominate: most jobs and housing development.	Regional development strongly backed by government.	Most regions are healthy and diverse; fairly equal spread in GDP among them.	SE* domination; central England competitive too.
	Urban & rural policy	Rigid planning—aesthetic & nature dominates.	Urban regeneration. Local neighbourhoods flourish. Rural areas seen as major ecosystem services providers.	Loss of planning powers. Slow blurring or rural/urban.	State controlled; emphasis on protecting and expanding agriculture and energy production.	Based on equality of resources. Food production just as likely to come from urban area.	Maintenance of countryside preservation (in terms of planning); rise in demand of 1 or 2 bedroom dwellings.
	Urban growth & change	Brown-field development. More rental flats.	Emphasis on improving building energy efficiency and urban greening.	Continued urban growth and ribbon development.	Urban development on Brown field; small-holdings and allotments increase but less space for leisure.	Reverse; housing stock diminishes, more green space.	Urban growth and redevelopment. More congestion in towns. Gradual push to better public transport.
	Rural & environmental economy	Subsidised agri and forestry provides reasonable income.	Flourishing, based on ecosystem services; IT well established across UK too.	Declines slightly, industrial farming maintains profit.	Slight increase in % of national economy but not equally shared. Env. given backseat.	Slow and low but sustainable and healthy. High levels of equality.	Dwindling. Fewer farmers and larger farms.

		Green and Pleasant Land	Nature@Work	World Market	National Security	Local Stewardship	Go with the Flow
	Rural growth & change	Farming provides more jobs; other rural service industry grows.	Countryside restoration includes farming, leisure and tourism.	Loss in population. Rise in exclusive gated communities.	Heavy push for energy and food prod. More people working in land-based industry.	Radical changes. Revitalised and burgeoning. Diverse.	Static. Fewer people working in rural industry. Farming more industrial.
	Land use & landscape	Highly protected, diverse, local character.	Highly protected; 'optimised' balance of ecosystem services provision.	More homogenous and industrial.	For production. Food and energy come first. Homogenised.	Very diverse, different regional characters.	Token efforts towards biodiversity protection doesn't hide further homogenisation of countryside.
	Agriculture & forestry	Extensive farming low-input, agri-environment schemes popular.	Reduction in meat – replaced by crop protein. more sustainable, precision techniques. More woodlands managed.	Industrialised and GM dominate.	Heavily subsidised. Technology advances push yields; GM adopted.	Localised, value added, regional products. Woodlands managed for timber, firewood and non-timber forest products.	Increasingly industrialised. Forestry industry dead - pulp and timber imported.
Socio-economic context continued	**Transport demand & supply**	Well maintained road network but reliable and comfortable rail too.	Large investment in rail network and cycle lanes. Less car use but electric and hydrogen popular.	Continuation of road building, congestion. Short-hop flights.	Car use increases as does internal flights. Fossil fuels and biofuels dominate.	National decline; emphasis on local bus, cycle networks. some mono-rail.	Move towards road tolls and privatisation of motorways. Rail network struggles to keep up with demand. Air travel still popular.
	Leisure & tourism	Very important part of economy and high investment and management.	Increased access to countryside (open access in most places).	Traditional areas under greater pressure; increase in south coast.	Less important and less attractive UK. Luxury that most people less concerned with.	Local. Different. Outdoors. Historical. More festivals.	Resurgence in south. More privately sponsored events.
	What technologies are in use?	IT, Biotechnology etc. all strong	IT, Biotechnology, Sustainable Technology	IT, transport, military, pharmaceutical, GM	GM, Biotechnology	Sustainable technology. Increase energy efficiency etc.	IT, vehicle
	Role of family	Traditional	Evolved. More emphasis on community involvement in family roles.	More divorce, disparate, breakdown of 'traditional values'.	Government incentive to stay traditional nuclear family.	Strong family units, children stay local.	Higher rates of divorce, single unit households common.
	Dominant cultural norm (art, philosophy, religion)	Aestheticism	Utilitarianism and pragmatism.	'Low art' and consumerist movements.	'Low art' and consumerist movements.	Pragmatism and strong local emphasis.	Cross section: consumerist but also increasingly environmentalist.
	Nature of education	State and private	Heavy investment in state education. Greater emphasis on languages, environment.	State sector in poor cond. More people take out mortgage to send children to private school.	Traditional. Focus on science and vocational. Loss of languages and arts.	Vocational emphasis alongside traditional subjects. Local authorities control and funding.	Mix of state and private. Increase in faith-based schools.
	Are people mobile? How do they travel?	Yes, car and very good public transport.	Yes, better use of public transport systems.	Yes, car dominates, flying too.	Yes, but expensive.	Not very, at least nationally. Major use of bicycles and buses.	Yes, car and flying.
	What do people eat	Traditional	More crop protein; less meat, more fresh food.	Fast food, processed meals.	Fast food, processed meals; less meat though.	Different regional and local products. Fresh, meat, fish etc.	Convenience food for poor and overworked.

Table 25.5 continued. Key storyline attributes for the UK NEA scenarios.

25.3.3.3 Main drivers

Arguably, the dominant drivers in this storyline are a change in the cultural appreciation of the UK's natural assets as well as a rise in affluence. Economic growth is assumed to be strong (2% of GDP/year) but is less immune to economic slumps.

However, the UK is also sufficiently healthy economically to instigate a long-term change in the rural economy that, whist damaging for traditional agricultural and forestry industries, provides greater opportunities for recreation and conservation. This loss of agricultural productivity comes at

		Green and Pleasant Land	Nature@Work	World Market	National Security	Local Stewardship	Go with the Flow
Environment and ecosystem services	*State of the environment*	Good, protected landscapes	Very good. Provisioning optimised but careful balance with regulation and biodiversity.	Poor in most places	Agriculture and energy decrease biodiversity few areas protected.	'Optimised' landscape but high biodiversity.	Many habitats in favourable condition. Loss of some species to climate change though.
	Climate change adaptation	Focus on biodiversity and flood	Major part of societal focus. Involves Ecosystem based adaption as much as possible.	Areas of high investment protected. Otherwise little attention.	Taken seriously and seeks tech solutions.	Yes, agriculture adapt in full swing. Strong cooperation between regions though.	Adaptation in agriculture and private sector.
	Energy mix & renewables	Nuclear, imported	Massive development of Renewables; nuclear also major source.	Fossil fuels, nuclear and biomass.	Drive to secure UK-based energy includes fossil fuels, renewable, gas and nuclear.	Localised. Based on optimising national resources. Small-scale.	Imports of gas and fossil fuels maintained. 15% renewables and nuclear.
	Ecosystems management	Co-benefit of landscape preservation.	Underlying concept. Includes education.	Some trading of ecosystem services (mostly energy) otherwise little regard.	Little regard. Other things over-ride it.	Full understanding of how to maintain ecosystem services. Local pride in management.	Some landscape management in flood areas.
	Water management	Public sector, high water quality.	Public sector; heavy investment involving education on use and managing storage, leaks etc.	Private sector ownership. Little investment. Frequent water shortages.	Public sector management. Increase in desalination and recycled water plants in south and east.	Regions focus on maintaining their own supply and conservation. Some trans-country delivery from northwest & west to east.	Private control. Expansion of desalination plants in south and east.
	Average UK wheat yield (other crops, milk and meat products follow similar trends)	8.5 tonnes/ha	10.5 tonnes/ha	11 tonnes/ha	10 tonnes/ha	8.5 tonnes/ha	9 tonnes/ha

*South East

a price though: national debt exists mainly due to a reliance of imported foodstuffs and other resources, although this is tempered by an increasing emphasis on the financial and service industries. The UK imports large amounts of raw materials but also exports high-quality goods. Employment is high but is mainly within the tertiary and quaternary sectors. The UK population increases very slowly and tighter controls on immigration exist compared to other scenarios. The majority of the UK's population still live in the south-east of England. Clearly then, land use change is a major driver in this storyline although one that is beneficial for biodiversity.

The energy industry is heavily focused on the development of renewable conversion technologies. Despite the UK's wealth of wind, wave and tidal power, new energy plant development can only proceed after passing stringent environmental impact assessments. However, as for biomass, much of the UK's energy is imported from overseas.

Adaptation to climate change is led through government initiatives, although the emphasis is on ecosystem-based adaptation programmes. Less money is spent on mitigation directly or reserved for autonomous adaptation. The higher climate change impacts results in a further reduction in arable and improved grassland area in the South East because it becomes more difficult to farm without recourse to irrigation,

which is problematic given reduced water; the consequence of this loss of agricultural land is further expansion of Semi-natural Grassland. Under the high climate change version of this scenario, the expansion of broadleaved woodland is less than that assumed for the low climate change trajectory because the preference for native species is strong, and planting options are more limited. In this respect the scenario contrasts markedly with *Nature@Work*, where southern European tree species are used to maintain and expand woodland cover.

Planning is strictly controlled in rural, urban and coastal areas. Housing development is all but impossible in rural areas and urban (re)development is the norm. There is heavy investment in the transport network and road pricing schemes are common. The rail system has been improved and new high-speed lines are replacing the old routes.

Globally, the US, EU, China, India, Russia and Brazil are the dominant economic forces and most countries appear to have embraced capitalism in various forms. International trade increases each year and new markets are created as more countries strive for a western standard of living whilst shifts occur as climate change affects some traditional production areas. Global environmentalism is, however, stronger than ever before, but still struggles to make progress in places

Table 25.6 Projected regional population breakdown for the UK NEA storylines.

		Green and Pleasant Land	Nature@ Work	World Market	National Security	Local Stewardship	Go with the Flow
UK population		65 million	68 million	77 million	70 million	65 million	75 million
Population (as % of UK total)	North East	4	4	3.8	3.9	4.8	4.2
	North West	10.9	11	8.2	11.3	12	11.2
	Yorkshire	8	9	8	8.7	9	8.5
	Humber						
	East Midlands	7	7.5	6	7.4	8	7.2
	West Midlands	9.1	9	8	9	10	8.8
	East	9.2	9.5	7	9.7	10	9.3
	London	13	11	18.1	11	10	12.5
	South East	13.7	10.5	16	13.8	8	13.6
	South West	8.5	10	9.2	8.8	9	8.5
	England	83.4	81.5	84.3	83.6	80.8	83.8
	Wales	5.1	5.5	3.5	4.9	6	4.9
	Scotland	8.5	10	9.5	8.5	10	8.4
	Northern Ireland	3	3	2.7	3	3.2	2.9
Population % in Urban (>10,000)		85	76	90	76	70	80

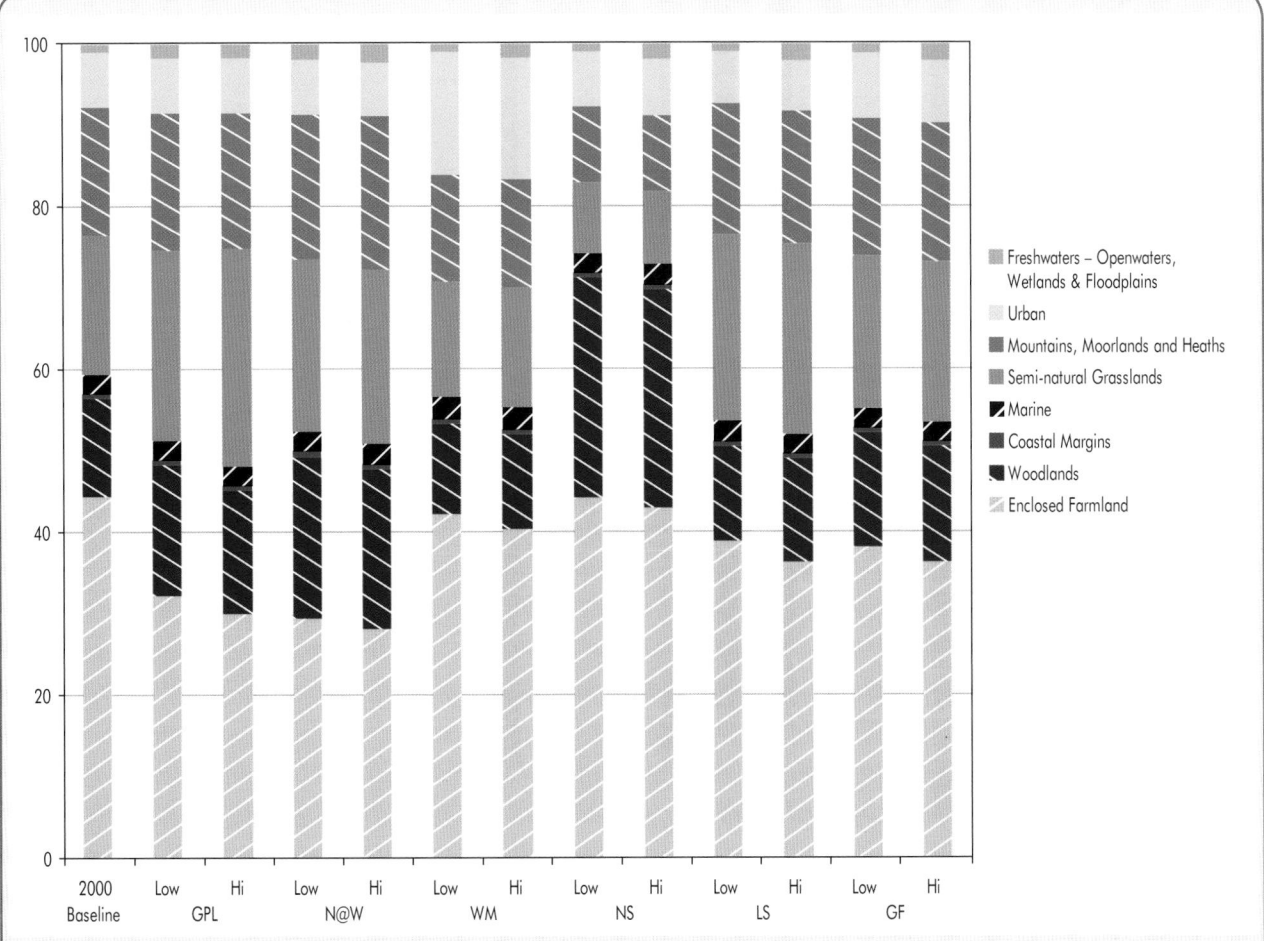

Figure 25.3 Projected changes in stock of UK NEA habitats for Great Britain for the six scenarios. The UK NEA looked at ecosystem services across eight Broad Habitat types. For the terrestrial space this is how their area might change proportionally under each of the scenarios. Note: Marine is under represented because the analysis only includes the immediate coastal areas. The Scenarios are as follows: GPL = Green and Pleasant Land; N@W = Nature@Work; WM = World Markets; NS = National Security; LS = Local Stewardship; GF = Go with the Flow. Low and Hi refer to Low and High climate change impacts.

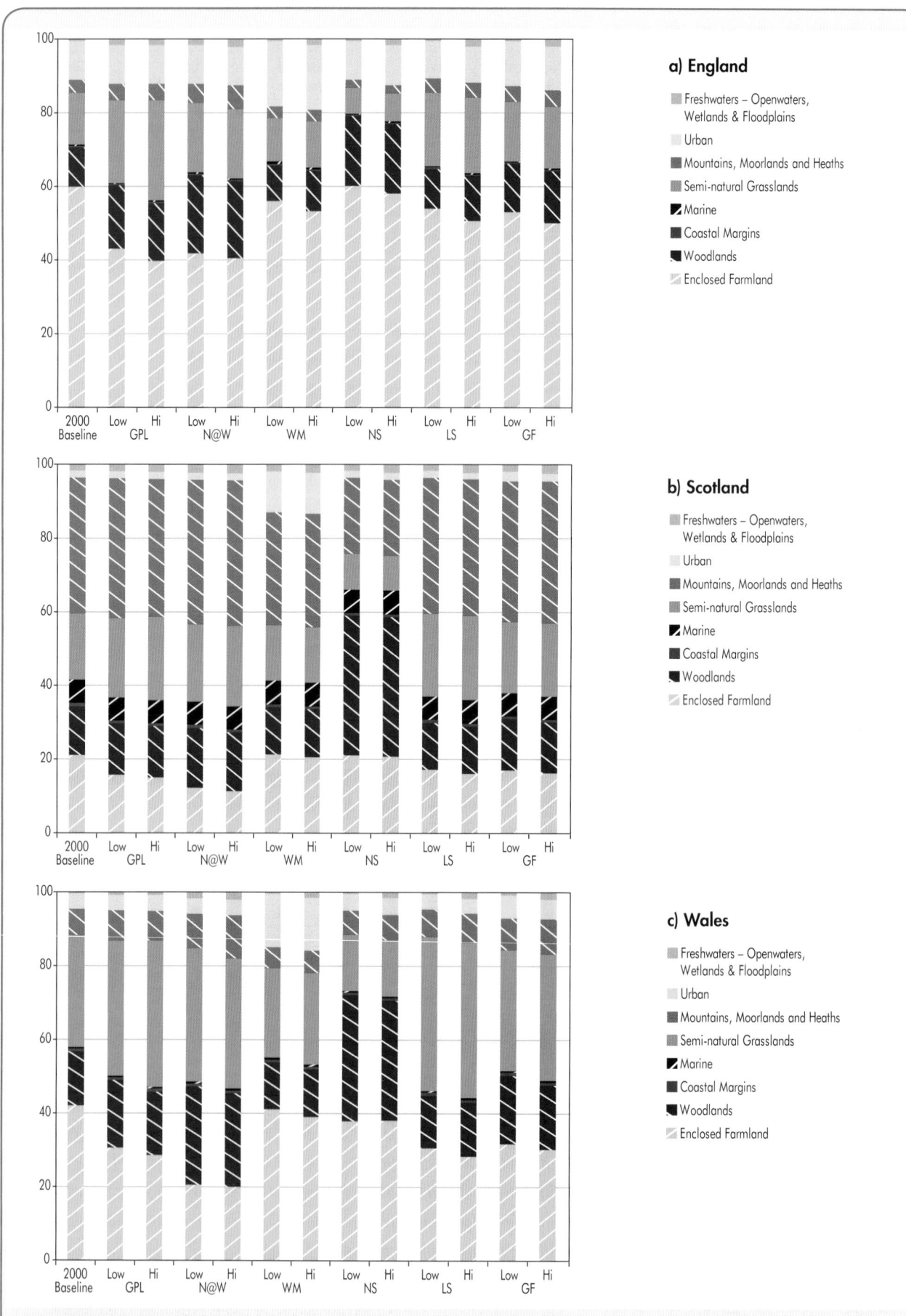

Figure 25.4 Projected changes in the stock of the UK NEA habitats for the six scenarios a) England, b) Scotland and c) Wales. The Scenarios are as follows: GPL = Green and Pleasant Land; N@W = Nature@Work; WM = World Markets; NS = National Security; LS = Local Stewardship; GF = Go with the Flow. Low and Hi refer to Low and High climate change impacts.

where a free market economy is dominant. One success is the burgeoning use of products which are sustainably certified (timber, biofuel, many foodstuffs) and increasingly, these products dominate the western markets. For wealthier people, the UK becomes a desirable country to live in even if, ultimately, its continued economic growth is heavily—and unsustainably—dependent on the provision of key ecosystem services from overseas.

24.3.3.4 Land and sea use

Pressure to improve the conservation and landscape value of the countryside results in Enclosed Farmland decreasing in area by 2060. As a consequence, major biodiversity and climate change corridor projects are established, which help to connect habitats or soften the landscape enough to ease the dispersal of species. Rural industries also have a strong focus on sustainable management. For example, many farmed landscapes have long since converted to organic or agro-ecological production and all farms are encouraged to adopt various farmland conservation options.

As a result of societal and environmental pressures on intensive livestock farming in the earlier part of the 21st Century, it is assumed that consumption of cheap meat has declined by 2060, resulting in a reduction in specialised (grain-fed) livestock farms. However, the number of mixed farms has grown and this helps to increase landscape heterogeneity and boost biodiversity levels in rural areas. A loss of agricultural area in lowland and upland rural UK results in greater conversion to nature conservation and woodlands. Landscape heterogeneity increases, but more so in areas with high concentrations of ancient, semi-natural woodlands (ASNW), or in other landscapes whose character is heavily influences by trees. The changes in woodland cover suggested by the analysis based on land cover transition matrices are shown in **Figure 25.5**. In upland rural areas there is a loss of livestock farming with concomitant rises in Moorland, native Woodlands and Semi-natural Grassland habitats. Restoration and the creation of native Woodlands is a major land use driver in uplands areas of the UK—as a consequence, and due to the lack of support for home-grown goods, conifer plantations are slowly converted to broadleaved woods. Particular attention is paid to the removal of invasive exotic species in freshwater systems. A programme of sustainable river management has introduced greater structural heterogeneity by increasing the number of bends, shallows, pools and riffles; this improves biodiversity and helps flood alleviation.

Marine ecosystems are given a high priority and the UK adopts all global, EU and many new national biodiversity and sustainable fishing laws and protocols. Sea fish stocks are given far better protection and a small rise in sustainably farmed offshore fisheries partly meets the demands for quality British fish, although most fish is sourced from overseas. A few areas of biodiversity importance around the coast of Britain are given strong conservation protection and very little fishing or other harmful activities are allowed. Sea-level rise is combated by a programme of widespread managed retreat, which results in more coastal habitats and less farmland. Where possible, ecosystem-based adaptation strategies are also adopted, rather than the hard defences that were traditionally applied. Offshore wind turbines are sited in a few places around the UK, creating additional sea habitats.

Despite stringent controls on rural housing development and a general acceptance that almost all new housing will be within existing urban boundaries, new urban greenspace is created and increases by 10%. However, there is a stronger focus on developing semi-natural greenspace as well as public parks and gardens and other amenity spaces. Urban housing development follows similar 'green' lines by adopting environmental techniques like green roofs. In peri-urban zones, tree planting increases near existing Woodland areas. Smaller organic farms selling direct to the public via

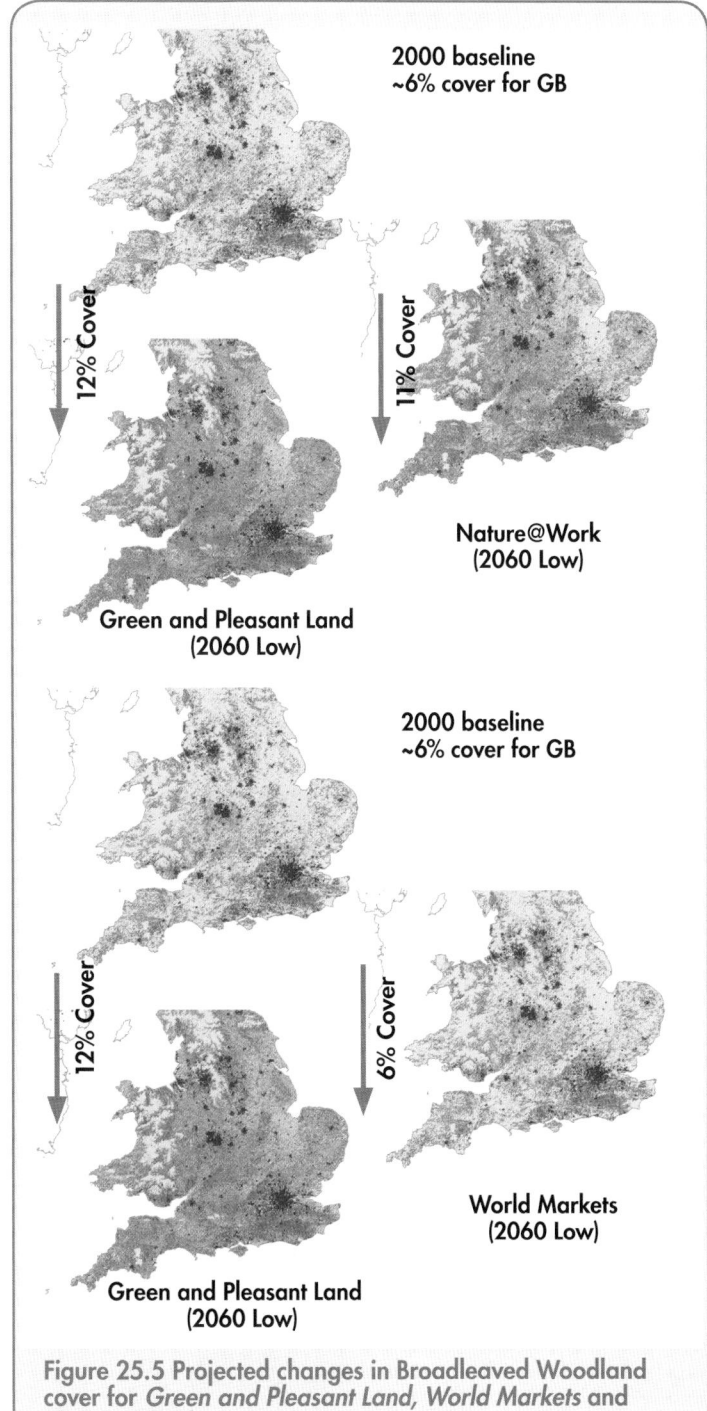

Figure 25.5 Projected changes in Broadleaved Woodland cover for *Green and Pleasant Land*, *World Markets* and *Nature@Work*.

organic box schemes or in farm shops are common. Most housing remains much as in 2010, except for a small increase in urban areas. New developments are kept to brownfield sites—the further decline in primary industries frees up a number of sites. However, an overall lack of new housing and a rise in rental costs results in more young people living with their parents until marriage; multi-occupancy flat sharing is common too.

25.3.3.5 Human well-being

Despite a large societal concern for the environment and biodiversity, in terms of material needs, many people still enjoy a consumer lifestyle, although there is conspicuous consumption of ethical and sustainable goods. Eating out patterns change and there is a greater emphasis on local, quality food and drink for those who can afford it. The increase in jobs in service and professional sectors results in a greater average income in the UK than is the case in most other storylines.

Health improves across all social groups in the UK, although the wealthiest still lead healthier lifestyles. Cleaner air, water, and food (a greater percentage of organic products) as well as a switch from junk food to more balanced diets (through education schemes) lead to overall health gains. The state continues to provide free healthcare but there is also private provision. Mental health is also improved—increasing habitats for biodiversity throughout Urban and rural parts of the UK is paying off in terms of the wider social benefits they can offer.

In terms of social relations and security, people are generally more relaxed and friendly, which partly reflects living in a more attractive environment. Communication systems are more advanced and people are better connected too. Literacy levels are higher and more children attain higher levels of performance at school. Local communities experience more 'togetherness', partly due to shared pride in the environment. There is also less vandalism, and people feel safer. Thus in relation to freedom and choice, there is a greater tolerance of different attitudes (except, perhaps, for non-environmentally friendly viewpoints). On the whole, there is a live and let live attitude, an increase in civil liberties (there is a ban on CCTV) as well as access to information and expression of views. However, freedom and choice are arguably greater for the richer than for the poor.

25.3.3.6 Effect on UK ecosystem services, goods and benefits

The main outcome of this storyline is a strong emphasis on preserving cultural services at the expense of provisioning services. Regulating services often coincide with the main

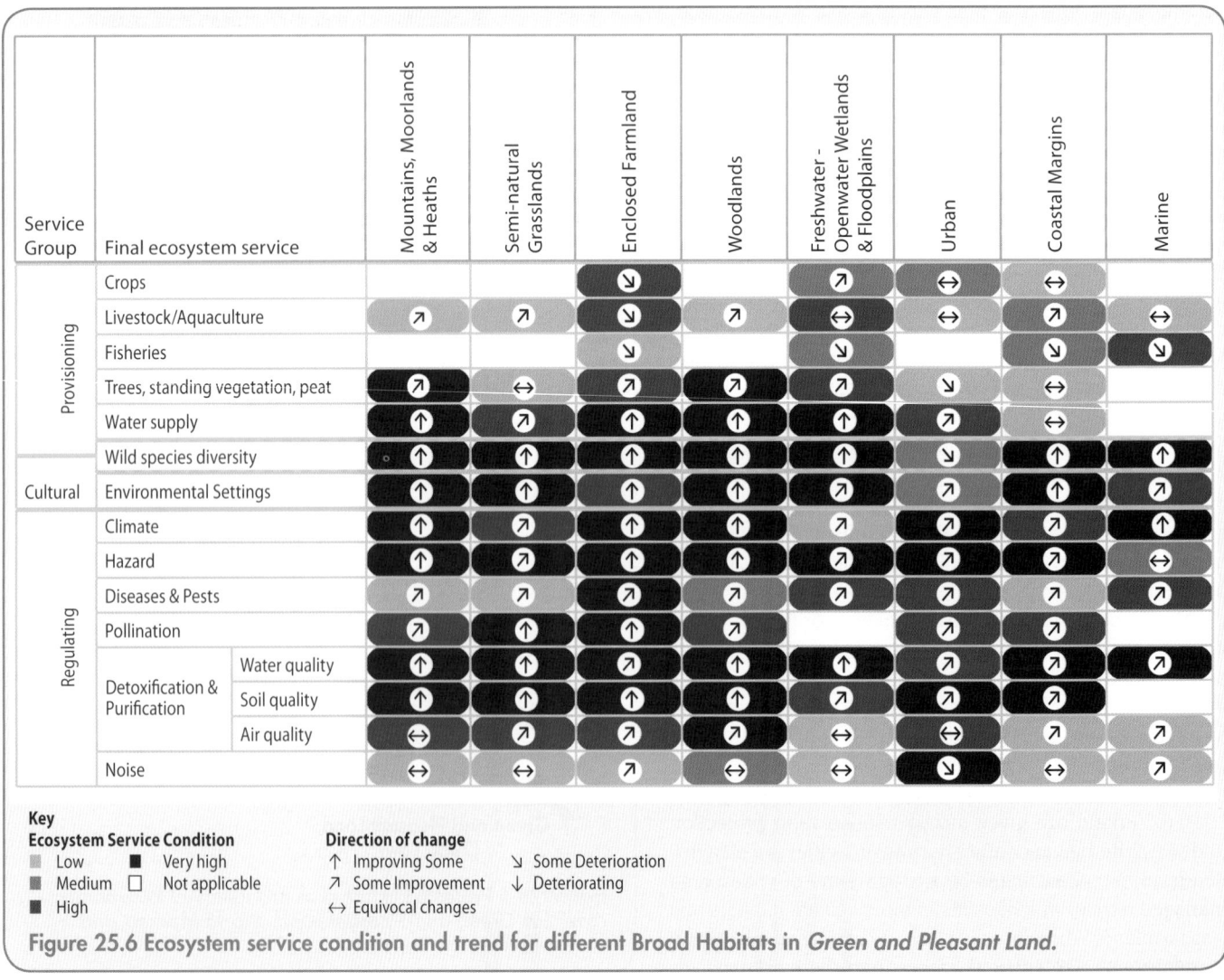

Figure 25.6 Ecosystem service condition and trend for different Broad Habitats in *Green and Pleasant Land*.

cultural service objectives, although they can sometimes clash. For example, areas prone to flooding may be better served by creating Woodlands, but, if the existing habitat is diverse wet grassland, afforestation would be unlikely. **Figure 25.6** summarises the status of ecosystem services for 2060 under this scenario. The colour intensity indicates the assumed condition of the each habitat for a given service at that time[2], while the arrow indicates the anticipated trend in the stock of that habitat up to that time. **Figure 25.7** provides an estimate of the changes in land cover proportions compared to 2000 across the UK NEA habitats for GB and the impact of the high and low climate trajectories; the analysis only shows change for terrestrial areas; 'sea' denotes only the area of open water in coastal areas.

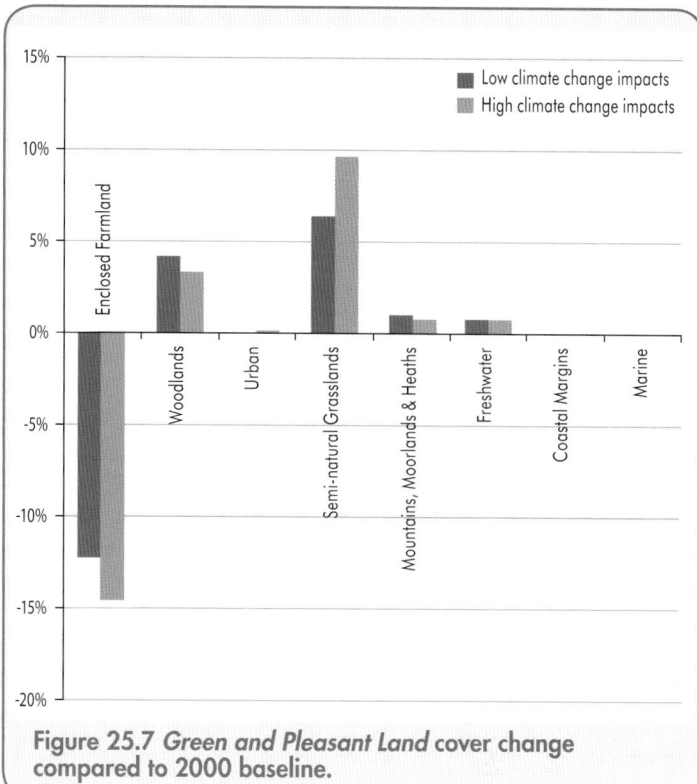

Figure 25.7 *Green and Pleasant Land* cover change compared to 2000 baseline.

Provisioning

- Timber production—there is a minimal increase compared to the present, despite a much greater area of broadleaved woodland, as most woods are managed for conservation or fuelwood (i.e. through coppice). Small pockets of quality timber production woods are encouraged, and these mainly supply a very small, high-quality furniture industry.

- Fuelwood production—this is stimulated by the increases in Woodland areas, coupled with widespread use of wood fuel energy boilers or log burners. A return to traditional coppice management is encouraged to promote rural employment, improve biodiversity and reduce fossil fuel use for heating. Sales to urban areas increase also with the use of clean wood burners.

- Crop provision—there are increases in crop yields compared to 2010 due to climate change and agronomic improvements. However, these increases cannot compensate for the large decrease in crop area. Crop-based food production is one of the biggest losers in this storyline and the UK depends heavily on food imports.

- Fisheries—natural ocean stocks are strictly controlled and protected. Fish farms increase but are carefully managed to ensure they do not harm the surrounding ecosystems. Locally abundant, but unfashionable fish are caught and markets for them are developed.

- Animal products—there is a reduction in overall national production and there are no significant improvements in breeding. Traditional, hardier beef and dairy breeds make a comeback (partly to help manage Semi-natural Grasslands) but imports of milk, beef, pork and other livestock products are higher than ever before.

Regulation

- Carbon—there is an overall gain due to land use change and better management; soil carbon increases, mainly due to the conversion of land from arable to semi-natural habitats (mostly grasslands and woodlands or scrub) and adoption of mixed and sustainable farming systems. Also, external nutrient inputs are lowered because of the greater utilisation of leguminous break crops in the rotation. Organic and low-till systems have increased soil carbon stocks too.

2 Condition determines the output of a given service per unit area.

- Flood alleviation—this is helped immensely, mainly due to the greater area of semi-natural vegetation or grassland (vs arable). Coastal flooding is dealt with by encouraging managed retreat.

- Water quality—there is an increase in water quality: incidents of pollution and diffuse pollution decline dramatically due to the smaller farmland area and better management. Watercourses are given higher protection too, with tight controls on industry.

- Erosion control—this is improved due to agri-environment schemes like field margins and conversion to woodland. Also, better soil management (through stricter regulation) is more common (use of no-till, better use of farmyard manure and other compost).

Cultural

- Recreation—stronger 'environmental settings' means that there are improved opportunities in peri-urban and rural areas, although even urban areas are more appealing. The countryside as a whole is more attractive and more people use it for weekends and longer breaks; taking a holiday in rural Britain is very common now too, partly as Spain, Italy and southern France are too hot for most people. A Sunday walk in the country has become a very common pastime—partly due to the scenery, but also because walking has been promoted as a healthy national pastime. High visitor numbers may result in conflicts with conservation aims, but generally this is carefully managed and understood by a sympathetic public. The public's appreciation of a sense of place is very high in this storyline; pride in traditional landscapes and seascapes is high and many people feel very connected to the countryside.

- Historical—a strong shift in cultural appreciation of local history is developed and many historical and archaeological monuments, buildings, etc. are conserved. This historical interest even extends to long-extinct species (e.g. beavers) and reintroduction schemes are encouraged and well supported.

25.3.3.7 Ecosystem service trade-offs and changes since today

The main gains in ecosystem service provision offered by this scenario compared to today are in the rise in the output of cultural services, driven by the availability of a more preserved, accessible and scenic countryside (stronger environmental settings) and of regulating services (**Figure 25.6**). The prioritisation of cultural services in this storyline does have a clear effect in terms of reducing the area devoted to provisioning services, particularly food from Enclosed Farmlands (**Figure 25.7**). Despite some gains in improving crop and livestock yields (and hence productivity per unit area), loss of agricultural area reduces overall UK productivity. To counter this, food supply in the UK becomes more dependent on imports from overseas. The shifts to Semi-natural Grassland, Mountains, Moorlands and Heaths and broadleaved Woodland brings with it benefits for many regulating services, including maintaining soil quality, flood alleviation, air quality, water quality, etc. These changes also help to ameliorate the impacts of climate change, although the higher impact scenario starts to reduce some regulating service provision by affecting Woodland habitats in the south (e.g. climate and hazard regulation). In common with all the scenarios, it is difficult to estimate how the overall balance in service output would change, however, because we lack any clear indication of how the output of services varies per unit area of each habitat type, either under present conditions or in the future. The implications of this knowledge gap for the interpretation of the scenario outcomes generally will be considered in Section 25.4.

25.3.4 Nature@Work

25.3.4.1 Origin

This scenario arose from the need, identified in the consultation work, for a green storyline that relates to increased interest in ecosystem services and their management as a model for sustainability. It attempts to outline a future where balancing trade-offs in delivering ecosystem services are one of the main challenges in society, and the overall goal is to create a multifunctional landscape. As the title of this scenario suggests, people have a utilitarian outlook on nature. They value it because of what it provides or does. Many of the focal questions asked were about the trade-offs that would have to be made with ecosystem services, and this storyline attempts to provide a pragmatic approach to balancing multiple aims; there is no attempt to prioritise any one ecosystem service group over another.

25.3.4.2 Rationale

The belief that the promotion of ecosystem services through the creation of multifunctional landscapes is essential for maintaining the quality of life in the UK is now widely accepted. This has resulted from a heavily promoted education programme, and a growing awareness in society that a more sustainable UK is a necessity. Society accepts and understands that some trade-offs have to be made and as a result, becomes more environmentally aware and sophisticated. Habitat restoration and creation is seen as an important component of this campaign, but the explicit conservation of species is sometimes overruled by a 'greater' ecosystem service benefit; this sometimes results in habitat conversion (e.g. Semi-natural Grassland to Woodland). Climate change is accepted as a very important driver of change so, as well as carbon mitigation, an important focus is the enhancement of society's resilience to climate change through 'ecosystem-based adaptation'. Modern technology is used were appropriate, though, and biotechnology is adopted where it can be shown to enhance ecosystem services. This includes the use of drought-tolerant crops to maintain production and reduce soil erosion.

This storyline is a heavily 'top-down' in terms of how ecosystems are managed. There is policy prescription through UK and EU legislation (ecosystem services have influenced legislation in many different sectors), and strong incentives via a range of environmental schemes (not just directed at farmers). Education has been a major contributor to the shift towards sustainability and environment is a central part of the curricula in all schools. Backing for maintaining the balance between different ecosystem services is provided by regional planning teams made up of experts from different fields—this feeds into a national ecosystem services accounting system and efforts are made to ensure a balance at the national level.

'Balanced service provision' is a key feature of this scenario, and the management of 'bundles' of ecosystem services is a result of careful examination of the trade-offs through scientific review: this entails an examination of the needs at local, landscape and regional levels. Areas with a strong potential to produce high-yield crops sustainably are maintained and kept in arable production, for example. Areas known to be at high flood risk would have mitigation plans instigated (e.g. conversion of arable or intensive grazing to woodland).

25.3.4.3 Main drivers

The population has continued to age, but numbers have increased steadily through immigration, which is one of the main drivers in this scenario. Economic growth is strong (3% of GDP/year), sustainable and increasingly based on the 'green economy'. National debt is low (but exists) and the balance of trade is slightly negative (despite an emphasis on more sustainable consumerism), due to a continuation of some food imports. This scenario is one in which science and technology are embraced, and in which most of society are appreciative of public funding in these sectors. There is a drive to develop technologies that solve environmental problems, and this includes a widespread adoption of many different forms of biotechnology (e.g. to deal with pathogens, drought or flooding, or to enhance salt tolerance in crops). The national government has introduced ecosystem services as the dominant policy paradigm, which is backed up by a fully integrated national 'ecosystem service account'.

As in other storylines, land cover change is an important driver of ecosystem service output; in this vision, semi-natural and wooded land covers generally increase at the expense of improved grassland. This is a radical and important change to the UK and is a result of a slow change in societal attitudes towards meat production (rather than meat consumption); UK meat becomes more of a luxury and dependence on crop-based protein is far higher than ever before (although cheaper meat is still imported).

The energy industry is encouraged to develop renewable conversion technologies as well as nuclear power. However, despite the UK's wealth of wind, wave and tidal power, new energy plant developments only go ahead if their impact on ecosystems is minimal, resulting in a greater number of small-scale plants; domestic energy systems become very popular.

The national response to climate change is a well-funded programme of carbon mitigation schemes alongside planned adaptation programmes focusing on increasing the resilience of communities so that they are better able to adapt autonomously. Invasive species are a constant threat to ecosystem service delivery throughout the UK, but a huge and well-funded national programme to screen and manage them has been successful. Of all the storylines, this is the best adapted to climate change, and differences in proportions of land cover between the low and high impact scenarios are marginal.

This scenario sits into a world where the 'business as usual' has evolved into 'green business as usual'. Global environmentalism is stronger than ever before. Sustainable development is finally beginning to mean something tangible to people. The US, EU, China, Russia, India and Brazil are dominant economic forces but many other countries with the capacity to export vitally important ecosystem services are gaining importance. Global trade increases each year and includes a growing share of trade in ecosystem services.

25.3.4.4 Land and sea use

Farmers are paid to provide services based on locally determined market prices. Soil erosion, water storage, water quality improvement, flood alleviation, carbon sequestration, and recreation, as well as food and fuel provision, are all targeted throughout the country. As meat production decreases, the nation's protein requirements are easily met by an increase in pulse production (and other protein crops such as quinoa, hempseed and buckwheat); large areas of grassland are converted to biofuels or Woodland, resulting in a higher percentage of Woodland in the north and western parts of the country where beef, sheep and dairy production previously dominated. Floodplain woods are encouraged in the main river landscapes in the UK (e.g. the Thames, Severn, and Trent). However, ecosystem service provision is ubiquitous throughout the UK, so most regions see an increase in Woodland area (to meet carbon mitigation, recreation and shade needs). Organic farming, as well as no-till cultivation, is widespread, as soil management is very important. Lowland rural farmed areas become slightly more heterogeneous; Woodland area increases and there is some increase in mixed farming in eastern counties. Many areas with high concentrations of ancient and semi-natural

Woodland or with major river networks also increase Woodland cover.

Woodlands are seen as a potential solution to many problems and the conservation of existing ancient and semi-natural woodlands is maintained; mixed-plantation woods are almost equally important though, and home-grown timber production is encouraged (although clear-cut systems are rare and more sophisticated shelterwood or selection systems are common). New Woodland creation is also heavily supported, especially near to where people live. Some localised woody biomass (short rotation coppice) production is found on large estates wanting to mechanise as much as possible (large harvesters are used as opposed to men with chainsaws) and similar projects crop up where villages and towns have started community heat and power generation systems. New floodplain woodlands utilise willow, alder, birch and poplar, but also ash and oak. Livestock farms in the west and north diversify and reduce their beef and sheep enterprises. More land is used for recreation as well, and many large, privately owned estates are opened up for free public access.

Most Semi-natural Grasslands are protected from Woodland or Enclosed Farmland encroachment but they are also utilised for service provision. This includes traditional uses such as grazing land for sheep and beef breeds, but increasingly, payments for recreation and education services are seen. Areas of traditional species-rich grasslands are restored (e.g. chalk grasslands), often taking poor quality arable land out of production (this is a good example of optimising ecosystem services and providing synergies). Wet grasslands are conserved for floodplain health; in mountain regions, wind farms are often deemed more important than other land uses.

The conservation and protection of freshwater is one of the highest priority aims. In the case of farming, this involves measures such as 25 m buffer strips bordering rivers to protect them from any potentially damaging operations, including organic farming systems.

Coastal Margins, in particular, are protected from development, and in certain areas, coastal erosion and sea level rise are allowed to progress through a system of managed retreat. Marine and Coastal Margin habitats are given greater conservation protection through a number of European and British laws. However, as in terrestrial ecosystems, despite seeking synergies, there are inevitably some trade-offs between biodiversity, food provision and energy. The UK's marine energy resources are particularly valuable and are developed considerably to the point where some energy is exported. A co-benefit here, though, is an increase in Marine habitats around energy farms as they cease to become fishing grounds, and an additional benefit is the conservation of carbon-rich seabeds. Sustainable fishing is very important, but there is research investment into farmed species to maintain an adequate supply for the UK market (another benefit of increased research and development are marine biotechnology spin-offs).

In urban areas there is an emphasis on the role of urban trees, gardens, urban farms and green roofs; urban greenspace increases by nearly 6% and a large percentage of that is in semi-natural habitats. The housing stock stays static, with an emphasis on restoring and upgrading old buildings to improve energy efficiency. Compared to today, a more holistic approach to town planning is taken, which incorporates energy use and transmission, waste removal, transport and dwellings. Many towns have been 'greened' so that they become net exporters of some ecosystem services, e.g. water purification. Similarly, urban food production becomes common and takes advantage of allotment and park space as well as roof space. This increase in small market producers, urban farms and forest gardens helps meet the demand for produce with low food miles. The South East still houses the largest proportion of people in the UK, although this is mainly due to a fairly static building construction programme elsewhere.

A precondition of this scenario is the implementation of an extensive programme of renewable energy development across the UK to harness wind, sea, solar and biomass resources in the most effective manner. Conflicts between landscape aesthetics and energy are much rarer and most people are more accepting of local wind farms, etc. Nuclear power is also a major provider of energy.

Most of the UK sees far greater recreation in rural and urban areas. Urban areas, in particular, have increased greenspace and many cities have seen increases in visitor numbers. Traditionally popular rural areas continue to attract many people (although there is greater use of extended public transport systems to get there), but most rural counties develop recreational activities and consequently boost visitor numbers.

The decarbonisation of the road transport system is all but complete. New technologies and improvements in electric vehicle systems mean that air pollution from the internal combustion engine does not plague the towns and cities of the UK. Aviation, shipping and heavy transport now use biofuel, much of which is grown in the UK and the EU. Short-hop air travel has disappeared from the UK (replaced by high-speed rail); short-distance travel is largely undertaken by bicycle, and cycle lane networks are extensive, well maintained and easy to use.

In summary, the main land cover changes are a huge decline in Improved Grassland cover, a slight decline in Arable and Horticultural cover and increases in Woodland (broadleaved and conifer), upland (Mountains, Moorlands and Heaths) and Semi-natural Grassland.

25.3.4.5 Human well-being

Compared to 2010, society's material needs are lower and less frivolous; there is still a strong demand for electrical goods for domestic and leisure purposes and, in most aspects, people are happier with possessions that work well and last longer (but cost more because they are of higher quality). Locally produced items are very important and in many parts of the UK, regional variations in clothing style can be seen.

Society in the UK benefits from improved nutrition; cleaner air, water, and food; better access to information about health and medicine; reduced stress; and better mental health. The concept of the green gym takes off and is a common prescription for many people; more importantly, it is seen as a preventative measure and is

heavily promoted. Technological improvements have also advanced surgical techniques and drug development; the UK, US and other EU countries inject considerable funding into a global initiative to developing 'drugs for all' that allow even the poorest citizens access to the latest medicines. Bioprospecting for pharmaceuticals is considered a global good for all, and patents are not allowed on drugs derived from natural fauna and flora (funding for development is provided by tax).

Society is more secure, mainly due to greater equality and better standards of living for all. People are connected with each other, both within the UK and overseas. Cheap communication systems are universal and high-speed and high-bandwidth internet connection is ubiquitous throughout the urban and rural UK (indeed, a large part of the economy is utterly dependent on it).

Tolerance and 'live and let live' attitudes are the main credos. Increased political freedom, civil liberties, information flow, movement, expression, and association are values held highly and rarely contravened. All environmental data are available to everyone, to ensure that supplies of ecosystem services are equitable and justifiable. An important part of ecosystem service provision is that flows of ecosystem services go to the poor as well as to the rich.

25.3.4.6 Effect on UK ecosystem services, goods and benefits

The essence of this storyline is the development of an understanding of how to balance and create synergies between ecosystem services. Inevitably some ecosystem services will become less common 'luxuries'. Climate change is also important within the environmental agenda and service provision heavily incorporates mitigation and adaptation. **Figure 25.8** summarises the status of ecosystem services for 2060 under this scenario. The colour intensity indicates the assumed condition of each habitat for a given service at that time, while the arrow indicates the anticipated trend in the stock of that habitat up to that time. **Figure 25.9** provides an estimate of the changes in land cover proportions compared to 2000 across the UK NEA habitats for GB and the impact of the high and low climate trajectories; the analysis only shows change for terrestrial areas; 'sea' denotes only the area of open water in coastal areas.

Provisioning
- Timber production—home-grown timber is encouraged and supported by the public. Everyone wants to live in a house 'made in Britain'; large plantations (sustainably managed) in the traditional areas (Wales, the Borders) are joined by new Woodland planting in carefully chosen sites in the north of Scotland. Timber from broadleaved Woodlands is also utilised and, more importantly, managed properly, and becomes an increasingly common building material.
- Fuelwood production—as with *Green and Pleasant Land*, this increases considerably due to short rotation coppice production as well as conservation coppice woodlands. The area of Woodlands is also much higher than in 2010, helping to meet the nation's timber requirements.

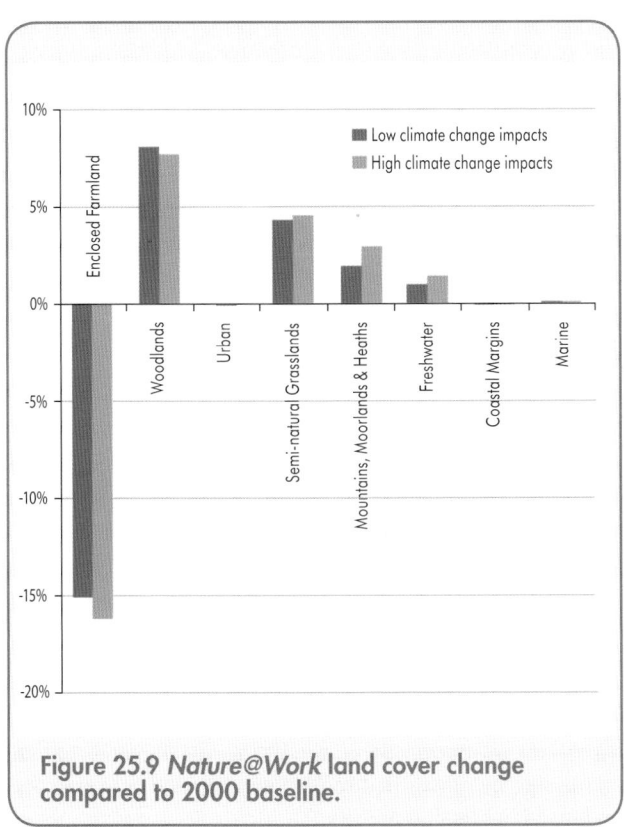

Service Group	Final ecosystem service		Mountains, Moorlands & Heaths	Semi-natural Grasslands	Enclosed Farmland	Woodlands	Freshwater - Openwater Wetlands & Floodplains	Urban	Coastal Margins	Marine
Provisioning	Crops				↑			↗		
	Livestock/Aquaculture		↗	↗	↘	↗	↗	↗	↔	↗
	Fisheries				↗		↗		↗	↗
	Trees, standing vegetation, peat		↗	↔	↑	↑	↗	↗	↗	
	Water supply		↑	↗	↑	↗	↑	↗	↔	
Cultural	Wild species diversity		↑	↑	↗	↑	↑	↗	↑	↑
	Environmental Settings		↑	↑	↑	↑	↑	↗	↗	↗
Regulating	Climate		↗	↗	↑	↑	↑	↗	↗	↑
	Hazard		↑	↗	↑	↑	↑	↗	↗	↗
	Diseases & Pests		↗	↗	↗	↑	↗	↗	↔	↔
	Pollination		↗	↑	↑	↗		↔	↔	
	Detoxification & Purification	Water quality	↑	↑	↑	↑	↑	↗	↗	↗
		Soil quality	↗	↗	↑	↑	↗	↗	↗	
		Air quality	↗	↗	↗	↑	↗	↗	↗	↗
	Noise		↔	↔	↔	↔	↔	↗	↔	↔

Key

Ecosystem service condition
- Low
- Medium
- High
- Very high
- Not applicable

Direction of change
- ↑ Improving Some
- ↗ Some Improvement
- ↔ Equivocal changes
- ↘ Some Deterioration
- ↓ Deteriorating

Figure 25.8 Ecosystem service condition and trend for different Broad Habitats in Nature@Work.

Figure 25.9 Nature@Work land cover change compared to 2000 baseline.

- Biofuel production—the quantity of biofuels from cropped land increases considerably to meet energy requirements. However, biofuels are only ever grown on poor quality agricultural land and do not displace high-yielding food crops.
- Crop production—overall production declines slightly as the cropped area reduces, but technological advances in agronomy and a warmer climate maintain the trend of increasing yields. There is a major switch from meat production to crop protein so that the UK's supply of protein for human consumption increases.
- Animal production—meat consumption declines and the super-high yielding dairy and beef breeds of 2010 have almost disappeared to make way for better adapted animals and a focus on flavour, not quantity. Meat and dairy production are still important, but they are focused on quality rather than quantity.
- Marine production—natural sea and freshwater stocks are strictly protected and only harvested under a sustainable catch regime. The total natural catch is far lower than today's. Farmed fisheries proliferate (offshore) but follow careful management guidelines so they do not affect natural ecosystems. Energy from the marine environment is hugely important; there are networks of wind farms and the use of wave energy is widespread.

Wild species diversity—in general, biodiversity conservation is boosted in this storyline and many species' populations are in better health than in 2010, despite climate change. Conflicts between biodiversity and ecosystem service provision will only occur if any given species has a healthy population outside the target area.

Regulation

■ Carbon—there are overall gains in lowland areas previously dominated by arable production; soil carbon increases mainly due to the conversion of land from arable to semi-natural habitats (mostly grasslands and woodlands or scrub) and adoption of mixed farming systems. Also, external nutrient inputs are lowered because of the greater utilisation of leguminous break crops in the rotation. Organic and low-till systems have increased soil carbon stocks dramatically. Upland areas also improve above and below-ground carbon through better management and habitat restoration.

■ Flood alleviation—the restoration and creation of floodplain Woodlands becomes a major factor in reducing flood impacts throughout the UK. This involves conversion of vulnerable areas from intensive arable or improved grassland use to appropriate alternatives (often Woodlands but also Semi-natural Grassland).

■ Erosion control—problem areas throughout the UK are targeted and controlled by implementing new management regimes (e.g. change to woodland, grassland or no-till cultivation). This is one of the main success stories of this scenario.

■ Water quality—this is vastly improved everywhere. Polluters are heavily fined and so rarely make mistakes, while sustainable land management technologies have allowed farmers to grow crops with minimal risk of pollution from fertiliser and pesticides.

Cultural

■ Recreation—outdoor activities become more popular in urban, peri-urban and rural areas, as environmental settings are strengthened generally. The countryside as a whole is more attractive and more people use it for weekend and longer breaks. A Sunday walk in the country has become a very common form of recreation, partly due to the scenery, but also because walking has been promoted as a healthy national pastime. Some key areas have been nationalised in order to maintain them for public use. Urban regeneration has transformed many cities, making them more attractive places to live in and to visit. In contrast to *Green and Pleasant Land*, society in this storyline does not have quite the same romantic ideals and 'sense of place' towards the countryside, although it is still a very important aspect of human well-being.

25.3.4.7 Ecosystem service trade-offs and changes since today

The goal in this storyline is to balance and provide synergies between ecosystem services within a region and, indeed, nationally (**Figure 25.8**, **Figure 25.9**). Maintenance and promotion of multifunctionality is the key; comparing

Figure 25.8 with **Figure 25.5**, for example, suggests that there is a more even pattern of improvement across all habitats and services. In terms of projected land cover changes, there is also a more even gain of area across the Woodlands, Semi-natural Grasslands, Mountains, Moorlands and Heaths, and Freshwaters—Openwaters, Wetlands and Floodplains categories for *Nature@Work* compared to *Green and Pleasant Land*. Inevitably, in some areas certain ecosystem services will be reduced in favour of others, but the emphasis is on achieving synergies and where possible no net loss. Within the Enclosed Farmland landscape there will probably be a greater loss of improved pasture to Semi-natural Grasslands under this scenario compared to *Green and Pleasant Land*. Perhaps one crucial element to the goal represented in the *Nature@Work* scenario is that although biodiversity is valued for its intrinsic worth, this can sometimes clash with the an ecosystem service value. For example, in some parts of the South East, climate change may slowly change the structural composition of Woodlands, even to the point that they become more scrub than woodland. In certain circumstances, tree species from southern Europe that are drought tolerant may be used to maintain a woodland's structure and function.

This storyline, along with *Local Stewardship*, shows the starkest difference with the current suite of ecosystem service provision in the UK. As the dominant paradigm in society and government policy, the goal of improving provisioning, regulating and cultural services is taken very seriously and largely succeeds in improving them all. Climate change mitigation and adaptation is a high priority policy (and societal) goal and many habitats are managed to cope with extremes of temperature and precipitation (both wetter winters and drier summers). In areas of particular vulnerability to climate change impacts (e.g. drought in the South East, sea-level rise in low lying coastal areas), the appropriate response to optimise ecosystem service provision is taken (e.g. the adoption of drought- and heat-tolerant crops or coastal retreat schemes). However, as with the discussion of *Green and Pleasant Land* (and in common with all the scenarios), it is difficult to estimate how the overall balance in service output would change, because we lack any clear indication of how the output of services varies per unit area of each habitat type.

25.3.5 World Markets

25.3.5.1 Origin

This storyline is a very common one in many published studies of scenarios, and provides an opportunity to examine how a suite of dominant socioeconomic and demographic drivers could affect the UK's ecosystem services. It also reflects the desire from some potential users of the UK NEA to see how a relaxation in rural and green belt regulation (and hence a spread of urbanisation) would affect ecosystem services in the UK. Other influencing focal questions raised issues about increasing dependence on commodities from overseas, rises in global food prices, a societal rejection of the importance of climate change, continuing increases in atmospheric nitrogen pollution and increases in housing density.

25.3.5.2 Rationale

The fundamental characteristic of this scenario is high economic growth driven by short-term profit, with a greater focus on removing impediments to trade. International trade barriers are assumed to have dissolved or to have limited impact as markets are liberalised. The UK's agricultural area declines slightly in the face of global competition, and there is a small shift from Improved Grassland to arable, but overall it becomes more industrial and large-scale in character. Demand for land is very competitive and housing or small-scale industrial units are often the winners. However, food production is still deemed more important than many other 'uneconomic' land uses, and food is produced in a highly industrial manner.

As in land-based food production, the food supply from the seas is seen as resource that does not require recourse to sustainable management. Fish stocks subsequently decline further and a few species have become locally extinct in the North Sea. Most fish is now imported from Asia. Desalination plants are built in areas along the east coast to meet water demand for the southern and eastern counties. 'Home-grown' fossil fuel energy production is dwindling and has been overtaken by imports of gas from Eastern Europe and privately funded nuclear industry in the UK. Consequently, coastal areas are built upon to accommodate power plants and gas pipeline stations. Supplies of other ecosystem services increasingly become privatised where they can become profitable.

The underlying policy prescription in this storyline is essentially a 'hands off' approach, i.e. there is very little legislation or incentive geared towards ecosystem service delivery in the UK. Market forces dominate and, along with population growth, are among the main drivers of change. Legislation relating to land use planning is greatly diminished. The consequence of this is a radical change in the rural and urban fabric of the UK: Urban areas continue to grow with very little curbing them; traditional conservation and landscape areas do not have the same restrictions on development; and threats to land cover (floods, sea-level rise) are only targeted if considerable financial loss is likely.

25.3.5.3 Main drivers

The UK's population rises through immigration, which is encouraged in this truly libertarian storyline, and there is an increase in the 60+ age group. Also, more people wish to live alone and the average household is smaller than in 2010. As a consequence there is a strong demand for new housing. Planning restrictions on green belt and rural areas are relaxed throughout the UK, often resulting in conversion of agricultural, woodland and grassland habitats to housing development. The influence of local groups and rural communities on development is somewhat limited and large business often gets its own way with little effective opposition. Many small towns are either subsumed by larger neighbours or become part of ribbon developments along major road and rail corridors.

In this scenario it is assumed that the UK is determined to be part of an expanding global trade system. New business models that maximise some ecosystem service provision (but not most) are created. Economics, based on monetary valuation of stocks and flows of critical natural capital, becomes the preferred option for tacking environmental problems that urgently need addressing (this way at least some ecosystem services are conserved). Investments in technology are mostly privately funded and the state plays a smaller role in everyday life. There are large differences in income levels within society, and divisions in terms of equality are greater than ever.

Although there are strong centralised government structures in the different parts of the UK, there is an emphasis on allowing people freedom to choose in many of the important aspects of life (health, education, etc.). There are minimal sets of environmental standards that maintain important aspects of urban life (e.g. air quality) but otherwise there are few restrictions on economic growth unless a market is created to protect some services (e.g. the rural beauty of some charismatic areas). Climate change is hardly given any attention in national policy and there is limited investment in mitigation. Climate change is considered 'natural' and is assumed that the market will take care of responses. Thus adaptation is mostly local and autonomous (and often led by business innovators and early adopters). Any recourse to renewable energy production is solely down to a decline in fossil fuel resources rather than a concern for the environment. The consequences of this attitude are that the differences between the high and low climate change trajectories for this scenario are amongst the greatest observed: arable and Improved Grassland are lost to Semi-natural Grassland through abandonment, and even some broadleaved woodland suffers dieback.

The US, EU, China, India, Russia and Brazil are dominant economic forces and global trade increases each year; global environmental legislation and conventions have become somewhat toothless and are rarely adopted by governments.

25.3.5.4 Land and sea use

In a free-trade world all land-based subsidies have been removed and the agricultural industry is dominated by large agri-businesses, which include the large retail supermarkets. Technological advances in agriculture push yields to new heights; biotechnology is very much a part of this. Specialisation is normal in farming and there are very few mixed farms; farm size continues to increase, as does the average field size. Large factory pig/dairy/beef/poultry units, which produce cheap meat efficiently, rise up throughout lowland areas, and increasingly in northern areas because they are cooler in the summer; increasingly, food produced in large glasshouses becomes more common too. Petroleum prices increase significantly in the UK, so woody biomass cropping and other cropped biofuels increase to meet demand where this can be competitive. Agricultural production intensifies on the best land as well as lower grade land (although this is also utilised for biofuels), and areas of semi-natural habitats are also converted to agricultural land. Climate change presents a problem but advanced husbandry, air-conditioned livestock units and biotechnology crop-breeding result in high adaptation in the sector (possibly the only sector where adaptation to climate change is taken seriously).

Modern arable farms are industrialised and homogeneous, with large fields of cereal or protein crops; this trend has resulted in hedges and some woodlands being grubbed out. Apart from a huge increase in willow for short-rotation coppice, most surviving woods have been replanted with exotic species to maintain timber production. Woodlands for conservation and recreation have minimal importance. Intensive management of existing Woodlands is promoted (including the coppicing of ancient and semi-natural woodlands). Semi-natural Grasslands are not considered a high priority and consequently, many are converted to biofuel cropping or housing. Some grassland on steep slopes gradually reverts to scrub and woodland. Lowland rural areas see a decrease in existing woodland but woody biofuel area increases. Housing stock increases with new towns being built, resulting in an overall decrease of farm area. In upland rural areas the cooler climate is utilised for housed livestock production in valley bottoms—most feed is imported. Overall, however, there is still a decrease in farm area; Improved Grassland decreases as more livestock is housed in larger feedlot complexes.

Some parts of mountainous areas are maintained for the most competitive services they can supply (i.e. freshwater provision, wind for energy generation and also recreation near large conurbations). However, in many mountainous areas, deregulation and lack of environmental protection have resulted in development or conversion to woodland in the warmer climate; large conifer and *Eucalyptus* woodlands have begun to appear in many hilly areas of the UK.

Water quality regulations are less strict than in 2010; the UK's rivers are in poor condition in terms of biodiversity, water quality and the presence of invasive species.

Coastal erosion is a continuing problem in many areas and requires state intervention, especially where huge investment (affluent housing, major ports, desalination plants) is threatened. Since the removal of the Common Fisheries Policy, the seas around the UK have become a free-for-all, except in the exclusive economic zone (EEZ) of 200 nautical miles from the coast. Even within the EEZ, however, the UK seas are more open to consumption of resources, including increases in fishing and aggregate extraction, with little regard to sustainable management. Most commercial fish populations have been overharvested and marine aggregate extraction has also increased in many areas. Shipping increases due to greater trade with other countries, particularly countries with whom the UK has entered into exclusive trade agreements to harvest resources.

An expansion of housing into green belts, parks and gardens results in a loss of nearly 30% of greenspace (resulting in greenspace accounting for only 39% of Urban cover). Built-on surfaces increase by nearly 80% to represent one-third of all Urban cover. Street trees are replaced as they die, but otherwise there is little urban woodland planting. Urban space has diminished considerably as the demand for housing targets every space available. In peri-urban areas there is a large decrease in Woodland and Enclosed Farmland due to housing expansion and small-scale industry.

Dependency on nuclear power and fossil fuels continues and there is very little use of renewable energy (with the exception of biofuels), although large tidal barrage schemes

do provide around 5% of the UK's energy requirements. Technology continues to improve efficiencies in most energy sectors.

The UK sees a huge decline in internal and overseas tourism, partly due to a gradual erosion of the country's cultural services (both in rural and urban areas); the wealthy middle classes around the globe still travel extensively, but the UK is losing out as a tourism destination. Recreation in the UK is now more home-based.

The transport network is heavily biased in favour of cars and air travel. Motorway-widening schemes reduce farmland and semi-natural areas, and a few new toll motorways are created between London and the Manchester-Leeds belt. Nearly all the major airports expand, including Heathrow and Birmingham, and in east London an airport is built in the Thames Estuary. The major land use winner in this scenario is Urban—large increases in Urban cover throughout the UK occur, although there is a stronger growth in the South East. The main losers are Semi-natural Grasslands and upland habitats.

25.3.5.5 Human well-being

People strive for personal wealth and material possessions or experiences. This is truly the age of mass consumerism. Mean income is higher than ever before and the poor have higher incomes too (but see below). The private education sector has increased considerably, as state-funded schooling is underfunded and in decline. Many services are provided by private companies.

Health standards are very high for those who can afford it; the NHS survives with many private providers included but struggles to cope with ensuring quality service provision. Obesity increases due to poorer diets and less exercise (linked to more people spending their leisure time at home in virtual worlds). There is a rise in diabetes, cancers, stress and depression, and other 'affluenzic' diseases. Every decade there is an increase in human health pandemics in the UK. Increasingly, unwell people are forced to pay for their health care if it can be shown that they are responsible for their condition (e.g. smoking-, drug- and drink-related diseases).

This is a disjointed and unfriendly society. People feel secure if they can afford to pay for security services or live in gated communities. Despite a higher standard of living for the poor, there is great resentment of the rich, who almost live in a different world. Street violence, mass protest and other civil unrest is common. Further afield, the UK frequently has to assert itself in a struggle for diminishing resources.

Freedom is more restricted for all, although the rich have more access, more say and more influence than the poor. Many goods that were once public are now private, and this affects access to recreation, food and decision-making more generally. Increasingly, politics is becoming a commercial enterprise and it becomes more difficult for someone to enter national politics without significant funding. Underground political movements spring up, but are controlled.

25.3.5.6 Effect on UK ecosystem services, goods and benefits

Ecosystem services that have monetary value and are easy to trade are protected, but in this unregulated, urbanising world,

Service Group	Final ecosystem service		Mountains, Moorlands & Heaths	Semi-natural Grasslands	Enclosed Farmland	Woodlands	Freshwater - Openwater Wetlands & Floodplains	Urban	Coastal Margins	Marine
Provisioning	Crops				↔					
	Livestock/Aquaculture			↓	↗		↔			
	Fisheries				↔		↓		↓	↓
	Trees, standing vegetation, peat		↓	↔	↓	↘		↘	↓	
	Water supply		↔	↘	↘	↘	↘	↘	↔	↗
Cultural	Wild species diversity		↘	↘	↓	↘	↘	↘	↘	↘
	Environmental Settings		↔	↓	↓	↓	↓	↓	↓	↘
Regulating	Climate		↔	↓	↓	↘	↘	↓	↓	↓
	Hazard		↘	↘	↓	↘	↓	↘	↓	↓
	Diseases & Pests		↘	↘	↘	↘	↘	↘	↓	↓
	Pollination		↘	↓	↓	↓		↘	↘	
	Detoxification & Purification — Water quality		↔	↘	↓	↘	↓	↓	↓	↓
	Detoxification & Purification — Soil quality		↔	↓	↓	↘	↘	↔	↔	
	Detoxification & Purification — Air quality		↔	↔	↘	↔	↔	↓	↔	↔
	Noise		↔	↔	↘	↘	↘	↓	↘	↘

Key

Ecosystem service condition
Low   Very high
Medium   Not applicable
High

Direction of change
↑ Improving Some   ↘ Some Deterioration
↗ Some Improvement   ↓ Deteriorating
↔ Equivocal changes

Figure 25.10 Ecosystem service condition and trend for different Broad Habitats in Nature@Work.

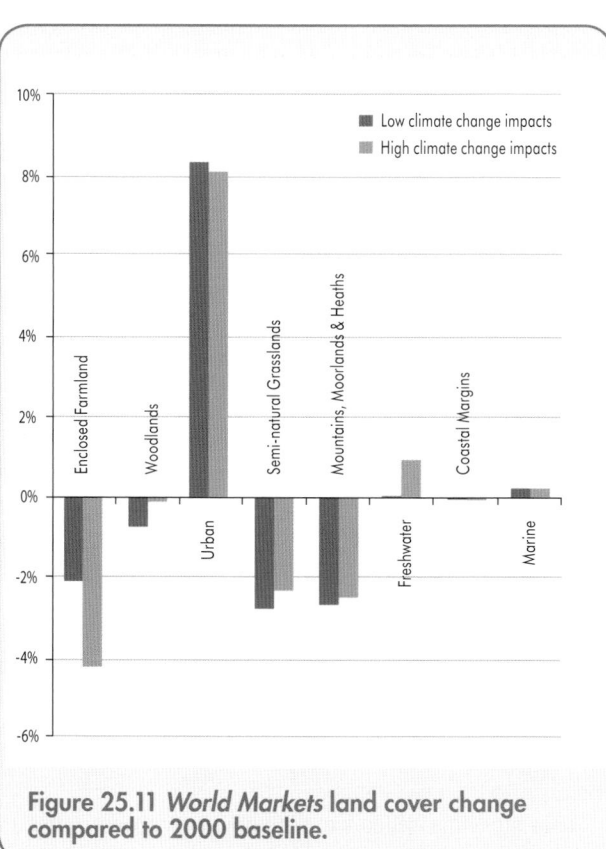

Figure 25.11 *World Markets* land cover change compared to 2000 baseline.

many others are not. The major transfer is to Urban land, driven mainly by the larger population size anticipated under this storyline. The growth is uneven geographically, with the major changes occurring in England, particularly in the South East and the Midlands, although there is also growth around existing urban centres elsewhere. **Figure 25.10** summarises the status of ecosystem services for 2060 under this scenario. The colour intensity indicates the assumed condition of each habitat for a given service at that time, while the arrow indicates the anticipated trend in the stock of that habitat up to that time. **Figure 25.11** provides an estimate of the changes in land cover proportions compared to 2000 across the UK NEA habitats for GB and the impact of the high and low climate trajectories. The analysis only shows change for terrestrial areas; 'sea' denotes only the area of open water in coastal areas.

Provisioning

- Timber production—despite a similar land cover to 2010, very little timber production is UK-based, with a high dependence on imports from Eastern Europe (despite high transport costs). Many woods are neglected or become privately owned.
- Fuelwood production—there is an increase due to high fossil fuel costs. More efficient boiler designs means that some affluent local communities adopt fuelwood as their energy source for heating.

- Crop production—this increases dramatically: free market enterprise has increased research and development, and the arable area has also expanded; a large proportion of crop production is used for animal feed.
- Animal production—there is a similar increase in yield per head but overall, national production stays the same as 2010 levels because of the demand for cheap, low quality meat. The vast majority of meat and dairy production systems are indoors.
- Wild species diversity—there are declines in most habitats: climate change, land use change and pollution are all major contributors to the decline. Increases in invasive species also reduce native species diversity.

Regulation
- Carbon—land carbon stocks decrease due to loss of semi-natural and upland habitat and conversion of Improved Grassland to housing. A decline in good soil management also diminishes soil carbon levels further.
- Flood alleviation—nothing is done to prevent the impacts of flood events on vulnerable communities. Those who can afford it move away; otherwise, people cope as best they can. Land management in the surrounding countryside does not change to help mitigate flood impact.
- Erosion control—this is a neglected problem, which increases in some areas due to lack of vegetation or inappropriate land management.
- Water quality—this declines to mid-1980s levels in the UK due to lower environmental standards across industry and agriculture.
- Invasive species—numbers increase due to more unregulated trade with other countries, an increase in traffic (a main vector for many species) and climate change; very little is done to control species except in affluent areas.

Cultural
- Recreation—there are declining opportunities for woodland, upland and farmland recreation, with a general weakening of environmental settings. Most woods are privately owned or managed for fuel to supply local heat generation systems; farming has reduced the beauty of much of the countryside. Upland areas are often privately controlled and the right to roam statute has been repealed. 'High quality' rural recreation remains an expensive pastime; game shooting (and even a day in the country) is an exclusive treat for the few.
- Historic and spiritual—values throughout the UK have been degraded or lost. These are seen as non-tangible, pointless and not worth conserving. Beautiful landscapes remain in areas almost exclusively utilised by the wealthy (homes and services here are too costly for most people).

25.3.5.7 Ecosystem service trade-offs and changes since today

The emphasis on provisioning services at the expense of almost all others is the notable pattern that arises in this storyline, although even food and timber production in the UK has to compete in a market driven by value (hence a reliance on cheaper food imports from overseas). Thus the loss of Enclosed Farmland under this scenario is much less than that assumed for *Green and Pleasant Land* and *Nature@ Work* (compare **Figure 25.11**, **Figure 25.9** and **Figure 25.7**). However, sustainable land and sea management is not always practised, which results in losses of regulating and cultural services.

The pattern of large-scale loss of semi-natural habitat, as well as the unsustainable management of land and sea resources in this storyline, explains the overall ecosystem service provision compared to 2010. Whilst there is the potential for increases in ecosystem service provision (technology driving crop and livestock yields, for example), the demand for land for housing and industrial development results in a further overall decline in provisioning, regulating and cultural services. Climate change significantly reduces the already eroding ecosystem services in this storyline: worst hit are provisioning services (loss of food production) and regulating services (from a decline in woodland cover). Once again, however, although we can project potential changes in the area of the different habitats, it is difficult to estimate how the overall balance in service output will change because we lack information on how the output of services varies per unit area.

25.3.6 National Security

25.3.6.1 Origin
This storyline is also very common in the published scenarios. The survey of focal questions also highlighted a number of issues that could be explored with this narrative, including: where the UK will get its ecosystem services from; the impacts of trying to secure national food, fibre and bioenergy supplies; the consequences for ecosystem services if there were an increase to 70% self-sufficiency in food; the consequences of maximising domestic food production to protect overseas ecosystems; and the future of CAP. Many of these questions helped to design a storyline that shared a lot of aspects with the *World Markets* storyline, except that global trade would be much reduced and there would be an emphasis on home-grown provisioning services.

25.3.6.2 Rationale
Under this scenario it is assumed that climate change results in increases in global energy prices, forcing many countries to attempt greater self-sufficiency and efficiency in many of their core industries. The UK is no exception and agricultural and other primary industries intensify accordingly. Society understands that a move towards sustainable resource management is a desirable way forward, although it is not always attainable. For example, many farmers are better at maintaining good soil quality, but this is more out of a desire to maintain food production rather than for any long-term environmental goals. Food and energy production to meet UK demands is the main priority and often comes at an environmental price if it ensures the UK's self-reliance.

This storyline relies on a heavy government hand in setting policy for the provision of ecosystem services; it also reduces the scope of market-driven forces (at least externally to the UK) to have an effect. Trade barriers provide a relatively competition-free environment for industry within the UK; subsidies for food and timber production exist also, to encourage their growth. Removal or weakening of environmental legislation results in a greater switch from semi-natural and Woodland habitats to Arable and Horticultural and Improved Grassland, and conifer plantations also make huge gains in upland areas.

25.3.6.3 Main drivers

Society is UK-focused. Immigration is strictly controlled and allows entry to only the most skilled workers. The housing stock increases to meet the demand for single-occupancy households, but this is mainly concentrated in brownfield development and results in an increase in new flat complexes. Population growth is 0.5% per year. Economic growth is lower than in the *World Markets* scenario. Planning is strongly controlled by the state: the expansion of home-grown industry is allowed if it provides jobs and benefits for the wider community and does not threaten green belts or rural land. Every last resource in the UK is utilised for the provision of services, and this results in: the reactivation of many coalmines; greater protection of the UK's fisheries; and the conversion of much non-productive land to farming. Resource consumption is somewhat curbed, and a slightly more sustainable and less profligate society develops. Protectionism and trade barriers are put in place to secure the health of the UK's industries.

The drive towards self-sufficiency is seen as a necessary step forward by many countries throughout the world, although trade still exists. Diminishing energy and freshwater resources have resulted in countries refocusing their efforts towards ensuring sustainable supplies of their own ecosystem services (albeit mainly regulatory and provisioning). No longer can countries guarantee supplies of many goods, but some countries will still export where they have an excess in supply and where there is demand.

Climate change is a driver of change in this storyline, but its greatest impact is felt in a reduction in arable area in the high impact scenario. Although technology plays a major role in this storyline, the insularity of the country results in a lower adoption of better adapted crop cultivars. In other habitats, climate change adaptation is more developed, e.g. suitable drought- and heat-tolerant conifer species are planted.

25.3.6.4 Land and sea use

Precision farming and other sustainable techniques are promoted and constantly evolve. Biotechnology crops are also heavily utilised and are considered essential to sustainable land management. Plant-based protein is a more efficient use of agricultural land and meat production is heavily taxed with a climate change levy (and thus declines becoming a food for the affluent); this results in some surplus grassland becoming available for arable, short rotation coppice bio-ethanol production, as well as new forest plantations for timber. Forestry is an important sector and home-grown timber production is promoted. Climate change has put pay to the promotion of conserving native species and foresters are free to experiment with exotic trees, with the exception of some potentially problematic species. Ancient semi-natural woodlands are managed for fuelwood, but in some cases also for quality timber or furniture products; although in places conservation objectives are met too. Plantations are by far the dominant Woodland type and increases in conifer cover are seen through the UK, especially in the uplands in Wales and Scotland.

Semi-natural Grassland becomes a conservation luxury that society cannot afford and it is now either planted for bioethanol or converted to Woodland if the topography is too difficult for farm machinery. Many of these Mountain, Moorland and Heath habitats have increased Woodland cover to accommodate the drive for home-grown timber. Overseas conifer species are widely used (Monterey and Corsican pines cope well with the climate and soils). Freshwater supply is controlled and use is governed by licence, e.g. for irrigation or drinking water. New desalination plants are built along the east coast; more reservoirs for potable water are built also.

Coastal resources are protected if they are important for the economic growth of the UK; desalination plants, nuclear power stations and some built-on areas are given priority for defence against sea-level rise. In other areas, high value farmland is also protected from sea intrusion. The fish resources of the waters around the UK are harvested as before, but under strict sustainable catch quotas and protection measures. However, subsidised low trophic-level aquaculture has developed into an important food resource and is pursued in many areas around the UK. Renewable energy schemes are also heavily promoted and include a huge programme of offshore wind farms and wave energy units. Large tidal barrage schemes provide around 5% of the UK's energy requirements.

Large market gardens, urban gardens (not just allotments) and even urban 'forest gardens' are developed and represent nearly 20% of all urban greenspace in the UK. However, as a consequence, greenspace for recreation, in the form of public parks and gardens and amenity areas, declines dramatically although these can provide space for relaxation despite their prime food-producing role. The housing stock is maintained and improved for energy efficiency; new housing is built to high-energy standards but is small and functional. Peri-urban zones are similar to Urban, but small agricultural fields also dominate; market gardens thrive and even previously, large private gardens are converted to food production.

Wind energy is heavily subsidised and much of the coast around the UK is utilised. Nuclear power is also developed through a programme of international control of uranium resources. However, uranium is one of the few overseas resources required for energy production and much of the UK relies on a continuation of fossil fuels use from North Sea gas reservoirs and the remaining coal seams. The major road networks are maintained and car use increases in the UK. Internal flights remain, although more people use rail travel to commute too. More people holiday at home than overseas compared to the present. Fossil fuels are in decline and are rationed; electric and biofuels dominate.

Service Group	Final ecosystem service		Mountains, Moorlands & Heaths	Semi-natural Grasslands	Enclosed Farmland	Woodlands	Freshwater - Openwater Wetlands & Floodplains	Urban	Coastal Margins	Marine
Provisioning	Crops				↑			↗		
	Livestock/Aquaculture			↓	↘		↔	↗	↔	↗
	Fisheries				↔		↓		↓	↓
	Trees, standing vegetation, peat		↗	↗	↘	↑		↘	↓	
	Water supply		↗	↘	↘	↘	↘	↘	↔	↗
	Wild species diversity		↘	↘	↓	↘	↘	↘	↓	↓
Cultural	Environmental Settings		↔	↓	↓	↔	↘	↘	↘	↘
Regulating	Climate		↔	↘	↘	↑	↘	↔	↔	↔
	Hazard		↘	↔	↘	↔	↘	↘	↘	↘
	Diseases & Pests		↘	↘	↘	↘	↘	↘	↘	↘
	Pollination		↓	↓	↓			↓		
	Detoxification & Purification	Water quality	↔	↘	↓	↘	↓	↓	↘	↘
		Soil quality	↔	↘	↓	↘	↔	↔	↔	
		Air quality	↔	↔	↘	↔	↔	↓	↔	↔
	Noise		↔	↔	↘	↘	↘	↘	↘	↘

Key

Ecosystem service condition
- Low
- Medium
- High
- Very high
- Not applicable

Direction of change
- ↑ Improving Some
- ↗ Some Improvement
- ↔ Equivocal changes
- ↘ Some Deterioration
- ↓ Deteriorating

Figure 25.12 Ecosystem service condition and trends for different Broad Habitats in *National Security*.

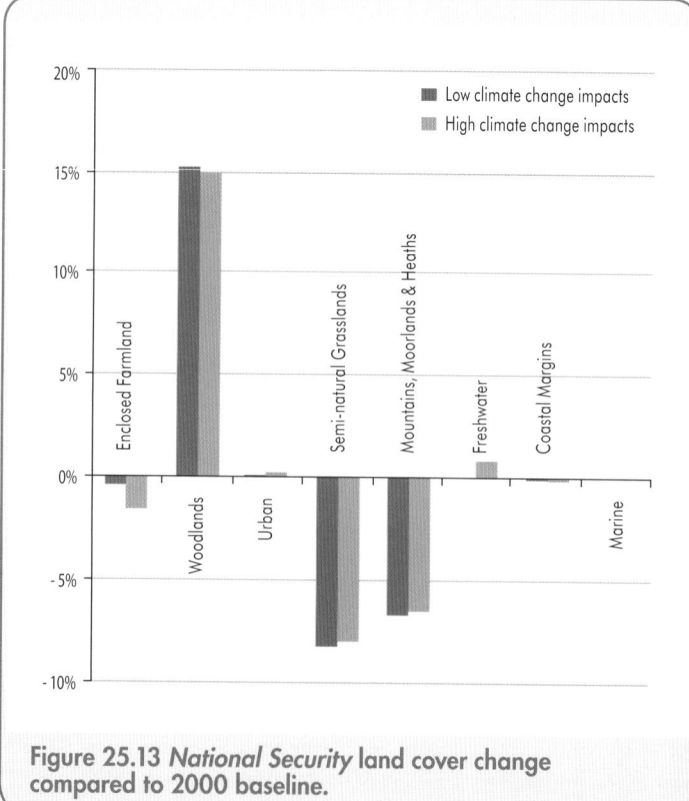

Figure 25.13 *National Security* land cover change compared to 2000 baseline.

25.3.6.5 Human well-being

Consumerism is down, largely due to lack of supply rather than personal preference, but there is also a trend towards local crafts and high quality, long-lasting goods over cheap, disposable wares. Recycling and reuse are common. Many people have returned to more traditional pastimes including reading. Technology has not been abandoned though, and most people are connected through the internet.

The health service is state funded and supported by a programme of education throughout the UK. A move to more manual labour employment also has health benefits, and obesity is declining. Junk food is comparatively rare and although the average diet is not inspiring, it is fairly well balanced. Meat consumption declines due to the high cost of production; this also has health benefits for the nation.

A decrease in availability of many luxury goods and even some staple foods increases inequality; the affluent manage to maintain a relatively higher standard of living, but the poor have a higher standard of living due to lower unemployment. The government takes more power away from citizens (this is seen almost as a time of war) and the media is also heavily monitored and censored in the name of national security. Crime reduces slightly. A rise in nationalism follows the drive towards self-sufficiency.

25.3.6.6 Effect on UK ecosystem services, goods and benefits

The goal of self-sufficiency and security of supply dominate in this future. Provisioning services are prioritised over the other ecosystem service types. **Figure 25.12** summarises the status of ecosystem services for 2060 under this scenario. The colour intensity indicates the assumed condition of each habitat for a given service at that time, while the arrow indicates the anticipated trend in the stock of that habitat up to that time. **Figure 25.13** provides an estimate of the changes in land cover proportions compared to 2000 across the UK NEA habitats for GB and the impact of the high and low climate trajectories. The analysis only shows change for terrestrial areas; 'sea' denotes only the area of open water in coastal areas. A key feature of the projected changes is the transfer of land (mainly Semi-natural Grasslands and Mountains, Moorlands and Heaths) to Woodland, especially Coniferous Woodland.

Provisioning

- Timber production—there are dramatic increases due to the larger Woodland area and because of better adapted species to a changing climate, high adoption of tree breeding technology and better forestry management.
- Fuelwood production—this also increases because it provides a relatively easy fuel to source, as well as providing home-grown jobs.
- Food production—a huge increase in arable area, coupled with gains in crop yields, results in higher production than at any time in the UK's history. Protein-based crops as well as more traditional grain and starch crops increase to offset a reduction in meat production.
- Marine fish stocks—dwindling wild fish stocks are protected and the UK's fishing territory is vigilantly controlled. Aquaculture becomes a vitally important source of fish-based food for the UK.
- Marine energy—there are dramatic increases to help meet the demands for self-sufficient energy supplies through the use of wind and tidal power.
- Wild species diversity—although declines in diversity are not as great as is the case in *World Markets,* biodiversity suffers from a range of drivers including climate change, land use change and pollution.

Regulation

- Carbon—there are increases in above and below-ground carbon use, mainly due to biofuel and woodland expansion. A reduction in meat production also reduces carbon emissions.
- Flood alleviation—rural, flood-prone areas are afforded protection against flood if they are major agricultural production areas. This is achieved through a series of better soil management, river-re-channelling and hard defence systems. Afforestation also improves flood mitigation provision in some areas.
- Erosion control—to maintain soil resources, strict control in the agricultural sector and good practice reduces the incidence of erosion.

- Water quality—this decline to mid-1980s levels due to a high use of pesticides and fertilisers and an increase in arable area.
- Invasive species—new incursions of invasive species decrease due to a reduction in overseas trade; current species are controlled in areas where they pose the largest threat to the provision of food.

Cultural

- Recreation—this decreases significantly with the weakening of environmental settings generally; people have less time (and resources) to visit the countryside and are more likely to spend time close to home in gardens etc. Rural UK is less attractive and many scenic areas have lost their aesthetic appeal through further agricultural expansion or large-scale coniferous planting.
- Historic and spiritual—such values are preserved and celebrated throughout the UK, however. Some beautiful and iconic landscapes that have not been altered too much by the drive towards production remain the most popular places to visit.

25.3.6.7 Ecosystem service trade-offs and changes since today

This storyline heavily emphasises provisioning services in the UK and results in a decline in regulating and cultural services. In some circumstances (e.g. an increase in broadleaved woodland), benefits are made for regulating services (although there is little for benefit for cultural services, except to increase the aesthetic value of the landscape by adding more Woodlands). An increase in food and timber production in this storyline results in gains in provisioning services compared to contemporary UK; however, in nearly all other instances, regulating and cultural services decline. It is difficult to estimate how the overall balance in service output would change, however, because we lack any clear indication of how the output of services varies per unit area of each habitat type. It would seem, nevertheless, that climate change would have the severest impact on arable land, with a significant reduction in Arable and Horticultural area under the high impact scenario due to poor adaptation capacity. For this reason, arable land is largely converted or abandoned to Semi-natural Grassland.

25.3.7 Local Stewardship

25.3.7.1 Origin

This storyline is a twist on the *National Security* narrative. *National Security* emphasises an effort to maintain economic development and current patterns of consumption, despite external pressures. In contrast, the *Local Stewardship* storyline describes an inherently greener world. It assumes a more conscious acceptance that a reduction is needed in the intensity of economic activity, and in the high levels of consumption that had characterised the earlier part of the century. It also envisages a migration pattern of counter-urbanisation. Many of the focal questions influencing the *Nature@Work* storyline are also relevant here, together with some aspects of *National Security*. In particular, this storyline tries to address issues raised about the future importance of localism and balancing ecosystem service delivery. It also seeks to describe a future where economic growth has not continued unabated and so provides us with a picture of how the UK could evolve sustainably under a global decline in economic growth and reduced access to dwindling resources.

25.3.7.2 Rationale

Local Stewardship is a future where society is more concerned with its immediate surroundings (community, land, etc.) and strives to maintain a sustainable focus on life within that area. However, unlike the *National Security* storyline, and despite the local focus, people are connected and have more solidarity with communities in other countries.

This scenario assumes that societal equity goes alongside environmental equity. People travel less and depend more on local resources; more of our food production and leisure activities take place in our immediate surroundings. The implementation of the sustainable management of resources is emphasised and society relies less on technological innovation for meeting social and environmental needs compared to the other scenarios. Low carbon economies spring up everywhere and there is a greater use of alternative economies such as LETS (Local Exchange Trading Systems) schemes. National GDP accounting has been complemented with GPI (Genuine Progress Indicator) to take into account environmental aspects and human welfare. Waste is considered an anathema: very little food is wasted, and, for example, farmers and smallholders utilise every last part of the animal. Many families keep chickens, pigs or geese.

Self-sufficiency is a key concept and so many exports and imports are reduced considerably, but still exist for commodities not produced in the UK. Agricultural land declines only slightly from 2010, and the population in this storyline is the lowest of all the scenarios. The overall levels of biodiversity increase and many ecosystems, including farmland and woodland, are managed more sustainably. Climate change is taken seriously and mitigation (an example of the 'think global' aspect) and adaptation projects spring up around the country. The main land cover changes due to climate change are seen in arable and grassland (small declines in area with concomitant rises in Semi-natural Grassland and broadleaved woodland). However, the low input and heterogeneous nature of the farm enterprises in *Local Stewardship* increase the adaptation capacity, so losses are minimal.

Through local specialisation the UK becomes less homogenised—the landscapes become more distinct and local economies vary considerably. Technological development occurs in localised areas due to private innovation and a government initiative for embedding sustainability into the development of technology. Social and environmental regulation have advanced, particularly in workers' welfare and rights and in environmental protection. Policy encourages smaller businesses and small and medium-sized enterprises proliferate. Although economic growth is slower compared to some storylines, the economy is more stable and does not suffer periodic dips and crashes.

The 'localism' aspect of this storyline is enabled by a reduction in state interference in the everyday life. UK government has largely devolved much of the day-to-day running of many aspects of life (e.g. education, health) but it still plays a role in environmental governance through legislation. Most environmental policy and legislation is related to the protection of semi-natural habitats and wildlife; other than this, there are no incentives for environmental management. Instead, the national government helps to provide education on sustainability and other environmental issues: environmentalism is generally based on a 'bottom-up' approach.

Land cover transitions are driven by a greater appreciation and desire for sustainability, but are also permitted to a large extent because of a lower demand for food provision due to smaller national population and shifts in diet. Biodiversity is afforded greater protection, and the desire to produce food locally results in greater heterogeneity in the landscape. This also improves the conservation value of the countryside.

25.3.7.3 Main drivers

Immigration is reduced and internal migration between regions falls dramatically too. Population growth relative to 2010 is very small, mainly due to a government policy of encouraging small families. However, the population continues to age; the age of retirement reflects the better health of the old and rises to 70. A focus on sustainable households results in more people living together under one roof. As a result, there is no housing crisis and as a consequence, much poor quality housing from the 20th Century is demolished to make way for greenspace.

One consequence of this scenario is lower overall GDP (but higher GPI). However, the country as a whole is healthier, happier and the environment is better protected. Unemployment is much lower than 2010 and although average income is reduced, there is much greater employment security and more people are engaged in labour-intensive jobs.

An investment in water and energy efficiency is one area where some technological advancement is made. A greater desire to develop diverse energy resources locally means that the energy industry is radically changed. Domestically, more houses take up a mix of solar, ground-source heat and wind. Fossil fuel is still used; some abandoned coalmines are reworked and energy is generated using cleaner technologies and carbon storage. Society is wary of nuclear power and no new power plants are created.

Internationally, the drive towards self-sufficiency is seen as a necessary step forward by many countries, although trade still exists. Diminishing energy and freshwater resources have resulted in countries refocusing their efforts towards ensuring sustainable supplies of their own ecosystem services (albeit mainly regulatory and provisioning services). No longer can countries guarantee supplies of many goods although, of course, some countries will still export goods where they have an excess of supply and where there is demand.

25.3.7.4 Land and sea use

Agriculture changes considerably as a consequence of two factors: the drive towards self-sufficiency means that some crops are reduced in area (e.g. wheat exports reduce, to be replaced by more protein and vegetable crops); mixed farms (many organic or low-input) become more common too. One major difference from many of the other storylines is the continued presence of Improved Grassland to maintain livestock production. However, whilst the overall land cover may stay the same, the location of Improved Grassland has changed and many arable farms have become mixed. These changes are largely driven by the local market. Some meat production becomes more extensive and traditional British breeds do well, although increasingly, breeds with a high tolerance to heat are kept. The second factor is the promotion, through market forces and policy, coupled with bottom-up demand for local production, of a distinct local or regional character for food production. Traditional areas for specialist foods return. Agriculture is subsidised by the government and is focused on an integrated programme of biodiversity conservation and sustainable management practices.

Most woodlands have a similar species composition to today's, but are better managed through coppice (used for local domestic energy or other craft products) and other (sustainable, like shelterwood) high forest silvicultural systems. Lower grade agricultural land is converted to woody biofuel in peri-urban areas and in lowland rural counties. Overall agricultural land area declines only slightly compared with 2010 but changes considerably in type. It is more heterogeneous and average farm size is smaller. Perhaps the most significant change is a large increase in Semi-natural Grassland ecosystems that are maintained by grazing and provide opportunities for recreation and biodiversity too. Mountain habitats are protected from development and provide grazing for sheep and hardy cattle breeds. Recreation is important but often locally based.

The quality of water in all freshwater habitats improves as a result of better agricultural management and more extensive production systems. A reduction in freshwater provision in the South East due to climate change is partly met by better water use efficiency and delivery from western and northern parts of the UK. Invasive species are controlled and new introductions from overseas decline due to greater border control.

In coastal areas, managed retreat is common (landowners are well compensated) and hard defences are actively removed in favour of 'softer', more natural approaches. Areas of valuable agricultural land are protected, but some systems are changed from highly drained farmland to wetland farm systems (e.g. rice production). Coastal development for shipping, oil and gas is reduced and the UK's coastline and Marine habitats reap the benefits. Renewable energy from the sea is encouraged and backed by government schemes— wave and tidal energy sources become common but do not conflict with areas of high biodiversity. Marine bioresources are managed sustainably, with local quotas implemented and managed through local groups, and the number of small fishing vessels increases. Local fish-based cuisine is very popular. Mobile fish populations (i.e. transboundary) are managed by national quota systems and a new fisheries committee. Despite a lower overall fish haul than in 2010, fish catches are more diverse. Carbon sequestration in Marine environments is also taken seriously; local marine areas are rewarded by the national government for maintaining carbon stocks.

The UK settlement pattern is very similar to 2010 except in areas prone to flooding, where some of the housing stock has been removed. Existing housing development occurs only in relatively safe and 'climate-proof' areas. There is a small outflow of people from urban to rural areas. Thus counter-urbanisation is a feature of this scenario. In urban areas the housing stock diminishes to make way for more greenspace (gardens both for leisure and food production) and the total city greenspace is the second highest proportion of Urban cover, after *Green and Pleasant Land* (57%). Street trees are planted and maintained and urban farms crop up throughout the UK. In peri-urban areas there is a large increase in working woodlands and conservation areas due to the contraction of housing. Small tenanted farms arise from the break-up of larger units.

Domestic energy supply is very important in this scenario and many houses are installed with a combination of wind, solar and ground-source heat systems. Energy efficiency is also improved across the national housing stock. Transport adopts a combination of biofuel, electric and fossil fuels. Large-scale renewable energy also plays an important part, but only where it does not conflict with biodiversity: e.g. wind farms crop up around the coast but avoid major bird migratory routes as well as important Marine habitats.

25.3.7.5 Human well-being

The belief in sustainable production systems pervades attitudes towards consumption and lifestyles; most people do not want or miss high-tech goods and enjoy a more relaxed pace to life. Simple things provide simple and rewarding pleasures. Food is very important, though: many people pride themselves on their cooking abilities and local food is easily sourced.

Although there are regional differences, the overall health of the nation increases due to a lower stress lifestyle, better nutrition, better education, more outdoor work and better housing standards. However, technological developments in medicine have not progressed as much as they have in other storylines, but mental health is much better than ever before. Overall the UK is a much happier place. There are lower incidences of crime and aggressive behaviour toward others; tolerance of minorities and different viewpoints is high and many local communities are so well connected and supported that any transgressions are easily dealt with if they arise. Community pride and peer pressure to 'behave' is strong.

Localism does not mean inconsistent standards in law or freedom. Everyone in the UK has a voice, a vote and freedom to do what they want within the laws of a civil society. Many local customs are maintained, but these do not encroach on equality and civility. Access to land and production systems is good and anyone has the opportunity to do well in life if they work hard.

25.3.7.6 Effect on UK ecosystem services, goods and benefits

Figure 25.14 summarises the status of ecosystem services for 2060 under this scenario. The colour intensity indicates the assumed condition of each habitat for a given service

Service Group	Final ecosystem service		Mountains, Moorlands & Heaths	Semi-natural Grasslands	Enclosed Farmland	Woodlands	Freshwater - Openwater Wetlands & Floodplains	Urban	Coastal Margins	Marine
Provisioning	Crops				↓	↗		↗		
	Livestock/Aquaculture		↗	↑	↗	↗	↗	↗	↔	↗
	Fisheries				↔		↗	↗	↑	↗
	Trees, standing vegetation, peat		↗	↔	↑	↑	↗	↗	↗	
	Water supply		↑	↗	↑	↗	↑	↗	↔	
Cultural	Wild species diversity		↑	↑	↑	↑	↑	↑	↑	↑
	Environmental Settings		↑	↑	↑	↑	↑	↑	↑	↑
Regulating	Climate		↗	↗	↑	↑	↗	↗	↗	↗
	Hazard		↗	↗	↑	↑	↗	↗	↗	↗
	Diseases & Pests		↗	↗	↑	↑	↑	↗	↗	↗
	Pollination									
	Detoxification & Purification	Water quality	↑	↑	↑	↑	↑	↗	↗	↗
		Soil quality	↗	↗	↑	↑	↗	↗	↗	
		Air quality	↗	↗	↑	↑	↗	↗	↗	↗
	Noise		↔	↔	↗	↔	↔	↗	↔	↔

Key

Ecosystem service condition
- ▪ Low
- ▪ Medium
- ▪ High
- ▪ Very high
- ☐ Not applicable

Direction of change
- ↑ Improving Some
- ↗ Some Improvement
- ↔ Equivocal changes
- ↘ Some Deterioration
- ↓ Deteriorating

Figure 25.14 Ecosystem service condition and trends for different Broad Habitats in *Local Stewardship*.

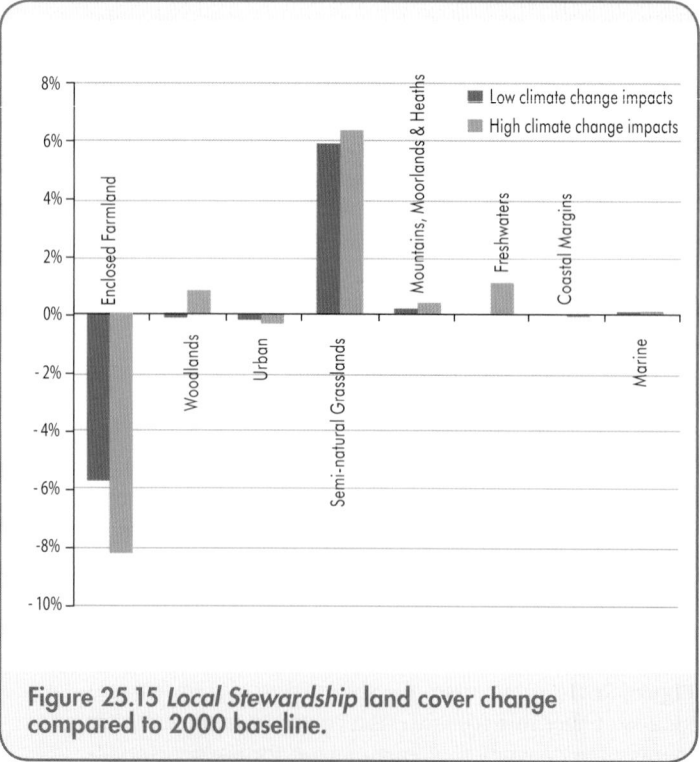

Figure 25.15 *Local Stewardship* land cover change compared to 2000 baseline.

at that time, while the arrow indicates the anticipated trend in the stock of that habitat up to that time. **Figure 25.15** provides an estimate of the changes in land cover proportions compared to 2000 across the UK NEA habitats for GB and the impact of the high and low climate trajectories. The analysis only shows change for terrestrial areas; 'sea' denotes only the area of open water in coastal areas. The goal of using resources in a more sustainable way, and managing them at local scales, is reflected in the outcomes, in that habitats and services are regarded as important across the board, and most show improving trends. The less intensive approaches to land management are reflected in the expansion of Semi-natural Grasslands, compared to the present.

Provisioning

■ Timber production—there are huge increases in some areas (i.e. traditional wooded regions like the South East) due to an emphasis in restoring silvicultural systems and a slight increase in Woodland area. Many farm woods are also renovated and become working woods again. Local wooden products are easy to find in shops (everything from spoons to broom handles, tables and joists).

- Fuelwood production—there are increases due to high fossil fuel costs and because more woods are being restored or worked for underwood. More efficient boiler designs mean that many local communities adopt fuelwood as their energy source for heating.
- Crop production—this declines slightly where old varieties have been adopted. There is less use of pesticides and inorganic fertilisers, but the rise in sustainable and diverse farming systems means that many farmers are far better adapted to climate change extremes.
- Animal production—there is a similar decline in yield to crops although the land area used and total livestock numbers remain fairly constant.
- Marine—popular wild fish species from the 20th Century are largely replaced by sustainable catches of local species.
- Wild species diversity—as a result of less intensive land management and greater landscape heterogeneity, biodiversity in the UK is fairly healthy. Climate change still poses a threat, but a 'softer' landscape aids species' migration as well as providing greater structural diversity to help provide more niche space for species.

Regulation
- Carbon—terrestrial carbon stocks increase due to better management of woodlands, farms and grasslands. Marine carbon stocks are protected.
- Flood alleviation—locally designed adaptation plans are implemented, often resulting in land cover change to Woodlands or other semi-natural habitats. Planned adaptation is widespread and some housing developments in floodplains have been removed and returned to natural ecosystems.
- Erosion control—the main problem areas on farmland are managed to control or prevent soil erosion.
- Water quality—the quality of water improves to almost complete UK-wide favourable status as a result of more sustainable agricultural practice and tighter environmental legislation.

Cultural
- Recreation—there are increasing opportunities for woodland and farmland recreation, and local service provision is key. Environmental settings have a strong influence. Fewer people travel far for leisure and pride in local landscapes runs high. Most woods are intensively managed for fuel to supply local heat generation systems, but also incorporate trails and paths for recreation. The traditional English mosaic landscapes of small fields and villages among rolling hills, with vibrant hedgerows and small woods, are returning and many people love walking in the countryside.
- The historical wealth of the UK is greatly appreciated and conserved and provides a very popular source of recreation for many people. This storyline is the most rural too and as localism is a dominant paradigm in society, people have a great 'sense of place'. This is not necessarily accompanied by greater spiritual awareness as many people adopt a pragmatic approach to life.

Local Stewardship has more in common with *Nature@Work* than *National Security* with regard to seeking synergies and making trade-offs between ecosystem services. However, despite the focus on local food production in *Local Stewardship*, this would never override the provision of regulating or cultural services. In this sense, *Local Stewardship* also sits slightly closer to *Green and Pleasant Land* too, inasmuch as biodiversity is regarded as very important, both for its intrinsic and instrumental value. It must also be remembered that it is easier to optimise service provision than is the case in the *Nature@Work* scenario, because the overall impact from the drivers of change are lower (e.g. population). In this storyline, the output of most ecosystem services improves compared to current levels; food provisioning stays constant or increases slightly, but nearly all regulating and cultural services increase dramatically. However, as before, it is difficult to estimate the changing balance overall and the extent to which the gains compensate for the losses. Climate change reduces provisioning services slightly in farmland, which is particularly evident in the South East (where temperatures and drought are most extreme). This farmland loss is broadleaved woodland's gain, as more drought-tolerant native species are planted.

25.3.8 Go with the Flow

25.3.8.1 Origin
This storyline attempts to imagine how current trends or targets might carry forward. In one sense it is a kind of comparator, but it is perhaps best viewed as a scenario in its own right because it does explore a particular set of assumptions about the processes that drive change and the responses to them. In many ways this storyline represents a world with sometimes conflicting objectives and the need for compromise. A number of the focal questions identified in the stakeholder consultation raised issues concerning the effectiveness of current environmental and socioeconomic policies, and this storyline provides one way of exploring these issues.

25.3.8.2 Rationale
This scenario is essentially a qualitative projection based on current trends and societal attitudes and results in a future UK that is loosely based on today's ideals and targets. In this sense it is not a 'do nothing' storyline, but a projection of current approaches. Thus, it leans towards improving environmental performance and sustainability in the UK but maintains an eye on growing the economy in a globalised world. Many current ideas being discussed in academic, government and the business sectors have been used as the basis of this narrative. The scenario assumes that environmental improvements are still important in the national vision for a future UK, but that the public are somewhat reluctant to adopt many global or national environmental standards if doing so challenges living standards (business and industry even less so). In this scenario, this stand-off continues to dominate and much

environmental progress is hindered, although some lead businesses are developing sustainability as a core driver of long-term business strategy.

Policy development in this storyline continues the current pattern of improving and tightening environmental legislation and incentives. It is backed up by more awareness of environmental issues in society and a more comprehensive and efficient extension service ready to support and advise farmers and other landowners. Land cover changes largely follow the patterns of the last few decades: broadleaved Woodland continues to increase slowly through grant aid, more Semi-natural Grassland is restored, and Urban development continues very slowly and expands into target areas (e.g. former farmland near good transport links).

25.3.8.3 Main drivers

The average household size of 2.4 persons in 2010 declines slightly as more people enjoy living alone, the divorce rate continues to rise and the birth rate declines. Immigration is controlled and only skilled migrants are allowed entry (immigration falls to around 250,000/year, although emigration rises to 350,000/year). Population growth slows, but *Go with the Flow* is second only to *World Markets* for total UK population size. A slow progression towards a low-carbon economy and better environmental standards across industry and society is maintained, albeit with bumps along the way. There are brief spurts and setbacks depending on the government at the time, but climate change mitigation and adaptation is kept on the agenda.

The employment rate increases from 72% in 2010 to 77%; unemployment falls from 7.9% to 3%. Export of goods to the EU and other countries grows to a value of £30 billion in 2060. The UK follows a similar pattern of privatisation or public/private partnerships running public institutions to that of the present day. Technology and science are considered critical components of economic growth and are maintained, although increased private sector investment is encouraged. The UK's gross domestic expenditure on research and development has increased from £25.6 billion in 2008 to £35 billion in 2060; this represents about 1.5% of GDP.

The global context is the same as is found in *Green and Pleasant Land*. The US, EU, China, India, Russia and Brazil are the dominant economic forces in the world and capitalism drives the economy of most countries. Global trade increases each year. New markets are created as more countries strive for a western standard of living and climate change affects many traditional production areas. Global environmentalism is stronger, but struggles to make any headway in places where free markets dominate. A global climate change deal was never achieved, but one success has been the burgeoning use of products that are sustainably certified (timber, biofuel and many foodstuffs) and increasingly, these products dominate the western markets.

25.3.8.4 Land and sea use

The current area of agricultural land in the UK (17.5 million hectares) stays roughly the same, although cropping changes to reflect the impacts of climate change occur; these include new crop species, more perennial crops and biofuels.

Agriculture is a varied and dynamic industry. In some parts of the country, large, intensive farm units supply cheap milk, pork, poultry and beef to supermarkets, while in others there is greater emphasis on organic farming and quality beef, lamb, chicken and pork production. The area of grassland declines slightly compared to now, as more livestock is housed, and some areas are converted to woody biomass. Arable production starts to encroach into traditional animal production areas in the western and northern parts of the UK under the influence of climate change.

The current area of Woodlands in the United Kingdom increases, reflecting 50 years of support for woodland creation; of this, a large percentage is sustainably managed. Greater public access to Woodlands is achieved through an amendment to the Countryside and Rights of Way (CRoW) Act. All conservation-designated grasslands are maintained, mainly by local conservation organisations as the emphasis of government, EU and Convention on Biological Diversity (CBD) conservation programmes shifts to focus on ecosystem service delivery and climate change adaptation schemes. Mountain, Moorland, and Heath habitats are threatened by afforestation and localised grazing pressure, but continue to be a dominant sink for soil carbon in the UK. Upland peat soils, in particular, are protected from land use change. Recreation increases in mountain areas, although traditional farm-based mountain communities are in decline and more people are engaged in the tourism and leisure industry. Mountain biodiversity shows a steady decline from 2010 for the next few decades, primarily due to climate change; conservation programmes to curb this are expensive and largely unsuccessful.

One success story in this storyline is the continued progress in cleaning the rivers of the UK. However, all is not rosy: the number of invasive species increases and they prove difficult to control with the limited funding provided by the government.

In 2060 UK ports handle around 750 million tonnes of freight, up from 562 million in 2008; most of this consists of imports. Some areas of coastland are placed under managed retreat regimes but on the whole, hard sea defences are employed to hold back rising sea levels. The UK sea fish (including shellfish) catch is down to 270 thousand tonnes in 2060, almost half the 2010 figure. Development of offshore wind farms has slowly picked up and threatens some Marine ecosystems.

Government ambitions to build a quarter of a million new houses every year until 2030 (when the UK reached 27.8 million households) were extended indefinitely and housing development continued. This has resulted in an average density of 50 dwellings per hectare (up from 45 in 2010). Most of this housing is concentrated in the South East, but all major conurbations in the UK see a rise in housing development. Building in green belt areas rises, and about 15% has changed to residential use since 2010. Development in areas of high flood risk has also continued, and by 2060 about 20% of all dwellings built since 2010 are found within such areas.

The UK pushes its 2010 target of 3% of energy sourced from renewables to 8%. An emphasis on nuclear energy has helped alleviate the dwindling fossil fuel resources available

Figure 25.16

Service Group	Final ecosystem service		Mountains, Moorlands & Heaths	Semi-natural Grasslands	Enclosed Farmland	Woodlands	Freshwater - Openwater Wetlands & Floodplains	Urban	Coastal Margins	Marine
Provisioning	Crops			↔	↑		↘	↘	↔	
	Livestock/Aquaculture		↘	↘	↘	↔	↘		↘	↔
	Fisheries				↔		↘		↘	↔
	Trees, standing vegetation, peat		↗	↔	↗	↑		↘	↔	
	Water supply		↗	↘	↗	↔	↗	↗	↔	
Cultural	Wild species diversity		↔	↘	↗	↔	↘	↔	↔	↘
	Environmental Settings		↗	↗	↗	↑	↗	↔	↗	↔
Regulating	Climate		↗	↗	↗	↗	↔	↗	↗	↔
	Hazard		↗	↔	↗	↗	↔	↔	↔	↗
	Diseases & Pests		↔	↔	↗	↔	↔	↗	↔	↗
	Pollination		↗	↗	↗	↗		↔	↗	
	Detoxification & Purification	Water quality	↗	↗	↗	↗	↗	↗	↗	↗
		Soil quality	↗	↗	↗	↗	↗	↔	↗	
		Air quality	↗	↗	↗	↗	↗	↗	↗	↗
	Noise		↔	↔	↔	↗	↔	↘	↔	↔

Key

Ecosystem service condition
- Low
- Medium
- High
- Very high
- Not applicable

Direction of change
- ↑ Improving Some
- ↗ Some Improvement
- ↔ Equivocal changes
- ↘ Some Deterioration
- ↓ Deteriorating

Figure 25.16 Ecosystem service condition and trends for different Broad Habitats in *Go with the Flow*.

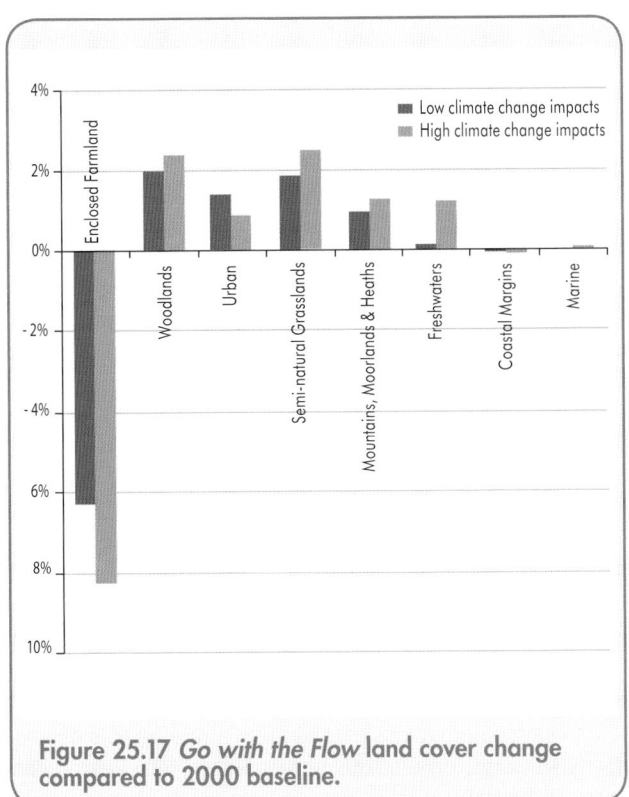

Figure 25.17 *Go with the Flow* land cover change compared to 2000 baseline.

to the UK. Biofuels from cropped land are also heavily promoted. Energy efficiency continues to improve at a steady pace and cars with poor fuel economy are heavily taxed. New high-speed rail networks are developed, greatly reducing intercity travel time. Car use also continues, although the vast majority of vehicles in 2060 do not use diesel or petrol any more (hydrogen, bioethanol and electric cars are common). Urban congestion is still a huge problem in most cities.

25.3.8.5 Human well-being

UK society is divided between the haves and have-nots. Mean income is higher than in 2010 but so is the gap between rich and poor; there is still a glass ceiling for some sectors in society (although things have improved for women). This breeds resentment and creates a divisive society. Freedom is more restricted than in 2010. Human rights are squeezed in the name of protecting democracy.

Many goods that were once public are now private—this affects access for recreation, food and decision making. More of the health service is funded through private finance initiatives, which has a detrimental effect on national health (i.e. the needs of patients are not always met). The affluent sections of society generally have better access to medical care and education (smoking, drinking and obesity remain mainly lower class issues). Global health pandemics occasionally have impacts on the UK.

25.3.8.6 Effect on UK ecosystem services, goods and benefits

The theme of this scenario is a continuation of today's aims and objectives. Thus, ecosystem services that have monetary value and are easy to trade are protected, while many others are not. **Figure 25.16** summarises the status of ecosystem services for 2060 under this scenario. The colour intensity indicates the assumed condition of each habitat for a given service at that time, while the arrow indicates the anticipated trend in the stock of that habitat up to that time. **Figure 25.17** provides an estimate of the changes in land cover proportions compared to 2000 across the UK NEA habitats for GB and the impact of the high and low climate trajectories. The analysis only shows change for terrestrial areas; 'sea' denotes only the area of open water in coastal areas. Enclosed Farmland declines in area and there are small increases in Woodlands, Semi-natural Grasslands and Mountains, Moorlands and Heaths.

Provisioning

- Timber production—very little timber is produced in the UK, as imports from Eastern Europe are cheaper for the UK consumer. The area of Coniferous Woodland declines slightly and although Broadleaved Woodlands increase in area, very little is managed for timber.
- Fuelwood production—this increases due to high fossil fuel costs and the larger Broadleaved Woodland area; some local communities adopt fuelwood as their energy source for heating.
- Crop production—this increases steadily; government and private research and development have pushed yields higher despite climate change. National production of cereals and protein crops increases overall.
- Animal products—milk, beef, poultry and pork yields continue to increase due to a demand for cheap, low quality meat; much of it is reared indoors.
- Wild species diversity—although conservation legislation is tighter than ever before, and the uptake of agri-environmental scheme is very high, biodiversity in many parts of the UK has declined (but this varies across different habitats). Farmland biodiversity has slowly recovered to pre-1970 levels (but not to pre-1940 levels), freshwater habitats are in rude health and mountain habitat biodiversity is also healthy. However, Woodland biodiversity is suffering from the effects of climate change as well as from competition from invasive species.

Regulation

- Carbon—terrestrial carbon stocks increase slightly, due to better carbon management across sectors (including agriculture); an increase in the area of Broadleaved Woodland also contributes.
- Flood alleviation—there are localised improvements, mostly in the southern counties of England; housing development continues in flood zones, often with little or no implementation of flood mitigation programmes.
- Erosion control—there is a slow improvement in management through concerted government and farm industry efforts.

- Water quality—there is continued improvement throughout the UK through better farmland management and tighter environmental legislation.
- Invasive species—numbers increase due to more unregulated trade, an increase in traffic (a main vector for many species) and climate change; control methods are implemented, but without real funding are fruitless.
- Marine fish stocks—some wild fish stocks have been all but depleted, despite protection from the UK and EU. Aquaculture increases production to maintain local fish supplies but increasingly, fish is imported from overseas.
- Energy—the nuclear industry is renewed and nuclear energy and gas imports are the main energy sources for the UK. Renewables make a small contribution, with a mix of land- and sea-based wind generation the main source.

Cultural

- Recreation—there are increasing opportunities for countryside recreation in National Parks and other publicly protected landscapes; however, access to private land in the UK is becoming increasingly difficult.
- Some historic and spiritual ecosystem services in the UK have been degraded or lost, due to a lack of government funding and little enthusiasm from business or civil society to take on the responsibility.

25.3.8.7 Ecosystem service trade-offs and changes since today

In this storyline, synergies in efforts to enhance ecosystem services are difficult to achieve and trade-offs are much more common. While there is a gradual shift away from provisioning to regulating and cultural services (although not in all areas), there is a constant battle with other socioeconomic forces to improve the UK's environment. There are also large geographical differences in ecosystem service delivery in this storyline; for example, the South East has a lower overall suite of services than many other parts of the UK.

Production of food increases, due mainly to technological advances increasing crop and livestock yields. However, sustainable farming is also more popular and as a result, regulating services also improve slightly (although there is still a widespread adoption of 'industrial' farming practice).

The main difference to note in ecosystem service delivery compared to 2010 is that there is a marked improvement for all services. While this storyline compares unfavourably with *Nature@Work*, *Green and Pleasant Land* and *Local Stewardship*, it is certainly an advance on today's situation as well as *World Markets* and *National Security*. Climate change adaptation is increasingly more important to society, and as a result of adopting greater technology and better management strategies, differences in land cover change under the high and low climate impact versions of this narrative are small; there is a small loss of farmland in those areas where climate impacts are most extreme, such as the South East. However, sea-level rise does result in a loss of land area, although this occurs partly through a programme of managed retreat in some parts of the UK.

25.4 The Six Scenarios: Land Cover Change and Impacts on UK Ecosystem Services and Habitats

25.4.1 Comparing Scenario Outcomes

A comparison of the sustainability of ecosystem service outputs was made for each scenario by counting the number of services that appeared to be increasing, stable or declining under the assumptions of each storyline. The approach used was similar to that described in the assessment of current status and trends, which estimated that 12 services were increasing and 21 were declining across those habitats that were considered important.

These same target habitats are considered in the analysis of the scenario outcomes. The results are shown in **Figure 25.18**; the data are shown as an aggregate of all services and separately for the three main ecosystem service groups.

The indicative analysis for the scenarios showed that while current policy approaches, as characterised in *Go with the Flow*, may lead to some improvements in service output, the UK can make significant gains where policy takes the approach outlined in three scenarios: *Green and Pleasant Land*, *Nature@Work* and *Local Stewardship*. In each of these, the majority of services appeared to show increasing trends, compared to the present where a more mixed picture has been reported. By contrast, *World Markets* and *National Security* showed significant losses compared to the present and *Go with the Flow*.

The advantages of *Green and Pleasant Land*, *Nature@Work* and *Local Stewardship* over the other scenarios is constant across the three main service groups, although

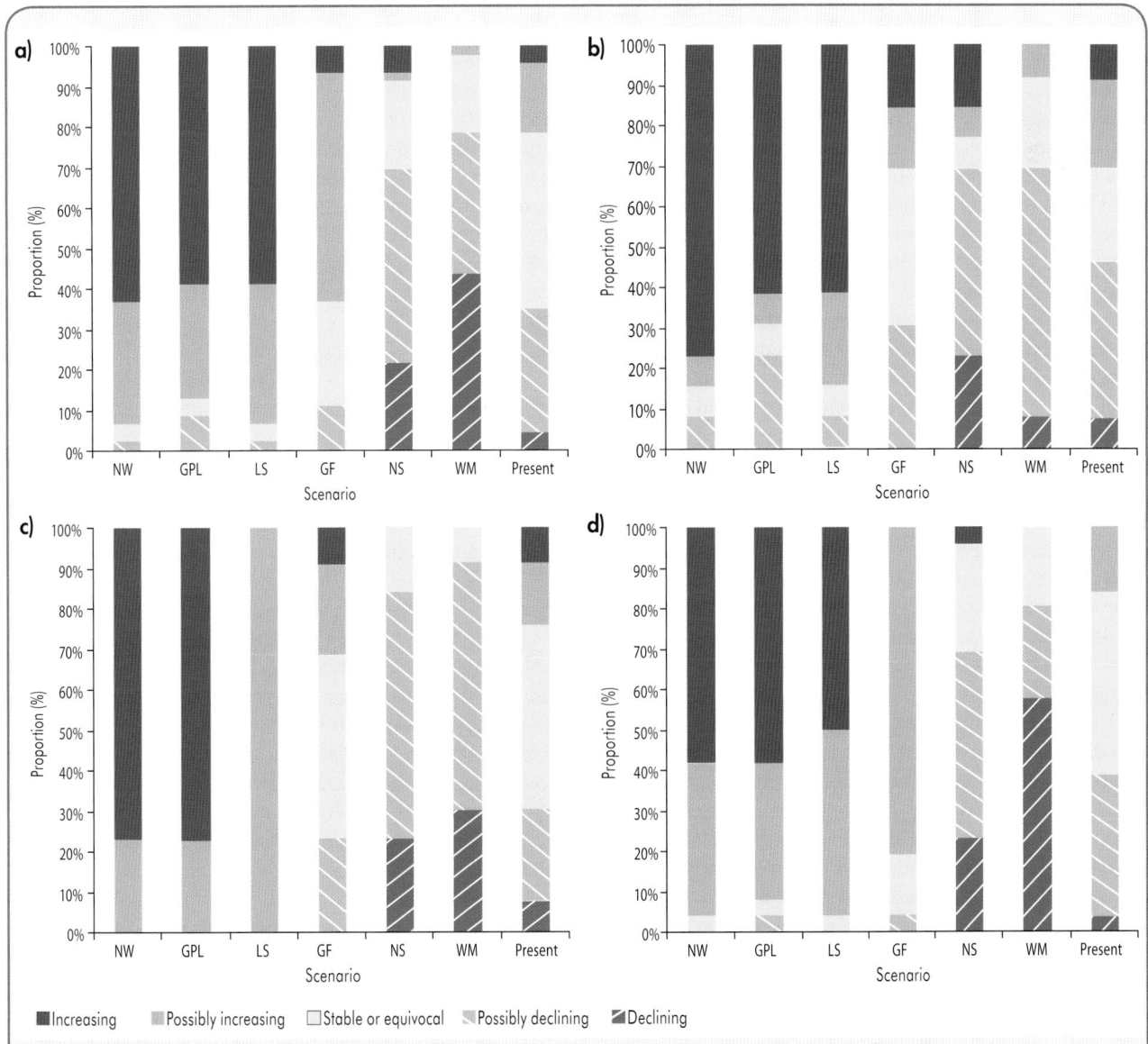

Figure 25.18 a) Change in ecosystem services across six scenarios compared to the present, b) Change in provisioning services across six scenarios to the present, c) Change in cultural services across six scenarios to the present, d) Change in regulating services across six scenarios to the present. The Scenarios are as follows: N@W = Nature@Work; GPL = Green and Pleasant Land; LS = Local Stewardship; GF = Go with the Flow; NS = National Security; WM = World Markets.

the gains in cultural services in *Green and Pleasant Land* compared to *Local Stewardship* do suggest that the balance between them may shift according to priorities. The marked deterioration of regulating services associated with the *World Markets* narrative is also apparent.

The outcome of *Go with the Flow* is of particularly interest because it suggests that current policies and interventions should have a positive effect in the long term. However, it is clear that the gains are modest and opportunities to adapt to make best use of our natural capital may be missed. This scenario outcome must not be interpreted as a 'do-nothing' option because it is premised on the assumption that the levels of present interventions to secure ecosystem services are maintained, and are equally effective in the future. In fact, the hands-off approach would be closer to *World Markets* than *Go with the Flow*.

25.4.2 Quantifying Differences

The quantification of scenario outcomes is particularly important if detailed comparisons are to be made between the different storylines. The task is a challenging one, however, because the science community presently lacks the kind of process-response models needed to link changes in drivers and ecosystem service outputs in an integrated way. Faced with this difficulty this scenario work has, as a first step, attempted to develop quantitative projections of changes in land cover as a way of exploring some of the consequences that the different storylines might have for ecosystem services. The work is based on the assumption that service output is dependent upon two key variables, namely: habitat condition, measured in terms of the habitat's capacity to supply a given service for a given unit area; and the stock of that habitat in the overall mix of land cover.

The use of a transition matrix to make projections of changes in future land cover has been described above. The outputs from this work are valuable in their own right because the mapping can be used to illustrate some of the consequences of each storyline. If the storylines can be used to gain an insight into changes in habitat condition, then an analysis of overall output can be attempted and provisional estimates of the marginal changes in value of some ecosystem services under the different storylines can be made (see Chapter 26).

The account of each of the storylines presented above included a summary Figure describing the projected status and trends of services in 2060; the diagrams were derived from qualitative estimates of changes in habitat stock and condition. To make a more quantitative assessment, the expert-based condition rating has been combined with the projected change in proportional cover of each habitat to construct a quantitative index of service outcomes for the different storylines. The analysis includes all the habitat service pairs considered important for each narrative.

For each storyline two indices have been calculated. The first presents the overall service output by habitat; the habitat index sums the condition score assigned to each service/habitat combination, weighted by the estimated proportional area of each habitat in 2060. The results are shown in **Figure 25.19 (series a)**, which also depicts the present situation. The second index breaks down results by service group (**Figure 25.19 series b);** for this metric the change in condition relative to the present is multiplied by the proportional change in amount of each habitat, and summed for each service group.

Using both these indices, three narratives, *Green and Pleasant Land, Nature@Work* and *Local Stewardship* appear to show significant gains in the general output of ecosystem services compared to *Go with the Flow*. However, the latter did show that compared to the present, some small improvements in service output are possible with current policy approaches. *World Markets* and *National Security* appeared to show significant losses compared to the present and *Go with the Flow*. The loss of provisioning services in *National Security* is, however, notable given the emphasis that this storyline places on self-sufficiency. The decline is partly driven in the data by the loss of Enclosed Farmland, but may also reflect the arbitrary nature of the scoring system used to estimate changes in condition.

Inspection of the high and low climate change versions of each scenario suggests that overall, the differences between them were smaller than those observed between scenarios. Future land use change may, therefore, potentially have as much impact on ecosystem services as the direct effects of climate. This is an important conclusion that needs to be examined further. On the basis of the analysis shown in **Figure 25.19**, a more detailed picture of the changes by UK NEA Broad Habitat may be built up; further detail is provided by **Figure 25.20**, which breaks down the changes in cover type projected for each scenario by England, Wales and Scotland.

25.4.2.1 Mountains, Moorlands and Heaths

For this habitat group, land cover patterns do not differ significantly from the present, except in the *World Markets* and *National Security* storylines, which show the largest losses compared to the present (**Figure 25.19**). *Green and Pleasant Land, Nature@Work* and *Local Stewardship* all show small gains in upland habitats (*Nature@Work* has the largest), reflecting the importance that cultural and regulating services are given in these storylines. Increases in *Nature@Work* are due to better management of these habitats for hazards, climate, pests and diseases, and water and soil regulation; this pattern is particularly strong in Wales and Scotland, but even in England there are gains. *Green and Pleasant Land* also shows increases in the cover of Mountains, Moorlands and Heaths, although the emphasis in this scenario is on trying to maintain the wild beauty of the UK's uplands, which has many synergies with efforts to promote regulating services.

World Markets shows a decline in upland habitats. This is partly due to the expansion of arable land (which also increases under the warmer and drier conditions of the high climate change scenario), but is also due to a reduction in land planning control, which results in patchy (but expanding) housing development in easily accessible upland areas. The largest land cover transition for uplands habitats is in *National Security*: this storyline aims to increase provisioning services as much as possible, which results in a significant expansion of coniferous plantations in many Welsh and Scottish upland areas.

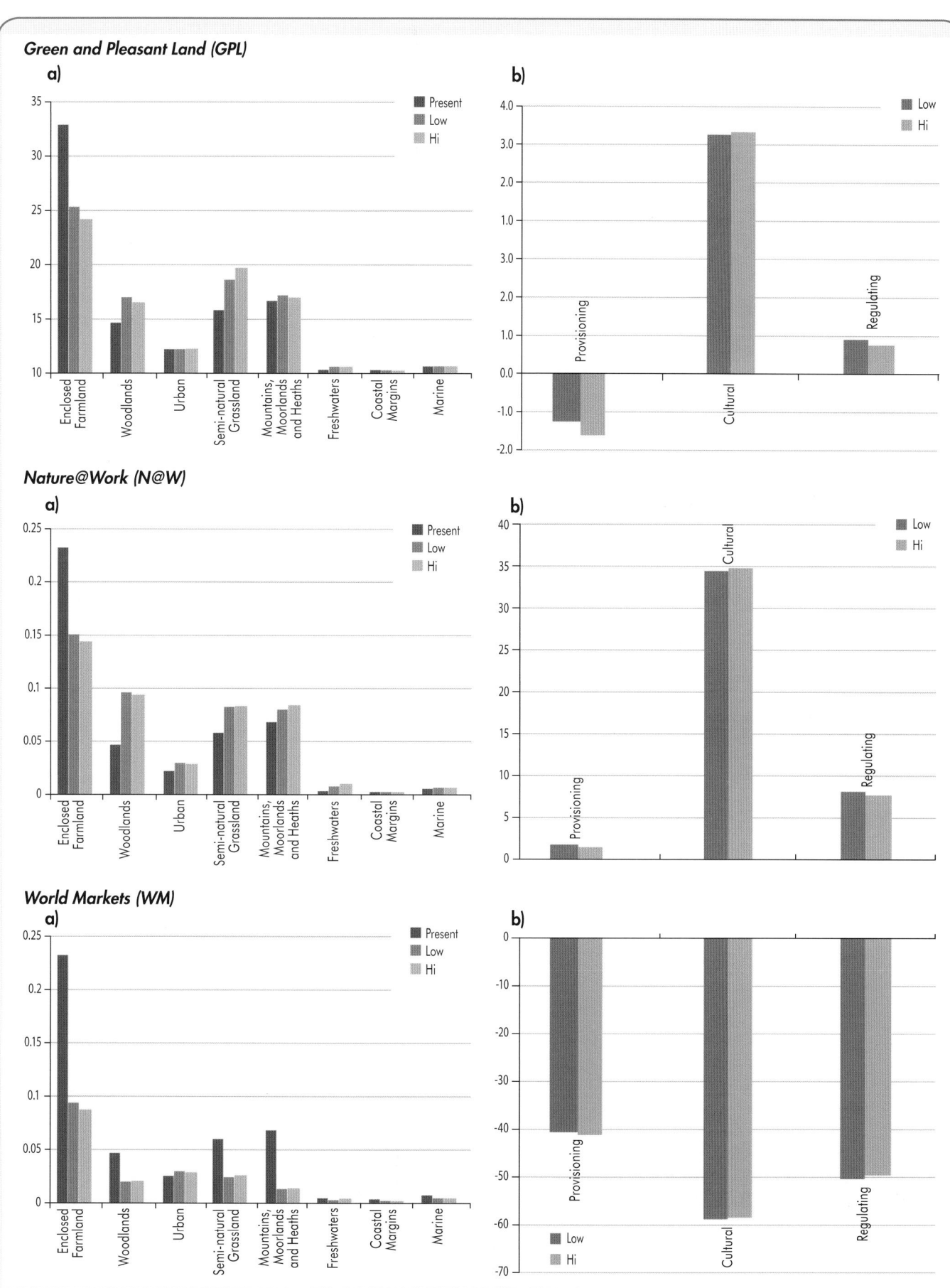

Figure 25.19 Change in ecosystem services across six scenarios compared to the present based on projected changes in habitat stock and condition. For *Green and Pleasant Land*: a) Broad Habitats and b) ecosystem services. For *Nature@Work* a) Broad Habitats and b) ecosystem services. For *World Markets* a) Broad Habitats and b) ecosystem services. Present, Low and Hi refer to Present, Low and High climate change impacts.

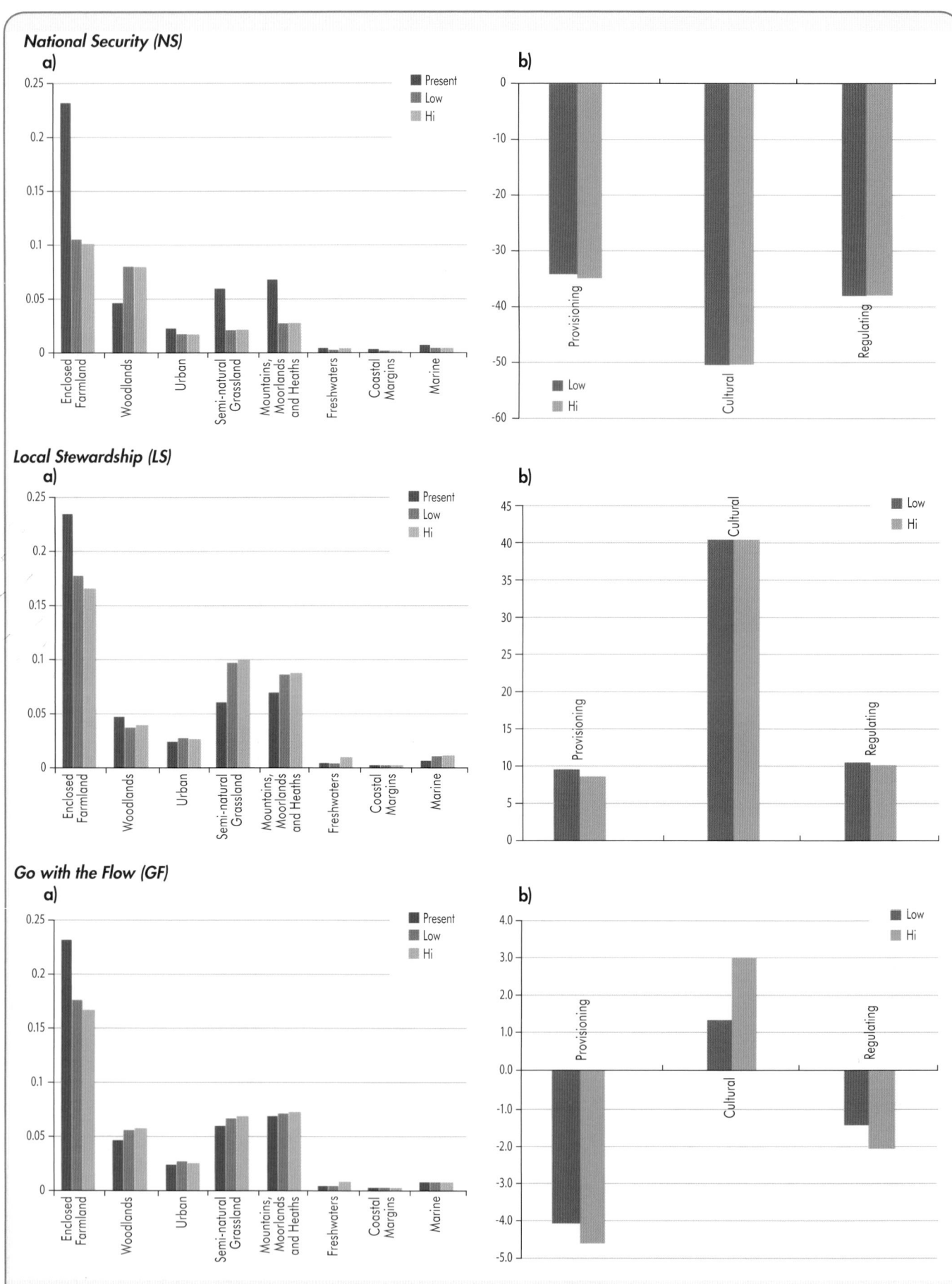

Figure 25.19 continued. Change in ecosystem services across six scenarios compared to the present based on projected changes in habitat stock and condition. For *National Security* a) Broad Habitats and b) ecosystem services. For *Local Stewardship* a) Broad Habitats and b) ecosystem services. For *Go with the Flow* a) Broad Habitats and b) ecosystem services. Present, Low and Hi refer to Present, Low and High climate change impacts.

25.4.2.2 Semi-natural Grasslands

As with the Mountain, Moorland and Heath habitats, *Nature@Work*, *Local Stewardship*, *Green and Pleasant Land* and *Go with the Flow* all show increasing Semi-natural Grassland cover and increase service outputs associated with this group (**Figure 25.19**). *Green and Pleasant Land* and *Local Stewardship* show the largest gains, especially in England, although Wales and Scotland also show increases (**Figure 25.20**). This partly reflects the impact that climate change has on Improved Grassland and Arable and Horticultural in the south, but it is also explained by England reclaiming a greater area of Semi-natural Grasslands. These increases have multiple ecosystem service benefits, even if the restoration objectives vary among the storylines (cultural service provision in *Green and Pleasant Land* and *Go with the Flow*, regulating service provision in *Nature@Work*, *Go with the Flow* and *Local Stewardship* and some provisioning in *Local Stewardship*). *World Markets* and *National Security* lose Semi-natural Grassland cover: to Broadleaved Woodland, Coniferous Woodland and Arable and Horticultural in *National Security*; and to Arable and Horticultural and Urban in *World Markets*.

25.4.2.3 Enclosed Farmland

Enclosed Farmland continues to be the dominant land cover in all six storylines (**Figure 25.19**), although the ratio between Arable and Horticultural and Improved Grassland varies between them. In *National Security*, food production is of prime importance and consequently arable area increases. Despite the importance of self-sufficiency, Improved Grassland declines due to a pragmatic approach to food production; crop-based protein is a more efficient use of land than livestock. In *World Markets*, the area of Enclosed Farmland declines, mainly to due to encroaching urban development, but greater intensification and industrial agricultural models do increase productivity. *Nature@Work* sees a reduction in Arable and Horticultural and Improved Grassland area, although production increases as a result of advances in technology and sustainable management techniques. Most of the farmland lost is converted to Semi-natural Grassland and Broadleaved Woodland, and some also to conifer plantations.

Green and Pleasant Land and *Local Stewardship* adopt a low-input agricultural model that seeks to conserve a range of ecosystem services; this results a large reduction in farmland area. Both Arable and Horticultural land and Improved Grassland decline in *Green and Pleasant Land*, but there is a much smaller loss of Improved Grassland in *Local Stewardship* (**Figure 25.19**). They both lose farmland to Semi-natural Grassland and Broadleaved Woodland, with higher transitions in areas of greater biodiversity where, for example, the density of ancient semi-natural woodlands is highest. *Go with the Flow* maintains and improves agricultural productivity through technological advances, but loses a larger area of Improved Grassland to Broadleaved Woodland and Semi-natural Grassland, partly because more livestock is reared indoors.

25.4.2.4 Woodland

The area of Woodland in 2060 increases in all the storylines except *World Markets*, which loses Woodland to urban development (**Figure 25.19**). The ratio of broadleaved to conifer also varies between the scenarios, with a greater emphasis on conifer woodland in *National Security* due to its better productivity. By contrast, in *Nature@Work,* the aim is for a mix of broadleaved and conifer. The former are planted to provide both cultural and regulating services, while the latter are encouraged to increase provisioning. In *National Security*, conifer plantations are created mainly in mountain and moorlands in Wales and Scotland, whilst existing heathland is targeted in England.

Go with the Flow and *Local Stewardship* create new forest area through planting broadleaved woodland on arable land; there is a higher conversion rate in *Go with the Flow,* which also converts Improved Grassland to broadleaved woodland. In *Go with the Flow*, *Nature@Work*, and *Green and Pleasant Land* woodland cover also expands in areas close to major conurbations as there are multiple ecosystem service benefits derived from locating forests there; these benefits are not just cultural, but also include hazard regulation. A further benefit is derived from shade provision in hotter summers in the high climate change scenario.

25.4.2.5 Freshwaters – Openwaters, Wetlands and Floodplains

Freshwater extent increases or remains the same in all the storylines, but for different reasons. In the more environmentally benign storylines (*Green and Pleasant Land*, *Nature@Work* and *Local Stewardship*), the restoration of old, traditional wetland and riverine habitats is an important goal. This has cross-benefits for biodiversity and recreation as well as flood mitigation, erosion regulation and water quality. Land cover adjacent to riverine habitats also benefits from conversion from Improved Grassland or Arable and Horticultural to wetland grazing or marshland. This pattern is further enhanced in the high climate change scenario, partly due to greater winter flood pressures.

In *World Markets* and *National Security*, freshwater expansion still occurs in the high climate change scenario, but is due to land abandonment from a lack of investment or inclination to adapt to greater flood incidence. Changes to freshwater habitats in *Go with the Flow* sit somewhere between the two contrasting approaches outlined above. In some areas, riverine habitat restoration is an important goal; in others a laissez-faire approach to climate change impacts is more prevalent.

25.4.2.6 Urban

The land cover of urban areas in the UK remains fairly constant in all the storylines except two (**Figure 25.19).** In *World Markets* a large population increase and a reduction in planning restrictions results in significant urban sprawl, with a greater concentration in the South East. In contrast, *Local Stewardship* is a storyline with a static population and a modest return to primary industries; this results in a pattern of counter-urbanisation which provides an opportunity for urban greening and 'softening'.

The development of greenspace in urban areas is a common theme for *Nature@Work*, *Green and Pleasant Land*, *Go with the Flow* and *Local Stewardship*. This is achieved

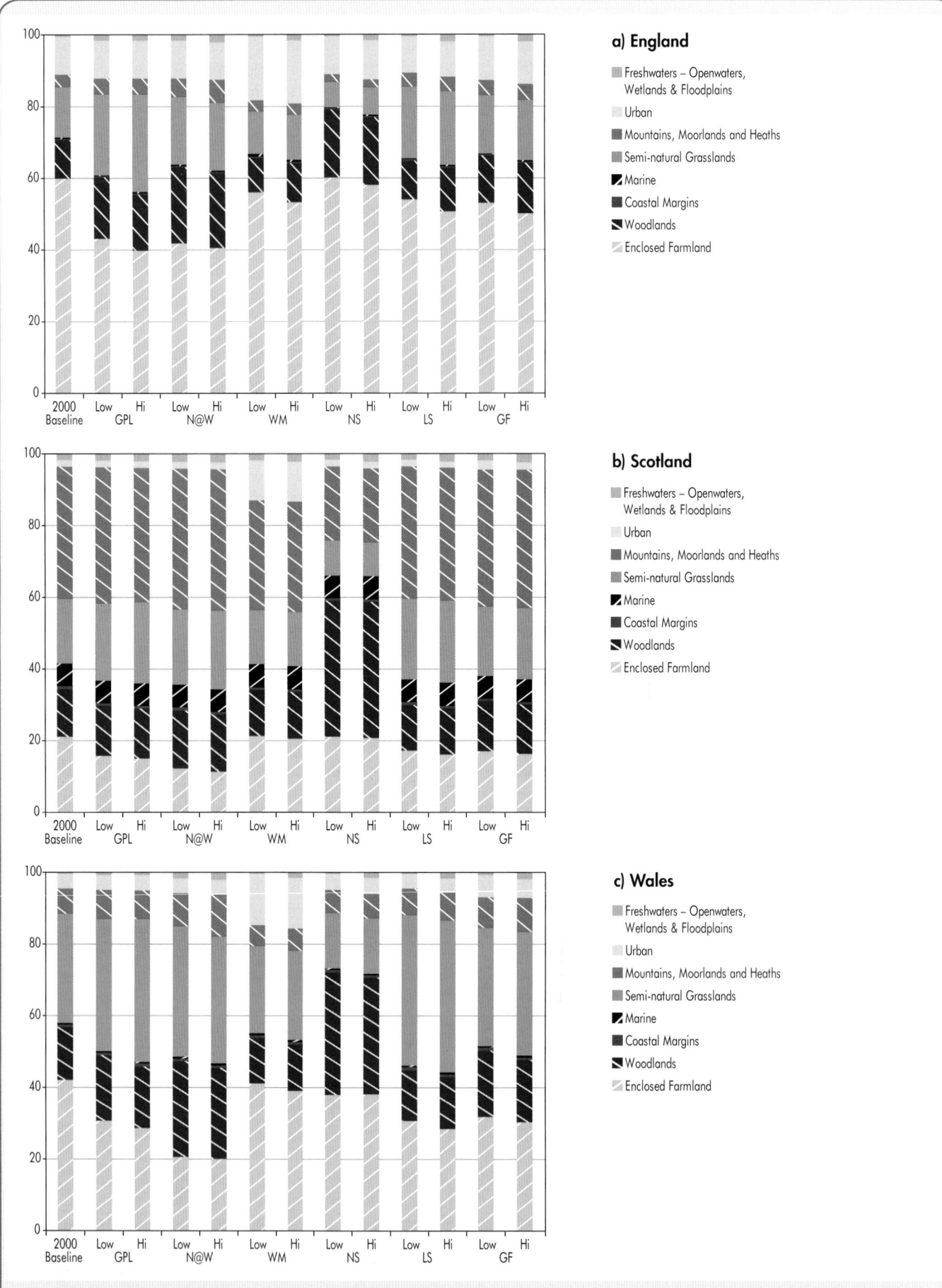

Figure 25.20 Projected change in stock of the Broad Habitats under the six scenarios, a) England, b) Scotland and c) Wales. The Scenarios are as follows: GPL = Green and Pleasant Land; N@W = Nature@Work; WM = World Markets; NS = National Security; LS = Local Stewardship; GF = Go with the Flow. Low and Hi refer to Low and High climate change impacts.

either through creating parks, gardens or open spaces (*Green and Pleasant Land, Go with the Flow*) or through the creation of green areas with a focus on food production as well as recreation (allotments, permaculture gardens and urban farms in *Nature@Work* and *Local Stewardship*). The management of water in urban areas is also considered important. In *Nature@Work, Green and Pleasant Land* and *Go with the Flow*, rivers, lakes and ponds are restored, protected, re-channelled and managed to ensure connectivity for wildlife through towns and cities. Recreation and flood mitigation is also improved.

25.4.2.7 Coastal Margins and Marine

The extent of Coastal Margin habitats is constant in all the storylines except for *World Markets*. In this narrative, industrial expansion in the form of ports, petrochemical plants, desalination plants, housing (particularly in the south) and tourism squeeze much of the remaining Coastal Margins habitat out. Better management of coastal habitats is assumed to occur in *Nature@Work, Green and Pleasant Land* and *Local Stewardship*, and all adopt a stronger ecosystem and land-/seascape approach to ecosystem service delivery; this results in the conversion of Arable and Horticultural , Improved Grassland and some conifer patches being to Coastal Margins habitats. In *Go with the Flow* (as well as *Nature@Work, Green and Pleasant Land* and *Local Stewardship*), climate change adaptation is important, and some Arable and Horticultural and Improved Grassland is lost to coast habitats due to the pressure of sea-level increases. Extreme sea-level rise results in a small amount of coastal habitat being lost to sea in all the storylines; this loss is probably lower in *Nature@Work* and *National Security* (both with very proactive adaptation schemes in place) and higher in *Green and Pleasant Land* (a laissez-faire approach) and *World Markets* (no planned adaptation).

The comparison between scenarios shown in **Figure 25.19** is exploratory and further research is required to establish more robust, evidence-based measures of the output of each service per unit area. Only then could reliable comparisons between scenarios be made using the different projections of land cover change. Two significant gaps in our knowledge that need to be resolved before the scenario work can be taken forward are a better understanding of the way modifications in habitat condition impact on service output, and the relative importance of the different habitats in terms of overall service output.

To illustrate the kind of analysis that might be possible if we had a better understanding of how the capacity to supply a service varied between habitats, the land cover projections for each scenario have been used to estimate differences in the amount of carbon stored in vegetation in 2060 (**Figure 25.21**). The estimates of carbon density for the major land cover types are taken from Milne & Brown (1997), and they have been assumed not to change over the period covered by the scenarios. For comparison, **Figure 25.21** includes an inset of the mapping by Milne & Brown (1997) for present conditions. Some of the differences between our mapping of the present (**Figure 25.21a**) and that of Milne & Brown (1997) arise because they used the Institute of Terrestrial Ecology (ITE) Land Classes to make their assessment, which

resulted in a somewhat coarser picture. However, in general terms there appears to be good agreement between the two maps. The high levels of vegetation carbon in the South East are apparent in both maps, as is the belt north east from Hampshire into Lincolnshire. The high values in the South West, Wales and north east Scotland are also apparent on both maps.

Figure 25.21 b & c show projections for vegetation carbon in 2060 for two scenarios, *Nature@Work* and *World Markets*. In both cases the low climate change projection has been used. The scenarios suggest that there are significant changes in the geographical patterns, with increases observed under *Nature@Work* in the south and west compared to the present. This is driven by the expansion of Woodland cover and the conversion of some Enclosed Farmland to Semi-natural Grasslands. The patterns under *World Markets* are much more similar to the present in the lowlands. For this scenario the greatest changes appear to be in the uplands where some increases are apparent due to abandonment and Woodland expansion.

The analysis presented in **Figure 25.21** clearly makes a number of simplifying assumptions about the nature of land cover change (e.g. that Woodland expansion has resulted in fully mature stands by 2060), and takes no account of the differences in carbon storage in soils. However, it illustrates the kind of analysis based on land cover that might be attempted if we had better unit area estimates of service output for particular habitats or habitat groups. The issue of how we can use projections of land cover change to model ecosystem service outcomes is also addressed in the UK NEA chapter dealing with the economic valuation of scenario outcomes (Chapter 26).

25.5 The UK NEA and Scenario Methodologies

25.5.1 Scenarios: Products or Processes?

Although the methods for scenario building developed in the MA set the context for the UK NEA work (see Ash *et al.* 2010), the complexities of such exercises should not be underestimated. Although widely applied and discussed, the use of scenarios is controversial and there is no single approach that is acceptable to all. Bradfield *et al.* (2005) observe, for example, that while scenarios have been used for more than three decades, a number of methodological issues are unresolved. In preparation for the UK NEA exercise, a reading of the large body of work concerned with scenario development (e.g. De Jouvenel 2000; Alcamo 2001; van Notten *et al.* 2003; Börjeson *et al.* 2006; Bishop *et al.* 2007; O'Neill *et al.* 2008; Wilkinson & Eidinow 2008) confirmed this view. The situation arises, Bradfield *et al.* (2005) suggest, because of the many conflicting definitions, principles and ideas about scenarios that exist in the literature, and the fact that terms such as 'planning', 'thinking', 'forecasting', 'analysis' and 'learning' are all variously used in describing

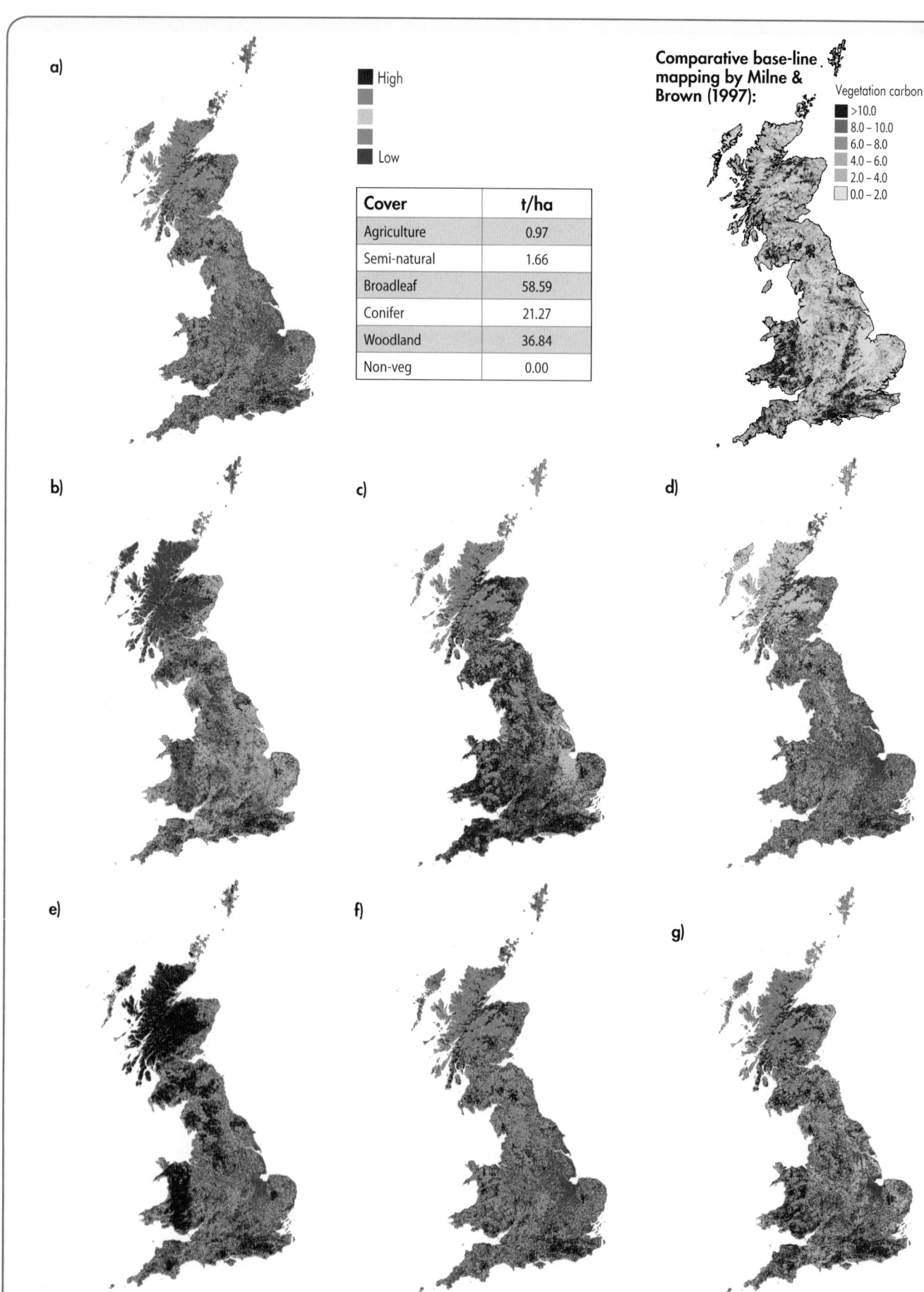

Cover	t/ha
Agriculture	0.97
Semi-natural	1.66
Broadleaf	58.59
Conifer	21.27
Woodland	36.84
Non-veg	0.00

Figure 25.21 Vegetation carbon densities using the low climate change projections, a) 2000 baseline, b) *Green and Pleasant Land*, c) *Nature@Work*, d) *World Markets*, e) *National Security*, f) *Local Stewardship*, and g) *Go with the Flow*.
Milne & Brown (1997): copyright (1997), map reproduced with permission of Elsevier.

what scenarios might be used for. The tension between the forecasting and learning perspectives is particularly acute, and it is one that has recurred throughout the current work.

O'Neill *et al.* (2008) have recently set out some of the issues, and suggest that a theme that is evident in recent debates is the dichotomy between two contrasting perspectives on the role of scenarios, namely 'scenarios as products and scenarios as processes'. Wilkinson & Eidinow (2008) make a similar point, and argue that often '... environmental scenarios are produced with enthusiasm but deployed with limited effect' because this dichotomy is not fully addressed. This situation comes about, they claim, because people often neglect to examine the nature and scope of the knowledge and beliefs that underlie the different scenario approaches, and as a result they fail to get to grips with 'wicked' problems that characterise debates about environmental change. They propose a new typology for scenario studies to help guide future work and resolve the tension between 'problem-focused' and 'actor-centric' approaches to scenario construction. It involves a more hybrid approach to scenario construction.

These discussions about the different purposes of scenario construction are relevant in any review of the approach used in the UK NEA, which has sought to assemble and make available the best current scientific information to users and stimulate new approaches to monitoring and planning for ecosystem services based on their importance for human well-being. It is useful, therefore, to consider the methodological questions surrounding scenarios in more detail so that the work can be better located in these different conceptual frameworks.

The 'product' perspective recognised by O'Neill *et al.* (2008) is one that views scenarios as mainly helping users to understand 'environmental outcomes produced, how they relate to the various factors driving them, and what the results tell us about the prospects for future environmental change, for impacts, and for mitigation' (O'Neill *et al.* 2008). This perspective often leads to the belief that scenarios ultimately have 'lives of their own, divorced from the processes that generated them...' (O'Neill *et al.* 2008). By contrast, the 'process-perspective' emphasises the importance of scenario building as a way of encouraging social learning within and between diverse groups, of finding synergies between different viewpoints, of consensus building, and of developing shared responsibilities for problem solving. From this perspective, the scenarios themselves are perhaps less important than the dialogue generated in their production, and the legacy that those dialogues leave.

Thus, although the MA framework provided a guide for the UK NEA, it was felt that the *process* aspect of the framework was one that needed greater emphasis in the UK. While the importance of deliberation is emphasised in the published overview of the MA approach, given the time that has elapsed since their publication, the MA scenarios tend now to be regarded more as products to be used, rather than modified and refined through further discussion. The tendency to treat the MA scenarios as a 'given' is strengthened by the fact that they were, to a large extent, model-based and are therefore inherently more difficult to manipulate in any follow-up study. It was therefore concluded that the MA scenarios could not

simply be customised or scaled down for UK NEA purposes, because this approach would not fully capture UK concerns.

The extent to which the MA approach to scenario building was essentially product- or process-orientated must be debated elsewhere. For those constructing the UK NEA scenarios, the important point was to pursue an approach that was most appropriate in the national context. Thus, it was considered important that the work should take account of, and build on, other national scenario exercises that had been undertaken, such as *Land Use Foresight* (FLUF 2010) and the UKCIP (Hulme *et al.* 2002). It was also felt that the scenarios should be built around a set of focal questions generated by potential users of the UK NEA outputs, and that the work should, where appropriate, reflect any differences between the countries that make up the UK. As a result, a purpose-built set of storylines has been constructed using a more deliberative, process-based approach.

It could be argued that the process/product dichotomy is not as stark as that described by other commentators, because it is clear that different types of approach may be needed at different points in the development of policy or management responses. The early stages of scenario building are inevitably exploratory and when different stakeholders are involved, they must involve a significant learning process, as people try to make sense of a complex range of drivers and driver interactions that describe different aspects of the future. If these shared understandings result in a distinct and interesting set of narratives that people can begin to work with (whether they have been involved in the scenario building or not), the scenarios may take on more of the character of a product—as they must if they are to contribute to the later phases of policy development. It is in these later phases when people start to use scenarios more as products to identify policy options (e.g. by asking such questions as, *'What would we do if we found ourselves in this future?'*), or to test identified policy options (as in, *'If we apply this policy idea, will it have the impact we want it to?'*). The key, it seems, to avoiding the problem that scenarios can be deployed with 'limited effect' (Wilkinson & Eidinow 2008) is to ensure that participants understand what stage of the policy cycle they are in, and how engaging with the scenarios can deliver the required outcomes.

One view of the current UK NEA scenarios is, therefore, that they are transitional between the process and product phases of development. The work presented here documents a range of concerns of potential users and translates them into a set of storylines that must be refined further. Although we have sought to quantify them, at this stage the mapping is intended more to help people examine their plausibility and implied contrasts, than to draw any firm conclusions about current policy or management approaches. The questions that further work needs to address must include: whether the contrasts represented by the different narratives sufficiently capture user concerns; whether their internal logics are sufficiently robust to justify the projections of change; how the process-response evidence on which they are based can be refined; and, how we might better quantify the scenario outcomes and the differences between the storylines so that the implications of the different sets of assumptions can be examined in detail.

25.5.2 Judging Success

Recent discussions of methodological questions have identified a second aspect of scenario construction that needs to be considered, namely: what criteria are used to judge the success of any exercise. Although it is widely acknowledged that scenario building is not about trying to predict the future, but is about identifying a range of possible futures that might unfold, notions of 'predictive success' often enter into and sometimes shape discussions—and these issues need to be addressed here when reviewing the outcomes of the UK NEA work.

In the context of climate change studies, Hulme & Dessai (2008) have looked at the 'predictive success' of scenarios alongside two other potential outcome measures, namely 'decision success' and 'learning success', and emphasised just how misleading it can be in scientific terms to regard them as the 'prophetic devices'. Problems include the fact that, by looking to predictive success we often try, inappropriately, to make a judgement about which scenario from a family of scenarios is 'better' or 'more accurate', when the actual outcomes are within the plausible or probable range of many of them. We might add that if we have to wait for outcomes to judge the success of a scenario study, then there is little point in building them in the first place. They therefore suggest that perhaps other ways of judging the success of scenarios are needed.

For Hulme & Dessai (2008), the idea of 'decision success' involves asking whether the judgments made on the basis of a scenario-building exercise were 'good ones'. They find this also to be problematic. Like notions of predictive efficacy, they feel that this measure also embodies an 'instrumentalist position' that essentially regards scenarios as products. These authors argue that measures based on 'decision success' only make sense if we move away from judging decisions by some kind of retrospective analysis of outcomes, to look at the robustness of the decision-making processes themselves. A key test, they suggest, is whether the scenario exercise allowed the full range of uncertainties surrounding an issue to be considered by the decision makers. This suggestion helps bring the assessment of the success of scenario building into the 'here and now', but as a measure it is difficult to apply, because we cannot know what should be included if situations are uncertain.

This is certainly the case with the UK NEA scenarios. It is clearly too soon to consider the nature of any decisions that might be made in relation to them. As indicated above, further deliberation with stakeholders is needed to ensure that they capture the full range of concerns. However, while the present work is still at a preliminary stage, it is clear that even in their present form, the scenarios do start to pose challenges that decision makers might want to consider and examine further. For example, the contrasts between *Green and Pleasant Land* and *Nature@Work* do seem to suggest that there might be gains in developing policies around ecosystem service rather than biodiversity and conservation alone, and that both are probably better than *Go with the Flow*.

Although difficult to measure, the extent to which scenario building leads to effective social learning is, according to Hulme & Dessai (2008), probably the most appropriate test of the success of such studies. In fact, this kind of measure is closer to the original intention of scenario studies, which was to introduce ideas about alternative and multiple views of possible futures into discussions so that different strategies and plans could be examined. Learning success is, they suggest, also more lasting that 'product outcomes', because these can rapidly become outdated as the relationships between the science, society and policy communities continue to evolve. In this context it is worth noting how many of the questions suggested in our consultations with potential users were about wanting to understand mechanisms and processes, rather than the implications for future trends (**Appendix 25.1**). These responses suggest that the UK NEA in general must address these broader social-learning or awareness-raising issues if progress is to be made.

Garb *et al.* (2008) have argued that if we recognise that scenarios 'shape and embed their social contexts', they can be used more effectively as decision-support tools. If we consider the set of focal questions suggested by the UK NEA stakeholders, then it is undoubtedly the case that they reflect the concerns of a particular interest group. They obviously focus heavily on ecosystem services and the conditions under which they might flourish or be diminished, and in many cases possibly give a higher priority to environmental issues than others might do. The UK NEA itself represents a particular environmental paradigm, one that seeks to explore a utilitarian view of nature. Thus, while further work might involve refining the storylines with UK NEA stakeholders, it is probably just as important to go beyond these groups to examine other reactions. All storylines will involve both 'goods' and 'bads', and only by talking to others might a richer understanding of the implications of particular sets of assumptions be established.

The argument about the importance of process in scenario development is not, it seems, just about encouraging greater levels of participation. As Wilkinson & Eidinow (2008) suggest, it is perhaps more about ensuring that participatory processes are *effective*. These authors reviewed current scenario typologies and concluded overall that a modified approach to the process of developing scenarios was needed. It is not simply a matter, they argue, of understanding who is involved and their respective world views, but understanding better the '... aims, intentions and underlying epistemological assumptions of those participating in the process' (Wilkinson & Eidinow 2008, p6). They proposed a reflexive interventionist or multi-agent-based approach (RIMA) to scenario building that tries to avoid simple consensus, but accepts that 'knowledge is multiple, temporary and dependent on context—with different points of view providing a constant challenge to any existing viewpoint or system' (Wilkinson & Eidinow 2008). Moss *et al.* (2010) have also argued that more pluralistic and iterative approaches to the construction of scenarios may be appropriate in the context of the climate change debate, in order to better explore and evaluate different adaptation needs and strategies, the options available for mitigation, and the understanding of feedbacks between biophysical and social systems. Both positions imply that future deliberations on the UK NEA scenarios must include wider circles of views.

The conclusion one may draw from these debates about scenario methodologies is that there is no 'best way' of building them, or any simple recipe that guarantees success. Having argued the case for RIMA, Wilkinson & Eidinow (2008), for example, 'draw back' from prescribing how the approach might be made operational. However, on the basis of their review, O'Neill *et al.* (2008) do usefully set out a number of points that those embarking on scenario construction might consider in relation to the lessons that might be drawn from recent debates (**Table 25.7**). These points are useful in judging the current work undertaken for the UK NEA.

The issue of transparency (**Table 25.7** point 2), for example, has been highlighted as an important part of the work, as well as the need to structure the exercise around a set of user-defined focal questions (point 1, **Table 25.7**). The need to include reference to social processes in the scenarios (point 4), so as to help understand different future transition pathways, was also acknowledged in emphasising the links that had to be made to the discussions of the response group (see Chapter 27). Finally, disaggregation of outputs (points 3 and 6, **Table 25.7**) was also flagged up as an early aim of the scenario work, as evidenced by the recognition that outputs would have to be differentiated across different types of users (especially to take account of the various 'country interests')

Table 25.7 Recommendations for Improving Scenario Development. Source: adapted from O'Neill *et al.* (2008).

1.	Focus scenario exercises on specific questions so that results from multiple models can be more illuminating.
2.	Enhance scenario transparency so as to enable extensions by users, rather than further expanding representation in global scenarios themselves.
3.	Incorporate relatively simple measures (such as sub-national disaggregation of income distributions and climate change impacts) to boost the equity sensitivity of scenarios.
4.	Recognise topics where social science inputs are becoming important for improving modelling and model relevance, such as providing a logic for how societies manage to transition from historical paths to the various future development paths foreseen in the scenarios, or developing measures of well-being which are independent of income levels, and include in global environmental scenario teams more representatives of social science professionals.
5.	Invest greater resources in assessing scenario results, and in understanding and overcoming the barriers to carrying out such assessment.
6.	Disaggregate the variety of global change decision makers targeted as audiences for scenarios.
7.	Develop an additional 'reflective interventionist' scenarios approach that involves different epistemologies for active learning in the public interest.
8.	Draw on the extensive toolkit of social science research methods to analyse the social work of scenarios.
9.	Create new institutions and scenario activities that can adapt and extend global scenarios to specific, often local or regional decision contexts.
10.	Create fora in which scenario practitioners, modellers, decision-makers, and social scientists of various kinds can discuss the process of scenario construction and use.

---

and across space (to help identify how potential synergies and trade-offs express themselves and to understand where particular sensitivities lie in relation to different drivers of change). The value of making scenarios spatially explicit was not one that was highlighted as important by O'Neill *et al.* (2008) and others. Nevertheless, it is an important feature of the UK NEA exercise, because mapping outcomes could potentially help make assumptions clearer and allow plausibility to be looked at more closely (cf. Hulme & Dessai 2008). It has also enabled economic valuation tools to be applied in the context of scenario work, and provide insights into the sorts of marginal gains and losses that might be associated with different kinds of future (Chapter 26).

The issue of confronting and building on the different world views represented by the various interest groups associated with the UK NEA (point 7) was also captured by the attempt to ground the exercise on a set of focal questions. To help in this process, those consulted were encouraged to forecast and extrapolate from the present using different assumption sets, and also to 'backcast' from some set of desired goals. With backcasting, users are asked to identify some target future and think through the kinds of pathway that might achieve it, and identify the barriers that might lie in the way. However, our work with stakeholders and expert contributors to the UK NEA has revealed that there are very different world views, and the tension between those who see scenarios mainly from the 'product' and 'process' perspectives was certainly evident in the group.

It has been recognised from the outset, however, that it was important that the UK NEA should leave a legacy, and it is clear that part of this must be the social learning that is begun or achieved through the initiative. Many of the remaining points made in **Table 25.7** concern these social and institutional issues, and while they are important, they are not ones that can be resolved just by devising the scenarios. Rather, they must be judged in the context of the success of the UK NEA as a whole. The gaps in knowledge that we faced in building scenarios are the same gaps that have be to confronted by the whole assessment exercise, and ultimately the robustness of the scenarios depends on the strength of the current evidence base that is available.

25.6 Working with the UK NEA Scenarios

The UK will not be guaranteed the ecosystem services it needs automatically, and all parts of the country will not necessarily be guaranteed access to these services. Consequently, the government and its stakeholders will need to work together to make choices about the levels and patterns of investment required to secure the quality of life that we want now and for future generations. Making choices of this type is not always straightforward. In a world of rapid change and increasing uncertainty, it can be difficult to know what the right choices are, and different stakeholders may have different priorities and ideas about what is desirable or necessary, and may not have a shared view of how the future will develop.

It is in these uncertain and complex situations that scenarios studies can be most useful, if they can help stimulate a strategic conversation between different stakeholder groups. While such conversations must, of necessity, be wide-ranging, three areas stand out as important starting points for discussion: identifying the choices that may have to be made; monitoring and interpreting the significance of change; and, finally, reviewing and testing the implications of different policy and project options.

The scenarios provide a range of possible futures in which the challenge will be to secure benefits from ecosystem services while simultaneously protecting the habitats and biodiversity that provide them. Exploring society's capacity to achieve that balance in the different scenarios can help identify the important choices that we need to make. One way to do this is to identify the questions of strategic importance for the future and test them across the scenario set. Different stakeholder groups will want to identify issues that reflect their own strategic priorities, but they may also want to consider a range of generic questions such as the following:

- How resilient are ecosystem services in each scenario? Are specific categories of ecosystem services more at risk in one scenario than another? Why might this be the case? How should we respond to mitigate risks?
- How resilient are the UK and its different geographical areas in each scenario? Are there specific shocks or events that affect the resilience of different types of locality?
- Is there anything that can be done now in order to mitigate potential shocks? Are there particular policies or approaches that we should explore now to increase resilience?
- Who is responsible for maintaining ecosystem services, and are there sufficient incentives for them continue to do so in each scenario?
- How do society and markets ascribe economic value to ecosystem services in the different futures? Is the economic value of ecosystem services understood sufficiently well now to help us make future decisions?
- Which habitats are under threat in the different scenarios and what are the impacts on ecosystem services? What are the possible impacts on human well-being?
- What do the scenarios tell us about the environmental management practices that need to be in place to protect habitats, ecosystems and biodiversity? Are current management practices sufficient?

The valuation exercise undertaken during the Assessment (Chapter 26) has, for example, illustrated how the framework we use for valuation can affect policy choices. It showed, for example, how interpretation of scenario outcomes (and by implication, policy decisions) can be different, depending on whether we consider only marginal changes in market values or total monetised values, which also includes monetary estimates for non-market goods. Response options in the UK NEA also emphasise the importance of looking closely at the frameworks in which choices are made (Chapter

27). This analysis used the scenarios to identify how the key characteristics, behaviours and practices of a range of stakeholders (governments, local authorities, the private sector, NGOs, civil society organisations and individuals and communities) differ in each scenario. **Table 25.8** highlights the key differences (and similarities) between the storylines in terms of the major policy response typologies: *Foundational* (or *knowledge*) responses form the basis for *Enabling* responses (legislation, policies, institutions, governance and behaviour) which in turn provide the preconditions for *Instrumental* responses (markets and incentives, technology). The storylines help to characterise and possibly envisage the ecosystem service consequences of our current and/or imminent policy responses. Another important issue that is highlighted in the scenarios that deliver the highest level of ecosystem services is that certain responses are likely to require a large degree of integration as well as collaboration between the numerous actors.

The defining characteristics, behaviours and practices of each storyline provide a range of indicators that can be used to monitor the future direction of travel, and perhaps understand what might be driving change. Thus, if the prevailing market condition is growth, but with greater exposure to global fluctuations, the prevailing policy approach is a shrinking of the welfare state and strong, centralised national government. In addition, if the prevailing approach to technology is that industry drives innovation for private profit, it might be argued that the world is on a trajectory which is more likely to lead to *World Markets* than any other scenario. In that case, scientists and policy makers can review the consequences of *World Markets* on ecosystem services provision and identify where the UK needs to strengthen its approach to securing services. Conversely, if technology drives sustainable development, with a stronger welfare state and a focus on the sustainable management of natural resources, but stable economic growth is maintained, then a *Nature@Work*-type trajectory may be more likely.

Finally, the scenarios can be used to test policies and projects designed to secure ecosystem services provision. Once a stakeholder group has identified a possible approach they can, for example:

- carry out a SWOT analysis of the project or policy in each scenario, perhaps from different stakeholder perspectives;
- identify the factors supporting—and barriers holding back—successful implementation of the policy or project in each scenario;
- clarify how the policy or project needs to be modified in each scenario to achieve its goal; and
- identify the aspects of the policy or project design that are robust across all scenarios and the aspects which need further modification or design work to provide flexibility over the range of futures.

The UK NEA scenarios are not predictions. In themselves, they are not offered here as a set of choices about what futures we might or ought to pursue. Rather, their purpose is to capture what we know about the way ecosystem services could change if we make different assumptions about the various driving forces that impact upon them. By working

Table 25.8 Key differences and similarities between the storylines in terms of the major policy response typologies.

	Knowledge	Legislation	Policies, institutions and governance	Behaviour	Markets and incentives	Technologies and practice	Voluntary actions
Green and Pleasant Land	Investment in green technologies; less focus on biotechnology. Romanticist view of Nature.	Strong links to EU and global Biodiversity obligations.	Globally minded government; slow down in investment in public services (e.g. more people switch to private health care).	Stewardship and responsibility; intrinsic values of nature. Pride in beautiful landscapes. NIMBYism rife.	Support for agri-env schemes.	Adoption of sustainable management in agriculture and woodlands.	In support of maintaining and conservbing the landscape. Local pride drives volunteers.
Nature@Work	Technology industry focused on sustainable resource use.	Strong links to EU and global obligations – focus on ecosystem function rather than biodiversity.	Globally minded government; investment in public services. Commitment to global free trade.	Utilitarian view, recognising the importance of 'nature's services'. Society seeks high standard of living but through sustainable methods.	Growth of market delivering economic progress.	Industry drives technological innovation in the context of resource use.	Strong sense of local and global community; people equally willing to volunteer for local and global environmental projects.
World Markets	Technology largely driven by private profit motive.	Reversal of devolution. Deregulated markets. Few environmental policies.	Shrinking of the welfare state. Strong, centralised national government. Deregulation of environmental protection.	Narrowly utilitarian, failing to recognise values of nature. Material consumption and greed good. Gesellschaft (compared with Local Stewardship).	Growth of market but greater exposure to global fluctuations.	(Global) Industry driving technological innovation for private profit.	Very little volunteering.
National Security	Technology industry focused on sustainable resource use.	Trade barriers and protectionist measures to protect UK interests.	Protectionist policies to protect UK interests.	Society values landscapes and features of nature that characterise 'national identity'.	Protection-led growth, but periods of stagnation and global crises. Markets protected.	UK industry focused on UK problems – state funded in some areas.	Very little volunteering; some support for community allotments and small horticultural enterprises.
Local Stewardship	Sustainability: understanding management of natural resources. Pragmatism, and respect for knowledge of 'older generation'.	Tight controls on immigration. Greater devolution to local governments.	Tax raising powers devolved to local levels.	Utilitarian view, recognising the importance of 'nature's services'. Self-sacrifice more prevalent. Gemeinschaft.	Slow but steady economic growth. Incentives for small families.	Technology focuses on self-sufficiency and construction goods.	Strong sense of community, voluntary action starts and often ends locally; however, strong sense of place in world.
Go with the Flow	Rapid development of technology through government investment. Increasing understanding of environmental issues.	Oscillation between pro-EU and more narrowly nationalistic approaches.	Oscillation between pro-EU and more narrowly nationalistic policies. Slow shrinking of public services.	Society values landscapes and features of nature that characterise 'national identity'. Split appreciation of nature – increasing appreciation but still industrial elite sceptical.	Growth of market but greater exposure to global fluctuations.	Technology driven by government investment.	Volunteering popular in some areas; increasingly shift towards localism and away from global environmentalism.

with scenarios we can try to understand how sensitive these systems are and start to think about how we might intervene if we need to protect or restore them. However, scenarios are only as good as our understandings of the way in which ecosystem structure and function support the output of ecosystem services. Unfortunately in many cases we lack this vital knowledge. Thus an important next step would be to develop a new generation of data-driven, multifunctional ecosystem models to explore the future of ecosystem services in the UK.

References

Alcamo, J. (2001) Scenarios as tools for international environmental assessments. Environmental issue report: 24. European Environment Agency, Copenhagen.

Alcamo, J., Vuuren, D. v., Ringler, C., Alder, J., Bennett, E. M., Lodge, D. M., Masui, T., Morita, T., Rosegrant, M., Sala, O. E., Schulze, K., Zurek, M., Eickhout, B., Maerker, M., & Kok, K. (2006) 6: Methodology for Developing the MA Scenarios. In S.

R. Carpenter, P. L. Pingali, E. M. Bennett, & M. B. Zurek (Eds.), Ecosystems and Human Well-being: Scenarios (pp. 145-172). Island Press, Washington, D.C.

Ash, N., Blanco, H., Brown, C., Garcia, K., Henrichs, T., Lucas, N., Raudsepp-Hearne, C., Simpson, D., R., Scholes, R., Tomich, T.P., Vira, B. & Zurek, M. (eds) (2010) Ecosystems and human well-being: a manual for assessment practitioners. Island Press.

Audsley, E., Pearn, K., Simota, C., Cojocaru, G., Koutsidou, E., Rousevell, M., Trnka, M. & Alexandrov, V. (2006) What can scenario modelling tell us about future European scale agricultural land use, and what not? *Environmental Science and Policy,* **9**, 148–162.

Beddington, J. (2009) Land use futures – land use policy journal introduction. *Land Use Policy,* **26**, S1-S1.

Bishop, P., Hines, A. & Collins, T. (2007) The current state of scenario development: An overview of techniques. *Foresight,* **9**, 5–25.

Börjeson, L., Höjer, M., Dreborg, K., Ekvall, T. & Finnveden, G. (2006) Scenario types and techniques: Towards a user's guide. *Futures,* **38**, 723–739.

Bradfield, R., Wright, G., Burt, G., Cairns, G. & van der Heijden, M. (2005) The origins and evolution of scenario techniques in long range business planning. *Futures,* **37**, 795–812.

Carpenter, S., Pingali, P., Bennett, E., & Zurek, M., eds. (2006b) Ecosystems and human well-being: Scenarios, volume 2, pp 561. Island Press, London.

Cork, S., Peterson, G., Bennett, E., Petschel-Held, G. & Zurek, M. (2006a) Synthesis of the storylines. *Ecology and Society,* **11**, 11.

Cork, S., Peterson, G., Petschel-Held, G., Alcamo, J., Alder, J., Bennett, E., Carr, E., Deane, D., Nelson, G., Ribeiro, T., Butler, C., Mendiondo, E., Oluoch-Kosura, W. & Zurek, M. (2006b) Four Scenarios. Ecosystems and Human Well-being: Scenarios, 223–294pp. Island Press.

Creedy, J., Doran, H., Duffield, S., George, N. & Kass, G. (2009) England's natural environment in 2060 – issues, implications and scenarios. Natural England, Sheffield.

Dahlstrom, K. & Salmons, R. (2005) Building Economic and Social Information for Examining the Effects of Climate cHange - BESEECH: Generic socio-economic scenarios. Building Economic and Social Information for Examining the Effects of Climate cHange. Final report. Policy Studies Institute, London, 59pp.

De Jouvenel, H. (2000) A brief methodological guide to scenario building. *Technological Forecasting and Social Change,* **65**, 37–48.

Environment Agency (2001) Water resources for the future: a strategy for England and Wales. Environment Agency, London.

Environment Agency (2009) Water for people and the environment: Water resources strategy for England and Wales. [online]. Available at: <http://publications.environment-agency.gov.uk/pdf/GEHO0309BPKX-E-E.pdf> [Accessed 17.03.11].

European Observation Network for Territorial Development and Cohesion (2007) Scenarios on the territorial future of Europe. [online]. <www.espon.eu/main/Menu_Projects/Menu_AppliedResearch/climate.html> [Accessed 13.04.11].

FEUFAR (The Future of European Fisheries and Aquaculture Research) (2008) Global review of horizon scanning and foresight exercises in the marine sector. 1–42.

FLUF (Foresight Land Use Futures) (2010) Making the most of land in the 21st century: Final project report. The Government Office for Science, London.

Garb, Y., Pulver, S. & VanDeveer, S. (2008) Scenarios in society, society in scenarios: Toward a social scientific analysis of storyline-driven environmental modeling. *Environmental Research Letters,* **3**, 045015.

Godet, M. (2000) The art of scenarios and strategic planning: Tools and pitfalls. *Technological Forecasting and Social Change,* **65**, 3–22.

Hulme, M. & Dessai, S. (2008) Predicting, deciding, learning: Can one evaluate the 'success' of national climate scenarios? *Environmental Research Letters,* **3**, 045013.

Hulme, M., Jenkins, G.J., Lu, X., Turnpenny, J.R., Mitchell, T.D., Jones, R.G., Lowe, J., Murphy, J.M., Hassell, D., Boorman, P., McDonald, R. & Hill, S. (2002) Climate Change Scenarios for the United Kingdom: The UKCIP02 Scientific Report, Tyndall Centre for Climate Change Research, School of Environmental Sciences, University of East Anglia, Norwich, UK. 120pp.

Langmead, O., McQuatters-Gollop, A. & Mee, L. D. (2007) European lifestyles and marine ecosystems: exploring challenges for managing Europe's seas. University of Plymouth Marine Institute, Plymouth.

MA (Millennium Ecosystem Assessment) (2005) Ecosystems and human well-being: Synthesis. Island Press, London.

Milne, R. & Brown, T.A. (1997) Carbon in the Vegetation and Soils of Great Britain. *Journal of Environmental Management,* **49**, 413–433.

Moore, K., Haines-Young, R., Paterson, J., Potschin, M. & Silfwerbrand, G. (2010): Assessing User Needs Of the NEA Scenarios through Focal Questions. CEM Working Paper No 4.

Moss, R., Edmonds, J., Hibbard, K., Manning, M., Rose, S., Vuuren, D., Carter, T., Emori, S., Kainuma, M., Kram, T., Meehl, G., Mitchell, J., Nakicenovic, N., Riahi, K., Smith, S., Stouffer, R., Thomson, A., Weyant, J. & Wilbanks, T. (2010) The next generation of scenarios for climate change research and assessment. *Nature,* **463**, 747–756.

Murphy, J.M., Sexton, D.M.H., Jenkins, G.J., Booth, B.B. B., Brown, C.C., Clark, R. T., Collins, M., Harris, G.R., Kendon, E.J., Betts, R.A., Brown, S. J., Humphrey, K.A., McCarthy, M.P., McDonald, R.E., Stephens, A., Wallace, C., Warren, R., Wilby, R., Wood, R. (2009), UK Climate Projections Science Report: Climate change projections. Met Office Hadley Centre, Exeter.

Nakicenovic, N., Davidson, O., Davis, G., Grübler, A., Kram, T., Lebre La Rovere, E., Metz, B., Morita, T., Pepper, W., Pitcher, H., Sankovski, A., Shukla, P., Swart, R., Watson, R. & Dadi, Z. (2009) IPCC special report on emissions scenarios. Cambridge University Press, Cambridge.

O'Neill, B., Pulver, S., VanDeveer, S. & Garb, Y. (2008) Where next with global environmental scenarios? *Environmental Research Letters,* **3**, 1–4.

Office of Science & Technology (2003) Foresight Futures 2020: Revised scenarios and guidance.Office of Science & Technology, London.

ONS (Office of National Statistics) (2010) UK national population projections – principals and variants, 2008–2083. [online]. Available at: <http://www.statistics.gov.uk/nationalprojections/flash_pyramid/projections.html> [Accessed 04.04.11].

Paterson, J.S., Haines-Young, R., Potschin, M., Moore, K. & Silfwerbrand, G. (2010) The utility of existing scenario frameworks for the National Ecosystem Assessment. Interim Report, May 2010, CEM Working Paper No 2, 11 pp.

Pinnegar, J., Viner, D., Hadley, D., Dye, S., Harris, M. & Simpson, F. (2006) Alternative future scenarios for marine ecosystems: technical report. Centre for Environment, Fisheries and Aquaculture Science, Lowestoft.

Prime Minister's Strategy Unit (2004) Net benefits: a sustainable and profitable future for UK fishing. London.

Raskin P., Banuri, T., Gallopin, G., Gutman, P., Hammond, A., Kates, R. & Swart, R. (2002) Great Transition – The Promise and Lure of the Times Ahead. Stockholm Environment Institute, Sweden.

Ritchey, T. (2010) General morphological analysis – a general method for non-quantified modelling. [online]. Available at: <http://www.swemorph.com/pdf/gma.pdf> [Accessed 17.03.11].

Rounsevell, M., Reginster, I., Araujo, M.B., Carter, T., Dendoncker, N., Ewert, F., House, J., Kankaanpaa, S., Leemans, R., Metzger, M., Schmit, C., Smith, P. & Tuck, G. (2006) A coherent set of future land use change scenarios for Europe. *Agriculture, Ecosystems and Environment,* **114**, 57–68.

Rounsevell, M. & Metzger, M. (2010) Developing qualitative scenario storylines for environmental change assessment. *Wiley Interdisciplinary Reviews: Climate Change,* **1**(4), 606–619.

Settele, J., Hammen, V., Hulme, P., Karlson, U., Klotz, S., Kotarac, M., Kunin, W.E., Marion, G., O'Connor, M., Petanidou, T., Peterson, K., Potts, m., Pritchard, H., Pysek, P., Rounsevell, M., Spangenberg, J., Steffan-Dewenter, N., Sykes, M.T., Vighi, A., Zobel, M. & Kühn, I. (2010) ALARM: Assessing Large-scale environmental Risks for biodiversity with tested Methods. *Gaia-Ecological Perspectives for Science and Society,* **14**, 69–72.

UKCIP (UK Climate Impacts Programme) (2001) Socio-economic scenarios for climate change impact assessment: A guide to their use in the UK Climate Impacts Programme. UKCIP, Oxford.

UNEP & RIVM (United Nations Environment Programme & National Institute of Public Health and the Environment)(2003). Four scenarios for Europe. Based on UNEP's third Global Environment Outlook. UNEP/DEIA&EW/TR.03-10 and RIVM 402001021.

van Notten, P.W.F., Rotmans, J., van Asselt, M.B.A. & Rothman, D.S. (2003) An updated scenario typology. *Futures,* **35**, 423–443.

Volkery, D.A. (2007) Land use scenarios for Europe – Qualitative and quantitative analysis on a European scale. European Environment Agency, Copenhagen.

Westhoek, H., van den Berg, M. & Bakkes, J. (2006) Scenario development to explore the future of Europe's rural areas. *Agriculture, Ecosystems and Environment,* **114**, 7–20.

Wildlife Conservation Society (2007) Futures of the Wild. WCS, New York.

Wilkinson, A. & Eidinow, E. (2008) Evolving practices in environmental scenarios: A new scenario typology. *Environmental Research Letters,* **3**, 1–11.

Appendix 25.1 User Responses for Focal Questions

Topic	Provisioning	Regulating	Cultural
Cross-cutting issues across all services (Provisioning, Regulating and Cultural)	What will be the impact of increased renewable energy production on ecosystem services, e.g. impact of increased areas of bioenergy crops and increased deployment of marine environments for wind/wave/tidal power and algae farming? Response		
	What are the possible roles of market-based instruments, such as habitat banking, in biodiversity protection and in the management of species adaptation to climate change? Response		
	How will our view of the 'countryside' from towns change in a changing climate? Landscape, Cultural		
	How will different environmental drivers affect service delivery? General		
	What are the synergies and trade-offs between different services? General		
	What are the likely impacts on urban biodiversity that could occur as a result of climate change, and could the effects of multiple drivers for change result in cumulative impacts?		
	What will be the impact of non native invasive species, including new pests and diseases? (There are the obvious problem species like Japanese knotweed but there are others that may be lying dormant or still in their population lag phase that may be able to benefit from climate change. Phytophthora is of particular concern and could have widespread impacts as it spreads geographically and taxonomically).		
	How will the management of habitat composition within an area, to maximise service production, be achieved? i.e. balancing extent of habitat according to service provision. Response		
	Impact of changes in habitat extent—how will the proposed expansion of woodland/forest cover in the UK impact of the provision of key ecosystem services?		
	How do synergies and trade-offs between services vary according to scale/management unit? Response		
	Climate change scenario—what would be the impact of a specific set of UK climate change predictions (many options to consider) by a specific year (2050?) on the continued delivery of provisioning and regulating services across a range of UK broad ecosystems? Sustainability		
	Will people be more dependent on ecosystem services and will they be aware of this. Response		
	What percentage of GDP will be made up by Ecosystem Services Economic		
	Will the coastal defence ability of Coastal Margin habitats be an increasing or a decreasing component of coastal flood defence (for Urban, SNG, Farmland etc.) under predicted rates of sea-level rise?		
	What are the services we should be getting from elsewhere?		
	Do we make policy that relies on and uses ecosystems or relies on technology and protects the 'best bits' of ecosystems?		
	What happens if you implement all the sustainable management option chapters in the UK NEA?		
	Will reversal of habitat fragmentation (e.g. through networks) affect services?		
	What will be the consequences of focusing on enhancing only those ecosystem services that we can value economically?		
	How will land use conflict impact on ecosystem services?		

Topic	Provisioning	Regulating	Cultural
Issues cross-cutting habitats	How can we change consumer behaviour to recognise the new 'reality' of agriculture in a changing climate and global food shortage situation?	How can we integrate climate adaptation strategies, energy needs and waste management together with maintenance of quality habitats to ensure continuity of ecosystem regulation? Response	How best can we encourage people to value natural ecosystems and landscape when their priorities are on short term crises? Response
	How best can we integrate the issues of climate change (adaptation and mitigation), energy security and price and global economic drivers to deliver a viable UK agriculture industry fit for the future?	How can we create multi-functional landscapes to promote regulating services alongside provisioning and cultural?	What is the role and significance of different habitats (and combination of habitats) in contributing to cultural services?
	How will food production impact on other services?	Are regulating services considered to be as important as provisioning and cultural to a general audience? If not how can their importance best be communicated?	Is there a conflict between public perception of culturally valuable habitats and landscapes and those habitats required for other services such as biodiversity and carbon storage?
	Will issues of food security and reducing carbon footprint of food prioritise food production above other services?	Green Belt provides a wide range of regulating, provisioning and cultural services that contribute to the quality of life in urban areas. Can ecosystem assessment help to inform decisions on future Green Belt use and designations? Response	
	Will impacts be limited to restricted geographical areas and other services prioritised elsewhere? or will a balance between services be attempted generically?	How would relaxation of green belt regulation and increased urbanisation in these areas affect the ecosystem service provision (of all types) in farmland and grassland—what are the trade-offs?	
	Given the predicted challenges of climate change and an increasing population creating possible food shortages, the UK appears to be well positioned to play a key role in meeting, not just UK food needs, but also global food demands. What can be done to use land to meet these demands—to produce more but at the same time to have less of an impact on the environment? Response		
	How do we manage the need for resilient habitats for climate change—should we have thresholds beyond which the objective of conservation of existing ecosystems change to an objective of redefining future ecosystem provision from an area? Response		
	How do we trade off the impacts on ecosystems overseas against domestic impacts when trying to secure national food, fibre (timber) and bioenergy supplies?		
	Does food security prevent change of land use from agriculture?		
	Does global trade in commodities (e.g. food and timber) remain the same, increase or decrease?		
	How will we prioritise energy verses food security from land?		

Topic	Provisioning	Regulating	Cultural
	What would 70% food security mean for UKs ecosystems?		
	How will global food prices impact on ecosystem services?		
	How should we be producing food without destroying ecosystems?	How will biomass demands in semi-natural habitats, including inshore waters, impact on biodiversity and other ecosystem services?	
	What impact will new crops have on UK's ecosystems?	What will be the consequences of recasting biodiversity targets in terms of ecosystem services? General	
	What will be the impact of low carbon agriculture?	How may new policies such as habitat banking enhance ecosystem services?	
	What would be the impact of another foot and mouth outbreak?	What would a shift towards managing BAP habitats and SSSIs for complexity and heterogeneity deliver in terms of ecosystem services?	
	What would a shift to naturalistic grazing / re-wilding deliver?	Do future climates emerge in line with expectations (projections)?	
	What impact will loss of single farm payments have on ecosystem services?	What habitat has most potential to sequester carbon?	
	How will new energy technology affect society (e.g. wind, solar, wave)?	How will future scenarios impact on the integrity of the ozone layer / protection it brings?	
	How will future UK energy policy impact on ecosystems?	How do ecosystems modify atmospheric concentrations of air pollution in the future?	
	How would large-scale release of chemical, biological, radiological and nuclear materials impact on ecosystems?	What would 'fixing' diffuse pollution deliver for ecosystem services?	
	What will the impact of continuing atmospheric nitrogen pollution (including methane) be on ecosystem services?	How do different amounts of habitat per nation affect what is important? (e.g. Wales has little arable)	
			What is the impact of public attitude change to environmental issues?
			Does leisure time increase or decrease? Is it spent inside or outside?
			How do people react to a changing landscape? How does its value change?
			What are the ecosystem service implications of a continuing growth in leisure use of the countryside?
			How does one 'account' for cultural services in future scenarios (e.g. is forest increase at the expense of grassland good)?

Topic	Provisioning	Regulating	Cultural
	How do we manage the need for resilient habitats for climate change—should we have thresholds beyond which the objective of conservation of existing ecosystems change to an objective of redefining future ecosystem provision from an area? Response	Are carbon stocks in soil in these habitats increasing, decreasing or remaining stable? Are there land-use trends that are likely to change the current situation with regard to soil carbon stocks? What are the net greenhouse gases fluxes for these habitats and how can they be optimised?	
Mountains, Moorlands, Heaths	WALES – How do the Common Agriculture Policy and Glastir agri-environmental scheme affect upland ecology and services?		WALES – For cultural services and recreation what are the renewable energy and 'landscape' Trade-offs?
Semi-natural Grasslands	Are semi-natural grasslands becoming more or less productive in terms of meat and milk production per unit of greenhouse gases emissions (carbon dioxide equivalent)? What are the reasons for any increase or decrease in production efficiency where production per unit of greenhouse gas emissions is used as the measure of efficiency? Trends	What trends in management practices for semi-natural grasslands are evident if any and what are the primary drivers for these trends? What are the implications of any trends observed for emissions of greenhouse gases from grassland and the efficiency of milk and meat production?	
	How can other services e.g. wild species diversity, carbon storage be enhanced whilst maintaining appropriate levels of production? Does enhancement require loss of production? Trade-offs	How do changes in stocking levels impact on regulating services?	
	How can providing provisioning services help maintain/improve quality/quantity of semi-natural grassland? Trade-offs	What are the optimum grazing levels for sheep and cattle for maintaining habitats, yet minimising GHG emissions?	
		How do you overcome the tacit view that 'improved grassland' improves all services?	
		How will continuing loss of species from grasslands (and other habitats) affect other services? Driver	
Enclosed Farmland	Is Enclosed Farmland more or less productive in terms of energy produced in edible output per unit of greenhouse gas emission? What are the primary causes of any trends in efficiency of production observed and how are these likely to change over the coming decades?	How is efficient natural nutrient cycling in the soil likely to be affected by temperature increase (1–2 degrees) from climate change?	What is the impact of increased tree planting on regulating and cultural services? Response
	Can long-term sustainability be incorporated into valuation of yield? i.e. accounting for regulating and supporting services as well as short term provisioning.	Are greenhouse gas emissions from Enclosed Farmland increasing or decreasing per unit of edible output (in joules) and what is the basis for any trends observed. What will the consequences for greenhouse gas emissions be if significantly more land than is currently the case is used for food production as compared to increasing production efficiency?	

Topic	Provisioning	Regulating	Cultural
	What are the implications of climate change, increasing water stress and a growing population on the productivity of farmland?	Some options within the agri-environment stewardship schemes are targeted at benefiting ecosystem services, for example in terms of soil quality, water quality, boosting pollinators and natural enemies. Under what (economic or otherwise) conditions is the policy of paying farmers for agri-environment schemes likely to change, or alternatively can it be predicted under what conditions farmers would stop taking the schemes up? And if they were no longer paid for or taken up, will this have a real and calculable effect on regulatory service provision?	
	How can we balance domestic food supply versus imports? Should we seek to limit domestic production to protect UK ecosystems and rely increasingly on imported food as population grows (and with it food demand) or should we maximise domestic production to protect overseas ecosystems?	Payment for water yields and flood regulation in land management?	
	How will most food be grown after climate change?		
	Does technological change continue to increase farming yields and therefore competition for land?		
	How could Common Agriculture Policy reform help delivery of services other than 'provisioning' from farmland?		
Woodland		Taking account of carbon fixation and nitrous oxide emissions, is the overall contribution of UK woodland to greenhouse gas emissions in terms of carbon dioxide equivalents positive, negative or neutral—and over what time scales? If positive, what is the annual amount of above and below ground carbon sequestered in UK woodland?	What kind of woodland do people prefer and value culturally? i.e. dense or well-spaced, coniferous or broadleaved, species-rich or species-poor?
		In converting semi-natural grassland to woodland, what are the net greenhouse gas emissions, and to what extent will they be affected by climate change?	
		In converting semi-natural grassland to woodland, what are the net GHG emissions, and to what extent will they be affected by climate change?	Seeing the trees for the wood? What is the impact of increased tree planting on regulating and cultural services?
		Does a market for carbon (or biofuels) develop to shape many land related decisions?	
		How do forests and woodland affect water regulation in catchments?	

Topic	Provisioning	Regulating	Cultural
		ENGLAND – Does forest cover expand as per policy aspirations?	
		SCOTLAND – Does forest cover expand as per policy aspirations?	
Rivers, lakes and lowland wetlands	What are the implications of climate change and a growing population on the availability of water for agriculture?	When will water quality or quantity become a limiting factor on development in the South East of England?	Helping the public value what lies below water level.
	Given the pressure for more food and more trees, how will future trends in farming practice and land management impact on water resources and flood control? Trade-offs	Will the Water Framework Directive help the regulating services in wetland systems?	
	WALES – How should English users pay for the ecosystem service of water production from Wales?		
	Is water abstraction from lowland rivers and wetlands likely to increase and what will be the impact on other services? Trade-offs		
Urban	Urban provisioning services appeared to peak in the 1940s. What are the viable options for increasing urban productivity? Where are the synergies with other ecosystem services and the trade-offs? Could investment in crop production through increased efforts in domestic gardens, allotments, containers on hard surfaces, green roofs etc. make a significant difference to all ecosystem service delivery?	Are housing densities likely to continue to increase across cities, and what will be the impact on regulating services?	How will our view of the 'countryside' from towns change in a changing climate?
		Tree planting is cited as a viable option for reducing temperatures and improving air quality. How viable is this option given the cost of planting and maintaining trees. How much would the added benefits to soil regulation, biodiversity and cultural services offset management costs?	Given the increasing cultural multiplicity of our towns and cities, how relevant will be the traditional native ecologies of the UK in the future?
	Ecological connectivity—green or grey infrastructure opportunities?	The extent of impermeable surfaces in urban areas is increasing severely compromising regulating services. How viable are the options for increasing areas of exposed soil and the use of permeable materials in urban centres and what are the additional benefits?	If future growth is restricted to existing urban areas, is development on green spaces with low recreational value likely to increase, and what will be the impacts on other cultural services, and regulating services?
		How can impermeable surfaces be reduced to improve services and benefits?	Which would people living in urban areas value more; local environmental services e.g. habitats for recreation which may be of poor quality or services which they have to travel to but may be more numerous and varied?
		How will loss of green infrastructure due to increasing housing density in urban centres impact on regulating and cultural services?	
		Arrest and reverse extent of impermeable surfaces—effects on hazard regulation and water quality	Valuing urban green spaces and trees?
Marine, coastal and estuarine	How will changes in terrestrial ecosystems impact on marine/coastal ecosystems delivery e.g. shell fisheries	What effect will the establishment of a marine conservation zone have?	How will sea-level rise alter the current coastal defence function provided by coastal margin habitats?
	Marine renewables and impacts		

Appendix 25.2 Indirect Drivers of Change and their Component Parts for Each of the Six UK NEA Scenarios

Green and Pleasant Land

Demographic	Socio-political	Economic	Science and technological	Cultural and religious
Population grows steadily through ageing and immigration. The average family size is larger than today.	Strong, centralised national government. Devolved power has been taken away. Markets have very little regulation; there are few environmental policies. The welfare state is reduced considerably.	Moderate economic growth with global free trade. Growth continues seemingly without any downturn.	Rapid development of technology through greater government investment.	A strong sense of stewardship and responsibility towards nature. The intrinsic value of biodiversity is heavily supported. The Judeo-Christian old-world view is disappearing.
Population grows steadily through ageing and immigration.	Local government gains considerable powers from Westminster and almost creates a mini-United States of GB & NI. A higher % of tax raised locally is spent locally.	Strong initial economic growth but characterised by occasional global market crises and periods of stagnation.	The private sector undercuts technology advancement and it flourishes but benefits a smaller proportion of society.	A strong utilitarian view dominates but also a greater understanding that nature supplies finite goods and services.
Population grows but slowly; immigration is very tightly controlled and only rich & skilled workers may enter the UK. Small families are encouraged. There is an expanding elderly cohort.	A globally-minded government. Decision-making is strongly influenced by EU and other countries ideas. Global issues are dealt with in a global manner. Public services are a priority.	Fairly static but reasonably healthy—most needs are catered for although excess supplies of goods are hard to come by.	Science and technology advancement slows in some areas (e.g. biotechnology) but in others increases (social network enhancements; green tech.).	Society values landscapes and much of the beauty nature provides—particularly those which embody national identity. In 'uglier' areas though nature is given less respect.
	The government interferes with the free market to protect UK interests and institutes trade barriers and other protectionist measures.	Modest growth but sustained and steady without any major perturbations.	Strong technological industry guided by improving sustainable resource use.	Utilitarian without greater understanding of nature's benefit to mankind. A return to the traditional Christian stewardship values.
	Government continues to move between bouts of EU-friendly policies and stronger nationalist identity. A slow removal of public services.		Moderate development but greater focus on self-sufficiency in food and construction goods.	

Nature@Work

Demographic	Socio-political	Economic	Science and technological	Cultural and religious
Population grows steadily through ageing and immigration. The average family size is larger than today.	Strong, centralised national government. Devolved power has been taken away. Markets have very little regulation; there are few environmental policies. The welfare state is reduced considerably.	Moderate economic growth with global free trade. Growth continues seemingly without any downturn.	Rapid development of technology through greater government investment.	A strong sense of stewardship and responsibility towards nature. The intrinsic value of biodiversity is heavily supported. The Judeo-Christian old-world view is disappearing.
Population grows steadily through ageing and immigration.	Local government gains considerable powers from Westminster and almost creates a mini-United States of GB & NI. A higher % of tax raised locally is spent locally	Strong initial economic growth but characterised by occasional global market crises and periods of stagnation.	The private sector undercuts technology advancement and it flourishes but benefits a smaller proportion of society.	A strong utilitarian view dominates but also a greater understanding that nature supplies finite goods and services.
Population grows but slowly; immigration is very tightly controlled and only rich & skilled workers may enter the UK. Small families are encouraged. There is an expanding elderly cohort.	A globally-minded government. Decision-making is strongly influenced by EU and other countries ideas. Global issues are dealt with in a global manner. Public services are a priority.	Fairly static but reasonably healthy—most needs are catered for although excess supplies of goods are hard to come by.	Science and technology advancement slows in some areas (e.g. biotechnology) but in others increases (social network enhancements; green technology)	Society values landscapes and much of the beauty nature provides—particularly those which embody national identity. In 'uglier' areas though nature is given less respect.
	The government interferes with the free market to protect UK interests and institutes trade barriers and other protectionist measures.	Modest growth but sustained and steady without any major perturbations.	Strong technological industry guided by improving sustainable resource use.	Utilitarian without greater understanding of nature's benefit to mankind. A return to the traditional Christian stewardship values.
	Government continues to move between bouts of EU-friendly policies and stronger nationalist identity. A slow removal of public services.		Moderate development but greater focus on self-sufficiency in food and construction goods.	

World Markets

Demographic	Socio-political	Economic	Science and technological	Cultural and religious
Population grows steadily through ageing and immigration. The average family size is larger than today.	Strong, centralised national government. Devolved power has been taken away. Markets have very little regulation; there are few environmental policies. The welfare state is reduced considerably.	Moderate economic growth with global free trade. Growth continues seemingly without any downturn.	Rapid development of technology through greater government investment.	A strong sense of stewardship and responsibility towards nature. The intrinsic value of biodiversity is heavily supported. The Judeo-Christian old-world view is disappearing.
Population grows steadily through ageing and immigration.	Local government gains considerable powers from Westminster and almost creates a mini-United States of GB & NI. A higher % of tax raised locally is spent locally	Strong initial economic growth but characterised by occasional global market crises and periods of stagnation.	The private sector undercuts technology advancement and it flourishes but benefits a smaller proportion of society.	A strong utilitarian view dominates but also a greater understanding that nature supplies finite goods and services.
Population grows but slowly; immigration is very tightly controlled and only rich & skilled workers may enter the UK. Small families are encouraged. There is an expanding elderly cohort.	A globally-minded government. Decision-making is strongly influenced by EU and other countries ideas. Global issues are dealt with in a global manner. Public services are a priority.	Fairly static but reasonably healthy—most needs are catered for although excess supplies of goods are hard to come by.	Science and technology advancement slows in some areas (e.g. biotechnology) but in others increases (social network enhancements; green technology)	Society values landscapes and much of the beauty nature provides—particularly those which embody national identity. In 'uglier' areas though nature is given less respect.
	The government interferes with the free market to protect UK interests and institutes trade barriers and other protectionist measures.	Modest growth but sustained and steady without any major perturbations.	Strong technological industry guided by improving sustainable resource use.	Utilitarian without greater understanding of nature's benefit to mankind. A return to the traditional Christian stewardship values.
	Government continues to move between bouts of EU-friendly policies and stronger nationalist identity. A slow removal of public services		Moderate development but greater focus on self-sufficiency in food and construction goods.	

National Security

Demographic	Socio-political	Economic	Science and technological	Cultural and religious
Population grows steadily through ageing and immigration. The average family size is larger than today.	Strong, centralised national government. Devolved power has been taken away. Markets have very little regulation; there are few environmental policies. The welfare state is reduced considerably.	Moderate economic growth with global free trade. Growth continues seemingly without any downturn.	Rapid development of technology through greater government investment.	A strong sense of stewardship and responsibility towards nature. The intrinsic value of biodiversity is heavily supported. The Judeo-Christian old-world view is disappearing.
Population grows steadily through ageing and immigration.	Local government gains considerable powers from Westminster and almost creates a mini-United States of GB & NI. A higher % of tax raised locally is spent locally	Strong initial economic growth but characterised by occasional global market crises and periods of stagnation.	The private sector undercuts technology advancement and it flourishes but benefits a smaller proportion of society.	A strong utilitarian view dominates but also a greater understanding that nature supplies finite goods and services.
Population grows but slowly; immigration is very tightly controlled and only rich & skilled workers may enter the UK. Small families are encouraged. There is an expanding elderly cohort.	A globally-minded government. Decision-making is strongly influenced by EU and other countries ideas. Global issues are dealt with in a global manner. Public services are a priority.	Fairly static but reasonably healthy—most needs are catered for although excess supplies of goods are hard to come by.	Science and technology advancement slows in some areas (e.g., biotechnology) but in others increases (social network enhancements; green technology)	Society values landscapes and much of the beauty nature provides—particularly those which embody national identity. In 'uglier' areas though nature is given less respect.
	The government interferes with the free market to protect UK interests and institutes trade barriers and other protectionist measures.	Modest growth but sustained and steady without any major perturbations.	Strong technological industry guided by improving sustainable resource use.	Utilitarian without greater understanding of nature's benefit to mankind. A return to the traditional Christian stewardship values.
	Government continues to move between bouts of EU-friendly policies and stronger nationalist identity. A slow removal of public services.		Moderate development but greater focus on self-sufficiency in food and construction goods.	

Local Stewardship

Demographic	Socio-political	Economic	Science and technological	Cultural and religious
Population grows steadily through ageing and immigration. The average family size is larger than today.	Strong, centralised national government. Devolved power has been taken away. Markets have very little regulation; there are few environmental policies. The welfare state is reduced considerably.	Moderate economic growth with global free trade. Growth continues seemingly without any downturn.	Rapid development of technology through greater government investment.	A strong sense of stewardship and responsibility towards nature. The intrinsic value of biodiversity is heavily supported. The Judeo-Christian old-world view is disappearing.
Population grows steadily through ageing and immigration.	Local government gains considerable powers from Westminster and almost creates a mini-United States of GB & NI. A higher percentage of tax raised locally is spent locally	Strong initial economic growth but characterised by occasional global market crises and periods of stagnation.	The private sector undercuts technology advancement and it flourishes but benefits a smaller proportion of society.	A strong utilitarian view dominates but also a greater understanding that nature supplies finite goods and services.
Population grows but slowly; immigration is very tightly controlled and only rich & skilled workers may enter the UK. Small families are encouraged. There is an expanding elderly cohort.	A globally-minded government. Decision-making is strongly influenced by EU and other countries ideas. Global issues are dealt with in a global manner. Public services are a priority.	Fairly static but reasonably healthy—most needs are catered for although excess supplies of goods are hard to come by.	Science and technology advancement slows in some areas (e.g. biotechnology) but in others increases (social network enhancements; green technology)	Society values landscapes and much of the beauty nature provides—particularly those which embody national identity. In 'uglier' areas though nature is given less respect.
	The government interferes with the free market to protect UK interests and institutes trade barriers and other protectionist measures.	Modest growth but sustained and steady without any major perturbations.	Strong technological industry guided by improving sustainable resource use.	Utilitarian without greater understanding of nature's benefit to mankind. A return to the traditional Christian stewardship values.
	Government continues to move between bouts of EU-friendly policies and stronger nationalist identity. A slow removal of public services.		Moderate development but greater focus on self-sufficiency in food and construction goods.	

Go with the Flow

Demographic	Socio-political	Economic	Science and technological	Cultural and religious
Population grows steadily through ageing and immigration. The average family size is larger than today.	Strong, centralised national government. Devolved power has been taken away. Markets have very little regulation; there are few environmental policies. The welfare state is reduced considerably.	Strong economic growth with global free trade. Growth continues seemingly without any downturn.	Rapid development of technology through greater government investment.	A strong sense of stewardship and responsibility towards nature. The intrinsic value of biodiversity is heavily supported. The Judeo-Christian old-world view is disappearing.
Population grows steadily through ageing and immigration.	Local government gains considerable powers from Westminster and almost creates a mini-United States of GB & NI. A higher % of tax raised locally is spent locally	Strong initial economic growth but characterised by occasional global market crises and periods of stagnation.	The private sector undercuts technology advancement and it flourishes but benefits a smaller proportion of society.	A strong utilitarian view dominates but also a greater understanding that nature supplies finite goods and services.
Population grows but slowly; immigration is very tightly controlled and only rich & skilled workers may enter the UK. Small families are encouraged. There is an expanding elderly cohort.	A globally-minded government. Decision-making is strongly influenced by EU and other countries ideas. Global issues are dealt with in a global manner. Public services are a priority.	Fairly static but reasonably healthy—most needs are catered for although excess supplies of goods are hard to come by.	Science and technology advancement slows in some areas (e.g. biotechnology) but in others increases (social network enhancements; green technology)	Society values landscapes and much of the beauty nature provides—particularly those which embody national identity. In 'uglier' areas though nature is given less respect.
	The government interferes with the free market to protect UK interests and institutes trade barriers and other protectionist measures.	Modest growth but sustained and steady without any major perturbations.	Strong technological industry guided by improving sustainable resource use.	Utilitarian without greater understanding of nature's benefit to mankind. A return to the traditional Christian stewardship values.
	Government continues to move between bouts of EU-friendly policies and stronger nationalist identity. A slow removal of public services.		Moderate development but greater focus on self-sufficiency in food and construction goods.	

Chapter 26:
Valuing Changes in Ecosystem Services: Scenario Analyses

Coordinating Lead Author: Ian J. Bateman
Lead Authors: David Abson, Barnaby Andrews, Andrew Crowe, Amii Darnell, Steve Dugdale, Carlo Fezzi, Jo Foden, Roy Haines-Young, Mark Hulme, Paul Munday, Unai Pascual, James Paterson, Grischa Perino, Antara Sen, Gavin Siriwardena and Mette Termansen

Key Findings

This chapter sets out to illustrate the decision making potential of the ecosystem service approach by valuing certain goods arising from changes in land use in Great Britain under a range of alternative future options. This analysis is extended to include both market and non-market goods and is given, as far as possible, in monetary terms. Where monetary valuation is not deemed reliable, alternative, quantitative assessments are made to permit an analysis of the cost-effectiveness of providing non-monetised goods.

The UK NEA Scenarios team provided six alternative futures, each of which is described in terms of land use, incomes and population in 2060. Furthermore, each scenario was presented with both a high and low climate change variant. Comparisons of the predicted situation in 2060 with a contemporary baseline allow us to identify the changes implied under each scenario. The novel work presented in this chapter applies various modelling techniques to quantify the impacts which these changes are expected to have upon the following five key ecosystem services:
- agricultural food production;
- terrestrial carbon storage and annual greenhouse gas emissions;
- biodiversity (assessed using birds as an indicator species);
- open-access recreation; and
- urban greenspace amenity.

Economic valuation techniques were applied to provide monetary assessments of the changes in the value of all these ecosystem services with the exception of biodiversity. In this latter case assessment was left in purely quantitative terms due to reservations about our ability to generate robust economic values for such effects.

Of these various ecosystem services, only agricultural food production has its value reflected in market-priced goods; remaining services all generate non-market values. Setting aside biodiversity for the moment, analysis of the scenarios revealed that in many cases, increases in market values could only be generated at the expense of those non-market ecosystem services. Furthermore, allowing decision making to be guided by market values alone (as per most contemporary decisions) often resulted in negative overall impacts for society, with total values (market plus non-market) falling substantially from the baseline. There were options which generated win-win increases in both market and non-market values; however, the greatest improvements in overall social well-being were generated by options which sought to treat both market and non-market values in an even-handed manner.

Bringing in the non-monetised measures of biodiversity effects allowed us to examine the costs of adopting options which avoided any such impacts. This provides an alternative perspective to decision making, highlighting options which deliver both increases in social values (assessed across both market and non-market goods) and avoids further pressures upon biodiversity. Interestingly, this shows that individuals may have to forgo attaining the highest possible gains in other values if they wish to avoid any loss of biodiversity.

All of the analyses conducted in this chapter adopt a unified methodology which captures the trade-offs in ecosystem services both across scenarios and across the country. The UK is highly heterogeneous and even under the same scenario, the changes induced in any given ecosystem service can vary from positive to negative depending upon which area of the country is considered. This methodology is highly appropriate for a localism agenda of decision-making systems which place great emphasis upon the distribution of costs and benefits across different areas and social groups.

26.1 Introduction

The purpose of economic analysis is to aid decision making. As discussed in the Economic Analysis chapter, (Chapter 22) decision making seeks to examine the trade-offs implied by each of a set of feasible options, so identifying that option which offers the best net benefits for society. For this reason, economic analysis is less interested in the total value of ecosystem services (not least because, for essential services, total values may be infinite) than in the change in value generated under one state as opposed to another. A key measure, then, will be the change in value arising from a move from a particular baseline to an alternative state. The present chapter assesses moves from a common baseline to each of the states described under the UK National Ecosystem Assessment (UK NEA) Scenarios (Chapter 25). In each case we consider the changes they imply for selected ecosystem services and the value of those changes.

This chapter does not pretend to value the impact of future scenarios upon all ecosystem services. This is, in part, a reflection of the state of available data and knowledge (and as such is an indicator of the need for further research in this area). As discussed at some length in Chapter 22 and supporting documents, economic values (for any good, not just ecosystem services) are contextual. By this we mean that marginal values (the value of a single unit change in a good) vary across space and time. So, for example, the value of a recreational visit may vary according to the location of that visit (e.g. because of the habitat type at that location). Similarly, the value of sequestering a tonne of carbon is likely to alter over time as the state of the climate alters. This information is not available for all of the ecosystem services considered in Chapter 22. Because of this we focus upon a subset of ecosystem service-related goods for which we do have sufficient data to undertake defensible valuations. Obviously, this subset does not represent the totality of values generated in the move from one state to another. Consequently, the valuations reported in the present chapter are necessarily partial and provisional. As a result, these analyses should not be taken as indicating the overall value of ecosystem service changes arising under each scenario.

A further caveat concerns the scenarios themselves. As discussed in Chapter 25, these are not the product of a modelling exercise in which trends are extrapolated and estimates of the future produced. Rather, the scenarios are hypothetical future worlds drawn in major part from a process of interaction with relevant agencies. As such they represent, in some considerable part, a wide spectrum of hypothetical but plausible future states. Another issue is that, as these are pre-generated outcomes, no information was provided on any transition path between the present and the scenario description. Where necessary, we have had to assume linear transition paths between the present and the future scenario. However, in the absence of further information we cannot improve on this assumption. A further caveat concerns the fact that these scenarios concern consumption of domestically produced ecosystem services and deliberately omit direct or indirect imports of such services. In effect, these are omitted from the total, future UK consumption of ecosystem services.

Despite these caveats, the present chapter does, we feel, amply demonstrate one very important and fundamental result: that methods now exist to unite natural sciences with economic assessments so as to estimate the value of changes arising under different states and thereby inform decision analysis. This is, arguably, the most important finding of the UK NEA in terms of its implications for the future. It paves the way for a new approach to decision making in which ecosystem services can be directly incorporated into policy choice. That this incorporation does not require a wholesale rejection of standard approaches to decision analysis, but rather an extension of current approaches, should significantly facilitate the acceptance and uptake of such techniques. In effect, these techniques facilitate an evolution, rather than a revolution, in decision making.

26.1.1 Valuing Scenarios of Ecosystem Service Change: Goods and Scenarios

Our demonstration of this evolution in decision making is executed through a series of highly comparable scenario analyses. These concern a consistent set of ecosystem service goods for which we can generate spatially and temporally sensitive data for each of the states described in Chapter 25. This work was conducted for the UK NEA by the SEER project[1] at the Centre for Social and Economic Research on the Global Environment (CSERGE), University of East Anglia in collaboration with colleagues at the British Trust for Ornithology and the School of Earth and Environment at the University of Leeds.

Five integrated ecosystem service goods are considered, as follows:
- agricultural food production;
- terrestrial carbon storage and annual greenhouse gas emissions;
- biodiversity (assessed using birds as an indicator species);
- open-access recreation; and
- urban greenspace amenity.

In each case, changes are calculated between a baseline[2] and the envisioned state of the UK in 2060 under the six UK NEA Scenarios. Ideally we would use the present day as the baseline; however, data availability prevented this[3] and the physical situation of land use, population and its characteristics in the year 2000 was adopted. However, to adjust somewhat to the present day, all baseline monetary values were adjusted to 2010 levels.

---

1   The Social and Environmental Economic Research (SEER) into Multi-Objective Land Use Decision Making project is held by the Centre for Social and Economic Research on the Global Environment (CSERGE) at the School of Environmental Sciences, University of East Anglia. SEER is funded by the Economic and Social Research Council (ESRC; Funder Ref: RES-060-25-0063).
2   As discussed subsequently, our analysis of farmland bird biodiversity adopts a somewhat different baseline.
3   While we would have liked to have used a more recent baseline, crucial sources of data such as Land Cover Map 2007 and 2011 Census details were not available at the time of the analysis. Consequently the analysis uses land use information from the CEH Land Cover Map 2000 while population, socioeconomic and demographic data is taken from the UK Census 2001.

- **Go with the Flow** essentially follows today's sociopolitical and economic trends and results in a future Britain that is roughly based on today's ideals, with some leaning towards improving the environmental performance and sustainability of the UK. Current ideas being developed in academic circles, government and the media about the way forward for the UK have been adopted. Environmental improvements are still important in the government's vision for a future UK, but the public are less keen on adopting many global or national environmental standards (business and industry even less so). This stand-off continues to dominate, and a lot of environmental progress is hindered. **It is very important to note that this scenario does not conform to that usually used as a baseline in an economic analysis.** The present approach is justified by noting both that it refers to a very long time horizon over which modelling would be problematic and that the scenarios listed here are designed to explore the how different drivers of change might shape the future. Typically, an economic analysis would define a baseline case under which existing trends and expected shifts are modelled to generate an estimate of how the world might look in the absence of particular policy changes. Economists typically refer to these as 'business as usual' or 'do-nothing' baselines. Other scenarios which embody such drivers such as policy change can then be analysed to assess their likely impact. This is not the case here and economists or other decision-makers should not infer that the *Go with the Flow* scenario is a 'do-nothing' baseline. To overcome this problem **we take the situation in 2060 under each scenario** (including *Go with the Flow*) **and compare this with our baseline.**

- **Green and Pleasant Land** is a storyline where the conservation of biodiversity and landscape are the dominant driving forces. Whilst it is recognised that biodiversity often provides essential benefits to society, its intrinsic value is accorded a pre-eminence in policy and legislation. A preservationist attitude arises because the UK can afford to look after its own backyard without diminishing standards of living. Tourism and leisure are consequently boosted by this drive and increase their share of overall UK GDP (Gross Domestic Product)— and by the decline in popularity of many of late 20th Century holiday destinations because of climate change (e.g. France, Spain and Italy). The countryside is very much a managed, cultural landscape but the focus is now on trying to maintain, protect and improve the aesthetic appeal. In general, landscape preservation often coincides with biodiversity conservation, although one major source of conflict is between the importance of recognising habitat and ecosystem change and the preservation of landscapes.

- **Local Stewardship** has localism as a dominant paradigm, yet is also more environmentally aware and open to international trade than some other scenarios (e.g. *National Security*, see below). Here political power has been devolved and many major issues are decided at a regional or local level (except crucial national aspects like defence); local timber and energy production is encouraged and there is great pride in the numerous local food products. This scenario focuses on optimising resources and consumption is reduced to more sustainable (and healthy) levels—GDP is low but sustainable. The 'tragedy of the commons'[4] would not be recognised in the UK; societal equity fits alongside environmental equity. People travel less and depend more on local resources; more of our food and leisure activities take place in the immediate locale. Technological development occurs in localised areas due to private innovation and a government initiative for developing sustainable technology. The implementation of the sustainable management of resources is a priority and society relies less on technological innovation. Low carbon economies spring up and there is greater use of alternative economies such as LETS (Local Exchange Trading Systems) schemes. Through local specialisation the UK becomes less homogenised—landscapes become more distinct and even local economies vary considerably. Social and environmental regulation has advanced, though, particularly regarding workers' welfare and rights, and environmental protection. Although economic growth is slower compared to other storylines, the economy is more stable.

- Under the **National Security** scenario, UK industry is protected from foreign investors and imports. Trade barriers and tariffs are increased to protect jobs and livelihoods in the UK; immigration is also very tightly controlled. Technological development is state-funded and many industries are subsidised by the state (including agriculture). Food, fuel, timber and mineral resources are prioritised over the conservation of biodiversity. Climate change results in increases in global energy prices, forcing many countries to attempt greater self-sufficiency (and efficiency) in many of their core industries. Britain is no exception, and agricultural and other primary industries 'optimise' (rather than intensify) accordingly.

- In the **Nature@Work** scenario, the conservation of biodiversity as an end in itself is less of a priority compared to maintaining and enhancing the output of ecosystem services. Adapting to climate change is also a priority, which means that some non-native species are introduced to provide food, energy or shade. A campaign of promoting ecosystem services in multifunctional landscapes as essential to maintaining the quality of life in the UK is now embedded in all walks of society (from primary schooling all the way to large industry). Society accepts that some trade-offs have to be made and as a result, becomes more environmentally aware. Habitat restoration and creation are seen as important components of this campaign, but the explicit

---

4   This derives from the seminal work of Hardin (1968) who observed that, in the absence of mediating economic incentives or social rules, unfettered access to common property resources could lead to over-exploitation and even destruction of such resources.

conservation of species is sometimes overruled by a 'greater' ecosystem service benefit; this sometimes results in habitat conversion (e.g. Semi-natural Grassland to Woodlands). As well as carbon mitigation, an important focus is the enhancement of societies' resilience to climate change through 'ecosystem-based adaptation'. Modern technology is used where appropriate, though, and even GM biotechnology is adopted if it can be shown to enhance ecosystem service provision. This includes the use of drought-tolerant crops to maintain production and reduce soil erosion. 'Optimal service provision' is key, and many ecosystem services in the landscape are a result of careful examination of the trade-offs through scientific and community review.

- In the **World Markets** storyline, unfettered economic growth through the complete liberalisation of trade is the main goal. International trade barriers dissolve, agriculture subsidies disappear and farming, for example, is now industrial and large scale. Consumption in society is high, which results in greater resource use and more imports. There is competition for land and this, coupled with reduced rural and urban planning regulations on housing, agriculture and industry mean that biodiversity is often the loser. Technological development in all industries is mainly privately funded but nevertheless is

burgeoning. Food is cheap and plentiful but of low quality. As in land-based food production, food supplies from the seas are equally seen as a resource for exploitation without recourse to any sustainable management. Fish stocks plummet and a few species have been wiped out; most fish is imported from Asia. Desalination plants are built in areas on the east coast to meet water demand for the southern and eastern counties. 'Home-grown' fossil fuel energy production is declining and has been overtaken by imports of gas from abroad and privately funded nuclear industry in the UK. Consequently, coastal areas are built upon to accommodate power plants and gas pipeline stations. Supplies of other ecosystem services increasingly become privatised.

Table 26.1 provides an overview of the UK NEA Scenarios described according to a number of common dimensions. These were used to synthesise a series of GIS-based maps articulating each scenario into a consequent land use allocation. The procedures used to generate these land uses are described in Chapter 25 and are summarised at a Great Britain (GB) scale in **Table 26.2**.

All of these scenarios were further modified according to two different responses to climate change as taken from the simplified UKCIP-09 Low and High Emissions scenarios for 2050–2079, discussed in Chapter 25. In sum then, we assess

---

Table 26.1 Overview of the UK NEA Scenarios.

Scenario	Knowledge	Legislation	Policies, institutions and governance	Behaviour	Markets and incentives	Technologies and practice
Green and Pleasant Land	Investment in green technologies; less focus on biotechnology.	Strong links to EU and global obligations.	Globally minded government; investment in public services.	Stewardship and responsibility; intrinsic values of nature.		
Nature@Work	Technology industry focused on sustainable resource use.	Strong links to EU and global obligations.	Globally minded government; investment in public services. Commitment to global free trade.	Utilitarian view, recognising the importance of 'nature's services'.	Growth of market delivering economic progress.	Industry drives technological innovation in the context of resource use.
World Markets	Technology largely driven by private profit motive.	Reversal of devolution. Deregulated markets. Few environmental policies.	Shrinking of the welfare state. Strong, centralised national government. Deregulation of environmental protection.	Narrowly utilitarian, failing to recognise values of nature.	Growth of market but greater exposure to global fluctuations.	Industry driving technological innovation for private profit.
National Security	Technology industry focused on sustainable resource use.	Trade barriers and protectionist measures to protect UK interests.	Protectionist policies to protect UK interests.	Society values landscapes and features of nature that characterise 'national identity'.	Protection-led growth, but periods of stagnation and global crises. Markets protected.	
Local Stewardship		Tight controls on immigration. Greater devolution to local governments.	Tax-raising powers devolved to local levels.	Utilitarian view, recognising the importance of 'nature's services'.	Slow but steady economic growth. Incentives for small families.	Technology focuses on self-sufficiency and construction goods.
Go with the Flow	Rapid development of technology through government investment.	Oscillation between pro-EU and more narrowly nationalistic approaches.	Oscillation between pro-EU and more narrowly nationalistic policies. Slow shrinking of public services.	Some leaning towards improved environmental performance but with limited public support.	Growth of market but greater exposure to global fluctuations.	Technology driven by government investment.

Table 26.2 Mean land use coverage and population figures for Great Britain: Year 2000 baseline and UK NEA 2060 Scenarios. Cells are shaded so as to indicate the magnitude of change from the 2000 baseline under each of the UK NEA Scenarios. Unshaded cells indicate that there is no significant change; green cells indicate significant increases over the baseline (with bold text indicating more substantial increases); purple cells indicate significant reductions from the baseline (with bold text indicating more substantial reductions). Scenarios are as follows: GF-H = *Go with the Flow* High emissions; GF-L = *Go with the Flow* Low emissions; GPL-H = *Green and Pleasant Land* High emissions; GPL-L = *Green and Pleasant Land* Low emissions; LS-H = *Local Stewardship* High emissions; LS-L = *Local Stewardship* Low emissions; NS-H = *National Security* High emissions; NS-L = *National Security* Low emissions; N@W-H = *Nature@Work* High emissions; N@W-L = *Nature@Work* Low emissions; WM-H = *World Markets* High emissions; MW-L = *World Markets* Low emissions; LSOA = Census lower super output areas.

UK NEA Broad Habitat	Land cover	Baseline	GF-H	GF-L	GPL-H	GPL-L	LS-H	LS-L	NS-H	NS-L	NW-H	NW-L	WM-H	WM-L
Coastal Margins	% Coast	0.48	0.44	0.47	0.47	0.47	0.44	0.47	0.41	0.44	0.45	0.46	0.42	0.45
Marine	% Freshwater	0.77	1.95	0.90	1.54	1.51	1.82	0.77	1.63	0.77	2.12	1.69	1.62	`0.78
Semi-natural Grassland	% Grasslands	15.9	18.34	17.64	25.3	22.1	21.9	21.5	8.42	8.15	20.20	20.03	13.7	13.28
Mountains, Moorlands & Heaths	% Mountains & Heathlands	13.8	15.04	14.75	14.62	14.82	14.22	14.06	8.16	8.02	16.6	15.6	11.7	11.5
Marine	% Other Marine	7.08	7.12	7.09	7.09	7.09	7.12	7.09	7.09	7.08	7.11	7.11	7.46	7.35
Urban	% Urban	6.72	7.61	8.06	6.74	6.71	6.36	6.50	6.95	6.81	6.61	6.72	14.3	14.57
Woodlands	% Conifer Wood	5.32	4.23	4.23	3.82	3.77	4.77	4.77	18.91	18.2	8.54	8.79	6.18	5.01
	% Broadleaved Wood	6.34	9.76	9.37	11.06	11.94	7.69	6.73	6.40	7.21	10.57	10.57	5.25	5.75
Enclosed Farmland	% Enclosed Farmland	43.5	35.5	37.49	29.25	31.53	36.6	38.06	42.04	43.22	27.75	28.85	39.32	41.2
	LSOA mean population	1,518	1,781	1,781	1,543	1,543	1,524	1,524	1,660	1,660	1,612	1,612	1,831	1,831
	Change in total real income	0	+1.5%	+1.5%	+2%	+2%	+0.5%	+0.5%	+1%	+1%	+3%	+3%	+2%	+2%
	Change in proportion retired	0	+20%	+20%	+22%	+22%	+19.5%	+19.5%	+19.5%	+19.5%	+20%	+20%	+21%	+21%

changes to all five of our ecosystem service-related goods under 12 scenarios.

We re-emphasise that the *Go with the Flow* scenario is not a conventional economic 'business as usual' baseline in that it does not attempt to model future trends based upon best available data (on policy and market trends and environmental change forecasts) but is rather a product of the ideologies summarised in the discussion given above. As such, it does not constitute an economically conventional baseline for comparison with other scenarios. Consequently, all economic analyses in this chapter compare the situation envisioned in 2060 under each of the above scenarios with a consistent baseline for the year 2000.[5]

The valuation of changes under each scenario informs decision analysts of the trade-offs across the set of goods under consideration. Such information is clearly an important input to decision making. However, alongside caveats regarding the incomplete set of goods being considered, we also emphasise the point raised in Chapter 22 that, while the valuation of ecosystem service flows is a very important improvement over sole reliance upon market prices, sustainability requires that we also consider the impacts of flow changes upon the levels of stocks of relevant ecosystem services. This is again highlighted as an important area for future research.

26.2 Valuing Scenarios for Agricultural Food Production

26.2.1 Introduction and Methodology

Our agricultural scenario analysis is decomposed into two parts. First, we analyse the variation in agricultural land types and livestock numbers under the baseline and under each scenario. Second, we derive the economic impact on farmers in terms of farm gross margin (FGM), defined as the

5   Land use under the baseline is taken from the CEH Land Cover map 2000, while population data is taken from the UK Census 2001 (on the assumption that any error this slight discrepancy causes will be insignificant).

difference between revenues from agricultural activities and associated variable costs.[6]

The agricultural land and livestock scenarios are derived by applying the CSERGE econometric agricultural land use model (Fezzi & Bateman 2010; Fezzi *et al.* 2010a) to the area of farmland predicted under each of the UK NEA Scenarios. The CSERGE model then determines the specific land use and (where appropriate) livestock numbers which are consistent with the behavioural patterns observed throughout its large cross-sectional and time series database.

As discussed in Chapter 25, each scenario is used to generate maps describing the corresponding land use for all of the UK. Following some harmonisation of scales[7] and categorisations,[8] the CSERGE land use model was applied to the area of each 2 km grid square across GB that was predicted to be farmland under each scenario. Within each of these grid squares the CSERGE model predicts the share of farmland under each agricultural land use type and predicts livestock numbers (dairy cows, beef cows and sheep) where appropriate. As discussed in Chapter 22, these shares are predicted from the estimated effect that policy, prices and the natural environment have upon farm land use and, therefore, differ between the low and high emission scenarios because

of the varied impact of climate change. Note, however, that we do not allow for the effect of new technologies such as the possible introduction of new crop varieties or husbandry practices. This is a potentially important caveat and means that the present results should not be over-interpreted.[9]

26.2.2 Agricultural Land Use Under the Baseline and Scenarios

26.2.2.1 Baseline

The baseline for our analysis describes agriculture in GB in the year 2000. The area of each land use and livestock numbers are reported in **Table 26.3**. This shows a highly heterogeneous picture, with the flatter and warmer lowlands of south-east England dominated by arable cultivation and the hilly North West primarily devoted to grazing systems. Wales and Scotland are also characterised by the presence of a high percentage of low-quality agricultural land, which translates into the highest shares of rough grazing in the whole of GB. Livestock rates are strongly related to land use, with dairy stocking rates being higher in the south and west, while sheep numbers are highest in England's northern upland areas and in Scotland.

Table 26.3 Average land use (hectares/2 km grid square) and livestock numbers (head/2 km grid square) in the year 2000 baseline. OSR = oilseed rape; CE = cereals; RC = root crops; OA = other arable; TG = temporary grassland; PG = permanent grassland; RG = rough grazing; D = dairy; B = beef; S = sheep.

Region	OSR	CE	RC	OA	TG	PG	RG	D	B	S
East Midlands	19.0	132.2	1.7	59.9	11.3	53.3	52.1	15.5	69.6	336.3
East of England	21.2	158.5	2.3	73.9	3.7	19.9	46.5	4.9	29.2	124.9
London	2.8	25.5	0.5	4.9	4.0	27.9	46.4	23.3	44.0	162.8
North East	10.0	66.2	0.3	24.7	21.0	64.5	122.7	19.8	105.9	593.2
North West	2.3	34.9	0.4	10.6	21.3	112.8	130.1	49.3	129.9	761.6
South East	11.7	96.8	1.1	26.1	14.9	69.9	52.8	31.4	72.2	296.4
South West	6.4	83.2	1.3	29.5	24.5	124.8	48.1	52.9	121.4	611.9
West Midlands	10.9	85.8	1.4	28.6	23.4	100.7	58.2	45.2	117.0	533.9
Humber	12.6	96.3	1.2	40.7	12.7	56.0	101.7	14.5	80.2	523.6
Scotland	3.5	25.4	0.1	8.0	14.3	36.2	227.6	9.9	53.2	509.6
Wales	0.5	12.6	0.3	5.1	21.8	125.1	150.6	48.9	124.8	903.0
GB	**7.9**	**64.8**	**0.8**	**24.5**	**16.0**	**66.7**	**131.1**	**24.8**	**79.5**	**511.8**

6   As stressed in Chapter 22, while this is a commonly applied approach, it is not a theoretically ideal measure, being only a fair approximation of the net economic value. That said, the trends in relative values provide some useful information regarding the likely changes in agricultural productivity in the four scenarios. Note, however, that in practice it is likely that any increases in FGM are likely to be ultimately capitalised into rents. Therefore it should not be assumed that any such increases will represent long-term gains to farmers.

7   The UK NEA Scenario maps are generated at a 1 km grid square scale. These are rescaled to the 2 km grid square basis used in the CSERGE agricultural land use model.

8   The UK NEA Scenarios team used a somewhat different land categorisation to both the CSERGE model and the Broad Habitats definitions used in previous chapters of the UK NEA. For example, the Enclosed Farmland Broad Habitat was split into further subdivisions such as 'arable' and 'improved grassland' To make this categorisation compatible with the CSERGE model the Scenarios team's categories 'upland', 'improved grassland' and 'arable' were classified as 'agricultural' land, with the 'upland' category taken as indicating rough-grazing land. Similarly the 'improved grassland' category was split into permanent or temporary grassland according to the shares of each land use predicted by the CSERGE model. A similar approach was taken to reallocate the area defined by the Scenarios team as 'arable' into 'cereals', 'oilseed rape', 'root crops' (potatoes and sugar beet) and 'other arable'.

9   The impact of unanticipated technical change upon the valuation of the UK NEA Scenarios is somewhat difficult to assess. The land use changes envisioned by the scenarios are themselves not modelled and hence do not respond to technological change. However, one would expect the absence of new technologies to lead to an underestimate of agricultural performance in the future. This issue could be addressed with further research. A possible approach would be to develop a full econometric model including not only land use allocation and livestock equations, but also profit and yield equations. This, however, requires farm-level data which were not available at the time of the analysis. Another strategy would be to use a hybrid econometric-simulation model as per Antle & Capalbo (2001).

Figure 26.1 illustrates the baseline distribution of selected land use types: cereals (the dominant arable crops), temporary grassland (rich grassland used mainly for dairy and beef cows) and rough grazing. The distribution of beef cattle is also shown. Cereals are located in most of the lowland, flatter areas of the country, such as the south and east coast of England and eastern Scotland. Temporary grassland, on the other hand, is concentrated in the wetter south-west of England and in the lowland areas of Scotland and Wales. While rough grazing has some minor presence in all areas, it is concentrated in the uplands of northern England, Scotland and Wales, in which it is the major,

if not the only, type of agricultural land use. Beef cattle are abundant in areas where there is either temporary or permanent grassland, but become absent in the more extreme upland areas.

26.2.2.2 Comparing the Baseline with the UK NEA Scenarios

Fezzi et al. (2011) present detailed comparisons of the changes in land use from the baseline to each of the UK NEA Scenarios. Given that we have six Scenarios, each with a high and low emissions variant, and that we are primarily interested in the value of changes rather than the land use

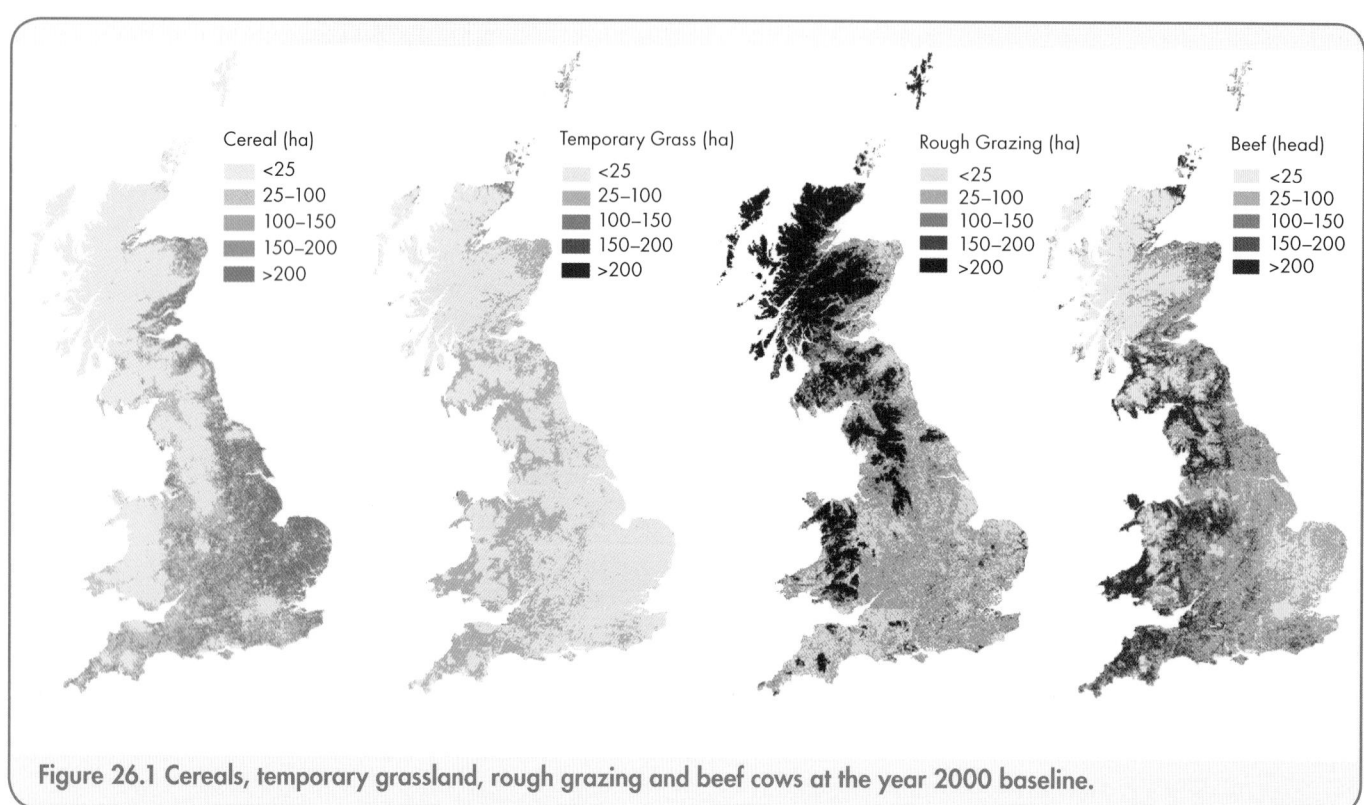

Figure 26.1 Cereals, temporary grassland, rough grazing and beef cows at the year 2000 baseline.

Table 26.4 Average change in amount of land used (hectares/2 km grid square) and livestock numbers (head/2 km grid square) in the *Green and Pleasant Land* High emissions scenario compared to the 2000 baseline. OSR = oilseed rape; CE = cereals; RC = root crops; OA = other arable; TG = temporary grassland; PG = permanent grassland; RG = rough grazing; D = dairy; B = beef; S = sheep.

Region	OSR	CE	RC	OA	TG	PG	RG	D	B	S
East Midlands	-16.4	-87.3	1.1	38.0	6.1	-26.9	53.3	32.2	-66.7	-261.8
East of England	-19.8	-113.2	2.1	49.6	8.8	-16.4	57.4	41.4	-29.0	-124.0
London	-2.8	-25.5	8.6	8.7	11.5	-21.8	19.9	28.6	-43.6	-162.3
North East	-6.1	-26.7	0.8	2.6	-10.1	-18.0	41.7	8.3	-65.9	-95.0
North West	-2.2	-29.4	4.7	12.7	-3.5	-39.8	38.3	3.8	-90.5	-294.5
South East	-11.6	-91.2	4.8	47.3	19.8	-52.4	62.3	34.9	-71.3	-295.7
South West	-6.4	-80.5	11.9	29.8	12.5	-70.2	74.5	19.0	-114.1	-486.5
West Midlands	-10.8	-71.2	2.1	39.3	9.3	-49.7	56.1	23.8	-102.1	-398.8
Humber	-10.1	-53.8	1.1	17.9	-3.0	-20.4	44.2	19.7	-69.3	-205.2
Scotland	-2.3	-10.2	0.6	1.3	-8.2	-6.5	21.4	1.3	-29.3	66.2
Wales	-0.5	-11.6	3.7	2.4	-0.5	-46.6	41.2	-0.2	-94.6	-341.5
GB	**-6.9**	**-46.7**	**3.0**	**18.9**	**1.1**	**-28.8**	**42.6**	**14.5**	**-62.2**	**-171.0**

shifts that precipitate the changes, we do not present all of these analyses here. Instead, we illustrate the comparison process with respect to a single scenario, comparing land use under the baseline with that predicted under the high emissions variant of the *Green and Pleasant Land* scenario.

Comparing the baseline with the high emissions variant of the *Green and Pleasant Land* scenario. The changes in land use and livestock numbers between the baseline in 2000 and the high emissions *Green and Pleasant Land* scenario in 2060 are reported in **Table 26.4**. In the *Green and Pleasant Land* scenario, a high amount of land is converted from intensive land uses to more extensive ones. In particular, cereals and oilseed rape decrease significantly, substituted partly by other arable and temporary grassland. Furthermore, rough grazing increases throughout the country, replacing permanent grassland and arable land. Finally, beef and sheep numbers decrease, while numbers of dairy cows grow as a result of the increase in temporary grassland.

Figure 26.2 presents maps of changes in selected land use types and livestock (cereals, rough grazing and dairy cows) under this scenario change. We observed a significant decrease in cereals in the entire country, a widespread increase in rough grazing and small, positive changes in stocking rates of dairy cows in the lowlands, particularly in the south and East of England.

26.2.3 Valuation of Scenario Changes: Farm Gross Margin Effect

We now move to consider the value of changes in agricultural provisioning services under each scenario. As mentioned in Chapter 22, these are measured as FGM. Two important limitations need to be acknowledged. First, since FGM is defined as the difference between revenues and variable costs, all farm fixed costs (e.g. machinery, buildings, rent, etc.) are not included in the analysis. Secondly, conversion costs are also not included; in other words, all changes in land use and FGM refer to equilibrium conditions, but do not take into account possible costs encountered in order to reach these new equilibriums. Bearing these caveats in mind, FGMs can be used to analyse the trends in overall agricultural productivity in the different scenarios.

We begin by considering the FGM under the 2000 baseline. These are reported in the first column of **Table 26.5** and mapped in **Figure 26.3**. The figure shows that those farms with the highest FGM are located in the lowland and southern areas of the country, while those in upland areas have relatively low FGM levels. This principally reflects the variation in physical environmental conditions across the country.

We can now use the type and amount of each land use estimated under each of the scenarios to generate corresponding FGM values. These are then contrasted with the baseline to estimate the change in value induced under each scenario. We can map the distribution of changes in FGM per hectare for all scenarios under both their low emission (**Figure 26.4**) and high emission (**Figure 26.5**) variants (full details presented in Fezzi *et al.* 2011).

In almost all scenarios the lowland south of the country appears to fare best (possibly with the exception of the low emission variants of the *Green and Pleasant Land* and *Nature@ Work* scenarios), while it is the upland and northern areas which bear the highest losses (partial exceptions being the low emission *World Markets* and *National Security* scenarios). Generally, patterns within scenarios are less marked than those across the different scenarios, although the variability of impacts appears greater in the high emission variants.

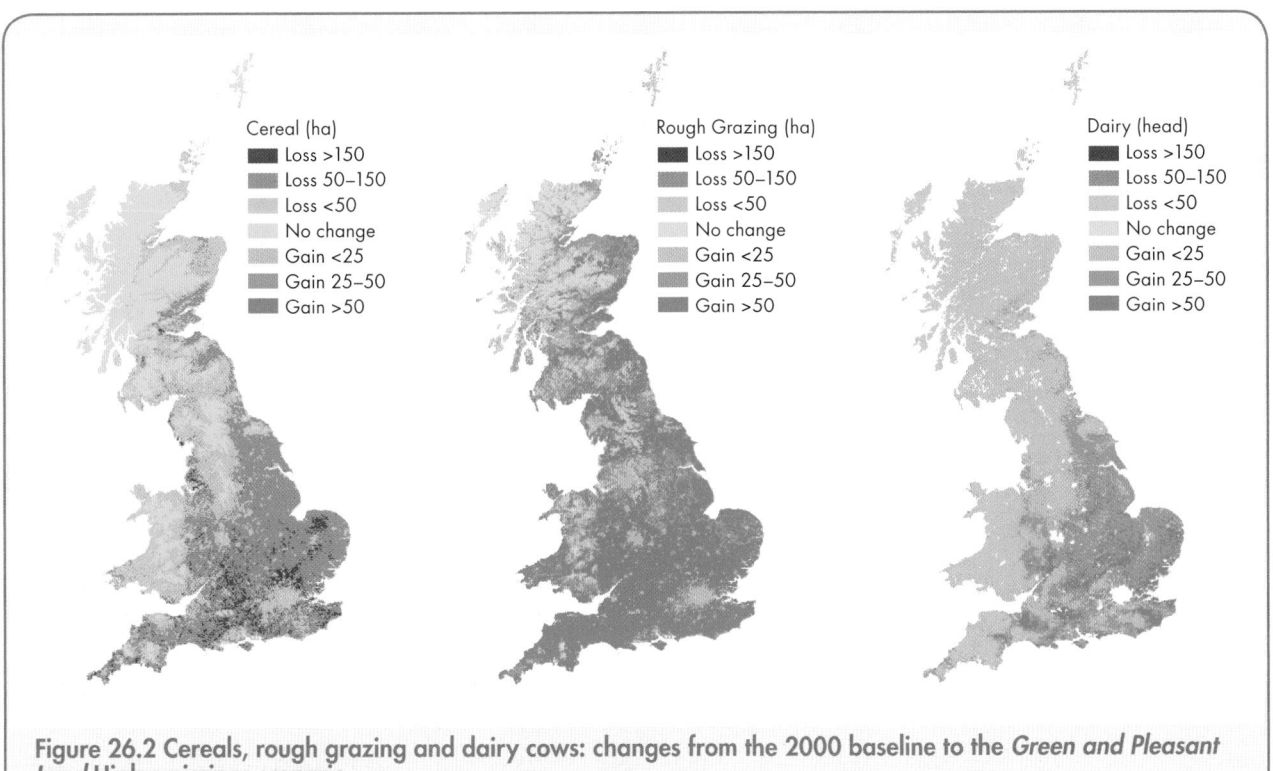

Figure 26.2 Cereals, rough grazing and dairy cows: changes from the 2000 baseline to the *Green and Pleasant Land* High emissions scenario.

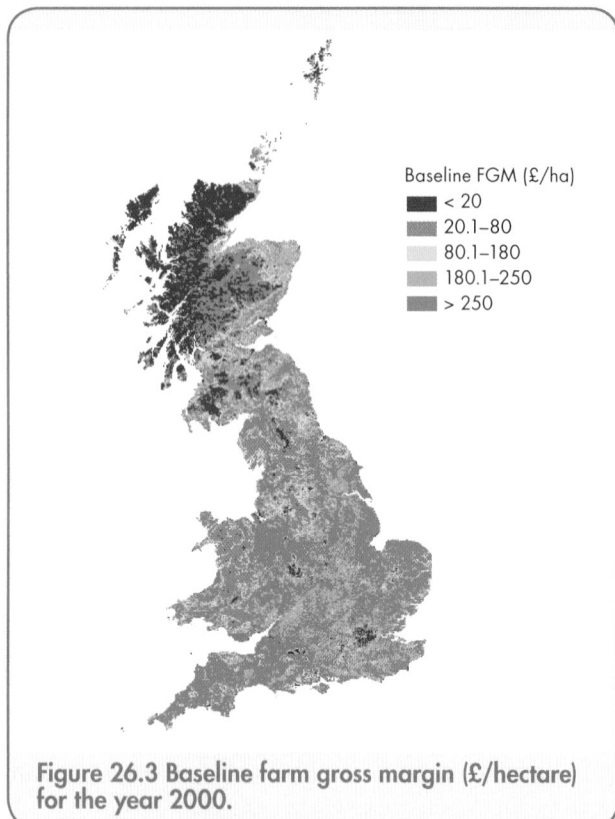

Figure 26.3 Baseline farm gross margin (£/hectare) for the year 2000.

Baseline FGM (£/ha)
- ■ < 20
- ■ 20.1–80
- 80.1–180
- 180.1–250
- ■ > 250

The patterns shown here are in marked contrast to those reported in Chapter 22 during discussion of the impacts of forecast climate change (where the spatial trend was reversed, with the south suffering declines in FGM due to increased droughtiness, and the north and uplands benefiting from higher temperatures and alterations in rainfall patterns). This serves to reinforce the fact that the UK NEA Scenarios are not forecasts but are instead, at least in considerable part, based upon a range of assumptions about the future. The contrasting patterns of land use envisaged by the UK NEA Scenarios show the value implications of future worlds, but do not shed light on the feasibility or paths of policy change required to attain such worlds.

The change in values from the 2000 baseline to each scenario in 2060 is calculated for each 2 km grid square across GB. This spatially explicit approach to valuation allows decision-makers the possibility of targeting policies at those areas which will generate the most efficient use of resources. Grid square values can also be summed to generate national level estimates of the values of changes induced under each scenario, as detailed in **Table 26.6**. Here the upper row details the baseline, which highlights the significant heterogeneity which characterises the present GB farming system (for example, the FGM/ha of the third quartile is more than seven times that of the first quartile).

In **Table 26.6**, the *Go with the Flow* scenarios imply that, at the national level, farm incomes will increase (particularly under high emissions) due to the warmer climate. However, the increase in FGM is not evenly distributed across all farms, and incomes at the lower quartile remain unaffected. Climate change is also incorporated into the other scenarios, but in those worlds the changes in land use and FGM are also influenced by various other social, economic and political drivers which somehow conceal the climate effect as compared to *Go with the Flow*.

Considering other scenarios, achieving higher environmental quality (*Green and Pleasant Land* and *Nature@ Work*) would come at some costs to the farming community (overall between 1% and 10% of total FGM for *Green and Pleasant Land* and between 4% and 20% for *Nature@Work*).

Table 26.5 Farm gross margin per hectare (FGM/ha) in the baseline and changes in farm gross margin per hectare (Δ FGM/ha) in the UK NEA Scenarios (high and low emissions). FGM is as follows: cereals = £290/ha, root crops = £2,425/ha, oilseed rape = £310/ha, dairy = £576/head, beef = £69/head, sheep = £9.3/head. Scenarios: GF = Go with the Flow; GPL = Green and Pleasant Land; NS = National Security; NW = Nature@Work; WM = World Markets; LS = Local Stewardship. Source: Fezzi et al. (2010b).

Region	Base (FGM/ha)	GF (Δ FGM/ha) high	GF (Δ FGM/ha) low	GPL (Δ FGM/ha) high	GPL (Δ FGM/ha) low	NS (Δ FGM/ha) high	NS (Δ FGM/ha) low	NW (Δ FGM/ha) high	NW (Δ FGM/ha) low	WM (Δ FGM/ha) high	WM (Δ FGM/ha) low	LS (Δ FGM/ha) high	LS (Δ FGM/ha) low
East Midlands	250.2	25.6	10.6	-16.3	-32.3	60.1	35.5	-12.8	-29.6	32.7	10.4	29.0	27.8
East of England	262.3	55.8	35.2	3.4	-17.6	90.6	57.2	18.6	-3.4	49.5	23.9	61.6	59.2
London	157.0	280.9	49.2	174.7	26.4	418.3	83.9	222.5	9.5	232.8	51.0	178.4	104.3
North East	172.5	-8.5	-10.1	-24.4	-26.4	16.6	10.7	-45.7	-45.6	7.1	2.7	-1.4	3.1
North West	183.8	25.0	9.3	-1.8	-17.4	90.3	57.2	-28.7	-41.8	68.8	32.8	11.8	11.6
South East	245.5	94.6	26.9	27.7	-23.3	132.4	48.1	31.9	-36.7	95.9	33.7	69.7	40.3
South West	257.0	136.0	69.0	34.0	-2.0	195.1	122.6	62.5	-19.4	163.9	95.4	89.7	62.3
West Midlands	250.0	25.6	5.1	-15.2	-30.7	61.8	33.2	-26.1	-50.8	37.3	14.8	16.8	17.1
Humber	201.6	12.6	4.7	-19.4	-29.1	43.0	25.7	-22.9	-31.6	27.2	9.3	16.0	15.7
Scotland	77.1	-2.4	-3.8	-7.7	-8.9	9.0	4.9	-20.7	-20.6	8.5	3.8	-2.9	-0.4
Wales	159.7	14.1	-5.5	-11.1	-17.9	79.5	47.1	-29.6	-57.2	66.4	33.5	-6.2	-2.3
GB	**173.1**	**32.8**	**12.2**	**-1.6**	**-16.2**	**66.7**	**37.7**	**-6.1**	**-28.7**	**49.1**	**23.4**	**23.7**	**19.5**

However, here the distributional impact of these losses is progressive, with poorer farmers being relatively unaffected (the first quartile income does not change) while incomes amongst richer farms decline noticeably (note the fall in third quartile incomes).

Encouraging agricultural production under the *National Security* and *World Markets* scenarios will, as one would expect, boost agricultural incomes, increase arable land shares and stocking rates. However, the total amount of agricultural land decreases significantly under these scenarios, depressing aggregate gains. In particular, the scenarios envisage a loss of low-productivity rough grazing and permanent grassland. However, the overall value of agricultural output is expected to increase. While the *World*

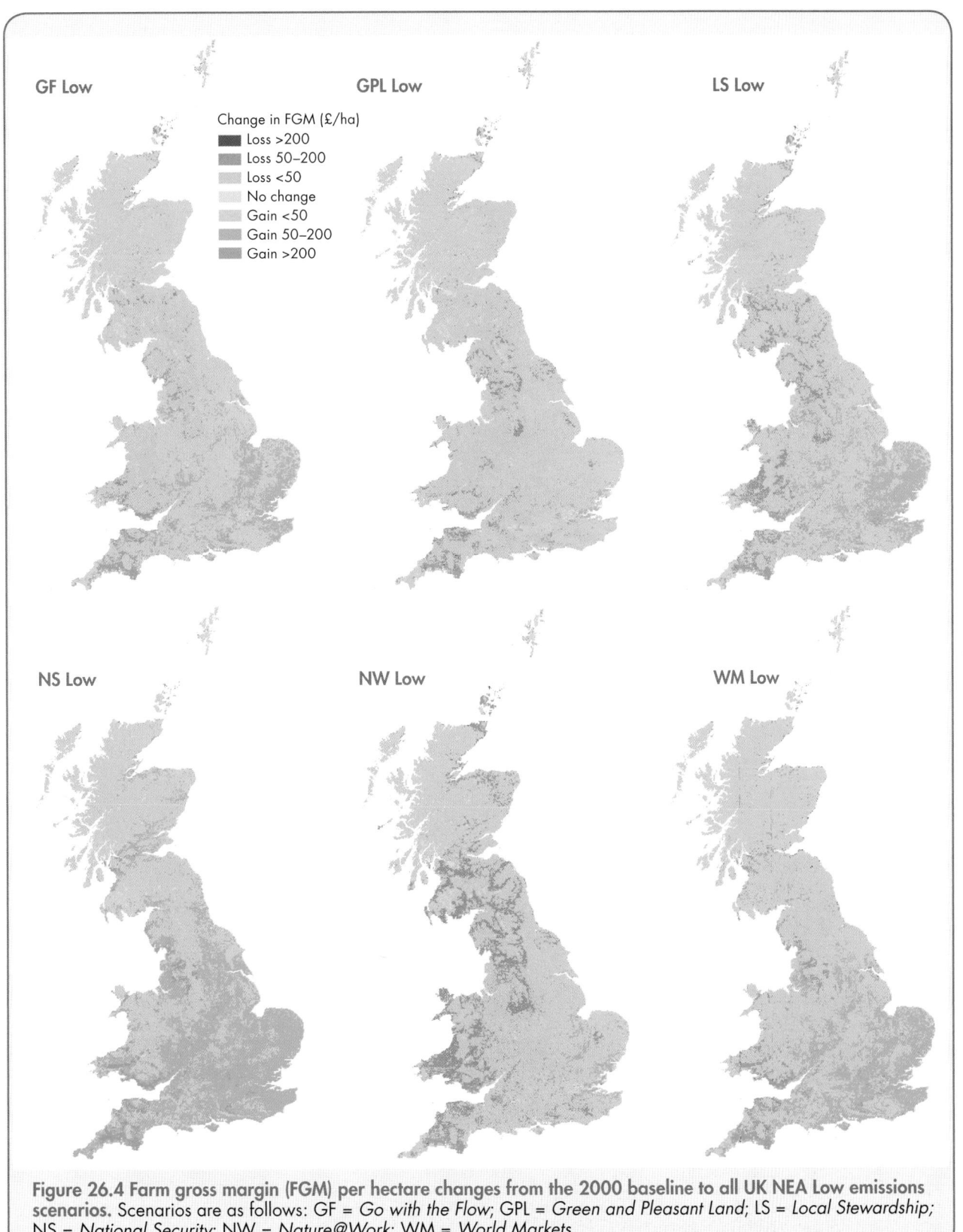

Figure 26.4 Farm gross margin (FGM) per hectare changes from the 2000 baseline to all UK NEA Low emissions scenarios. Scenarios are as follows: GF = *Go with the Flow*; GPL = *Green and Pleasant Land*; LS = *Local Stewardship*; NS = *National Security*; NW = *Nature@Work*; WM = *World Markets*.

Markets scenario leads to income increases for all farming groups, incomes for the poorest farms decline under the *National Security* scenario (e.g. first quartile income declines from £34.9/ha under the baseline to £25.3/ha under the *National Security* high emissions scenario). A similar pattern is observed for the *Local Stewardship* scenario where, on average, agricultural incomes increase (both per hectare and at the national level) but low income farms experience a small decline in FGM levels.

Table 26.7 summarises the changes in FGM/ha occurring under each scenario. Interestingly, even those scenarios which deliver the highest agricultural values overall (*National Security*, *World Markets* and *Local Stewardship*) still result in some farms being worse off.

Figure 26.5 Farm gross margin (FGM) per hectare changes from the 2000 baseline to all UK NEA High emissions scenarios. Scenarios are as follows: GF = *Go with the Flow*; GPL = *Green and Pleasant Land*; LS = *Local Stewardship*; NS = *National Security*; NW = *Nature@Work*; WM = *World Markets*.

Indeed, the first quartile of FGM changes is negative in all but one scenario (*World Markets* high emissions being the exception). Conversely, the third quartile of changes is positive in all scenarios, highlighting that there is a substantial proportion of farms which benefit from all scenarios, even when overall incomes are expected to decrease (e.g. the *Green and Pleasant Land* and *Nature@ Work* worlds). As a further illustration, **Table 26.8** reports the percentage changes relative to **Table 26.7**.

Table 26.6 Summary statistics and change (Δ) for farm gross margin (FGM) per hectare (ha) in the 2000 baseline and in the various UK NEA 2060 Scenarios (real values, £2010). FGM is as follows: cereals = £290/ha, root crops = £2,425/ha, oilseed rape = £310/ha, dairy = £576/head, beef = £69/head, sheep = £9.3/head. Minimum values are zero throughout. Q1 and Q3 are the first and third quartiles respectively. Scenarios are as follows: GF = *Go with the Flow*; GPL = *Green and Pleasant Land*; NS = *National Security*; NW = *Nature@Work*; WM = *World Markets*. Source: Fezzi *et al.* (2010b).

Scenario	Mean £/ha	Standard error ±£/ha	Q1 £/ha	Median £/ha	Q3 £/ha	Max £/ha	Total GB £ million p.a.	Δ Total GB £ million p.a.	Δ Total GB £ p.a.
Baseline	173.1	113.3	34.9	223.4	268.6	1,182	3,100	0	
GF High	205.9	184.1	34.8	227.4	301.3	1,980	3,690	590	19.0%
GF Low	185.3	151.5	35.0	214.6	280.5	2,073	3,320	220	7.1%
GPL High	171.5	133.7	34.8	198.0	254.8	1,721	3,070	-30	-1.0%
GPL Low	156.9	114.8	35.1	188.4	236.7	1,777	2,810	-290	-9.4%
LS High	196.8	164.0	33.3	223.8	299.7	2,272	3,530	430	13.9%
LS Low	192.6	145.6	36.7	224.6	297.7	1,697	3,450	350	11.3%
NS High	239.8	218.6	25.3	269.2	340.1	2,202	4,300	1,200	38.7%
NS Low	210.8	186.1	25.8	247.5	311.1	2,221	3,780	680	21.9%
NW High	167.0	159.0	31.5	164.8	253.3	1,697	2,990	-110	-3.5%
NW Low	144.4	120.3	32.0	147.4	227.4	1,871	2,590	-510	-16.5%
WM High	222.2	205.4	38.9	242.3	308.9	6,039	3,980	880	28.4%
WM Low	196.5	169.9	40.5	229.0	284.7	6,047	3,520	420	13.5%

Table 26.7 Summary statistics for change in farm gross margin per hectare (ΔFGM/ha) in the 2000 baseline and in the various UK NEA Scenarios. FGM is as follows: cereals = £290/ha, root crops = £2,425/ha, oilseed rape = £310/ha, dairy = £576/head, beef = £69/head, sheep = £9.3/head. Scenarios are as follows: GF = *Go with the Flow*; GPL = *Green and Pleasant Land*; LS = *Local Stewardship*; NS = *National Security*; NW = *Nature@Work*; WM = *World Markets*. Q1 and Q3 are the first and third quartiles respectively. Source: Fezzi *et al.* (2010b).

	ΔFGM mean (£/ha)	ΔFGM median (£/ha)	ΔFGM standard error (£/ha)	ΔFGM Q1 (£/ha)	ΔFGM Q3 (£/ha)
GF High	33	7	124	-7	39
GF Low	12	3	87	-10	19
GPL High	-2	-7	74	-30	6
GPL Low	-16	-19	56	-39	0
LS High	24	7	98	-9	39
LS Low	20	8	72	-5	37
NS High	67	29	155	-4	77
NS Low	38	14	121	-5	48
NW High	-6	-7	112	-45	9
NW Low	-29	-20	74	-63	1
WM High	49	13	148	0	43
WM Low	23	8	112	-2	21

Table 26.8 Summary statistics for change in farm gross margin per hectare (ΔFGM/ha) in the 2000 baseline and in the various UK NEA Scenarios. FGM is as follows: cereals = £290/ha, root crops = £2,425/ha, oilseed rape = £310/ha, dairy = £576/head, beef = £69/head, sheep = £9.3/head. Scenarios are as follows: GF = *Go with the Flow*; GPL = *Green and Pleasant Land*; LS = *Local Stewardship*; NS = *National Security*; NW = *Nature@Work*; WM = *World Markets*. Q1 and Q3 are the first and third quartiles respectively. Source: Fezzi *et al.* (2010b).

	ΔFGM mean (%)	ΔFGM median (%)	ΔFGM standard error (%)	ΔFGM Q1 (%)	ΔFGM Q3 (%)
GF High	19	3	109	-21	15
GF Low	7	1	77	-28	7
GPL High	-1	-3	66	-86	2
GPL Low	-9	-8	49	-110	0
LS High	14	3	87	-26	15
LS Low	11	4	64	-14	14
NS High	39	13	137	-10	29
NS Low	22	6	107	-14	18
NW High	-4	-3	99	-128	3
NW Low	-17	-9	65	-180	0
WM High	28	6	131	1	16
WM Low	14	4	99	-5	8

26.3 Terrestrial Carbon Storage and Annual Greenhouse Gas Emissions: A Scenario Analysis[10]

26.3.1 Introduction

This section presents an analysis of the changes in annual greenhouse gas emissions from terrestrial ecosystems resulting from changes in land use and associated land management, as envisaged under the UK NEA Scenarios. We then provide an economic valuation of the changes in climate regulation arising from the comparison of the 2000 baseline with each of the UK NEA Scenarios.

Our assessment of carbon storage and greenhouse gas emissions, while based on the land use patterns defined by the UK NEA Scenarios, draws directly on the CSERGE land use change model (Fezzi & Bateman 2010) as reported in the preceding section. It therefore shares the same methodology and assumptions in determining both detailed agricultural land use and livestock intensities. Both of these are important determinants of greenhouse gas balance. For example, land use influences carbon storage while methane and nitrous oxide emissions from grazing livestock represent important sources of terrestrial greenhouse gases. The limitations imposed by the prior focus upon agricultural land were in part relaxed by incorporating information on changes in Woodland extent over time directly from the UK NEA Scenarios analysis.

26.3.2 Scenario Analyses: Quantifying Changes in UK Terrestrial Greenhouse Gas Emissions

Three major categories of greenhouse gas emissions were considered when estimating changes in annual greenhouse gas emission flows:[11]

i) Direct and indirect emissions from land use and land management. Within this category three sources of emissions were considered: 1) the indirect emissions due to energy use from farmland activities such as tillage, sowing, spraying, harvesting and the production, storage and transport of fertilisers and pesticides. Per hectare estimates of greenhouse gas emissions for typical farming practices were applied to each type of land use in order to map these emissions across the UK.[12] 2) Emissions of nitrous oxide and methane from livestock, including beef

cattle, dairy cows and sheep through the production of manure and enteric fermentation.[13] 3) Direct emissions of nitrous oxide emissions from artificial fertilisers applied to agricultural land.

ii) Annual flows of carbon from soils due to land use changes. For example, permanent grassland converted from arable farming will be accumulating soil organic carbon (SOC), while permanent grassland on land that was previously under rough grazing may be losing SOC. For the baseline year (2000) annual flows of SOC were only estimated for organic (peat) soils as there is insufficient data on land use change prior to the baseline to accurately model changes in SOC in non-organic soils. In the analysis of the UK NEA Scenarios, SOC flows due to land use change in both organic and non-organic soils are included in the annual greenhouse gases emission estimates.

iii) Emissions and accumulations of carbon in terrestrial vegetative biomass. Estimates of the predicted annual accumulations of carbon in existing[14] and UK NEA Scenario-predicted future Woodlands were combined with annualised changes in the stock of vegetative biomass on agricultural land. Where the annual accumulation of carbon in terrestrial vegetative biomass under a scenario was lower than in the baseline, this was considered a net emission of greenhouse gases.

For the baseline year (2000) we estimate the annual greenhouse gases emissions from terrestrial ecosystems to be approximately 26 million tonnes of carbon dioxide equivalent (MtCO$_2$e). Land use management represents the dominant source of emissions in the baseline, with this category of emissions itself dominated by emissions from enteric fermentation and the direct release of nitrous oxide from both artificial fertilisers and the application of farmyard manure. The emissions from land use management, and to a lesser extent SOC, were partially counterbalanced by estimated annual accumulations in woodland biomass of approximately 7.6 MtCO$_2$e, with around a further 3 MtCO$_2$e accumulating annually as SOC in woodland soils.

Figure 26.6 and **Figure 26.7** map the change in terrestrial ecosystem emissions (tonnes of CO$_2$e/ha/yr) between the baseline (2000) and 2060 under each of the UK NEA Scenarios. Comparison of these figures shows that changes induced by a move from the low to high emission variants yield only modest variation in results. However, changes in greenhouse gas emissions across scenarios are highly significant. Perhaps not surprisingly, both the *Green and Pleasant Land* and *Nature@Work* scenarios generate less

---

10 This sections draws on Abson *et al.* (2010).

11 Here it should be noted that this does not represent a complete inventory of greenhouse gas emissions. The analysis is limited by the information provided by the scenarios and therefore does not account for emissions from land use practices (for example peat extraction) that cannot be inferred from the scenarios land use data. Moreover, the spatial modelling of greenhouse gas emissions required the use of coefficients that might not fully coincide with those used in other inventories.

12 Estimates of greenhouse gas emissions for forestry practices (such as application of fertilisers and energy use in harvesting) were not included as such data were not available.

13 The scenarios do not provide explicit data on livestock densities. Therefore, livestock densities were calculated using the CSERGE land use model and the land use patterns provided for the scenarios.

14 Estimates of the annual accumulations of carbon in woodland were taken from Thomson *et al.* (2007), based on the assumption that GB woodland planted before 1921 is in carbon balance (ibid). In the absence of spatially explicit data regarding the planting date of GB woodland, it was assumed that the post-1921 (carbon accumulating) woodland is distributed evenly across the total GB woodland extent. Consequently, a single (per hectare) estimate of carbon accumulation in woodland was applied to the baseline data.

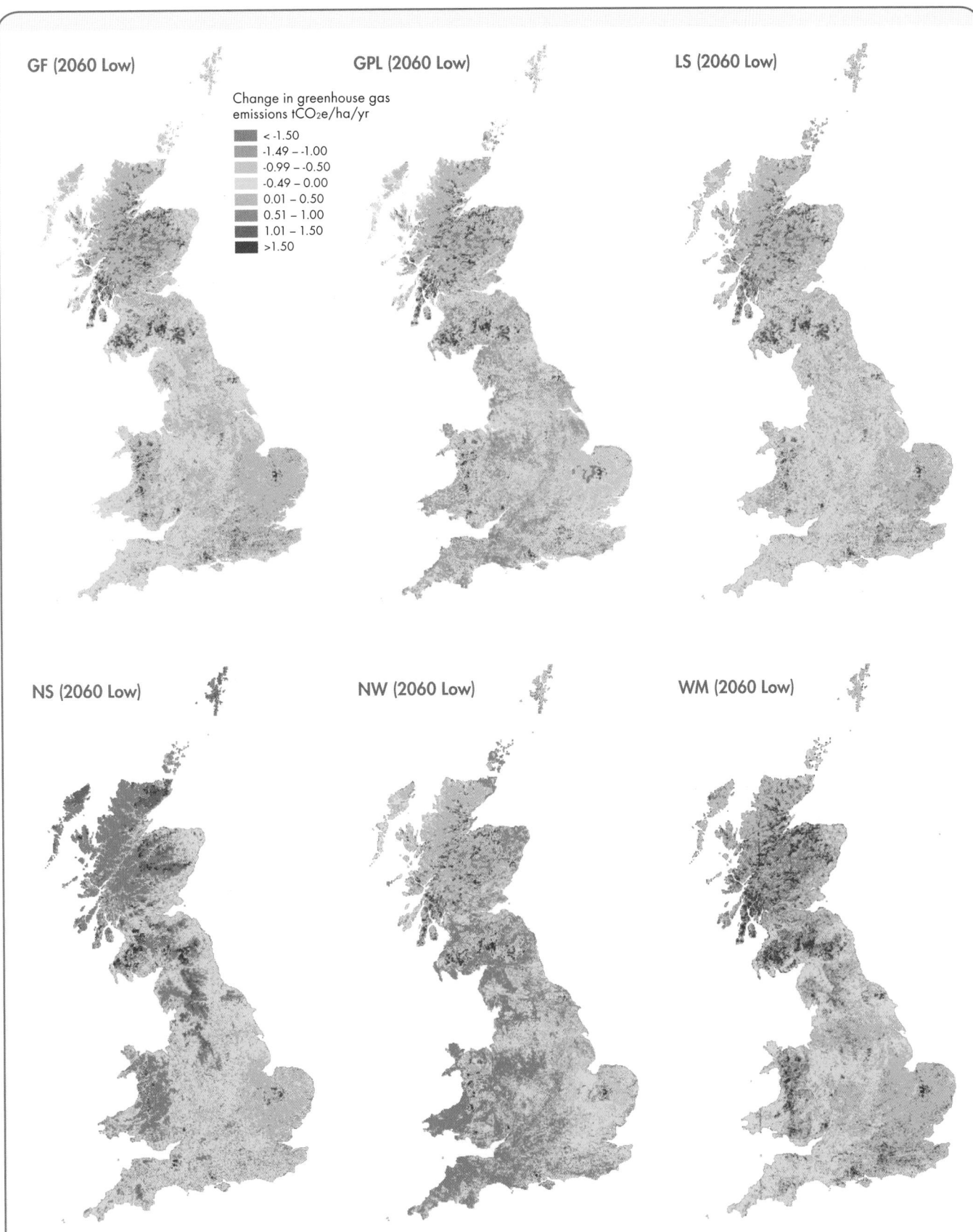

Figure 26.6 Estimated changes (from 2000 baseline) in terrestrial ecosystem carbon dioxide equivalent emissions (tCO₂e) for UK NEA Scenarios under the UKCIP low emissions climate scenario. Mapped changes in greenhouse gas emissions include: emissions from agricultural machinery; enteric fermentation from livestock; nitrous oxide emissions from artificial fertilisers and livestock origin manures; changes in all vegetative agricultural annual stocks; changes in Woodland not currently in carbon balance allowing for transition to balance over time adjusted for planting dates; allowances for estimates of future Woodland planting; changes in soil organic carbon (SOC). Scenarios are as follows: GF = *Go with the Flow*; GPL = *Green and Pleasant Land*; LS = *Local Stewardship*; NS = *National Security*; NW = *Nature@Work*; WM = *World Markets*.

Figure 26.7 Estimated changes (from 2000 baseline) in terrestrial ecosystem carbon dioxide equivalent emissions (tCO₂e) for the UK NEA Scenarios under the UKCIP high emissions climate scenario. Mapped changes in greenhouse gas emissions include: emissions from agricultural machinery; enteric fermentation from livestock; N₂O emissions from artificial fertilisers and livestock manures; changes in all vegetative agricultural annual stocks; changes in Woodland not currently in carbon balance, allowing for transition to balance over time adjusted for planting dates; allowances for estimates of future Woodland planting; changes in soil organic carbon (SOC). Scenarios are as follows: GF = *Go with the Flow*; GPL = *Green and Pleasant Land*; LS = *Local Stewardship*. NS = *National Security*; NW = *Nature@Work*; WM = *World Markets*.

emissions than the baseline. These scenarios show relatively uniform decreases in greenhouse gas emissions in lowland areas, driven by an extensification of agriculture, with conversion of arable land and improved grasslands to semi-natural grasslands and rough grazing. This in turn results in lower stocking densities of beef and sheep and reduced emissions from both enteric fermentation and nitrous oxide emissions from fertilisers than in the baseline case. However, the *Green and Pleasant Land* and *Nature@Work* scenarios show moderate increases in greenhouse gas emissions in upland areas, largely driven by increased livestock densities and a decline in carbon accumulation in afforested and upland areas. The *Local Stewardship* scenarios show similar patterns of greenhouse gas emissions as the *Green and Pleasant Land* scenarios, but with less extensive land use changes and therefore less dramatic changes in emissions. The *National Security* scenarios show significant decreases in emissions (relative to the baseline), but with very different patterns of emissions from *Green and Pleasant Land* and *Nature@Work*. In the *National Security* scenario, a move to boost agricultural output leads to increased emissions in the most productive areas of southern and eastern England, combined with significantly elevated emissions from upland peatlands. This is somewhat counterbalanced by large decreases in emissions in Scotland, northern England and Wales due to increased afforestation in those regions. The *World Markets* and *Go with the Flow* scenarios show generally increased emissions compared to the baseline. However, falls in emissions in some upland areas means that the *Go with the Flow* scenarios overall result in only moderate increases in emissions of around 0.13 tonnes of CO_2e/ha/yr by 2060, compared to 0.46 tonnes of CO_2e/ha/yr by 2060 for the low emissions climate variant of the *World Markets* scenario.

Table 26.9 summarises the national changes in total greenhouse gas emissions under the UK NEA land use scenarios, where positive values represent net increases (from the 2000 baseline) in greenhouse gas emissions. At a national scale, only the *World Markets* and *Go with the Flow* scenarios show consistent increases in annual emissions

compared to the baseline. Increases in emissions from the *World Markets* scenarios are driven by reductions in the extent of Woodlands and moderate expansions in arable and dairy production, largely at the expense of Semi-natural Grasslands. Emission increases in the *Go with the Flow* scenarios (of approximately 2.9 $MtCO_2e$/yr for both the *Go with the Flow* climate variants) occur mainly in Scotland and are driven largely by a reduction in carbon accumulation in Woodland. In contrast, Scotland sees significant declines in greenhouse gas emissions under the *National Security* scenario. Decreases in arable farming and the extent of Improved Grassland across lowland England result in significant decreases in emissions (between 8 and 13 $MtCO_2e$/yr) under the *Green and Pleasant Land* and *Nature@Work* scenarios.

Figure 26.8 shows in more detail how the three major sources of terrestrial carbon emissions/accumulations (land management, SOC changes and carbon accumulation/release for vegetative biomass) interact in the six scenarios. Note that only the UKCIP low emissions variants of the scenarios are presented here, as the patterns of emissions are broadly similar to those recorded for the high emissions scenario variants. *World Markets* and *Go with the Flow* are the only scenarios with consistently large increases in emissions relative to the baseline. This arises through declines in the annual accumulation of carbon in vegetative biomass in both these scenarios, exacerbated by additional emissions due to soil disturbance through land use change on peat soils in the *World Markets* scenarios. Nevertheless, as with the other four scenarios, the *World Markets* and *Go with the Flow* scenarios indicate consistent declines in emissions from land use management, driven by aggregate declines in arable farming, improved grassland and livestock numbers. Only the *Green and Pleasant Land* and *Nature@Work* scenarios show increased accumulation in SOC. Further investigation showed that this was due to increases in Woodlands and Semi-natural Grasslands (rough gazing) on non-organic soils. In contrast, aggregate emissions from SOC are predicted to increase in the *National Security* scenario as peat soils are disturbed through tree

Table 26.9 National (GB) analysis of changes (from the 2000 baseline) in total annual greenhouse gas emissions ('000s of tonnes CO_2 equivalent/yr) in 2060 under each UK NEA Scenario (positive values represent increases in annual greenhouse gas emissions). Scenarios are as follows: GF = *Go with the Flow*; GPL = *Green and Pleasant Land*; LS = *Local Stewardship*; NS = *National Security*; NW = *Nature@Work*; WM = *World Markets*.

	GF	GPL	LS	NS	NW	WM
UKCIP low emissions variant						
England	835	-8,355	-518	-4,327	-12,609	2,357
Scotland	1,986	330	1,404	-6,610	-1,791	4,813
Wales	92	-803	-522	-2,185	-2,381	600
GB	2,913	-8,828	364	-13,122	-16,781	7,770
UKCIP high emissions variant						
England	1,467	-8,020	-2,513	-3,550	-12,219	1,394
Scotland	1,676	189	1,201	-6,728	-2,104	4,360
Wales	-173	-979	-762	-2,126	-2,384	370
GB	2,970	-8,810	-2,073	-12,405	-16,707	6,124

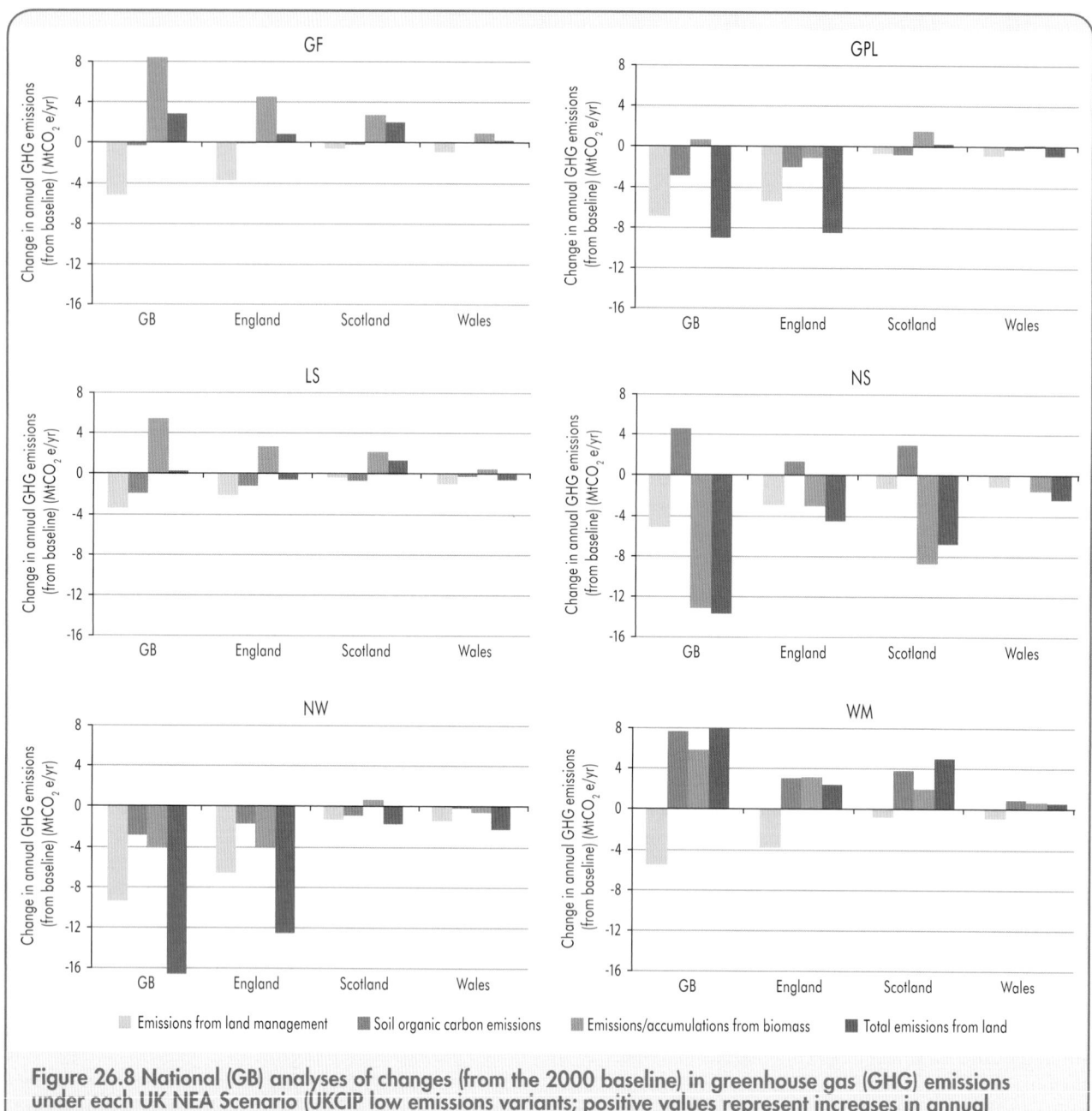

Figure 26.8 National (GB) analyses of changes (from the 2000 baseline) in greenhouse gas (GHG) emissions under each UK NEA Scenario (UKCIP low emissions variants; positive values represent increases in annual GHG emissions). Scenarios are as follows: GF = *Go with the Flow*; GPL = *Green and Pleasant Land*; LS = *Local Stewardship*; NS = *National Security*; NW = *Nature@Work*; WM = *World Markets*.

planting and the conversion of Semi-natural Grasslands to arable land uses in Scotland and upland England.

26.3.3 The Value of Terrestrial Climate Regulation

The UK government's official non-traded marginal abatement cost of carbon (MACC) prices (DECC, 2009) are used to value the changes in annual emissions from 2000 to 2060 under each scenario.[15] This means that carbon prices are set at £41.28 per tonne of CO_2e in 2000, and are increasing to £273.50 per tonne of CO_2e in 2060.[16] **Table 26.10** shows the change in the annual costs of greenhouse gas emissions from GB terrestrial ecosystems compared to the baseline year (2000) for each scenario. This represents the difference in value generated by each of the scenarios (in 2060) compared to that under the baseline land use patterns in 2000. This means that positive (negative) values represent an increase (decrease) in costs. Three of the scenarios (*Green and Pleasant Land*, *National Security* and *Nature@Work*), in both their low and high emission

15 Only the Department of Energy and Climate Change (DECC) central estimates of carbon prices are reported here, the upper and lower bound estimates are ± 50% of the central estimate. Here it should be noted that the official DECC carbon price is an estimate of the cost of abating greenhouse gas emissions and not the social cost of the damage caused by greenhouse gas emissions. The analysis uses a simplified approach to carbon valuation compared to that discussed in Chapter 22. Interested readers should consult the accompanying report by Abson *et al.* (2010) for further discussion of carbon pricing issues.
16 All values in 2010 prices.

Table 26.10 Change in the value from baseline year (2000) of annual greenhouse gas emissions from Great Britain terrestrial ecosystems in 2060 under the UK NEA Scenarios (£million/yr). Negative values represent increases in annual costs of greenhouse gas emissions. Scenarios are as follows: GF = *Go with the Flow*; GPL = *Green and Pleasant Land*; LS = *Local Stewardship*; NS = *National Security*; NW = *Nature@Work*; WM = *World Markets*.

	GF	GPL	NS	NW	LS	WM
	UKCIP low emissions variant					
England	-228	2,285	1,183	3,449	142	-645
Scotland	-543	-90	1,808	490	-384	-1,316
Wales	-25	220	598	651	143	-164
GB	-797	2,414	3,589	4,590	-100	-2,125
	UKCIP high emissions variant					
England	-401	2,193	971	3,342	687	-381
Scotland	-458	-52	1,840	575	-328	-1,192
Wales	47	268	581	652	208	-101
GB	-812	2,410	3,393	4,569	567	-1,675

UKCIP variants, show significant reductions in annual costs associated with emissions of greenhouse gas compared to the baseline land use configuration. The majority of these savings occur in England for the *Green and Pleasant Land* and *Nature@Work* scenarios, while Scotland generates most benefits under the *National Security* scenario.

If we assume that the changes in projected emissions occur linearly over the period, then we can calculate present values for 2000–2060 (**Table 26.11**) and convert these to annual equivalents[17] (**Table 26.12**).

The analysis shows marked differences between scenarios with the highest benefit attributed to the *Nature@Work* scenario. Only the *World Markets*, *Go with the Flow* and *Local Stewardship* (low UKCIP emissions variant) scenarios show an increase in the greenhouse gas costs associated with terrestrial ecosystems. As expected, an increase in the discount rate reduces the absolute values associated with the service/disservice.

Table 26.11 National (GB) cumulative present value of the changes in greenhouse gas emissions between the 2000 baseline and 2060 under each UK NEA Scenario (£1,000 million); calculated for various discount rates (negative values represent additional costs relative to the baseline). Scenarios are as follows: GF = *Go with the Flow*; GPL = *Green and Pleasant Land*; LS = *Local Stewardship*; NS = *National Security*; NW = *Nature@Work*; WM = *World Markets*.

	Discount rates (%)								
	0.00	1.50	2.00	2.50	3.00	3.50	4.00	4.50	5.00
Scenario	**UKCIP low emissions variants**								
GF	-13.8	-7.0	-5.6	-4.6	-3.7	-3.0	-2.5	-2.1	-1.7
GPL	41.9	21.2	17.0	13.8	11.2	9.2	7.5	6.2	5.2
LS	-1.7	-0.9	-0.7	-0.6	-0.5	-0.4	-0.3	-0.3	-0.2
NS	62.2	31.5	25.3	20.5	16.7	13.6	11.2	9.3	7.7
NW	79.6	40.3	32.4	26.2	21.3	17.4	14.3	11.9	9.9
WM	-36.9	-18.6	-15.0	-12.1	-9.9	-8.1	-6.6	-5.5	-4.6
	UKCIP high emissions variants								
GF	-14.1	-7.1	-5.7	-4.6	-3.8	-3.1	-2.5	-2.1	-1.7
GPL	41.8	21.1	17.0	13.8	11.2	9.2	7.5	6.2	5.2
LS	9.8	5.0	4.0	3.2	2.6	2.2	1.8	1.5	1.2
NS	58.8	29.8	24.0	19.4	15.8	12.9	10.6	8.8	7.3
NW	79.2	40.1	32.3	26.1	21.2	17.4	14.3	11.8	9.8
WM	-29.0	-14.7	-11.8	-9.6	-7.8	-6.4	-5.2	-4.3	-3.6

Table 26.12 Cumulative annuity values for Great Britain of the changes in greenhouse gas emissions between the 2000 baseline and 2060 under each UK NEA Scenario (£million); calculated for various discount rates (negative values represent additional costs relative to the baseline). Scenarios are as follows: GF = *Go with the Flow*; GPL = *Green and Pleasant Land*; LS = *Local Stewardship*; NS = *National Security*; NW = *Nature@Work*; WM = *World Markets*.

	Discount rates (%)								
	0.00	1.50	2.00	2.50	3.00	3.50	4.00	4.50	5.00
Scenario	**UKCIP low emissions variants**								
GF	-230	-177	-162	-147	-134	-121	-110	-100	-91
GPL	698	538	490	446	405	368	334	302	275
LS	-29	-22	-20	-18	-17	-15	-14	-12	-11
NS	1,037	800	729	663	602	547	496	450	408
NW	1,326	1,022	932	848	770	699	634	575	522
WM	-614	-473	-432	-393	-357	-324	-294	-266	-242
	UKCIP high emissions variants								
GF	-235	-181	-165	-150	-136	-124	-112	-102	-92
GPL	696	537	489	445	404	367	333	302	274
LS	164	126	115	105	95	86	78	71	64
NS	981	756	689	627	569	517	469	425	386
NW	1,321	1,018	928	844	767	696	631	572	520
WM	-484	-373	-340	-309	-281	-255	-231	-210	-190

17 Present Value, $PV = \sum_{t=0}^{60} P_{CO_2}^t \times E_{CO_2}^t \times (1+r)^{-t}$, where $P_{CO_2}^t$ and $E_{CO_2}^t$ are the carbon price and emissions, respectively, at time t, and r is the discount rate. $PV = AEQ \times a_{\overline{60}}|_r$, where *AEQ* is the equivalent annual value shown in Table 26.11, and $a_{\overline{60}}|_r = \dfrac{1 - 1/(1+r)^{60}}{r}$

A constant discount rate assumed.

26.4 Biodiversity Impacts: Using Birds as an Indicator Species

As discussed in Chapter 22, while there are a variety of methods available for estimating the use value of biodiversity, to date monetary estimates of its non-use existence value[18] can only be obtained via stated preference (SP) methods.[19] While a number of such studies have been undertaken, critics question whether the values estimated by SP analyses for such a low-experience[20] good as biodiversity are based upon the robust preferences required for admission within cost-benefit analyses. While we do not pass judgement on this matter, we use the present analysis to demonstrate that, even in the absence of monetary estimates of non-use existence values, there are useful inputs which economic analyses can provide to decision-makers. In particular, economists can advise on the cost-effectiveness of different situations by comparing the levels of both biodiversity and other economic values arising in different situations. Each of the UK NEA Scenarios imply a different array of ecosystem services for which robust values can be estimated. These can be contrasted with the consequences of each scenario in terms of levels of biodiversity, and a trade-off can be observed. Suppose that, for argument's sake, we observe one scenario where monetised benefits are high but biodiversity levels are poor, whereas in another state monetised values are lower but biodiversity improves. Decision makers now have the costs of improving biodiversity. We term this a 'cost-effectiveness analysis' (CEA). Clearly this is not as desirable as knowing the monetary value of that biodiversity and entering it within a cost-benefit analysis (CBA); nevertheless, at least the feasible trade-off is now explicit. Furthermore, additional analyses might find win-win situations where both biodiversity and the monetary value of other goods increase. In the present section of this chapter we discuss quantitative assessments of the impacts of each scenario upon biodiversity. In the final section we go on to compare the valuation of all monetised outcomes of each scenario with their impacts upon biodiversity. By comparing across scenarios we see the trade-off between monetary values and biodiversity, thus revealing the cost-effectiveness of providing different levels of biodiversity.

While the other analyses in this chapter provide us with an (albeit partial) economic valuation of the ecosystem-related goods under consideration, we now need to assess some measure of biodiversity in each scenario before we can complete our CEA. This section provides that assessment through two analyses, both of which use birds as indicators of biodiversity. Birds are a highly visible and widely studied feature of UK biodiversity. Furthermore they are high in the food chain and are often considered to be good indicators of wider ecosystem health (e.g. Gregory *et al.* 2005). Birds are more mobile than most other groups, and so will respond to, and reflect, environmental quality at a rather broader scale than mammals or terrestrial insects, for example. This probably makes them better indicators at the landscape scale and less good locally. However, no single animal or plant group, and especially no small set of variables describing that group, can ever provide a comprehensive summary of all aspects of biodiversity and we do not suggest that they do so. Rather, we note the value that birds have as indicators and make use of the important pragmatic benefit that they are better monitored than any other aspect of UK biodiversity. Our first analysis takes a wide view across almost all GB bird species, while the second focuses upon farmland birds as the group that has suffered the most dramatic declines over the past half century and earlier. In both cases, measures of bird success are modelled as a function of land use, because aspects of this have a proven impact upon biodiversity. These models are then used to assess the predicted impact upon these bird measures as a result of the differing land uses envisioned under each of the UK NEA Scenarios.

26.4.1 Breeding Bird Diversity as a Function of Land Cover[21]

26.4.1.1 Methods

The model used for this analysis is overviewed in Chapter 22 and discussed in detail by Hulme & Siriwardena (2010). Essentially, it links GB data collected in and around the year 2000 by the BTO/JNCC/RSPB Breeding Bird Survey (BBS) with land use information provided by the CEH Land Cover Map 2000. After excluding extremely rare species, the composition of the bird community represented by the presence and abundance of all remaining bird species in each survey square was summarised using Simpson's Diversity Index (D), calculated in each year following Equation (1).

$$D = \frac{1}{\displaystyle\sum_{i=1}^{s} P_i^2} \qquad (1)$$

Where S = number of bird species recorded at a focal site in that year, pi = proportion of birds of species i relative to the total number of birds of all species.

---

18 This refers to the value which individuals may obtain from the pure knowledge that a species or entity continues to exist, quite separately from any use of that species or entity. For further discussion see Chapter 22.

19 Stated preference monetary valuation methods are overviewed in the opening sections of Chapter 22. Methods for the non-monetary assessment of various values are considered in the UK NEA discussion of shared social values (Chapter 24).

20 Non-use values concern goods which the valuing individual typically has no direct experience of (e.g. the preservation of a pristine Antarctica). A further concern is that the individual may lack understanding of that good (e.g. the role of a species within the sustainable functioning of an ecosystem). Low experience and understanding may well affect the values individuals attribute to a good. While this does not necessarily invalidate SP responses (in such circumstances a willingness-to-pay response may indeed reflect underlying preferences) there is evidence to suggest that in such circumstances responses may be more vulnerable to 'framing' effects, i.e. they may be biased by elements of study design and question phrasing which economic theory would see as irrelevant to well formed, stable preferences. For further discussion see Chapter 22 of the UK NEA and the closing chapter of Bateman *et al.* (2002).

21 This section draws from Hulme & Siriwardena (2010).

The mean value of D was calculated for each square across all years within the study period in which that square was surveyed and this was modelled alongside the habitat and land-use classes from the CEH Land Cover Map 2000.[22] Models were run with all different combinations of land-cover classes, the relative importance of the classes in predicting diversity was calculated from these results and diversity across the whole of the UK was predicted at the 1 km² level using these values. Diversity was then predicted using the same models for each of the UK NEA land-cover scenarios, considering both low and high climate change predictions for land-use change. The difference between these diversity predictions and those for the Land Cover Map 2000 data were then calculated and summary statistics generated for the full set of 12 scenarios.

26.4.1.2 Results

Records for some 3,468 BBS 1 km grid squares across GB were analysed and 96 bird species were included in the diversity calculation. The best model of those that were run contained all land cover classes except for coastal habitats and inland water cover, indicating that all were associated with a variation in bird diversity.

All land cover variables, except for upland habitats, displayed generally positive, but non-linear, influences on bird diversity which levelled off or declined at high percentages of cover. Upland habitats had a negative influence on diversity but this levelled off at high cover. The coastal habitat cover had a negative influence on diversity and inland water cover had a positive influence but these effects were weaker than for the other land cover classes. Overall the largest influence on diversity in the models was geographic region (a control in the analyses), with large differences in diversity between 100 km squares across the UK.

The predicted change in bird diversity between the 2000 baseline and each of the UK NEA Scenarios for both high and low emissions climate change were calculated. **Figure 26.9** illustrates the resulting spatial patterns for each of these scenarios using high emissions assumption.

Considering the various spatial distributions mapped in **Figure 26.9** we can see that, in general, the *Go with the Flow, Green and Pleasant Land* and *Nature@Work* scenarios all lead to some modest increase in bird diversity in lowland areas. While this might be as expected for the overtly pro-environmental *Green and Pleasant Land* and *Nature@Work* scenarios, the increase in diversity under the *Go with the Flow* scenario indicates that this is set against the ongoing commitment across society to biodiversity-friendly management, for example as reflected by the Common Agricultural Policy 'Pillar 2' investment in agri-environment measures, as well as a general leaning towards biodiversity under this scenario. However, all three of these scenarios also reveal a slightly more pronounced decrease in diversity in upland areas as climate change induces increases in relative agricultural intensity within these areas. This trend is broadly reversed for the *Local Stewardship* and *National*

Security scenarios and becomes most extreme under the *World Markets* scenario, although here we also see some declines in upland areas. Indeed, across all scenarios, it is the *World Markets* high emissions case which gives both the greatest declines (-0.131) and largest increases (0.040) in predicted bird diversity.

To illustrate what the predicted changes may mean in terms of real changes in the bird community, the diversity for one high-diversity, lowland square in south-east England and one low-diversity, upland square in Scotland was calculated for the year 2000, altering bird numbers slightly to show their effects on the diversity index. The lowland square had 26 species in 2000, including 15 blackbirds, one blackcap, 11 chaffinches, 16 great tits and 37 wood pigeons, giving a diversity index of 9.087. Removing the blackcap resulted in a reduction of 0.123 in the index, removing all eight species with only one individual resulted in a reduction of 0.953, removing one chaffinch reduced the index by 0.043 and redistributing the total number of individuals as if all 26 species had been recorded in equal numbers seen increased the index by 16.913. The upland square had four species, comprising six golden plovers, 24 meadow pipits, one red grouse and two skylarks, giving a diversity index of 1.765. Removing the red grouse reduced the index for the upland square by 0.103, removing one of the golden plovers reduced the index by 0.075, removing one of the meadow pipits reduced the index by 0.0351 and removing 14 meadow pipits reduced the index by 0.795.

Most of the hypothetical changes envisioned in the above illustration lie outside the minimum-to-maximum ranges predicted under any of the scenarios. The patterns of change predicted under each of these scenarios are summarised in **Table 26.13** and all present changes in absolute diversity values that are well below 10%. Thus, all of the changes predicted would represent, in practice, rather minor changes in bird communities, rather than local extinctions or colonisations.

26.4.1.3 Discussion

An uncritical assessment of the results of this analysis would suggest that the average impact of the *Go with the Flow, Green and Pleasant Land, National Security* and *Nature@Work* scenarios would be a modest increase in bird diversity while only the *Local Stewardship* and *World Markets* scenarios would lead, on average, to reductions in diversity. Such an assessment oversimplifies the messages of the analysis and underplays important caveats spelt out in detail by Hulme & Siriwardena (2010), to which the interested reader is directed (chief amongst these is the issue that simple species diversity does not necessarily reflect the presence or diversity of species of conservation interest). However, as outlined in the introduction to this chapter, our purpose here is not to produce a complete analysis to answer any specific policy question, but rather to demonstrate that techniques now exist to change the approach to policy formulation and decision making. As such, the present analysis provides an

---

22 Regional variations in bird diversity were controlled for by including the 100 km Ordnance Survey grid square in which each BBS square is located within the analysis. A regional bias in survey effort across the UK towards highly populated areas with a higher number of volunteers was accounted for by weighting regions with lower survey effort more highly.

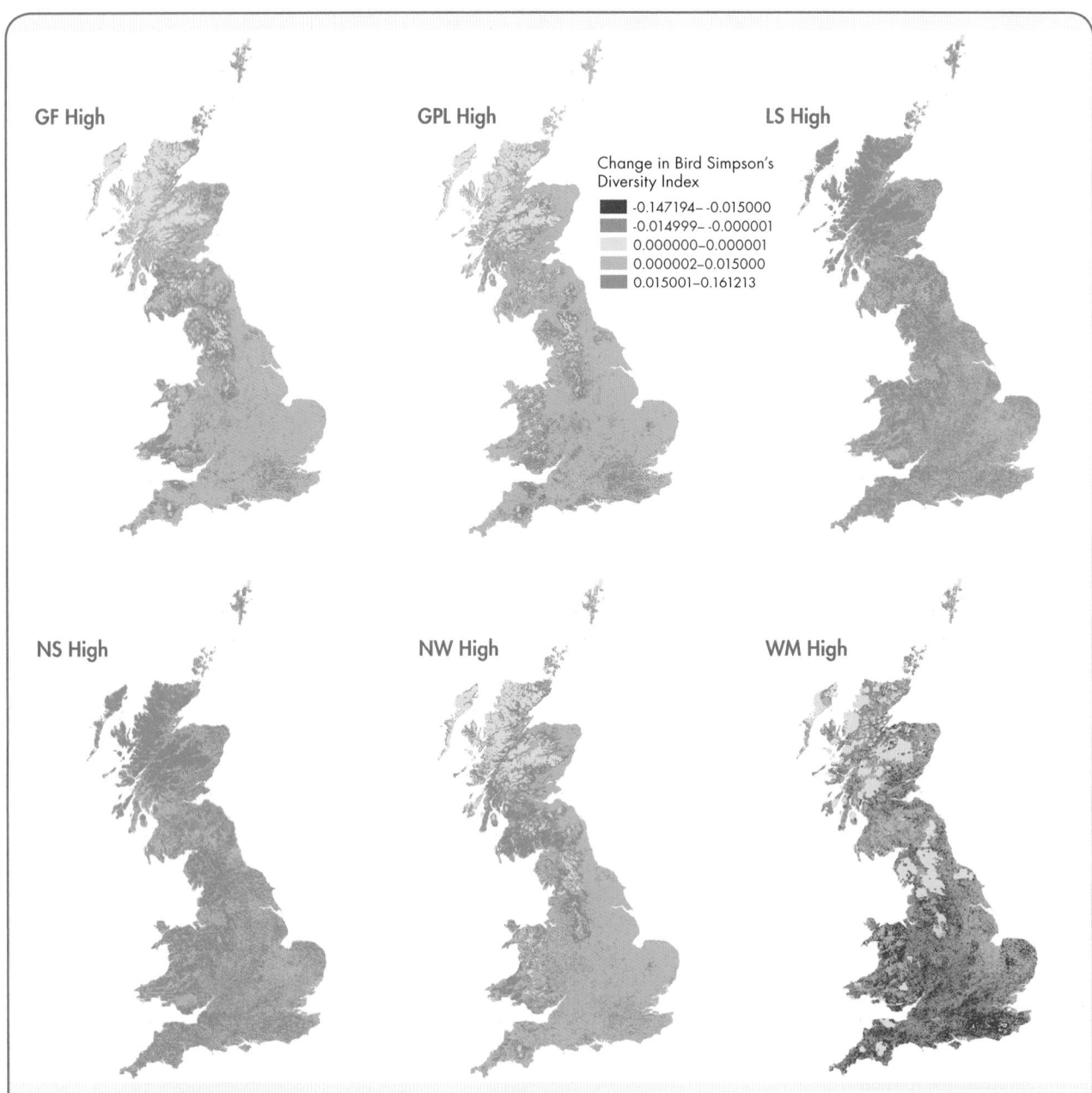

Figure 26.9 Predicted change in Simpson's Diversity Index for British birds arising from a shift from the 2000 baseline to the UK NEA Scenarios under high emission climate change. Scenarios are as follows: GF = *Go with the Flow*; GPL = *Green and Pleasant Land*; LS = *Local Stewardship*; NS = *National Security*; NW = *Nature@Work*; WM = *World Markets*.

Change in Bird Simpson's Diversity Index
- -0.147194– -0.015000
- -0.014999– -0.000001
- 0.000000–0.000001
- 0.000002–0.015000
- 0.015001–0.161213

indication of the type of quantitative biodiversity analysis which can be generated to set aside economic benefit valuations within a cost-effectiveness analysis.

26.4.2 Habitat Association Modelling for Farmland Birds[23]

Changes in farming practices have contributed to a 52% decrease in the Farmland Bird Index for England between 1970 and 2009 (Defra 2010). Such bird species are important, not only as indicators of wider biodiversity, but also in their own right.

The model used for this analysis is discussed in Chapter 22 and presented in detail by Dugdale (2010). The analysis considers a single 'guild'[24] of 19, primarily farmland, bird species. Guild richness was measured as the number of these species present in each 10 km grid square in England and Wales, with data being taken from Gibbons *et al.* (1993). Models were developed linking guild richness to data on land use, Woodland and Urban extent. The percentages of each 10 km grid square utilised for cereals, temporary grassland, Coniferous Woodland and Urban use, along with the mean altitude, were found to be highly significant predictors of measures of the number of farmland bird species present. The analysis was adjusted for spatial autocorrelation using geographically weighted regression techniques. The analysis was undertaken for a baseline period (which for data

23 For full details see Dugdale (2010).
24 Defined as a group in terms of the common foods they consume; in this guild primarily seeds and invertebrates.

Table 26.13 Summary of statistics showing the predicted changes in bird diversity from the 2000 baseline to each UK NEA Scenario (Low and High emissions) for 2060. All statistics are summaries across all 235,974 1-km squares in Great Britain for which mapped predictions were available and so represent the average changes across the whole country and the variability in these patterns. Mean standard error <0.00005 in all cases. Scenarios are as follows: GF = *Go with the Flow*; GPL = *Green and Pleasant Land*; LS = *Local Stewardship*; NS = *National Security*; NW = *Nature@Work*; WM = *World Markets*. Q1 and Q3 are the first and third quartiles respectively.

Scenario	Mean	SD	Min	Q1	Median	Q3	Max	Range
GF Low	0.00141	0.00262	-0.00480	0.00000	0.00054	0.00220	0.01689	0.02169
GPL Low	0.00684	0.00570	-0.01561	0.00097	0.00654	0.01172	0.02880	0.04441
LS Low	-0.00080	0.00348	-0.01424	-0.00237	0.00000	0.00116	0.00777	0.02200
NS Low	0.01034	0.01213	-0.00722	0.00093	0.00442	0.01864	0.04681	0.05403
NW Low	0.00557	0.00556	-0.00552	0.00078	0.00432	0.00852	0.03199	0.03751
WM Low	0.00019	0.00465	-0.02124	-0.00211	0.00020	0.00286	0.01085	0.03209
GF High	0.00175	0.00271	-0.00774	0.00000	0.00118	0.00336	0.01526	0.02300
GPL High	0.00467	0.00497	-0.01995	0.00000	0.00372	0.00879	0.02577	0.04572
LS High	-0.00024	0.00369	-0.01541	-0.00203	0.00015	0.00195	0.01057	0.02598
NS High	0.00870	0.01154	-0.01477	0.00022	0.00327	0.01522	0.03838	0.05315
NW High	0.00396	0.00519	-0.00959	0.00000	0.00243	0.00659	0.03032	0.03992
WM High	**-0.00434**	**0.01215**	**-0.12531**	**-0.00735**	**-0.00087**	**0.00139**	**0.02533**	**0.15064**

Table 26.14 Summary statistics for the change in guild richness for 19 species of farmland birds from the baseline to 2060 under each of the UK NEA Scenarios (High and Low emissions). Note: The baseline here is 1988 rather than the year 2000 baseline used for all other analyses in this chapter. Scenarios are as follows: GF = *Go with the Flow*; GPL = *Green and Pleasant Land*; LS = *Local Stewardship*; NS = *National Security*; NW = *Nature@Work*; WM = *World Markets*.

	GF High	GF Low	GPL High	GPL Low	LS High	LS Low	NS High	NS Low	NW High	NW Low	WM High	WM Low
Mean	-0.42	-0.32	-0.37	-0.27	-0.39	-0.30	-0.84	-0.72	-0.62	-0.54	-0.47	-0.30
Mean (% change)	-2.2	-1.7	-1.9	-1.4	-2.1	-1.6	-4.4	-3.8	-3.3	-2.8	-2.5	-1.6
± Standard deviation	2.35	2.21	2.34	2.21	2.32	2.19	2.30	2.16	2.38	2.25	2.28	2.12
Lower quartile	-1.89	-1.68	-1.85	-1.64	-1.85	-1.65	-2.26	-1.95	-2.10	-1.90	-1.91	-1.63
Median	-0.48	-0.40	-0.47	-0.36	-0.49	-0.38	-0.85	-0.75	-0.73	-0.65	-0.58	-0.41
Upper quartile	0.95	0.94	0.97	0.96	0.95	0.96	0.61	0.61	0.72	0.70	0.87	0.88

availability reasons was fixed at 1988; see Dugdale, 2010) and for all scenarios with changes to 2060 being calculated.

Results of the scenario analysis are summarised in **Table 26.14**. The mean impact of all scenarios is of a reduction in guild richness, although this is generally not large enough to generate a one species change in typical 10 km grid squares. Nevertheless, four scenarios reduce mean guild richness by more than 0.5 (*National Security* High, *National Security* Low, *Nature@Work* High and *Nature@Work* Low) suggesting that, on average, one species fewer would be present under these scenarios.[25] That these scenarios are the most negative for guild richness seems logical, as under *National Security* there

are major losses of grasslands and heaths accompanied by large increases in conifer plantations, while under the *Nature@Work* scenario the area of farmland (obviously important to this guild) decreases markedly. More generally, the lower quartile results suggest that, under almost all scenarios, more than one-quarter of all 10 km grid squares in England and Wales would suffer the loss of two species. However, this is partly offset by a further quarter of grid squares which would, typically, gain one species from this guild.

Figure 26.10 summarises the overall changes in the expected number of species for England and Wales. All scenarios lead to more grid squares which suffer losses

25 Note that the UK NEA Scenarios team only specify land use change and not changes in the intensity of that land use. If intensity also increases (for example in the *World Markets* scenario) then this might be expected to push impacts towards what is at present the lower quartile of estimates (as discussed subsequently).

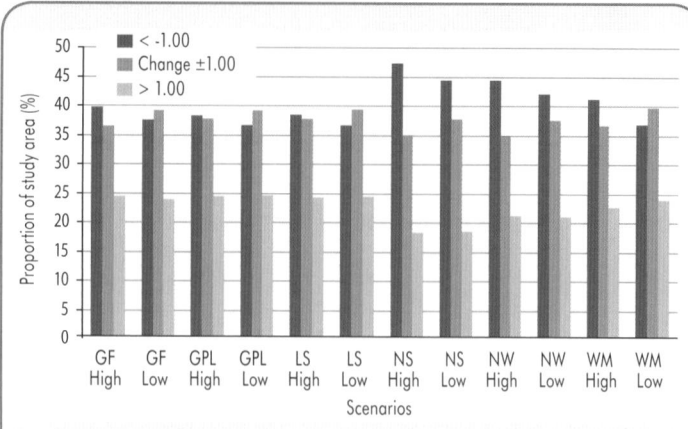

Figure 26.10 The impact of each UK NEA Scenario on predicted guild richness. The proportion (%) of England and Wales that is negatively impacted (predicted loss of more than one species), neutrally impacted (gain or loss of up to one species) or positively impacted (predicted gain of more than one species). Scenarios are as follows: GF = *Go with the Flow*; GPL = *Green and Pleasant Land*; LS = *Local Stewardship*; NS = *National Security*; NW = *Nature@Work*; WM = *World Markets*.

in the number of species than squares which enjoy gains. Furthermore, across all scenarios the high emission variant always leads to a reduction in guild richness in a larger proportion of England and Wales than in the case of the respective low emissions scenario.

Five scenarios predicted losses of more than one species in over 40% of England and Wales (*National Security* High and Low, *Nature@Work* High and Low and *World Markets* High). Overall the *National Security* high and low emissions scenarios had a negative or neutral effect over the largest area.

As suggested in **Table 26.14**, there is considerable spatial variation in predicted guild richness across scenarios. These spatial patterns are illustrated in **Figure 26.11** for the low emission scenarios, and **Figure 26.12** for the high emissions scenarios.

Considering **Figure 26.11** and **Figure 26.12**, the general spatial pattern is consistent across all 12 scenarios, with upland areas generally seeing an increase in guild richness and the English Midlands, Welsh borders and Yorkshire

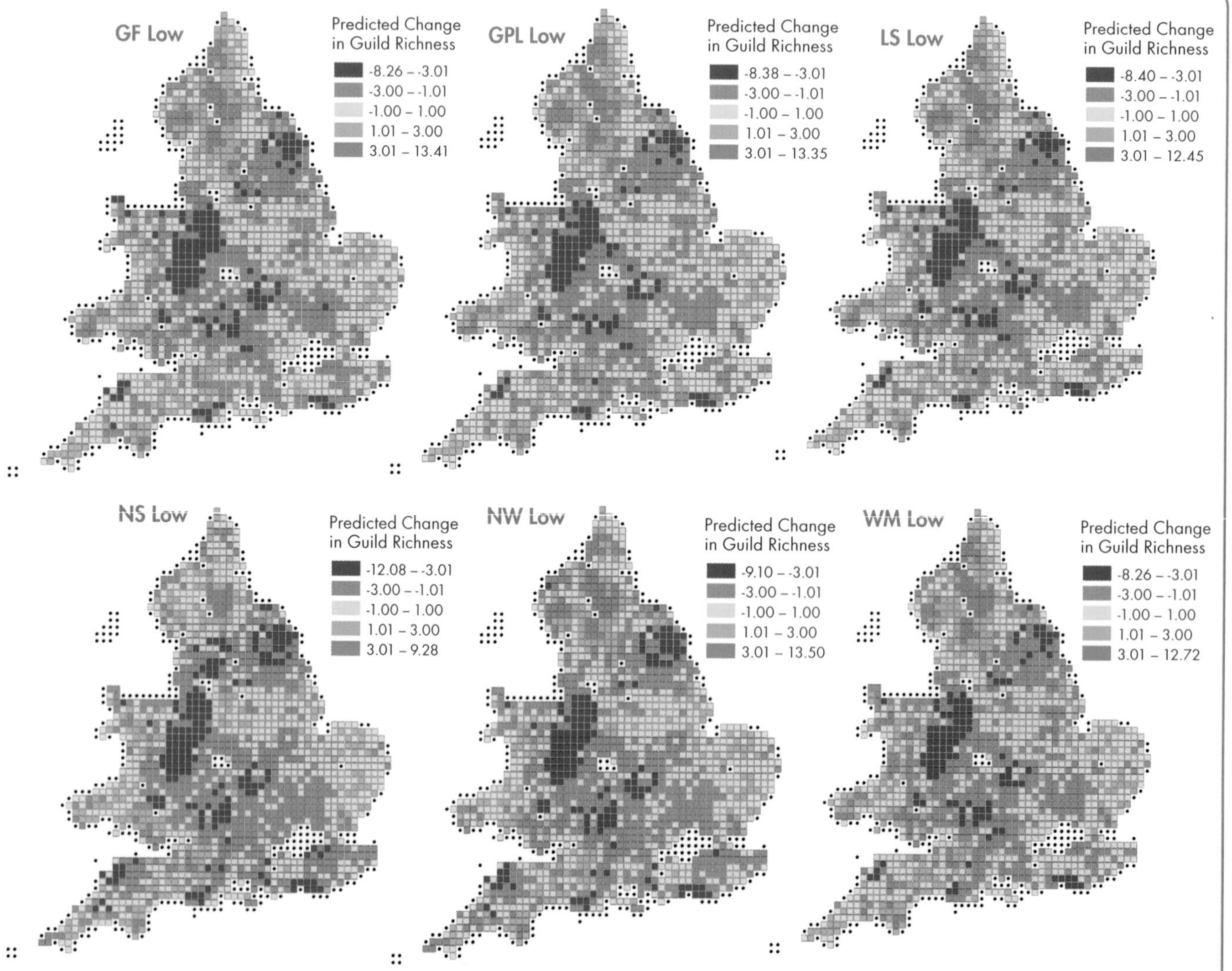

Figure 26.11 Spatial distribution of changes in predicted guild richness between the 1988 baseline and each of the Low emission UK NEA Scenarios for 2060 in England and Wales. Scenarios are as follows: GF = *Go with the Flow*; GPL = *Green and Pleasant Land*; LS = *Local Stewardship*; NS = *National Security*; NW = *Nature@Work*; WM = *World Markets*.

suffering the most significant reductions. The spatial patterns of predicted change in guild richness between the high and low emissions versions of each scenario were very similar. As might be expected, for any given scenario the high emission variant always leads to greater losses of guild richness than the respective low emission variant.

26.5 Open-access Recreation[26]

26.5.1 Introduction
This section applies the methodology developed in Chapter 22 for predicting the pattern and value of recreational day visits in GB under different scenarios. These predictions

are compared with the year 2000 baseline to calculate the changes in recreation values under each scenario.

26.5.2 Methodology
The general methodology is as described in Chapter 22. In essence this involves three linked analyses:

i) A site prediction model (SPM) is used to predict the number and location of recreation sites under each scenario. Here sites are predicted by examining data obtained from the Monitor of the Engagement with the Natural Environment (MENE) which was recently released by Natural England, Department for Environment, Food and Rural Affairs, and the Forestry Commission. These data are used to model the relationship between site location, land use and the proximity to and density of population.

ii) A trip generation function (TGF) is used to predict the number of day visits from any outset location to any specified site as a function of the availability of substitutes around the outset location, the population of that

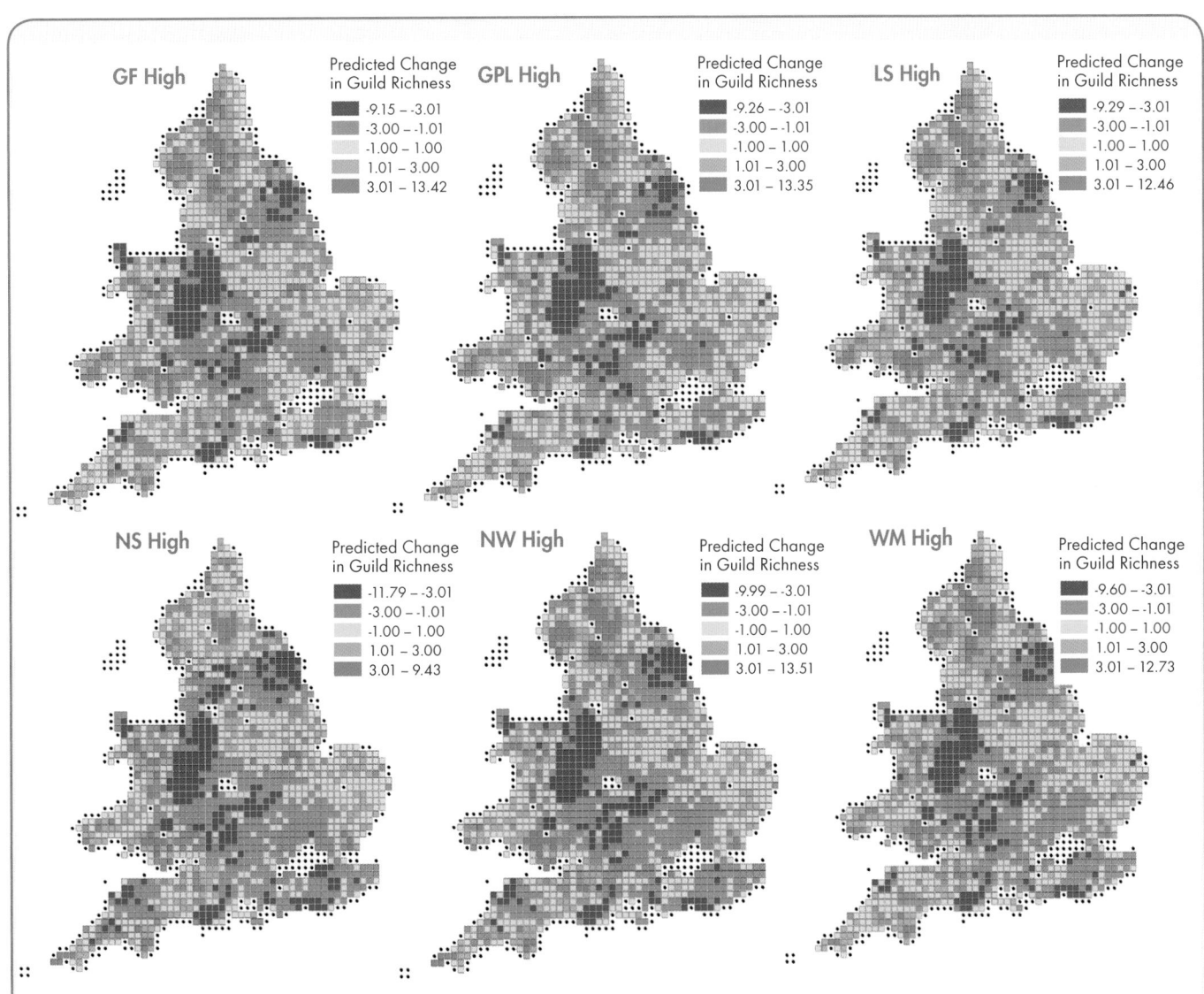

Figure 26.12 Spatial distribution of changes in predicted guild richness between the 1988 baseline and each of the High emission UK NEA Scenarios for 2060 in England and Wales. Scenarios are as follows: GF = *Go with the Flow*; GPL = *Green and Pleasant Land*; LS = *Local Stewardship*; NS = *National Security*; NW = *Nature@Work*; WM = *World Markets*.

26 For full details see Sen *et al.* (2011).

outset area and their socioeconomic and demographic characteristics, and the physical environmental characteristics of destination sites.

iii) A meta-analysis of estimates of the value of visits is undertaken, taking into account the nature of any visited site.

By combining outputs from the SPM and TGF analyses we can predict both where sites will be and how many day visitors they will attract. By feeding this estimate into the meta-analysis model we obtain an estimate of the value of those visits. Together this linked analysis yields estimates of recreational value which is sensitive to the spatial distribution of populations and their characteristics, and the spatial distribution of recreational sites and their environmental characteristics. This in turn ensures that the methodology is sensitive to the populations and land use changes envisaged under the UK NEA Scenarios.

The detailed methodology is presented in Chapter 22 and those discussions are not repeated here. However, a few adjustments are required in order to extend that approach to the valuation of recreation under the UK NEA Scenarios, as follows:

Census lower super output areas per Census data zone (LOSA/DZ) populations were calculated for 2060 in accordance with the population trends envisaged by the UK NEA Scenarios team (further discussion of these trends is given in Section 26.6.5 which covers Urban greenspace).

The UK NEA Scenarios team employed a 1 km grid resolution to define their maps of the baseline and scenario land use, whereas the SEER team at CSERGE employed a 25 m resolution map in their development of the methods described in Chapter 22. For consistency, the site prediction model (SPM) and trip generation function (TGF) were re-estimated using map information from the UK NEA Scenarios team (including recalculation of the explanatory variables used in those models). These re-estimated models are reported as **Table 26.15** and **Table 26.16**, respectively. Comparison with those reported in Chapter 22 shows that these are similar, with relatively minor changes in parameter values. Accordingly, the reader is referred to those previous models for discussion of the trends reported and the CSERGE team recommend their use for any future application as they are based upon more accurate data. Full details can be found in Sen *et al.* (2011).

26.5.3 Distribution and Value of Recreational Visits Under the Baseline

Our year 2000 baseline data on land use and population distribution and its characteristics was combined with

Table 26.15 Site probability model (SPM) predicting the number of recreational sites in each 5 km grid square. The model is estimated using a negative binomial model with robust standard errors. Tests on the SPM indicate that the over-dispersion parameter (alpha) is significant, justifying our choice of the negative binomial model. The dependent variable is the number of visited MENE sites in a 5 km cell. Statistical significance indicated by: *p<0.05, **p<0.01, ***p<0.001. Weighted population density variables (weights = 1.0 and 2.0) are only included in the model based on statistical significance. For full definition of variables and discussion of relationships see Chapter 22. Source: Sen *et al.* (2011).

	Coefficients	t-stat
% of coast in cell	0.0210**	2.699
% of freshwater in cell	0.0613***	6.160
% of grasslands in cell	0.00490**	3.220
% of mountains and heath in cell	-0.0169***	-5.267
% of other marine in cell	0.0110***	11.16
% of urban in cell	0.0542***	32.17
% of coniferous forests in cell	-0.00582	-1.358
% of broadleaved forests in cell	0.0267***	10.29
weighted population density (y=1) in cell	0.000000407***	5.407
weighted population density (y=2) in cell	-0.00000460***	-8.695
Constant	-0.811***	-20.40
Log alpha		
Constant	-0.627***	-12.04
Observations	5,526	

Table 26.16 Trip generation function (TGF) predicting the number of day visits to a site. The dependent variable is the number of visits from an LSOA/DZ to a site. The above model is estimated using a multilevel Poisson regression model. Statistical significance indicated by: *p<0.05, **p<0.01, ***p<0.001. For full definition of variables and discussion of relationships see Chapter 22. Source: Sen *et al.* (2011).

	Coefficients	t-stat
Travel time from LSOA to site	-0.0628***	-110.6
Coast substitute availability	-0.0233*	-2.151
Urban substitute availability	-0.0219***	-34.75
Freshwater substitute availability	-0.0827***	-6.349
Grasslands substitute availability	-0.0215***	-9.797
Woodland substitute availability	-0.0177***	-8.887
Sea/ocean substitute availability	-0.00198*	-2.164
Mountain substitute availability	0.0120**	2.971
% coast in site	0.0226***	11.12
% urban in site	-0.00222***	-4.617
% freshwater in site	0.0113***	4.812
% grasslands in site	0.00160	1.477
% woodlands in site	0.00364***	3.896
% of sea in site	0.0233***	9.804
% mountain/heath in site	0.0181***	7.980
% non-white ethnicity	-0.00546***	-6.162
% retired	0.00645***	3.661
Median household income	0.0000104***	11.19
Total population of outset area	0.000227***	5.902
Constant	-3.101***	-36.30
lnsig2u		
Constant	-0.912***	-25.47
Observations	4,047,387	

Ordnance Survey information on the road network and data on travel times (Jones *et al.* 2010). This allowed us to generate the range of variables required for our SPM and TGF analyses including: the characteristics of outset locations and potential destination sites, travel times, substitute availability, etc.

Estimation of the SPM provides us with the predicted distribution of sites across GB under the baseline conditions, as illustrated in **Figure 26.13a**. As per expectations, the immediate observation regarding this distribution is that it reflects, at least in some noticeable part, variation in population density across the country. However, there are also noticeable influences from variation in land use type. This is perhaps most clearly seen in areas such as the South West of England and the western coastal areas of Wales where, despite relatively low populations, site probability remains significant. Population pressures become the dominant factors when we consider the baseline predictions of our TGF as illustrated in **Figure 26.13b**. This predicts the number of visitors that there would be to each grid cell on the assumption that it does indeed contain a recreational site. Here the decay in visit rates away from population centres clearly demonstrates the vital importance of placing recreational sites in areas which are readily accessible to large numbers of people. **Figure 26.13c** combines the information given in both of the previous analyses to adjust the TGF predictions for the probability of sites given by the SPM. Note that we have also used this stage to adjust from the sample data given in the central figure

to the entire population of GB (Chapter 22 discusses this adjustment). Hence the distribution shows us the estimated total number of visits to each grid cell per annum.

The resulting distribution conforms strongly to prior expectations. Visit numbers reflect the very strong influence of travel time and associated costs. However, the land use and habitat types of each area clearly exert their influence. So, for example, prized landscapes such as large areas of south-west England, the north Norfolk coast, the western coast of Wales and the border areas of Scotland down into the Lakes all exert a pull on visitors which overcomes the fact that they have relatively low resident populations.

The total annual visitor numbers described in **Figure 26.13c** can then be fed into the meta-analysis model to convert visitor numbers into values, taking into account the land use and habitat characteristics of each visited site and their corresponding specific values. **Figure 26.14** maps the resultant values obtained from this analysis. The distribution is similar to, but not identical with, that shown in **Figure 26.13c** due to the different per visit values attached to visits in different habitat types. This is perhaps most noticeable in areas such as the Scottish highlands where, although the number of visits is low relative to the vast numbers around major conurbations, nevertheless the high per visit values attached to such habitats boosts the recreational value of such areas. **Table 26.17** presents a few descriptive statistics regarding the number of visits and their value in the baseline situation.

Figure 26.13 The baseline distribution of sites (a); predicted number of day visits (unadjusted for sample size) to sites (b); and the estimated total number of recreational day visits per annum across Great Britain (c); adjusted for sample size).

	GB	England	Scotland	Wales
Table 26.17 Predicted total annual visit numbers and their total value (£'000s) for the 2000 baseline period.				
Predicted visits per annum				
Mean (No. per 5 km cell)	394	559	130	94
Median (No. per 5 km cell)	72	133	12	24
Country total (visits)	3,231,000	2,860,000	290,000	81,000
Value of predicted visits per annum				
Mean (£/5 km cell)	1,223	1,732	414	303
Median (£/5 km cell)	241	436	44	79
Country total (£)	10,040,000	8,854,000	926,000	260,000

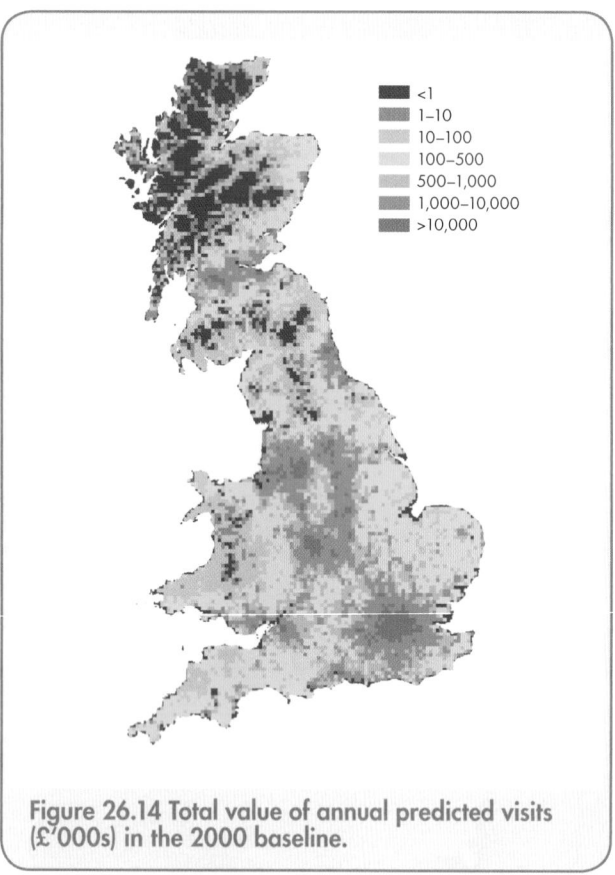

Legend:
- <1
- 1–10
- 10–100
- 100–500
- 500–1,000
- 1,000–10,000
- >10,000

Figure 26.14 Total value of annual predicted visits (£'000s) in the 2000 baseline.

26.5.4 Scenario Analysis

While Chapter 22 discusses the development and estimation of our underlying models in some detail, it does not discuss their use within scenario analyses at any length. Therefore in this section we first describe a single such analysis in some detail. That methodology is then simply repeated to generate results for the remaining scenarios.

Our more detailed discussions concern the estimation of values generated by moving from the baseline situation to that envisaged under the high emissions variant of the *Green and Pleasant Land* scenario.

The UK NEA Scenarios team envision the *Green and Pleasant Land* high emissions scenario as one in which conservation of biodiversity and landscape are the dominant driving forces. There are substantial relative increases in broadleaved woodland, freshwater and grassland habitats and declines in Coniferous Woodland and Enclosed Farmland. Although overall population increase is modest, the proportion who are retired increases more than under any other scenario and incomes also rise substantially. Taken together, these factors would be expected to play out through the SPM and TGF models to increase both the number and value of recreational visits. This is indeed what our analysis reveals, as illustrated in **Figure 26.15** which reworks the format of **Figure 26.13**, although now for the *Green and Pleasant Land* high scenario. The maps are now coloured such that decreases from the baseline are shown in purple and increases are coloured in green. In both cases darker tones indicate more substantial changes from the baseline.

Considering the maps shown in **Figure 26.15**, the immediate observation is the dominance of green tones indicating increases over the baseline. This is least true of the distribution of sites where both upland and high density Urban locations see declines. However, even here there is a noticeable increase in the prevalence of lowland sites, driven in major part by the increases in broadleaved woodland, freshwater and grassland habitats and declines in Coniferous Woodland and Enclosed Farmland in such areas. The contrast between high density Urban locations and areas just outside those centres is particularly noticeable, reflecting an increased availability of urban fringe recreational sites. Increased incomes and an increase in the numbers of retired people enables the population to take advantage of these sites, resulting in a significant increase in predicted day visits. The growth in Urban fringe sites leads to very substantial increases in recreational activity for those who live in highly populated areas, despite a reduction in the availability of recreational sites within the Urban environment. Indeed it is only the more remote areas which do not experience increased recreational visit numbers under the *Green and Pleasant Land* high emissions scenario. These visitor numbers are applied to the meta-analysis model to convert them into values that take account of the new habitat distribution envisioned under the *Green and Pleasant Land* high emissions scenario. **Figure 26.16** maps this distribution of values which again is similar to, but not identical with, that of the number of visitors, the difference being due to the variation in per visit values across habitats.

Table 26.18 presents selected descriptive statistics regarding the change in the number of visits and their value generated by a shift from the baseline situation to the *Green and Pleasant Land* high emissions scenario.

Inspection of **Table 26.18** confirms the message of **Figure 26.16**, that the *Green and Pleasant Land* high emissions scenario delivers a substantial increase in recreation values over the baseline. We now repeat this analysis for each of the scenarios with the resulting distribution of values being mapped in **Figure 26.17** for their low emission variants while **Figure 26.18** repeats this for the high emission scenarios.

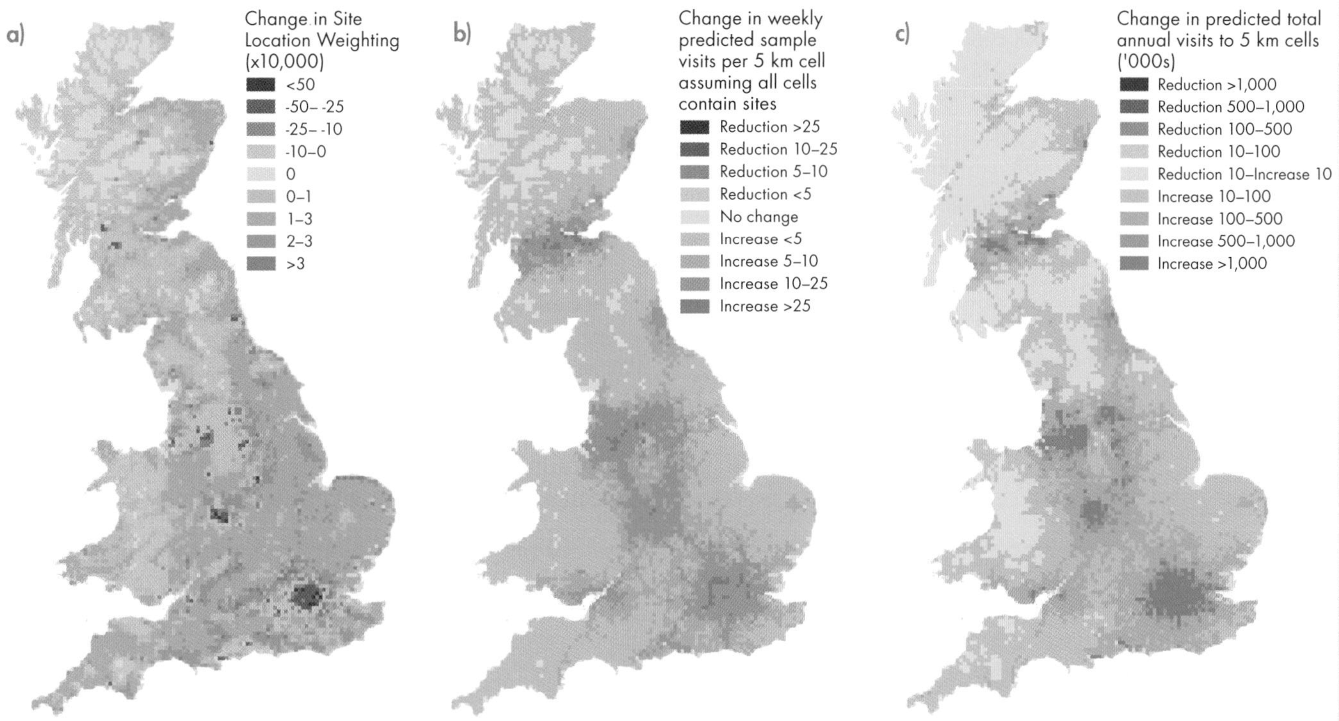

a)

Change in Site Location Weighting (x10,000)
- ■ <50
- ■ -50– -25
- ■ -25– -10
- -10–0
- 0
- 0–1
- 1–3
- 2–3
- >3

b)

Change in weekly predicted sample visits per 5 km cell assuming all cells contain sites
- ■ Reduction >25
- ■ Reduction 10–25
- Reduction 5–10
- Reduction <5
- No change
- Increase <5
- Increase 5–10
- Increase 10–25
- Increase >25

c)

Change in predicted total annual visits to 5 km cells ('000s)
- ■ Reduction >1,000
- ■ Reduction 500–1,000
- Reduction 100–500
- Reduction 10–100
- Reduction 10–Increase 10
- Increase 10–100
- Increase 100–500
- Increase 500–1,000
- Increase >1,000

Figure 26.15 Changes induced by a move from the 2000 baseline to the *Green and Pleasant Land* High emissions scenario in terms of the distribution of sites (a); the predicted number of day visits (unadjusted for sample size) to sites (b); and the estimated total number of recreational day visits per annum across Great Britain (c); adjusted for sample size.

In general the maps shown in **Figure 26.17** and **Figure 26.18** are dominated by increases in visit value. The *Nature@ Work* scenario displays the most substantial increases in the value of visits for large areas of GB both at high and low emissions. These gains are followed by those under the *Green and Pleasant Land* scenario, which are a little higher than those under *Go with the Flow*. In both of these scenarios, large increases are seen in and around Urban areas, while more rural areas see smaller increases in the annual value of visits. The *National Security* scenario also shows a similar geographic pattern to *Go with the Flow* and *Green and Pleasant Land*, but with some areas, such as the Scottish Highlands and the Pennines, experiencing a reduction in the predicted annual value of visits. Larger predicted reductions are seen under the *Local Stewardship* scenarios, particularly in the area south and west of London and in the urban centres, although London itself shows a substantial increase in the value of visits. The *World Markets* scenarios probably show the greatest difference both in comparison to the other scenarios and also in the response to high and low emissions. In both high and low scenarios London shows a very large decrease in value of visits with similar decreases in predicted visit value also seen in other urban centres across the country. However, in the low emissions scenario the Urban areas outside of London are expected to experience an increase in the value of visits. In all cases the remote uplands, because of their inaccessibility, remain unvisited and show no change in value.

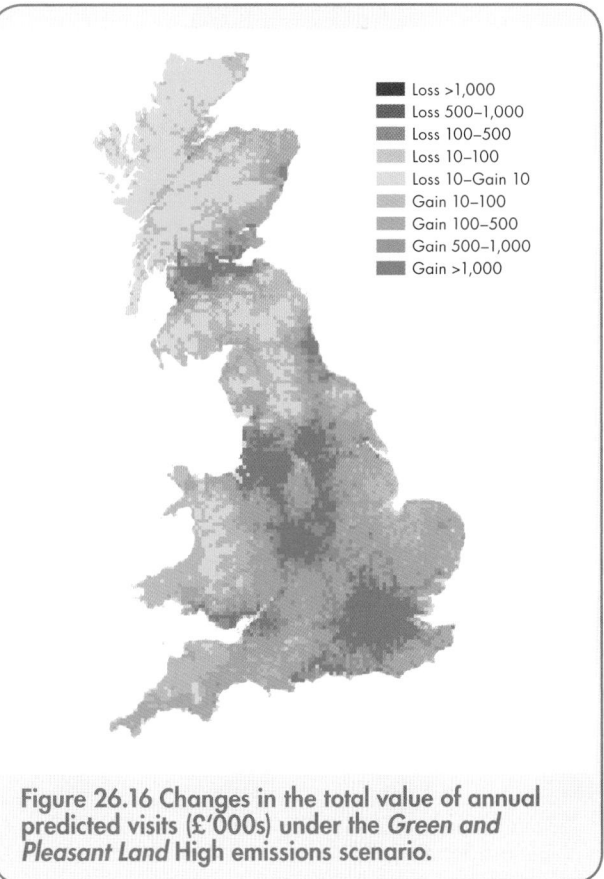

- ■ Loss >1,000
- ■ Loss 500–1,000
- ■ Loss 100–500
- Loss 10–100
- Loss 10–Gain 10
- Gain 10–100
- Gain 100–500
- Gain 500–1,000
- Gain >1,000

Figure 26.16 Changes in the total value of annual predicted visits (£'000s) under the *Green and Pleasant Land* High emissions scenario.

Table 26.18 Changes in the predicted total annual visit numbers and their total value arising from a move from the 2000 baseline situation to the *Green and Pleasant Land* High emissions scenario. All changes are positive under this scenario analysis. These changes must be added to the baseline figures in Table 26.17 to obtain absolute totals. All numbers are in thousands.

	GB	England	Scotland	Wales
Changes to predicted visits per annum				
Mean (No. per 5 km cell)	199	277	77	54
Median (No. per 5 km cell)	49	85	8	14
Country total (visits)	1,636,000	1,417,000	173,000	46,000
Changes in the value of predicted visits per annum				
Mean (£/5 km cell)	628	871	249	173
Median (£/5 km cell)	163	279	28	47
Country total (£)	5,156,000	4,451,000	556,000	149,000

Table 26.19 summarises the national level changes in value arising between the baseline and each of the scenarios. At this national level all of the scenarios generate increases in the annual value of visits except for the *World Markets* high emissions scenario. In general, we find large gains under the *Nature@Work*, *Green and Pleasant Land* and *Go with the Flow* scenarios and moderate increases for the *Local Stewardship* scenario.

The last row of **Table 26.19** divides the GB level values under the baseline and each scenario by the GB population to obtain per capita values. These adjust the national level results for the increases in population envisioned to occur, at different rates, under all scenarios. While the *Nature@Work* scenario still remains that which yields the highest per capita value, this analysis substantially differentiates the *Green and Pleasant Land* and *Go with the Flow* findings showing that, on a per person basis, the former more than double the value of the latter.

Figure 26.17 Total recreational value changes from the 2000 baseline to all UK NEA Low emissions Scenarios. Scenarios are as follows: GF = *Go with the Flow*; GPL = *Green and Pleasant Land*; LS = *Local Stewardship*; NS = *National Security*; NW = *Nature@Work*; WM = *World Markets*.

UK National Ecosystem Assessment: Technical Report

Figure 26.18 Total recreational value changes from the 2000 baseline to all UK NEA High emissions Scenarios.
Scenarios are as follows: GF = *Go with the Flow*; GPL = *Green and Pleasant Land*; LS = *Local Stewardship*; NS = *National Security*; NW = *Nature@Work*; WM = *World Markets*.

Table 26.19 Total (£million) and per capita (£) value of predicted annual visits in the 2000 baseline period and changes in total and per capita value of predicted annual visit under the various UK NEA Scenarios (High and Low emissions).
Scenarios are as follows: GF = *Go with the Flow*; GPL = *Green and Pleasant Land*; LS = *Local Stewardship*; NS = *National Security*; NW = *Nature@Work*; WM = *World Markets*.

Region	Baseline (£ million)	GF (£ million)		GPL (£ million)		LS (£ million)		NS (£ million)		NW (£ million)		WM (£ million)	
		High	Low	High	Low	High	Low	High	Low	High	Low	High	Low
England	8,854	3,624	5,048	4,451	5,327	898	1,400	3,061	4,125	21,084	21,428	-678	4,398
Scotland	926	370	488	556	602	162	84	189	249	2,262	2,190	-61	517
Wales	260	127	174	149	174	38	52	94	119	568	547	-84	122
GB	10,040	4,121	5,711	5,156	6,103	1,098	1,535	3,344	4,493	23,914	24,165	-823	5,037
GB population (millions)	55.4	62.8	62.8	65.6	65.6	74.5	74.5	67.5	67.5	62.0	62.0	72.4	72.4
GB per capita values (£ p.a.)	181	14	36	61	76	-1	6	17	34	337	341	-57	21

26.6 Urban Greenspace Amenity[27]

26.6.1 Urban Change Scenarios

Key ecosystem services provided by urban greenspace in the UK include recreation, aesthetics, physical and mental health, neighbourhood development, noise regulation and air pollution reduction. As such it is a bundled good[28] and should be valued as such. The benefits derived from domestic gardens are considered in Chapter 22 and are not included in what follows. Our methodology for such valuation is discussed in the Chapter 22, but in summary this undertakes a meta-analysis of prior studies, allowing us to estimate how amenity values decline with increasing distance between households and areas of urban greenspace. Capturing this distance dependence is vital if we are to accurately assess the value of changes in the number, extent and location of urban greenspaces as cities and their populations alter as envisioned in the UK NEA Scenarios.

The six UK NEA Scenarios detail a number of changes to key urban characteristics such as their physical extent, their population and the area of urban greenspace provided. **Table 26.20** presents the percentage changes for these key variables for each of the scenarios based on data provided by the UK NEA Scenarios team.[29] Note that the changes in urban extent shown in **Table 26.20** differ somewhat from those presented in **Table 26.2** of this chapter since the

former refers to cities with a population of at least 50,000 while the latter includes all urban areas.

The full narrative for each Scenario can be found in Chapter 25, but some brief illustrations are in order. Arguably, the *World Markets* scenario has the most extreme impact on urban areas. Here, by 2060, the UK experiences dramatic urbanisation, both in terms of urban extent and population. Informal greenspace, in particular, fails to keep up with increases in urban extent and population, a situation which, as we show subsequently, leads to losses in urban greenspace values. An expansion of housing into green belt, parks and gardens results in a loss of greenspace and developed areas increase substantially. A further extreme case is given under the *National Security* scenario. Here, although the increase in population is less extreme than under the *World Markets* scenario , now the drive for national self-sufficiency actually leads to a reduction in formal greenspace areas, as parks are used for provisioning purposes. One would expect that this would also yield reductions in the benefits provided by urban greenspace. A less extreme, but still negative, expectation arises with respect to the *Go with the Flow* scenario, where the combined change in overall (formal plus informal) greenspace only just outpaces very substantial growth in a population within a context of little alteration in the overall extent of urban areas. The combined effect of such changes is likely to be a small reduction in greenspace benefits. In contrast, the remaining scenarios (*Green and Pleasant Land, Local Stewardship* and *Nature@Work*) all envisage increases in combined greenspace which are clearly in excess of population growth. As such, urban greenspace benefits would be expected to increase in all three of these cases.

Table 26.20 Changes in urban characteristics from the 2000 baseline to 2060 for each of the UK NEA Scenarios.

Scenario	Change in urban area (%)	Change in urban population (%)	Change in the area of formal recreational space (%)	Change in the area of informal greenspace (%)
Go with the Flow	3.0	32.2	36.2	0.0
Green and Pleasant Land	0.0	21.7	38.9	5.4
Local Stewardship	-3.0	0.0	4.5	2.8
National Security	-3.0	17.2	-34.3	4.8
Nature@Work	-3.0	13.8	39.0	-4.9
World Markets	79.0	52.6	73.0	20.7

26.6.2 Methods for Calculating the Implications of Scenarios for Access to Urban Greenspace

The characteristics specified under the UK NEA Scenarios imply alterations in the size of urban areas and the formal and informal greenspace within them.[30] The implicit changes in access to greenspace (and hence distance decay in values) was assessed through GIS analysis of distance and accessibility relationships for the set of UK urban centres (ranging from relatively small cities like Norwich to major conurbations like Glasgow) discussed in Chapter 22. This analysis provided information on the proximity of each household[31] to urban greenspaces, both under the 2000

---

27 This section is drawn from Perino *et al.* (2011).

28 This means that some overlap with the previous analysis of open-access recreation is acknowledged.

29 With respect to the drivers of urban greenspace values, the UK NEA Scenarios do not differentiate between the high and low emission variants of a given scenario.

30 These changes are implemented by expanding or contracting existing areas of greenspace in line with the specifications of each scenario. This is likely to deliver a lower bound estimate of the value generated by such changes, as gaining or losing an entire park is expected to generate greater changes in value than simply changing an equivalent area of existing parks. The new percentage cover of general greenspace (as defined in Chapter 22) is calculated by increasing the areas covered by formal and informal greenspace as specified in the scenarios and then dividing the general greenspace cover by [1 + decimal percentage change in Urban area] to take account of the overall change in city size.

31 Note that proximity measurements were taken from the centroid of each full postcode, although as these typically contain just 20 households, any error induced by this assumption should be minor. This caveat applies throughout this section. These changes are implemented by the following simple procedures since it is beyond the scope of this project to more accurately simulate urban growth for the five cities. The change in Urban area is represented by multiplying distances to urban parks and other formal recreation sites, and city-edge greenspace by a factor equal to the square root of 1 plus the change in the Urban area (this is 0.98 for *Nature@Work*, *National Security* and *Local Stewardship*, 1.015 for *Go with the Flow* and 1.338 for *World Markets*). The square root is taken to translate a change in area into one in distance. The appropriateness of using a constant factor for all distances follows from the intercept theorems.

baseline and for each of the UK NEA Scenarios. The change in urban population is modelled by increasing the baseline population in each postcode by the growth rate specified under each scenario.[32] The distance between people's homes and the centre of urban greenspaces (>1 hectare) is a major driver of amenity values. Any change in the extent of urban areas will have a direct impact on this because (holding greenspace area constant) homes will be on average either further away (if the city grows) or closer (if the city shrinks) to urban greenspace. Since distances are measured to the centre of a park, a change in the park's size does not affect the distance measure but is captured separately. The marginal impact of an increase in both a park's size and its distance to a household are decreasing.

Although the UK NEA Scenarios include information on overall GDP growth, they do not specify changes in the relative distribution of income and so, for ease of exposition, we hold income constant throughout our analysis.[33] Furthermore, while the UK NEA Scenario descriptions specify the state of the world in 2060, they do not provide details about the intervening period. This does not cause a problem when we report the undiscounted value of changes. However, in order to determine discounted present values we assume that changes occur evenly across the time period and then apply the standard discounting rule specified in the HM Treasury's Green Book (2003, Annex 6, Table 6.1) that discounts any net changes at 3.5% for the first 30 years of a project and at 3% for years 31 to 60. We denote this as the 'HM Treasury–Standard Discounting' approach. However, applying these discount rates introduces a degree of internal inconsistency, as the Treasury bases these on the assumption of a 2% average growth rate of the UK economy. However, four of the six UK NEA Scenarios make different assumptions, with growth rates in the range between 0.5% (*Local Stewardship*) and 3% (*Nature@Work*). Using these growth rates instead of that assumed by the Treasury implies differentiated discount rates. These are calculated and used to define an 'HM Treasury–Scenario Specific Discounting' approach.[34]

26.6.3 Valuing Changes in Urban Greenspace Change

Using these various approaches, Perino *et al.* (2011) calculate values for the changes in urban greenspace envisaged under each scenario for both the set of cities considered and the implied values for the whole of GB[35]; it is these latter, national

level values that we focus upon here. In calculating these, value estimates are only made for cities with a population of 50,000 or more, as the methodology used is regarded as less suitable for smaller settlements. This is because urban greenspace is likely to play a lesser role in the provision of many ecosystem services in smaller settlements than it does in larger ones as, by their very nature, most households in smaller towns live relatively close to rural areas. The exclusion of smaller cities explains the difference in urban extent implied by each scenario given in **Table 26.2** and **Table 26.20**.

Our set of sampled cities allows us to calculate the value of changes in urban greenspace under each scenario for more than 1,600 urban areas (defined as LSOA in England and DZ in Scotland). Regression analysis linked these value estimates to a variety of small area characteristics. This analysis identified a number of highly significant (p<0.0001) predictors of the change in greenspace value generated by each scenario, including household density and socio-economic characteristics of those households such as their median income levels. Given that the predictors of value can be obtained for all census areas of all cities, the model can be used to extrapolate these value changes across GB. **Table 26.21** presents the resulting valuations of the urban greenspace changes envisioned under each scenario.

Table 26.21 presents estimates of the average changes in urban greenspace values under each scenario at national and household level. Undiscounted, standard and scenario-specific discounted values are reported, each being accompanied with its annuity equivalent. Note that in contrast to values reported in Perino *et al.* (2011) and Chapter 22, where a baseline of 2010 is used, the values in this and all other tables and figures are adjusted to reflect the common baseline of 2000. This does not affect the undiscounted value change reported in these tables but somewhat reduces all entries in subsequent rows. While these values should be regarded only as approximations, nonetheless they underline the very substantial changes in urban greenspace values which can arise across these scenarios. While more extreme scenarios such as *World Markets* lead to very substantial losses in urban greenspace values, even moderate scenarios show that feasible changes to urban greenspace can generate significant changes in values. We can see that in the *Go with the Flow* scenario, urban greenspace values decline by nearly £2 billion per

---

32 However, postcode centroids, i.e. the location of houses, are not changed over and above the inflation factor. The bias introduced by the artefact that some additional houses in postcode areas very close to existing parks, might be allocated to areas within the new boundaries of a park. This bias is limited by the adjustment of the marginal value function for such short distances as described in Chapter 22.

33 This is also a somewhat risk averse modelling strategy, as the estimated income effect is likely to dominate the aggregate change in benefits derived from ecosystem services across scenarios. This would be problematic to the extent that relative prices of all goods including substitutes for urban greenspace, e.g. private gardens and recreational trips, are held constant. Both, however, are expected to increase more in those scenarios that increase the scarcity of recreational greenspace in general. Holding income constant is considered to impose a smaller error than increasing it in line with general GDP growth but keeping relative prices constant.

34 This approach is discussed in further detail by Perino *et al.* (2011), who also discuss and present alternative approaches to dealing with the projected changes in population. Note that Stern (2006) deviated from the HM Treasury's guidelines on the grounds that the environmental good valued (climate change) involves intergenerational comparisons of benefit changes and hence should be guided by the moral principle of treating all generations equally. In terms of discounting, this implied a reduction of the 'pure rate of time preference' from the 1.5% used in HM Treasury (2003) to 0.1%. Stern (2006) also used a more cautious growth rate of 1.3%. This resulted in a discount rate of 1.4% (or an adjustment factor of 0.72 in the present case). Again, to be consistent with the growth rates in UK NEA Scenarios, the range of adjustment factors spans from 0.456 for *Nature@Work* to 0.865 for *Local Stewardship*. The 60-year time horizon considered in the UK NEA arguably involves intergenerational comparisons, although not exclusively.

35 Comparable data for Northern Ireland is not available. However, Urban areas in Northern Ireland represent only about 3% of total Urban area in the UK (Chapter 10, Section 10.1.2).

Table 26.21 Per household and aggregated benefit changes of UK NEA Scenarios for Great Britain. Note that per household values are based on the 15.2 million households living in the urban areas included in the extrapolation.

	Go with the Flow	Green and Pleasant Land	Local Stewardship	National Security	Nature@ Work	World Markets
Aggregate values (£ billion)						
Undiscounted value change	-118	141	129	-597	284	-1,440
Annuity (60 years)	-1.96	2.35	2.16	-9.94	4.73	-24.0
Net Present Value (HM Treasury–Standard Discounting)	-49	59	54	-250	119	-603
Annuity (infinite, 3.5%)	-1.73	2.06	1.90	-8.75	4.17	-21.1
Net Present Value (HM Treasury–Scenario Specific Discounting)	-55	59	76	-311	98	-603
Annuity (infinite, scenario specific)	-1.65	2.06	1.53	-7.79	4.41	-21.1
Per household values (£)						
Undiscounted value change	-7,800	9,300	8,500	-39,300	18,700	-94,700
Annuity (60 years)	-129	154	142	-655	312	-1,580
Net Present Value (HM Treasury–Standard Discounting)	-3,253	3,880	3,570	-16,500	7,840	-39,700
Annuity (infinite, 3.5%)	-114	136	125	-576	274	-1,390
Net Present Value (HM Treasury–Scenario Specific Discounting)	-3,600	3,880	5,030	-20,500	6,450	-39,700
Annuity (infinite, scenario specific)	-109	136	101	-513	290	-1,390

annum, while pro-environmental scenarios such as *Green and Pleasant Land* lead to value gains of over £2.3 billion annually, and that this is more than doubled under the *Nature@Work* scenario. These are major sums which would be likely to alter resource allocations if included within decision-making systems.

The changes in amenity value provided by urban greenspace under each scenario are driven by a combination of factors. A change in the size of a city changes the average distance to nearby greenspace and hence the amount of benefits (e.g. recreation, cleaner air, aesthetics) occurring to urban households. An increase in urban population, other things being equal, decreases per household benefits as parks get increasingly crowded. A change in the amount and type of urban greenspace provided is the last of the main factors. Each scenario is characterised by a specific combination and usually they point in different directions. For example, in the *World Markets* scenario the fact that greenspaces are both further away from people's homes and are more crowded dominates the (absolute but not relative) increase in provision.

Analysis of the geographic distribution of these value changes shows that, not surprisingly, they generally follow the distribution of population, being largest in England and smallest in Wales, as illustrated in **Figure 26.19**. However, **Figure 26.20** shows that, even after adjusting for this by considering values at the household level, there are still marked differences between the three countries. This is due to household level effects being highest in the largest conurbations, which are more prevalent in England than in Scotland and Wales.

Figure 26.21 presents the effects of moving from the HM Treasury's–Standard Discounting rule to one that takes

into account the different growth rates in the respective scenarios and hence is scenario-specific. Note that for the *Green and Pleasant Land* and *World Markets* scenarios the growth rate is equal to the 2% assumed by HM Treasury (2003) and hence there is no difference between the two discounting regimes. For *Nature@Work* the net present value is reduced by about 16%. For the *National Security*, *Local Stewardship* and *Go with the Flow* scenarios the

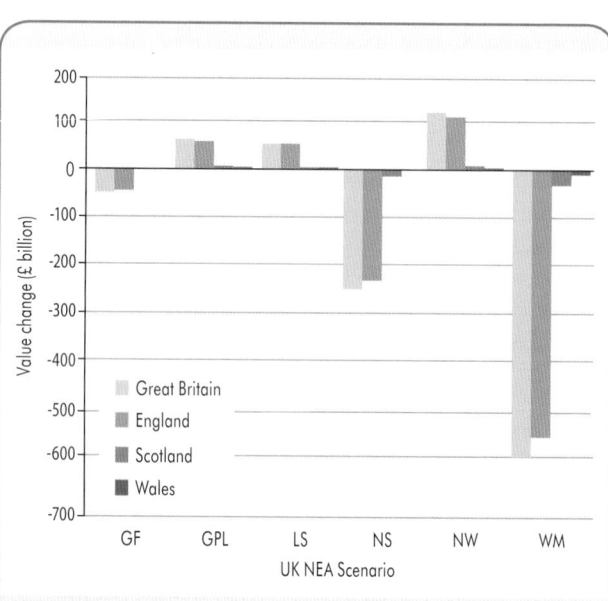

Figure 26.19 Distribution of UK NEA Scenario value changes across countries. Scenarios are as follows: GF = *Go with the Flow*; GPL = *Green and Pleasant Land*; LS = *Local Stewardship*; NS = *National Security*; NW = *Nature@Work*; WM = *World Markets*.

UK National Ecosystem Assessment: Technical Report

absolute value of the benefit change increases by up to one-third as their growth rates are below the one used by HM Treasury.

The spatial distribution of gains and losses is presented in **Figure 26.22** and **Figure 26.23**. The former figure presents the spatial pattern for the three scenarios (*Green and Pleasant Land*, *Nature@Work* and *Local Stewardship*) that yield net gains, and differences between these can be assessed with reference to the different scales given at the bottom of this figure. Similarly, **Figure 26.23** illustrates those three scenarios (*World Markets*, *National Security* and *Go with the Flow*) that generate net losses in terms of urban greenspace amenity.

The distribution of value changes under the scenarios differs substantially in the scale and direction of changes. Generally speaking, value changes are greatest in the centres of large Urban areas such as London, Birmingham and Manchester, with smaller cities being less affected. This supports our earlier decision to focus on cities with populations of 50,000 and above, but also suggests that any error induced through the omission of smaller towns might be relatively minor. Note that all values presented in **Figure 26.22** and **Figure 26.23** are per household changes in benefits. Hence, the weight of large Urban areas for the final outcome is even more pronounced than apparent from the maps, as they are home to more people.

26.6.4 Distributionally Weighted Values for Urban Greenspace Change

The aim of a cost-benefit analysis is to test whether a particular policy or project improves social welfare. Strictly speaking, summing up the monetary values of benefit changes across individuals only allows us to draw conclusions about changes in social welfare if the marginal utility of consumption is equal across all individuals. There is strong empirical evidence suggesting that the marginal utility of consumption decreases with income (i.e. the utility of £1 gained by a poor person is greater than if that amount were received by a rich person).[36] To adjust for this factor we follow HM Treasury (2003, Annex 5) and apply distributional weights to the benefits and costs of urban greenspace change. This procedure assumes that the elasticity of marginal utility with respect to consumption is one. This implies that someone with twice the median income receives a weight of one half compared to someone with median income. The distributional weight for each LSOA is calculated by dividing the median UK household income by the median household income in the LSOA or DZ using data provided by Experian (2010).[37]

Figure 26.24 and **Table 26.22** illustrate the impact of distributional weights on the net present value per urban household of each scenario. The benefit changes increase by up to about 30% if distributional weights are applied. This indicates that any reduction (increase) in the amount of urban greenspace would disproportionally hurt (benefit) the poor.

As **Figure 26.25** demonstrates, the impact of applying distributional weights is particularly pronounced for Scotland, where the impact of scenarios almost doubles as a result of the generally lower urban incomes relative to other areas of Great Britain.

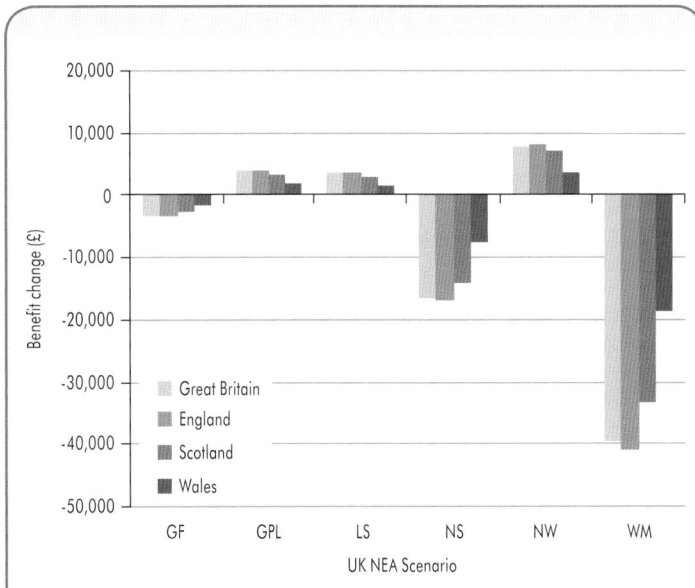

Figure 26.20 Distribution of benefit changes per household across countries. Aggregate net present value calculated using with HM Treasury–Standard Discounting. Scenarios are as follows: GF = *Go with the Flow*; GPL = *Green and Pleasant Land*; LS = *Local Stewardship*; NS = *National Security*; NW = *Nature@Work*; WM = *World Markets*.

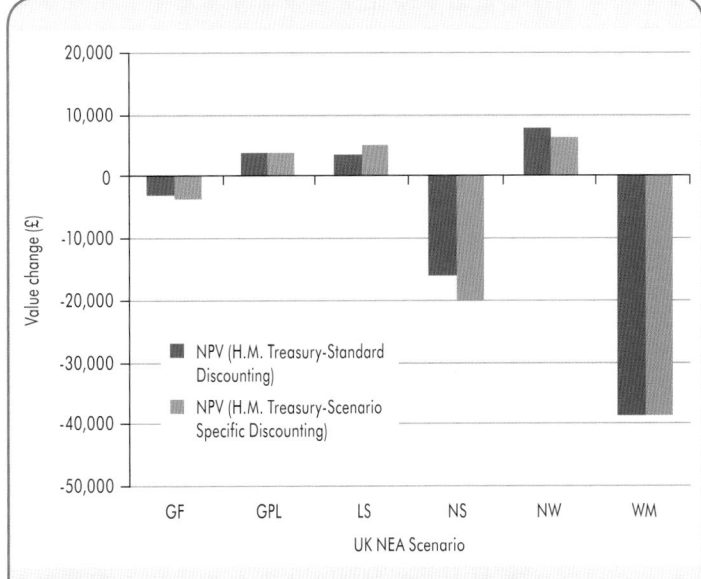

Figure 26.21 Comparing the HM Treasury–Standard Discounting rule with a scenario-specific discounting rule. NPV = Net Present Value. Scenarios are as follows: GF = *Go with the Flow*; GPL = *Green and Pleasant Land*; LS = *Local Stewardship*; NS = *National Security*; NW = *Nature@Work*; WM = *World Markets*.

36 Note that the sensitivity of the social discount rate to the rate of economic growth discussed above rests on the same concept.
37 The Experian Mosaic database contains median household incomes and the number of households for all LSOAs. Ordering all LSOAs with respect to income and computing the cumulative number of households allows us to obtain an estimate of the median household annual income for the UK, which in 2008 was £25,275.

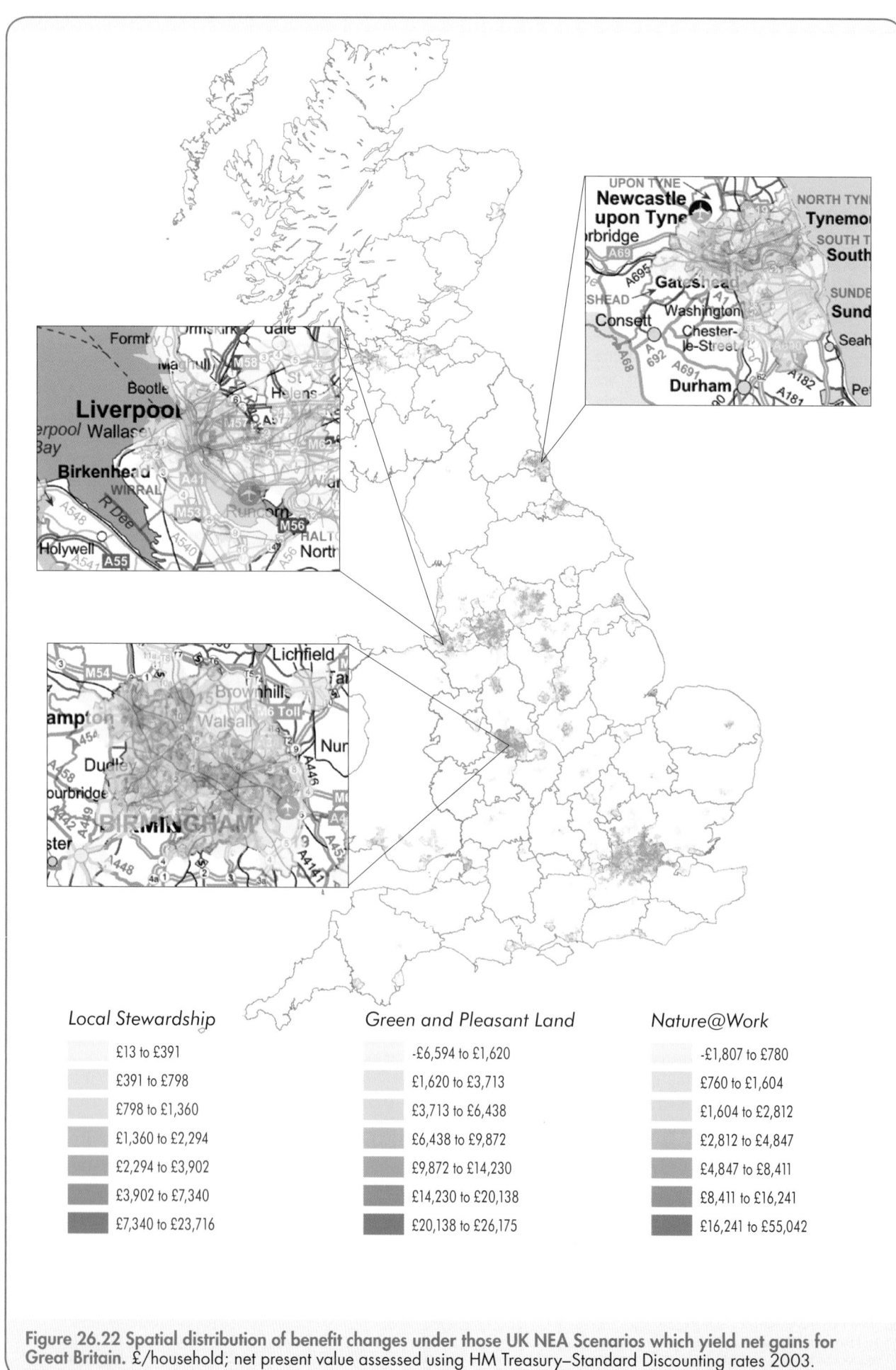

Local Stewardship
- £13 to £391
- £391 to £798
- £798 to £1,360
- £1,360 to £2,294
- £2,294 to £3,902
- £3,902 to £7,340
- £7,340 to £23,716

Green and Pleasant Land
- -£6,594 to £1,620
- £1,620 to £3,713
- £3,713 to £6,438
- £6,438 to £9,872
- £9,872 to £14,230
- £14,230 to £20,138
- £20,138 to £26,175

Nature@Work
- -£1,807 to £780
- £760 to £1,604
- £1,604 to £2,812
- £2,812 to £4,847
- £4,847 to £8,411
- £8,411 to £16,241
- £16,241 to £55,042

Figure 26.22 Spatial distribution of benefit changes under those UK NEA Scenarios which yield net gains for Great Britain. £/household; net present value assessed using HM Treasury–Standard Discounting rates 2003.

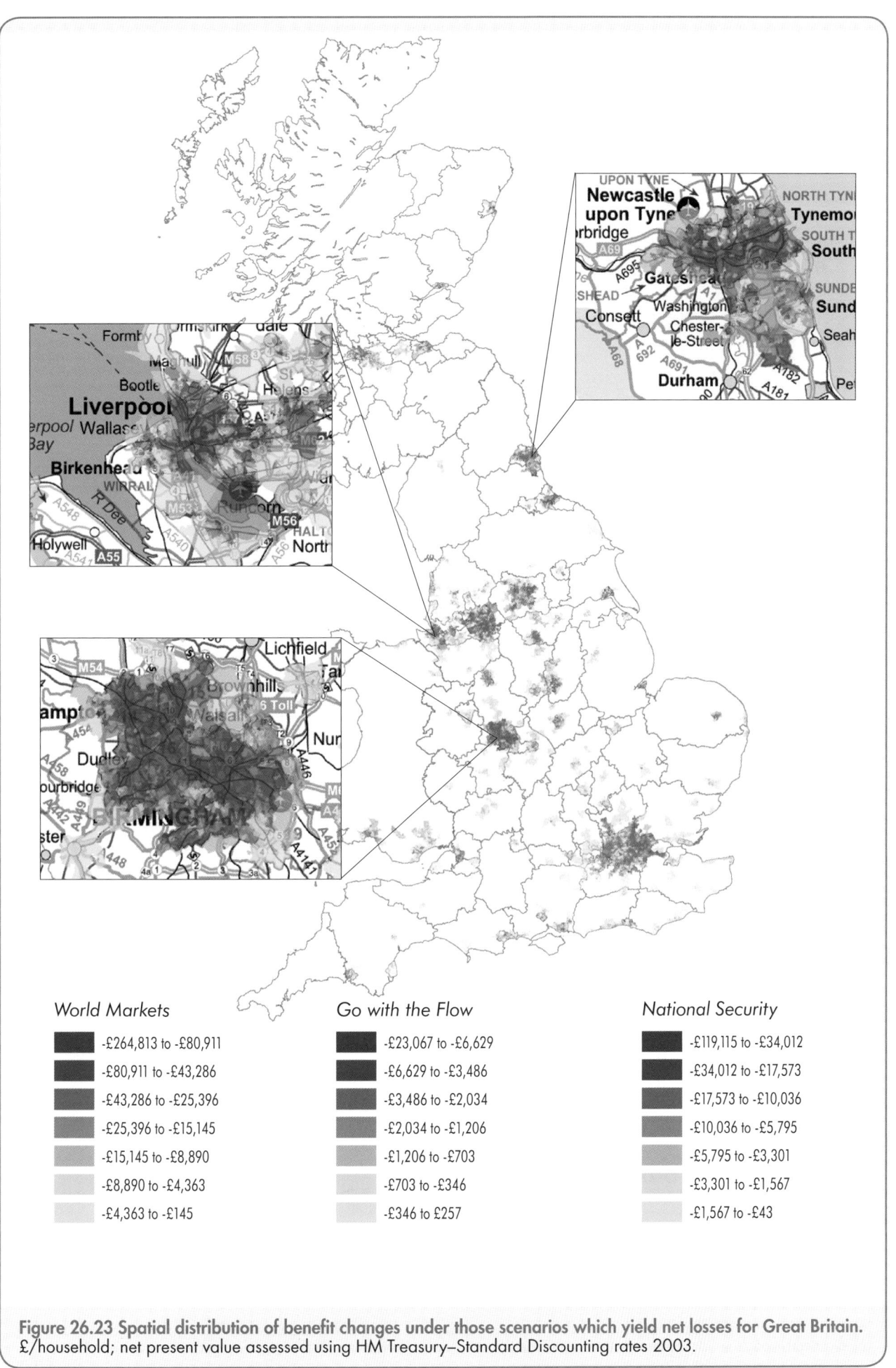

World Markets

- -£264,813 to -£80,911
- -£80,911 to -£43,286
- -£43,286 to -£25,396
- -£25,396 to -£15,145
- -£15,145 to -£8,890
- -£8,890 to -£4,363
- -£4,363 to -£145

Go with the Flow

- -£23,067 to -£6,629
- -£6,629 to -£3,486
- -£3,486 to -£2,034
- -£2,034 to -£1,206
- -£1,206 to -£703
- -£703 to -£346
- -£346 to £257

National Security

- -£119,115 to -£34,012
- -£34,012 to -£17,573
- -£17,573 to -£10,036
- -£10,036 to -£5,795
- -£5,795 to -£3,301
- -£3,301 to -£1,567
- -£1,567 to -£43

Figure 26.23 Spatial distribution of benefit changes under those scenarios which yield net losses for Great Britain. £/household; net present value assessed using HM Treasury–Standard Discounting rates 2003.

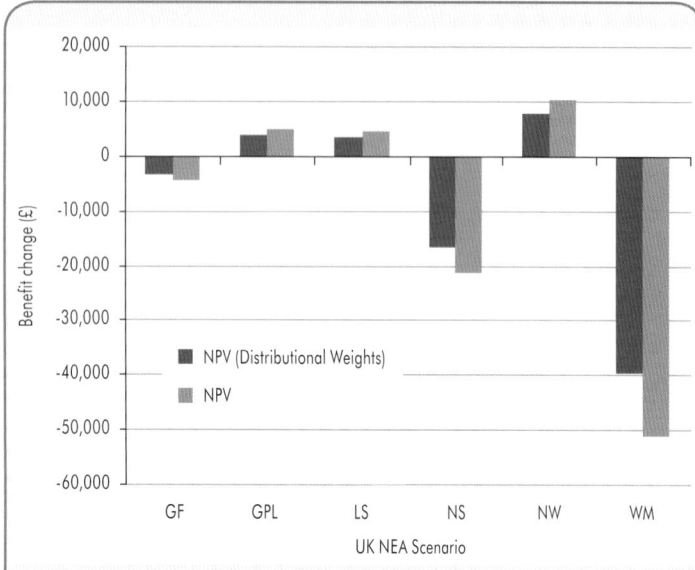

Figure 26.24 The effect of applying distributional weights on per household benefit changes across Great Britain. Net present value (NPV) per household calculated using with HM Treasury–Standard Discounting. Scenarios are as follows: GF = *Go with the Flow*; GPL = *Green and Pleasant Land*; LS = *Local Stewardship*; NS = *National Security*; NW = *Nature@ Work*; WM = *World Markets*.

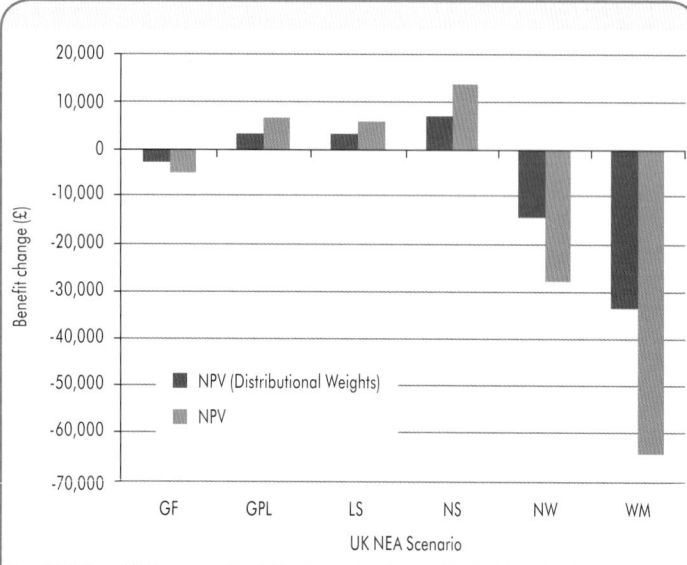

Figure 26.25 The effect of applying distributional weights on per household benefit changes in Scotland. Net present value (NPV) per household calculated using with HM Treasury–Standard Discounting. Scenarios are as follows: GF = *Go with the Flow*; GPL = *Green and Pleasant Land*; LS = *Local Stewardship*; NS = *National Security*; NW = *Nature@ Work*; WM = *World Markets*.

26.6.5 The Value of Urban Greenspace Change: Conclusions

While Perino *et al.* (2011) note a number of caveats and assumptions underlying their analysis, nevertheless their work provides an initial systematic attempt to estimate values for urban greenspace across GB. While under constant pressure due to the increasing demand for housing and commercial development, urban greenspace generates substantial benefits to local communities. This analysis shows that changes in the provision of urban greenspace can create, or destroy, billions of pounds worth of benefits to local residents.

26.7 Conclusions

26.7.1 Overview
The analysis presented in this chapter has considered five ecosystem service goods, as follows:

- agricultural food production;
- terrestrial carbon storage and annual greenhouse gas emissions;
- biodiversity (assessed using birds as an indicator species);
- open-access recreation; and
- urban greenspace amenity.

For each of these goods we have examined the changes in provision between a baseline[38] set as the situation in 2000 and the envisioned state of the UK in 2060 under the UK NEA Scenarios, which are as follows:

- *Go with the Flow*;
- *Green and Pleasant Land*;
- *Local Stewardship*;
- *National Security*;
- *Nature@Work*;
- *World Markets*.

With the exception of biodiversity, all of the goods are valued in monetary terms. As discussed in Chapter 22, while the use values of biodiversity are readily amenable to monetary valuation, its non-use existence value is the subject of some controversy. While some argue that monetary values can be robustly estimated, others question this. While we do not comment upon the veracity of these competing arguments, in the present analysis of scenarios we have adopted non-monetary, objective indicators such as the number of species becoming locally extinct in an area. These can then be compared against the monetary costs and benefits of each scenario, and most particularly those such as agricultural output, which has a direct impact upon bird diversity, so that we can undertake an analysis of the trade-offs between monetary and non-monetary measures occurring under each scenario. Admittedly this does not provide that clear guidance to decision making that a full cost-benefit analysis (CBA) would. However, CBA is just an informational input to the decision-making process, it is not the decision per se. Therefore we feel justified that our approach is consistent with an extension of existing decision analysis techniques.

---

38 As discussed, our farmland bird analysis adopts a somewhat earlier baseline. As this would lead our analysis to yield an upper bound prediction of impacts (as all changes are on average negative), this means that ours is a risk averse assessment and hence is considered acceptable for the present purposes.

	Go with the Flow	Green and Pleasant Land	Local Stewardship	National Security	Nature@ Work	World Markets
	Aggregate values in £billion (using distributional weights)					
Undiscounted value change	-154	180	166	-776	368	-1,850
Annuity (60 years)	-2.56	3.01	2.77	-12.9	6.14	-30.8
Net Present Value (HM Treasury – Standard Discounting)	-64	76	70	-325	154	-775
Annuity (infinite, 3.5%)	-2.25	2.65	2.43	-11.4	5.40	-27.1
Net Present Value (HM Treasury - Scenario Specific Discounting)	-72	76	98	-405	127	-775
Annuity (infinite, scenario specific)	-2.15	2.65	1.96	-10.1	5.72	-27.1
	Per household values in £ (using distributional weights)					
Undiscounted value change	-10,100	11,900	10,900	-51,100	24,300	-122,000
Annuity (60 years)	-169	198	182	-852	404	-2,030
Net Present Value (HM Treasury – Standard Discounting)	-4,240	4,980	4,580	-21,400	10,200	-51,100
Annuity (infinite, 3.5%)	-149	174	160	-750	356	-1,790
Net Present Value (HM Treasury – Scenario Specific Discounting)	-4,720	4,980	6,450	-26,700	8,370	-51,100
Annuity (infinite, scenario specific)	-142	174	129	-667	377	-1,790

26.7.2 Synthesis of Scenario Values

With the analysis of scenario impacts on individual ecosystems services complete, we can begin to synthesise results together. Great care has to be exercised in the interpretation of such findings. Most obviously, while this analysis goes beyond the normal decision remit of purely market values, it only considers a small subset of ecosystem service-related goods. Many market and non-market values are omitted here and so the analysis is necessarily partial and incomplete. Similarly, we are not considering the extent to which different scenarios impinge upon international trade and the effective import of ecosystem services (e.g. water embodied in agricultural imports) and resultant export of an ecological footprint. While these are important caveats, they do not undermine the fundamental objective of this analysis, which is to demonstrate that methods for the integrated valuation of highly varied goods have now been developed. However, there is an obvious danger of a simplistic acceptance of the following results as representing the value of all changes induced under any scenario. This would be highly erroneous and must be resisted. Nevertheless, what this demonstration does illustrate is that methods exists which address many of the key challenges to the incorporation of ecosystem services and the wider values of the natural environment within practical decision making. Furthermore, even this partial analysis amply shows that such incorporation can radically alter the apparent value of a given scenario or policy option. As such, these techniques point to a superior basis for future decision making.

Table 26.23 summarises comparable results from the various analyses reported in this chapter. It is important to recall that all of the values and impacts recorded here relate to changes rather than totals. So, for example, the agricultural values reported are simply for the change in value relative to the baseline. Total values could readily be computed by adding these to the baseline value. However, while we acknowledge that total values can be of some political use, such as underlining the importance of environmental resources as opposed to, say, the contribution of the health sector to well-being, the same example serves to show that no policy maker would ever wish to take a decision which placed either total value in jeopardy.[39] Instead it is the change in value induced by policy or other drivers which should be the focus of decision analysis allowing an informed choice between options.

Examining the monetary values reported in **Table 26.23** reveals a number of interesting findings. A general observation is that the magnitude of value changes within the farm provisioning services is generally lower than those of other monetised goods. This is immediately important, as it is only agricultural values which are reflected in market prices. This means that, from the outset, we can see that simple reliance upon market values is likely to yield an inaccurate assessment of the overall economic value of the different scenarios to society. In simple terms, analyses such as those provided by the UK NEA are vital if we are to ensure efficient decision making and an optimal allocation of resources.

39 It is also worth noting that for methodological reasons, the accuracy of total values is considerably smaller than that of value changes. While small deviations from the status quo can be reliably valued, a comparison of the status quo to an extreme and highly hypothetical state of the world where no ecosystem services are provided is on much shakier grounds.

Turning to consider the various scenarios under analysis we can see that the contrasting land uses, pollutions, urban extents and other characteristics of these scenarios are reflected in correspondingly different overall valuations. We can summarise these as follows:[40]

■ **Go with the Flow**: Here, overall agricultural incomes rise (although our geographical analysis shows that this is driven by gains in the south and lowlands offsetting losses in the north and uplands). As expected, these gains are largest under high climate change, reflecting the increased productivity arising from higher temperatures. (This reflects our analysis in Chapter 22; indeed, impacts on national farm incomes are always more positive under the high emissions variant of each scenario). These gains are added to by increases in recreational values, especially in areas where there are

high urban population levels. Furthermore, there are generally positive trends in general bird diversity and farmland birds, which have declined significantly over the past half century, remain at present levels. However, the increase in agricultural production envisioned under this scenario results in a substantial increase in carbon emissions. There is also a marked reduction in the amenity value of urban greenspace, which results from a combination of two effects. First, the expansion of Urban areas increases the average distance to the nearest urban greenspace. Second, substantial urban population growth exacerbates both crowding in greenspaces and population density in general. The provision of additional formal recreation sites under this scenario is insufficient to compensate for this, leaving urban households with an average annual loss in the order of £129/annum.

Table 26.23 Summary impacts for the change from the 2000 baseline to 2060 under each of the UK NEA Scenarios for Great Britain (High and Low Emissions). All values given in £ million per annum. Scenarios are as follows: GF = *Go with the Flow*; GPL = *Green and Pleasant Land*; LS = *Local Stewardship*; NS = *National Security*; NW = *Nature@Work*; WM = *World Markets*.

	GF High	GF Low	GPL High	GPL Low	LS High	LS Low	NS High	NS Low	NW High	NW Low	WM High	WM Low
	£millions p.a. (real values, £2010)											
Market agricultural output values[*]	590	220	-30	-290	430	350	1,200	680	-110	-510	880	420
Non-market greenhouse gas emissions[†]	-810	-800	2,410	2,410	570	-100	3,400	3,590	4,570	4,590	-1,680	-2,130
Non-market recreation[‡]	4,120	5,710	5,160	6,100	1,100	1,540	3,340	4,490	23,910	24,170	-820	5,040
Non-market urban greenspace[¶]	-1,960	-1,960	2,350	2,350	2,160	2,160	-9,940	-9,940	4,730	4,730	-24,000	-24,000
Total monetised values[§]	1,940	3,170	9,890	10,570	4,260	3,950	-2,000	-1,180	33,100	32,980	-25,620	-20,670
	Non-monetised impacts[**]											
Change in farmland bird species[‡‡]	0	0	0	0	0	0	-1	-1	-1	-1	0	0
Bird diversity (all species)[††]	++	++	++	++	-	-	++	+++	++	++	- -	+
Rank: Market values only	4	8	9	11	5	7	1	3	10	12	2	6
Rank: All monetary values	8	7	4	3	5	6	10	9	1	2	12	11
Rank: positive monetary values & number farmland bird losses	6	5	2	1	3	4						
Rank: positive monetary values & biodiversity gains	4	3	2	1								

* Change in total GB farm gross margin.
† Change from baseline year (2000) in annual costs of greenhouse gas (greenhouse gas) emissions from GB terrestrial ecosystems in 2060 under the UK NEA Scenarios (millions £/yr); negative values represent increases in annual costs of greenhouse gas emissions.
‡ Annual value change for all of GB.
¶ Annuity value; negative values indicate losses of urban greenspace amenity value.
§ We acknowledge some double counting between urban recreation and urban greenspace amenity values. Further data is needed to correct for this.
** Note that some commentators prefer to use monetised values for biodiversity. See discussion in Chapter 22.
†† Based on relative diversity scores for all species.
‡‡ Expected impact on the mean number of species in the seeds and invertebrates guild (including many farmland bird species) present in each 10 km square in England and Wales from 1988 to 2060 (rounded to the nearest whole number)—the 2000 baseline has 19 species in this guild (Dugdale 2010).

40 All of the assessments of monetary values presented in Table 26.23 are indifferent to the allocation of gains and losses across society. However, as discussed previously, this need not be the case. Indeed, policy makers have an explicit remit to consider distributional issues. Generally, the economist would argue that these should not be dealt with through the manipulation of values for any given good, preferring instead that these issues are dealt with directly through explicit redistribution policies such as progressive taxation (Just *et al.* 1987). While our instinct (as, in the main, economists) is to agree with the mainstream view, some would argue that the allocation of non-market environmental benefits can itself be used as a tool of redistribution and indeed this is allowed for in the Treasury Green Book which supplies a methodology for redistribution weighting of benefits.

Taking these various and opposing effects together, this scenario implies a modest overall net benefit. Two caveats are important, though. First, as mentioned, we are only considering a subset of market and non-market values here. While this seems preferable to the standard pure focus upon market values alone, it is still a partial and provisional analysis and should not be interpreted as implying that overall such a scenario improves welfare. Secondly, as emphasised at the start of this chapter, the *Go with the Flow* scenario does not conform to a standard economic 'do-nothing' baseline. Therefore it should not be interpreted as implying that an absence of any policy response will somehow lead to a beneficial outcome for society.

- **Green and Pleasant Land**: The reduction in agricultural intensity envisioned under this scenario leads to a decline in farm incomes (driven by losses in northern and upland areas which are only partly offset by gains in the southern lowlands), although this becomes relatively small when mitigated by a more rapidly warming climate. However, this pro-environment scenario results in substantial benefits in terms of reduced emissions. The scenario also generates very high gains in recreational value (second only to the *Nature@Work* scenario). Urban greenspace amenity improves as the average distance to urban parks remains constant but their size increases substantially and urban population growth and hence crowding is less than in the *Go with the Flow* scenario. Given that *Green and Pleasant Land* replicates the impact on birdlife exhibited by the *Go with the Flow* scenario, it is clear that, from a social value perspective, *Green and Pleasant Land* dominates *Go with the Flow*. Again, this result underlines the vital importance of analyses such as the UK NEA; if we were to restrict our analysis solely to market prices then the loss in agricultural values would reverse this outcome and reject a scenario which clearly benefits society as a whole.

- **Local Stewardship**: While the *Go with the Flow* and *Green and Pleasant Land* scenarios implied trade-offs between market and non-market (environmental) values, the *Local Stewardship* scenario appears to offer a win-win situation in terms of its monetised benefits. Agricultural incomes, recreation values and urban greenspace amenity all improve. Benefits derived from urban greenspace increase by about £142 per urban household per year as the urban population remains constant and provision of urban greenspace improves. However, returning to consider agricultural impacts, increases in farm incomes are confined to lowland areas, while upland regions exhibit falling incomes. Elsewhere, impacts upon greenhouse gas emissions are somewhat equivocal and themselves depend upon the rate of climate change. The *Local Stewardship* scenario also results in our first decline in overall bird diversity, although noticeably, this does not extend to our high-concern farmland species. Contrasting this scenario with, say, *Green and Pleasant Land*, gives us an analysis of the costs of avoiding that former decline. The analysis

cannot provide a cost-benefit assessment of whether or not those costs represent a suitable trade-off for the improvement in general bird diversity they would deliver, as we do not have robust non-use biodiversity values. However, if we contrast, say, the low emission *Local Stewardship* value (£3,950 million/annum), which does impose some decline in biodiversity, with the low emissions *Go with the Flow* value (£3,170 million/ annum), which maintains biodiversity, we can see that the opportunity cost of avoiding that biodiversity loss is roughly £780 million per annum.

- **National Security**: This scenario delivers the greatest gain in market-priced goods as agricultural incomes increase markedly. Net greenhouse gas emissions fall, due, in part, to the envisioned investment in Woodland, which in turn contributes to the modest increase in recreational values. However, the prioritisation of provisioning output results in very substantial falls in urban greenspace values to the extent that they dominate the other monetary values generated. The decline in urban greenspace values is driven by a marked loss in urban formal recreation sites, accompanied by a substantial increase in the urban population. Our biodiversity indicators extend trends seen from the middle of the last century, i.e. overall measures of general bird diversity improve, but our priority farmland bird indicators record the first localised species loss. Clearly, a decision rule which precluded options that result in such extinctions would reject such a scenario.

- **Nature@Work**: The headline prioritisation of multifunctional landscapes results in a marked decline in agricultural lands and with it, farm income. While this does generate strong improvements in our general biodiversity indicator, it actually results in a fall in our priority farmland bird indicator. Impacts upon greenhouse gas show the greatest reduction in emissions (compared to the baseline) of any of the scenarios. Moreover, the emphasis given to multifunctional landscapes results in by far the largest gains in both recreational values and urban greenspace amenity. The latter is driven by a substantial expansion in the provision of formal recreation sites, with only a moderate increase in urban population. These gains mean that, in monetary terms, the sum of market and non-market values is far larger in this than in any other scenario. In short, if society is prepared to accept the local loss of some farmland bird species, then this is by far the scenario yielding the highest net benefits. However, that caveat highlights the problem of dealing with a non-use value for biodiversity which, we argue, cannot be robustly established. In the end this is a problem which decision-makers would have to tackle.

- **World Markets**: The drive for unfettered economic growth envisioned under this scenario leads to substantial market-priced gains in agricultural output value. Where these are most extreme (under the high emission variant) they lead to the only losses of recreational value generated by any scenario, although these are slightly less than the increase in agricultural output values. However, these values are dwarfed by the losses in urban greenspace value and the rise in greenhouse gas emissions, both of which are larger than under any other scenario. In terms of urban growth, the *World Markets* scenario models an extreme case. The urban population increases by more than half, and the increase in urban greenspace is not sufficient to compensate for the fact that households live on average much further away from parks that are now more crowded. However, while *World Markets* clearly has

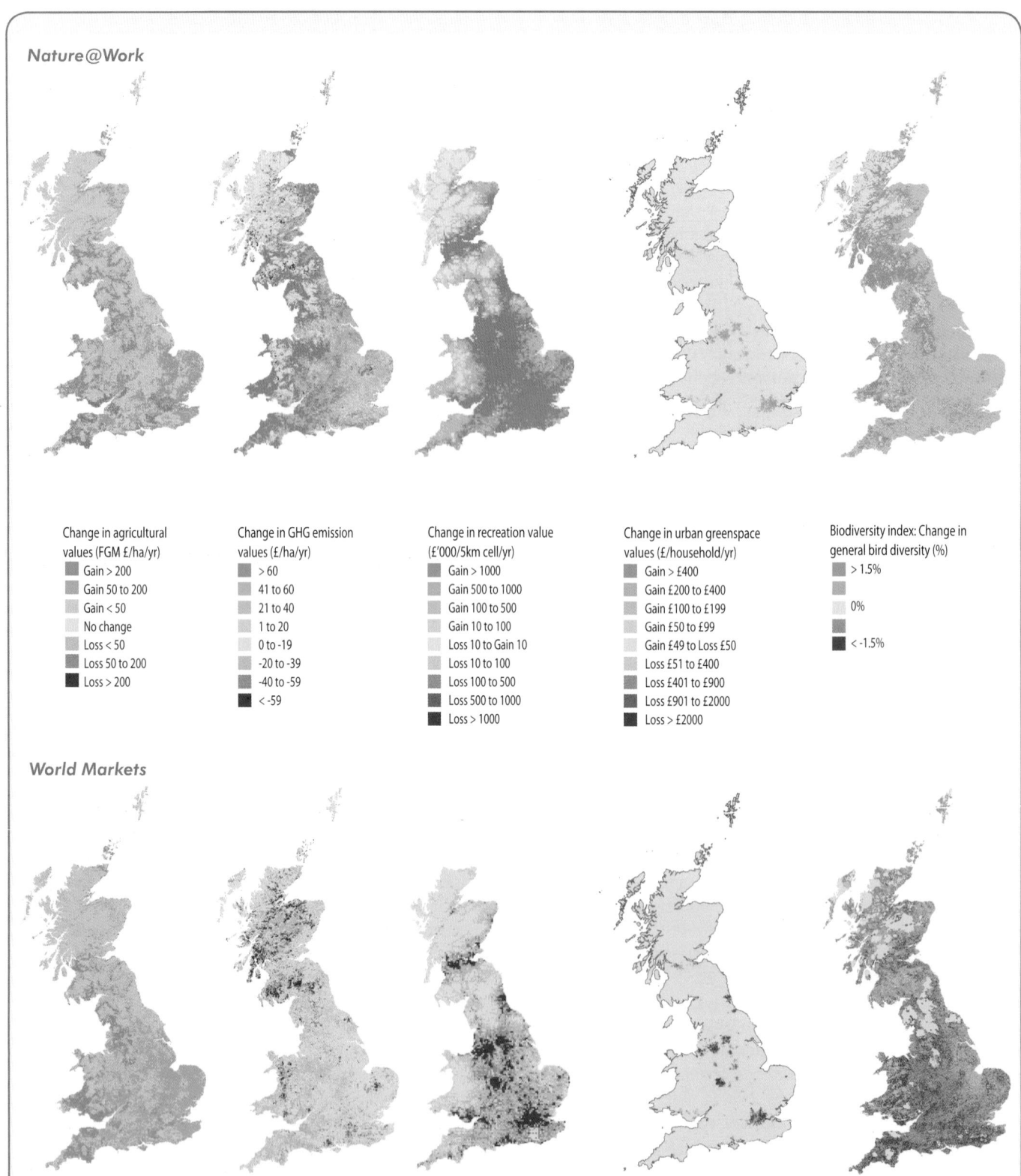

Nature@Work

Change in agricultural values (FGM £/ha/yr)
- Gain > 200
- Gain 50 to 200
- Gain < 50
- No change
- Loss < 50
- Loss 50 to 200
- Loss > 200

Change in GHG emission values (£/ha/yr)
- > 60
- 41 to 60
- 21 to 40
- 1 to 20
- 0 to -19
- -20 to -39
- -40 to -59
- < -59

Change in recreation value (£'000/5km cell/yr)
- Gain > 1000
- Gain 500 to 1000
- Gain 100 to 500
- Gain 10 to 100
- Loss 10 to Gain 10
- Loss 10 to 100
- Loss 100 to 500
- Loss 500 to 1000
- Loss > 1000

Change in urban greenspace values (£/household/yr)
- Gain > £400
- Gain £200 to £400
- Gain £100 to £199
- Gain £50 to £99
- Gain £49 to Loss £50
- Loss £51 to £400
- Loss £401 to £900
- Loss £901 to £2000
- Loss > £2000

Biodiversity index: Change in general bird diversity (%)
- > 1.5%
- 0%
- < -1.5%

World Markets

Figure 26.26 Spatial distribution of the changes induced by moving from the year 2000 baseline in five ecosystem service related goods (agricultural production (FGM: Farm Gross Margin); greenhouse gas (GHG) emissions; recreation; urban greenspace; biodiversity) under the *Nature@Work* scenario (upper row) and the *World Markets* scenario (lower row) for Great Britain.

a strongly negative effect on urban greenspace amenity, the actual monetary value derived should be treated with some caution as the scenario requires extrapolation well beyond the range of observable data. Clearly, the lunge for market values here generates outcomes which are undesirable in terms of overall social welfare. Furthermore, while the prioritisation of agriculture means that changes in farmland birds are not significant, the high emissions variant of *World Markets* generates the largest reduction in our general biodiversity indicator. In summary, this scenario does not offer an efficient allocation of resources for British society.

Considering all of the scenarios together underlines the vital importance of extending conventional decision analysis techniques to incorporate the generally non-market values generated by ecosystem services. The last four rows of **Table 26.23** underscore this message. The first of these ranks the UK NEA Scenarios solely according to the market value goods they generate: here represented by agricultural produce. We can see that most of the scenarios generate improvements in agricultural values (as indicated by the green shading of cells), particularly under their high climate change variants, with the *National Security* and *World Markets* scenarios providing the highest value, while the *Nature@Work* and *Green and Pleasant Land* scenarios produce, respectively, the greatest and second greatest losses of all scenarios. The following row extends our analysis to include all monetised values, irrespective of whether they are generated in markets or not. Here the ranking of scenarios changes dramatically, with the *Nature@Work* scenario moving from being the worst to now being the best option in terms of social value and the *Green and Pleasant Land* scenario coming second. In a similar manner, the *National Security* and *World Markets* scenarios, which were ranked as best in terms of market values alone, now appear to yield the two worst outcomes in terms of their overall social value. This is a major message of the UK NEA: omission of non-market values can result in socially sub-optimal situations, or even outcomes which actually reduce overall social welfare.

The final two rows of the table progressively exclude scenarios purely on the basis of their outcomes in terms of biodiversity. The penultimate row ranks outcomes only for those scenarios which both generate net social benefits and which avoid any further losses to our priority farmland bird diversity measure. This leads to the rejection of the *Nature@ Work* scenario, because its reduction in agricultural area results in localised losses of some farmland bird species. However, the opportunity costs of rejecting this scenario (which actually improves other biodiversity measures) are substantial, amounting to a loss of net social benefits of over £20,000 million/annum or two-thirds of the net value of the *Nature@Work* scenario. The final row of **Table 26.23** further restricts the analysis to only those scenarios which actually deliver biodiversity gains; although in this application the optimal scenario does not alter.

26.7.3 Spatial Patterns of Change

Our analysis has demonstrated that market and non-market values and non-monetary assessments vary substantially

across both scenarios and locations. We end our analysis by demonstrating the versatility of the methodology developed in capturing this variation. In **Figure 26.26** we compare two contrasting scenarios, *Nature@Work* high emissions and *World Markets* high emissions, in terms of each of the dimensions of change they generate. As can be seen, even when a scenario generates net benefits at a national scale, there are still winners and losers across different areas. The methodology developed provides decision-makers with the quantitative information required to incorporate this variation within the policy process. Long term, we feel that this constitutes one of the major contributions of this work. While we recognise that the analyses presented here are far from complete, nevertheless we contend that they constitute an agenda for future development in improving the incorporation of real world environmental complexity within economic assessments and decision-making analyses.

References

Abson, D.J., Termansen, M., Pascual, U., Fezzi, C., Bateman, I.J. & Aslam, U. (2010) Valuing regulating services (climate regulation) from UK terrestrial ecosystems. Report to the Economics Team of the UK National Ecosystem Assessment, School of Earth and Environment, University of Leeds, Department of Land Economy, University of Cambridge, and Centre for Social and Economic Research on the Global Environment (CSERGE), University of East Anglia. [online] Available at: <http://uknea.unep-wcmc.org/Resources/tabid/82/Default.aspx> [Accessed 18.03.11].

Antle, J. & Capalbo, S. (2001) Econometric-process models for integrated assessment of agricultural production systems. *American Journal of Agricultural Economics*, **83**, 389–401.

Bateman, I.J., Carson, R.T., Day, B., Hanemann, W.M., Hanley, N., Hett, T., Jones-Lee, M., Loomes, G., Mourato, S., Özdemiroglu, E., Pearce, D.W., Sugden, R. & Swanson, J. (2002) Economic Valuation with Stated Preference Techniques: A Manual. Edward Elgar Publishing, Cheltenham.

DECC (Department of Energy and Climate Change) (2009) Carbon valuation in UK policy appraisal: a revised approach. Departmant of Energy and Climate Change, London.

Defra (Department for Environment, Food and Rural Affairs) (2010) Wild populations: farmland birds in England 2009. Statistical release, Department for Environment, Food and Rural Affairs. [online] Available at: < http://www.defra.gov.uk/statistics/environment/biodiversity/england-biodiversity-indicators/> [Accessed 23.03.11].

Dugdale, S. (2010) Habitat Association Modelling for Farmland Birds, Report to the Economics Team of the UK National Ecosystem Assessment. CSERGE, University of East Anglia, Norwich. Experian (2010) Mosaic UK 2009/2008. [online] Available at: <http://uknea.unep-wcmc.org/Resources/tabid/82/Default.aspx> [Accessed 23.03.11].

Fezzi, C. & Bateman, I.J. (2010) Structural Agricultural Land Use Modelling for Spatial Agro-Environmental Policy Analysis. Centre for Social and Economic Research on the Global Environment (CSERGE), School of Environmental Sciences, University of East Anglia, Norwich.

Fezzi, C., Bateman, I.J., Askew, T., Munday, P. Pascual, U., Sen, A. & Coombes, E. (2010a) Enclosed Farmland 1: Provisioning services, Report to the Economics Team of the UK National Ecosystem Assessment. Centre for Social and Economic Research on the Global Environment (CSERGE), School of Environmental Sciences, University of East Anglia, Norwich. [online] Available at: <http://uknea.unep-wcmc.org/Resources/tabid/82/Default.aspx> [Accessed 18.03.11].

Fezzi, C., Hutchins, M., Rigby, D., Bateman, I.J., Posen, P. & Deflandre-Vlandas, A. (2010b) Integrated assessment of Water Framework Directive nitrate reduction measures. *Agricultural Economics*, **41**, 123–134.

Fezzi, C., Crowe, A., Abson, D., Bateman, I.J. & Haines-Young, R. (2011) Agricultural food production scenarios. Report to the UK National Ecosystem Assessment. Centre for Social and Economic Research on the Global Environment (CSERGE), School of Environmental Sciences, University of East Anglia, Norwich. [online] Available at: <http://uknea.unep-wcmc.org/Resources/tabid/82/Default.aspx> [Accessed 23.03.11].

Gibbons, D.W., Reid, J.B. & Chapman, R.A. (1993) The New atlas of breeding birds in Britain and Ireland: 1988-1991. T. & A.D. Poyser, London.

Gregory, R.D., van Strien, A., Voríšek, P., Meyling, A.W.G., Noble, D.G., Foppen, R.P.B. & Gibbons, D.W. (2005) Developing indicators for European birds. *Philosophical Transactions of Royal Society B*, **360**, 269–288.

Hardin, G. (1968) The tragedy of the commons. *Science*, **162**, 1243–1248.

HM Treasury (2003) The Green Book: Appraisal and Evaluation in Central Government. HMSO, London.

Hulme, M. & Siriwardena, G. (2010) Breeding bird diversity as a function of land cover. Report to the Economics Team of the UK National Ecosystem Assessment, British Trust for Ornithology, Thetford. [online] Available at: <http://uknea.unep-wcmc.org/Resources/tabid/82/Default.aspx> [Accessed 23.03.11].

Jones, A.P., Wright, J., Bateman, I.J. & Schaafsma, M. (2010) Estimating arrival numbers for informal recreation: A geographical approach and case study of British woodlands. *Sustainability*, **2**(2), 684–701. DOI:10.3390/su2020684.

Just, R.E., Hueth, D.L. & Schmitz, A. (1982) Applied Welfare Economics and Public Policy. Prentice Hall, Englewood Cliffs, New Jersey.

Perino, G., Andrews, B., Kontoleon, A. & Bateman, I.J. (2011) Urban Greenspace Amenity: Economic Assessment of Ecosystem Services provided by UK Urban Habitats. Report to the UK National Ecosystem Assessment, University of East Anglia, Norwich. [online] Available at: <http://uknea.unep-wcmc.org/Resources/tabid/82/Default.aspx> [Accessed 23.03.11].

Sen, A., Darnell, A., Crowe, A., Bateman, I.J. & Munday, P. (2011) Economic Assessment of the Value of Open-Access Recreation in UK Ecosystems: A Scenario Analysis. Report to the UK National Ecosystem Assessment, Centre for Social and Economic Research on the Global Environment (CSERGE), School of Environmental Sciences, University of East Anglia, Norwich. [online] Available at: <http://uknea.unep-wcmc.org/Resources/tabid/82/Default.aspx> [Accessed 23.03.11].

Stern, N. (2006). Stern Review on The Economics of Climate Change: Executive Summary. HM Treasury, London.

Thomson, A.M., Mobbs, D.C. & Milne, R. (2007) Annual inventory estimates for the UK. Inventory and projections of UK emissions by sources and removals by sinks due to land use, land use change and forestry (eds A.M. Thomson & M. Van Oijen). Centre for Ecology and Hydrology/Defra, London.

Chapter 27:
Response Options

Coordinating Lead Author: Bhaskar Vira
Lead Authors: Lindsey C. Elliott, Matthew Fortnam and Susie Wilks

Key Findings

There are three **tiers** of response options for sustainably managing ecosystems and their services:
1. **Foundational:** the generation and distribution of knowledge and information.
2. **Enabling:** legislation; policies, institutions and governance; changing social attitudes.
3. **Instrumental:** markets and incentives; technologies and practices; voluntary actions.

Knowledge (Foundational). The evidence base supporting ecosystems and their services continues to grow, as demonstrated by the richness of the UK National Ecosystem Assessment, and the large underlying literature base. However, there is a need to better understand linkages between biodiversity, ecosystem structure, functions and services. There is also an important need to develop monitoring and reporting frameworks that are better aligned with the ecosystem approach.

Legislation (Enabling). The role of the global and EU context, within which the UK has to frame policy responses, is important and often provides a strong push towards a more integrated and collaborative approach. In the context of environmental policy, external obligations should not necessarily be seen as a constraint, and often enable the adoption of more effective responses, while allowing scope for variation in national models of implementation. Many recent improvements in flows of ecosystem services have been due to effective legislative drivers.

Examples of important legislation include the Habitats Directive and the Birds Directive aimed specifically at the protection and conservation of wild animals, plants and habitats. Legislation from a wide range of sectors can positively impact on biodiversity, e.g. the Natural Environment and Rural Communities (NERC) Act 2006, and the Marine Strategy Framework Directive (MSFD) 2008. Pillar 2 of the Common Agricultural Policy (CAP) has provided an important source of funding for land managers to better align farming practices with the delivery of biodiversity through agri-environment schemes.

Policies, Institutions and Governance (Enabling). The UK Biodiversity Action Plan (UK BAP) led to the development of a framework of BAPs implemented by a broad array of stakeholders, with biodiversity targets expressed at the UK and country levels. The UK BAP contains 1,150 species and 65 habitats for which Species Action Plans and Habitat Action Plans have been published. As part of this national framework, more than 170 Local BAPs have been developed through local partnerships and community engagement for priority habitats and species.

Changing Social Attitudes (Enabling). The importance of the engagement of local communities and the general public in conservation is acknowledged in national biodiversity strategies and policies because public understanding and opinion of the value of biodiversity have strong implications for the acceptance and adoption of measures. While there has been a positive change in environmental attitudes, at present, the terms and concepts of biodiversity, ecosystems, and their services are not meaningful for the vast majority of people. Culturally, the concepts which have most meaning are those of nature, place and landscape.

Markets and Incentives (Instrumental). While incentives (e.g. CAP pillar 1) have long been used as an instrument to increase agricultural production, often degrading natural habitats and resulting in the loss of non-provisioning ecosystem services, recent incentive schemes (e.g. CAP pillar 2) have successfully contributed to the conservation of biodiversity. Agri-environmental schemes, especially the Higher Level Stewardship schemes, have generally led to the maintenance and restoration of existing habitats, with associated biodiversity benefits. Reform of the CAP could further safeguard biodiversity and promote multifunctional land use by rewarding, for example, the provision of carbon stores, promoting integrated pest management, and responding to new disease threats linked to climate change. Other market-based schemes that have proved effective include certification schemes such as the UK Woodland Assurance Standard.

Technologies and Practices (Instrumental). Agricultural production has been greatly increased by the application of technology for breeding, cultivation, management and protection from pests and diseases. The wider negative effects of fertilisers, pesticides and livestock manures have been reduced due to improved storage, new chemicals and more efficient applications. Nevertheless, habitats that are highly productive in terms of food are, inevitably, uniform and species-poor. In some areas, biodiversity is being supported by allocating non-productive areas for its conservation using biodiversity offsetting mechanisms such as agri-environment schemes. This support is occurring on a range of levels from single fields (promoting pollination and biological pest control), to whole catchments (promoting landscape and water quality), and even to higher scales (such as wilderness areas) and has the potential for enhancing biodiversity in the wider countryside. For example, the practice of set-aside (i.e. taking land out of agricultural production) was found to have a wide range of environmental benefits, despite not being explicitly designed for this purpose.

In the Marine environment, seabed trawling technologies have significantly damaged biodiversity. However, new, more environmentally friendly technologies and practices are now being developed, e.g. fishing technology to minimise harm to non-target species and juveniles.

Voluntary Actions, Education and Awareness (Instrumental). Education, at all ages, is essential for increasing public knowledge and understanding of the importance of conserving biodiversity. Statutory requirements stipulate that the science curriculum must include sustainable development, life processes and living things. Awareness creation leads to voluntary and civil society action, which plays an important role in the conservation of biodiversity. A prominent important example of voluntary action is the Campaign for the Farmed Environment.

Evidence shows that managing ecosystems and their services sustainably (economically, environmentally and socially) will be facilitated by employing an appropriate mix of approaches including legislation and regulations supporting attitudinal changes, underpinning markets and incentives, technological innovation, and voluntary compliance. The evidence shows that local initiatives have been invaluable for a range of local conservation activities and improving the delivery of some ecosystem services, but no national, regional or global environmental issue (e.g. air and water quality) has ever been successfully addressed without an appropriate enabling framework using a mix of regulations, technology, financial incentives and behavioural changes.

Evidence also shows that managing ecosystems and their services sustainably will be facilitated through the use of integrated approaches, recognising the scope for a wide range of actors to participate and collaborate, acknowledging the importance of spatial and temporal scales in formulating appropriate response mechanisms, and using flexible adaptive management frameworks.

Broadly, trends suggest that responses are becoming more integrated and reflective of ecosystem thinking, which suggests that the overall direction of change is positive. Moreover, in an international context, EU and UK approaches to ecosystem management reflect more integrated and collaborative modes of intervention. However, considerable challenges remain and should not be underestimated.

Evidence from the regional assessments (England, Northern Ireland, Scotland and Wales) demonstrates some divergence in approaches, which provides useful benchmarks for a comparison of policy options. In many ways, the UK context provides a 'controlled experiment' environment in which policies are differently implemented across the Devolved Administrations, and there is considerable scope for innovation at country level and shared learning from these divergent approaches.

Integrated Approaches. In order to reflect ecosystem thinking in the consideration of policy responses, the evidence suggests that decision-makers need integrated approaches that cut across narrow sectoral boundaries and recognise that the impact of actions in one sector has implications for other sectors and their associated ecosystem services (as well as human well-being). Promoting multifunctionality requires the identification of win-win opportunities which conserve and enhance multiple services (such as through strategies like managed realignment), while also recognising the importance of potential trade-offs between services. Responses that are initiated within a single sector often impact on other sectors and services—a key aspect of ecosystem service-based thinking. For example, agri-environment schemes provide markets and incentives shaped by EU law, albeit with variations in implementation in each region of the UK. The goal is to secure non-production ecosystem services from the farmed landscape to supplement income farmers make from provisioning services, e.g. crop, livestock and dairy production. Agri-environment schemes have been shown to have the following effects on ecosystem services:

- There is growing evidence that there have been considerable biodiversity improvements.
- There is potential to deliver other services, e.g. the prevention of soil erosion, better water quality and improvements to quantity and recharge flood control, and recreation.
- Evidence suggests that working across spatial scales is required to gain full potential, i.e. joint participation schemes for farmers to deliver ecosystem services from spatially connected farms which cannot be accomplished by individual farms.

Actors. There is considerable evidence that in each sector action has been undertaken by actors at every level, suggesting that there is scope for a wide range of actors to participate in the management of ecosystems. Different actors may be differently placed to undertake particular types of responses, but it is important to recognise that responses are not the exclusive domain of official/government actors, and that effective responses have been led by a range of private, non-governmental and community actors. An appropriate policy mix may require a combination of different types of responses (drawing upon the typology of responses that are considered, i.e. foundational, enabling and instrumental, with different actors playing different roles in each of the three tiers). Governments are primarily involved in foundational and enabling activities; the scientific community in foundational activities; the private sector primarily in foundational and instrumental activities, but also in enabling activities, especially in shaping social attitudes; and individuals and communities are mostly involved in enabling activities by changing social attitudes and values and instrumental activities by responding to incentives and undertaking voluntary activities.

Collaboration Between Actors. In order to be effective and to deliver lasting improvements in ecosystem services and human well-being, responses need to recognise the importance of collaboration between actors. While responses may be typically initiated by particular actors, they are rarely implemented in isolation, and usually require synergistic inputs from other actors to be successful. For example, the Water Framework Directive is an enabling piece of legislation which is implemented at local/regional scales, and necessitates collaboration between actors in order to develop River Basin Management Plans (RBMPs). While the lead stakeholders are competent government authorities in each river basin district (e.g. the Environment Agency, the Scottish Environment Protection Agency and the Northern Ireland Environment Agency), extensive consultations have taken place with stakeholders in the agricultural sector and water industry, and with planning authorities, businesses, environmental organisations, and anglers, boaters and other water users in the development of RBMPs. This engagement has established the foundation for continued collaboration between stakeholders in this context.

Temporal and Spatial Scale. Spatially, institutional mechanisms that link across scales provide opportunities for stakeholder engagement and greater collaboration between actors, and for the involvement of local groups and non-governmental organisations. Strategic spatial planning of habitats (terrestrial, freshwater and marine) is important for ecosystem service delivery, and this is happening in some cases, but needs to be better reflected in future responses. Temporally, recognising potential trade-offs between short-term goals and medium/long-term targets may require the adoption of longer planning horizons.

One example of thinking across spatial scales is marine planning. The Marine and Coastal Access Act is an enabling piece of legislation, which is under implementation in each region. The goal is an overarching framework for marine spatial planning, recognising linkages across scales. Key features include: consistency at the UK level across Devolved Administrations; recognition of competing demands taking an integrated ecosystems approach across scales; and engagement of all stakeholders/actors. Relevant evidence for the effectiveness of such an approach is the enactment of the Belgium Marine Protection Act in 1999, which established a master plan for Belgium's North Sea marine area, making it one of the first countries to develop an operational, multi-use marine spatial planning system with effective engagement of relevant stakeholders.

An example of thinking across temporal scales is Forest Schools, which seek to influence long-term social attitudes (enabling) through education in woodland. The goal is to use woodlands as a learning tool and site for education; there are about 140 Forest Schools in the UK. Evidence shows that outdoor learning environments enhance physical health and mental well-being of participants. There are also positive long-term impacts on the attitudes of participants towards nature and forested landscapes, resulting in greater local involvement in forest stewardship.

Flexible, Adaptive Management Frameworks. Planning responses in the face of uncertainty (such as in the context of climate change) requires the adoption of more flexible, adaptive management frameworks that are implemented within reflexive learning environments and which recognise that mistakes often help to construct more effective future responses. Knowledge frameworks need to support this adaptive approach, and lay and local knowledge needs to be adequately recognised as part of this broader learning environment, especially to get greater involvement of a wide range of stakeholders in response strategies.

27.1 Introduction

The UK National Ecosystem Assessment (UK NEA) has assessed a range of ecosystem types and associated flows of services, and has considered their contributions to human well-being. This chapter considers response options undertaken by a wide range of stakeholders which impact on these habitats, their ecosystem services and ultimately on health and human well-being. The chapter adapts a framework for assessing response options developed for the Millennium Ecosystem Assessment's Manual for Practitioners (Simpson & Vira 2010), and applies it to the UK experience. These responses are considered in the devolved UK context, and the chapter pays particular attention to the regionally diverse experiences within the different countries. The material is presented in a sectorally specific manner, in order to be accessible to readers who are likely to occupy roles in particular areas of ecosystem management. However, the overall message of the chapter is that sectorally focused approaches to responses are unlikely to be effective, given the connectedness of ecosystems and their functions, and the interdependence of different stakeholders. Responses that are initiated in one sector often have impacts in other sectors, and an integrated approach is a key element of ecosystem-based thinking for the delivery of multifunctional habitats. This chapter also emphasises the need for stakeholder collaboration since responses that are initiated by particular actors usually require engagement with others for successful implementation. Furthermore, the chapter highlights the necessity to recognise the need to adopt an appropriate mix of complementary responses, with knowledge, legislation and regulations supporting attitudinal changes, underpinning markets and incentives, driving technological innovation, and creating space for voluntary compliance.

This chapter is limited both by the availability of time for the actual assessment process, and by space, so inevitably falls short of a comprehensive survey of all response options that have been considered in the UK context. The examples that are used in the discussion of sectoral responses are illustrative of a much more complex reality, but have been chosen because of their relative importance and potential for further use. The chapter authors have consulted widely to aid this selection process, and have benefited greatly from the process of peer review and stakeholder engagement, which has widened the range of examples that have been considered, and has also added considerable nuance to their interpretation of the material that is under review.

This chapter needs to be seen as a contribution to the policy debate, being policy relevant, but not policy prescriptive (Ash *et al.* 2010). It does not provide any specific recommendations for policy, but reviews a range of responses and considers the evidence for their impacts. In this sense, the chapter documents a number of responses that have been undertaken in the UK context, by actors at different levels and cutting across a range of sectors, but does not provide prescriptive guidance for decision-makers. The choice among policies cannot be separated from the political context in which alternatives are considered, and

the objectives that are important for the decision-maker. These political choices will determine the intended outcome of any particular intervention, and the metric against which the relative success of a chosen measure is assessed. This chapter helps this process of policy choice by reviewing the evidence for the impacts of different responses, specifically focused on the UK context.

27.1.1 Typology of Response Options and Key Actors

This assessment adapts the typology of response options described in the Millennium Ecosystem Assessment's Manual for Practitioners (Simpson & Vira 2010). **Figure 27.1** presents a cascade, in which knowledge (at a fundamental, or 'foundational' level) creates the context within which governments enact legislation, adopt policies, institutions and governance-based interventions, and influence social attitudes towards habitats and ecosystem services. These provide the 'enabling' conditions within which actors undertake specific 'instrumental' strategies that frequently involve the use of markets and incentives for action, the deployment of specific technologies and practices, or the adoption of voluntary approaches.

Knowledge and information (in Tier 1 of the typology) are fundamental to any response as they provide the context within which a decision-maker recognises the need for intervention. This includes the emergence of new information about the impacts of production systems on natural ecosystems and their potential consequences for human well-being, as well as the monitoring of longer-term trends in habitat change and ecosystem functions and the likely risks that these might pose. An adequate knowledge base for action is a prerequisite for any intervention as it would be impossible to structure meaningful strategies without information about basic ecological and social relationships. Within the context of the UK NEA, the assessment of the status and trends of the UK's ecosystems and the services that they provide, the key drivers that are affecting ecosystem change, and the impacts of these on human well-being all constitute the knowledge base which shapes our consideration of potential responses. Importantly, this emerges from multiple sources; while research within conventional knowledge-producing sectors (such as universities and research organisations) is clearly very influential, there is an increasing role for other sources of information, especially from business and industry, but also from the 'lay' perceptions and experiences of citizens, which often form an important source of disaggregated data that can be effectively harnessed for monitoring purposes.

Tier 2 in the typology of responses provides an important link between the recognition of a problem and the adoption of specific instrumental strategies in response to that problem. This is characterised as a set of enabling mechanisms which provide the basis for particular approaches. Most importantly, perhaps, is the legislative and legal framework within which governments apply explicit policies, create particular institutional mechanisms and adopt specific strategies for governance. These are clearly influenced by a wider set of stakeholders, including businesses and industry, and the concerns of citizens and civil society organisations.

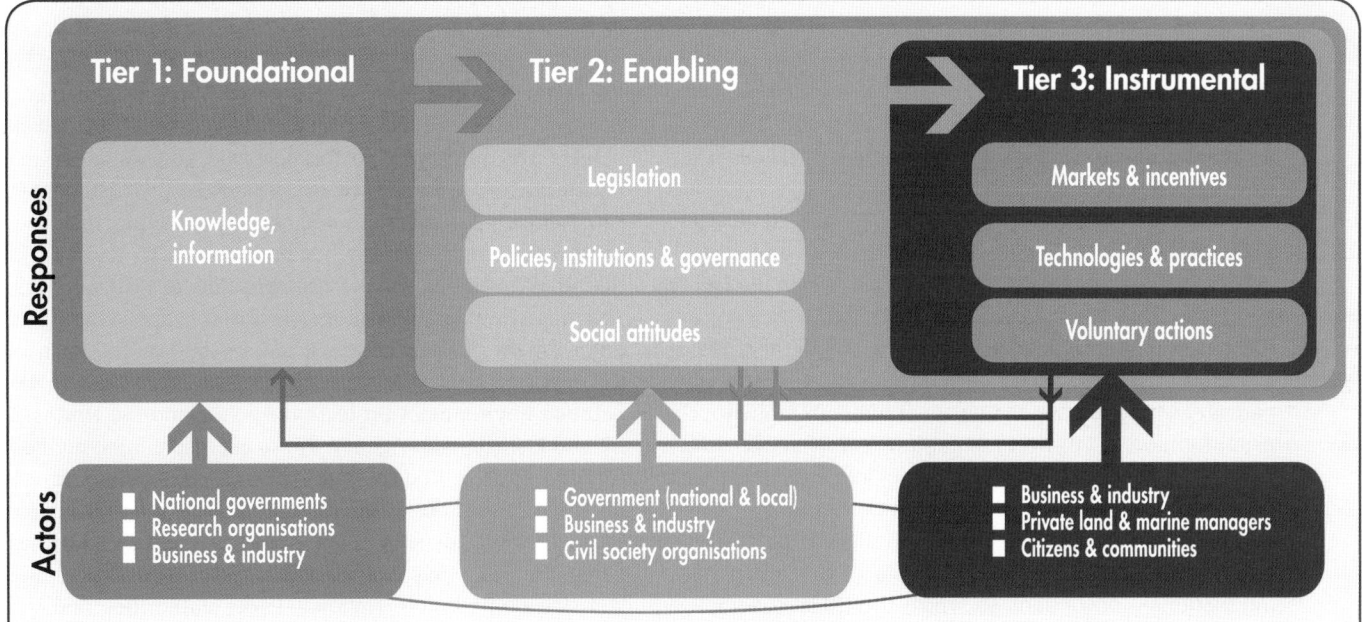

Figure 27.1 Cascade of responses. Knowledge (at a fundamental or 'Foundational' level) creates the context within which governments enact Legislation, adopt Policies, Institutions and Governance-based interventions, and influence Social Attitudes towards habitats and ecosystem services. These provide the 'Enabling' conditions within which actors undertake specific 'Instrumental' strategies that frequently involve the use of Markets and Incentives for action, the deployment of specific Technologies and Practices, or the adoption of Voluntary Approaches. The figure also shows the role that key actors play in the initiation and implementation of responses at each of these three tiers. Source: adapted from Simpson & Vira (2010).

Apart from the official adoption of these specific aspects of policy, it is also important to recognise the role of social attitudes, which shape the wider societal context within which responses are enacted. Attitudes to nature, the environment and to different components of human well-being are fundamental to the ways in which societies react to ecosystem change, and influence the range of interventions that can be implemented. These attitudes vary over time and space and are subject to a range of influences, including the crucial role of education as well as the persuasive power of advertisers and businesses, which shape social aspirations and attitudes to consumption.

Tier 3 in the typology describes specific actions that attempt to achieve particular outcomes; these include the use of markets and incentives to shape individual choices; the adoption of particular technological choices and everyday practices; and voluntary acts. While the enabling structures shape the opportunities and constraints that confront individual actors, much of the activity at this instrumental level is undertaken by businesses and industry, individual land and marine managers, and by citizens and communities. The role of governments at this level is to provide the conditions within which certain activities are rewarded and others are restricted, and to guide the actions of stakeholders towards improving the condition of ecosystems and enhancing the services that they provide.

Figure 27.1 shows the typology of response options, as well as the key stakeholders who exert a significant influence at each tier of the typology. While the role of governments at national and local levels is clearly important, the framework emphasises the need to recognise a wider range of stakeholders who shape responses including businesses and industry, private land and marine managers, civil society organisations (including non-governmental

organisations: NGOs), research organisations, and citizens and communities. Each of these actors has a particular domain within which they are able to exert an influence, but effective responses inevitably require interaction between the three tiers, and collaboration across actors. **Figure 27.1** also illustrates the importance of feedbacks between the three tiers. For example, the emergence of new technologies can lead to the generation of new information, as well as potentially requiring the reform of legislation and regulatory institutions and changes in social attitudes. Each tier of the typology influences, and is influenced by, the other tiers, and effective responses typically involve a combination of approaches across these different tiers.

27.1.2 Policy Context: European/ International Obligations

In order to understand the context within which UK decision-making on the environment takes place, it is important to recognise the impact of the country's wider global obligations and its membership of the European Union (EU). The UK is a party to many international conventions dealing with a huge number of environmental issues such as the United Nations Framework Convention on Climate Change (UNFCCC), the Convention on Biological Diversity (CBD), the Ramsar Convention (wetlands conservation), the Espoo Convention on Environmental Impact Assessment in a Transboundary Context, and the Convention for the Protection of the Marine Environment of the North-East Atlantic (the OSPAR Convention). Some, like UNFCCC, are more or less global in coverage, while others, like OSPAR, are regional, only applying to a certain area or set of countries. Some of these conventions, including UNFCCC, contain legally binding obligations; most do not, however, consisting of political pledges and aspirational targets instead. As a general rule, standards contained in international conventions require some kind of implementation in national law to have effect. International conventions tend to lack enforcement mechanisms or sanctions for breach, although there may be monitoring and reporting obligations which can exert pressure to comply with commitments.

The key EU legislative instruments are Regulations (which are legally binding in their entirety and directly applicable in national law) and Directives (which are legally binding as to the result to be achieved, but leave the choice of form and method for implementation to the Member State). Regulations impose entirely uniform standards and rules and are relatively rare in the environmental sphere. The usual form for EU environmental law is a Directive, which must be transposed (by a set deadline) into national law via primary or secondary legislation at the national level. There will be a varying degree of discretion left to the national governments as to the precise detail of implementation. International conventions to which the EU is a signatory also become EU law and are directly applicable in all of the Member States (under Article 216 of the Treaty on the Functioning of the EU: TFEU).

The EU and Member States have shared competence in environmental matters (under Article 4 of the TFEU), which means (under Article 2) that both may adopt legally binding acts in that area, the national governments acting to the extent that the EU does not. There are also shared competencies in other sectors, such as agriculture, energy and transport, which have significant environmental impacts. Fisheries management is a shared competence, but measures relating to the conservation of marine biological diversity belong to the exclusive competence of the EU. A key principle of EU law governing to what extent the EU will legislate in these areas is subsidiarity—meaning that the EU should only act if the objectives of the proposed action cannot be sufficiently achieved by the Member States acting alone. Due to the transboundary nature of many environmental issues (for example, water quality, climate change, migratory threatened species and marine pollution) this will often be the case.

Article 191 of the TFEU sets out some important principles for EU environmental law: that it shall aim at a high level of environmental protection, and apply the precautionary and polluter pays principles. Article 193 of the TFEU expressly preserves the right of Member States to maintain or introduce in their national law environmental protection measures that are more stringent than those introduced by the EU. The European Commission (EC) and, ultimately, the European Court of Justice are responsible for making sure that EU environmental law is transposed and implemented properly, but, in practice, enforcement is frequently lacking.

27.1.3 Policy Context: UK and Devolved Administrations

In the UK, legislation can be passed by the UK Parliament in Westminster for the whole of the country. Following devolution in 1998, powers were granted to the devolved Parliament in Scotland and Assemblies in Wales and Northern Ireland. The Westminster Parliament continues to legislate for England on issues that have been devolved to other Parliaments, and can still legislate for the UK, although by convention, this is only done by agreement. The legislation establishing devolution sets out which powers are transferred to the devolved governments, and which powers are reserved by Parliament in Westminster. Environmental matters are not, broadly speaking, reserved, so the devolved governments have power to legislate in this area, including for the transposition of EU Directives. The main regulators responsible for the application and enforcement of environmental law in the UK and each of the devolved jurisdictions are the Environment Agency, the Scottish Environment Protection Agency and the Northern Ireland Environment Agency. There are also a large number of other public bodies with specific responsibilities for implementation, enforcement, administrative and scientific research, and advisory roles, some of the key examples being Natural England, Scottish Natural Heritage, the Forestry Commission, National Parks authorities and the Rural Payments Agency.

Devolution has the potential to be an important influence on UK environmental law and some divergences of approach in environmental sectors have emerged (although, because a large proportion of environmental law is derived from the EU, the divergence may not be as great as could otherwise be expected). Waste management is a good example of an environmental sector where key differences exist under devolved mechanisms. Scotland has put in place more ambitious targets for waste management than are required under EU legislation or by Westminster, in the form of a 70% waste recycling target. Scotland's laws on countryside access also differ from those in England, with diverging rules on the evidence of habitual use leading to different public right of way designations in these two jurisdictions. Northern Ireland has differences in its waste and contaminated land regime, and Wales differs from England in certain rules implementing EU legislation like the Nitrates Directive (discussed in Section 27.3.3.2), and also in respect of its countryside access rules.

There are differing views on whether divergence of laws has a positive or negative effect as far as environmental protection is concerned—on the one hand it may lead to regulatory competition, encouraging an ambitious policy environment and establishment of best practice, on the other it may create inefficiencies, inequalities and perverse outcomes. Whether it works to promote or frustrate environmental protection will vary from case to case, as explored in some of the more detailed sectoral analyses in this document.

27.1.4 Sectoral Approaches and the Need for Integration

The majority of the assessment of response options that is presented in this chapter has been undertaken by sector. We have assessed response options available to the full range of actors within each sector by response type across the three tiers: foundational, enabling and instrumental. We have reviewed evidence for the impacts of these responses on habitats, their ecosystem services, and human health and well-being. Rather than undertaking specific assessments of each country, examples and case studies have been drawn from England, Scotland, Northern Ireland and Wales to illustrate response options and highlight success stories. The specific sectors that are addressed in subsequent sections of this chapter are: a) biodiversity; b) water; c) agriculture; d) forestry; e) fisheries; f) marine and coasts; g) recreation and tourism; and h) urban planning, transport and energy.

This sectoral approach is a somewhat artificial division of the material into sections that are likely to be accessible to our readers based on familiar areas within which policy responses can be conventionally subdivided. However, there is considerable overlap in our discussion, partly because specific responses, even if they are initiated within particular sectors, often have impacts on other sectors. The chapter provides cross-references within each section to identify these influences. More importantly, however, the chapter emphasises the need to adopt approaches that go beyond sectoral divides and are able to adopt a more holistic and integrated approach to habitats and ecosystem management. Thus, readers would be advised to read the sectoral material as a guide to some of the key responses that are most relevant within that particular context, but also be cognisant of the cross-cutting nature of much of the material that we have reviewed, and to read the chapter in its entirety to get a holistic overview of the range of responses that have been assessed.

Ecosystems are non-discrete units where assemblages of living organisms interact with each other and with the chemical and physical environment. Researchers have defined ecosystems at multiple scales, from biota in soil to large global systems like the oceans. The recognition of these interactions is fundamental for understanding how to holistically manage the natural environment. Ignoring this knowledge in the design of responses can lead to unintended consequences. The ecosystem approach, as defined by the CBD, is "a strategy for the integrated management of land, water and living resources that promotes conservation and sustainable use in an equitable way". It embodies knowledge of how complex, dynamic, interacting ecological and physical systems operate at different scales, and the ecosystem services provided to humanity. The approach also highlights that environmental limits must be adhered to if the land and sea are to continue to provide a wide range of ecosystem services in the future.

Internationally, the ecosystem approach has gained currency as a powerful framework for the assessment, planning and management of the natural environment and resources. It underpins the CBD, and at the World Summit on Sustainable Development (WSSD 2002) states were encouraged to apply the ecosystem approach by 2010. Since the publication of the Millennium Ecosystem Assessment (MA) in 2005 policy interest has risen further. As this chapter demonstrates, marine, coastal and water policy is currently being reconfigured in the UK in line with the broad principles of the ecosystems approach, and is adopting a more holistic and integrated perspective on response options. While these movements are important, there remain many challenges to embedding the ecosystem approach more widely in policy outside of the traditional domain of the 'environment' and especially into the decision-making processes of other

government departments that influence pressures on ecosystems.

The Department for Environment, Food and Rural Affairs (Defra) and others are increasingly interested in how the ecosystems approach can be embedded into multifunctional land use and management to secure rich and diverse landscapes delivering multiple ecosystem services (LUC 2008). In December 2007, Defra published Securing a Healthy Natural Environment: an Action Plan for Embedding an Ecosystem Approach. This action plan sets out a number of actions that Defra and its partners can follow to apply the ecosystem approach in managing the natural environment. The action plan's core principles are:

- A more **holistic approach to policy making** and delivery, with the focus on maintaining healthy ecosystems and ecosystem services.
- Reflecting the **value of ecosystem services in decision-making.**
- Respecting **environmental limits** in the context of sustainable development.
- Taking decisions at the **appropriate spatial scale**, while recognising the cumulative impacts of decisions.
- Applying **adaptive management** of the natural environment to respond to changing pressures, including climate change.

The main aim of the plan was to shift policy making and delivery away from 'silo' thinking towards a more holistic approach, and to ensure the value of ecosystem services is reflected in decision-making in Defra and across government. An update of the action plan was published at the beginning of 2010 and reviewed progress since 2007. The updated action plan stressed the fundamental importance of stakeholder participation in decision-making for delivering an ecosystems approach, especially ensuring that the right stakeholders are engaged. Work on developing Defra's Climate Change Plan (2011c) also emphasised the importance of taking a whole systems approach and the need for a policy framework that enables adaptive management, allowing actions to change in response to fluctuating pressures and new knowledge.

An ecosystems approach is now reflected in the plans and activities of Natural England, the Environment Agency and the Forestry Commission, and each organisation is exploring a variety of ways to embed this thinking into their work; for example, the Environment Agency are undertaking catchment management work with Defra, Natural England are running ecosystem service pilots, and the Forestry Commission has developed a Delivery Plan for England's Trees, Woods and Forests. These organisations have increased cooperation with local authorities to find ways to support the delivery of environmental objectives.

Multifunctional land use has been placed at the heart of how to deliver improved ecosystems. Land use determines the social and economic functions of landscapes such as food and timber production, infrastructure and housing. The Scottish Government has, for the first time, set out a high level strategy for sustainable land use across the country. They aim to guide and support those involved in land use management decisions by providing a long-term vision and objectives that will enable an integrated approach to land use in Scotland (Scottish Government 2010a).

Decisions about land use can be taken at various scales and by different sectors and actors. Many decisions taken on land use today are made within sectors such as agriculture, forestry and housing. While it is certainly important to account for the specifics of each sector in decisions, many of the big challenges going forward, such as climate change and optimising ecosystem service delivery, require a broader perspective on land use (Foresight 2010). In the UK, multipurpose land use is arguably one of the most important ways to maintain ecosystem services vital for the well-being and quality of life of UK citizens (LUC 2008). The Foresight Land Use Future report (Foresight 2010) called for a better understanding of how the various demands on land made by different sectors interact and the consequences of those interactions, and recommends "a broad and overarching perspective across sectors and different levels of governance".

Embedding an integrated ecosystem approach into land use management will demand shifts in world views. It will require fundamental changes to established policy mechanisms as focusing on individual sectors and the segregation of land use have been entrenched for a long time (Lowe *et al.* 2009). However, the ecosystem approach offers unprecedented opportunities to rethink how the UK's landscapes could look and function in the future. New, multifunctional landscapes could revitalise the distinctiveness of a place, and land use functions could be matched to a desired landscape character (LUC 2008). Section 27.10 provides more detail on the different areas within which an integrated approach to habitat and ecosystem management is being adopted in the UK. It also revisits the

sectoral evidence to demonstrate the substantial overlap in response options that cut across these boundaries.

Figure 27.2 provides a structural overview of the detailed content of this chapter, which is organised across eight sectoral sections. These sectoral sections are followed by a more synthetic discussion which reiterates the need for an integrated ecosystems approach, and examines potential synergies between interventions across different sectors.

Each sectoral section follows the typology of responses in **Figure 27.1** and discusses responses at each tier, as well as the roles of different stakeholders in adopting and implementing response options. The chapter finds that action has been undertaken by actors at every level, suggesting that there is scope for a wide range of actors to participate in the management of ecosystems. Different actors may be differently placed to undertake particular types of responses, but it is important to recognise that responses are not the exclusive domain of official/government actors, and that effective responses have been led by a range of private, non-governmental and community actors. Governments are primarily involved in foundational and enabling activities; the scientific community in foundational activities; the private sector primarily in foundational and instrumental activities, but also in enabling activities, especially in shaping social attitudes; and citizens and communities are mostly involved in enabling activities by changing social attitudes and values and instrumental activities by responding to incentives and undertaking voluntary activities.

The evidence reviewed in this chapter shows that managing ecosystems and their services sustainably (economically, environmentally and socially) requires an appropriate mix of approaches including regulations,

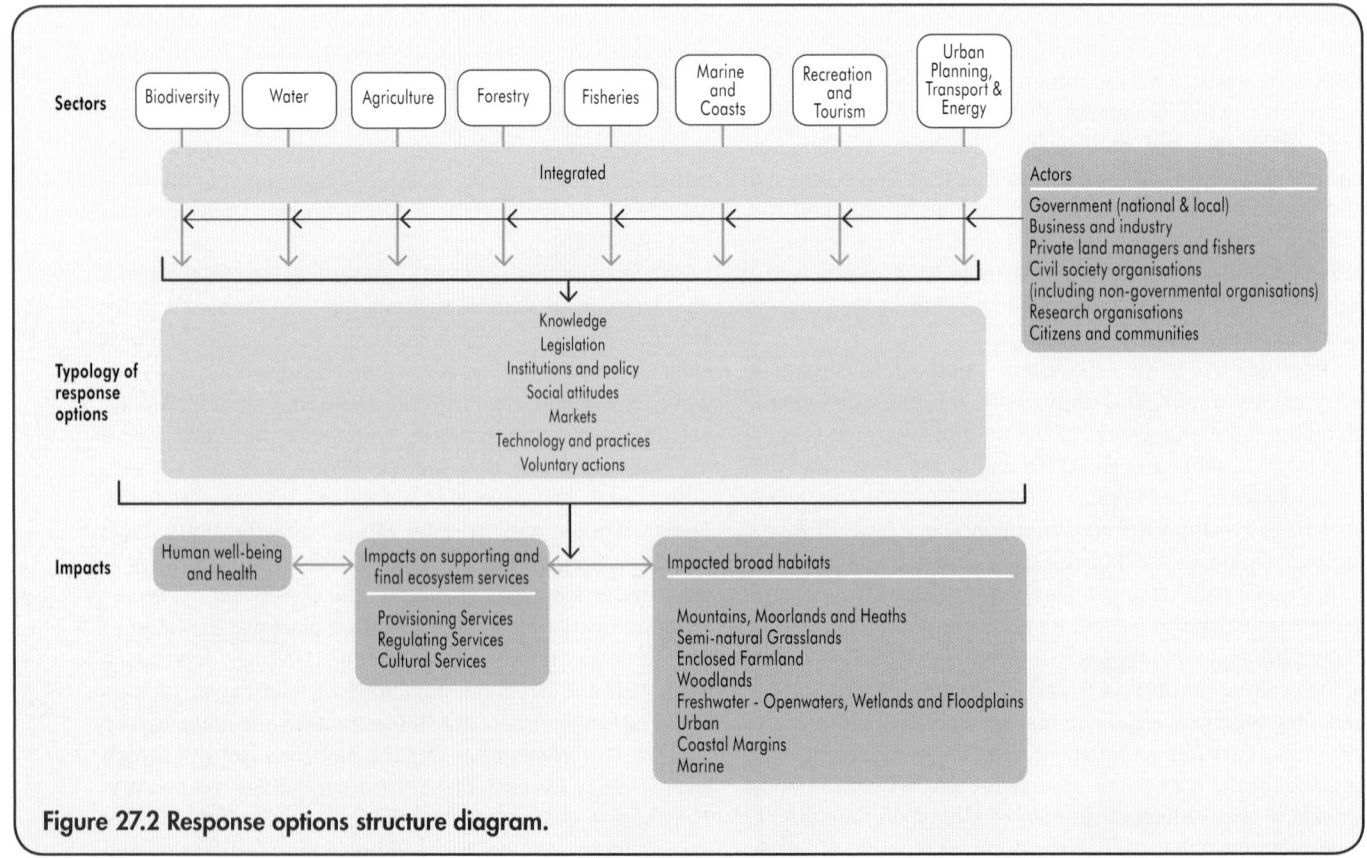

Figure 27.2 Response options structure diagram.

technology, financial incentives and behavioural changes. Evidence also shows that managing ecosystems and their services sustainably will be facilitated through the use of integrated approaches. Broadly, trends over the last 60 years suggest that responses are becoming more integrated and reflective of ecosystem thinking, which suggests that the overall direction of change is positive. Moreover, in an international context, EU and UK approaches to ecosystem management reflect more integrated and collaborative modes of intervention. However, considerable challenges remain and should not be underestimated.

27.2 Biodiversity

27.2.1 The Relationship Between Biodiversity, Ecosystem Services and Human Well-being

"The natural environment provides us with a range of benefits—ecosystems services...—and biodiversity underpins most, if not all, of them." (Lawton *et al.* 2010, p.v)

Biodiversity is a unique case within the UK NEA in that it simultaneously defines and differentiates each habitat, underpins ecosystem services, and can even be seen as an ecosystem service in its own right (Chapter 4; **Box 27.1**). It will be tackled as a sector for the purposes of this chapter, with full acknowledgement of its truly cross-sectoral nature. The focus here will be to capture the range of response options that promote the conservation of biodiversity, allowing it to serve its many functions.

Chapter 4 suggests that there are two different challenges in considering response options in this context. Where there is relatively good understanding of the impacts of drivers on biodiversity (such as land-use change, pollution and exploitation), it is important to improve the effectiveness of policy and practice responses (e.g. land-use change). In the case of other drivers (such as climate change), we need better understanding of biodiversity impacts. Continued research into all drivers of biodiversity change will help to fill existing gaps and improve our overall understanding of this complex sector at different scales.

Most of the drivers impacting biodiversity are not uniform in their importance across biodiversity groups or habitats, although land use change and pollution are acknowledged to have a major general impact (Chapter 4). **Figure 27.3** summarises the key drivers and their impacts on ecosystem services. Many of these drivers interact with one another, and in some cases, such as land use change, are important both as an ultimate driver and as the proximate result of changes in other drivers (climate change, exploitation, etc.).

27.2.2 Challenges within the Biodiversity Sector

Previous chapters have described in depth the habitats and ecosystem services of the UK and biodiversity plays an

Box 27.1 Defining biodiversity.

For the purposes of the UK NEA, the Biodiversity Chapter (Chapter 4) defines 'biodiversity' as follows:

"The term biodiversity describes the diversity of life on Earth. Diversity can occur at a number of levels of biological organisation from genes, through individuals, populations, species and communities, to entire ecosystems."

This is consistent with the definition adopted by the UN Convention on Biological Diversity. Use of the term 'biological diversity' became commonplace among members of the scientific community in the 1980s following publications such as Conservation Biology (Soulé & Wilcox 1980). The contraction 'biodiversity' was first published by Edward O. Wilson in 1988 (Novacek 2008).

While there is reasonable scientific consensus around the meaning of the term, there is continued concern about the lack of public understanding and engagement with biodiversity as a concept, despite evidence that there is great affinity with nature in a more general sense (Defra 2002b; Christie *et al.* 2006).

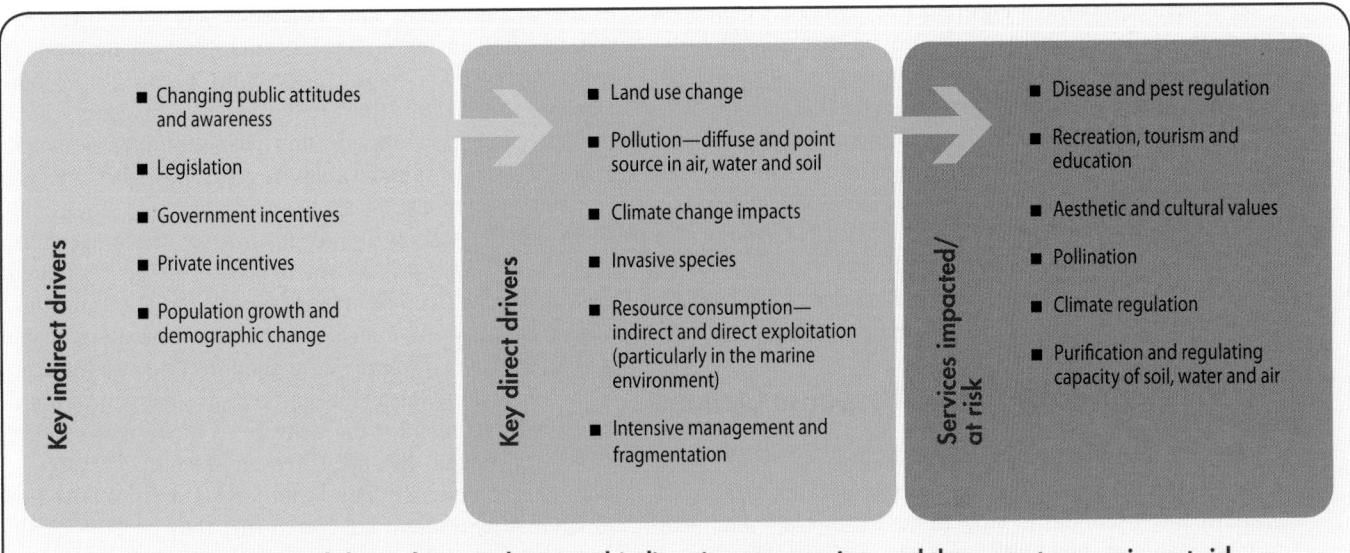

Figure 27.3 Key indirect and direct drivers relevant to biodiversity conservation, and the ecosystem services at risk.

important role in all of them. Because of its importance, we face numerous challenges to increase our understanding of this cross-cutting issue while simultaneously striving to preserve the biodiversity which underpins ecosystem services, well-being and our future.

In 2001, the EU Heads of State and Government undertook to halt the decline of biodiversity by 2010 (Presidency Conclusions 2001). Under the CBD, the 6th Conference of Parties in 2002 adopted the strategic plan "to achieve by 2010 a significant reduction of the current rate of biodiversity loss at the global, regional and national level as a contribution to poverty alleviation and to the benefit of all life on earth." (CBD 2002). Despite these commitments, by 2008 it was recognised that it was unlikely that the 2010 target would be achieved, and dramatic loss of biodiversity still continues in the UK today (The Environmental Audit Committee 2009).

Most biodiversity value cannot be expressed in monetary terms (Chapter 22). Consequently, a major recurring challenge is the trade-off between provisioning services and impacts on biodiversity and other ecosystem services. There are countless examples, from all habitat types, which demonstrate that increased productive capacity, often the result of technological advances, can lead to decreased biodiversity. For example, wasteful discards from mixed fisheries as a result of unselective fishing gear and the quota system of the Common Fisheries Policy impact marine biodiversity (**Box 27.30**, Section 27.6.3.6). Mechanisms to support less intensive management may improve the situation in some cases, but may also lead to a change in the composition of habitats dependent on active management such as Semi-natural Grassland. The development of improved spatial planning mechanisms is needed to ensure that the adverse biodiversity impacts of land use change are targeted through management at appropriate scales (Section 4.6).

One important concern within the conservation community is that the ecosystem service approach may not maximise biodiversity. There is little evidence that directly correlates biodiverse areas with high ecosystem service delivery (Section 22.3.2). There is, however, evidence of significant decline in biodiversity in the UK as a result of the drivers described in **Figure 27.3**. It will be a challenge to maintain biodiversity within groups that appear to be more vulnerable to these drivers, such as amphibians, lichens, bryophytes and land plants (Chapter 4, Table 4.5). In particular, the impacts of climate change, offshore energy development and invasive species have the potential to increase in the future. These impacts will also cause and interact with land use change to drive changes in biodiversity. A decline in biodiversity affects the resilience and stability of ecosystems and the services they provide, feeding back to further compound many of the drivers.

27.2.3 Biodiversity-related Response Options

27.2.3.1 Knowledge (foundational)
The evidence base supporting the role and importance of biodiversity continues to grow in the UK through a number of programmes and initiatives. The Countryside Survey has provided scientifically reliable evidence about the UK

countryside since 1978, reporting in 1984, 1990, 1998 and, most recently, 2007 (Carey *et al.* 2008b). Results in the form of a Land Cover Map and field surveys are compared over this period to analyse change. One important application of the data is to determine status and trends in aspects of biodiversity, Broad Habitats and linear features such as hedgerows, walls and streams (Carey *et al.* 2008a). For instance, findings indicate that between 1998 and 2007: common plant species became more abundant; plant species richness in arable land increased by 30% (in GB); the lengths of managed hedges decreased by 6%; the area of broadleaved woodlands increased by 6.9%; competitive species have increased in heathlands and bog; and the condition of freshwater has continued to improve. A number of other monitoring programmes exist throughout the UK for particular groups of organisms (**Box 27.7**, Section 27.2.3.7).

In England, the State of the Natural Environment 2008 report provides a comprehensive account of the evidence on the state of, threats to, and actions taken to secure, the natural environment (Natural England 2008b). The Key Scottish Environment Statistics have been published annually since 2000 to provide an easily accessible reference for information and trends about the state of Scotland's environment (National Statistics Scotland 2010). Most recently, Scotland's Wildlife: an Assessment of Biodiversity in 2010 reported on Scotland's progress towards biodiversity targets (Mackey & Mudge 2010). In Wales, reports are updated twice a year and published as an annual bulletin overviewing the progress made against the Environmental Strategy of the Welsh Assembly Government (Statistics for Wales 2010b) since the first Progress Report was published in 2007 (WAG 2007). The State of the Environment of Northern Ireland was first assessed and reported in 2008 (Environment & Heritage Service 2008) and, subsequently, the Northern Ireland Statistics Report was published in 2009 and updated in 2010 (Northern Ireland Statistics & Research Agency 2010).

The UK has adopted biodiversity targets and indicators to report on biodiversity status and trends (Section 4.1). The use of indicators in assessing broad trends in the ecological integrity of different habitats has been widely incorporated into policies and regulations (Carignan & Villard 2002). In the UK, an initial suite of biodiversity indicators were first reported in 2007 (Defra 2010k). The UK Biodiversity Indicators in Your Pocket 2010 report (Defra 2010k) now presents 18 indicators that are indicative of the general state of biodiversity in the UK, forming a basis for the assessment of progress towards biodiversity targets. The report indicates that 46% of all measures show an improvement since 2000, while only 27% show improvement over the longer-term (*ibid.*). A review of targets and indicators for the ecosystem approach by the Department for Environment, Food and Rural Affairs (Defra 2008d) concluded that "the currently available suite of indicators do provide a good overview of the state of the natural environment but there are gaps in terms of their ability to monitor the delivery of ecosystem services and, in particular, the pressures on specific ecosystems." (p.2). The review also found that targets are not based on 'functional' limits and suggested that they be periodically reviewed so that they take into account the latest scientific understanding.

Scotland's Biodiversity Indicators report (Donnelley 2007) presents the state of 17 indicators of Scotland's biodiversity and 5 indicators describing the engagement of people with its conservation and enhancement. These indicators are used to assess progress towards the achievements outlined in Scotland's Biodiversity Strategy.

In terms of the Marine environment, the UK Marine Monitoring and Assessment Strategy (UKMMAS) was set up in 2005 by the UK Government and Devolved Administrations to provide a more integrated understanding of the seas (Defra 2010i). The Charting Progress 2 (CP2) report (UKMMAS 2010), updating the earlier report from 2005, provides the best evidence currently available for UK Marine environments, and was positively received by government (Defra 2010i). Despite these achievements, many knowledge gaps remain, and much work is needed to provide sufficient data for robust assessments (Section 27.7.3.1).

The UK Terrestrial Biodiversity Strategy adopts a systematic approach to improve the surveillance and monitoring of biodiversity, fill knowledge gaps and address future needs (JNCC 2011). Development of a Biodiversity Surveillance Strategy for Scotland is currently underway by Scottish Natural Heritage and aims to address knowledge gaps for habitats and species of statutory and policy importance in the country.

Efforts have been made to increase the accessibility of information about biodiversity and the environment, and it is now commonplace for environmental statistics and analyses to be freely available online. The Biological Records Centre (BRC) was established in 1964 as a national focus for recording terrestrial and freshwater species (other than birds) into a database (Hill *et al.* 2006). In 2000, the National Biodiversity Network (NBN) Trust was established as a partnership between a range of conservation NGOs and government agencies to build a network of shared information about UK wildlife. One way this is achieved is through the NBN Gateway website (http://data.nbn.org.uk/) which acts as an accessible online database of biodiversity information and receives contributions from government and country agencies, environmental agencies, wildlife conservation organisations, local records centres and numerous volunteers.

There remains a 'cultural divide' in the collection of monitoring data, with a bias towards culturally important biodiversity groups, sometimes at the expense of those that matter most for the delivery of provisioning and regulating ecosystem services (Section 4.7, Figure 4.7). There is a lack of data and information about trends for some groups of invertebrates, lower plants, fungi and microorganisms, limiting our understanding of the services in which these groups play a part. Knowledge gaps also exist for rare habitats such as Semi-natural Grasslands in Scotland (Section 19.4.2).

As biodiversity is increasingly linked to ecosystem services, there is a need to shift to a more functional understanding of biodiversity (Section 4.7). The MA (2005) highlighted, for the first time, the functional roles biodiversity plays in the context of ecosystem services and its benefits to humans and well-being. Existing functional data is limited to small-scale or highly simplified systems; hence there is a need to study the functional relationships between biodiversity and

ecosystem services at appropriate scales. This will require the development of new research tools and techniques to measure and describe the functional components of biodiversity (NERC 2007). Research programmes focusing on functional links at large scales have begun to emerge—for example, those under the Water Framework Directive (WFD) and the Insect Pollinators Initiative (BBSRC 2009; **Box 27.2**)—but a number of challenges remain. Continued research on broad drivers, such as climate change and invasive species, is needed to better understand their potential future impact. The role of biodiversity indicators to assess climate change, economics and ecosystem services is likely to increase and evolve (Parliamentary Office of Science and Technology 2008). Most significantly, a better understanding of *how* biodiversity underpins ecosystem

---

Box 27.2 Insect Pollinators Initiative. Source: BBSRC (2009).

As presented in Chapter 14:

"Pollination is a primary/intermediate ecosystem service which potentially has a large impact on regulating the provision of final ecosystem services such as crops and other plants (delivering, for example, food and fibre)… It is well established that both managed pollinators (honeybees) and wild pollinators (primarily non-managed bees and hoverflies) have been in severe decline for at least the last 30 years and it is very likely that this trend will continue. Twenty percent of the UK cropped area comprises pollinator dependent crops and a high proportion of wild flowering plants depend on insect pollination for reproduction."

Pollinators are essential for the maintenance of biodiversity in natural ecosystems. As such, the Insect Pollinators Initiative was established to "promote innovative research aimed at understanding and mitigating the biological and environmental factors that adversely affect insect pollinators." The Initiative is administering a fund of up to £10 million over five years which is jointly sponsored by the Biotechnology and Biological Sciences Research Council (BBSRC), the Department for Environment, Food and Rural Affairs (Defra), the Natural Environment Research Council (NERC), the Scottish Government and the Wellcome Trust under their Living With Environmental Change (LWEC) Programme. Currently, nine projects are receiving funding from the Initiative.

One of the projects, led by Dr Geraldine Wright at Newcastle University, is attempting to answer the question: can bees meet their nutritional needs in the current UK landscape? Changes in land management practices worldwide have impacted the ability of pollinators to obtain adequate nutrition. The research will examine the nutritional needs and foraging habits of honeybees (**Figure 27.4**) and bumblebees, and explore how nutrition influences disease and toxin susceptibility. The project aims to identify the most important floral food sources for pollinators in the UK as a basis for the development of artificial food sources.

Figure 27.4 A honeybee pollinating a flower through the collection and transport of nectar. *Image © Mirek Srb, 2011. Used under license of Shutterstock.com.*

services needs to be developed: "While we often have a broad understanding of which biodiversity groups are important in underpinning specific ecosystem services, such assessments are frequently hampered by a critical lack of quantitative data on biodiversity and ecosystem service relationships at the scales (spatial and temporal) typical of real world ecosystems" (Section 4.1).

A significant knowledge gap is the lack of economic values for the benefits or services of biodiversity; this limits the potential for market mechanisms to promote the conservation of biodiversity. The Economics of Ecosystems and Biodiversity (TEEB) study was conceived in 2007 to "initiate the process of analysing the global economic benefit of biological diversity, the costs of the loss of biodiversity and the failure to take protective measures versus the costs of effective conservation." (TEEB 2010). Three (from the many) pertinent conclusions of the TEEB study state that:

- an ecosystem services perspective should inform economic valuations of biodiversity which include its multiple benefits and intangible values;
- a realignment of incentive structures, guided by the principles of 'polluter pays' and 'full-cost-recovery', is needed in order to take account of the full range of ecosystem services;
- and new positive incentives, such as payments for ecosystem services and tax breaks, can be a powerful means to encourage public and private actors to provide ecosystem services.

'Natural capital', which refers to "those aspects of the natural environment that deliver socio-economic value through ecosystem services", needs to be integrated into economic statistics and policy making (GLOBE International 2010). Cost-benefit analyses which do not account for ecosystem services may lead to the adoption of solutions which deteriorate natural capital. To prevent this, a System of Environmental and Economic Accounting (SEEA), or 'green accounting', could be implemented, along with an economic appraisal of government policies and cooperation from all government departments (GLOBE International 2010). In the UK, the Office for National Statistics produces online 'Environmental Accounts' twice each year, which provide data on the environmental impact of UK economic activity and the use of the environment by the economy (Office for National Statistics 2010). This includes data on: atmospheric emissions; energy consumption; estimates of oil and gas reserves; production and stock of solid radioactive waste; UK imports and exports of material resources; government revenues from environmental taxes; and UK environmental protection expenditure by industry. However, there is a need to account for additional intangible benefits from ecosystem services.

27.2.3.2 Legislation (enabling)

The Habitats Directive (Directive 92/43/EC) and the Birds Directive (Directive 2009/47/EC) are the major pieces of EU legislation aimed specifically at the protection and conservation of wild animals, plants and their habitats. The Birds Directive is one of the oldest pieces of EU environmental legislation—created in 1979, it recognised that the protection of migratory birds from pressures such as over-hunting

and habitat loss was an issue of shared concern for all EU Member States. The Habitats Directive was adopted in 1992 with an overall aim to maintain or restore (at 'favourable conservation status') certain natural habitats and wild plants and animals. Favourable conservation status has a particular definition within the legislation, covering factors such as the natural range of species and habitat types, species population dynamics, and the existence of structural and functional attributes necessary to maintain habitats over the long-term (European Council 1992). It refers to the status of habitats or species across the territory of the EU, not just at a specific site. However, habitats and species at each site contribute significantly to the overall network, reflecting natural range and the diversity of populations; hence, each occurrence of a protected habitat or species contributes integrally to its overall, EU-wide status.

The Birds Directive obliged the UK to set up Special Protection Areas (SPAs) consisting of the habitats of particular species of birds. There are 195 species and subspecies singled out for protection via SPAs listed in an Annex to the Directive; they broadly consist of species which are in danger of extinction, vulnerable to habitat changes, or rare due to small populations or restricted local distributions. Migratory birds are also covered. The Habitats Directive also required the creation of protected areas, known as Special Areas of Conservation (SACs). These contain representatives of particular habitat types and species, as well as habitats of particular species which are considered to be in need of protection. The Directive contains lists of individual species and habitat types to be covered by SACs (for example, coastal dunes, temperate heath, rocky habitats, etc.) (European Council 1992). Together, the SPAs and SACs make up a European network of protected areas given the title 'Natura 2000'.

In the UK, the obligations in the Birds and Habitats Directives are implemented in national legislation through the Habitats Regulations (1994 and 2010) and the Wildlife and Countryside Act 1981 (plus the Offshore Marine Conservation (Natural Habitats &c.) Regulations 2007, and certain equivalent regulations in devolved jurisdictions). The protected areas set up as part of the Natura 2000 network fit into a broader picture of protected areas at the national level including Sites of Special Scientific Interest (SSSIs; which also underpin Ramsar wetland sites of international importance), Areas of Outstanding Natural Beauty (AONBs) and National Parks. They may overlap—for example all terrestrial SACs in England are also SSSIs. The different legal regimes for each area (**Table 27.1**) impose different levels of protection, dictating what human activities can occur either in, or near to, an area.

The Birds and Habitats Directives, and their implementing laws in the UK, are widely seen by NGOs and the government as a useful and powerful tool for the conservation of biodiversity. This framework has had much success, but problems still exist. According to the Joint Nature Conservation Committee's analysis of the most recent six-year report on the operation of the regime in the UK (produced in accordance with monitoring and reporting requirements under the Habitats Directive) (JNCC 2007), there has been some improvement in the number of UK

Table 27.1 The main designations of protected area recognised in the UK and the associated legislation. Source: data from JNCC (2010a).

Protected area	Where	Description and statutory basis
Special Areas of Conservation (SACs)	EU	Part of Natura 2000 network, strictly protected sites best representing the range and variety within the EU habitats and non-bird species under **EC Habitats Directive**.
Special Protected Areas (SPAs)	EU	Part of Natura 2000 network, strictly protected sites of the most important habitat for rare and migratory birds under **EC Birds Directive**.
Sites of Special Scientific Interest (SSSIs)	England, Scotland, Wales	Sites of statutory protection for the best examples of UK's flora, fauna or geological or physiological features, also used to underpin other national/international designations under the **National Parks and Access to the Countryside Act 1949**, renotified under the **Wildlife and Countryside Act 1981** with improved provisions under the **Countryside and Rights of Way Act 2000 (England and Wales)** and **Nature Conservation (Scotland) Act 2004**.
Areas of Special Scientific Interest (ASSIs)	Northern Ireland	(Equivalent to above)
Ramsar Sites	Ratified by the UK	Wetlands of international importance designated under the **Ramsar Convention**.
Areas of Outstanding Natural Beauty (AONBs)	England, Wales, Northern Ireland	To conserve natural beauty under the **National Parks and Access to the Countryside Act, 1949** (amended in **Environment Act 1995**), **Countryside and Rights of Way Act 2000**.
National Scenic Areas	Scotland	(Equivalent to above)
Areas of Special Protection (AoSP)	England, Scotland, Wales	Sanctuary areas under the Protection of **Birds Acts 1954**, amended to **Wildlife and Countryside Act 1981**.
Wildlife Refuges	Northern Ireland	(Equivalent to above) under **Wildlife (Northern Ireland) Orders 1985**.
Country Parks	England, Wales	Statutorily declared and managed under local authorities under the **Countryside Act 1968**.
Country Parks	Scotland	(Equivalent to above), under **Countryside (Scotland) Act 1967**.
Country Parks	Northern Ireland	Non-statutory designation
Historic Gardens and Designated Landscapes	Scotland	Gardens and landscapes identified for natural heritage and cultural importance under the **Town and Country Planning (General Development) (Scotland) Order 1992 (GDPO)**.
Local Nature Reserves (LNRs)	England, Scotland, Wales	Declared and managed for nature conservation under the National Parks and Access to the **Countryside Act 1949**.
Local Authority Nature Reserves (LANRs)	Northern Ireland	(Equivalent to above)
Marine Conservation Zones (MCZs)	England, Wales (inshore), UK (offshore)	To protect important marine wildlife, habitats, geology and geomorphology under the **Marine and Coastal Access Act (2009)**.
Marine Nature Reserves (MNRs)	England, Scotland, Wales	To conserve marine flora fauna and provide study opportunities under the **Wildlife and Countryside Act 1981** (in Northern Ireland under **Nature Conservation and Amenity Lands (Northern Ireland) Order 1985**).
Voluntary Marine Nature Reserves (vMNRs)	UK	Non-statutory by agreement between non-governmental organisations, stakeholders and user groups.
National Nature Reserves (NNRs)	England, Scotland, Wales	Managed to conserve their habitats or for scientific study under the **National Parks and Access to the Countryside Act 1949** and the **Wildlife and Countryside Act 1981** (in Northern Ireland under **Amenity Lands Act (Northern Ireland) 1965**).
National Parks	England, Wales	To conserve and enhance landscapes whilst promoting public enjoyment under the **National Parks and Access to the Countryside Act 1949**.
National Parks	Scotland	(Equivalent to above) but in addition designed to promote the sustainable use of the natural resources of the area and the sustainable social and economic development of its communities under the **National Parks (Scotland) Act 2000**.
Natural Heritage Areas	Scotland	Large discrete areas of countryside with a large range of nature conservation and landscape interests where integrated management is encouraged under the **Natural Heritage (Scotland) Act 1991**. None have been designated.
Regional Parks	Scotland	Extensive areas where public access and informal recreation are allowed with existing land use under the **Wildlife and Countryside (Scotland) Act 1981**.

species listed at favourable conservation status. However, a lot of action is still needed for those species and habitats which are continuing to deteriorate.

The kind of ecosystem services which may be either fostered or discouraged by this legal framework needs to be considered against a background of human engagement with protected sites. In addition, it is clear that the effect of the Birds and Habitats Directives on ecosystem services cannot be understood in isolation because the system interacts with laws and policies regulating various human activities (agriculture, forestry, fishing and recreational activities) which may take place on the protected sites. Generally, habitat and species protection will require strong controls on the overexploitation of provisioning services, such as intensive agriculture and overfishing (CEC 2006). However, this will be to the benefit of certain regulating services, including: water regulation through preserving wetlands; climate regulation though preserving peatlands or woodland habitats; and pollination services through the protection of invertebrate and bird abundance and diversity. Cultural services are another clear gain, with protected habitats and species providing highly valued recreational, aesthetic and spiritual outlets.

Legislation from a wide range of sectors impacts biodiversity. The CAP involves a number of legislative measures at devolved, UK, and EU-levels. Reform of CAP via Pillar 2 (Axis 2) has promoted environmental improvement including biodiversity conservation (Section 27.4.3.1; Section 27.4.3.5). In the realm of rural legislation, the Natural Environment and Rural Communities (NERC) Act 2006 contains a Biodiversity Duty (Section 40[1]) that requires every public authority in England and Wales to have regard for the purpose of conserving biodiversity. The Department for Environment, Food and Rural Affairs published a report of guidance for local authorities on implementing the biodiversity duty (Defra 2007c). A review of the impacts of this duty (Defra 2010a) found that further improvement could be achieved through better integration of biodiversity across the whole suite of public authorities' functions. In Wales, the promotion of this duty has involved annual audits of National Park Authorities' and local authorities' performance with respect to the duty. The Nature Conservation (Scotland) Act 2004 contains a similar duty to 'further' the conservation of biodiversity in Scotland.

The Marine Strategy Framework Directive 2008 (Directive 2008/56/EC) puts in place a system designed to combine environmental protection and economic use objectives. It specifically states that marine strategies shall apply an ecosystem-based approach to the management of human activities, ensuring that, by 2020, those activities are kept within levels compatible with achieving good environmental status, while also enabling the sustainable use of Marine goods and services (Section 27.7.3.2). Biodiversity considerations are integral—assessments of Marine waters should cover descriptions of habitat types and biological communities. A list of descriptors for determining good environmental status contained in an Annex to the Directive includes the maintenance of biological diversity, and refers specifically to the diversity of Marine food webs and the minimisation of biodiversity losses through eutrophication. The EC recently published a decision explaining in more detail how the biodiversity indicator should be applied at species, habitat and ecosystem levels (EC 2010a).

For biodiversity conservation, the spatial protection requirements of the MSFD and its interaction with the Habitats and Birds Directives are important. The MSFD requires Member States to provide a progress report on the establishment of Marine Protected Areas (MPAs) (including Marine SACs and SPAs) by 2013. It is essential that this operates to speed up the designation of MPAs including the Marine element of the Natura 2000 network. According to the EU's most recent BAPs (CEC 2006, Objective A1.1.1), Marine SACs and SPAs should have been designated by 2008, with management priorities and necessary conservation measures identified by 2012. The process is significantly behind schedule, although 15 new sites were submitted to the EC in August 2010 (Defra 2010b).

The Marine and Coastal Access Act 2009 has provided for the creation of a network of Marine Conservation Zones (MCZs) across the UK by 2012. These will protect nationally important Marine wildlife, habitats, geology and geomorphology. The sites of MCZs are currently being identified; they build on MPAs designated under the Habitats and Birds Directive, but also take account of social and economic considerations (Section 7.3.2).

Much of the legislation designed to control pollution has successfully restricted harmful impacts on biodiversity, and has even permitted recovery in some cases. The success of the Clean Air Act 1956, and more recent EU legislation on air quality and emissions, in drastically reducing air pollution in the UK has had positive impacts on biodiversity in many habitats. The EU WFD has already achieved positive impacts on Freshwater and Wetland biodiversity in the UK (Section 9.4.1). Despite the positive track record of improvements to air and water quality through statutory measures, there remains a need for specific legislation to protect the regulating capacity of soils and its associated biodiversity (Section 14.7.1). A number of different statutory measures and policies do contribute to soil protection, and a Soil Framework Directive has been proposed at EU level (EC 2010b). So far, Member States have not been able to agree on how to take it forward (Defra 2008a). Legislation in the context of provisioning services, especially food and fisheries, is discussed separately in their sectoral contexts, but there is increasing recognition of the need to minimise the impacts of intensive provisioning practices on biodiversity.

27.2.3.3 Policies, institutions and governance (enabling)

The UK framework for biodiversity conservation is shaped by international commitments under the CBD, and by European obligations. As presented in Chapter 4 (Section 4.1), significant loss of biodiversity worldwide "culminated in the Convention on Biological Diversity (CBD) in 1992, which established policies for the conservation of biodiversity, the sustainable use of its components, and the fair and equitable sharing of benefits arising from biodiversity." In 1994, the UK Government published the UK BAP which combined new and existing conservation initiatives in response to the CBD and emphasised a partnership approach (Secretaries of State for the Environment 1994). This led to the development of a framework of BAPs implemented by a broad array of stakeholders who form the UK Biodiversity Partnership. Biodiversity targets are expressed at both UK and country levels (**Table 27.2**) and progress towards achieving these

---

Table 27.2 The strategic framework of national Biodiversity Action Plans (BAPs) in the UK. Source: adapted from Defra (2007e).

UK strategic framework			
Working with the grain of nature: a biodiversity strategy for England (Defra 2002)	Northern Ireland biodiversity strategy (2002)	Scotland's biodiversity: It's in your hands (Scottish Executive 2004)	Environment strategy for Wales (Welsh Assembly Government 2006)

targets is recorded by the Biodiversity Action Reporting System (BARS 2010). The list of UK BAP priority species and habitats was revised in 2007 and has grown in size reflecting improved data availability and the continuing decline of some species (Defra 2007e). It now contains 1,150 species and 65 habitats for which Species Action Plans (SAPs) and Habitat Action Plans (HAPs) are published.

More than 170 Local BAPs have also been developed through local partnership and community engagement to address the needs for priority habitats and species in a given local area (JNCC 2008).

'Conserving Biodiversity—the UK Approach' (Defra 2007e) presents the ecosystem approach as a key underlying principle for conserving biodiversity in the UK. This approach recognises that priority species and habitats cannot be considered in isolation and must be addressed through coordination at appropriate levels. One example is the ecosystem approach framework for action in Scotland as proposed by Scottish Natural Heritage (SNH 2010a) and endorsed by the Scottish Biodiversity Committee.

The role and responsibility of local authorities to assist with conserving and enhancing biodiversity is increasing, so fostering technical capacity and partnerships at this level will be a priority (Natural Capital Initiative 2010). Non-governmental conservation organisations also play an important role to stimulate support from the government and public alike for conservation initiatives (Lawton *et al.* 2010). Growth of membership numbers in these organisations—many of whom own or manage large areas of land important for biodiversity—has led to significant increases in expenditure and action for nature conservation purposes over recent decades (JNCC 2010a). Businesses, including developers, are investing more in biodiversity and this could be further encouraged through the accreditation of business initiatives that reduce detrimental impacts to biodiversity (Natural Capital Initiative 2010).

The designation of a protected areas network is one mechanism for addressing concerns of loss of habitat and species diversity. The institution of protected areas in the UK has continually grown to the complex network in place today; however, further improvements are needed to ensure that it is coherent and resilient to future challenges. The designations having the greatest impact on biodiversity are listed in **Table 27.1**. The extensive Making Space for Nature review of wildlife sites in England (Lawton *et al.* 2010) found that there has been recent progress in the condition of sites (particularly SSSIs), with 95.8% of SSSIs in favourable or recovering status in 2010, compared with 57% in the same condition in 2003. However, the review pointed out that many sites are too small, and extensive losses of certain habitats are likely to lead to further loss of biodiversity. It identified that most semi-natural habitats (outside SSSIs and Natura 2000 sites) are under-managed or insufficiently protected and that natural connections in the countryside have been lost. It recommends that "some form of national framework is required to ensure coherence and cost-effectiveness across the network," and that "the sooner we act to establish a coherent and resilient ecological network, the lower the eventual cost and the greater the benefits for us all." (p.ix).

At the moment, biodiversity, landscapes and historic environments are governed by separate systems in the UK. There is a need to coordinate these systems to support landscape planning mechanisms that both better connect protected areas and positively influence biodiversity outside these designated sites. An ecosystem services approach to land management could provide a valuable way of achieving these aims (Foresight 2010).

In 2002, the UK committed to halt biodiversity loss by 2010 as part of the EU Sustainable Development Strategy; however, significant biodiversity loss still continues today (JNCC 2008). At the tenth CBD Conference of the Parties held in Nagoya, Japan, a new Strategic Plan of the Convention was adopted for the period 2011 to 2020 (CBD 2010). It states that "there has been insufficient integration of biodiversity issues into broader policies, strategies, programmes and actions, and therefore the underlying drivers of biodiversity loss have not been significantly reduced." These results are predicted to act as a key driver of biodiversity policy.

Despite failing to meet its target, the public sector in the UK has demonstrated its commitment to biodiversity by doubling expenditure in this area between 2000 and 2008 as shown in **Figure 27.5** (Defra 2009g). Biodiversity policy is guided in each country by national strategies and BAPs (**Table 27.2**). A number of policy areas relating to biodiversity are emerging as present and future priorities. Marine planning policy development has recently been recognised as important (Section 27.7.3.3), and fisheries policy restricting fleet numbers, days at sea, and catch quotas has decreased landings (Section 27.6.3.3). Increases in Semi-natural Grassland are being promoted through policy, emphasising the fact that policy has begun to account for non-market public goods. Much effort is going into the development of climate change policy backed by results from major assessments of the threats of climate change to biodiversity (SNIFFER 2007; EA 2010d). The control of

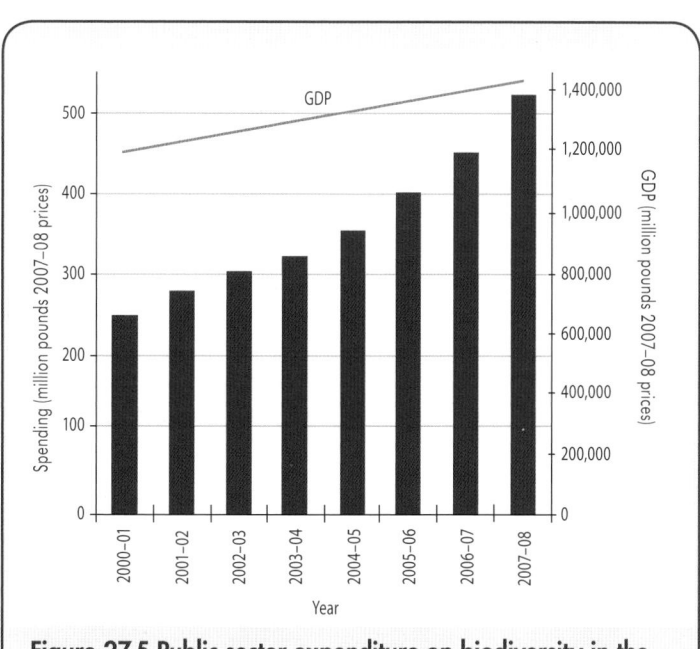

Figure 27.5 Public sector expenditure on biodiversity in the UK from 2000 to 2008. Source: reproduced from Defra (2009g) © Crown Copyright 2009.

invasive species is another policy priority as it is the second greatest threat to biodiversity worldwide (Wilcove *et al.* 1998). One example is the Invasive Species in Ireland Project (Invasive Species Ireland 2010), which started in 2006 as a joint venture between the Northern Ireland Environment Agency and the National Parks and Wildlife Service, and involves policy relating to specific species.

Improved soil management and protection has been encouraged through Safeguarding our Soils (which defines a strategy for England) (Defra 2009h) and The Scottish Soil Framework (Scottish Government 2009e), which seek to protect the biodiversity and ecosystem services derived from soils. Peat soils are of particular importance because they form three protected UK BAP habitats—fens, raised bogs, and blanket bogs—and store half of the 10 billion tonnes of carbon stored in all UK soils (Defra 2009h; Natural England 2011c). Minimising emissions from this source is, therefore, a policy priority, and measures aiming to protect and enhance peatlands for conservation and biodiversity reasons will additionally benefit climate change mitigation efforts (Scottish Government 2009e).

Policy that explores how a multifunctional ecosystem services approach might work is now being piloted (**Box 27.4**). A multifunctional approach will be necessary for the protection of certain biodiversity groups requiring coordinated actions. Conservation of lichen, for example, requires both a decrease in pollution and maintenance of high density and high quality mixed habitat. There is already a push towards more integrated and interdisciplinary approaches of biodiversity conservation; integration is occurring between government departments (such as planning, environment, energy, etc.), between national, regional and local levels of delivery, and between policy makers, practitioners and the public. The new framework for securing biodiversity in England (Natural England 2008a) emphasises the important role of partner organisations to

drive delivery and report on progress for species requiring urgent attention. In Scotland, there is a desire to further integrate biodiversity into planning and to encourage local approaches to conservation which may be more flexible and opportunity-based (Dick *et al.* 2009). The Scotland Rural Development Programme is a major policy of the Scottish Government which aims to better integrate biodiversity with other benefits in the rural sector, with particular links to water quality and climate change (*ibid.*).

27.2.3.4 Changing social attitudes (enabling)

"We need to engage more people in taking action to maintain and enhance biodiversity as part of their everyday lives" (Defra 2007e, p.11).

The public are increasingly aware of the loss of biodiversity and actively involved in its conservation (Dick *et al.* 2009). Highly publicised campaigns to save charismatic species from extinction have pushed biodiversity into the public domain, and provided a greater role for local communities. According to some, "we are currently witnessing a paradigm shift in biodiversity conservation, away from the establishment and maintenance of protected nature reserves towards community-based conservation" (Goddard *et al.* 2010, p.95). There is also growing evidence and enthusiasm about the importance of biodiversity in Urban areas for the provision of health and well-being benefits and ecosystem services (**Box 27.5**). This includes the maintenance of the abundance of relatively common species which contribute towards the provision of ecosystem services. The need to further engage local communities and non-experts in matters of conservation is acknowledged by the government in national biodiversity strategies and policy, and by a range of organisations. Public understanding and opinion about the value of biodiversity have strong implications for the acceptance and adoption of measures (Natural Capital

Box 27.4 Multifunctional ecosystems approach at the Otmoor Protected Area, Oxfordshire. Source: McInnes *et al.* (2008).

Defra has funded a number of case studies aiming to explore the potential applications of an ecosystems approach in a range of situations. One of these projects involved the application of an ecosystems approach in the management of the Otmoor protected area in Oxfordshire from 2006 to 2007. The area covers 1,100 hectares (ha) of farmland involving differing management practices within the designations: SSSI, RSPB reserve and Upper Thames Tributaries Environmentally Sensitive Area (ESA).

The four objectives of the pilot were as follows:
To demonstrate approaches for identifying policy objectives for a protected site that takes into account the views of stakeholders.
The range of national-level policies which drive decisions and actions at Otmoor were explored. These included European legislation (Birds and Habitats Directives, WFD, etc.), Common Agricultural Policy, Acts of Parliament (Town and Country Planning Act 1990, Countryside and Rights of Way Act 2000, etc.), and government strategies. To assess understanding and application of an ecosystems approach, 44 stakeholders were consulted during the project (**Table 27.3**).

To demonstrate a method for measuring, predicting and communicating the actual and potential cumulative impacts of different stressors on these policy objectives, based upon common monetary and ecological currencies.

To demonstrate a method for identifying, predicting and valuing the ecosystem services provided by the site.
Four ecosystem services were investigated:
- **Regulating:** Water purification and waste treatment (removal of phosphorus and nitrogen)
- **Regulating:** Natural hazard regulation (reducing the likelihood of extreme flood events)
- **Provisioning:** Food (conversion of light, energy and nutrients into agricultural biomass)
- **Cultural:** Recreation (provision of recreational opportunity)

Table 27.3 Points of agreement and disagreement among stakeholders concerning the Otmoor protected area. Source: information from McInnes *et al.* (2008).

Points of agreement	Points of disagreement
The conservation of all species should be a priority	Finding an appropriate balance between profitable farming and achievement of biodiversity goals
Flooding should be allowed to occur naturally across Otmoor (at least in the long-term)	The extent to which flooding can and should be managed for the benefit of farming and conservation
A large increase in the number of visitors to Otmoor should not be encouraged	The extent to which M40 runoff is responsible for pollution of the area

In order to improve decisions regarding wetland ecosystem management, the importance of these services to human society must be assessed. It will not be possible here to describe the conceptual framework in full (see McInnes *et al.* 2008), however the annual economic value of water purification (£15–£20/ha), food (£259–£355/ha) and recreational (£8–£31/ha) ecosystem services were quantified. The economic benefit of natural hazard regulation was not quantified due to the lack of reliable information (although a possible approach is provided). An uncertainty assessment, including sensitivity analysis, was conducted under two climate change scenarios to assess both data and model uncertainty.

To evaluate the applicability of elements of an ecosystems approach against the current level of understanding of a protected area and to demonstrate a prioritisation framework for balancing policy objectives against the value of ecosystem services and potential impacts.
The key driver at Otmoor is land management for food production. One conclusion of the project was: "to ensure that the wetland conservation interest are maintained in perpetuity the economics of agricultural production, including their role in protecting and enhancing biodiversity, need to be resolved and delivered by the market to the local land manager" (p.23). Through this pilot project, a conceptual and empirical method for quantifying and valuing ecosystem services was developed. Based on this experience, the strengths and weaknesses of the ecosystem approach are presented in **Table 27.4**.

This case study demonstrates that, by using an ecosystem service framework involving consultation with stakeholders, it is possible to discuss the trade-offs and synergies between different ecosystem services from an area, to determine the most appropriate management strategy.

Table 27.4 Strengths and weaknesses of the ecosystem approach based on experience from the Otmoor protected area pilot project. Source: information from McInnes *et al.* (2008).

	Implementation of an ecosystem approach at the Otmoor protected area
Strengths	■ Stakeholders recognise that Otmoor provides many benefits
	■ Some ecosystem services are recognised and reflected in decision-making
	■ Decision-making is devolved to several levels
	■ Some environmental limits are recognised and respected
Weaknesses	■ Several policy drivers do not recognise the interconnected nature of the natural environment
	■ Perverse incentives may exist which promote agricultural production at the expense of maintaining and enhancing biodiversity
	■ Ambiguity exists regarding the identification and evaluation of ecosystem services
	■ Opportunities for a more effective delivery of environmental outcomes are being missed
	■ Prescriptive rather than adaptive management is routinely applied

Box 27.5 Biodiversity in Urban Gardens project (BUGS2).

Following a successful first study in Sheffield, the second Biodiversity in Urban Gardens (BUGS) (BUGS2 2009) project was carried out between 2004 and 2007 in five cities: Leicester, Oxford, Cardiff, Belfast and Edinburgh. The study explored the extent and nature of domestic gardens, the features they include, and their floristic diversity. Garden features such as trees, mature shrubs, ponds, lawn areas, compost heaps and nest boxes are important for the maintenance of biodiversity, the provision of ecosystem services, and for human health and well-being. "[Urban green spaces] provide opportunities for people to interact with nature and are, therefore, vital in fostering interest in nature conservation issues." (Goddard et al. 2010, p.90).

Some of the results of the BUGS2 project published by Gaston et al. (2007) indicated that a significant number of households were participating in wildlife gardening, and that the most common form of participation was the feeding of wild birds. It was found that access to gardens and garden size were positively associated with activities aimed at encouraging wildlife. Interestingly, neither household density nor socioeconomic status of households were found to strongly effect participation in activities to encourage wildlife. The study suggests that, in order to increase awareness and participation in wildlife gardening, advice and opportunities should be carefully tailored to the kinds of spaces that are available in different areas.

Spatial scale is an important factor in the conservation of biodiversity. Many organisms operate at scales larger than individual gardens, so coordinated management at larger scales (from groups of gardens up to Urban green space planning) may be required (Goddard et al. 2010). **Figure 27.6** shows a conceptual framework of the socioecological characteristics which influence garden management.

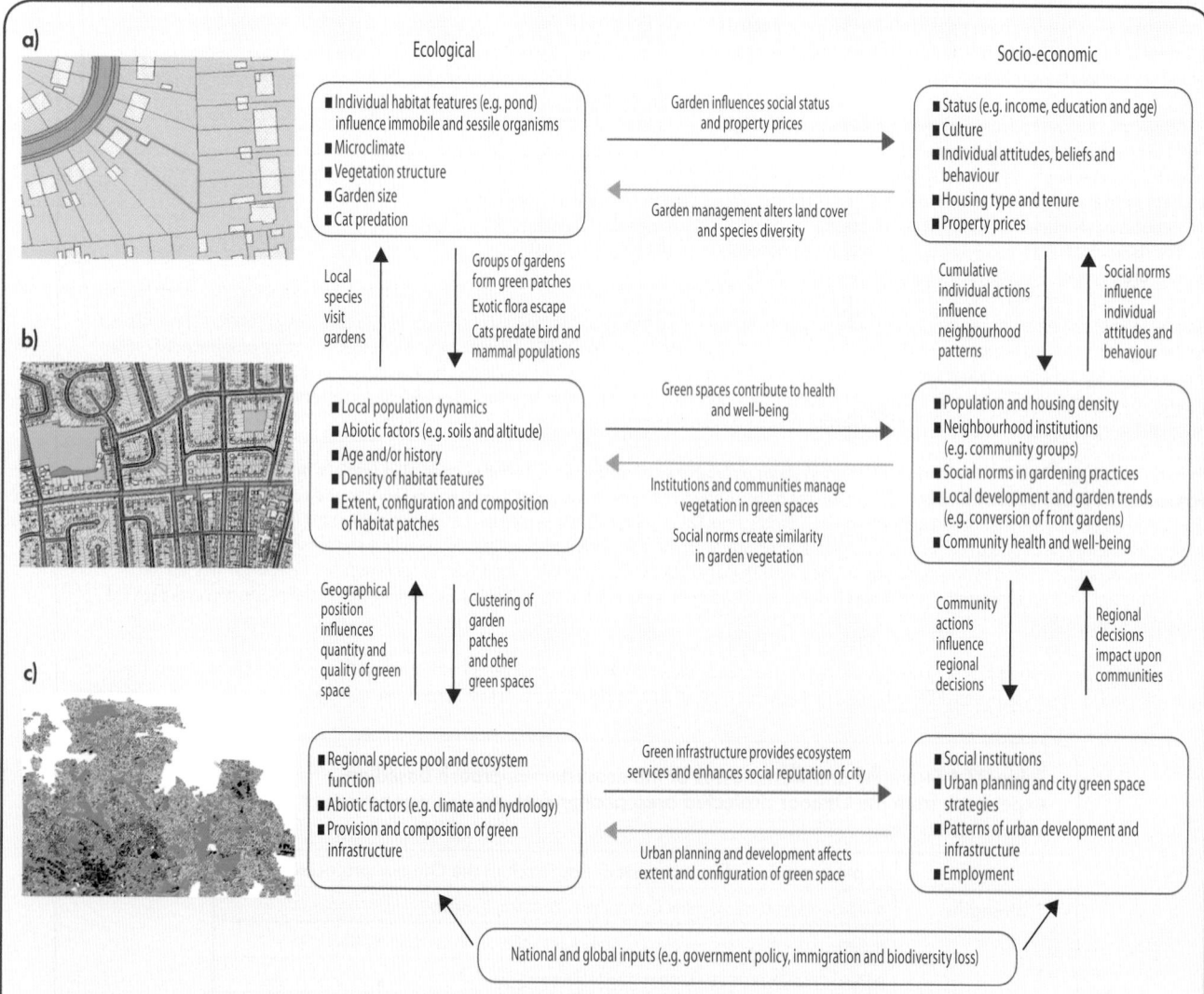

Figure 27.6 Gardens as socio-ecological constructs. A conceptual framework showing the key ecological and socio-economic components impacting on private gardens at multiple spatial scales. A nested hierarchy in garden management was identified that spans three scales: a) the individual garden or household; b) the neighbourhood or garden 'patch'; and c) the city or landscape scale. In reality, many of the ecological and socio-economic factors can act at more than one scale along this continuum (e.g. vegetation structure or social status) and interactions exist between scales to illustrate feedbacks within the garden ecosystem (black arrows). Ecological factors influence socio-economic factors through the provision of ecosystem services and economic and health benefits (green arrows). Socio-economic factors influence ecological conditions via human decision-making and subsequent management (orange arrows). Research and management is necessary at multiple scales to maximise the utility of private gardens for native biodiversity conservation. Source: Goddard et al. (2010). Copyright (2010), reproduced with permission from Elsevier.

UK National Ecosystem Assessment: Technical Report

Initiative 2010). Mechanisms of decision-making and trade-off negotiation should be transparent.

The government plays an important role in enabling and encouraging behavioural change. In Securing the Future, the sustainable development strategy from 2005 (HM Government 2005), a behaviour change model for policy making is presented (**Figure 27.7**).

This approach can apply to the promotion of biodiversity conservation—it helps to conserve natural habitats, wildlife, quality of greenspace, and generally brings people closer to nature. 'Enabling' involves educating people about the benefits of biodiversity, allowing people to make responsible choices based on the evidence. 'Encouraging' involves the use of many of the instruments presented in this section to provide positive incentives to reward good behaviour, and to enforce regulations and penalties when necessary. 'Engagement' through public involvement over long periods is imperative in changing behaviours through examples people can relate to. Finally, the government needs to lead by example ('exemplify') through its own operations and in creating consistent policies.

Public support to halt the loss of biodiversity is also fostered through local action by local authorities, Statutory Agencies, NGOs, and collaborations between these actors (Defra 2007e). It is important that key messages are targeted through communication strategies to different audiences in order to maximise their impact. The report Conserving Biodiversity—the UK Approach (Defra 2007e) emphasises the need to be 'positive', 'practical' and 'personal' when communicating biodiversity issues. The report promotes the following behaviours (*ibid.*, p.15):

- **Create**, or encourage others to create, **wildlife-friendly spaces**—at home, in your local community and through work.
- **Enjoy** (and value) your local wildlife-friendly space and share this enjoyment with others.
- **Support** the work of wildlife conservation organisations.

- **Think before you buy**, for example, wildlife-based products or souvenirs from overseas trips; buy wildlife/environmentally friendly/sustainably-sourced products.
- **Record** what you see and send results to your Local Records Centre.
- **Exercise** your civic duties to ensure those that represent your views reflect your environmental concerns.

There is a need to better craft the message that biodiversity is enormously important for the sustainability of the environment, the provision of ecosystem services and for our own well-being. The term 'biodiversity' itself lacks recognition or understanding among the public (Novacek 2008; Defra 2009a). Public interest in species, habitats and sites is highly responsive to stories and pictures made available through television programmes and the news. One example is the Nature Tales posters and activity guides made available through the BBC's Breathing Places initiative (BBC 2011a). Providing an inspiring message, however, is only the first step; lasting engagement with environmental issues, such as biodiversity loss, is often the result of a connection between people and nature through active involvement and participation (Section 27.2.3.7).

Education is a "key vehicle for increasing public knowledge and understanding of the importance of conserving biodiversity... this is true for all age groups" (Defra 2007c). Local authorities are encouraged to enhance biodiversity of school grounds and statutory requirements stipulate that the science curriculum must include 'sustainable development', 'life processes and living things,' and 'global citizenship' (*ibid.*). The Department for Children, Schools and Families (now the Department for Education) published a booklet entitled Top Tips for Schools to Engage with Biodiversity (DCSF 2010) which emphasises the benefits of engaging with biodiversity in schools.

The power of behavioural change to induce human action cannot be underestimated. We know more about culturally

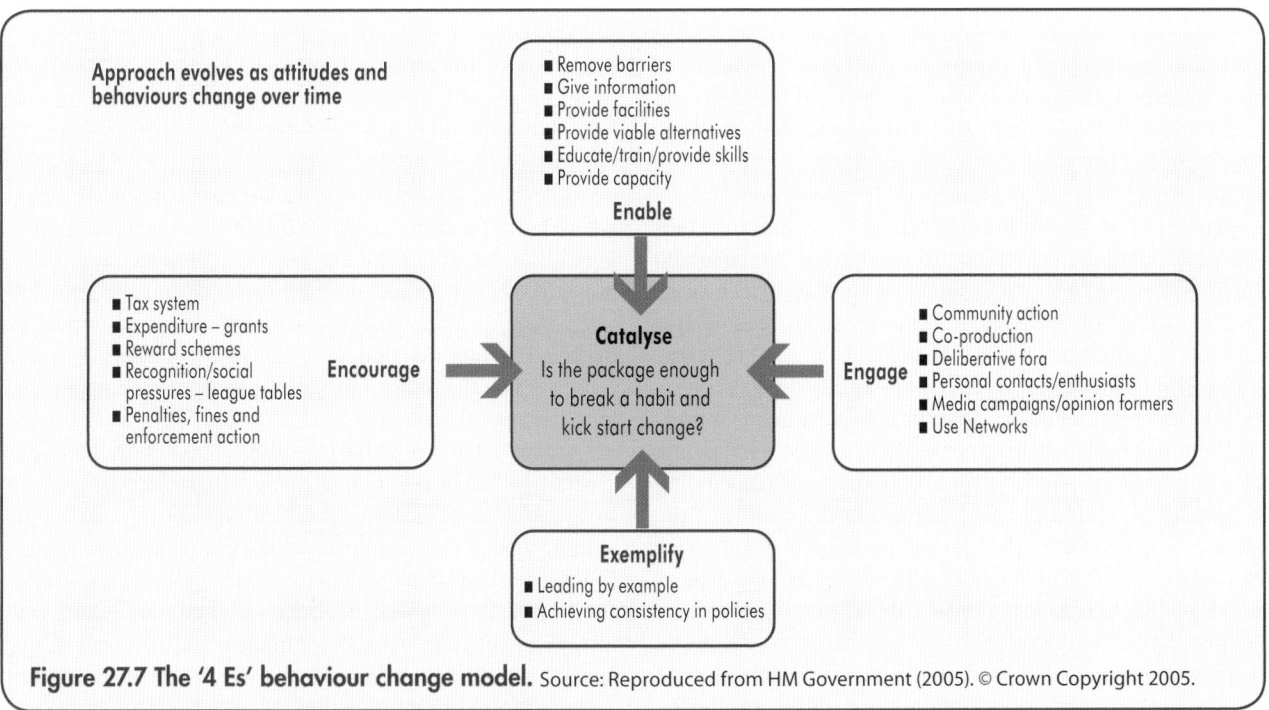

Figure 27.7 The '4 Es' behaviour change model. Source: Reproduced from HM Government (2005). © Crown Copyright 2005.

important biodiversity groups because they have received a bias in terms of research effort and funding (Section 4.7). The conservation of rare breeds, varieties and genetic resources is dependent on government and societal preference. Chapter 25 demonstrates the importance of social attitudes in shaping the future. Each storyline is dependent on the adoption of prevalent 'attitudes', 'beliefs', or 'societal concerns'. An appreciation of the importance of social attitudes in enabling the conservation of biodiversity is paramount.

27.2.3.5 Markets and incentives (instrumental)

Incentives have long been used in the UK as an instrument to influence production. Historically, this has negatively impacted habitats, such as moorland and grassland, through conversion to maximise production from agriculture and forestry (Section 19.4.2). More recently, incentive schemes have aimed to conserve biodiversity in agricultural landscapes. A review of the achievements of agri-environment schemes over the past 20 years in England (Natural England 2009a) highlighted specific successes. Some of the options under this scheme have significantly increased breeding populations of nationally scarce farmland birds and have benefited other farmland biodiversity. Higher Level Stewardship (HLS) schemes have been the main mechanism used to increase the condition of SSSIs, and have generally led to the maintenance and proactive restoration of existing habitats. Of the BAP priority habitat, 84% is under agri-environment agreements, as is 41% of actively managed hedgerows and 24% of actively managed stone walls. Agri-environment schemes protect 250,000 in-field trees and have supported the planting of 2,000 new parkland and hedgerow trees. Despite these achievements, it was found that the free choice and balance of options selected under many agreements were not ideal for achieving desired outcomes. Unexpected landscape-scale consequences, such as detrimental impacts to specialist species due to comparatively uniform management, have arisen, and there is a need for greater flexibility and a better evidence base at the landscape-scale.

Davey et al. (2010b) found that there was limited evidence of short-term effects of Environmental Stewardship schemes on lowland farmland birds, except for corn bunting and common starling under Entry Level Stewardship (ELS). They also found insufficient evidence of specific management options increasing the abundance of the species which they were targeted at. The authors expect, however, that time lags in bird populations responding to changes in the farmland environment mean that it is too early to draw conclusions on the success of the schemes. One potential reason they cite for the possible underachievement of ELS schemes is that the current pattern of options taken up by farmers focuses predominantly on boundary management options (accounting for 50% of all options selected). The rebalancing of option uptake to address gaps in option coverage (including in-field options), and the improvement of the quality of the options, may determine the future success of the ES scheme. The schemes will also need to mitigate against the loss of set-aside (Section 27.4.3.5). Given the voluntary nature of Environmental Stewardship, however, precaution has to be taken when changing the scheme to ensure options remain sufficiently attractive to maintain good levels of uptake

(Defra 2008b). At present, ELS schemes do not "account for spatial heterogeneity in species' responses to management" and it is suggested that scheme targeting could be improved in the future (Davey et al. 2010b, p.126).

Results from the Monitoring and Evaluation of Agri-environment Schemes study in Scotland, undertaken from 2004 to 2008, suggest that during this period implementation of the three agri-environment schemes in Scotland (Organic Aid Scheme, Countryside Premium Scheme, and the Rural Stewardship Scheme) had little impact on the biodiversity measures investigated (Scott Wilson Scotland Ltd. 2009).

Support via the CAP has evolved through a number of reforms which have increased environmental management and protection (Section 27.4.3.2). It is suggested that further reform of the CAP is needed to safeguard biodiversity and ensure that a wide range of public benefits are provided at appropriate scales (Davey et al. 2010b). A recent study by the UK Research Councils' Rural Economy and Land Use Programme suggested that building an ecosystem services approach into agri-environment schemes could promote multifunctional land use through a stronger role in the following areas (RELU 2010a):

1. Rewarding the provision of carbon stores.
2. Promoting integrated pest management.
3. Reducing risks to public health from livestock waste in water.
4. Responding to new disease threats linked to climate change.
5. Reviewing support for organic conversion in intensively farmed regions.

Civil society organisations and charities are increasingly seen as a financial support mechanism for the conservation of biodiversity outside the public domain.

27.2.3.6 Technologies and practices (instrumental)

Many forms of technology have inadvertently led to the destruction of biodiversity. Excess application of chemicals (including fertilisers and pesticides) developed to increase productivity in agricultural and aquacultural systems have negatively impacted biodiversity as pollution, but have subsequently been reduced through environmental regulations (Section 15.4). These chemicals have also made it possible to expand productive agriculture into other habitats, where land was previously unsuitable. The mechanisation of agriculture, peat removal and fishing industries have heavily impacted terrestrial and marine biodiversity. Seabed trawling technology, in particular, has had a widespread impact on benthic habitats (Section 12.3.1.3). Advancements in motor pumps since the 1940s have made moorland drainage and land reclamation possible.

As we learn from these lessons, technology has been created to reverse or minimise many of these adverse impacts. In lowland conservation areas, machinery is used for re-wetting, and in upland mires, 'grip blocking' maintains water levels, benefiting both biodiversity and carbon sequestration (Section 3.3.5.1). Fishing technology has come a long way in specialising the catch to minimise harm to non-target species and juveniles through the use of enhanced netting and sonar technology (Section 27.6.3.6).

The practice of set-aside, taking land out of agricultural production, was traditionally practised and, more recently, enforced through policy to control overproduction (Section 27.4.3.5). It was found to have the potential to deliver a range of environmental benefits including: introducing wildlife habitat into farmland; buffering and reducing diffuse pollution; improving soil quality and preventing erosion; and contributing to the adaptation and mitigation of climate change (IEEP 2008b). Set-aside was abolished in the CAP Health Check reform, so other measures will be needed to retain the benefits of this practice (Scottish Government 2009a). One such measure is the Campaign for the Farmed Environment which aims "to retain and exceed the environmental benefits that used to be provided by set-aside" (Section 27.4.3.7; CFE 2010).

An interesting development has been the potential to use 'biodiversity offsetting' in the UK as a mechanism for enhancing biodiversity in the wider countryside. It can be defined as:

> "Measurable conservation outcomes resulting from actions designed to compensate for significant residual adverse biodiversity impacts arising from development plans or projects after appropriate prevention and mitigation measures have been taken" (BBOP 2008).

A successful pilot of this mechanism from Australia is explored in **Box 27.6**. Monitoring and enforcement are necessary components of an offsetting mechanism which could be implemented through market or regulatory methods. A scoping study by the Department for Environment, Food and Rural Affairs (Treweek *et al.* 2009) concluded that the situation in England could lend itself to greater use of this mechanism to move towards no net loss or net gain of biodiversity, but that further work is needed to determine what additional policy may be required. A workshop addressing the practical challenges for biodiversity offsetting in the UK (Natural Capital Initiative 2010) concluded that, "current methodologies, tools and evidence are sufficient to begin encouraging increased use of biodiversity offsetting." The process of developing a framework should involve local planning authorities, land owners, businesses and the public. Pilot projects are currently underway in the UK (Environment Bank 2010) to determine the application of this mechanism in practice, and to ascertain the costs and benefits involved. Safeguards are essential, as are currently in place under the Habitats Directive, in order to avoid a shift towards a permissive regime in which access to easy offsetting options will encourage development in sensitive areas. However, if offsets are well managed, transparent and as close as possible both physically and ecologically to the converted sites, they do potentially have a role and could encourage greater private sector involvement in conservation and habitat creation.

27.2.3.7 Voluntary actions (instrumental)

Voluntary and civil society action plays an important role for biodiversity conservation in the UK. A review of literature relating to volunteering in the natural outdoors by the Institute for Volunteering Research (Ockenden 2007) stated that:

> "The conservation and environmental sectors appear to have become increasingly receptive to the concept

---

Box 27.6 BushBroker exchange pilot biodiversity offsetting initiative, Australia. Source: Plott *et al.* (2008).

There is an obvious trade-off between economic development and environmental conservation in Victoria, Australia, where 66% of the native vegetation has been cleared due to growth and economic development; this has left a total of 7.4 million hectares (ha) of native vegetation on public land and 1.1 million ha on private land. Because native vegetation is not seen to have monetary value, it has traditionally been considered an externality. Policies to limit its destruction, such as taxes and penalties attempting to approximate the economic value of environmental goods, have failed to be economically viable. The BushBroker vegetation offset scheme has been piloted as a mechanism to directly link decisions of economic development with environmental conservation using a market-based mechanism.

"Complex trading rules govern the transactions in the vegetation offset market in order to ensure equivalency in the biodiversity conservation value of the vegetation cleared and that used as an offset" (*ibid.*, p.8). The project's environmental metric incorporates data on the quality, quantity, type, significance level and location of the native vegetation to be cleared in order to allow ecologists to make informed decisions about what type of offset should be required. Using landscape classifications (28 bioregions, 300 ecological vegetation classes), conservation status significance levels, and techniques to evaluate the quality and quantity of native vegetation, appropriate offset areas are determined. 'Like-for-like' trading rules require that vegetation gains from an offset are 'commensurate' to the vegetation loss with respect to conservation significance, habitat and vegetation type, and quality. The loss resulting from the clearing of old trees is given special attention due to their ecological importance.

Offsets are traded in the form of contracts which require active vegetation management over ten years and then permanent site protection. The scheme is dependent on the fulfilment of these obligations, and endogenous risks (e.g. insufficient incentive) and exogenous risks (e.g. bushfire) have been minimised as far as possible through contract design.

The performance of the electronic BushBroker exchange software was tested experimentally and found to be a "simple and effective solution to the complex environment of native vegetation trading" (p.23). Plott *et al.* (2008) concluded that "successful implementation of the electronic BushBroker exchange will enable meaningful trade-offs to take place between economic development and environmental conservation…this will be an important step in allowing environmental conservation to compete on equal grounds with economic interests" (p. 33).

---

of involving people in the management of nature and providing opportunities for volunteers... People are increasingly seen as playing a central role in the solution to environmental and conservation problems... this has directly contributed to the development of 'community-based conservation', and an end to 'expert-based' solutions and management" (p.10).

'Citizen science' involves non-expert volunteers in the collection and/or processing of data and, therefore, aims to increase participation in formal scientific research (**Box 27.7**). The role of citizen science has grown tremendously over the past few years due to the availability of technical tools for disseminating information (e.g. the internet, mobile computing, etc.), increased realisation by the scientific community of this free source of labour and skills, and requirements by funding agencies for grant-holders to undertake science outreach (Silvertown 2009).

A comparison between 47 countries found that the USA and the UK have the highest percentage (8%) of people volunteering in the 'environment' (Hodgkinson 2003). The UK Biodiversity Indicators in Your Pocket 2010 report (Defra 2010k) found that between 2000 and 2009 there was a 51% increase in the time spent volunteering at eight major UK

Box 27.7 Volunteer-based biodiversity monitoring programmes.
Two examples of volunteer-based monitoring programmes in the UK:

1. The **Breeding Bird Survey** (BBS) is run by the British Trust for Ornithology (BTO) and is jointly funded by BTO, the Joint Nature Conservation Committee (JNCC), and the Royal Society for the Protection of Birds (RSPB) (Risely *et al.* 2010). Since 1994, the survey has recorded population trends for over 100 breeding bird species across the UK which are used by government and NGOs to set conservation priorities. The survey method involves volunteer visits during the April to June survey period to an assigned 'square'. During the visit, the volunteers record all birds encountered while walking two 1 km transects across their square. Habitat and mammal sightings are also recorded during transects. Additional data has been collected by professional fieldworkers from under-represented areas, including upland areas in England since 2006, and wooded areas in Scotland since 2007. Inclusion of these habitats results in more robust trend analysis. In 2003, the survey introduced an online recording system (www.bto.org/bbs), and in 2009, 76% of the results (from a total of 3,243 squares) were submitted online, thereby saving paper.

2. The **National Bat Monitoring Programme** (NBMP) has involved more than 2,200 volunteers in bat monitoring activities since 1996 (BCT 2011). The collection of data allows the:

- assessment of the conservation needs of the UK's 18 bat species;
- identification of any rapid population declines;
- selection of conservation priorities and informing of conservation policy;
- and the distribution of limited resources to where they are most needed.

"Without the valuable information collected by volunteers we would be unable to track how the UK's bat species are faring." (BCT 2011).

conservation charities[1], totalling around 1 million working days in 2009. Environmental programmes run by these and other conservation organisations have demonstrated the ability to raise public awareness and understanding of environmental concerns, and to engage communities (Binley *et al.* 2008).

There is considerable collaboration between biodiversity actors. A number of partnerships have formed between local authorities, statutory agencies and NGOs, particularly through the Local BAP mechanism, to deliver local action for biodiversity (Defra 2007e). For example, the Scottish Biodiversity Forum is a working partnership between public, private and voluntary organisations that has created an online communications toolkit which can help public and private enterprises communicate the benefits of biodiversity (SNH 2010b). As part of the Northern Ireland Biodiversity Strategy, Biodiversity Delivery Groups bring together Departmental, Agency and non-government partners to implement the targets and actions of the 37 Northern Ireland HAPs (NIEA 2010).

The Community Infrastructure Levy is a voluntary mechanism that came into force in 2010 in England and Wales allowing local authorities to raise funds from developers (DCLG 2010a). Money raised can be used to fund a range of infrastructure, including parks and green spaces, according to the needs of the local area. Levy rates are set in consultations with local communities and developers and expand the minimal contributions required under the planning obligations system.

Table 27.5 Biodiversity Summary

	Established responses	Early implementation, pilots	Proposed, under development
Knowledge	■ Country Surveys ■ State of Environment Reports ■ National Biodiversity Network Gateway	■ Biodiversity Indicators Reports ■ The Economics of Ecosystems and Biodiversity	■ Research on functional relationships (e.g. Insect Pollinators Initiative)
Legislation	■ Habitats Directive ■ Birds Directive ■ Common Agricultural Policy ■ Natural Environment and Rural Communities Act ■ Marine Strategy Framework Directive		
Policies, institutions and governance	■ UK Biodiversity Action Plans and national strategies ■ Local Biodiversity Action Plans	■ Scotland Rural Development Programme ■ Scottish Soils Framework ■ Invasive Species in Ireland Project	■ Multifunctional ecosystems approaches
Changing social attitudes		■ Biodiversity in Urban Gardens project ■ BBC Breathing Places Initiative ■ Department for Children, Schools and Families – guidance on biodiversity for schools	■ UK Sustainable Development strategy ■ Conserving Biodiversity – the UK approach
Markets and incentives	■ Agri-environment schemes		
Technologies and practices			■ Reformed set-aside practices ■ Biodiversity offsetting
Voluntary actions	■ Conservation volunteers ■ Volunteer-based biodiversity monitoring programmes	■ Campaign for the Farmed Environment ■ Scottish Biodiversity Forum ■ Northern Ireland biodiversity delivery groups	

1 Including: Bat Conservation Trust, BTCV, British Trust for Ornithology, Butterfly Conservation, Plantlife, Royal Society for the Protection of Birds, The Wildlife Trusts, Woodland Trust, and the public body Natural England.

The Campaign for the Farmed Environment encourages voluntary management by farmers to benefit the environment while ensuring profitable food production (Section 27.4.3.7).

An example of action to raise awareness about biodiversity in the Marine environment is Natural England's Under England's Seas campaign (Natural England 2011b). The campaign provides regional information about the wildlife found in underwater landscapes.

27.2.4 Biodiversity Summary

Table 27.5 summarises the key insights from this review of responses in the context of biodiversity, highlighting those that have been well-established, but also identifying a set of responses that are either in early implementation or are proposed. It is important to learn from these early pilots across all sectors to scale-up the adoption of an integrated ecosystem approach to the management of the UK's diverse habitats, which is one key policy direction that this review recommends.

27.3 Water

27.3.1 Freshwater Ecosystem Services and Human Well-being

The myriad services provided by Freshwater are critical for human well-being (Chapter 9). While water is used directly to supply homes, industry and agriculture, and generate power, it also sustains a variety of ecosystems, such as rivers, wetlands and lakes, which provide multiple benefits to people (MA 2005; **Figure 27.8**). In the UK, Freshwater ecosystems are a source of many cultural services—millions enjoy the diversity of wildlife and natural beauty of the UK's waterscapes. Freshwater ecosystems regulate water quality, flooding and local climates, and play a fundamental role in sustaining essential supporting services that ensure both water- and land-based goods and services continue to be delivered to our society and economy. **Figure 27.9**

Figure 27.8 Rocky stream waterscape in the Lake District, England. *Photo by Rick Harrison, available under a Creative Commons Attribution-ShareAlike license.*

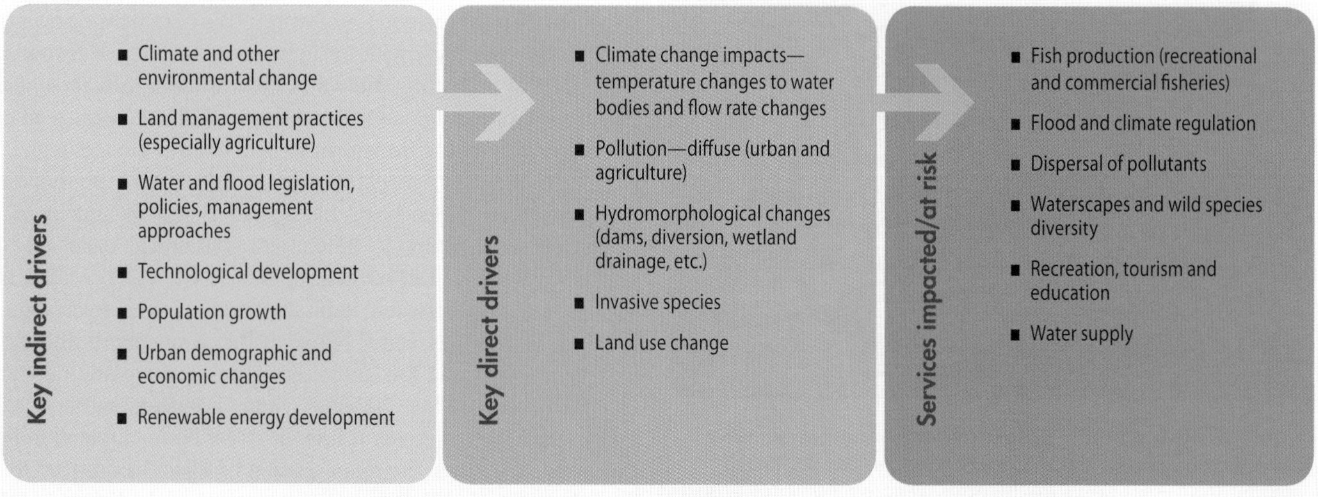

Key indirect drivers	Key direct drivers	Services impacted/at risk
■ Climate and other environmental change ■ Land management practices (especially agriculture) ■ Water and flood legislation, policies, management approaches ■ Technological development ■ Population growth ■ Urban demographic and economic changes ■ Renewable energy development	■ Climate change impacts—temperature changes to water bodies and flow rate changes ■ Pollution—diffuse (urban and agriculture) ■ Hydromorphological changes (dams, diversion, wetland drainage, etc.) ■ Invasive species ■ Land use change	■ Fish production (recreational and commercial fisheries) ■ Flood and climate regulation ■ Dispersal of pollutants ■ Waterscapes and wild species diversity ■ Recreation, tourism and education ■ Water supply

Figure 27.9 Key indirect and direct drivers relevant to the water sector, and the ecosystem services at risk.

summarises the major water-related direct and indirect drivers and their impact on ecosystem services. Given the cross-cutting nature of water, this sector should not be considered in isolation from the other sectors; response options for agriculture (Section 27.4.3) have particular relevance to Freshwater ecosystems.

27.3.2 Challenges for Water Management

Significant progress has been made improving the quality of the UK's rivers over the past two decades. Point source pollution from industry and urban areas has dramatically decreased, largely as a result of a European-driven regulatory framework that has led to investments in wastewater treatment. Although some point sources of pollution are still significant, diffuse source pollution from agriculture and urban areas remains an elusive issue, demanding a more comprehensive response. Nitrate concentrations have increased in approximately 4,000 km of rivers in the last two decades, and biological quality has declined in approximately 2,500 km of hill-rivers in Wales and the Welsh borders (Chapter 9).

Figure 27.10 Topmouth gudgeon eradication programme, Surrey. It may be less than 3 inches in size, but this tough invader from Asia preys on the eggs of native fish, breeds fast and spreads disease via a parasite that attacks other fish. *Photo © Environment Agency.*

Historically, Wetlands have been drained, dams built, dikes raised and channels straightened, deepened and widened in a bid to control water. Freshwater ecosystems have become highly fragmented, and flow rates have been modified, resulting in the loss of valuable Freshwater habitats and an increased flood risk. Severe flooding in 2007 emphasised the economic and social costs of flooding (Pitt 2008), the risk of which is expected to increase as a result of climate change (Defra 2009b).

According to evidence in Chapter 9, aquatic ecosystems appear particularly vulnerable to catastrophic regime shifts that, once incurred, can lead to large service losses which are difficult to restore. Emerging data also show that rivers, lakes and other Wetlands are especially sensitive to climate change, with temperatures in some UK rivers already rising and impacting river biodiversity (Chapter 9, Section 4). Hot, dry summers are apparently reducing juvenile populations of brown trout, salmon and eels (*ibid.*). Climate change is also likely to increase pressure on water supplies, particularly groundwater resources in some areas like south-east England. In addition to climate change, water stress is likely to become more widespread due to population growth and increasing environmental protection measures which reduce abstraction (Weatherhead & Howden 2009).

Non-native species that become invasive are a growing problem in UK Freshwater ecosystems (Strayer 2010; **Figure 27.10**), although there is insufficient evidence of their consequences. Novel pollutants, such as endocrine-disrupting substances, nanoparticles, and the effects of synthetic biology are emerging issues (Chapter 9). Changes in land use and climate, and increases in flood risk, are likely to continue to be important drivers of change in the water environment.

27.3.3 Water-related Response Options

27.3.3.1 Knowledge (foundational)

The way we perceive and manage water is very different today than it was 60 years ago. Historically, water was mainly valued for its supply for domestic, industrial and agricultural purposes, a place to dispose of wastes, and for game and course fisheries. There was little understanding of the multiple additional services it supports or our impact on them through the misuse of water. This has changed over the last two decades, with an increasing number of responses aimed at protecting the water environment. Advancements in environmental and social research have been a major driver behind the transformation of water management.

In the past, research has focused more on building knowledge of the basic biological, chemical and physical processes relating to catchment dynamics, especially in relatively undisturbed ecosystems. This has revealed the connections between habitats and how the hydrological cycle exchanges water between the atmosphere and land, the uplands and lowlands, terrestrial and aquatic habitats, fresh and saline habitats, and between surface and groundwater systems (Chapter 9). By better understanding these processes, the management of water has moved from administrative districts, such as counties and regions, to the natural units of river basins and catchments, embodied in Integrated Water Resource Management (IWRM).

We now know, with a high degree of certainty, that rivers, lakes, ponds and wetlands provide critical services to society, and that these services have been threatened by human activities, resulting in among the fastest rates of habitat modification in the UK (Chapter 9). Rivers are the most monitored environments in the UK, reflecting the importance placed on Freshwater through legislation, the effect of water quality on human activities, and the value of river organisms as indicators of wider environmental change. Long-term data are available for over 25,000 km of rivers in England, Wales and Scotland. Such data have allowed water quality trends to be tracked, prompting the enactment of legislation such as the Integrated Pollution Prevention and Control (IPPC) Directive in 1996 (Directive 96/61/EC) which led to the better protection of aquatic ecosystems and their services (*ibid.*).

The role of Freshwater ecosystems in reducing flood risk is increasingly being recognised. Based on this knowledge, government policy is moving away from engineered flood protection and towards working with nature by capitalising on the flood storage capacity of ecosystems—an approach endorsed in the Department for Environment, Food and Rural Affairs' Making Space for Water (Defra 2005), the government strategy for flood and coastal erosion in England. The Pitt Review (2008) was an independent inquiry carried out following devastating flooding in Gloucestershire (and other parts of England) in the summer of 2007. It resulted in a series of recommendations for improving the way flood risk is managed in England, which the government and relevant agencies are responding to, including improving the ability to predict the timing and extent of flooding (Defra 2009c).

In order to have a more integrated approach to water management, local and regional planners in the UK are adopting more holistic assessment tools. Water cycle studies are one way of providing a more comprehensive assessment of the impacts of proposed developments on the water environment. These studies assess existing information, identify knowledge gaps and consider options for sustainable development (EA 2009c).

However, considerable knowledge gaps remain (Chapter 9, Section 7); the benefits of Freshwater ecosystems are insufficiently quantified or valued in a meaningful way for policy makers. Monitoring networks currently misalign with the ecosystem service approach, making it difficult to quantify the links between ecosystem services and ecosystem functioning, structure and species composition. An increased understanding of how Freshwater can be managed sustainably within an ecosystem services approach is needed to ensure short-term uses do not undermine longer-term capacity. We also need to understand how Freshwater systems interact with different land types to deliver ecosystem services (Maltby 2009). The linkages between ecosystem functioning and ecosystem services are poorly understood, as is the importance of connectivity between wetlands, rivers, lakes and land for delivering ecosystem services. Climate change is likely to place greater pressure on aquatic ecosystems, the full effect of which is unclear, yet monitoring programmes are mainly targeted at stressors that were most dominant in the past (Hering *et al.* 2010). Further research is required to support efforts to optimise catchment management under climate change.

27.3.3.2 Legislation (enabling)

Command-and-control regulatory responses applied to Freshwater services (such as technological, end-of-pipe controls and discharge permits) are typically targeted at point sources of pollution (MA 2005). The European IPPC Directive is partly responsible for the significant reduction in industrial pollution across Europe, including in the UK. Industrial installations are issued permits that require them to employ Best Available Techniques in their production processes. Regulations for the collection and treatment of waste from homes (sewage) and industry stipulated in the Urban Wastewater Treatment Directive (Directive 91/271/EEC) has further reduced point source pollution loads in UK rivers (**Figure 27.11**).

Long-term monitoring data demonstrate significant improvements in chemical water quality, and the biological and chemical classification of 7,000 km of rivers in England and 12,000 km in Wales has dramatically improved over the past two decades (Chapter 9). The investments in wastewater treatment and other end-of-pipe solutions have, through regulation, monitoring and enforcement, been a major driver of these improvements, enhancing the delivery of multiple ecosystem services (Defra 2008c).

Although greatly reducing some point sources of pollution, these regulations have been less effective at achieving wider ecological objectives and there remain issues with some point sources. Phosphorus is elevated in many localities, probably due to continued discharges from wastewater treatment works, with more modest amounts from agriculture (e.g. Jarvie & King 2010). Diffuse sources of pollution from agricultural and urban areas, and water system fragmentation remain problematic (Chapter 9).

The WFD (2000/60/EC) was introduced with the aim of consolidating water legislation while also providing a framework to facilitate additional measures, allowing wider ecological objectives to be met. It obliges all 27 EU Member States to protect, enhance and restore water bodies, with the aim of achieving 'good' ecological, chemical and quantitative status in those water bodies by 2015. Extensions to the

Figure 27.11 Wastewater treatment works have significantly reduced point sources of pollution.
Sewage treatment plant. *Photo by Chesapeake Bay Program, available under a Creative Commons Attribution license.*

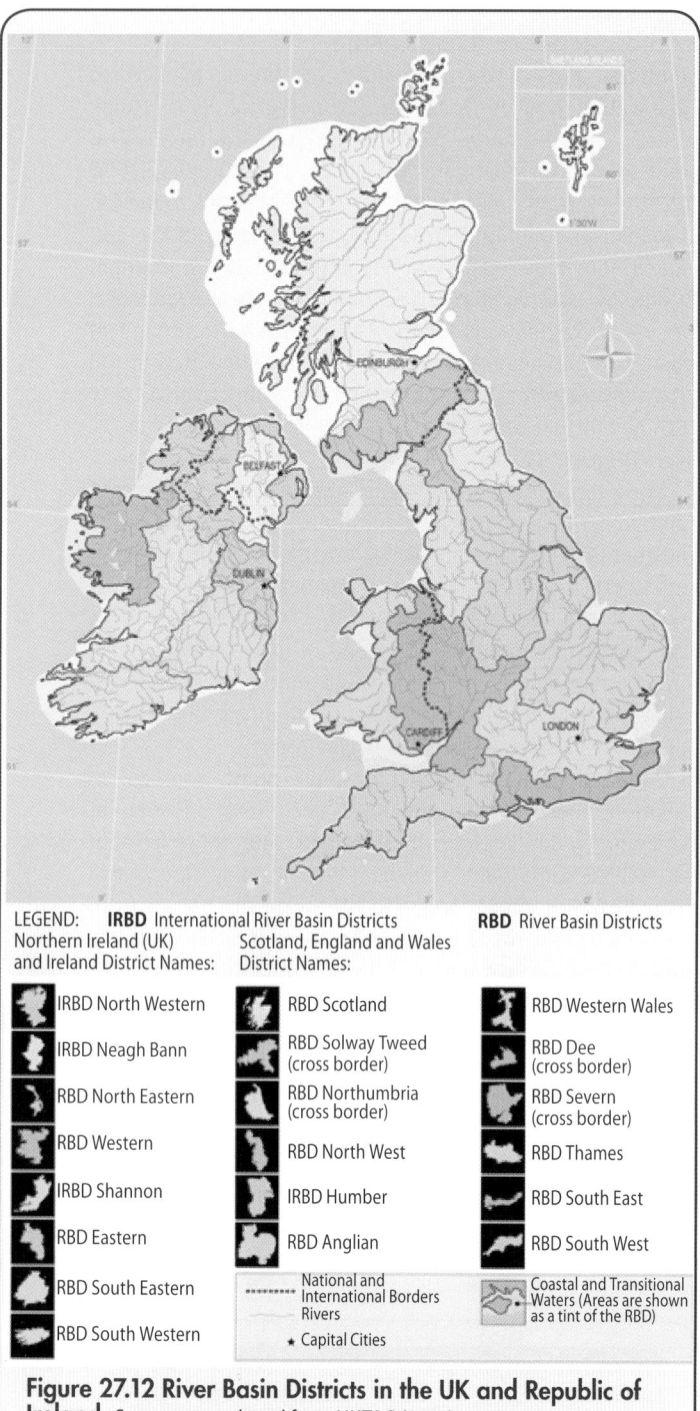

LEGEND: **IRBD** International River Basin Districts   **RBD** River Basin Districts
Northern Ireland (UK)   Scotland, England and Wales
and Ireland District Names: District Names:

IRBD North Western

IRBD Neagh Bann

RBD North Eastern

RBD Western

IRBD Shannon

RBD Eastern

RBD South Eastern

RBD South Western

RBD Scotland

RBD Solway Tweed
(cross border)

RBD Northumbria
(cross border)

RBD North West

IRBD Humber

RBD Anglian

National and
International Borders
Rivers

★ Capital Cities

RBD Western Wales

RBD Dee
(cross border)

RBD Severn
(cross border)

RBD Thames

RBD South East

RBD South West

Coastal and Transitional
Waters (Areas are shown
as a tint of the RBD)

Figure 27.12 River Basin Districts in the UK and Republic of Ireland. Source: reproduced from UKTAG (2005).

District, using this as the natural hydrological unit rather than political or administrative boundaries (**Figure 27.12**). This means that for river basins which cross national frontiers there must be cross-border cooperation (Northern Ireland shares three international River Basin Districts with the Republic of Ireland). The overall purpose of the WFD (set out in Article 1) is to prevent further deterioration of aquatic ecosystems, and to protect and enhance their status. It requires that objectives are set for water bodies taking into account ecological, as well as chemical and physical, criteria.

Secondly, the WFD combines at-source pollution control and quality standards regulatory approaches. This integrated strategy is intended to close the gaps left open in the past by using one or other strategy in isolation. Pollution emission limits applied at source can fail to deal with cumulative effects, while focusing on water quality standards can underestimate the effects of a particular substance in complex environments, especially where scientific understanding of the ecology of that environment is incomplete. As such, the strategy under the WFD is to make sure that source controls, including best available technologies, are applied as rigorously as possible. It also requires additional measures where source control alone is not enough to reach set quality objectives.

The WFD requires the production of River Basin Management Plans (RBMPs) by the competent authorities for each River Basin District. These must contain details of the analyses carried out for each water body including a summary of its current status, the pressures on it due to human activity, the specific objectives set for it and the measures planned to achieve those objectives.

In 2009, RBMPs which had been prepared for each of the UK jurisdictions were finalised according to the WFD timetable. The preparation of the RBMPs was a complex task, involving in depth consultation with stakeholders. Their publication illustrated the scale of the task ahead: in England and Wales only 27% of water bodies were assessed as currently being at or above good status. Current statistics (EA 2008b) show that over 84% of rivers, 85% of lakes, 97% of estuaries and 58% of coastal waters by length in England and Wales are failing to meet good status. The RBMPs set out predictions for the increase in the number of water bodies to reach good status by 2015 according to the programmes of measures which they set out. The Department for Environment, Food and Rural Affairs (2008c) estimates that £5 billion will need to be invested to improve the number of water bodies meeting good status by 5% by 2015. Scotland's water resources are in a better state, with 65% of water bodies assessed as good. The RBMPs will be updated on a six-yearly cycle, enabling changes to the pressures on a water body to be identified and new measures developed to overcome them. New knowledge from better monitoring and data can be incorporated into future planning cycles.

The WFD employs an ecosystem approach, aiming at holistic and ecologically sound management. Economic concepts are also a fundamental feature of the legislation. An economic analysis of water use is specifically required, and Member States must take account of the principle of recovery

2015 target may be permitted under specific circumstances, such as where the objectives are technically infeasible or disproportionately expensive, provided that no further deterioration in status occurs. The WFD aims to integrate water quality, quantity and ecological objectives, as well as all water users, functions and values. In doing so, it accounts for water use in the environment, health, consumption, recreation and other economic sectors.

The WFD deals with the management of all inland water bodies, including surface waters, groundwater, coastal waters and estuaries. Its introduction represented a step-change from previous water legislation in two major ways. Firstly, it designed a system for water management along ecological boundaries, and with ecological objectives. Water management under the WFD is structured by River Basin

of costs of water use, making sure that water pricing policies contribute to the Directive's environmental objectives, and reflect the polluter pays principle. The disproportionate expense analysis under Article 4 must consider monetised and non-monetised benefits of healthy water ecosystems. There is potential for these economic approaches to be used very effectively to promote water management methods with multiple ecosystem service benefits—for example, wetland restoration over more traditional end-of-pipe solutions to water management.

The EC (2010) has suggested that the cyclical outlook of the WFD should be leveraged in the process of adapting water body management to climate change impacts. The WFD itself does not make reference to climate change, but the importance of the issue is reflected in EU guidance on WFD implementation. This notes that climate change is projected to lead to major changes in yearly and seasonal precipitation and water flow, flooding and coastal erosion risks, water quality, and the distribution of species and ecosystems. Strategies for monitoring scientific forecasts on climate change impacts and designing robust adaptation strategies are recommended to be built into RBMPs (EC 2010).

The RBMPs of England and Wales have been criticised as demonstrating a lack of ambition for improving water body status (RSPB 2010b). The issue is not restricted to the UK—across the EU, RBMPs have been received critically. For England and Wales, allegations of inadequacies in the RBMPs relate to a number of issues: extensive reliance on deadline extensions; failure to specify the measures that will be taken; non-compliance of monitoring programmes with WFD requirements; and an unlawful approach to disproportionate costs (EEB 2010).

The WFD overlaps geographically with the MSFD (Section 27.7.3.2) in so far as both deal with coastal waters. The environmental status objectives of the MSFD (which operates a similar framework to the WFD) apply to coastal waters which are not covered by actions taken under the WFD. This arrangement is designed to avoid overlap, and will require cooperation by relevant authorities.

The laws dealing with flood risk management have been overhauled recently in the UK, first by the EU Floods Directive (2007/60/EC on the assessment and management of flood risks), and second by the Flood and Water Management Act 2010. The latter was enacted following the recommendations of the Pitt Review (2008).

Until these developments, the laws dealing with flood prevention and response in the UK had been dispersed in several different pieces of legislation. Relevant provisions were to be found in the Water Act 2003, Environment Act 1995, Water Resources Act 1991, and Land Drainage Act 1991. For example, certain local authority powers concerning drainage were set out in the Land Drainage Act, while the Environment Agency's powers in relation to flood defence actions were introduced through the Environment Act. The legislative picture was not very clear, and had developed in a piecemeal fashion alongside institutional developments. One of the Pitt Review's key recommendations was to bring flood control within one unifying legal framework. As yet, this has not quite been achieved, but there has been a significant degree of consolidation.

The EU Floods Directive was also introduced as a response to various serious flooding incidents in Europe during the last decade. It aims to put in place a proactive system of flood risk assessment and management. It is implemented in England and Wales by the Flood Risk Regulations 2009, in Scotland by the Flood Risk Management (Scotland) Act 2009, and in Northern Ireland by the Water Environment (Floods Directive) Regulation (Northern Ireland) 2009. It requires preliminary assessments identifying river basins and coastal areas most at risk of flooding to be carried out by 2011. Flood risk maps for those areas must be drawn up by 2013, and flood risk management plans must be in place by 2015. For England, the responsibility for these flood risk management plans is divided between the Environment Agency (for sea, major river and reservoir risks) and local authorities for other flooding sources in their areas. In Scotland, the task is allocated between the Scottish Environment Protection Agency and local authorities. For Northern Ireland, the main authority responsible is the Department of Agriculture and Rural Development. The Directive requires that flood risk management plans take into account the role to be played by natural floodplains. The Scottish implementing legislation is notable for imposing an express duty on the Scottish Environment Protection Agency to assess whether alteration (including enhancement) or restoration of natural features and characteristics of any river basin or coastal area in a flood risk management district could contribute to the management of flood risk for the district.

These flood risk management plans must have regard for the WFD, i.e. consider the effect of proposed flood management measures on achieving the ecological status objectives set out under the WFD. The flood risk maps and management plans are organised to correspond with WFD River Basin Districts. Northern Ireland has a duty to cooperate with Ireland in respect of shared River Basin Districts.

The Pitt Review (2008) noted that many of the defects it had identified in the UK's flood legislation could be addressed through the Floods Directive (at that time, awaiting implementation), but not all. In England and Wales, the Flood and Water Management Act 2010 was, in part, a response to this. It is not in full force yet; its first provisions commenced in October 2010, requiring the Environment Agency and local authorities to begin implementing flood risk management strategies.

Designated freshwater areas play an important role in protecting biodiversity and preserving landscapes, especially Wetlands (Section 27.2.3.2). Approximately two thirds of Wetlands designated as SSSIs are in target condition, and it is thought that non-statutory Wetlands are likely to be in poorer condition (Chapter 9). Although a successful conservation regulatory instrument, designated areas, including SSSIs and SACs, are argued to be too rigid to protect and maintain other ecosystem services in a changing environment (Section 27.2.3.3).

Nitrate Vulnerable Zones (NVZs), first described in 1998 under the Nitrates Directive, are designated areas draining into waters polluted by nitrates from agriculture. Farmers with land in NVZs must follow mandatory rules to tackle nitrate loss from agriculture, specifically rules for the application of fertiliser and manure. Currently, about

62% of England and 4% of Wales are designated as NVZs (EA 2011b). A re-survey of a sample of farms located within NVZs found that manure nitrate loading had decreased between the baseline taken in 1996–97 and 2003, and rates of compliance are almost absolute (ADAS 2004). The study also found that farmers were taking into account more factors, such as type of crop, application rates and fertiliser analysis, before spreading inorganic fertilisers on the field. Recent unpublished evidence suggests that nitrate levels may have fallen in rivers over the last decade (Bowman *et al.* unpublished), but more research is required to test this result and to understand the contribution of NVZs. Improvements in groundwater quality are likely to take time, but some reduction of nitrate levels in rivers would be expected (EA 2007a). New regulations were introduced in 2008, the impact of which on nitrate levels is not known yet.

Water Protection Zones (WPZs) are a regulatory instrument aimed at addressing diffuse pollution and hydromorpholgical changes. They give additional powers to the Environment Agency in England and Wales to use measures to prohibit or manage activities that could pollute or degrade water. The Environment Agency is currently undertaking desk studies of candidate sites.

27.3.3.3 Policy, institutions and governance (enabling)

There is a high degree of agreement internationally that traditional, fragmented, sectoral approaches to the management of water have failed to prevent the unsustainable use of water resources and their associated ecosystems (MA 2005; UNEP 2007). It is increasingly evident that the delivery of Freshwater services is dependent on the management of all habitats in a river basin—the soil, forests, woodlands and freshwater. The most effective management is, therefore, only likely to occur by considering how land and water is managed across entire catchments, not just riparian areas. The provision of Freshwater services is also determined by a complex system of interdependent environmental, social and economic components, further complicated by uncertainties associated with changes in climate, markets and society. Set within this context, piecemeal and rigid policies are unlikely to be able to meet the challenges ahead.

The principles of Integrated Water Resource Management (IWRM) provide for a more holistic approach to water management. The Global Water Partnership (GWP 2010) defines IWRM as "the coordinated development and management of water, land and related resources in order to maximise economic and social welfare without compromising the sustainability of vital ecosystems and the environment." The principles of the IWRM informed, in part, the WFD and the changes to water management in the UK that its implementation entails. The WFD provides an opportunity to move from fragmented to more integrated approaches. It sets objectives for water bodies to be of 'good status', with the intention that if rivers, lakes and groundwater are healthy then the catchment from which the water drains is also healthy. In this way, the management of the land has become integral to managing water. A healthy river catchment (including both land and water) is better

able to deliver a wide range of ecosystem services from food production to recreation (Quevauviller 2010).

The ecosystem services approach may prove a useful framework for accounting for the interconnections of water systems, and for framing wider economic and social considerations (RELU 2010a). By valuing the full range of freshwater ecosystem services in decision-making processes, synergies and trade-offs can be identified and programmes of measures in RBMPs tailored to optimise the mix of services. This may offer a practical approach to meeting the triple challenge of climate change, food security and water allocation (Chapter 9). The ecosystem approach may also be effective at engaging stakeholders around commonly understood beliefs, helping to identify innovative and equitable solutions through participative decision making (EA 2009a).

Integrated ecosystem approaches intrinsically consider the linkages and interactions between hydrological entities that cross multiple boundaries—geographic, political or administrative. This requires planning and management to align with the natural management unit, i.e. the catchment or river basin. The WFD has established River Basin Districts (a single system of water management) and assigned competent basin authorities responsible for the development of RBMPs. Since the first round of RMBPs were only completed in 2009, there is no evidence yet of their outcomes in terms of ecosystem service delivery.

The Environment Agency in England and Wales, the Northern Ireland Department for the Environment and the Scottish Environment Protection Agency are the competent authorities in the UK. In the first round of RBMPs, the Environment Agency established 'liaison panels' (stakeholder groups) in each River Basin District to represent local interests, but coordinated planning at a national level to ensure consistency (EA 2009c).

Some countries in the EU have devolved greater responsibility for the WFD's implementation to local government institutions and their local partners. In the UK, there may be opportunities to learn from their experiences of implementing the Directive (RELU 2010a) and from international experiences of catchment management. The argument for giving more responsibility to local and regional government is that they have a direct interest in water problems affecting their area, and have responsibility for development and planning in their region. The Rural Economy and Land Use (RELU) Programme's (2010a) Catchment Management Project studied water management programmes in the New York City water supply catchment, alongside other international examples and UK experiences; it found that local solutions are needed to better reflect local land use and diffuse pollution. The Project proposed that adaptive management, including applied research and stakeholder deliberation, and supported by multilevel partnerships and enabling regulations, could create the conditions for such local solutions. Such adaptive management may provide the necessary flexibility in water management to deal with uncertainties associated with changes in climate and society. The greater involvement of local authorities and local partners in environmental policy delivery (as is the case in most other European countries), and the integration of spatial planning with river basin planning, could provide for better local participation and ownership in water management (Quevauviller 2010). These principles broadly align with those of localism. Further discussion on collaborative approaches for integrated land-water management can be found in Section 27.10.

A challenge for the UK is that the management of water has traditionally been top-down, with limited connections between the policy making level and implementation activities at local levels. Quevauviller (2010) argues that the current, centralised institutional framework does not enable the flexibility necessary for more informed, participative and adaptive approaches. The use of existing data, knowledge and governance structures in the first round of the RBMPs may have perpetuated a top-down, uniform approach, with only limited local influence. This may have hindered the ability to consider trade-offs, conflicts and synergies that exist when several policies and regulations affect multiple ecosystem services (*ibid.*).

Stakeholder engagement in river basin planning can enhance the effectiveness of decisions since it can improve understanding of impacts and vulnerability, account for the distribution of benefits and costs, and co-create a wider range of response options (MA 2005). Conventionally, decision-making followed a path of: problem definition, response options development by experts, public consultation, political decision-making and final implementation ('Decide-Announce-Defend'; RELU 2010a). Increasingly, people's values, as well as facts, are recognised as contributing relevant knowledge, and it is considered that one can neither presume that people have values nor that experts have facts. In the West Wales River Basin District, the Environment Agency used deliberative analysis—a systematic process that incorporates analysis and deliberation as two complementary approaches to form understanding on the basis of knowledge, and reaching agreement through logical argument and reasoning (EA 2009b). These decision-making processes can be described as 'Engage-Deliberate-Decide' (RELU 2010b).

There are a growing number of projects that address the management of land and water interactions within a catchment; these projects are typically initiated and managed locally and independently from national policy frameworks. Interestingly, several water companies (e.g. South West Water, United Utilities, Dwr Cymru, Northumbrian Water) are trialling catchment interventions. As a result of investments in land management upstream of their treatment facilitates, they expect to reduce the treatment costs of water supply (**Box 27.8**). Given that the contamination of drinking water supplies by farming costs an estimated £129 million a year (Jacobs 2008), substantial savings could be made. Other water companies intend to join the early adopters of 'upstream thinking'. A total of seventeen companies plan to undertake 100 'catchment management schemes' taking action or investigation at the catchment-level to address deteriorating water quality, rather than pursuing traditional, capital-intensive treatment solutions (OFWAT 2009). The Mersey Basin Campaign, another local catchment intervention, was launched with government support to clean up the Mersey River and its tributaries by 2010. It successfully engaged many organisations, authorities, businesses, communities

---

Box 27.8 Catchment interventions by water companies and non-governmental organisations.
Source: South West Water (2010); West Country Rivers Trust (2010); www.unitedutilities.com/scamp; RSPB (2011); EA (2009a).

'Upstream Thinking'
South West Water has developed a scheme called 'Upstream Thinking', which aims to improve the water and ecological quality of the rivers of South West England in order to protect the company's assets (**Figure 27.13**). The water company hopes to make cost savings by working with landowners to change land management practices in upland areas to decrease the costs of water treatment for supply. One-to-one advice is offered to farmers, and farm plans were developed in cooperation with the West Country Rivers Trust and incentivised through a capital grant scheme. Above the Upper Tamar Lake, improvements in water quality have been realised through this scheme. Post-scheme monitoring revealed the quality of water downstream of farms involved in the project is now better than the inflows. Wider benefits for the river system are expected in addition to the protection of the water source for water supply.

SCaMP project
United Utilities developed the SCaMP Project in partnership with the Royal Society for the Protection of Birds on land they own in in the Bowland and Peak District area, North West England. Overgrazing by sheep, air pollution, historic drainage of blanket bog, the erosion of peat, and the loss of native trees were all impacting on wildlife and water quality. The upland area gathers water through heath and blanket bogs, where oxidised, exposed peat causes the water to become discoloured so requires treatment before being supplied to homes. The project aimed to address the land management problems at source, rather than at the end-of-pipe through water treatment. By working with farmers they developed management plans that identified how the land could be restored and managed to benefit water quality and wildlife. Twenty tenant farmers made use of agri-environment schemes, such as the English Higher Level Stewardship and Woodland Grant schemes, to receive compensation for changing their practices and for capital investments.

SCaMP has resulted in 2,000 less sheep on the uplands, which has allowed vegetation to recover; the blockage of over 100 km of drainage grips to improve raw water quality; and the revegetation of 5 km² of once bare peat. Moreover, 500,000 deciduous trees have been planted near the banks of streams and on steep cloughs, and 95% of the SSSIs located on United Utilities' land are now in favourable or unfavourable recovering condition. The important role of the peats in storing carbon for climate change mitigation was considered in the second phase of SCaMP. Restoration of the peatlands is anticipated to maintain the carbon store and enhance its ability to sequester carbon.

Figure 27.13 Upstream Thinking site on Exmoor, England.
Photo courtesy of South West Water.

---

and volunteers through 20 Action Partnerships, which resulted in significant improvements in river and estuary water quality, and the provision of ecosystem services and associated social benefits (Mersey Basin Campaign 2010; Quevauviller 2010).

The involvement of the third sector may have increased the trust of stakeholders in these schemes. Interventions in the River Tamar catchment carried out by the West Country Rivers Trust, including the Tamar 2000 project, improved the ecology of the River Tamar through advice to landowners and managers. The Environment Agency (EA 2009a) observed that because the West Country Rivers Trust led the Tamar 2000 project it was more bottom-up than the government's Catchment Sensitive Farming scheme, which consequently had less acceptance of prescribed actions by landowners, despite close similarities between the schemes.

Because most of these projects were intended to improve a particular ecosystem service, such as water quality, there may be scope to improve their design to optimise a wider range of ecosystem services. They also operate in isolation, and may benefit from support from regional or national policy. Furthermore, there are likely to be opportunities to learn from such schemes about what form of collaboration can work (Quevauviller 2010).

Until recently, flood management has concentrated on engineered solutions such as building flood banks, and deepening and straightening channels (Pitt 2008). Not only are they expensive to construct, but often shift the problem downstream, rather than providing a sustainable solution. However, a growing number of ecosystem-based alternatives exist (Natural England 2009g). The Department for Environment, Food and Rural Affairs' Making Space for Water Strategy (Defra 2005) lays out a more strategic approach to flood risk management with a wider portfolio of responses. This implies the wider employment of land use solutions, including the restoration of Wetlands and washlands, coastal realignment, river corridor widening and river restoration. 'Slowing water down' through ecological engineering has been suggested as a win-win-win solution: reducing flood risk while also improving water quality and increasing security of supply (Chapter 9). Woodlands, Mountains, Moors and Heaths, Semi-natural Grasslands and Wetlands have significant water storage capacity and slow surface water before it reaches streams and rivers. Water can also be slowed by restoring natural rivers and Floodplains (Sections 27.3.3.5, 27.3.3.6).

Policies to address water stress are likely to focus on demand management and water-saving, rather than resource development (e.g. reservoirs), as it is both cheaper and less carbon intensive (Weatherhead & Howden 2009). Because the distribution of water stress is uneven, with South East England particularly at risk, large-scale water transfers by rivers or canals from other river basins is feasible. However, this is less likely to be sustainable than demand management. Another option is to discourage land uses that increase evapotranspiration and runoff rates in water-stressed regions, and encourage land uses which increase infiltration (Weatherhead & Howden 2009) through, for example, catchment sensitive farming and agri-environment schemes (Section 27.4.3.5).

27.3.3.4 Changing social attitudes (enabling)

Water is impacted by the behaviour of a wide range of actors and land managers—from farmers and businesses to the public—so responses discussed in Agriculture (Section 27.4.3.4), Forestry (Section 27.5.3.4), and Urban planning, transport and energy (Section 27.9.3.4) have relevance to changing social attitudes about the water environment as well.

The adoption of more integrated, adaptive and participatory approaches (Section 27.3.3.3) to water management will likely require cultural changes in society if they are to be effective. Social attitudes are crucial for understanding barriers to the adoption of technologies and new management strategies. Social learning in river basin management involves different authorities, experts, interest groups and the public working collaboratively, and requires stakeholders to learn about their interdependence and differences, and to deal with them to resolve conflicts. Social learning should lead to increased capacity to address catchment issues. Information in this context is often a means to support communication rather than providing expert advice (Pahl-Wostl et al. 2008).

The Pitt Review (2008) made a number of recommendations for improving public awareness about flood risk and for how the public should respond to flood warnings. If residents of flood-prone regions took appropriate self-protective behaviour they could reduce the monetary damage of floods by up to 80%, thus reducing the need for public flood risk management (Grothmann & Reusswig 2006). Frequently, the public fail to respond appropriately to flood warning information, probably due to issues of lack of understanding, mistrust of authority and a lack of ownership on flood risk reduction actions (Parker et al. 2009). Many people living in flood-prone areas are in denial about the risk and expect protection from authorities, making them unprepared to respond to flood warnings. Parker et al. (2009) recommend several principles for improving flood warning response in the UK. Flood communication and education is likely to be more effective if it reduces uncertainty in people's minds and is targeted at specific audiences. There is also some evidence of a willingness among floodplain residents to engage in flood risk management including participating in informal communication networks within local communities and making arrangements to help the elderly and infirm in an emergency (ibid.).

People's perception of drought and climate change may be an important barrier to behaviour change for sustainable water management in areas facing water stress, such as South East England. A survey found that the public are more willing to accept restrictions than agree to pay higher water bills to ensure supply (Dessai & Catherine 2010). While respondents to the survey were concerned about the impacts of climate change, they did not necessarily take action to use water more efficiently. Barriers to engagement with climate change and water efficient behaviour included a lack of accessible information, a lack of resources and a perceived lack of institutional engagement. A number of water-saving initiatives have been established by the government including activities by the Water Saving Group and the Scottish Water Saving Network, and engagement programmes by Waterwise aimed at changing public behaviour towards water use.

27.3.3.5 Markets and incentives (instrumental)

Market-based instruments, incentives and pricing policies can alter demand for water and the way in which water and its associated ecosystem services are exploited. In the past, many Freshwater ecosystem services have been undervalued economically. Market-based instruments include appropriate pricing of water resources, metering of water use to reflect the cost of water supply, tradeable quotas, fees, permits and subsidies (UNEP 2007). Disincentives can be deployed in water-stressed regions to discourage land use that increases evapotranspiration or that increases surface runoff, thereby reducing the recharge of soil moisture or groundwater. Conversely, incentives can be used to encourage land uses that conserve water (Weatherhead & Howden 2009).

Household use is the main component (52%) abstracted from the public water supply and has increased by more than 30% since 1970 (Foresight 2010). Water metering is a long-established measure for reducing domestic water demand by connecting water use to water bills. Less than one third of homes in England have a water meter (Defra 2008c) and even fewer are in place in Scotland; in the remaining unmetered homes, there is little financial incentive to use water wisely. According to the Department for Environment, Food and Rural Affairs (Defra 2008c), fitting a meter reduces water consumption by about 10%. Although the take-up of meters is usually due to consumer choice, the regulatory framework was changed in 2007 to allow water companies in regions of water stress to implement compulsory water metering. The Environment Agency found the cost of near-universal water metering to be good value compared to water provision options (**Table 27.6**).

While research has been underway to understand the value of ecosystem services, mechanisms for integrating these values into decision-making processes are needed. The concept of Payments for Ecosystem Services (PES) has received growing interest as a way of establishing a market for ecosystem services. Landowners are currently unrewarded financially for services their land provides that have wider benefits to society. Providing PES could reward landowners for delivering multiple ecosystem services from their land (Natural England 2009g). Within catchments this could involve, for example, downstream users paying

upstream landowners to maintain water quality or quantity. Agri-environment schemes could provide a mechanism to reward farmers for taking action to reduce flood risk by, for example, reducing runoff rates or storing floodwater (RELU 2010a). Some recent studies have demonstrated a willingness from the public to pay for improved water quality (**Box 27.9**).

A system of licences issued by the environment agencies of each country governs the abstraction of water from all sources of supply, including rivers, lakes, canals and groundwater, in order to minimise impacts on the environment. The availability of licences is determined at a local level using Catchment Abstraction Management Strategies (CAMS) in England and Wales, and Water Resource Management Strategies in Scotland. Licensees must pay water abstraction charges in all UK countries. In England and Wales, there is also a system of water rights trading, introduced following the publication of Taking Water Responsibly in 1999. Water rights trading involves the transfer of licensed water rights from one party to another to use water that is already licensed rather than abstracting

---

Box 27.9 The Norfolk Broads. Source: Turner *et al.* (2004); Pretty *et al.* (2002).

During the 1980s, the Environmentally Sensitive Area scheme was pioneered in the Norfolk Broads, and by 1989, the Broads Authority had been established to take responsibility for conservation, planning, recreation and waterways in the area (**Figure 27.14**). The Broads Authority has experimented with a number of fen management measures (from ponies to mechanical fen-harvester machines), and has run a publicly funded flood alleviation initiative (which includes soft engineering) for 20 years. More recently, the Authority has begun to adopt the ecosystem services approach and has put initial values on some of the services it manages.

A 'willingness to pay' survey by Turner *et al.* (2004) showed that individual households in the region were willing to pay around £75 per year to improve wastewater treatment in order to prevent algal blooms. This equates to annual benefits of £169 million if all households in East Anglia were to make this payment—a figure which far exceeds the amount of money required to make similar improvements across the whole of England and Wales: an estimated £50 million per year (Pretty *et al.* 2002). This demonstrates that, in some cases, if the value of ecosystem services are fully understood, the willingness to pay for them can exceed the amount required to sustain them (Pretty *et al.* 2002; Turner *et al.* 2004).

Figure 27.14 Welsh ponies at How Hill National Nature Reserve in the Norfolk Broads, East of England. © Broads Authority. *Photo by Ian Aitkin.*

Table 27.6 The cost of near-universal water metering relative to other options. Source: EA (2009d).
*Costs taken from EA (2008c); †Average incremental social costs of other options are taken from EA (2007b).

Option	Range of costs (pence per cubic metre)
Near-universal (90%) metering *	140–160
Groundwater development †	100–500
Surface water development †	100–500
New reservoir †	300–1,000
Desalination plant †	400–800

more water, and to encourage abstractions to be transferred to locations where more water is available (EA, 2011).

The Cave Review (2009) looked at competition and innovation in the water markets in England and Wales, and identified a number of weaknesses in the current abstraction licensing system. It reported that the licences are issued on a first-come first-served basis, and charges are limited to cost-recovery and are fairly crude. Historically, issued licences are also not limited by time. As a result of these characteristics, the system fails to ensure water is delivered to those who value it most, or to the environment. The Review recommended that "where license levels are sustainable, licenses should be fully tradable subject only to modification for direct environmental impacts and the impact on other users from a change of use or location." It also recommends that in cases where the licensed volume of water is unsustainable "legislation should empower the Environment Agency to facilitate the return of licenses through reverse auctions and negotiated agreements", and that a scarcity charge should be introduced to restore sustainable licence volumes. The price of water would be uniform across overabstracted catchments and rise over time (above that required for cost-recovery) to encourage licence holders to trade or retire their rights and realise the true value of the water (*ibid.*). The Department for Environment, Food and Rural Affairs and the Welsh Assembly Government are currently considering these recommendations.

27.3.3.6 Technologies and practices (instrumental)

In the past, technological responses have been perhaps the most important tools for addressing water quality issues. Industry standards, such as Best Available Technology, Best Environmental Practice and Best Environmental Management, have also driven and shaped the development and improvement of technologies (UNEP 2007). The most common application of technological responses in the UK has been in the treatment of wastewater and for water reuse, including pollution source control (e.g. clean technology, recycling municipal and industrial wastes) and centralised wastewater treatment facilities. While there remains considerable wastage of water from leakages in the distribution system, the amount of water abstracted for the public water supply is slowly decreasing due to an overall reduction in leakages (Orr *et al.* 2007). Non-point source pollution, however, is difficult to control with high-tech applications, instead requiring ecological approaches and educational and awareness building responses.

Ecosystem restoration is now a popular option, with the overall aim to restore degraded ecosystems in order to enhance the services that they provide (UNEP 2007). However, restoration projects—including controlling invasive species, restoring hydrological regimes and ecological engineering—are normally more expensive than the protection of existing ecosystems (UNEP 2007).

Floodplains store water that would otherwise increase flood magnitude downstream (Acreman *et al.* 2003). They also provide benefits in terms of carbon sequestration, wild species diversity and purifying water of pollution. Restoring Floodplains is, therefore, held up as a win-win-win response. Meyerhoff & Dehnhardt (2004) found that the water quality

benefits provided by Floodplain restoration projects can have gains outweighing costs by a factor of 2.5 to 4. Yet raising water levels in Floodplains may not reduce flood risk. Although this response has mostly beneficial outcomes for ecosystem services overall (such as carbon sequestration), it cannot reduce flood storage in the long-term since saturated wetland soils with a water table near the surface have no, or limited, water storage capacity (Section 9.2.2.1).

Other types of restoration may, therefore, be better at reducing flood risk. Sustainable catchment drainage involves managing land to increase water infiltration rates and slow water down, providing benefits in terms of flood mitigation, maintaining low flows and purifying polluted water to reduce contamination of aquatic ecosystems and water supplies (Chapter 9). Encouraging water infiltration through appropriate land use practices in urban infrastructure development, land management and farming can also be effective at recharging aquifers and maintaining summer flows (HM Government, 2010b).

River restoration often involves the reinstatement of linkages between primary channels and nearby floodplains to increase flood attenuation. Morris *et al.* (2004) found that rivers restored with well-vegetated river channels can slow floodwaters down and enable them to infiltrate undeveloped floodplains, thus reducing the magnitude of flooding in built up areas. The re-creation of water and sediment transfers may not only reduce the flood severity downstream, but also improve the ecological water quality of rivers and create biodiverse Wetlands and washlands (Wharton & Gilvear 2006), offering opportunities for recreation, education and conservation. **Box 27.10** describes the environmental benefits that were achieved through the restoration of the River Glaven in North Norfolk.

Naturally occurring Wetlands can improve water quality by intercepting pollutants. This can offer a particularly useful way of addressing diffuse pollution from agriculture and urban sources (MA 2005), but their effectiveness depends on the Wetlands being situated in locations that intercept the pathway of the pollutant (Blackwell *et al.* 2009 in Chapter 9). Constructed Wetlands have long been used as a more cost-effective way of treating contaminated water than engineered solutions, with more than 1,000 projects in the UK (Cooper 2007; Section 9.2.2.4). Where such projects have been planned, implemented and managed well, they have

---

Box 27.10 Brown trout restoration work on the River Glaven, North Norfolk. Source: EA (2010c).

The Environment Agency established the River Glaven Sea Trout Restoration project with the primary aim to restore populations of brown trout in the river. Reconnecting the river laterally and longitudinally, and restoring the health and functions of the river, achieved this aim, but also brought a number of other benefits. While the project benefited anglers through the greater abundance of fish, more widespread benefits came from improving habitats for other species and increasing recreation and tourism. The extension of the project to provide routes for fish to bypass major obstructions on the river is also expected to provide benefits for flood risk management. The Environment Agency found that in cases like this, where the positive outcomes of a restoration project clearly outweigh the costs, an economic valuation of the benefits is not always necessary.

UK National Ecosystem Assessment: Technical Report

been successful long-term responses to pollution, and have also provided a range of other services such as increased wild species diversity and the supply of reeds for thatching. In cases without appropriate management, constructed Wetlands have become a source of pollution. Riparian buffer zones, a strip of protected habitat between the top of the riverbank and the river channel, can also protect wildlife and incept sediments and pollutants before reaching the river (**Box 27.11**).

27.3.3.7 Voluntary actions (instrumental)

In the UK, the Rivers Trusts (which collectively fall under the umbrella organisation of the Association of Rivers Trusts) and fisheries boards carry out river improvements by attracting charitable funds. Each individual Rivers Trust was formed due to a particular trigger such as a growing awareness of the environment, a decline of certain indicator species, or a pollution event (ART, 2009). The Trusts draw upon teams of volunteers, typically from angling clubs and riparian landowners. They offer the advantage of gaining the trust of local communities and actors (Raven 2011). As decision-making is moved from central and regional government to local authorities and communities, the River Trusts may be able to play a greater role in the management of catchments (*ibid.*). As discussed previously under *Policies, Institutions and Governance*, local action in catchments can be effective (Section 27.3.3.3). A good understanding of catchment-scale processes is also required, however (Newson 2010), with some coordination needed to ensure that action taken

locally does not have untended consequences downstream. Raven (2011) expresses concern that cuts in government funding for land management grants, monitoring, research and conservation projects could hinder River Trusts and other voluntary groups in making river improvements.

Many stakeholders are voluntarily involved in the management of water through, for example, Stakeholder Groups that work with the Environment Agency to develop CAMS, and Catchment Flood Management Strategies. River Trusts and fora, such as the National Flood Forum, enable the Environment Agency to connect with communities and find solutions to complex local problems (Orr *et al.* 2007).

In addition to Rivers Trusts, there are also a wide range of other trusts and NGOs involved in the conservation of rivers, lakes, Wetlands and Freshwater species. Voluntary conservation organisations, including The Wildlife Trusts, the National Trust and the RSPB, own considerable Wetland areas, affording them protection and managing them appropriately for biodiversity gain. Such organisations also mobilise significant numbers of volunteers. For instance, the Water for Wildlife partnership between The Wildlife Trusts, water companies and the Environment Agency involved nearly 5,000 volunteer working days to help the partners achieve the maintenance and restoration of 95,000 ha of Wetland and 750 km of rivers, and conduct otter (*Lutra lutra*) and water vole (*Arvicola terrestris*) surveys (The Wildlife Trusts 2010).

In some nations, community volunteerism plays a larger role in land-water management. In Australia, the government has emphasised voluntary action as a key instrument in river basin management, and invested heavily in participatory approaches. Almost all river rehabilitation schemes are implemented with volunteer involvement, with regional authorities and the Natural Heritage Trust providing support to volunteer groups (Fryirs *et al.* 2008). The aim is for participatory decision-making through regional governance, decentralisation, accountability, equity and empowerment. The intention is for management strategies to be designed for regional conditions and circumstances to increase the likelihood of success, but there are often problems with the process being influenced by vested interests and the exclusion of important stakeholders (*ibid.*). The Landcare movement in Australia has been the main mechanism through which volunteers have been engaged. It is a type of community-based natural resource management that involves individuals with varying backgrounds in local groups to cooperate with government and non-government stakeholders to manage the natural environment (Prager & Vanclay 2010). Read more about the Landcare groups in **Box 27.57**. Rivercare programmes were a spin-off of the Landcare movement, addressing specifically water quality and river system issues. Participants in Rivercare establish plans for the rehabilitation of rivers (Fryirs *et al.* 2008).

If the role of voluntary action in the management of UK catchments increases, it would be wise to learn from the experiences of countries with a stronger tradition of decentralised natural resource management. In addition to Australia, Landcare is also found in Germany, for instance, and Canada has a strong focus on decentralised and participatory management approaches.

Box 27.11 Providing ecosystem services in the Upper Bristol Avon through the creation of a buffer zone.
Source: EA (2010b).

A 330 m buffer zone along one bank in the Upper Bristol Avon catchment (North Wiltshire) was created following concerns raised by Somerford's Fishing Association: the field boundary near the river edge had been poached by grazing dairy cattle, and had eroded the riverine habitat; and diffuse pollution from sediments was impacting the river habitat and fish populations. Following discussions with the landowner and the Environment Agency, a buffer zone was created in 2008 at a cost of £4,700.

By the end of 2009, the area had been revegetated to such an extent that the riverbank was stabilised and the river channel narrowed. Not only did this reduce the runoff of pollutants into the river, but also improved the scour of the riverbed and increased flow and habitat diversity. The buffer zone created a suitable habitat for the breeding and protection of game and course fish species, and provided them with a source of food. The semi-static water and vegetation cover also provided a nursery area where juvenile fish can shelter from predators and where warmer shallow waters aid fry growth rates. Residents and visiting anglers report high numbers of birds and other wildlife, and an improved waterscape.

The project is estimated to have created gross lifetime benefits valued at £144,860—a benefit-to-cost ratio of 31:1. The project demonstrates that, by restoring the functioning of ecosystems, wider benefits to society can be achieved other than just the primary focus of the intervention (in this case, the fisheries). Buffer zones may be a useful measure to provide social and economic benefits, and for supporting the achievement of 'good ecological status' required under the Water Framework Directive.

27.3.4 Water Summary

Table 27.7 summarises the key insights from this review of responses in the water sector, highlighting those that have been well-established, but also identifying a set of responses that are either in early implementation or are proposed. It is important to learn from these early pilots across all sectors to scale-up the adoption of an integrated ecosystem approach to the management of the UK's diverse habitats, which is one key policy direction that this review recommends.

27.4 Agriculture

27.4.1 Agriculture, Ecosystem Services and Human Well-being

The agricultural sector is still managed and valued primarily for food production, and to a lesser extent forage, fibre, bioenergy and pharmaceuticals. Arable crop yields have grown significantly (for example, wheat yields have risen by 300% during the period 1940 to 2008), but the sector's contribution to the national economy has declined since the 1970s, and livestock numbers have fallen in the last decade, particularly in upland grazing areas (Section 7.3.1). In addition to agri-products, agricultural land delivers many other ecosystem services—from drinking water supply to climate regulation—that are fundamental to the well-being of UK citizens. Upland grazing areas, for example, not only provide food, but are known for their outstanding beauty and provide a range of public benefits such as carbon sequestration, drinking water and recreation opportunities.

Up until the 1990s, maximising food provision often caused unintentional losses of other ecosystem services on farmland. Disservices of the sector included declines in farmland wildlife, nutrient loading of watercourses, and a significant contribution to the UK's greenhouse gas

Table 27.7 Water Summary.

	Established responses	Early implementation, pilots	Proposed, under development
Knowledge	■ Research on catchment dynamics ■ River monitoring ■ Flood prediction	■ Understanding how freshwater ecosystems reduce flood risk ■ Holistic assessment tools (e.g. water cycle assessment)	Research: ■ Valuation of freshwater ecosystem services (ES) ■ Land-water interactions delivering ES ■ Monitoring of climate change impacts ■ Linkages between ecosystem functioning and services, and connectivity between water bodies
Legislation	■ Command and control regulations (e.g. IPPC Directive) ■ Designated areas (e.g. SACs, SSSIs, Nitrate Vulnerable Zones)	■ Water Framework Directive ■ Floods Directive ■ National flood and water legislation ■ Water Protection Zones	
Policies, institutions and governance	■ Top-down, sectoral water management ■ Decide-announce-defend decision-making ■ Engineered flood defences ■ Resource development (e.g. reservoirs) and demand management	■ Integrated Water Resources Management ■ Catchment management (land and water), e.g. by water companies ■ Stakeholder engagement ■ Third sector led schemes (e.g. River Trusts) ■ Flood risk management, including ecosystem-based approaches	■ Ecosystem services approach ■ Management responsibilities devolved to local and regional authorities and actors ■ Collaborative approaches ■ Engage-deliberate-decide decision-making ■ Support of local schemes by regional and national policy and funding, and catchment-scale coordination
Changing social attitudes	■ Water saving initiatives ■ Land manager education & awareness raising programmes	■ Flood risk awareness raising	■ Social learning in river basin management
Markets and incentives	■ Water fees ■ Water metering ■ Abstraction license trading	■ Payments for ecosystem services (e.g. through agri-environment schemes to reduce flood risk)	■ Disincentives to discourage land-use which increases evapotranspiration and decreases infiltration in water stressed regions ■ Universal water metering
Technologies and practices	■ Wastewater treatment and water re-use technologies ■ Reducing leakage from water supply system ■ Ecosystem restoration (e.g. rivers, wetlands)	■ Ecosystem restoration designed to deliver multiple ecosystem services ■ Buffer zones to provide multiple ecosystem services	
Voluntary actions	■ Rivers Trusts and voluntary activity ■ Volunteer conservation organisations buying and restoring important freshwater habitat sites		■ Volunteers integrally involved in catchment decision making and restoration activities (e.g. Rivercare, Australia)

emissions. As evidenced in this section, however, some responses have led to a reduction, or even a reversal, in the deterioration of ecosystem services associated with agricultural landscapes (Chapter 7).

Agriculture also benefits from ecosystem service flows from nature. It relies on supporting services such as soil structure and fertility, nutrient cycling, water cycling and genetic biodiversity used in the improved breeding of crops and livestock. Pollinators visiting from adjacent unmanaged land can increase yields, while wild species can control pests (Chapter 14). Ecosystems can also purify and regulate the supply of inflowing water, improving plant growth (Power 2010).

Public access to agricultural landscapes offers opportunities for education and recreation, including exercise and relaxation that can support healthy lifestyles (Section 27.8). Farmers can manage the land to better conserve and enhance biodiversity and landscapes, which can attract tourism and, therefore, provide a source of income for rural economies. Promising evidence considered in this chapter suggests that agriculture can also reverse the negative ecosystem trends associated with its activities and enhance a suite of other benefits as well, such as food, energy, climate change mitigation, flood regulation, wild species diversity and water purification. Occupying almost 74% of the terrestrial UK (Foresight 2010), agriculture defines how the majority of land is managed and, thus, the range of ecosystem services provided to the public (**Box 27.12**). Therefore, the decisions taken by the sector in the coming

> **Box 27.12 Ecosystem services and public goods.**
> Source: ENRD (2010).
>
> Pubic goods refer to a range of goods, services and other matters of societal interest that are typically not delivered through the market. Public goods include environmental goods, such as biodiversity or cultural landscapes, which are termed ecosystem services in the UK NEA. Please refer to literature from the European Network for Rural Development for further discussion of public goods in the agricultural context.

years are not only important for food security, but for many other socially and economically important objectives, too.

Figure 27.15 summarises the key drivers impacting on the agricultural sector and related ecosystem services. The sector has a significant influence on, and is influenced by, the other sectors discussed in this chapter. Readers are especially advised to read the water (Section 27.3), biodiversity (Section 27.2) and recreation and tourism (Section 27.8) sectors, in addition to the integrated responses section (Section 27.10), to gain a wider perspective. Biocrops are discussed in more detail under energy (Section 27.9) and forestry (Section 27.5).

27.4.2 Challenges for Agriculture

Global demand for food and other agricultural products, including biofuels, is expected to increase substantially over the next 50 years due to population growth, changing diets and government policy (Chapter 3). World market prices for agricultural commodities influence land use and practices, and largely determine the income of farms. Agriculture in the UK is, therefore, highly sensitive to world market volatility (Foresight 2010). Globally and nationally there are also growing concerns about food and energy security. At the same time, climate change and natural resource limitations will require more food to be produced sustainably.

The public value of non-production ecosystem services provided by agriculture is increasingly reflected in legislation, markets and subsidies, both nationally and internationally. The Foresight Land Use Futures report (Foresight 2010) estimates that the value of these services is about £1.74 billion per year, whereas the impact agriculture has on ecosystem services is as much as £2.57 billion—a net cost to the UK of about £830 million per year. Although these figures need to be treated with caution, it asks whether this balance could be turned around, with agriculture becoming a net contributor of environmental value.

Demand for agricultural land is not uniform across the four countries of the UK; demand from other land uses has decreased the area of farmland in England (Angus *et al.* 2009), while remote grazing areas in Scotland are experiencing depopulation with implications for the maintenance of agri-

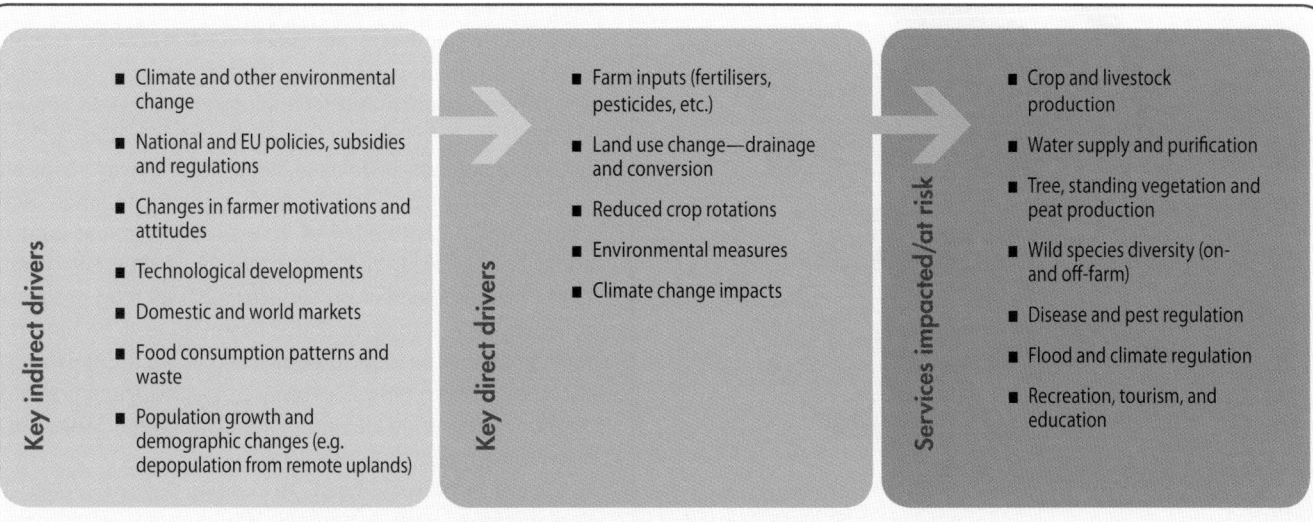

Figure 27.15 Key indirect and direct drivers relevant to the agricultural sector, and the ecosystem services at risk.

landscapes (SAC 2008; **Figure 27.16**). Pressure on essential inputs of water, energy and nutrients is intensifying, and the costs of such inputs is rising; to increase productivity, farmers will need to reduce waste, use precision application of chemicals and use water more efficiently (Foresight 2010). Climate change further complicates the sector's outlook and may increase risk to ecosystem service delivery. Moreover, the loss of productive land in other parts of the world due to climate change is likely to increase pressure on food production in the UK. The agricultural sector will also be asked more and more to play its part in climate change mitigation efforts. The UK NEA Economic valuation found that the loss in carbon storage on Enclosed Farmlands since 2004 will come at a cost of £600 per capita every year under a United Kingdom Climate Impacts Programme (UKCIP) high carbon emissions scenario for 2050 (Chapter 22).

The challenges for agriculture are therefore great: farmers must produce more food and energy with fewer inputs (energy, nutrients and water), and they must be productive in the provision of other ecosystem services, while becoming more resilient to climate change and world market volatility. A further major challenge is managing trade-offs between food production and environmental goals to optimise the provision of multiple ecosystem services for both public and private good.

27.4.3 Agricultural-related Response Options

27.4.3.1 Knowledge (foundational)

The monitoring of biodiversity, water and soil quality, and a body of academic studies in multiple disciplines, have revealed the dramatic declines in environmental quality resulting from the intensification, mechanisation and specialisation of agriculture since the Second World War (WWII). Responding to this knowledge (and public sentiment), agricultural policy has provided increasing protection to the environment, reflected in reforms to the CAP and the establishment of agri-environment schemes.

In the past, research developments have contributed to the political debate on various farming technologies. For example, the toxicity of organochloride and organophosphate insecticides to humans and wildlife was publicly revealed in the book *Silent Spring* by Carson (1962), and following further investigation, several harmful pesticides are now controlled in the UK under the Food and Environmental Protection Act (FEPA 1985—as amended) and the Control of Pesticides Regulations (COPR 1986).

In the near future, the agricultural sector is set to change in response to advances in climate science that have predicted significant environmental changes in the UK and globally. The work of the UKCIP has revealed a number of ways that climate change will impact agriculture, including greater pressure on water supplies, and changes to the growing season and types of diseases and pests (Section 7.2.2.1). Tools and guidance based on this science are being developed to help farmers adapt to future climate change (UKCIP 2011). Research organisations and agro-technology industries will also play a role in finding climate change adaptation solutions. The development of resilient crop varieties, for example, seeks to develop plant types that are productive under environmental stresses imposed by climate change. Furthermore, knowledge of the greenhouse gas contribution from agriculture (7% of the UK's total emissions; DECC 2009) and the potential for reducing emissions has resulted in concerted efforts from government and the industry to integrate climate change mitigation into farming practices (Section 27.4.3.3).

Despite significant advances, new research, spanning several disciplines, needs to further develop agricultural knowledge, science and technology to meet this century's challenges for farming. Spatial optimisation of land management has been suggested as one way to provide multiple ecosystem services from agricultural lands. Better understanding is needed of how such integrated land use could be achieved, and of the impact of different types of land use management on services such as food production (Chapter 7). A strong evidence base will also be important for supporting the food strategies of the four administrations (Scottish Government 2009b). A cross-government strategy for Food Research and Innovation has been launched to coordinate research in this area.

Decision-makers need to know how to meet the demand for ecosystem services in a changing environment. Understanding how to create resilient agro-ecosystems will be important for coping with climate shocks and market

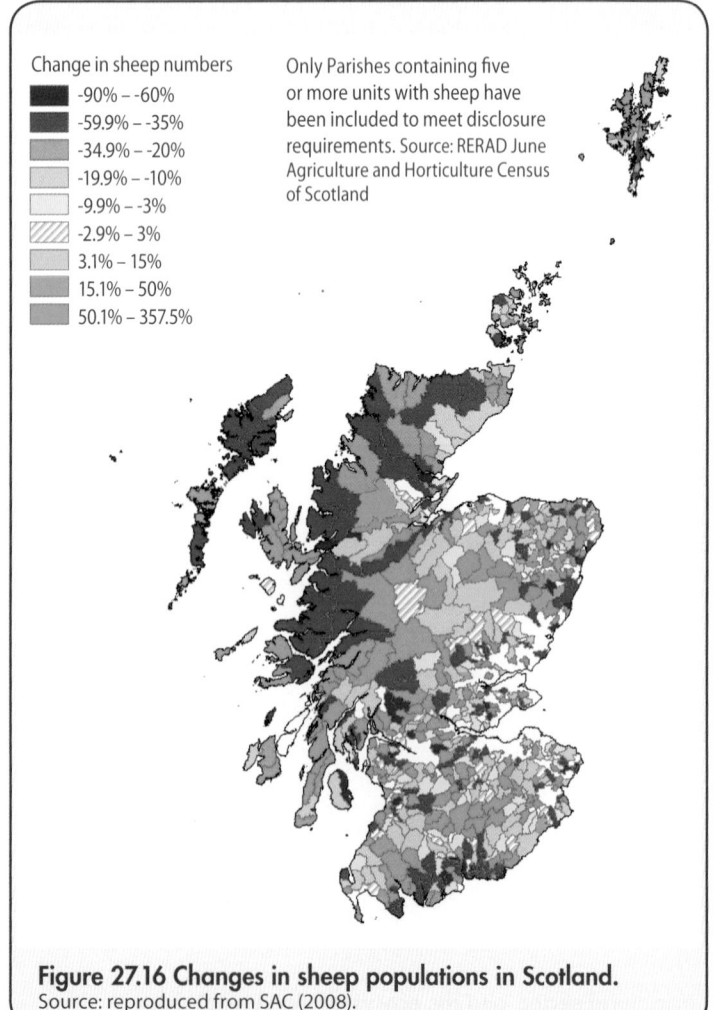

Change in sheep numbers
- -90% – -60%
- -59.9% – -35%
- -34.9% – -20%
- -19.9% – -10%
- -9.9% – -3%
- -2.9% – 3%
- 3.1% – 15%
- 15.1% – 50%
- 50.1% – 357.5%

Only Parishes containing five or more units with sheep have been included to meet disclosure requirements. Source: RERAD June Agriculture and Horticulture Census of Scotland

Figure 27.16 Changes in sheep populations in Scotland.
Source: reproduced from SAC (2008).

volatility. This may include research on farm- and catchment-scale systems, including the social and economic context of farmers and how they will deliver ecosystem services.

Knowing how to respond to likely cost increases of nitrogen inputs and potential shortages of phosphorus will be important. Food 2030 (Defra 2010e) highlighted the need to develop crop varieties that require fewer chemical inputs, but still meet consumer demands and agri-environment goals. Such research should consider the value of, and impact on, agricultural biodiversity and relatives of the crop in the wild.

Given the multifaceted influence of agricultural management on ecosystem services and human well-being, further investment in science, technology and skills is necessary to maximise the benefits from agricultural landscapes. The development of knowledge networks and collaborative mechanisms between public, private and non-governmental stakeholders will aid this process. Collaboration between researchers and the agricultural industry can identify the challenges that need to be understood (Defra 2010e), and better incorporation of farmers' local knowledge could improve the design and delivery of agri-environment initiatives.

A new Sustainable Agriculture and Food Innovation Platform, led by the Technology Strategy Board, was established with funding from the Department for Environment, Food and Rural Affairs and the Biotechnology and Biological Sciences Research Council (BBSRC) of £90 million over five years. The platform aims to support innovative technological research and development in areas such as crop productivity, sustainable livestock production, waste reduction and management, and greenhouse gas reduction (Defra 2010e).

27.4.3.2 Legislation (enabling)

Agriculture is affected by a large number of different pieces of legislation at EU, national and devolved level. The summary below focuses on the CAP as an example of legislation governing farming practice. Some other pieces of legislation relevant to farming in the UK, such as the WFD, Nitrates Directive, and Habitats and Birds Directives, are discussed in the Water and Biodiversity sections of this chapter.

The CAP embodies a raft of legislation governing the application of the EU's system of agricultural subsidies which currently account for over 40% of the total EU budget. The CAP has evolved over the years from its roots as a post-war food security policy towards a gradually increasing emphasis on rural development and environmental protection. Most recently, significant reforms took place in 2003, followed by a number of further amendments via the CAP Health Check in 2008. Further large-scale reforms will be developed in time for implementation in the next EU budgetary period, 2014 to 2020. The EC has begun developing proposals for the new legislation, and will issue more details during 2011 (EC 2010c).

The CAP is implemented separately by England, Scotland, Wales and Northern Ireland, so different sets of regulations exist and different agencies are responsible for allocating the payments and enforcing the rules in each jurisdiction.

In its current form, the CAP is organised into two 'Pillars'. Pillar 1 contains rules allocating around two thirds of the total subsidy amount in the form of direct payments to farmers. This system is known as the Single Farm Payment Scheme. The origins of Pillar 1 payments are production-linked subsidies of the early CAP, which largely took the form of guaranteed prices: the more farmers produced, the more subsidy they received. Following the 2003 reforms, payments are no longer directly 'coupled' to production in this manner for the majority of agricultural products, although some direct production-linked elements remain, as do a limited number of price intervention mechanisms. The goal is for production linkages to be phased out completely by 2012 (although Scotland will retain some production-linked payments through the Scottish Beef Calf Scheme). However, it is crucial to note that the allocation of the Single Farm Payment currently still reflects the historical, production-linked position, which means it is biased towards large, high intensity farms.

The Single Farm Payment is linked to a system called 'cross compliance'. This means that there is a set of standards concerned with food safety, environmental management and animal welfare which farmers must comply with as a condition of receiving their subsidy. Some of these cross compliance standards are obligations of existing EU legislation. These are known as the Statutory Management Requirements. Further standards have been introduced explicitly through the cross compliance scheme; these are known as Good Agricultural and Environmental Condition (GAEC) standards and are set broadly by the EU legislation and defined in more detail at national or regional level. For example, the Department for Environment, Food and Rural Affairs has implemented a GAEC requirement for soil protection by requiring farmers to complete an annual Soil Protection Review. Cross compliance is intended to promote sustainable agriculture, while lending legitimacy to the direct payment system by making it conditional on farmers complying with basic rules, including for environmental protection (CEC 2007).

Pillar 2 refers to the second main financial instrument of the CAP, accounting for approximately one third of the budget. This is the European Agricultural Fund for Rural Development. The overarching rules are set out in the Rural Development Regulation (1698/2005 as amended) and supplemented by Commission Regulations 1974/2006 and 1975/2006, dealing with further details of how the scheme should be implemented and enforced. Under this regime, payments may be targeted at specific types of action, which are categorised under three headings: Axis 1, improving competitiveness in the agriculture and forestry sectors; Axis 2, improving the environment ('agri-environment'); and Axis 3, improving quality of life and diversification for rural communities. These payments are designed to compensate farmers for additional costs and income foregone through undertaking the environmental improvement measures. In the UK, for the 2007 to 2013 EU budgetary period, approximately 80% of Pillar 2 money is allocated under Axis 2 (Defra 2009d).

In England, Axis 2 subsidies take the form of Environmental Stewardship schemes, administered by Natural England and the Rural Payments Agency. There currently include the Entry Level Stewardship (ELS) and

Higher Level Stewardship (HLS) schemes, plus particular schemes for organic and uplands farming. Both ELS and HLS involve environmental obligations going beyond the baseline standards set by cross compliance. Entry Level Stewardship payments are allocated per hectare of land, and farmers must apply particular land management actions to the area covered. A range of management options is available, and points are awarded for each action undertaken, building up to a points target. The options include the protection of in-field trees, the management of hedgerows, maintaining buffer zones, and providing in-field grass areas to prevent soil erosion and runoff. Higher Level Stewardship schemes involve tailored management agreements undertaken over ten-year periods and intended to address specific local targets.

In Scotland, previous agri-environment schemes have been incorporated into the Scotland Rural Development Programme, which also contains schemes for forestry, rural enterprise and business development. All support provided through Pillar 2 of the CAP (i.e. Axis 1, 2 and 3) in Scotland is managed through the programme, and priorities for achieving national outcomes are set by stakeholders at a regional level. More details of the operation of agri-environment schemes in each of the UK jurisdictions are given under Markets and Incentives (Section 27.4.3.5).

In terms of their effects on ecosystem services, the production-linked subsidies of the CAP (still reflected in the current direct payments system) were aimed at dramatically increasing provisioning services by encouraging high intensity, monocultural production, with high inputs of energy, water and chemicals. But these subsidies had unintended consequences for regulating, supporting and cultural services. The intensification of agriculture, promoted by the CAP (Baldock *et al.* 2002; EEA 2009), has correlated strongly with a substantial decline in farmland biodiversity (BirdLife International n.d.; Donald *et al.* 2006). Although some biodiversity declines have levelled off more recently, the CAP has not yet changed enough to protect against further losses (Biala *et al.* 2010). Supporting services reliant on biodiversity, such as invertebrate pollination, biological pest control and soil nutrient cycling, continue to be at risk as a result. Favouring large-scale and intensive farming practices in subsidy allocation (EEA 2009) has also led to the loss of valued landscapes (Ellison 2001) and countryside features, and fails to account for the role farming can play in maintaining the countryside for the provision of cultural ecosystem services (CPRE & NFU 2006).

A major challenge for the latest reform round will be how to design a CAP capable of supporting a much wider range of public goods provision including soil functionality, water quality, carbon sequestration, flood resilience, biodiversity and landscape goals (Cooper *et al.* 2009). Cross compliance and agri-environment schemes have aimed to tackle this objective, but various features of the way the current legal framework is structured continue to stand in the way. Three examples of these weaknesses are as follows:

1. *Lack of efficacy of cross compliance penalties.* Cross compliance is intended to form a baseline standard for good environmental practice, animal welfare and public, plant and animal health in agriculture. However,

significant problems with enforcing the system mean that it fails to fully meet its environmental objectives (CEC 2007; European Court of Auditors 2008; Boccaccio *et al.* 2009b). Environmental cross compliance obligations are, in many cases, vaguely worded and difficult to check, varying in stringency across different regions. The legal requirement for the frequency of farm inspections is very low. In addition, the main sanction for a breach of cross compliance rules is a percentage reduction in the amount of subsidy payment, up to a maximum of 5%. The European Court of Auditors has criticised the fact that the size of the subsidy, rather than the severity of the breach, may be the main factor determining the penalty, with the outcome that a big polluter receiving low subsidies may pay a low fine, while a small polluter receiving larger payments pays more. Overall, the likelihood and size of the sanction may be offset by the gain to be made from committing the breach, such as benefiting from high prices gained from the extra productivity (*ibid.*). In addition, the system has been criticised for effectively turning a set of mandatory legal obligations into a voluntary arrangement (Boccaccio *et al.* 2009b). The Statutory Management Requirements of cross compliance are all pre-existing legal rules which must be complied with in any event, not simply to avoid a reduction in subsidy.

2. *Non-inclusion of certain important environmental standards in cross compliance.* Simplification of cross compliance during the 2008 Health Check led to mixed outcomes, including the removal of certain items considered by some stakeholders (such as the RSPB and the Institute of European Environmental Policy) to be of crucial importance for sound environmental management (IEEP 2008a; Boccaccio *et al.* 2009b). Of particular concern was the removal of certain biodiversity protections, like Article 8 of the Birds Directive and Article 15 of the Habitats Directive, which prohibit indiscriminate methods of killing birds and other animals (such as using poisoned bait and traps). The EC believed that these standards were not relevant in an agricultural context (EC 2009b). Conservationists believe that a broader vision of rural land management is necessary, bearing in mind the overlapping uses of land for agricultural and other purposes such as recreational hunting and fishing (Boccaccio *et al.* 2009, p.19, 21).

3. *Implementation of Axis 2 measures.* Generally, the fact that Axis 2 payments are, according to the legislation, compensation for income foregone rather than incentives, is seen as a constraint on the ability of scheme organisers to set up dynamic and ambitious environmental stewardship programmes (Defra 2008b). In addition, the organisation of ELS schemes makes it difficult to encourage ambitious environmental outcomes. From the range of management options available, the least onerous or most affordable measures may be chosen. While this system may have encouraged greater uptake of the scheme by farmers, environmental NGOS have voiced concern that there are insufficient mechanisms to make sure that more complex measures, with as much or more ecological significance, are not neglected (Boccaccio *et al.* 2009a). A recent study tracking 70 Scottish farms over seven years has indicated the added benefits to be gained from properly targeted agri-environment measures over more generic management options (Perkins *et al.* 2011). Rural Priority Setting by the Scottish Government is an example of a system designed to help ensure that Axis 2 CAP payments are aligned with regional conservation priorities: payments are awarded to those applicants whose management proposals fit best with delivering the priority outcomes for their region.

A further weakness is that the consideration of conflicts is not built into the legal framework. This means there is potential for conflicts to arise between payments for environmentally sensitive farming, and farm modernisation measures that have adverse effects on habitats and biodiversity such as infrastructure installations. Clearer mechanisms for identifying positive links between environmental protection actions and economic development outcomes could be considered in future CAP reform.

In November 2010, the EC released a communication setting out its high level proposals for the next round of CAP reform (EC 2010c). The Commission envisages three main objectives for the future CAP: viable food production; sustainable management of natural resources and climate action; and balanced territorial development. The proposals maintain the two Pillar structure, noting that Pillar 1 payments must become 'greener' and more equitably distributed. Linking payments to actions involving permanent pasture, green cover, crop rotation and ecological set-aside are specifically mentioned. With regard to environmental measures under Pillar 2, the communication states that these "should be more closely tailored to the specific needs of regions and even local areas such as Natura 2000 and [High Nature Value] areas"; however, the detail of the framework will be crucial and remains an open question. It is not yet resolved whether the new legislation will be an adjustment or a far-reaching reform with a strong focus on environment and climate change objectives.

Conservation groups have welcomed the proposals for the greening of Pillar 1 and the recognition that both an enhanced cross compliance baseline and incentive payments for ecosystem protection will have a role to play. Nevertheless, there is strong criticism of the proposal for its failure to recognise the importance of agri-environment schemes (IEEP 2010). The UK Government has called on the EU to be more ambitious in its plans, and has emphasised the importance of maximising the scope of Pillar 2 to reward farmers for the provision of public goods (Defra 2011).

Robust environmental protection rules under a reformed CAP will be vital to the success of the Birds and Habitats Directives. A large proportion of Natura 2000 sites are on farmland, and extensive agricultural practices (e.g. low impact grazing and sustainable forestry) are essential to Natura site management. Clearly, environmentally damaging agricultural practices would breach the Habitats and Birds Directives provisions. The wider impact of agriculture generally on Natura 2000 sites, for instance through diffuse pollution effects, must also be considered. The EC has emphasised that "Natura 2000 and the conservation of threatened species will not be viable in the long term without a wider terrestrial, freshwater and marine environment favourable to biodiversity" (CEC 2006).

The Nitrates Directive and the WFD (Section 27.2.3.2) are also important areas of legislation which seek to influence the way agricultural practice impacts on other sectors, in this case affecting the health of inland and coastal water systems. Diffuse pollution from agricultural land, particularly from nitrates, remains one of the major pressures on aquatic systems (EEA 2010); hence, robust monitoring of pollution control requirements under the CAP and the Nitrates Directive are essential to the success of the WFD.

27.4.3.3 Policies, institutions and governance (enabling)

In the mid-1970s, food self-sufficiency was the prevailing agricultural policy, which resulted in food provisioning services being maximised, with unintended negative consequences for other ecosystem services. Today, none of the UK governments and assemblies have targets for national self-sufficiency. Instead, the UK's Food 2030 Strategy (Defra 2010e), for example, seeks to achieve food security through "strong UK agriculture and international trade links with EU and global partners".

As self-sufficiency priorities have given way to international markets, subsidies have been rolled back from supporting food production, and have moved towards protecting the environment. This is evident in CAP reforms and European Directives, such as the WFD, as well as in the extensive enrolment of farmers in agri-environment schemes (Section 27.4.3.2; 27.4.3.5). Agri-environment schemes have been an effective means of widening the remit of rural land management to protect the environment, and their further development is likely to be an important mechanism for policy makers to bring about real change.

Under the schemes, land managers are currently rewarded with annual payments for adopting management practices which protect soils and water, and maintain or enhance biodiversity. These practices can protect some of the services provided by farmland that currently do not have a market value by compensating farmers for the opportunity costs. A policy direction that is receiving growing support (e.g. in the Foresight Report, Foresight 2010) proposes a more integrative view of land planning where the value of non-production public goods are considered and land managers are rewarded for managing them. To achieve this integrated approach, the Rural Economy and Land Use Programme (RELU 2010a) recommend the adoption of an ecosystem service approach to agri-environment policy (**Box 27.13**)

Deliberately managing a more diverse range of ecosystem services from agricultural land will inevitably require trade-offs to be made, but there are also likely to be opportunities for management options to conserve or enhance more than one service. The key trade-off in agriculture is between increased food and energy production, and regulatory and cultural services. For instance, habitat and species diversity normally declines with increases in agricultural production, although environmental management practices are available that can minimise the impact on biodiversity without negatively affecting production. Further examples include food competing for land with bioenergy (Section 27.9.2), and changes to livestock management to reduce greenhouse gas emissions impacting livestock managed habitats (Defra 2010e). Food security, climate change mitigation and the implementation of the WFD are current policy priorities, and may determine which ecosystem services are prioritised, with the risk of conservation becoming "marginalised as an 'added value' element of multi-objective landscapes" (Bradbury *et al.* 2010).

New research, however, is revealing opportunities for win-win policies and demonstrating that trade-offs between agricultural production and regulatory and cultural services are not always necessary. The appropriate management of ecosystems that provide services to agriculture can increase production as a result of enhanced pollination, pest control, soil fertility and retention, and regulation of nutrient cycling (Power 2010). Badgley *et al.* (2007) analysed yields from agro-ecosystems from around the world and found that agricultural systems that use measures that protect ecosystem services (e.g. minimum tillage, grassland management, biological control and less agrochemical inputs) perform as well as intensive, high input systems. In the UK, farmers have managed to increase yields since the 1990s, while reducing greenhouse gas emissions and inputs of artificial fertilisers. For example, potato yields have increased by 18%, sugar beet by 45% and wheat yields by 8%, while the application of fertiliser has decreased by up to 52% between 1990 and 2007, and total greenhouse gas emissions have fallen by 20% (although this is largely due to a reduction in livestock numbers) (Defra 2010e). However, more research is needed to identify beneficial synergies (Chapter 7).

Low intensity agricultural landscapes, where food production is limited by environmental conditions, may prove easier areas in which to establish win-win management that provides multiple environmental public goods (Bradbury *et al.* 2010). Livestock-grazing managed by many generations of farmers has played a fundamental role in shaping the aesthetics and culture of the UK's countryside. The provision of ecosystem services from moors, heathlands and grasses are typically dependent on the continuation of low intensity livestock grazing systems (Section 5.1.3). But livestock numbers are decreasing in many upland areas (SAC 2008), which may have negative impacts for some of these services. The High Nature Value (HNV) farming concept recognises the nature conservation value of such landscapes, which the EC

hopes to protect through the Rural Development Programmes (**Box 27.14**). While there may be some benefits of destocking to revegetate bare or eroding peats to enhance carbon storage, a substantial decline in sheep population in the uplands could have unexpected consequences (Section 5.2.1). It may be necessary to consider how sufficient stocking densities can be maintained to ensure current upland landscapes and their ecosystem services are retained. Chapter 5 discusses options for the sustainable management of these uplands in more detail, and recommends that management of Mountains, Moorlands and Heaths should be sufficiently flexible to allow adaptation to uncertain changes in condition.

When considering how to optimise the delivery of ecosystem services from farmland, scale is important, both spatially and temporally. Win-win measures, as described above, often take time before benefits to production are realised, and the short-term provision of one service can affect its provision and other services in the future (Power 2010). Policy makers should also consider the scale of implementation that is required for a measure to achieve its objective (Bradbury *et al.* 2010). For example, the control of arable weeds requires management at the field-scale, farmland birds need a mixture of habitat at the landscape-scale, and water quality is likely to be best considered at the catchment-scale. Moreover, climate change adaptations that increase the resilience of farmland habitats may need regional-scale strategies, and planning for carbon sinks, a national-level strategy (RELU 2010a). This suggests that there is no one scale that agri-environment policy should be implemented at, and that schemes need to target appropriate scales or risk being ineffective. RELU (2010a) recommend designing agri-environment schemes that can be applied at multiple scales to maximise their impact. In the case of mobile species, such as butterflies and birds, schemes would go beyond actions at the farm-scale, requiring multiple farmers to collaborate to achieve landscape-scale benefits. Section 27.10.5 discusses incentive options for encouraging collaboration between farmers.

Current agricultural governance arrangements are unlikely to be appropriate for managing these multi-scale issues, especially at landscape- and catchment-scales, or delivering ecosystem services cost-effectively (Chapter 7). The Foresight Land Futures report (Foresight 2010) described policy pertaining to agriculture as fragmented and sometimes conflicting, and recommends the development of new governance structures to reward farmers for providing ecosystem services. Greater stakeholder engagement is likely to be critical in a governance structure that adopts the ecosystem services approach to land management. Involving stakeholders can help to understand who benefits and loses from policies, and can strengthen and validate the setting of priorities, values and the fair management of agri-ecosystems. RELU (2010a) suggest that policies designed to enhance a wider range of ecosystem services from a given area of land will only be successful if they manage these distributional aspects. Involving stakeholders, especially farmers, in the design of agri-environment schemes at a local scale, such as a catchment or landscape, from the outset and through continued engagement may encourage greater local ownership (RELU 2010a). Readers are strongly

Box 27.14 The High Nature Value (HNV) of Scottish farming systems.
Source: McCracken (2009).

The HNV farming concept recognises that many European habitats and landscapes considered to be of high value for nature conservation are dependent on the continuation of specific low intensity farming systems such as those found on the islands, and in the hills and uplands of Scotland (**Figure 27.17**). These farming systems are becoming economically unviable due to market, policy and social pressures; for example, Europe-wide changes to the CAP reduced support for low intensity farming activity in Scotland. The abandonment of these farms would change the nature conservation value of these landscapes.

The HNV concept has been adopted by the EC, requiring Member States to ensure that Axis 2 (environmental improvements) of their Rural Development Programmes is targeted at "biodiversity and preservation of high nature value farming and forestry systems, water and climate change". The implementation of HNV through Scotland's Rural Development Programme will provide financial support for low intensity farming that maintains HNV. Scottish Natural Heritage is currently establishing a baseline of how much and where HNV farming occurs in Scotland. McCracken (2009) suggests there is also a need to consider what support mechanisms are most appropriate and what policy framework is needed to ensure that support can be implemented effectively.

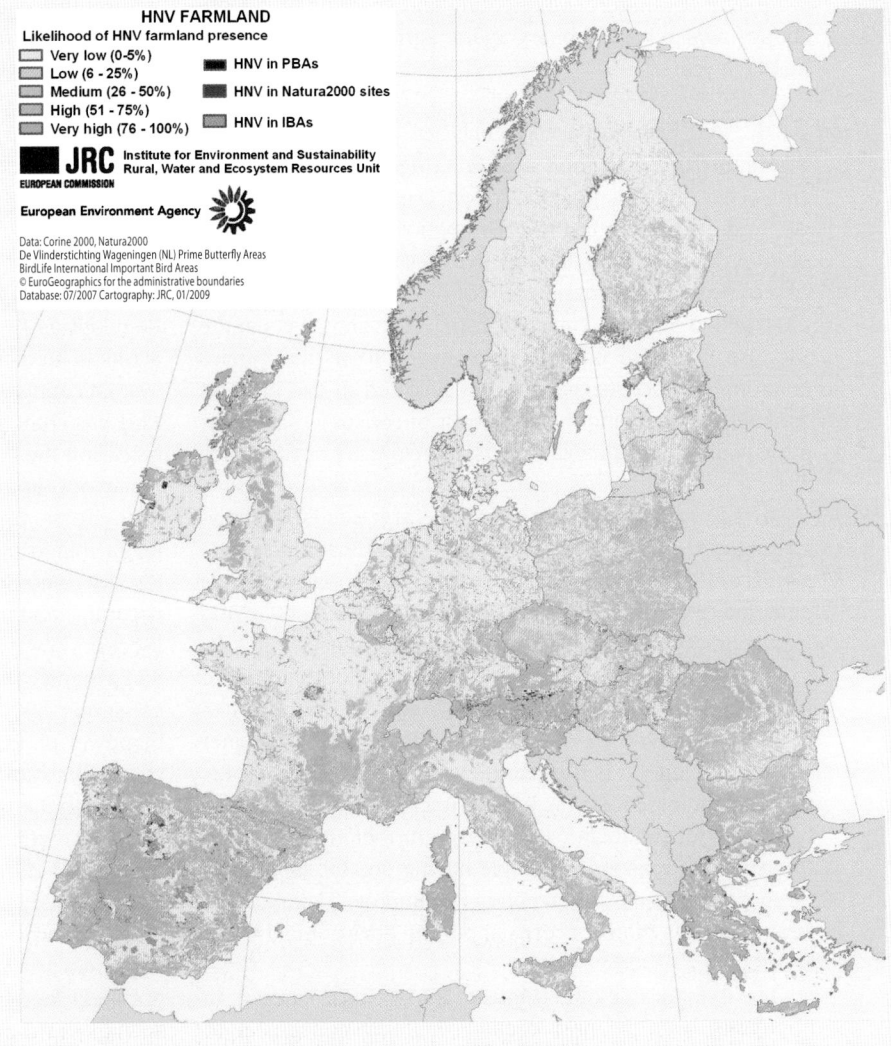

HNV FARMLAND

Likelihood of HNV farmland presence

- ☐ Very low (0-5%)
- ☐ Low (6 - 25%)
- ☐ Medium (26 - 50%)
- ☐ High (51 - 75%)
- ☐ Very high (76 - 100%)
- ■ HNV in PBAs
- ■ HNV in Natura2000 sites
- ■ HNV in IBAs

JRC EUROPEAN COMMISSION — Institute for Environment and Sustainability Rural, Water and Ecosystem Resources Unit

European Environment Agency

Data: Corine 2000, Natura2000
De Vlinderstichting Wageningen (NL) Prime Butterfly Areas
BirdLife International Important Bird Areas
© EuroGeographics for the administrative boundaries
Database: 07/2007 Cartography: JRC, 01/2009

Figure 27.17 Map of potential High Nature Value (HNV) areas in Europe.
Source: KnowledgeScotland.org.

advised to examine lessons on engagement identified during the RELU projects (RELU 2010a).

It may even be necessary to look beyond agricultural management to think more holistically about all land uses—the spatial optimisation of land management may be more effective at delivering a greater range of ecosystem services. Scotland's A Forward Strategy for Scottish Agriculture aims to "promote an integrated, landscape-scale approach to environmental improvement". The Scottish Government is also developing their first national Land Use Strategy to guide an integrated approach to land use management (Section 27.10.3, **Box 27.51**).

Future challenges due to environmental change are likely to demand landscape-level responses. **Box 27.15** discusses

Box 27.15 Agricultural policy and climate change.

Climate change has emerged as a major issue for the agricultural sector both in terms of adaptation and mitigation, with a number of important government policies driving responses. Agriculture can reduce its emissions of greenhouse gases by changing practices, storing carbon within agri-ecosystems, and also through the production of bioenergy (where energy input is less than energy produced).

Each of the Devolved Administrations has produced an action plan for tackling greenhouse gas emissions from agriculture. The UK Low Carbon Transition Plan resulted in the industry-led development of the Agriculture Industry Greenhouse Gas Action Plan 2010, whereby English farmers have agreed to reduce their collective emissions by 3 million tonnes carbon dioxide equivalent by 2020, from a level of 44 million tonnes carbon dioxide equivalent in 2008. The Land Use Climate Change Group (2010) reported to the Welsh Assembly in March 2010. Its key suggestions for reducing emissions from agriculture are: the introduction of anaerobic digestion to reduce methane emissions; improving farm productivity; using manure, fertilisers and energy more efficiently; the expansion of woodlands; and the development of renewable energy sources.

Existing agri-environment policies have already made a contribution to climate change mitigation and have the potential to be targeted more effectively. According to the Department for Environment, Food and Rural Affairs (Defra 2007b), the Environmental Stewardship scheme (Section 27.4.3.5) saves an estimated 3.46 million tonnes of carbon dioxide per year, and emissions from agriculture would be 11% higher without it. The value of these savings has been estimated at between £600 million and £1.8 billion.

the role of agriculture in mitigating and adapting to climate change, which has become a major agricultural policy area in recent years.

27.4.3.4 Changing social attitudes (enabling)

Public attitudes to food and farming. Overconsumption and obesity are major health concerns and costs in the UK, and are related to the consumption of unhealthy (and often processed) food and inactive lifestyles. The economic cost of people being overweight or obese is estimated to be £49.9 billion by 2050 (Foresight 2007). Prevailing diets in the UK also comprise intensively produced food that carries environmental costs that are not reflected in the price to consumers. Changing the behaviour of consumers towards more healthy, sustainable diets is, therefore, a priority policy area.

In contrast to these general dietary trends, demand for organic and ethically produced food has increased significantly, and an interest in local, seasonal food has emerged (**Figure 27.18**). The number of consumers buying locally produced food has almost doubled from 15% in 2006 to 27% in 2009, while those buying organic food increased from 12% to 24% between 2006 and 2008, but fell back to 19% in 2009 (Defra 2009e). The recent dip in demand for higher value organic food is likely to be a response by consumers to the economic recession, but it is unclear whether demand has reached a plateau or will grow further in the future. However, the reasons for people buying organic foods may be more the result of perceptions of improved quality and health benefits than concerns about the environment (Wier *et al.* 2008).

Local food markets (**Figure 27.19**) have grown in popularity over the past decade, enabling consumers to interact with producers and better understand where their food is grown and by whom. Moreover, an increasing number of households are growing their own food in their gardens and at allotments: an activity that can have a number of benefits for mental and physical health, and community cohesion. Novel community food projects are also appearing across the country, with the potential to increase food produced in urban areas. Supermarkets have played a role in enabling products with an added environmental value to reach a wider consumer base than that of local markets by stocking them in their extensive network of retail outlets and promoting them widely (Chapter 7). The purchasing power of supermarkets has been a driver of change throughout the food chain.

In addition to government support for the conversion of agricultural land to organics (e.g. Organic Farming (Aid) Regulations 1994), the rise in demand for 'ethical' foods has acted as an incentive for farmers to convert land to organic systems and adopt more environmentally friendly practices. This has changed the environmental impact of these farms, reflecting the power of consumers to alter markets, farmer behaviour and, ultimately, the impact of agriculture on ecosystems. Organic farming, for instance, can be beneficial for farmland biodiversity (Hole *et al.* 2005), long-term soil fertility (Watson *et al.* 2002), and tends to have more semi-natural habitats capable of providing multiple benefits (Section 27.4.3.6). Concerns over intensive agriculture have had a significant influence on policy as well as markets, and consumer resistance to new agricultural technologies can be powerful. Public objections to genetically modified (GM) crops, for example, have prevented them being commercially planted in the UK to date (Section 27.4.3.6).

The certification of food that meets standards of production allows consumers to feel confident of the ethical claims made by the producer and retailer; this makes them more willing to pay the high prices the food commands. This is particularly true where the consumer and producer do not meet face-to-face (as is the case at farmers' markets), such as in supermarkets where the majority of organic food is purchased in the UK (Daugbjerg & Sønderskov 2009). Certification schemes also set criteria that can guide farmers to use best practice. In addition to organic certification that restricts the use of agrochemicals, farms that meet the Conservation Grade protect wildlife habitat, while Linking Environment and Farming (LEAF) promotes integrated and

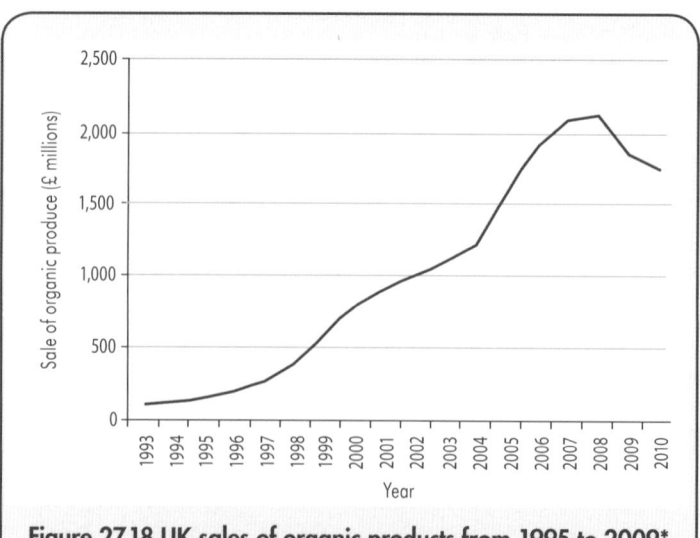

Figure 27.18 UK sales of organic products from 1995 to 2009*.
Source: reproduced from Soil Association (2010); www.soilassociation.org.
*Soil Association Organic Market Reports/Organic Food and Farming Reports 1999–2009.

Figure 27.19 Fresh vegetables at Borough Market, London. *Photo by Stacy Cashman at RamblingTraveler.com, available under a Creative Commons Attribution-ShareAlike license.*

UK National Ecosystem Assessment: Technical Report

precision crop management (Section 27.4.3.6). The Assured Foods Standards' Red Tractor scheme, which has over 78,000 members, brought together several food assurance schemes to set standards for food safety and hygiene, animal welfare and environmental protection. The scheme only restricts members to minimum standards for environmental protection due to concerns that stricter standards would harm the competitiveness of producers (Snowdon 2002). With the exception of the organic food label, studies have found that the range of eco-labelling logos and schemes often confuse consumers (Foresight 2011).

The Department for Environment, Food and Rural Affairs' Food Strategy (Defra 2010e) sets a vision for 2030: people are connected to their food and are more involved in cooking and growing healthy food; they understand the impacts of their diet on health, the environment and other people; and they minimise their waste. Changes to diets will have implications for the management of agricultural land. For instance, reduced demand for carbon-intensive produce, such as beef, lamb and dairy products, would lower the emissions from the agricultural sector (Sutherland *et al.* 2010). Some consumers are already concerned about the climate change impacts of their food (Defra 2010e).

Every year, 8.3 million tonnes of food and drink is wasted by UK households (65% of which is avoidable), representing 22% of all purchases by weight (WRAP 2009). This costs people in the UK £12 billion annually (**Figure 27.20**). Shifting behaviour further up the waste hierarchy towards the initial prevention of waste is the preferred response option (Defra 2010o); the use of campaigns and advice aimed at households is a particularly popular response (**Box 27.16**). In theory, reducing food waste should reduce food demand, and thus reduce pressure on agricultural land and create space for other land uses such as conservation and carbon sequestration. Given that food waste produces the greenhouse gas equivalent of 20 million tonnes of carbon dioxide every year (WRAP 2009), reducing it could also make a significant contribution to climate change mitigation. While households contribute over one half of the UK's food waste, food and drink is also wasted on farms, and during manufacture, distribution and retail (**Table 27.8**). Waste and Resources Action Programme (2010) estimate that the

diversion of food waste from landfill to animal feed could save a manufacturing company £85 per tonne, and £555 per tonne if they avoided the waste altogether (in terms of saved raw materials, energy and labour).

Farmer attitudes and values. The decisions farmers make can have a wide-ranging impact on ecosystem integrity both on- and off-farm. Understanding the motivations for their decisions and behaviour is, therefore, important for finding ways to move towards more sustainable agricultural systems (Feola & Binder 2010). A number of instruments can be employed to initiate behaviour change among farmers including regulatory and economic incentives and disincentives, provision of advice, and voluntary collective actions (Blackstock *et al.* 2010). Here, we discuss knowledge sharing networks and engagement of farmers in decision-making as a means to change behaviour.

A review of theoretical and applied evidence of farmer behaviour (Defra 2008e) found that the decisions made by individual farmers are shaped by their own specific contexts: not every farmer seeks to maximise

---

Box 27.16 Love Food Hate Waste—a campaign to reduce food waste. Source: www.lovefoodhatewaste.com; Defra (2010o).

Waste and Resources Action Programme (WRAP)'s Love Food Hate Waste campaign aims to raise awareness about the environmental and social costs of avoidable food waste and provide practical advice to households on how to reduce food waste. Research has shown that consumers are generally interested and willing to reduce their waste. The campaign highlights the benefits of reducing waste through positive messages that promote easy, practical changes to behaviour such as better planning of shopping and cooking. Information to help reduce food waste, such as recipes for leftovers and guidance on storage, is provided on a website and through local roadshows which visit supermarkets, businesses and community groups. WRAP also hope that the campaign will contribute towards reducing carbon dioxide emissions from the production and disposal of wasted food.

Table 27.8 Food waste in the supply chain. Source: data extracted from WRAP (2010); data from Food & Drink Federation, Environment Agency, WRAP/DHL, WRAP & Eurostat.

Supply chain stage	Food
Manufacturing*	2,591,000
Distribution†	4,000
Retail	362,000
Household‡	8,300,000
Total	11,257,000

* The manufacturing data is from 2006.
† Scaled up from information supplied from one major supermarket company.
‡ Food and drinks waste including that sent for sewer disposal (an additional 1.8 million tonnes) and not recorded in the other stages.

Figure 27.20 Food waste costs the UK £12 billion per year.
Photo by Nick Saltmarsh, available under a Creative Commons Attribution license.

profits, decisions are made based on a range of long-term attitudes, and behaviours are rational to the individual. Hence, a segmented approach to designing policy options to change farmer behaviour may be more effective than 'one size fits all' approaches. Agri-environment schemes have often failed to persuade farmers that they can, or need to, change their behaviour (Macgregor & Warren 2006). This is particularly the case when the impact of an activity or the benefit of an option is felt downstream rather than on the farm. A literature review by Blackstock *et al.* (2010) stressed the importance of providing strong and consistent messages which convince the farmer that the problem is serious and affects them, but that they are also capable of performing the requested actions.

Individual farmers and other land managers are nested within networks and communities (for example, around farming type) that influence attitudes and decisions. Within such networks, there are key individuals who can be targeted and engaged to bring about wider change (Defra 2008e). Advice coming from a trusted source, particularly from the farming community, is known to have more resonance with farmers (Blackstock *et al.* 2010). This suggests that voluntary initiatives established by the industry, such as the Campaign for the Farmed Environment, may be well-placed to communicate advice (Section 27.4.3.7). Furthermore, influencing individual behaviour at the farm-scale may not always be the most appropriate scale to manage ecosystem services delivered by agricultural landscapes (Section 27.4.3.3). Collective action at landscape- or catchment-scales may enable agri-environment schemes to be more effective (RELU 2010a). Understanding how to strengthen and influence farm group dynamics is, therefore, essential. **Box 27.57** (Section 27.10.7) gives an example of collective action at a catchment-scale and outlines potential options for fostering collaboration amongst farmers through agri-environment schemes (Section 27.10).

Inclusive approaches and the engagement of farmers in decision-making can prove successful because farmers understand the reasoning for change and so, are better motivated and more inclined to comply with regulations. Appropriate engagement with farming networks and organisations may also help to establish well-designed programmes and a sense of cooperative effort (ENRD 2010). Farmers have demonstrated a willingness to maintain and develop their skills and knowledge through advice, informal and formal education, and knowledge exchange programmes. The industry owned Agri-skills Forum, for example, was formed to re-skill and raise professional standards (www.agriskillsforum.co.uk). These approaches are likely to be important for improving the uptake of new technologies and practices. The expansion and widespread recruitment of farmers to agri-environment schemes has exposed them to environmental management and offers opportunities for future knowledge development and transfer to, from and among farmers (Natural England 2009a). The involvement of farmers in monitoring is being trialled by the English Beef and Lamb Executive as one approach to help farmers better understand the impact of their activities and improve cooperation between them and regulatory authorities under the Better Returns Programme.

27.4.3.5 Markets and incentives (instrumental)

Government incentive schemes, in combination with regulatory guidance, have been used to alter agricultural practices with some success in terms of ecosystem service provision. Financial incentives are only required to encourage land management practices that go beyond the legislative baseline (ENRD 2010). Direct subsidy payments to farmers for cross compliance, with minimum standards for food safety, environmental management and animal welfare, have been delivered through the Single Payment Scheme (Section 27.4.3.2). Cross compliance is compulsory, whereas agri-environment schemes are voluntary, incentive-based schemes that reward farmers for higher standards of environmental management than that required under the Single Payment Scheme.

Set-aside is a compulsory instrument that was introduced in 1992 to take land out of production in order to reduce the overproduction of cereals. By 2007, set-aside land accounted for 10% of the UK's arable land area (Foresight 2010), creating fallow arable land across the UK which enhanced a number of ecosystem services (IEEP 2008b). Set-aside land has substantially higher biodiversity than intensive arable land, with strong evidence of benefits to declining farmland birds, as well as plants, invertebrates and mammals. Set-aside land has also been found to reduce soil erosion and increase fertility, while buffering watercourses from diffuse pollution. The fragmentation of habitats that resulted from the intensification of agriculture had been partly counteracted by set-aside increasing the size and connectivity of habitats. This service could be particularly important in helping species to migrate in response to climate change. The success of set-aside in delivering ecosystem services depends on the location of the set-aside and the way it is managed (*ibid.*). Whether the set-aside is rotational or non-rotational determines the types of ecosystem services it provides, with each type providing different environmental benefits to different extents (*ibid.*).

In 2007, the EC reduced the set-aside requirement due to high international prices for cereal crops in response to global shortages, and later abandoned the scheme altogether. There is little evidence, so far, of the impact of the discontinuation of the scheme, but it is widely assumed that it will cause a major loss of environmental benefits if it is not substituted with other measures (IEEP 2008b). A recent study (Levin & Jepsen 2010) found that the re-cultivation of set-aside land in Denmark had negatively affected the spatial structure of semi-natural habitats. Another study (Gillings *et al.* 2010) concluded that the zero set-aside rate rapidly reduced fallow land in the UK; as a result, 25–50% of farmland bird populations could be affected, and birds, such as skylark (*Alauda arvensis*) and yellowhammer (*Emberiza citronella*), would be required to migrate to other habitats in winter, causing a small increase in the rate of population decline.

Agri-environment schemes have been the main supporting mechanism for protecting and enhancing the environment. Farmers are paid to manage the land to provide specific environmental benefits. Agri-environment schemes were launched in the UK in 1987, under the banner of Environmentally Sensitive Areas (ESAs), in response to marked declines in environmental quality and wildlife.

In 1991, this was supplemented by a national scheme, Countryside Stewardship Schemes (CSS), which targeted those areas that fell outside of ESAs.

In 2005, Environmental Stewardship succeeded these early schemes in England, although many farms are still managed under the old schemes. Agri-environment agreements total more than 58,000 (**Figure 27.21**) and cover over 66% of English agricultural land (6 million ha). Environmental Stewardship has two tiers of management. Entry Level Stewardship (ELS) is open for entry to all eligible applicants for supporting sustainable land management with a focus on short-term results. Farmers can select any land management options from a scheme menu. While this has made overall uptake of Environmental Stewardship more attractive, it has resulted in a tendency for the less arduous options to be implemented, and prevents a more systematic, or ecosystem, approach to farmland management. Higher Level Stewardship (HLS) is a competitive scheme that has a greater number of management options, but choice is restricted to those options stipulated in a farm management plan (Natural England 2009a). It is particularly targeted at delivering significant environmental improvements, over the long-term, on farms with SSSIs and BAP targets. Unsurprisingly, HLS has greater potential to deliver a wider range of ecosystem services than ELS. There is also an equivalent two-tiered agri-environment scheme for organic farms.

Similar schemes are run in Wales—Tir Gofal is the more rigorous scheme level, and Tir Cynall is the Welsh entry-level scheme. They will be replaced by a single scheme, Glastir, in 2012, which aims to address challenges, such as climate change, outlined in CAP Health Check proposals. Interestingly, the upper level element of Glastir considers land-water interactions through prescribed actions that aim to work at a collaborative or catchment-scale (WAG 2011).

In Northern Ireland, 39% of farmland is registered in an agri-environment scheme, with the Countryside Management and Organic Farming schemes being active since 2008.

In Scotland, previous agri-environment schemes were incorporated into the Scottish Rural Development Programme in 2007, which also contains schemes for forestry, rural enterprise and business development. The Scottish Rural Development Programme offers non-competitive rural development contracts where land managers apply for

funding for a range of options under Axis 1, 2 and 3 of the CAP; these are called Land Manager Options. In addition to LMOs, land managers can apply for competitive funding for options that meet 'Rural Priorities' which indicate outcomes that are considered to be of greatest importance to the region. Sections 27.4.3.2 and 7.2.2.9 discuss the schemes of each country in more detail.

Each of the four governments and assemblies have given different attention to agri-environment schemes within their rural development programmes. In England, Environmental Stewardship is the most dominant component of its rural development programme, and even received an increase in funding in the Comprehensive Spending Review in 2010. The Scottish Rural Development Programme (2007 to 2013) places, perhaps, more importance on social and economic concerns. Specific support, for example, is available for crofting, an historic form of agriculture that it describes as being "of major cultural importance". Upper and entry level tiered schemes operate in Northern Ireland, Wales, and England, whereas Scotland has a single scheme which covers Axes 1, 2 and 3 of the CAP Pillar 2.

The mitigation of climate change has already been identified as a new policy imperative of the CAP, and will play an increasing role in agri-environment schemes across the UK. Notably, the Welsh Glastir agri-environment scheme will include an Agricultural Carbon Reduction and Efficiency Scheme, which will provide capital grants for energy efficiency improvements and the installation of renewable energy technologies (Cardwell 2010).

Box 27.17 illustrates the impact of agri-environment schemes on ecosystems services and human well-being, taking the English Environmental Stewardship scheme as an example. An evaluation of the Scottish Rural Stewardship Scheme found that farms participating in the scheme had greater biodiversity than those that were not. While some management prescriptions did enhance wildlife populations, the higher biodiversity on scheme farms is likely to be due to the farms that signed up to the scheme already having prescribed habitats (Scott Wilson Scotland Ltd. 2009). The RSPB (2007) cites the lack of investment in the Rural Stewardship Scheme as a major reason for biodiversity objectives not being met. Scott Wilson Scotland Ltd. (2009) conclude, however, that there is insufficient evidence and it is

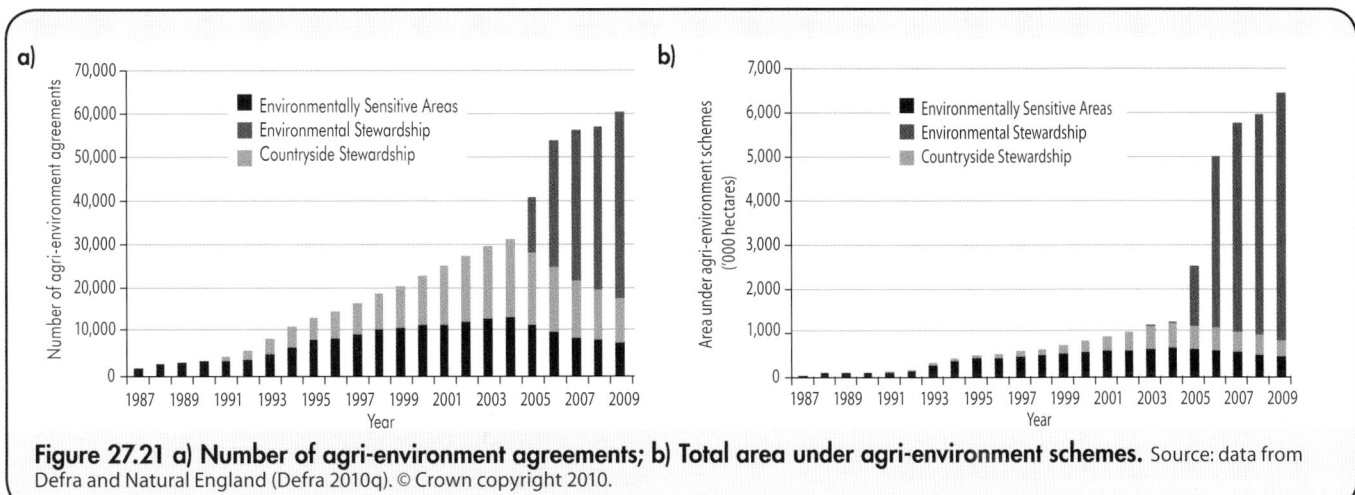

Figure 27.21 a) Number of agri-environment agreements; b) Total area under agri-environment schemes. Source: data from Defra and Natural England (Defra 2010q). © Crown copyright 2010.

too early to draw meaningful conclusions about biodiversity improvements since the scheme began. McCracken (2010) acknowledged that designated sites and targeted actions have improved the habitats for particular species, but that these gains have been offset by continuing declines in the quality of much of Scotland's farmland.

Despite indications of some successes achieved by agri-environment schemes, there are likely to be opportunities to improve their design in the future. **Box 27.17** includes some suggestions made to improve the English Environmental Stewardship scheme, indicating that there is scope to design agri-environment options which deliver objectives like climate change mitigation, resource protection and flood mitigation in synergy with more established priorities such as biodiversity, landscape and public access.

Embedding the ecosystem services approach into the design of agri-environment schemes—which might better deliver this wider range of services—would require the assessment of the extent to which current scheme options recognise and reward the full range of potential ecosystem services, and would require adjusting the schemes appropriately (RELU 2010a). The schemes could also be adapted so that payments are made to farmers for achieving biodiversity objectives rather than being paid to adopt management options that are assumed to deliver environmental benefits. Payments-by-results could be more cost-effective at delivering biodiversity actions on the ground (McCracken 2010).

Findings of the RELU programme (RELU 2010a) suggest that while improvements in biodiversity for some groups of species, such as plants and butterflies, were consistent in different localities, for others, such as solitary bees and birds, the impact of options varied considerably between regions. This suggests that agri-environment schemes could be more effective if they were more flexible, allowing management options to be adapted to regional conditions and targeted species types. In this respect, payments could be linked to the provision of ecosystem services in places that are best placed to deliver them. For example, in the case of farmers located in Less Favoured Areas (designated under

---

Box 27.17 The ecosystem service impacts of the Environmental Stewardship scheme in England. Source: Natural England (2009a); LUC (2009).

Environmental Stewardship was launched in England in 2005, as a response to learning from the earlier Environmentally Sensitive Areas and Countryside Stewardship Schemes. It is a multi-objective scheme with primary objectives of protecting wild species diversity, increasing soil and water quality, and providing cultural benefits from, and public access, to agricultural landscapes. It also has secondary objectives for flood management and conserving genetic resources, and climate change mitigation and adaptation was a recent addition in 2008.

Natural England's (2009a) Review of Results and Effectiveness of Agri-environment schemes reports considerable biodiversity improvements. Arable options, for example, have increased breeding populations of scarce farmland birds There has also been a notable slowing and, in some cases, reversal of declines in UK BAP priority butterfly species. In addition to an increase in wild species diversity, landscape and habitat enhancements by Environmental Stewardship have improved access for education and recreation, and improved countryside aesthetics. In 2007, there were 6,800 education visits which resulted in 170,000 people visiting farms.

Despite the multifunctional intent of Environmental Stewardship, there has generally been a focus on biodiversity objectives until recently (also see Section 27.2). A review of the Provision of Ecosystem Services Through the Environmental Stewardship Scheme (LUC 2009) found that most Environmental Stewardship options have significant potential to deliver a greater range of ecosystem services than they were originally designed for (**Table 27.10**). The review found, for example, that 120 different Environmental Stewardship options can prevent soil erosion, yet only four options were actually designed to deliver this service. It also found that Environmental Stewardship options for woodlands, hedgerows, upland moorland, semi-natural grassland and blanket bogs already impact over 15 services (**Table 27.10**). Detailed evidence of improvements to these other ecosystem services is lacking, however. Water and soil protection, for instance, have only been addressed since 2005, and there is little evidence, so far, of the effect of agri-environment schemes on them. Although climate change mitigation only became an objective in 2008, according to Natural England (2009a), Environmental Stewardship management options indirectly reduced greenhouse gas emissions from the agriculture, forestry and land management sector by 11% in England. This represents a saving of 3.46 million tonnes of carbon dioxide equivalent emissions through the promotion of lower intensity farming practices.

In future, there needs to greater targeting and monitoring of improvements of non-biodiversity related ecosystem services if the multi-objective emphasis of Environmental Stewardship is to be realised (LUC 2009). Although Environmental Stewardship supports a range of ecosystem services already, the current option menu may benefit from it being systematically designed for broad, multi-service delivery. The latest integrated, map-based targeting of ecosystem services delivery launched by Natural England in 2008 demonstrates a movement in this direction. **Table 27.9** shows the ecosystem services that agri-environment schemes have the most potential to enhance, but actions to optimise the delivery of these services are required, particularly to achieve results at landscape-scales.

The Department for Environment, Food and Rural Affairs (Defra 2008d) has already adapted Environmental Stewardship based on early evaluations in order to increase overall uptake, encourage the uptake of in-field options, provide more advice to farmers, and improve the appropriateness of choices made by farmers in relation to geographic priorities. The continued monitoring and evaluation of schemes, fed into policy and scheme design, will be critical for their development and improvement in the future (Davey et al. 2010a).

Table 27.9 Ecosystem services that Environmental Stewardship has the greatest potential to enhance. Source: information from Land Use Consultants (2009).

Supporting	Provisioning	Regulating	Cultural
■ Biodiversity ■ Protection of soil organic matter	■ Genetic conservation ■ Water supply	■ Water infiltration ■ Water quality ■ Flood regulation and coastal protection ■ Erosion control ■ Pollination	■ Recreation ■ Education ■ Cultural heritage ■ Aesthetics ■ Sense of place

---

Box 27.17 continued.

Table 27.10 The impacts of Environmental Stewardship on ecosystem service delivery. Green = positive impact; maroon = negative impact; orange = positive and negative impact. Source: reproduced from LUC (2009).

Feature type	Habitat or feature	Provisioning Services					Regulating Services									Cultural Services					Supporting			
		Food	Fibre	Fuel	Genetics	Fresh water	Air quality	Climate	Water regulation	Erosion	Water quality	Disease	Pest	Polination	Hazards	Recreation	Cultural heritage	Education	Aesthetics	Sense of place	Soil formation	Photosynthesis	Primary production	Biodiversity
Boundary features	Hedgerows (basic)																							
	Hedgerows (enhanced)																							
	Stone faced hedgebanks																							
	Ditches																							
	Hedges & ditches combined (basic hedge management)																							
	Hedges & ditches combined (enhanced hedge management)																							
	Stone walls																							
Trees & woodland	In-field trees																							
	In-field trees (ancient)																							
	Woodland fences																							
	Woodland edges																							
	Wood pasture & parkland																							
	Woodland																							
	Scrub																							
	Orchards																							
Historic & landscape	Archaeology under grassland																							
	Archaeology under cultivated soils																							
	Archaeology & high water levels																							
	Designed water bodies																							
	Water meadows																							
	Traditional farm buildings																							
Buffer strips, field margins / corners	Buffer strips (2 m and 4 m)																							
	Buffer strips (6 m)																							
	Enhanced buffer strips (with grazing)																							
	Enhanced buffer strips (without grazing)																							
	Buffer strips beside ponds & streams																							
	Uncropped cultivated margins																							
	Conservation headlands																							
	Conservation headlands (no fertiliser or harvesting)																							
	Field corners																							
Arable land	Seed mixtures sown for birds																							
	Fallow plots																							
	Low input cereals																							
	Undersown spring cereals																							
	Overwintered stubbles																							
	Whole crop silage & over-wintered stubbles																							
	Fodder crops & overwintered stubbles																							
	Beetle banks																							
Grassland	Low input grassland																							
	Species rich grasslands																							
	Rough grazing (basic)																							
	Rough grazing (enhanced)																							
	Rush pastures																							
	Wet grassland																							
	Mixed stocking																							
	Rare breeds (supplement)																							
Moor/Heath	Moorland																							
	Shepherding (supplement)																							
	Lowland heathland																							
Coast	Coastal saltmarsh																							
	Sand dunes																							
Wetlands	Ponds																							
	Reedbeds																							
	Fens																							
	Lowland raised bogs																							
Soils	Maize crops & resource protection (without cover crop)																							
	Maize crops & resource protection (with cover crop)																							
	Arable reversion to grassland (no fertiliser)																							
	Arable reversion to grassland (low input)																							
	In-field grass areas																							
	Intensively managed grassland & soils (low input)																							
	Seasonal livestock removal on intensive grasslands																							
	Watercourses & erosion																							
Access	Open access																							
	Linear access																							
	Educational access																							

EU regulations dating back to the 1970s), compensation is currently provided for the physical disadvantages of farming in the uplands. Instead, RELU (2010a) propose that farmers are rewarded in these areas for the provision of public goods, and are supported in maximising the potential of the land to deliver them. Payments for such public goods could also benefit the local economies and create jobs in such areas (**Box 27.18**).

Targeting agri-environment schemes at multiple scales—farm, landscape, catchment and regional—could also yield improvements, as discussed above in Section 27.4.3.3. There may also be issues of temporal scale that need to be addressed in scheme design. Managing carbon and restoring or linking wildlife habitats, for example, require long-term commitments that may require new contractual mechanisms (RELU 2010b).

It has been estimated (Cao 2009) that overall annual payments in the UK through Pillar 2 may have to be in the region of £1–3 billion (compared to today's £3.9 billion allocated over seven years from 2007 to 2013) in order to achieve the environment policy objectives of the UK Government; this estimate is based on current indicator areas and agri-environment option payment rates. Additional challenges set out in future CAP reform would increase this figure further.

In addition to agri-environment schemes, the government has introduced incentives to promote the production of bioenergy crops. The Energy Crops Scheme provided grants for short rotation coppice willow and *Miscanthus* (Section 27.5.3.5). By 2006, when the scheme closed to applicants, 1,200 ha of willow and 3,400 ha of *Miscanthus* had been planted, accounting for 7% and 68% of the original targets, respectively (Sections 27.9.3.3, 7.2.2.9). Grants have also been used to encourage the establishment of farm woodlands on land that was formerly used for agricultural production. The 1998 Farm Woodland Scheme (now replaced with different schemes in the devolved countries) made annual payments to farmers to compensate for loss of income from converted agricultural land; while the Forestry Commission made payments to farmers for the initial set-up of woodlands under the Woodland Grant Scheme. Between 1988 and 2005, these schemes established 120,000 ha of new woodland across the UK (Chapter 7; Section 27.5.3.5).

Payment for some non-production services can be made through the markets, such as holiday accommodation in the countryside. The adding of value to food products through certification (e.g. organic, LEAF) can also compensate farmers for loss of productivity due to better environmental care. Offsets of greenhouse gas emissions may, in the future, be paid to agriculture from other sectors in return for carbon sequestration and storage services. This could be integrated into emission trading schemes and linked to payments for other services such as natural resource conservation

(Foresight 2010). Carbon offsetting schemes may provide a source of funding to manage and restore peatlands for carbon storage (CREDIT 2011). There is also scope for agri-environment schemes to include options that prevent the loss of carbon and/or support carbon sequestration (RELU 2010a).

The markets will continue to play a major role in the future. The food market dominance of supermarkets—accounting for 75% of sales of food in the UK—has favoured large, intensive farmers, but has also promoted some environmental improvements (Foresight 2010). As discussed in Section 27.4.3.4, if consumer awareness on environmental issues continues to rise, demand for sustainably produced food should rise as well.

27.4.3.6 Technologies and practices (instrumental)

Conventional farming practices still dominate UK agriculture, but a number of alternative farming systems are available that adopt practices with variable impacts on ecosystem services:

Integrated Farm Management (IFM) uses a whole farm system approach with an aim to be both profitable and environmentally responsible. It makes use of regulatory ecosystem services, traditional farming methods and the responsible use of technologies. LEAF is the main advocate of IFM in the UK and has a membership of 1,500 farms, covering over 707,000 ha of farmland (www.leafuk.org). Produce from their members carries the LEAF Marque Label. It differs from organic farming by not barring the use of artificial fertilisers, but instead encourages farmers to use them in a more targeted way, based on detailed information on farm soil structure and fertility. This gives greater flexibility than organic farming for site-specific characteristics (Trewavas 2001).

Typically, IFM includes mixed arable and livestock enterprises, fallow land, conservation headlands, bird cover crops, and sympathetic field margin and hedgerow management (Vickery *et al.* 2004). Nutrient management plans and auditing systems are characteristic of this farming approach (Burgess & Morris 2009). Vickery *et al.* (2004) found that IFM field management practices, such as crop rotation and use of manures, maintains crop structural diversity, soil organic content and biological activity (e.g. earthworms). A complex crop rotation can benefit farmland birds by providing more breeding and foraging opportunities, and IFM farming methods outlined above would also be expected to have benefits for water quality and pest regulation, and reduce soil erosion.

The distinction between 'intensive' and 'integrated' farming is becoming increasingly blurred as intensive farm systems adopt integrated practices that they perceive to be beneficial (Burgess & Morris 2009). Agri-environment schemes have also mainstreamed IFM practices by including them in the menu of land management options.

Extensification of production can include a reduction in inputs to crops, and/or sparser crop and livestock densities. This typically lowers productivity and increases the value of the produce—niche markets are willing to pay these extra costs, however, in return for higher quality products that have a lower impact on the environment (Section 27.4.3.4). Whether such systems can meet the needs of, and be

---

Box 27.18 Agri-environment payments can create local jobs. Source: ENRD (2010).

A farmer on a remote, 1,400 ha livestock farm in a Less Favoured Area in the north-west of England entered an agri-environment scheme. He reduced the number of sheep, and time they spent grazing, on moorland, and chose management options for drystone walls, hedgerows, woodland restoration, in-field trees, traditional farm buildings and the management of archaeological features on grassland. The farmer also used a specialist local contractor to restore moorland. For every £1 the farmer was paid by the scheme, the local economy benefited by £3.70. At least 10 new jobs were created in the local area, reflecting the growing jobs market for contractors specialising in landscape and habitat restoration work.

affordable to, all of society is widely debated (Section 7.5.4). Extensive systems are known to increase biodiversity and reduce pollution, but their overall effect on other ecosystem services can be variable. Although extensive cattle- or sheep-grazing in upland habitats, for example, can maintain biodiversity and may protect carbon stocks in soils, slower growth rates may result in higher methane (greenhouse gas) emissions over their lifetime than intensive production systems. High energy costs may encourage more farmers to be less intensive, which is likely to reduce yield per hectare (Foresight 2010).

Organic farming systems prohibit the use of external inputs such as artificial fertilisers and most pesticides; instead, they internalise inputs, especially nutrients, for crop and livestock production (Chapter 7). The integration of biological processes, such as pest control, and the rotation of crops, remove the need for external inputs, but result in organic systems normally having lower yields per hectare than conventional systems. Standards for organic production are regulated by European law (EC Regulation 834/2007) and administered by non-government organisations; for instance, the Soil Association is the largest organic food certifier in the UK, accounting for 70% of all organic farmland (Section 7.2). Although it is widely agreed that organic farming methods offer benefits to biodiversity, intensive agriculture can arguably produce more food on less land and, therefore, create space for the delivery of other ecosystem services (Section 7.5.4). In this instance, agri-environment schemes can be used to encourage farmers to include wildlife habitat in field boundary strips (**Figure 27.22**) and non-cropped areas, leaving cropped areas to be intensively managed (RELU 2010a).

Government policy in the UK has increasingly promoted practices that are embodied in organic farming. However, due to fears over the need for more land to produce the same amount of food, and an unwillingness by the majority of consumers to pay more for their food despite the benefits, it is unlikely that organics will be adopted as a model for

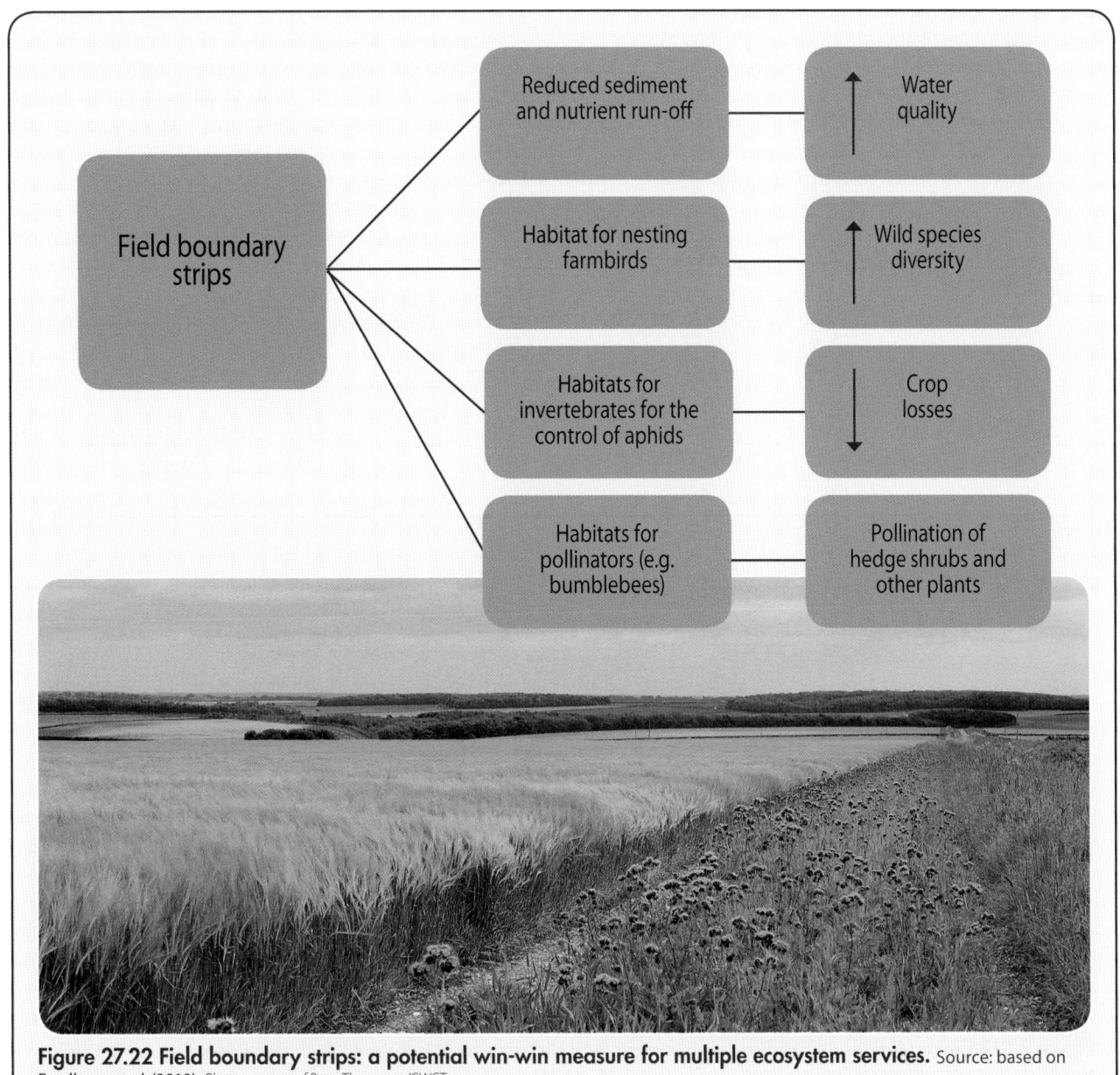

Figure 27.22 Field boundary strips: a potential win-win measure for multiple ecosystem services. Source: based on Bradbury *et al.* (2010). *Photo courtesy of Peter Thompson/GWCT.*

a sustainable farming system (Tomlinson 2008). Organic systems are likely to be useful to extend into areas where environmental factors limit productivity and habitat needs to be protected from intensive agriculture. Reducing demand for food by, for example, reducing food waste or making improvements in organic technologies to increase yields per hectare, may make the widespread uptake of organics more attractive in the future.

The types of soil management employed on a farm can influence the provision of supporting, provisioning and regulatory services. Soil management strategies that better utilise natural processes offer opportunities for improving the sustainability of agro-ecosystems (Section 13.3.4). Bulk fertilisers (such as manures and composts) and crop rotations with ley crops (**Figure 27.23**) can improve soil fertility and structure, increase water and nutrient storage, remove pollutants that could otherwise enter the food chain or water supplies, and can improve soil biodiversity (Section 13.2.4). The use of bulk fertilisers can also reduce soil erosion and increase concentrations of soil organic carbon (SOC), although this generally does not constitute an additional transfer of carbon from the atmosphere to land (Powlson *et al.* 2011). Contour tillage can reduce surface runoff, and other tillage changes or no-till strategies can have benefits for soil quality, nutrient cycling and reduce erosion (Section 14.3.4.2). Reduced tillage, however, appears to increase SOC by much less than previously thought, at least in temperate regions such as the UK (Powlson *et al.* 2011). The more efficient use of fertilisers, the wider use of perennial crops and legumes, and rotational cropping can improve nutrient cycling and nutrient uptake by plants, and minimise losses of nitrogen from the farm (Section 13.3.4). There is potential for agri-environment schemes to better support farmers who adopt beneficial farming practices, including the biocontrol of soil-living pests through the provision of habitats for predators, as well as the other soil management techniques outlined here. **Table 27.11** shows a selection of management options for lowland farmland that can influence regulating ecosystem services.

Moorlands and heaths are often burned for the rearing of sheep and red grouse, but little is known about the effects of this practice on ecosystem services. Importantly, there is contradictory evidence on the influence of burning on carbon sequestration and storage (Section 5.5.2.1). One alternative to burning is heather-cutting, which is often used in places where fire could pose a risk to people and property. While cut material can be used to regenerate heather restoration sites, this practice is deemed uneconomical by land managers and there is some evidence that it can reduce plant vigour over the long-term (*ibid.*). Reductions in the number of sheep grazing on moors and heathland can benefit some species in areas where there is high grazing pressure. The challenge is calculating the number of livestock that is sustainable in a specific location with specific conditions. Re-wilding initiatives allow natural processes to re-establish, but normally with a minimal level of grazing to maintain the existing ecosystem services (Section 5.5.2.2).

The increasing occurrence of drought and water shortages in the UK (especially in South East England), and concerns over energy security and climate change, are heightening the need for arable farming to become more water efficient. Many water-efficient technologies already exist, including water-efficient crop varieties, drip irrigation and low pressure sprinklers. Measures to reduce water loss, such as greenhouses and plastic tunnels, and the development of alternative water sources, such as rainwater harvesting, are also likely to become increasingly important (Section 7.2.2.7). The biggest greenhouse complex in the UK, Thanet Earth, is under development in Kent; once completed, it will increase salad crop production by 15% in the UK. It is heated and powered by a neighbouring combined heat and power plant (www.thanetearth.com).

Biotechnology has the potential to contribute to meeting future agricultural challenges. Crop and livestock breeding

Figure 27.23 Crop rotations can reduce weeds, pests and diseases by interrupting their lifecycles. They can also replenish nutrients and maintain soil fertility. *Photo © Environment Agency (2008a).*

Table 27.11 A selection of management options on lowland farmland that can influence regulating ecosystem services.
Source: Bradbury *et al.* (2010). Copyright © 2010 British Ecological Society. Reproduced with permission of Blackwell Publishing Ltd.

Final Service	Benefit	Land management objectives	Management options
■ Carbon sequestration ■ Greenhouse gas emission reduction	■ Climate change mitigation	■ Reduce soil carbon oxidation ■ Reduce energy consumption ■ Increase soil carbon sequestration ■ Reduce nitrous oxide emissions ■ Reduce methane emissions	■ Convert arable land to permanent grassland, in particular on organic soils. ■ Reduce cultivation intensity. ■ Grow woody vegetation: hedgerows, woodland, biomass crops. ■ Improve crop nitrogen use, manure nitrogen use, tailor nutrient supplied in feed to livestock nutrient requirement. ■ Provide high quality feed, reduce stocking levels, digest manures anaerobically.
■ Water regulation ■ Erosion regulation	■ Usable water ■ Flood risk management ■ Hazard control	■ Improve soil infiltration ■ Reduce surface run-off	■ Ameliorate soil structural damage and compaction. ■ Create/restore semi-natural habitats including scrub, plant trees. ■ Maintain/create flow barriers: hedgerows, earth banks, buffer strips, beetle-banks. ■ Restore vegetation cover on bare soils, under-sow arable crops such as maize. ■ Implement minimal cultivation or no-till techniques on arable land.
■ Water purification	■ Clean water	■ Reduce fertiliser leaching & pesticides	■ Tailor nitrogen, phosphorus and potassium inputs to crop requirements. ■ Use plants with improved nitrogen use efficiency. ■ Use manure nitrogen efficiently. ■ Create low input grassland and conservation headlands. ■ Avoid application in inappropriate (e.g. wet / frozen) conditions. ■ Prevent pollutant surface run-off, create physical buffer zones. ■ Provide reed beds / wetlands to filter water before entry to water courses. ■ Reduce / prevent soil erosion.

and selection can increase productivity and quality through improved strains. Sylvester-Bradley & Wiseman (2005, cited in Burgess & Morris 2009) estimate that current average UK wheat yields could be increased by about 50% by 2050 through genetic improvement; they also anticipate that breeders will produce varieties that require less agrochemicals, water and nutrients. The main focuses for livestock breeding will be to increase reproductive rates, and use genetic improvement, diet manipulation and containment to reduce greenhouse gas emissions (Section 7.2.2.7).

Genetic modification may be important for the development of new crop varieties with, for example, improved drought tolerance. Public resistance to GM crops has been extremely strong, with awareness of the potential risks greater than awareness of the potential benefits (Gaskell *et al.* 2000 in Burgess & Morris 2009). The use of GM crops is now considered on a case-by-case basis following the lift of the European moratorium in 2004.

Farmers receive advice and information on agricultural best practices and technologies from a variety of sources including: individuals and informal communication networks (perhaps the most significant source); non-government organisations, such as farmers associations and research organisations; commercial enterprises that provide inputs and services; and public bodies, such as the Environmental Agency and Natural England. The government and the industry have established a number of schemes to provide information and advice to farmers, including the Campaign for the Farmed Environment (Section 27.4.3.7) and the Catchment Sensitive Farming Initiative (**Box 27.19**).

27.4.3.7 Voluntary actions (instrumental)
Voluntary action by farmers is complementary to the growing burden of litigation, economic sanctions and government subsidies which they face (Sabatier *et al.* 2005 in Blackstock *et al.* 2010). Moreover, voluntary action is argued to be more likely to be embedded in social norms (Ayer 1997 in Blackstock *et al.* 2010).

> **Box 27.19 The Catchment Sensitive Farming Initiative.**
>
> The Catchment Sensitive Farming Initiative uses advice, regulation and various schemes to reduce the agricultural contribution of diffuse pollution to water. Farming is a significant source of diffuse pollution, especially nutrients from fertilisers and manure. The Initiative promotes land management that reduces diffuse sources of pollution to levels that maintain ecological quality in watercourses. A range of advice is given to farmers and land managers working in priority catchments, including guidance on the appropriate use of fertilisers, manures and pesticides, how to avoid runoff and erosion, and how to protect watercourses from diffuse pollution. The advice is complemented with management options delivered through the Environmental Stewardship scheme in England, and through the future creation of water protection zones—a new regulatory tool for protecting watercourses (Section 27.3.3).

In recent years, a trend for the agricultural sector establishing its own initiatives to tackle environmental issues has developed. The industry-led Voluntary Initiative led by the Crop Protection Association, aims to minimise the environmental impacts of pesticide use and make environmental improvements (EA 2007a). The scheme was established by the agricultural sector to avoid statutory controls on pesticide application through collective voluntary action (Blackstock *et al.* 2010); **Box 27.20** outlines some of the outcomes of the scheme since 2001. Furthermore, the industry has established its own Agriculture Industry Greenhouse Gas Action Plan 2010, which sets targets for reducing emissions (Box 27.16).

The Campaign for the Farmed Environment is a new industry-led initiative that aims to extend participation in ELS and offset the loss of environmental benefits from the abandonment of set-aside by encouraging voluntary environmental management outside of the agri-environment schemes. Supported by a large consortium of organisations, it has specific work themes for protecting water and soils, and for supporting bird species and other farmland wildlife. The Campaign was launched at the end of 2009, so it is too early to assess its impact on ecosystem services.

At a regional and local level, there are some examples of individual farmers voluntarily working together to achieve positive commercial and environmental outcomes (**Box 27.21**).

27.4.4 Agriculture Summary

Table 27.12 summarises the key insights from this review of responses in the context of agriculture, highlighting those that have been well-established, but also identifying a set of responses that are either in early implementation or are proposed. It is important to learn from these early pilots across all sectors to scale-up the adoption of an integrated ecosystem approach to the management of the UK's diverse habitats, which is one key policy direction that this review recommends.

27.5 Forestry

27.5.1 Forestry-related Ecosystem Services and Human Well-being

Throughout history, forestry has been a sector of high economic and cultural importance in the UK. Over the past 30 years, the key trend in this sector has been increased multifunctionality and the diversification of ecosystem services delivered by Woodlands or forests (synonymous for the purposes of this section). **Figure 27.25** summarises the key drivers impacting the forestry sector, and the resulting risks to ecosystem services.

Table 27.12 Agriculture Summary.

	Established responses	Early implementation, pilots	Proposed, under development
Knowledge	■ Farm monitoring ■ Predicting impacts of climate change on agriculture	■ Research on climate change adaptations, e.g. development of resilient crop varieties ■ Collaboration between researchers and the farming community	■ Research on spatial optimisation of agriculture, and impact of different management practices on ecosystem services (ES) ■ Sustainable Agriculture and Food Innovation Platform ■ Creating resilient agro-ecosystems ■ Further development of low input crop varieties
Legislation	■ Common Agricultural Policy (CAP) ■ Nitrates Directive ■ Habitats and Birds Directives	■ Water Framework Directive	■ CAP reform
Policies, institutions and governance	■ Agri-environment policy ■ CAP Cross Compliance	■ UK Food 2030 Strategy ■ Agriculture Industry GHG Action Plan	■ ES approach to agri-environment policy ■ High Nature Value farming concept ■ Agri-environment schemes (AES) applied at multiple spatial and temporal scales ■ Collaboration between farmers to achieve objectives at landscape scale ■ Increased stakeholder engagement, especially farmers in the design of agri-environment schemes ■ Land use strategies to optimise delivery of ES
Changing social attitudes	■ Food certification to encourage sustainable diets ■ Awareness raising, campaigns and advice on healthy and sustainable diets, and food waste ■ Advice to farmers ■ Enrolment of farmers in AES	■ Raising awareness of climate impacts of food ■ Advice given to farmers from trusted sources, e.g. from farming community	■ Segmented approach to changing farmer behaviour ■ Strengthening farmer group dynamics for collective action ■ Engagement of farmers in decision-making
Markets and incentives	■ Removal of production-based incentives ■ Set-aside ■ AES	■ Competitive funding for options that meet 'rural priorities' (Scotland Regional Development Programme) ■ Integrated map-based targeting of ecosystem services delivery by AES ■ Restoration of peatlands funded by carbon offsetting schemes	■ AES adjusted to reward the full range of ecosystem services, and to encourage collaborative actions at landscape and catchment scales ■ In Less Favoured Areas reward farmers for providing public goods rather than compensating for physical disadvantages ■ Agricultural Carbon Reduction and Efficiency Scheme (Welsh Glastir AES)
Technologies and practices	■ Integrated Farm Management ■ Extensification of production ■ Organic farming ■ Water efficient technologies ■ Biotechnology ■ Advice on best practice and technologies ■ Catchment Sensitive Farming Initiative	■ Re-wilding initiatives ■ Biotechnology ■ Genetic modification	■ Calculating the sustainable number of livestock for specific locations ■ Biotechnology to develop crop varieties that have higher yields and require less inputs, and to improve livestock breeding
Voluntary actions	■ Voluntary Initiative (VI; pesticides)	■ Voluntary collective action by farmers ■ Campaign for the Farmed Environment	

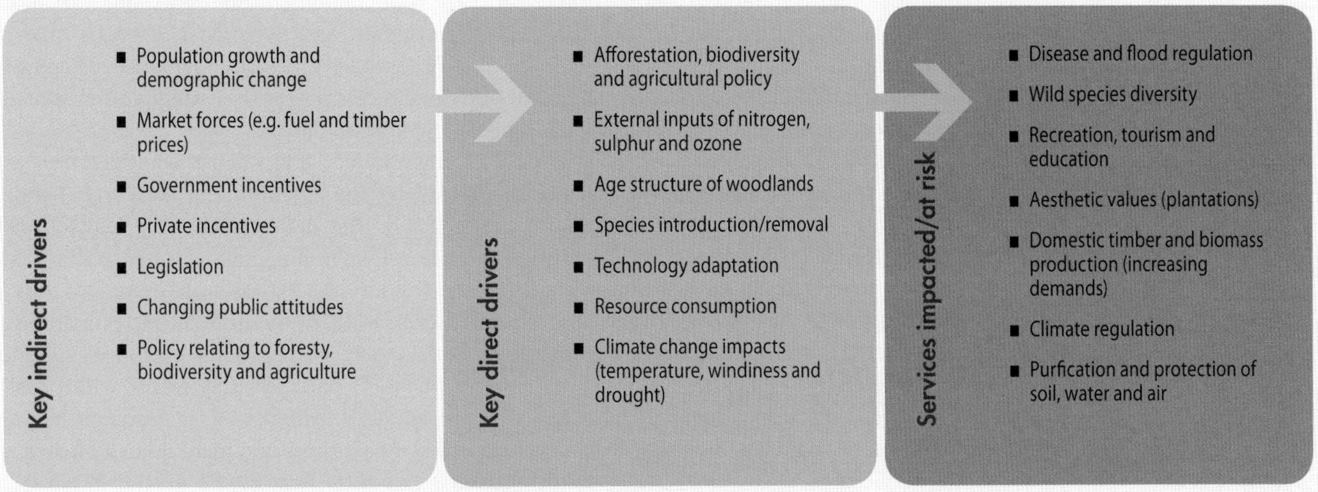

Figure 27.25 Key indirect and direct drivers relevant to the forestry sector, and the ecosystem services at risk.

Key indirect drivers	Key direct drivers	Services impacted/at risk
■ Population growth and demographic change ■ Market forces (e.g. fuel and timber prices) ■ Government incentives ■ Private incentives ■ Legislation ■ Changing public attitudes ■ Policy relating to foresty, biodiversity and agriculture	■ Afforestation, biodiversity and agricultural policy ■ External inputs of nitrogen, sulphur and ozone ■ Age structure of woodlands ■ Species introduction/removal ■ Technology adaptation ■ Resource consumption ■ Climate change impacts (temperature, windiness and drought)	■ Disease and flood regulation ■ Wild species diversity ■ Recreation, tourism and education ■ Aesthetic values (plantations) ■ Domestic timber and biomass production (increasing demands) ■ Climate regulation ■ Purification and protection of soil, water and air

Forestry does not operate in isolation, but interacts with many other sectors. For the development of Green Infrastructure (GI; the green areas in both urban and rural places) and access to woodlands, forestry is integrated into planning and infrastructure and there is a growing need for spatial planning of forests at a landscape-scale. The role of forestry in the energy sector is ever–increasing, particularly with a resurgence of the use of wood biomass for heating and as technological advances increase the potential for electricity generation from biomass on a large scale. Forests have an important potential role to play in the mitigation of the impacts of climate change through carbon sequestration, and forest management will have to adjust to prepare forests to face a changing climate. Woodland recreation and tourism is in high demand, and forests are acknowledged for the benefits they provide to human health and well-being. Semi-natural forests are valued sites of high biodiversity, the preservation and appreciation of which needs to be promoted through the network of protected areas. Finally, trees and forests provide a number of regulating and supporting services which underpin activities outside the forestry sector. These include: the maintenance of water quality; the protection and formation of soil and the cycling of nutrients; disease regulation; the decontamination of air, water and soil; and the regulation of floods, local climate and noise.

27.5.2 Challenges for the Forestry Sector

In contrast to other sectors, forestry operates over long timescales, which creates a number of challenges. It can take time for changes in forestry management plans to match changes in societal attitudes and forest policy (Section 8.2.5). Instruments for change, such as incentives, need to be introduced with sufficient lead times in order to achieve their intended impact (Foresight 2010). In terms of provisioning services, it is anticipated that demand for forest products will increase in the coming decades due to population growth and trends favouring wood over more carbon intensive materials and processes (Section 15.7). Responses adopted in the near future will prepare the forestry industry for future change, and determine what proportion of this demand will be met through domestic production (Section 8.2.5.1).

In addition to meeting provisioning demands, there are increasing expectations for the delivery of multiple services from forests, and that these services are used sustainably (Section 8.4.1). Achieving multifunctionality will be a challenge in light of increased pressure on forests from climate change, settlement and infrastructure expansion, renewable energy development, the spread of invasive pests and diseases, and population growth. There is increasing demand for access to woodland for the achievement of human health benefits, and for woodlands to play a part in climate change mitigation; all in addition to the provisioning of timber and other wood products. Current and future financial pressures will further challenge the achievement of multifunctional forestry. As such, there is a need to strengthen policies which promote multifunctionality, especially regarding regulating services.

Woodland biodiversity is threatened by the impacts of deer, the intensity of provisioning and climate change

(Section 8.2.4.3). Functional connectivity of woodlands across the landscape to reduce the isolation of biodiverse fragments will be increasingly important in the face of a changing climate (Section 8.2.4.1). Expansion of our knowledge about the risks of climate change will potentially require forest managers to adapt their practices and also to improve the mitigation of climate change through carbon sequestration efforts.

Another challenge will be the development of a framework for landscape-scale planning involving coordination across land uses and collaborative management among diverse sectors (Section 8.5.5). The increasing devolution of the forestry sector could create further issues for landscape planning, hence it is anticipated that capacity-building at local levels will become a priority.

27.5.3 Forestry-related Response Options

27.5.3.1 Knowledge (foundational)

Knowledge and scientific evidence about forestry act as a foundation to inform developments in legislation, policy, institutions, governance and social attitudes. This process is not linear, as research priorities also respond to the experience of such developments and the instruments that they enable. Sustainable forest management and multifunctionality have been the dominant paradigms and focus for research over the past few decades. In 2005, the MA provided further foundational knowledge of the diversity of ecosystem services provided by forest habitat (MA 2005).

The Forest Research Agency, the research arm of the Forestry Commission GB, restructured their operations in 2009 into three research centres which reflect current priorities for knowledge and practical solutions in UK forestry (Forest Research 2010a). The Centre for Forestry and Climate Change investigates topics which include the interaction of climate change with pest and pathogen behaviour, the mitigation of the effects of increased greenhouse gases, adaptive forest management practices, and the development of GI (Forest Research 2010b). The Centre for Forest Resources and Management aims to understand and advise on the measurement and management of the UK's forests, and increasingly focuses on how forest management can minimise risks from climate change and sequester carbon. The Centre for Human and Ecological Sciences takes an interdisciplinary approach to researching and developing the role that trees and forests play within integrated, sustainable landscapes and within society.

In 2003, 'environment and health' was identified as a research priority by the Environment Research Funders' Forum (NERC 2004). The understanding of health benefits derived from natural environments and greenspaces, which include forests (Section 16.3.3), has since expanded through programmes such as NERC's Environment and Human Health Programme (2006-2009). There is some evidence suggesting trees capture pollutant particles and gases, with possible benefits for air quality (Section 14.8.1). Research has also begun to uncover the physical and mental health benefits of forests (Lovell & Roe 2009; **Box 27.22**, Section 27.5.3.4).

Previous chapters have identified some key knowledge gaps in the forest sector (e.g. Chapter 8). The evidence base would benefit from the better incorporation of lessons learned from past responses and improved valuation methods (Section 8.3.7.3). There is also a need to support the coordination of land uses across landscapes through more interdisciplinary research.

We need to determine long-term rates of carbon storage and to model long-term future scenarios which integrate both socioeconomic and emission models (Sections 8.6, 14.3.5). Clearer scientific evidence is needed concerning changes in soil carbon, while mechanisms to increase the carbon-carrying capacity of different UK soils need to be further developed (Ostle *et al.* 2009). Biosecurity continues to be a serious threat to UK forests through the unintentional introduction of invasive pathogens as world trade expands, and especially through the importation of live plants (Brasier 2008). Continued investment into international procedures to prevent invasions is necessary. The wider implications of land use policy aimed at reducing emissions or conserving carbon sinks need to be more fully understood, as do the effects of land use management. In addition, there remains a need to quantify the regional-scale biophysical effects of climate change regulation.

Further research on the sustainable harvest of non-timber forest products (including knowledge about ecology, reproduction and population structures) is warranted, as is the development of markets for deer, orchard fruit, and other potentially profitable forest products (Section 8.6).

27.5.3.2 Legislation (enabling)

The Forestry Act 1967 is the statutory basis for forestry in the UK. Much of the legislation which governs forestry is cross-sectoral in nature and regulates other commercial enterprises, such as agriculture, which lie outside the scope of planning law (Forestry Commission 2009c). A list of some of the laws governing forestry in the UK can be found in **Table 27.13**.

An Environmental Statement is required under the Environmental Impact Assessment (Forestry) England and Wales Regulations (SI 1999/2228) and Scotland Regulations (SI 1999/43)—both of which were further amended in 2006—for any afforestation, deforestation, forestry road or quarry activity anticipated to significantly impact the environment (Forestry Commission 2009a). Consent for proposed activity is achieved through screening by the Forestry Commission, and parties carrying out work without prior consent will be served with an Enforcement Notice to stop the work, apply for consent, or restore land and alleviate damage caused. Failure to obey this notice carries a fine of up to £5,000 (Forestry Commission 2007b).

It is an offence to fell a tree without a licence to do so, unless the case falls under a number of exceptions: the tree to be felled is located in a garden, orchard, churchyard or designated open space (Commons Act 1899); activities to be carried out involve lopping, topping, pruning and pollarding; felling is under a specified volume and diameter; or if permission has been granted under a grant scheme or with planning permission (Town and Country Planning Act) (Forestry Commission 2007b). Exceptions are also made for the felling of dangerous or nuisance trees or to prevent the spread of pests and disease as stipulated by a Forestry

Table 27.13 A list of some of the laws governing forestry practice in the UK. Source: information from Forestry Commission (2007).

Forestry Legislation
Forestry Act 1967 as amended
The Forestry Regulations 1979 (SI 1979 No 792) as amended by the Forestry (Amendments) Regulations 1985 (SI 1985 No 1572) and by the Forestry (Amendment) Regulations 1988 (SI 1988 No 970)
The Forestry Regulations 1985 (SI 1985 No 1958)
The Plant Health (Forestry) (Great Britain) Order 1993 (SI 1993 No 1283, as amended by SI 1994 No 3094, SI 1995 No 1989, SI 1996 No 751, SI 1998 No 2206, SI 1998 No 3109, SI 2001 No 299, SI 2002 No 295)
The Watermark Disease (Local Authorities) Order 1974 (SI 1974 No 768, as amended by SI 1984 No 688, SI 1986 No 1342 and SI 1992 No 44)
The Dutch Elm Disease (Local Authorities) Order 1984 (SI 1984 No 687, as amended by SI 1988 No 604)
Nature Conservation (Scotland) Act 2004
Environmental Impact Assessment (Forestry) England and Wales Regulations 1999 (SI 1999/2228), as amended 2006
Environmental Impact Assessment (Forestry) Scotland Regulations 1999 (SI 1999/43), as amended 2006
Tree Preservation Orders
Habitats Regulations 2010
Wildlife and Countryside Act 1981
Habitats Directive (Directive 92/43/EC)
Birds Directive (Directive 2009/147/EC)
Countryside and Rights of Way Act 2000; Land Reform (Scotland) Act 2003; Access to the Countryside (Northern Ireland) Order 1983
Planning Policy Statement 9

Commission Plant Health Officer. The penalty for felling a licensable tree without prior permission is a fine up to £2,500 or twice the value of the trees (whichever is higher).

Tree preservation orders are made by a Local Planning Authority to prohibit the cutting down, uprooting, topping, lopping, wilful damage or wilful destruction of trees or woodland (DCLG 2000; DCLG 2009). The orders lie under the Town and Country Planning Act 1990, and the Town and Country Planning (Trees) Regulation 1999. Separate legislation (Environment Act 1995 and the Hedgerows Regulations 1997 (SI 1997, No 1160)) is in place to regulate hedgerow removal.

In the UK, the Habitats Regulations 2010 and the Wildlife and Countryside Act 1981, along with Natura 2000 protected areas under the Habitats Directive (Directive 92/43/EC) and Birds Directive (Directive 2009/147/EC) across the EU, provide legal protection SACs, SPAs, National Nature Reserves (NNRs) and SSSIs which include woodland. Improvements to the protection of SSSIs and ancient woodlands have been achieved through amendments to the Countryside and Rights of Way Act in 2000 (Pryor & Peterken 2001), and through Planning Policy Statement 9 (PPS9) (ODPM 2005).

Legislation from a number of other sectors also acts as an indirect driver of UK forestry. The smoke control provisions of the Clean Air Acts of 1956 and 1968 (subsequently consolidated into the Clear Air Act 1993) gave powers to local authorities to declare part or all of their region a 'smoke control area' in which coal, oil and wood could not be used unless burnt on an exempted fireplace without smoke emissions (Defra 2010g). Wood was preferred to coal as a fuel, but this placed a considerable restriction on the use of wood for heating and stove purposes, subsequently impacting forest management practices providing such fuels. More recently, greater take-up by heating appliance manufacturers and fuel producers of the exemption and authorisation provisions has led to a resurgence in the use of wood fuels in 'smoke control areas' (**Figure 27.26**).

Within the energy sector, the Renewables Obligation Order 2002 (as ammended) (Wilson 2002) in particular has had a major impact on forestry. The order stipulated that from April 1st 2010 until March 31st 2027, 10.4% of the total electricity supplied must come from renewable sources, which includes wood biomass. Due to the many pressures on land in the UK, bioenergy can only act as a small part of the solution to climate change, and checks and balances are required to prevent inappropriate displacement of food production, sites for conservation and places for recreation (Woodland Trust 2010b). That being said, there is great potential for bioenergy development to offer co-benefits including: the expansion of native woodland and tree cover; buffering of sensitive woodland; bringing woodlands under appropriate management for biodiversity and social benefits; and the renewal of political and public appreciation of woodland value (*ibid.*). The overall purpose of the WFD (Section 27.3.3.2) is to prevent further deterioration, and protect and enhance the status, of aquatic ecosystems. Forests and their management have a positive role to play in regulating water quality and flood risk as outlined in the Forest and Water Guidelines (Forestry Commission 2003). River Basin Management Plans consider forest design, management and planning, which impact water quality, quantity and habitat structure.

27.5.3.3 Policies, institutions and governance (enabling)

In 1999, the UK Government devolved responsibility for forestry to the National Assembly for Wales and to Scottish Ministers; forestry in Northern Ireland has been fully devolved since 1922 (Interdepartmental Group 2002). The

Figure 27.26 Wood is commonly used as fuel for domestic heating. *Image © viki2win, 2011. Used under license of Shutterstock.com.*

Forestry Commission reports separately in each country to the respective ministry, each of which is responsible for developing a national Forest Strategy. A review conducted by an Interdepartmental Group (2002) concluded that there was a need to further integrate the Forestry Commission's National Offices with the rural departments in each country. In 2003, the Forest Enterprise agency of the Forestry Commission was devolved to separate bodies in England, Scotland and Wales. In Wales, the Forest Enterprise was reabsorbed into the Forestry Commission to form a single devolved body in 2004. The Forest Research agency has remained a GB entity, but the responsibilities of the Devolved Administrations in determining research priorities have grown.

In the UK, forest policy is devolved and outlined in the forestry strategy of each country. The UK Forestry Standard contains UK-relevant requirements and guidelines for woodland managers to achieve sustainable forestry management in line with international protocols (Forestry Commission 2004). Its most recent revision in 2009 strengthens the role of forest planning and incorporates developments in scientific understanding and international climate change initiatives (Forestry Commission 2009c). A revised edition of this document is due in 2011.

There is a continuous reassessment of forest policy in the UK to meet changing public attitudes and legislation. Carbon sequestration policy is likely to become a major driver of forest policy in the future (Section 8.2.5). The Scottish Forestry Strategy (Scottish Executive 2006b), for example, calls for an increase in area of new woodland and short rotation forestry to help achieve the targets set out in Scotland's Climate Change Programme through carbon sequestration (Scottish Executive 2006a). Forestry is also embedded in the Climate Change Strategy for Wales (WAG 2010c), while the Woodlands for Wales strategy (WAG 2009) outlines policy promoting the diversification of tree age and species in order to improve the ability of forests to survive climate change and pest and disease outbreaks. Site-appropriate management systems, such as continuous cover forestry, are encouraged by the strategy in place of clearfelling. The trade-off between the aim of diversifying plantation species and structure and the desire to maximise carbon sequestration needs to be addressed (Mason *et al.* 2009). Future planting programmes should consider species carbon content and the potential of new productive genotypes.

Biomass energy policy (DTI *et al.* 2007; Scottish Executive 2007; WAG 2010b) is likely to increase the management of previously unproductive woodlands and could have synergistic cultural, regulating and biodiversity benefits. Renewable energy requirements under the Renewables Obligation Order 2002 (Section 27.9.3.3; Wilson 2002) and wood fuel policy, such as the UK Renewable Energy Strategy (HM Government 2009b) and A Woodfuel Strategy for England (Forestry Commission 2007a), are driving increasing demand for domestically grown timber. In combination, issues of carbon sequestration and biomass production have led to renewed policy interest in forest expansion in GB.

At the other end of the spectrum, recent policy developments, such as the Open Forest Policy in England (Forestry Commission England 2010) and the Policy on

Control of Woodland Removal in Scotland (Forestry Commission Scotland 2008b), outline regulations for the permanent conversion of woods and forest to restore priority open habitats, enhance populations of priority species, enhance important landscapes, or to improve the conservation of soil and water regulation services. These policies aid the achievement of UK BAP targets for priority open habitats (Section 8.1.3). Felling is regulated through licences and requirements for long-term Forest Plans, and Forestry Commission and Northern Ireland Department of Agriculture and Rural Development Forestry Service policy requires that all felled areas not authorised under planning regulations or for environmental improvement be replanted or naturally regenerated (Forestry Commission 2004).

Successful policy has driven a reduction in nitrogen oxides and sulphur and has subsequently decreased negative impacts on forests. However, nitrogen deposition is still above critical loads for lower plants, and remains a policy challenge (Section 8.2.5.2). Policy controls exist to reduce grazing pressure in forests (such as CAP reform which reduced the number of free-ranging sheep in the uplands and stocking level requirements within Environmentally Sensitive Areas); yet grazing and browsing by both wild and domestic herbivores remains one of the primary drivers of biodiversity change in UK forests (Section 8.2.5.4). Additionally, there remains a general need to strengthen policies which promote multifunctional forests, especially those supporting regulating services such as flood control and water quality (Foresight 2010).

There has been a general transition in the UK from public to private forest ownership. This was exemplified by the recent proposal by the Department for Environment, Food and Rural Affairs in England to fundamentally reform the ownership of the public forest estate (Defra 2010d). There were concerns that private industry would have the deepest pockets in terms of bidding for parts of the public forestry estate, and that local access could be negatively affected if such outside acquisition was widespread. There were also concerns about the safeguards (and their associated costs) needed to both secure the existing rights of those who enjoy access to public forests and woodlands, and to ensure that these areas continue to deliver a range of ecosystem services, many of which could prove difficult to measure, quantify and potentially transact over (Adams & Hodge 2010). Due to public unease and resistance during the consultation period, the government removed the forestry clauses from the Public Bodies Bill and established an independent panel to consider forest policy in England (Defra 2011b).

In general, there is an increasing reliance in the UK on NGOs, voluntary schemes and government partnerships which are experienced at engaging local communities and managing forest resources (Pryor & Peterken 2001; Defra 2007a). The key challenge, from an ecosystem services perspective, is to maintain the public benefits from forestry and woodlands (especially those that are difficult to monetise or quantify), while allowing a greater role for non-state actors (both in the private sector and local communities) to participate in forestry activity.

There is a trend towards greater community involvement in forestry decision-making and management, and this is

expected to continue (Moffat *et al.* 2009). Community Forests play an important role in raising the profile and relevance of greenspace and the countryside, and in influencing policy and planning of GI in England (Countryside Agency 2005). The Community Forest Programme involves working partnerships between public, private and voluntary sector actors at all levels. Successful examples of cross-boundary Community Forests which extend across multiple local authority areas exist, achieving strategic landscape- scale change. With increasing urbanisation, the Community Forestry movement will play an increasing role in the realisation of social, environmental and economic benefits (Moffat *et al.* 2009). Policy to improve public access to woodlands is enabled by the Countryside and Rights of Way Act 2000, the Land Reform (Scotland) Act 2003 and the Access to the Countryside (Northern Ireland) Order 1983 (Section 27.8.3.2). The Forests for People Strategy in Scotland (Forestry Commission Scotland 2008a), for example, outlines the recreation infrastructure that is provided by the Forestry Commission Scotland across the national forest estate to facilitate outdoor access (Forestry Commission Scotland 2008a). The principal priorities of this strategy are to promote outdoor recreation, provide facilities in order to improve local health and well-being, and support local economic development.

Planning for sustainable forest management occurs at a number of scales, but there is a need for these levels to be better coordinated (Section 8.5.5). In Scotland, for example, the National Forest Estate Strategic Plan 2009-2013 (Forestry Commission Scotland 2009) provides the context for how Forest Enterprise Scotland contributes to the delivery of the Scottish Forestry Strategy (Scottish Executive 2006b). Ten District Strategic Plans further define how the national strategic plan will be implemented at a local level. In Wales, the Woodlands for Wales Action Plan indicates what needs to happen over the next five years in order to achieve the outcomes presented in the 50-year Woodlands for Wales Strategy (WAG2009). Forest Design Plans (Forest Enterprise) or Forest Plans (non-Forest Enterprise) are used in the UK for medium to long-term planning of public estate forests in the context of relevant national and district plans. Site-level planning (operational site assessment) is also carried out prior to the start of operations. Incentive schemes, such as the Woodland Improvement Grant in Scotland, encourage an increase in the coverage of Forest Plans; however, only half of UK Woodlands currently have a management plan, so "increasing the coverage of management plans is central to sustainable forest management and the delivery of ecosystem services." (Section 8.5.5.3).

27.5.3.4 Changing social attitudes (enabling)

Forest extent, composition and structure across the UK are strongly influenced by changes in societal behaviour and the prevalent trends of the time. Historically, large-scale felling of forest during WWII stimulated extensive afforestation and the desire to increase the domestic timber market. Current concerns about the overexploitation of tropical hardwood forests, in addition to aspirations for self-sufficiency, support the need to maintain and increase domestic production of wood products; however, hardwood production has declined in the UK over the past 40 years (Section 15.7). The motivations for hardwood afforestation tend to be the promotion of conservation, aesthetic, recreational and other public services, while the motivations for softwood afforestation are climate regulation through carbon sequestration and the provision of wood products including wood fuel. Increased societal understanding about species and habitat protection, and pressure from conservation organisations, have recently led to the formulation of policy to allow the conversion of selected afforested areas back to grassland, moorland and wetlands (Section 8.1).

Historically, provisioning landscape services dominated other concerns, resulting in the loss of non-woodland trees through agricultural intensification and mechanisation, and the abandonment of less productive, traditional forestry practices. The protection and conservation of semi-natural woodland and trees is increasingly being promoted as the role of multipurpose forestry gains social acceptance (**Figure 27.27**). The popularity and value of conservation is demonstrated by the considerable increase in membership of environmental NGOs and their subsequent increase in power and responsibility (Section 16.2). Governments now aim to further strengthen partnerships with these organisations.

The principles of sustainable forest management, multifunctionality and ecosystem service thinking have renewed interest in traditional forms of forest management and natural regeneration (Section 8.2.4.3). The appeal for increased recreational services from forests has acted as a driver for improved management and regeneration of mixed and broadleaved forests in place of commercial conifer plantations. Efforts have also been made to encourage the use of conifer woodlands for recreational purposes (Section 8.2.5.3). Local access to greenspace and sites of forest recreation are predicted to continue gaining importance as awareness about the health and well-being benefits of forests increases and as the UK makes the transition to low carbon living (Section 8.3.5.1). The popularity of woodlands

as a learning tool and site for education also continues to grow (**Box 27.22**).

Public awareness about climate change has generated interest in biomass as a source of energy and the use of wood fuel for heating. A five-fold increase in the area of short rotation coppice of *Miscanthus* and reed canary grass was recorded from 2005 to 2007 (Section 15.2.5). As the value of wood fuel continues to increase, it is likely that additional small, privately owned forests will be brought under management to increase production. The substitution of fossil fuel-derived materials with forest products is also becoming more commonplace in the construction and industry sectors. In combination, these trends act to increase the finance available from forests and should lead to higher numbers of people actively managing forests, providing gradual improvements in the state of many woodlands that were not previously managed due to financial constraints.

A number of organisations and agencies actively encourage community involvement with woodlands for the numerous benefits they provide. 'Community forestry', which differs among the devolved countries (Lawrence *et al.* 2009), has an important role in shaping social attitudes towards forestry by actively involving citizens with their local woods. In Wales, there are 138 active Community Woodland Groups undertaking a wide range of activities, such as environmental improvements, community regeneration and school visits or education, on a total of 1,795 ha of woodland (Griffiths 2010). These groups were found to work with elderly people, young offenders and people with health issues. Research about Community Woodland Groups suggests that there is scope for further development and that they provide a double benefit in policy terms because they play an important role in achieving both socioeconomic and woodland objectives (*ibid.*). Another example is the Tree Warden Scheme, which originated in England in the early 1980s, and has grown into a national scheme of 8,000 volunteer Tree Wardens (The Tree Council 2010).

27.5.3.5 Markets and incentives (instrumental)

International market forces strongly impact forestry in the UK. Anticipated increases in fuel prices are likely to raise the profitability of wood fuel, leading to the growth of local wood markets (Section 3.3.3). The relatively low current value of UK timber further encourages the transition to the management of woodland for conservation and recreation services. Certification schemes and standards are also influential market mechanisms to improve the quality and sustainability of woodland management: 45% of wood in the UK is now certified (Forestry Commission 2009b). The UK Woodland Assurance Standard (UKWAS) is a voluntary independent certification standard meeting international protocols and suited specifically to UK forestry. It was amended in 2008 to become more accessible for the small and low intensity managed woodlands (UKWAS 2008). The Forest Stewardship Council (FSC) is an international NGO that runs a global forest certification system for forest management and chain of custody (FSC 2011); it is a registered UK charity which supports the market-based instrument allowing businesses and enterprises to benefit from sound

Figure 27.27 The native Scots Pine woodlands of Glen Affric National Nature Reserve in Scotland. *Image © johnbraid, 2011. Used under license of Shutterstock.com.*

Forest School is an outdoor learning approach that has been used in the UK since the mid-1990s. Research commissioned by the Forestry Commission Scotland has shown that it "has the potential to significantly benefit children and young people's physical health and mental well-being" (**Figure 27.28**).

There are currently about 140 Forest School programmes in the UK which are broadly defined by three common factors:

1. They take place within a forest or woodland which is ideally near to the participants' school.
2. Participants at the school take part in activities which normally include small and achievable tasks, exploration of the environment and physically active games—all with an emphasis on education in the outdoors.
3. The learning experience is sustained over an extended period, for example once per week or fortnight for a minimum of 12 weeks.

The approach has proved to be advantageous to mood in all behavioural groups, but especially to adolescents suffering from 'mental disorders'; it has also been found to be particularly effective at reducing anger levels. These findings support prior research which has shown that exposure to a park settings elevates attention performance in the general population and also in populations with Attention Deficit Hyperactivity Disorder (ADHD) (Faber Taylor & Kuo 2009). Another study has demonstrated a relationship between childhood visits to woodlands or greenspaces and preparedness to visit such sites alone as an adult (Thompson *et al.* 2008). Findings suggest that childhood experiences strongly reflect the physical and emotional benefits of accessing such places.

Figure 27.28 Children exploring a woodland habitat. *Image © Morgan Lane Photography, 2011. Used under license of Shutterstock.com.*

forest stewardship. There is little evidence, however, of the impact certification has on forest management and ecosystem services in the UK (Section 8.5.4).

It is well-established that the doubling of forest cover since WWII is primarily in response to incentives, in the form of grants, and favourable economic and tax conditions (Chapter 3; Chapter 8). In fact, the forestry sector is so reliant on incentives that between 1961 and 1986 expenditure in forestry exceeded income in all but two years, with a mean deficit over this period of £70/ha (Chapter 22). Incentive schemes have improved since the 1980s, when grants financially supported tree plantation with primary regard for timber production. Woodland creation grants now incorporate scoring and eligibility criteria in order to assess the delivery of the greatest public and environmental benefits (**Box 27.23**); however, there are still concerns that new planting could damage important sites of biodiversity such as Semi-natural Grassland (RSPB 2008). Forestry incentives intersect with incentive schemes from agriculture (e.g. agri-environment schemes), recreation and tourism (e.g. the Wildspaces! Scheme), biodiversity (e.g. support for SSSI management), and energy (e.g. biomass grants) sectors as grant schemes become increasingly integrated.

Devolved forestry grant schemes run by the Forestry Commission and the Northern Ireland Department of Agriculture and Rural Development incentivise action towards the aims of the Forest Strategy in each country: the Woodland Grant Scheme operates in England (Forestry Commission England 2009); Glastir Woodland Grants were recently introduced for woodland creation in Wales (replacing the Better Woodlands for Wales scheme; **Box 27.23**) (Forestry Commission Wales 2010); Rural Development Contracts— Rural Priorities are part of the Scotland Rural Development

Programme in Scotland (Scottish Government 2010g); and Forest Grants exist in Northern Ireland (Forest Service 2007). Common to all of these schemes is the availability of funding for woodland creation and for management improvements. Northern Ireland and Scotland both have grants available specifically for the planting of new woodland to be managed under short rotation forestry for the production of wood fuel and renewable energy (**Box 27.24**). In England, the Energy Crops Scheme supports the establishment of short rotation coppice (Natural England 2009c).

Outside the public forestry grants mentioned above, private forestry incentives are available. Some energy providers now offer contracts to local farmers who supply biomass (Section 15.2.5). Non-governmental organisations and charities are increasingly supporting tree planting initiatives privately through membership fees and donations. One example is the MOREwoods scheme of the Woodland Trust which offers finance and technical support for native tree planting to landowners across the UK (Woodland Trust 2010a).

Taxation is also used as an economic instrument to achieve desired policy objectives. In the UK, favourable tax conditions currently exist which encourage people to purchase woodland and to invest in forest management. All profits and income from timber sales are free from Income and Corporation Tax, and there is no Capital Gains Tax (CGT) on the increase in value of standing timber over time (Forestry Commission Wales 2003). Additionally, commercial woodland that has been owned for at least two years prior to being transferred or upon death qualifies for 100% relief from Inheritance Tax. While Inheritance Tax breaks are desirable, (Render 2004; Lawrence *et al.* 2010) found that grants "can be preferred to tax incentives for the

Box 27.23 Glastir Woodland Creation Scheme.

In Wales, the Better Woodlands for Wales grants scheme closed to new applications in 2010 (Forestry Commission Wales 2010). In its place, the Glastir Woodland Creation Scheme has been launched by the Forestry Commission Wales as an instrument to increase the area of native and mixed woodland as set out in the Woodlands for Wales strategy of the Welsh Assembly Government (WAG 2010d). Options for woodland management are currently under development and have been proposed for inclusion under the Targeted Element of the Glastir scheme which will be operational in spring 2013 (Forestry Commission Wales 2010).

Under the new Glastir Woodland Creation Scheme there are three grants available (**Table 27.14**): 1) establishment grants; 2) fencing grants (only available for new planting); and 3) income foregone payments. Establishment grants at various rates are available for five woodland categories as follows:

A collaboration of partners has worked to develop strategic woodland creation maps for both native and mixed woodlands. These indicate where planting can go ahead without consultation (green), where planting can go ahead without consultation, but with specific prescriptions (green hatched), where planting plans need to be further informed by local consultation or where other barriers need to be overcome (amber), and where sites are inappropriate and planting is not allowed (red).

The maps are available via a web-based mapping browser (http://maps.forestry.gov.uk/imf/imf.jsp?site=fcwales_ext&), allowing applicants to quickly check the eligibility of an area (Forestry Commission Wales 2011).

Table 27.14 Woodland category, specifications and grant rates under the Glastir Woodland Creation scheme. Source: reproduced from WAG (2010d).

Woodland Category	Specification	Grant £/ha (yr 1/yr 2/yr 3)
Small simple woodland	■ No species restriction providing they are suited to site and woodland meets UKFS and environmental standards ■ Stocking density 2,500/ha	500 / 150 / 150
Basic mixed woodland	■ Minimum of 3 species with no more than 75% of any one species ■ Minimum of 25% broadleaved species inclusive of woody shrub element ■ Maximum of 10% woody shrub element ■ Stocking density 2,500/ha	980 / 500 / 500
Enhanced mixed woodland	■ Minimum of 5 major species (at least 10% of each) ■ Minimum of 25% broadleaved inclusive of woody shrub element ■ Maximum 10% woody shrub element ■ No more than 50% of a single species ■ Stocking density 2,500/ha	2,350 / 500 / 500
Native woodland—carbon	■ Native species mix should be site-native ■ Suitable provenance planting stock* ■ Maximum 20% woody shrubs allowed ■ Stocking density 2,500/ha	3,500 / 500 / 500
Native woodland— biodiversity	■ Native species mix should be site-native and largely conform to HAP types; however, local conditions may necessitate some variation from these ■ Suitable provenance planting stock* ■ Maximum 20% woody shrubs allowed ■ Clumped distribution of species with variable spacing ■ Stocking density 1,600/ha	1,890 / 500 / 500

* Indications from research are that the use of locally native provenance alone may not be resilient enough to cope with predicated climate change. Guidance is being developed on widening the genetic material used within a species.

Box 27.24 The Big Tree Plant campaign.

The Big Tree Plant is a campaign to encourage people and communities to plant more trees in England's towns, cities and neighbourhoods. It is a partnership bringing together national tree-planting organisations and local groups working with the Department for Environment, Food and Rural Affairs and the Forestry Commission. The initiative has been launched in response to a decline in tree planting in urban areas. It is backed by funding of £1 million, but the emphasis is on community groups and organisations establishing or extending projects to plant and care for trees, in line with the 'Big Society' (localism) approach. Further information: http://thebigtreeplant.direct.gov.uk

provision of certain public benefits (particularly landscape protection and nature conservation)".

27.5.3.6 Technologies and practices (instrumental)

Intensive management made possible through the adoption of mechanisation in forestry operations, particularly timber harvesting, has allowed woodland enterprises to increase their profitability and domestic markets to grow

(Section 8.2.5.3). Intensive practices have affected the age-distribution, structural diversity, habitat quality and biodiversity of productive forests. Chemicals are used both to directly increase woodland productivity, and to allow growth of conifer plantations in areas where this was previously uneconomical (Chapter 3.3). Modern technology has improved harvesting practice to minimise impacts on regulating services by reducing sediment losses, nitrate peaks and other threats to water quality downstream of plantations (Section 14.9.4).

Tree development through breeding has a long history in the UK. The Forestry Commission established its first hybrid trial in 1926 and, by 1948, a research station was established to undertake work in forest genetics (Forest Research 1998). Biotechnological tools are used both for genetic conservation strategies and to increase the desirability of morphological traits. Applications have included biochemical and molecular studies to enable seed origin to be determined and the use of vegetative propagation techniques to genetically improve commercial species (Lee *et al.* 2004). Biotechnology is used to increase the quality of commercially grown tree species through breeding and genetic conservation programmes use advanced molecular techniques to conserve native tree biodiversity (Wilson & Samuel 2003).

An important recent application is the use of genetic strategies to reduce the impacts of climate change on UK forests (Hubert & Cottrell 2007). Three potential strategies have been identified to accommodate climate change: 1) maintain genetic variation and promote natural regeneration; 2) adopt a portfolio approach and plant a mix of provenances alongside the current population; and 3) use assisted migration by planting a different provenance or species (*ibid.*).

There is also scope for the future development of a biochemical industry based on forest foliage compounds to produce products like essential oils, herbal supplements and resin acids.

Sophisticated technology, such as automatic, high efficiency boilers and power installations, can efficiently create energy from wood biomass as an economical and low carbon alternative to fossil fuels (Forest Research 2006). Wood fuel boilers can produce heat or electricity from logs, chips, or pellets with variable requirements for moisture content and consistency (**Box 27.25**). Combined Heat and Power (CHP) plants can produce both electricity and heat which can be used for hot water or district heating for industries or local communities. Electricity can also be generated through 'co-firing' where different techniques are used to combine up to 20% biomass with coal in existing power stations (Perry & Rosillo-Calle 2008). As the price of gas rises, wood fuel is an increasingly cost-effective source of heat.

An ecosystem service of increasing importance is noise regulation which can be moderated through tree planting, especially in the case of strip planting along motorways to minimise undesirable noise from road traffic (Section 14.6). Tree belts are also used in a regulating capacity to capture or reduce the transport of point source pollution (for example, ammonia from agricultural livestock production), reducing negative impacts on vulnerable habitat (Defra 2002a). When appropriately planned, trees and greenspaces can play an important role in controlling Urban climates by improving flood control and air quality, countering threats to biodiversity, and reducing Urban heat island effects (Wilby & Perry 2006). Tree planting in Urban areas has also become a commonplace activity for the benefits of human health and recreation opportunities. The realisation of these benefits from trees is dependent on species choice used and where they are located.

There is a need for the development of decision-analysis tools which account for ecosystem services. Multi-criteria decision analysis is a subjective method for decision-makers to evaluate alternative courses of conflicting action (Section 8.5). Decision-support tools aid forest owners and managers to model different management options to determine the impacts of future climate change. Payments for ecosystem services involving forestry have high potential in the UK, and technological advances in remote sensing and GIS will be important in this field.

Box 27.25 Stevens Croft biomass power station, Lockerbie, Scotland. Source: Scottish Executive (2007); Perry & Rosillo-Calle (2008); Net Resources International (2010).

Commissioned in 2007, Stevens Croft biomass power station (**Figure 27.29**) is the largest plant in Scotland solely dedicated to burning wood biomass. The plant, which is carbon neutral, burns 480,000 tonnes of sustainable wood fuel in a year; it is capable of using a maximum of 95,000 tonnes per year from short rotation coppice in the blend of fuel. E.ON UK won Best Renewable Project 2007 at the Scottish Green Energy Awards for the project which cost an estimated €132 million. Each year, the plant will save up to 140,000 tonnes of greenhouse gas emissions.

Using new technology from Siemens and Metso Power, the power plant can reach full generating capacity (42.2 megawatts export) even with high moisture fuel, such as freshly cut small round wood, sawmill co-products, and short rotation coppice willow of different grades.

The site, which was already occupied by a sawmill, is near to densely forested areas, minimising the cost and emissions of fuel transport. The project has generated 40 direct jobs, and has created or safeguarded an additional 300 jobs in forestry or farming.

Figure 27.29 The Stevens Croft biomass power station in Lockerbie, Scotland: the UK's largest solely wood biomass-burning plant. *Photo courtesy of E.ON UK.*

27.5.3.7 Voluntary actions (instrumental)

Voluntary actions are increasingly powerful instruments of change in forestry. As public awareness about issues of climate change and habitat and species conservation expands, there is increasing incentive for businesses to adopt voluntary measures to improve corporate social responsibility. One new example in the UK is the Woodland Carbon Code, a piloted standard for voluntary carbon sequestration projects (Forestry Commission 2010b). The code is designed to provide reassurance to businesses and individuals wishing to plant trees for the purpose of sequestering carbon by encouraging a consistent approach to woodland carbon projects. Projects meeting the requirements of a forestry standard, long-term management plan, and provide carbon benefits that are accurately measured, can carry the Woodlands Carbon Code label of approval. In doing so, the process also provides reassurance to carbon-conscious consumers.

Voluntary organisations also play an important role in encouraging the support of traditional forest management practices such as coppicing. Voluntary partnerships among government departments, organisations, businesses and individuals are becoming more common in the forestry sector (**Box 27.26**). In 1994, a National Native Woodland Accord was signed between the Association of National Park Authorities and the Forestry Commission to formally recognise the importance of semi-natural Woodlands to the landscapes and ecosystems of English National Parks (DNPA, *et al.* 2004). This was reinforced in 2002 with an Accord to widen the scope and depth of the partnership "to provide a framework for the two organisations to work together to enhance the contribution that trees and woodlands can make to society within some of the finest landscapes in England and Wales." (Forestry Commission 2002). Another example is the Wales Forest Business Partnership, a voluntary group of businesses and organisations across the forestry sector in Wales (Wales Forest Business Partnership 2011). The aim of this partnership is to strengthen the forestry sector as a whole and to encourage forestry-related businesses to compete and be successful within a wider market.

27.5.4 Forestry Summary

Table 27.15 summarises the key insights from this review of responses in the forestry context, highlighting those that have been well-established, but also identifying a set of responses that are either in early implementation or are proposed. It is important to learn from these early pilots across all sectors to scale-up the adoption of an integrated ecosystem approach to the management of the UK's diverse habitats, which is one key policy direction that this review recommends.

27.6 Fisheries

27.6.1 Fisheries, Ecosystem Services and Human Well-being

Fisheries benefit people in the UK and overseas through the provision of fish and shellfish for human consumption (sourced from wild capture and aquaculture fisheries), fishmeal for aquaculture, fish oil for food supplements, and bait for sea angling. The polyunsaturated fatty acids (e.g. omega-3 oils) contained in fish can contribute to a healthy

---

Box 27.26 The Treegeneration project, North East Wales. Source: Forest Research (2008).

The aim of the Treegeneration pilot project (2004 to 2008) was to determine the scope for a national urban forestry initiative in Wales. Funding for the project was attained through a partnership between: the Countryside Council for Wales, the two County Councils involved (Wrexham and Flintshire), and the Forestry Commission Wales. Partnerships were also made with other organisations, such as BTCV, the Groundwork Trust, schools, businesses and community groups, to provide match funding.

Treegeneration was a grant-giving project for Urban tree planting, but also provided practical assistance and expert advice on other Urban planting schemes. A total of 20 projects were given financial assistance (totalling £113,000) and an additional six projects received non-monetary assistance. By the end of project delivery in 2008, 59,300 native and 308 non-native trees had been planted; by 2,200 people, and a total of 30 ha of Urban woodland had been created.

The project was found to be successful in promoting integrated working through direct partnerships; but these partnerships were found to be short-lived. A review of the project determined that it had been valuable and had played an important role in providing support and expertise for urban greening which was otherwise unavailable. Interestingly, the business community resisted the project, fearing that Urban tree cover would exacerbate anti-social behaviour and crime. Experiences from this project support recommendations to strengthen the partnership approaches of the Forestry Commission Wales.

---

diet (NHS 2011). Despite its declining contribution to the UK's economy, it remains an important industry for some coastal communities, especially in remote areas of Scotland, Wales and south-west England. In 2007, the UK's commercial marine fishery landed 611,000 tonnes of fish and shellfish into the UK and abroad, worth almost £650 million at first sale (UKMMAS 2010). The expansion of aquaculture in Scotland has been substantial—it is now the largest salmon producer in the EU and generates £327 million from farmed finfish alone (**Figure 27.30**). Recreational sea, coarse and game angling provides a valuable source of income for coastal and rural communities; recreational sea fishing generated £538 million for England and Wales in 2003 and £141 million for Scotland in 2008 (UKMMAS 2010); Section 27.8).

Marine ecosystems provide a number of services that support commercial fisheries (Section 12.3). They break down waste and purify water, ensuring seafood is safe to eat. Marine microbial organisms cycle nutrients (such as carbon, nitrogen and phosphorus) that are essential for the maintenance, growth and production of essential Marine organisms that underpin Marine food webs and commercial fisheries. Marine living habitats, such as mussel beds, form feeding, breeding and nursery grounds that are important for the recruitment of commercial species. Despite the importance of these services to the fishing industry, the general trend has been to unintentionally degrade the environment that delivers them. Seabed trawl nets and dredging gear destroy living reefs and deep-water corals, which have slow recovery times, and affect benthic invertebrate communities that are an important food source for commercial fisheries. Chapter 12 reports that several stocks in the North Sea and Irish Sea are fished beyond biological limits of exploitation. Not only does the

Table 27.15 Forestry Summary.

	Established responses	Early implementation, pilots	Proposed, under development
Knowledge	▪ Forest Research Agency ▪ Environment and Human Health Programme (Natural Environment Research Council)		▪ Research on physical and mental health benefits of forests
Legislation	▪ Forestry Act 1967 ▪ Forestry Regulations ▪ Environmental Impact Assessment (forestry) Regulations ▪ Protected areas legislation (**Table 27.5**) ▪ Countryside and Rights of Way Act	▪ Renewables Obligation Order	
Policies, institutions and governance	▪ National Forestry Strategies ▪ UK Forestry Standard	▪ Biomass energy policy ▪ Open Forest Policy and Policy on Control of Woodland Removal ▪ Grazing Policy	▪ Carbon sequestration policy ▪ Multifunctional forestry approaches ▪ Public-private partnership
Changing social attitudes	▪ Tree Warden Scheme in England	▪ Physical and mental benefits of 'Forest School' ▪ Community Woodland Groups in Wales	▪ Local access to greenspace
Markets and incentives	▪ UK Woodland Assurance Standard ▪ Forest Stewardship Council UK	▪ English Woodland Grant Scheme ▪ Glastir Woodland Grants ▪ Rural Development Contracts in Scotland ▪ MOREwoods Scheme	▪ The Big Tree Plant Campaign
Technologies and Practices	▪ Tree development through breeding ▪ Biomass power station technology		▪ Biotechnology improvements to reduce impacts of climate change ▪ Biochemical industry
Voluntary actions	▪ National Native Woodland Accord ▪ Wales Forest Business Partnership	▪ Woodland Carbon Code ▪ Treegeneration Project	

Figure 27.30 Scotland is now the largest salmon producer in the EU. Salmon farm on the Island of Skye, Scotland.
Photo by Eric, available under a Creative Commons Attribution-NonCommercial-NoDerivs license.

unsustainable exploitation of the fisheries threaten the long-term survival of the industry, it also impacts the supporting and regulating services of the Marine environment.

Due to the interdependencies between the state of the fisheries and the Marine and Freshwater environment, responses need to be considered within the wider context of marine planning and river basin management. The fisheries also have a significant influence on Marine biodiversity, and marine energy development may impact the habitats of commercial species. The reader should, therefore, also refer to: Biodiversity (Section 27.2); Water (Section 27.3); Marine and Coasts (Section 27.7); and Urban Planning, Transport and Energy (Section 27.9).

27.6.2 Challenges for the Fisheries Sector

Figure 27.31 summarises the major fisheries-related direct and indirect drivers and their impact on ecosystem services. The major challenge for fisheries is to move towards a sustainable path where landings of fish fall within safe biological limits of exploitation, so an appropriately sized fishing industry can prosper. Some progress has been made towards achieving this aim. In the early 1990s, only about 10% of scientifically monitored fish stocks were considered to be at full reproductive capacity, but this rose to 50% by 2008 (Armstrong & Holmes 2008). While this is a positive trend, Chapter 12 reports that several stocks in the North Sea and Irish Sea are still overfished and subject to recovery

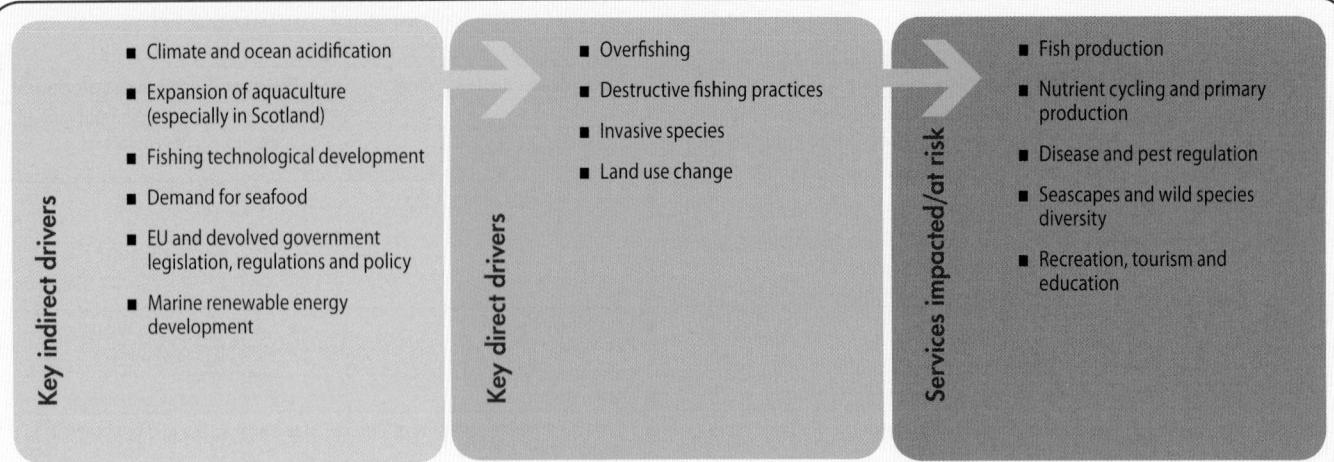

Figure 27.31 Key indirect and direct drivers relevant to the fisheries sector, and the ecosystem services at risk.

plans, while other commercial species have not yet been assessed due to sparse data. Fish mortality in most stocks remains above levels that would enable maximum sustainable yields in the long-term. The provision of food from Marine ecosystems is at its lowest in over 100 years (Chapter 12). Although regulations have protected some deep-sea corals, the use of seabed trawling is still widespread in UK waters and has a severe impact on benthic communities.

In the future, demand for fish is expected to increase globally, but remain stable in the UK and the rest of Europe; fish landings are likely to remain stable or decline if stocks remain overexploited (Delgado *et al.* 2003; Pinnegar *et al.* 2006). At worst, fish stocks could collapse, with widespread impacts on employment in the sector and their communities. But it is more likely that stocks will remain fairly stable or fall as trade barriers are removed (UK Cabinet Office 2004).

Aquaculture is set to expand to meet global demand for fish protein, with more farms in Scotland and the emergence of an industry in England and Wales. While this expansion could create 2,000 jobs and a first sale value of £100 million, it will also require more fish feed, putting pressure on wild species (Section 22). Care must be taken to manage the potential environmental impacts of this development.

Climate change impacts, including increased sea temperatures, ocean acidification and changes in primary production, may alter the Marine environment and fisheries in ways that are not yet known. By 2050, the warming of the seas may increase the abundance of warm water species, but some seas are likely to have lower yields (e.g. Irish Sea and English Channel). Stocks of cod could disappear completely by 2100 (Pinnegar *et al.* 2010).

The enactment of the Marine and Coastal Access Act (2009), and the creation of Marine Scotland, the Marine Management Organisation and Inshore Fisheries and Conservation Authorities in England, illustrate a shift towards a more integrated approach to managing the marine environment (Section 27.6.3.2; Section 27.6.3.3). This is likely to necessitate the rebalancing of fisheries exploitation and the delivery of other Marine ecosystem services. Enhancing the latter, however, is also likely to support the restoration of commercial fish stocks that are highly dependent on the

supporting services of these ecosystems. Creating adaptive systems of management will be important for responding to the uncertainty associated with environmental change. Regulations will struggle to achieve their intended goals without better compliance from the fishing industry.

27.6.3 Fisheries-related Response Options

27.6.3.1 Knowledge (foundational)

Since very few people actually get see the underwater world, science has been the prevailing driver of policies to protect the fisheries. Knowledge of the status of fish stocks has been the subject of research for more than 100 years. The International Council for the Exploration of the Sea (ICES), established in 1902, is responsible for scientific assessments on the sustainability of European fish stocks. In the UK, the Fisheries Science Partnership and the Scottish Industry/Science Partnership provide national data on fish stock abundance and distribution, and various government agencies publish statistics on the UK fishing and processing industry.

In addition to recording landings and logbook schemes, fisheries observers are deployed on-board fishing vessels to record catches. For example, Marine Scotland Science observers record all catches of the whitefish and *Nephrops* fleets, data which is then fed to national scientists and ICES. A second observer initiative run by the Scottish Government and the Scottish Fishermen's Federation focuses primarily on cod catches, and has also trialled new gears. In place of observers, Closed Circuit TV is currently being trialled (e.g. on Scottish whitefish and *Nephrops* vessels, and in Devon, England) as a more economic and easier means of recording fishing activities. This system of observation has already proved effective during trials in Denmark (WWF 2009).

Recorded declines in fish stocks led to the development of approaches to calculate sustainable catch levels. Maximum Sustainable Yield is the largest size of catch that can be sustained by the fisheries for the foreseeable future. When there is adequate data on specific stocks, Maximum Sustainable Yield can be a useful point of reference for the recovery of a stock. Developments in science, however, have revealed the limitations to the concept. It does not consider environmental variability, the age and sex structure of stocks, or by-catch. Each species is effectively managed individually under this concept, whereas, in reality, several species are caught together making it difficult to ensure all species are fished within Maximum Sustainable Yield (Horwood *et al.* 2006). Maximum Sustainable Yield has been improved to account for natural mortality by using mortality rates to measure Maximum Sustainable Yield rather than catch size (Natural England 2009h). The UK ratified the 1995 UN Fish Stocks Agreement, which contains a commitment to meet Maximum Sustainable Yield. The agreement stipulates that Maximum Sustainable Yield should be the upper limit for fishing, rather than a target; in doing so, it takes account of the uncertainties associated with natural variability and inaccurate stock assessments. The UK Government also has a commitment made at The World Summit on Sustainable Development (WSSD 2002) in Johannesburg to manage stocks at Maximum Sustainable Yield levels by 2015.

Increased knowledge is urgently required to support an ecosystems approach to marine resource management. Untangling human influences from natural variability and future environment change in Marine bioresources is a theme of research currently being undertaken by Ocean 2025, a multi-institutional and interdisciplinary project funded by the Natural Environment Research Council (Oceans 2025 2010). Any advances in knowledge need to be translated into policy-relevant advice and decision-support tools for marine and fisheries managers. The Centre for Environment, Fisheries and Aquaculture Science, an executive fisheries management agency of the Department for Environment, Food and Rural Affairs, is undertaking research on the ecosystem approach to fisheries management by developing a pilot for the south-west of England (Cefas 2011). Research in this area requires the integration of ecosystem knowledge and social and economic considerations to find effective solutions.

Chapter 12 (Section 12.6) identified many gaps in knowledge for marine resource management. Some of the most important challenges for researchers include quantifying the linkages between ecosystem functions and services, and the likely impact on fisheries from expected environmental changes (e.g. pH and temperature). The Chapter also emphasises the importance of research into tipping points and thresholds in the Marine environment, which could have indirect effects on fish population structure and abundance.

The availability and quality of credible scientific data is essential for achieving sustainable fisheries. In addition to stock assessments, better understanding of the impact of fishing on Marine ecosystems, and the basic biology, ecology and socioeconomics of fisheries, is needed. It will be necessary for scientists to work with fishermen and managers to collect and analyse this data (Defra 2009i).

27.6.3.2 Legislation (enabling)

The Common Fisheries Policy (CFP) was formally established in 1983. Its origins are in the assurance of mutual access by EU Member States to each other's territorial waters for fishing purposes. It was organised to reflect historical fishing patterns in European waters, and its underlying goal was to avoid territorial disputes.

Growing awareness of declines in fish stocks triggered attempts to use the CFP to manage fisheries more sustainably. This culminated, in 2002, with the most recent set of CFP reforms. These reforms acknowledged the growing severity of unsustainable and environmentally destructive fishing practices. They identified and attempted to address various long-standing, worsening failures of the CFP: the prioritisation of short-term objectives in decision-making over quota allocations; the complexity of technical regulations; fishing fleet overcapacity; and poor compliance and enforcement. Lack of stakeholder involvement was also tackled through the setting up of Regional Advisory Councils, consisting of representatives of the fisheries sector and other interest groups (but dominated by the former). The framework for the post-2002 CFP mechanisms is set out in the Basic Regulation (2371/2002/EC). Key elements of the framework are as follows.

1. Total Allowable Catches (TACs). These are agreed each December by the EU Council of Fisheries Ministers, and set an overall weight limit for the amount of a particular species which may be landed. This overall amount is then divided up by nation, according to a methodology (known as 'relative stability') which reflects historical catch levels. In theory, TACs are based on advice from the ICES regarding sustainable levels of catches. Since the 2002 reforms, in an effort to promote long-term management and avoid quotas being ruled by short-term economic interests, some TACs are subject to multi-annual management plans.

2. Technical regulations. These are described by the EC as the qualitative element of the CFP, and complement the quantitative limits it imposes in the form of quotas. They consist of a series of rules intended to encourage selectivity in fishing methods and prohibit particularly environmentally destructive practices. They include minimum mesh sizes for nets (to allow small fish below reproductive age to escape), minimum landing sizes, and limits on by-catch as a percentage of total catch.

3. Fleet overcapacity controls. Fisheries around the world, including in Europe, are under intense pressure because fishing fleets have grown so much in size and efficiency. Economic subsidies have exacerbated this. The CFP 2002 rules have attempted to restructure the EU fleet and reduce overcapacity by, for example, funding vessel-scrapping schemes, and banning using public money to add capacity to, or modernise, ships. Member States have flexibility as to how to carry out capacity reduction obligations. In addition, there are 'effort limiting' rules such as days-at-sea limits.

4. Enforcement. Compliance has been a major issue for the CFP, particularly as the combination of fleet overcapacity and diminishing stocks degrades the industry's competitiveness and pressure builds on fishermen to break the rules (EC 2008). National governments have responsibility for policing fisheries regulations (in England, the Marine Management Organisation is the main coordinator for this; in Scotland, Marine Scotland is the coordinator). The EU performs a role inspecting the standard of national enforcement activities: 'controlling the controllers'. If national-level enforcement is found to be falling short, it is possible for the EU Commission to bring infringement proceedings; for instance, infringement proceedings were brought against Italy and France over failures to properly control their bluefin tuna fishing industries. Recently, new regulations have tightened enforcement procedures, such as the Control Regulation, and the Regulation on Illegal, Unreported and Unregulated Fishing. However non-compliance remains pervasive. A European Court of Auditors report (2007) criticised the UK (as well as five other EU countries) over incomplete and unreliable data collection, badly targeted inspection activities and failure to apply sanctions robustly enough to provide an effective deterrent (European Court of Auditors 2007).

Overall, the 2002 reforms have not succeeded, and it is now almost universally recognised that EU fisheries are in an extremely poor state. According to the EU Commission's Green Paper (2009) on CFP reform, over 80% of European fish stocks are over fished, and 30% of species assessed are outside safe biological limits (i.e. they may be incapable of replenishing). In ecosystem services terms, the provisioning services of EU Marine waters have been vastly overexploited, to the extent that future capacity is in grave doubt.

In short, a number of systemic failures mean that the CFP in its current form is incapable of delivering sustainability objectives. The Commission's Green Paper identified five structural failings: fleet overcapacity, short-term decision-making, imprecise policy objectives, poor compliance, and insufficient industry responsibility.

Efforts to take a more long-term stock management approach are consistently undermined. Short-term decision-making remains dominant, with economic, political and social objectives overriding ecological objectives (EC 2008). Fleet overcapacity creates a vicious circle, as competition among fishing businesses with very low economic resilience encourages ever-harder fishing (ibid.). Policies to reduce overcapacity have, so far, led to reductions of about 2% per year (EU Commission CFP User's Guide, 2009), but this is compensated for by technological advances. The system of technical regulations is complex, costly and, in some cases, contradictory. Methods are found by fishing fleets to counteract short-term negative economic effects of technical restrictions, leading to the imposition of ever-more detailed measures. The incentive for fishers to break the rules in the absence of efficient enforcement mechanisms is strong. Discarding is perhaps the most severe unintended outcome of the current CFP, an effect created by the combination of quotas and minimum limits on the size of fish which may be brought to shore. **Box 27.30**, Section 27.6.3.6 discusses the issue of discards in more detail and outlines options for tackling it.

There is agreement among government (at EU and national levels), environmentalists and the fishing industry that the CFP is not working. Likewise, it is agreed that the next round of reform must entail a comprehensive overhaul, not further piecemeal development of the current flawed system (OCEAN2012 2011 ; ClientEarth 2009; CEC 2009; UKPREU 2009). A complete picture of proposals for a new framework is not possible in this space, but some of the essential elements can be outlined.

A reformed CFP should contain certain fundamental objectives and basic management mechanisms. In order to ensure the system is applied consistently, these should be legally binding, not simply aspirational targets. They could, for example, be enacted in a new Basic Regulation. **Box 27.27** outlines some of the fundamental objectives that are being considered in the CFP reforms.

The Marine Strategy Framework Directive (2008/56/EC) was enacted in 2008. It follows a similar strategy to the WFD, obliging Member States to ensure the 'good environmental status' of all seas under their jurisdiction by 2020. The overall objectives of the MSFD are discussed in more detail in Section 27.7.3. The interaction of the MSFD with the CFP is of crucial importance.

The reformed CFP will need to include an obligation to manage resources so as to comply with the MSFD. This means taking ecological factors—such as the indicators of characteristics, pressures and impacts on marine environmental status set out in the MSFD—into account in fisheries management plans and when allocating fishing opportunities. In particular, this includes the consideration of the descriptors which help to establish good environmental status under the MSFD such as: biological diversity at a regional ecosystem level; populations of fish stocks within safe biological limits and with mortality levels equal to, or lower than, Maximum Sustainable Yield; all elements of Marine food webs (including large fish); seafloor integrity; and contaminants in fish (Section 27.7.3.2).

The Marine and Coastal Access Act 2009 has provided for the creation of a network of Marine Conservation Zones (MCZs) across the UK by 2012. They will protect nationally important Marine wildlife, habitats, geology and geomorphology. The sites of MCZs are currently being identified; Lundy Island became England's first MCZ in January 2010. They build on MPAs designated under the Habitats and Birds Directives, but also take account of social and economic considerations. Levels of protection for MCZs will range from highly protected areas where no extraction, deposition or other damaging activities are allowed, to areas where only minimal restriction on activities is required to protect features. Designation as a MCZ, therefore, does not mean a no-take zone unless it is required. Highly protected (or reference) areas, where fishing and other extractive and disturbing activities are prohibited, are intended to create reference, or near unimpacted, conditions. This will help MCZ managers to understand the value of intact Marine ecosystems compared to areas impacted by activities, including the benefits that closures offer the fisheries (Ashworth et al. 2010).

To date, there are only two statutorily designated MPAs within the area of influence of the Marine and Coastal Access Act: Skomer Island and Lundy Island. There are only three no-take zones (NTZ) in the UK: the east side of Lundy Island, in the Bristol Channel (established in 2003); Lamlash Bay, a community marine conservation area on the Isle of Arran in Scotland (2008); and Flamborough Head in Yorkshire, closed following the signing of a bylaw in 2010. While it is too early for there to be evidence of benefits of the Flamborough Head NTZ, an early study of the Lamlash Bay no-take zone by Howarth (2010) concluded that the NTZ does seem to be providing early scallop fishery benefits, but future monitoring will be needed to detect any substantial improvements in scallop stocks. Natural England have been monitoring the Lundy NTZ, the first of its kind in the UK, and found that, by 2007, lobsters were seven times more abundant inside the NTZ than outside, and that adjacent areas are benefiting from the higher number of lobsters (Natural England 2010c). Scientists are now tagging the lobsters inside the NTZ and fishermen are being encouraged to report catches of tagged animals. This will show how far the lobsters migrate from the NTZ and have implications for commercial fisheries. Closing areas to fisheries may provide benefits to biodiversity and even fisheries production, but there may also be trade-offs in terms of diverting fishing pressure to other localities (Section 27.6.3.6).

27.6.3.3 Policies, institutions and governance (enabling)

The current problem of overfishing originally stemmed from a history of fish being a common pool resource open to anyone to exploit (MA 2005). Without government intervention based on knowledge of the limits of exploitation, individual fishermen have little short-term incentive to limit the quantity of fish they harvest.

The introduction of quotas through the CFP to help stocks recover has resulted in landings of demersal fish decreasing by over 50%. Set by the EC, TAC limits (Section 27.6.3.2) control the amount of fish that can be removed from a stock. Total Allowable Catches should be based on assessments by ICES that draw from scientific surveys by Member States on the estimated size of the fish stock and the size of total landings that will not place stocks outside of MSY limits.

Today, 88% of European quota stocks are still overfished, suggesting that the current TAC quota system needs revision to deliver sustainable fisheries (Roberts *et al.* 2005). The drawbacks of the system include its targeting of specific species, problems associated with its high information requirements, that it does not consider by-catch and damage to habitats, and it fails to protect the genetic and population structure of stocks. Precautionary quotas recognise the uncertainties in stock assessment and reduce the risk of exceeding sustainable catch levels, but still have the same inherent drawbacks (Roberts *et al.* 2005). Because of these reasons, quota systems are not compatible with an ecosystems approach.

The principle of relative stability in the CFP divides quota rights proportionately between nations who have historically exploited the fishery. Nations are able to negotiate for changes in their allocation to ensure the quota can support their fleet or at least its managed downsizing. If the EC agree to an increase in quota size, then the quotas of the nations with rights to the fishery will also increase to maintain the same ratio as before the CFP, even if this goes beyond the agreed TAC. This makes the system biased to economic sustainability at the cost of ecological sustainability and the long-term viability of the fisheries (WWF 2007). Fisheries Ministers also tend to set TAC levels higher than that recommended by scientists to protect fishing communities (**Figure 27.32**; Roberts *et al.* 2005). In the long-run this will only jeopardise the viability of the industry.

The fall in domestic fish landings due to quotas has shifted demand for popular fish species to import markets (**Figure 27.33**): imports of fish into the UK increased by 46% from 1998 to 2008. This shifts the pressure on fish stocks to other parts of the world with often weaker regulations and management of fisheries than in European waters.

With growing acknowledgement that the current quota system is not achieving its objectives, and perhaps has the

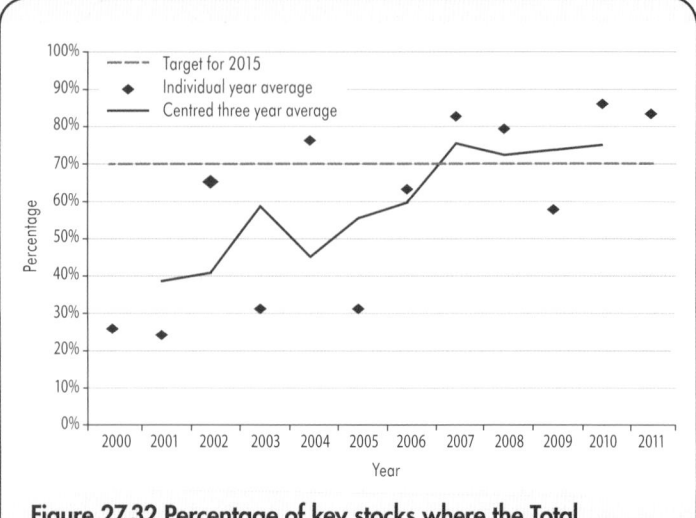

Figure 27.32 Percentage of key stocks where the Total Allowable Catch (TAC) limit is consistent with scientific advice. Source: data from Scottish Government Marine Directorate (2010).

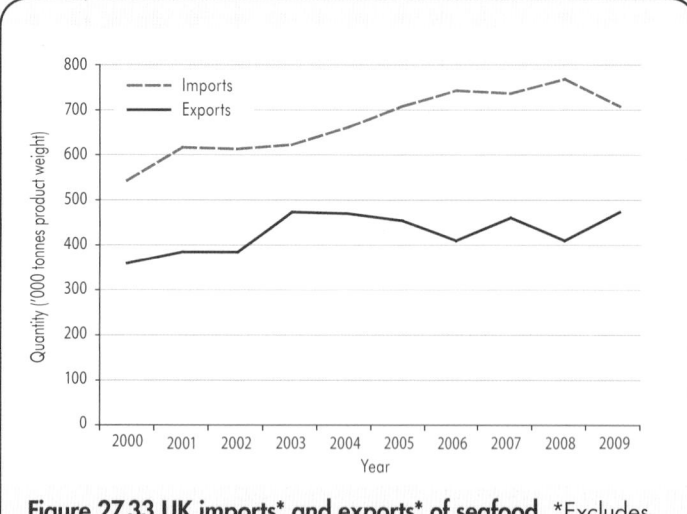

Figure 27.33 UK imports* and exports* of seafood. *Excludes fish products. Source: data from MMO (2010c).

least conservation value out of any of the management options available, alternative policies and measures are being considered including incentive-based schemes (Section 27.6.3.5), effort and spatial management alternatives, and gear restrictions (Section 27.6.3.6). Fisheries management is moving away from conventional approaches that focus on target species with little consideration of species with limited or no commercial value. The realisation that the entire Marine food web sustains commercial fish stocks has led to the acceptance, in principle, of the ecosystem approach in the management of fisheries, whereby the whole system is assessed and managed. More research and applied management is needed to explore how it could be attained in practice; one current example is the Centre for Environment, Fisheries and Aquaculture Science's Ecosystem Approach to Fisheries Management Project which is working to develop knowledge in this area.

A true ecosystem approach requires that the fisheries are not managed in isolation from other marine activities such as renewable energy, recreation and aggregate extraction. All these activities compete for space, and they impact on the ecosystems that support the fisheries and vice versa.

Decisions made by the fisheries sector, therefore, need take account of the environmental effects of fishing (FAO 2008). The Marine and Coastal Access Act (MCA 2009) aims to create a strategic planning system that provides for a more integrated approach to Marine management and the sustainable use of marine resources including fisheries (Section 27.7). Recent changes to UK fisheries management, such as reforms associated with the Marine and Coastal Access Act and new inshore fisheries arrangements (see below), have the potential to improve the status of commercial fish stocks. Chapter 12 expressed concern, however, that these measures may not address the disturbance of benthic habitats. Targeted measures may be required to protect the seabed, especially where environmentally sensitive or functionally important species are present.

The fisheries were previously managed by the Scottish Fisheries Protection Agency and Marine and Fisheries Agency in English and Welsh waters who were responsible for enforcing seas fisheries regulations, licensing UK fishing vessels and enforcing quotas. Marine Scotland and the Marine Management Organisation assumed their responsibilities in 2009 and 2010, respectively, including fisheries management activities related to the CFP, fisheries data collection and Marine nature conservation. Their jurisdiction is beyond six nautical miles offshore, with the inshore fisheries controlled by differing institutional arrangements in the four countries of the UK (e.g. Inshore Fisheries and Conservation Authorities (IFCAs) in England; **Box 27.28**). The Marine Management Organisation and Marine Scotland both also hold responsibility for the planning and management of the full range of marine activities to ensure that the integrated approach called for in the Marine and Coastal Access Act and Scotland Marine Act is met. The Marine Management Organisation has new responsibilities including the power to establish nature conservation bylaws that will have implications for the fisheries sector.

A consensus is now emerging among fishers, processors, retailers, consumers, conservation organisations and governments that something has to be done to increase the abundance and diversity of fish and improve the health of the Marine environment (Natural England 2009h). This shared objective creates an opportunity for collaborative action to address overfishing and destructive practices. It is argued that 'top-down' fisheries approaches associated with the CFP have not been effective at achieving either ecological or social sustainability (Thompson 2008b). In the Green Paper on CFP reform (EC 2009a), a lack of stakeholder engagement in decision-making was highlighted as a key failure of the CFP. The centralised approach, where regulations apply a 'one size fits all' approach, failed to take account of local circumstances (*ibid.*).

Allowing fishers to be more involved in the management of the resource upon which they depend is seen as one way to correct this. Co-management is thought to provide several benefits such as providing opportunities for social learning (Section 27.6.3.4), building trust and improving compliance with regulations and reducing enforcement costs (Pinkerton 1989; Borrini-Feyerabend & Borrini 1996; Schusler *et al.* 2003). Fisheries organisations at a local level can provide a useful forum for knowledge generation and cooperation to solve problems through deliberation and joint learning (Berkes 2009). Inshore fisheries management in England and Wales is one of the oldest examples of co-management of fisheries, but is currently being reformed (**Box 27.28**).

Furthermore, since there are significant knowledge gaps in and uncertainties about the linkages between Marine ecosystem functions and services, and on the impact of environmental changes (Section 27.6.3.1), management needs to be flexible enough to be changed as information becomes available and the impact of fisheries and other Marine management actions become apparent ('learning by doing'). Adaptive management, whereby decision-makers continuously gather and integrate appropriate social, economic and ecological information to improve measures, is particularly relevant for the sustainable management of fisheries (Costanza *et al.* 1998).

27.6.3.4 Changing social attitudes (enabling)

Public awareness and consumer choice. In the past, raising public awareness of the threat to the UK's Marine ecosystem was problematic. Only a limited number of people, mainly SCUBA divers, have the opportunity to view and interact with the UK's underwater seascapes. The decline of UK fish stocks is also masked by the industry shifting fishing effort to other fish stocks and species further from land, and using more sophisticated technologies. Imports and aquaculture make up the shortfall from wild capture fisheries. These innovations prevent the reduction in supply from UK waters being represented in the price of fish.

The British do, however, have a strong affinity with the sea, and seaside leisure activities continue to grow in popularity. The media, particularly natural history documentaries, enable people to experience the underwater world for themselves. Recent environmental documentaries (e.g. The End of Line) and televised campaigns (e.g. Channel 4's *Fish Fight*) have been instrumental in raising awareness about the plight of the fisheries. Section 12.3.3 highlights the importance of membership in recreational clubs for engaging users of the sea, such as sea anglers, in conservation activities that benefit Marine ecosystems. Educational programmes and aquariums help children and adults to learn about Marine ecosystems and fisheries (Section 27.7.3.4).

Influencing consumer choice can alter the market for fisheries products by, for example, reducing demand for the most overfished species, reducing consumption of seafood overall, and raising demand for fish caught in a more sustainable manner. In 2008, consumers in GB bought 385,000 tonnes of seafood from retail outlets. According to research by the Seafood Choices Alliance, in 2007, 74% of those consumers believe environmental considerations to be important, and 90% would be more likely to buy seafood that is labelled as 'environmentally responsible'. More than 50% would pay 5–10% more for sustainable seafood (Natural England 2009h).

Certification schemes help to respond to consumer demands for sustainably sourced seafood. The certification of fish products by the Marine Stewardship Council (MSC)

Box 27.28 Inshore fisheries management in the devolved UK context: decentralised management in practice. Source: Phillipson & Symes (2010).

Two different systems of inshore fisheries management had emerged in the UK by the 2000s. England and Wales decentralised responsibility to twelve Sea Fisheries Committees (SFCs) over a century ago with jurisdiction up to six nautical miles offshore for regulations, stock management, monitoring and enforcement. This exemplifies one of the first cases in Europe of co-management between the local fishing industry and local government. The strengths of SFCs were in their local knowledge of the fisheries, the ability to design management appropriate for local circumstances, and the engagement of the fishing industry. Giving responsibility to the committees for the management of their inshore fisheries broadly aligns with current notions of localism. Since the mid-1990s, the remit of SFCs in England and Wales expanded to include environmental management as well, but insufficient funding and inflexible regulations have been attributed to slow progress in this area. In Scotland, a more centralised approach to inshore fisheries management emerged. This has been attributed to opposition to local management stemming from conflicts of interest between local, small-scale fishing fleets in the west, and larger, capitalised fleets in the north-east. Few local management arrangements existed.

The Marine and Coastal Access Act triggered a reorganisation of inshore fisheries management in England with the replacement of SFCs with Inshore Fisheries and Conservation Authorities (IFCAs) in 2011. The IFCAs will not be significantly different, but will have changes to structure, duties and powers to address identified weaknesses. The environmental management representation will be strengthened on these authorities. The aim of the IFCAs is to ensure sea fisheries are "carried out in a sustainable way", and balance the "social and economic benefits [...] with the need to protect the marine environment". They are also responsible for meeting the conservation objectives of MCZs. The Department for Environment, Food and Rural Affairs will announce further reforms of inshore fisheries management in 2011 based on the research and consultation undertaken in the Sustainable Access to Inshore Fisheries project (Defra 2010h). It is expected that these reforms will attempt to address issues relating to the displacement of inshore fisheries due to the increasing number of MPA designations.

In Wales, SFCs were abolished in 2008 and management responsibilities were assumed by the Welsh Assembly Government. Following sustained opposition to the changes from environmental and fisheries organisations, a stakeholder advisory group was established in 2009 that recommended the establishment of three Inshore Fisheries Groups for South, Mid and North Wales, and a national advisory group of stakeholders (e.g. commercial sea fishing, aquaculture, recreational fishing and nature conservation). The Inshore Fisheries Groups will represent the interests of local fisheries.

In Scotland, the drawbacks of the centralised approach were exposed by an inquiry in 2005. The inquiry led to the establishment of six Inshore Fisheries Groups who are developing local management plans to cover stock management, market initiatives and local development. The Inshore Fisheries Groups are voluntary groups with no environmental management responsibilities. Within the Groups there is an Executive Committee representing fishing industry interests, and a separate advisory group where other stakeholders represent a diverse range of interests including fisheries research and environment and conservation concerns.

It is too early to conclude how each system of inshore fisheries management will influence the provisioning service of fish or change the impacts of the industry on Marine ecosystems. Each places differing degrees of power and responsibility with various actors with an interest in coastal zone resource management.

enables consumers to be confident that they are buying from sustainable fisheries, and allows fisheries to prove their practices are more sustainable than alternatives. In addition to fish stock considerations, the MSC also uses Food and Agriculture Organization (FAO) guidelines to set standards for its eco-label to minimise impacts on wider ecosystems, including impacts on habitats from fishing gear. Transparency in the supply chain is critical in maintaining consumer trust in such schemes. In 2010, a total of 101 fisheries were certified by MSC (and a further 131 were undergoing assessment), including 13 of the UK's fisheries (18 under assessment; MSC 2010). The higher market-value of these products can encourage fishers to become certified, thereby bringing benefits to the long-term sustainability of fish provision and a reduction in harm to Marine ecosystems. Although awareness of MSC eco-labels has grown, Kaiser & Edwards-Jones (2006) identified barriers that may prevent its wider uptake including: a lack of concern by the public for marine fish or the need for sustainable fisheries; whether fishers will continue to receive added financial rewards; and difficulties of quality assurance.

Businesses, particularly supermarkets, can play an important role in reducing demand for depleted fish species through their purchasing policies (for example, only stocking fish certified from sustainable fisheries) and through their advertising (**Box 27.29**). These purchasing policies typically respond to the attitudes and values of their customers. The media is extremely powerful in changing shopping behaviours, at least in the short-term, as evidenced by soaring sales of sustainable fish following Channel 4's *Fish Fight* television series (Smithers 2011). Purchasing decisions in the public sector can also stimulate markets for sustainable fisheries. The MSC's Fish & Kids project is working with schools in England to serve MSC certified food. Since the project began in 2007, demand for, and supply of, MSC fish in the food service sector has dramatically increased. The Fish & Kids project assists nearly 4,000 primary schools to serve MSC fish, and the world's largest contract caterer recently achieved MSC certification for all its UK sites (more than 700) (MSC 2010).

27.6.3.5 Markets and incentives (instrumental)

Incentive-based schemes are beginning to emerge as an alternative to regulations that control effort and gear (Section 27.6.3.6). The Scottish Conservation Credits Scheme, the first of its kind in the EU, aims to reduce cod mortality and whitefish discards by providing incentives, in the form of extra days at sea, to fishermen who adopt best practice in stock conservation (Seafood Scotland 2010). The scheme is run by the Scottish Government, but has been successful at securing the support of the industry (**Figure 27.34**). It is focused on meeting the requirements of the EU Cod Recovery Plan of December 2008. It provides credits to fishermen for the adoption of a variety of practices that avoid catching cod, such as closures and gear restrictions These measures are complemented with effort management and a ban on 'high grading', whereby only larger, fresher fish are retained and less valuable, but still marketable, fish are discarded (WWF 2009). The measures implemented under the Scottish Conservation Credits Scheme have already reduced cod discards in the North Sea, but other stocks, such as haddock and whiting, remain at risk (WWF 2009). The scheme could be extended to target these in the same way that cod has been protected. Several other countries have replicated the scheme in part or completely.

The Marine Conservation Society and ClientEarth (2010b) have developed proposals for an alternative Fishing Credits System. The system is built on an ecosystems approach, which means (among other things) rules reflect ecosystem regions and up-to-date scientific advice. At its core is a credits allocation system for sustainable mixed catch quotas. The Fishing Credits System would assign credits annually to all species likely to be impacted within a particular marine region (including by-catch species). Different species and stocks are given differing credit weightings according to sustainability (ecosystems) criteria, such as the species' ecological vulnerability and stock level. Each fisher is given a credit allowance per licence, and everything caught (including by-catch) is counted towards that maximum credit allowance. Therefore, the entire catch will need to be landed (with very limited exceptions). Fishers can choose what they catch, and in what quantity for each species, as long as it does not exceed their total credit allowance, so discarding and over-quota issues are eliminated. Micromanagement and detailed technical rules are abolished under the Fishing Credits System. 'Results based management' means only an outcome is specified and it is left to the fishers to decide how they achieve that (i.e. what gear is used, and what mesh size and twine thickness is preferred). To provide more flexibility, part of each fisher's annual credit allocation will be transferable. The Fishing Credits System incentivises and rewards best

---

Box 27.29 Supermarkets sourcing sustainable seafood. Source: Natural England (2009h).

Supermarkets control the majority of the UK market for fish. The purchasing decisions they make can, therefore, have a tremendous influence on the fishing industry and, ultimately, the ecosystems that they impact. Consumers are increasingly concerned about where fish products are sourced and many want to purchase and pay more for sustainable seafood. In a bid to demonstrate their 'green' credentials, and in response to high profile campaigns by environmental organisations, especially Greenpeace, several supermarkets have stopped the sale of some species and/or are stocking more eco-labelled products.

For instance, Waitrose "does not take any flatfish caught from beam trawlers, which are inefficient in terms of fuel consumption and potentially damaging to the marine environment" (Waitrose 2011). Marks & Spencer claim to ensure that all their seafood is traceable to the vessel that it was caught on and that it was caught within their quota. It has also banned undeclared landings (Greenpeace 2006). Sainsbury's, which has a 21.4% market share in fresh fish, had pledged to stock only MSC certified fish, but was unable to source adequate quantities of fish to meet demand. Instead, they use a traffic light colour-coded scheme to indicate which fish are sustainably sourced, and stocked over 80 products with an MSC label by early 2011. At the beginning of 2011, Tesco announced that, by 2012, it will only be sourcing tuna caught by line or pole.

practice in order to encourage fishers to target species deemed sustainable in a selective manner. For example, fishers are rewarded with extra catch allowances for using and/or developing best practice (such as improved selective gear technology and avoiding closed areas) and there is preferential access for those with a good compliance record (ClientEarth 2010b).

27.6.3.6 Technologies and practices (instrumental)

Management of fishing effort. The failure of the quota system to make the fisheries more sustainable and the urgent need to reduce fishing effort, especially to help the recovery of North Sea cod, led to the introduction of 'days at sea restrictions' in 2003 for the North Sea and Irish Sea as part of cod recovery plans; as a result, Roundfish vessels were limited to 16 days at sea per month (**Figure 27.35**). Restricting the time spent at sea by fishers has merely encouraged more intensive fishing and incentivised the fishermen to improve catch efficiency by using larger nets, more hooks and faster tows (Catchpole *et al.* 2005). Concentrating fishing effort into shorter, intense periods not only risks the safety of crews, but also floods the market with fish, thus driving prices down (Roberts *et al.* 2005).

Decommissioning schemes were introduced to reduce the capacity of the UK's fishing fleet. The number of UK fishing vessels fell by 17% between 2000 and 2009 in the UK, and the number of fishermen decreased by 22% over the same period (**Figure 27.36**; (MMO 2010c). While this has made important reductions in fleet size, technological improvements to maximise efficiency, such as detection and capture advances, have largely offset reductions in fishing effort resulting from the downsizing of the fleet. In fact, the scheme may have inadvertently enabled fishing companies to receive compensation for decommissioning older vessels, allowing them to invest in the modernisation of their remaining vessels (Natural England 2009h).

Gear restrictions aim to control the types of fishing gear that is used in designated locations and/or for certain species. Improvements in the selectivity of gear can reduce by-catch and other modifications can reduce impacts on Marine habitats. The adoption of such gear usually results in decreased catch efficiency, so either it needs to be enforced by law, or added value is given to fish caught using the gear through certification schemes. Mesh size restrictions can avoid the capture of young fishes, but such nets can become ineffective if towed in such a way that the mesh closes when they are full, and when the fishermen are targeting species of different sizes. **Box 27.30** describes the problem of discards and ways to tackle it. The banning of gear can remove destructive fishing practices, but can be met with resistance from the fishing industry if there has been considerable investment in the technology.

Research conducted for the Centre for Environment, Fisheries and Aquaculture Sciences (Corporate Culture 2010) on increasing the uptake of more sustainable gear and practices by fishers recommended conducting local trials to test solutions, making it as easy as possible for them to adopt new behaviour (e.g. they do not lose money), and communicating progress along the way. One way to encourage wider adoption of new gear is to reward fishers who adopt selective fishing gear with more days at sea, and penalise those with more intensive fishing technologies by deducting days.

Spatial management options. In addition to spatial restrictions on gear use, a number of other spatial options exist for fisheries management. The cessation of fishing in

Figure 27.35 Sussex Inshore Fisheries and Conservation Authorities Patrol. *Photo courtesy of Sussex IFCA.*

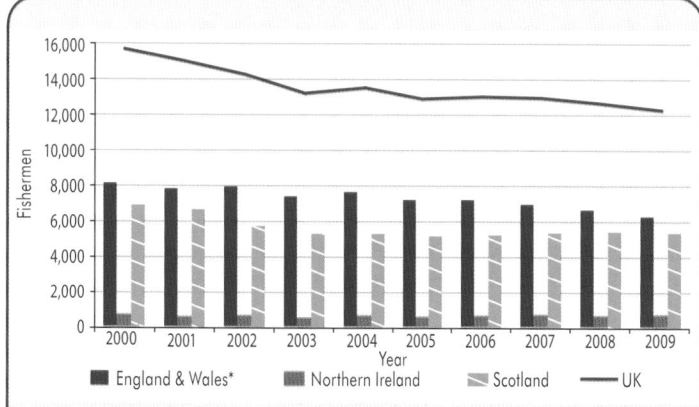

Figure 27.34 Fishing boats in Kirkwall harbour, Orkney Islands, Scotland. *Photo by joeri-c, available under a Creative Commons Attribution-ShareAlike license.*

Figure 27.36 The number of fishermen in the UK from 2000 to 2009. Source: data from MMO (2010c).

certain areas can protect or increase the abundance of fish that are particularly susceptible or overfished. Permanent closures of such areas are expected to protect habitats, but can also benefit surrounding fisheries as fishes increase and leave the closed area. Meanwhile, temporary or seasonal closures control fishing effort on migratory species at certain times of the year or in certain locations. Closures can be a highly effective way of reducing fishing mortality and improving spawning (Gell & Roberts 2003). In the Barents Sea, the Norwegian Government enforce temporary closures that have helped with the recovery of cod and haddock. In this case, the government conduct real-time sampling of fish size to judge whether to close an area. In contrast, a pilot of the closure method in Scotland gave responsibility to fishers to call for closures instead (**Box 27.31**). One of the main benefits of schemes such as that in the Barents Sea is that an economic incentive is provided for fishermen to adopt selective fishing gear that allows them access to closed areas.

Area closures can also have consequences for other species and habitats. The displacement of trawling (for example, from

---

Box 27.31 Scottish real-time closures pilot. Source: Catchpole & Gray (2010).

In 2007, real-time closures were piloted in the North Sea by Scottish skippers in partnership with the Scottish Government and scientists from the Fisheries Research Services. The fishermen agreed that they would record when they caught more than 60 fish smaller than 35 cm in length in one hour. If this happened three times over a 48-hour period, an area of 15 x 15 miles would be closed for 21 days. There was a maximum of nine closures at a time and no more than three within a 45 x 45 mile square. The fishers were responsible for notifying the authorities of the need for the closures and for abiding the closure in return for extra days at sea and an 11% increase in cod quota.

An estimated 300,000 juvenile cod avoided capture. During the pilot, however, the minimum fish length was increased from 35 to 50 cm and the schemes objective changed to protect spawning stock rather than juveniles. It is unclear whether discards were reduced as a result of the pilot.

According to a study of 15 different discard pilot projects from across Europe by Catchpole & Gray (2010) there are seven important determinants of improving the viability of projects: fisheries crises, incentivisation, funding, expertise, leadership, and enforcement. The Scottish pilot met all of these criteria except for enforcement.

Box 27.30 What can we do about discards?

Discarding—when fish are thrown back to the sea dead or alive—is perhaps the most perverse outcome of the current CFP, an effect created by the combination of quotas and minimum limits on the size of fish which may be brought to shore. Both of these measures were intended to assist sustainability by making sure that not too many fish, particularly those which have not had a chance to reproduce, are taken out of the ecosystem. In fact, they have created the opposite effect. Discarding occurs in mixed fisheries, such as those in the North Sea, where boats fish for a number of different species. Once a vessel runs out of quota for one species (e.g. cod), it continues fishing for another species (e.g. haddock), but because it is not possible to fish completely selectively it also catches more cod. It is illegal for this cod catch to be brought to shore, so instead it is thrown overboard. Likewise, prohibiting fish below a certain size from being landed may not prevent them from being caught—they are simply discarded. The extent of discards depends on the fishery and the type of gear used. It has been estimated that for beam trawl catch in the North Sea, as much as 60% is discarded (EC 2007). Overall, in the North Sea mixed fishery, nearly a third of the total weight landed is discarded annually, which amounts to 10% of the estimated total biomass of fish in the North Sea (Catchpole et al. 2005).

Days at sea and decommissioning only serve to reduce discards by reducing the proportion of fishing effort; instead, they create an incentive to fish less selectively in the limited time available (Catchpole et al. 2005). Because the rate of discards is not reduced, any increase in fishing effort will also increase discards.

Using more selective fishing gear, such as different mesh sizes and escape panels for non-target species, can lower by-catch rates. The fitting of square mesh panels onto Nephrops trawls, for example, can enable juvenile and non-target fish to escape. The modification of North Sea Nephrops trawls in such a manner was legislated in 2002. If a second square mesh is fitted, however, by-catch of undersized fish can be reduced by an extra 43%, and there is potential to increase its efficiency further (Revill et al. 2007). Such gear modifications have their limitations. If non-targeted species have a similar habitat range, morphology and size as catch species, selective gear can be ineffective.

Project 50%, piloted by the Centre for Environment, Fisheries and Aquaculture Sciences and fishermen, aimed to reduce discards from 12 Devon beam trawlers by 50%. The vessels involved in the project fitted new trawl nets with larger meshes, square mesh escape panels and novel headlines in their construction. Each skipper designed their own trawl to meet their fishing patterns, but with the aim to allow juvenile fish to escape. The results from the project are impressive: the fishermen participating in the scheme threw an average of 52% fewer fish back into the sea, with some in the trial reducing their discards by over 65% compared to traditional nets (Cefas 2010; **Figure 27.37**).

Another option that takes the opposite approach to the CFP (under which it is illegal to bring discards ashore) is the banning of discards. The Norwegian Government has been operating this policy since 1983. All commercial fish species caught in Norwegian waters are landed and deducted from quotas with the aims of making use of the food source and better recording catches. Because smaller fish have a low value, it provides an incentive for fishers to find ways of reducing the capture of non-target and juvenile fish. On the downside, it can encourage capture of smaller fish if there is profit to be made. The ban is also difficult to enforce, and some compensation is required to encourage fishers to comply with it (Catchpole et al. 2005). In March 2011, the EC Fisheries Commissioner proposed the possibility of a European-wide discard ban as part of CFP reforms in 2013 (BBC 2011b).

2½ baskets of discards from new nets   **4 baskets of discards from old nets**

3 baskets of discards from new nets   **6 baskets of discards from old nets**

Figure 27.37 Fishermen participating in Project 50% threw an average of 52% fewer fish back into the sea. Source: Cefas (2010), photos courtesy of Simon Armstrong.

overfished and degraded habitats to other areas) can often have a significant impact on benthic communities in the new fishing grounds since these areas were previously less disturbed (Hiddink *et al.* 2006). To avoid such incidents there is a need to have a sufficient understanding of the region's biology, benthic habitats and the effects of shifting fleet pressure and trawling to elsewhere (Catchpole *et al.* 2005; Hiddink *et al.* 2006). In the North Sea, a 12-week closure to protect spawning cod inadvertently redirected fishers to areas with high juvenile haddock stocks. Fishers reported a 95% discard rate which led to them voluntarily suspend fishing. Unfortunately, they set to sea again after three weeks when compensation was refused in favour of long-term decommissioning (Catchpole *et al.* 2005).

Marine reserves have received increasing attention recently as an effective response for achieving both fisheries management and conservation objectives. Reserves offer permanent protection from fishing to sensitive habitats and vulnerable species. They can also support surrounding fisheries by providing a refuge for stocks to replenish and migrate outside the Marine reserve (Roberts *et al.* 2005). Within 5–10 years, stocks of commercial species can increase by 3–5 times (Gell & Roberts 2003). Marine reserves are known to redevelop natural age structures, protect genetic diversity and provide a safety net for management failures (*ibid.*). In addition to commercial benefits, reserves can restore ecosystem functioning and be highly valuable for biodiversity conservation, as well as providing tourism and educational opportunities. The UK has three no-take zones, where fishing is prohibited, which are discussed, along with MCZs, in Section 27.6.3.2.

27.6.3.7 Voluntary actions (instrumental)

There are a number of options for changing the behaviour of fishers which complement co-management and decentralised fisheries management approaches. Public pressure for certified fish products encourages fishers to meet this demand through the adoption of sustainable fishing practices (**Box 27.32**) (Natural England 2009h).

Box 27.32 The North Sea Haddock Fishery. Source: Moody Marine Ltd. (2010).

The MSC certified the North Sea Haddock Fishery in 2011, which became the first Scottish whitefish to receive certification. The fishery supports 192 vessels which fish offshore using seine and trawl nets. In 2009, 27,507 tonnes of haddock were landed.

The North Sea Haddock Fishery is a large-scale, industrial fishery which has invested heavily in sustainable gear and equipment for monitoring and targeting haddock. The fishery was assessed as being well-managed and effective management strategies are in place to assist the recovery of two (cod and whiting) out of the five retained by-catch species which are currently outside safe biological limits. However, to continue being certified after 2015 the fishery must address a number of conditions. These include implementing further mitigation measures to reduce by-catch, such as working with research organisations to find and use more selective gear, and to provide accurate quantitative information on total catch including discarded catch. By setting such conditions, the MSC can ensure improvements continue to be made by the fishery and best practices are adopted as they become available.

Education and social learning are important attributes of the co-management of natural resources (Schusler *et al.* 2003). Environmental education programmes for fishers aim to build their capacity to make informed decisions. Social learning involves the participation of a diverse range of stakeholders in a process of open communication and deliberation whereby multiple sources of knowledge are used to solve problems. Such processes in the co-management of fisheries allows the fishing industry, environmental agencies and NGOs, government representatives and other stakeholders to share their perspectives, experiences and knowledge, and develop a common understanding for joint action. Social learning involves learning-by-doing and, given time, can become adaptive management where management changes in response to lessons learnt from previous actions (Berkes 2009). There is also some scope to use these consultative mechanisms to explore new alternative livelihood opportunities for fishers and boat owners, such as through marine-based wildlife tourism (Section 27.8).

Fishermen have shown a commitment to improve the sustainability of the fisheries through a number of voluntary codes of conduct; for example, within the Loch Torridon *Nephrops* creel fishery a code of conduct has been agreed in order to increase the size, and improve the quality, of the shellfish caught (Gray & Hatchard 2007). The industry and Seafish developed the Responsible Fishing Scheme in 2006, whereby fishermen sign a commitment to fish responsibly. Responsible Fishing Scheme certified fishing vessels minimise discards of non-target species and the impact of fishing gear. They also commit to ensuring their activities do not result in by-catch of seabirds and dolphins (Seafish 2011). Although these measures do not address fundamental issues of overfishing, they demonstrate the industry's willingness to move towards more sustainable fishing. Unfortunately, the benefits of this scheme for ecosystems have not been quantified.

27.6.4 Fisheries Summary

Table 27.16 summarises the key insights from this review of responses in the fisheries context, highlighting those that have been well-established, but also identifying a set of responses that are either in early implementation or are proposed. It is important to learn from these early pilots across all sectors to scale-up the adoption of an integrated ecosystem approach to the management of the UK's diverse habitats, which is one key policy direction that this review recommends. A number of proposals focus on the future direction of the Common Fisheries Policy, which is currently under discussion.

27.7 Marine and Coasts

27.7.1 Marine and Coastal Ecosystem Services and Human Well-being

The Marine and Coastal Margin habitats of the UK provide a variety of valuable ecosystem services and benefits to society. In addition to the food provisioning services discussed under Section 27.6, Marine ecosystems provide

Table 27.16 Fisheries Summary.

	Established responses	Early implementation, pilots	Proposed, under development
Knowledge	■ Fish stock assessments ■ Monitoring of landings ■ Logbook schemes ■ Calculating Maximum Sustainable Yield	■ CCTV monitoring onboard fishing vessels ■ Applied research on the ecosystem approach to fisheries management ■ Research collaborations between scientists and fishermen	■ Quantify linkages between ecosystem functions and services ■ Research on tipping points and thresholds ■ Better understanding of the impacts of fisheries on marine ecosystems
Legislation	■ Common Fisheries Policy ■ Total Allowable Catches ■ Regulations governing fishing practices ■ National level enforcement ■ Conservation bylaws	■ Marine Strategy Framework Directive ■ Marine Conservation Zones	■ Common Fisheries Policy reform: prioritisation of ecological sustainability; full adoption of ecosystem approach (based on ecosystem regions); integration of the Common Fisheries Policy with the Marine Strategy Framework Directive; setting of legally binding fishing opportunities based on scientific advice; management of total catch (not landings); discard ban.
Policies, institutions and governance	■ Sectoral management of fisheries ■ Management of target species ■ Fisheries agencies ■ Co-management of inshore fisheries (England and Wales)	■ Ecosystem-based approaches ■ Management of fisheries with other marine activities (integrated) ■ Coordination through Marine Management Organisation, etc. ■ New inshore fisheries (co-) management arrangements	■ Greater involvement of fishermen in decision-making ■ Adaptive management
Changing social attitudes	■ Media, e.g. documentaries, raising awareness ■ Membership in recreation clubs ■ Educational programmes and aquarium ■ Certification schemes		
Markets and incentives	■ Fishing vessel decommissioning schemes	■ Scottish Conservation Credits Scheme ■ Extra 'days at sea' awarded for adoption of more sustainable practices	■ Fishing Credits Scheme
Technologies and practices	■ Days at sea restrictions ■ Selective fishing gear ■ Closure of areas to fishing (seasonal, permanent, and temporary)	■ Trials of new selective fishing gear ■ Participation of fishermen in developing selective gear (e.g. Project 50%) ■ Real-time closures ■ No take zones and marine reserves	
Voluntary actions	■ Fisheries joining certification schemes ■ Voluntary codes of conduct, e.g. Responsible Fishing Scheme ■ Voluntary involvement in decision making processes		

industrial inputs (e.g. blue biotechnology) and fertiliser (e.g. seaweed), regulate the climate, breakdown waste and detoxify pollution. Coastal ecosystems protect coastlines from flooding and erosion: a service that will be increasingly tested under rising sea levels and increased storm activity. Both the coast and sea are popular for recreation, leisure and tourism—over 250 million visits are made to the coast every year—providing physical and mental health benefits for visitors (Section 27.8; **Figure 27.38**). Coastal Margin and Marine habitats are also likely to store and sequester substantial amounts of carbon, but this has yet to be quantified (Thompson 2008a). In the future, marine sources of energy are expected to account for a larger proportion of the UK's energy mix, both from physical processes (e.g. wave and tidal) and biofuels (e.g. algae; Section 27.9). The total value of services provided by coastal habitats is estimated to be £48 billion (Chapter 11).

The way we plan our coastlines and seas, and the human activities that operate on and in them, affects the ability of ecosystems to provide services. Human activities have impacted the seafloor by, for example, extracting aggregates

Figure 27.38 Southwold Beach, Suffolk. *Photo by Gerry Balding available under a Creative Commons Attribution-NonCommercial-NoDerivs license.*

and constructing offshore windfarms, coastal defences, ports and coastal developments. The disturbance of the seabed has had localised impacts on benthic organisms and the regulating and supporting services they provide (Section 12.3). The value of coastal protection afforded by ecosystems has been overlooked in coastal planning until recently. The building of sea defences replaced multifunctional ecosystems with single service structures (Chapter 11.3). Some infrastructure developments, however, such as offshore windfarms and artificial reefs, can create habitats that provide benefits for conservation, commercial fisheries, recreation and tourism. **Figure 27.39** summarises the major marine and coastal-related direct and indirect drivers and their impact on ecosystem services.

27.7.2 Challenges for Marine and Coastal Planning

The challenge for coastal and marine planners is to manage the demands of multiple users of the UK's increasingly crowded coasts and seas—a highly dynamic and complex environment which is continually changing in response to weather variations, sediment supply, land use and other human influences (Section 11.2). Coastal planning must address threats from sea-level rise, as well as pollution and continued development pressures. These pressures are compounded by the position of the coast between rising seas and encroaching land uses, which leaves little space for safe coastal habitat except at protected sites. Sea-level rise is likely to result in increased wave energy reaching shorelines (Section 11.2.3), thus impacting on the sea defence services of Coastal Margins. Shoreline planning decisions made now can, therefore, have long-term repercussions.

Managing trade-offs between marine activities competing for space and resources, while minimising their impacts on Marine biodiversity is the task of marine planners. Leisure and commercial uses of the Marine environment continue to expand and include renewable energy development, increasing shipping traffic, further gas pipe and cable-laying, and the growing popularity of marine recreational activities.

Marine and coastal planning is in a period of massive transformation in response to new marine and coastal legislation across the UK (Section 27.7.3.2). The challenge is to ensure that the ambitious goals of this new legislation are met.

27.7.3 Response Options for Marine and Coastal Planning

27.7.3.1 Knowledge (foundational)

Knowledge of the Marine environment has typically trailed behind our understanding of terrestrial systems. Charting Progress 2 (UKMMAS 2010), the most comprehensive report of the state of the UK's seas, prioritised several areas where efforts are needed to improve understanding of the relationships between pressures and impacts:

Better criteria to determine whether the seas are clean, healthy, safe, productive and biologically diverse. Clearly defined criteria are needed of what 'good' status of the Marine environment means under the MSFD (Section 27.7.3.2).

Setting appropriate baselines and targets. Some targets use the state that was 'natural' before human pressures were introduced (e.g. MSFD); others use sustainable levels (e.g. Maximum Sustainable Yields in fisheries management).

A truly integrated approach to assessments remains a challenge. Progress has been made understanding the impacts of specific pressures on the sea, but the impact of multiple, interacting pressures is problematic. Adopting an ecosystem approach requires an understanding of how the various pressures change the structure and functioning of ecosystems.

More data coverage. Expert judgement and inadequate datasets were used to make assessments of the state of the sea. More detailed knowledge would enable more informed marine planning.

The ecosystem approach to Marine management, where human activities and the supporting ecosystems are managed together, is embodied in current initiatives under the MSFD (Section 27.7.3.2). It requires that both ecological

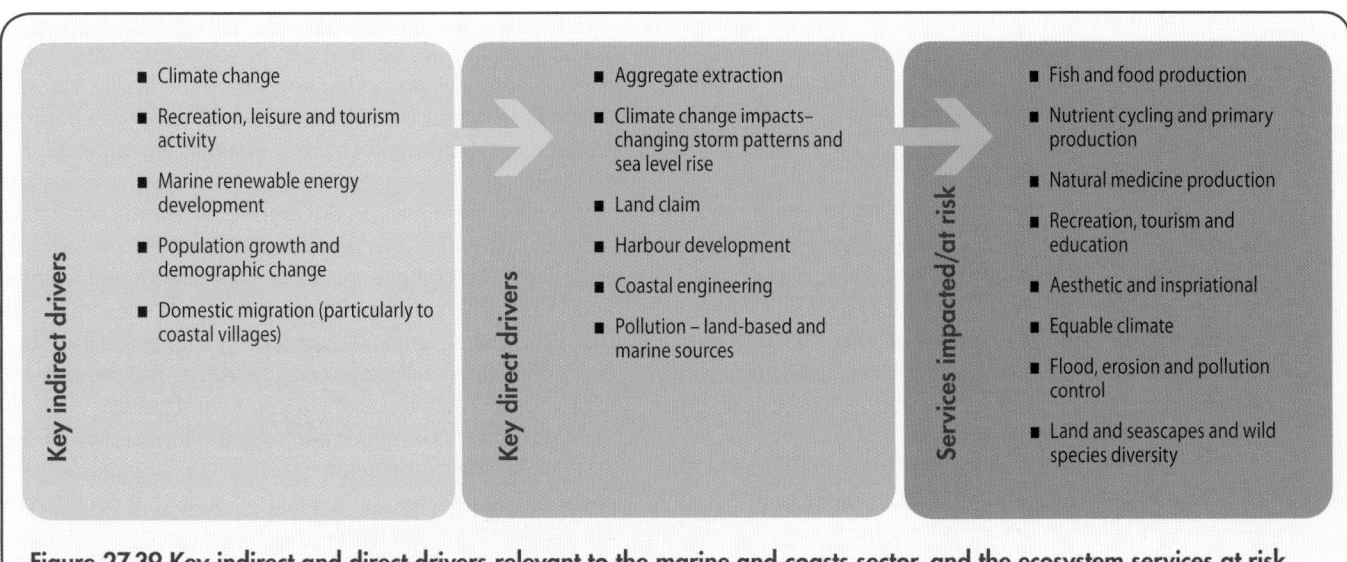

Figure 27.39 Key indirect and direct drivers relevant to the marine and coasts sector, and the ecosystem services at risk.

health and human well-being be optimised. This approach, however, needs a stronger science base and the testing of practical tools to make the concept operational. In marine planning, conflicts between the multiple uses of the Marine environment are common, requiring improved criteria for analysing the costs and benefits of measures. KnowSeas, a collaborative project under the EC's Seventh Framework Programme (FP7), aims to strengthen the science base for managing European waters based on the ecosystems approach and systems thinking (KnowSeas 2011).

Chapter 12 highlights sparse mapping of the biodiversity and habitats of the UK's seabed as an impediment to quantifying ecosystems services in a meaningful way that supports policy and the implementation of marine spatial planning. Only 10% of the UK's continental shelf is mapped (UKMMAS 2010). New marine legislation has not provided for the establishment of a marine information network to support the new marine planning regime (WWF 2010). The Department for Environment, Food and Rural Affairs has established, however, the Marine Environmental Data and Information Network and the UK Directory of Marine Observing Systems to better coordinate knowledge generation.

Major knowledge gaps also exist with regards to Coastal Margins (Section 11.6). Consistent survey methodologies for each coastal habitat would allow a more coherent analysis of trends. The lack of a national perspective of the expected impacts on geomorphology and ecosystems from higher sea levels and greater storm activity presents a major hindrance for coastal planning. Chapter 11 (Section 11.6) recommends the identification of priorities for a national strategic monitoring programme and the testing of management options, such as managed realignment, in different coastal habitat types.

Chapter 12 emphasises the importance of understanding and quantifying the ecological links between Marine biodiversity, ecosystem function and goods and services, and the effects of human impacts on these. Although the Charting Progress 2 and State of Scotland's Seas assessments collated significant evidence, there remain substantial data gaps in the Marine environment. The management of trade-offs between competing uses of the Marine environment would benefit from a stronger evidence base. Geographic Information System and spatial modelling tools are likely to play a constructive role in supporting participatory processes (Jude *et al.* 2006), and decisions on where and when activities take place, such as coastal and offshore renewable energy development.

27.7.3.2 Legislation (enabling)

A number of pieces of legislation already exist that are relevant to the protection and management of Marine ecosystems. The discussion below focuses on two recent and key legislative developments: the MSFD and Marine and Coastal Access Act 2009. A number of other laws with marine and coastal relevance, such as the Habitats Directive and the Flood and Water Management Act 2010, are covered in other sectoral discussions in this chapter.

The MSFD (Directive 2008/56/EC) was adopted in June 2008 and has as its overall goal the achievement of 'good environmental status' for all EU marine waters by 2020. It obliges Member States to implement marine strategies with the aim of protecting, preserving and restoring the Marine

environment, and preventing or reducing inputs into the Marine environment with a view to phasing out pollution. It covers waters within Member States' exclusive economic zones (including the seabed and subsoil) as defined by the UN Convention on the Law of the Sea. It also covers coastal waters in so far as they are not dealt with under the WFD.

The MSFD sets out various actions to be taken towards the achievement of the 2020 goal, with legally binding deadlines. By 2012, Member States must carry out assessments of the current state of their marine waters, determine a set of characteristics for good environmental status, and provide a set of targets and indicators. A monitoring programme must be put in place by 2014, and by 2016, a programme of measures designed to take marine waters from their initial state to good environmental status must be implemented. Exceptions to the deadline are permitted for certain reasons: natural causes or conditions, factors for which the Member State concerned is not responsible, and overriding reasons of public interest which outweigh the negative impact on the environment. The Directive specifically demands that the programmes of measures include spatial protection measures, "contributing to coherent and representative networks of marine protected areas, adequately covering the diversity of the constituent ecosystems" (Article 13 (4) MSFD). This network can include SACs and SPAs designated under the Habitats and Birds Directives (Section 27.2.3.2).

In UK law the Directive was transposed by the Marine Strategy Regulations 2010, and is in the process of being implemented by the Department for Environment, Food and Rural Affairs and the Devolved Administrations. Recognising that transboundary efforts are required to control the Marine environment, the MSFD contains express duties of regional cooperation. Existing regional institutions and Regional Seas Conventions are to be utilised. For the UK, the OSPAR Convention is the key regional mechanism, and the OSPAR Secretariat is taking on the role of facilitating MSFD commitments. Under the OSPAR Convention, the UK has committed to a number of marine environmental protection objectives, particularly tackling various forms of marine pollution. The MSFD should assist by effectively bringing these international law obligations into a more rigorously binding, EU law basis.

Integration of environmental concerns into other policies and laws is another key aim of the MSFD. It states that it shall "contribute to coherence between, and aim to ensure the integration of environmental concerns into, the different policies, agreements and legislative measures which have an impact on the marine environment" (MSFD Article 1(4)). The EU Commission describes it as the environmental component of the EU's Integrated Maritime Policy (EC 2011). It has been designed to dovetail with the WFD, and employs similar mechanisms including assessments, monitoring, and integrated programmes of measures towards a target environmental status.

Also of crucial importance is the interaction of the MSFD with the CFP (Section 27.6.3.2). Descriptors of good environmental status in the MSFD include that commercial fish stocks should be within safe biological limits and that the integrity of seafloor ecosystems is maintained. The MSFD's preamble states that the "Common Fisheries Policy, including in the future reform, should take into account the environmental impacts of fishing and the objectives of this Directive". In addition, paragraph 39 of the preamble notes that fisheries measures can be taken in the context of the CFP, based on scientific advice aimed at helping to achieve the MSFD's objectives. In order to ensure policy consistency with the MSFD, the reformed CFP will need to make sure fish stocks are able to recover by 2020 and fisheries management is coherent with the ecosystems approach of the MSFD. The full closure of certain areas to fisheries, to enable the integrity, structure and functioning of ecosystems to be maintained or restored, is specifically foreseen. The reformed CFP should also secure some degree of regional cooperation to manage fisheries within the areas identified in the MSFD.

The MSFD is clearly designed to safeguard the future economic potential of the oceans, as well as to protect habitats and species in their own right. The EU Commission notes that one of its purposes is protecting the resource base on which marine-related social and economic activities depend (EC 2011). Economic analyses are incorporated into the directive as part of its ecosystem approach, and the potential economic cost of degradation of Marine ecosystems is expressly acknowledged. Guidance produced for the Department for Environment, Food and Rural Affairs (Turner *et al.* 2010) on the economic and social analysis required as part of the initial assessment of marine waters under the MSFD details various approaches to ecosystem service valuation in the marine context. It highlights various examples of the most prominent Marine ecosystem services for which valuation has been attempted, such as food provision, amenity and recreation, carbon storage, and raw material provision (*ibid.*). The MSFD will be one of the first pieces of legislation to apply such ecosystem service valuation techniques.

The Marine and Coastal Access Act 2009 creates an overarching framework for marine planning in the form of a Marine Policy Statement. This will be a strategic and coordinated programme for future marine development. Prior to the Marine and Coastal Access Act, there was no comprehensive planning regime for UK marine waters. It is being formulated by all four Devolved Administrations to ensure there is consistency at the UK-level, and is expected to be released in spring 2011, having undergone a consultation which finished in October 2010. The MPS will apply to all UK territorial waters and, therefore, must be jointly adopted by the UK and Devolved Administrations. The Marine and Coastal Access Act also sets up marine planning regions. For each of these regions there will be a marine plan identifying activities, resources and impacts for the area (Section 27.7.3.3). The planning provisions in the Act apply to the English inshore and offshore regions, the Welsh inshore and offshore regions, the Scottish offshore region and the Northern Ireland offshore region. The Scottish inshore region is covered by the Marine (Scotland) Act 2010, and provisions for marine planning and marine nature conservation in Northern Ireland's territorial waters will be contained in the Northern Ireland Marine Bill, due to come into force in 2012.

In addition to the new planning framework, the Marine and Coastal Access Act contains important new nature conservation provisions. It requires the setting up of MCZs in offshore waters around the whole of the UK, plus in inshore waters for England and Wales. The Marine (Scotland) Act 2010 sets up equivalent designations for Scottish inshore waters. Legislation for Northern Ireland's inshore waters is expected to follow. The MCZ designations are to be made on the basis of conserving Marine flora, fauna or habitats, or geological or geomorphological features. The designation order must set out conservation objectives for the area. The overall objective under the Marine and Coastal Access Act is to create an 'ecologically coherent network' of MPAs, including both MCZs and other protected areas (e.g. Natura 2000 marine sites), taking into account that the conservation of certain features may require their protection in more than one designated area. The sum total of the network should add up to more than the benefits provided by individual protected areas. One design principle is that MPAs are spaced appropriately to ensure connectivity between them (Ashworth *et al.* 2010), which will be paramount if the initiative is to be successful (WWF 2010).

Public authorities whose actions are capable of affecting an MCZ are under a duty to exercise their functions in a manner which furthers the conservation objectives of the MCZ, or if that is not possible, in a manner which least hinders those objectives. There are similar duties in respect of the authorisation of activities which may hinder the achievement of MCZ conservation objectives. Public authorities must not issue such licences unless it can be demonstrated by the licence applicant that there is no significant risk of damaging the conservation objectives of the site. If this is not possible, the licence must only be granted if it is shown that there are no alternatives to the proposed activity, that the benefit to the public of proceeding outweighs the risk of damage, and the licensee will undertake measures of equivalent environmental benefit. This system of protection has parallels with the development control provisions of the Habitats Directive. The Marine and Coastal Access Act also makes it an offence to knowingly perform a prohibited act which may significantly damage the achievement of the conservation objectives of an MCZ. Prohibited acts include killing or destroying animals and plants, or taking or damaging features which are protected within that MCZ.

The process of designating the MCZs is ongoing via a series of stakeholders such as environmental groups, scientists and industry. The RSPB (2010a) has raised concerns about the role of socioeconomic factors in determining the designations. Consideration of such factors is permitted by the Marine and Coastal Access Act, but conservationists stress that science must be the overriding consideration or important conservation sites may be lost (*ibid.*). Finalised recommendations for the network will be submitted to the government by the end of November 2011.

Another important legislative development, the Flood and Water Management Act 2010 aims to provide a more comprehensive management framework for flood risk. Of relevance to coastal zone management, the Act gives the Environment Agency in England and Wales overall responsibility for flood and coastal erosion risk management and local authorities responsibility for managing the risk of local floods. The Environment Agency in England and Welsh

Ministers in Wales have a duty to develop and implement a strategy for flood and coastal erosion risk management.

27.7.3.3 Policies, institutions and governance (enabling)

Marine planning policy. The establishment of marine planning arrangements as a result of the Marine and Coastal Access Act and the Marine (Scotland) Act has the potential to make positive changes to the delivery of ecosystems from both Coastal Margin and Marine environments. The Marine Policy Statement, expected to released in Spring 2011, is the first step towards implementing marine planning in the UK (Section 27.7.3.2). The vision of the government for the Marine environment is for "clean, healthy, safe, productive, and biologically diverse oceans and seas", and the draft Marine Policy Statement identifies the following aims:

- promote sustainable economic development;
- enable the UK's move towards a low carbon economy, in order to mitigate the causes and adapt to the effects of climate change and ocean acidification;
- recognise that the demand for use of the seas, and the resulting pressures on them, will continue to increase;
- manage competing demands on the marine area, taking an ecosystem-based approach;
- enable the coexistence of compatible activities wherever possible; and
- integrate with terrestrial planning.

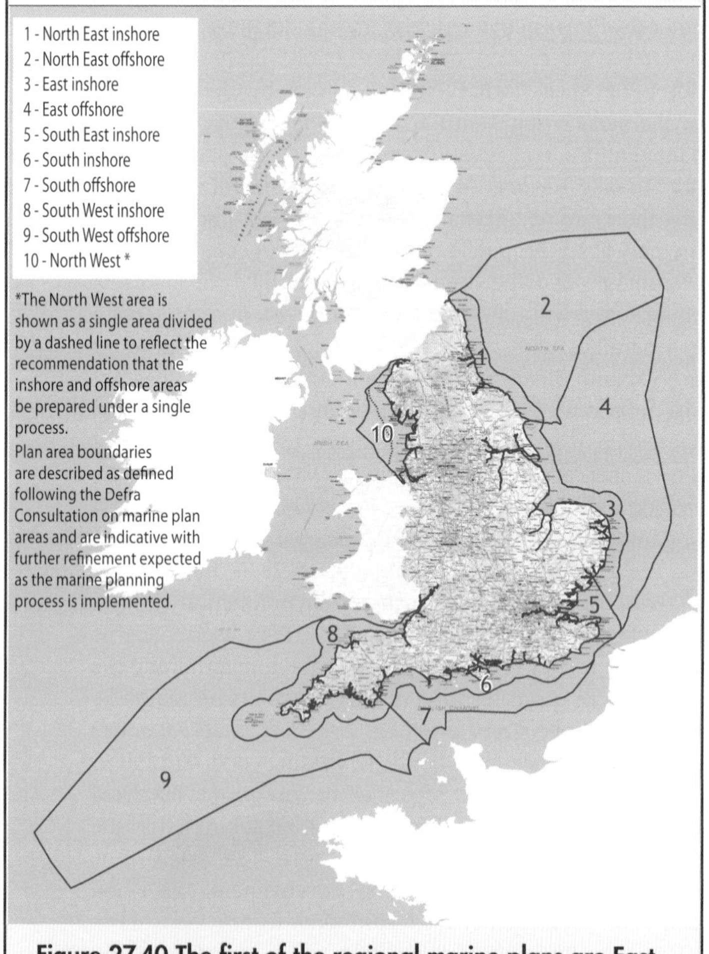

The Marine and Coastal Access Act and Marine (Scotland) Act also set up marine planning regions. For each of these regions there will be a marine plan identifying activities, resources and impacts for the area. Each regional marine plan must take into account sustainable development objectives and must conform to the Marine Policy Statement. The regime will function in a similar fashion to terrestrial planning, in that individual licence applications will be decided within the parameters set down in the regional plans. So far, two areas have been selected to be the first to have regional marine plans developed: the coast around Flamborough Head in East Riding, Yorkshire, named East Inshore; and Felixstowe in Suffolk,; named East Offshore (MMO 2010b) (see also **Figure 27.40**). It is critical that the marine plans address not only Marine biodiversity and habitats, but also the fundamental functioning of ecosystems (Section 12.5).

While it will be some time before the impact of the UK's marine planning system on ecosystem services can be assessed, lessons can be learnt from earlier adopters of spatial marine planning in other regions of the world. An evaluation by WWF-UK (2010) of the implementation of marine spatial planning in Canada, Australia, New Zealand, the United States (California) and Belgium (**Box 27.33**) led to a number of recommendations of relevance to the UK:

- deliver an ecosystem-based Marine Policy Statement;
- ensure ecologically sustainable development;
- ensure clear accountability;
- develop open and transparent processes;
- deliver effective and frequent communication;
- facilitate early stakeholder engagement;
- provide ongoing political leadership; and
- provide adequate funding and resources.

The new marine planning regime will particularly affect offshore renewable energy developments, such as windfarms and wave power projects. Commercial commentators have received the new regime positively because it will increase certainty for developers and should also simplify licensing processes, although concerns exist as to how MCZ designation will restrict development (Norton Rose 2010). From a conservation viewpoint, there are also concerns about whether the plans will be capable of dealing effectively with cumulative development effects, and how far the precautionary principle will be applied in areas where there may be scientific uncertainty about the effects of marine development or the state of Marine resources. Application of the precautionary principle is not an express requirement of the legislation, but consideration of sustainable development objectives is, and this should incorporate a precautionary approach (WWF-UK 2010). The benefits of marine planning are expected to be substantial. In 2007, a Regulatory Impact Assessment of the then Marine Bill found that the costs of implementation over a 20-year period would be considerably

1 - North East inshore
2 - North East offshore
3 - East inshore
4 - East offshore
5 - South East inshore
6 - South inshore
7 - South offshore
8 - South West inshore
9 - South West offshore
10 - North West *

*The North West area is shown as a single area divided by a dashed line to reflect the recommendation that the inshore and offshore areas be prepared under a single process.

Plan area boundaries are described as defined following the Defra Consultation on marine plan areas and are indicative with further refinement expected as the marine planning process is implemented.

Figure 27.40 The first of the regional marine plans are East Inshore (3) and East Offshore (4), located off the coast between Flamborough Head (East Riding, Yorkshire) and Felixstowe (Suffolk). Source: MMO (2010a). © SeaZone Solutions Limited 2005 [SZ042010.001]. © Crown Copyright and database right 2010. All rights reserved. Ordnance Survey Licence No. 100022861.

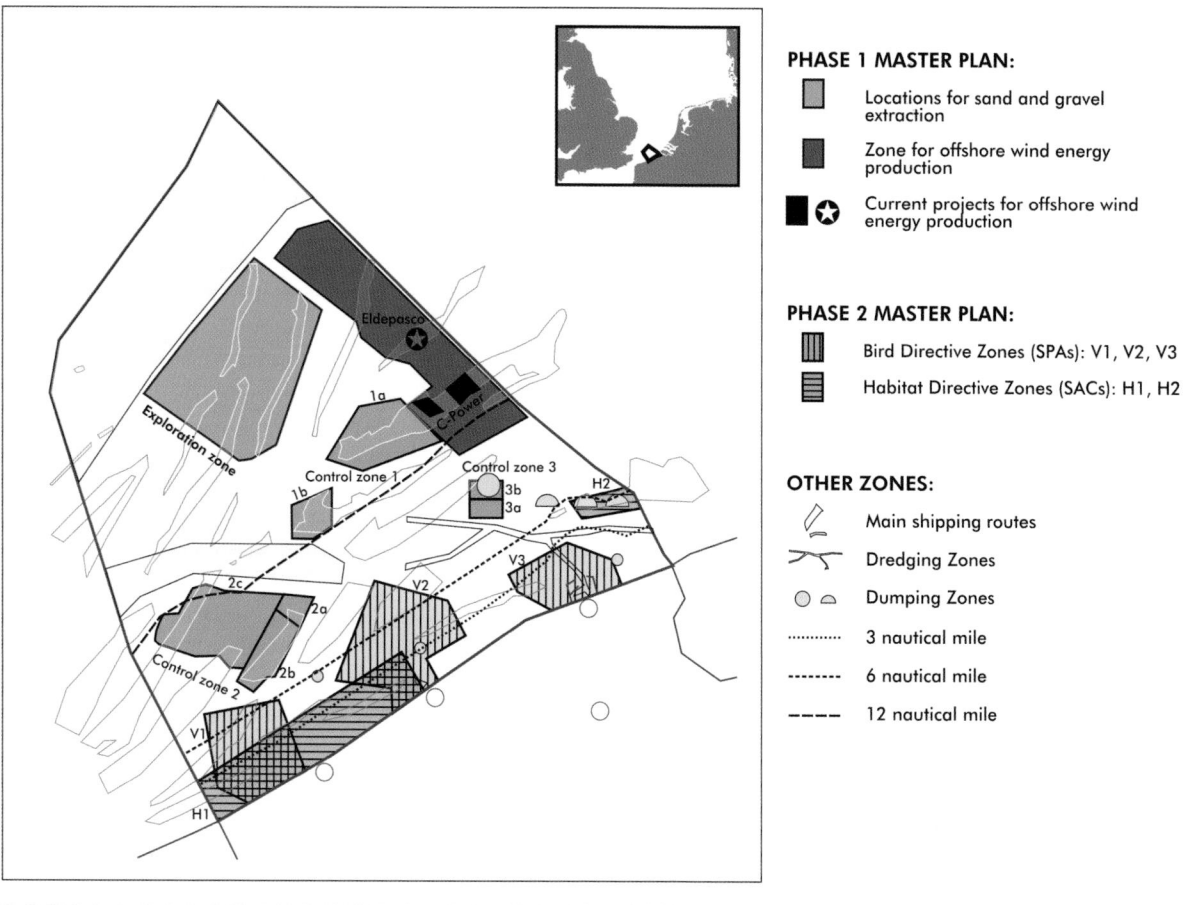

Box 27.33 Lessons learnt from marine spatial planning in Belgium (North Sea). Source: WWF-UK (2010).

The North Sea is one of the most intensively used seas in the world, and the Belgium portion is at the core of marine activity. Historically, a top-down approach to marine management prevailed in Belgium, with little common understanding and weak interaction between stakeholders, and lacklustre political will within the Belgium Government. In 1999, this began to change following the enactment of Belgium's Marine Protection Act which established a master plan for Belgium's North Sea marine area, making it one of the first countries to develop an operational, multi-use planning system. **Figure 27.41** shows a map of the master plan.

Stakeholder engagement and a transparent system were considered to have been fundamental in making the planning process effective. The management of land-based activities has had a beneficial impact on the quality of coastal waters, and strict Marine reserves forbid all activities. Including zoning and seasonal closures within the marine plan was also found to be valuable. However, user agreements to avoid the Marine reserves are voluntary and thus have the potential to unfold. In the early stages, discontinuity within government departments also slowed progress. Given the dynamism of the North Sea as a whole, an international approach would bring advantages, whereby issues are considered within the context of the entire sea.

PHASE 1 MASTER PLAN:

- Locations for sand and gravel extraction
- Zone for offshore wind energy production
- Current projects for offshore wind energy production

PHASE 2 MASTER PLAN:

- Bird Directive Zones (SPAs): V1, V2, V3
- Habitat Directive Zones (SACs): H1, H2

OTHER ZONES:

- Main shipping routes
- Dredging Zones
- Dumping Zones
- 3 nautical mile
- 6 nautical mile
- 12 nautical mile

Figure 27.41 Phase 1 and 2 of the master plan for Belgium's North Sea marine area. Source: reproduced from Douvere *et al.* (2007). Copyright (2007), with permission from Elsevier.

outweighed by benefits expected to accrue over the same period (ABP 2007).

The Marine and Coastal Access Act and Marine (Scotland) Act led to the creation of the Marine Management Organisation and Marine Scotland. The Welsh Assembly Government has equivalent responsibilities as the Marine Management Organisation in Welsh waters, but at the time of writing the Northern Ireland Government had not made any commitments to establish a Marine Management Organisation equivalent to manage their seas. Each country has responsibility for planning in their inshore and offshore waters. Marine planning at a regional scale is not addressed in the new legislation, but in the future it may be beneficial to coordinate and implement planning between all countries that share a common body of water.

The Marine Management Organisation, Marine Scotland, Welsh Assembly and Northern Ireland Assembly are responsible for preparing the marine plans in their respective seas. They will regulate most activities in their country's territorial waters, including fisheries (Section 27.6.3.3), dredging, aggregate extraction, laying of submarine cables, marine renewable energy development and environmental protection. A key responsibility will be to ensure stakeholder buy-in from the full range of marine activities. The Marine Management Organisation must work closely with Welsh and Northern Ireland Ministers and Marine Scotland to manage the linkages between reserved and devolved responsibilities to ensure ecosystem-based management is joined up throughout the UK's Marine environment. The Marine Management Organisation, and its equivalent authorities in Wales, Scotland and Northern Ireland, are expected to be the centre of marine expertise, provide a consistent and unified approach, and coordinate information and data. In England, Natural England and the Joint Nature Conservation Committee will work with the Marine Management Organisation to integrate marine planning with MCZs (WWF-UK 2010). Although the Marine Management Organisation has significant powers, since the discontinuation of the Infrastructure Planning Commission (IPC), the Secretary of State makes the final decision on large-scale infrastructure projects in the UK including major offshore developments, ports and harbours.

Coastal zone management. Historically, coastal management policies and decisions in the UK were made by the sector involved, for example, transport, environment, economic growth or waste management. Responsibilities for marine and coastal management remain dispersed across a variety of government agencies and departments. This traditional sectoral approach to management and planning is being modified due to growing pressures on the coastal zone from competing human activities.

Integrated Coastal Zone Management (ICZM) provides a holistic approach to management that acknowledges natural dynamics and the interdependence of the Coastal Margin with other habitats such as the Marine environment. It also means adopting a joined-up approach to the management of many different interests in coastal areas. Although the principles of ICZM are broadly accepted in the UK, implementation has been a slow and long-term process (Defra 2006).

An audit (called the Stocktake) of the framework for coastal management of the UK was commissioned by the Department for Environment, Food and Rural Affairs and the Devolved Administrations following a Recommendation by the EU in 2002 to adopt a strategic approach to the management of the coastal zone based on a number of key principles. The Stocktake (Atkins 2004) looked at current practices, legislation, institutions and stakeholders, and reported that there was a mixed picture of how the principles of ICZM were being implemented in the UK in 2004. While there were good examples of local-level voluntary initiatives that successfully supported integrated approaches to resolve conflict, the dominant framework reflected sectoral approaches. Coastal forums were highlighted in the report as a way of involving stakeholders, facilitating exchange of information, breaking down sectoral barriers and moving ICZM forward at a local level.

The findings of the report were fed into the development of different coastal zone management strategies in England (Defra 2008f), Wales (WAG 2008b), Scotland (Scottish Government 2005), and Northern Ireland (DOE 2006). Although the coastal policies of the four countries differ somewhat as a result of devolution, they are all influenced by European legislation, including the Habitats Directive, the WFD, Flood Directive and the EU Recommendation on Coastal Zone Management (Section 11.2). Based on a set of common guiding principles, the Department for Environment, Food and Rural Affairs is committed to achieving a strategic framework for ICZM that recognises UK-wide policy objectives, but that can be applied in a flexible manner within each Devolved Administration. As well as the individual strategies of the four nations, actions will also be taken at a UK-level to achieve the aims of ICZM.

Chapter 12 (Section 12.5) emphasises the importance of considering the linkages between deep-sea, shelf, coastal, estuarine, freshwater and terrestrial systems in marine plans. In this respect, the new marine planning regime may provide an opportunity to reinvigorate coastal zone management so that marine and coastal management are aligned. The Marine and Coastal Access Act incorporated principles of ICZM, providing an opportunity to link together marine management with existing terrestrial arrangements, and the act will be the key vehicle for delivery of many of the actions within the coastal zone management strategy for England.

A review of progress in implementing ICZM between 2006 and 2010 was submitted to the EC (Defra 2010f). Wales is reported to be making good progress, but integration remains a challenge; the Welsh Assembly's development of marine planning in Wales will attempt to address this issue. The Scottish Strategy has included significant coastal partnership work on ICZM, and the Scottish Sustainable Marine Environment Initiative involved pilots in Firth of Clyde, Sound of Mull, and the seas around the Shetland Islands (**Box 27.34**). The continued development of voluntary partnerships was highlighted as important to progressing the ICZM agenda.

Shoreline Management Plans (SMPs) are the primary strategy for coastal flood and erosion risk management in England and Wales, and some also exist in Scotland. Northern Ireland does not have a strategic approach to shoreline management (Section 11.2). Shoreline Management Plans assess risks associated with coastal processes and provide a strategic and long-term policy framework to reduce risks to people, property, and the historic and natural environment. The SMPs support decisions on which sections of coastline should be defended and which should be left to more natural processes. Coastal groups, comprising of local authorities and other bodies with coastal defence responsibilities, discuss options and contribute to the formulation of SMPs. Because the plans are updated every five years, new scientific research and national policy guidance can be incorporated (Hewett & Fletcher 2010).

Box 27.34 Scottish Sustainable Marine Environment Initiative. Source: Defra (2010f).

The Scottish Sustainable Marine Environment Initiative involved four pilot projects which considered spatial planning, habitat mapping and conflict resolution. The Shetland project ran from 2006 to 2010 and developed a Marine Spatial Plan to create a more integrated and robust framework for wider marine planning and management in Shetland. The plan provides guidance for the positioning of different marine activities and reflects extensive public involvement, consultation and consensus to ensure that communities understand and participate more effectively in decision-making. In contrast, the Berwickshire pilot focused primarily on the socioeconomic benefits of a high quality Marine environment on the local economy through work packages that address fisheries, and integrated harbour and visitor management. The Firth of Clyde and Sound of Mull pilot projects prepared, and are implementing, Marine Spatial Plans with a view to deliver more integrated and sustainable management of their marine and coastal areas.

The first SMPs were produced in the mid-1990s and set out how each length of shoreline is managed. Several major studies since then, including Futurecoast, Foresight and UK Climate Impacts Programme, Catchment Flood Management Plans, and Strategic Flood Risk Assessments (by local authorities), have provided evidence that the original SMPs may not be practical in the long-term. These reports highlighted the threat of sea-level rise and that maintaining and improving current defences may not be economically or environmentally viable in the future. To account for these risks, a second generation of SMPs are currently being prepared to cover the entire coast of England and Wales. The new plans will outline approaches to managing the risks to the coast in the short (0–20 years), medium (20–50 years) and long-term (50–100 years). Again, coastal groups, mainly made up of the Environment Agency and local authorities, will develop the SMPs.

In Northern Ireland, flood and coastal erosion risk management operates without statutory guidance, and without formal shoreline management plans. Dodds *et al.* (2010) attribute this to the fact that Northern Ireland receives less frequent, and less severe, flooding than other parts of the UK. The EU Floods Directive has recently helped to highlight and identify policy and knowledge gaps. Northern Ireland's Rivers Agency has now moved directly to flood risk management. However, flood management remains focused on asset and sector-based coastal protection, with limited consideration of the cross-cutting nature of coastal hazards. Climate change and associated changes to coastal processes are likely to require a more integrated, strategic approach to increase coastal resilience in the future (Dodds *et al.* 2010).

In England and Wales, the Environment Agency and local authorities have various responsibilities for coastal management, but there is not one institution with overall responsibility for coastal management, although SMPs are intended to provide some coordination (**Figure 27.40**). It is now increasingly recognised that more transparent decision-making processes are needed—involving participatory approaches—given the complex coastal management arrangements and many stakeholders involved.

Coastal partnerships have been the main champion of ICZM since the early 1990s—there are now over 60 voluntary coastal partnerships around the UK (Stojanovic & Barker 2008). The partnerships involve a variety of stakeholder engagement activities including coastal fora, networks and partnerships. They all aim to promote integrated approaches to regional or local coastal management, but have differing concerns and activities. The partnerships facilitate cooperation and resolve conflicts, and disseminate information among stakeholders (**Box 27.35**). Initially, the partnerships were supported solely by local authorities and statutory conservation bodies, but now a wide range of stakeholders participate, including sea fisheries committees, port authorities, energy companies, local voluntary groups and NGOs, reflecting a broader remit than purely conservation. The partnerships operate at a variety of scales, from local (e.g. Hamble Estuary Partnership), to regional (e.g. Devon Maritime Forum) to national (e.g. the Scottish Coastal Forum) (Hewett & Fletcher 2010).

The extent to which coastal partnerships have made a positive contribution to ICZM is contested. A study by Stojanovic & Ballinger (2009) found that the partnerships enhance local decision-making processes, and they are also good value for money (Entec 2008). They can assist in integration, share information, and their officers can provide specialist advice and local knowledge (Entec 2008). The ability of the partnerships to provide engagement with local stakeholders from a platform perceived as independent and neutral is seen as a key strength and benefit by the UK Government (Defra 2010f). Nevertheless, others (Hewett & Fletcher 2010) report that partnerships suffer from a lack of financial and sometimes political support due, perhaps, to the non-statutory basis of the bodies, uncertain success, and the mismatch of expectations between funders and partnership officers. Potential internal failures include: problems with communication and engagement, especially with the private sector; variable performance in achieving aims; and the challenge of undertaking a resource intensive, consensus approach (Stojanovic & Ballinger 2009).

Box 27.35 Tay Estuary Forum.

Coastal partnerships are defined by Fletcher (2003, p.229) as:

"voluntary groupings of stakeholders and lay public bound together by a shared sense of place concerning a discrete coastal area. Such groups use the rationale of deliberative consensus building to develop and implement broadscale coastal management strategies".

Coastal partnerships emerged as a key mechanism to address the concerns of coastal management in the UK in the early 1990s; however, a survey found that unclear decision-making procedures and representative structures can lead to misrepresentation and poor inclusivity (*ibid.*). Some coastal partnerships have addressed these issues, and one such positive example is from the Tay Estuary in Scotland.

The Tay Estuary Forum was established in 1997 to promote the wise and sustainable use of the estuary and adjacent coastline (Booth & Duck 2010). Central to this partnership has been community engagement and voluntary partnership, and the forum has acted as a local mediator to resolve coastal issues. The area covered by the Tay Estuary Forum (including three major estuaries) is designated as an SPA because it is of national and international importance for populations of wildfowl and waders. It also includes the largest continuous stand of reedbed in Britain, and extensive dune systems. Maintenance of water quality is a priority for the Tay Estuary Forum which operates in an area that is under pressure from local population, environmental and economic demands.

The Tay Estuary Forum is made up of a membership over 450 organisations, groups and individuals. The organisation is neutrally housed at the University of Dundee, and the Steering Group comprises representatives from four local authorities. While early studies of the Tay Estuary Forum reported a lack of representation and participation, awareness of the forum has been raised through events, workshops and the media, and participation and representation have been improved through the Annual Conference (with audiences consistently reaching more than 65 since 2005) and through the quarterly newsletter.

Following discussions at the Annual Conference and subsequent consultation, the Tay Estuary Forum launched its non-statutory five-year Management Plan in 2009 to guide the work of the Forum from 2009 to 2014. The Plan aims to remain dynamic in reflecting the changing needs of stakeholders around the estuary over time.

27.7.3.4 Changing social attitudes (enabling)

It is argued in Chapter 12 that the introduction of new marine legislation (Marine and Coastal Access Act 2009) signals an increasing awareness of the cultural and societal importance of the Marine ecosystem, habitats and biodiversity. Marine flagship species, including cetaceans (whales, porpoises, dolphins), turtles and seals, are commonly used for public awareness and fundraising purposes (Section 12.3.5). Raising awareness about the Marine environment is challenged, however, by the relative difficulty in accessing some Marine habitats.

Educational programmes present opportunities for children and adults to learn about Marine ecosystems and the impact of humans upon them. The National Curriculum covers Coasts and Coastal management in the Geography syllabus, and the use of coastal education packs by teachers can further encourage coverage of marine issues (Defra 2008f). Chapter 12 discusses a number of education programmes run by environmental NGOs such as the Marine Conservation Society's Cool Seas programme which has reached over 120,000 school children since 2006. School trips to the coast and aquaria can also nurture interest in children for the Marine environment. Natural England's marine campaign Under England's Seas aims to raise awareness and excitement about Marine environments among the public using maps, videos, events and children's activities (Natural England 2010b). On the other hand, some campaigns arise from target groups with an interest in the health of the UK's seas. Surfers Against Sewage (**Figure 27.42**) gathered significant public support to pressurise water companies and the government to properly treat wastewater before its discharge to rivers and coastal waters.

A study looking at human and wildlife coexistence in the Marine environment of the Moray Firth in Scotland found that the public were highly concerned with factors that directly harmed Marine animals such as fishing gear, oil spills and litter entanglement (Zapponi 2006). Local community support for conservation of the Marine environment was demonstrated through public participation in voluntary beach-clean operations. While more than 70% of the inhabitants and visitors interviewed were aware of the three main cetacean species in the area (bottlenose dolphin, Minke whale and harbor porpoise), most did not know the protection status of these species, nor did they identify the Inner Firth SAC as an example of a MPA.

Policies are now actively seeking to change social behaviours towards Marine environments. The Strategy for Promoting an Integrated Approach to the Management of Coastal Areas in England (Defra 2008f) recognises the importance of promoting awareness to encourage participation in the management process. It highlights the progress made in raising public awareness through coastal partnerships that have organised events, conferences, educational websites, and guided tours and walks. The Strategic Plan for Water-related Recreation in Wales (Church *et al.* 2008) encourages increased participation in water-related recreation for the economic, social and health benefits such activities provide. In many cases, public perception is as, if not more, important than actual conditions. In a study of perceived welfare benefits resulting from policy and legislation to improve bathing water quality, it was found that perceived water quality, as opposed to actual water quality, affected the number of trips people plan to the coast (Hanley *et al.* 2003).

A body of research has explored social acceptance of offshore renewable energy development (Wüstenhagen *et al.* 2007; West *et al.* 2010; Haggett 2011), acknowledging the power of social behaviour to constrain the achievement of government renewable energy targets. Haggett (2011) argues that the role of the public should not be underestimated, and that they should be involved in decision-making about offshore windfarm development. The designation of MCZs across British waters has been met with some resistance from fishermen. They are concerned about issues of displacement for fishermen, the consequences for their communities, and the knock-on effects on adjacent or distant fisheries (NFFO 2011).

27.7.3.5 Technologies and practices (instrumental)

Several alternative coastal management practices are available to decision-makers, and are under consideration for the development of revised SMPs.

Hold the line. The traditional approach to flooding and erosion has been to 'hold the line' through sea defence and coastal protection. These responses have been effective at addressing the problem locally, but, due to downdrift of the built structure, there are typically adverse effects as previously eroded sediments are unable to supply beaches, dunes and saltmarshes which are then not able to fulfil their protective role. Sea-level rise and declining sediment supply is leading to a decrease in intertidal habitats that defend the coast from storm surges and erosion (Natural England 2009g). Sea defence and stabilisation measures should, therefore, be deployed sparingly. In the 2009/10 financial year, a total of £349 million was spent on capital investments in defences and projects, yet it is not enough to keep up with increasing rates of erosion (Defra 2009f). Second generation SMPs need to assess the impacts of their package of measures on soft cliffs, and sediment supply and dynamics. In the future, holding the line is likely to become increasingly untenable in many cases given the severe effects of changing sediment dynamics and the prospect of sea-level rise. The coast will not be confined to its current configuration.

Figure 27.42 Surfers Against Sewage: a special interest group that campaigns for cleaner seas. Photo © David/Flickr.com.

Nowadays, there is recognition of the role of cliff erosion supplying sediments to beaches and shorefronts, and ultimately their role in flood and erosion mitigation. This has led to a wider spectrum of options being considered in shoreline management, with a focus on working with natural processes.

Saltmarsh restoration and protection. Chapter 11 (Section 11.3.2.1) reports on the effectiveness of Saltmarshes in regulating flooding and coastal erosion—pioneer Saltmarsh was found to reduce wave energy by up to 82% and Saltmarsh could bring a capital cost saving of £2.17 billion for sea defence in the UK. Given that Saltmarsh is rapidly declining across the UK, there is an urgent need to protect and restore this habitat (**Figure 27.43**). Managed realignment has proved to be an effective and simple response to restore Saltmarshes while providing several additional environmental benefits (**Box 27.36**).

Beach nourishment. A shortage of sediment in many coastal systems has increased the risk of erosion, overwashing and breaching (Section 11.2.1); hence, artificial protection is now not seen as the only coastal protection option. Instead, coastal managers have increasingly turned to beach nourishment schemes. The additional sediment provided to the system affords coastal protection, has a lower impact than permanent constructed defences, and can help create conditions for vegetation to develop and provide further protection to the coastline. The sustainability of sediment supply to beach nourishment schemes, and the impacts caused by extraction of sediments off- and onshore, should be considered carefully in SMPs. There are also variable impacts on components of beach ecosystems such as microphytobenthos and terrestrial arthropods (Speybroeck *et al.* 2006).

Figure 27.43 Saltmarsh habitat created by the National Trust at Northey Island, Southeast Essex. *Photo © Natural England.*

The south-east of England, in particular, has seen a proliferation of beach nourishment schemes since the 1970s. The volume of cliff erosion in this region is insufficient to make up for losses of beach sediment, with beach nourishment used to reduce the deficit. The costs of such schemes have increased five-fold since the late 1980s. Expected rises in sea level due to climate change could make this practice too costly and/or ineffective in the medium to long-term (Moses & Williams 2008).

Box 27.36 Alkborough Flats: managed realignment delivering multiple ecosystem services.

Alkborough Flats, on the south bank of the Humber Estuary, is the UK's largest realignment scheme, covering 440 ha of low-lying land. In 2006, a 20 m-wide breach was made in the flood defence bank, converting 170 ha of land into intertidal mudflat, Saltmarsh and reedbed; the remaining land was made available as storage capacity during extreme storm surges. The project has created many valuable ecosystem services (**Figure 27.44**).

There are now 23 coastal realignment projects in England and three in Scotland, delivering a range of cost-effective ecosystem services.

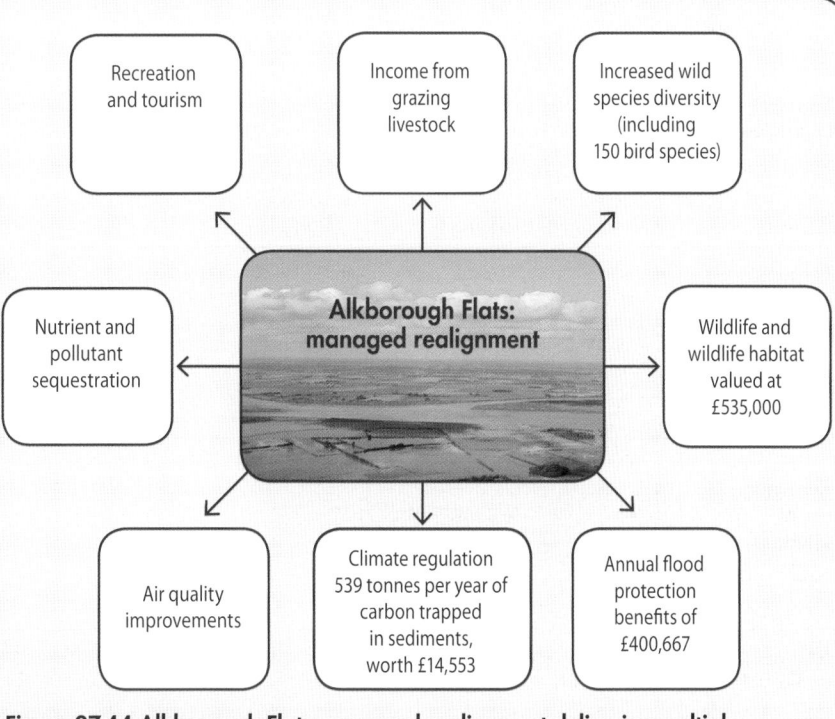

Figure 27.44 Alkborough Flats: managed realignment delivering multiple ecosystem services. Source: information adapted from (Natural England 2009g); *Photo © Environment Agency.*

Managed realignment. Managed realignment (adaptive management) has become an important management option. Flooding and erosion threaten coastal habitats, such as Saltmarshes and Sand Dunes. By recreating these habitats landward of their existing position, the coast can retreat in a sustainable manner and continue to dissipate wave energy and protect against floods. Although these habitats could migrate landward on their own if given space, active realignment is often necessary given the pace of climatic changes. This approach allows coastal geomorphology and habitats to respond dynamically to environmental changes such as sea-level rise and increased storm activity. To date, coastal realignment schemes have predominantly involved recreating Saltmarsh, but could be extended to other habitat types, including Sea Cliffs and Coastal Lagoons.

Managed realignment schemes have been found to reduce the cost of hard defences. An 80 m-deep zone of intertidal habitat fronting seawalls can save £4,600 per metre in sea defence costs (Natural England 2009g). However, such schemes do not only have sea defence and coastal protection benefits, but also provide a range of other valuable services demonstrated by the Alkborough Flats managed realignment scheme in the Humber Estuary (**Box 27.36**). Saltmarshes and mudflats store substantial amounts of carbon. Shepherd *et al.* (2007) recorded 0.44–1.7 tonnes of carbon per ha per year could be stored by recreating intertidal habitats in the Blackwater Estuary, Essex (Natural England 2009g).

Managed realignment can be controversial since it sacrifices land that provides its own range of ecosystem services (e.g. food from agricultural land) (Luisetti *et al.* 2011). Low-lying, sparsely populated areas that would once have been protected by coastal defences may not be protected in the future, raising issues about balancing efficiency in the use of public resources with the equity of changing the coastal management arrangements that local people have come to rely upon (RCEP 2010). The wider deployment of a managed realignment strategy in the UK will inevitably involve complex trade-offs, particularly where productive farmland or valuable property and infrastructure assets are located. A complex mixture of political, social, economic and ethical concerns will need to be considered in such strategies (Luisetti *et al.* 2008). Where there are significant numbers of people, property and other assets, cost-benefit analyses can be useful, but should not be decisive in managing trade-offs (*ibid.*).

27.7.4 Marine and Coasts Summary

Table 27.17 summarises the key insights from this review of responses in the marine and coastal context, highlighting those that have been well-established, but also identifying a set of responses that are either in early implementation or are proposed. It is important to learn from these early pilots across all sectors to scale-up the adoption of an integrated ecosystem approach to the management of the UK's diverse habitats, which is one key policy direction that this review recommends.

Table 27.17 Marine and Coasts Summary.

	Established responses	Early implementation, pilots	Proposed, under development
Knowledge	■ Charting Progress (report of the state of UK seas)	■ Knowseas project (ecosystem approach to marine management) ■ Marine environmental data and information network	■ Integrated approach to marine assessments ■ More data coverage, with use of GIS to support participatory decision-making ■ National strategic monitoring programme
Legislation	■ Convention for the Protection of the Marine Environment of the North-East Atlantic (OSPAR Convention) ■ Common Fisheries Policy	■ Marine Strategy Framework Directive ■ Marine Conservation Zones ■ Water Framework Directive ■ EU Floods Directive and national flood legislation	
Policies, institutions and governance	■ Sectoral management of marine and coastal activities ■ Integrated Coastal Zone Management ■ Coastal forums and partnerships ■ Shoreline Management Plans	■ Marine planning regions ■ Marine Management Organisation, Marine Scotland, etc. ■ National coastal zone management strategies ■ Strengthening of Integrated Coastal Zone Management ■ Scottish Sustainable Marine Environment Initiative	■ Marine Planning Policy Statement ■ Integrating coastal zone management and marine management ■ Second generation Shoreline Management Plans
Changing social attitudes	■ Educational programmes (in National Curriculum and by non-governmental organisations) ■ Special interest campaign groups ■ Coastal partnerships raising public awareness		■ Greater involvement of public in decision-making
Technologies and practices	■ 'Hold the line' (sea defences) ■ Managed realignment ■ Saltmarsh restoration and protection ■ Beach nourishment	■ Managed realignment in habitats other than saltmarshes	

27.8 Recreation and Tourism

27.8.1 Recreation and Tourism-related Ecosystem Services and Human Well-being

"Recreation in the countryside is a widespread activity and continues to be an important policy objective, especially within the ecosystem services approach..., being one of the benefits of the natural environment" (CRC 2010).

As defined in Chapter 16 (Section 16.3.2), "'recreation' describes what we do with, or at, our 'leisure', while tourism encompasses the travel and accommodation required to gain access to some recreation and leisure activities". Put differently, 'tourism' is the economic consumption and production of services to support 'recreation'. There is a broad range of outdoor recreation activities undertaken in the UK as listed in **Table 27.18**. Recreational ecosystem services, classified as cultural in nature, are often associated with meaningful landscapes of aesthetic or social value—the places where people choose to spend their leisure time. Local places of

recreation are of particular importance because they foster a sense of place, and because they are easily and frequently accessed, thereby enhancing benefits to well-being. The appeal of certain landscapes may also be dependent on the presence of rare species (such as birds, flowers or amphibians) or high levels of biodiversity or geodiversity. For this reason, there will be overlap of this sector with Biodiversity, especially concerning the protection and enjoyment of biodiversity and habitats in designated areas. There is also a close relationship with Urban planning, Transport and Energy because tourism involves transport to preferred locations, and planning is required to maximise the utility of greenspaces for recreational purposes, and to avoid or minimise adverse impacts on our most valued natural assets.

A broad set of direct and indirect drivers impact recreation and tourism, which, in turn, affects other ecosystem services. These are summarised from earlier chapters of the UK NEA in **Figure 27.45**.

The countryside is both actively managed to accommodate different recreational and tourism pursuits, and passively impacted by these activities. In this way, there may be trade-offs or synergies between recreation and tourism and other ecosystem services and sectors. For example, increased stocking density of sheep for the

Table 27.18 Popular outdoor recreation activities in the UK (listed from most to least popular from most recent survey sources). Source: * Natural England (2010d); † Forestry Commission Wales (2009); ‡ TNS Research International (2010); ¶ LUC (2006).

England*	Wales†	Scotland‡	Scotland – specialist marine/coastal recreation¶
Walking with a dog	Short walk	Walking (2–8 miles)	Sea angling
Walking	Dog walking	Walking (<2 miles)	Sailing/dinghy sailing
Playing with children	Long walk	Family outing	Birdwatching and wildlife tours
Eating or drinking out	Hill walking	Sightseeing/visiting attractions	Sub-aqua and snorkelling
Visiting an attraction	Visiting playgrounds	Other wildlife/nature-watching	Other specific activity
Informal games/sport	Wildlife-watching	Walking (>8 miles)	Speed boating/personal water craft/water skiing
Running	Sightseeing	Cycling on paths/tracks	Windsurfing
Wildlife-watching	Running	Picnicking	Land yachting
Road cycling	Informal games	Birdwatching	Motorbike scrambling/4x4 off-roading
Appreciating scenery from car	Picnicking	Cycling on public roads	
Picnicking	Road cycling	Running/jogging	
Visit to beach/sunbathing	Off-road cycling	Walking the dog	
Horse riding	Horse riding	Fishing	
Off-road cycling/Multi-Terrain Biking		Hill walking	
Fishing		Golf	
Water sports		Other sports	
Swimming outdoors		Swimming in sea/rivers/locks	
Field sports		Water sports	
		Horse riding	
		Shopping	
		Just a day out	
		Playing/watching football	
		Just a day out	
		Playing/watching football	

Figure 27.45 Key indirect and direct drivers relevant to the recreation and tourism sector, and the ecosystem services at risk.

Key indirect drivers
- Personal and family wealth (relatively higher disposable income)
- Changing public attitudes and awareness
- Legislation
- Financial incentives
- Population growth and demographic change
- Domestic mirgation (particularly to coastal villages)

Key direct drivers
- Climate change impacts
- Land-use change
- Pollution (especially of marine environments)
- Biodiversity (presence of iconic species)
- Resource consumption (fishing, logging, peat extraction)
- Intensive management and fragmentation

Services impacted/at risk
- Meaningful and sociall valued landscapes
- Aesthetic, spiritual and cultural values
- Production of renewable energy and other products (trade-off)
- Human health and well-being
- Regulation of soil (erosion of footpaths) and fire risk
- Biodiversity

production of lamb decreases the quality of that landscape as red grouse habitat, thereby impacting recreational hunting opportunities. Recreation and tourism are considered to be synergistic with the benefits of education, spirituality and physical health (Section 16.3.2). Certain habitats, such as mountains, crags, hills, limestone rocks, woodlands, lakes, upland streams, beaches, sea, parks and open spaces, are of great value for the unique recreational opportunities that they provide (**Figure 27.46**). Recreational activities can broadly be divided into 'benefit enhancing services' (such as biodiversity and aesthetic services) or 'resource extractive services' (such as fishing and hunting) (Chapter 22).

27.8.2 Challenges for the Recreation and Tourism Sector

With an increasing domestic population and international tourism to the UK predicted to double by 2020, it will be a challenge to manage a significant increase in demand for these outdoor services without adversely impacting the provision of other ecosystem services (Foresight 2010). As a result of the economic downturn and the increasing cost of international travel, there has been a shift from outbound to domestic tourism, also known as 'staycations';

Figure 27.46 The Carrick-a-Rede rope bridge in Northern Ireland allows coastal tourists, including fishers and climbers, to access the island. The site and surrounding area is recognised as a SSSI due to its unique geology, flora and fauna, which is also an attraction for tourists. *Image © Joe Gough, 2011. Used under license of Shutterstock.com.*

meanwhile, the depreciation of the pound sterling has increased the financial attractiveness of UK tourism to foreigners (Webber *et al.* 2010). This will result in both opportunities for, and threats to, the natural environment, and management interventions will be key to ensuring that ecosystems are not over-used. "Physical development of resorts, consumption of fuel by buildings, aircraft, trains, buses, taxis and cars, overuse of water resources, pollution by vehicle emissions, sewage and litter all contribute to substantial, often irreversible, environmental degradation, as well as to dramatic social consequences" (Davenport & Davenport 2006, p.281).

More people will mean more pressure on transportation infrastructure to popular destinations, and increased congestion on road and rail networks could, in turn, discourage travel and have social and economic consequences (Section 27.9). Local recreation, reachable by foot, bicycle or public transport, directly reduces traffic and greenhouse gas emissions; however, these benefits need to be balanced against visitor impacts at these sites. Meeting increasing demands for Green Infrastructure will also be a challenge in increasingly dense urban areas where trade-offs will need to be made between greenspace and other forms of development. Appropriate planning and design for long-term management and development will be essential (Section 27.9.3.3).

As cultural services, recreation and tourism depend on a number of ecosystem characteristics that can be difficult to measure and quantify—especially aesthetic and spiritual qualities and biodiversity. Social attitudes about the characteristics which add value to recreational and leisure activities are generally poorly understood, posing a challenge for the improvement of these services. For example, provision of renewable energy from windfarms has been deemed by some to negatively impact the aesthetic value of the countryside, but further studies are needed to better understand these attitudes. Conflicts between users and between different uses of a location can arise, for example, between walkers, dog walkers, bicycle riders and horseback riders on trails. Activities undertaken by some visitors may adversely impact other visitors' enjoyment of an area. In some cases, certain seabirds and mammals that are valued for recreation and leisure compete directly with humans for resources, such as fish and food, creating a trade-off between food provision, cultural services and conservation (Chapter 12).

Recreation and tourism activities often directly impact the ecosystems in which they take place. The development of infrastructure to support tourism has the greatest impact on the environment (Davenport & Davenport 2006); however, activities such as hiking and camping can also cause soil compaction through trampling, soil erosion, and disturbance to wildlife and vegetation (Cole 2004). Future climate change will exacerbate these impacts as habitats become more fragile (**Box 27.37**). The quality of bathing waters is predicted to be affected by impacts of both population growth and climate change, leading to increasing amounts of sewage and overflows as a result of heavy rainfall (EA 2010a).

27.8.3 Recreation and Tourism-related Response Options

27.8.3.1 Knowledge (foundational)

A large number of surveys about outdoor recreation and tourism have been conducted in the UK, providing a wealth of data and statistics (**Table 27.19**). Early surveys that recorded basic data about the location, frequency and cost of visits have been superseded by more advanced surveys which aim to provide information about the characteristics of visitors, their motivations for visiting, and patterns in

---

> ### Box 27.37 The impact of visitors on coastal habitat under a changing climate. Source: Coombes & Jones (2010).
>
> In their paper, Coombes & Jones (2010) make the argument that climate change will not only impact vulnerable environments, but a warmer and drier climate is also likely to increase participation in ecologically damaging activities. The study looks specifically at coastal recreation at two East Anglian beach sites where tourism is economically valuable and the coast is sensitive to climate change because it is low-lying and easily erodible should sea levels rise.
>
> Using data from visitor surveys, the study predicts that climate change will generally increase both the numbers of visitors to these sites and their participation in activities promoted by dry, warm weather. Under a high emissions scenario, visitor numbers are predicted to experience a 46% net increase. However, impacts on biodiversity are not likely to be directly proportional to this increase since warmer temperatures are also likely to encourage low impact activities. In the case of shorebirds, increased visitor numbers will create disturbance irrespective of visitor activity level. Decreased beach width, as a result of climate change, might compound visitor impact as it is restricted to a reduced area and is, therefore, more concentrated.
>
> The results suggest that additional management will be required to minimise trampling and bird disturbance in response to changes in coastal recreation. Recommendations include:
> - restricting access to a single entrance point;
> - targeting management strategies specifically to each user group such as birdwatchers, sunbathers, players/paddlers, walkers and dog walkers;
> - preventing access to sensitive areas;
> - creating defined paths to limit wandering and minimise trampling;
> - raising environmental awareness (i.e. through information centres) to promote responsible use; and
> - aligning coastal defence strategies to meet visitor preferences.

---

the use of the natural environment. VisitBritain (http://www.visitbritain.com/en/GB/), and its devolved partners VisitEngland, VisitScotland and VisitWales, are also a source of information about recreation and tourism in the UK.

Increased attention is being paid to research on the physical and mental health benefits of being outdoors and in contact with nature (Section 16.3). Physical activity in the presence of nature, otherwise known as 'green exercise', not only has positive health benefits, but also promotes ecological knowledge, fosters social bonds, and influences behavioural choices. Similarly, a growing body of empirical evidence supports the benefits of Urban greenspaces. In particular, research has shown that open greenspaces and access to nature promotes healthy development of children (Section 16.3.1).

Disadvantaged people often live in the worst environments, where air quality is poor and there is less access to greenspace (EA 2011a). Low income households are also less able to travel (due to lower car ownership, less disposable income for recreation, etc.) and are, therefore, more dependent on local greenspaces for the health and well-being benefits they provide (Mitchell & Popham 2008). A body of research about environmental inequality, transport disadvantage, and the relationship between greenspace, inequality, ethnicity, health and well-being exists in the UK (Defra 2008g; Mitchell & Popham 2008; CABE Space 2010; EA 2011a). Early research on this subject in England led to formal policy recognition by the Social Exclusion Unit, resulting in the internationally recognised Making the Connections (Socail Exclusion Unit 2003) report and the subsequent development of cross-departmental policy guidance on the delivery of Local Transport Plans (Lucas & Currie 2011).

A number of important knowledge gaps remain, however. Generally speaking, knowledge about the impacts of drivers influencing cultural services is needed, as is a better understanding of the ways in which social and environmental systems interact (Section 19.7). Further investigation of public attitudes towards aesthetic values, especially concerning renewable energy production, is warranted (Section 19.5.3.12). The Foresight Land Use Futures Project (Foresight 2010) highlighted the need for policy-relevant research on the value of different landscapes for recreation and tourism in urban, urban fringe and rural settings—including consideration of their contribution to the UK economy and to individual and community well-being. Data on the capital and labour costs of deer stalking as a recreation activity is needed, along with primary data on the number of deer taken and the level of paid stalking (Chapter 22). Some form of hedonic or travel cost analysis is needed to identify features which add value to the stalking experience. This would allow a more accurate representation of the potential value of this service. Fuller data is also required for grouse shooting in England and Wales to ensure data comparability.

As the recognition of the importance of greenspace grows, additional research is required to improve the safety and design of these spaces, and to further explore green exercise as a therapeutic intervention in order to maximise its utility (Section 19.5.4.3).

Table 27.19 A summary of important sources of recreation and tourism-related data in the UK. This list is by no means exhaustive.

Survey	Scope and Latest Reference	Aims and Key Findings
Leisure Day Visits Survey	Great Britain (Natural England 2003)	Initiated in 1998 and repeated in 2002–2003 in Great Britain to measure the extent of, and participation in, leisure day visits, and to estimate their value.
UK Countryside Survey	UK and devolved areas (Carey *et al.* 2008a)	Reports on the state of the countryside and identifies change through comparison with previous surveys (1978, 1984, 1990, 1998, 2007).
UK Tourism Survey (UKTS)	UK (VisitBritain 2010)	This national consumer survey annually measures the volume and value of tourism trips taken by UK residents.
Monitor of Engagement with the Natural Environment (MENE)	England (Natural England 2010d)	This survey aims to understand how people use, enjoy, and are motivated to protect the natural environment, and to provide data about changes in the use of the natural environment at different spatial scales over time for key groups within the population.
State of the Countryside Report	England, 11th Edition (CRC 2010)	Covers official social, economic and environmental statistical and analytical evidence for rural England—now includes greater detail at smaller spatial scales, and information about the effects of the recession.
Countryside Quality Counts (CQC)	England (Haines-Young 2007)	Starting in 2002, this indicator of countryside quality was developed and monitored. It incorporates biodiversity, tranquillity, heritage and landscape character.
The Welsh Outdoor Recreation Survey	Wales (Forestry Commission Wales 2009)	This first survey presents findings on the use of the outdoors by Welsh residents, places visited, motivations and barriers to using the outdoors and 'latent demand' for outdoor recreation.
The Scottish Recreation Survey	Scotland (TNS Research International 2010)	Since 2003, this survey has provided information about levels of participation in outdoor recreational activities in Scotland including transport used and awareness of the Scottish Outdoor Access Code.
A Review of Marine and Coastal Recreation in Scotland	Scotland (Land Use Consultants 2006)	Using a web-based approach, this survey provided the first reasonably complete picture of marine and coastal recreation in Scotland.

27.8.3.2 Legislation (enabling)

The legislative framework in the UK has evolved to favour the protection of environmental and societal rights for the benefits of community good (Chapter 3). Since 1945, a large number of UK and EU statutory protection schemes have aimed to conserve socially valued landscapes, as shown in the biodiversity sector (Section 27.2). The 'access movement' in the 1950s, supported by parts of the urban working class, led to the formation of National Parks under the National Parks and Access to the Countryside Act 1949 (CRC 2010). This act has two statutory purposes (CNP 2010):

1. To conserve and enhance the natural beauty, wildlife and cultural heritage of the National Parks.
2. To promote opportunities for the public understanding and enjoyment of the special qualities of the Parks.

Since this time, the area open for public access and enjoyment outside National Parks has increased. In England and Wales, the Countryside and Rights of Way Act 2000 amends the law regarding public rights of way and strengthens wildlife enforcement legislation, including increased protection of SSSIs and improved management of AONBs (JNCC 2010b). Increased access to open land (mountain, moor, heath, down, and registered common land) is provided through a new right of public access under this act, which also contains provisions to safeguard landowners, occupiers and wildlife. The Land Reform (Scotland) Act 2003 established the rights to be on and to cross land for the purposes of recreation and educational activity if they are exercised responsibly (Scottish Executive 2003). This act imposes duties requiring local authorities to design and adopt a plan of core paths for access on and over their area, and requires Scottish Natural Heritage to draw up and issue the Scottish Outdoor Access Code. In Northern Ireland, district councils have the

authority to identify walking and horse riding routes, and the responsibility to maintain and signpost these public rights of way is legislated under the Access to the Countryside (Northern Ireland) Order 1983.

The Marine and Coastal Access Act 2009 sets out the legal framework for the provision of public access around the English and Welsh coastline. It makes provisions for the establishment of an English coastal walking route and rights of access to the English coast (EA 2010e). In Wales, the act enables Assembly Measures in relation to coastal routes for recreational journeys and rights of access to land near the Welsh coast. Under this act, marine planning and conservation of the offshore region surrounding Scotland (from 12–200 nautical miles) is devolved to Scottish Ministers; and the new Marine (Scotland) Act 2010 creates a system of planning, licensing and conservation for Scotland's territorial seas from 0–12 nautical miles offshore (Scottish Government 2010e).

Specific statutory instruments exist in Scotland to regulate recreational hunting activities. The Deer (Scotland) Act 1996 makes it an offence to kill a deer by means other than shooting, stipulates 'closed seasons' for each species of deer (during which they cannot be shot), and regulates the types of ammunition and guns permitted (SNH 2010c). The Deer Commission of Scotland, which recently merged with Scottish Natural Heritage under the Public Services Reform (Scotland) Act 2010, was assigned the role to coordinate action to implement the national strategy for wild deer (Scottish Government 2008). The Environmental Protection (Restriction on Use of Lead Shot) (Scotland) (no.2) Regulations 2004 (SSI No. 2004/358)(Scottish Ministers 2004) differs from legislation in place in England and Wales to restrict the use of lead shot for hunting in that it follows a habitat-based approach (BASC Scotland). In England and Wales, it is illegal to use lead shot on a number of SSSIs, or to shoot any duck or goose; however, in Scotland, lead shot is permissible as long as shooting does not occur on, or over, Wetlands. This legislation prevents water pollution and the poisoning of waterfowl through lead ingestion.

Due to the increasing popularity and economic importance of angling in the UK as a recreational activity, legislation is in place to maintain sustainable fisheries (Aprahamian *et al.* 2010). In Scotland, fishing rights are private, and 14 Protection Orders under the Salmon and Freshwater Fisheries (Consolidation) (Scotland) Act 2003 protect freshwater fish (Scottish Government 2011a). In England and Wales, national and regional rod fishing bylaws are implemented by the Environment Agency and applied to all waters to protect fish stocks and fisheries (EA 2011c). The use of lead sinkers in angling was banned in the UK due to detrimental impacts on mute swans (Cooke & Cowx 2006).

The EU Bathing Water Directives (76/160/EEC and 2006/7/EC) are administered by the relevant Devolved Administrations in the UK to protect the environment and public health from faecal pollution at popular bathing areas (Defra 2010c). As a result of this legislation, great progress has been made in improving the quality of bathing waters at coastal and inland sites, especially in Wales, where 96% of designated sites already meet the more demanding standards of the revised directive (EA 2010a).

27.8.3.3 Policy, institutions and governance (enabling)

The recreation and tourism sector involves a large number of government departments dealing with a broad range of interacting topics which include, among others: environment, sustainability, countryside and landscape, public access, protected areas, coastal issues, forestry, natural heritage, culture, land use strategy, communities, health, landscapes, recreation and sport, transport, climate change, planning, and rural affairs. Much of the work in this sector is devolved to reflect the specific characteristics of recreation and tourism in each country. The Department of Culture, Media and Sport is specifically responsible for supporting the British tourism industry in partnership with VisitBritain which is the national tourism agency responsible for the promotion of Britain globally (DCMS 2010).

The Countryside Recreation Network, covering the UK and the Republic of Ireland, has promoted research, cooperation and the development of best practice regarding countryside recreation since 1968 (CRN 2011). It publishes the journal Countryside Recreation twice yearly, which includes information from professionals in this field. The Tourism Alliance, made up of trade associations and bodies, influences quality standards and policy within the recreation and tourism industry (Tourism Alliance 2010b). It comprises almost 50 Tourism Industry Organisations that together represent some 200,000 businesses of all sizes throughout the UK. In Northern Ireland, the Countryside Access and Activities Network brings together actors with an interest or involvement in outdoor recreation to develop, manage and promote outdoor activities (CAAN 2010).

The institution of protected areas is discussed in the Biodiversity section (Section 27.2) In addition to protecting biodiversity, protected areas are designed to allow people to come into contact with the natural environment. The issue most relevant to recreation and tourism is the public access afforded under each of these designations. Some protected areas, such as SPAs, prohibit public access during certain periods to protect or prevent disturbance to vulnerable bird species (UK Clearing House Mechanism for Biodiversity 2010). Other areas are designated specifically to actively encourage public access and recreation activities. Country Parks are located near population centres for leisure and recreation opportunities and are not necessarily of nature conservation importance (JNCC 2010a). National Parks are in place for the purpose of promoting public enjoyment while conserving and enhancing these environments. In Scotland, National Parks additionally serve the purpose of promoting the sustainable use of natural resources, and sustainable social and economic development of communities. National Nature Reserves are managed for conservation and provide opportunities for scientific study, while Local Nature Reserves (LNRs) are managed for nature conservation, but are also meant to encourage contact with nature and offer opportunities for research and education. The multitude of designations making up the network of protected areas promotes participation in the natural environment while restricting access to sensitive sites of high conservation value. Additionally, National Trails (England and Wales) and Long Distance Routes (Scotland) link gaps between existing footpaths, bridleways and minor roads to increase the accessibility of landscapes for walking, cycling and horse riding activities (Natural England 2011d; VisitScotland 2011). In England and Wales, there are 2,500 miles (4,000 km) of National Trail (Natural England 2011d).

Since 1945, there has been a growing number of protection schemes to conserve socially valued landscapes (Section 16.2.3). Back in 2000, the government published the Rural White Paper (DETR 2000) which aimed, among other things, to ensure that everyone has the opportunity to enjoy an attractive and accessible countryside. It specifically aimed to increase the number of people from under-represented groups able to access the natural environment, culminating in the Outdoors for All Action Plan (Defra 2008g). Public consultation about the action plan highlighted the need to make policies and services relating to the outdoor recreation sector more coherent.

A Walking and Cycling Action Plan for Wales 2009-2013 (WAG 2008a) intends to change behaviour to encourage more people, young and old, to walk and cycle more often (**Figure 27.47**). Policy objectives to achieve this aim integrate with other strategies of the Welsh Assembly Government including: the Wales Transport Strategy—to promote sustainable travel options; the Wales Climate Change Strategy—highlighting the contribution made through sustainable travel; the Physical Activity Action Plan; and One Wales—which commits to supporting greater participation in walking and cycling. Monitoring of the action plan is performed by the Transport Statistics Branch of the Statistical Directorate, which has found that, although targets have not yet been reached, there has been a significant increase since 2004-05 in the percentage of adults cycling for recreation (Statistics for Wales 2010a). The new Local Transport White Paper—Creating Growth, Cutting Carbon—aims to make travelling on foot, by bike or

Figure 27.47 A group cycling through the countryside for recreational purposes. *Image © mega, 2011. Used under license of Shutterstock.com.*

on public transport more attractive in England by offering choices that deliver a shift in behaviour towards more sustainable transport (Department for Transport 2011). In Scotland, a range of government policies seek to encourage more people to enjoy the outdoors (SNH 2007). Policy priorities for work until 2011 can be divided into five major categories: paths, access rights, participation, rangers and places (SNH 2010d).

A draft of the UK Marine Policy Statement was published by the Department for Environment, Food and Rural Affairs and the Devolved Administrations for consultation in 2010 (HM Government 2010c). The Marine Policy Statement, which will apply to all UK waters, will provide the framework for making decisions that affect the Marine environment, and for preparing Marine Plans (Section 27.7.3.2; Section 27.7.3.3). It includes consideration of marine tourism and recreation, and stresses the importance of both economic and environmental factors. Consultation responses are currently being analysed, and the UK Government and Devolved Administrations aim to adopt the Marine Policy Statement in 2011 (Defra 2010m). A Coastal Tourism Strategy exists in Wales to sustainably develop the tourism potential of the coastline (VisitWales 2008). It involves cooperation between relevant divisions and departments of the Welsh Assembly Government, and external partners including local authorities, the Countryside Council for Wales, the Environment Agency, the National Trust and the RSPB. Through the Wales Coastal Access Improvement Programme there is a proposal to create an all-Wales coastal path by 2012, and the Environment Agency Wales is aiming for a substantial increase in all water-related recreation, especially recreational fishing (Chapter 20). The Scottish Coastal Forum published A Strategy for Scotland's Coast and Inshore Waters (Scottish Coastal Forum 2004), which consists of a national strategy for the sustainable use of Scotland's coast, and a vision for the next 25 years. It outlines the need to promote sustainable tourism and responsible recreational use by raising awareness, and identifies the need to find suitable locations for the development of specific activities and the enhancement of visitor experiences. In the UK, there remains a need to limit the acidification of water which leads to widespread ecological damage and consequently reduces opportunities for recreational water use (Section 14.9).

Recent policy has emphasised re-wilding and the planting of native woodland, and grazing and burning regimes have been changed to allow woodland cover to increase (Section 27.5.3.3, Chapter 22). The number of livestock on the Scottish hills has fallen dramatically since 1999, due, in part, to CAP reform which decoupled livestock numbers from payments to farmers (SAC Rural Policy Centre 2008). Alteration of the number of grazing upland livestock impacts landscape character, influencing the aesthetic appeal of this environment and the opportunities for recreational activities such as game shooting (Sections 19.2, 19.4.1).

Planning policy also has an important enabling role to play in the recreation and tourism sector. In England, Planning Policy Guidance 21: Tourism (PPG21) was replaced in 2006 with the Good Practice Guide on Planning for Tourism (DCLG 2006a) which brought together guidance about a number of policies relevant to tourism including Town Centres Planning (PPG6), Countryside and Rural Economy Planning (PPG13), Transport Planning (PPG13), and Green Belt Planning (PPG2) (DCLG 2006b). The guide outlines the vital role that the planning system plays in facilitating the development and improvement of tourism in England. For example, Green Belt Policy (PPG2; ODPM 2006) safeguards the countryside by protecting open land from urban sprawl and directly relates to other mechanisms, including landscape, countryside and nature conservation, sustainable transport, open space, green networks, and access, which all have important implications for recreation and tourism. In Scotland, the Scottish Planning Policy (SPP; Scottish Government 2010c) identifies the tourism industry as one of Scotland's largest business sectors, and covers policy which impacts tourism such as: rural development, coastal planning, historic environment, landscape and natural heritage, renewable energy, and transport. Planning policy for open space, sport and outdoor recreation (PPS8; The Planning Service 2004) facilitates appropriate recreational activities in the countryside of Northern Ireland through policy to: safeguard open spaces, ensure access to these spaces and to sporting facilities by all sections of society, and ensure provision of new spaces and facilities.

Much has been said up to this point about the responses adopted by government, but NGOs and charities also have an important role as actors in the recreation and tourism sector. These organisations have a long history of involvement with the public to encourage collaboration and responsible participation in the natural environment. Many of the organisations devoted to conserving habitats and species in the UK also campaign for increased participation in outdoor activities in the natural environment. One example is the National Trust: with more than 3.7 million members, it actively encourages people to visit and enjoy the natural environment through its website and publications (National Trust 2010). Other organisations are devoted entirely to recreation in the natural environment (**Box 27.38**). The Ramblers Association, Britain's largest walking charity, has evolved over the last 75 years into a vocal advocate of outdoor recreation. It is made up of 125,000 members across Britain, "working to safeguard the footpaths, the countryside and other places we go walking, and to encourage more people to take up walking" (Ramblers 2010).

The role of businesses within the tourism sector is significant as there are currently 146,000 businesses in the hospitality, leisure, travel and tourism industry in GB, employing 1,887,700 people (7% of all UK jobs) and accounting for 4.5% of the UK's total economic output (People 1st 2010). One example of a response by businesses to reduce impacts on the environment is the Green Tourism Business Scheme: a certification scheme for energy and water efficiency, waste management and biodiversity (The Green Tourism Business Scheme 2011). The tourism sector includes 14 industries: visitor attractions, holiday parks, events, restaurants, contract food service, membership clubs, pubs, bars and nightclubs, self-catering accommodation, gambling, tourist services, travel services, hotels, hostels, and hospitality services (People 1st 2010). Businesses in this sector continue to recover from the recession, and it is possible that they will play an even more important role in responding to the challenges of ecologically sustainable tourism in the future.

27.8.3.4 Changing social attitudes (enabling)

It is important to understand the individual behaviours and aggregated social categories which influence decision-

> **Box 27.38 Sustrans and the delivery of smarter travel choices.** Source: Sustrans (2010a,b,c).
>
> Sustrans is a leading UK charity that influences changes in travel behaviour and shapes policy to make smarter travel choices possible. The charity employs more than 400 full- and part-time staff, and has over 3,000 volunteers working across the UK.
>
> In 1995, Sustrans began work on the National Cycle Network which now extends 12,600 miles and comes within one mile of 57% of the UK's population. Sustrans has been monitoring progress since 2000 and, in 2009, it found that:
> - the network was used by 1.5 million cyclists and 1.6 million pedestrians;
> - nearly one quarter of all journeys made on the network (95 million) were commuting trips;
> - 79% of trips were made by foot or bike alone, emitting zero carbon;
> - 42% of users got at least 30 minutes of physical activity at least five days a week;
> - 10% of trips were made by people over the age of 65, 17% of users described themselves as black or minority ethnic, and women users increased by 8%.
>
> It is the only national transport network in the UK "with no obligations by government to support it, develop it or maintain it, either at a local or national level" (Sustrans 2010b, p.6). Public transport information was distributed to 40,000 households, resulting in a reduction of car use between 460–875 miles per household per year. In monetary terms, the health benefits from the network equate to £288 million from cycling trips and £96 million from walking trips, and potential carbon savings are worth an additional £32 million.
>
> "The Network is a catalyst proving that when you create the right environment for people of all ages and abilities to walk and cycle, people will use it, and will often choose to leave their car behind" (Sustrans 2010b, p.6).

making about the environment (Section 16.1.3). As declared in Chapter 16, "one notable characteristic of the UK is the depth and breadth of our cultural engagement with nature and wildlife which continues to flourish despite the blandishment of contemporary consumer culture.". The trend of decreasing opportunities for aesthetic experiences with socially valued landscapes during the post-war period led to the creation of parks, AONBs, Landscape Character Assessments, and coastal and marine protection.

Evidence for increased enthusiasm about the environment is demonstrated by the popularity of nature television programmes, growing membership of societies involved with landscape and nature interests, and the high numbers of people utilising Urban parks, greenspaces and allotment gardens (**Box 27.39**; Section 27.9.3.6) on a regular basis. The media plays an important role in influencing people's interest in recreational pursuits. The BBC's Springwatch and Autumnwatch are examples of popular television programmes which encourage wildlife-watching and direct engagement with the natural environment. The extent of local community participation through informal residents' networks and associations is also substantial.

Public Attitudes and Behaviours Towards the Environment is a survey that was conducted by the Department for Environment, Food and Rural Affairs (Defra 2009a). It found that 80% of respondents worry about changes to the countryside in the UK and loss of native animals and plants, while 67% actively encourage wildlife in their garden. Interestingly, the number of respondents who said that they used public gardens, parks, commons and other greenspaces at least once a week decreased slightly between 2007 and 2009 from 54% to 48%, respectively; however, local greenspaces are evidently of considerable importance

Box 27.39 Allotment gardening as a recreational activity.

Allotment gardening is one of the only recreational activities to have specific legislation. Benefits from this activity include low-cost physical exercise, community involvement and direct access to fresh produce (Scottish Parliamentary Corporate Body 2000; **Figure 27.48**). Allotment gardens can also provide regulating services and support biodiversity.

The legislative basis for allotment gardening in Scotland is the Allotment (Scotland) Act 1982, as amended by the Land Settlement (Scotland) Act 1919 and the Allotment (Scotland) Acts of 1922 and 1950. The Allotments Act (Northern Ireland) 1932 remains in place in Northern Ireland, while in England and Wales, the Small Holdings and Allotments Act 1908 was followed by Allotments Acts 1922, 1925 and 1950.

The resurgence of interest in allotments has sparked policy development in this area. As part of the National Food and Drink Policy, the Scottish Government has committed to providing more support for 'grow your own' initiatives (Scottish Government 2010f). According to the same source there are approximately 3,000 people on allotment waiting lists in Scotland. Growing in the Community: a good practice guide for the management of allotments (Local Government Association 2006) provides guidance for allotment officers and societies and Planning Policy Guidance 17 (ODPM 2002) "encourages local authorities to undertake robust assessments of the need for different forms of open space" (Wiltshire 2010). The same reference estimates that 76,300 names were on allotment waiting lists in England in 2009.

In the UK, local authorities are typically responsible for providing a sufficient number of allotment plots to meet demand in their area (Campaign for More Allotments 2010). Wiltshire (2010) recommends that management of current allotment sites could be improved through: re-definition of non-cultivation, adjustment of plot sizes to accommodate more gardeners, fair and efficient management of waiting lists, and support to devolved management associations to adopt good practices.

Figure 27.48 An allotment garden filled with flowers and vegetables. *Image © joingate, 2011. Used under license of Shutterstock.com.*

Numerous funds and societies exist to support allotment gardening. The National Society of Allotment & Leisure Gardeners is the recognised national body for the allotment movement in the UK (National Society of Allotment & Leisure Gardeners Limited 2010). The Society offers information and advice concerning allotment leases, rental agreements and consultations with local authorities and government offices. The Allotments Regeneration Initiative (ARI 2010) is a project that was launched in 2002 to support and develop allotment regeneration and support the creation of new allotment sites in the UK. It is funded by the Big Lottery Fund, Department for Communities and Local Government, and the Fund for the Environment and Urban Life.

in the UK. The English public recently demonstrated their concern for the future of the Public Forest Estate during consultations about the proposed change of management of lands controlled by the Forestry Commission (Defra 2011b). The Public Opinion of Forestry Survey showed that an increasing proportion of respondents said that they had visited woodland between 2005 and 2009 for walks, picnics or other recreation; Scotland was an exception to this rule, showing a large decrease in woodland visits during the same period (Forestry Commission 2010a). Visits to the seaside make up 5% of all leisure visits in the UK (4% in England, 9% in Scotland and 12% in Wales) (Natural England 2003), and an increasing proportion of trips away from home involve wildlife-watching or nature study (Chapter 12).

Key trends since 2004 include an increase in the number of shorter duration visits made closer to home, a greater proportion of visits taken on foot, and a decrease in visits taken by car (Section 16.2.1). Nonetheless, car travel is still a prominent means of travel for recreation. In England, the car was the main form of transport for 59% of trips, and was used for 78% of trips to National Parks (typically, longer distance trips) (Research International Ltd. 2006). A more recent survey found that 31% of visits to the natural environment in England were made by car or van (Natural England 2010d). While the mobility of the urban population has increased, in the future, infrastructural access to the countryside may be less important as improvements in information and communication technology increase and

restrictions on car use come into force (Foresight 2010). Some people have begun to adopt "new approaches to lifestyle based on a creative (re)connection with the land and environment in a positive, productive way." (Chapter 16). This may indicate a greater connection to local ecosystems.

The link between health and proximity to natural environments as a catalyst for healthy behaviour continues to be strengthened as the body of empirical evidence grows (Chapter 22). The average time spent walking or cycling for travel purposes in the UK decreased between 1995 and 2007 (National Statistics 2010). We are living more sedentary lives than we used to; overall, energy expenditure has dropped by 800kcal/day between 1945 and 1995 (Section 16.3.3.1). There has also been a trend towards a substantial loss of direct contact with nature in deprived areas in the UK. For these reasons, increased attention is being given to the physical and mental health benefits of being outdoors and being in contact with nature. There is considerable participation in outdoor sports, the most popular of which are swimming, cycling and golf (Section 16.3.2). The Scottish uplands are highly regarded as a landscape for many recreational activities including: hiking, biking, climbing, skiing, camping, nature-watching, fishing and hunting (Section 19.4.1). The future of game hunting is highly dependent on social attitudes towards these activities (Chapter 16). If negative attitudes were to develop, it would be difficult to justify large public spending for game management.

27.8.3.5 Markets and incentives (instrumental)

"Most tourism in the UK is domestic. British residents take well over 1 bn overnight trips and day visits each year (an average of 17 per person). This travel results in the circulation of over £67 bn around the UK economy, with much of that expenditure being redistributed from large towns and cities to rural and seaside communities" (Tourism Alliance 2010a).

The devastating outbreak of Foot and Mouth Disease in 2001 "showed how the economic benefits of the countryside were more dependent on tourism and recreation than had been previously realized." (Chapter 16). The recreation and tourism sector is an important source of income, employment and economic activity, especially in rural areas (**Figure 27.49**). Although only three in ten visits to the natural environment in England were shown to involve expenditure (Natural England 2010d), large sums are spent on specialist recreation activities such as game shooting, angling, birdwatching, sailing, kayaking, etc. In Scotland, for example, all forms of wildlife-watching tourism are estimated to generate 7,446 jobs and £156 million in income (Chapter 12). A survey of marine and coastal recreation in Scotland found that the greatest proportion of spending was close to home versus on the web or close to the coast (LUC 2006). In England, leisure visits to the countryside account for £9.4 billion being spent in the countryside, £1.4 billion spent in seaside coast, £400 million spent in National Parks, and £200 million spent in open access land (CRC 2010).

Although incentive schemes are not as commonly utilised as instruments in this sector as they are in others, examples do exist, and indirect impacts from other payment schemes also affect recreation and tourism. As mentioned previously, the CAP single payment schemes impact tourism by altering livestock density and landscape character. Specialist grant schemes to support conservation activities, which have increased 1,000% from 1992 to the mid-2000s, encourage protection of habitats and species that attract visitors and improve the aesthetic, spiritual and inspirational values of outdoor recreation and tourism (Section 3.1). One example of a grant scheme designed specifically to incentivise tourism-based enhancements to LNRs is the Wildspace! scheme (**Box 27.40**) Access to Nature, funded by Natural England and the Big Lottery Fund's Changing Spaces Programme, is also a popular, £28.75 million grant scheme that financially supports projects encouraging people from all backgrounds to understand, access and enjoy the natural environment (Natural England 2010a). It aims to have benefited 1.7 million people from urban, rural and coastal communities by 2014. Another grant scheme is Splash—the water recreation challenge fund for Wales (EA 2010f). In this scheme, the Welsh Assembly Government offers up to 100% grants to projects which improve public access to lakes, waterways, reservoirs and coastal areas to promote recreational and educational activities.

Certification schemes acting to improve standards can also add value to recreation and tourism services. One example is the WiSe (WIldlife SafE) Scheme which aims to promote responsible marine wildlife-watching through training, accreditation and awareness-raising (WiSe Scheme 2011). The development of marine wildlife-based tourism

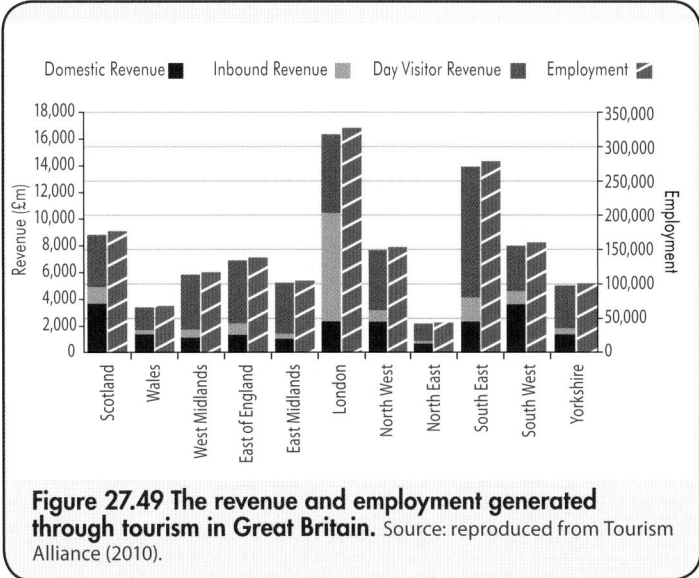

Figure 27.49 The revenue and employment generated through tourism in Great Britain. Source: reproduced from Tourism Alliance (2010).

can generate income for coastal communities, and act as alternative sources of income for fishers and private and commercial boat owners (Dobson 2008).

27.8.3.6 Voluntary actions and technology (instrumental)

There are a large number of voluntary codes of practice and conduct that exist to promote responsible recreation in the natural environment. Countryside codes are non-statutory mechanisms which provide guidance for responsible recreation and tourism in the countryside. The Countryside Code in England and Wales helps members of the public "respect, protect, and enjoy the countryside" (Natural England 2010f). The Code also provides guidance to land managers about how to encourage visitors to act responsibly, and to know their rights. The Scottish Outdoor Access Code provides detailed guidance about the responsibilities of those exercising their access rights (Scottish Outdoor Access Code 2010). This code, which has been approved by Ministers and the Scottish Parliament, is based on three key principles: respect the interests of other people, care for the environment, and take responsibility for your own actions. The Countryside Code in Northern Ireland provides advice on how to enjoy visits to the countryside while helping to protect it (NIDirect Government Services 2010). These Codes act as an important practical means to create public awareness about the access rights contained in the Land Reform (Scotland) Act 2003, the Countryside and Rights of Way Act 2000 and the Access to the Countryside (Northern Ireland) Order 1983.

The Accessible Natural Greenspace Standard (ANGSt) is a tool produced by Natural England to assess levels of accessible natural greenspace, and to plan for better provision (Natural England 2010e). It was initially developed in the early 1990s, and was subsequently reviewed in 2008. The underlying principles of the standard are: to improve access to greenspaces, to improve naturalness of green spaces, and to improve connectivity with greenspaces. Specifically (Natural England 2010e):

"ANGSt recommends that everyone, wherever they live, should have an accessible natural greenspace:

Box 27.40. The Wildspace! grant scheme. Source: Natural England (2006a); Natural England (2006b).

With funding from the Big Lottery Fund, English Nature (now Natural England) launched the Wildspace! initiative in England back in 2001. By mid-2006, 169 grants totalling £7 million had been distributed to Wildlife Trusts, charitable groups and local authorities to support work on Local Nature Reserves (LNRs), with a particular focus on disadvantaged areas lacking access to natural open space (**Table 27.20**).

In terms of the social benefits perceived to be gained from LNR designation, 60% of surveyed grantees identified "greater awareness and understanding; opportunities for education, learning, training and developing skills, and increased interest" as the most important (**Figure 27.50**). In addition, 94% of grantee respondents agreed that projects had made LNRs safe, accessible and enjoyable places to visit.

The evaluation concluded that the Wildspace! scheme was a success not only at reaching its targets, but also in realising wider social and environmental gains. A valuable recommendation for future schemes was to extend the life of revenue support targeting 'hard-to-reach' communities because these areas were more time consuming to engage due to low levels of initial interest and awareness. The evaluation also recommended that reporting requirements be reduced to harbour trust, and that a tapering of the period of revenue grants could allow local authorities to find necessary additional funding to sustain posts.

Figure 27.50 The Wildspace! grant scheme provided opportunities for environmental education and learning in Local Nature Reserves. Photo © Natural England (2006a).

Table 27.20 The aims, targets and outcomes of the Wildspace! grant scheme. Source: information from Natural England (2006a).

Aims	Targets	Outcomes
To increase the number of Local Nature Reserves (LNRs) in England.	Create 200 new LNRs over the lifetime of the scheme.	As a result of the grant, 230 new LNRs were designated.
To realise the potential of LNRs for wildlife and the community by enhancing the quality of experience for users.	To give grants towards the 'visitor friendly' enhancement of two LNRs per region that can be used as examples of best practice from which others will learn.	Two sites in each of the nine English regions were enhanced as exemplars of 'visitor friendly' LNRs.
To enable the employment of Community Liaison Officers to facilitate community participation in the management and development of LNRs.	To give grants towards the employment of 46 Community Liaison Officers throughout the life of the scheme.	Grants were awarded for the employment of 89 Community Liaison Officers, almost twice the number first envisaged. Of these, 63 were employed by local authorities and 26 by a mixture of conservation groups and other organisations.
To promote the use of LNRs for environmental education.	To give grants towards the development of two LNRs per region as centres of excellence for environmental education from which others will learn.	Two sites in each of the nine Regions were developed as centres of excellence for environmental education.

- Of at least 2 hectares in size, no more than 300 metres (5 minutes walk) from home;
- At least one accessible 20 hectares site within two kilometres of home;
- One accessible 100 hectare site within five kilometres of home; and
- One accessible 500 hectare site within ten kilometres of home; plus
- A minimum of one hectare of statutory Local Nature Reserves per thousand population."

Since the review, the standard also aims to identify appropriate delivery of tools and partners, and to "collect information on the role of accessible natural greenspace in improving quality of life and reducing negative impacts of climate change" (ibid., p.19). Natural England has also developed Visitor Service Standards to encourage excellence in terms of both recreation and nature conservation at three levels: NNRs, Country Parks and LNRs. Greenspace quality standards apply criteria that ensure these spaces reach their full potential. In 2009, Natural England also launched the Country Parks Accreditation Scheme which

identifies and officially recognises sites delivering the core facilities and services expected of a Country Park (Natural England 2011a).

The Green Flag Awards scheme has become the benchmark of excellence for recreational green areas in the UK (Keep Britain Tidy 2110; Section 27.9.3.4). The scheme, which was initiated in 1996, judges applicants against eight criteria: a welcoming place; healthy, safe and secure; clean and well-maintained; sustainability; conservation and heritage; community involvement; marketing; and management. The scheme was piloted in parts of Scotland in 2007, after which, it was evaluated by Greenspace Scotland (Gibb 2008). It was found that working towards the Green Flag criteria helped green areas to make improvements at site level and in management approaches, in interdepartmental working, and in raising awareness. Additionally, it was determined that the award had the potential to influence greenspace planning and investment. Following this evaluation, the Green Flag Awards scheme was extended to the rest of Scotland.

The Best of Both Worlds is a management approach designed with the aim of improving and increasing opportunities for outdoor sports and recreation in ways that respect and safeguard natural and cultural heritage (BoBW n.d.). The approach promotes the use of tools like codes of good management practice, management agreements or consents, and permit arrangement systems. There exist a number of documented case studies of how the Best of Both Worlds' principles have successfully resolved conflicts and led to collaboration between conservationists and recreationalists with regards to the use of a variety of habitats for a number of different activities taking place on land, in the water and in the air (*ibid.*).

There is evidence to support an increase in the number of people engaging with the natural environment through volunteering (**Figure 27.51**). This trend is "important for the protection, management and enhancement of habitats and ecosystems, for the delivery of policies, and it is likely to improve the volunteers' sense of well-being" (CRC 2010, p.172). In 2009, BTCV worked with more than 620,000 volunteers to improve the environment (BTCV 2010), and it aims to actively support a total of 1.5 million people to take part in environmental action by 2013 (BTCV 2009). The National Trust currently has more than 52,000 volunteers (National Trust 2011) and The Wildlife Trusts have over 35,000 volunteers (The Wildlife Trusts 2011).

Footpaths are used in the recreation and tourism sector to minimise the impact visitors have on the natural environment (**Box 27.41**). A more recent technological

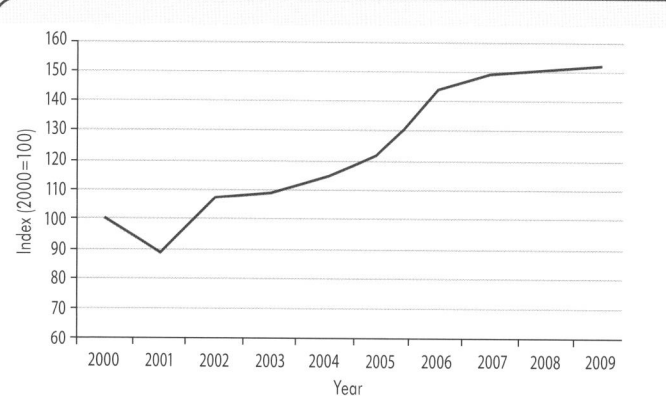

* Where possible organisations have used records of actual volunteer hours, or where this is unavailable, volunteer numbers along with an estimate of hours per volunteer.
† The decline in volunteer hours seen in 2001 was a real effect caused by the Foot and Mouth outbreak that year.
‡ Defra estimates have been used in the index calculation for Woodland Trust (2000 and 2001), Butterfly Conservation (2000 to 2002), and the Wildlife Trusts (2000 to 2004).
¶ As data provided by the Royal Society for the Protection of Birds (RSPB) were for financial years as opposed to calendar years, 2008–2009 data were allocated to 2008 and Defra estimates were made for 2009.

Figure 27.51 Index of conservation volunteering in the UK from 2000 to 2008[*][†]. Source: data from Bat Conservation Trust, British Trust for Conservation Volunteers, British Trust for Ornithology, Butterfly Conservation[‡], Natural England, Plantlife, Royal Society for the Protection of Birds[¶], The Wildlife Trust[‡], Woodland Trust[‡], Defra (2010k).

Box 27.41 Use of the Pennine Way footpath to minimise recreational disturbance of the golden plover (*Pluvialis apricaria*). Source: Finney *et al.* (2005).

Legislation and policy has drastically increased access to the countryside for recreational purposes. In turn, this has fuelled concern for the conservation of wildlife that faces increased human disturbance. Human presence can illicit defensive behaviour in animals and can increase the risk of predation. This is especially true for ground-nesting birds such as the golden plover (**Figure 27.52**) —a priority species for conservation.

A study by Finney *et al.* (2005) assessed the effect of recreational disturbance on the reproductive performance and breeding distribution of the golden plover along the Pennine Way long-distance

footpath in the Peak District National Park. A fence was erected along the edge of the road, and a 4-km section of the path was paved with flagstones in 1993–1994 (**Figure 27.53a**). This significantly affected the behaviour of hikers, reducing the proportion of people who strayed from the path from 30% to just 4% after the resurfacing of the path.

Figure 27.52 Golden plover (*Pluvialis apricaria*). Image © Leksele, 2011. Used under license of Shutterstock.com.

Before the path was resurfaced, golden plovers were found to be 54% less likely to occupy areas within 200 m of the path on weekends during the chick-rearing period due to recreational disturbance. After the Pennine Way was resurfaced, golden plovers were only 24% less likely to occupy areas within 50 m of the path during weekends, and during the week they were not found to avoid areas near the footpath at all, despite the number of visitors doubling after the path was improved. In other words, 96% of walkers stayed on the path after it was resurfaced, allowing the birds to exploit habitat closer to the footpath.

Under the Countryside and Rights of Way Act, people have the right to freely access mapped open access areas; this could have adverse impacts on breeding populations of golden plover, and other upland waders. The results from this study demonstrate how simple technology, such as flagstone footpaths (**Figure 27.53b**) and fencing, can significantly minimise the negative impacts of recreation by altering visitor behaviour.

Figure 27.53 a) The Pennine Way long-distance footpath; b) Type of footpath at Arthur's Seat, Edinburgh. Source: a) image © David Hughes, 2011. Used under license of Shutterstock.com; b) photo courtesy of Lindsey Elliott.

development is the use of pervasive computing to support mass engagement environmental campaigns. Pervasive, or ubiquitous, computing describes the integration of information processing capabilities into everyday objects. The UK Participate project, which began in 2006, brings together industry and academic actors to "collectively explore how the convergence of mobile, online and broadcast media can enable a broad cross-section of the public to contribute to, as well as access, environmental information—on the move, in public places, at school and at home" (Paxton 2008). The schools strand of the project involves the BBC, ScienceScope, BT, the University of Nottingham and the University of Bath to determine how primary and secondary schools in the UK can be supported to collect environmental data and to share their outcomes via the internet (Participate 2011). Social networking sites and new media technologies provide novel opportunities to engage the public with nature.

A final example is the potential use of market segmentation technology to identify the specific needs, requirements and preferences of various groups to enable efforts to focus on making the natural environment more interesting, accessible and relevant. A research project entitled Understanding What People Want from the Natural Environment using Customer Segmentation is currently being run by the Department for Environment, Food and Rural Affairs, Natural England, the Forestry Commission, the Environment Agency and British Waterways to develop a segmentation model.

27.8.4 Recreation and Tourism Summary

Table 27.21 summarises the key insights from this review of responses in the context of recreation and tourism, highlighting those that have been well-established, but also identifying a set of responses that are either in early implementation or are proposed. It is important to learn from these early pilots across all sectors to scale-up the adoption of an integrated ecosystem approach to the management of the UK's diverse habitats, which is one key policy direction that this review recommends.

27.9 Urban Planning, Transport and Energy

27.9.1 Urban Planning, Transport and Energy and Ecosystem Services and Human Well-being

Urban ecosystems deliver essential services which have an important, yet undervalued, impact on human well-being. Towns and cities are dependent on ecosystems beyond their boundaries for food, products and other goods and services, but also benefit from a range of local services such as air

Table 27.21 Recreation and Tourism Summary.

	Established responses	Early implementation, pilots	Proposed, under development
Knowledge	■ Numerous established surveys such as UK Countryside Survey, Countryside Quality Counts and The Scottish Recreation Survey	■ Monitor of Engagement with the Natural Environment ■ The Welsh Outdoor Recreation Survey ■ A Review of Marine and Coastal Recreation in Scotland ■ Research about environmental inequality & transport disadvantage	■ Green exercise, physical and mental benefits of outdoor recreation ■ Research about public attitudes and values relation to recreation
Legislation	■ National Parks and Access to the Countryside Acts ■ Countryside and Rights of Way Act ■ Land Reform (Scotland) Act 2003 ■ Access to the Countryside (Northern Ireland) Order	■ Marine and Coastal Access Act ■ Marine (Scotland) Act	
Policies, institutions and governance	■ Countryside Recreation Network ■ Tourism Alliance ■ The Countryside Access and Activities Network in Northern Ireland ■ Institution of Protected Areas ■ Outdoors for All Action Plan ■ A Strategy for Scotland's Coast and Inshore Waters	■ A Walking and Cycling Action Plan For Wales 2009–2013 ■ Transport Strategies ■ Climate Change Strategies ■ Coastal Tourism Strategy ■ Good Practice Guide on Planning for Tourism ■ Sustrans National Cycle Network	■ UK Marine Policy Statement
Changing social attitudes	■ Nature television programming (e.g. BBC's Springwatch) ■ Public Attitudes and Behaviours Towards the Environment ■ Public Opinion of Forestry Survey	■ The Allotments Regeneration Initiative	
Markets and incentives	■ Wildspace! Grant Scheme	■ Wildlife Safe (WiSe) Scheme ■ Splash – water recreation challenge fund for Wales	
Voluntary actions and Technology	■ Countryside Codes ■ Green Flag Awards scheme ■ British Trust for Conservation Volunteers ■ Pennine Way footpath	■ Accessible Natural Greenspace Standard (ANGSt) – reviewed ■ Country Parks Accreditation Scheme ■ The Best of Both Worlds (BoBW) management approach	■ Market segmentation technology

filtration, micro-climate regulation, noise reduction, flood regulation, and recreational, cultural and health-related benefits. Perhaps most importantly, greenspace (parks, playing fields, gardens, allotments, etc.) has been found to be beneficial for mental and physical health (Chapter 10; Section 27.5.3.4; **Figure 27.54**). The potential to increase the provision of Urban ecosystem services is substantial—largely because, in the past, the spatial planning system did not reflect their value appropriately, compared to other factors, when making planning decisions.

To date, most supporting and regulating services in Urban habitats have been constrained, with little realisation of the consequences. Urban soils, for example, regulate flooding by storing and slowing water down, but development and infrastructure have compacted and sealed them, thus increasing flood risk. Vegetation in cities and towns can contribute to climate change adaptation and mitigation by regulating temperatures and absorbing carbon dioxide. Urban environments support biodiversity and can be understood and managed as a distinct and valuable habitat type (**Box 27.5**, Section 27.2.3.4; Section 27.7.3.4). The impacts and demands created by urban living need to be analysed in relation to the potential impacts of that number of people if they were not concentrated in an urban area (Newman 2006). Urban areas have considerable ecological footprints, however, drawing on vast quantities of resources and energy from outside their limits—hence, cities have become a major driver of environmental change (Rees 2001). So urban areas both mitigate and generate the demographic pressures that human numbers and urban lifestyles impose on the environments from which they import ecosystem services.

According to the Department for Transport (TfL 2008), demand for air travel continues to grow rapidly and car use remains high. While the number of passengers travelling by bus has risen over the last decade in some regions, such as London, and rail travel has increased by 70% since the 1980s, walking and cycling has declined significantly (Section 27.8.3.4). These transport trends affect ecosystems and people's relationship with nature. Firstly, while transportation networks allow people to access the countryside and seaside for recreation and tourism,

conversion of land to accommodate the expansion of transport infrastructure effects biodiversity and fragments habitats, and can adversely impact the aesthetic and cultural values of landscapes (Section 27.8). Secondly, transport is a significant source of air pollution and greenhouse gas emissions, which indirectly affect ecosystems in the UK, the latter through climate change. Lastly, the travel choices people make effect the level of interaction people have with nature with implications for health and well-being.

Energy underpins our society and economy. It heats our homes, powers our transport systems, produces the food we eat, and is used to make every product we buy. It is essential for our quality of life. The majority of our energy is derived from the burning of fossil fuels. In the 1970s, the UK became increasingly dependent on imports of fossil fuels, with domestic production accounting for less than half of the total primary energy consumption (Foresight 2010). Since the 1970s, energy demand has been met by imports, the construction of nuclear power stations, and the exploitation of North Sea gas and oil reserves to fuel gas and oil power stations. More recently, policy is shifting towards supporting a wider portfolio of energy sources, including renewable energy.

The impact of fossil fuel energy production on the global climate is well-established (IPCC 2007). Climate change is expected to become a major driver of change for UK ecosystems, and their ability to provide services, this century (Chapter 25). Reducing demand for energy, and switching to alternative low carbon sources of energy, will be required to mitigate climate change. Decarbonising the UK economy would contribute to the protection of ecosystems both globally and domestically, and help avoid irreversible change that would undermine essential ecosystem services that we depend on for our well-being. In this section, however, we focus on responses to the immediate impacts of the energy sector on ecosystem services and human well-being through, for example, habitat loss, visual intrusion, and air and water pollution.

In the past, fossil fuel combustion has had major impacts on health through emissions of sulphur dioxide and particulate matter. The introduction of legislation and technologies have reduced air pollutants from power stations and transportation, although exhaust fumes from vehicles still have substantial health impacts (RCEP 2007). Although the development of renewable energies is likely to play a vital role in climate change mitigation, it will have a predominantly localised impact on the environment. The planned expansion of renewable energy production (including biofuel crops, off- and onshore windfarms, and tidal and hydropower) is likely to have local implications for ecosystems in the UK in the near future. Nevertheless, given the importance of decarbonising energy supplies in the longer-term, it will be necessary to consider and minimise the impacts on ecosystem services of renewables and all the low carbon energy options.

27.9.2 Challenges to Urban Planning, Transport and Energy Development

Figure 27.55 summarises the major urban planning, transport and energy-related direct and indirect drivers

Figure 27.54 Parks are important for good mental and physical health. *Photo: Holyrood Park, Edinburgh, courtesy of Lindsey Elliott.*

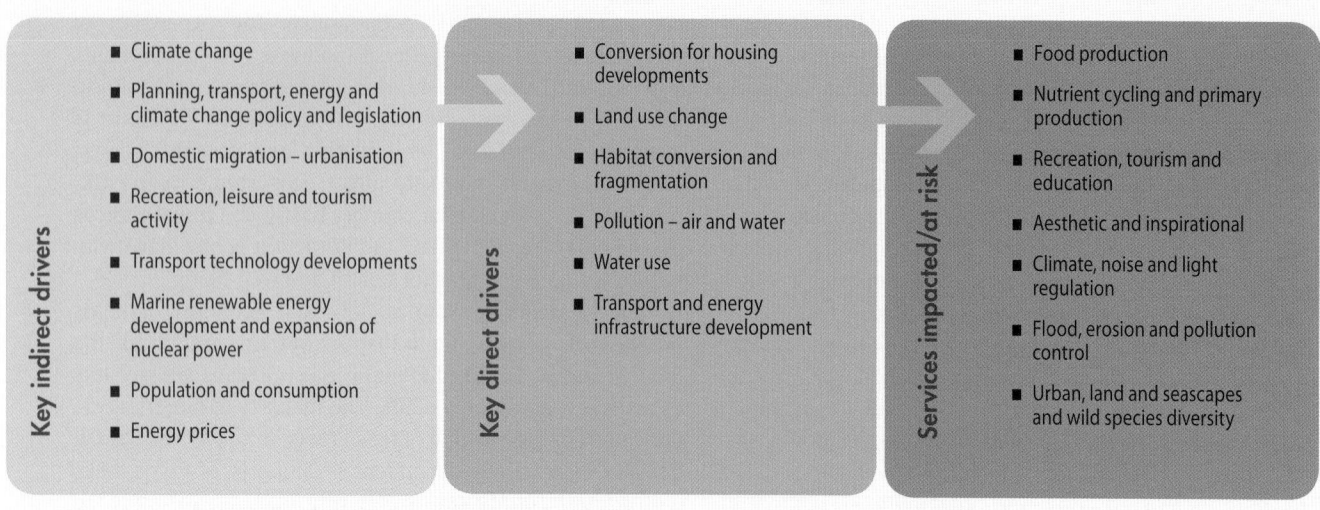

Figure 27.55 Key indirect and direct drivers relevant to urban planning, transport and energy, and the ecosystem services at risk.

Key indirect drivers	Key direct drivers	Services impacted/at risk
■ Climate change ■ Planning, transport, energy and climate change policy and legislation ■ Domestic migration – urbanisation ■ Recreation, leisure and tourism activity ■ Transport technology developments ■ Marine renewable energy development and expansion of nuclear power ■ Population and consumption ■ Energy prices	■ Conversion for housing developments ■ Land use change ■ Habitat conversion and fragmentation ■ Pollution – air and water ■ Water use ■ Transport and energy infrastructure development	■ Food production ■ Nutrient cycling and primary production ■ Recreation, tourism and education ■ Aesthetic and inspirational ■ Climate, noise and light regulation ■ Flood, erosion and pollution control ■ Urban, land and seascapes and wild species diversity

and their impact on ecosystem services. The challenges discussed here are in relation to maximising the potential of Urban ecosystems to provide services, rather than global environmental sustainability, including the decarbonisation of cities.

Bolund and Hunhammar (1999) argue that consideration of ecosystem services needs to be integral to land use planning given the potential of Urban ecosystems to improve quality of life. Monitoring of Urban ecosystems is weak, preventing the quantification of ecosystem goods and services. Without such information it will be difficult for the true potential of these habitats to be recognised in decision-making processes (Chapter 10). One reason for this lacuna is that cultural services, which are arguably one of the most important types of Urban ecosystem service, are intangible and are linked to human perceptions, cultural values, norms and behaviours that resist quantification (Price 2008).

The lack of value placed on greenspace in planning processes and inadequate funding for maintenance has, until the 2000s, progressively decreased the amount and quality of greenspace in towns and cities. For example, around 10,000 playing fields were lost in the UK between 1979 and 1997 (DCMS 2009). In recent years, local authorities and community groups have rejuvenated many greenspaces across the country. Ensuring these improvements are maintained and continued in the coming years will be challenging for budget-constrained authorities. Local authorities are also under increasing pressure to increase the UK's housing stock. At the same time, there is a growing recognition of the importance of Urban ecosystems for human well-being. Planners are likely to be required to design cities that can cater for both of these objectives.

It is widely accepted that current transport trends cannot be maintained without harming the natural environment and human well-being. The further expansion of transport infrastructure will cause the additional loss and fragmentation of habitats and culturally valued landscapes, while increases in road and air traffic will exacerbate light, noise and air pollution levels. It is well-established that air pollution causes significant impacts to the natural environment, not least through acidification. Air pollution reduces the life expectancy of every person in the UK by an average of six months, with equivalent health costs of up to £19 billion a year (Defra 2011a). Furthermore, noise pollution can have deleterious effects on health, work productivity and happiness. Pockets of tranquillity, such as parks, are likely to increase in value in this context (**Box 27.42**, Section 27.9.3.2), while sustainable solutions to transport, both through demand management and encouraging modal shift, would reduce air and noise pollution.

The concept of urban heat islands, where an urban area is warmer than its surrounding rural areas, is well-established. Preparing cities for the expected increases in temperature, and the duration, frequency and maxima of heatwaves associated with climate change, is a priority for urban planners. Urban ecosystems can play a significant role in climate change adaptation in cities and towns. Securing these opportunities, as well as those for climate change

---

Box 27.42 Quiet Areas. Source: POST (2009).

The Environmental Noise Directive requires Member States to identify and aim to preserve 'Quiet Areas'. Quiet Areas are understood to be important for well-being in urban areas, reducing annoyance and stress. A recent survey by Environmental Protection UK found that 91% of people think that it is important to protect Quiet Areas from an increase in noise.

In the first round of Noise Action Plans, the Environmental Noise Directive requires Member States to identify Quiet Areas in large urban areas. Eventually, it is expected that Quiet Areas in open country will also be designated. Scotland began with parks and national heritage sites and then selected candidate sites based on a set of criteria including land type, noise level and area. Wales asked local authorities to identify quiet open spaces that are of importance to the local community. Their list includes parks, playing fields, allotments and cemeteries, reflecting the fact that many different types of open space may be valued for their quietness. England and Northern Ireland intend to adopt an approach similar to Wales. The consequences of designating an urban site as a Quiet Area, and how this fits in with the other government policies, such as the aim to deliver greener public spaces, are not yet clear.

mitigation, against a background of increasing competition for land will be challenging.

The challenge for the energy sector is finding ways to produce more energy from low carbon sources without undermining the flows of ecosystem services. According to the Department of Energy and Climate Change, a quarter of the UK's electricity generation will need to be replaced in the next decade as many nuclear and coal-fired power stations are decommissioned. Furthermore, the EU Renewable Energy Directive requires the UK to source 15% of its energy from renewables by 2020 (Foresight 2010); Section 27.9.3.2). Switching to renewable energy is an essential component of the UK's efforts in tackling climate change. However, many renewable energy projects do have impacts on the environment and may be publicly opposed. The construction of windfarms and transmission lines to convey energy from remote, windy areas has been met with stout resistance from local residents due to the visual intrusion and noise produced from turbines (Devine Wright 2005); Section 27.9.3.4). For example, the upgrading of a key transmission line for renewables in Scotland attracted 18,000 objections in the Beauly-Denny planning inquiry (BBC 2010).

27.9.3 Response Options for Urban Planning, Transport, and Energy

27.9.3.1 Knowledge (foundational)

In the past, research has predominantly focused on understanding the impact of urban areas on distant ecosystems that are essential for global sustainability. Research is now emerging from several disciplines on the importance of local ecosystems for the quality of life of urban dwellers. To date, this has focused on valuing the economic (benefits and savings), social-ecological (e.g. resilience), psychological (well-being), cultural (e.g. inspiration) and health benefits provided by Urban ecosystems.

Many urban local authorities have mapped their network of public greenspaces as part of developing Greenspace Strategies (**Box 27.43**), and have an understanding of the benefits they provide (CABE 2010a). Scottish Heritage has used maps of greenspace based on aerial photographs to plan habitat networks and recreation areas (Section 10.5.3). Mapping tools may also be useful for understanding the links between ecosystem character, ecosystem connectivity and ecosystem services that people benefit from within a cityscape (Andersson 2006).

Currently, no comprehensive, national information source on the quality, quantity and use of Urban greenspaces exists in the UK, although a recent study by CABE (2010b), Urban Green Nation, collected available data and research, and identified data gaps. Chapter 10 also found that data was dispersed across many organisations, with no central collection or analysis. Without a consistent framework for data collection on greenspaces, comparison between urban areas and Urban subhabitat types will not be possible (Section 10.6). A key message from the Urban Green Nation report was that the collection and management of baseline data on Urban greenspaces would enable a strategic overview, coordinate the provision of ecosystem services, and allow the evaluation of the effects of measures. For more information on research

> **Box 27.43 Greenspace maps in Scotland.** Source: greenspace scotland (2009).
>
> In 2005, the Glasgow and Clyde Valley Structure Plan Committee commissioned work to map the distribution and typology of all open spaces in the area. The work was intended to develop an information resource which would be owned and maintained by the eight Glasgow and Clyde Valley local authorities. An Ordnance Survey Master Map and aerial photography was used to map open space types across each local authority area; these maps were then verified by staff with knowledge of the area or by sample site visits. The data is held on a Geographic Information System (GIS) which can be accessed and updated by local authority staff.
>
> The methodology was subsequently applied by a number of other central Scotland local authorities including Falkirk and Edinburgh. The success of the datasets as the basis for auditing greenspace led to Greenspace Scotland applying for Scottish Government support to roll-out mapping to other parts of Scotland in 2006-07. There are now consistent distribution and typology maps for greenspace in 25 of the 32 Scottish local authority areas. These 'greenspace maps' provide a baseline for mapping data on quality and fitness for purpose of spaces, and also to compare greenspace provision with population data relating to age, gender, levels of social deprivation and health statistics.

gaps and monitoring, data collection and mapping related to Urban ecosystems refer to Section 10.6.

Undertaking Urban ecosystem assessments, as a first step to inform decisions about GI and enable trade-offs to be identified, could facilitate the delivery of multiple ecosystem services. Economic analytical tools for valuing Urban ecosystem services need further development, but are useful in demonstrating to decision-makers the benefits of and costs saved by GI (Section 10.5.3).

Chapter 10 reports that data, research and decision-making tools are needed to improve the evidence base on regulatory services (e.g. climate, noise, light, flood regulation) provided in urban settings and to support their integration into planning policy. Further research is also required on the role of biodiversity in urban areas and its relationship with human well-being (Section 10.6.4). Response options (presented here and in Chapter 10) could be improved and better transformed into actions through greater collaboration between research organisations and implementation bodies (Section 10.6.5).

Our understanding of the impacts of climate change on urban areas, including rises in temperature, has improved. Considerable investment has been made recently in research on options for adapting to these potential climate changes, including the Sustainable Cities: Options for Responding to Climate Change Impacts and Outcomes and the Development of a Local Urban Climate Model and its Application to the Intelligent Development of Cities projects (**Table 27.22**). The Sustainable Urban Environment programme is a £38 million Engineering and Physical Sciences Research Council initiative involving 30 UK Universities that is exploring various aspects of sustainability in an urban context including waste and water management, transport planning and spatial planning.

Research gaps related to the impacts of transportation on ecosystems include: understanding the effects of noise, lighting and air pollution on wildlife and tranquil areas; establishing the effectiveness of environmental mitigation techniques (e.g. tree barriers) used in transport development; the contribution of transport to habitat fragmentation and implications for

Table 27.22 UK research programmes: new approaches to urban design and development.

Research programme	Aim
Sustainable Urban Environment (SUE)	To investigate different ways of improving sustainability in the urban environment.
Sustainable Cities: Options for Responding to Climate Change Impacts and Outcomes (SCORCHIO)	To develop tools for the analysis of adaptation options in urban areas, with a particular emphasis on heat and human comfort in the built environment.
The Development of a Local Urban Climate Model and its Application to the Intelligent Design of Cities (LUCID)	To calculate local climates in the urban environment and the impact on the internal built environment, energy use and the consequences for health.
Urban River Corridors and Sustainable Living Agendas	To produce innovations, tools and knowledge to help guide the regeneration of urban river corridors.

resilience to climate change; and the cumulative impact on ecosystems from transport infrastructure.

Our understanding of climate change, energy consumption and the impacts they have on ecosystems has significantly improved over the last few decades. The UK Energy Research Council was established in 2004 to conduct research on sustainable future energy systems. It focuses on five major themes including: technology and policy assessment, energy and environment, energy supply, energy demand, and energy systems. Another source of information within the sector is the Living with Environmental Change partnership between government departments and agencies, Devolved Administrations, local government and research councils (LWEC 2011). Living with Environmental Change supports long-term science and policy-driven research activities related to energy including: the Marine Renewable Energy activity to predict the environmental impacts of large offshore wind, wave, and tidal energy devices; and the Biofuels Executive Research Board which, among other things, monitors and manages research into biofuels.

A number of collaborative research centres in the UK have contributed to our understanding of energy and climate change issues such as the Tyndall Centre for Climate Change Research, the Centre for Climate Change Economics and Policy (est. 2008), the Centre for Social and Economic Research on the Global Environment (est. 1991), and the Centre for Business Relationships, Accountability, Sustainability and Society (est. 2001). The Energy Generation and Supply Knowledge Transfer Network links industrial, academic and government organisations in the areas of: offshore wind; wave and tidal; carbon abatement technologies; fuel cells and hydrogen technologies; maximising oil and gas resources; and future and emerging energy generation and supply opportunities (Technology Strategy Board 2011).

There remains a need to broaden the evidence base for several energy technologies, and to increase our understanding of the impacts of climate change and energy use on ecosystem service delivery. For example, evidence of the environmental impacts of marine renewable energy installations remains limited (Inger *et al.* 2009). To allow for the full range of biodiversity impacts to be assessed, additional multi- and interdisciplinary research will be needed (*ibid.*). The UK Strategic Environmental Assessment

(SEA) on marine wind, oil and gas licensing and carbon sequestration revealed several knowledge gaps (Dolman & Simmonds 2010). In response, the Joint Nature Conservation Committee identified a number of steps to address these gaps: "(1) gap analysis of environmental information; (2) comprehensive Environmental Impact Assessment guidance (including criteria for site selection); (3) targeted survey work (large scale and collaborative approach); (4) a preliminary round of development based on a precautionary threshold coupled with adoption of an iterative approach to consenting; (5) structured and funded monitoring (all stages of pre-development planning, construction and operation) and (6) commitment to full, well-resourced SEA for licensing rounds" (*ibid.*, p.1024).

27.9.3.2 Legislation (enabling)

The system of planning laws in the UK has undergone a number of major reforms in recent years, and remains in a state of flux as the government plans a further series of amendments. Until recently, it operated along a hierarchical structure comprising national level Planning Policy Statements, Regional Strategies and Local Development Frameworks. The legislation laying the basis for this framework is the Town and Country Planning Act 1990, but this has been amended several times, and a number of elements of the current system are set out by the Planning and Compulsory Purchase Act 2004. Recent and proposed changes to the planning system include the discontinuation of the Regional Strategy tier and associated targets for housing development, and a review of planning policy with the intention to consolidate Planning Policy Statements, circulars and guidance documents into a single National Planning Policy Framework.

The new framework is still in preparation, with little detail of its content available at the time of writing. A Ministerial Statement in December 2010 cited the reason for the reform of the planning system in England as "the current suite of planning policy statements and guidance notes is too centralist in its approach...", and that the new framework will ensure "the majority of planning decisions are made at the local level" (Clark 2010). These changes are aligned with the Decentralisation and Localism Bill 2011, discussed below.

Until the new national framework is in force, planning policy will continue to be stipulated in Planning Policy Statements (PPS). Some selected PPSs are considered below. Regional Strategies were (until their abolition) set on a 15 to 20-year timescale, and set out the spatial strategy proposed for the region showing the scale and, broadly, the location for developments including housing, transport, retail and GI. Local Development Frameworks are sets of documents dealing with the detail of planning at local level, but prepared with regard to national planning policy, and also conforming to the regional strategy.

The Planning and Compulsory Purchase Act 2004 required the authorities preparing local and regional plans to have regard to sustainable development. In addition, that act required a sustainability appraisal of the strategies and policies in the regional and local plans (ss 5(4) and 19(5)). The sustainability appraisal incorporates the requirements of the Strategic Environmental Assessment Directive.

A number of national policy documents contain provisions for the incorporation of environmental protection into the planning system. Among them is PPS9 on Biodiversity and Geological Conservation, which states in its key principles that planning decisions should aim to prevent harm to biodiversity (Section 27.2.3.2). Planning decisions should favour less biodiversity-damaging alternatives, plus provide mitigation and compensation measures where damage is unavoidable. Planning Policy Statement 9 also incorporates duties in relation to consideration of protected sites designated at international, EU and national level. According to Natural England (2009e), planning policy has generally protected the UK's designated areas adequately. Planning Policy Statement 1 deals with the delivery of sustainable development, stating that this is the core principle underpinning planning. Planning Policy Guidance (PPG) 2 describes the designation of green belt land and sets out a presumption against inappropriate development in the green belt. Planning Policy Statement 7 on Sustainable Development in Rural Areas requires priority to be given to brownfield over green-field land for development, and for strict control of development in the open countryside. It is important to bear in mind that the sustainable development objectives of planning policy are constantly being weighed against economic development pressures, and economic development goals also feature heavily in the national planning policy documents. A specific principle of PPS7, for example, is the maintenance of high levels of economic growth and employment in rural areas.

The EU has put in place a common set of rules for the consideration of the environmental impacts of development. There are two impact assessment regimes. Each lays down procedures for the systematic consideration of possible environmental impacts before planning decisions are made. One set of rules (the Environmental Impact Assessment Directive) operates at the level of individual projects, while the other (the Strategic Environmental Assessment Directive) governs the consideration of impacts flowing from government development programmes. There is broad consensus that the Environmental Impact Assessment regime has had positive effects and succeeds in many cases in building environmental considerations into planning processes (EC 2009a). This has beneficial effects for environmental protection, but also for the better design, and public acceptance, of developments (ibid.). A particularly helpful aspect of both Environmental Impact Assessments and Strategic Environmental Assessments is that they employ wide-ranging concepts of environmental effect. This means that impact assessments can, and should, cover the effects of a project or plan on almost any aspect of the environment.

However, the framework contains a number of weaknesses. In short, the requirements are procedural only, i.e. the law does not actually specify that projects with significant adverse effects on the environment must not be carried out, just that there must be an assessment to identify and describe those effects. In practice, there are many cases where a policy decision is made to authorise a project, plan or programme despite dangers shown by an impact assessment. Other problems (especially with the project-level system) have their roots in the fact that the developer,

with a vested interest in seeing the project authorised, is generally the party determining what information is contained in an environmental assessment and where that information comes from. This means there is potential for major problems with quality of data contained in environmental reports and the independence of conclusions drawn. Environmental statements should be clear, accurate, comprehensive and objective—but the current law does not contain mechanisms to ensure this is the case (EC 2009a).

A separate set of planning rules for large infrastructure developments of national significance is contained in the Planning Act 2008. This established a system of National Policy Statements (NPSs) for setting out government policy on Nationally Significant Infrastructure Projects including in the sectors of energy, transport (ports, national roads and rail networks), water and waste management. National Policy Statements include matters such as the amount, type and size of such development which is appropriate nationally, and the criteria to be applied in deciding whether a location is suitable for it. It may even identify specific locations as particularly suitable.

The Planning Act also set up a new body, the Infrastructure Planning Commission, to take decisions on the planning of NPSs. The draft Decentralisation and Localism Bill (being debated in Parliament at the time of writing) abolishes the Infrastructure Planning Commission on the grounds that it is unelected and unaccountable. Instead, the bill returns to a position where the Secretary of State takes the final decision on major infrastructure projects of national importance.

The overall theme of the Decentralisation and Localism Bill is to return power for planning decisions to local authorities and communities. The move to planning decisions being decided locally will be supported through the new National Planning Policy Framework that "will be used as a mechanism for delivering Government objectives only where it is relevant, proportionate and effective to do so" (DCLG 2010b). The regional tier of the planning hierarchy, whereby Regional Strategies were developed by unelected regional bodies, will be removed. In particular, this is intended to free local planning authorities from housing targets imposed at regional and national level. As well as improving the ability of the planning system to reflect local needs and sentiments, this measure is designed to remove 'red tape' and reduce costs. Environmental groups have pointed out that a certain level of regional planning and coordination will need to be maintained in order to avoid parochialism or competition for economic growth between different areas (CPRE 2010; FoE 2010). The new bill includes a duty for local planning authorities to liaise and cooperate with each other in this context.

The EU Directive on Environmental Noise (Directive 2002/49/EC) was enacted in 2002. It requires governments to draw up strategic noise maps for major roads, railways, airports and large urban areas, using harmonised noise indicators. Action plans must then be developed to reduce noise where necessary. In addition, where environmental noise quality is shown to be good, this must be maintained and designated as Quiet Areas (**Box 27.42**). The directive does not contain any specific noise limit values. The process of identifying and dealing with noise issues through mapping and action plans is intended to complement other EU legislation dealing with noise emissions from specific sources (Defra 2010p).

The requirements of EU Directives such as the Renewable Energy Directive (2009/28/EC) to increase renewable energy in order to decrease carbon emissions may conflict with those safeguarding areas of biodiversity importance (Chapter 17). In addition, conflicts may arise over locations for renewable energy developments, such as tidal and wind power, and rules for biodiversity and water quality protection under the Habitats and Birds Directives, MSFD and WFD. For example, the environmental regulation of water quality and water usage as a result of the WFD, the MSFD and the Habitats Directive limits the nature and location of future operating thermal plants.

Climate change presents one of the greatest long-term risks to ecosystem service delivery, and the energy sector is embarking on massive changes to decarbonise energy production, driven by legislation such as the EU carbon emissions trading scheme and the Renewables Obligation [Order 2009] for electricity suppliers. The Renewables Obligation Order 2009 (as amended) in England, Wales and Northern Ireland, and the Renewables Obligation (Scotland) Order 2009 (as amended), require electricity providers to supply, during a given period, a specified number of renewable obligation certificates which guarantee a renewable source. Eligible renewable sources include biomass and waste of which less than 90% is derived from fossil fuels. Similarly, the Renewable Transport Fuel Obligations Order 2007 (as amended) stipulates that 4.17% (during the period commencing 2011, and 5.26% after the 2012 period) of the transport fuel provided by a supplier must come from renewable sources, thereby regulating an increase in the proportion of renewable transport fuel.

There are a large number of statutory measures in place to minimise climate impacts. The Climate Change Act 2008 and the Climate Change (Scotland) Act 2009 set carbon targets and budgets, and cover the carbon trading scheme and adaptation to climate change. The Climate Change and Sustainable Energy Act 2006 sets targets for micro-generation of energy, provisions for energy efficiency, and building regulations. The Energy Act 2010 covers financial assistance schemes for carbon capture and storage, and for decarbonisation. The purpose of the Green Energy (Definition and Promotion) Act 2009 is to promote "the generation of electricity or heat from renewable or low-carbon sources by the use of any equipment".

The energy sector is also subject to several further pieces of European legislation: the Large Combustion Plant Directive, the National Emissions Ceilings Directive and Integrated Pollution Prevention and Control Directive. Sulphur dioxide and nitrous oxide emissions have reduced by 92% and 47%, respectively, between 1980 and 2009, which can, in part, be attributed to legislation governing thermal energy plants (Passant et al. 2011). Many ecosystems are consequently recovering from acidification (Ormerod & Durance 2009). Also, the environmental regulation of water usage and water quality is progressively tightening as a result of the WFD, MSFD and Habitats Directive, with implications for the energy sector.

27.9.3.3 Policies, institutions and governance (enabling)

The planning system aims to implement sustainable development, whereby economic, social and environmental objectives are met together. Government planning policy (PPS1: Delivering Sustainable Development) demands that planning authorities make land available to meet expected 'needs' for housing, industrial development, the extraction of raw materials, retail and commercial development, and leisure and recreation. However, careful assessment of the difference between 'demands' and 'needs' is required. Meeting demand for growth is already problematic in many regions of the UK, and increasing supply indefinitely is unlikely to be possible within the capacity of the environment, particularly in areas of especially high demand such as the south-east of England. Increasing the sustainability of homes has the potential to minimise damage to the environment; but avoiding unacceptable loss or modification of ecosystems will be challenging. Demand for housing is rising, partly due to family break-up and more people living alone and for longer, and the UK Government is concerned about the affordability of homes for young people and families. House prices have doubled in real terms in the last decade, and the average house now costs more than eight times the average salary (DCLG 2007). In addition to increasing the housing stock, there may be potential to better control demand and find alternative long-term solutions that do not exceed environmental capacity.

Environmental capacity (or limits) is one of five key components of the UK's Sustainable Development Strategy (HM Government 2005). In the planning context, it refers to the ability of ecosystems to sustain development without irreversible damage or decline in services or benefits derived from them. Yet there is still inadequate guidance on how practitioners can operationalise the concept at the regional and local scales in spatial plans (Smith & Pearson 2008). Trials and studies have been undertaken to address this shortcoming in the South East, East, and North West regions of England (**Box 27.44**).

Ecosystem services approach to development. The adoption of an ecosystem service approach in the design of new developments could yield significant benefits to occupants and the wider community. The incorporation of GI into development plans with explicit objectives to supply a range of services (e.g. recreation, flood attenuation, micro-climate regulation) could significantly increase the value of developments for society beyond direct social and economic benefits. Several PPSs already implicitly protect ecosystem services: PPS 9: Biodiversity and Geological Conservation, emphasises the importance of protecting and enhancing the quality of the natural environment; while PPS 24: Noise recommends the use of natural noise barriers.

Natural England's (2009e) Policy Position on Spatial Planning acknowledges that the adoption of the sustainable development agenda in planning policy has increased the environmental performance of developments. However, it finds that the planning system does not sufficiently capitalise on the multifunctional opportunities that GI in developments could offer (see below, this section). Enhancement of the environment, including habitat creation and landscape restoration, could

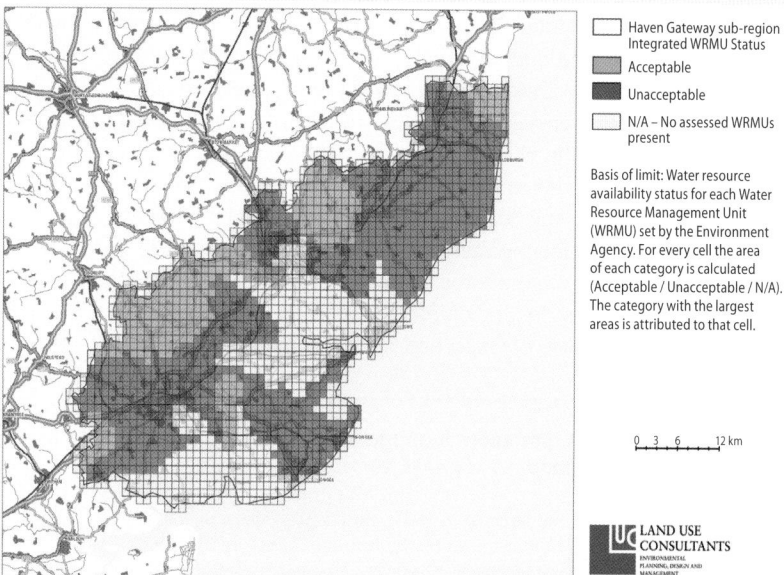
provide benefits for ecosystem functioning and people. Moreover, by considering the landscape and ecosystem setting of the development location, existing landscape distinctiveness could be enhanced and the connectivity of onsite GI with that offsite could be improved (*ibid.*).

Designing developments to create opportunities for people to access and enjoy the natural environment could bring substantial health and well-being benefits for occupants. Rather than adding landscape features as a 'finishing touch', environmental assets could be at the core of development design from the outset; currently, priority is instead given to grey infrastructure in land use planning at the cost of valuable ecosystem services (Landscape Institute 2009). How new buildings are designed will also determine the ease and ability of occupants to behave sustainably. Natural England (2009e) recommends that spatial plans should aim for net improvements in environmental quality and increased environmental capacity, rather than merely minimising damage. The services provided by the natural environment could be multiplied and enhanced substantially if they were planned for and integrated into planning policies from the beginning (Landscape Institute 2009).

Policy support for multifunctional Green Infrastructure. Green Infrastructure refers to parks, green spaces, public squares, trees, allotments, woodlands and waterways and how they are spatially connected as networks of public spaces that benefit local communities. Green Infrastructure can provide green routes for safe travel by foot and bicycle, filter polluted air, attenuate floodwaters, reduce the urban heat island effect through cooling and shading, supply local food and biofuel, and provide habitats and corridors for wildlife to move around urban areas. Green Infrastructure, such as parks and woodland, can also be designated as quiet and dark areas where noise and light levels are limited (**Box 27.43**). It is well-established that

these features improve perceptions of an area, can provide stimulus to local economies, and can bring health benefits (CABE 2010a). Chapter 10 discusses the potential benefits of GI in more detail.

Green Infrastructure is increasingly recognised in planning policy as an important response to creating sustainable communities. The role of GI in addressing climate change adaptation is cited in a supplement to PPS1 (2007). Natural England (2009d) recommends that local authorities should develop GI strategies to ensure its integration into development processes from the outset.

Localism and greenspace management. The government's move towards devolving power to local authorities, set out in the Decentralisation and Localism Bill, is likely to change the way greenspace is owned and managed. Local actors will be expected to play a larger role in managing community open spaces. Some local authorities are considering whether to transfer ownership of public open spaces to communities as a way of reducing costs. Many community groups are already active in influencing the way their greenspaces are managed and contribute volunteer time to their upkeep and improvement. The idea of getting these groups more involved in the management of these spaces is growing in popularity. Underused or neglected space can be managed by groups or leased or licensed by a local authority to restore them for the benefit of their local community. Transfer of ownership is rising: a survey of local authorities in 2009 found that about 1,000 transfers were being made at that time in England (CABE 2010a).

The Community-led Spaces Report by CABE (2010a) states that the benefits of community group ownership of greenspaces include: the maintenance of funds by the group irrespective of budget cuts by local government; savings in terms of staffing costs as volunteers donate their time; and better management because people living close to a greenspace care most about it and know the specific needs and priorities. Community groups are also thought to respond to opportunities more rapidly, such as converting land to food production, and can build trust between local authorities and communities. The establishment of trusts to manage open spaces has proven successful in cases where sufficient resources and skills are available (**Box 27.45**). Building the skills and capacity of volunteers and providing sufficient funding support will be essential if greater responsibility for the management of greenspaces is to be transferred to communities. However, the risks of relying excessively on local volunteers need to be recognised, particularly lack of expertise, diseconomies of operating

---

---

in relatively small-scale units, and competing pressures on people's time and finances. There are also risks associated with the capacity of local authorities to support and liaise with community groups.

Minimising the negative impacts of transport on ecosystems. In the past, the UK government's transport policy typically backed the expansion of transport infrastructure to support economic growth and reduce congestion. In terms of congestion, at least, this rationale was flawed. Evidence suggests that the expansion of road capacity, for example, is eroded over time as new and longer journeys fill the extra space. The London Orbit Multi-Modal Study (2001) found that the M25 could be widened indefinitely and still fail to stop congestion unless demand control measures were implemented, such as road pricing. Expansion of transport infrastructure, and road and air traffic, impacts ecosystems through conversion and fragmentation of habitats, light, noise and air pollution, and loss of valued landscapes and tranquillity (Natural England 2009f).

More recently, the government has sought to reduce emissions from the transport sector and to encourage a modal shift from private cars, road and airfreight to more sustainable forms of travel and transportation such as walking, bicycle, rail, bus/coach and boat (Section 27.8.3.3). Progress towards this objective has been slow; car use remains high and air travel continue to increase (DfT 2009). Expanding the capacity for public transport within and between urban areas could reduce congestion and have limited overall direct effects on ecosystems. Not only would a substantial modal shift reduce the transport sector's contribution to climate change, but it would also (**Figure 27.57**) minimise the space required for transport infrastructure and avoid the associated environmental impacts. The logic is clear, but the challenges for its attainment great.

Figure 27.57 The amount of space required to transport the same number of people by car, bus or bicycle. Source: a poster in the Press Office, city of Münster, Germany.

In 2011, the government published the Local Transport White Paper (DfT 2011). It focuses on improving the quality of existing public transport primarily at the local level with limited expansion of infrastructure (notably a high speed rail network). A Local Sustainable Transport Fund of £560 million will be available for local authorities to develop local transport initiatives.

The government also intends to support the development of the electric car market in the UK.

Current transport planning policy attempts to minimise damage to ecosystems, particularly if there is potential to impact protected areas such as SSSIs, AONBs, National Parks and SACs. Even with protection, these areas can still be impacted by increasing noise, air and light pollution from increasing traffic, and major transport projects are still regularly proposed in AONBs and National Parks. Green infrastructure, such as tree barriers, can be useful instruments for reducing noise impacts (Section 27.5.3.6). A report by The Royal Commission on Environmental Pollution (RCEP 2009) found that sufficient evidence exists to "generate concern regarding the adverse ecological consequences of artificial lighting schemes"; but further research is required on this subject. The report also noted that, between 1993 and 2000, the UK became more intensely lit at night, and outdoor lighting continues to grow at around 3% every year. Although there is currently inconclusive evidence at an ecosystem level of the impact of light pollution, including on protected areas, there is sufficient information to warrant concern and to prompt actions to reduce light pollution.

In the future, there is potential for transport policies to deliver net environmental gains. Ecosystem services can be better valued in transport decision-making processes, and transport choices that are less harmful to ecosystems have the potential to be made more attractive. By integrating transport and spatial planning, towns and cities could be designed to minimise the need to use a car (Stantchev & Whiteing 2010). Making environmentally sustainable modes of transport more convenient, affordable and more enjoyable than travelling by car is likely to be important in encouraging a modal shift. The Land Use Futures report (2010) warned that the "failure to integrate transport into land use strategy over the next two decades will have serious consequences for congestion, pollution and managing climate change, and will lead to mismatches between the location of housing development and the availability of jobs."

Energy policy. According to the Foresight Land Use Futures report (Foresight 2010), the future energy of the UK is likely to be obtained from a mix of nuclear, renewables, coal-fired powered stations with carbon capture and storage, and conventional fossil fuels such as gas. How much each of these will contribute is still under debate and may vary between the four countries of the UK. It will depend on a range of factors including the incentives provided by government, fuel prices, regulations and technological developments. Electricity demand could double, according to the government's 2050 Energy Pathways report (HM Government 2010a), meaning that the decarbonisation of electricity generation will be a major priority.

In 2009, the UK Government published the UK Low Carbon Transition Plan (HM Government 2009a) which sets out the policies needed to achieve the targets set by the 2008 Climate Change Act to reduce emissions by at least 34% below 1990 levels by 2020, and by 80% by 2050. The plan aims to reduce emissions through energy efficiency gains, the increased use of renewable energy and the EU Emissions Trading System. The Climate Change (Scotland) Act sets the ambitious target of reducing emissions by 42% below 1990 levels by 2020.

Renewable energy is further promoted by the UK Renewable Energy Strategy (HM Government 2009b), and through devolved policy. The strategy sets the legally binding target of 15% of energy coming from renewable sources by 2020. In order to achieve this overall target, it is proposed that 30% of electricity, 12% of heat and 10% of transport energy are generated from renewables. Legislation including the Renewables Obligation 2009 (amended 2010), the Renewables Transport Fuel Obligation (Amendment) Order 2009 and the new Renewables Heat Incentive will further encourage the development of the renewables sector. The UK Biomass Strategy (DTI *et al.* 2007) evaluates the contribution biomass can make as a sustainable resource. It predicts that 35,000 ha of perennial energy crops will be needed by 2020 to meet targets, plus an additional 740,000 ha for transport biofuel. Land conversion at this scale will conflict with food production, protection of water resources, biodiversity and other services unless it is appropriately planned and managed (Section 7.2.2.1).

The Scottish Government has backed renewables through the Renewables Action Plan 2009 (as updated in 2010, 2011; Scottish Government 2009c), with a pledge to generate 20% of its energy and 50% of its electricity from renewable energy sources by 2020; it is already on course to exceed its 2011 interim target for 31% of electricity to come from renewable sources (Scottish Government 2010a). Other relevant Scottish policies include: the Energy Efficiency Action Plan (Scottish Government 2010c), the Renewable Heat Action Plan (Scottish Government 2009d), the Low Carbon Scotland Public Engagement Strategy (Scottish Government 2010d), and the Roadmap for Carbon Capture Storage (Scottish Government 2010b).

The Climate Change Strategy for Wales (WAG 2010c), The Energy Policy Statement (WAG 2010a), the Renewable Energy Route Map for Wales (WAG 2008c) and the Bioenergy Action Plan for Wales (WAG 2010b) form the a framework for renewable electricity generation and energy efficiency in the Welsh context. In Northern Ireland, the Strategic Energy Framework (DETI 2010) outlines aims for a more secure and sustainable energy system.

The Department of Energy and Climate Change has opened a consultation on the reform of the electricity market with the aim of creating a new market framework that favours the development of low carbon energy, including nuclear power. This is the most important assessment of the electricity market since it was privatised, and an appropriate reform will accelerate the transition to a low carbon electricity mix. The modelling used in the Energy 2050 study estimates that the UK can maintain its energy supplies while still complying with its international environmental obligations for low carbon energy and without causing catastrophic change (UKERC 2010).

The backing of wind energy will have substantial implications for ecosystem services. Windfarms are located in exposed areas to ensure sufficient average wind speeds that maximise energy generation—these places are often coastal, upland and offshore locations which frequently contain environmentally sensitive habitats that could be threatened by inappropriate wind energy projects. WWF-UK *et al.* (2001) recommend that if a windfarm development is likely to have adverse effects on a site of regional or local nature conservation importance, it should only be permitted if there are strong reasons for the project that outweigh the need to safeguard nature conservation. There are some examples emerging, however, where both nature conservation and renewable energy can benefit, such as at Black Law windfarm in Scotland (**Box 27.46**). Due to local resistance towards the noise and visual impacts of turbines, windfarms are often subject to planning delays and the industry worries that lengthy planning processes and guidelines could hamper the achievement of onshore renewable energy targets (POST 2009). Although there are many complaints about noise from wind developments in the UK, issues can often be resolved by limiting turbine rotation speed (*ibid.*).

The UK has an extensive coastline, exposed to strong winds, currents and waves, providing enormous potential to generate energy from the Marine environment. Plans are afoot for substantial development of marine renewable energy infrastructure to harness this energy. In February 2009, the Crown Estate announced ten sites for the development of offshore windfarms within Scottish territorial waters. These sites are spread out on the east and west coasts, and will contribute to delivering an additional 25 gigawatts from offshore wind. Prior & McMath (2008) postulate that the expansion of marine windfarms and marine energy generators will be the most large-scale engineering intervention in the UK's coastal waters in the coming decades. **Figure 27.59** maps the locations of marine windfarms planned in the UK. The Marine Energy Action Plan (HM Government 2010b) sets out the vision for the marine energy sector upto 2030, and covers wave, tidal range and tidal stream energy across the UK. It incorporates a full sector engagement approach, encouraging collaboration between government and industry for the development of the sector. The plan recommends delivery of the full Strategic Environmental Assessment for Wave and Tidal Energy involving engagement of all relevant stakeholders. The Scottish Government has also proposed Strategic Environment Assessments for marine wind energy.

Concerns over the potential impacts on biodiversity of marine renewable energy installations include habitat loss, collision risks, noise and electromagnetic fields (Inger *et al.* 2009) Cetacean species are at significant risk due, for example, to the noise from pile-driving (Simmonds & Brown 2010). Conversely, marine renewable energy installations may also offer some biodiversity benefits by providing hard surfaces for fouling organisms to colonise, which might, in turn, provide a habitat for fishes (Inger *et al.* 2009). Furthermore, the areas around large installations, especially wave energy and tidal stream generating sites, will probably need to be closed zones to fishing due to the risks of collision and gear entanglement, and may, in effect, act as MPAs where certain activities are limited or banned through bylaws. Effectively managed MPAs can increase biodiversity compared to surrounding areas (Halpern 2003). Further research is required, however, to fully understand the positive and negative impacts of the deployment of marine renewable energy installations (Chapter 12), and how to enhance the positives and mitigate the negatives (Simmonds & Brown 2010). The deployment of marine renewable energy installations is a potentially contentious issue between

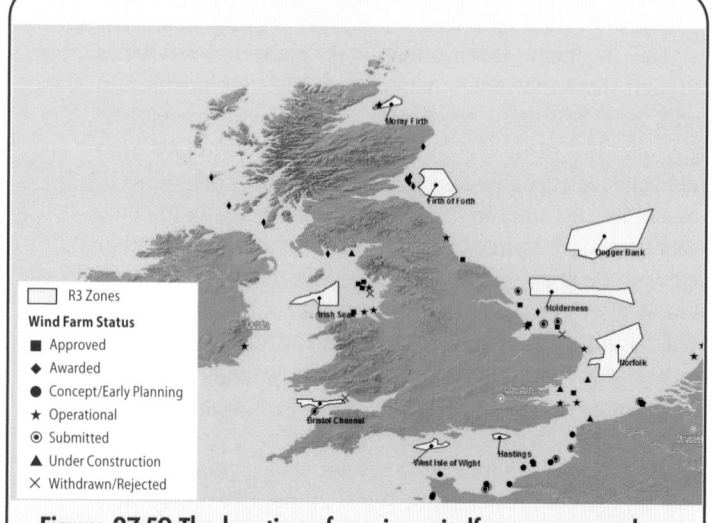

Figure 27.59 The location of marine windfarm zones and sites in UK waters. Source: updated from Simmonds & Brown (2010).

Box 27.46 Win-win for renewable energy and conservation at Black Law windfarm. Source: RSPB Scotland (2010).

Black Law windfarm (**Figure 27.58**), a 124-megawatt, 54-turbine renewable energy development, is located in an area of North and South Lanarkshire and West Lothian that was extensively damaged by mining, afforestation and drainage of wet heath. During the development of the windfarm, Scottish Power Renewables, Scottish Natural Heritage, the three local councils, and RSPB Scotland worked together to protect and enhance the habitats of farmland birds and a locally important population of breeding waders, and to restore blanket bog. The project developed a Habitat Management Plan that covers 1,440 ha and is now the largest heathland restoration scheme in the region. Habitat was created in a former opencast coal mine, conifer plantations were removed, and a watercourse was restored to benefit water voles and otters.

Black Law windfarm has been operational since summer 2005 and was awarded the Best Renewable Project in the 2005 Green Energy Awards. An application for extending the wind farm by a further 23 turbines is currently being considered.

Figure 27.58 Black Law windfarm, Lanarkshire, Scotland. *Photo by Stuart Brooks (geographic.org.uk), available under a Creative Commons Attribution-Share Alike license.*

environmental groups, the fishing sector and energy companies (Inger *et al.* 2009). Clearly, evidencing potential environmental benefits, and integrating stakeholders into the design, construction, and installation phases, could minimise conflicts.

27.9.3.4 Changing social attitudes (enabling)

Interaction with nature is believed to be essential for nurturing an understanding of the value of ecosystems and an interest in protecting them (Nisbet *et al.* 2009). Urban dwellers are often less connected with nature than those living in rural areas because there are less opportunities within cities to spend time in natural environments and there may be negative associations with some Urban wildlife (Johnson & Catley 2009). Since over 90% of the UK's population live in urban areas (GreenLINK 2010), designing places where people work and live to maximise exposure to meaningful interactions with the natural world could support widespread change to more sustainable behavioural patterns (Miller 2005 in Andersson 2006). Providing opportunities for volunteers to manage Urban greenspaces can foster a greater awareness of the wider environment (GreenLINK 2010), and more contact with nature can also have benefits for physiological and physical health (Chapter 10).

Since the 1990s, the trend of a decline in quality of greenspace has been stopped, and even reversed, in many cases. This has resulted in people using and valuing greenspace more (CABE 2010b). The benefits of using greenspace have not reached everyone though, with variable quality and quantity of greenspace in different regions of the UK. A study by CABE (2010) found depravation and affluence to be the most significant determinants of greenspace provision and quality (**Figure 27.60**). People from certain socioeconomic and cultural backgrounds do not have equal access to greenspace—this has implications for health, their relationship with nature, and the potential for behavioural change (Section 27.8.3.1).

The CABE report also found that by improving the quality of greenspace (for example, by providing more facilities and improving safety) more people will actively use it, including for exercise. If parks and greenspaces are well-managed, research has shown that communities use their local spaces more, have better relationships with their local councils and take pride in the area where they live and the quality of life of individuals is enhanced (CABE 2010b). Concern about personal safety is the most common reason for people not using parks, and constraints on personal time (perceived and real) make the proximity of greenspace to homes and workplaces another important determinant. Once-avoided greenspace can be rejuvenated, however, into popular amenities for communities through good design, management and maintenance (CABE 2005). The Green Flag Award allows greenspaces to be compared with the national standard and encourages authorities managing the parks and greenspaces to improve performance and gain national recognition (Section 27.8.3.6; **Figure 27.61**). Likewise, successful community-managed greenspace can be recognised by the Green Pennant Award.

Public and organisational behaviour change will be necessary in order for sustainable travel to become widely

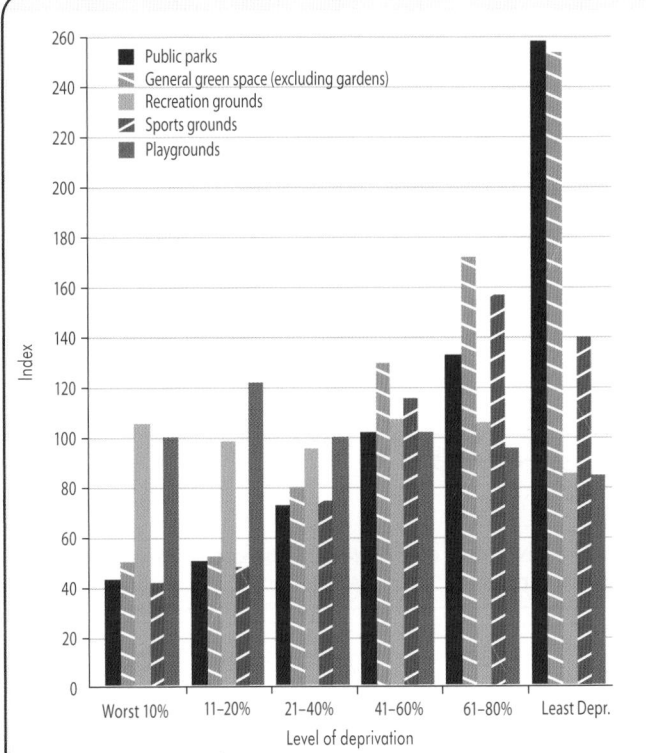

Figure 27.60 Quantity and type of greenspace and area deprivation. Source: CABE (2010); data from CIPFA Leisure, culture and recreation statistics 2007/08 and Municipal Year Book (recreation grounds); CABE Space urban green space inventory (public parks); Generalised Land Use Database (general green space); Sport England Facilities data 2009 (sports grounds); Ordnance Survey Points of Interest information (playgrounds). All measures based on area (hectares) of green space per 1,000 population.

adopted, thus reducing emissions and the pressure from the transport sector on the natural environment. Perhaps the greatest 'value-action gap' is on transport behaviour: even those with strong 'green' values are unwilling to give up, or accept restrictions on, private car use and aviation. More 'social invention' action research could find new approaches and frameworks that effectively reduce travel distances and encourage modal shift to 'green' modes (e.g. car share clubs and city-wide bike hire schemes such as Velib in Paris and London's 'Boris bikes'; **Figure 27.62**).

In fact, a fundamental cultural shift in the way the public view travel is required. 'Smart' travel measures, such as travel plans and personalised journey planning, can encourage walking, cycling and public transport use, but these also need to be complemented with hard measures, such as cycle routes and priority bus lanes, to make sustainable travel choices more attractive (Natural England 2009f). Forming a network of greenways by closing some residential streets to cars and establishing trees, cycle and walking paths, and recreational facilities is one option for improving the appeal and safety of walking and cycling in urban areas (Chapter 10, Box 10.2).

To embed the value of the natural environment in the planning system, the UK Man and Biosphere Committee's Urban Forum (UK MAB Urban Forum 2010) recommend providing adequate training on ecological considerations in the education of planners. Such knowledge will be essential for the development of robust GI plans.

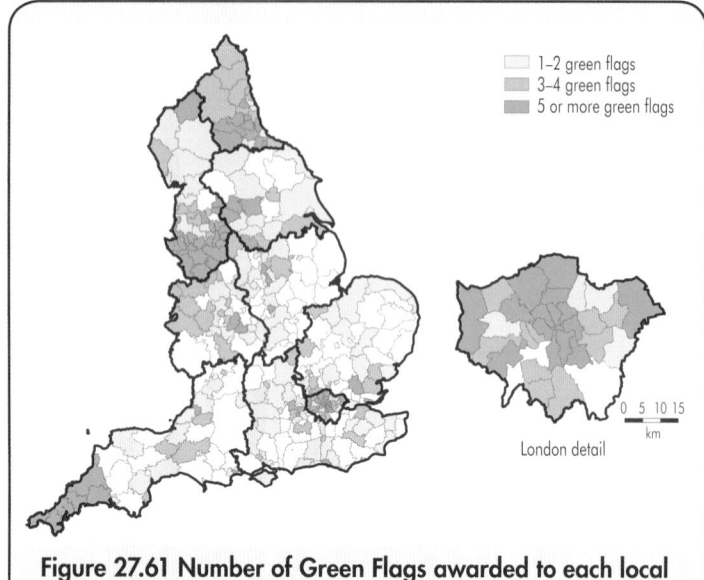

Figure 27.61 Number of Green Flags awarded to each local authority in England. Source: CABE 2010b.

Legend:
- 1–2 green flags
- 3–4 green flags
- 5 or more green flags

London detail

0 5 10 15 km

Figure 27.62. Research is needed on innovative approaches—such as the London bicycle hire scheme—to encourage a shift in travel behaviour towards 'green' modes. *Photo by Seth Anderson available under a Creative Commons Attribution-Share Alike license.*

The process of researching and understanding public perceptions and acceptance of renewable energy development is of great importance. The development of different forms of renewable energy is supported by central government, and the public have a generally favourable attitude towards renewables overall, but there is strong resistance to specific developments, coined 'not in my back yard' sentiments, or 'NIMBYism' (Devine Wright 2005; Owens & Driffill 2008, p.4413). Upreti (2004) found that, in England and Wales, public opposition is one of the major obstacles in the promotion of biomass energy. Much research has been conducted on public attitudes towards windfarm development. Public oppositions to such developments include: visual impacts, noise, perceived unreliability, high cost, dangerous impacts on birds and wildlife, perceived inefficiency (vs. coal-fired power stations), suspicion on motives of development, and annoyance towards idle turbines (Devine Wright, 2005). Even when people recognise the necessity to promote renewable energy, they would prefer it does not take place in their locality. In this respect, public participation in the delivery of renewable energy is of great importance.

Studies have shown that local involvement positively influences public perceptions of windfarms. A study by Warren & McFadyen (2010) in south-west Scotland found that "a change in development model towards community ownership [as opposed to developer-owned] could have a positive effect on public attitudes towards windfarm development in Scotland" (p.204). In order to address the complexities involved in behaviour change towards climate change, the Scottish Government has developed the Climate Change Behaviours Research Programme (CCBRP; Scottish Executive 2006a). Between 2010 and 2012, the programme aims to better understand mechanisms for stimulating, facilitating and supporting behaviour change to feed into policy development.

The approach commonly taken to transform social attitudes in energy and environmental fields is awareness raising and education, but the provision of information often has little impact on behaviour, especially when counter to social norms or prices (Owens & Driffill 2008). Attitudes are additionally influenced by social, political and cultural factors. Many examples demonstrate that domestic energy consumption campaigns have failed to lead to the take-up of energy efficiency measures. Owens & Driffil (2008) highlight the need for more interactive and deliberative communications between a broad spectrum of actors. Contextual constraints also limit capacity for effective action; for example, physical infrastructure, spatial separation of activities and availability of public services may limit people's ability to minimise driving in order to mitigate climate impacts (*ibid.*).

The Energy Saving Trust is one example of a non-profit organisation acting in the energy sector to provide a range of resources for citizens, businesses and the public sector to minimise energy wastage and inform green behaviour (EST 2011a). Their Green Communities programme aims to support, facilitate and promote community-based energy projects through the provision of advice and expert support. Collaborative networks also exist in this field.

27.9.3.5 Markets and incentives (instrumental)

To encourage a shift to more sustainable transport modes, pricing can be an important driver of behavioural change. Currently, the external costs of transportation are not reflected in the cost of travel by car. Fiscal instruments, such as road pricing, fuel tax and vehicle excise duty, can reduce traffic growth and make more sustainable forms of transport more financially attractive. These policies, however, often need to be complemented with other measures, such as behavioural change, technology and regulations, to be successful (Natural England 2009f). A review of evidence by the Land Use Futures study (2010) found that "rationing road use in cities by pricing is economically and environmentally sound, but may accelerate the rate of decentralisation of economic activities to fringe locations ('Edge Cities')." The Central London Congestion Charge, introduced in 2003, successfully reduced congestion by 20–30% in the zone (**Figure 27.63**). Congestion has increased again in London recently due to high levels of road works and more road allocated to cycling and buses, not due to increased traffic (Albalate & Bel 2008; TfL 2008). Transport for London estimated that the scheme was responsible for up to one-half of the bus patronage increases seen over the period 2002 to 2003 in London. Attempts to replicate the London system in other towns and cities have been met with resistance from the public. In Manchester, congestion charging was rejected—almost 80% voted against the introduction of the scheme—and the government removed financial support for congestion charging when it discontinued the Transport Innovation Fund in March 2010. The downsizing of the London congestion zone in 2011 also demonstrates the lack of public and, therefore, political acceptability of such schemes. This is despite there being no discernable impacts on the economy of London (TfL 2008).

The government is reviewing market arrangements for electricity supply to determine how to deliver major new investments in low carbon electricity generation. This is likely to result in market and incentive arrangements to drive low carbon electricity, in addition to existing instruments such as the EU Carbon Emissions Trading Scheme and the Renewables Obligation for electricity suppliers. Grants exist for home energy saving, domestic renewable projects, commercial renewables, and for infrastructure for alternative fuels. The Low Carbon Building Programme is now closed to new applications due to cost saving measures; however, the Feed-in Tariff (FIT) for electricity-generating technologies was introduced as a government incentive (in GB) in April 2010 (EST 2011b). The aim of FITs is to incentivise small-scale renewable energy generation from, for example, solar photovoltaics and wind turbines, by energy suppliers making regular, minimum payments to individuals, communities and businesses for the electricity they supply the national grid. The new Renewable Heat Incentive (RHI) financial support scheme is due to be put in place in 2011 following consultations on the proposal (DECC 2010). This scheme proposes to support a range of technologies including: "air, water and ground-source heat pumps (and other geothermal energy), solar thermal, biomass boilers, renewable combined heat power, use of biogas and bioloquids and the injection of biomethane into the natural

gas grid" (ibid., p.3). The Energy Crops Scheme in England provides establishment grants for short rotation coppice (of willow, poplar, ash, alder, hazel, silver birch, sycamore, sweet chestnut and lime), and Miscanthus (a tall woody grass) (Natural England 2009c); (Section 27.5.3.5).

27.9.3.6 Technologies and practices (instrumental)

Multifunctional Green Infrastructure. Green Infrastructure is acknowledged as one of the most promising ways to enhance ecosystem service provision in urban areas. Rural GI will be covered in less detail here since many of the responses are discussed under other sectors including Biodiversity (Section 27.2.), Water (Section 27.3.), and Forestry (Section 27.5.).

Green Infrastructure is a planned network of greenspaces and other environmental assets (**Box 27.47**). The intention of GI is to provide multiple ecosystem services that have benefits for the quality of life of local communities. The development of GI involves a process of planning, design, implementation and management of a network of greenspaces, habitats and places which, if managed together, exceed the sum of the individual parts (Landscape Institute 2009).

The human well-being benefits of greenspaces are substantial. There is strong evidence that greenspace provides health benefits, and increases informal and physically active recreational opportunities. Coombes et al. (2010) found that people living closest to formal greenspace are more likely to meet recommended levels of physical activity; reducing the sedentary population by just 1% would save an estimated £1.44 billion per year in costs to the economy (Natural England 2009e). Ensuring people don't have to travel far to use greenspaces and that they are of a high quality has a significant influence on user levels and equal access (Section 27.9.3.4). Green Infrastructure can also provide for Quiet Areas (**Box 27.43**). A growing body of literature indicates that access to greenspace reduces long-term noise annoyances (Gidlof-Gunnarsson & Ohrstrom 2007).

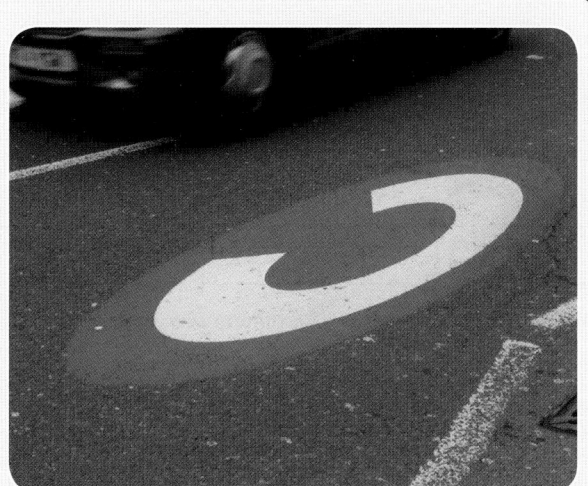

Figure 27.63 The Central London Congestion Charge reduced congestion by 20–30%. *Photo by audreym available under a Creative Commons Attribution-NonCommercial-ShareAlike license.*

Box 27.47 Green Infrastructure definition and typology (Table 27.23). Source: Natural England (2009d).

Green Infrastructure is defined in PPS 12 as:
"a network of multi-functional green space, both new and existing, both rural and urban, which supports the natural and ecological processes and is integral to the health and quality of life of sustainable communities"

Table 27.23 Green Infrastructure typology. Source: Natural England (2009d).

Parks and gardens	Urban parks, Country and Regional Parks, formal gardens
Amenity greenspace	Informal recreation spaces, housing greenspaces, domestic gardens, village greens, urban commons, other incidental space, green roofs
Natural and semi-natural urban greenspaces	Woodland and scrub, grassland (e.g. downland and meadow), heath or moor, wetlands, open and running water, wastelands and disturbed ground), bare rock habitats (e.g. cliffs and quarries)
Green corridors	Rivers and canals including their banks, road and rail corridors, cycling routes, pedestrian paths, and rights of way
Others	Allotments, community gardens, city farms, cemeteries and churchyards

SuDS attenuation pond → Policy priorities:
- **Environmental**
- **Economic**
- **Social**

→ Functions:
- **Flood attenuation and water resource management**
- **Access, recreation, movement and leisure**
- **Landscape setting and context for development**
- **Habitat provision and access to nature**
- **Healthy communities, health and well being**

Figure 27.64. Ecosystem services delivered by Sustainable Urban Drainage Systems (SuDS). Source: Natural England (2009d).

Water management and urban drainage. Increased flooding in towns and cities has prompted interest in the role that town planning can play in reducing flood risk. The replacement of hard impermeable surfaces with semi-permeable surfaces (such as honeycomb structures) can reduce surface runoff by retaining water (Shaw *et al.* 2007). Water features, such as ponds and lakes, can have a substantial cooling effect, as well as providing recreational and aesthetic benefits and habitats for wildlife. As rivers have become cleaner, they have become a focus of urban regeneration; since cleaner rivers support wildlife, and are aesthetically pleasing, they bring improvements in well-being and are a source of economic benefits (EA 2002). Sustainable Urban Drainage Systems (SuDs) fulfil a range of functions including the attenuation of surface water runoff and the enhancement of biodiversity and recreation opportunities (**Figure 27.64**). They include rainwater re-use, soakaways, permeable surfaces, ponds and wetlands. The runoff of pollutants into watercourses can be reduced by slowing down the flow of rainwater so that it passes through soils where pollutants are retained and broken down. Reedbeds are also extremely effective at removing contaminants from water. SuDS have also been used in transport infrastructure schemes to minimise impacts on water quality (**Box 27.48**).

Allotments and community gardens (Chapter 10, Box 10.4, Section 27.8.3.4, **Figure 27.65**). During WWII, urban food production played a significant role in meeting the nutritional needs of the urban population, but today, cities are fed by an enormous inflow of food and other goods that have impacted ecosystems, both within the UK and globally, during their production. Food production may once again be returning to the Urban landscape, however, with a rise in the number of city dwellers working allotments and gardens

Figure 27.65 Allotments in Bristol, England. *Photo courtesy of William Bolton/Ecojam.org.*

(Chapter 10; **Box 27.40**). There has also been a proliferation of community food projects. The Landshare scheme aims to bring together people who have land to share with those who need land for cultivating food. Since its launch in 2009, it has grown into a community of more than 55,000 growers, sharers and helpers (Landshare 2011).

By creating more space for allotments, community gardens and orchards to meet rising demand, spatial planning can increase access to healthy food, provide educational opportunities, contribute to food security, and reconnect communities with their local environment and source of food (Landscape Institute 2009) (Section 27.8.3.4). Practices to reduce the extent and levels of soil contamination in urban areas would support the expansion of food production in cities.

Energy—practices and technologies. New technologies are expected to make a significant contribution to decarbonising energy supply, including carbon capture and

Box 27.48 Using Sustainable Drainage Systems to minimise the impact of a bypass—A5 Newtownstewart, Northern Ireland. Source: NIEA (2009).

The construction of the 2.6 km single carriageway trunk road near Newtownstewart in Northern Ireland, and two bridges over the River Strule, posed a risk to the scenic and environmentally sensitive Strule Valley. The river is important for recreational fishing and a fish farm is located downstream of the bypass. A number of measures were implemented to mitigate the environmental impacts of the project and those from traffic following construction. To protect the quality of the river water, Sustainable Drainage Systems were incorporated into the project's design.

The road was constructed without kerbs, and an open, stone filter, with a perforated pipe at its base, was installed along both sides of the road. Surface water flows from these drains to five detention basins that are planted with reeds to purify contaminants. Water from the basins is discharged to the river via penstocks, which can be closed in the event of a hazardous spillage.

storage of fossil fuel emissions, and the electricification of transport and heating. Geothermal technology is one area of research and development in the UK. The UK Government has committed £6 million to explore the potential of deep geothermal power generation in the country (HM Government 2009a). A field trial of heat pumps by the Energy Saving Trust (EST 2010) revealed that well-installed heat pumps can lead to domestic carbon savings in the UK, and that the simplest systems perform with higher efficiencies.

With respect to energy crops, empirical models using GIS can be used to produce yield maps for energy-generation potential, taking into account environmental and socioeconomic factors (Lovett *et al.* 2009). The use of this technology will optimise trade-offs between land uses at regional and local scales. Lovett *et al.* (2009) conclude that increased planting of biofuels crops on 350,000 ha (as proposed in Section 27.9.3.3) would utilise 4–28% of lower grade land and would not necessarily impact on UK food security. The use of hay as a biomass fuel from Semi-natural Grasslands could create synergies between bioenergy production and conservation (Section 17.4.2.2).

Dolman & Simmonds (2010) identified a number of steps to minimise the negative consequences of the marine renewable energy industry in Scotland including appropriate criteria for site selection, marine and spatial planning, Strategic Environmental Assessments, providing best practice guidance to developers, real-time monitoring, and measures to mitigate potential impacts.

27.9.4 Urban Planning, Transport and Energy Summary

Table 27.24 summarises the key insights from this review of responses in the context of urban planning, transport and energy, highlighting those that have been well-established, but also identifying a set of responses that are either in early implementation or are proposed. It is important to learn from these early pilots across all sectors to scale-up the adoption of an integrated ecosystem approach to the management of the UK's diverse habitats, which is one key policy direction that this review recommends.

27.10 Adopting an Ecosystems Approach: Integrated Responses

The MA (2005) defined integrated responses as those that "intentionally and actively address ecosystem services and human wellbeing simultaneously". So far, this chapter has reviewed responses that have been tried within a selection of sectors which have a major influence on ecosystems and the services they provide. Such a sectoral approach represents

Table 27.24 Urban Planning, Transport and Energy Summary.

	Established responses	Early implementation, pilots	Proposed, under development
Knowledge	■ Mapping of public green space ■ Collaborative interdisciplinary research centres and programmes ■ Strategic Environmental Assessments	■ Research on adaptation to climate change in urban areas	■ National database on green spaces ■ Urban ecosystem assessments, including valuation studies ■ Research on regulatory services and biodiversity in urban areas; cumulative impact of transport on ecosystems; energy technologies and their impacts on ecosystems
Legislation	■ Town & Country Planning Act 1990, Planning and Compulsory Purchase Act 2004 ■ Environment impact assessment Directives ■ Environmental Noise Directive ■ Energy related EU legislation, e.g. Combustion Plant Directive	■ Designation of 'Quiet Areas' ■ Climate change and energy legislation, e.g. Climate Change Act 2008 ■ Renewable Energy Directive (2009)	■ National Planning Policy Framework ■ Decentralisation and Localism Bill (2011)
Policies, institutions and governance	■ Planning Policy Statements ■ Regional Strategies (discontinued), Local Development Frameworks ■ UK Sustainable Development Strategy	■ Operationalising the concept of environmental limits in spatial plans ■ Management and ownership of green space by local communities ■ Improving sustainable modes of transport ■ Low Carbon Transition Plan ■ Renewable energy developments designed to also benefit biodiversity	■ Ecosystem services approach and Green Infrastructure in development planning ■ Integrate transport and spatial planning to minimise car use and improve public transport ■ Local Transport White Paper
Changing social attitudes	■ Awareness raising and education ■ Energy Saving Trust	■ Volunteer opportunities to manage urban greenspace ■ Improve appeal of sustainable travel modes to change attitudes towards travel	■ Changing attitudes to travel and public transport ■ Training of planners to consider ecosystem services ■ Public participation in the delivery and ownership of renewable energy to reduce local opposition
Markets and incentives	■ EU Emissions Trading System ■ Road pricing, congestion charging	■ Feed-in-tariffs (energy)	■ Reform of electricity market to favour low-carbon energy
Technologies and practices	■ Water management and sustainable urban drainage systems (SuDS) ■ Measures to minimise impacts of energy installations and energy crops	■ Multi-functional Green Infrastructure ■ New renewable energy technologies, carbon capture and storage ■ New renewable energy technologies, carbon capture and storage ■ Measures to minimise impacts of energy installations and energy crops	

how the impacts of human activities in the UK have been historically managed. Sector-by-sector approaches normally result in fragmented responses that do not adequately recognise the realities of the interconnections among natural and social systems. This has resulted in failures to achieve broader sustainable development goals. As the previous UK NEA chapters have demonstrated, it has also prevented the full potential and value of the goods and services provided by the UK's natural environment to be utilised.

Protecting the environment does not need to come at the expense of the economy and competitiveness. A growing body of evidence outlined in this chapter suggests that investment in nature can produce benefits that far outweigh costs. In the current economic climate, short-term political priorities of job creation and economic growth and stability are not necessarily incompatible with long-term imperatives of social, economic and environmental sustainability. Sustainable economic growth depends on healthy ecosystems delivering essential goods and services, whereas growth that undermines the UK's ecosystems also risks jeopardising the nations' future prosperity. This section will discuss approaches to integrated responses in a cross-sectoral context and options for collaboration between actors.

27.10.1 Knowledge (Foundational)

Our worldview has shifted from regarding human and natural systems as separate entities to an appreciation that the two are fundamentally interwoven. Humans impact ecosystems and environmental conditions, while ecosystems and the physical environment sustain and constrain human well-being and development. Both ecosystems and societies are complex and evolving through dynamic interactions at various scales, from local to global. Such linked natural and social systems are coined as socioecological systems. Our growing knowledge of the UK's socioecological systems provides a foundation upon which integrated responses can be formulated.

The MA (2005) provided a foundational review of our knowledge of ecosystems and the consequences of ecosystem change for human well-being. In addition to research since its publication, there is a need to better understand the relationships between different ecosystem services (provisioning, regulating and cultural) and the underpinning biophysical processes (supporting services). In the UK, data from the Countryside Survey and national datasets have been used in a Countryside Survey Integrated Assessment (Smart et al. 2010) to report on the ecosystem services provided by the countryside and how they respond to different pressures. The UK NEA takes the ecosystem research agenda forward further and identifies where more research is required to support improved decision-making. Essentially, we need to know how natural processes support the delivery of ecosystem services and how they might be best managed to deliver multiple ecosystem services, while respecting environmental limits.

The Scottish Government is encouraging an ecosystem approach, reflected in the Rural Affairs and Environment Strategic Research Programmes 2011–16, with ecosystem services as the first of eight research themes (Scottish

Government 2010h). The theme is structured to incorporate economics and natural and social sciences to encourage interdisciplinary research among research institutions.

Living with Environmental Change is a partnership of UK Government departments and agencies, Devolved Administrations, local government and research councils which provides a coordinated platform for funding multidisciplinary research in the context of environmental change (http://www.lwec.org.uk). The partnership has six identified challenges around which its programmes are structured: a) climate challenge; b) ecosystem challenge; c) resources challenge; d) health challenge; e) infrastructure challenge; and f) social challenge. Living with Environmental Change has a strategic role in coordinating activities for environmental evidence-gathering in the UK. Living with Environmental Change partners also engage in the co-design, co-delivery and coproduction of accredited activities, which involve long-term science and policy-driven research (including research programmes, monitoring, centres and networks) to address the six challenges.

One promising approach to assess the effects of policy changes on biodiversity is interdisciplinary modelling, although the use of this approach is still not widespread (Acs et al. 2009). Integrated ecological-economic modelling can be used to simultaneously address biodiversity conservation and economic viability for land managers. In order to be successful, in-depth knowledge of both disciplines is required, in addition to the identification of the problem and a common understanding among economists and ecologists of scales and modelling (Wätzold et al. 2006). One example of an integrated model applied in the Peak District National Park explored the effects of policy changes on biodiversity (bird species richness) and farm incomes (Acs et al. 2009). The results of the study showed that impacts of policy reform (such as changing from headage payments to single farm payments) differ across farm types and depend on policy design (for example, agri-environment options), suggesting that "policy initiatives which are uniform across farm types and bird species will not always produce results which are helpful for biodiversity conservation" (ibid., p.11).

Historically, only ecosystem services that are bought and sold in markets at a price, such as food and timber, have been managed to maximise their provision. By recognising the value of ecosystem services not valued by markets, such as flood and climate regulation, we are better able to account for them in decision-making. A growing number of studies have made the link between various ecosystem services and attributes of human well-being, including economic (benefits and savings), socioecological (e.g. resilience), psychological (well-being), cultural (e.g. inspiration) and health benefits.

The valuation of ecosystem services has received continued interest from policy communities in the UK and abroad. In addition to this assessment, the United Nations Environment Programme's The Economics of Ecosystems and Biodiversity programme was established to understand the economics of biodiversity in the same way that the Stern Review drew attention to the economics of climate change. The Natural Capital project in the USA has developed a network of institutions working on valuing ecosystem services, and the Natural Environment Research Council has recently established a Valuation Network to build research capacity in the valuation of ecosystem services in the UK. The Economic and Social Research Council, the Biotechnology and Biological Sciences Research Council and the Natural Environment Research Council jointly supported the Rural Economy and Land Use (RELU) programme which suggested considerable policy benefits from the adoption of an ecosystems approach (**Box 27.49**).

Behavioural change responses are increasingly seen as an essential long-term strategy for addressing environmental issues by encouraging pro-environmental behaviour among the public and organisations. Interdisciplinary research is rising to the challenge of providing the much-needed science-base upon which to develop behavioural change responses. A review by Upham *et al.* (2009) found that literature on public attitudes to environmental change was extremely variable in quantity. Most studies focus on UK attitudes to climate change and energy infrastructure rather than landscapes, species change and ecosystems. Dobson (2010) identified a number of research needs to better understand how to encourage environmental citizenship including: how many people are environmental citizens and how they influence others in their lives; evaluate the effectiveness of campaigns such as 10:10; and understand whether the wider public have values associated with environmental behaviour that are currently latent. The Department of Energy and Climate Change's Low Carbon Communities Challenge is likely to generate interesting findings from testing packages of responses to reduce energy use through community engagement.

27.10.2 Legislation (Enabling)

In Europe and the UK, environmental legislation really began to develop during the 1970s, in most cases, with single issue instruments addressing particular environmental media or pollution from a specific source. It developed on an *ad hoc* basis including in response to public sentiment on particular issues, or to environmental disasters. At EU-level (which is the source of large amount of environmental law affecting the UK), much focus was on water and waste. Early water legislation addressed quality objectives for drinking water, bathing waters, fish and shellfish waters, and was followed in later years by specific directives focusing on nitrate pollution and urban wastewater treatment. An early Waste Framework Directive (1975) addressed a number of specific waste issues such as hazardous waste disposal, landfill, packaging waste and waste shipment. Generally, an 'end-of-pipe' approach responded to environmental issues by introducing measures ex-post to deal with waste and pollution consequences rather than addressing source/systemic issues.

The drawbacks of this fragmented approach were recognised by the time of the Fourth EU Environmental Action Programme (1987–1991). Legislation began to move towards a more sectoral approach, attempting to analyse the overall environmental impact of economic sectors such as agriculture, manufacturing and transport. In the late 1990s, the pattern was towards consolidation and framework legislation, such as the Ambient Air Quality Directive, the WFD and the Directive on Integrated Pollution Prevention and Control. These attempted to put together long-term and coordinated work programmes for particular sectors.

Box 27.49 The Rural Economy and Land Use (RELU) Programme: benefits to policy making from adopting the ecosystem approach. Source: RELU (2010b).

A review of the outcomes from several projects run by the Rural Economy and Land Use (RELU) programme (2010b) identified a number of benefits that the full adoption of an ecosystem approach could have for policy making:

- Identify and quantify the range of services provided by land and water under different management options, drawing on evaluations of diverse datasets for any one area.
- Understand the synergies and trade-offs between the different types of benefits and costs associated with different options for land and water management.
- Reconcile competing objectives with policy measures which reward land managers for providing environmental public goods that are not rewarded by markets for food, fibre and energy.
- Appreciate how benefits and costs are distributed among different public and private interests, facilitate dialogue among them, and show what can and cannot be achieved through collaborative working.
- Design and promote new forms of land and water management that can deliver intended outcomes more cost-effectively.
- Design targeted policies that reward land and water managers for providing a wider range of beneficial services, within a single framework.
- Support the 'joining up' of hitherto fragmented policy objectives and funding mechanisms.
- Adapt policies to future challenges (political, economic, social, technological, legal and environmental), incorporating new knowledge as it becomes available.

More profound than a consolidation exercise is the recent movement towards incorporation of ecosystem principles. The WFD and the MSFD are both examples of EU legislation that provide frameworks within which there are opportunities to embed an ecosystem approach similar to that outlined in the Department for Environment, Food and Rural Affairs' Action Plan. These laws require management by ecologically delineated units, with monitoring and assessment against a range of ecological indicators. Both contain provisions for economic analysis of water or marine water use, with the WFD, in particular, requiring prices for water provisioning and treatment to reflect environmental costs. In national legislation, the Marine and Coastal Access Act applies holistic marine spatial and conservation planning in line with ecosystem principles. Neither, however, systematically recognise the economic value of ecosystem services, or provide a procedure to understand and manage trade-offs and synergies.

In EU law, an integration principle is specifically delineated in Article 11 of the Treaty on the Functioning of the European Union. According to this, environmental protection requirements must be integrated into the definition and implementation of the Union's policies and activities, i.e. across its activities in all sectors. In practice, although progress has been made in incorporating environmental parameters, for example in CAP or via requirements for Environmental Impact Assessments in various sectors, integration is still to be achieved. Systematic recognition of the economic value of environmental services might be the first step towards genuine legislative integration.

27.10.3 Policies, Institutions and Governance (Enabling)

Internationally, the ecosystem approach has gained currency as a powerful framework for the assessment, planning and management of the natural environment and resources.

The Department for Environment, Food and Rural Affairs has embraced the ecosystem approach as an important contribution to 'securing a healthy natural environment' through a more strategic and integrated process (Defra 2007d). The new marine planning regime is an example of how the Department for Environment, Food and Rural Affairs, together with the Devolved Administrations, are embedding an ecosystem approach in marine planning, as discussed in Section 27.7.3. There has been substantial piloting of the ecosystem approach in managing flooding and water quality (Section 27.3), whereby the accumulative impacts and responses are considered across catchments. Research has also been undertaken in three regions to understand how the concept of environmental limits can be integrated into decision-making (**Box 27.44**). The updated plan stressed the fundamental importance of stakeholder participation in decision-making for delivering an ecosystems approach, especially ensuring that appropriate stakeholders are engaged.

The Department for Environment, Food and Rural Affairs has embedded the ecosystem approach in several key policies and legislation. 'Ecosystem services' is one of three priority challenges for evidence gathering in the Evidence Investment Strategy. The Department for Environment, Food and Rural Affairs' Future Water sets out a vision for water in 2030, and acknowledges the need to adopt a whole systems approach to managing water. The Appraisal of Flood and Coastal Erosion Risk Management states that opportunities to improve the capacity of the environment to provide services should be identified and the benefits valued. The Marine and Coastal Access Act (2009) also sets out an integrated approach to the management of marine activities with the ecosystem approach, at least in principle, if not yet in practice.

Multifunctional land use has been placed at the heart of how we can deliver ecosystem services and will be an essential contributor to climate change mitigation and adaptation. **Box 27.50** gives an example of how, by thinking outside a single land-use perspective, areas previously seen as unproductive can have significant value. There are numerous examples like this for upland areas but multipurpose land use in lowland areas is presently relatively rare. Currently, the two primary mechanisms for influencing land use are the planning system for developed areas and agri-environment and forestry schemes (LUC & GHK Consulting 2009).

Neither the UK in its entirety nor England, Wales and Northern Ireland as individual countries have a land use strategy. The Scottish Government has taken a lead in this area, and its first Land Use Strategy was laid in Parliament on 17 March 2011 (**Box 27.51**). The advantage of developing a land use strategy is that it can give a more integrated and consistent approach to managing land use, rather than piecemeal or incremental change; it can also identify opportunities for multifunctional land use (Foresight 2010) that can produce synergies for ecosystem service provision. The formulation of a strategy needs to be framed by political decisions, such as the scale at which decisions are made, and the environmental capacity of land.

Integration of science and policy across sectors can ensure the transition between urban, rural, freshwater and marine habitats is more carefully managed. There is increasing interest in landscape-scale planning rather than planning by sector (Natural Capital Initiative 2009). To achieve more integrated management of land, water and sea there would need to be better connections across sectors, government departments, local authorities, the devolved countries and the rest of Europe. The Department for Environment, Food and Rural Affairs is already working more with other departments by encouraging the adoption of the ecosystem approach where appropriate. A range of government departments, including the Department for Communities and Local Government, the Department for Transport, Her Majesty's Treasury, the Department for International Development, and the Department for Energy and Climate Change, are considering how taking better account of the value of ecosystem services can enhance the delivery of their own policy objectives in specific policy areas or through appraisal mechanisms.

Working with the Department of Communities and Local Government will be critical for using the planning system to protect and enhance rural and Urban ecosystems (Section 27.9). The Marine Management Organisation has

---

Box 27.50 Land use for conservation and aquifer protection. Source: extracted from LUC (2008).

"The chalk aquifers of the South East provide 70% of the water needs of the South East—the most populous region in England. In the face of climate change these aquifers are becoming increasingly threatened by ground water pollution and falling water levels with rising water abstraction and reduced recharge. They require nurturing and appropriate management to ensure that their enormous economic value is retained for future generations. Here there are clear synergies with other conservation objectives. The conservation of aquifers requires careful management of the land surface that overlies them, with low fertiliser levels and improved water infiltration, best provided by low input and extensively managed grasslands—objectives that are shared with the conservation and restoration of chalk grassland, one of the main habitats of international importance associated with the downlands."

Box 27.51 Scotland's Land Use Strategy: land use to provide ecosystem services. Source: Scottish Government (2010a; 2011b).

The Scottish Government has, for the first time, set out a high level strategy for sustainable land use across the country. It aims to guide and support those involved in land use management decisions by providing a long-term vision and objectives that will enable an integrated approach to land use in Scotland. The Land Use Strategy focuses on common goals for different land users, and provides a set of principles for sustainable land use to inform policy making by government and across the public sector.

The Scottish Government is developing an action plan to take forward the proposals that are included in the Land Use Strategy. It has also produced an information note on applying an ecosystems approach to land use. The ecosystems approach is summarised in the form of three key principles: i) the consideration of natural systems by using knowledge of interactions in nature and how ecosystems function; ii) taking account of the services that ecosystems provide, especially those that underpin social and economic well-being; and iii) involving people, especially those who benefit from ecosystem services and those who manage them.

been formed to be responsible for the integration of sectors (including fisheries, marine energy and seabed cable-laying) into the UK's new marine planning regime. The ecosystem approach may also require that links between ecosystem services and public health be formalised in policy and delivery through institutional cooperation. Cooperation and co-management between local authorities is essential for managing the environment at appropriate scales to deliver ecosystem services. For example, managing water at the catchment-scale and managing GI cannot be confined to administrative districts since natural units do not align with them (RELU 2010b). This also extends to natural units that cross the borders of the UK's nations. The WFD, for example, has required cross-border working among countries in the UK to develop RBMPs. The Solway-Tweed River Basin District, for example, crosses south-east Scotland and north-east England, requiring that the Scottish Environment Protection Agency and the Environment Agency (and appropriate stakeholders from each side of the border) work together to develop and implement the RBMP. Additionally, for the Marine and Coastal Access Act and Marine (Scotland) Act to improve fisheries management, cross-border cooperation between the Marine Management Organisation and Marine Scotland will be fundamental.

There is also scope for the UK to learn from other countries and their experiences of integrated policy making. The different ways that European countries are implementing the WFD and MSFD will provide many valuable lessons. Australasia and North America, although in different contexts, have many positive examples of approaches to nature resource management that could have resonance here as well. Watson (2004) argues that inter-organisational collaboration, rather than coordination, is essential for addressing land and water management problems under increasing complexity and uncertainty. Coordination may overcome problems of administrative fragmentation, but collaboration provides an open-ended, iterative approach to river basin management. Taking lessons from experiences in the Fraser Basin in British Columbia, Canada, key institutional conditions and arrangement for successful collaboration to take place in river basin management include: a common vision of the desired future conditions in the river basin among stakeholders; adaptive capacity to cope with changes in knowledge and circumstances; resources to fund the collaborative process and implement decisions; independence from government control, but with government involvement; fair representation of the various interests of groups; outputs to ensure the process is action orientated and not just a forum for debate; and outcomes to demonstrate that collaborative efforts have a positive impact on the sustainability of river basins.

27.10.4 Changing Social Attitudes (Enabling)

Historically, policy makers have tried to change the behaviour of individuals and organisations through legislation, fiscal measures, or market-based measures such as carbon trading (Dobson 2010). Engagement and communications can also be used to change behaviour, and have had mixed success in the UK. Communications involve a one-way

transmission of information and messages, whereas other approaches to behavioural change involve dialogue and the participation of the public in activities and decision-making. By positively changing attitudes towards environmental issues, pro-environmental policies and decisions are more likely to be accepted by the public (Waylen & Fischer 2010). Current government approaches are mainly one-way communications through mass media, such as the Act on CO_2 campaign. There have been concerns about the cost-effectiveness of communication campaigns and whether they are able to exert any long-term influence on behavioural change (POST 2010).

The Department for Environment, Food and Rural Affairs' pro-environmental behaviour framework (Defra 2008e) seeks to protect and improve the environment by primarily encouraging more sustainable consumption patterns, particularly in reference to reducing carbon emissions. The framework broadly follows a social marketing methodology, a technique adapted from commercial marketing practices. Social marketing breaks down whole systems into groups of people and organisations based on commonalities of behaviour, motivations and/or activities, and targets messages and marketing at them accordingly. This acknowledges that a campaign must take account of how messages are received and interpreted by a target audience, and what the target audiences' motivators and barriers to change are likely to be (Anable et al. 2006). Best practice in social marketing on environmental issues includes using influential people within communities to deliver messages, using positive messages rather than arousing fear and guilt that can cause people to 'switch off', and using non-environmental messages that fulfil other motivations such as saving money and health benefits (POST 2010). Consistency of messages is also important, as messages from different government departments can sometimes be contradictory. For example, people are being encouraged to eat more fish for health reasons yet overconsumption of fish could further threaten depleted fish stocks.

Rather than communicate messages to the public and organisations, engagement involves a two-way communication among individuals, groups and a change-maker. To change behaviours and attitudes, it is important to understand the factors that shape behaviour, including knowledge (of environmental issues), psychological factors (beliefs, values, attitudes), social norms (what people perceive as 'normal'), habits (routines), structural conditions (institutions, society, technology), and socio-demographic patterns. Research has shown a number of techniques for encouraging behavioural change such as making the impacts of behaviour visible (e.g. Smart Meters for electricity use), making the behavioural change aspirational, and providing information that enables action (e.g. the Department for Transport's 'Smarter Choices' personalised travel plans). Working with a whole group or community can be effective since people feel part of a collective movement (POST 2010; **Box 27.52**).

Because the factors which shape behaviour are so complex, a 'whole system approach' may be required to encourage behavioural change. Policy makers increasingly acknowledge the need for a multi-instrument approach

(Darnton 2006) where innovative policies, practical measures and consistent messages are targeted across sectors, within and among organisations, and at every level of society (Lucas *et al.* 2008). Joined-up working within and between government departments would be important in a whole system approach. Alongside social marketing and engagement, other incentives to change behaviour may be needed such as financial incentives (e.g. to take up electric cars) or regulations to encourage wider uptake once there is support from a significant proportion of the population to make it politically feasible. Other measures such as eco-labelling can make it easier for people to change their behaviour.

Many members of the public have become disconnected from the natural environment. By not being in touch with nature, people are less inclined to understand our reliance on ecosystem services and that it is within our self-interest to protect and enhance them (Natural Capital Initiative 2009). In Section 27.9.3.4, we report on the importance of urban dwellers having contact with greenspace to provide opportunities for further engagement in environmental activity. Spending time in nature also has significant mental and physical health benefits. Ensuring all sections of society have access to greenspace would have benefits for well-being and may encourage pro-environmental behaviour. Making use of the natural environment as a teaching resource can help to produce environmentally active citizens.

The formal education system offers substantial potential to change the behaviour of an entire generation. Not only could this bring benefits in the future, but the 'nag factor' from children has been found to be very influential on the behaviour of parents as well. Environmental education has been present in the UK since the 1970s, and since the 1990s, the UK Government has included sustainable development in the national curriculum. Education for sustainable development encompasses many different aspects of sustainability such as environmental education, development education, and global citizenship. Each of the Devolved Administrations has its own approach to sustainable development education. In England, education has largely been through government-led education (e.g. formal, further and higher education). In Northern Ireland and Scotland, there are bodies and policies specifically for education for sustainable development, whereas the Welsh Assembly Government has placed it at the heart of their frameworks and activities, and have a strong global citizenship element in their curriculum. Northern Ireland has made guidance on good practice on education for sustainable development a component of initial teaching training (Dobson 2007). Increasing awareness and knowledge among teachers in all subjects of the value of nature to human well-being and of environmental issues, in general, would increase their capacity and passion to convey information to children and develop citizenship qualities.

The Eco-schools programme has perhaps had the most success in engaging schools and children in environmental and sustainability activities. Eco-schools is an international award programme that guides schools to improve their sustainability. In Scotland and Wales, 80% and 90% of schools have taken up the scheme, respectively, whereas, in England, 55% have taken up the scheme and Northern Ireland has almost half its schools registered as Eco-schools. The programme uses a flag system (eco-school, bronze, silver and gold) to reward schools for progress in several areas, such as waste, energy, transport and global perspective. By embedding principles of sustainability at school, the programme not only reduces the impact of the school, but also engages pupils about sustainability (**Box 27.52**).

Consumption choices influence market forces, which, in turn, affect land management, the exploitation of natural resources and pollution. Ultimately, what and how much people consume impacts ecosystems and their ability to provide services. Choices made on price alone, for example, would favour intensive food production with low costs. The factors noted above that shape behaviour, however, result in consumer choices that favour production techniques that have a lower impact on ecosystems. Eco-labelling and certification schemes enable consumers to know and trust how products are produced. Organic food certification (see Section 27.4.3.6) and the MSC's label for fish (Section 27.7) are prime examples. In addition to the behavioural change responses above, the media has an enormous role to play in encouraging pro-environmental behaviour. The widespread switch from single-use plastic bags to reusable bags (**Box 27.54**) demonstrates how a mix of community action, media coverage and supermarket power can lead to a large proportion of the population changing their habits.

Box 27.52 Collective change: Ecoteam's group-based approach. Source: POST (2010).

'Ecoteams' is an initiative run by the environmental charity Global Action Plan since 1990. Groups of between six and eight people attend regular meetings over five months, guided by a trained facilitator. The participants share information, discuss actions and monitor their progress on criteria such as energy use.

The scheme is claimed to cut emissions by 17% and a high proportion of participants appear to maintain their change in behaviour. Global Action Plan state that the reason for the programme's success is that the information comes from peers who they trust; individuals are motivated by support from the group and by comparing their progress, and actions focus on small changes that fit existing lifestyles. However, the risk of schemes like this is that they tend to attract those who are already engaged and don't reach a mainstream audience.

Box 27.53 Eco-schools success story: Pembroke Dock Community School, Wales.

Pembroke Dock Community School, located in rural Pembrokeshire, Wales, has won the international Green Flag three times—the highest award within the Eco-schools programme.

The school has 70 members on its Eco-schools committee who coordinate activities and maintain momentum. The pupils are engaged in the work through focus groups which meet weekly to work on key activities, such as an Eco-newsletter and school-wide projects. An ideas box is available for any pupil to suggest ideas and thoughts. The children have been involved in activities ranging from daily recycling, watering plants and providing bird seed for birds, to one-off events such as the production of a school musical on pollution and its effects. The school has also embedded outdoor learning as part of their school curriculum; children visit a local organic farm, and have regular excursions.

27.10.5 Markets and Incentives (Instrumental)

Market- and incentive-based instruments have been some of the most powerful drivers of ecosystem change over the past three decades. Fiscal incentives and disincentives can create positive outcomes very shortly after a charge is introduced (for example, congestion charging in Central London, Section 27.9). Given the immediacy and perceived importance of many environmental problems (such as climate change), they can be useful tools for bringing about timely behavioural change. On the downside, since people are responding to the financial incentive rather than underlying ethical principles, they may return to their previous behaviour once the incentive is removed (Dobson 2010). Furthermore, the New Economics Foundation (New Economics Foundation 2005) argue that in instances where people are naturally motivated to 'do the right thing' and feel bad if they don't, a punishment, such as a fine, can have a counter-productive effect by cleansing the conscience of the guilty party in return for accepting a punishment. This legitimises, rather than deters, the behaviour. However, incentive-based approaches, which can change behaviour quickly, can be combined with measures to change social attitudes that take longer to establish, but are more likely to prove sustainable and durable.

European and government subsidies for the agriculture, energy and fisheries sectors have expanded and intensified production at the cost of the provision of services not valued by markets. The narrow objective approach of these subsidies failed to acknowledge the consequences for the attainment of wider policy goals, such as sustainable development. The reform of subsidies that have caused unintended consequences is likely to be one of the most cost-effective means of delivering multifunctional land, water and sea use. Reform of the CAP is discussed in detail in Section 27.4.3.2, and reform of the CFP in Section 27.6.3.2.

Conventionally, the taxation system is sparingly used as an instrument to change behaviour, focusing predominantly on raising revenue in the most efficient (Natural England 2009g) and politically acceptable way possible. If taxes are used to dissuade damaging or undesirable behaviour and activities, they can be a powerful driver of positive change. Not only can they reduce social costs, but they can also raise revenue for the government. The introduction of an environmental tax can be market 'correcting' in that the costs to the environment are better represented in the price of a product or service. Several environmental taxes have been introduced in the UK including the Aggregates Levy, Landfill Tax (**Box 27.55**) and Climate Change Levy. There is some evidence that these taxes have been served their purpose well, both for the environment and the exchequer. The public and political acceptability of taxation and other disincentives, however, can be problematic. Some taxes, such as fuel duty and Landfill Tax, are more likely to transcend different governments due to their importance as revenue sources. Others can be removed or decreased resulting in the behaviour of the target audience returning to pre-tax patterns if their underlying social attitudes and values have not changed (Dobson 2010).

The potential to use environmental taxes more widely is substantial, for example, by shifting taxation from 'goods' like labour to 'bads' like pollution. It is argued that such a shift to 'green taxes' would have benefits for the natural environment and the services derived from it, and also have economic advantages by making employment more attractive through reduced taxes, thereby yielding a double dividend. This may have the potential to increase UK employment and economic growth during a period of economic recovery (Green Fiscal Commission 2009; Natural England 2009g).

Environmental markets attempt to use market forces that have already been effective in driving innovation to initiate positive change that protects or enhances the environment. Markets have already been established internationally to encourage more efficient resource use and incentivise the provision of ecosystem services. In Europe, the EU Emissions Trading Scheme uses a cap and trade approach favoured by business and governments (CEMEP 2007). The effectiveness of the scheme is contested, but it is widely agreed that a persistently low price per tonne of carbon has reduced the impetus for investment and innovation to cut emissions.

Overseas, markets have been established for water abstraction (e.g. Australia) and for individual transferable quotas for fishing in Norway and New Zealand (Natural England 2009g). Biodiversity offsetting is gaining popularity, but there are significant risks associated with its use (Section 27.2). Government intervention is normally needed to create the institutional arrangements and incentives necessary to establish markets.

Payment for Ecosystem Services (PES) is an innovative approach to accounting for the value of ecosystem services in decision-making. It involves paying land managers and others to undertake measures to protect and enhance the quantity and quality of ecosystem services (Defra 2010n). By putting a price on ecosystem services that are not conventionally valued by markets, it alters the economic incentives that motivate the actions taken by land managers, and corrects existing market failures. The payment under PES is paid directly by the beneficiary of the ecosystem service, and the transaction is voluntary.

The Environmental Stewardship scheme is a variation of a PES scheme. It makes payments to farmers who volunteer to take measures that can enhance ecosystem service delivery, such as leaving field boundaries uncultivated to create habitat for biodiversity, intercept agrochemical runoff from fields and store carbon. However, the scheme makes payments based on income foregone from participating, rather than the value of the benefits provided. The Rural Economy and Land Use Programme (RELU 2010b) proposes making payments for environmental public goods from farmland which reflect the true cost of providing them, rather than the opportunity costs of farming the land. Payments for ecosystem services have also been paid indirectly through, for example, the value added to food via organic certification schemes and eco-labelling.

New examples of PES are rapidly emerging. The Westcountry Rivers Trust's WATER project aims to establish a market-based catchment restoration scheme. The National Forest in England uses a novel approach where land managers design schemes to supply specific ecosystem services, quoting a cost and time period of commitment, and then competitively implement them (RELU 2010b). Natural England has launched three upland pilots to explore whether packages of ecosystem services can be turned into business opportunities using the PES concept (**Box 27.56**).

27.10.6 Technologies and Practices (Instrumental)

Technological responses have been the prevailing reactions to many environmental issues. Technologies have tended to be deployed as a response to single issues with some success. Wastewater treatment plants, for example, have significantly improved water quality across the UK (Section 27.3). However, in many cases, decisions to use technology have failed to consider the broader implications for other locations and ecosystem services. For example, Coastal planning (Section 27.7) describes how sea defences and coastal protection have served their purpose locally, but have exacerbated erosion and flooding downdrift. Furthermore, they have reduced intertidal habitat for wildlife, which also stores carbon and detoxifies water.

Technologies will continue to play an important role in addressing many of the problems identified in this assessment. Such technological responses are discussed under each of the sectors in this chapter. However, in future, decisions to use technologies need to better account for unintended consequences throughout their lifecycle on whole systems. Opportunities to achieve multiple benefits simultaneously should be exploited (Foresight 2010); for instance, offshore windfarms may create Marine habitat through the creation of 'artificial reefs', thus enhancing recruitment in commercial fisheries.

Ecological innovations are likely to play an increasing role given recent evidence of their performance in providing multiple benefits and cost-effectiveness. For example, green roofs insulate buildings, making them more energy efficient; regulate temperature and humidity; attenuate surface runoff rates; and reduce air and noise pollution (Chapter 10, Box 10.9. Many of the case-studies of multifunctional innovations already discussed in this chapter, such as managed realignment schemes and GI, have been proven to deliver benefits significantly outweighing costs and with relatively short payback periods. To realise the full value of services that could be provided by the UK's natural environment, public investment will be required in protecting, maintaining and enhancing the UK's ecosystems.

27.10.7 Voluntary Actions (Instrumental)

In the past, decision-making processes have followed a linear path of 'propose-announce-decide', whereby a problem was diagnosed, response options were recommended by experts, the public was consulted, a political decision was made, and then implementation was enacted (RELU 2010b). A participatory approach is core to the goals of an ecosystems approach. The reasons for involving stakeholders in decision-making include: that they have the right to participate in decisions that impact them; engagement builds trust and legitimacy in decision-making; and that decisions and their outcomes become more informed (Fish *et al.* 2011). Moving from the 'propose-announce-decide pathway to an

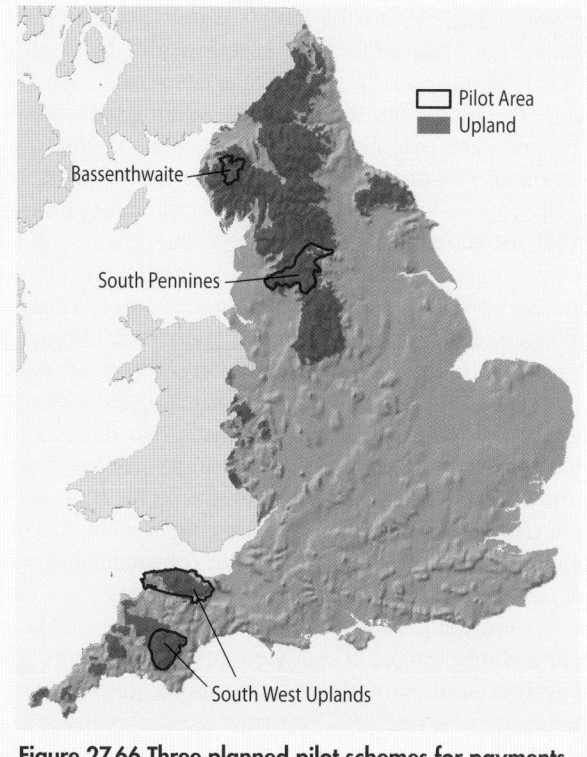
making in the Great Lakes region of the USA and Canada concluded that public involvement had mostly positive outcomes, but that the legitimacy of those representing wider interests of the public is important for achieving successful results (Beierle & Konisky 1999). The USA has moved to more participatory governance of water in the last decade, representing a shift from top-down decision-making to bottom-up approaches. This change emerged due to frustrations with tackling multiple water management issues, which require detailed knowledge of local situations and the coordination of multiple agencies. The collaborative approach that they adopted involved face-to-face information exchange and problem-solving among stakeholders, with an emphasis on finding creative, win-win solutions to a variety of problems. Although the process takes time, it is likely to build mutual understanding and trust among the stakeholders, enhance collaborative efforts to tackle interrelated problems, and improve the support for implementation (Sabatier *et al.* 2005)

The balance between national, regional and local decision-making influences how land is managed to deliver ecosystem services, what priorities are set, and who is involved. Decentralisation approaches propose to transfer considerable powers from central government to local authorities and, ultimately, to local communities who are argued to have the most interest and knowledge of what is best for their local area. This could have significant implications for nature resource management in rural and urban areas.

Decentralisation would mean giving communities, voluntary organisations, trusts and cooperatives a greater role in enhancing the natural environment in their local area. The activation of volunteers, the formation of new types of community groups and environmental awareness raising campaigns could form part of such a package of measures (RELU 2010b; **Box 27.57**). Volunteers can bring knowledge to the management of natural resources that experts can't; anglers and fishery managers, for example, have first-hand knowledge of the water environment and care about it. Combining such local knowledge with scientific expertise will improve the performance of response options (Woods 2009). The Rural Coalition provided several recommendations for empowering local communities including embedding community-led planning, building local capacity for delivery (e.g. advice and training for local enablers), and Parish and Town Councils facilitating community-led plans (The Rural Coalition 2010). Pilots are needed to test new local approaches, building on initiatives such as Community Forests (Section 27.5).

Despite the benefits of a community-based approach, a balance needs to be struck with management at a local level and ensuring strategic management at appropriate scales for the ecosystem services involved in order to account for services that might be consumed some distance from their source. For example, management decisions made locally for water supply and flood risk could have potentially substantial cumulative effects at the catchment-scale. Mitigating and adapting to climate change is also likely to require a more integrated, strategic perspective. Broad principles and a common approach to decision-making processes at a national level are likely to be complemented by detailed implementation at regional or local levels (Foresight 2010). A more centralised

approach of 'engage-deliberate-decide' can better engage land managers, local communities and other stakeholders to effectively rise to future challenges. This latter approach has been adopted by the Environment Agency in the development of RBMPs in order to engage a diverse range of stakeholders who have an interest in, or are involved in activities that impact on, , the water environment (e.g. spatial planning, highways, agriculture, forestry, sewage, research, water industry) (see Section 27.3). There is, however, significant scope to go further in devolving responsibilities for land and water management to local stakeholders.

A study of public participation in environmental decision-

approach would involve greater direction from national government responsible for achieving the strategic and sustainable management of land (Foresight 2010).

27.10.8 Cross-sectoral Synergies and Integration

The review of responses in this section has focused on attempts to adopt a more integrated approach to ecosystem management. In previous sections, the discussion of sectorally specific responses also identified a number of interventions that are adopting a more integrated approach. These are reviewed here, to highlight the possibility for cross-sectoral synergies in responses which allow the delivery of multiple ecosystem services.

The Biodiversity section (Section 27.2) identified the role of green accounting as a mechanism for including values for natural capital and ecosystem services alongside an economic appraisal of national wealth. The UK NEA economics chapter (Chapter 22) provides further guidance on methods for valuing ecosystem services, and complements initiatives discussed here, such as the Natural Environment Research Council's Valuation Network. Other **knowledge-based responses** that offer possibilities for integration are the water cycle studies that attempt a more comprehensive assessment of the impacts of development on the water environment (Section 27.3). These overlap with similar approaches to integrated assessment such as the Countryside Survey Integrated Assessment.

In the context of **legislation**, the most significant opportunities for integration discussed in previous sections emerge from discussions around reforms to the CAP (see Section 27.4) and the CFP (see Section 27.6). In both cases, embedding ecosystem-based thinking in proposals for reform will allow for a more cross-sectoral approach to be adopted, which will deliver multifunctional and resilient

habitats, and recognise the importance of these activities in broader ecosystem management.

There are a number of areas of **policy-, institutional- and governance-based** responses discussed in a sectoral context that are beginning to reflect a more integrated approach. Adopting principles of Integrated Water Resource Management and strategic flood risk management allows for a more coordinated approach to manage water and land resources to secure ecosystem health and human well-being, and to minimise vulnerability (Section 27.3). The impact of forested land uses on water quality and quantity is an important consideration in both the Water and Forestry sectors. The recognition of a holistic approach to land use may require collaboration between farmers to achieve landscape-scale benefits that secure habitats for certain mobile species such as butterflies and birds (Section 27.4); this complements more integrated land use planning such as Scotland's Land Use Strategy. Multifunctional forested landscapes have scope to deliver potentially synergistic recreational, conservation and climate change mitigation outcomes, and are being promoted (Section 27.5). Within the Marine context, marine spatial planning and Integrated Coastal Zone Management can reflect integrated ecosystem-based thinking and deliver substantial benefits (Section 27.7). Spatial planning in an Urban context and the promotion of GI also provides potential benefits for ecosystem functioning and human well-being (Section 27.9).

The educational system offers opportunities to **change social attitudes**, especially of the young, such as in the case of Forest Schools (Section 27.5). There are additional benefits from outdoor learning opportunities including improved mental and physical health, and greater community engagement with local forests. Similarly, improving access to greenspace in Urban areas can provide health benefits and improve environmental awareness (Section 27.9). In a wider context, changing social attitudes to issues such as forest certification (Section 27.5), the certification of fish products (Section 27.6) and food sourcing (Section 27.4) are important reflections of the sustainable consumption agenda that has become more prominent in recent years.

Agri-environment schemes (Sections 27.2, 27.3, 27.4) are an important example of the ways in which **markets and incentives** can be harnessed to deliver an integrated approach to ecosystem management. Payments for Ecosystem Services can also reward landowners for the delivery of multiple ecosystem benefits (Section 27.3). Similarly, there is scope for rewarding marine managers and fishers for the delivery of conservation outcomes alongside the provision of sustainable fish for consumers through conservation credits schemes (Section 27.6). These innovative uses of price mechanisms complement existing systems of environmental taxation and congestion charging which seek to use the power of markets to promote pro-environmental behaviour.

The use of new **technologies and practices**, such as biodiversity offsetting, can be used to enhance ecosystem values in the wider countryside, and can encourage the involvement of private sector stakeholders in habitat creation (Section 27.2). Similarly, restoring natural rivers and Floodplains, including through the reintroduction of vegetation and forest cover, helps to slow water down, reducing flood risk and improving water quality and security of supply (Sections 27.3; 27.5). Also, promoting sustainable catchment drainage and restoring and managing Wetlands in order to intercept pollutants provides improvements in water quality, as well as increased wild species diversity and the supply of materials, such as reeds for thatching (Section 27.3). In the coastal context, managed realignment schemes have been shown to significantly reduce the costs of hard sea defences, while also acting as a store of carbon and providing a useful habitat for wild species (Section 27.7). Within the farmed landscape, techniques such as Integrated Farm Management can benefit species abundance, as well as benefiting water quality, pest regulation and controlling soil erosion (Section 27.3). Soil conservation efforts that focus on peat soils provide synergies between biodiversity conservation and climate change mitigation agendas (Section 27.2). In the energy context, some renewable technologies offer win-win opportunities with conservation, such as large wave and tidal generation sites which may need to be closed zones for fishing, thereby acting as MPAs (Section 27.9).

Multi-stakeholder approaches to river basin management require an acceptance of collaborative possibilities between authorities, experts, interests groups and the public (Section 27.3). Similarly, farmers may need to learn to collaborate more closely in the delivery of landscape- or catchment-scale ecosystem services (Section 27.4). Each of these provides considerable opportunities for the integration of **voluntary actions** across different stakeholder groups, and complements the discussion of participatory approaches (such as Australia's Landcare movement; **Box 27.57**) in this section.

Table 27.25 summarises the key insights from this review of integrated approaches to ecosystem and habitat management, based both on the material presented in this section and in earlier parts of this chapter. There is considerable evidence of cross-sectoral and synergistic approaches in a number of key areas, cutting across all types of responses. A number of these are still in relatively early stages of implementation; it is important to learn from these early pilots in order to scale-up the adoption of an integrated ecosystem approach to the management of the UK's diverse habitats, which is one key policy direction that this review recommends.

27.11 Summary and Conclusions

This chapter has reviewed a wide range of responses in the context of UK ecosystem and habitat management implemented by stakeholders at every level. The chapter has distinguished between responses that are *foundational*, typically involving the generation of knowledge and information; those that are *enabling*, which include legislation, policies, institutions and governance, and changing social attitudes; and those that are *instrumental*, which include the use of markets and incentives, technologies and practices, and voluntary actions. Actors at every level—national and local governments, business and industry, private land managers and fishers, civil society organisations and NGOs, research organisations, and citizens and communities—undertake these responses. This chapter has discussed the impacts of these responses on habitats and associated ecosystem services, and their ultimate effects on human well-being.

Table 27.25 Integrated Responses Summary.

	Established responses	Early implementation, pilots	Proposed, under development
Knowledge	■ Countryside Survey Integrated Assessment ■ Rural Economy and Land Use programme ■ Living With Environmental Change programme	■ UK National Ecosystem Assessment ■ Scotland Rural Affairs and Environment Strategic Research Programmes	■ Green accounting ■ Water cycle studies ■ Natural Environment Research Council Valuation Network
Legislation	■ EU Water Framework Directive ■ EU Marine Strategy Framework Directive ■ Common Agricultural Policy ■ Common Fisheries Policy ■ Marine and Coastal Access Act		
Policies, institutions and governance		■ Department for Environment, Food and Rural Affairs Ecosystem Approach ■ Scotland Land Use Strategy ■ Marine Management Organisation ■ River Basin Management Plans	■ Integrated Water Resource Management ■ Strategic flood risk management ■ Multifunctional forests ■ Integrated Coastal Zone Management ■ Urban spatial planning
Changing social attitudes	■ Eco-schools programme ■ Eco-labelling and certification schemes	■ Forest schools ■ Urban greenspaces	■ Sustainable consumption
Markets and incentives	■ Environmental taxes ■ Congestion charges ■ Agri-environment schemes	■ Payment for Ecosystem Services schemes	■ Fishing conservation credits schemes
Technologies and practices	■ Restoring hydrological regimes ■ Wetland restoration ■ Managed realignment	■ Conservation of peat soils ■ Green Infrastructure ■ Urban agriculture and allotments	■ Biodiversity offsets ■ Integrated Farm Management ■ Renewable energy
Voluntary actions		■ Participation in River Basin Management Plans	■ Collaboration of farmers at the landscape-scale

Evidence in this chapter shows that the sustainable management of ecosystems and their services typically involves a mix of approaches including regulations, policies, attitudes, incentives, technologies and voluntarism. The chapter emphasises the need to manage ecosystems through the adoption of holistic and integrated approaches, which recognise the impacts of actions across a range of sectors and provide opportunities for collaboration between actors at different levels. Broadly, over the period under review, the evidence suggests that approaches are moving away from relatively isolated sectoral responses towards more integrated strategies that are reflective of ecosystem thinking. Promoting multifunctionality requires the identification of synergies between different ecosystem services, but also needs to acknowledge that there may be difficult choices to be made where trade-offs exist. Responses that are initiated in one sector almost always have associated impacts in other sectors, and these impacts need to be understood and managed to promote human well-being.

This chapter has drawn on examples from the devolved UK context, but these are not intended to be an exhaustive catalogue of the entire spectrum of responses that have been implemented or discussed over the last 60 years. The material that has been presented here is illustrative, but not comprehensive. However, through an extensive review process and stakeholder engagement, the chapter does cover several of the most important initiatives that have had significant impacts on the management of habitats and landscapes within the UK, paying particular attention to differences at country level. In many ways, the UK offers an empirical context that provides excellent lessons from the experiences of the different Devolved Administrations since common principles are often implemented to reflect the particular circumstances within each country. Innovation at country level, and divergence between these approaches, provide a controlled experimental environment which fosters very useful learning opportunities.

This chapter has emphasised the importance of sensitivity to spatial and temporal scale. Institutional mechanisms that link across scales provide opportunities for stakeholder engagement and collaboration between actors. Strategic spatial planning of terrestrial, freshwater and marine habitats is important for the delivery of ecosystem services; while this is happening in some cases, it needs to be better reflected in future responses. In a temporal sense, recognising potential trade-offs between short-term goals and medium/long-term targets is important, and ecosystem management strategies need to reflect a dynamic perspective on the delivery of resilient and robust flows of services to enhance human well-being over time. This is particularly important in the face of considerable uncertainty about the drivers of ecosystem change in the medium-term, and the associated need for the adoption of more flexible and adaptive management frameworks that are implemented within self-reflexive learning environments. Knowledge frameworks need to support this adaptive approach, and lay and local knowledge needs to be adequately reflected in this broader learning environment, especially as it helps to secure the involvement of a wider range of stakeholders in ecosystem management.

References

ABP (2007) Cost impact of Marine Biodiversity Policies on Business—The Marine Bill, Final report to Defra, CRO378. ABP Marine Environment Research Ltd, Risk and Policy Analysts, and Jan Brooke Environmental Consultants Ltd. [online] Available at: <http://randd.defra.gov.uk/Document.aspx?Document=WC0602_6734_FRP.pdf> [Accessed 09.05.11].

Acreman, M., Riddington, R. & Booker, D. (2003) Hydrological impacts of floodplain restoration: a case study of the River Cherwell, UK. *Hydrology and Earth System Sciences*, **7**, 75–85.

Acs, S., Dallimer, M., Hanley, N., Gaston, K.J. & Armsworth, P.R. (2009) Linking biodiversity, land-use and incomes at the farm level: an interdisciplinary modelling approach. Agricultural Economics Society.

Adams, W.M. & Hodge, I. (2010) The Crown Jewels and the Big Society – What future for National Nature Reserves? *ECOS*, **31** 28–35.

ADAS (2004) Nitrate Vulnerable Zones – 2003 Re-Survey Report. ADAS report to Defra.

Albalate, D. & Bel, G. (2008) Shaping urban traffic patterns through congestion charging: What factors drive success or failure? *IREA Working Papers*.

Anable, J., Lane, B. & Kelay, T. (2006) An evidence base review of public attitudes to climate change and transport behviour. The Department for Transport, London.

Andersson, E. (2006) Urban landscapes and sustainable cities. *Ecology and Society*, **11**, 34.

Angus, A., Burgess, P., Morris, J. & Lingard, J. (2009) Agriculture and land use: Demand for and supply of agricultural commodities, characteristics of the farming and food industries, and implications for land use in the UK. *Land Use Policy* **26**, S230–S242.

Anon (2002) Northern Ireland Biodiversity Strategy. [online] Available at: <http://www.doeni.gov.uk/niea/nibs2002.pdf> [Accessed 23.05.11].

Aprahamian, M., Hickley, P., Shields, B. & Mawle, G. (2010) Examining changes in participation in recreational fisheries in England and Wales. *Fisheries Management and Ecology*, **17**, 93–105.

ARI (Allotments Regeneration Initiative) (2010) Welcome to the Allotments Regeneration Initiative. [online] Available at: <http://www.farmgarden.org.uk/ari/home> [Accessed 10.12.10].

Armstrong, M. & Holmes, I. (2008) An indicator of sustainability for marine fin-fish stocks around the UK: 1990–2008. Centre for Environment, Fisheries and Aquaculture Science.

Ash, N., Bennett, K., Reid, W., Irwin, F., Ranganathan, J., Scholes, R., Tomich, T., Brown, C., Gitay, H., Raudsepp-Hearne, C. & Lee, M. (2010) Assessing ecosystems, ecosystem services, and human well-being. Ecosystems and Human Well-Being (eds N. Ash, H. Blanco, C. Brown, K. Garcia, T. Henrichs, N. Lucas, C. Ruadsepp-Heane, R.D. Simpson, R. Scholes, T. Tomich, B. Vira & M. Zurek), pp 1–32. Island Press, London.

Ashworth, J., Aish, A. & Stoker, B. (2010) MCZ Project Ecological Network Guidance Natural England and JNCC.

Atkins (2004) ICZM in the UK : A Stocktake. Final Report. [online] Available at: <http://www.scotland.gov.uk/Resource/Doc/921/0030726.pdf> [Accessed 09.05.11].

Ayer, H. (1997) Grass roots collective action: agricultural opportunities, *Journal of Agricultural and Resource Economics*, **22**, 1–11.

Badgley, C., Moghtader, J., Quintero, E., Zakem, E., Chappell, M.J., Aviles-Vazquez, K., Samulon, A. & Perfecto, I. (2007) Organic agriculture and the global food supply. *Renewable Agriculture and Food Systems*, **22**, 86–108.

Baldock, D., Dwyer, J. & Sumpsi Vinas, J. (2002) Environmental Integration and the CAP: a report to the European Commission, DG Agriculture. IEEP. [online] Available at: <http://www.ieep.eu/assets/139/EnvironmentalintegrationandCAP.pdf> [Accessed 16.02.11].

BARS (Biodiversity Action Reporting System) (2010) Biodiversity Action Reporting System. [online] Available at: <http://www.ukbap-reporting.org.uk/> [Accessed 01.12.10].

BASC Scotland (The British Association for Shooting & Conservation) Protecting Waterfowl from Lead in Wetlands – a practical guide to the Lead Shot Regulations in Scotland. The British Association for Shooting and Conservation. [online] Available at: <http://www.unep-aewa.org/surveys/hunting_and_trade/brochure_on_lead_shot_scotland.pdf> [Accessed 10.02.11].

BCT (Bat Conservation Trust) (2011) NBMP – Monitoring Bats. [online] Available at: <http://www.bats.org.uk/pages/nbmp.html> [Accessed 13.12.10].

BBC (2010) Power line upgrade given go-ahead. [online] Available at: <http://news.bbc.co.uk/1/hi/scotland/highlands_and_islands/7853756.stm> [Accessed 11.03.11].

BBC (2011a) Breathing Places: a place for nature near you. [online] Available at: <http://www.bbc.co.uk/breathingplaces/> [Accessed 02.03.11].

BBC (2011b) 'Unethical' fish discards must end, says EU commission. [online] Available at: <http://www.bbc.co.uk/news/science-environment-12598660> [Accessed 02.03.11].

BBOP (The Business and Biodiversity Offsets Program) (2008) The Business and Biodiversity Offsets Program (BBOP). [online] Available at: <http://bbop.forest-trends.org/index.php > [Accessed 05.12.10].

BBSRC (Biotechnology and Biological Sciences Research Council) (2009) Insect Pollinators Initiative. [online] Available at: <http://www.bbsrc.ac.uk/funding/opportunities/2009/insect-pollinators-initiative.aspx > [Accessed 02.12.10].

Beierle, T.C. & Konisky, D.M. (1999) Public Participation in Environmental Planning in the Great Lakes Region. Resources for the Future. *Discussion Paper, 99–50.*

Benson D. (2010) The Australian National Heritage Trust / Caring for Our Country, extract from an unpublished working paper prepared as part of the Rural Economy and Land Use funded project RES-229-25-0009-A, Catchment Management for Protection of Water Resources, SOAS, University of London, and University of East Anglia.

Berkes, F. (2009) Evolution of co-management: Role of knowledge generation, bridging organizations and social learning. *Journal of Environmental Management*, **90**, 1692–1702.

Biala, K., Makarewicz, K., Zisenis, M., Richard, D., Evans, D., Bailly-Maitre, J., Ellmauer, T., Moser, D., Halada, L., Gajdos, P. & Oszlanyi, J. (2010) 10 messages for 2010: Agricultural ecosystems. EEA. [online] Available at: <http://www.eea.europa.eu/publications/10-messages-for-2010-agricultural-ecosystems> [Accessed 12.12.10].

Binley, A., Cheshire, S. & Bridgwood, A. (2008) Green Spaces and Sustainable Communities (GSSC) and Transforming Waste evaluation summary. Big Lottery Fund Research. Issue 48.

BirdLife International. New challenges, new CAP: BirdLife International's vision for the future of the EU Common Agricultural Policy. BirdLife International. [online] Available at: <http://www.rspb.org.uk/Images/New%20challenges%20new%20CAP2_tcm9-172261.pdf> [Accessed 09.05.11].

Blackstock, K.L., Ingram, J., Burton, R., Brown, K.M. & Slee, B. (2010) Understanding and influencing behaviour change by farmers to improve water quality. *Science of The Total Environment*, **408**, 5631–5638.

Blackwell, M.S.A., Hogan, D.V., Pinay, G. & Maltby, E. (2009) The role of wetlands as buffer zones for nutrient removal from agricultural runoff. The Wetlands Handbook (eds E.B. Maltby & T. Barker), pp.417–439. Wiley-Blackwells, Chichester.

BoBW (Best of Both Worlds) (n.d.) Outdoor Recreation and Conservation is the Best of Both Worlds. [online] Available at: <http://www.bobw.co.uk/Default.aspx?page=home> [Accessed 28.02.11].

Boccaccio, L., Brunner, A. & Powell, A. (2009a) Could do better–How is EU Rural Development policy delivering for biodiversity? Report of BirdLife International, Brussels, Belgium.

Boccaccio, L., Hegarty, J. & Brunner, A. (2009b) Through the green smokescreen: how is CAP cross compliance delivering for biodiversity? BirdLife International. [online] Available at: <http://www.birdlife.org/eu/pdfs/Through_the_green_smokescreen_November_2009.pdf> [Accessed 10.02.11].

Bolund, P. & Hunhammar, S. (1999) Ecosystem services in urban areas. *Ecological Economics,* **29**, 293–301.

Booth, L.M. & Duck, R.W. (2010) A Decade of Delivering Sustainable Coastal Zone Management: The Tay Estuary Forum, a Voluntary Local Coastal Partnership in Scotland. *Littoral 2010.* London.

Borrini-Feyerabend, G. & Borrini, G. (1996) Collaborative management of protected areas: tailoring the approach to the context. IUCN.

Bowman, A., Furguson, C., Lee, D., Magdalina, A. & Scott, E. Unpublished. Spatiotemporal modelling of nitrate and phosphorous for river catchments. Science Report – SC080041/SR. Environment Agency.

Bradbury, R.B., Stoate, C. & Tallowin, J.R.B. (2010) FORUM: Lowland farmland bird conservation in the context of wider ecosystem service delivery. *Journal of Applied Ecology*, **47**, 986–993.

Brasier, C.M. (2008) The biosecurity threat to the UK and global environment from international trade in plants. *Plant Pathology,* **57**, 792–808.

BTCV (British Trust for Conservation Volunteers) (2009) Investing in Sustainable Futures: BTCV Strategic Plan 2009–2013. BTCV, Doncaster. [online] Available at: <http://www2.btcv.org.uk/btcv_strategy_09-13.pdf> [Accessed 03.03.11].

BTCV (British Trust for Conservation Volunteers) (2010) Mobilising communities: annual review 2009/10. BTCV, Doncaster. [online] Available at: <http://www2.btcv.org.uk/BTCV_Annual_Review_2010.pdf> [Accessed 03.03.11].

BUGS2 (2009) Biodiversity in Urban Gardens 2. [online] Available at: <http://www.bugs.group.shef.ac.uk/BUGS2/bugs2-index.html> [Accessed 15.02.11].

Burgess, P.J. & Morris, J. (2009) Agricultural technology and land use futures: The UK case. *Land Use Policy*, **26**, S222–S229.

CAAN (Countryside Access & Activities Network) (2010) Countryside Access & Activities Network: Inspiring Outdoor

Recreation. [online] Available at: <http://www.countrysiderecreation.com/> [Accessed 14.12.10].

CABE (the Commission for Architecture and the Built Environment) (2005) Decent parks? Decent behaviour? The link between the quality of parks and user behaviour. Commission for Architecture and the Built Environment, London.

CABE (the Commission for Architecture and the Built Environment) (2010a) Community-led spaces: A guide for local authorities and community groups. Commission for Architecture and the Built Environment, London.

CABE (the Commission for Architecture and the Built Environment) (2010b) Urban green nation: Building the evidence base. Commission for Architecture and the Built Environment, London.

CABE Space (2010) Community green: using local spaces to tackle inequality and improve health. Commission for Architecture and the Built Environment, London.

Campaign for More Allotments (2010) Allot more allotments. [online] Available at: <http://www.allotmoreallotments.org.uk/about_us.htm#h> [Accessed 09.12.10].

Cao, Y., Elliott, J., McCracken, D., Rowe, K., Whitehead, J. & Wilson, L. (2009) Estimating the Scale of Future Environmental Land Management Requirements for the UK. ADAS UK Ltd and Scottish Agricultural College.

Cardwell, M. (2010) Rural development in the United Kingdom: continuity and change. *International Journal of Land Law and Agricultural Science*, **4**, 1–12.

Carey, P.D., Wallis, S., Chamberlain, P.M., Cooper, A., Emmett, B.A., Maskell, L.C., McCann, T., Murphy, J., Norton, L.R., Reynolds, B., Scott, W.A., Simpson, I.C., Smart, S.M. & Ullyett, J.M. (2008a) Countryside Survey: UK Results from 2007, 105pp.

Carey, P.D., Wallis, S.M., Emmett, B.E., Maskell, L.C., Murphy, J., Norton, L.R., Simpson, I.C. & Smart, S. (2008b) Countryside Survey: UK headline messages from 2007. NERC/Centre for Ecology & Hydrology.

Carignan, V. & Villard, M. (2002) Selecting indicator species to monitor ecological integrity: a review. *Environmental Monitoring and Assessment*, **78**, 45–61.

Carson, R. (1962) Silent spring. Houghton Mifflin, Boston.

Catchpole, T.L., Frid, C.L.J. & Gray, T.S. (2005) Discards in North Sea fisheries: causes, consequences and solutions. *Marine Policy*, **29**, 421–430.

Catchpole, T.L. & Gray, T.S. (2010) Reducing discards of fish at sea: a review of European pilot projects. *Journal of Environmental Management*, **91**, 717–723.

CBD (Convention on Biological Diversity) (2002) Report of the sixth meeting of the conference of the parties to the Convention on Biological Diversity. Decision VI/26: Strategic Plan for the Convention on Biological Diversity. UNEP/CBD/COP/6/20.

CBD (Convention on Biological Diversity) (2010) Updating and revision of the strategic plan for the post-2010 period: Decision as adopted (advance unedited version). CBD.

CEC (Commission of the European Communities) (2006) Communication from the Commission: Halting the Loss of Biodiversity by 2010 – and Beyond: Sustaining ecosystem services for human well-being. COM(2006) 216 final.

CEC (Commission of the European Communities) (2007) Report from the Commission to the Council on the application of the system of cross-compliance. Brussels. COM(2007) 147 final.

CEC (Commission of the European Communities) (2009) Green Paper: Reform of the Common Fisheries Policy. Brussels. COM(2009) 163 final.

Cefas (Centre for Environment, Fisheries & Aquaculture Science) (2010) Project 50% Final Report. Centre for Environment, Fisheries and Aquaculture Sciences.

Cefas (Centre for Environment, Fisheries & Aquaculture Science) (2011) Ecosystem Approach to fisheries. Cefas. [online] Available at: <http://www.cefas.defra.gov.uk/our-science/ecosystems-and-biodiversity/ecosystem-approach-to-fisheries.aspx?RedirectMessage=true> [Accessed 09.05.11].

CEMEP (Commission on Environmental Markets and Economic Performance) (2007) Commission on Environmental Markets and Economic Performance report. Defra, London. [online] Available at: <http://archive.defra.gov.uk/environment/business/innovation/commission/documents/cemep-report.pdf> [Accessed 09.05.11].

CFE (Campaign for the Farmed Environment) (2010) Campaign for the Farmed Environment: record your environmental management. [online] Available at: <http://www.cfeonline.org.uk/> [Accessed 06.12.10].

Chase, M. & Hampole, N. (2010) Building Long Term Solutions: Retail Shopping Bag Impacts and Options, BSR. [online] Available at: <http://www.bsr.org/reports/Bags_and_Brands_Report1.pdf> [Accessed 09.05.11].

Church, A., Ravenscroft, N., Hughes, G. & Taylor, B. (2008) A Strategic Plan for Water Related Recreation in Wales. University of Brighton.

Clark, G. (2010) Planning: National planning policy framework. Written Ministerial Statement by Minister for Decentralisation (Gred Clark). [online] Avaliable at: <http://www.publications.parliament.uk/pa/cm201011/cmhansrd/cm101220/wmstext/101220m0001.htm> [Accessed 09.05.11].

ClientEarth (2009) Common Fisheries Policy Green Paper response – the legal issues. ClientEarth. [online] Available at: <http://www.clientearth.org/cfp-green-paper-response> [Accessed 12.12.10].

ClientEarth (2010a) Concept Paper: The proposed legal framework for a reformed Common Fisheries Policy including options for regionalisation. ClientEarth. [online] Available at: <http://www.clientearth.org/proposed-legal-framework-for-reformed-cfp> [Accessed 13.12.10].

ClientEarth (2010b) The Fishing credits system: an industry guide. ClientEarth and Marine Conservation Society. [online] Available at: <http://www.clientearth.org/the-fishing-credits-system-an-industry-guide>. [Accessed 13.12.10].

CNP (Campaign for National Parks) (2010) National Park Legislation. [online] Available at: <http://www.cnp.org.uk/content/national-park-legislation> [Accessed 09.12.10].

Cole, D.N. (2004) Impacts of hiking and camping on soils and vegetation: a review. *Environmental Impacts of Ecotourism*, (ed R. Buckley), pp. 41-60. CABI.

Cooke, S.J. & Cowx, I.G. (2006) Contrasting recreational and commercial fishing: searching for common issues to promote unified conservation of fisheries resources and aquatic environments. *Biological Conservation*, **128**, 93–108.

Coombes, E., Jones, A.P. & Hillsdon, M. (2010) The relationship of physical activity and overweight to objectively measured green space accessibility and use. *Social Science & Medicine*, **70**, 816–822.

Coombes, E.G. & Jones, A.P. (2010) Assessing the impact of climate change on visitor behaviour and habitat use at the coast: A UK case study. *Global Environmental Change*, **20**, 303–313.

Cooper, P. (2007) The Constructed Wetland Association UK database of constructed wetland systems. *Water, Science and Technology*, **50**, 1–6.

Cooper, T., Hart, K. & Baldock, D. (2009) Provision of public goods through agriculture in the European Union. Institute for European Environmental Policy, London. [online] Available at: <http://ec.europa.eu/agriculture/analysis/external/public-goods/report_en.pdf> [Accessed 22.02.11].

Corporate Culture (2010) Actionable insight into the discarding behaviours of fishermen in the North West. Centre for Environment, Fisheries and Aquaculture Sciences.

Costanza, R., Andrade, F., Antunes, P., den Belt, M.v., Boersma, D., Boesch, D.F., Catarino, F., Hanna, S., Limburg, K., Low, B., Molitor, M., Pereira, J.o.G., Rayner, S., Santos, R., Wilson, J. & Young, M. (1998) Principles for Sustainable Governance of the Oceans. *Science*, **281**, 198–199.

Countryside Agency (2005) Evaluation of the Community Forest Programme. Land Use Consultants with SQW Ltd.

CPRE (Campaign to Protect Rural England) (2010) The Bigger Picture: the case for strategic planning. A briefing by the Campaign to Protect Rural England.

CPRE & NFU (Campaign to Protect Rural England and the National Farmers Union) (2006) Living landscapes: hidden costs of managing the countryside. [online] Available at: <http://www.cpreoxon.org.uk/campaigns/landscape/living-landscapes-summary.pdf> [Accessed 09.05.11].

CRC (Commission for Rural Communities) (2010) State of the Countryside 2010. Commission for Rural Communities.

CREDIT (Carbon Reduction and Investment Techniques) (2011) Carbon reduction and investment techniques. [online] Available at: <http://www.see.leeds.ac.uk/credit/> [Accessed 21.11.10].

CRN (Countryside Recreation Network) (2011) Countryside Recreation Network: past, present and future. [online] Available at: <http://www.countrysiderecreation.org.uk/index.asp> [Accessed 23.02.11].

Darnton, A., Elster-Jones, J., Lucas, K. & Brooks, M. (2006) Promoting Pro Environmental Behaviour: Existing evidence to inform better policy making. The Centre for Sustainable Development, University of Westminster & Defra.

Daugbjerg, C. & Sønderskov, K. (2009) Organic labelling systems and consumer confidence. *ICROFS news*, (2/2009) 3–4.

Davenport, J. & Davenport, J.L. (2006) The impact of tourism and personal leisure transport on coastal environments: A review. *Estuarine, Coastal and Shelf Science*, **67**, 280–292.

Davey, C.M., Vickery, J.A., Boatman, N.D., Chamberlain, D.E., Parry, H.R. & Siriwardena, G.M. (2010a) Regional variation in the efficacy of Entry Level Stewardship in England. *Agriculture, Ecosystems & Environment*, **139**, 121–128.

Davey, C.M., Vickery, J.A., Boatman, N.D., Chamberlain, D.E., Parry, H.R. & Siriwardena, G.M. (2010b) Assessing the impact of Entry Level Stewardship on lowland farmland birds in England. *Ibis*, **152**, 459–474.

DCLG (Department for Communities and Local Government) (2000) Tree Preservation Orders: a guide to the law and good practice. Department for Communities and Local Government. London.

DCLG (Department for Communities and Local Government) (2006a) Good Practice Guidance on Planning for Tourism. Department for Communities and Local Government, London.

DCLG (Department for Communities and Local Government) (2006b) Review of Planning Policy Guidance Note 21 (PPG21) on tourism – consultation. DCLG, London.

DCLG (Department for Communitire and Local Government) (2007) Homes for the future: more affordable, more sustainable. Cm 7191. DCLG, London.

DCLG (Department for Communities and Local Government) (2009) Tree Preservation Orders: a guide to the law and good practice – addendum May 2009. Department for Communities and Local Government, London.

DCLG (Department for Communities and Local Government) (2010a) The Community Infrastructure Levy: An Overview. Department for Communities and Local Government. London.

DCLG (Department for Communities and Local Government) (2010b) National Planning Policy Framework. Department for Communities and Local Government, London.

DCMS (Department for Culture, Media and Sport) (2009) The Number of School Playing Fields – Case 101795. [online] Available at: <http://www.culture.gov.uk/reference_library/foi_requests/5523.aspx> [Accessed 11.03.11].

DCMS (Department for Culture, Media and Sport) (2010) Tourism. [online] Available at: <http://www.culture.gov.uk/what_we_do/tourism/default.aspx> [Accessed 14.12.10].

DCSF (Department for Children, Schools and Families) (2010) Top tips for schools to engage with biodiversity. DCSF Publications, Nottingham. [online] Available at: <https://www.education.gov.uk/publications/eOrderingDownload/00227-2010BKT-EN.PDF> [Accessed 09.05.11].

DECC (Department of Energy and Climate Change) (2009) The UK Low Carbon Transition Plan. DECC, London.

DECC (Department of Energy and Climate Change) (2010) Renewable Heat Incentive – Consultation on the proposed RHI financial support scheme. DECC, London.

Defra (Department for Environment, Food and Rural Affairs) (2002a) Ammonia in the UK. Defra, London. [online] Available at: <http://archive.defra.gov.uk/environment/quality/air/airquality/publications/ammonia/documents/ammonia-in-uk.pdf> [Accessed 17.05.11].

Defra (Department for Environment, Food and Rural Affairs) (2002b) Working with the grain of nature: a biodiversity strategy for England. Defra, London.

Defra (Department for Environment, Food and Rural Affairs) (2005) Making space for water: taking forward a new government strategy for flood and coastal erosion risk management in England. Defra, London.

Defra (Department for Environment, Food and Rural Affairs) (2006) Report from the United Kingdom: Implementation of (2002/413/EC) Recommendation of the European Parliament and of the Council, of 3 May 2002, concerning the implementation of Integrated Coastal Zone Management in Europe. Defra, London

Defra (Department for Environment, Food and Rural Affairs) (2007a) A strategy for England's Trees, Woods and Forests. Defra, London. [online] Available at: <http://archive.defra.gov.uk/rural/documents/forestry/20070620-forestry.pdf> [Accessed 17.05.11].

Defra (Department for Environment, Food and Rural Affairs) (2007b) Research into the current and potential climate change mitigation impacts of Environmental Stewardship. Defra, London.

Defra (Department for Environment, Food and Rural Affairs) (2007c) Guidance for local authorities on implementing the biodiversity duty. Defra, London. [online] Available at: <http://www.defra.gov.uk/publications/2011/03/30/pb12584-biodiversity-duty/> [Accessed 17.05.11].

Defra (Department for Environment, Food and Rural Affairs) (2007d) Securing a healthy natural environment: An action plan for embedding an ecosystems approach. Defra, London. [online] Available at: <http://archive.defra.gov.uk/environment/policy/natural-environ/documents/eco-actionplan.pdf> [Accessed 17.05.11].

Defra (Department for Environment, Food and Rural Affairs) (2007e) Conserving Biodiversity – the UK approach. Defra, London. [online] Available at: <http://archive.defra.gov.uk/environment/biodiversity/documents/conbiouk-102007.pdf> [Accessed 17.05.11].

Defra (Department for Environment, Food and Rural Affairs) (2008a) EU thematic strategy for soil protection. Defra, London. [online] Available at: <http://archive.defra.gov.uk/environment/quality/land/soil/europe/> [Accessed 10.03.11].

Defra (Department for Environment, Food and Rural Affairs) (2008b) Environmental Stewardship: Review of progress. Defra, London. [online] Available at: <http://www.arthurrankcentre.org.uk/projects/rusource_briefings/rus08/633.pdf> [Accessed 17.05.11].

Defra (Department for Environment, Food and Rural Affairs) (2008c) Future Water: the Government's water strategy for England. Defra, London. [online] Available at: <http://archive.defra.gov.uk/environment/quality/water/strategy/pdf/future-water.pdf> [Accessed 17.05.11].

Defra (Department for Environment, Food and Rural Affairs) (2008d) Research Project Final Report: Reviewing Targets and Indicators for the Ecosystem Approach. Defra, London. [online] Available at: <http://www.esindicators.org/files/esid/reviewing_targets_and_indicators_for_the_ecosystem_approach.pdf> [Accessed 17.05.11].

Defra (Department for Environment, Food and Rural Affairs) (2008e) A Framework for Pro-environmental Behaviours. Defra, London. [online] Available at: <http://archive.defra.gov.uk/evidence/social/behaviour/documents/behaviours-jan08-annexes.pdf> [Accessed 17.05.11].

Defra (Department for Environment, Food and Rural Affairs) (2008f) Understanding Behaviours in a Farming Context: Bringing theoretical and applied evidence together from across Defra and highlighting policy relevance and implications for future research. Defra, London. [online] Available at: <http://archive.defra.gov.uk/evidence/statistics/foodfarm/enviro/observatory/research/documents/ACEO%20Behaviours%20Discussion%20Paper%20%28new%20links%29.pdf> [Accessed 17.05.11].

Defra (Department for Environment, Food and Rural Affairs) (2008g) A strategy for promoting an integrated approach to the management of coastal areas in England. Defra, London. [online] Available at: <http://archive.defra.gov.uk/environment/marine/documents/protected/iczm/iczm-strategy-england.pdf> [Accessed 17.05.11].

Defra (Department for Environment, Food and Rural Affairs) (2008h) Outdoors for All? An Action Plan to increase the number of people from under-represented groups who access the natural environment. Defra, London. [online] Available at: <http://archive.defra.gov.uk/rural/documents/countryside/dap-ofa.pdf> [Accessed 17.05.11].

Defra (Department for Environment, Food and Rural Affairs) (2009a) Public attitudes and behaviours towards the environment - tracker survey. Defra, London.

Defra (Department for Environment, Food and Rural Affairs) (2009b) Adapting to climate change: UK Climate Projections. Defra, London. [online] Available at: <http://www.defra.gov.uk/publications/2011/03/28/pb13274-uk-climate-projections-090617/> [Accessed 17.0511].

Defra (Department for Environment, Food and Rural Affairs) (2009c) The Government's Response to Sir Michael Pitt's Review of the summer 2007 Floods. Defra, London. [online] Available at: <http://www.defra.gov.uk/publications/2011/03/30/pb13193-flood-review-2007/> [Accessed 17.05.11].

Defra (Department for Environment, Food and Rural Affairs) (2009d) Rural Development Programme Budget. Defra, London. [online] Available at: <http://archive.defra.gov.uk/rural/rdpe/secta.htm> [Accessed 09.03.11].

Defra (Department for Environment, Food and Rural Affairs) (2009e) Food Statistics Pocketbook. Defra, London. [online] Available at: <http://www.defra.gov.uk/statistics/files/defra-stats-food-pocketbook-2009.pdf> [Accessed 17.05.11].

Defra (Department for Environment, Food and Rural Affairs) (2009f) Investment allocation: flooding. Defra, London. [online] Available at: <http://archive.defra.gov.uk/environment/flooding/funding/allocation.htm> [Accessed 13.12.10].

Defra (Department for Environment, Food and Rural Affairs) (2009g) The environment in your pocket 2009. Defra, London. [online] Available at: <http://www.defra.gov.uk/publications/2011/03/28/eiyp-2009-pb13319/> [Accessed 17.05.11].

Defra (Department for Environment, Food and Rural Affairs) (2009h) Safeguarding our Soils: A strategy for England. Defra, London. [online] Available at: <http://www.defra.gov.uk/publications/2011/04/08/pb13297-soil-strategy/> [Accessed 17.05.11].

Defra (Department for Environment, Food and Rural Affairs) (2009i) Achieving sustainable fisheries through CFP reform. Defra, London. [online] Available at: <http://archive.defra.gov.uk/foodfarm/fisheries/documents/fisheries/cfp-discuss.pdf> [Accessed 17.05.11].

Defra (Department for Environment, Food and Rural Affairs) (2009j) Ecosystem approach case-studies. Defra, London. [online] Available at: <http://www.defra.gov.uk/environment/policy/natural-environ/research/case-studies.htm> [Accessed 15.02.11].

Defra (Department for Environment, Food and Rural Affairs) (2010a) CTX 0811: Review of the Biodiversity Duty contained in section 40 of the NERC Act 2006. Defra, London. [online] Available at: <http://www.biodiversitysouthwest.org.uk/docs/BiodiversityDutyReviewFullReport.pdf> [Accessed 17.05.11].

Defra (Department for Environment, Food and Rural Affairs) (2010b) Fifteen new areas to give protection to UK seas. Defra, London. [online] Available at: <http://www.defra.gov.uk/news/2010/08/20/protection-uk-seas/> [Accessed 09.03.11].

Defra (Department for Environment, Food and Rural Affairs) (2010c) Bathing Waters and the Bathing Water Directive. Defra, London. [online] Available at: <http://archive.defra.gov.uk/environment/quality/water/waterquality/bathing/> [Accessed 09.12.10].

Defra (Department for Environment, Food and Rural Affairs) (2010d) Forestry in England: a new strategic approach. Defra, London. [online] Available at: <http://www.defra.gov.uk/news/2010/10/29/forestry/> [Accessed 17.05.11].

Defra (Department for Environment, Food and Rural Affairs) (2010e) Food 2030. Defra, London. [online] Available at: <http://archive.defra.gov.uk/foodfarm/food/pdf/food2030strategy.pdf> [Accessed 17.05.11].

Defra (Department for Environment, Food and Rural Affairs) (2010f) United Kingdom Report to the European Commission, Implementation of the ICZM Recommendation, 2006 – 2010. Defra, London. [online] Available at: <http://archive.defra.gov.uk/environment/marine/documents/interim2/201012-iczm-report.pdf> [Accessed 17.05.11].

Defra (Department for Environment, Food and Rural Affairs) (2010g) UK Smoke Control Areas. Defra, London. [online] Available at: <http://smokecontrol.defra.gov.uk/index.php> [Accessed 28.11.10].

Defra (Department for Environment, Food and Rural Affairs) (2010h) Sustainable access to inshore fisheries (SAIF). Defra, London. [online] Available at: <http://archive.defra.gov.uk/foodfarm/fisheries/policy/saif/> [Accessed 17.05.11].

Defra (Department for Environment, Food and Rural Affairs) (2010i) Government commentary on charting progress 2: the state of UK seas. Defra, London. [online] Available at: <http://chartingprogress.defra.gov.uk/Government-Commentary-on-Charting-Progress-2.pdf> [Accessed 17.05.11].

Defra (Department for Environment, Food and Rural Affairs) (2010j) What happens to waste. Defra, London. [online] Available at: <http://archive.defra.gov.uk/environment/waste/topics/> [Accessed 18.12.10].

Defra (Department for Environment, Food and Rural Affairs) (2010k) UK Biodiversity Indicators in Your Pocket 2010. Defra, London. [online] Available at: <http://archive.defra.gov.uk/evidence/statistics/environment/wildlife/download/pdf/biyp2010.pdf> [Accessed 17.05.11].

Defra (Department for Environment, Food and Rural Affairs) (2010l) Municipal Waste Management Stastics For England 2009/10. Defra, London. [online] Available at: <http://www.defra.gov.uk/news/2010/11/04/waste-stats-q40910/> [Accessed 17.05.11].

Defra (Department for Environment, Food and Rural Affairs) (2010m) An initial summary of responses to The UK Marine Policy Statement: A draft for consultation. Defra, London. [online] Available at: <http://archive.defra.gov.uk/corporate/consult/marine-policy/100721-marine-policy-responses.pdf> [Accessed 17.05.11].

Defra (Department for Environment, Food and Rural Affairs) (2010n) Payments for Ecosystem Services: A short introduction. Defra, London. [online] Available at: <http://archive.defra.gov.uk/environment/policy/natural-environ/documents/payments-ecosystem.pdf> [Accessed 17.05.11].

Defra (Department for Environment, Food and Rural Affairs) (2010o) Understanding and influencing behaviours: a review of social research, economics and policy making in Defra. Defra, London. [online] Available at: <http://archive.defra.gov.uk/evidence/series/documents/understand-influence-behaviour-discuss.pdf> [Accessed 17.05.11].

Defra (Department for Environment, Food and Rural Affairs) (2010p) Environmental Noise. Defra, London. [online] Available at: <http://www.defra.gov.uk/environment/quality/noise/environment/index.htm> [Accessed 17.05.11].

Defra (Department for Environment, Food and Rural Affairs) (2010q) Observatory Programme Indicators. Defra, London. Available at: <http://archive.defra.gov.uk/evidence/statistics/foodfarm/enviro/observatory/indicators/index.htm> [Accessed 03.03.11].

Defra (Department for Environment, Food and Rural Affairs) (2011a) EU policies. Defra, London. [online] Available at: <http://www.defra.gov.uk/environment/quality/air/air-quality/eu/> [Accessed 08.12.10].

Defra (Department for Environment, Food and Rural Affairs) (2011b) The Future of Forestry in England. Defra, London. [online] Available at: <http://www.defra.gov.uk/news/2011/02/17/futureforestry/> [Accessed 18.02.11].

Defra (Department for Environment, Food and Rural Affairs) (2011c) Climate Change Plan 2010. [online] Available at: <http://www.defra.gov.uk/publications/2011/03/26/climate-change-plan-2010-pb13358/> [Accessed 30.03.11].

Delgado, C.L., Wada, N., Rosegrant, M.W., Meijer, S. & Ahmed, M. (2003) Fish to 2020: supply and demand in changing global markets. International Food Policy Research Institute, Washington, D.C.

Department for Transport (2011) Creating Growth, Cutting Carbon: Making sustainable local transport happen. The Stationary Office (TSO). [online] Available at: <http://www.dft.gov.uk/pgr/regional/sustainabletransport/pdf/whitepaper.pdf> [Accessed 22.05.11].

Dessai, S. & Catherine, S. (2010) Public perception of drought and climate change in southeast England. *Environmental Hazards*, **9**, 340-357.

DETI (Department of Enterprise, Trade and Investment) (2010) A Strategic Framework for Northern Ireland. Department of Enterprise, Trade and Investment, Belfast.

DETR (Department of the Environment Transport and the Regions) (2000) Our Countryside: the future – a fair deal for rural England. HMSO, London.

Devine Wright, P. (2005) Beyond NIMBYism: towards an integrated framework for understanding public perceptions of wind energy. *Wind Energy*, **8**, 125-139.

DfT (Department for Transport) (2009) Transport Trends: 2009 Edition. Department for Transport, London.

DfT (Department for Transport) (2011) Local Transport White Paper: Creating Growth, Cutting Carbon – Making Sustainable Local Transport Happen. The Stationary Office, London.

Dick, D., Price, M. & Russell, G. (2009) Scotland's changing rural biodiversity: policy and action needs. A forum organised by the Edinburgh Consortium for Rural Research in association with Aberdeen Research Consortium and the Scottish Biodiversity Forum. Summary of the presentations and discussions. Scottish Natural Heritage Battleby Centre. [online] Available at: <http://www.ecrr.org.uk/forum_biodiversity_summary.pdf> [Accessed 22.05.11].

DNPA (Dartmoor National Park Authority), Forestry Commission & Exmoor National Park Authority (2004)

Woodland Accord: an accord between the Dartmoor and Exmoor National Park Authorities and the Forestry Commission.

Dobson, A. (2007) Environmental citizenship: towards sustainable development. *Sustainable Development*, **15**, 276–285.

Dobson, A. (2010) Environmental citizenship and pro-environmental behaviour: Rapid research and evidence review. Sustainable Development Research Network, London.

Dobson, J. (2008) Shark! A new frontier in tourist demand for marine wildlife. Marine Wildlife and Tourism Management: Insights from the Natural and Social Sciences (eds J. Higham & M. Lück), pp. 49–65. CABI, Wallingford, Oxfordshire.

Dodds, W., Cooper, J. & McKenna, J. (2010) Flood and Coastal Erosion Risk Management Policy Evolution in Northern Ireland. *Ocean & Coastal Management*, **53**, 779–786.

DOE (Department of the Environment Northern Ireland) (2006) An Integrated Coastal Zone Management Strategy for Northern Ireland 2006 – 2026. Department of the Environment Northern Ireland, Belfast. [online] Available at: <http://www.doeni.gov.uk/iczm_document-2.pdf> [Accessed 22.05.11].

Dolman, S. & Simmonds, M. (2010) Towards best environmental practice for cetacean conservation in developing Scotland's marine renewable energy. *Marine Policy*, **34**, 1021–1027.

Donald, P.F., Sanderson, F.J., Burfield, I.J. & Van Bommel, F.P.J. (2006) Further evidence of continent-wide impacts of agricultural intensification on European farmland birds, 1990-2000. *Agriculture, Ecosystems & Environment*, **116**, 189–196.

Donnelley, R.R. (2007) Scotland's Biodiversity Indicators. The Scottish Government Edinburgh. [online] Available at: <http://www.scotland.gov.uk/Resource/Doc/202855/0054080.pdf> [Accessed 22.05.11].

Douvere, F., Maes, F., Vanhulle, A. & Schrijvers, J. (2007) The role of marine spatial planning in sea use management: The Belgian case. *Marine Policy*, **31**(2):182–191.

DTI (Department of Trade and Industry), DfT (Department for Transport) & Defra (Department for Environment, Food and Rural Affairs) (2007) UK Biomass Strategy. Defra, London.

EA (Environment Agency) (2007a) The unseen threat to water quality: Diffuse water pollution in England and Wales. Environment Agency, Bristol.

EA (Environment Agency) (2007b) Water Efficiency in the South East of England: retrofitting existing homes. Environment Agency, Bristol.

EA (Environment Agency) (2008a) Best farming practices. Environment Agency, Bristol.

EA (Environment Agency) (2008b) Water resources in England and Wales – current state and future pressures. Environment Agency, Bristol.

EA (Environment Agency) (2008c) The costs & benefits of moving to full water metering. Science Report – SC070016/SR1 (WP2). Environment Agency, Bristol.

EA (Environment Agency) (2009a) Ecosystem services case studies. Environment Agency, Bristol.

EA (Environment Agency) (2009b) River Basin Management **Plan,** Western Wales River Basin District. Environment Agency, Bristol.

EA (Environment Agency) (2009c) Water for life and livelihoods: River Basin Management Plans. Environment Agency, Bristol.

EA (Environment Agency) (2009d) Water for people and the environment: water resources strategy for England and Wales.

Environment Agency, Bristol. [online] Available at: <http://waterwiki.net/images/a/a6/Eng%26WalesEnvAgency.pdf> [Accessed 23.05.11].

EA (Environment Agency) (2010a) Bathing Waters: Working in partnership in England and Wales. Environment Agency, Bristol.

EA (Environment Agency) (2010b) Ecosystem services assessment of buffer zone installation on the upper Bristol Avon, Wiltshire. Environment Agency, Bristol.

EA (Environment Agency) (2010c) Ecosystem services assessment of sea trout restoration work on the River Glaven, North Norfolk. Environment Agency, Bristol. [online] Available at: <http://publications.environment-agency.gov.uk/pdf/SCHO0110BRTZ-e-e.pdf>

EA (Environment Agency) (2010d) Managing the environment in a changing climate. Environment Agency, Bristol.

EA (Environment Agency) (2010e) Marine and Coastal Access Act. [online] Available at: <http://www.environment-agency.gov.uk/research/planning/40191.aspx> [Accessed 09.12.10].

EA (Environment Agency) (2010f) Splash. Environment Agency, Bristol. [online] Available at: <http://www.environment-agency.gov.uk/homeandleisure/recreation/100081.aspx> [Accessed 05.01.11].

EA (Environment Agency) (2011a) Addressing Environmental Inequalities. Environment Agency, Bristol. [online] Available at: <http://www.environment-agency.gov.uk/research/library/position/41189.aspx> [Accessed 23.02.11].

EA (Environment Agency) (2011b) Nitrate Vulnerable Zones (NVZs). Environment Agency, Bristol. [online] Available at: <http://www.environment-agency.gov.uk/business/sectors/54714.aspx> [Accessed 16.12.10].

EA (Environment Agency) (2011c) Rod Fishing Byelaws. Environment Agency, Bristol. [online] Available at: <http://www.environment-agency.gov.uk/homeandleisure/recreation/fishing/31465.aspx> [Accessed 03.03.11].

EC (European Commission) (2007) A policy to reduce unwanted by-catches and eliminate discards in European fisheries. Commission of the European Communities. COM(2007) 136 final. European Commission, Belgium.

EC (European Commission) (2008) The Common Fisheries Policy: A user's guide. European Commission, Belgium.

EC (European Commission) (2009a) Green Paper on the Reform of the Common Fisheries Policy. European Commission, Belgium.

EC (European Commission) (2009b) "Health Check" of the Common Agricultural Policy. European Commission, Belgium. [online] Available at: <http://ec.europa.eu/agriculture/healthcheck/index_en.htm> [Accessed 09.03.11].

EC (European Commission) (2009c) Report From The Commission To The Council, The European Parliament, The European Economic And Social Committee And The Committee Of The Regions COM(2009) 378 final. European Commission, Belgium.

EC (European Commission) (2010a) Commission Decision on criteria and methdological standards on good environmental status of marine waters. European Commission. European Commission, Belgium. [online] Available at: <http://eur-lex.europa.eu/LexUriServ/LexUriServ.do?uri=OJ:L:2010:232:0014:0024:EN:PDF> [Accessed 17.05.11].

EC (European Commission) (2010b) Soil. European Commission, Belgium. [online] Available at: <http://ec.europa.eu/environment/soil/index_en.htm> [Accessed 10.03.11].

EC (European Commission) (2010c) The CAP towards 2020: Meeting the food, natural resources and territorial challenges of the future. European Commission, Belgium. [online] Available at: <http://ec.europa.eu/agriculture/cap-post-2013/communication/com2010-672_en.pdf> [Accessed 17.05.11].

EC (European Commission) (2011) A Marine Strategy Directive to save Europe's seas and oceans. European Commission, Belgium. [online] Available at: <http://ec.europa.eu/environment/water/marine/index_en.htm> [Accessed 17.05.11].

EEB (European Environemental Bureau) (2010) 10 years of the Water Framework Directive: A Toothless Tiger? A snapshot assessment of EU environmental ambitions. European Environmental Bureau, Belgium.

Ellison, M. (2001) A New Role for Recreation? *Countryside Recreation*, **9**, 26–30.

ENRD (European Netword for Rural Development) (2010) Public good and public intervention in agriculture. European Network for Rural Development, Belgium.

Entec (2008) The Financial Benefits to Working in Partnership at the Coast. DEFRA/LGA Coastal SIG/Coastal Partnerships Working Group. Entec, Bristol, England.

Entrust (2010) Annual Report 2009/2010. Entrust.

Environment Bank (2010) Biodiversity is the next big issue. [online] Available at: <http://www.environmentbank.com/docs/pilot%20scheme%20launch.pdf> [Accessed 01.04.11].

Environment & Heritage Service (2008) Our Environment, Our Heritage, Our Future: State of the Environment Report for Northern Ireland. Northern Ireland Department of the Environment. Belfast, Environment and Heritage Service.

EST (Energy Saving Trust) (2010) Getting warmer: a field trial of heat pumps. Energy Saving Trust, London. [online] Available at: <http://www.energysavingtrust.org.uk/Publication-Download/?oid=1801485&aid=4898250> [Accessed 10.03.11].

EST (Energy Saving Trust) (2011a) Energy Saving Trust: Welcome! [online] Available at: <http://www.energysavingtrust.org.uk/> [Accessed 08.03.11].

ENRD (European Netword for Rural Development) (2010) Public good and public intervention in agriculture. Seminar. European Network for Rural Development, Brussels. [online] Available at: <http://enrd.ec.europa.eu/index.cfm?5D0C00D7-E927-179B-3F79-74061EE7F80B> [Accessed 08.03.11].

EST (Energy Saving Trust) (2011b) Feed-in Tariff Scheme. [online] Available at: <http://www.energysavingtrust.org.uk/Generate-your-own-energy/Sell-your-own-energy/Feed-in-Tariff-scheme> [Accessed 08.03.11].

European Council (1992) Council Directive 92/43/EEC on the conservation of natural habitats and of wild fauna and flora. European Council, Belgium. [online] Available at: <http://eur-lex.europa.eu/LexUriServ/LexUriServ.do?uri=CELEX:01992L0043-20070101:EN:NOT> [Accessed 22.05.11].

European Court of Auditors (2007) Special Report No. 7/2007: on the control, inspection and sanction systems relating to the rules on conservation of Community fisheries resources together with the Commission's replies. *Official Journal of the European Union*, **C317**, 1–33.

European Court of Auditors (2008) Special Report No. 8/2008: is cross compliance an effective policy? European Court of Auditors, Luxembourg. [online] Available at: <http://eca.europa.eu/portal/pls/portal/docs/1/2246310.PDF> [Accessed 22.05.11].

EEA (European Environment Agency) (2009) Distribution and targeting of the CAP budget from a biodiversity perspective. European Environment Agency, Luxembourg. [online] Available at: <http://www.eea.europa.eu/publications/distribution-and-targeting-of-the-cap-budget-from-a-biodiversity-perspective/at_download/file> [Accessed 22.05.11].

EEA (European Environment Agency) (2010) The European Environment – state and outlook 2010: synthesis. European Environment Agency, Copenhagen. [online] Available at: <http://www.eea.europa.eu/soer/synthesis/synthesis/at_download/file> [Accessed 22.05.11].

Faber Taylor, A. & Kuo, F. (2009) Children with attention deficits concentrate better after walk in the park. *Journal of Attention Disorders*, **12**, 402.

FAO (Food and Agricultural Organisation) (2008) Fisheries Management: 2. The Ecosystem Approach to fisheries. Food and Agriculture Organisation.

Feola, G. & Binder, C.R. (2010) Towards an improved understanding of farmers' behaviour: The integrative agent-centred (IAC) framework. *Ecological Economics*, **69**, 2323–2333.

Finney, S.K., Pearce-Higgins, J.W. & Yalden, D.W. (2005) The effect of recreational disturbance on an upland breeding bird, the golden plover *Pluvialis apricaria. Biological Conservation*, **121**, 53–63.

Fish, R., Burgess J., Chilvers J., Footitt A., Haines-Young R., Russell D., Turner, K. & Winter, M. (2011) Participatory and Deliberative Techniques for Embedding an Ecosystems Approach into Decision Making. Full Technical Report to Defra (Project Code: NR0124). Defra, London.

Fletcher, S. (2003) Stakeholder representation and the democratic basis of coastal partnerships in the UK. *Marine Policy*, **27**, 229–240.

FoE (Friends of the Earth) (2010) Briefing: The Localism Bill. [online] Available at: <http://www.foe.co.uk/resource/briefing_notes/localism_bill.pdf> [Accessed 22.05.11].

Foresight (2007) Tackling Obesities: Future Choices–Modelling FutureTrends in Obesity & Their Impact on Health. [online] Available at: <http://news.bbc.co.uk/1/shared/bsp/hi/pdfs/22_11_07_modelling_fat.pdf> [Accessed 19.05.11].

Foresight (2010) Foresight Land Use Futures Project: Final Project Report. The Government Office for Science, London. [online] Available at: <http://www.bis.gov.uk/assets/bispartners/foresight/docs/land-use/luf_report/8614-bis-land_use_futures_exec_summ-web.pdf> [Accessed 03.03.11].

Foresight (2011) Foresight Project on Global Food and Farming Futures: Synthesis Report C8: Changing consumption patterns. Government Office for Science. [online] Available at: <http://www.bis.gov.uk/assets/bispartners/foresight/docs/food-and-farming/synthesis/11-628-c8-changing-consumption-patterns.pdf> [Accessed 25.11.10].

Forest Research (1998) 50 Years of Tree Breeding in Britain. Forest Research, Farnham. [online] Available at: <http://www.forestry.gov.uk/fr/INFD-5WNJBW> [Accessed 21.02.11].

Forest Research (2006) Woodfuel meets the challenge. Forest Research, Farnham.

Forest Research (2008) Treegeneration: a review of the urban forestry pilot project for North East Wales. Forest Research, Farnham.

Forest Research (2010a) Annual report and accounts 2009–2010. Crown copyright, The Stationery Office Limited, Edinburgh.

Forest Research (2010b) Benefits of green infrastructure. Forest Research, Farnham.

Forest Service (2007) Forestry Grant Information. Forest Service, Department of Agriculture and Rural Development, Northern Ireland. [online] Available at: <http://www.forestserviceni.gov.uk/index/publications/forestry-grant-information.htm> [Accessed 28.11.10].

Forestry Commission (2002) An accord between the Association of National Park Authorities and the Forestry Commission. Forestry Commission, Edinburgh.

Forestry Commission (2003) Forests & Water Guidelines – Fourth Edition. Forestry Commission, Edinburgh. [online] Available at: <http://products.ihs.com/cis/Doc.aspx?AuthCode=&DocNum=275579> [Accessed 19.05.11].

Forestry Commission (2004) The UK Forestry Standard: the Government's approach to sustainable forestry, Edinburgh. [online] Available at: <http://www.forestry.gov.uk/website/publications.nsf/WebpubsbyISBN/0855386266> [Accessed 20.11.10].

Forestry Commission (2007a) A Woodfuel Strategy for England. [online] Available at: <http://www.forestry.gov.uk/pdf/fce-woodfuel-strategy.pdf/$FILE/fce-woodfuel-strategy.pdf> [Accessed 10.03.11].

Forestry Commission (2007b) Tree Felling: getting permission. Forestry Commission, Edinburgh. [online] Available at: <http://www.forestry.gov.uk/pdf/wgsfell.pdf/$FILE/wgsfell.pdf> [Accessed 26.11.10].

Forestry Commission (2009a) Environmental impact assessment of forestry projects. Grants and Licences, Edinburgh. [online] Available at: <http://www.forestry.gov.uk/pdf/wgseia.pdf/$FILE/wgseia.pdf> [Accessed 26.11.10].

Forestry Commission (2009b) Forestry Facts & Figures 2009: A summary of statistics about woodland and forestry. Forestry Commission, Edinburgh. [online] Available at: <http://www.forestry.gov.uk/pdf/FCFS209.pdf/$FILE/FCFS209.pdf> [Accessed 26.11.10].

Forestry Commission (2009c) The UK Forestry Standard: Consultations Draft. Forestry Commission, Edinburgh.

Forestry Commission (2010a) Forestry Statistics 2010 – Recreation. Forestry Commission, Edinburgh. [online] Available at: <http://www.forestry.gov.uk/website/forstats2010.nsf/0/FF517AC1769965F68025734E0055883B> [Accessed 10.12.10].

Forestry Commission (2010b) Woodland Carbon Code. [online] Available at: <http://www.forestry.gov.uk/carboncode> [Accessed 28.11.10].

Forestry Commission England (2009) General Guide to English Woodland Grant Scheme. Forestry Commission England, Cambridge.

Forestry Commission England (2010) When to convert woods and forests to open habitat in England: Government policy, Edinburgh. Forestry Commission England, Cambridge.

Forestry Commission Scotland (2008a) Forests for People: Access, recreation & tourism on the national forest estate. Forestry Commission Scotland, Edinburgh.

Forestry Commission Scotland (2008b) Policy on control of woodland removal. Forestry Commission Scotland, Edinburgh.

Forestry Commission Scotland (2009) The National Forest Estate Strategic Plan 2009–2013. Forestry Commission Scotland, Edinburgh.

Forestry Commission Wales (2003) Forestry and Taxation. Forestry Commission Wales, Aberystwyth, Ceredigion. [online]

Available at: <http://www.forestry.gov.uk/pdf/ForestryandTaxation.pdf/$FILE/ForestryandTaxation.pdf> [Accessed 22.05.11].

Forestry Commission Wales (2009) First Release: Headline Results – Welsh Outdoor Recreation Survey 2008. Forestry Commission Wales, Aberystwyth, Ceredigion. [online] Available at: <http://www.forestry.gov.uk/forestry/INFD-7VQEPA> [Accessed 22.05.11].

Forestry Commission Wales (2010) Glastir woodland management briefing paper. Forestry Commission Wales, Aberystwyth, Ceredigion.

Forestry Commission Wales (2011) Glastir Woodland Creation: mapping and eligibility guide. Forestry Commission Wales, Aberystwyth, Ceredigion.

FSC (Forest Stewardship Council) (2011) Forest Stewardship Council United Kingdom. [online] Available at: <http://www.fsc-uk.org/?page_id=5> [Accessed 01.03.11].

Fryirs, K., Chessman, B., Hillman, M., Outhet, D. & Spink, A. (2008) The Australian River Management Experience. River Futures: an Integrative Scientific Approach to River Repair (eds G.J. Brierley & K.A. Fryirs), pp. 149–173. Society for Ecological Restoration International, Island Press, Washington.

Garrod, G., Garratt, J., Kennedy, A. & Willis, K. (2007) A mixed methodology framework for the assessment of the Voluntary Initiative. *Pest Management Science*, **63**, 157–170.

Gaskell, G., Allum, N., Bauer, M., Durant, J., Allansdottie, A., Bonfadelli, H., Boy, D., de Chveigné, S., Fjaestad, B., Gutteling, J.M., Hampel, J., Jelsøe, E., Correia Jesuino, J., Kohring, M., Kronberge, N., Midden, C, Nielsen, T.H., Przestalski, A., Rusanen, T., Sakellaris, G., Torgersen, H., Twardowski T. & Wagner, W. (2000) Biotechnology and the European public. *Nature Biotechnology*, **18**, 935–938.

Gaston, K.J., Fuller, R.A., Loram, A., MacDonald, C., Power, S. & Dempsey, N. (2007) Urban domestic gardens (XI): variation in urban wildlife gardening in the United Kingdom. *Biodiversity and Conservation*, **16**, 3227–3238.

Gell, F.R. & Roberts, C.M. (2003) Benefits beyond boundaries: the fishery effects of marine reserves. *Trends in Ecology and Evolution*, **18**, 448–455.

Gibb, E. (2008) Greenspace Scotland. Paper 3(08)8: Green Flag Award Scheme. greenspace scotland. [online] Available at: <http://www.greenspacescotland.org.uk/upload/File/30808greenflag.pdf> [Accessed 22.05.11].

Gidlof-Gunnarsson, A. & Ohrstrom, E. (2007) Noise and well-being in urban residential environments: The potential role of perceived availability to nearby green areas. *Landscape and Urban Planning,* **83**, 115–126.

Gillings, S., Henderson, I., Morris, A. & Vickery, J. (2010) Assessing the implications of the loss of set-aside for farmland birds. *Ibis*, **152**, 713–723.

Glass, C.R., Boatman, N.D., Brown, C.B., Garthwaite, D. & Thomas, M. (2006) Evaluation of the Performance of the Voluntary Initiative for Pesticides in the United Kingdom. International Advances in Pesticide Application (eds L.S. Alexander, P.I. Carpenter, S.E. Cooper, C.R. Glass, P. Gummer Andersen, B. Magri, T.H. Robinson, D. Stock, W.A. Taylor, E.W. Thornhill & J. van de Zande), pp 163–166. Cambridge, UK.

GLOBE International (2010) The GLOBE Natural Capital Action Plan. GLOBE International Secretariat, London.

Goddard, M., Dougill, A. & Benton, T. (2010) Scaling up from gardens: biodiversity conservation in urban environments. *Trends in Ecology & Evolution*, **25**, 90–98.

Gray, T.S. & Hatchard, J. (2007) Environmental stewardship as a new form of fisheries governance. *ICES Journal of Marine Science: Journal du Conseil*, **64**, 786–792.

Green Fiscal Commission (2009) Lessons from Two Green Tax Shifts in the United Kingdom. Green Fiscal Commission, London.

GreenLINK (2010) Blue Sky Green Space: Understanding the importance of retaining good quality parks and green spaces, and the contribution they make to improving people's lives. GreenSpace, London.

Greenpeace (2006) A recipe for change: supermarkets responding to the challenge of sourcing sustainable seafood. Greenpeace. [online] Available at: <http://www.greenpeace.org.uk/files/images/migrated/MultimediaFiles/Live/FullReport/7988.pdf> [Accessed 09.05.11].

greenspace scotland (2009) Making the links: greenspace for a more successful and sustainable Scotland. greenspace scotland, Stirling.

Griffiths, E. (2010) A survey of Community Woodland Groups in Wales – Report of main findings. Forestry Commission Wales, Aberystwyth, Ceredigion.

Grothmann, T. & Reusswig, F. (2006) People at Risk of Flooding: Why Some Residents Take Precautionary Action While Others Do Not. *Natural Hazards*, **38**, 101–120.

GWP (Global Water Partnership) (2010) What is IWRM? Global Water Partnership. [online] Available at: <http://www.gwp.org/en/The-Challenge/What-is-IWRM/> [Accessed 09.05.11].

Haggett, C. (2011) Understanding public responses to offshore wind power. *Energy Policy*, **39**, 503–510.

Haines-Young, R. H. (2007) Tracking Change in the Character of the English Landscape, 1999–2003. Catalogue Number NE42. Natural England, Sheffield.

Halpern, B.S. (2003) The impact of marine reserves: do reserves work and does reserve size matter? *Ecological Applications*, **13**, 117–137.

Hanley, N., Bell, D. & Alvarez-Farizo, B. (2003) Valuing the benefits of coastal water quality improvements using contingent and real behaviour. *Environmental and Resource Economics*, **24**, 273–285.

Hering, D., Haidekker, A., Schmidt-Kloiber, A., Barker, T., Buisson, L., Graf, W., Grenouillet, G., Lorenz, A., Sandin, L. & Stendera, S. (2010) Monitoring the Responses of Freshwater Ecosystems to Climate Change. Climate Change Impacts on Freshwater Ecosystems (eds M. Kernan, R. W. Battarbee & B. Moss). Wiley-Blackwell, Oxford, UK.

Hewett, T. & Fletcher, S. (2010) The emergence of service-based integrated coastal management in the UK. *Area* **42**, 313–327.

Hiddink, J.G., Hutton, T., Jennings, S. & Kaiser, M.J. (2006) Predicting the effects of area closures and fishing effort restrictions on the production, biomass, and species richness of benthic invertebrate communities. *ICES Journal of Marine Science: Journal du Conseil*, **63**, 822–830.

Hill, M.O., Arnold, H.R., Broad, G.R., Brown, P.M.J., James, T.J., McLean, I.F.G., Preston, C.D., Rowland, F. & Roy, D.B. (2006) Biological Records Centre Annual Report 2005–2006. JNCC, Peterborough.

HM Government (2005) Securing the future: delivering UK sustainable development strategy. The Stationary Office (TSO). [online] Available at: <http://www.defra.gov.uk/publications/files/pb10589-securing-the-future-050307.pdf> [Accessed 19.05.11].

HM Government (2009a) The UK Low Carbon Transition Plan – National strategy for climate and energy. The Stationary Office (TSO). [online] Available at: <http://centralcontent.fco.gov.uk/central-content/campaigns/act-on-copenhagen/resources/en/pdf/DECC-Low-Carbon-Transition-Plan> [Accessed 19.05.11].

HM Government (2009b) The UK Renewable Energy Strategy. The Stationary Office (TSO). [online] Available at: <http://www.official-documents.gov.uk/document/cm76/7686/7686.pdf> [Accessed 19.05.11].

HM Government (2010a) 2050 Pathways Analysis DECC. [online] Available at: <http://www.decc.gov.uk/assets/decc/what%20we%20do/a%20low%20carbon%20uk/2050/216-2050-pathways-analysis-report.pdf> [Accessed 19.05.11].

HM Government (2010b) Marine Energy Action Plan 2010: Executive Summary & Recommendations. DECC. [online] Available at: <http://www.oreg.ca/web_documents/marineactionplan.pdf> [Accessed 03.03.11].

HM Government (2010d) UK Marine Policy Statement: A draft for consultation. [online] Available at: <http://www.doeni.gov.uk/marine_policy_statement_consultation.pdf> [Accessed 03.03.11].

Hodgkinson, V.A. (2003) Volunteering in global perspective. The values of volunteering: cross-cultural perspectives. (eds P. Dekker, & L. Halman), pp. 35–53. Springer, New York.

Hole, D.G., Perkins, A.J., Wilson, J.D., Alexander, I.H., Grice, P.V. & Evans, A.D. (2005) Does organic farming benefit biodiversity? *Biological Conservation*, **122**, 113–130.

Horwood, J., O'Brien, C. & Darby, C. (2006) North Sea cod recovery? *ICES Journal of Marine Science*, **63**, 961–968.

Howarth, L.M. (2010) Is there early evidence of the Lamlash Bay No Take Zone providing scallop fishery benefits? University of York, York.

Hubert, J. & Cottrell, J. (2007) The role of forest genetic resources in helping British forests respond to climate change. Forestry Commission, Edinburgh. [online] Available at: <http://www.forestry.gov.uk/pdf/FCIN086.pdf/$FILE/FCIN086.pdf> [Accessed 22.05.11].

IEEP (Institute for European Environmental Policy) (2008a) IEEP Cap Health Check Review: Cross Compliance. [online] Available at: <http://cap2020.ieep.eu/2008/12/2/ieep-cap-health-check-review-cross-compliance?s=2&selected=archive&y=2008&m=12> [Accessed 09.03.11].

IEEP (Institute for European Environmental Policy) (2008b) The Environmental Benefits of Set-aside in the EU. A Summary of Evidence. Institute for European Environmental Policy, study prepared for Defra.

IEEP (Institute for European Environmental Policy) (2010) CAP Communication Responses. [online] Available at: <http://www.cap2020.ieep.eu/2010/11/22/cap-communication-responses?s=2&selected=latest> [Accessed 09.03.11].

Inger, R., Attrill, M.J., Bearhop, S., Broderick, A.C., James Grecian, W., Hodgson, D.J., Mills, C., Sheehan, E., Votier, S.C. & Witt, M.J. (2009) Marine renewable energy: potential benefits to biodiversity? An urgent call for research. *Journal of Applied Ecology*, **46**, 1145–1153.

Interdepartmental Group (2002) Forestry devolution review. Interdepartmental group report. [online] Available at: <http://www.forestry.gov.uk/pdf/fdr~full~final.pdf/$FILE/fdr~full~final.pdf> [Accessed 22.05.11].

Invasive Species Ireland (2010) Welcome to the Invasive Species Ireland Website. [online] Available at: <http://invasivespeciesireland.com/> [Accessed 04.12.10].

IPCC (Intergovernmental Panel of Climate Change) (2007) Contribution of Working Group II to the Fourth Assessment Report of the Intergovernmental Panel on Climate Change, 2007. (eds O.F. Canziani, M.L. Parry, J.P. Palutikof, P.J. van der Linden and C.E. Hanson). Cambridge University Press, Cambridge, UK.

Jacobs (2008) Environmental Accounts for Agriculture: Final Report. Report to Department for Environment, Food and Rural Affairs; Welsh Assembly Government, Scottish Government, Department of Agriculture & Rural Development (Northern Ireland). Jacobs UK Ltd. [online] Available at: <http://www.dardni. gov.uk/environmental-accounts.pdf> [Accessed 22.05.11].

Jarvie, H.P. & King S.M. (2010) Just scratching the surface? New techniques to show how surface functionality of nanoparticles influences their environmental fate. *Nano Today*, **5**, 248–250.

JNCC (Joint Nature Conservation Committee) (2007) Second Report by the UK under Article 17 on the implementation of the Habitats Directive from January 2001 to December 2006. JNCC, Peterborough. [online] Available at: <www.jncc.gov.uk/article17> [Accessed 19.05.11].

JNCC (Joint Nature Conservation Committee) (2008) The UK Biodiversity Action Plan: highlights from the 2008 reporting round. JNCC, Peterborough. [online] Available at: <http://jncc. defra.gov.uk/default.aspx?page=5398> [Accessed 19.05.11].

JNCC (Joint Nature Conservation Committee) (2010a) Protected Sites Designations Directory. JNCC, Peterborough. [online] Available at: <http://www.jncc.gov.uk/page-1527> [Accessed 01.12.10].

JNCC (Joint Nature Conservation Committee) (2010b) The Countryside and Rights of Way Act 2000. [online] Available at: <http://www.jncc.gov.uk/page-1378> [Accessed 09.12.10].

JNCC (Joint Nature Conservation Committee) (2011) The UK Terrestrial Biodiversity Surveillance Strategy. JNCC, Peterborough. [online] Available at: <http://www.jncc.gov.uk/ page-4409> [Accessed 01.03.11].

Johnson, E. & Catley, K. (2009) Urban soil ecology as a focal point for environmental education. *Urban Ecosystems*, **12**, 79–93.

Jude, S., Jones, A.P., Andrews, J.E. & Bateman, I.J. (2006) Visualisation for Participatory Coastal Zone Management: A Case Study of the Norfolk Coast, England. *Journal of Coastal Research*, 1527–1538.

Kaiser, M.J. & Edwards-Jones, G. (2006) The Role of Ecolabeling in Fisheries Management and Conservation. *Conservation Biology*, **20**, 392–398.

Keep Britain Tidy (2010) Green Flag Awards. [online] Available at: <http://www.keepbritaintidy.org/GreenFlag/Default. aspx> [Accessed 13.12.10].

KnowSeas (2011) Knowledge based sustainable management for Europe's seas. [online] Available at: <http://www.knowseas. com/> [Accessed 21.01.11].

Landscape Institute (2009) Green infrastructure: connected and multifunctional landscapes: Position statement. Landscape Institute, London.

Landshare (2011) Landshare: connecting growers to people with land to share. [online] Available at: <www.landshare.net> [Accessed 16.11.10].

Land Use Climate Change Group (2010) Land Use Climate Change Report to Welsh Assembly Government. Land Use Climate Change Group, Welsh Assembly Government. [online] Available at: <http://wales.gov.uk/topics/environmentcountryside/ farmingandcountryside/farming/landuseclimatechangegroup/lan duseclimatechangereport/?lang=en> [Accessed 22.05.11].

Lawrence, A., Anglezarke, B., Frost, B., Nolan, P. & Owen, R. (2009) What does community forestry mean in a devolved Great Britain? *International Forestry Review*, **11**, 281–297.

Lawrence, A., Dandy, N. & Urquhart, J. (2010) Landowners' attitudes to woodland creation and management in the UK. Forest Research, Alice Holt, Farnham. [online] Available at: <www. forestry.gov.uk/fr/ownerattitudes> [Accessed 22.05.11].

Lawton, J.H., Brotherton, P.N.M., Brown, V.K., Elphick, C., Fitter, A.H., Foreshaw, J., Haddow, R.W., Hilborne, S., Leafe, R., N., Mace, G.M., Southgate, M.P., Sutherland, W.J., Tew, T.E., Varley, J. & Wynne, G.R. (2010) Making space for nature: a review of England's wildlife sites and ecological network. Report to Defra. Defra, London. [online] Available at: <http://archive.defra.gov.uk/ environment/biodiversity/documents/201009space-for-nature. pdf> [Accessed 22.05.11].

Lee, S., Cottrell, J. & John, A. (2004) Advances in Biotechnology: Powerful tools for tree breeding and genetic conservation. Forestry Commission, Edinburgh. [online] Available at: <http://www.forestry.gov.uk/pdf/fcin059.pdf/$FILE/fcin059. pdf> [Accessed 22.05.11].

Levin, G. & Jepsen, M.R. (2010) Abolition of set-aside schemes, associated impacts on habitat structure and modelling of potential effects of cross-farm regulation. *Ecological Modelling*, **221**, 2728–2737.

Local Government Association (2006) Growing in the Community: a good practice guide for the management of allotments – Second Edition. Local Government Association, London. [online] Available at: <http://www.lga.gov.uk/lga/ aio/336363> [Accessed 22.05.11].

Lovell, R. & Roe, J. (2009) Physical and mental health benefits of participation in forest school. *Countryside Recreation*, **17**, 20–23.

Lovett, A.A., Sünnenberg, G.M., Richter, G.M., Dailey, A.G., Riche, A.B. & Karp, A. (2009) Land use implications of increased biomass production identified by GIS-based suitability and yield mapping for *Miscanthus* in England. *Bioenergy Research*, **2**, 17–28.

Lowe, P., Woods, A., Liddon, A. & Phillipson, J. (2009) Strategic Land Use for Ecosystem Services. What Is Land For?: The Food, Fuel and Climate Change Debate (eds. M. Winter & M. Lobley), pp. 23. Earthscan, Oxford.

LUC (Land Use Consultants) (2006) Review of Marine and Coastal Recreation F05AA608. Scottish Natural Heritage.

LUC (Land Use Consultants) (2008) Ecosytem Services and Multi-purpose Land Use. Land Use Consultants, London.

LUC (Land Use Consultants) (2009) Provision of Ecosystem Services Through the Environmental Stewardship Scheme: Final Report. Land Use Consultants and GHK Consulting Ltd, Bristol.

LUC & GHK Consulting (2009) Land use and environmental services. Environment Agency, Bristol. [online] Available at: <http://publications.environment-agency.gov.uk/pdf/ SCHO1009BRDG-e-e.pdf> [Accessed 22.05.11].

Lucas, K., Brooks, M., Darnton, A. & Jones, J.E. (2008) Promoting pro-environmental behaviour: existing evidence and policy implications. *Environmental Science & Policy*, **11**, 456–466.

Lucas, K. & Currie, G. (2011) Developing socially inclusive transportation policy: transferring the United Kingdom policy approach to the State of Victoria? *Transportation*, Online First, 4 February 2011.

Luisetti, T., Turner, K. & Bateman, I. (2008) An ecosystem services approach to assess managed realignment coastal policy in England. CSERGE Working Paper, 08-04, University of East Anglia, Norwich.

Luisetti, T., Turner, R.K., Bateman, I.J., Morse-Jones, S., Adams, C. & Fonseca, L. (2011) Coastal and marine ecosystem services valuation for policy and management: Managed realignment case studies in England. *Ocean & Coastal Management*, **54**, 212–224.

LWEC (Living With Environmental Change) (2011) Living with Environmental Change. [online] Available at: <http://www. lwec.org.uk/> [Accessed 08.03.11].

MA (Millennium Ecosystem Assessment) (2005) Millennium Ecosystem Assessment. Island Press, Washington.

Macgregor, C. & Warren, C. (2006) Adopting sustainable farm management practices within a Nitrate Vulnerable Zone in Scotland: The view from the farm. *Agriculture, Ecosystems & Environment*, **113**, 108–119.

Mackey, E.C. & Mudge, G. (2010) Scotland's Wildlife: an assessment of biodiversity in 2010. Scottish Natural Heritage, Inverness. [online] Available at: <http://www.snh.org.uk/pdfs/ biodiversityreport2010.pdf> [Accessed 19.05.11].

Maltby, E. (2009) Functional assessment of wetlands. Woodhead Publishing Ltd, Oxford.

Mason, W., L., Nicoll, B.C. & Perks, M. (2009) Mitigation potential of sustainably managed forests. Combating Climate Change – a role for UK forests. (National Assessment of UK Forestry and Climate Change Steering Group), pp. 100–118. The Stationary Office, Norwich.

MCA (Marine and Coastal Access Act) (2009) Marine and Coastal Access Act 2009. [online] Available at: <http:// www.legislation.gov.uk/ukpga/2009/23/contents> [Accessed 22.05.11].

McCracken, D. (2009) Identifying And Supporting High Nature Value Farming Systems. Knowledge Scotland. [online] Available at: <http://www.knowledgescotland.org/briefings. php?id=64> [Accessed 15.03.11].

McCracken, D. (2010) How Well Is Farmland Biodiversity Being Maintained In Scotland? Knowledge Scotland. [online] Available at: <http://www.knowledgescotland.org/briefings. php?id=136> [Accessed 26.02.11].

McInnes, R.J., Crane, M., Rodda, H.J.E., Danks, P.W., Hogan, D.V. & Field, A.I. (2008) Management of the Otmoor protected area (Oxfordshire). Multifunctional wetlands in agricultural landscapes: An evaluation of values, impacts and the application of the ecosystem-based approach. NR0112 Full Report. Wildfowl & Wetlands Trust Report to Defra. Wildfowl & Wetlands Trust, Slimbridge, UK.

Mersey Basin Campaign (2010) 1985–2010: Mersey Basin Campaign. [online] Available at: <http://www.merseybasin.org. uk/> [Accessed 09.05.11].

Meyerhoff, R. & Dehnhardt, A. (2004) The European Water Framework Directive and Economic Valuation of Wetlands: The Restoration of Floodplains along the River Elbe, Working Paper on Management in Environmental Planning. Technical University of Berlin.

Miller, J.R. (2005) Biodiversity conservation and the extinction of experience. *Trends in Ecology & Evolution*, **20**, 430–434.

Mitchell, R. & Popham, F. (2008) Effect of exposure to natural environment on health inequalities: an observational population study. *The Lancet*, **372**, 1655–1660.

MMO (Marine Management Organisation) (2010a) Marine plan areas. [online] Available at: <http://www. marinemanagement.org.uk/marineplanning/areas_all.htm> [Accessed 29.03.11].

MMO (Marine Management Organisation) (2010b) Press release: England's first marine plan areas announced. [online] Available at: <http://marinemanagement.org.uk/news/ press/101028.htm> [Accessed 05.12.10].

MMO (Marine Management Organisation) (2010c) UK Sea Fisheries Statistics 2009. [online] Available at: <http://www. marinemanagement.org.uk/fisheries/statistics/annual_archive. htm> [Accessed 09.11.10].

Moffat, A.J., Quine, C.P. & McKay, H. (2009) The state of the natural environment: land use and the future of forestry. Forest Research. [online] Available at: <http://www.bis.gov.uk/assets/ bispartners/foresight/docs/land-use/jlup/er32_the_state_of_the_ natural_environmenty_land_use_and_forestry.pdf> [Accessed 22.05.11].

Moody Marine Ltd. (2010) Final report: SFSAG North Sea Haddock Trawl & Danish Seine Fishery. [online] Available at: <http://www.msc.org/track-a-fishery/certified/north-east-atlantic/SFSAG-north-sea-haddock-fishery/assessment-downloads-1/17.09.2010-sfsag-haddock-final-feport-v4.pdf> [Accessed 22.05.11].

Morris, J., Bailey, A.P., Alsop, D., Vivash, R.M., Lawson, C.S. & Leeds-Harrison, P.B. (2004) Integrating flood management and agri-environment thgough washland creation in the UK. *Journal of Farm Management*, **12**, 33–48.

Moses, C.A. & Williams, R.B.G. (2008) Artificial beach recharge: the South East England experience. *Zeitschrift für Geomorphologie, Supplementary Issues*, **52**, 107–124.

MSC (Marine Stewarship Council) (2010) Pers Comm. R. Wescott.

National Society of Allotment & Leisure Gardeners Limited (2010) National Society of Allotment & Leisure Gardeners Limited. [online] Available at: <http://www.nsalg.org.uk/index. php> [Accessed 09.12.10].

National Statistics (2010) Transport Trends: 2009 Edition. Department for Transport. [online] Available at: <http://www. dft.gov.uk/pgr/statistics/datatablespublications/trends/current/ transporttrends2008> [Accessed 22.05.11].

National Statistics Scotland (2010) Key Scottish Environment Statistics 2010. National Statistics. [online] Available at: <http://www.scotland.gov.uk/ Publications/2010/09/08094058/0> [Accessed 22.05.11].

National Trust (2010) Days Out and Visits. [online] Available at: <http://www.nationaltrust.org.uk/main/w-vh/w-visits.htm> [Accessed 14.12.10].

National Trust (2011) Jobs at the Trust. [online] Available at: <http://www.nationaltrust.org.uk/main/w-trust/w-thecharity/w-jobs.htm> [Accessed 28.02.11].

Natural Capital Initiative (2009) Valuing Our Life Support Systems: Symposium Report. Natural Capital Initiative, London. [online] Available at: <http://www.naturalcapitalinitiative.org.uk/ files/nci_full_lo.pdf> [Accessed 22.05.11].

Natural Capital Initiative (2010) Addressing practical challenges for biodiversity offsetting in the UK. Summary report for policy makers on the first 'Towards no net loss, and beyond' workshop, 22nd June, 2010. Natural Capital Initiative, London.

Natural England (2003) GB Leisure Day Visits Survey 2002-03. [online] Available at: <http://www.naturalengland.org.uk/ourwork/enjoying/research/monitor/leisuredayvisits/default.aspx> [Accessed 07.12.10].

Natural England (2006a) Wildspaces! Evaluation – Volume 1: Main Report. Natural England. [online] Available at: <http://www.english-nature.org.uk/special/lnr/pdf/EvaluationReport.pdf> [Accessed 19.05.11].

Natural England (2006b) Wildspace! in Action. Natural England. [online] Available at: <http://www.english-nature.org.uk/special/lnr/pdf/WildspaceAction1.pdf> [Accessed 19.05.11].

Natural England (2008a) Securing biodiversity: a new framework for delivering priority habitats and species in England. Natural England. [online] Available at: <http://naturalengland.etraderstores.com/NaturalEnglandShop/NE127> [Accessed 19.05.11].

Natural England (2008b) State of the Natural Environment 2008. Natural England. [online] Available at: <http://www.naturalengland.org.uk/publications/sone/sone2008.aspx> [Accessed 16.12.10].

Natural England (2009a) Agri-environment schemes in England 2009: a review of results and effectiveness. Natural England. [online] Available at: <http://www.naturalengland.org.uk/Images/AE-schemes09_tcm6-14969.pdf> [Accessed 19.05.11].

Natural England (2009b) Delivering Nature's Services. Natural England. [online] Available at: <http://naturalengland.etraderstores.com/NaturalEnglandShop/NE225> [Accessed 19.05.11].

Natural England (2009c) Energy crops scheme: establishment grants handbook. Natural England. [online] Available at: <http://www.naturalengland.org.uk/Images/ECShandbook3ed_tcm6-12242.pdf> [Accessed 19.05.11].

Natural England (2009d) Green Infrastructure Guidance. Natural England. [online] Available at: <http://naturalengland.etraderstores.com/NaturalEnglandShop/NE176> [Accessed 20.03.11].

Natural England (2009e) Natural England's Position on Spatial Planning. Natural England.

Natural England (2009f) Natural England's Position on Transport and the Natural Environment. Natural England. [online] Available at: <http://www.naturalengland.org.uk/Images/transport_tcm6-16528.pdf> [Accessed 19.05.11].

Natural England (2009g) No charge? Valuing the natural environment. Natural England. [online] Available at: <http://naturalengland.etraderstores.com/NaturalEnglandShop/NE220> [Accessed 26.11.10].

Natural England (2009h) Sea fisheries: steps to sustainability Natural England. [online] Available at: <http://naturalengland.etraderstores.com/NaturalEnglandShop/NE193> [Accessed 06.02.11].

Natural England (2010a) Access to Nature. Natural England. [online] Available at: <http://www.naturalengland.org.uk/ourwork/enjoying/outdoorsforall/accesstonature/default.aspx> [Accessed 25.02.11].

Natural England (2010b) Lost life: England's lost and threatened species. Natural England. [online] Available at: <http://naturalengland.etraderstores.com/NaturalEnglandShop/NE233> [Accessed 19.05.11].

Natural England (2010c) Lundy Marine Conservation Zone. Natural England. [online] Available at: <http://www.naturalengland.org.uk/ourwork/marine/protectandmanage/mpa/mcz/lundy.aspx> [Accessed 09.02.11].

Natural England (2010d) Monitor of Engagement with the Natural Environment: The national survey on people and the natural environment. Annual Report from the 2009-10 survey. Natural England. [online] Available at: <http://www.naturalengland.org.uk/ourwork/enjoying/research/monitor/default.aspx> [Accessed 06.02.11].

Natural England (2010e) Nature Nearby – Accessible natural greenspace guidance. Natural England. [online] Available at: <http://naturalengland.etraderstores.com/NaturalEnglandShop/NE265> [Accessed 02.12.10].

Natural England (2010f) The Countryside Code. Natural England. [online] Available at: <http://www.naturalengland.org.uk/ourwork/enjoying/countrysidecode/default.aspx > [Accessed 13.12.10].

Natural England (2011a) Country Parks Accreditation Scheme. Natural England. [online] Available at: <http://www.naturalengland.org.uk/ourwork/enjoying/places/countryparks/accreditation/default.asp> [Accessed 28.02.11].

Natural England (2011b) Our Work: Under England's Seas. Natural England. [online] Available at: <http://www.naturalengland.org.uk/ourwork/marine/undersea/default.aspx> [Accessed 02.03.11].

Natural England (2011c) Peat. [online] Available at: <http://www.naturalengland.org.uk/ourwork/conservation/biodiversity/englands/peat.aspx> [Accessed 03.03.11].

Natural England (2011d) The National Trail Website. Natural England. [online] Available at: <http://www.nationaltrail.co.uk/> [Accessed 28.02.11].

NERC (Natural Environment Research Council) (2004) Report of the NERC web consultation on environment and health and the environment and human health workshop. NERC, Wellcome Trust, MRC, BBSRC & ESRC, Hixton.

NERC (Natural Environment Research Council) (2007) Next generation science for planet earth: NERC strategy 2007-2012. NERC Communications. [online] Available at: <http://www.nerc.ac.uk/publications/strategicplan/documents/strategy07.pdf> [Accessed 22.05.11].

Net Resources International (2010) Stevens Croft Wood Burning Plant, Lockerbie, Scotland, United Kingdom. [online] Available at: <http://www.power-technology.com/projects/stevenscroftbiomass/> [Accessed 28.11.10].

New Economics Foundation (2005) Behavioural economics: seven principles for policy makers. New Economics Foundation, London. [online] Available at: <http://www.neweconomics.org/sites/neweconomics.org/files/Behavioural_Economics_1.pdf> [Accessed 22.05.11].

Newman, P. (2006) The environmental impact of cities. *Environment and Urbanization*, **18**, 275.

Newson, M. (2010) Understanding hotspot problems in catchments: the need for scale sensitive measures and mechanisms to secure effective solutions for river management and conservation. *Aquatic Conservation: Marine and Freshwater Ecosystems*, **20**, S62-S72.

NFFO (National Federation of Fishermen's Organisations) (2011) MCZs: The Opposite of the Big Society. [online] Available at: <http://www.nffo.org.uk/news/mczs.html> [Accessed 03.03.11].

NHS (National Health Service) (2011) Healthy eating. [online] Available at: <http://www.nhs.uk/livewell/healthy-eating/Pages/Healthyeating.aspx> [Accessed 09.05.11].

NIDirect Government Services (2010) The Countryside Code. [online] Available at: <http://www.nidirect.gov.uk/index/information-and-services/leisure-home-and-community/leisure-and-recreation/outdoor-recreation/the-countryside-code.htm> [Accessed 13.12.10].

NIEA (Northern Ireland Environment Agency) (2009) Managing Stormwater: A Strategy for Promoting the Use of Sustainable Drainage Systems (SuDS) within Northern Ireland. Northern Ireland Environment Agency, Belfast.

NIEA (Northern Ireland Environment Agency) (2010) Biodiversity Delivery Groups. [online] Available at: <http://www.doeni.gov.uk/niea/biodiversity/biodiversity_delivery_groups.htm> [Accessed 06.12.10].

Nisbet, E.K., Zelenski, J.M. & Murphy, S.A. (2009) The nature relatedness scale. *Environment and Behavior*, **41**, 715.

Northern Ireland Statistics & Research Agency (2010) Northern Ireland Environmental Statistics Report. Northern Ireland Department of the Environment, Belfast. [online] Available at: <http://www.doeni.gov.uk/northern_ireland_environmental_statistics_report_2010-2.pdf> [Accessed 22.05.11].

Norton Rose (2010) The Marine and Coastal Access Act: opportunities and challenges for the energy industry. Norton Rose International Legal Practice, London. [online] Available at: <http://www.nortonrose.com/knowledge/publications/2010/pub32382.aspx?lang=en-gb&page=all#publication_page_main> [Accessed 22.05.11].

Novacek, M.J. (2008) Engaging the public in biodiversity issues. *Proceedings of the National Academy of Sciences*, **105**, 11571.

OCEAN2012 (2011) How to Transform European Fisheries Policy. [online] Available at: <http://assets.ocean2012.eu/publication_documents/documents/4/original/How_to_transform_European_fisheries_policy.pdf> [Accessed 09.03.11].

Oceans 2025 (2010) Oceans 2025. [online] Available at: <http://www.oceans2025.org/> [Accessed 09.05.11].

Ockenden, N. (2007) Volunteering in the natural outdoors in the UK and Ireland: a literature review. Institute for Volunteering Research, London. [online] Available at: <http://www.ivr.org.uk/NR/rdonlyres/436D85DF-7149-41E0-8484-F4031E6AD5D0/0/NatOutdoors.pdf> [Accessed 22.05.11].

ODPM (Office fo the Deputy Prime Minister) (2002) Planning Policy Guidance 17: Planning for Open space, Sport and Recreation. Department for Communites and Local Government, London. [online] Available at: <http://www.communities.gov.uk/documents/planningandbuilding/pdf/ppg17.pdf> [Accessed 22.05.11].

ODPM (Office fo the Deputy Prime Minister) (2005) Planning Policy Statement 9: Biodiversity and Geological Conservation. Controller of Her Majesty's Stationary Office, Norwich [online] Available at: <http://www.communities.gov.uk/documents/planningandbuilding/pdf/147408.pdf> [Accessed 22.05.11].

ODPM (Office fo the Deputy Prime Minister) (2006) Planning Policy Guidance 2: Green belts. Department for Communites and Local Government, London. [online] Available at: <http://www.communities.gov.uk/documents/planningandbuilding/pdf/155499.pdf> [Accessed 22.05.11].

Office for National Statistics (2010) United Kingdom Environmental Accounts. [online] Available at: <http://www.statistics.gov.uk/STATBASE/Product.asp?vlnk=3698> [Accessed 02.12.10].

OFWAT (The Water Services Regulation Authority) (2009) Future water and sewage charges 2010-15: Final Determinations, Birmingham. [online] Available at: <http://www.ofwat.gov.uk/pricereview/pr09phase3/det_pr09_finalfull.pdf> [Accessed 22.05.11].

Ormerod, S. J. & I. Durance (2009) Restoration and recovery from acidification in upland Welsh streams over 25 years. *Journal of Applied Ecology*, **46**: 164–174.

Orr, P., Colvin, J. & King, D. 2007. Involving stakeholders in integrated river basin planning in England and Wales. *Water Resources Management*, **21**, 331-349.

Ostle, N., Levy, P., Evans, C. & Smith, P. (2009) UK land use and soil carbon sequestration. Land Use Policy, **26**, S274–S283.

Owens, S. & Driffill, L. (2008) How to change attitudes and behaviours in the context of energy. *Energy Policy*, **36**, 4412–4418.

Pahl-Wostl, C., Tabara, D., Bouwen, R., Craps, M., Dewulf, A., Mostert, E., Ridder, D. & Taillieu, T. (2008) The importance of social learning and culture for sustainable water management. *Ecological Economics*, **64**, 484–495.

Parker, D.J., Priest, S.J. & Tapsell, S.M. (2009) Understanding and enhancing the public's behavioural response to flood warning information. *Meteorological Applications*, **16**, 103–114.

Parliamentary Office of Science and Technology (2008) Postnote: Biodiversity Indicators. [online] Available at: <http://www.parliament.uk/documents/post/postpn312.pdf> [Accessed 22.05.11].

Participate (2011) Participate. [online] Available at: <http://www.participateschools.co.uk/homepage> [Accessed 01.03.11].

Passant, N. R., Wagner, A., Murrells, T.P., Li, Y., Okamura, S., Thistlewaite, G., Walker, H.L., Walder, C., Whiting, R., Sneddon, S., Stewart, R.A., Brophy, N.C.J., MacCarthy, J., Tsagatakis, I., & Bush, T. (2011) UK Informative Inventory Report (1980 to 2009). National Atmospheric Emissions Inventory (NAEI). [online] Available at: <http://uk-air.defra.gov.uk/reports/cat07/1103150849_UK_2011_CLRTAP_IIR.pdf> [Accessed 22.05.11].

Paxton, M. (2008) Participate: Producing A Mass Scale Environmental Campaign for Pervasive Technology. Pervasive Persuasive Technology and Environmental Sustainability. Workshop held at the 6th International Conference on Pervasive Computing May 19th, 2008, Sydney, Australia. [online] Available at: <http://www.pervasive2008.org/Papers/Workshop/w2-11.pdf> [Accessed 25.02.11].

People 1st (2010) State of the Nation: Executive Summary 2010. People 1st, Sectors Skills Council for the Hospitality, Leisure, Travel and Tourism Industries, Uxbridge. [online] Available at: <http://www.people1st.co.uk/webfiles/Research/State%20Of%20The%20Nation/2010/State_of_the_Nation_2010_Executive_Summary.pdf> [Accessed 22.05.11].

Perkins, A.J., Maggs, H.E., Watson, A. & Wilson, J.D. (2011) Adaptive management and targeting of agri-environment schemes does benefit biodiversity: a case study of the corn bunting *Emberiza calandra*. *Journal of Applied Ecology*, 1–9.

Perry, M. & Rosillo-Calle, F. (2008) Recent trends and future opportunities in UK bioenergy: maximising biomass penetration in a centralised energy system. *Biomass and Bioenergy*, **32**, 688–701.

Phillipson, J. & Symes, D. (2010) Recontextualising inshore fisheries: The changing face of British inshore fisheries management. *Marine Policy*, **34**, 1207–1214.

Pinkerton, E. (1989) Co-operative management of local fisheries: new directions for improved management and community development. University of British Columbia Press, Vancouver.

Pinnegar, J.K., Viner, D., Hadley, D., Dye, S., Harris. M., Berkout, F. & Simpson, M. (2006) Alternative future scenarios for marine ecosystems: technical report. Cefas, Lowescroft.

Pinnegar, J.K., Cheung, W.W.L. & Heath, M. (2010) Fisheries in MCCIP Annual Report Card 2010–11 pp. 19. [online] Available at: <http://www.mccip.org.uk/annual-report-card/2010-2011.aspx> [Accessed 22.05.11].

Pitt, M. (2008) Learning Lessons from the 2007 Floods. Cabinet Office, London.

Plott, C., Nemes, V. & Stoneham, G. (2008) Electronic BushBroker exchange: designing a combinatorial double auction for native vegetation offsets. National MBI Pilot Program Rd 2: Project Final Report. [online] Available at: <http://www.marketbasedinstruments.gov.au/Portals/0/docs/R2-20%20Final%20Report.pdf> [Accessed 22.05.11].

Pontbren Farmers (2008) Our Environmental Work. Pontbren Farmers. [online] Available at: <http://www.pontbrenfarmers.co.uk/env_work.html> [Accessed 29.03.11].

POST (Parlimentary Office of Science and Technology) (2009) Environmental Noise. POST No. 338. The Parlimentary Office of Science and Technology, London. [online] Available at: <http://www.parliament.uk/documents/post/postpn338.pdf> [Accessed 22.05.11].

POST (Parlimentary Office of Science and Technology) (2010) Climate change: engagement and behaviour. POST No. 347. The Parlimentary Office of Science and Technology, London. [online] Available at: <http://www.parliament.uk/documents/post/postpn347.pdf> [Accessed 22.05.11].

Posthumus, H. & Morris, J. (2010) Implications of CAP reform for land management and runoff control in England and Wales. *Land Use Policy*, **27**, 42–50.

Power, A. (2010) Ecosystem services and agriculture: tradeoffs and synergies. *Philosophical Transactions of the Royal Society B*, **365**, 2959–2971.

Powlson, D.S., Whitmore, A.P. & Goulding, K.W.T. (2011) Soil carbon sequestration to mitigate climate change: a critical re-examination to identify the true and the false. *European Journal of Soil Science*, **62**, 42–55.

Prager, K. & Vanclay, F. (2010) Landcare in Australia and Germany: comparing structures and policies for community engagement in natural resource management. *Ecological Management & Restoration*, **11**, 187–193.

Presidency Conculsions (2001) Göteborg European Council, 15 and 16 June 2001. Göteborg, Sweden. SN 200/1/01 REV 1. [online] Available at: <http://ec.europa.eu/governance/impact/background/docs/goteborg_concl_en.pdf> [Accessed 22.05.11].

Pretty, J., Mason, C., Nedwell, D. & Hine, R. (2002) A preliminary assessment of the environmental costs of the eutrophication of fresh waters in England and Wales. University of Essex, UK.

Price, C. (2008) Landscape economics at dawn: An eye-witness account. *Landscape Research*, **33**, 263–280.

Prior, A. & McMath, M.J. (2008) Marine mammals and noise from offshore renewable energy projects – UK developments. Proceedings of the ASCOBANS/ECS Workshop on Offshore wind farms and marine mammals: impacts and methodologies for assessing impacts (ed G.H. Evans), pp. 14–18. San Sebastian, Spain.

[online] Available at: <http://www.wdcs.org/submissions_bin/wind_farm_workshop.pdf> [Accessed 22.05.11].

Pryor, S.N. & Peterken, G.F. (2001) Protected Forest Areas in the UK. WWF. Forestry Commission, Oxford Forestry Institute.

Quevauviller, P. (2010) The Water Framework Directive: Action Programmes and Adaptation to Climate Change. Royal Society of Chemistry, London.

Ramblers (2010) Our Work. [online] Available at: <http://www.ramblers.org.uk/aboutus> [Accessed 14.12.10].

Raven, P. J. (2011) How will river conservation cope with the global economic downturn? Observations from an international conference. *Aquatic Conservation: Marine and Freshwater Ecosystems*, **21**, 1-6.

RCEP (Royal Commission on Environmental Pollution) (2007) The Urban Environment. 26th Report. Royal Commission on Environmental Pollution, London. [online] Available at: <http://www.official-documents.gov.uk/document/cm70/7009/7009.pdf> [Accessed 22.05.11].

RCEP (Royal Commission on Environmental Pollution) (2009) Artificial Light in the Environment. The Royal Commission on Environmental Pollution, London. [online] Available at: <http://webarchive.nationalarchives.gov.uk/20090128002317/http://www.rcep.org.uk/light/httprcepd.light.htm> [Accessed 22.05.11].

RCEP (Royal Commission on Environmental Pollution) (2010) Adapting Institutions to Climate Change. 28th Report. The Royal Commission on Environmental Pollution, London. [online] Available at: <http://www.ukcip.org.uk/wordpress/wp-content/PDFs/RCEP_adaptation_final_report.pdf> [Accessed 22.05.11].

Rees, W.E. (2001) The Conundrum of Urban Sustainability. How green is the city? Sustainability assessment and the management of urban environments (ed. D.Devuyst), pp. 37–42. Columbia University Press, New York.

RELU (Rural Economy and Land Use) (2010a) Informing the Reform and Implementation of the Common Agricultural Policy Rural Economy and Land Use Programme. [online] Available at: <http://www.relu.ac.uk/news/briefings/BRIF%2012%20CAP/12674%20RELU%20CAP%20Briefing%20Paper.pdf> [Accessed 03.03.11].

RELU (Rural Economy and Land Use) (2010b) Shaping the Nature of England: policy pointers from the Relu programme. Rural Economy and Land Use Programme, Newcastle upon Tyne. [online] Available at: <http://www.relu.ac.uk/news/briefings/BRIF13/NatureofEngland.pdf> [Accessed 03.03.11].

Render, M.G. (2004) The Development of Sub-regional Policy for Sustainable Forestry, with Particular Reference to the Chilterns, UK. Brunel University, Uxbridge, Middlesex.

Research International Ltd. (2006) England Leisure Visits: Report of the 2005 Survey. Natural England, Sheffield. [online] Available at: <http://naturalengland.etraderstores.com/NaturalEnglandShop/product.aspx?ProductID=e21aa150-6e4c-4928-9e4b-f67c516f2d73> [Accessed 22.05.11].

Revill, A.S., Catchpole, T.L. & Dunlin, G. (2007) Recent work to improve the efficacy of square-mesh panels used in a North Sea *Nephrops norvegicus* directed fishery. *Fisheries Research*, **85**, 321–327.

Risely, K., Baillie, S.R., Eaton, M.A., Joys, A.C., Musgrove, A.J., Noble, D.G., Renwick, A.R. & Wright, L.J. (2010) The Breeding Birds Survey 2009. British Trust for Ornithology, Thetford.

Ritch, E., Brennan, C. & MacLeod, C. (2009) Plastic bag politics: modifying consumer behaviour for sustainable development. *International Journal of Consumer Studies*, **33**, 168–174.

Roberts, C.M., Hawkins, J.P. & Gell, F.R. (2005) The role of marine reserves in achieving sustainable fisheries. *Philosophical Transactions of the Royal Society B: Biological Sciences*, **360**, 123–132.

RSPB (Royal Society for the Protection of Birds) (2007) Lessons from the Rural Stewardship Scheme 2006. Royal Society for the Protection of Birds. [online] Available at: <http://www.rspb.org.uk/Images/rssreport_tcm9-156173.pdf> [Accessed 19.05.11].

RSPB (Royal Society for the Protection of Birds) (2008) Forestry Commission Scotland Discussion Paper: Woodland Expansion in Scotland – Response to consultation by the Royal Society for the Protection of Birds Scotland. [online] Available at: <http://www.rspb.org.uk/Images/woodlandexpansion_tcm9-200807.pdf> [Accessed 01.01.11].

RSPB (Royal Society for the Protection of Birds) (2010a) Marine Protected Areas for the UK. [online] Available at: <http://www.rspb.org.uk/ourwork/policy/marine/legislation/mpa/index.aspx> [Accessed 19.05.11].

RSPB (Royal Society for the Protection of Birds) (2010b) The Water Framework Directive. [online] Available at: <http://www.rspb.org.uk/ourwork/policy/water/policyissues/waterframeworkdirective.aspx> [Accessed 15.03.11].

RSPB (Royal Society for the Protection of Birds) (2011) SCaMP – Sustainable Catchment Management Programme. [online] Available at: <http://www.rspb.org.uk/ourwork/projects/details/218780-scamp-sustainable-catchment-management-programme> [Accessed 16.02.11].

RSPB Scotland (Royal Society for the Protection of Birds) (2010) Scotland's Land use future. Royal Society for the Protection of Birds, Edinburgh. [online] Available at: <http://www.rspb.org.uk/Images/Scotlands%20land%20use%20future1_tcm9-264606.pdf> [Accessed 19.05.11].

Sabatier, P.A., Focht, W., Lubell, M., Trachtenberg, Z., Vedlitz, A. & Matlock, M. (2005) Collaborative approaches to watershed management. Swimming upstream: Collaborative approaches to watershed management (eds. P.A. Sabatier, W. Focht, M. Lubell, Z. Trachtenberg, A. Vedlitz, & M. Matlock), pp. 3-22. MIT Press, Cambridge, UK.

SAC (Scottish Agricultural College) Rural Policy Centre (2008) Farming's Retreat from the Hills. Scottish Agricultural College Rural Policy Centre, Edinburgh. [online] Available at: <http://www.sac.ac.uk/mainrep/pdfs/retreatfromhillsfullreport.pdf> [Accessed 22.05.11].

Schusler, T.M., Decker, D. & Pfeffer, M. (2003) Social Learning for Collaborative Natural Resource Management. *Society and Natural Resources*, **16**, 309-326.

Scott Wilson Scotland Ltd. (2009) Monitoring and Evaluation of Agri-environment Schemes: Final Report. Scottish Government, Edinburgh. [online] Available at: <http://www.scotland.gov.uk/Resource/Doc/289188/0088491.pdf> [Accessed 22.05.11].

Scottish Coastal Forum (2004) A Strategy for Scotland's Coast and Inshore Waters. Scottish Coastal Forum, Edinburgh.

Scottish Executive (2003) Land Reform (Scotland) Act 2003: Explanatory Notes. HMSO, London.

Scottish Executive (2004) Scotland's Biodiversity: it's in your hands. A strategy for the conservation and enhancement of biodiversity in Scotland. The Scottish Government,
Edinburgh. [online] Available at: <http://www.scotland.gov.uk/Publications/2004/05/19366/37239> [Accessed 23.05.11].

Scottish Executive (2006a) Changing our Ways – Scotland's climate change programme. Scottish Executive, Edinburgh. [online] Available at: <http://www.scotland.gov.uk/Publications/2006/03/30091039/0> [Accessed 19.05.11].

Scottish Executive (2006b) The Scottish Forestry Strategy. Forestry Commission Scotland, Edinburgh. [online] Available at: <http://www.forestry.gov.uk/pdf/SFS2006fcfc101.pdf/$FILE/SFS2006fcfc101.pdf> [Accessed 19.05.11].

Scottish Executive (2007) Biomass Action Plan for Scotland. Scottish Executive, Edinburgh. [online] Available at: <http://www.scotland.gov.uk/Publications/2007/03/12095912/0> [Accessed 19.05.11].

Scottish Government (2005) Marine Strategy for Scotland's coast and marine environment. [online] Available at: <http://www.scotland.gov.uk/Publications/2005/08/26102543/25444> [Accessed 19.05.11].

Scottish Government (2008) Scotland's Wild Deer: A National Approach. Deer Commission for Scotland. [online] Available at: <Scotland's Wild Deer: A National Approach> [Accessed 19.05.11].

Scottish Government (2009a) Implementation of the common agricultural policy (CAP) health check in Scotland: a consultation paper. Scottish Government. [online] Available at: <http://www.scotland.gov.uk/Publications/2009/04/22113214/0> [Accessed 19.05.11].

Scottish Government (2009b) Recipe For Success: Scotland's National Food and Drink Policy. Scottish Government, Edinburgh. [online] Available at: <http://www.scotland.gov.uk/Resource/Doc/277346/0083283.pdf> [Accessed 19.05.11].

Scottish Government (2009c) Renewables Action Plan. Scottish Government, Edinburgh. [online] Available at: <http://www.scotland.gov.uk/Publications/2009/07/06095830/0> [Accessed 19.05.11].

Scottish Government (2009d) Renewable Heat Action Plan for Scotland: a plan for the promotion of the use of heat from renewable sources. Scottish Government, Edinburgh. [online] Available at: <http://www.scotland.gov.uk/Resource/Doc/290657/0089337.pdf > [Accessed 19.05.11].

Scottish Government (2009e) The Scottish Soil Framework. Scottish Government, Edinburgh. [online] Available at: <http://www.scotland.gov.uk/Resource/Doc/273170/0081576.pdf> [Accessed 19.05.11].

Scottish Government (2010a) A draft Land Use Strategy for Scotland. Scottish Government, Edinburgh.

Scottish Government (2010b) Carbon Capture and Storage - A roadmap for Scotland. Scottish Government, Edinburgh. [online] Available at: <http://www.scotland.gov.uk/Publications/2010/03/18094835/0> [Accessed 19.05.11].

Scottish Government (2010c) Conserve and Save: Energy Efficiency Action Plan. Scottish Government, Edinburgh. [online] Available at: <http://www.scotland.gov.uk/Publications/2010/10/07142301/0> [Accessed 19.05.11].

Scottish Government (2010d) Low Carbon Scotland: Public Engagement Strategy. Scottish Government, Edinburgh. [online] Available at: <http://www.scotland.gov.uk/Resource/Doc/336432/0110100.pdf> [Accessed 19.05.11].

Scottish Government (2010e) Marine Planning & Legislation. Scottish Government, Edinburgh. [online] Available at:

<http://www.scotland.gov.uk/Topics/marine/seamanagement> [Accessed 09.12.10].

Scottish Government (2010f) News Release: Growing Spaces Summit. Scottish Government, Edinburgh. [online] Available at: <http://www.scotland.gov.uk/News/Releases/2010/05/04125011> [Accessed 09.12.10].

Scottish Government (2010g) Rural Development Contracts - Rural Priorities. Scottish Government, Edinburgh. [online] Available at: <http://www.scotland.gov.uk/Topics/farmingrural/SRDP/RuralPriorities> [Accessed 19.05.11].

Scottish Government (2010h) Strategic Research 2011-2016 Themes document. Scottish Government, Edinburgh. [online] Available at: <http://www.scotland.gov.uk/Topics/Research/About/EBAR/StrategicResearch/future-research-strategy/Themes> [Accessed 19.05.11].

Scottish Government (2011a) Fishing Rights. Scottish Government, Edinburgh. [online] Available at: <http://www.scotland.gov.uk/Topics/marine/Salmon-Trout-Coarse/17519/8903> [Accessed 03.03.11].

Scottish Government (2011b) Getting the best from our land: a land use strategy for Scotland. Scottish Government, Edinburgh.

Scottish Government Marine Directorate (2010) National Indicator – Ensure 70% key commercial fish stocks at full reproductive capacity and harvested sustainably by 2015. [online] Available at: <http://www.scotland.gov.uk/About/scotPerforms/indicators/fishStocks#a2> [Accessed 03.05.11].

Scottish Ministers (2004) The Environmental Protection (Restriction on Use of Lead Shot) (Scotland) (No.2) Regulations 2004. Scottish Statutoty Instrument, Edinburgh. [online] Available at: <http://www.legislation.gov.uk/ssi/2004/358/pdfs/ssi_20040358_en.pdf> [Accessed 22.05.11].

Scottish Outdoor Access Code (2010) Scottish Outdoor Access Code. [online] Available at: <http://www.outdooraccess-scotland.com/outdoors-responsibly/access-code-and-advice/soac/> [Accessed 13.12.10].

Scottish Parliamentary Corporate Body (2000) Scottish Parliament: Research Briefings: RN 00-102 Allotments. Scottish Corpus of Texts and Speech. [online] Available: <http://www.scottishcorpus.ac.uk/corpus/search/document.php?documentid=1250> [Accessed 22.05.11].

Seafish (2011) Responsible Fishing Scheme. Seafish. [online] Available at: <http://rfs.seafish.org/> [Accessed 22.05.11].

Seafood Scotland (2010) Scottish Conservation Credits Scheme. [online] Available at: <http://www.seafoodscotland.org/en/responsible-sourcing/scottish-fisheries-management/scottish-conservation-credits-scheme.html> [Accessed 25.02.11].

Secretaries of State for the Environment (1994) Biodiversity: the UK Action Plan. HMSO, London.

Shaw, R., Colley, M. & Connell, R. (2007) Climate change adaptation by design: A guide for sustainable communities. Town and Country Planning Association (TCPA), London. [online] Available at: <http://www.tcpa.org.uk/data/files/bd_cca.pdf> [Accessed 22.05.11].

Shepherd, D., Burgess, D., Jickells, T., Andrews, J., Cave, R., Turner, R.K., Aldridge, J., Parker, E.R. & Young, E. (2007) Modelling the effects and economics of managed realignment on the cycling and storage of nutrients, carbon and sediments in the Blackwater estuary UK. *Estuarine Coastal and Shelf Science*, **73**, 355–367.

Silvertown, J. (2009) A new dawn for citizen science. *Trends in Ecology & Evolution*, **24**, 467–471.

Simmonds, M.P. & Brown, V.C. (2010) Is there a conflict between cetacean conservation and marine renewable-energy developments? *Wildlife Research*, **37**, 688–694.

Simpson, D. & Vira, B. (2010) Assessing Intervention Strategies. Ecosystems and Human Well-Being (eds N. Ash, H. Blanco, C. Brown, K. Garcia, T. Henrichs, N. Lucas, C. Ruadsepp-Heane, R.D. Simpson, R. Scholes, T. Tomich, B. Vira & M. Zurek), pp 221–253. Island Press, London.

Smart, S., Dunbar, M.J., Emmett, B.A., Marks, S., Maskell, L.C., Norton, L.R., Rose, P. & Simpson, I.C. (2010) An Integrated Assessment of Countryside Survey data to investigate Ecosystem Services in Great Britain. NERC/Centre for Ecology & Hydrology.

Smith, P. & Pearson, J. (2008) An environmental limits approach to spatial planning. *Town & Country Planning*, **2008**, 511-514. [online] Available: <http://www.landuse.co.uk/files/EnvironmentalLimitsSpatialPlanning_6.pdf> [Accessed 22.05.11].

Smithers, R. (2011) Sales of sustainable seafood soar in UK supermarkets. The Guardian. [online] Available at: <http://www.guardian.co.uk/environment/2011/jan/17/sustainable-seafood-supermarkets-fish-fight> [Accessed 22.05.11].

SNH (Scottish Natural Heritage) (2007) Enjoying the Outdoors: supporting participation and sharing the benefits. [online] Available at: <http://www.snh.gov.uk/docs/A129984.pdf> [Accessed 14.02.11].

SNH (Scottish Natural Heritage) (2010a) An Ecosystem Approach for Scotland. [online] Available at: <http://www.snh.gov.uk/protecting-scotlands-nature/safeguarding-biodiversity/working-with-others/ecosystem-approach-for-scotland/> [Accessed 14.02.11].

SNH (Scottish Natural Heritage) (2010b) Scotland's Biodiversity Communication Toolkit. [online] Available at: <http://www.snh.org.uk/biodiversitycommstoolkit/index.html> [Accessed 06.12.10].

SNH (Scottish Natural Heritage) (2010c) Deer. [online] Available at: <http://www.snh.gov.uk/protecting-scotlands-nature/protected-species/legal-framework/deer-protection/> [Accessed 09.12.10].

SNH (Scottish Natural Heritage) (2010d) Enjoying the Outdoors Policy. [online] Available at: <http://www.snh.gov.uk/land-and-sea/managing-recreation-and-access/access-and-recreation-policy/enjoying-the-outdoors-policy/> [Accessed 12.12.10].

SNIFFER (Scotland and Northern Ireland Forum For Environmental Research) (2007) Preparing for a changing climate in Northern Ireland. SNIFFER, Edinburgh. [online] Available at: <http://www.doeni.gov.uk/preparing_for_a_climate_change_in_northern_ireland_executive_summary.pdf> [Accessed 22.05.11].

Snowdon, P. (2002) Food production and environmental quality. Paper delivered at a seminar on Mountain Quality - from local initiatives to a European project, Toulouse, 1-2 February 2002. [online] Available at: <http://www.snh.org.uk/pdfs/strategy/rural/sr-pt.pdf> [Accessed 22.05.11].

Social Exclusion Unit (2003) Making the connections: Final report on transport and social exclusion – Summary. Social Exclusion Unit, London.

Soulé, M. & B. Wilcox (1980) Conservation biology: an evolutionary-ecological perspective. Sinauer & Associates, Sunderland.

Speybroeck, J., Bonte, D., Courtens, W., Gheskiere, T., Grootaert, P., Maelfait, J.-P., Mathys, M., Provoost, S., Sabbe, K.,

Stienen, E.W.M., Lancker, V.V., Vincx, M. & Degraer, S. (2006) Beach nourishment: an ecologically sound coastal defence alternative? A review. *Aquatic Conservation: Marine and Freshwater Ecosystems*, **16**, 419-435.

Stantchev, D. & Whiteing, T. (2010) Thematic Research Summary: Land Use Planning. DG Energy and Transport, European Commission, Belgium. [online] Available at: <http://www.transport-research.info/Upload/Documents/201002/20100215_150102_95903_TRS%20Land%20use%20planning.pdf> [Accessed 22.05.11].

Statistics for Wales (2010a) Statistical Bulletin: A Walking & Cycling Action Plan for Wales 2009 - 2013 Monitoring Report. Statistical Directorate, Welsh Assembly Government, Cardiff. [online] Available at: <http://wales.gov.uk/docs/statistics/2010/100803sb652010en.pdf> [Accessed 22.05.11].

Statistics for Wales (2010b) Statistical Bulletin: State of the environment, July 2010. Statistical Directorate, Welsh Assembly Government, Cardiff. [online] Available at: <http://wales.gov.uk/docs/statistics/2010/100722sb572010en.pdf> [Accessed 22.05.11].

Stojanovic, T.A. & Ballinger, R.C. (2009) Integrated Coastal Management: A comparative analysis of four UK initiatives. *Applied Geography*, **29**, 49–62.

Stojanovic, T.I.M. & Barker, N. (2008) Improving governance through local Coastal Partnerships in the UK. *Geographical Journal*, **174**, 344-360.

Strayer, D.L. (2010) Alien species in fresh waters: ecological effects, interactions and other stressors, and prospects for the future. *Freshwater Biology*, **55**, 152-174, Supplement 1.

Sustrans (2010a) Annual Review 2009. Sustans, Bristol. [online] Available at: <http://www.sustrans.org.uk/assets/files/Publications/sustrans_annual_review_2009_june10.pdf> [Accessed 22.05.11].

Sustrans (2010b) Moving Forward: a year of delivering smarter travel choice. Sustans, Bristol. [online] Available at: <http://www.sustrans.org.uk/assets/files/rmu/Moving%20forward%20Sustrans%20Monitoring%20Report%20to%20end%202009%20September%202010.pdf> [Accessed 22.05.11].

Sustrans (2010c) Sustrans Limited: Annual report for the year ended 31 March 2010. Sustans, Bristol. [online] Available at: <http://www.sustrans.org.uk/assets/files/general/sustrans_accounts_2010.pdf> [Accessed 22.05.11].

Sutherland, W.J., Albon, S.D., Allison, H., Armstrong-Brown, S., Bailey, M.J., Brereton, T., Boyd, I.L., Carey, P., Edwards, J., Gill, M., Hill, D., Hodge, I., Hunt, A.J., Le Quesne, W.J.F., Macdonald, D.W., Mee, L.D., Mitchell, R., Norman, T., Owen, R.P., Parker, D., Prior, S.V., Pullin, A.S., Rands, M.R.W., Redpath, S., Spencer, J., Spray, C.J., Thomas, C.D., Tucker, G.M., Watkinson, A.R. & Clements, A. (2010) Review: The identification of priority policy options for UK nature conservation. *Journal of Applied Ecology*, **47**, 955-965.

Sylvester-Bradley, R. & Wiseman, J. (2005) Yields of UK Crops and Livestock: Physiological and Technological Constraints and Expectations of Progress to 2050. Defra Project IS0210. ADAS/Nottingham University, Boxworth, Cambridge.

Technology Strategy Board (2011) Energy Generation and Supply Knowledge Transfer Network. [online] Available at: <https://ktn.innovateuk.org/web/energyktn/overview> [Accessed 08.03.11].

TEEB (The Economics of Ecosystems and Biodiversity) (2010) The Economics of Ecosystems and Biodiversity: Mainstreaming the economics of nature: a synthesis of the approach, conclusions and recommendations of TEEB. [online] Available at: <http://www.teebweb.org/LinkClick.aspx?fileticket=bYhDohL_TuM%3d&tabid=1278&mid=2357> [Accessed 22.05.11].

TfL (Transport for London) (2008) Central London Congestion Charging: Impacts Monitoring. Sixth Annual Report. Transport for London, London.

The Environmental Audit Committee (2009) Halting biodiversity loss: Government Response to the Committee's Thirteenth Report of Session 2007–08. House of Commons, London.

The Green Tourism Business Scheme (2011) The Green Tourism Business Scheme. [online] Available at: <http://www.green-business.co.uk/> [Accessed 01.04.11].

The Planning Service (2004) Planning Policy Statement 8: Open space, sport and outdoor recreation. Department of the Environment, Northern Ireland, Belfast.

The Rural Coalition (2010) The rural challenge: achieving sustainable rural communities for the 21st century. The Rural Coalition, London. [online] Available at: <http://www.eerf.org.uk/Documents/Latest%20news/2010/Rural%20Challenge%20Aug2010%20%28summary%29.pdf> [Accessed 09.05.11].

The Tree Council (2010) Tree Wardens. [online] Available at: <http://www.treecouncil.org.uk/tree-wardens> [Accessed 21.02.11].

The Wildlife Trusts (2010) Water for wildlife. [online] Available at: <http://www.wildlifetrusts.org/index.php?section=environment:wfw> [Accessed 13.04.11].

The Wildlife Trusts (2011) Volunteer your time. [online] Available at: <http://www.wildlifetrusts.org/index.php?section=helping:volunteer> [Accessed 28.02.11].

Thompson, C., Aspinall, P. & Montarzino, A. (2008) The Childhood Factor: Adult Visits to Green Places and the Significance of Childhood Experience. *Environment and Behaviour*, **40**, 111–143.

Thompson, D. (2008a) Carbon Management by Land and Marine Managers. Natural England Research Report NERR026. Natural England, Sheffield. [online] Available at: <http://naturalengland.etraderstores.com/NaturalEnglandShop/NERR026> [Accessed 22.05.11].

Thompson, M.H. (2008b) Fostering sustainable behaviours in community-based co-managed fisheries. *Marine Policy*, **32**, 413-420.

TNS Research International (2010) Scottish Recreation Survey: Annual summary report 2009, Scottish Natural Heritage Commissioned Report No. 395 (ROAME No. F02AA614/8).

Tomlinson, I. (2008) Re-thinking the Transformation of Organics: The Role of the UK Government in Shaping British Organic Food and Farming. *Sociologia Ruralis*, **48**, 133–151.

Tourism Alliance (2010a) What is the Tourism Allliance. [online] Available at: <http://www.tourismalliance.com/details.cfm?p=ab&s=w> [Accessed 12.14.10].

Tourism Alliance (2010b) Tourism: Britain's best opportunity for sustainable economic growth and new employment. Tourism Alliance, London. [online] Available at: <http://www.tourismalliance.com/downloads/TA_284_313.pdf> [Accessed 22.05.11].

Trewavas, A. (2001) Urban myths of organic farming. *Nature*, **410**, 409–410.

Treweek, J., Kate, K., Butcher, B., Venn, O., Garland, L., Wells, M., Moran, D. & Thompson, S. (2009) Scoping study for the design and use of biodiversity offsets in an English context. Final report to Defra (Contract NE 0801). Defra, London. [online] Available at: <http://www.forest-trends.org/documents/files/doc_2400.pdf> [Accessed 22.05.11].

Turner, R.K., Bateman, I.J., Georgiou, S., Jones, A., Langford, I.H., Matias, N.G.N. & Subramanian, L. (2004) An ecological economics approach to the management of a multi-purpose coastal wetland. *Regional Environmental Change*, **4**, 86-99.

Turner, R. K., Hadley, D., Luisetti, T., Lam, V.W.Y. & Cheung, W.W.L. (2010) An Introduction to Socio-economic assessment within a Marine Strategy Framework. Defra, London. [online] Available at: <http://archive.defra.gov.uk/environment/marine/documents/legislation/msf-socioeconomic.pdf> [Accessed 22.05.11].

UK Cabinet Office (2004) Net Benefits: A Sustainable and Profitable Future for UK Fishing, Prime Minister's Strategy Unit, UK Cabinet Office, London.

UKCIP (UK Climate Impacts Programme) (2011) UK Climate Impacts Programme. [online] Available at: <www.ukcip.org.uk/> [Accessed 09.05.11].

UK Clearing House Mechanism for Biodiversity (2010) Areas of Special Protection (for birds). [online] Available at: <http://uk.chm-cbd.net/default.aspx?page=7322> [Accessed 22.05.11].

UK MAB Urban Forum (2010) The UK UNESCO Man and Biosphere (MAB) Urban Forum's Response to the Pre consultation on the Nature of England White Paper. UK Man and Biosphere Committee.

UKERC (UK Energy Research Centre) (2010) Energy 2050: Making the Transition to a Secure Low-Carbon Energy System. Earthscan, Oxford. [online] Available at: <http://www.ukerc.ac.uk/support/tiki-index.php?page=Energy+2050+Overview> [Accessed 22.05.11].

UKMMAS (UK Marine Monitoring and Assessment Strategy) (2010) Charting Progress 2: An assessment of the state of UK seas. Published by the Department for Environment, Food and Rural Affairs on behalf of UKMMAS. TSO, London. [online] Available at: <http://chartingprogress.defra.gov.uk/resources> [Accessed 22.05.11].

UKPREU (UK Permanent Representation to the European Union) (2009) UK Response to the European Commission Reform Green Paper on the Common Fisheries Policy (COM(2009)163). [online] Available at: <http://archive.defra.gov.uk/foodfarm/fisheries/documents/fisheries/cfp-response.pdf> [Accessed 16.05.11].

UKWAS (UK Woodland Assurance Standard) (2008) The UK Woodland Assurance Standard: Second Edition. UKWAS, Edinburgh. [online] Available at: <http://www.forestry.gov.uk/pdf/ukwasguide.pdf/$FILE/ukwasguide.pdf> [Accessed 22.05.11].

UNEP (United Nations Environment Programme) (2007) Global Environmental Outlook 4. United Nations Environment Programme. [online] Available at: <http://www.unep.org/geo/geo4.asp> [Accessed 22.05.11].

Upham, P., Whitmarsh, L., Poortinga, W., Purdam, K., Darnton, A., McLachlan, C. & Devine Wright, P. (2009) Public Attitudes to Environmental Change: a selective review of theory and practice – executive summary. A reserach synthesis for the Living With Environmental Change research programme. Research Councils UK, Living With Environmental Change. [online] Available at: <http://www.esrc.ac.uk/_images/public-attitudes-to-environmental-change-exec-summary_tcm8-6383.pdf> [Accessed 22.05.11].

Upreti, B.R. (2004) Conflict over biomass energy development in the United Kingdom: some observations and lessons from England and Wales. *Energy Policy*, **32**, 785–800.

Vickery, J.A., Bradbury, R.B., Henderson, I.G., Eaton, M.A. & Grice, P.V. (2004) The role of agri-environment schemes and farm management practices in reversing the decline of farmland birds in England. *Biological Conservation*, **119**, 19–39.

VisitBritain (2010) United Kingdom Tourism Survey. VisitBritain. [online] Available at: <http://tourisminsights.info/STATISTICS/UKTS.htm> [Accessed 22.05.11].

VisitScotland (2011) Walking Scotland. Visit Scotland. [online] Available at: <http://walking.visitscotland.com/> [Accessed 28.02.11].

VisitWales (2008) Coastal Tourism Strategy. Visit Wales, Welsh Assembly Government, Cardiff. [online] Available at: <http://wales.gov.uk/docs/drah/publications/Tourism/090612coastaleng.pdf> [Accessed 22.05.11].

WAG (Welsh Assembly Government) (2006) Environment Strategy for Wales. Welsh Assembly Government, Cardiff.

WAG (Welsh Assembly Government) (2007) Environment strategy for Wales: report on grogress. Welsh Assembly Government, Cardiff.

WAG (Welsh Assembly Government) (2008a) A Walking and Cycling Plan for Wales 2009–2013. Welsh Assembly Government, Cardiff.

WAG (Welsh Assembly Government) (2008b) Making the Most of Wales' Coast: The Integrated Coastal Zone Management Strategy for Wales – Progress Report. Welsh Assembly Government, Cardiff.

WAG (Welsh Assembly Government) (2008c) Renewable Energy Route Map for Wales: consultation on way forward to a leaner, greener and cleaner Wales. Welsh Assembly Government, Cardiff.

WAG (Welsh Assembly Government) (2009) Woodlands for Wales: the Welsh Assembly Government's Strategy for Woodlands and Trees. Welsh Assembly Government, Cardiff.

WAG (Welsh Assembly Government) (2010a) A Low Carbon Revolution: The Welsh Assembly Government Energy Policy Statement. Welsh Assembly Government, Cardiff. [online] Available at: <http://wales.gov.uk/docs/desh/policy/100331energystatementen.pdf> [Accessed 22.05.11].

WAG (Welsh Assembly Government) (2010b) Bioenergy action plan for Wales: Progress report. Welsh Assembly Government, Cardiff.

WAG (Welsh Assembly Government) (2010c) Climate Change Strategy for Wales. Welsh Assembly Government, Cardiff.

WAG (Welsh Assembly Government) (2010d) Glastir Woodland Creation Scheme Rules. Welsh Assembly Government, Cardiff.

WAG (Welsh Assembly Government) (2011) An introduction to Glastir and other UK agri-environment schemes. Members' Research Service. Welsh Assembly Government, Cardiff.

Waitrose (2011) Aquaculture policies. [online] Available at: <http://www.waitrose.com/home/inspiration/food_issues_and_policies/sustainable_fishing/aquaculture_policies.html> [Accessed 09.05.11].

Wales Forest Business Partnership (2011) Wales Forest Business Partnership. [online] Available at: <http://www.wfbp.

co.uk/walesforestbusinesspartnership/default.htm> [Accessed 28.11.10].

Warren, C.R. & McFadyen, M. (2010) Does community ownership affect public attitudes to wind energy? A case study from south-west Scotland. *Land Use Policy*, **27**, 204–213.

Watson, C.A., Atkinson, D., Gosling, P., Jackson, L.R. & Rayns, F.W. (2002) Managing soil fertility in organic farming systems. *Soil Use and Management*, **18**, 239–247.

Watson, N. (2004) Integrated river basin management: A case for collaboration. *International Journal for River Basin Management,* **2**, 243–257.

Wätzold, F., M. Drechsler, Armstrong, C.W., Baumgärtner, S., Grimm, V., Huth, A., Perrings, C., Possingham, H.P., Shogren, J.F., Skonhoft, A., Verboom-Vasiljev, J. & Wissel, C. (2006) Ecological-Economic Modeling for Biodiversity Management: Potential, Pitfalls, and Prospects. *Conservation Biology*, **20**, 1034–1041.

Waylen, K. & Fischer, A. (2010) Understanding Public Attitudes For Biodiversity Management. Knowledge Scotland. [online] Available at: <http://www.knowledgescotland.org/briefings.php?id=156> [Accessed 05.12.10].

Weatherhead, E.K. & Howden, N.J.K. (2009) The relationship between land use and surface water resources in the UK. *Land Use Policy*, **26**, S243–S250.

Webb, B., Marshall, B., Czarnomski, S. & Tilley, N. (2006) Fly-tipping: Causes, Incentives and Solutions. Jill Dando Institute of Crime Science, University College London. [online] Available at: <http://www.ucl.ac.uk/scs/downloads/research-reports/flytipping-good-practice-guide> [Accessed 22.05.11].

Webber, D., Buccellato, T. & White, S. (2010) The global recession and its impact on tourists' spending in the UK. *Economic & Labour Market Review*, **4**, 65–73.

West, J., Bailey, I. & Winter, M. (2010) Renewable energy policy and public perceptions of renewable energy: A cultural theory approach. *Energy Policy*, **38**, 5739–5748.

Wharton, G. & Gilvear, D.J. (2006) River restoration in the UK: Meeting the dual needs of the European Union Water Framework Directive and flood defence? *International Journal for River Basin Management*, **4**, 1–12.

Wier, M., O'Doherty Jensen, K., Andersen, L.M., Millock, K. & Rosenkvist, L. (2008) The character of demand in mature organic food markets: Great Britain and Denmark compared. *Food Policy*, **33**, 406–421.

Wilby, R.L. & Perry, G.L.W. (2006) Climate change, biodiversity and the urban environment: a critical review based on London, UK. *Progress in Physical Geography*, **30**, 73.

Wilcove, D. S., Rothstein, D., Jason, D., Phillips, A. & Losos, E. (1998) Quantifying Threats to Imperiled Species in the United States. *BioScience,* 48, 607–615.

Wilson, B. (2002) The Renewables Obligation Order 2002. No. 914. Department of Trade and Industry. Statutory Instruments, London. [online] Available at: <http://www.legislation.gov.uk/uksi/2002/914/pdfs/uksi_20020914_en.pdf> [Accessed 22.05.11].

Wilson, S. McG. & Samuel, C.J.A. (2003) Genetic conservation of native trees. Forest Research Annual Report and Accounts 2002-2003, pp. 56-61. Forest Research. [online] Available at: <http://www.forestry.gov.uk/pdf/frgeneticcons0203.pdf/$FILE/frgeneticcons0203.pdf> [Accessed 22.05.11].

Wiltshire, R. (2010) A Place to Grow: a supplementary document to Growing in the community. Local Government Association, London.

WiSe Scheme (2011) WiSe Scheme. [online] Available at: <http://www.wisescheme.org/> [Accessed 25.02.11].

Woodland Trust (2010a) MOREwoods. Woodland Trust. [online] Available at: <http://www.woodlandtrust.org.uk/en/plant-trees/plant-a-wood/Pages/morewoods.aspx> [Accessed 28.11.10].

Woodland Trust (2010b) Position Statement: Bioenergy in the UK. Woodland Trust. [online] Available at: <http://www.woodlandtrust.org.uk/SiteCollectionDocuments/pdf/policy-and-campaigns/bioenergy-policy-100217.pdf> [Accessed 20.02.11].

Woods, A. (2009) Securing Integrated Land Management: Issues for policy, research and rural communities from the RELU programme. Commissioned by RELU. [online] Available at: <http://www.relu.ac.uk/research/Land_Use_Consultation/Securing_Integrated_Land_Man.pdf> [Accessed 22.05.11].

WRAP (Waste and Resources Action Programme) (2009) Household Food and Drink Waste in the UK. WRAP, Banbury.

WRAP (Waste and Resources Action Programme) (2010) Waste arisings in the supply of food and drink to households in the UK. Oakdene Hollins & WRAP, Banbury.

WSSD (World Summit on Sustainable Development) (2002) World Summit on Sustainable Development (WSSD) Johannesburg, August 26–September 4, 2002. [online] Available at: <http://www.worldsummit2002.org/> [Accessed 09.05.11].

Wüstenhagen, R., Wolsink, M. & Bürer, M.J. (2007) Social acceptance of renewable energy innovation: An introduction to the concept. *Energy Policy,* **35**, 2683-2691.

WWF (World Wildlife Fund) (2007) Mid-term Review of the Common Fisheries Policy. World Wide Fund for Nature, Brussels.

WWF (World Wildlife Fund) (2009) The Scottish Conservation Credits Scheme: moving fisheries management towards conservation. WWF Scotland. [online] Available at: <http://assets.wwf.org.uk/downloads/scottish_conservation_credits_scheme.pdf> [Accessed 22.05.11].

WWF-UK (World Wildlife Fund) (2010) Mobilising the Marine Act. WWF-UK. [online] Available at: <http://assets.wwf.org.uk/downloads/mobilising_the_marine_act.pdf> [Accessed 22.05.11].

WWF-UK (World Wildlife Fund), English Nature, RSPB & The British Wind Energy Association (2001). Wind Farm Development and Nature Conservation. World Wildlife Fund, UK.

WWCT (Warley Woods Community Trust) (2010) Warley Woods Community Trust. [online] Available at: <http://www.warleywoods.org.uk/> [Accessed 09.05.11].

Zapponi, L. (2006) Human and Wildlife Coexistence in the Marine Environment: A case study in the Moray Firth. University of Nottingham, Nottingham.

Glossary

Abatement cost: See *Marginal abatement cost.*

Abundance: The total number of individuals of a taxon or taxa in an area, population, or community. Relative abundance refers to the total number of individuals of one taxon compared with the total number of individuals of all other taxa in an area, volume, or community.

Acidification: Acidification is a natural process. The term is used to describe the loss of nutrient bases (calcium, magnesium and potassium) through the process of leaching and their replacement by acidic elements (hydrogen and aluminium).

Adaptation: Adjustment in natural or human systems to a new or changing environment. Various types of adaptation can be distinguished, including anticipatory and reactive adaptation, private and public adaptation, and autonomous and planned adaptation.

Adaptive capacity: The general ability of institutions, systems, and individuals to adjust to potential damage, to take advantage of opportunities, or to cope with the consequences.

Adaptive management: A systematic process for continually improving management policies and practices by learning from the outcomes of previously employed policies and practices. In active adaptive management, management is treated as a deliberate experiment for purposes of learning.

Afforestation: Planting of forests on land that has historically not contained forests.

Agrobiodiversity: The diversity of plants, insects, and soil biota found in cultivated systems.

Alien species: Species introduced outside its normal distribution.

Alien invasive species: See *Invasive alien species.*

Aquaculture: Breeding and rearing of fish, shellfish, or plants in ponds, enclosures, or other forms of confinement in fresh or marine waters for the direct harvest of the product.

Biodiversity (a contraction of biological diversity)**:** The variability among living organisms from all sources, including terrestrial, marine, and other aquatic ecosystems and the ecological complexes of which they are part. Biodiversity includes diversity within species, between species, and between ecosystems.

Biofuels: Liquid fuels derived from biomass and predominantly used in transportation. The dominant biofuels are ethanol and biodiesel. Ethanol is produced by fermenting starch contained in plants such as sugar cane, sugar beet, maize, cassava, sweet sorghum or beetroot. Biodiesel is typically produced through a chemical process called trans-esterification, whereby oily biomass such as rapeseed, soybeans, palm oil, jatropha seeds, waste cooking oils or vegetable oils is combined with methanol to form methyl esters (sometimes called "fatty acid methyl ester" or FAME).

Biogeographic realm: A large spatial region, within which ecosystems share a broadly similar biota. Eight terrestrial biogeographic realms are typically recognised, corresponding roughly to continents (e.g. Afrotropical realm).

Biological diversity: See *Biodiversity.*

Biomass: The mass of tissues in living organisms in a population, ecosystem, or spatial unit.

Biome: The largest unit of ecological classification that is convenient to recognise below the entire globe. Terrestrial biomes are typically based on dominant vegetation structure (e.g. forest, grassland). Ecosystems within a biome function in a broadly similar way, although they may have very different species composition. For example, all forests share certain properties regarding nutrient cycling, disturbance, and biomass that are different from the properties of grasslands. Marine biomes are typically based on biogeochemical properties.

Biotechnology: Any technological application that uses biological systems, living organisms, or derivatives thereof to make or modify products or processes for specific use.

Capacity building: A process of strengthening or developing human resources, institutions, organisations, or networks. Also referred to as capacity development or capacity enhancement.

Capture fisheries: see *Fishery.*

Carbon sequestration: The process of increasing the carbon content of a reservoir other than the atmosphere.

Catch: The number or weight of all fish caught by fishing operations, whether the fish are landed or not.

Coastal system: Systems containing terrestrial areas dominated by ocean influences of tides and marine aerosols, plus nearshore marine areas.

Collaborative (or joint) forest management: Community-based management of forests, where resource tenure by local communities is secured.

Community (ecological): An assemblage of species occurring in the same space or time, often linked by biotic interactions such as competition or predation.

Community (human, local): A collection of human beings who have something in common. A local community is a fairly small group of people who share a common place of residence and a set of institutions based on this fact, but the word 'community' is also used to refer to larger collections of people who have something else in common (e.g. national community, donor community).

Conceptual Framework: Is a concise summary in words and pictures of the relationship between people and nature including key components of interactions between humans and ecological systems. Conceptual frameworks assist in organising thinking and structuring work when assessing complex ecosystems, social arrangements and human-environment interactions.

Condition of an ecosystem: The capacity of an ecosystem to yield services, relative to its potential capacity.

Condition of an ecosystem service: The capacity of an ecosystem service to yield benefits to people, relative to its potential capacity.

Contingent valuation: Economic valuation technique based on a survey of how much respondents would be willing to pay for specified benefits.

Cost-benefit analysis: A technique designed to determine the feasibility of a project or plan by quantifying its costs and benefits.

Cost-effectiveness analysis: Analysis to identify the least cost option that meets a particular goal.

Critically endangered species: Species that face an extremely high risk of extinction in the wild. See also *Threatened species.*

Cultural landscape: See *Landscape.*

Cultural services: The nonmaterial benefits people obtain from ecosystems through spiritual enrichment, cognitive development, reflection, recreation, and aesthetic experience, including, e.g. knowledge systems, social relations, and aesthetic values.

Decision-maker: A person whose decisions, and the actions that follow from them, can influence a condition, process, or issue under consideration.

Decomposition: The ecological process carried out primarily by microbes that leads to a transformation of dead organic matter into inorganic mater.

Degradation of an ecosystem service: For *provisioning services*, decreased production of the service through changes in area over which the services is provided, or decreased production per unit area. For *regulating* and *supporting services*, a reduction in the benefits obtained from the service, either through a change in the service or through human pressures on the service exceeding its limits. For *cultural services*, a change in the ecosystem features that decreases the cultural benefits provided by the ecosystem.

Degradation of ecosystems: A persistent reduction in the capacity to provide ecosystem services.

Direct use value (of ecosystems): The benefits derived from the services provided by an ecosystem that are used directly by an economic agent. These include consumptive uses (e.g. harvesting goods) and nonconsumptive uses (e.g. enjoyment of scenic beauty). Agents are often physically present in an ecosystem to receive direct use value. (Compare *Indirect use value*).

Diversity: The variety and relative abundance of different entities in a sample.

Driver: Any natural or human-induced factor that directly or indirectly causes a change in an ecosystem.

Driver, direct: A driver that unequivocally influences ecosystem processes and can therefore be identified and measured to differing degrees of accuracy. (Compare *Driver, indirect*).

Driver, indirect: A driver that operates by altering the level or rate of change of one or more direct drivers. (Compare *Driver, direct*).

Ecological character: See *Ecosystem properties*.

Ecological degradation: See *Degradation of ecosystems*.

Ecosystem: A dynamic complex of plant, animal, and microorganism communities and their non-living environment interacting as a functional unit.

Ecosystem approach: A strategy for the integrated management of land, water, and living resources that promotes conservation and sustainable use. An ecosystem approach is based on the application of appropriate scientific methods focused on levels of biological organisation, which encompass the essential structure, processes, functions, and interactions among organisms and their environment. It recognises that humans, with their cultural diversity, are an integral component of many ecosystems.

Ecosystem assessment: A social process through which the findings of science concerning the causes of ecosystem change, their consequences for human well-being, and management and policy options are brought to bear on the needs of decision-makers.

Ecosystem change: Any variation in the state, outputs, or structure of an ecosystem.

Ecosystem function: See *Ecosystem process*.

Ecosystem interactions: Exchanges of materials, energy, and information within and among ecosystems.

Ecosystem management: An approach to maintaining or restoring the composition, structure, function, and delivery of services of natural and modified ecosystems for the goal of achieving sustainability. It is based on an adaptive, collaboratively developed vision of desired future conditions that integrates ecological, socioeconomic, and institutional perspectives, applied within a geographic framework, and defined primarily by natural ecological boundaries.

Ecosystem process: An intrinsic ecosystem characteristic whereby an ecosystem maintains its integrity. Ecosystem processes include decomposition, production, nutrient cycling, and fluxes of nutrients and energy.

Ecosystem properties: The size, biodiversity, stability, degree of organisation, internal exchanges of materials, energy, and information among different pools, and other properties that characterise an ecosystem. Includes ecosystem functions and processes.

Ecosystem resilience: See *Resilience*.

Ecosystem resistance: See *Resistance*.

Ecosystem robustness: See *Ecosystem stability*.

Ecosystem services: The benefits people obtain from ecosystems. These include *provisioning services* such as food and water; *regulating services* such as flood and disease control; *cultural services* such as spiritual, recreational, and cultural benefits; and *supporting services* such as nutrient cycling that maintain the conditions for life on Earth. The concept "ecosystem goods and services" is synonymous with ecosystem services.

Enabling conditions: Critical preconditions for success of responses, including political, institutional, social, economic, and ecological factors.

Endangered species: Species that face a very high risk of extinction in the wild. See also *Threatened species*.

Environmental settings: Are the locations and places where humans interact with each other and nature that give rise to the cultural goods and benefits that people obtain from ecosystems.

Equity: Fairness of rights, distribution, and access. Depending on context, this can refer to resources, services, or power.

Eutrophication: The increase in additions of nutrients to freshwater or marine systems, which leads to increases in plant growth and often to undesirable changes in ecosystem structure and function.

Evapotranspiration: See *Transpiration*.

Existence value: The value that individuals place on knowing that a resource exists, even if they never use that resource (also sometimes known as conservation value or passive use value).

Externality: A consequence of an action that affects someone other than the agent undertaking that action and for which the agent is neither compensated nor penalised through the markets. Externalities can be positive or negative.

Final ecosystem service: Are the outcomes from ecosystems that directly lead to good(s) that are valued by people.

Fishery: A particular kind of fishing activity, e.g. a trawl fishery, or a particular species targeted, e.g. a cod fishery or salmon fishery.

Fish stock: See *Stock*.

Fixed nitrogen: See *Reactive nitrogen*.

Functional diversity: The value, range, and relative abundance of traits present in the organisms in an ecological community.

Geographic information system: A computerised system organising data sets through a geographical referencing of all data included in its collections.

Goods: Are all use and non-use, material and non-material outputs from ecosystems that have value for people.

Governance: The process of regulating human behaviour in accordance with shared objectives. The term includes both governmental and nongovernmental mechanisms.

Habitat: Is an ecological or environmental area that is inhabited by a particular animal or plant species. 'Broad Habitats' are used to classify different ecosystems for reporting.

Health, human: A state of complete physical, mental, and social well-being and not merely the absence of disease or infirmity. The health of a whole community or population is reflected in measurements of disease incidence and prevalence, age-specific death rates, and life expectancy.

Heritage (cultural and natural): UNESCO defines heritage as 'our legacy from the past, what we live with today, and what we pass on to future generations'. Physical objects produced and used by past generations, ranging from small-scale domestic utensils to large-scale buildings, monuments, places and landscapes, may become valued as cultural heritage by their descendants. Equally, symbolic products of human creativity and imagination such as music, visual arts, poetry and prose, knowledge and know-how contribute to a society or group's understanding of its cultural heritage.

Human well-being: See *Well-being*.

Indirect use value: The benefits derived from the goods and services provided by an ecosystem that are used indirectly by an economic agent. For example, an agent at some distance from an ecosystem may derive benefits from drinking water that has been purified as it passed through the ecosystem. (Compare *Direct use value*).

Intermediate ecosystem services: Those whose ecological processes and functions support all life, and, by definition all other services.

Institutions: The rules that guide how people within societies live, work, and interact with each other. Formal institutions are written or codified rules. Examples of formal institutions would be the constitution, the judiciary laws, the organised market, and property rights. Informal institutions are rules governed by social and behavioural norms of the society, family, or community. Also referred to as organisations.

Integrated coastal zone management: Approaches that integrate economic, social, and ecological perspectives for the management of coastal resources and areas.

Integrated pest management: Any practices that attempt to capitalise on natural processes that reduce pest abundance. Sometimes used to refer to monitoring programs where farmers apply pesticides to improve economic efficiency (reducing application rates and improving profitability).

Integrated responses: Responses that address degradation of ecosystem services across a number of systems simultaneously or that also explicitly include objectives to enhance human well-being.

River basin management: Integration of water planning and management with environmental, social, and economic development concerns, with an explicit objective of improving human welfare.

Interventions: See *Responses*.

Intrinsic value: The value of someone or something in and for itself, irrespective of its utility for people.

Invasive alien species: An alien species whose establishment and spread modifies ecosystems, habitats, or species.

LA10,T: The A weighted level of noise exceeded for 10% of the specified measurement period (T). It gives an indication of the upper limit of fluctuating noise such as that from road traffic. LA10,18h is the arithmetic average of the 18 hourly LA10,1h values from 06.00 to 24.00.

LA90,T: The A weighted noise level exceeded for 90% of the specified measurement period (T). In BS 4142: 1990 it is used to define background noise level.

LAeq,T: The equivalent continuous sound level or ambient noise level is the sound level of a notional steady sound having the same energy as a fluctuating sound over a specified measurement period (T). LAeq,T is used to describe many types of noise and can be measured directly with an integrating sound level meter. It is written as Leq in connection with aircraft noise.

Land cover: The physical coverage of land, usually expressed in terms of vegetation cover or lack of it. Related to, but not synonymous with, *land use*.

Landscape: An area of land that contains a mosaic of ecosystems, including human-dominated ecosystems. The term cultural landscape is often used when referring to landscapes containing significant human populations or in which there has been significant human influence on the land.

Landscape unit: A portion of relatively homogenous land cover within the local-to-regional landscape.

Land use: The human use of a piece of land for a certain purpose (such as irrigated agriculture or recreation). Influenced by, but not synonymous with, *land cover*.

Marginal abatement cost: The cost of abating an incremental unit of, for instance, a pollutant or carbon.

Market-based instruments: Mechanisms that create a market for ecosystem services in order to improve the efficiency in the way the service is used. The term is used for mechanisms that create new markets, but also for responses such as taxes, subsidies, or regulations that affect existing markets.

Market failure: The inability of a market to capture the correct values of ecosystem services.

Marine system: Marine waters from the low-water mark to the high seas that support marine capture fisheries, as well as deepwater (>50 meters) habitats. Four sub-divisions (marine biomes) are recognised: the coastal boundary zone; trade-winds; westerlies; and polar.

Mitigation: An anthropogenic intervention to reduce negative or unsustainable uses of ecosystems or to enhance sustainable practices.

Net primary productivity: See *Production, biological*.

Nutrient cycling: The processes by which elements are extracted from their mineral, aquatic, or atmospheric sources or recycled from their organic forms, converting them to the ionic form in which biotic uptake occurs and ultimately returning them to the atmosphere, water, or soil.

Nutrients: The approximately 20 chemical elements known to be essential for the growth of living organisms, including nitrogen, sulphur, phosphorus, and carbon.

Open access resource: A good or service over which no property rights are recognised.

Opportunity cost: The benefits forgone by undertaking one activity instead of another.

Organic farming: Crop and livestock production systems that do not make use of synthetic fertilisers, pesticides, or herbicides. May also include restrictions on the use of transgenic crops (genetically modified organisms).

Policy-maker: A person with power to influence or determine policies and practices at an international, national, regional, or local level.

Pollination: A process in the sexual phase of reproduction in some plants caused by the transportation of pollen. In the context of ecosystem services, pollination generally refers to animal-assisted pollination, such as that done by bees, rather than wind pollination.

Population, biological: A group of individuals of the same species, occupying a defined area, and usually isolated to some degree from other similar groups. Populations can be relatively reproductively isolated and adapted to local environments.

Population, human: A collection of living people in a given area. (Compare *Community (human, local)*).

Precautionary principle: The management concept stating that in cases "where there are threats of serious or irreversible damage, lack of full scientific certainty shall not be used as a reason for postponing cost-effective measures to prevent environmental degradation," as defined in the Rio Declaration.

Primary production: See *Production, biological*.

Production, biological: Rate of biomass produced by an ecosystem, generally expressed as biomass produced per unit of time per unit of surface or volume. Net primary productivity is defined as the energy fixed by plants minus their respiration.

Productivity, biological: See *Production, biological*.

Projection: A potential future evolution of a quantity or set of quantities, often computed with the aid of a model. Projections are distinguished from "predictions" in order to emphasise that projections involve assumptions concerning, for example, future socioeconomic and technological developments that may or may not be realised; they are therefore subject to substantial uncertainty.

Provisioning services: The products obtained from ecosystems, including, for example, genetic resources, food and fibre, and fresh water.

Public good: A good or service in which the benefit received by any one party does not diminish the availability of the benefits to others, and where access to the good cannot be restricted.

Reactive nitrogen (or fixed nitrogen): The forms of nitrogen that are generally available to organisms, such as ammonia, nitrate, and organic nitrogen. Nitrogen gas (or dinitrogen), which is the major component of the atmosphere, is inert to most organisms.

Regulating services: The benefits obtained from the regulation of ecosystem processes, including, for example, the regulation of climate, water, and some human diseases.

Resilience: The level of disturbance that an ecosystem can undergo without crossing a threshold to a situation with different structure or outputs. Resilience depends on ecological dynamics as well as the organisational and institutional capacity to understand, manage, and respond to these dynamics.

Resistance: The capacity of an ecosystem to withstand the impacts of drivers without displacement from its present state.

Responses: Human actions, including policies, strategies, and interventions, to address specific issues, needs, opportunities, or problems. In the context of ecosystem management, responses may be of legal, technical, institutional, economic, and behavioural nature and may operate at various spatial and time scales.

Riparian: Something related to, living on, or located at the banks of a watercourse, usually a river or stream.

Salinisation: The build-up of salts in soils.

Scenario: A plausible and often simplified description of how the future may develop, based on a coherent and internally consistent set of assumptions about key driving forces (e.g. rate of technology change, prices) and relationships. Scenarios are neither predictions nor projections and sometimes may be based on a "narrative storyline." Scenarios may include projections but are often based on additional information from other sources.

Security: Access to resources, safety, and the ability to live in a predictable and controllable environment.

Service: See *Ecosystem services*.

Shared social values: Refers to the fulfillment, meaning or significance of the collective needs of society in relation to social, health and cultural services.

Soil fertility: The potential of the soil to supply nutrient elements in the quantity, form, and proportion required to support optimum plant growth. See also *Nutrients*.

Species: An interbreeding group of organisms that is reproductively isolated from all other organisms, although there are many partial exceptions to this rule in particular taxa. Operationally, the term *species* is a generally agreed fundamental taxonomic unit, based on morphological or genetic similarity, that once described and accepted is associated with a unique scientific name.

Species diversity: Biodiversity at the species level, often combining aspects of species richness, their relative abundance, and their dissimilarity.

Species richness: The number of species within a given sample, community, or area.

Stock (in fisheries): The population or biomass of a fishery resource. Such stocks are usually identified by their location. They can be, but are not always, genetically discrete from other stocks.

Storyline: A narrative description of a scenario, which highlights its main features and the relationships between the scenario's driving forces and its main features.

Strategies: See *Responses*.

Subsidy: Transfer of resources to an entity, which either reduces the operating costs or increases the revenues of such entity for the purpose of achieving some objective.

Subspecies: A population that is distinct from, and partially reproductively isolated from, other populations of a species but that has not yet diverged sufficiently that interbreeding is impossible.

Supporting services: Ecosystem services that are necessary for the production of all other ecosystem services. Some examples include biomass production, production of atmospheric oxygen, soil formation and retention, nutrient cycling, water cycling, and provisioning of habitat.

Sustainable use (of an ecosystem): Human use of an ecosystem so that it may yield a continuous benefit to present generations while maintaining its potential to meet the needs and aspirations of future generations.

Sustainability: A characteristic or state whereby the needs of the present and local population can be met without compromising the ability of future generations or populations in other locations to meet their needs.

Taxon (pl. taxa): The named classification unit to which individuals or sets of species are assigned. Higher taxa are those above the species level. For example, the common mouse, *Mus musculus*, belongs to the Genus *Mus*, the Family Muridae, and the Class Mammalia.

Threatened species: Species that face a high (*vulnerable species*), very high (*endangered species*), or extremely high (*critically endangered species*) risk of extinction in the wild.

Threshold: A point or level at which new properties emerge in an ecological, economic, or other system, invalidating predictions based on mathematical relationships that apply at lower levels. For example, species diversity of a landscape may decline steadily with increasing habitat degradation to a certain point, then fall sharply after a critical threshold of degradation is reached. Human behaviour, especially at group levels, sometimes exhibits threshold effects. Thresholds at which irreversible changes occur are especially of concern to decision-makers.

Total economic value framework: A widely used framework to disaggregate the components of utilitarian value, including *direct use value*, *indirect use value*, *option value*, *quasi-option value*, and *existence value*.

Total fertility rate: The number of children a woman would give birth to if through her lifetime she experienced the set of age-specific fertility rates currently observed. Since age-specific rates generally change over time, TFR does not in general give the actual number of births a woman alive today can be expected to have. Rather, it is a synthetic index meant to measure age-specific birth rates in a given year.

Trade-off: Management choices that intentionally or otherwise change the type, magnitude, and relative mix of services provided by ecosystems.

Travel cost analysis: Economic valuation techniques that use observed costs to travel to a destination to derive demand functions for that destination.

Uncertainty: An expression of the degree to which a future condition (e.g. of an ecosystem) is unknown. Uncertainty can result from lack of information or from disagreement about what is known or even knowable. It may have many types of sources, from quantifiable errors in the data to ambiguously defined terminology or uncertain projections of human behaviour. Uncertainty can therefore be represented by quantitative measures (e.g. a range of values calculated by various models) or by qualitative statements (e.g. reflecting the judgment of a team of experts).

Urbanisation: An increase in the proportion of the population living in urban areas.

Urban Heat Island: A metropolitan area which is significantly warmer than its surrounding rural areas.

Urban systems: Built environments with a high human population density.

Valuation: The process of expressing a value for a particular good or service in a certain context (e.g. of decision-making) usually in terms of something that can be counted, often money, but also through methods and measures from other disciplines (sociology, ecology, and so on). See also *Value*.

Value: The contribution of an action or object to user-specified goals, objectives, or conditions. (Compare *Valuation*).

Value systems: Norms and precepts that guide human judgment and action.

Voluntary measures/actions: Measures that are adopted by firms or other actors in the absence of government mandates.

Watershed (also catchment basin): The land area that drains into a particular watercourse or body of water. Sometimes used to describe the dividing line of high ground between two catchment basins.

Well-being: A context- and situation-dependent state, comprising basic material for a good life, freedom and choice, health and bodily well-being, good social relations, security, peace of mind, and spiritual experience.

Wetlands: Areas of marsh, fen, peatland, or water, whether natural or artificial, permanent or temporary, with water that is static or flowing, fresh, brackish or salt, including areas of marine water the depth of which at low tide does not exceed six metres. May incorporate riparian and coastal zones adjacent to the wetlands and islands or bodies of marine water deeper than six metres at low tide laying within the wetlands.

Abbreviations and Acronyms

AE	Actual Evaporation
AES	Agri-environment scheme
ANGSt	Accessible Natural Greenspace Standard
AOD	Above Ordnance Datum
AONB	Area of Outstanding Natural Beauty
AoSP	Areas of Special Protection
ASNW	Ancient Semi-natural Woodland
ASSI	Area of Special Scientific Interest
AWI	Ancient Woodland Inventory
BAP	Biodiversity Action Plan
BARS	Biodiversity Action Reporting System
BBS	Breeding Bird Survey
BBSRC	Biotechnology and Biological Sciences Research Council
BMI	body mass index
BoBW	Best of Both Worlds
BOD	Biochemical Oxygen Demand
BRC	Biological Records Centre
BSBI	Botanical Society of the British Isles
BSE	Bovine Spongiform Encephalopathy
bTB	Bovine Tuberculosis
BTO	British Trust for Ornithology
BTV	Bluetongue Virus
CABE	Commission for Architecture and the Built Environment
CAMS	Catchment Abstraction Management Areas
CAMSAR	Condition and Management Survey of the Archaeological Resource
CAP	Common Agricultural Policy
CBA	cost-benefit analysis
CBD	Convention on Biological Diversity
CCW	Countryside Council for Wales
CD&E	construction, demolition and excavation
CDOM	co-varying coloured dissolved organic matter
CEA	cost-effectiveness analysis
CEFAS	Centre for Environment, Fisheries and Aquaculture Science
CEH	Centre for Ecology & Hydrology
CFP	Common Fisheries Policy
CGT	Capital Gains Tax
CHD	coronary heart disease

CHP	Combined Heat and Power	FFCD	Foresight Flood and Coastal Defence
CI	confidence interval	FGM	farm gross margin
CITES	Convention on International Trade in Endangered Species of Wild Fauna and Flora	FIO	faecal indicator organism
		FIT	Feed-in Tariff
CME	Choice Modelling Experiments	FLUF	Foresight Land Use Futures
CMS	Convention on the Conservation of Migratory Species of Wild Animals	FLUFP	Foresight Land Use Futures Project
		FMD	Foot and Mouth Disease
CO_2	carbon dioxide	FOG	Fire Operations Group
CO_2e	carbon dioxide equivalent	FSC	Forest Stewardship Council
COGAP	Code of Good Agricultural Practice	FTE	full time employment
Confor	Confederation of Forest Industries	FWAG	Farm and Wildlife Advisory Group
COP	Conference of Parties	FWC	forest-wood-chains
COPR	Control of Pesticides Regulations	FWS	Farm Woodland Scheme
CP	Charting Progress	GAEC	Good Agricultural and Environmental Condition
CPRE	Campaign to Protect Rural England	GB	Great Britain
CQC	Countryside Quality Counts	GCR	Geological Conservation Review
CRoW	Countryside and Rights of Way	GDP	Gross Domestic Product
CS	Countryside Stewardship	GF	*Go with the Flow*
CSERGE	Centre for Social and Economic Research on the Global Environment	GHG	greenhouse gas
		GIS	geographic information system
CSO	Central Statistics Office	GLUD	Generalised Land Use Database
CSS	Countryside Stewardship Scheme	GM	genetically modified
DARD	Department of Agriculture and Rural Development	GMO	genetically modified organism
		GNI	Global National Income
DCLG	Department of Communities and Local Government	GPI	genuine progress indicator
		GPL	*Green and Pleasant Land*
DDT	dichlorodiphenyltrichloroethane	GPP	gross primary production
DECC	Department of Energy and Climate Change	GPS	Global Positioning System
Defra	Department for Environment, Food and Rural Affairs	GVA	gross value added
		GW	gigawatts
DMG	Deer Management Group	GWCT	Game & Wildlife Conservation Trust
DNA	deoxyribonucleic acid	ha	hectares
DOC	dissolved organic carbon	HAP	Habitat Action Plan
DoE	Department of Environment	HaRPPS	information retrieval system to support management of habitats and rare priority protected species
DON	dissolved organic nitrogen		
EA	Environment Agency		
EASAC	European Academies Science Advisory Council	HLS	Higher Level Stewardship
EAU	Environmental Advisory Unit	HMS	Harmonised Monitoring Scheme
EC	European Commission	HNV	High Nature Value
ECG	electrocardiogram	HPAI	Highly Pathogenic Avian Influenza
ECN	Environmental Change Network	HRV	heart rate variability
EEA	European Environment Agency	HSW	Habitat Survey of Wales
EEC	European Economic Community	HWP	Harvested Wood Products
EEZ	exclusive economic zone	ICES	International Council for the Exploration of the Sea
EIA	environmental impact assessment		
ELME	European Lifestyles & Marine Ecosystems	ICZM	Integrated Coastal Zone Management
ELS	Entry Level Stewardship	IEEP	Institute for European Environmental Policy
ELVS	English Leisure Visits Survey	IFM	Integrated Farm Management
END	European Directive on the Assessment and Management of Environmental Noise	IPC	Infrastructure Planning Commission
		IPCC	Intergovernmental Panel on Climate Change
EQS	Environmental Quality Standards	IPPC	Integrated Pollution Prevention and Control
ERICA	Environmental Risk from Ionising Contamination	ISPV	Israeli Acute Paralysis Virus
ES	ecosystem service	IT	Information Technology
ESA	Environmentally Sensitive Area	ITS	internal transcribed sequences
ESRC	Economic and Social Research Council	IUCN	International Union for Conservation of Nature
ET	evapotranspiration	IWA	Institute of Welsh Affairs
EU	European Union	JNCC	Joint Nature Conservation Committee
EUNIS	European Nature Information System	JULES	Joint UK Land Environment Simulator
FC	Forestry Commission	KE	knowledge exchange
FEPA	Food and Environmental Protection Act	Kw	kilowatt

LANR	Local Authority Nature Reserve	NICMS	Northern Ireland Countryside Management Scheme
LCM	Land Cover Map	NIEA	Northern Ireland Environment Agency
LCM2000	Land Cover Map 2000	NI-NFFO	Non-Fossil Fuel Obligations
LEAF	Linking Environment and Farming	NISMR	Northern Ireland Sites and Monuments Record
LETS	Local Exchange Trading Systems	NIWT	National Inventory of Woodlands and Trees
LFA	less favoured area	NLEPI	Net Landscape Ecological Potential Index
LNR	Local Nature Reserve	NM	nautical mile
LS	*Local Stewardship*	NNR	National Nature Reserve
LSOA	UK Census Lower Super Output Area	NOFS	New Organic Farming Scheme
LU	Livestock Unit	NOx	nitrogen oxides
LUCID	Local Urban Climate Model and its Application to the Intelligent Design of Cities	NP	National Park
m^3	cubic metres	NPP	net primary production
MA	Millennium Ecosystem Assessment	NPS	National Policy Statement
MACC	marginal abatement cost of carbon	NRoSO	National Register of Sprayer Operators
MAFF	Ministry of Agriculture, Fisheries and Food	NS	*National Security*
MCCIP	Marine Climate Change Impacts Partnership	NSAs	Nitrate Sensitive Areas
MCS	Marine Conservation Society	NSTS	National Sprayer Testing Scheme
MCZ	Marine Conservation Zone	NTFP	non-timber forest product
MEEB	Minimum Entry Environmental Benefit	NVC	British National Vegetation Classification
MEECE	Marine Ecosystem Evolution in a Changing Environment	NVZ	Nitrate Vulnerable Zone
MENE	Monitoring Engagement with the Natural Environment	NW	*Nature@Work*
		OAS	Organic Aid Scheme
MFA	Material Flow Analysis	OMHoPDL	Open Mosaic Habitats on Previously Developed Land
MMH	Mountains, Moorlands and Heaths		
MMO	Marine Management Organisation	ONS	Office for National Statistics
MNR	Marine Nature Reserve	OPW	Office of Public Works
MOD	Ministry of Defence	OSNW	Other Semi-natural Woodland
MONARCH	modelling natural resource responses to climate change	OSPAR	Convention for the Protection of the Marine Environment of the North East Atlantic
MORECS	Met Office Rainfall and Evaporation Calculation System	OTMS	Over Thirty-Month Scheme
		p.a.	per annum
MOSS	Management of Special Sites	PAN	Planning Advice Note
MPA	Marine Protected Area	PAWS	Plantations on Ancient Woodland Sites
MSC	Marine Stewardship Council	PCB	polychlorinated biphenyl
MSFD	Marine Strategy Framework Directive	PDL	Previously Developed Land
MSY	maximum sustainable yield	PDV	Phocine Distemper Virus
Mt	megatonnes	PE	Potential Evaporation
Mt CO_2	megatonnes of carbon dioxide	PEFC	Programme for Endorsement of Forest Certification
MtC	megatonnes of carbon		
$MtCO_2e$	megatonnes of carbon dioxide equivalent	PES	payment for ecosystem services
MW	megawatts	PFRA	Preliminary Flood Risk Assessment
Mwe	megawatts equivalent	PM	particulate matter
MWTP	marginal willingness to pay	PM10	air pollution with particle diameter < 10 microns
NAEI	National Atmospheric Emissions Inventory	PML	Plymouth Marine Laboratory
NAO	North Atlantic Oscillation	POC	particulate organic carbon
NBN	National Biodiversity Network	POM	particulate organic matter
NCC	Nature Conservancy Council	POP	persistent organic pollutant
NCMS	National Countryside Monitoring Scheme	PPG	Planning Policy Guidance
NDVI	Normalised Difference Vegetation Index	PPS	Planning Policy Statement
NEA	National Ecosystem Assessment	PRD	partial root drying
NEE	net ecosystem exchange	QALY	Quality Adjusted Life Year
NEP	net ecosystem productivity	Ramsar	Convention on Wetlands of International Importance
NERC	Natural Environment Research Council		
NERC	Natural Environment and Rural Communities	RBMP	River Basin Management Plan
NGO	non-governmental organisation	RCEP	Royal Commission for Environmental Pollution
NHS	National Health Service	REC	Regional Environmental Characterisation
NICE	National Institute for Health and Clinical Excellence	REP	Rural Environment Protection
		RFA	Renewable Fuels Agency
		RHI	Renewable Heat Incentive

RHS	River Habitat Survey	UKWIR	UK Water Industry Research
RIG	Regionally Important Geological and Geomorphological Sites	UN	United Nations
		UNECE	United Nations Economic Commission for Europe
RIMA	reflexive interventionist or multi-agent-based approach	UNEP	United Nations Environment Programme
		US	United States
RoTAP	Review of Transboundary Air Pollution	USA	United States of America
RPA	Rural Payments Agency	USD	United States dollar
RPI	Retail Price Index	UV	ultraviolet
RSPB	The Royal Society for the Protection of Birds	UVB	ultraviolet B
SAC	Special Area of Conservation	VI	Voluntary Initiative
SAF	Single Application Form	VMA	Valuation Meta-Analysis
SAMS	Scottish Association for Marine Science	VMNR	Voluntary Marine Nature Reserve
SAP	Species Action Plan	VMS	Vessel Monitoring System
SAS	Six Acre Standard	VOC	volatile organic compound
SCaMP	Sustainable Catchment Management Programme	VPF	value of a preventable fatality
SCC	social cost of carbon	VRP	Valleys Regional Park
SCORCHIO	Sustainable Cities: Options for Responding to Climate cHange Impacts and Outcomes	VTG	vitellogenin
		WAG	Welsh Assembly Government
SDA	Severely Disadvantaged Area	WATER	Wetted Land Assessment and Techniques for Restoration
SEA	Strategic Environmental Assessment		
SEEA	System of Environmental and Economic Accounting	WFD	Water Framework Directive
		WGS	Woodland Grant Scheme
SEER	Social and Environmental Economic Research	WHO	World Health Organization
SEP	Special Environmental Project	WHR	waist to hip ratio
SEPA	Scottish Environment Protection Agency	WiSe	Wildlife SafE
SFM	sustainable forest management	WM	*World Markets*
SGM	Standard Gross Margin	WPZ	Water Protection Zone
SLNCI	Sites of Local Nature Conservation Importance	WSSD	World Summit on Sustainable Development
SMP	Shoreline Management Plan	WTP	willingness to pay
SNG	semi-natural grassland	WWF	World Wide Fund for Nature
SOC	soil organic carbon	WWI	World War I
SP	Stated Preference	WWII	World War II
SPA	Special Protection Area	WWTW	wastewater treatment work
SPM	site prediction model		
SPP	Scottish Planning Policy		
SRDP	Scotland Rural Development Programme		
SRP	soluble reactive phosphorus		
SSSI	Site of Special Scientific Interest		
SuDS	Sustainable Urban Drainage Systems		
SUE	Sustainable Urban Environment		
TAG	Technical Advisory Group		
TANs	Technical Advice Notes		
TB	tuberculosis		
TEEB	The Economics of Ecosystems and Biodiversity		
TEV	Total Economic Value		
TFR	Total Fertility Rate		
TGF	trip generation function		
THC	tetrahydrocannabinol		
TMP	Tracking Mammals Partnership		
TOC	total organic carbon		
UHI	Urban Heat Intensity		
UK	United Kingdom		
UK NEA	United Kingdom National Ecosystem Assessment		
UKBAP	United Kingdom Biodiversity Action Plan		
UKCIP	United Kingdom Climate Impacts Programme		
UKCP	UK Climate Projection		
UKMMAS	United Kingdom Marine Monitoring and Assessment Strategy		
UKTS	United Kingdom Tourism Statistics/Survey		
UKWAS	UK Woodland Assurance Standard		

Contributors

Expert Panel, Authors, Reviewers, User Group, Client Group and Secretariat

Abson, David (University of Leeds)
Acreman, Mike (Centre for Ecology & Hydrology)
Ajax-Lewis, Nigel (Wildlife Trust for South & West Wales)
Albon, Steve (The James Hutton Institute)
Aleem, Mariam (Food Standards Agency)
Alexander, Richard (Natural England)
Allott, Tim (University of Manchester)
Alonso, Isabel (Natural England)
Anderson, Penny (Penny Anderson Associates)
Andrews, Barnaby (University of East Anglia)
Andrews, Julian (University of East Anglia)
Angus, Stewart (Scottish Natural Heritage)
Annett, Judith (Northern Ireland Biodiversity Group)
Archdale, Peter (Council for Nature Conservation & the Countryside)
Armitage, Heather (The James Hutton Institute)
Armitage, Will (Her Majesty's Treasury)
Armstrong, Aileen (Scottish Natural Heritage)

Asara, Viviana (University of Cambridge)
Ashley, Jayne (Sustainable Development Commission)
Ashmore, Mike (University of York)
Ashworth, Jen (Natural England)
Askew, Tom (University of Cambridge)
Aslam, Uzma (University of Leeds)
Aspinall, Richard (The James Hutton Institute)
Atkinson, Giles (London School of Economics)
Atkinson, Sian (Woodland Trust)
Austen, Melanie C. (Plymouth Marine Laboratory)
Bailey, Sallie (Forestry Commission)
Bailey, Mark (Centre for Ecology & Hydrology)
Baker, Julia (Balfour Beatty)
Baker, Sandra (University of Oxford)
Baker, Tom (University of Liverpool)
Balmford, Andrew (University of Cambridge)
Bankhead, Judith (Rivers Agency)
Bardgett, Richard D. (Lancaster University)
Barry, Caroline (Northern Ireland Environment Agency)
Barton, Jo (University of Essex)
Bashford, Jenny (National Farmers' Union)
Bateman, Ian J. (University of East Anglia)
Batty, Michael (University College London)
Bazley, Tony (Earth Science Ireland Magazine)
Beaumont, Nicola (Plymouth Marine Laboratory)
Beck, Helen (Commission for Architecture and the Built Environment)
Beharry-Borg, Nesha (University of Leeds)
Bell, Laverne (Quarry Products Association Northern Ireland)
Benjamins, Stephen (Joint Nature Conservation Committee)
Benton, Dustin (Campaign to Protect Rural England)
Berry, Pam (Oxford University)
Bide, Peter (Department of Communities and Local Government)
Biesmeijer, Koos (University of Leeds)
Biggs, Jeremy (Pond Conservation)
Birchall, Caroline (Natural England)
Bird, William (Natural England)
Black, Helaina (The James Hutton Institute)
Blackstock, Kirsty (The James Hutton Institute)
Blackstock, Tim H. (Countryside Council for Wales)
Blackwell, Martin (North Wyke Research)
Blaney, Ralph (Scottish Natural Heritage)
Blyth, Simon (UNEP World Conservation Monitoring Centre)
Bolt, Katharine (Royal Society for the Protection of Birds)
Bonn, Aletta (IUCN UK Peatland Programme)
Booker, Rob (The James Hutton Institute)
Boon, Phil (Scottish Natural Heritage)
Bradburne, Robert (Department for Environment, Food and Rural Affairs)
Bradbury, Richard (Royal Society for the Protection of Birds)
Bradley, Martin (Northern Ireland Environment Agency)
Bradshaw, Richard (University of Liverpool)
Brady, Emily (Edinburgh University)
Breen, Joe (Northern Ireland Environment Agency)
Breeze, Tom (University of Reading)
Brereton, Tom (Butterfly Conservation)
Brett, Hope (Environment Agency)
Brierley, Bill (Environment Agency)
Broadmeadow, Mark (Forestry Commission)

Brooke, Diane (Association of Electricity Producers)
Brown, Bob (Independent / Joint Nature Conservation Committee)
Brown, Claire (UNEP World Conservation Monitoring Centre)
Brown, Lee (University of Leeds)
Bruce, Lee (Woodland Trust)
Bruneau, Patricia (Scottish Natural Heritage)
Bubb, Philip (UNEP World Conservation Monitoring Centre)
Buckingham, David (Royal Society for the Protection of Birds)
Buckton, Seb (Wildfowl & Wetlands Trust)
Bullock, James M. (Centre for Ecology & Hydrology)
Burgess, Jacquelin (University of East Anglia)
Burgess, Paul (Cranfield University)
Burgess, Diane (Agri-Food & Biosciences Institute)
Burn, Alastair (Natural England)
Burnett, Emma (Oxford University)
Burrows, Michael (Scottish Association for Marine Science)
Butenschön, Momme (Plymouth Marine Laboratory)
Butler, Christine (Department of Agriculture & Rural Development)
Cahalan, Christine (Bangor University)
Campbell, Colin D. (The James Hutton Institute)
Carey, Martin (Mourne Heritage Trust)
Carter, Claire (University of Ulster)
Carvell, Claire (Centre for Ecology & Hydrology)
Casement, Patrick (Council for Nature Conservation & the Countryside)
Chamberlain, David (Royal Botanic Garden Edinburgh)
Christie, Mary (Scottish Natural Heritage)
Christie, Mike (Aberystwyth University)
Christie, Peter (Agri-Food & Biosciences Institute)
Christie, Susan J. (Northern Ireland Environment Link)
Church, Alistair (Northern Ireland Environment Agency)
Church, Andrew (University of Brighton)
Clarke, Barrie (Water UK)
Clarke, Michelle (National Soil Resources Institute)
Clarke, Stewart (Natural England)
Colbeck, Ian (University of Essex)
Cole, Matthew (University of Birmingham)
Collins, Murray (London School of Economics)
Comerford, Emma (Royal Society for the Protection of Birds)
Coombes, Emma (University of East Anglia)
Cooper, Nigel (Church of England / Anglia Ruskin University)
Cooper, David (Department for Environment, Food and Rural Affairs)
Cooper, Alan (University of Ulster)
Cooper, Andrew (University of Ulster)
Corker, Pat (Northern Ireland Environment Agency)
Corstanje, Ron (Cranfield University)
Costigan, David (Department for Environment, Food and Rural Affairs)
Counsell, Dominic (Scottish Natural Heritage)
Coupar, Andrew (Scottish Natural Heritage)
Crabbe, James (University of Bedfordshire)
Crang, Michael (Durham University)
Cregg, Patrick (Woodland Trust)
Crick, Mark (Joint Nature Conservation Committee)
Crone, Victoria (Department of Environment)
Cross, Paul (Bangor University)

Crowe, Andrew (University of East Anglia)
Crowle, Alistair (Natural England)
Crute, Ian (Agriculture and Horticulture Development Board)
Cush, Peter (Northern Ireland Environment Agency)
Darnell, Amii (University of East Anglia)
Dasgupta, Sir Partha (University of Cambridge)
Davies, Keith (Countryside Council for Wales)
Davies, Linda (Imperial College London)
Davies, Iain (Northern Ireland Environment Agency)
de Moor, Des (The Ramblers)
Delaney, Colum (Royal Society for the Protection of Birds)
Diack, Ian (Natural England)
Doody, Pat (National Coastal Consultants)
Dornbusch, Uwe (Environment Agency)
Downey, Philip (Department of Agriculture & Rural Development)
Drewitt, Joanna (Scottish Government)
Duck, Callan (Sea Mammal Research Unit)
Dugdale, Steve (University of East Anglia)
Duigan, Catherine (Countryside Council for Wales)
Dunbar, Michael (Centre for Ecology & Hydrology)
Duncan, Callan (Marine Conservation Society)
Dunn, Helen (Department for Environment, Food and Rural Affairs)
Durance, Isabelle (Cardiff University)
Early, John (Northern Ireland Environment Agency)
Easson, Lindsay (Agri-Food & Biosciences Institute)
Edmonds-Brown, Ronni (University of Hertfordshire)
Edward-Jones, Gareth (Aberystwyth & Bangor Universities)
Edwards, Martin (Sir Alister Hardy Foundation for Marine Science)
Elliot, Lindsey C. (UNEP World Conservation Monitoring Centre)
Elliot, Russell (Countryside Council for Wales)
Ellis, Christopher J. (Royal Botanic Garden Edinburgh)
Emmett, Bridget A. (Centre for Ecology & Hydrology)
Evans, Chris (Centre for Ecology & Hydrology)
Evans, Hugh (Forest Research (Wales))
Evans, Martin (University of Leeds)
Evans, Simon (National Forest Company)
Everard, Mark (Environment Agency)
Falconer, Roger (Cardiff University)
Falzon, Charles (C Falzon Associates)
Feest, Alan (University of Bristol)
Ferguson, Scott (Scottish Natural Heritage)
Fezzi, Carlo (University of East Anglia)
Firbank, Les (University of Leeds)
Fish, Robert (University of Exeter)
Fisher, Brendan (Princeton University)
Fisher, Jane (Liverpool John Moores University)
Fitter, Alastair (University of York)
Foden, Jo (University of East Anglia)
Foley, Nicola (Bangor University)
Fortnam, Matthew (UNEP World Conservation Monitoring Centre)
Freer, Jim (Bristol University)
Frogbrook, Zoe (Environment Agency Wales)
Frost, Peter (Countryside Council for Wales)
Frost, Mathew (Marine Biological Association of the UK)
Fyfe, Gillian (Convention of Scottish Local Authorities)

Gale, Andrew (Natural England)
Garbutt, Angus (Centre for Ecology & Hydrology)
Gaston, Kevin J. (University of Sheffield)
Gibbons, Steve (London School of Economics)
Gibby, Mary (Royal Botanic Garden Edinburgh)
Gibson, Chris (Queen's University, Belfast - retired)
Gilbert, Jack (Plymouth Marine Laboratory)
Gilchrist, Paul (University of Brighton)
Gilvear, David (University of Stirling)
Ginley, Sue (Forestry Commission)
Glass, Jayne (University of the Highlands and Islands)
Glerum, Jonathan (Construction Industry Research and Information Association)
Golshetti, Giles (Department for Environment, Food and Rural Affairs)
Gordon, John (Scottish Natural Heritage)
Goulding, Keith (Rothamsted Research)
Graham, Andrea (National Farmers' Union)
Grant, Gary (Green Roof Consultancy)
Green, David (University of Aberdeen)
Gregory, Richard (Royal Society for the Protection of Birds)
Grice, Phil (Natural England)
Griffin, John (Forest Service)
Griffiths, Richard (University of Kent)
Grime, Philip J. (University of Sheffield)
Gruffudd, Pyrs (Swansea University)
Gupta, Anil (Convention of Scottish Local Authorities)
Gurnell, Angela (Queen Mary, University of London)
Hails, Rosemary (Centre for Ecology & Hydrology / Natural Capital Initiative)
Haines-Young, Roy (University of Nottingham)
Halliday, Neil (Northern Ireland Environment Link)
Hanley, Nick (University of Stirling)
Hanna, Judith (Natural England)
Hansom, Jim (Glasgow University)
Harmer, Ralph (Forestry Commission)
Harrington, Lauren (University of Oxford)
Harrington, Richard (Rothamsted Research)
Harris, Ian (Bangor University)
Harris, Jim A. (University of Cranfield)
Harvey, Simon C. (Canterbury Christ Church University)
Hattam, Caroline (Plymouth Marine Laboratory)
Haygarth, Phil (University of Lancaster)
Heard, Matt (Centre for Ecology & Hydrology)
Heathwaite, Louise A. (University of Lancaster)
Helfer, Stephan (Royal Botanic Garden Edinburgh)
Henry, Clifford (Northern Ireland Environment Agency - retired)
Hesketh, Helen (Centre for Ecology & Hydrology)
Hess, Tim (Cranfield University)
Hester, Alison (The James Hutton Institute)
Hicks, Kevin (Imperial College London)
Hiddink, Jan (Bangor University)
Hills, Kate (Local Government Association)
Hine, Rachel (University of Essex)
Hinton, George (Natural England)
Hobson, Edward (Commission for Architecture and the Built Environment)
Hockley, Neal (Bangor University)
Holyoak, Vince (English Heritage)

Hopkins, John (Natural England)
Hoskins, Stephen (King Edward VI School, Southampton)
Houghton, Jane (Natural England)
Hourahane, Shelagh (Creu-Ad Consultants)
Hughes, Rob (Queen Mary University of London)
Hughes, Dermot (Ulster Wildlife Trust - retired)
Hulme, Mark (British Trust for Ornithology)
Hume, Carrie (Wildfowl and Wetlands Trust/Wildlife and Countryside Link)
Humphrey, Jonathan (Ecological consultant)
Ishwaran, Mallika (Department for Environment, Food and Rural Affairs)
Jackson, Emma (Marine Biological Association of the UK)
James, Philip (University of Salford)
Jarrett, Dafydd (National Farmers' Union - Wales)
Jefferson, Richard G. (Natural England)
Jenkins, Alan (Centre for Ecology & Hydrology)
Jenkins, Martin (UNEP World Conservation Monitoring Centre)
Jennings, Simon (Centre for Environment Fisheries & Aquaculture Science)
Jeavans, Mark (Department for Environment, Food and Rural Affairs)
Johnes, Penny (University of Reading)
Johns, David (Sir Alister Hardy Foundation for Ocean Science)
Johns, Tim (Environment Agency / Roehampton University)
Johnson, Sally (Scottish Natural Heritage)
Johnson, Andrew (Centre for Ecology & Hydrology)
Johnston, Robert (Fellow of the Society of Biology, Fellow of the Linnean Society)
Jones, Barbara (Countryside Council for Wales)
Jones, Glyn (Agricultural Development Advisory Service)
Jones, Laurence (Centre for Ecology & Hydrology)
Jones, Ceris (National Farmers' Union)
Jordan, Crawford (Agri-Food & Biosciences Institute)
Kasier, Michael (Bangor University)
Kass, Gary (Natural England)
Kay, David (Aberystwyth University)
Kearney, Eimear (Lough Neagh Partnership)
Keatinge, Ray (Department for Environment, Food and Rural Affairs)
Keith, Aidan (Centre for Ecology & Hydrology)
Kenney, Siobhan (UNEP World Conservation Monitoring Centre)
Killeen, Steve (Environment Agency)
King, Tony (Scottish Environment Link)
Kingham, Jonathan (Northern Ireland Environment Link)
Kirby, Keith (Natural England)
Kirkpatrick, Hilary (University of Ulster)
Kirkwood, Lisa (World Wildlife Fund)
Kontoleon, Andreas (University of Cambridge)
Korn, Julia (Countryside Council for Wales)
Kumar, Pushpam (University of Liverpool)
Kungu, Elizabeth (Royal Botanic Garden Edinburgh)
Kunin, William (University of Leeds)
Kwiatkowski, Lester (Imperial College London)
Laidlaw, Scott (Agri-Food & Biosciences Institute)
Landsberg, Florence (World Resources Institute)
Langmead, Olivia (University of Plymouth)
Lansdown, Richard (Ardeola Environmental Services)

Large, Andy (University of Newcastle)
Lawlor, Declan (Loughs Agency)
Lawson, Aileen (Ulster Farmers Union)
Le Vay, Lewis (Bangor University)
Lea, Chris (Welsh Assembly Government)
Leather, Simon (Imperial College London)
Lerch, Andreas (Marine Scotland)
Lilly, Allan (The James Hutton Institute)
Logan, Niall (Glasgow Caledonian University)
Long, David (Royal Botanic Garden Edinburgh)
Lovett, Andrew (University of East Anglia)
Lucas, Steve (Bat Conservation Trust)
Luisetti, Tiziana (University of East Anglia)
Lyme, Samantha (Natural England)
Maberly, Steve (Centre for Ecology & Hydrology)
Macdonald, David (University of Oxford)
Mace, Georgina M. (Imperial College London)
Mack, Kim (Scottish Government)
MacKerron, George (London School of Economics)
Mackey, Ed (Scottish Natural Heritage)
MacKintosh, Jane (Scottish Natural Heritage)
Maddison, David (University of Birmingham)
Madgwick, Genevieve (Natural England)
Maggs, Chris (Queen's University Belfast)
Maguire, Cathy (Queen's University Belfast)
Maguire, Orla (Belfast City Council)
Malcolm, Stephen J. (Centre for Environment, Fisheries & Aquaculture Science)
Mäler, Karl-Göran (The Stockholm School of Economics / Beijer International Institute of Ecological Economics)
Maltby, Edward (University of Liverpool)
Mangi, Stephen (Plymouth Marine Laboratory)
Mannion, Kathrina (Department for Environment, Food and Rural Affairs)
Marrington, Emma (Campaign to Protect Rural England)
Martin, John (Royal Society for the Protection of Birds)
Maskell, Lindsay (Centre for Ecology & Hydrology)
Maxwell, Simon (Department for Environment, Food and Rural Affairs)
May, Linda (Centre for Ecology & Hydrology)
McAdam, Jim (Agri-Food & Biosciences Institute)
McAuley, Marcus (Department of Culture, Arts & Leisure)
McCall, Rob (Countryside Council for Wales)
McCann, David (Northern Ireland Environment Link)
McCann, Thomas (University of Ulster)
McColgan, Ronan (Northern Ireland Environment Link)
McCracken, Davy (Scottish Agricultural College)
McCulloch, Neil (Northern Ireland Environment Agency)
McFerran, Damian (Centre for Environmental Data & Recording)
McHaffie, Heather (Royal Botanic Garden Edinburgh)
McKay, Hazel I. (Independant consultant)
McMorrow, Julia (University of Manchester)
McMullan, Melina (Northern Ireland Environment Agency)
McMurray, Philip (Department of the Environment)
McNee, Jonathan (Planning Service)
McQuarrie, Alison (Marine Scotland)
Meharg, Mike (Northern Ireland Environment Agency)
Memmott, Jane (Bristol University)
Merino, Gorka (Plymouth Marine Laboratory)

Metcalfe, Robert (Oxford University)
Middlebrook, Ian (Butterfly Conservation)
Mieszkowska, Nova (Marine Biological Association of the UK)
Miles, Alison (Environment Agency)
Mitchell, Arthur (Rural Development Council)
Mitchell, Diane (National Farmers' Union)
Mitchell, Ian (Joint Nature Conservation Committee)
Moeller, Iris (University of Cambridge)
Moffat, Andy (Forest Research)
Monteith, Don (Centre for Ecology & Hydrology)
Montgomery, Ian (Queen's University of Belfast)
Moore, Alan (Northern Ireland Water)
Moorhouse, Tom (University of Oxford)
Moran, Dominic (Scottish Agricultural College)
Morgan, Vicky (Joint Nature Conservation Committee)
Morling, Paul (Royal Society for the Protection of Birds)
Morris, Joe (Cranfield University)
Morris, Tony (Royal Society for the Protection of Birds)
Morwood, Stuart (Forest Service)
Moss, Brian (University of Liverpool)
Moss, Joan (Agri-Food & Biosciences Institute)
Mourato, Susana (London School of Economics)
Mudge, Greg (Scottish Natural Heritage)
Mulholland, Fiona (Northern Ireland Environment Agency)
Munday, Paul (University of East Anglia)
Murchie, Archie (Agri-Food & Biosciences Institute)
Neill, Ken (Northern Ireland Environment Agency)
Newman, Jonathan (Centre for Ecology & Hydrology)
Nicholls, Robert (University of Southampton)
Norris, Ken (University of Reading)
Nunn, Julia (Centre for Environmental Data & Recording)
Nurse, Jo (Department of Health)
Nuttall, Geoff (World Wildlife Fund)
O'Neill, John (Fisheries Division, Department of Agriculture & Rural Development)
Ogden, Peter (Campaign for the Protection of Rural Wales)
Oppenheimer, Sarah (Royal Society for the Protection of Birds)
Orford, Julian (Queen's University Belfast)
Ormerod, Steve (University of Cardiff)
Orr, Harriet (Environment Agency)
Osborne, Juliet (Rothamsted Research)
Osborne, Dan (Natural Environment Research Council)
Owen, Nicola (Mineral Products Association)
Owen, Roger (Scottish Environment Protection Agency)
Pagella, Saskia (Bangor University)
Pagella, Tim (Bangor University)
Pakeman, Robin J. (The James Hutton Institute)
Pascual, Unai (University of Cambridge)
Patterson, James (University of Nottingham)
Payne, Michael (National Farmers' Union)
Pearce-Higgins, James (British Trust for Ornithology)
Pearson, Jon (Land Use Consultants)
Peel, Steve (Natural England)
Perino, Grischa (University of East Anglia)
Perry, Suzanne (Natural England)
Phillips, Nick (Royal Society for the Protection of Birds)
Pickup, Roger (Centre for Ecology & Hydrology)
Pilgrim, Emma (Rothamsted Research)

Pimm, Eunice (Joint Nature Conservation Committee)
Pinnegar, Sally (Natural England)
Pitkin, Peter (Scottish Natural Heritage)
Polasky, Steve (University of Minnesota)
Poots, Brian (Northern Ireland Forest School Association)
Porter, Keith (Natural England)
Porter, David (Rivers Agency)
Potschin, Marion (University of Nottingham)
Potts, Simon G. (University of Reading)
Pretty, Jules N. (University of Essex)
Procter, Julie (Greenspace Scotland)
Purse, Beth (Centre for Ecology & Hydrology)
Pye, Kenneth (Kenneth Pye Associates Ltd.)
Pywell, Richard J. (Centre for Ecology & Hydrology)
Quine, Chris (Forest Research, Forestry Commission)
Quine, Timothy (University of Exeter)
Ragab, Ragab (Centre for Ecology & Hydrology)
Rahman, Amanna (Environment Agency)
Ravenscroft, Neil (University of Brighton)
Rawcliff, Peter (Scottish Natural Heritage)
Rayment, Mark (Bangor University)
Reading, Christopher (Centre for Ecology & Hydrology)
Rebane, Mick (Natural England)
Reed, Mark (University of Aberdeen)
Rees, Sue (Natural England)
Reid, Christine (Natural England)
Reid, Neil (Quercus)
Resende, Guliherme (London School of Economics)
Reynolds, Brian (Centre for Ecology & Hydrology)
Rhind, Peter (Countryside Council for Wales)
Rimes, Carrie (Countryside Council for Wales)
Roast, Stephen (Environment Agency)
Robertson, Anne (Roehampton University)
Robinson, Anna (Joint Nature Conservation Committee)
Robinson, David (Centre for Ecology & Hydrology)
Rogers, Kenton (Hi-Line Consultancy)
Rose, Paul (Joint Nature Conservation Committee)
Rosell, Robert (Agri-Food & Biosciences Institute)
Ross, Louise (University of Aberdeen)
Ross, Martin (South West Water)
Rowan, John (University of Dundee)
Rowntree, Clare (National Farmers' Union)
Ruddock, Diane (The National Trust)
Russell, Shaun (Wales Environment Research Hub)
Russell, Stephen (Landscape Institute)
Sadler, Jon (University of Birmingham)
Sajwaj, Todd (Unaffiliated)
Sanderson, Bill (Countryside Council for Wales)
Savill, Peter (University of Oxford)
Schaible, Richard (Forest Service)
Schoeman, Dave (University of Ulster)
Scholes, Lian (Middlesex University)
Scott, Robert (Belfast City Council)
Scowen, Matt (Bangor University)
Sen, Antara (University of East Anglia)
Service, Matthew (Agri-Food & Biosciences Institute)
Shannon, Delia (Mineral Products Association)
Sheate, William R. (Imperial College London)
Shepherd, Matthew (Natural England)
Sherry, Jan (Countryside Council for Wales)

Shimmield, Tracy (Scottish Marine Institute)
Silvertown, Jonathan (Open University)
Sime, Iain (Scottish Natural Heritage)
Simpson, Lucy (UNEP World Conservation Monitoring Centre)
Siriwardena, Gavin (British Trust for Ornithology)
Sizaret, Maxime (Causeway Coast & Glens Heritage Trust)
Skates, James (Welsh Assembly Government)
Skea, Jim (UK Energy Research Centre)
Skinner, Ann (Scottish Natural Heritage)
Small, Emma (Countryside Council for Wales)
Smith, Cecile (Scottish Natural Heritage)
Smith, Pete (University of Aberdeen)
Smith, Philip (Land Use onsultants)
Smith, Stuart (Countryside Council for Wales)
Smithers, Richard (Woodland Trust)
Smyth, Emily (University of Ulster)
Smyth, Tim (Plymouth Marine Laboratory)
Snowdon, Pat (Forestry Commission)
Somerfield, Paul (Plymouth Marine Laboratory)
Spence, Barbara (Forestry Commission)
Spode, Steve (Welsh Assembly Government)
Spray, Chris (University of Dundee)
Spurgeon, James (Environmental Resources Management)
Squire, Geoff (The James Hutton Institute)
Stein, Alexandra (Scottish Government)
Stentford, Grant (Centre for Environment, Fisheries & Aquaculture Science)
Stephens, Jude (Queen's University Belfast)
Stewart Roper, Charles (Scottish Government)
Stirrat, Craig (Built Environment Forum Scotland)
Stoate, Chris (Game and Wildlife Conservation Trust)
Storkey, Jonathan (Rothamsted Research)
Stott, Andrew (Department for Environment, Food and Rural Affairs)
Swart, Chloe (UNEP World Conservation Monitoring Centre)
Tallowin, Jerry (Rothamsted Research)
Taylor, Colin (EDF Energy)
Termansen, Mette (University of Leeds / Aarhus University)
Thomas, Huw (Department for Environment, Food and Rural Affairs)
Thomas, Clive (Forestry Commission)
Thompson, Des (Scottish Natural Heritage)
Thompson, Julian (University College London)
Thomson, Amanda (Centre for Ecology & Hydrology)
Tierney, Megan (UNEP World Conservation Monitoring Centre)
Tinch, Dugald (University of Stirling)
Tolia-Kelly, Divya (Durham University)
Tomlinson, Roy (Queen's University Belfast - retired)
Townsend, Mike (Woodlands Trust)
Treweek, Jo (Treweek Environmental Consultants)
Turley, Carol (Plymouth Marine Laboratory)
Turner, Kerry (University of East Anglica)
Turner, Sarah (Centre for Ecology & Hydrology)
Tyler, Charles (University of Exeter)
Upton, Andrew (Ulster Wildlife Trust)
Usher, Michael (University of Stirling)
Valatin, Gregory (Forest Research)
Van der Wal, René (University of Aberdeen)

van Soest, Daan (Tilburg University)
Vanbergen, Adam (Centre for Ecology & Hydrology)
Vaughan, Ian (University of Cardiff)
Vincent, Claire (Northern Ireland Environment Agency)
Vira, Bhaskar (University of Cambridge)
Volpi, Massimiliano (Natural Environment Research Council)
Wade, Rebecca (University of Abertay)
Wall, Diana (Colarado State University)
Waller, Paul (Paul Waller Consulting)
Walmsley, Clive (Countryside Council for Wales)
Walpole, Matt (UNEP World Conservation Monitoring Centre)
Walton, Paul (Royal Society for the Protection of Birds)
Ward, Rob (British Geological Survey)
Warren, Martin (Butterfly Conservation)
Warrington, Stuart (National Trust)
Waters, Ruth (Natural England)
Watkinson, Andrew (Living With Environmental Change)
Watson, Robert, T. (Department for Environment, Food and Rural Affairs & the Tyndall Centre, University of East Anglia)
Watt, Allan (Centre for Ecology & Hydrology)
Weighell, Tony (Joint Natural Conservation Council)
Wernham, Chris (British Trust for Ornithology)
Wharfe, Jim (Environment Agency)
Whitbread, Tony (Wildlife Trust)
Whitehouse, Andrew (Buglife – The Invertebrate Conservation Trust)
Whitmore, Andrew P. (Rothamsted Research)
Wilks, Susie (Client Earth)
Williams, James (Joint Nature Conservation Committee)
Williams, Prysor (Bangor University)
Willis, Graeme (Campaign to Protect Rural England)
Wilson, Alister (Waverley Management Consultants)
Wilson, Jeremy (Royal Society for the Protection of Birds)
Winn, Jonathan (UNEP World Conservation Monitoring Centre)
Winter, Michael (University of Exeter)
Wood, Carly (University of Essex)
Woodcock, Ben (Centre for Ecology & Hydrology)
Woodhurst, Ian (Campaign to Protect Rural England)
Wright, Mark (Northern Ireland Environment Agency)
Wright, Timothy (Economic and Research Council)
Young, Mark (University of Aberdeen)
Young, Michael (Geological Survey Northern Ireland)

Acknowledgements

The UK National Ecosystem Assessment (UK NEA) was funded by the Department for Environment, Food and Rural Affaris (Defra), Natural Environment Research Council (NERC), Economic and Social Research Council (ESRC), Northern Ireland Environment Agency (NIEA), the Scottish Government, the Countryside Council for Wales (CCW) and the Welsh Assembly Government (WAG).

We would like to acknowledge the contributions of all the authors of the UK NEA and the support provided by their institutions that enabled their participation. Writing this technical report would also not have been possible without the many comments and useful insights from the Expert Panel and Chairs, User Group and Client Group. We also wish to further acknowledge the many constructive comments provided by independent reviewers, ensuring the assessment's robustness. These comments were further complemented by the many stakeholders who took part in workshops during the two years of the assessment.

The UK NEA would not have been possible without the availability of data that underpins the assessment, and we wish to acknowledge all institutions and individuals who provided data, specifically the Centre for Ecology & Hydrology, Natural England, Scottish Natural Heritage, the Environment Agency, Forestry Commission, BTO, RSPB, The Woodlands Trust, Agri-Food & Biosciences Institute, Biotechnology & Biological Sciences Research Council, the Met Office, and Cranfield University. We would also like to thank all of those who provided high resolution versions of graphics and photos for inclusion in the UK NEA Technical Report.

Special thanks are due to the Secretariat staff who worked tirelessley on the UK NEA and especially to Kate Trumper, Rhonda Pike, Chloe Cryus-Kent, Helen Walsh, Rowena Millar and the designers at NatureBureau who worked with the Secretariat, and on the production of the Technical Report.

Specifically, the following author teams would like to acknowledge:

Mountains, Moorlands and Heaths

The authors are grateful for comments on earlier drafts from Edward Maltby (University of Liverpool), Ian Montgomery (Queen's University Belfast), Christine Reid (Natural England), Greg Mudge (Scottish Natural Heritage [SNH]), Mick Rebane (Natural England), Patrick Thompson (RSPB), Phil Burston (RSPB), Jeremy Wilson (RSPB), Penny Anderson (Penny Anderson Associates), Diane Mitchell (National Farmers' Union), Vicky Morgan (Senior Habitats Adviser JNCC), Sally Johnson (SNH), Andrew Coupar (SNH), Jo Treweek (Treweek Environmental Consultants), James Pearce Higgins (BTO), Chris Gibson (Queen's University, Belfast - retired), and Robin Pakeman (Macaulay Institute).

Woodlands

The authors are grateful for assistance from Peter Crow, Elaine Dick, David H. Evans, Justin Gilbert, Ralph Harmer, Helen McKay, James Morison, Jonathan Starling and others.

Marine

Some of the material for this chapter has been reproduced with permission from the Charting Progress 2 (CP2) Healthy and Biologically Diverse Seas Evidence Group Feeder Report 2010 (Frost 2010) and chapters therein. Reproduced information is highlighted in footnotes in the relevant sections. Information has also been sourced from the Productive Seas Evidence Group Feeder Report (Saunders 2010). Contributing authors from Plymouth Marine Laboratory and Scottish Association for Marine Science were partially funded through the NERC Oceans 2025 programme.

Supporting services

We are grateful to the many people who have contributed to the writing of this chapter specifically John Gordon, Alistair Rennie, Stewart Angus and Ness Kirkbride and several other colleagues and referees. We are especially indebted to: Robert Jones, Patricia Bruneau, John Gordon, Stephen Chapman, Alan Lilly, Nikki Baggaley and Willie Towers who provided valuable information for the soil formation section, Fangjie Zhao and Keith Goulding who made available unpublished data for the nutrient cycling section, and Brian Reynolds for information on trends in soil phosphorus. We are also grateful to several referees who provided helpful comments on previous versions of this chapter, and other Coordinating Lead Authors and members of the UK NEA Expert Panel who contributed through valuable comments and discussion.

Economic valuation

The economic analysis (Chapter 22 & 26) was in part funded by the ESRC Social, Economic and Environmental Research (SEER) project (funder ref: RES-060-25-0063) at CSERGE, University of East Anglia, UK. The work carried out on valuing of woodland recreation was funded in part by the Forestry Commission. The UK NEA economics team and many of the collaborating natural and social scientists were supported in part by the NERC Valuing Nature Network (funder ref: NE/I015086/1) which provides a forum for bringing together researchers and decision makers from across the ecosystem services spectrum. The authors are grateful to the UK NEA Economic Advisory Panel and in particular Sir Partha Dasgupta, Brendan Fisher, Karl-Göran Mäler, Steve Polasky and Kerry Turner.

Scenarios

The Scenarios chapter could not have been completed without the assistance, guidance and feedback from a large group of people: Megan Tierney, Matt Walpole, Jonathan Winn, Claire Brown and Lucy Simpson from UNEP-WCMC, Cambridge, UK; Bob Watson, Robert Bradburne, Giles Golshetti, Josef Hargrave, Peter Costigan, and Fiona Lickorish from Defra, London, UK; Steve Albon, The James Hutton Institute, Aberdeen, UK; Nicola George, Natural England; Alice Hardiman, RSPB, Sandy, UK; Kathryn Monk, Environment Agency Wales, Cardiff, UK; Jim Wharfe, Environment Agency, UK; Angela Wilkinson, Said Business School, University of Oxford, UK; Diane Mitchell, NFU, Stoneleigh, UK; Louise Heathwaite, Lancaster Environment Centre, UK; Chris Quine, Forest Research, Alice Holt, UK; also the Scenarios Expert Group, the UK NEA economics team and the members of the UK NEA stakeholder groups in England, Scotland, Wales and Northern Ireland. We are also grateful for input from former research assistants at CEM Kate Moore (now University of Leicester) and Gabrielle Silfwerbrand (now University of Stockholm, Sweden).